NORTH CAROLINA TEACHER'S EDITION

PRENTICE HALL MATHEMATICS

ALGEBRA 1

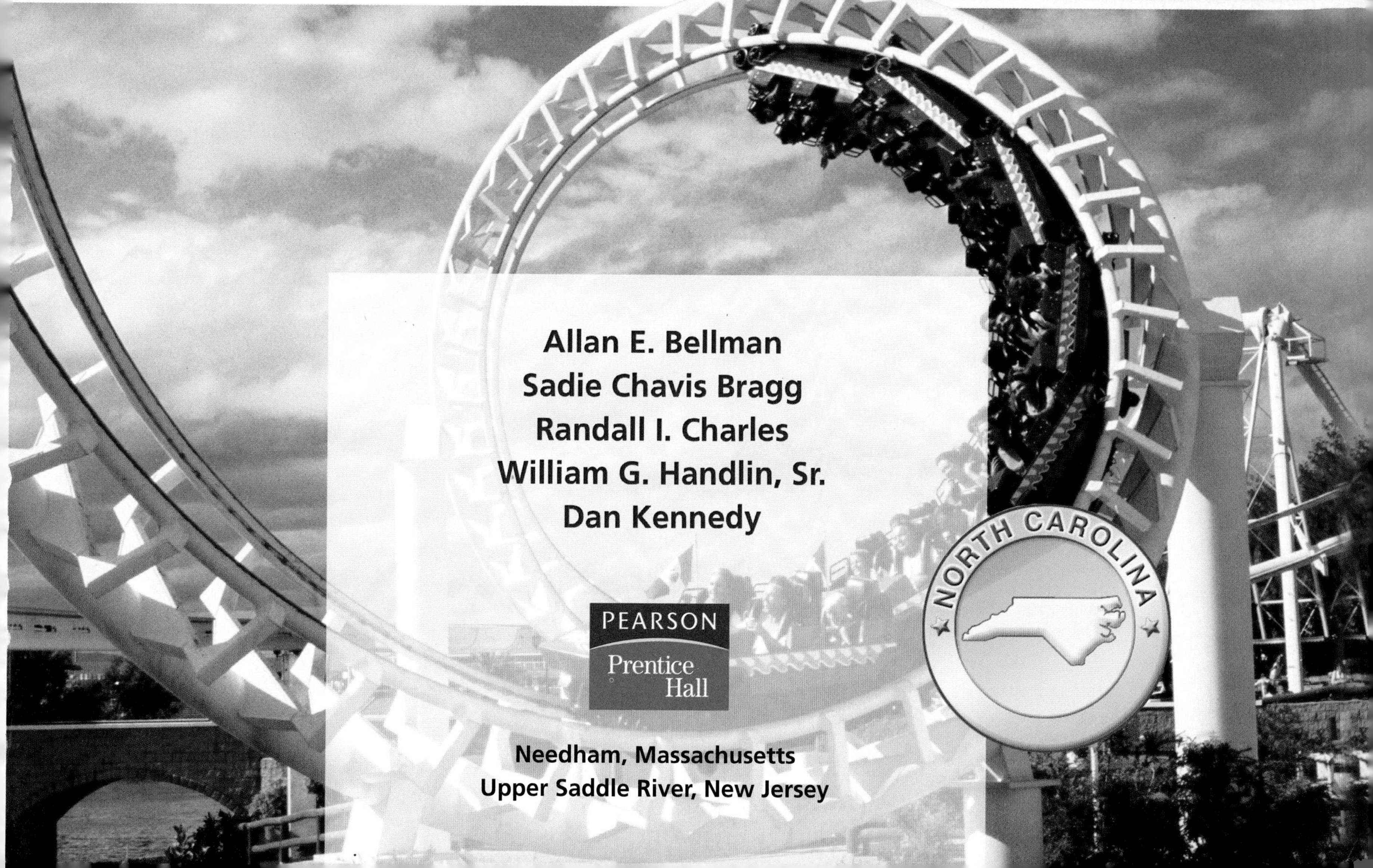

Allan E. Bellman

Sadie Chavis Bragg

Randall I. Charles

William G. Handlin, Sr.

Dan Kennedy

PEARSON

Prentice Hall

NORTH CAROLINA

Needham, Massachusetts
Upper Saddle River, New Jersey

Dorling Kindersley (DK) is an international publishing company that specializes in the creation of high-quality, illustrated information books for children and adults. Dorling Kindersley's unique graphic presentation style is used in this program to motivate students in learning about real-world applications of mathematics. DK is part of the Pearson family of companies.

ISBN 0-13-180862-1

2 3 4 5 6 7 8 9 10   07 06 05 04

North Carolina Algebra 1 Standard Course of Study Handbook

Correlation NC4

These pages provide a complete list of the Algebra 1 objectives of the North Carolina Mathematics Standard Course of Study and identify the Prentice Hall Mathematics lessons in this book that address each state objective.

Year-at-a-Glance NC6

These pages provide a brief overview of where each North Carolina mathematics objective is introduced, developed, and concluded in this book.

Lesson-by-Lesson Correlation NC8

These pages list each lesson along with all of the objectives addressed by each lesson. Pacing suggestions for two different teaching schedules – traditional and block – are also offered for each lesson.

Standards Progression NC12

These pages lay out the North Carolina Standard Course of Study for Algebra 1. The pages list the chapters where you can find each objective, as well as a sample item that addresses that objective. Also shown is the progression made in each benchmark from prior years to this year, and then in later years.

North Carolina Standard Course of Study Correlation

This correlation identifies sections on which the North Carolina Standard Course of Study objectives are addressed in this book. With the help of this chart you can find solid, fully developed instruction on any standard.

Standard	Prentice Hall Algebra 1 Lessons
Number & Operations	
1.01 Write equivalent forms of algebraic expressions to solve problems.	1-8
a) Apply the laws of exponents.	1-2, 1-7, 8-1, 8-2, 8-3, 8-4, 8-5, 11-1, 11-5
b) Operate with polynomials.	9-1, 9-2, 9-3, 9-4, 12-3, 12-4, 12-5, 12-6, 12-7
c) Factor polynomials.	9-5, 9-6, 9-7, 9-8, 11-4
1.02 Use formulas and algebraic expressions, including iterative and recursive forms, to model and solve problems.	1-1, 2-1, 2-2, 2-3, 2-4, 2-5, 2-6, 3-6, 4-1, 4-2, 4-3, 4-4, 5-6, 8-6, 10-7, 11-2, 11-3, 11-4
1.03 Model and solve problems using direct variation.	5-5, 12-1
Measurement & Geometry	
2.01 Find the lengths and midpoints of segments to solve problems.	11-3, 11-7
2.02 Use the parallelism or perpendicularity of lines and segments to solve problems.	6-5, 11-2
Data Analysis & Probability	
3.01 Use matrices to display and interpret data.	1-4, 1-5
3.02 Operate (addition, subtraction, scalar multiplication) with matrices to solve problems.	1-4, 1-5, 1-6
3.03 Create linear models for sets of data to solve problems.	1-9, 10-9
a) Interpret constants and coefficients in the context of the data.	6-4
b) Check the model for goodness-of-fit and use the model, where appropriate, to draw conclusions or make predictions.	6-6

Standard	Prentice Hall Algebra 1 Lessons
Algebra	
4.01 Use linear functions or inequalities to model and solve problems; justify results.	5-5, 6-1
a) Solve using tables, graphs, and algebraic properties.	3-1, 3-2, 3-3, 3-4, 3-5, 5-2, 5-3, 5-4, 7-5
b) Interpret constants and coefficients in the context of the problem.	6-2, 6-3, 6-4
4.02 Graph, factor, and evaluate quadratic functions to solve problems.	10-1, 10-2, 10-4, 10-5, 10-6, 10-7, 10-8, 10-9
4.03 Use systems of linear equations or inequalities in two variables to model and solve problems. Solve using tables, graphs, and algebraic properties; justify results.	7-1, 7-2, 7-3, 7-4, 7-6
4.04 Graph and evaluate exponential functions to solve problems.	8-7, 8-8, 10-9

North Carolina Standard Course of Study Year-at-a-Glance

The following chart provides an overview of where within Prentice Hall Algebra 1 each objective in the North Carolina Standard Course of Study is introduced, developed, and concluded.

Standard	|	PRENTICE HALL ALGEBRA 1 CHAPTERS										
	1	2	3	4	5	6	7	8	9	10	11	12
Number & Operations												
1.01 Write equivalent forms of algebraic expressions to solve problems.	I D C											
a) Apply the laws of exponents.	I							D		C		
b) Operate with polynomials.									I D			C
c) Factor polynomials.									I D		C	
1.02 Use formulas and algebraic expressions, including iterative and recursive forms, to model and solve problems.		I D		D	D	D				D	D	C
1.03 Model and solve problems using direct variation.					I D							D C
Measurement & Geometry												
2.01 Find the lengths and midpoints of segments to solve problems.											I D	
2.02 Use the parallelism or perpendicularity of lines and segments to solve problems.						I D					C	
Data Analysis & Probability												
3.01 Use matrices to display and interpret data.	I D C											
3.02 Operate (addition, subtraction, scalar multiplication) with matrices to solve problems.	I D C											
3.03 Create linear models for sets of data to solve problems.	I									D C		
a) Interpret constants and coefficients in the context of the data.						I D C						
b) Check the model for goodness-of-fit and use the model, where appropriate, to draw conclusions or make predictions.						I D C						

I = introduced   D = developed   C = concluded

Standard	PRENTICE HALL ALGEBRA 1 CHAPTERS											
	1	2	3	4	5	6	7	8	9	10	11	12
Algebra												
4.01 Use linear functions or inequalities to model and solve problems; justify results.					I D	D C						
a) Solve using tables, graphs, and algebraic properties.			I D		I D		C					
b) Interpret constants and coefficients in the context of the problem.						I D C						
4.02 Graph, factor, and evaluate quadratic functions to solve problems.										I D C		
4.03 Use systems of linear equations or inequalities in two variables to model and solve problems. Solve using tables, graphs, and algebraic properties; justify results.							I D C					
4.04 Graph and evaluate exponential functions to solve problems.								I D		C		

I = introduced   D = developed   C = concluded

North Carolina Standard Course of Study Lesson-by-Lesson Correlation

This chart provides pacing suggestions based on the objectives of the North Carolina Standard Course of Study for Algebra 1. It is designed to help you maximize your coverage of the objectives.

Chapter 1 Tools of Algebra		North Carolina Course of Study	Pacing		
			Traditional	Two Year	Block
1-1	Using Variables	1.02	1 day	1 day	1/2 day
1-2	Exponents and Order of Operations	1.01.a	2 days	3 days	1 day
1-3	Exploring Real Numbers		1 day	3 days	1/2 day
1-4	Adding Real Numbers	3.01, 3.02	1 day	2 days	1/2 day
1-5	Subtracting Real Numbers	3.01, 3.02	2 days	2 days	1/2 day
1-6	Multiplying and Dividing Real Numbers	3.02	2 days	3 days	1/2 day
1-7	The Distributive Property	1.01.a	1 day	3 days	1/2 day
1-8	Properties of Real Numbers	1.01	1 day	2 days	1/2 day
1-9	Graphing Data on the Coordinate Plane	3.03	1 day	3 days	1/2 day
Testing and Additional Activities			3 days	4 days	1 day

Chapter 2 Solving Equations		North Carolina Course of Study	Pacing		
			Traditional	Two Year	Block
2-1	Solving One-Step Equations	1.02	1 day	2 days	1/2 day
2-2	Solving Two-Step Equations	1.02	1 day	3 days	1/2 day
2-3	Solving Multi-Step Equations	1.02	1 day	3 days	1/2 day
2-4	Equations With Variables on Both Sides	1.02	1 day	3 days	1 day
2-5	Equations and Problem Solving	1.02	2 days	4 days	1 day
2-6	Formulas	1.02	1 day	3 days	1/2 day
2-7	Using Measures of Central Tendency		2 days	3 days	1 day
Testing and Additional Activities			3 days	4 days	1 day

Chapter 3 Solving Inequalities		North Carolina Course of Study	Pacing		
			Traditional	Two Year	Block
3-1	Inequalities and Their Graphs	4.01.a	1 day	2 days	1/2 day
3-2	Solving Inequalities Using Addition and Subtraction	4.01.a	1 day	2 days	1/2 day
3-3	Solving Inequalities Using Multiplication and Division	4.01.a	1 day	2 days	1/2 day
3-4	Solving Multi-Step Inequalities	4.01.a	2 days	4 days	1/2 day
3-5	Compound Inequalities	4.01.a	1 day	4 days	1/2 day
3-6	Absolute Value Equations and Inequalities	1.02, 4.01.a	1 day	3 days	1/2 day
Testing and Additional Activities			3 days	4 days	1 day

Chapter 4 Solving and Applying Proportions	North Carolina Course of Study	Pacing		
		Traditional	Two Year	Block
4-1 Ratio and Proportion	1.02	2 days	4 days	1/2 day
4-2 Proportions and Similar Figures	1.02	1 day	3 days	1/2 day
4-3 Proportions and Percent Equations	1.02	2 days	4 days	1 day
4-4 Percent of Change	1.02	2 days	4 days	1 day
4-5 Applying Ratios to Probability		1 day	3 days	1/2 day
4-6 Probability of Compound Events		1 day	3 days	1/2 day
Testing and Additional Activities		3 days	4 days	1 day

Chapter 5 Graphs and Functions	North Carolina Course of Study	Pacing		
		Traditional	Two Year	Block
5-1 Relating Graphs to Events		1 day	2 days	1/2 day
5-2 Relations and Functions	4.01.a	2 days	3 days	1 day
5-3 Function Rules, Tables, and Graphs	4.01.a	1 day	2 days	1/2 day
5-4 Writing a Function Rule	4.01.a	1 day	3 days	1/2 day
5-5 Direct Variation	1.03, 4.01.a	2 days	4 days	1 day
5-6 Describing Number Patterns	1.02	1 day	3 days	1/2 day
Testing and Additional Activities		3 days	4 days	1 day

Chapter 6 Linear Equations and Their Graphs	North Carolina Course of Study	Pacing		
		Traditional	Two Year	Block
6-1 Rate of Change and Slope	4.01	2 days	4 days	1/2 day
6-2 Slope-Intercept Form	4.01.b	2 days	4 days	1 day
6-3 Standard Form	4.01.b	1 day	2 days	1/2 day
6-4 Point-Slope Form and Writing Linear Equations	3.03.a, 4.01.b	2 days	3 days	1/2 day
6-5 Parallel and Perpendicular Lines	2.02	2 days	3 days	1/2 day
6-6 Scatter Plots and Equations of Lines	3.03.b	1 day	2 days	1/2 day
6-7 Graphing Absolute Value Equations		1 day	3 days	1/2 day
Testing and Additional Activities		3 days	4 days	2 days

Chapter 7 Systems of Equations and Inequalities	North Carolina Course of Study	Pacing		
		Traditional	Two Year	Block
7-1 Solving Systems by Graphing	4.03	1 day	3 days	1 day
7-2 Solving Systems Using Substitution	4.03	1 day	3 days	1/2 day
7-3 Solving Systems Using Elimination	4.03	2 days	3 days	1 day
7-4 Applications of Linear Systems	4.03	1 day	4 days	1 day
7-5 Linear Inequalities	4.01.a	1 day	2 days	1/2 day
7-6 Systems of Linear Inequalities	4.03	1 day	4 days	1 day
Testing and Additional Activities		3 days	4 days	2 days

Chapter 8 Exponents and Exponential Functions	North Carolina Course of Study	Pacing		
		Traditional	Two Year	Block
8-1 Zero and Negative Exponents	1.01.a	1 day	2 days	1 day
8-2 Scientific Notation	1.01.a	2 days	4 days	1/2 day
8-3 Multiplication Properties of Exponents	1.01.a	1 day	3 days	1 day
8-4 More Multiplication Properties of Exponents	1.01.a	2 days	4 days	1/2 day
8-5 Division Properties of Exponents	1.01.a	1 day	3 days	1/2 day
8-6 Geometric Sequences	1.02	2 days	4 days	1/2 day
8-7 Exponential Functions	4.04	2 days	4 days	1 day
8-8 Exponential Growth and Decay	4.04	1 day	3 days	1 day
Testing and Additional Activities		3 days	4 days	2 days

Chapter 9 Polynomials and Factoring	North Carolina Course of Study	Pacing		
		Traditional	Two Year	Block
9-1 Adding and Subtracting Polynomials	1.01.b	1 day	3 days	1/2 day
9-2 Multiplying and Factoring	1.01.b, c	1 day	2 days	1/2 day
9-3 Multiplying Binomials	1.01.b	2 days	3 days	1/2 day
9-4 Multiplying Special Cases	1.01.b	1 day	3 days	1/2 day
9-5 Factoring Trinomials of the Type $x^2 + bx + c$	1.01.c	2 days	3 days	1 day
9-6 Factoring Trinomials of the Type $ax^2 + bx + c$	1.01.c	1 day	3 days	1/2 day
9-7 Factoring Special Cases	1.01.c	2 days	3 days	1/2 day
9-8 Factoring by Grouping	1.01.c	2 days	3 days	1 day
Testing and Additional Activities		3 days	4 days	2 days

Chapter 10 Quadratic Equations and Functions	North Carolina Course of Study	Pacing		
		Traditional	Two Year	Block
10-1 Exploring Quadratic Graphs	4.02	1 day	3 days	1/2 day
10-2 Quadratic Functions	4.02	1 day	3 days	1/2 day
10-3 Finding and Estimating Square Roots		1 day	3 days	1/2 day
10-4 Solving Quadratic Equations	4.02	1 day	2 days	1/2 day
10-5 Factoring to Solve Quadratic Equations	4.02	1 day	4 days	1 day
10-6 Completing the Square	4.02	2 days	4 days	1 day
10-7 Using the Quadratic Formula	1.02, 4.02	2 days	4 days	1 day
10-8 Using the Discriminant	4.02	1 day	2 days	1 day
10-9 Choosing a Linear, Quadratic, or Exponential Model	3.03, 4.02, 4.04	2 days	3 days	1 day
Testing and Additional Activities		3 days	4 days	2 days

Chapter 11 Radical Expressions and Equations	North Carolina Course of Study	Pacing		
		Traditional	Two Year	Block
11-1 Simplifying Radicals	1.01.a	1 day	3 days	1 day
11-2 The Pythagorean Theorem	1.02, 2.02	2 days	4 days	1 day
11-3 The Distance and Midpoint Formulas	1.02, 2.01	2 days	4 days	1 day
11-4 Operations with Radical Expressions	1.01	1 day	4 days	1 day
11-5 Solving Radical Equations	1.01.a	1 day	3 days	1/2 day
11-6 Graphing Square Root Functions		1 day	2 days	1/2 day
11-7 Trigonometric Ratios	2.01	2 days	4 days	1 day
Testing and Additional Activities		3 days	4 days	1 day

Chapter 12 Rational Expressions and Functions	North Carolina Course of Study	Pacing		
		Traditional	Two Year	Block
12-1 Inverse Variations	1.03	2 days	3 days	1/2 day
12-2 Graphing Rational Functions		2 days	4 days	1 day
12-3 Simplifying Rational Expressions	1.01.b	1 day	3 days	1/2 day
12-4 Multiplying and Dividing Rational Expressions	1.01.b	2 days	3 days	1 day
12-5 Dividing Polynomials	1.01.b	1 day	3 days	1/2 day
12-6 Adding and Subtracting Rational Expressions	1.01.b	2 days	4 days	1 day
12-7 Solving Rational Equations	1.01.b, c	2 days	4 days	1 day
12-8 Counting Methods and Permutations		2 days	4 days	1 day
12-9 Combinations		1 day	4 days	1 day
Testing and Additional Activities		3 days	4 days	2 days

North Carolina Course of Study

Use these pages to acquaint yourself with the North Carolina Algebra 1 Standard Course of Study at this grade level with respect to where previous standards have brought the student and where this year's standards will lead their studies going forward.

Number & Operation

Progression

Prior Years	This Year	Going Forward
Students focus on developing number sense with real numbers and learn how to work with irrational numbers.	They will expand their understanding to include creating and solving algebraic expressions.	Students will expand their operations with algebraic expressions to include expressions with polynomials, radicals, and complex fractions.

1.01 Write equivalent forms of algebraic expressions to solve problems.
  a) Apply the laws of exponents.
  b) Operate with polynomials.
  c) Factor polynomials.

Math Background

In Algebra we use algebraic expressions and equations to model relationships, to state generalizations, and so on. Polynomials are the basic building blocks of expressions. Students may know that poly means many. This will help them remember that a polynomial is an expression that is a term or sum of terms. The terms are called monomials, mono meaning one.

Students may be confused by some aspects of the laws of exponents, as some may seem somewhat counterintuitive. Nonetheless, these principles will help students understand operations involving exponents. For example, when a base raised to a power is multiplied by the same base raised to a power, the product is the base raised to the sum of the two exponents (e.g., $4^2 \times 4^8 = 4^{10}$). Conversely, when a based raised to a power is divided by the same base raised to a power, the quotient is the base raised to the difference between the two powers (e.g., $4^{10} \div 4^2 = 4^8$).

Write an algebraic expression to represent the sum of an odd integer and the next three odd integers.

Use four odd integers for an example. Let the least integer be the variable n and create expressions equal to each of the other integers by using n. Then add them to find an algebraic expression that is equivalent to the word statement.

The correct answer is $4n + 12$.

The algebraic expression $x(4x^2 - x + 2)$ is equal to which of the following expressions?

A $4x^3 - x + 2$
B $4x^3 - 2x^2 + 2$
C $4x^3 - x^2 + 2x$
D $4x^3 - 3x^2 + 2x$

Answer: C

Progression

Prior Years	This Year	Going Forward
Students focus on solving problems using mental computation, estimation, calculators, and paper and pencil.	Students will expand their problem-solving skills to include modeling and solving problems using formulas with algebraic expressions.	Students will further expand their skills to include defining and computing with complex numbers and nonlinear functions.

1.02 Use formulas and algebraic expressions, including iterative and recursive forms, to model and solve problems.

Math Background

Students will be accustomed to formulas, but the notion of a recursive formula will probably be new to them. Recursion comes from Latin and means "running back." A recursive formula relates a new term in a sequence to a previous term.

$2, 4, 6, 8, \ldots$

A recursive formula for this sequence is:

Value of new term = value of previous term + 2.

Throughout the year, students will be asked to model, or represent mathematically, many real-world situations and problems. Students will need to use variables, expressions, and equations to model the relationship that exists in the situation or problem. Consequently, students will need to know how to translate the situation into numbers and symbols.

The cost of using a phone card is 85 cents per call and 10 cents per minute. Write and solve an equation to find the length, in minutes, of a $3.55 call.

Let n = the number of minutes. Next, write an equation such as $355 = 85 + 10n$. Then solve for n.

The correct answer is 27 min.

To weigh his new puppy, Sam holds the dog and steps on a scale. Alone, Sam weighs 140 lb. With the dog, he weighs 151 lb.

Write and solve an equation to find the weight of the dog.

Let n = the dog's weight. Next, write and solve an equation such as: $151 = 140 + n$. Then solve for n.

The correct answer is 11 lb.

Progression

Prior Years	This Year	Going Forward
Students focus on developing an understanding of functions.	Students will expand their understanding of modeling and solving problems using direct variation and all its implications relative to models and data.	Students will learn to identify different kinds of variation (direct, inverse, combined, and joint variation) and represent them in algebraic expressions.

1.03 Model and solve problems using direct variation.

Math Background

A good example of direct variation is the amount earned for the number of hours worked. The pay increases directly as the number of hours increases.

Students will also learn that there are other kinds of variation, such as inverse variation. An example of inverse variation is the relation between the number of gallons of water left in the hot water tank and the number of minutes used to take a shower.

Remind students that they can identify if a relationship is direct or inverse by analyzing the equation. A direct variation will take the form of $y = kx$, where k is the *constant of variation*. An inverse variation will have the form $y = \frac{k}{x}$.

A graphical representation of a direct variation will produce a graph of a line passing through the origin. The graph of an inverse variation produces a curve, with each end of the curve approaching the x- or the y-axis.

Which equation is a direct variation?

A $\quad y = 2x$

B $\quad y = 1 - 2x$

C $\quad y = 1 - \frac{2}{x}$

D $\quad y = 1 - \frac{2}{x^2}$

Answer: A

Write an equation of the direct variation that includes the point $(1, 2)$.

Use the function form of a direct variation: $y = kx$. Then, replace x with 1 and y with 2 to solve for k and write an equation.

The correct answer is $y = 2x$.

Progression

Prior Years	This Year	Going Forward
Students focus on learning fundamental geometric properties as they apply to algebra. They also learned to measure perimeter, area, and volume.	Students will expand their work in the application of algebra to geometry to include finding the lengths and midpoints of line segments.	Students will continue to use algebra with geometry. For example, students will use equations for determining other geometric quantities, including properties of circles and parabolas, to solve problems.

2.01 Find the lengths and midpoints of segments to solve problems.

Math Background

When you tell students that they are going to learn how to find the length of a segment or the midpoint of a segment, chances are they will think about getting out their rulers. But there is another curious way, and it involves a right triangle and the Pythagorean Theorem and showing the segment on a coordinate plane. Students calculate the distance between two points on the plane and divide by two to determine the midpoint. Since it involves the Pythagorean Theorem

$$a^2 + b^2 = c^2$$

it involves finding some square roots.

Students can also use formulas to find the distance between two points and the midpoint. The distance formula $(d = \sqrt{(x_2 - x_1)^2 + (y_2 - y_1)^2})$ is a practical application of the Pythagorean Theorem. One way to help the students understand the conceptual basis of the formula is by showing them how the distance formula is derived from the Pythagorean Theorem.

The idea of a midpoint will be more obvious to the students. As such, the formula for determining the midpoint of a segment will be more straightforward. However, point out that in finding the midpoint, they are finding the location of the midpoint of the segment. As with the derivation of the distance formula, demonstrating the derivation of the midpoint formula $(\frac{x_1 + x_2}{2}, \frac{y_1 + y_2}{2})$ will provide a foundation for understanding how and when to use this formula.

 A hiker is 2 km west and 3 km north of the campground. Another is 4 km east and 2 km south of the campground How far apart are the two hikers?

A $\sqrt{27}$ km
B 61 km
C 6 km
D $\sqrt{61}$ km

Answer: D

 Find the distance between (5, 10) and (10, 5). Use the distance formula:

$$d = \sqrt{(x_2 - x_1)^2 + (y_2 - y_1)^2}$$

to solve this problem.

The correct answer is $\sqrt{50}$.

Progression

Prior Years	This Year	Going Forward
Students focus on the properties of linear equations and writing equations of a line given points, slope, and/or *y*-intercept.	Students will expand their work with linear equations to better understand slope and the relationship of parallel and perpendicular lines.	Students will expand their use of linear equations to create and use best-fit models of linear equations to solve problems.

2.02 Use the parallelism or perpendicularity of lines and segments to solve problems.

Math Background

Most students will know that parallel lines do not meet. When they are considering two lines in a plane, that "definition" will give them a working knowledge of the concept. However, they will need to understand that just because two lines do not meet does not mean that they are parallel. Lines must be in the same plane to be parallel.

Example: Consider the line formed by two walls on the south side of a building. Then consider the line formed by the roof and a wall at the north side of the building. They do not meet, but they are not parallel because they are not in the same plane. We call those lines skew lines.

It might be useful to have students look around the classrooom and give other examples of skew lines.

Students have also encountered perpendicular lines— lines that intersect to form right angles. You can deepen their understanding of perpendicular lines (and parallel lines) through an exploration of the slope of these lines. Students will see that lines (as long as the lines are non-vertical) are parallel if they have the same slope and different *y*-intercepts. With perpendicular lines, the slope of one line is the negative reciprocal of the other line.

Which of the following equations represents a line perpendicular to $y = \frac{x}{3} - 5$?

A $\quad y = -\frac{2}{3}x + 5$

B $\quad y = \frac{x}{3} - 5$

C $\quad y = 3x + 15$

D $\quad y = -3x - 15$

Answer: D

Write an equation for the line that contains $(1, 1)$ and is parallel to $y = 2x + 1$.

Parallel lines have the same slope. To solve, substitute the points into the point-slope form and simplify.

$y - 1 = 2(x - 1)$

The correct answer is $y = 2x - 1$.

Progression

Prior Years	This Year	Going Forward
Students focus on using data tables and other basic statistical tools to organize and display data.	They will learn to use matrices to display and interpret bodies of data. They will also learn to perform calculations with matrices.	Students will expand their operations with matrices to model and solve problems.

3.01 Use matrices to display and interpret data.

Math Background

A matrix is a rectangular arrangement of numbers. In today's world of spreadsheets and charts of all sorts, matrices are all around us. Dimensions of matrices are given by the number of rows and columns. For instance, the matrix

$$\begin{bmatrix} 1 & 2 & 3 & 4 \\ 5 & 6 & 7 & 8 \\ 9 & 10 & 11 & 12 \\ 13 & 14 & 15 & 16 \\ 17 & 18 & 19 & 20 \end{bmatrix}$$

is a 5×4 matrix because it has 5 rows and 4 columns. Matrices are clearly very useful tools for displaying data. Students may be familiar with spreadsheets created on computers, one example of the use of matrices.

As students become more comfortable with matrices, you may wish to introduce some matrix terminology. Understanding these terms will facilitate teaching students matrix operations. For example, each number in a matrix is a *matrix element*. Additionally, a matrix element is identified by its position within the matrix (using a lowercase letter with subscripts). So, a_{21} is the matrix element in the second row, first column.

Write the data in the table below as a matrix.

Students in Mr. Glass's Class

	A	B	C
2000	3	10	7
2001	4	12	3
2003	5	14	1

The correct answer is:

$$\begin{bmatrix} 3 & 10 & 7 \\ 4 & 12 & 3 \\ 5 & 14 & 1 \end{bmatrix}$$

State the dimensions of each matrix.

$$A \begin{bmatrix} 4 & 5 & 7 \\ -1 & 0 & 11 \\ 0 & 3 & 2 \\ 10 & -4 & -3 \end{bmatrix}$$

$$B \begin{bmatrix} 3 & 7 \\ -8 & 2 \\ 6 & 3 \\ 1 & 1 \\ 2 & 9 \end{bmatrix}$$

$$C \begin{bmatrix} 2 & 1 & 1 \\ -4 & -2 & 1 \end{bmatrix}$$

Answer: A. 4×3; B. 5×2; C. 2×3

3.02 Operate (addition, subtraction, scalar multiplication) with matrices to solve problems.

Math Background

With the rising popularity and convenience of the use of spreadsheets, understanding how to perform operations with matrices has become more and more important. It is important to note that addition and subtraction of matrices can be performed only if the matrices have the same dimensions.

$$\begin{bmatrix} 7 & 8 \\ 4 & 7 \\ 2 & 9 \end{bmatrix} + \begin{bmatrix} 3 & 5 \\ 1 & 6 \\ 0 & 7 \end{bmatrix} = \begin{bmatrix} 10 & 13 \\ 5 & 13 \\ 2 & 16 \end{bmatrix}$$

One common error for students to make is to try to add matrices that are not the same size, as in the example below.

$$\begin{bmatrix} 2 & 5 \\ 1 & 8 \\ 3 & 6 \end{bmatrix} + \begin{bmatrix} 5 & 8 & -2 \\ 1 & -3 & 7 \\ 10 & 16 & 4 \end{bmatrix} = \begin{bmatrix} 3 & -2 & 10 \\ 10 & 16 & 4 \end{bmatrix}$$

While matrix addition and subtraction will appear to be a natural extension of what students have learned concerning these basic operations, matrix multiplication will appear to be much more complicated. However, in scalar multiplication, students will readily grasp the notion of multiplying each element in the matrix by the scalar.

For example,

$$3\begin{bmatrix} 2 & 4 \\ 7 & 9 \end{bmatrix} = \begin{bmatrix} 6 & 12 \\ 21 & 27 \end{bmatrix}$$

On the other hand, matrix multiplication, multiplying the elements of each row in the first matrix by the elements of each column in the second matrix, will be less obvious.

For example,

$$\begin{bmatrix} 2 & 4 \\ 5 & 6 \end{bmatrix}\begin{bmatrix} 3 & 1 \\ 9 & 2 \end{bmatrix} = \begin{bmatrix} 42 & 10 \\ 69 & 17 \end{bmatrix}$$

Find the product.

$$3\begin{bmatrix} 4 & \frac{1}{2} \\ 1.1 & 1 \end{bmatrix}$$

Multiply each element in the matrix by 3.

The correct answer is:

$$\begin{bmatrix} 12 & \frac{3}{2} \\ 3.3 & 3 \end{bmatrix}$$

A stationery store is having a sale on wrapping paper, candles, and calendars. The wrapping paper is on sale for $4.99, the candles are $9.99, and the calendars are $12.99. On the first day of the sale, the store sold 14 packages of wrapping paper, 20 candles, and 7 calendars. Find the store's gross income for the day.

First, set prices of the items as one matrix and the number of each sold as another matrix.

Prices

Wrapping paper	Candles	Calendars

$$\begin{bmatrix} \$4.99 & \$9.99 & \$12.99 \end{bmatrix}$$

Number Sold

Wrapping paper
Candles
Calendars

$$\begin{bmatrix} 14 \\ 20 \\ 7 \end{bmatrix}$$

Multiply each price by the number of items sold. Then, add the products.

$$[4.99 \quad 9.99 \quad 12.99]\begin{bmatrix} 14 \\ 20 \\ 7 \end{bmatrix}$$

$$[4.99(14) + 9.99(20) + 12.99(7)] = [360.59]$$

Progression

Prior Years	This Year	Going Forward
Students focus on interpreting and comparing properties of linear relationships and writing equations of lines.	Students will expand their use of linear equations to include creating linear models based upon given data for solving problems.	Students will expand their problem-solving skills to include creating models based on linear, exponential, and quadratic functions.

3.03 Create linear models for sets of data to solve problems.

a) Interpret constants and coefficients in the context of the data.

b) Check the model for goodness-of-fit and use the model, where appropriate, to draw conclusions or make predictions.

Math Background

One fundamental idea in mathematics is the concept of function. The functional relationship relates the value of one variable, such as y, to the value of another variable, such as x. Functions can be modeled through graphs. Linear functions are a special function whose graph is a line. Students will spend a good deal of time studying this all-important idea.

Not all data from the real-world will represent a function. However, students will need to study to see if there are patterns and if they can write a "function rule," or an equation, to represent that pattern. Once they have built an equation to express the relationship in the data, they are on their way in solving problems involving that data.

Students have familiarity with some aspects of analyzing and interpreting linear equations. However, they will need practice in translating between the graphical and the symbolic representations of a linear relationship. Consequently, they will learn to examine a linear equation in slope-intercept form ($y = mx + b$) to glean information such as the slope of the line (m) and the point at which the line crosses the y-axis. Based on this information alone, students should be able to translate the equation to draw its graph. Conversely, students will learn to examine the graph of a linear equation for its slope and y-intercept for purposes of translating the graph into an equation.

Which equation best models the data in the table below?

x	y
0	8
1	16
2	24
3	32

A $y = 8x$
B $y = 8x + 8$
C $y = x + 8$
D $y = 8x^2$

Answer: B

A telephone calling plan charges $1.00 per call and $.05 per minute. Write an equation for cost per call.

The correct answer is $y = 1.00 + .05x$.

Progression

Prior Years	This Year	Going Forward
Students focus on developing an understanding of ratio, proportion and rates, and solving problems using linear equations.	Students will expand their knowledge to include identifying, creating, and graphing linear functions.	Students will expand their problem-solving skills to include nonlinear functions. They will model real-life situations that use quadratic, cubic, and exponential functions.

4.01 Use linear functions or inequalities to model and solve problems; justify results.

a) Solve using tables, graphs, and algebraic properties.

b) Interpret constants and coefficients in the context of the problem.

Math Background

It is important for students to understand that the graph of a line represents all of the solutions of the corresponding linear equation for that line. Students should graph enough solutions for a linear equation so that they are convinced that every solution for that equation would be on that line.

Students who have limited exposure to geometry may be skeptical about how many points are needed to determine a line. A few minutes with a straightedge and a few non-collinear points will help them accept that only two are needed; however, it is wise to determine a few more in case they have made an error.

You can use the students understanding of linear functions as a stepping off point to discussing inequalities. The procedures used for solving inequalities are similar to those for solving equations. However, it will be important to emphasize the differences that exist between solving an equation and an inequality, most notably the multiplication and division properties of inequality. Multiplying or dividing both sides of an inequality by a negative number reverses the inequality symbol.

An average person burns 10 calories/minute biking and 7 calories/minute hiking. Write an equation to find the number of minutes a person would need to bike and hike to burn 500 calories.

Let $x =$ the number of minutes spent biking and $y =$ the number of minutes spent hiking.

The correct answer is $10x + 7y = 500$.

You want to spend less than $10 on snacks at the cinema. Chocolate mints cost about $4 per box. Popcorn costs about $5.50 per bag. Let c represent boxes of mints and d represent bags of popcorn.

Which inequality below models the given situation?

A $4c + 5.5d = 10$
B $4c + 5.5d < 10$
C $4c - 5.5d < 10$
D $4c \times 5.5d \geq 10$

Answer: B

Progression

Prior Years	This Year	Going Forward
Students focus on solving problems using linear equations.	Students will expand their algebraic understandings and interpretations to include quadratic equations.	Students will expand their problem-solving skills to include creating models using exponential, rational, logarithmic, and quadratic functions.

4.02 Graph, factor, and evaluate quadratic functions to solve problems.

Math Background

A quadratic function is a function that can be written in the form $y = f(x) = ax^2 + bx + c$.

The graph of a quadratic function is U-shaped, called a parabola.

Quadratic equations can be solved in a number of ways, by graphing, finding square roots, factoring, and completing the square. Quadratic equations can also be solved using the quadratic formula.

Quadratic equations have many everyday applications. One of the more common applications is the flight of a ball.

Because a quadratic function has a term that contains x^2, simplifying, graphing, and solving quadratic functions will involve using square roots. Consequently, a students will need to have a firm understanding of estimating and finding square roots.

Students will need help in learning to decide the best method for solving a quadratic equation. Graphing is preferable when the equation is simple or when a graphing calculator can be used. Finding square roots works well when there is no x-term in the equation, and the constant term is a perfect square. Factoring can be used with equations that can be factored. Finally, completing the square works best with equations that are easily transformed into perfect squares.

Which equation best models the data in the table below?

x	y
0	0
1	0.3
2	1.2
3	2.7
4	4.8

A $y = 0.3x$
B $y = 0.3x^2$
C $y = 0.6x^2$
D $y = x + 0.6$

Answer: B

Solve $x^2 + x - 6 = 0$ by factoring.

Factor: $(x + 3)(x - 2) = 0$.

Use the zero-product property:

$x + 3 = 0$ or $x - 2 = 0$,

and solve for x.

The correct answer is $x = -3$ or $x = 2$.

Progression

Prior Years	This Year	Going Forward
Students focus on the properties of and solving problems using linear equations and inequalities.	Students will expand their understanding to include solving and graphing systems of equations and inequalities.	Students will expand their operations with more complex systems (such as systems with three variables) of equations to model and solve problems.

4.03 Use systems of linear equations or inequalities in two variables to model and solve problems. Solve using tables, graphs, and algebraic properties; justify results.

Math Background

Two or more linear equations (or inequalities) together form a system of linear equations (or inequalities).

The solution of a system of equations is the point that is common to the equations of both graphs. In other words, the solution is the point where the lines intersect.

Systems of equations can also be solved algebraically, either by using substitution (replacing one variable with an equivalent expression containing the other variable) or by elimination (adding or subtracting equations to eliminate a variable).

Systems of equations have many practical applications, including the time or location where two travelers will meet, or finding how many products must be sold in order to make a profit.

Remind students that the solution set of a linear inequality is a region that has a boundary line. With a dashed boundary line, each point on the line is not part of the solution. On the other hand, points on a solid boundary line are part of the solution.

Just as two or more linear equations form a system of linear equations, two or more inequalities together form a system of linear inequalities. The solution of a system of linear inequalities is the region where the two inequalities overlap. This solution is a region with two boundary lines.

Solve the following system of linear equations.

$x + 2y = 10$

$8x + y = 50$

Eliminate the y variable and solve for x.

The correct answer is (6, 2).

The sum of two numbers is 25. The difference between four times the larger and three times the smaller is 50.

Which system describes this situation?

A $x + y = 25$
   $4x - 3y = 50$
B $x - y = 25$
   $4x + 3y = 50$
C $x + 3y = 25$
   $4x - y = 50$
D $x - y = 25$
   $4x - 3y = 50$

Answer: A

Progression

Prior Years	This Year	Going Forward
Students focus on understanding and using exponents, including scientific notation.	Students will expand their understanding of graphing and evaluating non-linear equations, such as exponential equations.	Students will work with rational exponents and learn to create and use models based on linear, exponential, quadratic, and cubic functions.

4.04 Graph and evaluate exponential functions to solve problems.

Math Background

An exponential function is a function in the form $y = a \cdot b^x$.

When b is greater than one, the function is modeling exponential growth. In this case, b is called the growth factor. When b is greater than zero, but less than one, the function is modeling exponential decay. In this case, b is called the decay factor.

The graph of an exponential function is a J-shaped curve.

One of the more common applications of exponential functions is modeling population growth. Other applications include depreciation, compound interest, and radioactive decay.

The graph of an exponential growth function rises from left to right. The graph of an exponential decay function falls from left to right.

Which of the following is a graph of the function $y = 2^x$?

A 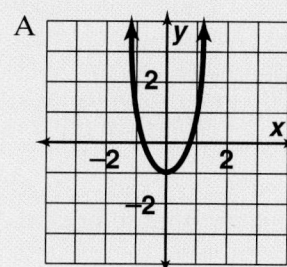   B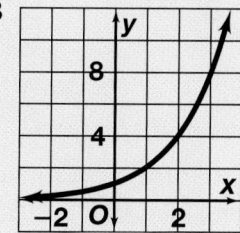

C 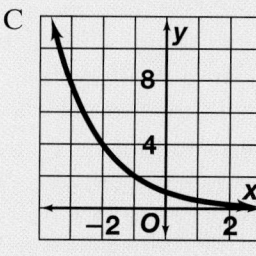   D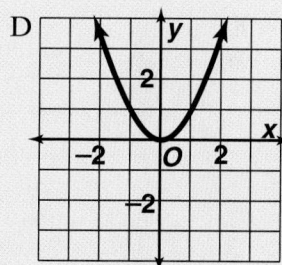

Answer: B

For the function $y = 3^x$, what is the value of y when $x = 3$?

Substitute the value of x in the equation and solved for y.

The correct answer is 27.

North Carolina Course of Study

Here is a complete list of the objectives of the North Carolina Standard Mathematics Course of Study for Algebra 1. These are provided so that you will know what you are expected to learn this year.

Following each objective is an example of how you might see that objective tested. These test questions will become more meaningful to you as the year unfolds. You might want to check back to this section of the book from time to time to check that you understand how to answer the questions.

NUMBER & OPERATION

1.01 Write equivalent forms of algebraic expressions to solve problems.
   a) Apply the laws of exponents.

What It Means to You

An exponent tells you how many times a number is multiplied by itself. For example, 2^4 is the same as $2 \times 2 \times 2 \times 2$. But what happens when you multiply or divide expressions that contain exponents? One way to simplify exponents is to write each expression in terms of its factors. For example, to simplify $3^3 \div 3^2$, you might write $\frac{3 \times 3 \times 3}{3 \times 3}$. You could then cross out factors in both the numerator and denominator and write $3^3 \div 3^2 = 3$. You may find, however, that sometimes there are too many factors for this method to be useful.

You have encountered sets of rules, such as the Order of Operations and the properties of addition and multiplication, which help you simplify expressions quickly and efficiently. You will learn a set of rules to help you simplify exponents.

Suppose you multiply x^2 times x^4. In this case, you add the exponents. So, $x^2 \times x^4 = x^6$. When you divide with exponents you subtract. If you divide x^6 by x^2, you will subtract the exponent 2 from the exponent 6. So $x^6 \div x^2 = x^4$. There is even a rule to simplify expressions when an exponent is raised to a power (expressions of the form $(x^a)^b$). You will use what you already know about exponents, the Order of Operations, and properties of multiplication to develop rules—called the laws of exponents—for simplifying expressions involving exponents. You will apply these rules to expressions with positive integer exponents. You will also see that rational exponents (exponents which are fractions and decimals) follow the same rules.

Where You'll Learn This
You will study this standard in chapters 1, 2, 8, and 9.

Simplify $(3xy^4)(4x^2y^5)$.

   A $7x^3y^9$
   B $12x^2y^{20}$
   C $12x^3y^9$
   D $-x^3y^9$

Answer: C

Simplify $3qp^4 \div 3p^3$.

   A qp
   B $3qp^7$
   C $\frac{1}{3}p$
   D $3qp^{12}$

Answer: A

b) Operate with polynomials.

What It Means to You

An algebraic expression is a math phrase. It includes numbers, variables (usually letters), and operation symbols. You have already worked with algebraic expressions in the form of monomials—expressions that are a single number, a single variable, or the product of numbers and variables, such as $4x$ and x^2. You know that you can add expressions with the same variable. For example, $3x + 4x = 7x$. Similarly, you can add expressions when variables are raised to powers, such as $3x^2 + 4x^2 = 7x^2$. Sometimes, you will want to work with expressions that are polynomials—expressions made up of one or more monomials. How do you add an expression like $3x^2 + 4x$? In this case, the variables are not raised to the same exponent, so they are not considered *like terms*. The expression is already in simplest form.

You will also encounter expressions in which you will multiply or divide monomials and polynomials. For example, you may want to multiply $2x(3y + x^2)$. You will learn that multiplying and dividing algebraic expressions is very similar to multiplying and dividing integer expressions. The properties of multiplication and addition that you learned in numeric expressions can also be applied to algebraic expressions. In this example, you can use the distributive property to simplify the expression.

You will apply what you already know about numeric expressions to algebraic expressions. You will learn how to simplify algebraic expressions. Some of these expressions will involve exponents; some will include more than one variable. You will learn how to add, subtract, multiply, and divide the parts of algebraic phrases to solve problems.

Where You'll Learn This

You will study this standard in chapters 1, 2, 8, and 9.

The algebraic expression $x(3x^2 - 2x + 1)$ is equal to which of the following expressions?

A $3x^3 - 2x + 1$
B $3x^3 - 2x^2 + 1$
C $3x^3 - 2x^2 + x$
D $4x^3 - 3x^2 + 2x$

Answer: C

Simplify the following expression:
$6(2x^2 + 3x - 1) - 2(4 - x^2)$. Show your work.

Answer: First, use the Distributive Property.
$12x^2 + 18x - 6 - 8 + 2x^2$

Then, combine like terms to simplify the expression.
$(12 + 2)x^2 + 18x - 6 - 8 = 14x^2 + 18x - 14$

Student's Guide

c) Factor polynomials.

What It Means to You

Numbers and symbols, such as 6, $3t$, $\frac{x}{8}$, $-4xy^2$, are examples of monomials—an expression that is a number, a variable, or a product of a number and one or more variables. A *polynomial* is a monomial or the sum or difference of two or more monomials. You can think of a polynomial as a group of monomials added together. Polynomials are also related to monomials through multiplication and division. You are familiar with finding the factors of a number. You know that two factors of 14 are 2 and 7. You use division to find integers that divide 14 without leaving a remainder. The factors of a polynomial, however, can be monomials and other polynomials. You can multiply monomials to create polynomials, and you can divide polynomials by monomials (and other polynomials) to find factors.

Just as there are many ways to find factors of integers—such as creating factor trees and division ladders, and using divisibility rules—there are many methods of factoring polynomials. In a method similar to dividing with integers, you can divide a polynomial by a monomial or another polynomial. For example, you may try to divide $x^2 + 6x + 8$ by $x + 2$ to see if $x + 2$ is a factor. You can also factor the individual parts of a polynomial to find common factors. These common factors will be factors of the polynomial. For example, in the polynomial $6x^2 + 3x$, the term $3x$ is a factor of both $6x^2$ and $3x$. It is also a factor of the polynomial. You can use this factor to find other factors. In any of the methods you choose, when you factor a polynomial, you look for factors whose product is the original polynomial. For example, $(x + 2)$ and $(x + 4)$ are factors of $x^2 + 6x + 8$.

Where You'll Learn This

You will study this standard in chapters 1, 2, 8, and 9.

 Find the factors of $x^2 - 8x + 12$.

A $(x + 6)$ and $(x + 2)$
B $(x + 2)$ and $(x + 4)$
C $(x - 6)$ and $(x + 2)$
D $(x - 6)$ and $(x - 2)$

Answer: D

 Which of the following is a factor of $4x^4 - 8x^8 + 2x^{16}$?

A $2x^4$
B $2x^{16}$
C $16x$
D x^8

Answer: A

1.02 Use formulas and algebraic expressions, including iterative and recursive forms, to model and solve problems.

What It Means to You

Sometimes you can use a formula or an expression to help solve a problem. In fact, many common types of problems have formulas that you can use. For example, to solve problems involving the area of a rectangle, you can use the formula for area of a rectangle. Many problems involve data that are related to other data and a formula gives the relationship, such as $F = 1.8C + 32$, relating temperatures in degrees Fahrenheit and degrees Celsius.

Sometimes data occur in an iterative (repeating) pattern or a recursive (applying a rule repeatedly) pattern. You may be able to solve a related problem by recognizing the pattern and modeling it with an expression or formula. Suppose for example, you are reading a book. You start on page one, and each day you read three pages. In three weeks, you are going to go on a vacation, and you want to know if you will have finished the book by then. From the iterations of three pages read each day, you can model the total numbers of pages read with the pattern 3, 3 + 3, 3 + 3 + 3, and so on. Or you can apply the recursive rule of adding 3 pages to the previous day's total for the pattern 3, 6, 9, 12, ...

In either case, you can model the pattern with the expression $3d$ for the total number of pages read in d days. You can iterate through 21 days, apply the recursive rule 20 times, or you can let $d = 21$ to determine whether you will finish the book by the time of your vacation.

Other situations will require more complicated formulas and equations. Many will involve exponents, fractions, and polynomials. You will learn how to model and solve real-world problems using algebraic expressions and formulas.

Where You'll Learn This

You will study this standard in chapters 2, 3, 4, 5, and 8.

Sarita called home using a phone card. The cost of using the card is $.85 per call and $.10 per minute. Her call cost $3.05. Write and solve an equation to find the length of the call in minutes. Show your work.

One way to answer this question is to let n equal the number of minutes. Then, you can write an equation:
$305 = 85 + 10n$

Solve the equation by first subtracting 85 from both sides as shown below:
$305 - 85 = 85 - 85 + 10n$

$220 = 10n$

Finally, solve for n by dividing both sides by 10:
$$\frac{220}{10} = \frac{10n}{10}$$

$22 = n$

So, the phone call took 22 minutes.

1.03 Model and solve problems using direct variation.

What It Means to You

There are many real-life examples of direct variation. For example, if you are paid $6.00 per hour that you work, then the amount you earn varies directly with the number of hours you work. In other words, the more hours you work, the more you are paid.

Two variables are said to vary directly with one another when changing one variable (your work hours) always changes the other variable (your paycheck) at the same rate. You can write an equation to model the relationship between the hours you work and the amount you are paid. If h is the number of hours you work and p is the amount you are paid, $p = 6h$. Other examples of direct variation include the relationship between rate, time, and distance traveled. If you are traveling at a certain rate, the distance you travel varies directly with the time spent traveling. The equation $d = rt$ models this relationship, where d is the distance, r is your constant speed, and t is the time spent traveling. Similarly, the force you must use to lift an object varies directly with the object's weight.

All of these relationships can be modeled with equations in the form $y = kx$, where k is a constant and x and y are variables that vary directly. To solve problems using direct variation, you will need to identify direct variation and represent it using algebraic expressions. You will learn to identify direct variation in problems and to write equations to model direct variation. You will then use your model to solve problems.

Where You'll Learn This

You will study this standard in chapter 5.

A winch turned by a crank is used to raise an anchor on a boat. It takes about half a pound of force to lift a 25-lb object using a winch on a certain boat. How much force would you need to apply to raise a 100-lb anchor? Show your work.

First, assume that the force you must apply to lift an object varies directly with the object's weight. Then you can solve by letting n equal the force you need to lift 100 lb. Set up a proportion like this one:

$$\frac{\text{Force 1}}{\text{Weight 1}} = \frac{\text{Force 2}}{\text{Weight 2}}$$

Plug in the amounts and cross multiply:

$$\frac{0.5}{25} = \frac{n}{100}$$

$$0.5 \times 100 = 25n$$

$$50 = 25n$$

Divide each side by 25.

$$2 = n$$

It will take 2 lb of force to lift the 100-lb anchor using the winch.

North Carolina Fact

Ocracoke Island, part of the Cape Hatteras National Seashore, was a hideout of Blackbeard the pirate and the site of many shipwrecks.

2.01 Find the lengths and midpoints of segments to solve problems.

What It Means to You

Measurements are an important part of geometry. You use dimensions of figures to calculate area, volume, and surface area. In real world situations, you use dimensions to determine if one object will fill a certain space or if a container is large enough for the material you want to put in it. One way to find measures is to measure them directly, using rulers or other measuring tools. You can measure a line segment to find its length or determine its midpoint.

In many cases, measuring with a ruler is impractical or the tools for measuring directly are not available. A line drawn in the coordinate plane is not always measured in terms of inches or centimeters. A figure may be too large or too small to measure directly. For example, suppose you know one friend is 3 miles east of the library and another friend is 4 miles north of the library, and you want to know how far from each other they are. You can draw a grid to represent their locations, and assign coordinates to each point.

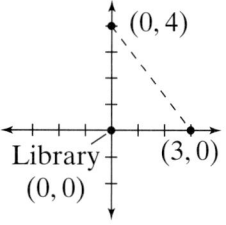

Measuring your diagram, however, will not give you an accurate measure of their distance. In these cases, you can use algebra to solve problems in geometry. You will learn to use algebraic formulas to find the length of a segment in the coordinate plane. You can also use a formula to find the midpoint of the segment (the point that divides a segment into two equal parts) in the plane. You can use this information to find the distance between two points, the length of the sides of a geometric figure, or the center of a circle.

Where You'll Learn This

You will study this standard in chapter 11.

The Smith and the Nguyen families are staying at the same campground. The Smiths hike 3 km west and 4 km south. The Nguyens hike 2 km east and 3 km north. How far apart are the two families?

A $\sqrt{2}$ km
B   2 km
C   6 km
D $\sqrt{74}$ km

Answer: D

Find the midpoint of a line segment with endpoints $(3, 7)$ and $(5, 3)$

A $(8, 10)$
B $(-2, 4)$
C $(4, 5)$
D $(3, 3)$

Answer: C

North Carolina Student Handbook **xxxiii**

Student's Guide

2.02 Use the parallelism or perpendicularity of lines and segments to solve problems.

What It Means to You

You may remember that the slope is the steepness of a line. You can use the slope of a line and its *y*-intercept or a point on the line to write an equation for the line in *slope-intercept form* or in *point-slope form*. Suppose that you know the equation of a line in slope-intercept form. You know another line is parallel to it (the two lines are in the same plane and never intersect), and you know its *y*-intercept, but you do not know its equation. You can use the first line to find the equation of the second. An important property of parallel lines is that they have the same slope and different *y*-intercepts. You can use this information to write the equation for the second line.

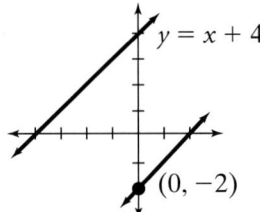

$y = x + 4$

$(0, -2)$

Perpendicular lines (lines that intersect at right angles) also have a special relationship to slope. If two lines are perpendicular, the product of their slopes is -1. This means that given the equation of a line in slope-intercept form (and a point on the perpendicular line), you can find the equation of another line perpendicular to it.

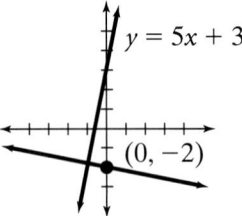

$y = 5x + 3$

$(0, -2)$

You will apply what you have learned about slope and equations of lines to parallel lines and perpendicular lines. You can use these line properties to solve many different kinds of problems.

Where You'll Learn This

You will study this standard in chapter 6.

A line contains the point $(6, 3)$ and is perpendicular to $y = \frac{x}{3} + 5$. Which of the following equations represents this line?

A $y = -\frac{x}{3} + 5$

B $y = \frac{x}{3} - 5$

C $y = -3x + 21$

D $y = \frac{1}{3}x + 15$

Answer: C

A line passes through the point $(2, -2)$ and is parallel to the line $y = 3x + 4$. What is its equation?

A $y = 3x + 8$
B $y = 2x + 4$
C $2x + y = 4$
D $3x - y = 8$

Answer: D

DATA ANALYSIS

3.01 Use matrices to display and interpret data.

What It Means to You

You often see data arranged in tables. When you need to compare different kinds of data, you can use a *matrix*. A matrix is a rectangular arrangement of numbers into rows and columns, not unlike a data table. In fact, you can think of a matrix as a type of table for organizing data. The plural of matrix is matrices.

Matrices are a convenient way to display and manipulate a large group of information. For example, if you have a data table with 20 rows and 20 columns, you may find it difficult to see the relationship between the data in a table. By writing the table as a matrix, you can more clearly see the relationship between the *elements*, or terms in the matrix.

You will see that matrices have many uses, from storing information about events, to describing groups of equations. You can use a matrix to model a system of equations, and manipulate the matrix to find the solution of the system. Matrices are also helpful when working with calculators and computers. Although you cannot enter a data table, many graphing calculators will allow you to input and manipulate a matrix. You will learn how to use matrices to write and draw conclusions about data.

Where You'll Learn This

You will study this standard in chapter 1.

Write the data in the table below as a matrix.

Olympic Medals Awarded in 2002

	Gold	Silver	Bronze
USA	10	14	11
China	2	2	4
Italy	4	4	4

Answer:

$$\begin{bmatrix} 10 & 14 & 11 \\ 2 & 2 & 4 \\ 4 & 4 & 4 \end{bmatrix}$$

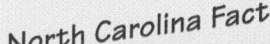

North Carolina Fact

Did you know that fossils of the Zatomus, a reptile that lived about 225 million years ago, have been found in North Carolina? This quadruped was known for its blade-like teeth.

Student's Guide

3.02 Operate (addition, subtraction, scalar multiplication) with matrices to solve problems.

What It Means to You

You often see data arranged in tables. When you need to use whole tables of data to solve problems, you can use matrices. Matrices provide a convenient method for storing and interpreting data, but they also make manipulating data easier.

You can add matrices that are the same size (have the same number of rows and columns). For example, if you represent the monthly book sales of two stores with one matrix, and the monthly magazine sales of the same two stores with another, you can add the matrices to find the total monthly sales.

To add matrices, you add each *element*, or term, in the first matrix to the corresponding term in the second matrix.

$$
\begin{array}{cc} \text{Store 1} & \text{Store 2} \end{array} \qquad \begin{array}{cc} \text{Store 1} & \text{Store 2} \end{array} \qquad \begin{array}{cc} \text{Store 1} & \text{Store 2} \end{array}
$$

$$
\begin{bmatrix} 300 & 415 \\ 560 & 325 \\ 481 & 382 \end{bmatrix} + \begin{bmatrix} 475 & 524 \\ 430 & 415 \\ 312 & 482 \end{bmatrix} = \begin{bmatrix} 775 & 939 \\ 990 & 740 \\ 793 & 864 \end{bmatrix}
$$

You can also multiply a matrix by a *scalar*, or a number. To multiply by a scalar, you multiply each element of the matrix by the same number. As you will see, you can add, subtract, and multiply bodies of data using matrices.

Where You'll Learn This

You will study this standard in chapters 1 and 7.

The matrices below show the number of first- and second-place ribbons two schools won in three swim meets. How many ribbons were won by both schools?

Johnson High

	First Place	Second Place
Meet 1	3	5
Meet 2	4	2
Meet 3	3	4

Frederick High

	First Place	Second Place
Meet 1	1	3
Meet 2	3	4
Meet 3	2	4

Answer:

To add two matrices, you add the corresponding elements.

Ribbons Won by Both Schools

	First Place	Second Place
Meet 1	4	8
Meet 2	7	6
Meet 3	5	8

3.03 Create linear models for sets of data to solve problems.
a) Interpret constants and coefficients in the context of the data.
b) Check the model for goodness-of-fit and use the model, where appropriate, to draw conclusions or make predictions.

What It Means to You

Real-world problems do not always follow model equations. However, you can examine data for patterns that look similar to the models you will learn about and find a best-fit model. For example, suppose you conduct a survey to compare memory to age. You have each participant examine a picture for a short time. You then ask a set of questions about the picture and record the number of correct responses and the person's age. You can plot your data in a *scatterplot*. In this situation, it is unlikely that the points will lie in a line. Some younger participants may have noticed certain aspects of the picture that older participants did not. In such cases, you can draw a *trend line* or a *line of best fit* to approximate the data. The line will represent the data, although it does not pass through each data point. You can then use the line to predict the correct number of responses a person with a certain age will give.

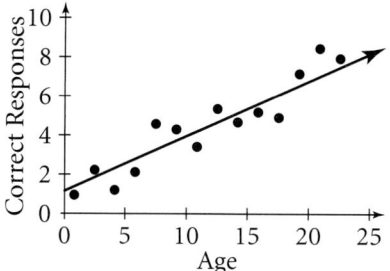

You will learn to construct models for data and different methods of creating trend lines. You will evaluate accuracy of trend lines and create lines of best fit—the trend line that most close approximates a set of data. Once you have a model to base the data on, you can use the model to draw conclusions or make predictions about that data.

Where You'll Learn This

You will study this standard in chapters 6 and 10.

Which equation best models the data in the table below?

Data Table

x	y
0	4
1	8
2	12
3	16
4	20
5	24

A $\quad y = 4x$
B $\quad y = 4x + 4$
C $\quad y = x + 4$
D $\quad y = 4x^2$

Answer: B

Student's Guide

ALGEBRA

4.01 Use linear functions or inequalities to model and solve problems; justify results.
    a) Solve using tables, graphs, and algebraic properties.
    b) Interpret constants and coefficients in the context of the problem.

What It Means to You

Many real-world situations can be modeled using the basic equation for a line or an inequality. To solve these kinds of problems, you often have to translate the information you know into an equation so you can make sense of it and understand the process used to obtain your answer. In some equations and inequalities, you will have a set of values to test. In these cases, you can substitute the values in the equation to see if they make a true statement. For example, suppose you have $25 to spend on CDs that cost $12 each. You want to buy two or three CDs. You can write an in-equality to represent this: $12c \leq 25$. You can then substitute 2 and 3 for c to see which makes a true statement. $12(2) = 24$, so you can buy two CDs. $12(3) = 36$, which is more than you have to spend. In more complicated situations, you may want to make a table to organize your work.

You will also learn to solve equations and inequali-ties using algebraic properties. For example, to solve $12c \leq 25$, you can divide both sides of the equation by 12 and find $c \leq 2\frac{1}{12}$. For other equations, you may find that graphing is the best way to solve the equation. You will learn to accurately draw graphs of linear equations and inequalities and interpret the graphs to find solutions. You will learn to write linear equations and inequalities to model problems and to decide which method is best for solving a problem.

Where You'll Learn This

You will study this standard in chapters 5, 6, and 10.

You want to spend less than $15 on snacks for a party. Chips cost about $3 per pound. The chip dip costs about $3.50 per pound. Let c represent pounds of chips and d represent pounds of dip.

Which inequality below models the given situation?

A $3c + 3.5d = 15$
B $3c + 3.5d < 15$
C $3c - 3.5d < 15$
D $3c \times 3.5d \geq 15$

Answer: B

Which of the following values of x is NOT a solution of $2x - 5 \geq 9$?

A $15\frac{1}{2}$
B   8.3
C   7
D   0

Answer: D

4.02 Graph, factor, and evaluate quadratic functions to solve problems.

What It Means to You

Functions that result in a line do not apply to all problems. Some problems are solved using a function that results in a U-shaped curve, called a *parabola*. You can recognize these equations by their squared variables (x^2). A function of the form $y = ax^2 + bx + c$ is called a *quadratic function*.

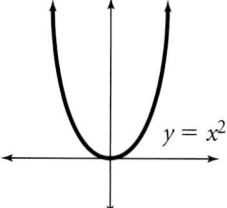

$y = x^2$

Quadratic equations appear in many physics problems. For example, the equation for the distance d an object dropped from a height h after time t seconds is given by the equation $d = -16t^2 + h$.

You will learn several methods of solving such equations, such as graphing the equation. You will also use what you have learned about factoring polynomials to factor quadratic equations. You can then use the *Zero-Product Property*, which says that you can find possible solutions by letting each factor equal zero and solving for the variable.

You will also derive and use the *quadratic formula*, which is written as $x = \dfrac{-b \pm \sqrt{b^2 - 4ac}}{2a}$. By substituting the coefficients and constants of a quadratic equation in the quadratic formula, you can solve any quadratic equation. Using these methods and the properties of quadratic equations, you will learn how to work with these functions and graph their curves to solve problems.

Where You'll Learn This
You will study this standard in chapter 10.

A ball is thrown into the air with an initial velocity of 56 ft/s. The ball's height, h, is given by the following quadratic equation:

$h = -16t^2 + 56t + 4$

Calculate the ball's maximum height. Show your work.

First, calculate the x-coordinate of the vertex:

$x = \dfrac{-b}{2a} = \dfrac{-(56)}{2(-16)} = 1.75$

Then, calculate the height.
$h = -16(1.75)^2 + 56(1.75) + 4$
$\quad = 53$

The ball is thrown 53 ft into the air.

Solve the equation $4z^2 + 18z = 10$. Show your work and explain which method you used.

Answer: First, subtract 10 from each side. Then, factor the quadratic expression.

$4z^2 + 18z - 10 = 2(2z - 1)(z + 5)$

Use the Zero Product Property to find $z = \frac{1}{2}$ and $z = -5$.

Student's Guide

4.03 Use systems of linear equations or inequalities in two variables to model and solve problems. Solve using tables, graphs, and algebraic properties; justify results.

What It Means to You

When two streets run into each other, they form an intersection. Similarly, when the graphs of two lines run into each other, they form an intersection at a point. The point of intersection represents a solution to both equations.

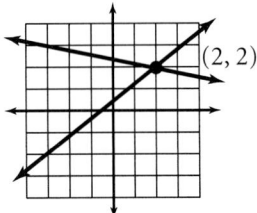

Similarly, when you graph two inequalities on a pair of axes, part of the graphs may overlap. The overlapping regions represent points that are solutions to both inequalities.

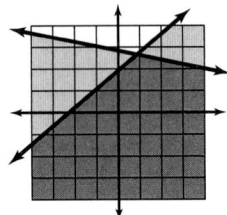

Once you have learned how to solve equations for lines and inequalities, you will learn to solve two or more of these equations together, which is known as a system of equations. You will learn how to find the *x*- and *y*-coordinates of the intersection points using a number of methods, including graphing and tables.

Sometimes you will find that a system is too complicated to graph or create a table easily. In such cases, you can substitute one equation into another, just as you have done with numbers. Other times, you will use algebraic properties to combine two or more equations into one equation with one variable.

Where You'll Learn This

You will study this standard in chapter 7.

Solve the following system of linear equations.
$$2x + 4y = 20 \qquad 16x + 2y = 100$$
Show your work.

One way to solve this system is to first eliminate a variable. To do this, multiply the first equation by 8:
$$8(2x + 4y = 20) \rightarrow 16x + 32y = 160$$

Then subtract the second equation from the product:
$$\begin{array}{r} 16x + 32y = 160 \\ -16x - 2y = -100 \\ \hline 0 + 30y = 60 \end{array}$$

Solve for y:
$$30y = 60$$
$$y = 2$$

Solve for x:
$$2x + 4(2) = 20$$
$$2x = 20 - 8$$
$$2x = 12$$
$$x = 6$$

Answer: (6, 2)

4.04 Graph and evaluate exponential functions to solve problems.

What It Means to You

Some things grow very rapidly, or exponentially. A bacterial population or a savings account with compound interest are examples of this kind of growth. These situations are modeled using an equation for a steep curve, called an *exponential function*. Exponential equations have a number raised to another power (a^x).

For example, think of a bacterial population that doubles every hour. If you start with one cell, how many cells will be in the population after x hours? In this case, the population is not changing by a fixed number every hour, so you cannot write a polynomial equation to describe the problem. Since the population doubles every hour, you will write $y = 2^x$ to represent the population.

If you graph the exponential equation, you will see that the curve has a J-shape. This shape models that rapid growth of an exponential function, and is one way to recognize the graph of an exponential function. You will also learn to recognize exponential functions that model exponential decay, or a rapid decrease in population or value. In the case of decay, the J-shape slopes downward.

You will learn how to graph these curves and work with their equations to solve problems.

Where You'll Learn This

You will study this standard in chapters 8 and 10.

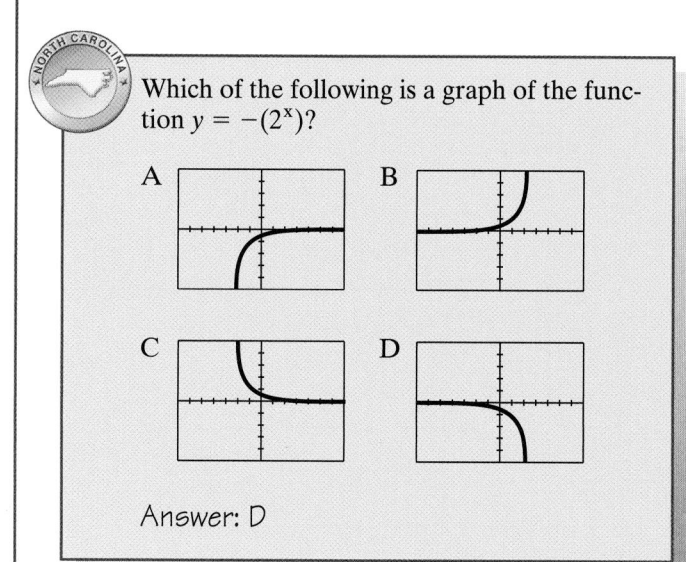

Which of the following is a graph of the function $y = -(2^x)$?

A   B

C   D

Answer: D

North Carolina Fact

Over 300 kinds of minerals and rocks are found in North Carolina, one of the most geologically diverse areas of the world.

Teacher's Edition Contents

Teacher Handbook

Program Overview **T4**

Authors and Reviewers **T8**

Student Edition Table of Contents **T12**

Research Overview **T26**

Mathematical Strands **T34**

Pacing Options **T39**

Student's Guide: Using Your Book for Success **T42**

Student Edition with Teacher Notes

Chapter 1: Tools of Algebra 2A

Chapter 2: Solving Equations 72A

Chapter 3: Solving Inequalities 132A

Chapter 4: Solving and Applying Proportions 180A

Chapter 5: Graphs and Functions 234A

Chapter 6: Linear Equations and Their Graphs 280A

Chapter 7: Systems of Equations and Inequalities 338A

Chapter 8: Exponents and Exponential Functions 392A

Chapter 9: Polynomials and Factoring 454A

Chapter 10: Quadratic Equations and Functions 508A

Chapter 11: Radical Expressions and Equations 576A

Chapter 12: Rational Expressions and Functions 634A

Extra Practice 702

Skills Handbook 714

Tables T748

Properties and Formulas T749

English/Spanish Illustrated Glossary T750

Answers to Instant Check System™ T758

Selected Answers T762

Additional Answers T770

Index T795

Acknowledgments T810

Prentice Hall Mathematics

A comprehensive program for North Carolina Grades 6-12

From middle school math to high school algebra and geometry, Prentice Hall has the solutions you need to guarantee math success for all students.

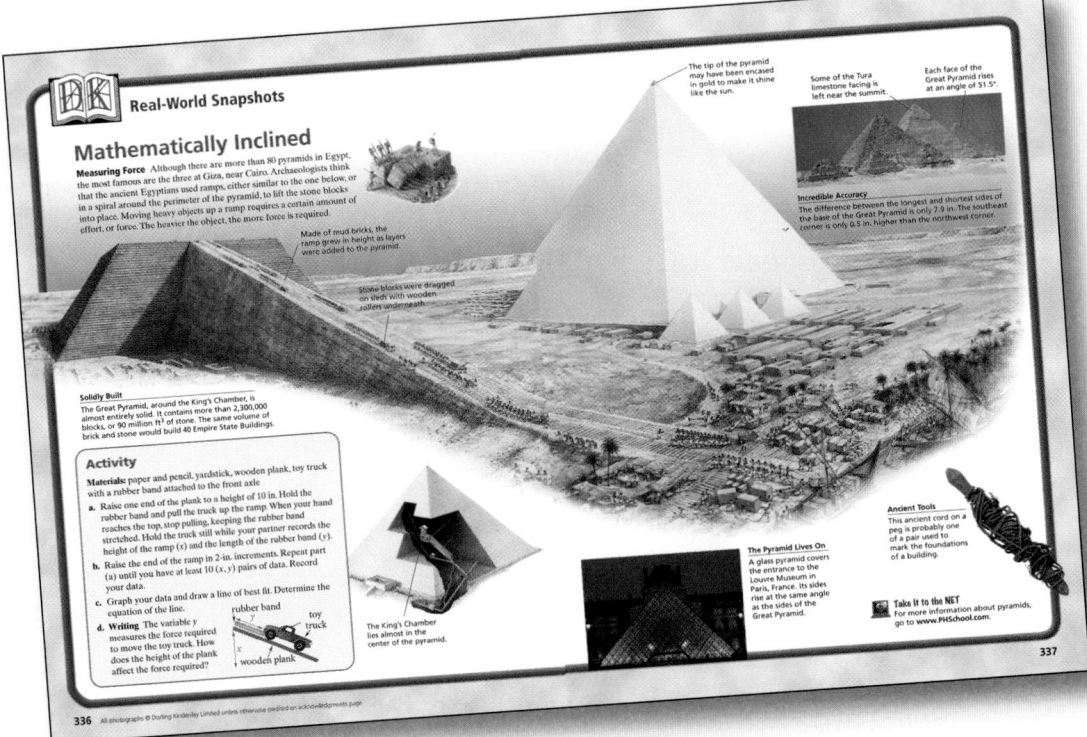

Reach Them ▶

Comprehensive Content Connects to Their World

Our comprehensive scope and sequence of content addresses the North Carolina Standard Course of Study, NAEP, and teacher expectations. Abundant real-world connections reinforce math applications, while unique *Dorling Kindersley Real-World Snapshots* bring math to life.

Empower Them ▶

Give Every North Carolina Student the Opportunity to Succeed

The *Instant Check System™* enables students to check their understanding at key points during instruction. No other program provides such an easy-to-use way to measure students' progress.
Leveled exercise sets allow you to easily craft just the right assignments for your classes. Plus, we've built in homework helpers along the way.

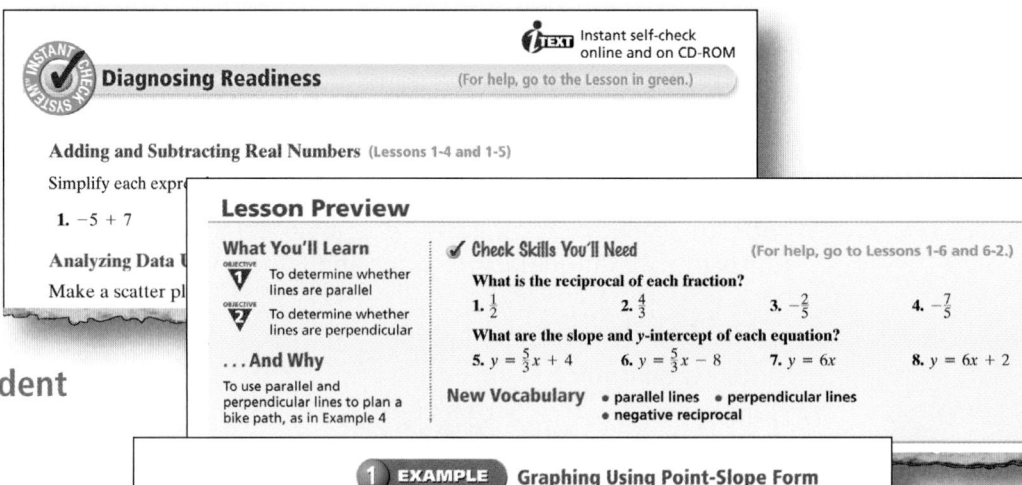

Diagnosing Readiness   (For help, go to the Lesson in green.)

iText Instant self-check online and on CD-ROM

Adding and Subtracting Real Numbers (Lessons 1-4 and 1-5)

Simplify each expression.

1. $-5 + 7$

Analyzing Data

Make a scatter plot

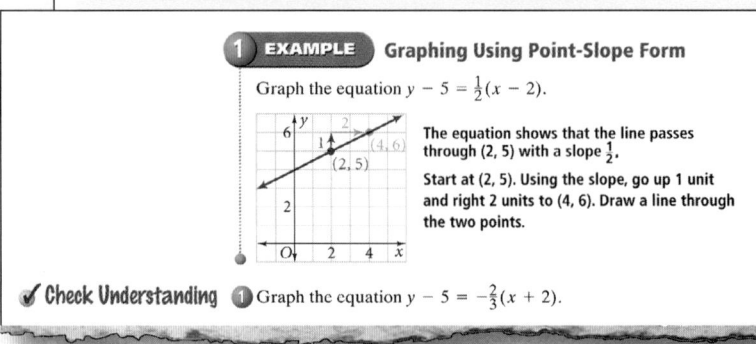

Lesson Preview

What You'll Learn

OBJECTIVE 1 To determine whether lines are parallel

OBJECTIVE 2 To determine whether lines are perpendicular

...And Why

To use parallel and perpendicular lines to plan a bike path, as in Example 4

✓ **Check Skills You'll Need**   (For help, go to Lessons 1-6 and 6-2.)

What is the reciprocal of each fraction?

1. $\frac{1}{2}$ 2. $\frac{4}{3}$ 3. $-\frac{2}{5}$ 4. $-\frac{7}{5}$

What are the slope and y-intercept of each equation?

5. $y = \frac{5}{3}x + 4$ 6. $y = \frac{5}{3}x - 8$ 7. $y = 6x$ 8. $y = 6x + 2$

New Vocabulary • parallel lines • perpendicular lines • negative reciprocal

1 EXAMPLE   Graphing Using Point-Slope Form

Graph the equation $y - 5 = \frac{1}{2}(x - 2)$.

The equation shows that the line passes through (2, 5) with a slope $\frac{1}{2}$.

Start at (2, 5). Using the slope, go up 1 unit and right 2 units to (4, 6). Draw a line through the two points.

✓ **Check Understanding** ❶ Graph the equation $y - 5 = -\frac{2}{3}(x + 2)$.

NORTH CAROLINA
MATH

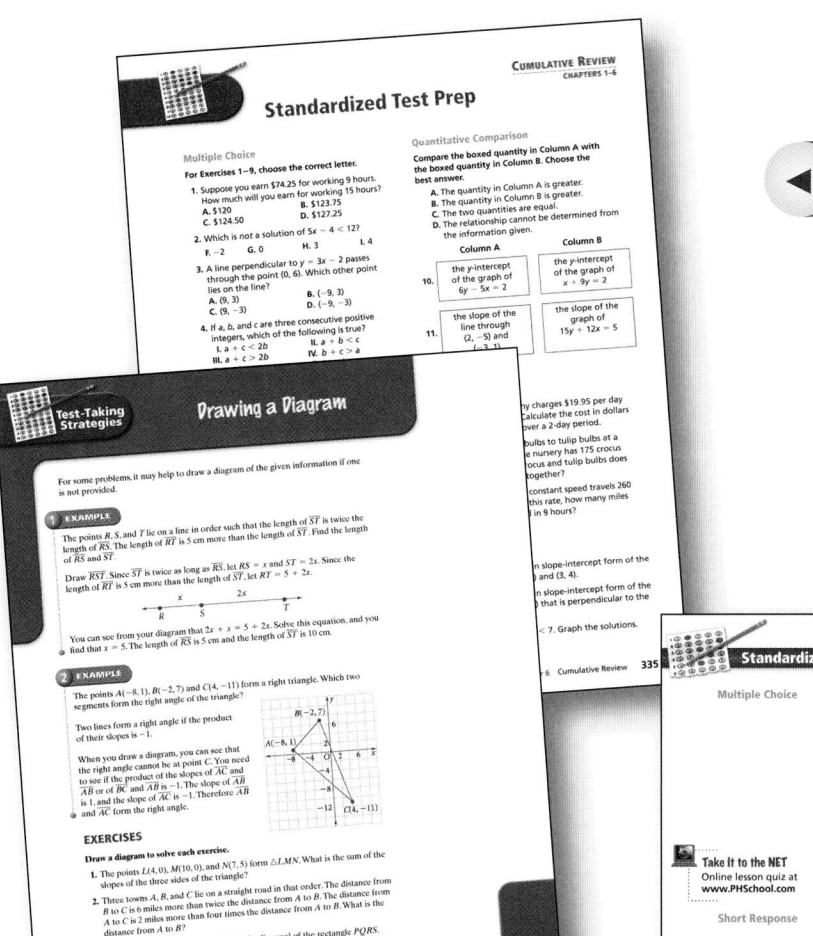

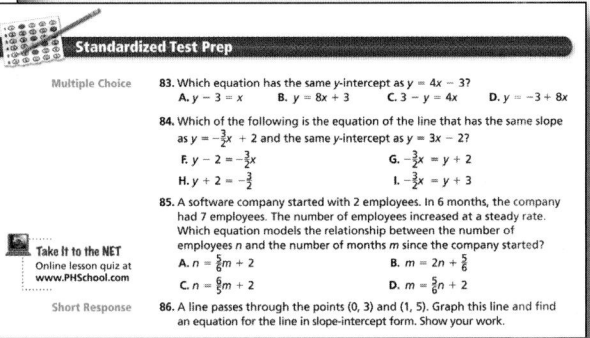

◀ Prepare Them

Test Prep Strand Guarantees EOC and NAEP Success

Reading comprehension activities and test-taking strategies are included throughout the program. Test prep practice in every lesson gives students the confidence they need to succeed on the North Carolina assessments.

◀ And Get the Support You Deserve

Outstanding Teacher Time Savers Allow for Effective Instruction

Our comprehensive *Presentation Assistant Plus!* provides all the material you need to teach every lesson step-by-step from beginning to end, while the unique *PH SuccessNet* unlocks a whole new set of online solutions for teaching success.

OVER
700
transparencies
per Grade
Level!

Prentice Hall Mathematics

Comprehensive content with a scope and sequence that helps you meet the North Carolina Standard Course of Study while focusing on specific student needs

Content Standards

Careful consideration of the North Carolina Standard Course of Study and the National Assessment of Educational Progress 2005 Guidelines was made prior to developing the scope and sequence of content for each text. In addition, North Carolina teacher input concerning content issues helped to determine the final content coverage of the entire program. Consequently, with *Prentice Hall Mathematics*, you can be assured that new content standards are covered along with the content North Carolina teachers know is important.

Strand Coverage

Important mathematics strands such as number theory, algebra, geometry, measurement, data analysis, statistics, and probability are thoroughly developed as appropriate to each level. Each text from *Pre-Algebra* through *Algebra 2* provides excellent coverage of the topics indicated for that level while other strands are reviewed and reinforced to help students make important connections

Reading and Math

Reading Math lessons are included throughout the program to help students to become more active in the learning process. Reading math vocabulary is carefully developed, and students learn a variety of techniques to help them more effectively read their textbook and mathematical text in general. Reading and Math Literacy Masters are also available.

Alternate Course Planning Guides

A Basic Algebra Planning Guide and an Informal Geometry Planning Guide help you structure alternative courses to meet the needs of less able students. In addition, Connections to Precalculus Masters accompany *Algebra 2* to help you highlight key skills that will ensure success for all your students who continue their study of mathematics.

Tables of Contents

PRE-ALGEBRA

1. Algebraic Expressions and Integers
2. Solving One-Step Equations and Inequalities
3. Decimals and Equations
4. Factors, Fractions, and Exponents
5. Operations with Fractions
6. Ratios, Proportions, and Percents
7. Solving Equations and Inequalities
8. Linear Functions and Graphing
9. Spatial Thinking
10. Area and Volume
11. Right Triangles in Algebra
12. Data Analysis and Probability
13. Nonlinear Functions and Polynomials

ALGEBRA 1

1. Tools of Algebra
2. Solving Equations
3. Solving Inequalities
4. Solving and Applying Proportions
5. Graphs and Functions
6. Linear Equations and Their Graphs
7. Systems of Equations and Inequalities
8. Exponents and Exponential Functions
9. Polynomials and Factoring
10. Quadratic Equations and Functions
11. Radical Expressions and Equations
12. Rational Expressions and Functions

GEOMETRY

1. Tools of Geometry
2. Reasoning and Proof
3. Parallel and Perpendicular Lines
4. Congruent Triangles
5. Relationships Within Triangles
6. Quadrilaterals
7. Area
8. Similarity
9. Right Triangle Trigonometry
10. Surface Area and Volume
11. Circles
12. Transformations

ALGEBRA 2

1. Tools of Algebra
2. Functions, Equations, and Graphs
3. Linear Systems
4. Matrices
5. Quadratic Equations and Functions
6. Polynomials and Polynomial Functions
7. Radical Functions and Rational Exponents
8. Exponential and Logarithmic Functions
9. Rational Functions
10. Quadratic Relations
11. Sequence and Series
12. Probability and Statistics
13. Periodic Functions and Trigonometry
14. Trigonometric Identities and Equations

  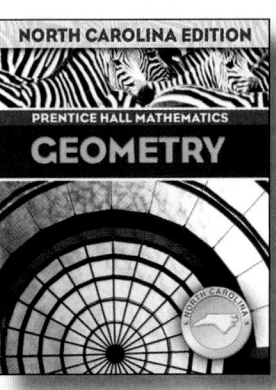 

NORTH CAROLINA EDITION — PRENTICE HALL MATHEMATICS — PRE-ALGEBRA | ALGEBRA 1 | GEOMETRY | ALGEBRA 2

Complete North Carolina Resources

 North Carolina Student Edition
iText—Interactive text online and on CD-ROM
North Carolina Teacher's Edition
Teaching Resources
- Grab & Go Chapter Support Files
  - Practice
  - Reteaching
  - Enrichment
  - Chapter Projects
  - Checkpoint Quizzes
  - Chapter Tests
  - Alternative Assessment
  - Cumulative Review
- Cumulative Assessment
- Solution Key

Reaching All Students

Practice Workbook
Reading and Math Literacy Masters
Guided Problem-Solving Masters
Hands-on Activities
Technology Activities
Prentice Hall MathNotes Folders
Skills Intervention Kit

Coming Soon— Online Intervention

Teacher Time Savers

Presentation Assistant Plus!
- Additional Examples on Transparencies
- Daily Skills Check and Lesson Quiz Transparencies
- Problem of the Day Transparencies
- Student Edition Answers on Transparencies
- Classroom Aid Transparencies
- Prentice Hall Presentation Pro CD-ROM

Assessment and Test Prep

Prentice Hall Assessment System
- North Carolina Computer Test Generator CD-ROM
- Algebra Readiness Tests
- Assessment Resources
  - Checkpoint Quizzes
  - Chapter Tests, Forms A & B
  - Alternative Assessment
  - Cumulative Assessment
- North Carolina Content Diagnostic Tests
- Skills and Concepts Review
- North Carolina EOC and NAEP Preparation Workbook with Teacher's Guide
- Test-Taking Strategies with Transparencies

Spanish Support

Student Edition, Spanish Version
Spanish Practice Workbook
Spanish Reading and Math Literacy Masters
Spanish Assessment Resources

Technology

iText—Interactive text online and on CD-ROM
Prentice Hall Presentation Pro CD-ROM
North Carolina Resource Pro® with Planning Express® CD-ROM
North Carolina Computer Test Generator CD-ROM
PH SuccessNet Teacher Center Web Site
PHSchool.com Textbook Site

Take a virtual tour of the program at
PHSchool.com/northcarolina

Authors

Series Authors

Dan Kennedy, Ph.D., is a classroom teacher and the Lupton Distinguished Professor of Mathematics at the Baylor School in Chattanooga, Tennessee. A frequent speaker at professional meetings on the subject of mathematics education reform, Dr. Kennedy has conducted more than 50 workshops and institutes for high school teachers. He is co-author of textbooks in calculus and precalculus, and from 1990 to 1994 he chaired the College Board's AP Calculus Development Committee. He is a 1992 Tandy Technology Scholar and a 1995 Presidential Award winner.

Randall I. Charles, Ph.D., is Professor Emeritus in the Department of Mathematics and Computer Science at San Jose State University, San Jose, California. He began his career as a high school mathematics teacher, and he was a mathematics supervisor for five years. Dr. Charles has been a member of several NCTM committees and is the former Vice President of the National Council of Supervisors of Mathematics. Much of his writing and research has been in the area of problem solving. He has authored more than 75 mathematics textbooks for kindergarten through college.

ISBN 0-13-052316-X

3 4 5 6 7 8 9 10   06 05 04 03

Test-Taking Strategies
Test-Taking Strategies in every chapter teach you strategies to be successful and give you practice in the skills you need to pass state tests and standardized national exams.

Standardized Test Prep
Standardized Test Prep pages in every chapter give you more opportunities to prepare for the tests you will have to take.

Test Item Formats
The *Standardized Test Prep* exercises in your book give you the practice you need to answer all types of test questions.
- *Multiple Choice*
- *Quantitative Comparison*
- *Gridded Response*, for which you write your answer in a grid
- *Short Response*, which are scored using a rubric
- *Extended Response*, which are scored using a rubric
- *Reading Comprehension*

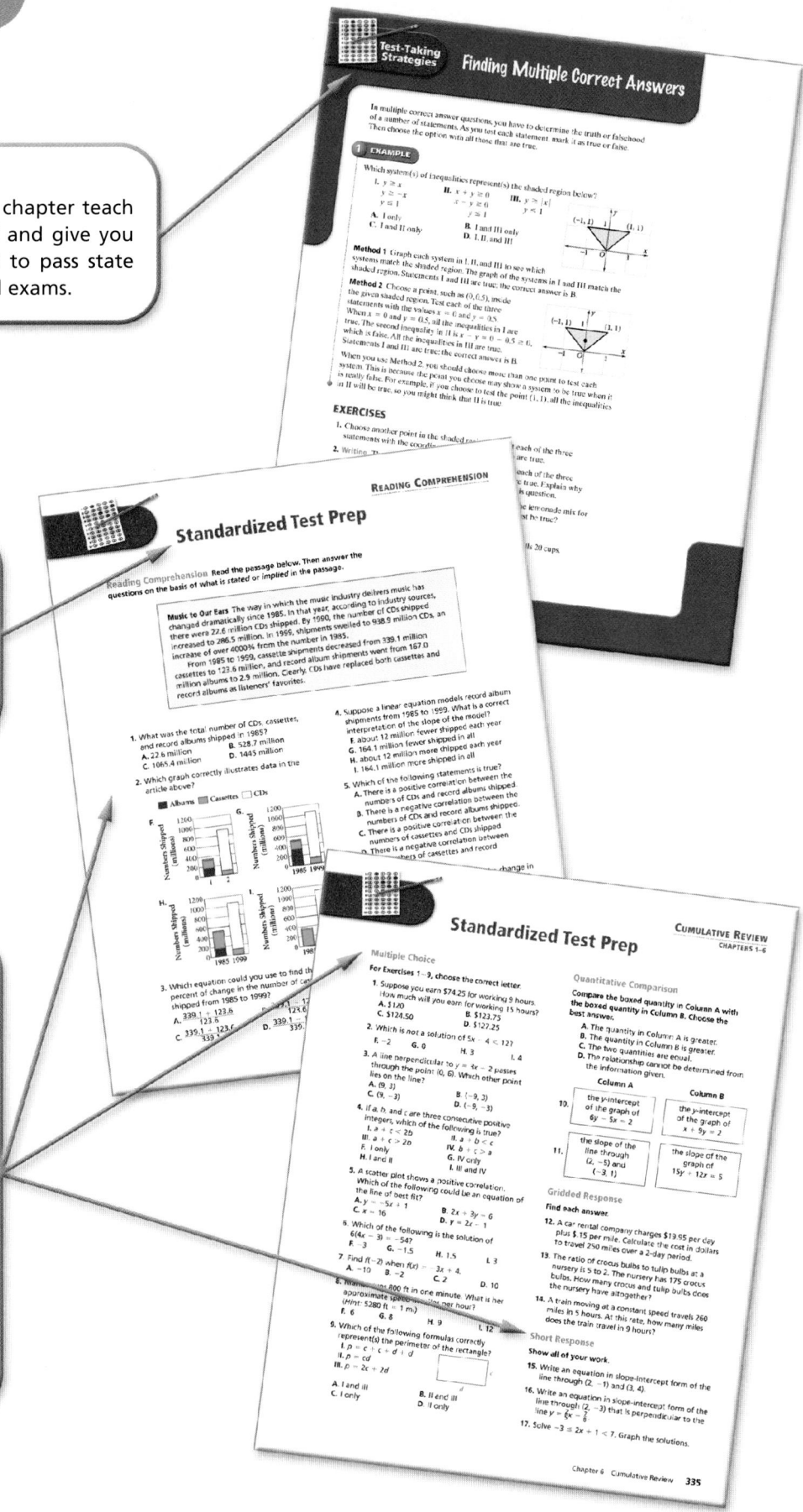

Reviewers

North Carolina Math Program Advisors

Kelly S. Crisp
Mathematics Teacher
Buncombe County Schools
Arden, North Carolina

Don McGurrin
Educational Math
Consultant
Clayton, North Carolina

Sheila S. Brookshire
Mathematics Teacher
AC Reynolds Middle School
Asheville, North Carolina

Cynthia Hanner Davis
Mathematics Teacher
Northeast High School
Greensboro, North Carolina

Judy Porter
Leesville Road High School
Raleigh, North Carolina

Dr. Ann R. Crawford
University of North Carolina
 at Wilmington
Wilmington, North Carolina

Algebra 1 Reviewers

Mary Lou Beasley
Southside Fundamental
 Middle School
St. Petersburg, Florida

Jane E. Damaske
Lakeshore Public Schools
Stevensville, Michigan

**Ann Marie Palmieri-
 Monahan**
Director of Mathematics
Bayonne Board of Education
Bayonne, New Jersey

Blanche Smith Brownley
Washington, D.C., Public
 Schools
Washington, D.C.

Stacy A. Ego
Warren Central High School
Indianapolis, Indiana

Marie Schalke
Woodlawn Middle School
Long Grove, Illinois

Joseph Caruso
Somerville High School
Somerville, Massachusetts

Earl R. Jones
Formerly, Kansas City
 Public Schools
Kansas City, Missouri

Julie Welling
LaPorte High School
LaPorte, Indiana

Belinda Craig
Highland West Junior High
 School
Moore, Oklahoma

Jeanne Lorenson
James H. Blake High School
Silver Spring, Maryland

Sharon Zguzenski
Naugatuck High School
Naugatuck, Connecticut

John T. Mace
Hibbett Middle School
Florence, Alabama

Geometry Reviewers

Marian Avery
Great Valley High School
Malvern, Pennsylvania

Mary Emma Bunch
Farragut High School
Knoxville, Tennessee

Karen A. Cannon
K–12 Mathematics Coordinator
Rockwood School District
Eureka, Missouri

Johnnie Ebbert
Department Chairman
DeLand High School
DeLand, Florida

Russ Forrer
Math Department Chairman
East Aurora High School
Aurora, Illinois

Andrea Kopco
Midpark High School
Middleburg Heights, Ohio

Gordon E. Maroney III
Camden Fairview High School
Camden, Arkansas

Charlotte Phillips
Math Coordinator
Wichita USD 259
Wichita, Kansas

Richard P. Strausz
Farmington Public Schools
Farmington, Michigan

Jane Tanner
Jefferson County International
Baccalaureate School
Birmingham, Alabama

Karen D. Vaughan
Pitt County Schools
Greenville, North Carolina

Robin Washam
Math Specialist
Puget Sound Educational
   Service District
Burien, Washington

Algebra 2 Reviewers

Josiane Fouarge
Landry High School
New Orleans, Louisiana

Susan Hvizdos
Math Department Chair
Wheeling Park High School
Wheeling, West Virginia

Kathleen Kohler
Kearny High School
Kearny, New Jersey

Julia Kolb
Leesville Road High School
Raleigh, North Carolina

Deborah R. Kula
Sacred Hearts Academy
Honolulu, Hawaii

Betty Mayberry
Gallatin High School
Gallatin, Tennessee

John L. Pitt
Formerly, Prince William
   County Schools
Manassas, Virginia

Margaret Plouvier
Billings West High School
Billings, Montana

Sandra Sikorski
Berea High School
Berea, Ohio

Tim Visser
Grandview High School
Cherry Creek School District
Aurora, Colorado

Mathematics Content Consultants

Courtney Lewis
Prentice Hall Senior National Consultant
Baltimore, Maryland

Deana Cerroni
Prentice Hall National Consultant
Las Vegas, Nevada

Kim Margel
Prentice Hall National Consultant
Scottsdale, Arizona

Sandra Mosteller
Prentice Hall National Consultant
Anderson, South Carolina

Rita Corbett
Prentice Hall Consultant
Elgin, Illinois

Cathy Davies
Prentice Hall Consultant
Laguna Niguel, California

Sally Marsh
Prentice Hall Consultant
Baltimore, Maryland

Dr. Barbara Rogers
Prentice Hall Consultant
Raleigh, North Carolina

Rose Primiani
Prentice Hall Consultant
Brick, New Jersey

Loretta Rector
Prentice Hall Consultant
Foresthill, California

Charlotte Samuels
Prentice Hall Consultant
Lafayette Hill, Pennsylvania

Margaret Thomas
Prentice Hall Consultant
Indianapolis, Indiana

Contents in Brief

Prentice Hall Web Codes xix

Using Your Book for Success xx

Chapter 1   Tools of Algebra 2

Chapter 2   Solving Equations 72

Chapter 3   Solving Inequalities 132

Chapter 4   Solving and Applying Proportions 180

Chapter 5   Graphs and Functions 234

Chapter 6   Linear Equations and Their Graphs 280

Chapter 7   Systems of Equations and Inequalities 338

Chapter 8   Exponents and Exponential Functions 392

Chapter 9   Polynomials and Factoring 454

Chapter 10   Quadratic Equations and Functions 508

Chapter 11   Radical Expressions and Equations 576

Chapter 12   Rational Expressions and Functions 634

Extra Practice 702

Skills Handbook

Problem Solving Additional Lessons
Draw a Diagram 714
Try, Check, Revise 715
Look for a Pattern and Make a Table 716
Solve a Simpler Problem 717
Use Logical Reasoning 718
Work Backward 719

Numbers and Operations Additional Lessons
Prime Numbers and Composite Numbers 720
Factors and Multiples 721
Divisibility 722
Using Estimation 723
Simplifying Fractions 724
Fractions and Decimals 725
Adding and Subtracting Fractions 726
Multiplying and Dividing Fractions 727
Fractions, Decimals, and Percents 728
Exponents 729

Geometry and Measurement Additional Lessons
Measuring and Classifying Angles 730
Perimeter, Area, and Volume 731
Translations 732
Reflections 733
Rotations 734

Data Analysis & Probability Additional Lessons
Line Plots 735
Bar Graphs 736
Histograms 737
Line Graphs 738
Circle Graphs 739
Box-and-Whisker Plots 740
Choosing an Appropriate Graph 741
Misleading Graphs 742
Probability Distributions 743
Simulations 744
Conducting a Survey 745
Interpreting Statistical Results 746
Spreadsheets 747

Tables
Measures 748
Symbols 749
Squares and Square Roots 750
Trigonometric Ratios 751

Properties and Formulas
Properties and Formulas 752
Formulas of Geometry 756

English/Spanish Illustrated Glossary ... 757

Answers to Instant Check System 787

Selected Answers 801

Index 833

Acknowledgments 847

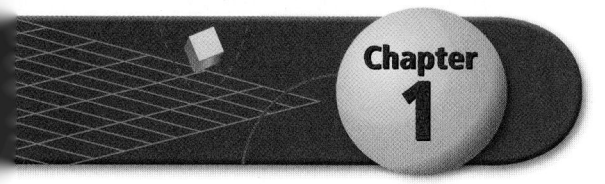

Chapter 1

Tools of Algebra

✓ **Diagnosing Readiness** 2

1-1 **Using Variables** 4

1-2 **Exponents and Order of Operations** 9
  • Reading Math: Reading an Example, 16

1-3 **Exploring Real Numbers** 17

1-4 **Adding Real Numbers** 24

✓ **Checkpoint Quiz 1** 31

1-5 **Subtracting Real Numbers** 32

1-6 **Multiplying and Dividing Real Numbers** 37
  • Technology: Matrices, 45

1-7 **The Distributive Property** 47
  • Investigation: The Distributive Property, 46

1-8 **Properties of Real Numbers** 54

✓ **Checkpoint Quiz 2** 58

1-9 **Graphing Data on the Coordinate Plane** [Data & Statistics] 59

Assessment
  • Test-Taking Strategies: Writing Gridded Responses, 66
  • Chapter Review, 67
  • Chapter Test, 70
  • Standardized Test Prep: Reading Comprehension, 71

Student Support

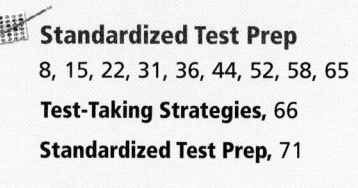 **Instant Check System**

Diagnosing Readiness, 2

Check Skills You'll Need, 4, 9, 17, 24, 32, 37, 47, 54, 59

Check Understanding, 4, 5, 6, 10, 11, 12, 17, 18, 19, 20, 25, 26, 27, 32, 33, 34, 38, 39, 40, 41, 47, 48, 49, 55, 56, 60, 61, 62

Checkpoint Quiz, 31, 58

Reading Math

Reading Math, 4, 5, 10, 18, 19, 40

Reading an Example, 16

Understanding Vocabulary, 67

Reading Comprehension, 71

Standardized Test Prep

8, 15, 22, 31, 36, 44, 52, 58, 65

Test-Taking Strategies, 66

Standardized Test Prep, 71

Real-World Connections

Music, 5
History, 14
Chemistry, 29
Archaeology, 35
Sports, 51
A Point in Time, 53
Nutrition, 64
. . . and more!

Table of Contents

Chapter 2

Solving Equations

✓ **Diagnosing Readiness** **72**

2-1 **Solving One-Step Equations** **74**

2-2 **Solving Two-Step Equations** **81**
   • Reading Math: Reading For Problem Solving, 87

2-3 **Solving Multi-Step Equations** **88**

✓ **Checkpoint Quiz 1** **94**

2-4 **Equations With Variables on Both Sides** **96**
   • Investigation: Modeling Equations, 95
   • Technology: Graphing to Solve Equations, 102

2-5 **Equations and Problem Solving** **103**

2-6 **Formulas** **111**
   • Extension: Developing Geometric Formulas, 116

✓ **Checkpoint Quiz 2** **115**

2-7 **Using Measures of Central Tendency** [Data & Statistics] . . **118**

Assessment
   • Test-Taking Strategies: Writing Short Responses, 124
   • Chapter Review, 125
   • Chapter Test, 128
   • Standardized Test Prep: Cumulative Review, 129

Real-World Snapshots: Applying Variation **130**

Student Support

✓ **Instant Check System**
   Diagnosing Readiness, 72
   Check Skills You'll Need, 74, 81, 88, 96, 103, 111, 118
   Check Understanding, 75, 76, 77, 82, 83, 88, 89, 90, 97, 98, 103, 104, 105, 106, 107, 111, 112, 113, 119, 120, 121
   Checkpoint Quiz, 94, 115

📖 **Reading Math**
   Reading Math, 75, 85, 90, 106
   Reading For Problem Solving, 87
   Understanding Vocabulary, 125

🏁 **Standardized Test Prep**
   80, 86, 93, 101, 110, 115, 123
   Test-Taking Strategies, 124
   Standardized Test Prep, 129

🌐 **Real-World Connections**
   Algebra at Work, 94
   Flying, 99
   Construction, 113
   Wildlife Management, 122
   Mechanics, 130
   Bicycles, 130
   . . . and more!

Solving Inequalities

Student Support

✓ **Instant Check System**

Diagnosing Readiness, 132

Check Skills You'll Need, 134, 140, 146, 153, 161, 167

Check Understanding, 134, 135, 136, 140, 141, 142, 147, 148, 149, 153, 154, 155, 161, 162, 163, 167, 168, 169

Checkpoint Quiz, 151, 166

Reading Math

Reading Math, 134, 135, 141, 150, 161

Reading to Analyze Errors, 152

Understanding Vocabulary, 175

Reading Comprehension, 179

Standardized Test Prep
139, 145, 150, 158, 166, 171

Test-Taking Strategies, 174

Standardized Test Prep, 179

Real-World Connections

Gymnastics, 143
Community Service, 148
Health Care, 157
Algebra at Work, 159
Chemistry, 162
Meteorology, 165
Elections, 170
. . . and more!

✓ **Diagnosing Readiness** **132**

3-1 Inequalities and Their Graphs **134**

3-2 Solving Inequalities Using Addition and Subtraction **140**

3-3 Solving Inequalities Using Multiplication and Division **146**
• Reading Math: Reading to Analyze Errors, 152

✓ **Checkpoint Quiz 1** **151**

3-4 Solving Multi-Step Inequalities **153**
• Extension: Interpreting Solutions, 160

3-5 Compound Inequalities **161**

✓ **Checkpoint Quiz 2** **166**

3-6 Absolute Value Equations and Inequalities **167**
• Extension: Algebraic Reasoning, 173

Assessment
• Test-Taking Strategies: Writing Extended Responses 174
• Chapter Review, 175
• Chapter Test, 178
• Standardized Test Prep: Reading Comprehension, 179

Chapter 4

Solving and Applying Proportions

Student Support

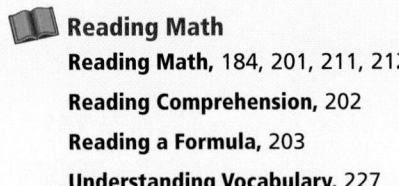 Instant Check System
Diagnosing Readiness, 180

Check Skills You'll Need, 182, 189, 197, 204, 211, 219

Check Understanding, 182, 183 184, 185, 190, 191, 197, 198, 199, 200, 204, 205, 206, 212, 213, 220, 221

Checkpoint Quiz, 195, 217

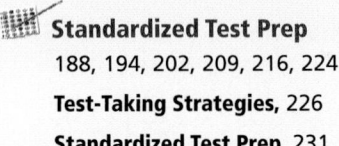 Reading Math
Reading Math, 184, 201, 211, 212

Reading Comprehension, 202

Reading a Formula, 203

Understanding Vocabulary, 227

Standardized Test Prep
188, 194, 202, 209, 216, 224

Test-Taking Strategies, 226

Standardized Test Prep, 231

Real-World Connections
Cycling, 184
Demographics, 187
Architecture, 193
Farming, 205
Radio, 215
Algebra at Work, 224
Baseball, 232
. . . and more!

✔ Diagnosing Readiness 180

4-1 Ratio and Proportion 182

4-2 Proportions and Similar Figures 189

✔ Checkpoint Quiz 1 195

4-3 Proportions and Percent Equations 197
• Investigation: Modeling Percents, 196
• Reading Math: Reading a Formula, 203

4-4 Percent of Change 204

4-5 Applying Ratios to Probability (Probability) 211
• Investigation: (Probability) Understanding Probability, 210
• Technology: (Data & Statistics) Conducting a Simulation, 218

✔ Checkpoint Quiz 2 217

4-6 Probability of Compound Events (Probability) 219
• Extension: (Data & Statistics) Sampling, 225

Assessment
• Test-Taking Strategies: Quantitative Comparisons, 226
• Chapter Review, 227
• Chapter Test, 230
• Standardized Test Prep: Reading Comprehension, 202
• Standardized Test Prep: Cumulative Review, 231

Real-World Snapshots: Applying Probability (Probability) . . 232

Chapter 5

Graphs and Functions

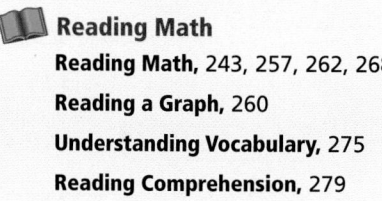

Student Support

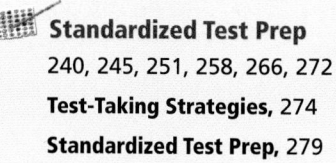

Instant Check System

Diagnosing Readiness, 234

Check Skills You'll Need, 236, 241, 247, 254, 261, 268

Check Understanding, 236, 237, 241, 242, 243, 248, 249, 254, 255, 262, 263, 264, 268, 269, 270

Checkpoint Quiz, 246, 267

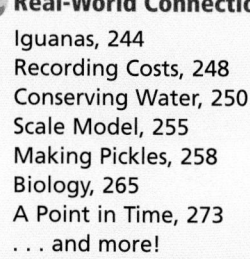

Reading Math

Reading Math, 243, 257, 262, 268

Reading a Graph, 260

Understanding Vocabulary, 275

Reading Comprehension, 279

Standardized Test Prep

240, 245, 251, 258, 266, 272

Test-Taking Strategies, 274

Standardized Test Prep, 279

Real-World Connections

Iguanas, 244
Recording Costs, 248
Conserving Water, 250
Scale Model, 255
Making Pickles, 258
Biology, 265
A Point in Time, 273
. . . and more!

✔ **Diagnosing Readiness** 234

5-1 Relating Graphs to Events 236

5-2 Relations and Functions 241

✔ **Checkpoint Quiz 1** 246

5-3 Function Rules, Tables, and Graphs 247
• Technology: Function Rules, Tables, and Graphs, 253

5-4 Writing a Function Rule 254
• Reading Math: Reading a Graph, 260

5-5 Direct Variation 261

✔ **Checkpoint Quiz 2** 267

5-6 Describing Number Patterns 268

Assessment
• Test-Taking Strategies: Using a Variable, 274
• Chapter Review, 275
• Chapter Test, 278
• Standardized Test Prep: Reading Comprehension, 279

Table of Contents

Chapter 6

Linear Equations and Their Graphs

 **Student Support**

Instant Check System

Diagnosing Readiness, 280

Check Skills You'll Need, 282, 291, 298, 304, 311, 318, 325

Check Understanding, 283, 284, 285, 292, 293, 299, 300, 305, 306, 307, 311, 312, 313, 319, 320, 325, 326, 327

Checkpoint Quiz, 303, 324

 Reading Math

Reading Math, 284, 285, 305, 307

Reading Math Vocabulary, 310

Understanding Vocabulary, 331

Standardized Test Prep

289, 297, 303, 309, 317, 323, 329

Test-Taking Strategies, 330

Standardized Test Prep, 335

 Real-World Connections

Skydiving, 286
A Point in Time, 297
Nutrition, 302
Environment, 308
Bird Eggs, 318
Population, 322
Pyramids, 336
. . . and more!

Diagnosing Readiness **280**

6-1   Rate of Change and Slope **282**

6-2   Slope-Intercept Form **291**
• Technology: Investigating $y = mx + b$, 290

6-3   Standard Form **298**

Checkpoint Quiz 1 . . . . **303**

6-4   Point-Slope Form and Writing Linear Equations **304**
• Reading Math: Reading Math Vocabulary, 310

6-5   Parallel and Perpendicular Lines **311**

6-6   Scatter Plots and Equations of Lines Data & Statistics . . **318**

Checkpoint Quiz 2 . . . . **324**

6-7   Graphing Absolute Value Equations **325**

Assessment
• Test-Taking Strategies: Drawing a Diagram, 330
• Chapter Review, 331
• Chapter Test, 334
• Standardized Test Prep: Cumulative Review, 335

Real-World Snapshots: Applying Slope Data & Statistics . . **336**

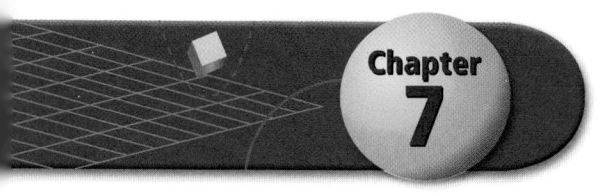

Chapter 7

Systems of Equations and Inequalities

Student Support

 Instant Check System

Diagnosing Readiness, 338

Check Skills You'll Need, 340, 347, 353, 362, 370, 377

Check Understanding, 340, 341, 342, 348, 349, 353, 354, 355, 356, 363, 364, 371, 372, 378, 379, 380

Checkpoint Quiz, 352, 376

 Reading Math

Reading Math, 342, 347, 359, 363, 366

Reading for Problem Solving, 369

Understanding Vocabulary, 387

Reading Comprehension, 391

Standardized Test Prep

345, 352, 359, 367, 375, 384

Test-Taking Strategies, 386

Standardized Test Prep, 391

Real-World Connections

Soccer, 344
Transportation, 349
Ticket Sales, 354
Electricity, 358
Publishing, 363
Algebra at Work, 368
Manufacturing, 373
. . . and more!

✔ **Diagnosing Readiness** **338**

7-1 Solving Systems by Graphing **340**

7-2 Solving Systems Using Substitution **347**
   • Investigation: Solving Systems Using Algebra Tiles, 346

✔ **Checkpoint Quiz 1** **352**

7-3 Solving Systems Using Elimination **353**

7-4 Applications of Linear Systems **362**
   • Technology: Matrices and Solving Systems, 360
   • Reading Math: Reading for Problem Solving, 369

7-5 Linear Inequalities **370**

✔ **Checkpoint Quiz 2** **376**

7-6 Systems of Linear Inequalities **377**
   • Technology: Graphing Linear Inequalities, 385

Assessment
   • Test-Taking Strategies: Finding Multiple Correct Answers, 386
   • Chapter Review, 387
   • Chapter Test, 390
   • Standardized Test Prep: [Data & Statistics] Reading Comprehension, 391

Table of Contents

Chapter 8

Exponents and Exponential Functions

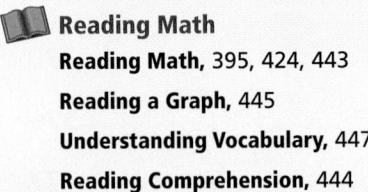

Student Support

✓ **Instant Check System**

Diagnosing Readiness, 392

Check Skills You'll Need, 394, 400, 405, 411, 417, 424, 430, 437

Check Understanding, 395, 396, 400, 401, 402, 405, 406, 407, 412, 413, 418, 419, 424, 425, 426, 427, 430, 431, 432, 438, 439, 440, 441

Checkpoint Quiz, 416, 435

Reading Math

Reading Math, 395, 424, 443

Reading a Graph, 445

Understanding Vocabulary, 447

Reading Comprehension, 444

Standardized Test Prep

399, 404, 409, 415, 423, 429, 434, 444

Test-Taking Strategies, 446

Standardized Test Prep, 451

Real-World Connections

Astronomy, 401
Medicine, 409
Algebra at Work, 416
Recycling, 418
Credit Card Balances, 443
Animals, 452
. . . and more!

✓ **Diagnosing Readiness** 392

8-1 **Zero and Negative Exponents** 394

8-2 **Scientific Notation** 400

8-3 **Multiplication Properties of Exponents** 405

8-4 **More Multiplication Properties of Exponents** 411

✓ **Checkpoint Quiz 1** 416

8-5 **Division Properties of Exponents** 417

8-6 **Geometric Sequences** 424

8-7 **Exponential Functions** 430

✓ **Checkpoint Quiz 2** 435

8-8 **Exponential Growth and Decay** [Data & Statistics] 437
   • Technology: [Data & Statistics] Fitting Exponential Curves to Data, 436
   • Reading Math: [Data & Statistics] Reading a Graph, 445

Assessment
   • Test-Taking Strategies: Testing Multiple Choices, 446
   • Chapter Review, 447
   • Chapter Test, 450
   • Standardized Test Prep: Cumulative Review, 451

Real-World Snapshots: Applying Systems of Equations . . **452**

Chapter 9

Polynomials and Factoring

Student Support

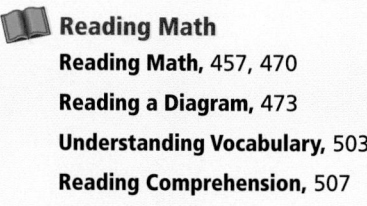

Instant Check System
Diagnosing Readiness, 454

Check Skills You'll Need, 456, 462, 467, 474, 481, 486, 490, 496

Check Understanding, 457, 458, 462, 463, 467, 468, 469, 475, 476, 477, 481, 482, 483, 486, 487, 491, 492, 496, 497, 498

Checkpoint Quiz, 472, 495

Reading Math
Reading Math, 457, 470

Reading a Diagram, 473

Understanding Vocabulary, 503

Reading Comprehension, 507

Standardized Test Prep
461, 465, 472, 479, 485, 489, 494, 500

Test-Taking Strategies, 502

Standardized Test Prep, 507

Real-World Connections
Graduation, 460
Building Models, 464
Construction, 470
Vegetables, 471
Dogs, 475
Biology, 478
A Point in Time, 501
. . . and more!

✔ **Diagnosing Readiness** 454

9-1 Adding and Subtracting Polynomials 456

9-2 Multiplying and Factoring 462

9-3 Multiplying Binomials 467
• Investigation: Using Models to Multiply, 466
• Reading Math: Reading a Diagram, 473

✔ **Checkpoint Quiz 1** 472

9-4 Multiplying Special Cases 474

9-5 Factoring Trinomials of the Type $x^2 + bx + c$ 481
• Investigation: Using Models to Factor, 480

9-6 Factoring Trinomials of the Type $ax^2 + bx + c$ 486

9-7 Factoring Special Cases 490

✔ **Checkpoint Quiz 2** 495

9-8 Factoring by Grouping 496

Assessment
• Test-Taking Strategies: Eliminating Answers, 502
• Chapter Review, 503
• Chapter Test, 506
• Standardized Test Prep: Reading Comprehension, 507

Table of Contents

Chapter 10

Quadratic Equations and Functions

Student Support

Instant Check System

Diagnosing Readiness, 508

Check Skills You'll Need, 510, 517, 524, 529, 536, 541, 547, 554, 559

Check Understanding, 511, 512, 513, 518, 519, 524, 525, 526, 530, 531, 536, 537, 542, 543, 548, 549, 550, 555, 560, 562, 563

Checkpoint Quiz, 534, 558

Reading Math

Reading Math, 524, 548

Using a Formula, 553

Understanding Vocabulary, 569

Reading Comprehension, 552

Standardized Test Prep

516, 523, 528, 533, 539, 546, 552, 557, 566

Test-Taking Strategies, 568

Standardized Test Prep, 573

Real-World Connections

Diving, 521
A Point in Time, 540
Population, 551,
Zoology, 562
Space Stations, 574
. . . and more!

✔ **Diagnosing Readiness** **508**

10-1 Exploring Quadratic Graphs **510**

10-2 Quadratic Functions **517**

10-3 Finding and Estimating Square Roots **524**

10-4 Solving Quadratic Equations **529**

✔ **Checkpoint Quiz 1** **534**

10-5 Factoring to Solve Quadratic Equations **536**
• Technology: Finding Roots, 535

10-6 Completing the Square **541**

10-7 Using the Quadratic Formula **547**
• Reading Math: Using a Formula, 553

10-8 Using the Discriminant **554**

✔ **Checkpoint Quiz 2** **558**

10-9 Choosing a Model Data & Statistics **559**
• Extension: Cubic Functions, 567

Assessment
• Test-Taking Strategies: Cannot Be Determined, 568
• Chapter Review, 569
• Chapter Test, 572
• Standardized Test Prep: Cumulative Review, 573

Real-World Snapshots: Applying Formulas **574**

Radical Expressions and Equations

Student Support

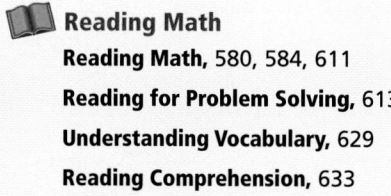 **Instant Check System**

Diagnosing Readiness, 576

Check Skills You'll Need, 578, 584, 591, 600, 607, 614, 621

Check Understanding, 578, 579, 580, 581, 585, 586, 587, 592, 593, 600, 601, 602, 607, 608, 609, 614, 615, 622, 623, 624

Checkpoint Quiz, 597, 619

Reading Math

Reading Math, 580, 584, 611

Reading for Problem Solving, 613

Understanding Vocabulary, 629

Reading Comprehension, 633

Standardized Test Prep

583, 590, 596, 605, 612, 618, 627

Test-Taking Strategies, 628

Standardized Test Prep, 633

Real-World Connections

Sightseeing, 579
Solar Power, 588
Archaeology, 595
Art, 602
Algebra at Work, 606
Firefighting, 617
Navigation, 623
. . . and more!

✓ **Diagnosing Readiness** **576**

11-1 Simplifying Radicals **578**

11-2 The Pythagorean Theorem **584**

11-3 The Distance and Midpoint Formulas **591**
• Extension: Special Right Triangles, 598

✓ **Checkpoint Quiz 1** **597**

11-4 Operations With Radical Expressions **600**

11-5 Solving Radical Equations **607**
• Reading Math: Reading for Problem Solving, 613

11-6 Graphing Square Root Functions **614**
• Extension: Rational Exponents, 620

✓ **Checkpoint Quiz 2** **619**

11-7 Trigonometric Ratios **621**

Assessment
• Test-Taking Strategies: Using Estimation, 628
• Chapter Review, 629
• Chapter Test, 632
• Standardized Test Prep: Reading Comprehension, 633

Table of Contents

Chapter 12

Rational Expressions and Functions

Student Support

 Instant Check System

Diagnosing Readiness, 634

Check Skills You'll Need, 636, 644, 652, 657, 662, 667, 672, 679, 686

Check Understanding, 637, 638, 639, 644, 645, 646, 648, 652, 653, 654, 657, 658, 659, 662, 663, 664, 667, 668, 669, 672, 673, 674, 680, 681, 682, 687, 688

Checkpoint Quiz, 656, 685

Reading Math

Reading Math, 637, 658, 673, 681

Reading an Example, 678

Understanding Vocabulary, 693

Standardized Test Prep

642, 650, 655, 661, 666, 671, 677, 684, 691

Test-Taking Strategies, 692

Standardized Test Prep, 697

Real-World Connections

Light, 649
Baking, 654
Loan Payments, 660
Algebra at Work, 671
Computers, 682
Guitars, 700
. . . and more!

 Diagnosing Readiness **634**

12-1 Inverse Variation **636**

12-2 Graphing Rational Functions **644**
• Technology: Graphing Rational Functions, 643
• Extension: Determining Limits, 651

12-3 Simplifying Rational Expressions **652**

Checkpoint Quiz 1 . . . . **656**

12-4 Multiplying and Dividing Rational Expressions **657**

12-5 Dividing Polynomials **662**

12-6 Adding and Subtracting Rational Expressions **667**

12-7 Solving Rational Equations **672**
• Reading Math: Reading an Example, 678

12-8 Counting Methods and Permutations **679**

Checkpoint Quiz 2 . . . . **685**

12-9 Combinations **686**

Assessment
• Test-Taking Strategies: Answering the Question Asked, 692
• Chapter Review, 693
• Chapter Test, 696
• Standardized Test Prep: Cumulative Review, 697

Real-World Snapshots: Applying Functions **700**

Take It to the Net

Throughout this book you will find links to the Prentice Hall Web site for *Algebra 1*. Use the Web Code provided with each link to gain direct access to online material.

Here's how to **Take It to the Net**:
• Go to **PHSchool.com**.
• Enter the Web Code.
• Click Go!

For a complete list of online features, use Web Code aek-0099

Lesson Quiz Web Codes

There is an online quiz for each lesson. Access these quizzes with Web Codes aea-0101 through aea-1209 for Lesson 1-1 through Lesson 12-9. See page 8.

88 Lesson Quizzes
Web Code format: aea-0204
02 = Chapter 2   04 = Lesson 4

Chapter Resource Web Codes

Chapter	Vocabulary Quizzes *See page 67.*	Chapter Tests *See page 70.*	Dorling Kindersley Real-World Snapshots *See pages 130–131.*	Chapter Projects
1	aej-0151	aea-0152		aed-0161
2	aej-0251	aea-0252	aee-0253	aed-0261
3	aej-0351	aea-0352		aed-0361
4	aej-0451	aea-0452	aee-0453	aed-0461
5	aej-0551	aea-0552		aed-0561
6	aej-0651	aea-0652	aee-0653	aed-0661
7	aej-0751	aea-0752		aed-0761
8	aej-0851	aea-0852	aee-0853	aed-0861
9	aej-0951	aea-0952		aed-0961
10	aej-1051	aea-1052	aee-1053	aed-1061
11	aej-1151	aea-1152		aed-1161
12	aej-1251	aea-1252	aee-1253	aed-1261
End-of-Course		aea-1254		

Additional Resource Web Codes

Data Updates Use Web Code aeg-2041 to get up-to-date government data for use in examples and exercises. *See page 27.*

Algebra at Work For information about each Algebra at Work feature, use Web Code aeb-2031. *See page 94.*

A Point in Time For information about each A Point in Time feature, use Web Code aee-2032. *See page 53.*

Graphing Calculator Procedures There are 27 procedures available online. Use Web Code aee-2100 for an index of all the procedures, or Web Codes aee-2101 through aee-2127 to access individual procedures. *See page 45.*

Table of Contents

Prentice Hall Mathematics programs are research-based and proven to work

The stakes for mathematics educators are high. You are expected to raise student achievement. Prentice Hall understands your dedicated efforts and gives you the confidence to meet this challenge. In developing Prentice Hall programs, the use of research studies is a central, guiding construct. Research on *Prentice Hall Mathematics* indicated key elements of a textbook program that ensure student success: constant review within instruction, support for reading and writing in mathematics, and an ongoing assessment strand. This research was conducted in three phases:

Phase ❶: Exploratory Needs Assessment

Phase ❷: Formative, Prototype Development and Field Testing

Phase ❸: Summative, Validation Research

1 Exploratory Needs Assessment

Along with periodic surveys concerning curriculum issues and challenges, we conducted specific product development research, which included discussions with teachers and advisory panels, focus groups, and quantitative surveys. We explored the specific needs of teachers, students, and other educators regarding each book we developed in *Prentice Hall Mathematics*.

In conjunction with Prentice Hall authors, secondary research was done to explore educational research about learning. This research was incorporated into our instructional strategy and pedagogy to make a more effective mathematics program.

2 Formative, Prototype Development and Field Testing

During this phase of research, we worked to develop prototype materials for each course in *Prentice Hall Mathematics*. Then we tested the materials, including field testing with students and teachers, and qualitative and quantitative evaluations of different kinds. We received solid feedback about our lesson structure in our early prototype testing. Results were channeled back into the program development for improvement. For example, teachers commented positively on motivational quality and richness of the mathematics in the Dorling Kindersley features.

3 Summative, Validation Research

Finally, we conducted and continue to conduct longer-term research based on scientific, experimental designs under actual classroom conditions. This research identifies what works and what can be improved in the next revision of *Prentice Hall Mathematics*. We also continue to monitor the program in the market. We talk to our users about what works, and then we begin the cycle over again. Highlights of this research follow in the next section.

Prentice Hall Research Time Line

Market Needs Assessment
(Quantitative & Qualitative)
- Teacher Interviews
- Classroom Observations
- Mail Surveys
- Conference Participation

Formative Research
(Quantitative & Qualitative)
- Field Testing of Prototypes
- Classroom Observations
- Teacher Reviews
- Supervisor Reviews
- Educator Advisory Panels
- Prentice Hall Sales Force Input

Summative Research
(Experimental and Quasi-Experimental Study Designs & Qualitative Research)
- Pre-Publication Learner Verification Research
- Post-Publication Validation Studies
- Classroom Observations
- Evaluation of In-Market Results on Standardized Tests

Prentice Hall Math programs get results!

Standardized Test End-of-Year Results
(adjusted for differences in pre-test levels)

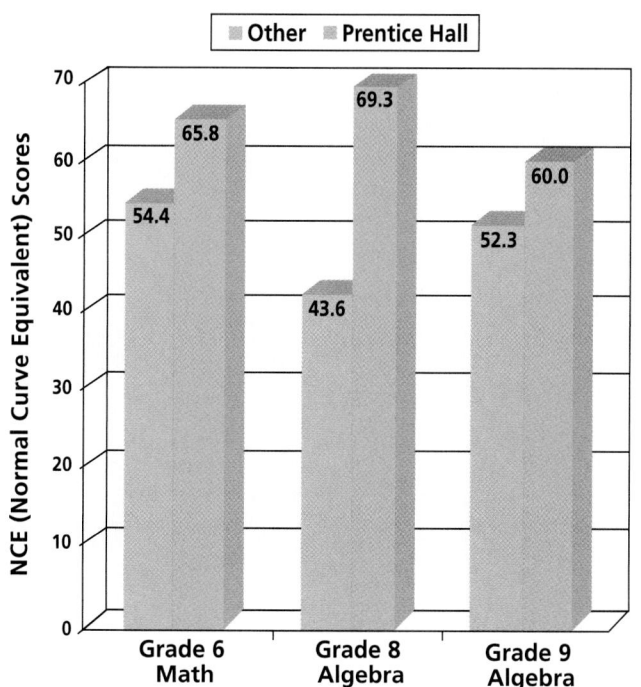

Prentice Hall mathematics programs are continually researched to determine "what works." Our programs are regularly revised to keep the best of what has worked in prior editions, and to improve them to meet changing market and curriculum needs. For example . . .

In a year-long study conducted in six states, students using Prentice Hall mathematics programs at grades 6, 8 (algebra), and 9 (algebra) outscored students using other math programs on a nationally normed standardized test.

The study followed a scientific, experimental design with two classes per school. The classes selected were of similar ability levels, and the assignment of the Prentice Hall program was done randomly. A total of eight schools (a mix of rural, suburban, and urban) participated, with 350 students involved in the study.

Classes were tested at the beginning of the school year using the TerraNova™ CTBS Basic Battery, and they were re-tested at the end of the school year. The final results, shown in the graph at the left, have been adjusted (via ANCOVA) to eliminate any contribution of higher or lower starting points on the pre-test to the observed post-test score.

All tests were scored by CTB/McGraw-Hill, the publisher of the TerraNova™ exam. Statistical analyses were conducted by an independent statistician from Pulse Analytics, Inc.

Additional studies of program effectiveness are under way, and many districts have demonstrated math improvement since adopting Prentice Hall mathematics programs.

Detailed results of this study can be obtained at **www.PHSchool.com**.

A unique progress-monitoring system that gives every student the opportunity to excel

What Research Indicates: Students' learning progresses to higher levels of understanding only if they have mastered a foundational understanding of preliminary concepts. If students are not functioning at a particular level of understanding, they are not ready to move on. Review plays a key role in promoting retention. Research clearly indicates that review should be systematically planned and incorporated into instruction. Before a new chapter or topic is begun, an inventory can help you ascertain whether any prerequisite knowledge is missing. Review should be continuous for students to attain mastery.

(Suydam, Marilyn N. *The Role of Review in Mathematical Instruction*. Columbus, Ohio: ERIC Clearinghouse for Science, Mathematics, and Environmental Education.)

Prentice Hall's Response: *Prentice Hall Mathematics* provides a unique **Instant Check System™** that is built right into the text to assess mastery and diagnose weaknesses before, during, and after each lesson's instruction. This ongoing monitoring strand allows students to check their understanding of skills before moving on to the next topic. If students have misconceptions or need to reinforce their skills, the green type throughout the text clearly indicates where they can go for help. All the answers for the *Instant Check System™* questions are available at the back of the student edition so students can check their work.

✓ Diagnosing Readiness

At the beginning of every chapter, students complete the *Diagnosing Readiness* exercises to see what prerequisite skills they may need to review before they begin the chapter. The Teacher's Edition prescribes specific *Examples* and *Exercises* that students can do for intervention.

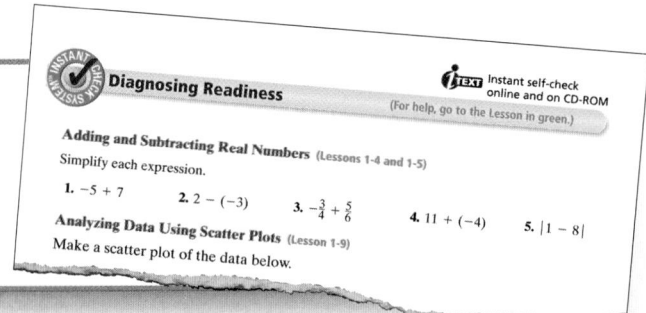

✓ Check Skills You'll Need

To begin each lesson, students complete the *Check Skills You'll Need* exercises to make sure they have the skills needed to successfully learn the concepts in the lesson. These questions with worked-out solutions are conveniently available as transparencies and on CD-ROM.

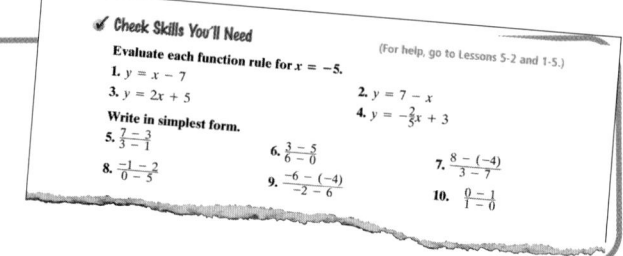

> *"If students do not have the proper level of understanding, they cannot further their knowledge of concepts and relationships in mathematics. Both the Instant Check System and the Diagnosing Readiness feature help teachers assess how well students have achieved understanding of related skills before having them move on to subsequent concepts."*
>
> —Art Johnson, *Prentice Hall Mathematics program author*

✓ Check Understanding

Every lesson includes numerous *Examples*, each followed by *Check Understanding* questions that students can do on their own. As skills and concepts are introduced, these questions focus students on the mathematics being presented and allow them to assess their understanding. More importantly, these questions will raise misconceptions that students have so that you may immediately address them.

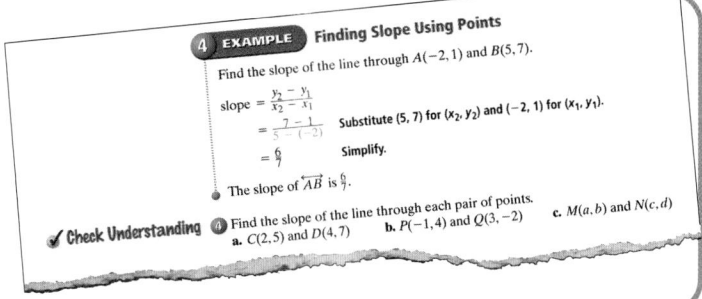

Leveled Exercises

The abundant *Exercises* in every lesson are organized by level to provide ample opportunity for students of all abilities to master the concepts. The *A: Practice by Example* exercises directly relate to the *Examples* in the lesson. The *B: Apply Your Skills* and *C: Challenge* exercises provide richer skill and application problems to extend students' thinking.

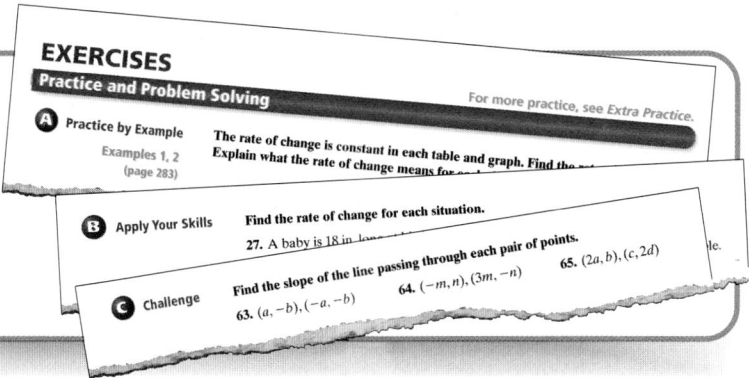

✓ Checkpoint Quizzes

Two *Checkpoint Quizzes* in every chapter provide students with opportunities for ongoing assessment. Each quiz provides a cumulative review of skills within specific lessons. Alternate versions are available in the Teaching Resources and online.

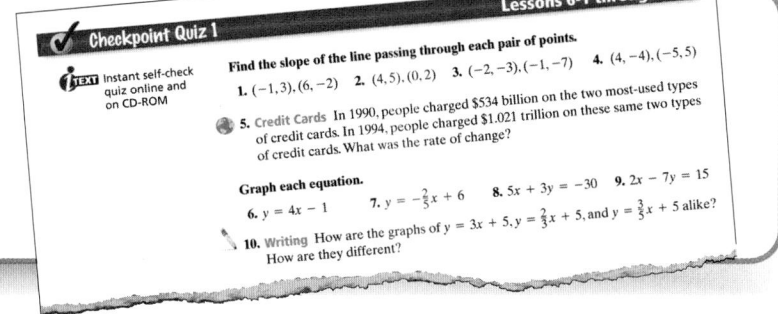

Prentice Hall Mathematics 🄸TEXT with Self-Grading Assessments

The *iText* provides the complete Student Edition online and on CD-ROM. The unique *Instant Check System™* is made interactive in the *iText* to allow students ongoing opportunities for checking their learning. Also, the click of a button lets students go back to a lesson or Example for additional help. Students get instant feedback so they know whether they're on track and where to go to get help.

Reading and Writing throughout build communication skills

What Research Indicates: Reading mathematics requires the same skills as reading in other content areas—decoding and comprehending what is read, analyzing and evaluating the content based on one's prior knowledge, and making inferences and generating conclusions. Mathematics text demands that readers also use additional, content-specific reading skills, for example, reading graphs. Students need to learn to focus on significant details, explanations, and the underlying logic in texts where there are more concepts per word, per sentence, and per paragraph than in any other kind of text.

(Barton, Mary Lee & Heidema, Clare. *Teaching Reading in Mathematics:* A Supplement to Teaching Reading in the Content Areas Teacher's Manual, 2nd Ed. Aurora, Colorado: Mid-continent Research for Education and Learning.)

The development of a student's power to use mathematics also involves learning the signs, symbols, and terms of mathematics. This is best accomplished in problem-solving situations in which students have an opportunity to read, write, and discuss ideas so that the use of the language of mathematics becomes natural. As students communicate their ideas, they learn to clarify, refine, and consolidate their thinking.

(*Curriculum and Evaluation Standards for School Mathematics.* Reston, Virginia: The National Council of Teachers of Mathematics, Inc.)

Prentice Hall's Response: *Prentice Hall Mathematics* provides a consistent emphasis on mathematics literacy with a special focus on reading and writing in mathematics. This program integrates even more ways for you to develop your students' ability to read and write mathematically so that they are successful in this course and on state tests.

Reading Math

The *Reading Math* tips within lessons help students to read and understand the language of mathematics. The *Reading Math* features help students read more effectively, so that they can write, speak, and think mathematically. Reading to Analyze Errors, Reading Math Vocabulary, and Reading an Example are just a few of the strategies included.

Writing in Math

Every lesson incorporates *Writing* exercises that help students learn to explain, describe, or compare in a mathematical situation. Special emphasis is also given to writing as it relates to Critical Thinking, Reasoning, and Error Analysis. Instruction in writing answers to rubric-scored questions helps students communicate successfully on today's tests.

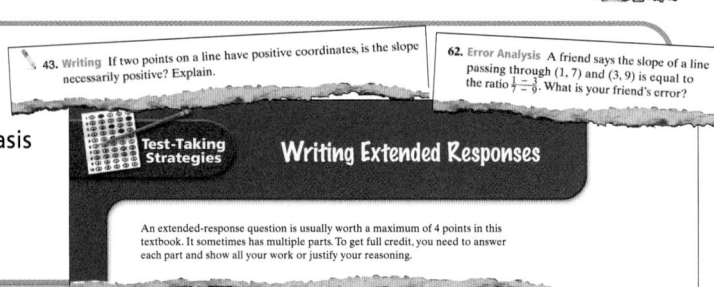

> "Success in subsequent mathematics courses and on standardized tests depends greatly on a student's ability to communicate in mathematics. The emphasis on reading and writing in *Prentice Hall Mathematics* through the Reading Tips and Reading Math features and through the Writing in Math opportunities enables all students to develop their communication skills."
>
> —Randy Charles, *Prentice Hall Mathematics* program author

Understanding Vocabulary

Prentice Hall Mathematics carefully develops the skill of reading math vocabulary. New vocabulary is conveniently listed at the beginning of each chapter and each lesson. Each new term is highlighted in yellow. The Chapter Review includes exercises that help students to correctly use the vocabulary presented in the chapter. The **iTEXT** reinforces students' vocabulary skills with an online vocabulary quiz for every chapter and an audio version of all glossary terms.

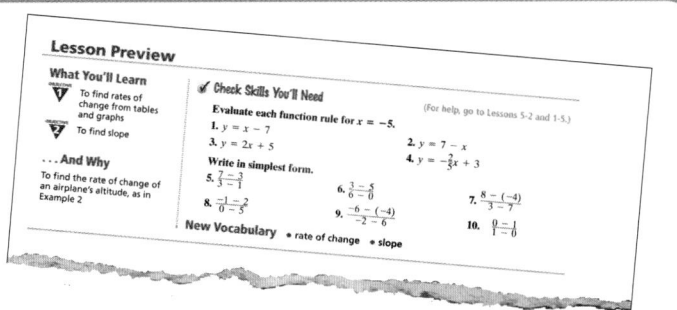

Reading and Math Literacy Masters

These unique blackline masters supplement the coverage of reading and math in the textbook. Students learn a variety of techniques to master mathematics vocabulary and symbols, read for problem solving, and increase comprehension.

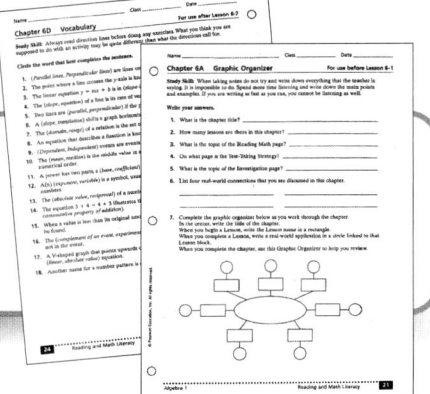

Reading for problem solving through Real-World Connections

Prentice Hall Mathematics incorporates abundant real-world connections within *Examples* and *Exercises* to provide a problem-solving context for applications of mathematics. Dorling Kindersley Real-World Snapshots bring math to life, with activities in which students gather data they need by reading graphic displays and captions.

Ongoing assessment and test preparation guarantee testing success

What Research Indicates: We assess students most fairly when we assess often and with a variety of different answers. Research also shows that assessment needs to measure and describe a student's growth and achievement in all domains of mathematics and at three levels of thinking. Because of this, there should be questions at all levels of thinking, of varying degrees of difficulty, and in all content domains.

(Shafer, Mary C. & Foster, Sherian. "The Changing Faces of Assessment." *Principled Practice in Mathematics and Science Education*, Volume 1, No. 2.)

Prentice Hall's Response: *Prentice Hall Mathematics* provides an ongoing assessment strand that begins within the lesson instruction and continues throughout the program components. The program exposes students to questions of varying difficulty and at different levels of thinking in the daily *Check Understanding* questions and in the leveled *Exercises*.

A variety of question formats, including those found on today's standardized tests, is built into the Student Edition to assess student learning and prepare students for high-stakes tests. The ability to demonstrate knowledge in short-answer and open-ended formats increases opportunities for students to be successful on today's tests and in gaining admission to higher schooling and to the workplace.

✓ Check Understanding

Check Understanding questions after worked-out *Examples* allow students to assess their progress on a daily basis. These questions often emphasize the processes of explaining or reasoning—mirroring the types of questions that students will encounter on today's tests. You can use these questions to address any misconceptions or weaknesses before moving on to new topics.

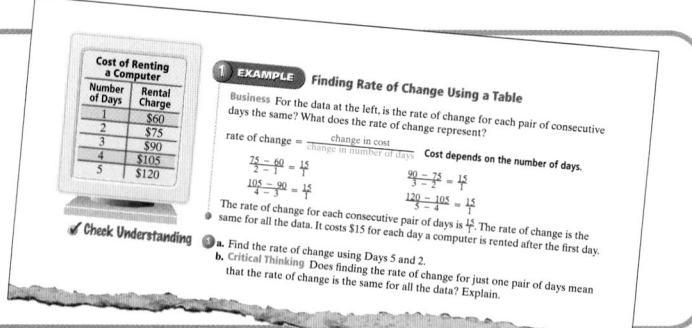

Quizzes and Tests—In Print and Online

You can assess student progress at key points with the *Lesson Quizzes*, *Checkpoint Quizzes*, and *Chapter Tests*. The Teaching Resources provides additional quizzes and tests, as well as alternative assessments. Online self-grading quizzes and tests are available on the Prentice Hall Web site at **www.PHSchool.com**.

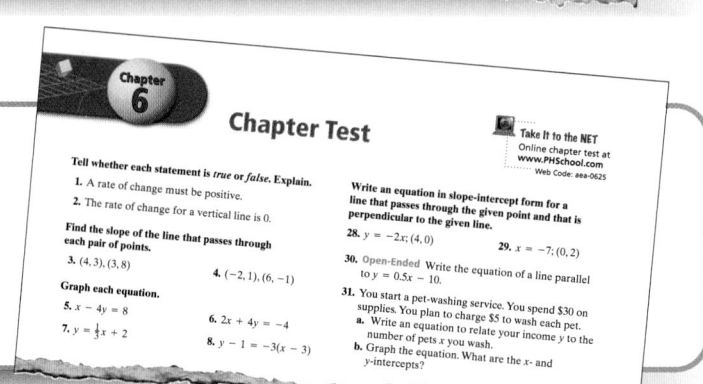

"Assessment is an integral part of a mathematics program. Prentice Hall Mathematics provides a strong formative and summative assessment strand. The formative assessment features—before and during instruction—offer a variety of modalities that speak to different kinds of learners. The summative assessment features—after instruction—further prepare students for success on today's tests."

—Sadie Chavis Bragg, *Prentice Hall Mathematics* program author

Standardized Test Prep Exercises

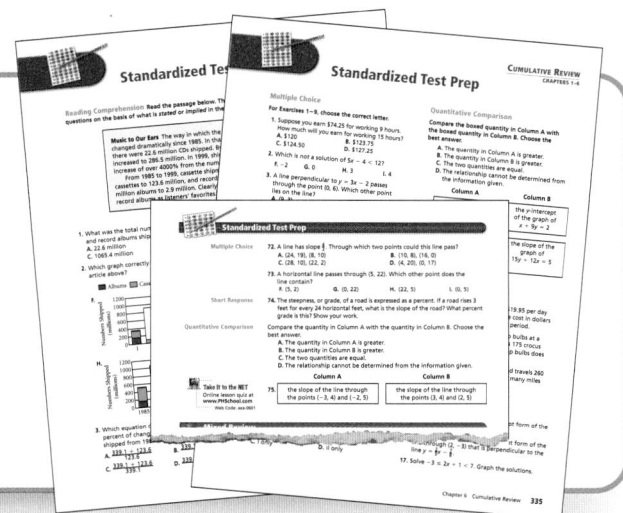

Standardized Test Prep exercises in every lesson give students daily practice with the types of test item formats that they will encounter on state tests. You can also provide students with the *Standardized Test Prep* page at the end of each chapter.

The daily exercises and the test prep pages include these most common test item formats:

- Multiple Choice
- Gridded Response
- Short Response
- Quantitative Comparison
- Reading Comprehension
- Extended Response

Test-Taking Strategies

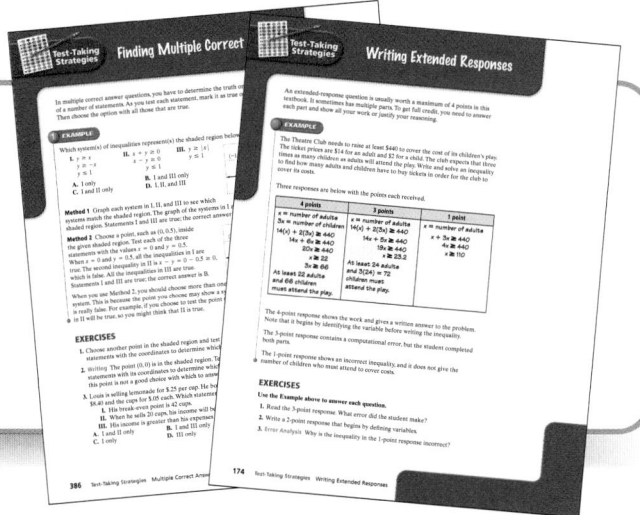

Test-Taking Strategies in every chapter teach students strategies to be successful and give them practice in the skills they need to pass state tests and standardized national exams. Several lessons focus on helping students answer rubric-based questions.

The *Test-Taking Strategies With Transparencies* provide instruction on overheads and include additional practice sheets for the strategies taught in each chapter.

Prentice Hall Assessment System

An innovative *Assessment System* gives you everything you need to assess student progress on the content covered in the course, and to prepare students for high-stakes testing. The system contains the program Assessment Resources and the Computer Test Generator CD-ROM with unlimited questions and ready-to-use Chapter Tests.

In addition, you can diagnose student knowledge with *Content Diagnostic Tests*, prescribe intervention with the *Skills and Concept Review*, and have students practice for standardized assessments with the *Test Preparation* booklet. A *Teacher's Guide* gives you correlations and answers. Also included is the *Test-Taking Strategies With Transparencies* described above.

Mathematical Strands

Overview and Background

Number and Operations

NCTM Standard for Grades 9–12

- Understand numbers, ways of representing numbers, relationships among numbers, and number systems
- Understand meanings of operations and how they relate to one another
- Compute fluently and make reasonable estimates

Key Content in Prentice Hall
Algebra 1, Geometry, Algebra 2

- Represent and compute with rational numbers and real numbers (A1: Ch 1, 11; A2: Ch 1, 7)
- Understand the properties and operations of matrices, vectors, and complex numbers (A1: Ch 1; G: Ch 9; A2: Ch 4, 5)
- Justify relationships within number systems and compare properties of number systems (A1: Ch 1; A2: Ch 1, 4, 5)
- Judge the effects of multiplying, dividing, computing powers, and computing roots on the magnitude of quantities (A1: Ch 8; A2: Ch 7)
- Use counting techniques, including permutations and combinations (A1: Ch 12; A2: Ch 6)
- Judge reasonableness of numerical computations (throughout A1, G, A2)

Background and Progression

Students usually enter an Algebra 1 course having some facility with integers, fractions, and decimals. They have worked with square roots and used the Pythagorean Theorem.

In *Algebra 1,* students build an understanding of real numbers by using symbolic, graphic, and numeric representations as they solve equations and inequalities. Work with rational and radical expressions, equations, and functions builds a wide base of experience with rational and irrational numbers. Matrices are introduced.

In *Geometry,* students' understanding of the properties of real numbers becomes a base for building reasoned geometric arguments. In this year, students first study vectors.

In *Algebra 2,* students study matrices and complex numbers—number systems that do not share all the properties of real numbers (for example, multiplication of matrices is not commutative, and complex numbers cannot be arranged in order).

Data Analysis and Probability

NCTM Standard for Grades 9–12

- Formulate questions that can be addressed with data and collect, organize, and display relevant data to answer them
- Select and use appropriate statistical methods to analyze data
- Develop and evaluate inferences and predictions that are based on data
- Understand and apply basic concepts of probability

Key Content in Prentice Hall
Algebra 1, Geometry, Algebra 2

- Construct and interpret histograms, box plots, and scatterplots (A1: Ch 6; A2: Ch 12)
- Compute statistics, including mean, median, mode, range, and standard deviation (A1: Ch 2; A2: Ch 12)
- Identify trends in bivariate data and find functions that model the data (A1: Ch 6, 10; A2: Ch 2, 5, 6, 8)
- Construct sampling distributions and use them for informal inference about the population (A2: Ch 12)
- Compute probabilities of simple and compound events, geometric probabilities, and conditional probabilities (A1: Ch 4; G: Ch 7; A2: Ch 1, 9, 12)

Background and Progression

In the middle grades, students have gathered, displayed, and interpreted many types of data, including one-variable (for example, test scores), two-variable (height vs. age), and data related to categories (numbers of students who like various foods). They can distinguish appropriate uses of bar, line, and circle graphs, and can find simple probabilities.

In *Algebra 1,* students work with scatter plots and functions to model two-variable, or bivariate, data. They compute probabilities for simple and compound events.

In *Geometry,* students maintain skills, with probability exercises found throughout the text, and are introduced to geometric probability.

In *Algebra 2,* students begin a study of histograms (probability distributions based on experimental results) and theoretical distributions, including binomial (based on two possible outcomes) and normal (representing many real-life random variables, such as adult heights). Students also use tree diagrams to analyze conditional probabilities.

 *For more **Math Background** on every lesson, see page B before each chapter and see each lesson's teaching notes.*

Algebra

NCTM Standard for Grades 9–12

- Understand patterns, relations, and functions
- Represent and analyze mathematical situations and structures using algebraic symbols
- Use mathematical models to represent and understand quantitative relationships
- Analyze change in various contexts

Key Content in Prentice Hall
Algebra 1, Geometry, Algebra 2

- Use various representations of functions and choose types to model quantitative relationships (throughout A1, A2)
- Analyze functions of one variable, including rates of change, intercepts, zeros, and asymptotes (A1: Ch 5, 6, 8, 10; A2: Ch 2, 5–9, 11, 13)
- Combine, compose, and invert common functions (A2: Ch 7, 8, 13, 14)
- Interpret functions of two variables and use parametric forms (A2: Ch 3, 10)
- Understand properties of different types of functions, including linear, quadratic, exponential, polynomial, rational, radical, logarithmic, and periodic functions (A1: Ch 6, 8, 10–12; A2: Ch 2, 5–9, 11, 13)
- Use symbolic algebra to represent and explain mathematical relationships (throughout A1, A2)
- Write equivalent forms of and solve equations, inequalities, and systems (throughout A1, G, A2)

Background and Progression

Today's middle school students are comfortable with tables, graphs, verbal rules, and variables in the representation of simple relationships. Many know how to solve linear equations.

In *Algebra 1,* students use tables, graphs, verbal rules, and symbolic rules to describe linear, quadratic, and exponential functions. They choose a best model for data from among these functions. Rate of change is studied in the context of direct variation, linear equations, and arithmetic and geometric sequences. Students learn how to write equivalent forms of polynomial, radical, and rational expressions.

In *Geometry,* Algebra 1 skills are reinforced with applications involving both linear and quadratic relationships.

In *Algebra 2,* students use multiple representations in studying polynomial, rational, radical, logarithmic, and periodic functions. Using technology, students study residuals as an indicator of the most appropriate model for data. Students first see functions of two variables in the concrete context of linear programming. Trigonometric functions are presented first in the unit circle, and then applied to solving triangles.

Geometry

NCTM Standard for Grades 9–12

- Analyze characteristics and properties of two- and three-dimensional geometric shapes and develop mathematical arguments about geometric relationships
- Specify locations and describe spatial relationships using coordinate geometry and other representational systems
- Apply transformations and use symmetry to analyze mathematical situations
- Use visualization, spatial reasoning, and geometric modeling to solve problems

Key Content in Prentice Hall
Algebra 1, Geometry, Algebra 2

- Analyze properties of plane and space figures. Solve problems involving them, and real-world applications in general (throughout G)
- Explore congruence and similarity (throughout G)
- Use deductive reasoning to establish the validity of conjectures, to prove theorems, and to critique arguments (G: Ch 2–12)
- Use coordinates to analyze shapes, solve problems, and prove relationships (G: Ch 3, 6, 12; A2: Ch 10)
- Understand and represent transformations in the plane using sketches, coordinates, vectors, functions, and matrices (G: Ch 12; A2: Ch 2, 4, 5, 7–10, 13)
- Visualize, draw, and construct plane and space figures, from different perspectives (G: Ch 1, 10; A2: Ch 3, 10)
- Use geometric models to solve problems in other areas of mathematics (A1: Ch 4; G: Ch 7, 9; A2: Ch 14)

Background and Progression

In the middle grades, students have explored various plane and space figures to identify and compare properties. This includes working with similarity, congruence, tessellations, symmetry, slides, flips, turns, and simple figures in the coordinate plane.

In *Algebra 1,* students begin to use geometric models with proportions, percent, and probability. They also explore ways to describe translations of familiar functions in both words and symbols.

In *Geometry,* all key strand content is covered. The first two chapters establish the tools of geometry—methods of reasoning, construction, the coordinate plane, and types of measurement. Subsequent chapters focus on properties and applications of lines, triangles, quadrilaterals, similarity, right triangle trigonometry, circles, and transformations.

In *Algebra 2,* students apply principles of translating in the coordinate plane to functions and conic sections. Geometric models for trigonometric relationships are also utilized.

Mathematical Strands

 *For more **Math Background** on every lesson, see page B before each chapter and see each lesson's teaching notes.*

Measurement

NCTM Standard for Grades 9–12

- Understand measurable attributes of objects and the units, systems, and processes of measurement
- Apply appropriate techniques, tools, and formulas to determine measurements

Key Content in Prentice Hall
Algebra 1, Geometry, Algebra 2

- Make decisions about appropriate units and scales in problems involving measurement (A1: Ch 6; G: Ch 8, 10; A2: Ch 1, 13, 14)
- Understand and use formulas for area, surface area, and volume (A1: Ch 2; G: Ch 7, 10; A2: Ch 6, 7)
- Apply concepts of successive approximation, upper and lower bounds, and limits (G: Ch 10; A2: Ch 11, 12)
- Use unit analysis (A1: Ch 4; G: Ch 7)

Background and Progression

Middle school students have usually experienced direct measurements (such as length, mass, and volume), indirect measurements (based on similar triangles), and derived measurements (such as rates). They are familiar with precision and accuracy in measurement, and have developed and used formulas for the perimeters, areas, and volumes of simple figures.

In *Algebra 1,* students make decisions about appropriate scales with graphical representations of data. They use formulas for the perimeters and areas of figures to find missing measures, and use unit analysis (sometimes called dimensional analysis) to help set up proportions and other equations.

In *Geometry,* students justify formulas for perimeter and area and apply them to composite and irregular plane shapes. Students use cross sections to develop formulas for the volumes of prisms, cylinders, pyramids, and cones. The approximation techniques used to help justify the formulas for the surface area and volume of a sphere anticipate calculus. Through work with arc length and the areas of circles and parts of circles, students become comfortable with exact measures (which are irrational and expressed in terms of π) and rational approximations of these measures.

In *Algebra 2,* students use polynomials to express the areas and volumes of figures, and polynomial equations to find missing measures. With geometric sequences they explore successive approximations and the concept of a limit. Various statistical measures lead to the concepts of statistical error and standard deviation. In their study of trigonometry, students learn how to use the parallel measuring scales of degrees and radians, and when to choose one over the other. In "solving" triangles (finding the measures of all sides and angles, and the area), they use trigonometric relationships to make indirect measurements.

Problem Solving

NCTM Standard for Grades 9–12

- Build new mathematical knowledge through problem solving
- Solve problems that arise in mathematics and in other contexts
- Apply and adapt a variety of appropriate strategies to solve problems
- Monitor and reflect on the process of mathematical problem solving

Key Processes in Prentice Hall
Algebra 1, Geometry, Algebra 2

- Solve problems taken from the student's current and future world (Real-World Connection Examples throughout each text)
- Use a variety of appropriate methods to solve problems (Examples showing two methods throughout each text)
- Construct an appropriate expression, equation, or function to solve a problem (Examples using the "Relate-Define-Write" model throughout A1 and A2)
- Use various problem solving strategies as appropriate (reviewed in the Skills Handbook of each text)
- Build understanding of new topics through problem solving (Investigations and Reading for Problem Solving throughout each text)
- Reflect on the process of problem solving (Checks for Reasonableness, Writing, Critical Thinking, Reasoning, and Error Analysis exercises throughout each text)

Background and Progression

The Prentice Hall Mathematics Program for the middle grades contains a rich problem solving strand, including lessons each year covering ten problem solving strategies.

In *Algebra 1, Geometry,* and *Algebra 2,* the strategies are reviewed in the Skills Handbook. In each text, students practice the critical skill of expressing mathematical relationships from real-world problems with symbolic models. Each text contains numerous real-world examples, many of which use the "Relate-Define-Write" format to guide the student in choosing and writing a correct model.

Where possible, examples show more than one method for solving a problem. Many examples include a check for reasonableness. Investigations found throughout each text allow students to form their understanding of a new math topic through guided discovery. The Reading for Problem Solving pages model the thinking of an inquiring student.

Writing, Critical Thinking, Reasoning, and Error Analysis exercises allow students to analyze and verbalize their own understanding of the problem solving process.

 *For more **Math Background** on every lesson, see page B before each chapter and see each lesson's teaching notes.*

Reasoning and Proof

NCTM Standard for Grades 9–12

- Recognize reasoning and proof as fundamental aspects of mathematics
- Make and investigate mathematical conjectures
- Develop and evaluate mathematical arguments and proofs
- Select and use various types of reasoning and methods of proof

Key Processes in Prentice Hall
Algebra 1, Geometry, Algebra 2

- Use inductive reasoning to make and investigate conjectures (Make a Conjecture exercises and Investigation pages throughout each text)
- Develop deductive proof in various formats, including paragraph, flow, two-column, indirect, and coordinate proof (A1: Ch 1; G: Ch 2–12; A2: Ch 6, 14)
- Apply appropriate reasoning to analyze mathematical statements (Checks for Reasonableness, Writing, Critical Thinking, Reasoning, and Error Analysis exercises throughout each text)
- Study and write proofs of geometric theorems (G: Ch 2–12)
- Study and write proofs of algebraic theorems, properties, and equivalences (A1: Ch 1; A2: Ch 6, 8, 14)
- Explain work and justify conclusions (Writing, Critical Thinking, Reasoning, Error Analysis, Short Response, and Extended Response exercises throughout each text)

Background and Progression

In middle grades, students identify the use of Commutative, Associative, Identity, Inverse, and Distributive properties. They use these properties and the Properties of equality to justify steps in solving equations. Students also differentiate deductive and inductive reasoning.

In *Algebra 1,* students solve equations using the properties of real numbers and of equality to justify their steps. These justifications are extended to simple algebraic proofs.

In *Geometry,* students develop an understanding of the structure and concepts of Euclidean plane geometry, building naturally on the step-by-step processes of algebra. They prove theorems in more than one way using paragraph proofs, flow proofs, and two-column proofs.

In *Algebra 2,* students further their understanding and ability to prove concepts not only by deduction but also by using mathematical induction.

Communication

NCTM Standard for Grades 9–12

- Organize and consolidate their mathematical thinking through communication
- Communicate their mathematical thinking coherently and clearly to peers, teachers, and others
- Analyze and evaluate the mathematical thinking and strategies of others
- Use the language of mathematics to express mathematical ideas precisely

Key Processes in Prentice Hall
Algebra 1, Geometry, Algebra 2

- Write about mathematical concepts by summarizing, comparing, analyzing, and explaining (Writing, Critical Thinking, Reasoning, Short Response, and Extended Response exercises throughout each text)
- Understand the language and notations of mathematics (Reading Math notes and Reading for Problem Solving pages throughout each text and Understanding Vocabulary exercises in each Chapter Review)
- Use appropriate notation to express mathematical relationships in real-world contexts (Examples using the "Relate-Define-Write" model throughout A1 and A2, Reading Comprehension exercises, and the Reading for Problem Solving pages in each text)
- Analyze sample work to find errors (Error Analysis exercises throughout each text)

Background and Progression

The Prentice Hall Mathematics Program for the middle grades gives students numerous opportunities to explain and justify their reasoning.

The *Algebra 1, Geometry,* and *Algebra 2* textbooks continue this rich communication strand. In-lesson Investigations and Investigation pages have students develop critical concepts, which students are encouraged first to summarize and then to use in exercises.

The Reading for Problem Solving pages focus on a variety of topics to help students read more effectively, so that they can write, speak, and think mathematically. The Reading Math hints in lessons help students use the language and notation of mathematics correctly and relate new mathematical vocabulary to English terms they already know.

Students are given instruction on answering Short Response questions with two-point rubrics and Extended Response questions with four-point rubrics. Throughout each text, students get ample opportunity to answer rubric-based exercises.

 *For more **Math Background** on every lesson, see page B before each chapter and see each lesson's teaching notes.*

Connections

NCTM Standard for Grades 9–12

- Recognize and use connections among mathematical ideas
- Understand how mathematical ideas interconnect and build on one another to produce a coherent whole
- Recognize and apply mathematics in contexts outside of mathematics

Key Processes in Prentice Hall
Algebra 1, Geometry, Algebra 2

- Solve problems in more than one way (A1 and A2: Examples showing two methods; G: Alternative proofs)
- Solve problems arising from real-world contexts (Real-World Connection Examples, Real-World Snapshots, and application and Reading Comprehension exercises throughout each text)
- Use algebraic concepts such as the coordinate plane, slope, vectors, matrices with transformations, and properties of geometric figures (A1: Ch 5; G: Ch 3, 5, 6, 9, 11,12; A2: Ch 4, 10)
- Use algebraic equations to solve measurement problems in geometry (throughout G)
- Use geometric concepts with probability, systems of equations, functions, and quadratic relations (A1: Ch 7, 10–12; G: Ch 7; A2: Ch 2, 3, 5–13)

Background and Progression

In middle grades, students make connections between geometric and algebraic concepts through graphing geometric figures in the coordinate plane and using slope to investigate the concepts of parallelism and perpendicularity.

In **Algebra 1,** students use algebra to develop formulas for geometric measurement and to describe statistical relationships (lines of best fit). Critical Thinking exercises have students make connections between previously learned material and lesson content. Students understand geometric relationships using slope, midpoint, and distance formulas.

In **Geometry,** students use algebra to interpret and apply geometric relationships. Students take an alternative look at many geometric facts by revisiting them in the coordinate plane.

In **Algebra 2,** students use matrices to describe transformations in the coordinate plane. They extend algebra-geometry connections to reinforce the structure and processes involving functions and conic sections.

Representation

NCTM Standard for Grades 9–12

- Create and use representations to organize, record, and communicate mathematical ideas
- Select, apply, and translate among mathematical representations to solve problems
- Use representations to model and interpret physical, social, and mathematical phenomena

Key Processes in Prentice Hall
Algebra 1, Geometry, Algebra 2

- Organize mathematical information in order to make and support conjectures (Investigations throughout each text)
- Use tables, graphs, verbal rules, and symbolic rules interchangeably as appropriate (A1: Ch 5–8, 10-12; A2: Ch 1, 3, 5, 6, 8–10, 12, 13)
- Choose an appropriate algebraic function model for two-variable measurement data (A1: Ch 10; A2: Ch 2, 5, 8)
- Solve real-world problems by creating a mathematical model to represent the essential mathematics involved (Examples using the "Relate-Define-Write" model in A1 and A2, application exercises, Reading Comprehension exercises, and Real-World Snapshots throughout each text)

Background and Progression

In the middle grades, students have experiences using tables, rules, and graphs to describe functional relationships. They also use tables in problem solving situations to organize real-world data.

In **Algebra 1,** students gain facility in graphing these families of functions: linear, quadratic, exponential, and rational functions. Using tables and graphs, students determine which function best models a given set of data.

In **Geometry,** students learn to recognize, apply, and interpret geometric principles in real-world settings, and frequently use coordinate methods to take another look at these principles.

In **Algebra 2,** students extend their knowledge of the families of functions to polynomial, logarithmic, and trigonometric functions. They also use three-variable equations to model problem situations.

 *For more **Math Background** on every lesson, see page B before each chapter and see each lesson's teaching notes.*

Pacing Options for Algebra 1

Pacing Guide

This chart is provided merely as a guide to help you customize your course. To accommodate flexible scheduling, most lessons are subdivided into objectives. Within the lessons of the Student Edition, these objectives are indicated in red by the symbol ▼. The Assignment Guide for each lesson indicates which exercises in the Student Edition correspond to each objective of the lesson.

Detailed Chapter Pacing Options precede each chapter and give you lesson-by-lesson pacing suggestions for that specific chapter.

CHAPTER	Traditional (45-minute class periods)	Two-Year (45-minute class periods)	Block (90-minute class periods)	Two-Year Block (90-minute class periods)
1	14 days	28 days	8 days	14 days
2	13 days	26 days	7 days	13 days
3	11 days	22 days	5 days	11 days
4	10 days	20 days	5 days	10 days
5	10 days	20 days	5 days	10 days
6	13 days	26 days	7 days	13 days
7	12 days	24 days	6 days	12 days
8	14 days	28 days	7 days	14 days
9	15 days	30 days	7 days	15 days
10	16 days	32 days	8 days	16 days
11	14 days	28 days	7 days	14 days
12	18 days	36 days	8 days	18 days
Total	160 days	320 days	80 days	160 days

Differentiated Scope of Course

B = Basic Course   C = Core Course   A = Advanced Course

Chapter 1 Tools of Algebra	B	C	A
1-1: Using Variables	✓	✓	✓
1-2: Exponents and Order of Operations	✓	✓	✓
1-3: Exploring Real Numbers	✓	✓	✓
1-4: Adding Real Numbers	✓	✓	✓
1-5: Subtracting Real Numbers	✓	✓	✓
1-6: Multiplying and Dividing Real Numbers	✓	✓	✓
• Technology: Matrices		✓	✓
• Investigation: The Distributive Property	✓	✓	✓
1-7: The Distributive Property	✓	✓	✓
1-8: Properties of Real Numbers	✓	✓	✓
1-9: Graphing Data on the Coordinate Plane	✓	✓	✓

Chapter 2 Solving Equations	B	C	A
2-1: Solving One-Step Equations	✓	✓	
2-2: Solving Two-Step Equations	✓	✓	✓
2-3: Solving Multi-Step Equations	✓	✓	✓
• Investigation: Modeling Equations	✓	✓	
2-4: Equations With Variables on Both Sides	✓	✓	✓
• Technology: Graphing to Solve Equations		✓	✓
2-5: Equations and Problem Solving	✓	✓	✓
2-6: Formulas	✓	✓	✓
• Extension: Developing Geometric Formulas			✓
2-7: Using Measures of Central Tendency	✓	✓	✓

Chapter 3 Solving Inequalities	B	C	A
3-1: Inequalities and Their Graphs	✓	✓	✓
3-2: Solving Inequalities Using Addition and Subtraction	✓	✓	✓
3-3: Solving Inequalities Using Multiplication and Division	✓	✓	✓
3-4: Solving Multi-Step Inequalities	✓	✓	✓
• Extension: Interpreting Solutions		✓	✓
3-5: Compound Inequalities		✓	✓
3-6: Absolute Value Equations and Inequalities		✓	✓
• Extension: Algebraic Reasoning			✓

Chapter 4 Solving and Applying Proportions	B	C	A
4-1: Ratio and Proportion	✓	✓	✓
4-2: Proportions and Similar Figures	✓	✓	✓
• Investigation: Modeling Percents	✓	✓	
4-3: Proportions and Percent Equations	✓	✓	✓
4-4: Percent of Change	✓	✓	✓
• Investigation: Understanding Probability	✓	✓	✓
4-5: Applying Ratios to Probability	✓	✓	✓
• Technology: Conducting a Simulation		✓	✓
4-6: Probability of Compound Events		✓	✓
• Extension: Sampling			✓

Chapter 5 Graphs and Functions	B	C	A
5-1: Relating Graphs to Events	✓	✓	✓
5-2: Relations and Functions	✓	✓	✓
5-3: Function Rules, Tables, and Graphs	✓	✓	✓
• Technology: Function Rules, Tables, and Graphs	✓	✓	✓
5-4: Writing a Function Rule	✓	✓	✓
5-5: Direct Variation	✓	✓	✓
5-6: Describing Number Patterns	✓	✓	✓

Chapter 6 Linear Equations and Their Graphs	B	C	A
6-1: Rate of Change and Slope	✓	✓	✓
• Technology: Investigating $y = mx + b$	✓	✓	✓
6-2: Slope-Intercept Form	✓	✓	✓
6-3: Standard Form	✓	✓	✓
6-4: Point-Slope Form and Writing Linear Equations		✓	✓
6-5: Parallel and Perpendicular Lines		✓	✓
6-6: Scatter Plots and Equations of Lines	✓	✓	✓
6-7: Graphing Absolute Value Equations			✓

Chapter 7 Systems of Equations and Inequalities	B	C	A
7-1: Solving Systems by Graphing	✓	✓	✓
• Investigation: Solving Systems Using Algebra Tiles	✓	✓	✓
7-2: Solving Systems Using Substitution	✓	✓	✓
7-3: Solving Systems Using Elimination	✓	✓	✓
• Technology: Matrices and Solving Systems			✓

	B	C	A
7-4: Applications of Linear Systems	✓	✓	✓
7-5: Linear Inequalities	✓	✓	✓
7-6: Systems of Linear Inequalities		✓	✓
• Technology: Graphing Linear Inequalities			✓

Chapter 8 Exponents and Exponential Functions

	B	C	A
8-1: Zero and Negative Exponents	✓	✓	✓
8-2: Scientific Notation	✓	✓	✓
8-3: Multiplication Properties of Exponents	✓	✓	✓
8-4: More Multiplication Properties of Exponents	✓	✓	✓
8-5: Division Properties of Exponents	✓	✓	✓
8-6: Geometric Sequences	✓	✓	✓
8-7: Exponential Functions	✓	✓	✓
• Technology: Fitting Exponential Curves to Data			✓
8-8: Exponential Growth and Decay		✓	✓

Chapter 9 Polynomials and Factoring

	B	C	A
9-1: Adding and Subtracting Polynomials	✓	✓	✓
9-2: Multiplying and Factoring	✓	✓	✓
• Investigation: Using Models to Multiply	✓	✓	✓
9-3: Multiplying Binomials	✓	✓	✓
9-4: Multiplying Special Cases	✓	✓	✓
• Investigation: Using Models to Factor	✓	✓	✓
9-5: Factoring Trinomials of the Type $x^2 + bx + c$	✓	✓	✓
9-6: Factoring Trinomials of the Type $ax^2 + bx + c$	✓	✓	✓
9-7: Factoring Special Cases	✓	✓	✓
9-8: Factoring by Grouping			✓

Chapter 10 Quadratic Equations and Functions

	B	C	A
10-1: Exploring Quadratic Graphs	✓	✓	✓
10-2: Quadratic Functions	✓	✓	✓
10-3: Finding and Estimating Square Roots	✓	✓	✓
10-4: Solving Quadratic Equations	✓	✓	✓

	B	C	A
• Technology: Solving Quadratic Equations by Graphing	✓	✓	✓
10-5: Factoring to Solve Quadratic Equations	✓	✓	✓
10-6: Completing the Square		✓	✓
10-7: Using the Quadratic Formula	✓	✓	✓
10-8: Using the Discriminant			✓
10-9: Choosing a Linear, Quadratic, or Exponential Model		✓	✓
• Extension: Cubic Functions			✓

Chapter 11 Radical Expressions and Equations

	B	C	A
11-1: Simplifying Radicals	✓	✓	✓
11-2: The Pythagorean Theorem	✓	✓	✓
11-3: The Distance and Midpoint Formulas	✓	✓	✓
• Extension: Special Right Triangles		✓	✓
11-4: Operations with Radical Expressions	✓	✓	✓
11-5: Solving Radical Equations	✓	✓	✓
11-6: Graphing Square Root Functions		✓	✓
• Extension: Rational Exponents			✓
11-7: Trigonometric Ratios		✓	✓

Chapter 12 Rational Expressions and Functions

	B	C	A
12-1: Inverse Variation	✓	✓	✓
• Technology: Graphing Rational Functions			✓
12-2: Graphing Rational Functions		✓	✓
• Extension: Determining Limits			✓
12-3: Simplifying Rational Expressions	✓	✓	✓
12-4: Multiplying and Dividing Rational Expressions	✓	✓	✓
12-5: Dividing Polynomials			✓
12-6: Adding and Subtracting Rational Expressions	✓	✓	✓
12-7: Solving Rational Equations	✓	✓	✓
12-8: Counting Methods and Permutations	✓	✓	✓
12-9: Combinations	✓	✓	✓

Using Your Book for Success

Welcome to Prentice Hall *Algebra 1*. There are many features built into the daily lessons of this text that will help you learn the important skills and concepts you will need to be successful in this course. Look through the following pages for some study tips that you will find useful as you complete each lesson.

Instant Check System
An *Instant Check System*, built into the text and marked with a ✔, allows you to check your understanding of skills before moving on to the next topic.

✔ Diagnosing Readiness
Complete the *Diagnosing Readiness* exercises to see what topics you may need to review before you begin the chapter.

✔ Check Skills You'll Need
Complete the *Check Skills You'll Need* exercises to make sure you have the skills needed to successfully learn the concepts in the lesson.

New Vocabulary
New Vocabulary is listed for each lesson. As each term is introduced, it is highlighted in yellow.

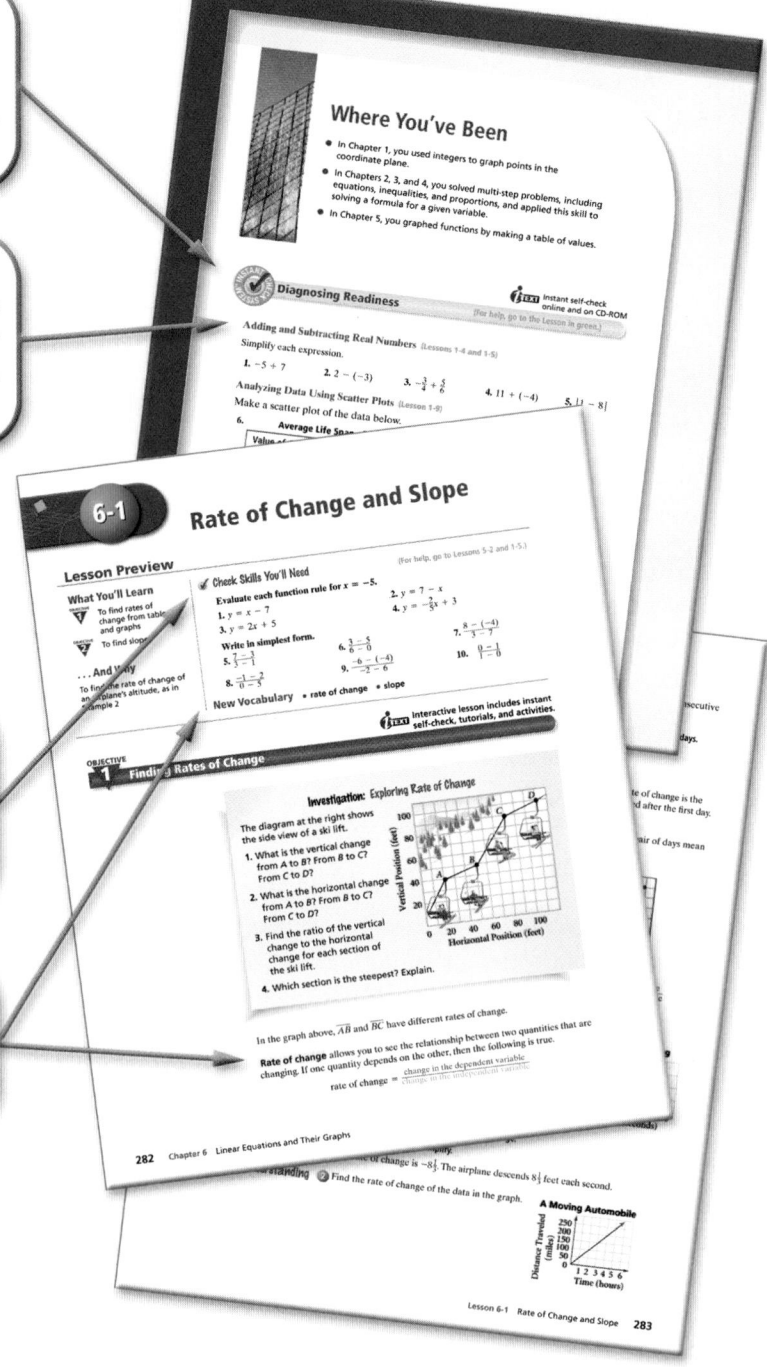

Need Help?

Need Help? notes provide a quick review of a concept you need to understand the topic being presented. You can also find help in the Skills Handbook at the back of the text.

Reading Math

The *Reading Math* hints help you to use mathematical notation correctly, understand new mathematical vocabulary, and translate mathematical symbols into everyday English so you can verbalize your learning.

✓ Check Understanding

Every lesson includes numerous *Examples,* each followed by a *Check Understanding* question that you can do on your own to see if you understand the skill being introduced. Check your progress with the answers at the back of the book.

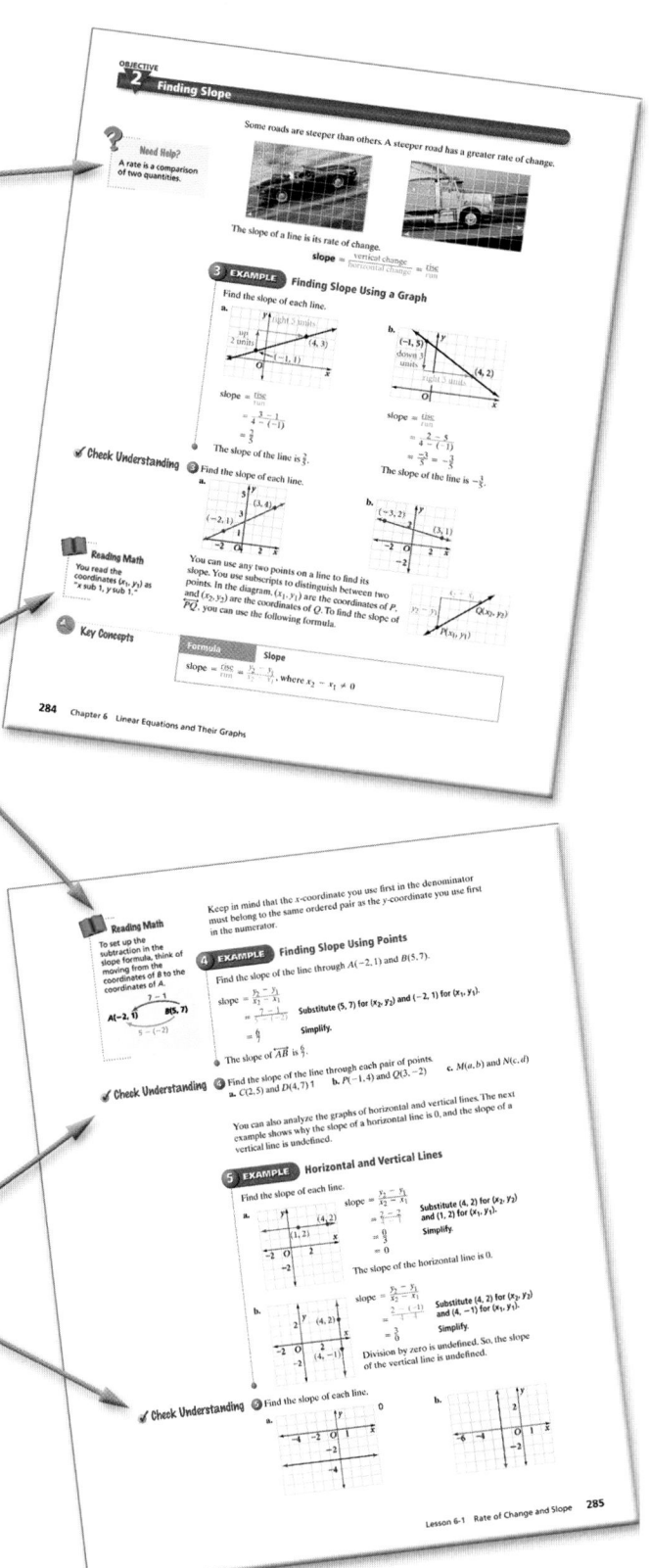

Exercises

There are numerous *Exercises* in each lesson that give you the practice you need to master the concepts in the lesson. Each practice set includes the following sections.

A: Practice by Example

The *A: Practice by Example* exercises refer you back to the Examples in the lesson, in case you need help with completing these exercises.

B: Apply Your Skills

The *B: Apply Your Skills* exercises combine skills from earlier lessons to offer you richer skill exercises and multi-step application problems.

C: Challenge

The *C: Challenge* exercises give you an opportunity to solve problems that extend and stretch your thinking.

Standardized Test Prep

Standardized Test Prep exercises give you daily practice with the types of test question formats that you will encounter on state and national tests.

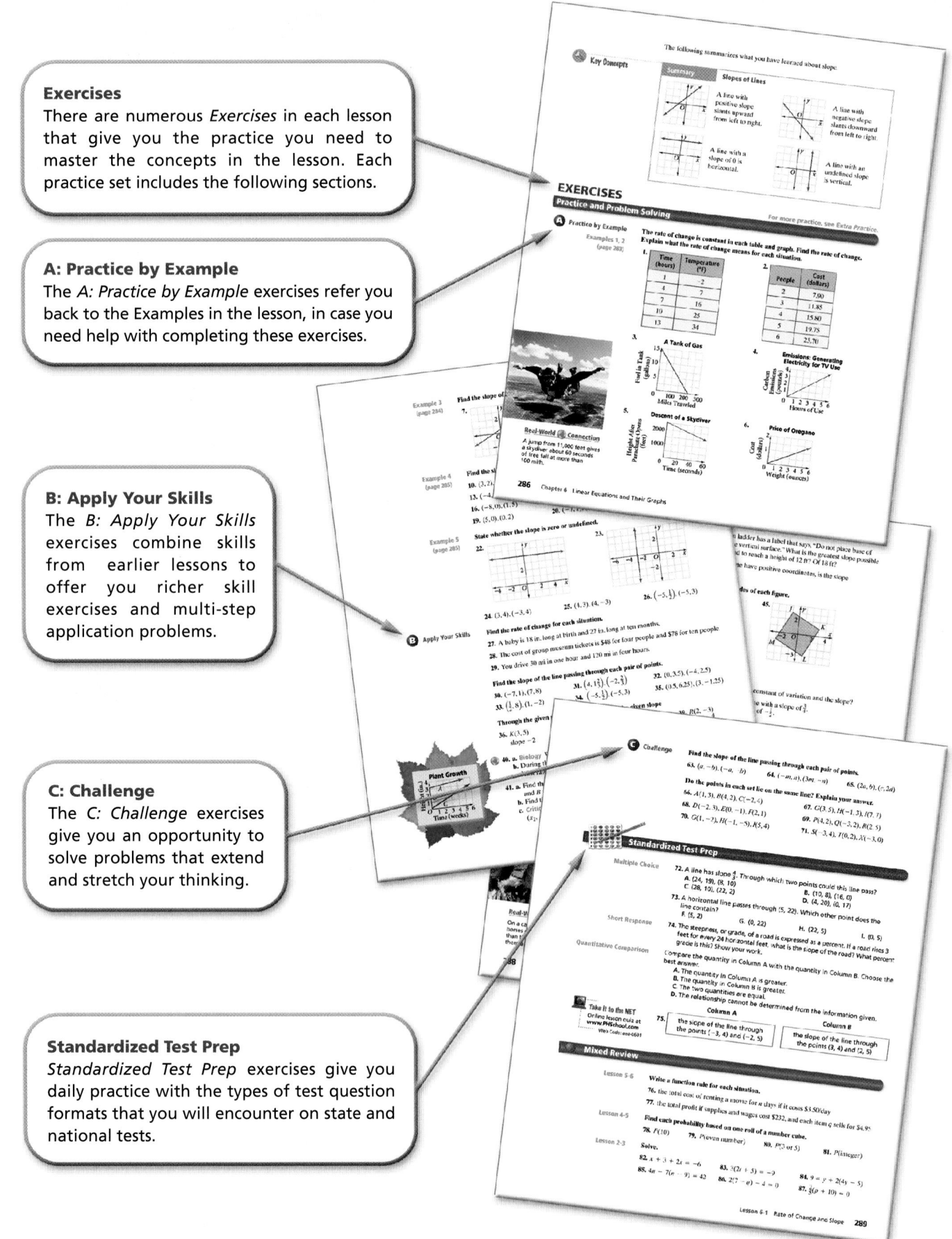

Test-Taking Strategies

Test-Taking Strategies in every chapter teach you strategies to be successful and give you practice in the skills you need to pass state tests and standardized national exams.

Standardized Test Prep

Standardized Test Prep pages in every chapter give you more opportunities to prepare for the tests you will have to take.

Test Item Formats

The *Standardized Test Prep* exercises in your book give you the practice you need to answer all types of test questions.
- *Multiple Choice*
- *Quantitative Comparison*
- *Gridded Response*, for which you write your answer in a grid
- *Short Response*, which are scored using a rubric
- *Extended Response*, which are scored using a rubric
- *Reading Comprehension*

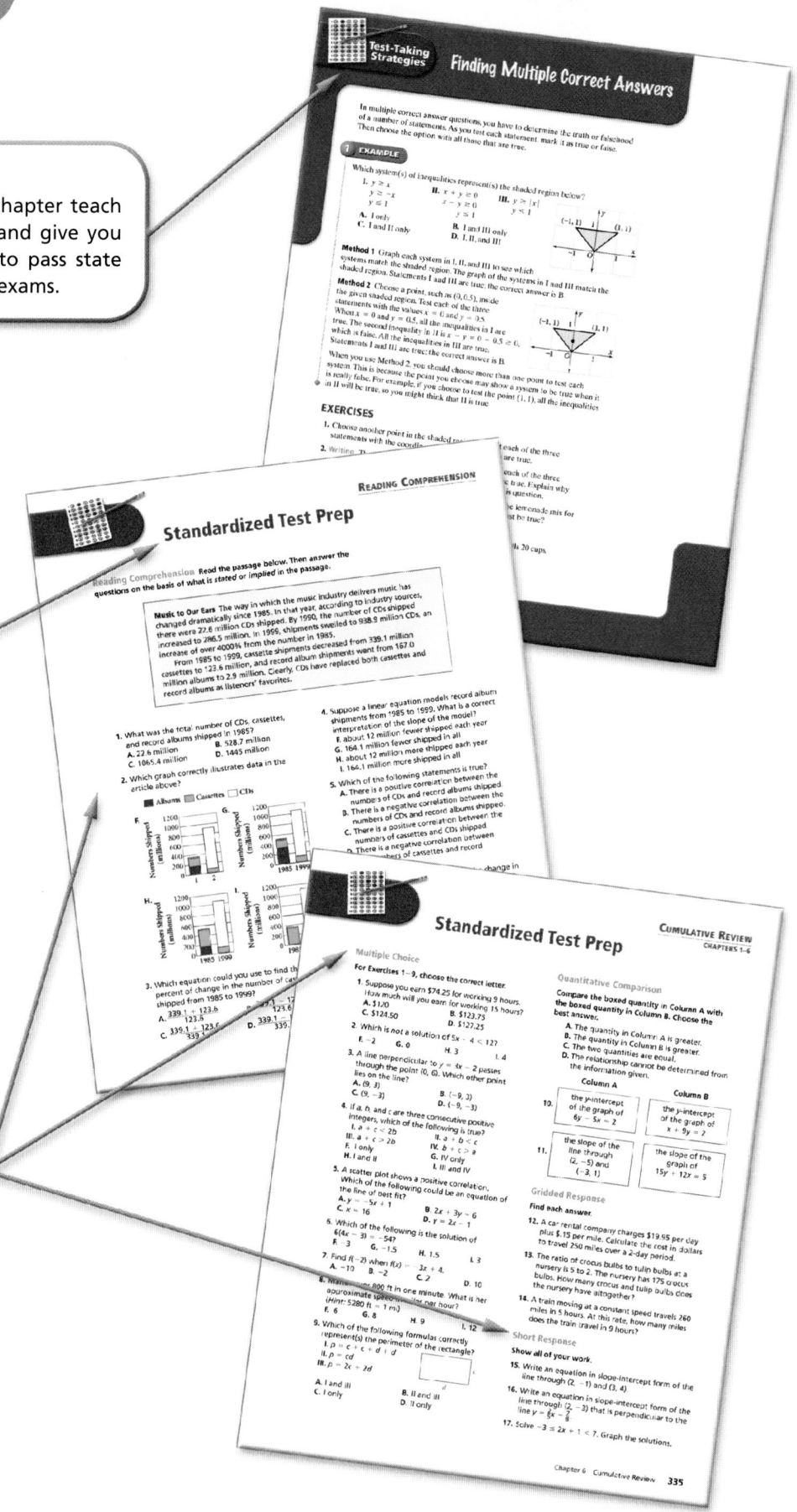

Reading to Learn

In addition to the Reading Math hints shown on page xxi, your *Algebra 1* text provides even more ways for you to develop your ability to read mathematically so that you are successful in this course and on state tests.

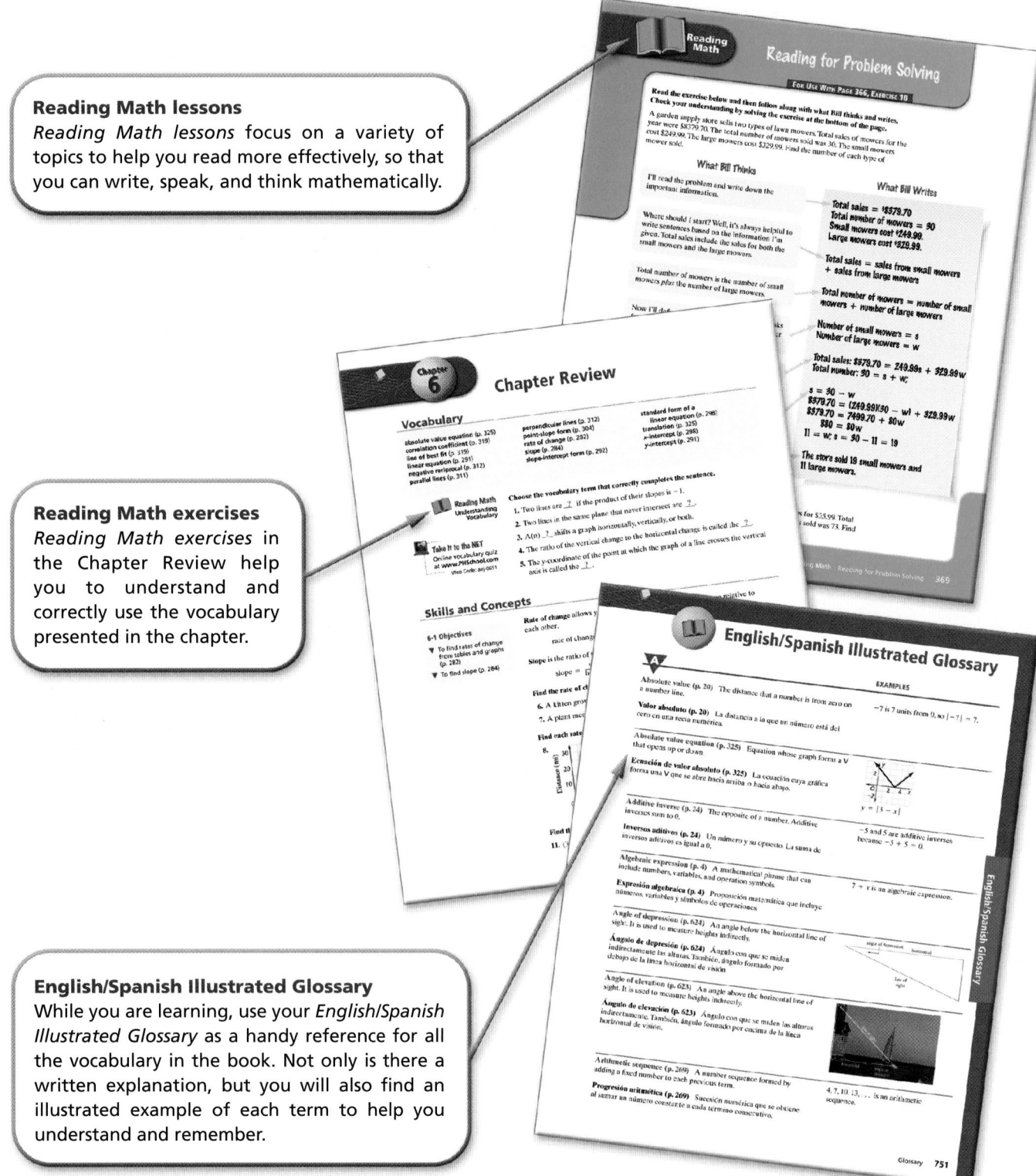

Reading Math lessons
Reading Math lessons focus on a variety of topics to help you read more effectively, so that you can write, speak, and think mathematically.

Reading Math exercises
Reading Math exercises in the Chapter Review help you to understand and correctly use the vocabulary presented in the chapter.

English/Spanish Illustrated Glossary
While you are learning, use your *English/Spanish Illustrated Glossary* as a handy reference for all the vocabulary in the book. Not only is there a written explanation, but you will also find an illustrated example of each term to help you understand and remember.

Dorling Kindersley (DK) Real-World Snapshots

 Dorling Kindersley (DK) is an international publishing company that specializes in the creation of high-quality, illustrated information books for children and adults. DK is part of the Pearson family of companies.

Real-World Snapshots
The *Real-World Snapshots* feature applies the exciting and unique graphic presentation style found in Dorling Kindersley books to show you how mathematics is used in real life.

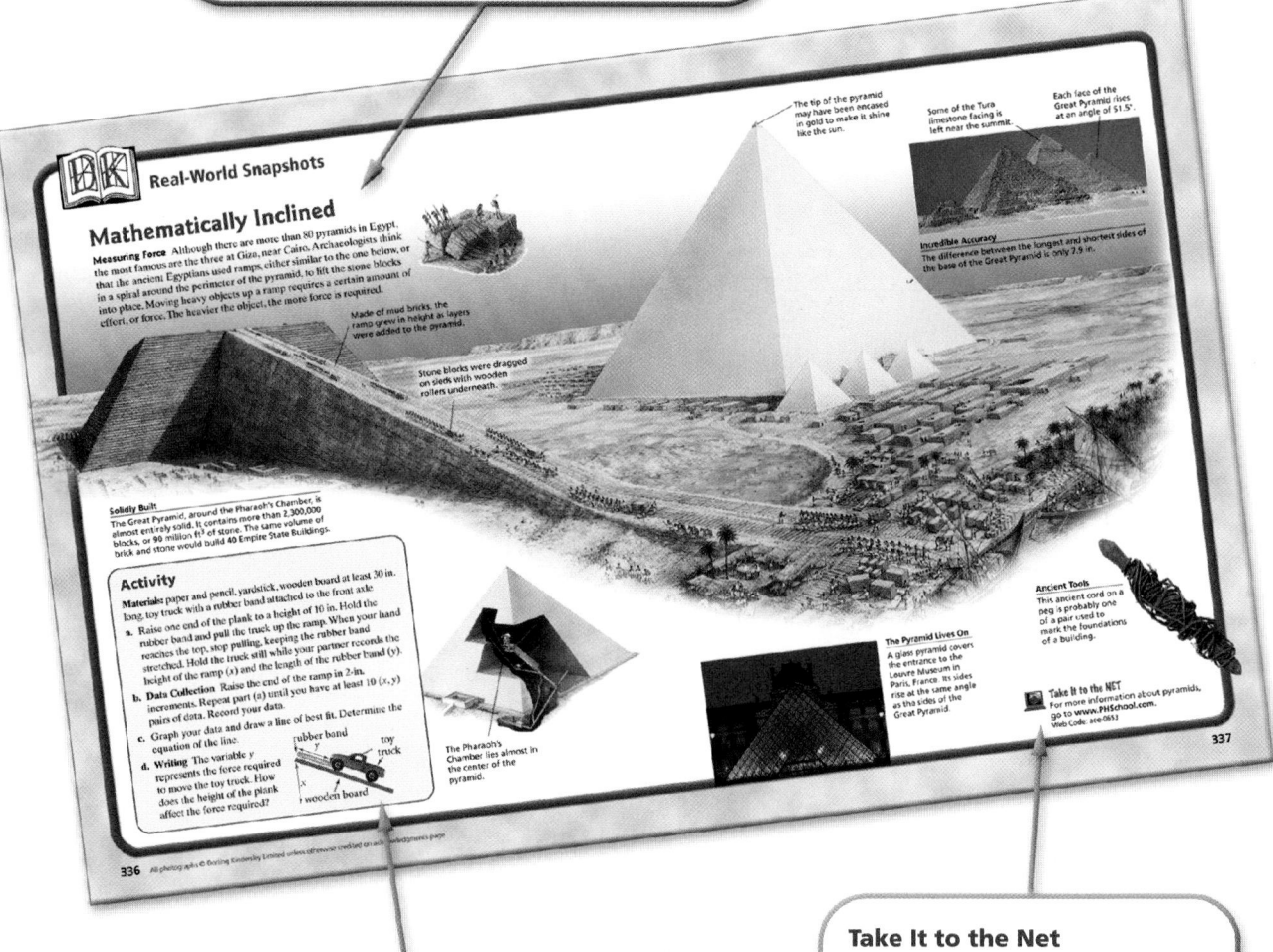

Activities
Using data from these pages and data that you gather, complete the hands-on *Activities* to apply the mathematics you are learning in real-world situations.

Take It to the Net
Enter the Web Code for online information you can use to learn more about the topic of the feature.

Tools of Algebra

Chapter at a Glance  North Carolina Objectives

1-1   **Using Variables**   1.02

NCTM   1, 2, 8, 10
- ▼ Modeling Relationships with Variables
- ▼ Modeling Relationships with Equations and Formulas

1-2   **Exponents and Order of Operations**   1.01a

NCTM   2, 3, 8, 9, 10
- ▼ Simplifying and Evaluating Expressions and Formulas
- ▼ Simplifying and Evaluating Expressions with Grouping Symbols

1-3   **Exploring Real Numbers**

NCTM   1, 2, 8, 9, 10
- ▼ Classifying Numbers
- ▼ Comparing Numbers

1-4   **Adding Real Numbers**   3.01, 3.02

NCTM   1, 2, 8, 9, 10
- ▼ Adding Real Numbers
- ▼ Applying Addition

1-5   **Subtracting Real Numbers**   3.01, 3.02

NCTM   1, 2, 9, 10
- ▼ Subtracting Real Numbers
- ▼ Applying Subtraction

1-6   **Multiplying and Dividing Real Numbers**   3.02

NCTM   1, 2, 8, 9
- ▼ Multiplying Real Numbers
- ▼ Dividing Real Numbers

1-7   **The Distributive Property**   1.01a

NCTM   1, 2, 9, 10
- ▼ Using the Distributive Property
- ▼ Simplifying Algebraic Expressions

1-8   **Properties of Real Numbers**   1.01

NCTM   1, 2, 7, 8, 10
- ▼ Identifying and Using Properties
- ▼ Using Deductive Reasoning

1-9   **Graphing Data on the Coordinate Plane**   3.03

NCTM   2, 5, 10
- ▼ Graphing Points on the Coordinate Plane
- ▼ Analyzing Data Using Scatter Plots

NCTM STANDARDS 2000

1	Number and Operations	6	Problem Solving
2	Algebra	7	Reasoning and Proof
3	Geometry	8	Communication
4	Measurement	9	Connections
5	Data Analysis and Probability	10	Representation

Pacing Options

This chart suggests pacing only for the lessons and their parts. It is provided as a possible guide. It will help you determine how much time you have in your schedule to cover other components, such as the features, Chapter Review, and Chapter Test.

Day	Traditional 45 min.	Two-Year 45 min.	Block 90 min.
1	1-1 ▼ ▼	1-1 ▼ ▼	1-1 ▼ ▼ 1-2 ▼
2	1-2 ▼	1-2 ▼	1-2 ▼ 1-3 ▼ ▼
3	1-2 ▼	1-2 ▼ ▼	1-4 ▼ ▼
4	1-3 ▼ ▼	1-2 ▼	1-5 ▼ ▼
5	1-4 ▼ ▼	1-3 ▼	1-6 ▼ ▼
6	1-5 ▼	1-3 ▼	1-7 ▼ ▼
7	1-5 ▼	1-4 ▼	1-8 ▼ ▼
8	1-6 ▼ ▼	1-4 ▼	1-9 ▼ ▼
9	1-7 ▼	1-5 ▼	
10	1-7 ▼	1-5 ▼	
11	1-8 ▼ ▼	1-6 ▼	
12	1-9 ▼ ▼	1-6 ▼	
13		1-7 ▼	
14		1-7 ▼ ▼	
15		1-7 ▼	
16		1-8 ▼	
17		1-8 ▼	
18		1-9 ▼	
19		1-9 ▼	

NAEP Correlation (National Assessment of Educational Progress 2000 Mathematics Objectives)

1-1	1-2	1-3	1-4	1-5	1-6	1-7	1-8	1-9
N2d, e	N3a; A5a, b	N2e, N3a	N3a; A5a, b	N3a	N3a, b; N7a, b	N3a, d; A5a	N3a, A5a, A7c	A3a, c; D5c

N = Number Sense, Properties, and Operations; **M** = Measurement; **G** = Geometry and Spatial Sense; **D** = Data Analysis, Statistics, and Probability; **A** = Algebra and Functions

Math Background

Chapter Overview

This chapter introduces variables and their use in establishing relationships among quantities, and connects them to the student's previous experience with arithmetic of real numbers. The properties are explained and illustrated with examples. These properties, and the order of operations, make it possible to write and simplify algebraic expressions so that there is no ambiguity in their meaning.

In order to model real-world situations and problems using algebra, it is necessary to know how to translate ordinary English words, such as "more than" into precise algebraic representations.

Using Variables, Exponents, and Order of Operations 1-1, 1-2

In algebra we use variables, expressions, and equations to model relationships. Solving problems modeled by algebra involves simplifying algebraic expressions using the order of operations. Students will see variables used in many ways. Among them are translating English expressions into algebraic expressions; as abbreviations in formulas; as unknowns in open sentences; as identifiers of points, segment lengths, or spreadsheet locations; and as identifiers for particular functions and sequences.

Exploring Real Numbers 1-3

Most students are familiar with the subsets of the real numbers as reflected in the Venn diagram in the lesson. They may not have had much exposure to *counterexample*. Testing proposed solution sets for inequalities is a good way to demonstrate the importance of understanding that only one counterexample is needed to reject a solution set, but that all possibilities must be true in order to accept a solution set. For example, consider the sets

$$\{x \mid 2x > 0\}$$

and

$$\{x \mid 2x \geq 0\}.$$

Discuss whether the set of whole numbers is the solution set for either set. Clearly 0 is not greater than zero, but is greater than or equal to zero, so the whole numbers are a solution set for only the second set. But discuss further the importance of algebra and its symbols in representing that every member of the set of whole numbers is a solution of this infinite set.

Adding, Subtracting, Multiplying, and Dividing Real Numbers 1-4, 1-5, 1-6

Real numbers can be combined by a number of different operations, including the four most basic operations. The properties of addition involve using 0 as the additive identity and introduce the idea of taking the opposite or inverse of a number. A sum of a number and its additive inverse is 0. Adding numbers is extended to adding numbers in arrays, or matrices. The dimensions of a matrix are given by its number of rows and columns; it is said to be an r by c, or $r \times c$ matrix. When two matrices have the same dimensions, the corresponding entries can be added or subtracted to form a new matrix of the same dimensions. Patterns and the usefulness of consistency can help students understand the various rules for combining numbers with like and unlike signs.

The Distributive Property 1-7

The Distributive Property is the only property that combines multiplication and addition. The property states that the coefficient of an expression within parentheses that contains a sum or difference multiplies (is distributed over) each term of the expression. An important use is in simplifying algebraic expressions. Be sure to have students explain their understanding of why $-(3x - 2y)$ can be rewritten as $-1(3x - 2y)$.

Properties of Real Numbers 1-8

The set of real numbers, combined with various operations, has certain properties that make it possible to rewrite algebraic expressions in different ways. Expressions that involve only addition, or only multiplication, can be rearranged and grouped without changing their value. These commutative and associative properties do not, in general, hold for subtraction and division, since $a - b$ is not the same as $b - a$, nor is $a \div b$ the same as $b \div a$. Discuss whether subtraction and division have identity and inverse elements.

Graphing Data on the Coordinate Plane 1-9

Forming a coordinate plane by drawing two perpendicular number lines makes it possible to name every point on the plane by using two numbers. One number shows the horizontal distance from the vertical line. A second number shows the vertical distance from the horizontal line. Distance to the right or up is indicated by a positive number; distance to the left or down is indicated by a negative number. The horizontal distance is always given first, so the order of the pair of numbers makes a difference. Thus every ordered pair of numbers can name a point on the plane, and every point on the plane can be named by an ordered pair.

Ongoing Assessment and Intervention

Tools for Monitoring Student Progress

The Prentice Hall *Algebra 1* program provides you with many options for assessment in the Student Edition, the Teacher's Edition and the teaching resources. From these options you may choose instructional materials and techniques that are appropriate for your students and support your district's curriculum requirements.

Instant Check System™ in Chapter 1

Allows students to check their own learning before, during, and after each lesson.

Diagnosing Readiness before the chapter (p. 2)

Check Skills You'll Need exercises in each lesson (pp. 4, 9, 17, 24, 32, 37, 47, 54, 59)

Check Understanding questions with each Example (pp. 4, 5, 6, 10, 11, 12, 17, 18, 19, 20, 25, 26, 27, 32, 33, 34, 38, 39, 40, 41, 47, 48, 49, 55, 56, 60, 61, 62)

Checkpoint Quiz (pp. 31, 58)

Test Prep in Chapter 1

Teaches students strategies and gives them practice with all the test item formats they will encounter on state tests and standardized national exams.

Standardized Test Prep exercises in each lesson (pp. 8, 15, 22, 23, 31, 36, 44, 52, 53, 58, 65)

Test-Taking Strategies (p. 66: Writing Gridded Responses)

Standardized Test Prep (p. 71: Reading Comprehension)

All your assessment needs in one place!

Program Assessment

Assess student progress throughout the *Algebra 1* text with blackline masters and CD-ROM.

Assessment Resources

- Checkpoint Quizzes 1 & 2
- Chapter Test, Forms A & B
- Chapter Alternative Assessment

Spanish versions available. Tests for Basic Algebra also available.

Computer Test Generator

- Unlimited questions of varying difficulty for every lesson objective.
- Create your own practice sheets, quizzes, and tests, or use the pre-made Chapter Tests.
- Diagnose readiness with questions on prerequisite skills.
- Prepare students by making tests based on standardized test objectives.
- Access Algebra 1, Geometry, and Algebra 2 content—all on one CD-ROM.

Test Preparation

A three-step approach to preparing students for high stakes, national, and state exams.

❶ Diagnose & Prescribe

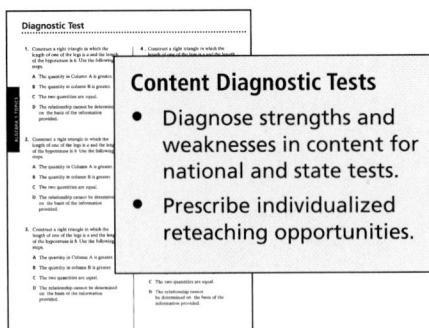

Content Diagnostic Tests
- Diagnose strengths and weaknesses in content for national and state tests.
- Prescribe individualized reteaching opportunities.

❷ Review & Reteach

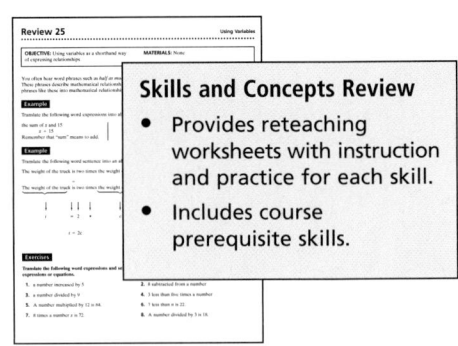

Skills and Concepts Review
- Provides reteaching worksheets with instruction and practice for each skill.
- Includes course prerequisite skills.

❸ Practice & Assess

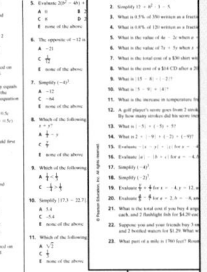

Test Preparation
- Features practice tests for End-of-Course and SAT/ACT exams.
- Includes standardized test practice by chapter for ongoing review.

Teacher's Guide with answers and correlations.

Test-Taking Strategies with Transparencies
- Support the Test-Taking Strategies pages in the Student Edition.
- Provide a teaching transparency and a practice worksheet for each strategy.

Reaching All Students

Support in the Student Text and Additional Resources

The textbook, the iText, and other technology components provide numerous opportunities to reach students of various ability levels and learning styles. Each Teacher's Edition lesson suggests how you can help *all* your students be successful and understand the mathematics in Chapter 1.

Below Level

Student Edition
- Diagnosing Readiness*: p. 2
- Check Skills You'll Need*: pp. 4, 9, 17, 24, 32, 37, 47, 54, 59

Reteaching
Chapter 1 Support File: pp. 10–18

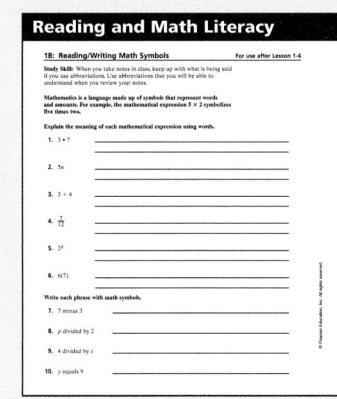

Basic Algebra Planning Guide
Chapter 1 Lesson Plans: pp. 1–9
Chapter 1 Tests: pp. 89–92

* Can be used with all ability levels to ensure mastery of prerequisite skills.

Advanced Learners

Student Edition
- Challenge exercises: pp. 8, 14, 22, 30, 36, 43, 44, 52, 57, 64

Enrichment
Chapter 1 Support File: pp. 19–27

Reading and Math Literacy

Student Edition
- Vocabulary: pp. 3, 67, *plus* in every Lesson Preview
- Reading Math: pp. 4, 5, 10, 16, 18, 19, 40, 67
- Illustrated Glossary: pp. 757–785

Reading and Math Literacy Masters
Chapter 1: pp. 1–4

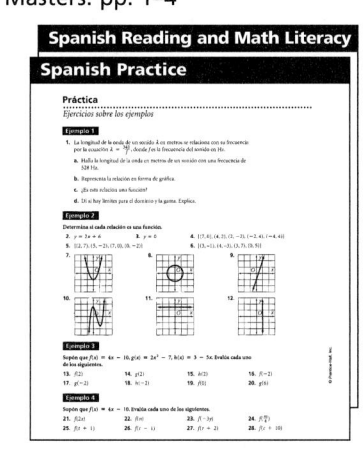

English Learners

Student Edition
- English/Spanish Illustrated Glossary: pp. 757–785

Workbook and Masters
Spanish Practice Workbook: pp. 1–9
Spanish Reading and Math Literacy Masters: pp. 1–4

Learning Styles

Student Edition
- Investigation: pp. 9, 37, 38
- Technology: pp. 11, 12, 45
- Writing: pp. 7, 14, 22, 29, 35, 42, 51, 57, 64, 70

Activity Masters
Hands-On Activities: 1, 2, 3
Technology Activities: 15

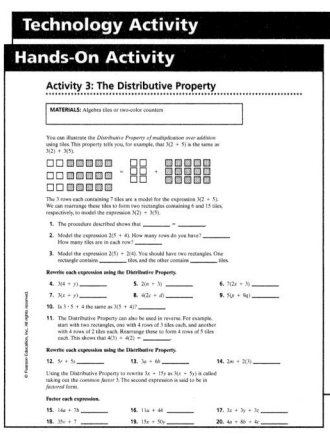

Program Resources

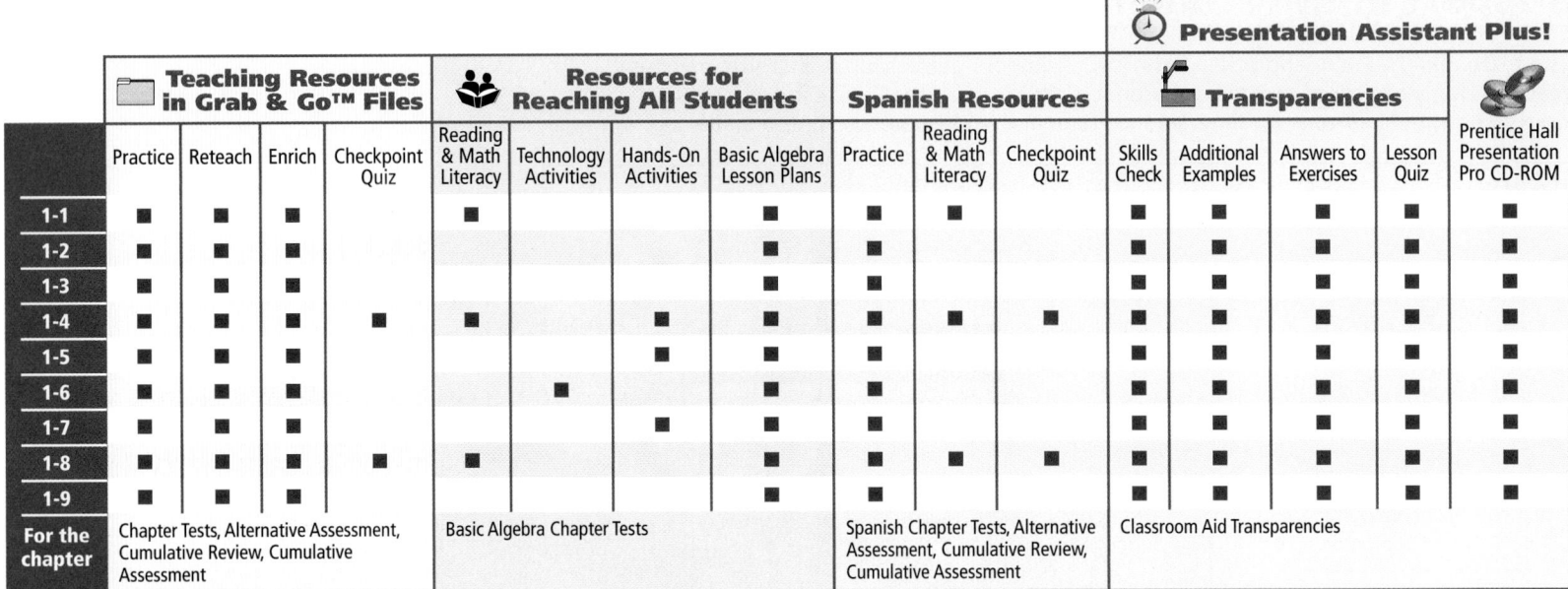

	Teaching Resources in Grab & Go™ Files				Resources for Reaching All Students				Spanish Resources			Presentation Assistant Plus! Transparencies				Prentice Hall Presentation Pro CD-ROM
	Practice	Reteach	Enrich	Checkpoint Quiz	Reading & Math Literacy	Technology Activities	Hands-On Activities	Basic Algebra Lesson Plans	Practice	Reading & Math Literacy	Checkpoint Quiz	Skills Check	Additional Examples	Answers to Exercises	Lesson Quiz	
1-1	■	■	■		■			■	■	■		■	■	■	■	■
1-2	■	■	■					■	■			■	■	■	■	■
1-3	■	■	■						■			■	■	■	■	■
1-4	■	■	■	■	■		■	■	■		■	■	■	■	■	■
1-5	■	■	■				■	■	■			■	■	■	■	■
1-6	■	■	■			■		■	■			■	■	■	■	■
1-7	■	■	■				■	■	■			■	■	■	■	■
1-8	■	■	■	■	■			■	■			■	■	■	■	■
1-9	■	■	■					■				■	■	■	■	■
For the chapter	Chapter Tests, Alternative Assessment, Cumulative Review, Cumulative Assessment				Basic Algebra Chapter Tests				Spanish Chapter Tests, Alternative Assessment, Cumulative Review, Cumulative Assessment			Classroom Aid Transparencies				

Also available for use with the chapter:

 *See page 2C.*

- Practice Workbook
- Solution Key

- For teacher support and access to student Web site materials, use Web Code aek-5500.
- For additional online and technology resources, see below.

Technology

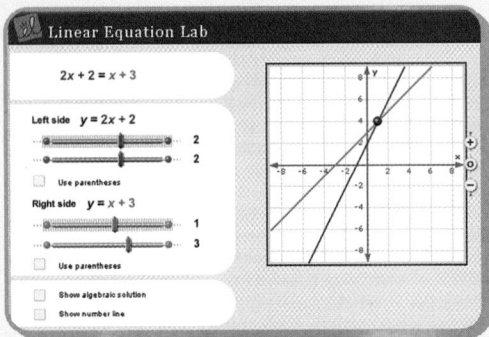

iTEXT — Online and on CD-ROM

Complete Interactive Student Text online and on CD-ROM—with instant feedback assessment, tutorial help, dynamic activities, instructional and real-world videos, audio, and additional practice.

www.PHSchool.com — For Students

Use **Web codes** for easy access to online activities, chapter projects, self-grading lesson quizzes and chapter tests, vocabulary quizzes, updated data sources, graphing calculator procedures, and more.

PH SuccessNet — For Teachers

Online lesson planning with built-in state correlations, all the teaching resources, complete reference library, your own calendar and Teacher Web page, professional development, and more.

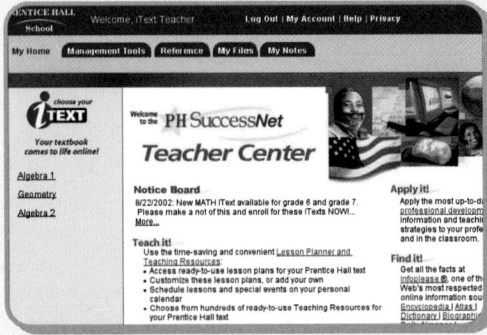

Presentation Assistant Plus!

The Prentice Hall *Presentation Assistant Plus!* provides you with the material you need to teach a lesson from beginning to end. Two easy-to-use formats—Transparencies and CD-ROM—allow you to present a lesson the way you are most comfortable.

 Transparencies

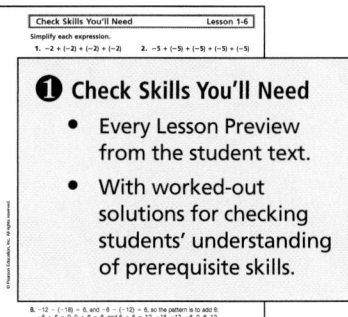

❶ Check Skills You'll Need
- Every Lesson Preview from the student text.
- With worked-out solutions for checking students' understanding of prerequisite skills.

 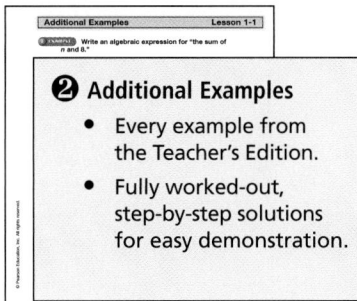

❷ Additional Examples
- Every example from the Teacher's Edition.
- Fully worked-out, step-by-step solutions for easy demonstration.

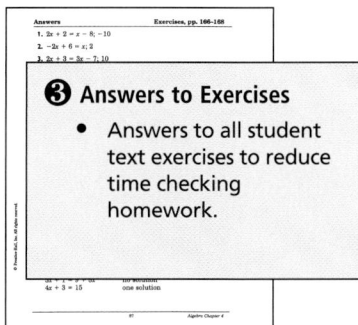

❸ Answers to Exercises
- Answers to all student text exercises to reduce time checking homework.

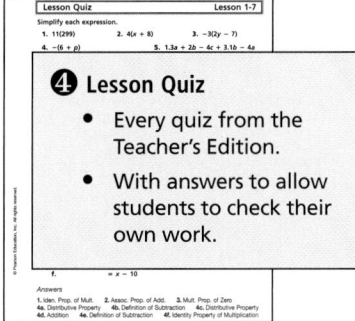

❹ Lesson Quiz
- Every quiz from the Teacher's Edition.
- With answers to allow students to check their own work.

 Throughout the Teacher's Edition, this symbol indicates material that is available on transparency in the Presentation Assistant Plus!

Prentice Hall Presentation Pro CD-ROM

- Includes all Transparencies.
- Conveniently organized by lesson so you can easily ❶ Introduce, ❷ Teach, ❸ Check Homework, and ❹ Assess each lesson.
- Animated examples allow step-by-step instruction at your own pace.
- Easy to edit so you can create custom presentations.

Teaching Chapter 1 Using Presentation Assistant Plus!

	❶ Introduce	❷ Teach	❸ Check Homework	❹ Assess
	Check Skills You'll Need	Additional Examples	Student Edition Answers	Lesson Quiz
1-1	p. 1	p. 1	✔	p. 89
1-2	p. 2	pp. 2–3	✔	p. 89
1-3	p. 3	pp. 3–4	✔	p. 90
1-4	p. 4	pp. 5–6	✔	p. 90
1-5	p. 5	pp. 6–7	✔	p. 91
1-6	p. 6	pp. 8–9	✔	p. 91
1-7	p. 7	pp. 9–10	✔	p. 92
1-8	p. 8	pp. 10–11	✔	p. 92
1-9	p. 9	pp. 11–12	✔	p. 93

 Prentice Hall Presentation Pro

CD-ROM with dynamic PowerPoint® presentations for every lesson. Helps you introduce and develop concepts, check homework, and assess progress. Part of Presentation Assistant Plus! *(See above.)*

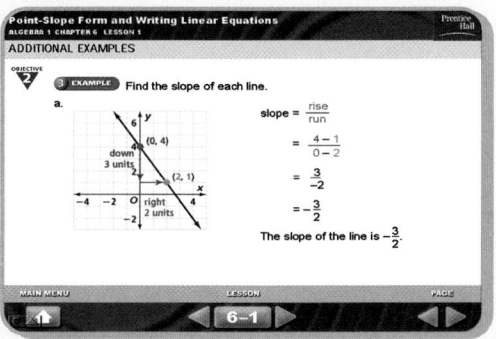

 Computer Test Generator

CD-ROM to create practice sheets and tests for course objectives and standardized tests. Includes Instant Chapter Tests™, online testing, and student reports. Part of the PH Assessment System. *(See page 2C.)*

Resource Pro® with Planning Express®

CD-ROM with a lesson planning tool that allows you to import state and local objectives. Includes electronic versions of all the teaching resources.

Tools of Algebra

 Diagnosing Readiness

Students will find answers to these exercises in the back of their textbooks.

For intervention, direct students to:

Simplifying Fractions
Skills Handbook: p. 724,
Example 2, Exercises 23–34

Adding and Subtracting Fractions
Skills Handbook: p. 726,
Example 2, Exercises 6–15
Example 3, Exercises 21–30

Exponents
Skills Handbook: p. 729,
Example 1, Exercises 1–6

Line Graphs
Skills Handbook: p. 738,
Exercises 1, 2

Where You've Been

In previous courses, you learned

● to perform calculations involving addition, subtraction, multiplication, and division with whole numbers, fractions, and decimals

● to compare numerical expressions using inequality and equality symbols

● to read and interpret graphs

 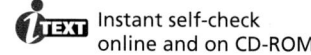 **Instant self-check online and on CD-ROM**

Diagnosing Readiness (For help, go to the Skills Handbook.)

Simplifying Fractions (Skills Handbook page 724)

Write in simplest form.

1. $\frac{12}{15}$ **4/5**
2. $\frac{20}{28}$ **5/7**
3. $\frac{33}{77}$ **3/7**
4. $\frac{8}{56}$ **1/7**
5. $\frac{48}{52}$ **12/13**

Adding and Subtracting Fractions (Skills Handbook page 726)

Add or subtract. Write each answer in simplest form.

6. $\frac{1}{8} + \frac{1}{6}$ **7/24**
7. $\frac{27}{33} - \frac{6}{22}$ **6/11**
8. $\frac{3}{4} + \frac{7}{10}$ **1 9/20**
9. $\frac{12}{13} - \frac{1}{3}$ **23/39**

10. $5\frac{7}{10} + 6\frac{7}{8}$ **12 23/40**
11. $7\frac{5}{6} - 3\frac{1}{4}$ **4 7/12**
12. $3\frac{5}{12} - 1\frac{7}{12}$ **1 5/6**
13. $4\frac{5}{7} + 8\frac{3}{4}$ **13 13/28**

Exponents (Skills Handbook page 729)

Write using exponents.

14. $9 \cdot 9 \cdot 9 \cdot 9 \cdot 9$ **9^5**
15. $8 \cdot 7 \cdot 7 \cdot 7 \cdot 7 \cdot 7 \cdot 7$ **$8 \cdot 7^6$**
16. $2 \cdot 2 \cdot 3 \cdot 3 \cdot 3 \cdot 3 \cdot 3 \cdot 3$ **$2^2 \cdot 3^6$**

Analyzing Graphs (Skills Handbook page 738)

Use the graph at the right.

17. What was the approximate difference in the voting-age populations of Texas and of Florida in 1988? **≈2,650,000**

18. Between 1992 and 1996 which state had the greater increase in voting-age population? Estimate that increase. **Texas; ≈1,000,000**

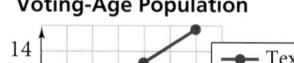
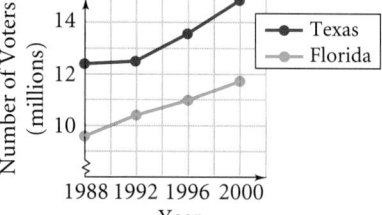

Voting-Age Population

Tools of Algebra

Where You're Going

- In this chapter, you will use variables to transform English phrases into mathematical expressions.

- You will extend your ability to calculate with whole numbers, decimals, and fractions to include integers.

- You will use the order of operations and the distributive property to simplify expressions.

- You will show the relationship between two sets of real-world data, using a scatter plot.

Real-World Connection You will use addition of integers to find the height of a mountain that has a base below sea level, on page 26.

LESSONS

1-1   Using Variables

1-2   Exponents and Order of Operations

1-3   Exploring Real Numbers

1-4   Adding Real Numbers

1-5   Subtracting Real Numbers

1-6   Multiplying and Dividing Real Numbers

1-7   The Distributive Property

1-8   Properties of Real Numbers

1-9   Graphing Data on the Coordinate Plane

Key Vocabulary

- absolute value (p. 20)
- coefficient (p. 49)
- constant (p. 49)
- coordinates (p. 59)
- equation (p. 5)
- exponent (p. 9)
- integers (p. 17)
- like terms (p. 49)
- ordered pair (p. 59)
- order of operations (p. 10)
- origin (p. 59)
- rational number (p. 17)
- real numbers (p. 18)
- reciprocal (p. 41)
- variable (p. 4)

Chapter 1 Overview

In this chapter, students model relationships using variables, expressions, and equations. They will apply the order of operations to simplify and evaluate expressions with grouping symbols such as parentheses, fraction bars, and absolute value symbols. Operating on real numbers, they evaluate expressions by applying properties, including the Distributive Property, the Commutative and Associative Properties and the Identity and Inverse Properties. Finally, students graph points on the coordinate plane and make scatter plots.

Reading Math
Reading an Example, p. 16

Vocabulary
A complete list of terms, plus vocabulary exercises, appears in the Chapter Review, p. 67.

Illustrated Glossary
Examples for each vocabulary term, plus definitions in both English and Spanish, appear starting on p. 757.

Test-Taking Strategies
Answering Gridded-Response Questions, p. 66

Real-World Connections
Some of the applications you will find in this chapter are CD sales (1-1), football (1-4), shopping (1-7), cars (1-9).

www.PHSchool.com
Internet support for this chapter includes:
- Self-grading Vocabulary and Chapter 1 Tests
- Chapter Project
- Chapter Planner
- Chapter 1 Resources

Plus **iTEXT**

3

1-1

1. Plan

Lesson Preview

✓ **Check Skills You'll Need**

Variables and Expressions
Use the worksheet on this topic found in the Skills and Concepts Review masters.

Lesson Resources

📁 **Teaching Resources**
Practice, Reteaching, Enrichment

👥 **Reaching All Students**
Practice Workbook 1-1
Spanish Practice Workbook 1-1
Reading and Math Literacy 1A
Spanish Reading & Literacy 1A
Basic Algebra Planning Guide 1-1

⏱ **Presentation Assistant Plus!**
Transparencies
• Check Skills You'll Need 1-1
• Additional Examples 1-1
• Student Edition Answers 1-1
• Lesson Quiz 1-1
PH Presentation Pro CD 1-1

PRENTICE HALL
ASSESSMENT SYSTEM

Computer Test Generator CD

💿 **Technology**
Resource Pro® CD-ROM
Computer Test Generator CD
Prentice Hall Presentation Pro CD

💻 **www.PHSchool.com**
Student Site
• Teacher Web Code: aek-5500
• Reasoning & Puzzles pp. 24, 29
• Self-grading Lesson Quiz
Teacher Center
• Lesson Planner
• Resources

Plus

1-1

Using Variables

1.02 Use formulas and algebraic expressions, including iterative and recursive forms, to model and solve problems.

Lesson Preview

What You'll Learn

 OBJECTIVE 1
To model relationships with variables

 OBJECTIVE 2
To model relationships with equations and formulas

. . . And Why

To model the relationship between the number and the cost of CDs, as in Example 3

✓ Check Skills You'll Need

Write the operation (+, −, ×, ÷) that corresponds to each phrase.

1. divided by ÷   2. difference −   3. more than +   4. product ×

5. minus −   6. sum +   7. multiplied by ×   8. quotient ÷

Find each amount.

9. 12 more than 9 **21**   10. 8 less than 13 **5**   11. 16 divided by 4 **4**   12. twice 25 **50**

New Vocabulary • variable • algebraic expression • equation • open sentence

---

Interactive lesson includes instant self-check, tutorials, and activities.

OBJECTIVE

1 Modeling Relationships With Variables

📖 **Reading Math**

Each expression below means 6.50 multiplied by *h*.

6.50 × *h*
6.50 · *h*
6.50(*h*)
(6.50)*h*
6.50*h*
(6.50)(*h*)

If you earn an hourly wage of $6.50, your pay is the number of hours you work multiplied by 6.5.

In the table at the right, the variable *h* stands for the number of hours you worked. A **variable** is a symbol, usually a letter, that represents one or more numbers. The expression 6.50*h* is an algebraic expression. An **algebraic expression** is a mathematical phrase that can include numbers, variables, and operation symbols. Algebraic expressions are sometimes called variable expressions.

Hours Worked	Pay (dollars)
1	6.50×1
2	6.50×2
3	6.50×3
h	$6.50 \times h$

1 EXAMPLE **Writing an Algebraic Expression**

Write an algebraic expression for each phrase.

a. seven more than *n*
$n + 7$ **"More than"** indicates addition. Add the first number 7 to the second number *n*.

b. the difference of *n* and 7
$n - 7$ **"Difference"** indicates subtraction. Begin with the first number *n*. Then subtract the second number 7.

c. the product of seven and *n*
$7n$ **"Product"** indicates multiplication. Multiply the first number 7 by the second number *n*.

d. the quotient of *n* and seven
$\frac{n}{7}$ **"Quotient"** indicates division. Divide the first number *n* by the second number 7.

✓ **Check Understanding** ❶ Write an algebraic expression for each phrase.
a. the quotient of 4.2 and *c* $\frac{4.2}{c}$ **b.** *t* minus 15 $t - 15$

 Ongoing Assessment and Intervention

Before the Lesson	During the Lesson	After the Lesson
Diagnose prerequisite skills using:	**Monitor progress using:**	**Assess knowledge using:**
• Check Skills You'll Need	• Check Understanding • Additional Examples • Standardized Test Prep	• Lesson Quiz • Computer Test Generator CD

To translate an English phrase into an algebraic expression, you may need to define one or more variables first.

2 EXAMPLE Writing an Algebraic Expression

Define a variable and write an algebraic expression for each phrase.

a. two times a number plus 5

Relate	two times	a number	plus 5

Define Let n = the number.

Write	2	·	n	+	5

$2n + 5$

Reading Math

In math, you write the phrase "seven less than twelve" as $12 - 7$. The order of the numbers in the math phrase is different than the order of the numbers in the English phrase.

b. 7 less than three times a number

Relate	7 less than	three times	a number

Define Let a = the number.

Write	3	·	a	−	7

$3a - 7$

✓ Check Understanding **2** Define a variable and write an algebraic expression for each phrase.
a. 9 less than a number   **b.** the sum of twice a number and 31
c. the product of one half of a number and one third of the same number
Let n be the number.   **b.** $2n + 31$

a. $n - 9$ **c.** $\frac{1}{2}n\left(\frac{1}{3}n\right)$

OBJECTIVE

2 Modeling Relationships With Equations and Formulas

You can use algebraic expressions to write an equation. An **equation** is a mathematical sentence that uses an equal sign. If the equation is true, then the two expressions on either side of the equal sign represent the same value. An equation that contains one or more variables is an **open sentence**. In everyday language, the word "is" often suggests an equal sign in the associated equation.

3 EXAMPLE Writing an Equation

Music Track One Media sells all CDs for $12 each. Write an equation for the total cost of a given number of CDs.

Relate	The total cost	is	12 times	the number of CDs bought.

Define Let n = the number of CDs bought.

Let c = the total cost.

Write	c	=	12	n

$c = 12n$

Real-World Connection

More than 940 million CDs were sold in the United States in the year 2000.

✓ Check Understanding **3 a.** Suppose the manager at Track One Media raises the price of each CD to $15. Write an equation to find the cost of n CDs. $c = 15n$
b. **Critical Thinking** Suppose the manager at Track One Media uses the equation $c = 10.99n$. What could this mean? **Each CD costs $10.99.**

👥 Reaching All Students

Below Level Have students substitute the values from the table in Example 4 into the equation. Ask them to verify that each set of values produces an equation that is true.	**Advanced Learners** Ask students to write an equation to calculate the total cost, including sales tax, for the CDs purchased in Example 3. Use your local sales tax.	**Error Prevention** See note on page 5.

---

2. Teach

Professional Development

Math Background

In algebra, letters, called *variables*, act as placeholders, in the same way boxes did in previous grades. The phrase $x + 17$ is called a *variable expression*.

OBJECTIVE
1 Teaching Notes

2 EXAMPLE Error Prevention

Some students may write $7 - 3a$ instead of $3a - 7$. Have them substitute 4 for a in each of these expressions and simplify each.

Additional Examples

1 Write an algebraic expression for each phrase.
a. the sum of n and 8 $n + 8$
b. six less than b $b - 6$

2 Define a variable and write an algebraic expression for each phrase.
a. ten more than twice a number
Let y = the number; $2y + 10$
b. three times a number minus six
Let n = the number; $3n - 6$

OBJECTIVE
2 Teaching Notes

Additional Examples

3 Write an equation to show the total income from selling tickets to a school play for $5 each. $i = 5t$

4 Write an equation for the data in the table. $m = 20g$

Gallons Used	4	6	8	10
Miles Traveled	80	120	160	200

Closure

Ask: *Why do you sometimes need variables when writing equations to represent real-world situations?* **Answers may vary. Sample: A situation may have several different values for the same types of data.**

5

3. Practice

Assignment Guide

 **Objective**
  Ⓐ Ⓑ **Core** 1–16, 25–38

 **Objective**
  Ⓐ Ⓑ **Core** 17–24, 39–42
  Ⓒ **Extension** 43–47

Standardized Test Prep 48–53

Mixed Review 54–66

Careers

Exercises 43–44 Physics is the study of physical forces. Physicists use equations to study matter, energy, force, and motion, and the ways they relate to each other.

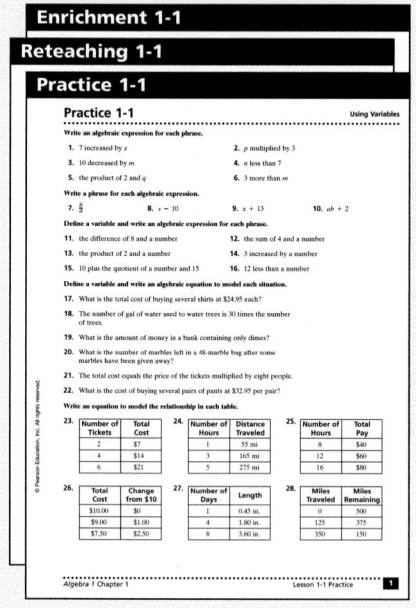

When you write an equation for data in a table, it may help to write a short sentence describing the relationship between the data. Then translate the sentence into an equation. Be sure to tell what each variable represents.

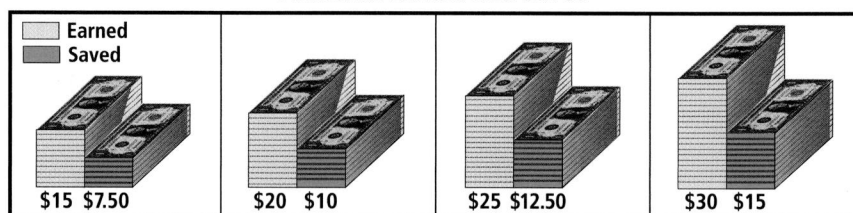

4 EXAMPLE   <u>Real-World</u> 🌎 **Problem Solving**

Sales Write an equation for the data in the table.

Cost of Purchase	Change From $20
$20.00	$0
$19.00	$1.00
$17.50	$2.50
$11.59	$8.41

Relate   Change   equals $20.00   minus   cost of purchase.

Define   Let c = cost of item purchased.
         Let a = amount of change.

Write a =   20   − c

&nbull; $a = 20 - c$

✓ **Check Understanding** ④ Write an equation for the data in the chart. **See left.**

4. Answers may vary.
   Sample:
   e = money earned,
   s = money saved,
   $s = \frac{1}{2}e$

Amounts Earned and Saved

☐ Earned
■ Saved

$15 $7.50 $20 $10 $25 $12.50 $30 $15

EXERCISES

For more practice, see *Extra Practice.*

Practice and Problem Solving

Ⓐ **Practice by Example**   **Write an algebraic expression for each phrase.**

Example 1
(page 4)

1. 4 more than p $p + 4$ **2.** y minus 12 $y - 12$

3. 12 minus m $12 - m$ **4.** the product of c and 15   **15c**

5. the quotient of n and 8 $\frac{n}{8}$ **6.** the quotient of 17 and k $\frac{17}{k}$

7. 23 less than x $x - 23$ **8.** the sum of v and 3 $v + 3$

Example 2
(page 5)

Define a variable and write an expression for each phrase.
9–16. Choice of variable for the number may vary.

9. 2 more than twice a number $2n + 2$ **10.** a number minus 11 $n - 11$

11. 9 minus a number $9 - n$ **12.** a number divided by 82 $\frac{n}{82}$

13. the product of 5 and a number   **5n**   **14.** the sum of 13 and twice a number $13 + 2n$

15. the quotient of a number and 6 $\frac{n}{6}$ **16.** the quotient of 11 and a number $\frac{11}{n}$

Example 3
(page 5)

Define variables and write an equation to model each situation. **17–20. See margin.**

17. The total cost is the number of cans times $.70.

18. The perimeter of a square equals 4 times the length of a side.

19. The total length of rope, in feet, used to put up tents is 60 times the number of tents.

20. What is the number of slices of pizza left from an 8-slice pizza after you have eaten some slices?

---

pages 6–8 Exercises

17. c = total cost,
   n = number of cans,
   $c = 0.70n$

18. p = perimeter,
   s = length of a side,
   $p = 4s$

19. ℓ = total length in feet,
   n = number of tents,
   $\ell = 60n$

20. ℓ = number of slices left,
   e = number of slices
   eaten, $\ell = 8 - e$

Example 4
(page 6)

21–24. Choices of variables may vary. Samples are given.

21. w = number of workers, r = number of radios, $r = 13n$

22. n = number of tapes, c = cost, $c = 8.5n$

23. n = number of sales, t = total earnings, $t = 0.4n$

24. n = number of hours, p = pay, $p = 8n$

B **Apply Your Skills**

25. $9 + k - 17$

27. $37t - 9.85$

29. $15 + \frac{60}{w}$

30. $7 - 3v$

Define variables and write an equation to model the relationship in each table.

21.

Number of Workers	Number of Radios Built
1	13
2	26
3	39
4	52

22.

Number of Tapes	Cost
1	$8.50
2	$17.00
3	$25.50
4	$34.00

23.

Number of Sales	Total Earnings
5	$2.00
10	$4.00
15	$6.00
20	$8.00

24.

Number of Hours	Total Pay
4	$32
6	$48
8	$64
10	$80

Write an expression for each phrase.

25. the sum of 9 and k minus 17

26. 6.7 more than 5 times n $5n + 6.7$

27. 9.85 less than the product of t and 37

28. the quotient of $3b$ and 4.5 $\frac{3b}{4.5}$

29. 15 plus the quotient of 60 and w

30. 7 minus the product of v and 3

31. the product of m and 5, minus the quotient of t and 7 $5m - \frac{t}{7}$

32. the sum of the quotient of p and 14 and the quotient of q and 3 $\frac{p}{14} + \frac{q}{3}$

33. 8 minus the product of 9 and r $8 - 9r$

Write a phrase for each expression. 34–38. See margin.

34. $q + 5$ 35. $3 - t$ 36. $9n + 1$ 37. $\frac{y}{5}$ 38. $7hb$

Define variables and write an equation to model the relationship in each table.

39.

Number of Days	Change in Height (meters)
1	0.165
2	0.330
3	0.495
4	0.660

39–40. See margin.

40.

Time (months)	Length (inches)
1	4.1
2	8.2
3	12.3
4	16.4

41. Use the table at the right.
   a. Does each statement fit the data in the table? Explain.
      i. hours worked = lawns mowed · 2   yes; 6 = 3 · 2
      ii. hours worked = lawns mowed + 3   yes; 6 = 3 + 3

Lawns Mowed	Hours
1	
2	
3	6

   b. **Writing** Which statement in part (a) better describes the relationship between hours worked and lawns mowed? Explain.
      See margin.

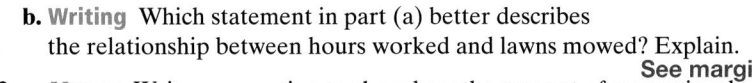 42. a. **Money** Write an equation to show how the amount of money in a bag of quarters relates to the number of quarters in the bag. See margin.
   b. The bag contains 13 quarters. How much money is this? $3.25

Real-World Connection

In 1998, people in the United States spent more than $8.5 billion on lawn care.

34–38. Answers may vary. Samples are given.

34. 5 more than q

35. the difference of 3 and t

36. one more than the product of 9 and n

37. the quotient of y and 5

38. the product of 7 times h and b

39–40. Choices of variables may vary. Samples are given.

39. n = number of days, c = change in height (m), $c = 0.165n$

40. t = time in months, ℓ = length in inches, $\ell = 4.1t$

Lesson Quiz 1-1

Write an algebraic expression for each phrase.

1. 7 less than 9 $9 - 7$

2. the product of 8 and p $8p$

3. 4 more than twice c $2c + 4$

Define variables and write an equation to model each situation.

4. The total cost is the number of sandwiches times $3.50. Let c = the total cost and s = the number of sandwiches; $c = 3.5s$

5. The perimeter of a regular hexagon is 6 times the length of one side. Let p = the perimeter and s = the length of a side; $p = 6s$

Alternative Assessment

Have students work in pairs. Each student writes an equation. Students exchange equations. Then, they write a situation that can be modeled by the equation, define the variables, and solve for one particular event.

41b. **Answers may vary.** Sample: i; it makes sense that an equation relating lawns mowed and hours worked would be a multiple of the number of lawns mowed.

42a. Let a = the amount in dollars and n = the number of quarters, $a = 0.25q$.

7

Standardized Test Prep

📁 **Resources**

For additional practice with a variety of test item formats:

• Standardized Test Prep, p. 71
• Test-Taking Strategies, p. 66
• Test-Taking Strategies with Transparencies

pages 6–8   Exercises

45–47. Answers may vary. Samples are given.

45. You walk at a rate of 5 miles per hour. How far do you walk in 2 hours? Let d = distance in miles and t = time in hours.

46. Anabel is three years older than her brother Barry. How old will Anabel be when Barry is 12? Let a = Anabel's age in years and b = Barry's age in years.

47. The Merkurs have budgeted $40 for a baby sitter. What hourly rate can they afford to pay if they need the sitter for 5 hours? Let h = the number of hours and c the cost per hour.

 **Challenge**  **Physics** The table at the left shows the height of the first bounce when a ball is dropped from different heights.

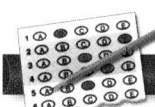

Drop Height (ft)	Height of First Bounce (ft)
1	$\frac{1}{2}$
2	1
3	$1\frac{1}{2}$
4	2
5	$2\frac{1}{2}$

a. d = drop height (ft), f = height of first bounce (ft), $f = \frac{1}{2}d$

43. a. Write an equation to describe the relationship between the height of the first bounce and the drop height.

b. Suppose you drop the ball from a window 20 ft above the ground. Predict how high the ball will bounce. **10 ft**

44. Suppose the second bounce is $\frac{1}{4}$ of the original drop height. Write an equation to relate the height of the second bounce to the drop height.

s = height of second bounce (ft), $s = \frac{1}{4}d$

Open-Ended Describe a real-world situation that each equation could represent. Include a definition for each variable. **45–47. See margin.**

45. $d = 5t$ **46.** $a = b + 3$ **47.** $c = \frac{40}{h}$

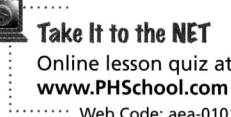

Standardized Test Prep

Multiple Choice

48. Which is an algebraic expression for "six less than k"? **D**

A. $\frac{6}{k}$ **B.** $\frac{k}{6}$ **C.** $6 - k$ **D.** $k - 6$

49. Which is an algebraic expression for "the product of a and 10"? **H**

F. $a + 10$ **G.** $a - 10$ **H.** $10a$ **I.** $\frac{a}{10}$

50. Which is an algebraic expression for "9 more than v"? **A**

A. $v + 9$ **B.** $v - 9$ **C.** $9 - v$ **D.** $9v$

51. A container of milk contains 64 ounces. Which equation models the number n of ounces remaining after you have drunk m ounces? **G**

F. $m - 64 = n$ **G.** $64 - m = n$ **H.** $n - 64 = m$ **I.** $n - m = 64$

52. Which equation models the relationship in the table if r represents the row number and t represents the number of tulips? **D**

A. $r = 3t$ **B.** $\frac{r}{t} = 3$

C. $t = r + 3$ **D.** $t = 3r$

Row Number	Number of Tulips
1	3
2	6
3	9
4	12

53. Which is an algebraic expression for "the quotient of $r + 5$ and b"? **F**

F. $\frac{r + 5}{b}$ **G.** $\frac{r}{b + 5}$ **H.** $\frac{b}{r + 5}$ **I.** $\frac{b}{r} + 5$

💻 **Take It to the NET**
Online lesson quiz at
www.PHSchool.com
Web Code: aea-0101

Mixed Review

Pre-Course

Add, subtract, multiply, or divide.

54. $0.2 + 0.7$ **0.9**   **55.** $0.13 + 0.91$ **1.04**   **56.** $0.6 + 0.75$ **1.35**   **57.** $1.09 + 0.37$ **1.46**

58. 0.9×0.7 **0.63**   **59.** $0.58 - 0.49$ **0.09**   **60.** $0.8 - 0.66$ **0.14**   **61.** $1.32 - 0.39$ **0.93**

62. 2×0.5 **1**   **63.** $0.69 \div 3$ **0.23**   **64.** $0.6 \div 0.2$ **3**   **65.** $1.21 \div 11$ **0.11**

66. List four prime numbers between 20 and 50. **any four of 23, 29, 31, 37, 41, 43, and 47**

1-2

Exponents and Order of Operations

 North Carolina Objectives

1.01   Write equivalent forms of algebraic expressions to solve problems. a) Apply the laws of exponents.

Lesson Preview

What You'll Learn

 OBJECTIVE 1
To simplify and evaluate expressions and formulas

 OBJECTIVE 2
To simplify and evaluate expressions containing grouping symbols

. . . And Why

To find the total cost of sneakers including sales tax, as in Example 3

✓ Check Skills You'll Need

Find each product.

1. 4 · 4 **16**   **2.** 7 · 7 **49**   **3.** 5 · 5 **25**   **4.** 9 · 9 **81**

Perform the indicated operations.

5. 3 + 12 − 7 **8**   **6.** 6 · 1 ÷ 2 **3**

7. 4 − 2 + 9 **11**   **8.** 10 − 5 − 4 **1**

9. 5 · 5 + 7 **32**   **10.** 30 ÷ 6 · 2 **10**

New Vocabulary
- simplify - exponent - base - power
- order of operations - evaluate

 iTEXT Interactive lesson includes instant self-check, tutorials, and activities.

OBJECTIVE

1 Simplifying and Evaluating Expressions and Formulas

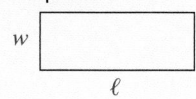

Problem Solving Hint
Drawing a diagram may help you understand the problem.

Investigation: Order of Operations

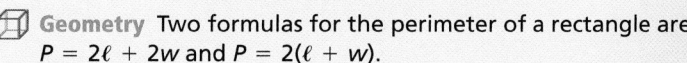

Geometry Two formulas for the perimeter of a rectangle are $P = 2\ell + 2w$ and $P = 2(\ell + w)$.

1. The length ℓ of a rectangle is 8 in. and its width w is 3 in. Find the perimeter of the rectangle using each of the formulas. **22 in.**

2. When you used $P = 2\ell + 2w$, did you add first or multiply first?
   multiply

3. When you used $P = 2(\ell + w)$, did you add first or multiply first?
   add

4. Which formula do you prefer to use? Why?
   Answers may vary. Sample: $p = 2(\ell + w)$; easier to use with mental math

To **simplify** a numerical expression, you replace it with its simplest name. The simplest name for 2 · 8 + 2 · 3 and for 2(8 + 3) is 22.

Expressions may include exponents. Using an exponent provides a shorthand way to show a product of equal factors.

$$\text{base} \rightarrow 2^4 = 2 \cdot 2 \cdot 2 \cdot 2$$

exponent ↓

power

An **exponent** tells how many times a number, the **base,** is used as a factor. A **power** has two parts, a base and an exponent.

You read the expression 2^4 as "two to the fourth power." To simplify 2^4, you replace it with its simplest name, 16. There are special names for 2^3, "two cubed," and 2^2, "two squared."

Lesson 1-2   Exponents and Order of Operations   **9**

 ## Ongoing Assessment and Intervention

Before the Lesson
Diagnose prerequisite skills using:
- Check Skills You'll Need

During the Lesson
Monitor progress using:
- Check Understanding
- Additional Examples
- Standardized Test Prep

After the Lesson
Assess knowledge using:
- Lesson Quiz
- Computer Test Generator CD

1-2

 North Carolina Objectives 1.01a

1. Plan

Lesson Preview

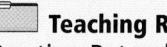 ✓ **Check Skills You'll Need**

Order of Operations
Use the worksheet on this topic found in the Skills and Concepts Review masters.

Lesson Resources

📁 **Teaching Resources**
Practice, Reteaching, Enrichment

👥 **Reaching All Students**
Practice Workbook 1-2
Spanish Practice Workbook 1-2
Basic Algebra Planning Guide 1-2

⏱ **Presentation Assistant Plus!**
Transparencies
- Check Skills You'll Need 1-2
- Additional Examples 1-2
- Student Edition Answers 1-2
- Lesson Quiz 1-2
PH Presentation Pro CD 1-2

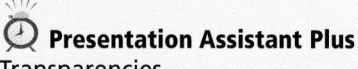 **PRENTICE HALL ASSESSMENT SYSTEM**

Computer Test Generator CD

 Technology
Resource Pro® CD-ROM
Computer Test Generator CD
Prentice Hall Presentation Pro CD

 www.PHSchool.com
Student Site
- Teacher Web Code: aek-5500
- Reasoning & Puzzles pp. 2, 25
- Graphing Calculator, Procedure 1
- Self-grading Lesson Quiz
Teacher Center
- Lesson Planner
- Resources

Plus  **iTEXT**

9

Math Background

Usually an exponent is placed to the right, raised from the base line, and written smaller.

 OBJECTIVE 1 Teaching Notes

Investigation (Optional)

After students have completed Question 4, write $\ell = \frac{5}{8}$ and $w = \frac{3}{8}$ on the board. Ask students which formula for the perimeter they would prefer to use. Lead students to notice the problem will be easier to solve using $P = 2(\ell + w)$.

1 EXAMPLE Math Tip

Tell students that a *numerical expression* is an algebraic expression that has only numbers in it.

2 EXAMPLE Tactile Learners

Have students suggest and demonstrate a series of at least three actions that are effective only if performed in the correct order. For example, (1) put socks on, (2) put shoes on, (3) tie shoelaces, is only effective if done in that order. Students may act out their series in the wrong order to demonstrate why the order of operations is necessary to assure that everyone achieves the same result.

3 EXAMPLE English Learners

The word *sneakers* may not be familiar to some students. Tell them *sneakers* is another name for tennis or athletic shoes. The rubber soles allow you to walk more quietly, as when you *sneak* up on someone.

Look at the expression below. It is simplified in two ways.

$$
\begin{array}{cc}
\underbrace{3 + 5} - 6 \div 2 & 3 + 5 - \underbrace{6 \div 2} \\
\underbrace{8 \quad - 6} \div 2 & \underbrace{3 + 5} - \quad 3 \\
\underbrace{2 \quad \div 2} & \underbrace{8 \quad - \quad 3} \\
1\ \textbf{✗} & 5\ \textbf{✔}
\end{array}
$$

↖ Different results! ↗

To avoid having two different results when simplifying the same expression, mathematicians have agreed on an order for doing operations.

🔧 Key Concepts

Summary	Order of Operations

1. Perform any operation(s) inside grouping symbols.
2. Simplify powers.
3. Multiply and divide in order from left to right.
4. Add and subtract in order from left to right.

---

1 EXAMPLE Simplifying a Numerical Expression

Simplify $25 - 8 \cdot 2 + 3^2$.

$$
\begin{aligned}
25 - 8 \cdot 2 + 3^2 &= 25 - \underline{8 \cdot 2} + 9 \qquad && \text{Simplify the power: } 3^2 = 3 \cdot 3 = 9. \\
&= \underline{25 - 16} + 9 && \text{Multiply 8 and 2.} \\
&= \quad 9 \quad + 9 && \text{Add and subtract in order from left to right.} \\
&= 18 && \text{Add.}
\end{aligned}
$$

✓ **Check Understanding** ① Simplify each expression.

 a. $6 - 10 \div 5\ 4$ **b.** $3 \cdot 6 - 4^2 \div 2$ **c.** $4 \cdot 7 + 4 \div 2^2$ **d.** $5^3 + 90 \div 10$

              10   29   134

You **evaluate** an algebraic expression by substituting a given number for each variable. Then simplify the numerical expression using the order of operations.

 Reading Math

For help with Example 2, see page 16.

2 EXAMPLE Evaluating an Algebraic Expression

Evaluate $3a - 2^3 \div b$ for $a = 7$ and $b = 4$.

$$
\begin{aligned}
3a - 2^3 \div b &= 3 \cdot 7 - 2^3 \div 4 \qquad && \text{Substitute 7 for } a \text{ and 4 for } b. \\
&= 3 \cdot 7 - 8 \div 4 && \text{Simplify the power.} \\
&= 21 - 2 && \text{Multiply and divide from left to right.} \\
&= 19 && \text{Subtract.}
\end{aligned}
$$

✓ **Check Understanding** ② Evaluate each expression for $c = 2$ and $d = 5$.

 a. $4c - 2d \div c\ 3$ **b.** $d + 6c \div 4\ 8$ **c.** $c^4 - d \cdot 2\ 6$ **d.** $40 - d^2 + cd \cdot 3$

                             45

10 Chapter 1 Tools of Algebra

👥 Reaching All Students

Below Level Remind students to write out all intermediate steps when simplifying and evaluating expressions. This will help them gain a better understanding and prevent errors.	**Advanced Learners** Challenge students to add grouping symbols in the correct places to make the following expression true. $34 \cdot 6^3 \div 2^2 \cdot 3^2 - 1 = 170$	**English Learners** See note on page 10. **Tactile Learners** See note on page 10.

You can use expressions with variables to model many real-world situations.

3 EXAMPLE   **Real-World Problem Solving**

Sales Find the total cost of the sneakers shown. Use the formula below.

$$\underset{\downarrow}{\text{cost}} \qquad \underset{\downarrow}{\text{original price}} \qquad \underset{\downarrow}{\text{sales tax}}$$

$$C = \qquad\qquad p \qquad\qquad + \qquad \overbrace{r \cdot p} \\ \qquad\qquad\qquad\qquad\qquad\qquad\qquad \underset{\uparrow}{\text{sales tax rate}}$$

$$C = p + r \cdot p$$
$$= 59 + (0.06)59 \qquad \textbf{Substitute 59 for } p\textbf{. Change 6\% to 0.06 and substitute 0.06 for } r.$$
$$= 59 + 3.54 \qquad\quad \textbf{Multiply first.}$$
$$= 62.54 \qquad\qquad \textbf{Then add.}$$

The total cost of the sneakers is $62.54.

✓ Check Understanding   **3** A shirt costs $24.95 plus sales tax of 5%. Find the total cost of the shirt. **$26.20**

OBJECTIVE

2   **Simplifying and Evaluating Expressions With Grouping Symbols**

When you simplify expressions with parentheses, work within the parentheses first. Inside parentheses, use the order of operations.

4 EXAMPLE   **Simplifying an Expression With Parentheses**

Simplify $15(13 - 7) \div (8 - 5)$.

$$15(13 - 7) \div (8 - 5) = 15(6) \div 3 \qquad \textbf{Simplify within parentheses first.}$$
$$= 90 \div 3 \qquad\quad \textbf{Multiply and divide from left to right.}$$
$$= 30 \qquad\qquad \textbf{Divide.}$$

✓ Check Understanding   **4** Simplify each expression.
   a. $(5 + 3) \div 2 + (5^2 - 3)$ **26**   **b.** $8 \div (9 - 7) + (13 \div 2)$ **10.5**

The base for an exponent is the number, variable, or expression directly to the left of the exponent. For $(cd)^2$, cd is the base. For cd^2, d is the base. Grouping symbols show which part of the expression is the base of the power.

5 EXAMPLE   **Evaluating Expressions With Exponents**

Evaluate each expression for $c = 15$ and $d = 12$.
   a. $(cd)^2$ **b.** cd^2

$$(cd)^2 = (15 \cdot 12)^2 \quad \leftarrow \textbf{Substitute 15 for } c \textbf{ and 12 for } d. \rightarrow \quad cd^2 = 15 \cdot 12^2$$
$$= (180)^2 \qquad\quad \leftarrow \textbf{Simplify within parentheses.} \qquad\qquad = 15 \cdot 144$$
$$= 32,400 \qquad\qquad\qquad \leftarrow \textbf{Simplify.} \rightarrow \qquad\qquad\qquad = 2160$$

✓ Check Understanding   **5** Evaluate each expression for $r = 9$ and $t = 14$.
   a. rt^2 **1764**   **b.** r^2t **1134**   **c.** $(rt)^2$ **15,876**

1 Simplify $32 + 6^2 - 14 \cdot 3$. **26**

2 Evaluate $5x + 3^2 \div p$ for $x = 2$ and $p = 3$. **13**

3 Find the total cost of a pair of jeans if the price is $32 and the sales tax rate is 8%. **$34.56**

OBJECTIVE

2   **Teaching Notes**

Ask students what would happen if there were no rules about whether to drive on the right side or the left side of a road. Explain to students that whether people drive on the right side or the left side of the road is not important, as long as everybody follows the same rule. Similarly, the rules for the order of operations are neither right nor wrong, but simply a convention everybody follows to avoid confusion.

5 EXAMPLE   **Alternative Method**

Let students input the expressions into a graphing calculator. They can press ▲ 2 or ▣ to square a term.

▣ Additional Examples

4 Simplify $3(8 + 6) \div (4^2 - 10)$. **7**

5 Evaluate each expression for $x = 11$ and $z = 16$.
a. $(xz)^2$ **b.** xz^2
a. 30,976   **b.** 2816

7 A carpenter wants to build three decks in the shape of regular hexagons. The perimeter p of each deck will be 60 ft. The perpendiuclar distance a from the center of each deck to one of the sides will be 8.7 ft. Use the formula $A = 3\left(\frac{pa}{2}\right)$ to find the total area of all three decks. **783 ft²**

6 EXAMPLE **Technology Tip**

If students use a graphing calculator, remind them that there are no brackets on the calculator. They must use parentheses for all grouping symbols. If the calculator display shows an error, students should check to make sure all parentheses have been input correctly. They should count the number of left parentheses and then make sure there is the same number of right parentheses.

7 EXAMPLE **Connection to Geometry**

Draw students' attention to the two boxes in the left corners of the figure. Explain that these boxes symbolize that the angles are right angles. Each angle has a measure of 90°.

Closure

Ask students to explain why the rules for the order of operations are necessary. *If everyone follows the same rules, they will get the same end result for the same problem.*

Calculator Hint

To simplify a power such as 6^3, press 6 y^x 3. On a graphing calculator, use 6 $\wedge$ 3. There is a special key for squares, so you can simplify 6^2 by pressing 6 x^2.

You can also use brackets [ ] as grouping symbols. When an expression has several grouping symbols, simplify the innermost expression first.

6 EXAMPLE **Simplifying an Expression**

Simplify $2[(13 - 7)^2 \div 3]$.

$$2[(13 - 7)^2 \div 3] = 2[(6)^2 \div 3] \quad \text{First simplify (13 − 7).}$$
$$= 2[36 \div 3] \quad \text{Simplify the power.}$$
$$= 2[12] \quad \text{Divide within the brackets.}$$
$$= 24 \quad \text{Multiply.}$$

✓**Check Understanding** **6** Simplify each expression.
 a. $5[4 + 3(2^2 + 1)]$ **95** **b.** $12 + 3[18 - 5(16 - 13)]$ **21** **c.** $5 + [(2 + 1)^3 - 3]$ **29**

A fraction bar is also a grouping symbol. For an expression like $\frac{2 + 8}{5 - 3}$, do the calculations above and below the fraction bar before simplifying the fraction.

7 EXAMPLE **Real-World** **Problem Solving**

Urban Planning A neighborhood association turned a vacant lot into a park. The park is shaped like the trapezoid below. Use the formula $A = h\left(\frac{b_1 + b_2}{2}\right)$ to find the area of the lot.

$$A = h\left(\frac{b_1 + b_2}{2}\right)$$
$$= 130\left(\frac{100 + 200}{2}\right) \quad \text{Substitute 130 for } h, \text{ 100 for } b_1, \text{ and 200 for } b_2.$$
$$= 130\left(\frac{300}{2}\right) \quad \text{Simplify the numerator.}$$
$$= 130(150) \quad \text{Simplify the fraction.}$$
$$= 19,500 \quad \text{Multiply.}$$

The area of the park is 19,500 ft².

$b_1 = 100$ ft

$h = 130$ ft

$b_2 = 200$ ft

✓**Check Understanding** **7** Find the area of a trapezoid with height $h = 300$ ft and bases $b_1 = 250$ ft and $b_2 = 170$ ft. **63,000 ft²**

EXERCISES

For more practice, see *Extra Practice*.

Practice and Problem Solving

A **Practice by Example**

Simplify each expression.

Example 1 (page 10)

1. $5 + 6 \cdot 9$ **59** **2.** $40 - 2 \cdot 3^2$ **22** **3.** $8 + 12 \div 6 - 3$ **7**

4. $8 \cdot 4 + 9^2$ **113** **5.** $5 \cdot 3^2 - 13$ **32** **6.** $21 + 49 \div 7 + 1$ **29**

Example 2 (page 10)

Evaluate each expression for $a = 5$, $b = 12$, and $c = 2$.

7. $a + b + 2c$ **21** **8.** $2b \div c + 3a$ **27** **9.** $b^2 - 4a$ **124**

10. $ca + a$ **15** **11.** $abc + ab$ **180** **12.** $5a + 12b$ **169**

12 Chapter 1 Tools of Algebra

Example 3
(page 11)

Sales Use the formula $C = p + r \cdot p$ to find the total cost of each purchase, where C is the total cost, p is the price, and r is the sales tax rate written as a decimal.

13. A coat costs $34.99. The sales tax is 6%. **$37.09**

14. A camcorder costs $329. The sales tax is 5.5%. **$347.10**

Example 4
(page 11)

Simplify each expression.

15. $2(5 + 9) - 6$ **22**   **16.** $(17 - 7) \div 5 + 1$ **3**   **17.** $(2 + 9) \cdot (8 - 4)$ **44**

18. $(7^2 - 3^2) \div 8$ **5**   **19.** $17 - 5^2 \div (2^4 + 3^2)$ **16**   **20.** $(10^2 - 4 \cdot 8) \div (8 + 9)$ **4**

Example 5
(page 11)

Evaluate each expression for $s = 11$ and $v = 8$.

21. sv^2 **704**   **22.** $(sv)^2$ **7744**   **23.** $s^2 + v^2$ **185**   **24.** $(s + v)^2$ **361**

25. $s^2 - v^2$ **57**   **26.** $(s - v)^2$ **9**   **27.** $2s^2v$ **1936**   **28.** $(2s)^2v$ **3872**

Example 6
(page 12)

Simplify each expression.

29. $6[13 - 2(4 + 1)]$ **18**   **30.** $[3(7 + 4) - 2]6$ **186**   **31.** $20 - [4(3 + 2)]$ **0**

32. $1^{11} + 3\left[\left(\frac{22}{11} + 8\right) \div 5\right]$ **7**   **33.** $27[5^2 \div (4^2 + 3^2) + 2]$ **81**   **34.** $9 + [4 - (10 - 9)^2]^3$ **36**

Example 7
(page 12)

Evaluate the formula $V = \frac{Bh}{3}$ for each pair of values.

35. $B = 4 \text{ cm}^2, h = 6 \text{ cm}$ **8 cm³**   **36.** $B = 21 \text{ in.}^2, h = 13 \text{ in.}$ **91 in.³**

37. $B = 7 \text{ ft}^2, h = 9 \text{ ft}$ **21 ft³**   **38.** $B = 8.4 \text{ cm}^2, h = 10 \text{ cm}$ **28 cm³**

39. $B = 500 \text{ ft}^2, h = 90 \text{ ft}$ **15,000 ft³**   **40.** $B = 118 \text{ m}^2, h = 66 \text{ m}$ **2596 m³**

B **Apply Your Skills**   **Simplify each expression.**

41. $(2 + 3)^2 - 10$ **15**   **42.** $2^3 + 3^2 - 10$ **7**   **43.** $(2^3 + 3)^2 - 10$ **111**

44. $(2^3 + 3^2) - 16$ **1**   **45.** $3 + 6 \cdot 8$ **51**   **46.** $(5.2 - 1) \cdot 12$ **50.4**

47. $3 \cdot 9^2 - 1$ **242**   **48.** $5 + (24 \div 3) \cdot 7^1$ **61**   **49.** $(9.8 \cdot 2) + 6.5 \cdot 8$ **71.6**

50. $4\frac{1}{3} + 6 \cdot 9$ **58$\frac{1}{3}$**   **51.** $\frac{8^2 - 4}{72}$ **$\frac{5}{6}$**   **52.** $28 \div [(19 - 7) \div 3]$ **7**

53. $1 + 2(3 + 4) \div (5 \cdot 6)$ **1$\frac{7}{15}$**   **54.** $4^3 \div 8 - 1 + 5 \div 8$ **7$\frac{5}{8}$**

55a. left side = 1
right side = 1

b. left side = 4
right side = 2

c. Answers may vary.
Sample: For $a = 2$ and
$b = 3$, left side = 25,
right side = 13

d. No; as seen in part (b),
$(a + b)^2 = a^2 + b^2$ is
not true for all values
of a and b.

55. A student wrote that $(a + b)^2 = a^2 + b^2$. **See left.**
  a. Evaluate each side of the equation for $a = 0$ and $b = 1$.
  b. Evaluate each side of the equation for $a = 1$ and $b = 1$.
  c. Open-Ended Choose another pair of values for a and b. Evaluate each side of the equation for those values.
  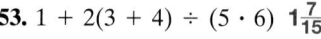 **d. Writing** An equation is true if each side of the equation simplifies to the same value or expression. Is the equation $(a + b)^2 = a^2 + b^2$ true? Explain.

Evaluate each expression for $m = 3$, $p = 7$, and $q = 4$.

56. $mp - q$ **17**   **57.** $m(p - q)$ **9**   **58.** $mp^2 - q$ **143**   **59.** $m(p^2 - q)$**135**

60. $(mp^2) - q$ **143**   **61.** $m(p - q)^2$ **27**   **62.** $m \div q + 2p$ **14$\frac{3}{4}$**   **63.** $qp^2 + pq$ **308**

64. a. Framing The frame at the left is 2 in. wide. The outer height h is 17.5 in., and the outer width w is 14 in. Use the formula $A = (h - 4)(w - 4)$ to find the area of the picture. **135 in.²**
  b. Critical Thinking Why is 4 subtracted from the height and from the width in the formula in part (a)?
  The frame is 2 in. wide, so it adds 2 in. on each side.

-2 in.

-2 in.

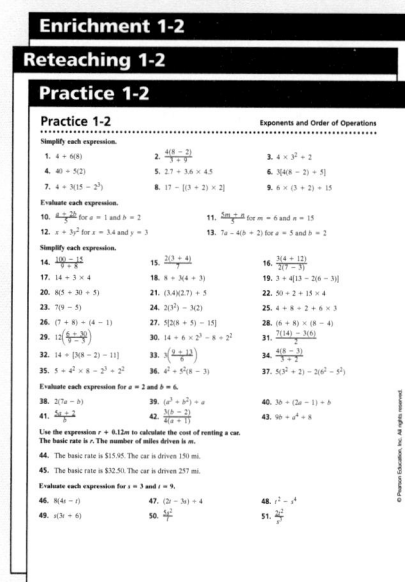

Assignment Guide

1 Objective
  A **B** Core 1–14, 42, 45, 47, 50, 54

2 Objective
  A **B** Core 15–41, 43–44, 46, 48–49, 51–53, 55–74
  C Extension 75–82

Standardized Test Prep 83–88

Mixed Review 89–106

Error Prevention

Exercises 13, 14 Remind students to rewrite the sales tax rates as decimals.

Exercises 35–40 Inform students that B represents the *area of the base* of a pyramid. That is why the units of measure are squared.

Simplify each expression.

1. $50 - 4 \cdot 3 + 6$ **44**

2. $3(6 + 2^2) - 5$ **25**

3. $2[(1 + 5)^2 - (18 \div 3)]$ **60**

Evaluate each expression.

4. $4x + 3y$ for $x = 2$ and $y = 4$ **20**

5. $2 \cdot p^2 + 3s$ for $p = 3$ and $s = 11$ **51**

6. $xy^2 + z$ for $x = 3$, $y = 6$, and $z = 4$ **112**

Alternative Assessment

Have students choose numbers to substitute for x and y in $6xy^2 + 3(xy)^2$ and evaluate the expression. Ask students to explain each step in their calculations.

pages 12–15   Exercises

80b. Yes; part a shows that the placement of parentheses can affect the value of the expression, when both add. and subtr. are involved.

J. E. MATZELIGER
LASTING MACHINE
No. 274,207.   PATENTED MAR. 20, 1883.
Fig.1.

Real-World Connection

Jan Matzeliger (1852–1889) immigrated to the United States and worked in a shoe factory in Lynn, Massachusetts.

65. History In 1883, Jan Matzeliger invented the shoe-lasting machine to attach the upper part of a shoe to its sole. Before that, each shoe was assembled and sewn by hand. You can estimate the wages at that time using the formula $w = 0.34\frac{p}{t}$, where w is the hourly wage in dollars, p is the price of a pair of shoes in dollars, and t is the time in minutes to assemble a pair of shoes.

In 1891, a worker who used the shoe-lasting machine could assemble one pair of shoes in two minutes. A pair of shoes cost about \$.94. Estimate the worker's hourly wage to the nearest cent. **\$.16**

66. Sports The formula for the volume of a sphere with radius r is $V = \frac{4\pi r^3}{3}$. Find the volume of a croquet ball that has radius 4.6 cm. Round your answer to the nearest hundredth. **407.72 cm³**

67. a. Food Use the formula for the volume of a sphere in Exercise 66. Find the volume of a seedless orange with radius 5 cm. **523.60 cm³**

   b. Suppose the peel of the orange is 0.5 cm thick. What volume of the orange is edible? **381.70 cm³**

   c. Express the edible part of the orange as a percent of the whole orange. Round your answer to the nearest percent. **about 73%**

Evaluate each expression.

68. $(5h^2 - 4) - h$, for $h = 3$ **38**

69. $[(5.2 + a) + 4]10$, for $a = 3.5$ **127**

70. $\frac{p + 4q}{3}$, for $p = 7$ and $q = 5$ **9**

71. $[x \div (y + 1)] y$, for $x = 12$ and $y = 5$ **10**

72. $h + (34 - g^2) \div g$, for $h = 2$ and $g = 3$ **$10\frac{1}{3}$**

73. a. Geometry The formula for the volume of a cylinder is $V = \pi r^2 h$. What is the volume of the cylinder below? Round your answer to the nearest hundredth of a cubic inch. **23.89 in.³**

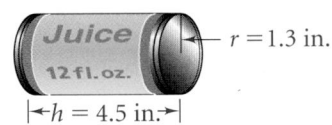

Juice
12 fl. oz.

$r = 1.3$ in.

$\leftarrow h = 4.5$ in. $\rightarrow$

   b. Critical Thinking About how many cubic inches does an ounce of juice fill? Round your answer to the nearest tenth of a cubic inch. **2.0 in.³**

   c. The formula for the surface area of a cylinder is $SA = 2\pi r(r + h)$. What is the surface area of the cylinder? Round your answer to the nearest hundredth of a square inch. **47.38 in.²**

 74. Writing Suppose you have a numerical expression. Is there only one number that is the simplest form of the expression? Explain.
Yes; the rules for simplifying are designed to produce exactly one result.

C Challenge

Use grouping symbols to make each equation true.

75. $10 + 6 \div 2 - 3 = 5$
   $(10 + 6) \div 2 - 3 = 5$

76. $14 - 2 + 5 - 3 = 4$
   $14 - (2 + 5) - 3 = 4$

77. $3^2 + 9 \div 9 = 2$ **$(3^2 + 9) \div 9 = 2$**

78. $6 - 4 \div 2 = 1$ **$(6 - 4) \div 2 = 1$**

79. a. Simplify $12 + (3 + 7)$ and $(12 + 3) + 7$. **22; 22**

   b. Does it seem that the placement of the parentheses affects the value of an expression when only addition is involved? Explain.
   No; part (a) shows the value is unaffected for the given numbers.

80. a. Simplify $(12 - 3) + 7$ and $12 - (3 + 7)$. **16, 2**

   b. Does it seem that the placement of the parentheses affects the value of the expression when both addition and subtraction are involved? Explain.
   See margin.

81. Open-Ended Use the numbers 1, 2, 4, and 5 in any order to write expressions to equal each integer from 1 to 20. Examples: **See margin.**

$$(2 \cdot 4) + 1^5 = 9 \qquad 4(5 - 2) + 1 = 13$$

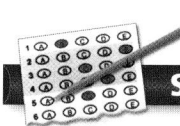 **82. a. Geometry** A trapezoid has height $h = 8$ ft, and bases $b_1 = 4$ ft and $b_2 = 5.5$ ft. Use the formula $A = h\left(\dfrac{b_1 + b_2}{2}\right)$ to find the area of the trapezoid. **38 ft²**

b. Critical Thinking Does the area of the trapezoid double if the height doubles? If one base doubles? If both bases double? Explain your answers. **See margin.**

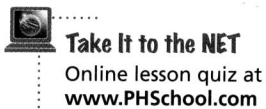

Standardized Test Prep

Multiple Choice

83. Simplify $5^3 - 15 \div 2 + 2$. **D**
A. 2   B. 57   C. 112   D. 119.5

84. Simplify $8(5 - 3)^3 + 9$. **F**
F. 73   G. 57   H. 40   I. 22

85. Evaluate $2ab + c$ for $a = 3.3$, $b = 4.5$ and $c = 2$. **B**
A. 18.4   B. 31.7   C. 32.8   D. 41.6

86. Evaluate $(r - s)^2$ for $r = 9$ and $s = 6.5$. **H**
F. 2.5   G. 3.5   H. 6.25   I. 12.25

87. A shirt is on sale for $25 at the local department store. There is also a 4% sales tax. What is the total cost of the shirt, including the sales tax? **B**
A. $25   B. $26   C. $29   D. $35

88. You can find the distance d an object falls in feet for time t in seconds using the formula $d = 16t^2$. Suppose a ball is dropped out of a window of a tall building. How far will the ball fall in 3 seconds? **F**
F. 144 ft   G. 96 ft   H. 48 ft   I. 16 ft

Take It to the NET
Online lesson quiz at
www.PHSchool.com
Web Code: aea-0102

Mixed Review

Lesson 1-1   **Write an expression for each phrase.**

89. 2 more than c **$c + 2$**   **90.** the product of m and 36   **$36m$**

91. the difference of t and 21   **$t - 21$**   **92.** the quotient of y and 5   **$\frac{y}{5}$**

Pre-Course   **Write each decimal as a percent.**

93. 0.5 **50%**   **94.** 0.34 **34%**   **95.** 0.95 **95%**   **96.** 1.45 **145%**   **97.** 0.06 **6%**

Find each percent.

98. What is 50% of 86? **43**   **99.** What is 18% of 105? **18.9**

100. What is 0.5% of 250? **1.25**   **101.** What is 67% of 90? **60.3**

Open-Ended **Write three multiples of each number.**   102–106. Answers may vary. Samples are given.

102. 8   **103.** 5   **104.** 11   **105.** 30   **106.** 13
8, 24, 56   55, 100, 250   44, 66, 121   60, 150, 240   26, 39, 52

Standardized Test Prep

📁 **Resources**
For additional practice with a variety of test item formats:
• Standardized Test Prep, p. 71
• Test-Taking Strategies, p. 66
• Test-Taking Strategies with Transparencies

Error Prevention

Exercises 85, 86 Suggest to students that they place parentheses around each substituted value to avoid confusion.

81. Answers may vary. Samples:
$2(4 - 1) - 5 = 1$
$5 + 2 - (1 + 4) = 2$
$(2^4 - 1) \div 5 = 3$
$1 + 2 + 5 - 4 = 4$
$2 \cdot 5 - (1 + 4) = 5$
$(5^2 - 1) \div 4 = 6$
$5 + 4 - 1 \cdot 2 = 7$
$2^5 \div (4 \cdot 1) = 8$
$2^5 \div 4 + 1 = 9$
$4^2 - (1 + 5) = 10$
$(4^2 - 5) \div 1 = 11$
$1 + 2 + 4 + 5 = 12$
$2^{(4 - 1)} + 5 = 13$
$2 \cdot 5 + 1 \cdot 4 = 14$
$5(4 - 1^2) = 15$
$2(1 + 5) + 4 = 16$
$5 + 4(2 + 1) = 17$
$4(5 - 1) + 2 = 18$
$4 \cdot 5 - 1^2 = 19$
$4^2 + 5 - 1 = 20$

82b. Yes; $2h\left(\dfrac{b_1 + b_2}{2}\right) =$

$2\left[h\left(\dfrac{b_1 + b_2}{2}\right)\right]$.

No; $h\left(\dfrac{2b_1 + b_2}{2}\right) \neq$

$2h\left(\dfrac{b_1 + b_2}{2}\right)$

since $b_2 \neq 0$.

Yes; $h\left(\dfrac{2b_1 + 2b_2}{2}\right) =$

$h\left(\dfrac{2(b_1 + b_2)}{2}\right) =$

$2\left[h\left(\dfrac{b_1 + b_2}{2}\right)\right]$.

15

Reading an Example

Reading an Example

Students read an example by following steps and explanations.

Teaching Notes

Have a volunteer read the paragraph that explains how to read an example.

Visual Learners

The use of color throughout this text will guide students through examples. Point out to students that the red variable is replaced by the value shown in red. Similarly the blue variable is replaced by the value shown in blue.

Exercise

Have students work independently to solve the problem. Have them show the steps they used to solve the problem. Then have volunteers share with the class what they were thinking as they wrote each step.

Reading an Example

FOR USE WITH PAGE 10, EXAMPLE 2

The description below explains how to read an example. Follow each step carefully. Then do the exercise at the bottom of the page to check your understanding.

Above an example there is usually a paragraph that will help you understand what the example is teaching. On page 10, the paragraph above Example 2 tells you that to evaluate an algebraic expression, you do the following:

- Substitute a given number for each variable and
- Simplify the numerical expression using the order of operations.

Examples show you how to use the concepts taught in each lesson. In an example, the steps are on the left and the explanations are in **bold** on the right. As you read an example, make sure you understand each step and its explanation. Checking the math in an example as you read it is one way to help you make sure you understand the concepts being taught.

EXAMPLE   **Evaluating an Algebraic Expression**

Evaluate $3a - 2^3 \div b$ for $a = 7$ and $b = 4$.

> Read the problem and locate the variables.

$3a - 2^3 \div b = 3 \cdot 7 - 2^3 \div 4$ **Substitute 7 for a and 4 for b.**

> The text in **bold** explains what is being done. Each variable is shown in color to help you see the substitution.

$= 3 \cdot 7 - 8 \div 4$ **Simplify the power.**

> To evaluate the expression, locate the power in the previous step. Check that it was simplified correctly by making sure that 2^3 is 8.

$= 21 - 2$ **Multiply and divide from left to right.**

> Check that $(3 \cdot 7)$ and $(8 \div 4)$ were simplified correctly.

$= 19$ **Subtract.**

> Check that $21 - 2$ was simplified correctly.

EXERCISE

After every example, you will see this heading. The problems in this section help you check how well you understand the concepts and techniques illustrated in the example. Try the one on page 10 under Example 2, which is shown below.

Evaluate each expression for $c = 2$ and $d = 5$.

  a. $4c - 2d \div c$ **3**   **b.** $d + 6c \div 4$ **8**   **c.** $c^4 - d \cdot 2$ **6**   **d.** $40 - d^2 + cd \cdot 3$ **45**

Exploring Real Numbers

Lesson Preview

What You'll Learn

 OBJECTIVE 1 To classify numbers

 OBJECTIVE 2 To compare numbers

. . . And Why

To determine which sets of numbers are appropriate for real-world situations, as in Example 2

✔ **Check Skills You'll Need** (For help, go to Skills Handbook page 725.)

Write each decimal as a fraction and each fraction as a decimal.

1. 0.5 $\frac{1}{2}$ **2.** 0.05 $\frac{1}{20}$ **3.** 3.25 $\frac{13}{4}$ **4.** 0.325 $\frac{13}{40}$

5. $\frac{2}{5}$ 0.4 **6.** $\frac{3}{8}$ 0.375 **7.** $\frac{2}{3}$ $0.\overline{6}$ **8.** $3\frac{5}{9}$ $3.\overline{5}$

New Vocabulary
- natural numbers
- whole numbers
- integers
- rational number
- irrational number
- real numbers
- counterexample
- inequality
- opposites
- absolute value

1-3

1. Plan

Lesson Preview

✔ **Check Skills You'll Need**

Fractions and Decimals
Skills Handbook: p. 725
Example 1, Exercises 1–12
Example 2, Exercises 13–24

Lesson Resources

📁 **Teaching Resources**
Practice, Reteaching, Enrichment

Reaching All Students
Practice Workbook 1-3
Spanish Practice Workbook 1-3
Basic Algebra Planning Guide 1-3

🕐 **Presentation Assistant Plus!**
Transparencies
- Check Skills You'll Need 1-3
- Additional Examples 1-3
- Student Edition Answers 1-3
- Lesson Quiz 1-3
PH Presentation Pro CD 1-3

PRENTICE HALL ASSESSMENT SYSTEM
Computer Test Generator CD

Technology
Resource Pro® CD-ROM
Computer Test Generator CD
Prentice Hall Presentation Pro CD

💻 **www.PHSchool.com**
Student Site
- Teacher Web Code: aek-5500
- Reasoning & Puzzles p. 54
- Self-grading Lesson Quiz
Teacher Center
- Lesson Planner
- Resources

Plus

 Interactive lesson includes instant self-check, tutorials, and activities.

OBJECTIVE

1 Classifying Numbers

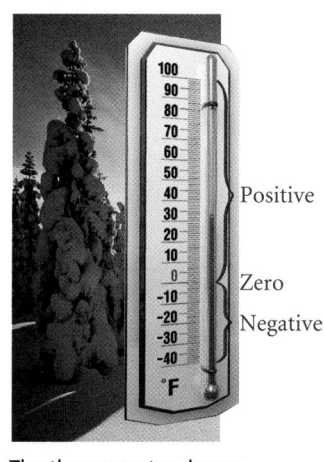

The thermometer shows positive numbers, zero, and negative numbers.

1a. integers, rational numbers

b. rational numbers

c. rational numbers

d. natural numbers, whole numbers, integers, rational numbers

Each of the graphs below shows a set of numbers on a number line. The number below a point is its coordinate on the number line.

Natural numbers	$1, 2, 3, \ldots$	
Whole numbers	$0, 1, 2, 3, \ldots$	
Integers	$\ldots -2, -1, 0, 1, 2, \ldots$	

As you can see, the set of integers has negative numbers as well as zero and positive numbers. There are also numbers that are not integers, such as 0.37 or $\frac{1}{2}$, which are rational numbers. A **rational number** is any number that you can write in the form $\frac{a}{b}$, where a and b are integers and $b \neq 0$. A rational number in decimal form is either terminating, such as 6.27, or repeating, such as $8.222\ldots$, which you can write as $8.\overline{2}$.

All integers are rational numbers because you can write any integer n as $\frac{n}{1}$.

1 **EXAMPLE** Classifying Numbers

Name the set(s) of numbers to which each number belongs.

a. $-\frac{17}{31}$ rational numbers

b. 23 natural numbers, whole numbers, integers, rational numbers $\left(\frac{23}{1}\right)$

c. 0 whole numbers, integers, rational numbers $\left(\frac{0}{1}\right)$

d. 4.581 rational numbers $\left(\frac{4581}{1000}\right)$

✔ **Check Understanding** ① Name the set(s) of numbers to which each number belongs. **a–d. See above left.**

a. -12 **b.** $\frac{5}{12}$ **c.** -4.67 **d.** 6

Ongoing Assessment and Intervention

Before the Lesson	During the Lesson	After the Lesson
Diagnose prerequisite skills using:	**Monitor progress using:**	**Assess knowledge using:**
• Check Skills You'll Need	• Check Understanding • Additional Examples • Standardized Test Prep	• Lesson Quiz • Computer Test Generator CD

Math Background

Every real number corresponds to a point on the number line. Any real number can be expressed as either a repeating ($3.\overline{10}$) or non-repeating ($3.10110111011110111110\ldots$) decimal number. The continuum hypothesis asserts that every point on the number line corresponds to a real number—there are no 'holes.'

OBJECTIVE

1 Teaching Notes

1 EXAMPLE Visual Learners

Explain natural numbers as being the numbers you naturally say when you count. Have students write "whole numbers." As a mnemonic device, instruct students to circle the o in *whole*. Stress that whole numbers are the natural numbers and 0. Integers are zero, and natural numbers and their opposites.

2 EXAMPLE Math Tip

Suggest to students that they refer to the number lines and information on page 17 for help in determining the most reasonable set of numbers.

Additional Examples

1 Name the set(s) of numbers to which each given number belongs.
a. -13 integers, rational numbers
b. 3.28 rational numbers
c. $\frac{13}{25}$ rational numbers
d. 42 natural numbers, whole numbers, integers, rational numbers

2 Which set of numbers is most reasonable for each situation? integers
a. outdoor temperatures integers
b. the number of beans in a bag whole numbers

You may need to determine the set of numbers that is reasonable for a given situation. For example, suppose 110 students are going on a field trip. Each bus can hold 40 students. To find the number of buses needed, divide 110 by 40. The answer is a rational number, 2.75. However, it is not the number of buses you would need. You would need a whole number of buses, or 3 buses.

2 EXAMPLE Real-World 🌐 Problem Solving

Which set of numbers is most reasonable for each situation?
a. the number of students who will go on the class trip   whole numbers
b. the height of the door frame in your classroom   rational numbers

✓ **Check Understanding** **2** Which set of numbers is most reasonable for the cost of a scooter? **rational numbers**

📖 **Reading Math**

π represents the ratio $\frac{\text{circumference}}{\text{diameter}}$ of a circle. This is not a rational number because either the circumference or the diameter is not rational.

An **irrational number** cannot be expressed in the form $\frac{a}{b}$, where a and b are integers. Here are three irrational numbers.

$$0.101001000\ldots \qquad \pi \qquad \sqrt{10}$$

Decimal representations of each of these are nonrepeating and nonterminating.

Together, rational numbers and irrational numbers form the set of **real numbers.**

The Venn diagram below shows the relationships of the sets of numbers that make up the real numbers.

🔑 **Key Concepts**

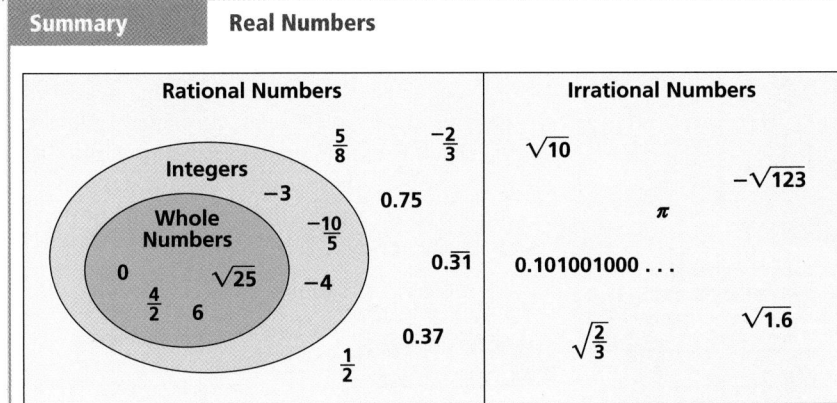

Suppose a friend says that all integers are whole numbers. You respond that -3 is an integer but not a whole number. You are using a counterexample to prove that a statement is false.

Any example that proves a statement false is a **counterexample.** You need only one counterexample to prove that a statement is false, while a proof to show that a statement is true may be more complicated.

👥 **Reaching All Students**

| **Below Level** Hand out copies of the Venn diagram on page 18 without the numbers included. Assist students in placing examples of all types of real numbers on the diagram. | **Advanced Learners** Discuss the expression $\frac{x^2}{y^2} > \frac{x}{y}$, where x and y are positive integers. If not always true, challenge students to give an example. | **Inclusion** See note on page 19. **Visual Learners** See note on page 18. |

3 EXAMPLE Using Counterexamples

Is each statement *true* or *false*? If it is false, give a counterexample.

a. All whole numbers are rational numbers.
Every whole number can be written in the form $\frac{n}{1}$, so all whole numbers are rational numbers. The statement is true.

b. The square of a number is always greater than the number.
The square of 0.5 is 0.25, and 0.25 is *not* greater than 0.5. The statement is false.

 Check Understanding **3 Critical Thinking** Is each statement true or false? If it is false, give a counterexample.

a. All whole numbers are integers. **true** **b.** No fractions are whole numbers.
b. False; answers may vary. Sample: $\frac{3}{1} = 3$ is a whole number.

OBJECTIVE

2 Comparing Numbers

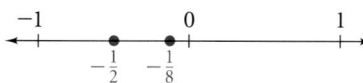

An **inequality** is a mathematical sentence that compares the value of two expressions using an inequality symbol, such as $<$ or $>$.

When you compare two real numbers, only one of these can be true:

$a < b$	or	$a = b$	or	$a > b$
is less than		**is equal to**		**is greater than**

There are three other symbols that compare two values.

$a \le b$	or	$a \ne b$	or	$a \ge b$
is less than or equal to		**is not equal to**		**is greater than or equal to**

Reading Math

You can read the inequality $3 < 5$ from right to left as "5 is greater than 3." Thus $3 < 5$ and $5 > 3$ are identical in meaning.

The number line below shows how values of numbers increase as you go to the right on a number line.

$$-1 \qquad 0 \qquad 1$$
$$-\tfrac{1}{2} \quad -\tfrac{1}{8}$$

$-\frac{1}{8}$ is to the right of $-\frac{1}{2}$, so $-\frac{1}{8} > -\frac{1}{2}$ and $-\frac{1}{2} < -\frac{1}{8}$.

To compare fractions, you may find it helpful to write the fractions as decimals and then compare the decimals.

4 EXAMPLE Ordering Fractions

Write $-\frac{3}{8}$, $-\frac{1}{2}$, and $-\frac{5}{12}$ in order from least to greatest.

$-\frac{3}{8} = -0.375$ **Write each fraction as a decimal.**

$-\frac{1}{2} = -0.5$

$-\frac{5}{12} = -0.4166\ldots = -0.41\overline{6}$

$-0.5 < -0.41\overline{6} < -0.375$ **Order the decimals from least to greatest.**

From least to greatest, the fractions are $-\frac{1}{2}$, $-\frac{5}{12}$, and $-\frac{3}{8}$.

Need Help?

You can review fractions and decimals in the Skills Handbook, page 725.

 Check Understanding **4** Write $\frac{1}{12}$, $-\frac{2}{3}$, and $-\frac{5}{8}$ in order from least to greatest. $-\frac{2}{3}, -\frac{5}{8}, \frac{1}{12}$

 **Additional Examples**

3 Determine whether the statement is true or false. If it is false, give a counterexample.
All negative numbers are integers.
false; Answers may vary.
Sample: $-\frac{2}{3}$

3 EXAMPLE Alternative Method

Have students work in pairs. Each person fills in one blank of the following sentence with a different choice of *natural numbers, whole numbers, integers, rational numbers, irrational numbers,* or *real numbers.* All _____ are _____. Together, students with their partners determine if the statement is true or false. If false, students provide counter-examples.

OBJECTIVE

2 Teaching Notes

4 EXAMPLE Inclusion

Ordering numbers can be very challenging to students who are dyslexic. Allow these students to have the numbers read to them. Instruct a partner to help find the numbers on the number line. Then they can move a finger from left to right along the number line to determine number comparisons.

5 EXAMPLE Tactile Learners

Students may need help in understanding that distance is always positive. Use masking tape to make a number line on the floor. Have students walk from 0 to 3 and from 0 to −3, making sure to step on every integer in their path. Ask: *How many steps did you take?* 3 *What do the positive and negative signs indicate?* direction

Additional Examples

4 Write $-\frac{3}{4}$, $-\frac{7}{12}$, and $-\frac{5}{8}$ in order from least to greatest.
$-\frac{3}{4}, -\frac{5}{8}, -\frac{7}{12}$

5 Find each absolute value.
a. $|-2.5|$ 2.5   b. $|7|$ 7

Closure

Ask: *What is a rational number? How can you express an integer as a rational number?* A rational number is any number you can write in the form $\frac{a}{b}$, where a and b are integers and $b \neq 0$. You can express an integer as $\frac{n}{1}$.

pages 20–23 Exercises

1. integers, rational numbers

2. rational numbers

3. rational numbers

4. natural numbers, whole numbers, integers, rational numbers

5. rational numbers

6. integers, rational numbers

7. whole numbers, integers, rational numbers

8. rational numbers

9. rational numbers

10. irrational numbers

Real-World **Connection**

The two teams pull in opposite directions. Depending on direction, a pull on the rope results in a positive or a negative direction for your team.

Two numbers that are the same distance from zero on a number line but lie in opposite directions are **opposites**.

3 units   3 units

-3 and 3 are the same distance from 0. So -3 and 3 are opposites.

The **absolute value** of a number is its distance from 0 on a number line. Both -3 and 3 are 3 units from zero. Both have an absolute value of 3. You write "the absolute value of -3" as $|-3|$.

5 **EXAMPLE** **Finding Absolute Value**

Find each absolute value.

a. $|12|$ 12 is 12 units from 0 on a number line. $|12| = 12$

b. $\left|-\frac{2}{3}\right|$ $-\frac{2}{3}$ is $\frac{2}{3}$ units from 0 on a number line. $\left|-\frac{2}{3}\right| = \frac{2}{3}$

c. $|0|$ 0 is at 0 on a number line. $|0| = 0$

✓ **Check Understanding** **5** Find each absolute value.

a. $|5|$ 5   b. $|-4|$ 4   c. $|-3.7|$ 3.7   d. $\left|\frac{5}{7}\right|$ $\frac{5}{7}$

EXERCISES

For more practice, see *Extra Practice*.

Practice and Problem Solving

A **Practice by Example**

Example 1
(page 17)

Name the set(s) of numbers to which each number belongs. 1–10. See margin.

1. -1 2. $\frac{1}{3}$ 3. -4.8 4. 7   5. $-\frac{32}{95}$

6. $-\frac{20}{4}$ 7. 0   8. -7.34 9. $\frac{7}{1239}$ 10. $\sqrt{5}$

Open-Ended Give an example of each kind of number. Answers may vary.

11. negative integer   12. whole number   13. positive real number
 Sample: -17 Sample: 53   Sample: 0.3

Example 2
(page 18)

Are *whole numbers, integers,* or *rational numbers* the most reasonable for each situation?

14. your shoe size **rational numbers**

15. the number of siblings you have **whole numbers**

16. a temperature in a news report **integers**

17. the number of quarts of paint you need to buy to paint a room **whole numbers**

18. the number of quarts of paint you use when you paint a room **rational numbers**

Example 3
(page 19)

Is each statement *true* or *false*? If the statement is false, give a counterexample.

19. All integers are rational numbers. **true**

20. All negative numbers are integers. **False; answers may vary. Sample:** $-\frac{2}{3}$

21. Every multiple of 3 is odd. **False; answers may vary. Sample: 6**

22. No positive number is less than its absolute value. **true**

23. No negative number is less than its absolute value.
 False; answers may vary. Sample: $-6 < |-6|$

Example 4
(page 19)

Use <, =, or > to compare.

24. $\frac{2}{3}$ ■ $\frac{1}{6}$ > **25.** $-\frac{2}{3}$ ■ $-\frac{1}{6}$ < **26.** $\frac{15}{8}$ ■ $1\frac{6}{8}$ > **27.** $\frac{3}{5}$ ■ 0.6 =

Order the numbers in each group from least to greatest. **28–33. See margin.**

28. 2.01, 2.1, 2.001   **29.** $-9\frac{2}{3}, -9\frac{7}{12}, -9\frac{3}{4}$ **30.** $-\frac{5}{6}, -\frac{1}{2}, \frac{2}{3}$

31. $-1.01, -1.001, -1.0009$ **32.** $\frac{7}{11}, 0.63, 0.636$ **33.** $\frac{22}{25}, \frac{8}{9}, 0.8888$

Example 5
(page 20)

Find each absolute value.

34. $|4|$ 4   **35.** $|-9|$ 9   **36.** $\left|\frac{-9}{14}\right|$ $\frac{9}{14}$ **37.** $|-0.5|$ 0.5

38. $\left|\frac{3}{5}\right|$ $\frac{3}{5}$ **39.** $|0|$ 0   **40.** $|-1295|$ 1295 **41.** $\left|-\frac{4}{5}\right|$ $\frac{4}{5}$

B **Apply Your Skills**

Write each number in the form $\frac{a}{b}$ using integers to show that it is a rational number. **42–46. Answers may vary. Samples are given.**

42. $0.2 \; \frac{1}{5}$ **43.** $5 \; \frac{5}{1}$ **44.** $21.3 \; \frac{213}{10}$ **45.** $1.034 \; \frac{1034}{1000}$ **46.** $-4 \; \frac{-4}{1}$

Name the set(s) of numbers to which each number belongs. **47–50. See left.**

47. $\left|\frac{93}{3}\right|$ **48.** $|-782|$ **49.** $|-1.93|$ **50.** $\left|\frac{37}{59}\right|$

Use <, =, or > to compare.

51. $|19|$ ■ $|-19|$ =   **52.** $|-18|$ ■ $|-17|$ >   **53.** $\left|\frac{1}{2}\right|$ ■ $|-0.51|$ <

54. $|-3.121|$ ■ $|3.12|$ > **55.** $\left|\frac{-8}{10}\right|$ ■ $\left|\frac{-16}{20}\right|$ = **56.** $\left|\frac{1}{3}\right|$ ■ $|-0.333|$ >

Simplify each expression. (*Hint:* Absolute value symbols are grouping symbols.)

57. $4 + |3 - 1|$ 6   **58.** $|41 - 38| + 6$ 9   **59.** $|a - a| + a$ a

60. $|24| + |-4|$ 28   **61.** $|12| \cdot |-4|$ 48   **62.** $|-6 + 4| + |3|$ 5 irrational

63. a. Math in the Media In the cartoon below, what type of number is pi (π)?
  b. Will the football ever be hiked? Explain. **No; π has no final digit.**

FoxTrot   by Bill Amend

Critical Thinking Use the number line for Exercises 64–66.

Q P R S T

64. If the coordinates of P and T are opposites, what is the coordinate of S? **0**

65. If the coordinates of Q and T are opposites, is R positive or negative? Explain.
  See left.

66. Reasoning If the coordinates of R and T are opposites, which point has the coordinate with the greatest absolute value? Explain. **See left.**

Real-World Connection

Careers Cartoonists may draw syndicated cartoons, such as the one at the right, that appear daily in newspapers.

65. Neg.; 0 is the point between R and S since the coordinates of Q and T are opposites, so if R is to the left of 0, then R is neg.

66. Q; 0 is the point to the right of S because the coordinates of R and T are opposites, therefore the point Q is the farthest from 0, so it has the greatest absolute value.

47. natural numbers, whole numbers, integers, rational numbers

48. natural numbers, whole numbers, integers, rational numbers

49. rational numbers

50. rational numbers

---

28. 2.001, 2.01, 2.1

29. $-9\frac{3}{4}, -9\frac{2}{3}, -9\frac{7}{12}$

30. $-\frac{5}{6}, -\frac{1}{2}, \frac{2}{3}$

31. $-1.01, -1.001, -1.0009$

32. $0.63, 0.636, \frac{7}{11}$

33. $\frac{22}{25}, 0.8888, \frac{8}{9}$

Lesson 1-3 Exploring Real Numbers   **21**

---

3. Practice

Assignment Guide

1 Objective
  A B Core 1–23, 42–46, 63, 72

2 Objective
  A B Core 24–41, 47–62, 64–71
  C Extension 73–78

Standardized Test Prep 79–85

Mixed Review 86–98

Exercises 14–18 Suggest to students that for each situation, they ask themselves whether they could have part of the item or could only express or use a complete amount.

Exercises 19–23 Suggest to students that they refer to the Venn diagram on page 18 and the number lines on page 17.

Error Prevention

Exercises 28–33 Suggest to students that they use calculators to find the decimal equivalent of each fraction.

Enrichment 1-3
Reteaching 1-3
Practice 1-3

Connection to Geometry

Exercise 63 You may want to tell students that π is the ratio of the circumference of a circle to its diameter. The approximations $\frac{22}{7}$ and 3.14 are commonly used when performing calculations with π.

Teaching Tip

Exercises 68–71 Point out to students that for *sometimes*, they need to find an example that shows the statement is true, and another example that shows it is false.

Connection to Science

Exercise 77 You may want to explain to students that density is the measure of a quantity per unit of space, such as mass per unit volume or electrical charge per unit volume.

Alternative Assessment

Ask students to name some rational numbers. Write them on the board. Repeat for irrational numbers. Instruct each student to identify the set(s) of numbers to which each given number belongs, and write the numbers in order from least to greatest.

Problem Solving Hint

Test each statement using a variety of numbers.

C Challenge

77. a. $2.75\ \frac{g}{cm^3}$, $19.3\ \frac{g}{cm^3}$, $10.5\ \frac{g}{cm^3}$, $3.5\ \frac{g}{cm^3}$

b. aluminum, diamond, silver, gold

---

67. **Open-Ended** Choose a real number. Find the sum of the absolute value of the number and the absolute value of its opposite.
Answers may vary. Sample: 25, $|25| + |-25| = 50$

Determine whether each statement is *sometimes*, *always*, or *never* true.

68. The difference of two rational numbers is an integer. **sometimes**

69. The product of two numbers is greater than either number. **sometimes**

70. The opposite of a number is less than the number. **sometimes**

71. The quotient of two nonzero integers is a rational number. **always**

72. ✏️ **Writing** Are natural numbers, whole numbers, and integers also rational numbers? Explain. **Yes; all can be expressed as ratios of themselves to 1.**

Evaluate each expression for $c = 5$, $d = 1$, and $e = 6$.

73. $-|c + d|$ **−6**   74. $2e + \left|\frac{c}{d}\right|$ **17**   75. $\frac{|e - d|}{c}$ **1**   76. $|d + 2| + |-7|$ **10**

77. a. **Science** Use the formula $d = \frac{m}{v}$ to find the density d of each substance in the table below. **a–b. See left.**

Densities of Some Substances

	Mass (m)	Volume (v)	Density (d)
Aluminum	38.5 g	14 cm³	■
Gold	38.6 g	2 cm³	■
Silver	42 g	4 cm³	■
Diamond	1.75 g	0.5 cm³	■

b. List the substances from least to greatest density.
78a–d. Answers may vary. Samples are given.

78. a. **Open-Ended** Find a number between -2 and -3 on a number line. **−2.2**

b. Find a number between -2.8 and -2.9. **−2.81**

c. Find a number between $-2\frac{1}{16}$ and $-2\frac{3}{8}$. **$-2\frac{1}{8}$**

d. **Make a Conjecture** On a number line, is it possible to find a number between any two different given numbers? Explain.
Yes; find the average of the two given numbers.

Standardized Test Prep

Multiple Choice

79. Which number has the same value as $-\left|-\frac{3}{4}\right|$? **A**
A. -0.75 B. -0.34 C. 0.34   D. 0.75

80. Which group of numbers is ordered from least to greatest? **G**
F. $-0.7, -\frac{3}{4}, -1$ G. $-1, -\frac{3}{4}, -0.7$ H. $-1, -0.7, -\frac{3}{4}$ I. $-\frac{3}{4}, -0.7, -1$

81. Suppose a is a nonzero integer. Which statement is never true? **D**
A. $a > -a$ B. $a < -a$ C. $|a| = -a$ D. $|a| = -|a|$

82. Which number is NOT an integer? **G**
F. -10 G. $-\frac{2}{3}$ H. 0   I. 5

83. Use the double bar graph below. In which year was there the least difference between the numbers of metal workers and of textile workers? **C**

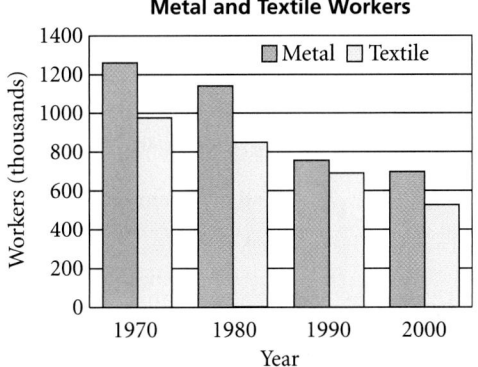

Metal and Textile Workers

SOURCE: U.S. Bureau of Labor Statistics

A. 1970   **B.** 1980   **C.** 1990   **D.** 2000

84. Suppose your brother says that fractions are rational numbers, but fractions are not integers. Which number is a counterexample for this statement? **I**

  F. $\frac{10}{3}$ **G.** $\frac{5}{3}$ **H.** $-\frac{5}{3}$ **I.** $-\frac{9}{3}$

85. Which set of numbers is most reasonable to use to describe the area of your kitchen floor? **C**

  A. whole numbers   **B.** integers

  C. rational numbers   **D.** real numbers

Take It to the NET
Online lesson quiz at
www.PHSchool.com
Web Code: aea-0103

Mixed Review

Lesson 1-2

Simplify each expression.

86. $3 + 5 \cdot 6$ **33**   **87.** $(3 + 5)6$ **48**   **88.** $3 + 5^2 \cdot 6$ **315**

89. $(33 + 9) \div 6$ **7**   **90.** $\frac{12 - 4 \cdot 3}{7 + 13 \cdot 15}$ **0**   **91.** $8 - 3 \div 6$ **$7\frac{1}{2}$**

Evaluate each expression for $g = 15$ and $k = 2$.

92. $5k + g$ **25**   **93.** $\frac{g + 1}{k^2}$ **4**   **94.** $g^2 - gk$ **195**

Lesson 1-1

Define a variable and write an expression to model each situation. 95–98. Choices of variables may vary.

95. the cost of several movie tickets that are $6.25 each
    n = **number of tickets, 6.25n**

96. the total cost of an item with a shipping fee of $3.98
    i = **cost of item, i + 3.98**

Define variables and write an equation to model the relationship in each table.

97. n = number of hours,
d = distance traveled,
$d = 7n$

98. c = total cost,
n = number of books,
$c = 3.5n$

97.

Number of Hours	Distance Traveled
1	7 mi
2	14 mi
3	21 mi
4	28 mi

97–98. See left.

98.

Number of Books	Total Cost
1	$3.50
2	$7.00
3	$10.50
4	$14.00

Resources

For additional practice with a variety of test item formats:
- Standardized Test Prep, p. 71
- Test-Taking Strategies, p. 66
- Test-Taking Strategies with Transparencies

Exercise 80 Remind students that it is a good idea to check all of their work. Suggest that they place the numbers on a number line to make sure their responses are correct.

1. Plan

Lesson Preview

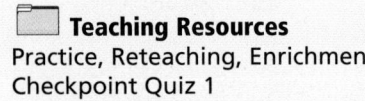 **Check Skills You'll Need**

Adding and Subtracting Fractions
Skills Handbook: p. 726
Example 2, Exercises 6–15

Lesson Resources

📁 **Teaching Resources**
Practice, Reteaching, Enrichment
Checkpoint Quiz 1

👥 **Reaching All Students**
Practice Workbook 1-4
Spanish Practice Workbook 1-4
Reading and Math Literacy 1B
Spanish Reading & Literacy 1B
Hands-On Activities 1
Basic Algebra Planning Guide 1-4

⏱ **Presentation Assistant Plus!**
Transparencies
• Check Skills You'll Need 1-4
• Additional Examples 1-4
• Student Edition Answers 1-4
• Lesson Quiz 1-4
PH Presentation Pro CD 1-4

PRENTICE HALL **ASSESSMENT** *SYSTEM*

Checkpoint Quiz 1
Computer Test Generator CD

💿 **Technology**
Resource Pro® CD-ROM
Computer Test Generator CD
Prentice Hall Presentation Pro CD

💻 **www.PHSchool.com**
Student Site
• Teacher Web Code: aek-5500
• Updated Data
• Reasoning & Puzzles pp. 3, 4, 16, 17
• Graphing Calculator, Procedure 13
• Self-grading Lesson Quiz
Teacher Center
• Lesson Planner
• Resources

Plus

24

 **1-4**

Adding Real Numbers

3.01 Use matrices to display and interpret data.
3.02 Operate (addition, subtraction, scalar multiplication) with matrices to solve problems.

Lesson Preview

What You'll Learn

 OBJECTIVE 1 To add real numbers using models and rules

 OBJECTIVE 2 To apply addition

. . . And Why

To use integers to represent yards gained and lost in a football game, as in Example 3

✓ **Check Skills You'll Need**   (For help, go to the Skills Handbook page 726.)

Find each sum.

1. $4 + 2$ **6**
2. $10 + 7$ **17**
3. $9 + 5$ **14**
4. $27 + 32$ **59**
5. $0.4 + 0.9$ **1.3**
6. $5.2 + 0$ **5.2**
7. $4.1 + 6.8$ **10.9**
8. $7.6 + 9.5$ **17.1**
9. $\frac{1}{5} + \frac{3}{5}$ **$\frac{4}{5}$**
10. $\frac{4}{9} + \frac{7}{9}$ **$1\frac{2}{9}$**
11. $\frac{1}{2} + \frac{3}{4}$ **$1\frac{1}{4}$**
12. $\frac{3}{8} + \frac{1}{4}$ **$\frac{5}{8}$**

New Vocabulary   • Identity Property of Addition   • additive inverse
• Inverse Property of Addition   • matrix   • element

 Interactive lesson includes instant self-check, tutorials, and activities.

OBJECTIVE 1 Adding Real Numbers

In previous math courses, you learned that the sum of a number and 0 is the original number. This is true for any number, whether it is positive or negative.

🔑 **Key Concepts**

Property	Identity Property of Addition
For every real number n, $n + 0 = n$.	
Examples $0 + 5 = 5$ $-5 + 0 = -5$	

The opposite of a number is its **additive inverse.** The number line shows the sum of $4 + (-4)$.

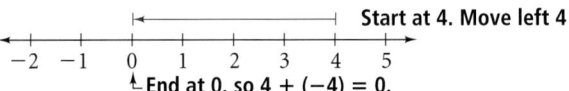

Start at 4. Move left 4 units.

End at 0, so $4 + (-4) = 0$.

The additive inverse of a negative number is a positive number. The number line below shows the sum of $-5 + 5$.

Start at -5. 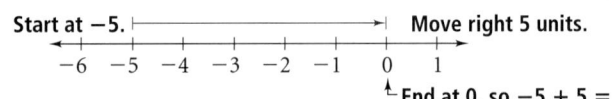 Move right 5 units.

End at 0, so $-5 + 5 = 0$.

🔑 **Key Concepts**

Property	Inverse Property of Addition
For every real number n, there is an additive inverse $-n$ such that $n + (-n) = 0$.	
Examples $17 + (-17) = 0$ $-17 + 17 = 0$	

Ongoing Assessment and Intervention

Before the Lesson
Diagnose prerequisite skills using:
• Check Skills You'll Need

During the Lesson
Monitor progress using:
• Check Understanding
• Additional Examples
• Standardized Test Prep

After the Lesson
Assess knowledge using:
• Lesson Quiz
• Computer Test Generator CD
• Chapter Checkpoint 1 (p. 31)

You can use number lines as models to add real numbers.

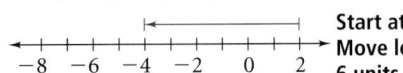 **EXAMPLE** Using a Number Line Model

Simplify each expression.

a. $2 + 6$ Start at 2. Move right 6 units. $2 + 6 = 8$

b. $2 + (-6)$ Start at 2. Move left 6 units. $2 + (-6) = -4$

c. $-2 + 6$ Start at −2. Move right 6 units. $-2 + 6 = 4$

d. $-2 + (-6)$ Start at −2. Move left 6 units. $-2 + (-6) = -8$

 Check Understanding ❶ Use a number line to find each sum.

a. $-6 + 4$ **−2**   **b.** $4 + (-6)$ **−2**   **c.** $-3 + (-8)$ **−11**   **d.** $9 + (-3)$ **6**

You can also find the sums in Example 1 using rules. Recall that numbers being added are called addends.

🔑 **Key Concepts**

Rule	Adding Numbers With the Same Sign

To add two numbers with the same sign, *add* their absolute values. The sum has the same sign as the addends.

Examples $2 + 6 = 8$ $-2 + (-6) = -8$

Rule	Adding Numbers With Different Signs

To add two numbers with different signs, find the *difference* of their absolute values. The sum has the same sign as the addend with the greater absolute value.

Examples $-2 + 6 = 4$ $2 + (-6) = -4$

❷ **EXAMPLE** Adding Numbers

Simplify each expression.

a. $-5 + (-6) = -11$ Since both addends are negative, add their absolute values. The sum is negative.

b. $13 + (-34) = -21$ The difference of the absolute values is 21. The negative addend has the greater absolute value, so the sum is negative.

c. $3.4 + 9.7 = 13.1$ Since both addends are positive, add their absolute values. The sum is positive.

d. $-1.5 + 3.4 = 1.9$ The difference of the absolute values is 1.9. The positive addend has the greater absolute value, so the sum is positive.

Check Understanding ❷ Find each sum.

a. $-7 + (-4)$ **−11**   **b.** $-26.3 + 8.9$ **−17.4**   **c.** $-\frac{3}{4} + \left(-\frac{1}{2}\right)$ **$-1\frac{1}{4}$**   **d.** $\frac{8}{9} + \left(-\frac{5}{6}\right)$ **$\frac{1}{18}$**

Lesson 1-4 Adding Real Numbers   **25**

Math Background

In general, matrices may be added when the entries in identical locations represent similar data.

OBJECTIVE

❶ **Teaching Notes**

❶ **EXAMPLE** Tactile Learners

Make a number line on the floor using tape. Have students walk along the number line to model the sums. You may also have students use their index fingers to trace the movement shown on the number lines in the book.

❷ **EXAMPLE** English Learners

Stress to students that when you add numbers with *different* signs, you actually find the *difference* in their absolute values. Remind students that the sum has the same sign as the addend with the greater absolute value.

❸ **EXAMPLE** Diversity

If any students are from other countries where football means soccer, have a few students explain what is meant by football in the United States.

Additional Examples

❶ Use a number line to simplify each expression.
a. $3 + (-5)$ **−2**
b. $-3 + 5$ **2**
c. $-3 + (-5)$ **−8**

❷ Simplify each expression.
a. $12 + (-23)$ **−11**
b. $-6.4 + (-8.6)$ **−15.0**

Additional Examples

3 The water level in a lake rose 6 inches and then fell 11 inches. Write an addition statement to find the total change in water level. **6 + (−11) = −5; The water level fell 5 inches.**

OBJECTIVE

2 Teaching Notes

4 EXAMPLE Error Prevention

Suggest to students that they write all substituted amounts in parentheses so that they will not forget any negative signs.

5 EXAMPLE Connection to Geography

Explain to students that there are areas of land that are below sea level. One of these areas is Death Valley. Death Valley is a desert region in southeastern California that is from 4 to 16 miles wide and about 140 miles long. It has the lowest elevation in the Western Hemisphere. Death Valley got its name from one of the 18 survivors of a group of 30 people who were crossing the area in 1849. The group was trying to find a shortcut to the goldfields in California.

You can use negative numbers to model real-world situations.

3 EXAMPLE Real-World Problem Solving

Football A football team gains 2 yd and then loses 7 yd in two plays. You express a loss of 7 yd as −7. Use addition to find the result of the two plays.

$$2 + (−7) = −5$$

● The result of the two plays is a loss of 5 yd.

✓ Check Understanding **3** **Temperature** The temperature falls 15 degrees and then rises 18 degrees. Use addition to find the change in temperature. **−15 + 18 = 3, rise of 3°**

OBJECTIVE

2 Applying Addition

You can evaluate expressions that involve addition. Substitute a value for the variable(s). Then simplify the expression. The expression $−n$ means the opposite of n. The expression $−n$ can represent a negative number, zero, or a positive number.

4 EXAMPLE Evaluating Expressions

Evaluate $−n + 8.9$ for $n = −2.3$.

$$−n + 8.9 = −(−2.3) + 8.9 \quad \textbf{Substitute −2.3 for } n.$$
$$= 2.3 + 8.9 \quad \textbf{− (−2.3) means the opposite of −2.3, which is 2.3.}$$
$$= 11.2 \quad \textbf{Simplify.}$$

✓ Check Understanding **4** Evaluate each expression for $t = −7.1$.
a. $t + (−4.3)$ **−11.4** **b.** $−2 + t$ **−9.1**   **c.** $8.5 + (−t)$ **15.6**   **d.** $−t + 7.49$ **14.59**

You can write and evaluate expressions to model real-world situations.

Real-World Connection

Rock climbers use helmets, harnesses, ropes, and a variety of other devices to help them ascend steep routes.

5 EXAMPLE Real-World Problem Solving

Climbing A rock climber climbs a mountain. The base of the mountain is 132 ft below sea level.
a. Write an expression to represent the climber's height below or above sea level.

Relate   132 ft below sea level   plus   feet the route rises

Define Let h = feet the route rises.

Write   −132   + h

$$−132 + h$$

b. Find the climber's height above sea level when he is 485 ft above the base of the mountain.

$$−132 + h = −132 + 485 \quad \textbf{Substitute 485 for } h.$$
$$= 353 \quad \textbf{Simplify.}$$

● His height is 353 ft above sea level.

✓ Check Understanding **5** **Temperature** The temperature one winter morning is −14°F. Define a variable and write an expression to find the temperature after it changes. Then evaluate your expression for a decrease of 11 degrees Fahrenheit.
Choices of variable may vary. Sample: c = change in temp., −14 + c; −25°F

26   Chapter 1 Tools of Algebra

U.S. School Enrollment (millions)

Level	Public	Private
Elementary	29.3	3.1
High School	14.6	1.2
College	12.1	3.3

SOURCE: *Statistical Abstract of the United States.*
Go to **www.PHSchool.com** for a data update.
Web Code: aeg-2041

You can use matrices to add real numbers. A **matrix** is a rectangular arrangement of numbers in rows and columns. The plural of matrix is matrices (pronounced MAY-truh-seez). The matrix below shows the data in the table.

$$\begin{array}{c} \\ \text{Elementary} \\ \text{High School} \\ \text{College} \end{array} \begin{array}{cc} \text{Public} & \text{Private} \\ \begin{bmatrix} 29.3 & 3.1 \\ 14.6 & 1.2 \\ 12.1 & 3.3 \end{bmatrix} \leftarrow \text{row} \end{array}$$
$$\uparrow$$
$$\text{column}$$

You identify the size of a matrix by the number of rows and the number of columns. The matrix above has 3 rows and 2 columns, so it is a 3×2 matrix. Each item in a matrix is an **element**.

Matrices are equal if the elements in corresponding positions are equal.

$$\begin{bmatrix} -1 & 2 \\ 4 & 0 \end{bmatrix} = \begin{bmatrix} -1 & \frac{4}{2} \\ \frac{20}{5} & 0 \end{bmatrix}$$

You add matrices that are the same size by adding the corresponding elements.

6 EXAMPLE Adding Matrices

Add $\begin{bmatrix} -5 & 2.7 \\ 7 & -3 \end{bmatrix} + \begin{bmatrix} -3 & -3.9 \\ -4 & 2 \end{bmatrix}$.

$$\begin{bmatrix} -5 & 2.7 \\ 7 & -3 \end{bmatrix} + \begin{bmatrix} -3 & -3.9 \\ -4 & 2 \end{bmatrix} = \begin{bmatrix} -5 + (-3) & 2.7 + (-3.9) \\ 7 + (-4) & -3 + 2 \end{bmatrix}$$ Add corresponding elements.

$$= \begin{bmatrix} -8 & -1.2 \\ 3 & -1 \end{bmatrix}$$ Simplify.

✓ **Check Understanding** **6** Find each sum.

a. $\begin{bmatrix} 5 \\ 3.2 \\ -4.9 \end{bmatrix} + \begin{bmatrix} -9 \\ -1.7 \\ -11.1 \end{bmatrix} \begin{bmatrix} -4 \\ 1.5 \\ -16 \end{bmatrix}$

b. $\begin{bmatrix} -4 & \frac{7}{8} \\ \frac{3}{4} & 0 \end{bmatrix} + \begin{bmatrix} -5 & -\frac{3}{4} \\ \frac{1}{2} & -1 \end{bmatrix} \begin{bmatrix} -9 & \frac{1}{8} \\ 1\frac{1}{4} & -1 \end{bmatrix}$

EXERCISES

Practice and Problem Solving

For more practice, see *Extra Practice*.

A Practice by Example

Example 1
(page 25)

Write the expression modeled by each number line. Then find the sum.

1. 6 + (−3); 3

2. −1 + (−2); −3

3.
−5 + 7; 2

4.
3 + (−4); −1

---

4 Evaluate 3.6 + (−t) for t = −1.7. **5.3**

5 A scuba diver who is 88 ft below sea level begins to ascend to the surface.
a. Write an expression to represent the diver's depth below sea level after rising any number of feet. **−88 + r**
b. Find the new depth of the scuba diver after rising 37 ft. **51 feet below sea level**

6 Add $\begin{bmatrix} -6 & 8.6 & 11 \\ 2.3 & 5 & -3 \end{bmatrix} +$

$\begin{bmatrix} 7 & -5.4 & 2 \\ 11.1 & 3 & -1 \end{bmatrix}$.

$\begin{bmatrix} 1 & 3.2 & 13 \\ 13.4 & 8 & -4 \end{bmatrix}$

6 EXAMPLE Alternative Method

At this time, you may wish to introduce students to adding matrices on a graphing calculator. See page 45 for specific instructions. Since students must first enter the size of the matrix, you can reinforce the idea that they can add only matrices that are the same size. Stress that when students enter the matrix size, they must first enter the number of rows, then the number of columns.

Closure

Ask: *How do you add two real numbers that have different signs?* You find the difference of their absolute values. The sum has the same sign as the addend with the greater absolute value.

Assignment Guide

1 Objective
- Ⓐ Ⓑ **Core** 1–27, 42–59, 68–69
- Ⓒ **Extension** 85–92

2 Objective
- Ⓐ Ⓑ **Core** 28–41, 60–67, 70–82
- Ⓒ **Extension** 83–84, 93–97

Standardized Test Prep 98–103

Mixed Review 104–114

Exercises 5–24 Encourage students to use a number line to check their answers.

Exercises 25–27 Suggest to students that they draw a diagram for each exercise.

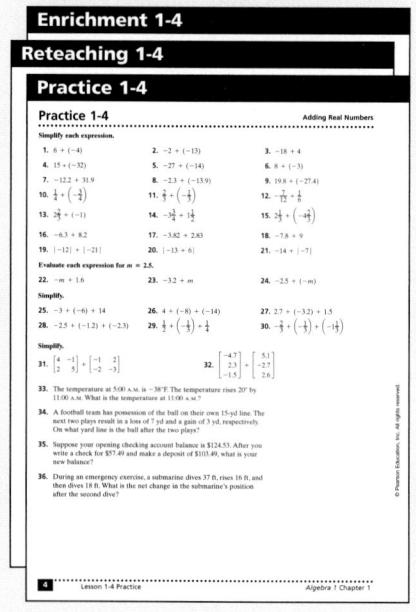

Example 2
(page 25)

Simplify.

5. $3 + 12$ **15**   **6.** $-7 + (-4)$ **−11**   **7.** $-8.7 + (-10.3)$ **−19**   **8.** $5.04 + 7.1$ **12.14**

9. $5 + (-9)$ **−4**   **10.** $-8 + 13$ **5**   **11.** $-27 + 19$ **−8**   **12.** $45 + (-87)$ **−42**

13. $-2.3 + 4.5$ **2.2**   **14.** $-8.05 + 7.4$ **−0.65**   **15.** $9.51 + (-17)$ **−7.49**   **16.** $3.42 + (-2.09)$ **1.33**

17. $\frac{4}{5} + \frac{2}{15}$ **$\frac{14}{15}$**   **18.** $-\frac{5}{9} + \left(-\frac{1}{3}\right)$ **$-\frac{8}{9}$**   **19.** $2\frac{1}{4} + 3\frac{15}{16}$ **$6\frac{3}{16}$**   **20.** $-4\frac{3}{8} + \left(-1\frac{3}{4}\right)$ **$-6\frac{1}{8}$**

21. $-\frac{2}{3} + \frac{4}{6}$ **0**   **22.** $\frac{1}{9} + \left(-\frac{5}{6}\right)$ **$-\frac{13}{18}$**   **23.** $-5\frac{7}{12} + 10\frac{3}{4}$ **$5\frac{1}{6}$**   **24.** $\frac{9}{7} + \left(-2\frac{3}{14}\right)$ **$-\frac{13}{14}$**

Example 3
(page 26)

25. A diver dives 47 ft below the surface of the water and then rises 12 ft. Use addition to find the diver's depth. **−47 + 12 = −35, 35 ft below the surface**

26. On two football plays, a team gains 8 yd, and then loses 5 yd. Use addition to find the result of the two plays. **8 + (−5) = 3, 3 yd gain**

27. The temperature at 6 A.M. is −6°F. The temperature rises 13 degrees Fahrenheit by noon. Use addition to find the temperature at noon. **−6 + 13 = 7, 7°F**

Example 4
(page 26)

Evaluate each expression for $n = 3.5$.

28. $5.2 + n$ **8.7**   **29.** $-5.2 + n$ **−1.7**   **30.** $-n + 5.2$ **1.7**   **31.** $-n + (-5.2)$ **−8.7**

32. $9.1 + n$ **12.6**   **33.** $-9.1 + n$ **−5.6**   **34.** $-n + 9.1$ **5.6**   **35.** $-9.1 + (-n)$ **−12.6**

36–37. Choices of variable may vary.

Example 5
(page 26)

36. Temperature The temperature one winter morning is −8°F. Define a variable and write an expression to find the temperature after each change below. Then evaluate your expression for each change. **c = change in temp., −8 + c**
a. a rise of 7°F **−1°F**   **b.** a decrease of 3°F **−11°F**   **c.** a rise of 19°F **11°F**

37. Money You have $74 in a checking account. Define a variable and write an expression to find the balance in your account after each deposit or withdrawal below. Then evaluate your expression for each change. **c = change in amount of money, 74 + c**
a. a deposit of $18 **$92**   **b.** a withdrawal of $29 **$45**   **c.** a withdrawal of $47 **$27**

Example 6
(page 27)

Simplify.

38. $\begin{bmatrix} 7 & -8 \\ -12 & 6.2 \end{bmatrix} + \begin{bmatrix} -8 & 9.4 \\ -9 & 17 \end{bmatrix}$ $\begin{bmatrix} -1 & 1.4 \\ -21 & 23.2 \end{bmatrix}$

39. $\begin{bmatrix} -7.2 \\ 3.2 \\ -4.9 \end{bmatrix} + \begin{bmatrix} -11 \\ 8.4 \\ 24 \end{bmatrix}$ $\begin{bmatrix} -18.2 \\ 11.6 \\ 19.1 \end{bmatrix}$

40. $\begin{bmatrix} \frac{1}{2} \\ 8 \\ -9 \end{bmatrix} + \begin{bmatrix} -\frac{1}{2} \\ 17 \\ -3 \end{bmatrix}$ $\begin{bmatrix} 0 \\ 25 \\ -12 \end{bmatrix}$

41. $\begin{bmatrix} 1.3 & 26 \\ \frac{1}{8} & -2 \end{bmatrix} + \begin{bmatrix} 0.5 & -4 \\ -\frac{5}{8} & 9 \end{bmatrix}$ $\begin{bmatrix} 1.8 & 22 \\ -\frac{1}{2} & 7 \end{bmatrix}$

Ⓑ **Apply Your Skills**

Simplify.

42. $2.4 + (-8.7) + 3.6$ **−2.7**   **43.** $-13.2 + 7 + (-6.8)$ **−13**

44. $0.9 + 6.4 + (-0.7)$ **6.6**   **45.** $\frac{1}{6} + 12 + \left(-\frac{3}{8}\right)$ **$11\frac{19}{24}$**

46. $|-4| + (-4) + 4$ **4**   **47.** $1\frac{4}{7} + \left(-8\frac{1}{5}\right) + 3$ **$-3\frac{22}{35}$**

48. $-17 + (-1.7) + 0.17$ **−18.53**   **49.** $2.47 + (-9.8) + (-13.5)$ **−20.83**

50. $-8.02 + |-5.9| + 0.4$ **−1.72**   **51.** $-\frac{1}{3} + \frac{1}{4} + \left(-\frac{1}{5}\right)$ **$-\frac{17}{60}$**

52. $-\frac{5}{12} + 1\frac{5}{8} + \left(-6\frac{3}{10}\right)$ **$-5\frac{11}{120}$**   **53.** $|-0.1| + |-0.7|$ **0.8**

54. $|-2| + \left(-\frac{2}{3}\right) + 3$ **$4\frac{1}{3}$**   **55.** $-4.3 + 1.2 + (-5.7)$ **−8.8**

Real-World Connection

The art of photography is changing because of the development of digital cameras.

🌐 **Art** Use the table for Exercises 56–59.

Number of People Who Participate in Art Activities (millions)

Ages	Drawing	Pottery	Weaving	Photography	Creative Writing
18–24	9.2	5.0	5.2	6.6	7.6
25–34	7.2	6.8	10.0	7.2	5.2
35–44	6.8	8.2	13.1	8.2	5.4
45–54	4.4	6.1	9.8	6.1	3.4
55–64	1.9	2.1	6.1	2.1	1.0

SOURCE: *Statistical Abstract of the United States*

56. How many people aged 18 to 34 participate in photography? **13.8 million people**

57. How many people aged 45 to 64 draw? **6.3 million people**

58. Which of the activities is most popular? Explain how you found your answer.
Weaving; add the numbers in each column.

59. a. Write a fraction to compare the number of people aged 25 to 34 who weave to the number of people aged 18 to 64 who weave. $\frac{100}{442} = \frac{50}{221}$
b. Write your answer from part (a) as a decimal to the nearest hundredth. **0.23**
c. What percent of the people who weave are aged 25 to 34? **about 23%**

Evaluate each expression for $a = -2$, $b = 3$, and $c = -4$.

60. $-a + 2 + c$ **0**   **61.** $-|a|$ **−2**   **62.** $a + b$ **1**   **63.** $a + (-b)$ **−5**

64. $a + 3b$ **7**   **65.** $c + 3b$ **5**   **66.** $c + a + 5$ **−1**   **67.** $-(c + a + 5)$ **1**

68. The sum of −227 and 319; the sum of −227 and 319 is positive, while the sum of 227 and −319 is negative.

 68. Writing Without calculating, which is greater, the sum of −227 and 319 or the sum of 227 and −319? Explain. **See left.**

69. Reasoning Explain what is wrong with the reasoning in the statement: *Since 20 is the opposite of −20, then 20°F must be very hot, because −20°F is very cold.* **See margin.**

Evaluate each expression for $b = -3.5$.

70. $b + 3.2$ **−0.3**   **71.** $-9 + b + (-1.2)$ **−13.7**   **72.** $b + |-2.9|$ **−0.6**

73. $8.5 + b + 3.7$ **8.7**   **74.** $|b| + (-3.4)$ **0.1**   **75.** $-5.6 + b + 7.2$ **−1.9**

🌐 **76. Chemistry** A charged atom of magnesium has 12 protons and 10 electrons. Each proton has a charge of +1, and each electron has a charge of −1. What is the total charge of the atom? **+2**

77. Open-Ended Write a 2 × 3 matrix. **Answers may vary. Sample:** $\begin{bmatrix} 2 & 0 & 1 \\ -1 & 3 & 0.5 \end{bmatrix}$

78. Error Analysis A student added two matrices as shown. What error did the student make? **The matrices are not the same size, so they can't be added.**

$$\begin{bmatrix} 4 & -1 \\ -3 & 2 \\ 1.5 & 6 \end{bmatrix} + \begin{bmatrix} -2 & 2.3 & 0 \\ 7 & -4 & 5.1 \end{bmatrix} = \begin{bmatrix} 11 & -3 \\ -7 & 4.3 \\ 6.6 & 6 \end{bmatrix}$$

Error Prevention

Exercises 38–41 Students may try to add the wrong entries. In each row of the matrix, have students circle the first term and put a square around the second term. When there are more than two terms in a row, students may use triangles or underline terms. This will help students identify the correct terms to add in each row.

Exercises 42–55 Suggest to students that they first add two numbers with the same sign.

Error Prevention

Exercises 56, 57 Draw students' attention to "millions" in the title of the table. Show them that 9.2 represents 9.2 million, or 9,200,000 people.

Exercises 60, 63 Students may expect −a or −b to be negative numbers. Have students say "opposite of" when a negative sign appears in front of a variable.

Diversity

Exercise 69 If you live in a warm climate, ask a student who has experienced 20°F to describe how cold it is. Remind students that water freezes at 32°F.

pages 27–31   Exercises

69. Answers may vary. Sample: Although 20 and −20 are opposite *numbers*, there is no such thing as opposite *temperatures*.

Alternative Assessment

Group students in pairs. Give each student two index cards. Have each student write a positive number on one and a negative number on the other. The partners choose two of the four cards to form an addition problem and solve it. Then they compare answers. They shuffle the cards and repeat.

Standardized Test Prep

pages 27–31   Exercises

80a. $\begin{bmatrix} 8 & 3 & 5 & 1 \\ 10 & 2 & 2 & 1 \\ 4 & 1 & 0 & 1 \end{bmatrix}$;

$\begin{bmatrix} 5 & 2 & 1 & 1 \\ 8 & 2 & 0 & 1 \\ 2 & 1 & 0 & 1 \end{bmatrix}$

b. $\begin{bmatrix} 13 & 5 & 6 & 2 \\ 18 & 4 & 2 & 2 \\ 6 & 2 & 0 & 2 \end{bmatrix}$

c. 4 employees

30

---

79. No; time and temperature are different quantities and can't be added.

Number of Employees

Saturday Schedule

Shift	Hourly Wage $6.25	$6.50	$7.00	$7.50
Day	8	3	5	1
Evening	10	2	2	1
Night	4	1	0	1

Sunday Schedule

Shift	Hourly Wage $6.25	$6.50	$7.00	$7.50
Day	5	2	1	1
Evening	8	2	0	1
Night	2	1	0	1

🔵 **Challenge**

94. Pos.; if m is neg., $-m$ is pos. and the sum of two pos. is pos.

95. Neg.; if n is pos., $-n$ is neg. and the sum of two neg. is neg.

96. Pos.; if m is neg., $-m$ is pos. and the sum of two pos. is pos.

97. Zero; sum of neg. and pos. is the difference of the abs. values. $|n| = |m|$ so $|n| - |m| = 0$.

30   Chapter 1   Tools of Algebra

e. Answers may vary. Sample: Multiply the entries in each column by the appropriate hourly wage, then by 8, and then add all entries to find the total wages.

---

79. **Math in the Media** In the cartoon below, does the total "12 27" make sense? Explain. **See left.**

Frank and Ernest

© 1980 Thaves / Reprinted with permission. Newspaper dist. by NEA, Inc.

🌐 80. **Jobs** Use the data in the tables at the left.
   a. Write the data in each table as a matrix. **See margin.**
   b. Add the matrices to find the total number of workers in each pay category for each work shift. **b–c. See margin.**
   c. How many weekend employees on the evening shift earn $6.50 per hour?
   d. How many weekend employees work the night shift? **10 employees**
   e. **Critical Thinking** Suppose all employees work 8-hour shifts both Saturday and Sunday. How would you use the matrix to find the total wages of the weekend employees? **See margin.**
   f. Find the total wages of the weekend employees. **$3230**

81. Suppose you overdrew your bank account. You have a balance of $-\$34$. You then deposit checks for $17 and $49. At the same time the bank charges you a $25 fee for overdrawing your account. What is your balance? **$7**

82. a. What is the value of $-n$ when $n = -4$? **4**
   b. What is the value of $-n$ when $n = 4$? **–4**
   c. **Reasoning** For what values of n will $-n$ be positive? Negative? **neg.; pos.**

Simplify the elements in each matrix. 83–84. See margin.

83. $\begin{bmatrix} \frac{5}{6} \div \frac{2}{3} & -4 + 2\frac{1}{2} \\ \left(3\frac{1}{3}\right)\left(\frac{3}{4}\right) & \frac{1}{2} + \left(\frac{2}{5}\right)\left(\frac{5}{4}\right) \end{bmatrix}$

84. $\begin{bmatrix} 8 + 2 \div 4 & 2^5 & -12 + (-15) \\ -45 + 5(13) & \frac{10 + 16}{4} & 4 - 2^2 \end{bmatrix}$

Simplify each expression.

85. $\frac{w}{5} + \left(-\frac{w}{10}\right)$ $\frac{w}{10}$

86. $-\frac{c}{4} + \left(-\frac{c}{4}\right)$ $-\frac{c}{2}$

87. $3\left(\frac{a}{7}\right) + 7\left(\frac{a}{3}\right)$ $\frac{58a}{21}$

88. $-1\left(\frac{b}{9}\right) + \left(-\frac{b}{9}\right)$ $-\frac{2b}{9}$

89. $\frac{-x}{4} + \frac{x}{3}$ $\frac{x}{12}$

90. $\frac{x}{4} + \left(-\frac{x}{3}\right) - \frac{x}{12}$

91. $\frac{2t}{3} + \frac{-3t}{6}$ $\frac{t}{6}$

92. $\frac{-m}{2} + \left(\frac{-m+1}{4}\right)$ $\frac{-3m+1}{4}$

93. $\frac{m}{6} + \left(-\frac{m}{18}\right)$ $\frac{m}{9}$

Tell whether each sum is *positive, negative,* or *zero.* Explain. 94–97. See left.

94. n is positive and m is negative. $n + (-m)$ is $\underline{\ ?\ }$.

95. n is positive, and m is negative. $-n + m$ is $\underline{\ ?\ }$.

96. $|n| = |m|$, n is positive, and m is negative. $n + (-m)$ is $\underline{\ ?\ }$.

97. $|n| = |m|$, n is positive, and m is negative. $-n + (-m)$ is $\underline{\ ?\ }$.

98. $n = m$, and n and m are negative. $n + (-m)$ is $\underline{\ ?\ }$.
   zero; $n + (-m) = n + (-n) = 0$

83. $\begin{bmatrix} 1\frac{1}{4} & -1\frac{1}{2} \\ 2\frac{1}{2} & 1 \end{bmatrix}$

84. $\begin{bmatrix} 8\frac{1}{2} & 32 & -27 \\ 20 & 6\frac{1}{2} & 0 \end{bmatrix}$

Standardized Test Prep

Multiple Choice

99. Simplify $10 + |-3| + (-3)$. **B**
  A. 16   **B.** 10   **C.** 7   **D.** 4

100. Evaluate $(3a + b) + (-20)$ for $a = 5$ and $b = -1$. **F**
  F. -6 **G.** -2 **H.** 20   **I.** 22

101. Which expression has a value different from the others? **D**
  A. $-7 + 3$ **B.** $5 + (-9)$ **C.** $-8\frac{2}{3} + 4\frac{2}{3}$ **D.** $-9 + 13$

102. In a 12-hour period, the temperature rose from $-12°F$ to $18°F$. Find the increase in temperature in degrees. **F**
  F. 30   **G.** 6   **H.** -6 **I.** -30

103. The value of $-(-(-27))$ is NOT the same as which expression? **C**
  A. $-29 + 2$ **B.** $-12.8 + (-14.2)$
  C. $-42 + 17$ **D.** $8 + (-35)$

104. Suppose you have \$95 in your checking account. You pay for a \$34 sweater using your debit card. Then you deposit a \$32 check. Later, you withdraw \$16 at the supermarket. What is the balance in your account? **H**
  F. \$145   **G.** \$81   **H.** \$77   **I.** \$13

Take It to the NET
Online lesson quiz at
www.PHSchool.com
Web Code: aea-0104

Mixed Review

Lesson 1-3

Use <, =, or > to compare.

105. $-1.23 \ \blacksquare \ -1.18$ **<**

106. $1\frac{2}{4} \ \blacksquare \ 1\frac{5}{10}$ **=**

107. $|-5| \ \blacksquare \ |-6|$ **<**

108. $|-4.1| \ \blacksquare \ |-3.9|$ **>**

109. $\left|-\frac{3}{10}\right| \ \blacksquare \ \left|\frac{2}{9}\right|$ **>**

110. $|1.2| \ \blacksquare \ \left|-\frac{6}{5}\right|$ **=**

Lesson 1-2

Simplify each expression.

111. $(5 - 2)^2$ **9**   **112.** $-4 + 3.1(2)$ **2.2**   **113.** $9[5 + (-3)]$ **18**   **114.** $4^2 + 3^2 - 2^2$ **21**

Checkpoint Quiz 1   Lessons 1-1 through 1-4

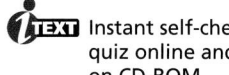 Instant self-check
quiz online and
on CD-ROM

Write a variable expression for each phrase. Then evaluate the expression for
$a = 3$, $b = -2$, and $c = 2.5$.

1. the sum of b and 4 $b + 4$; **2**

2. the quotient of c and 2 $\frac{c}{2}$; **1.25**

3. the product of a and 4.3 **4.3a; 12.9**

4. b plus c plus twice a $b + c + 2a$; **6.5**

5. 17 more than b $b + 17$; **15**

6. three times c **3c; 7.5**

7. the difference of 24 and a $24 - a$; **21**

8. the sum of b and twice a $b + 2a$; **4**

9. Is the statement "A number is always greater than its opposite" true? Explain.
  No; the statement is not true for nonpositive numbers.

10. What set of numbers is reasonable to use for the number of loaves of bread a bakery bakes in one day? **whole numbers**

To check understanding of Lessons 1-1 to 1-4:

Checkpoint Quiz 1 (p. 31)

📁 **Teaching Resources**
Checkpoint Quiz 1 (also in Prentice Hall Assessment System)

👥 **Reaching All Students**
Reading and Math Literacy 1B

Spanish versions available

1. Plan

Lesson Preview

✓ **Check Skills You'll Need**

Exploring Real Numbers
Lesson 1-3: Example 5
Exercises 34–41
Extra Practice, p. 702

Adding Real Numbers
Lesson 1-4: Example 2
Exercises 5–24
Extra Practice, p. 702

Lesson Resources

📁 **Teaching Resources**
Practice, Reteaching, Enrichment

👥 **Reaching All Students**
Practice Workbook 1-5
Spanish Practice Workbook 1-5
Hands-On Activities 2
Basic Algebra Planning Guide 1-5

⏲ **Presentation Assistant Plus!**
Transparencies
• Check Skills You'll Need 1-5
• Additional Examples 1-5
• Student Edition Answers 1-5
• Lesson Quiz 1-5
PH Presentation Pro CD 1-5

**PRENTICE HALL
ASSESSMENT SYSTEM**

Computer Test Generator CD

💿 **Technology**
Resource Pro® CD-ROM
Computer Test Generator CD
Prentice Hall Presentation Pro CD

📷 **www.PHSchool.com**
Student Site
• Teacher Web Code: aek-5500
• Reasoning & Puzzles pp. 16, 17
• Self-grading Lesson Quiz
Teacher Center
• Lesson Planner
• Resources

Plus

Subtracting Real Numbers

Lesson Preview

What You'll Learn

OBJECTIVE 1 To subtract real numbers

OBJECTIVE 2 To apply subtraction

. . . And Why

To find stock prices, as in Example 6

✓ **Check Skills You'll Need** (For help, go to Lessons 1-3 and 1-4.)

Find the opposite of each number.

1. 6 **−6**   **2.** −7 **7**   **3.** 3.79 **−3.79**   **4.** $-\frac{7}{19}$ **$\frac{7}{19}$**

Simplify.

5. 3 + (−2) **1**   **6.** 9.5 + (−3.5) **6**   **7.** 13 + (−8) **5**   **8.** $\frac{2}{3} + \left(-\frac{1}{6}\right)$ **$\frac{1}{2}$**

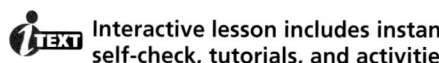 **Interactive lesson includes instant self-check, tutorials, and activities.**

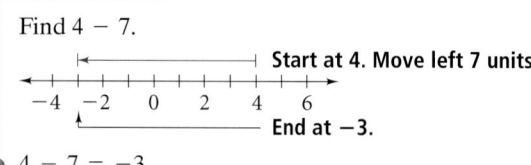
1 Subtracting Real Numbers

You have learned to add real numbers and to find the opposite of a number. You can use these two concepts to understand how to subtract real numbers.

1 EXAMPLE Using a Number Line Model

Find 4 − 7.

Start at 4. Move left 7 units.

−4 −2   0   2   4   6

End at −3.

• 4 − 7 = −3

✓ **Check Understanding** ① Use a number line to find each difference.
a. 2 − 6 **−4**   **b.** −1 − 4 **−5**   **c.** −3 − 8 **−11**   **d.** 7 − 2 **5**

You can use tiles to model subtraction. A ⬜ represents +1, and a ⬛ represents −1. A negative tile and a positive tile together (⬜⬛) represent zero. This is called a zero pair.

2 EXAMPLE Using a Tile Model

Find 3 − (−5).

Start with 3 positive tiles.

Add zero pairs until there are 5 negative tiles.

Remove 5 negative tiles.
There are 8 positive tiles left.

• 3 − (−5) = 8

✓ **Check Understanding** ② Draw tiles to find each difference.
a. 4 − 5 **−1**   **b.** 5 − (−9) **14**   **c.** −6 − (−10) **4**   **d.** 6 − 3 **3**

Ongoing Assessment and Intervention

Before the Lesson	**During the Lesson**	**After the Lesson**
Diagnose prerequisite skills using:	Monitor progress using:	Assess knowledge using:
• Check Skills You'll Need	• Check Understanding • Additional Examples • Standardized Test Prep	• Lesson Quiz • Computer Test Generator CD

The number line below models the sum $2 + (-6)$ *and* the difference $2 - 6$.

Start at 2. Move left 6 units.

Both $2 + (-6)$ and $2 - 6$ have the same value, -4. This illustrates the following rule for subtracting real numbers.

 Key Concepts

Rule	Subtracting Numbers
To subtract a number, add its opposite.	
Examples $\quad 3 - 5 = 3 + (-5) = -2 \qquad 3 - (-5) = 3 + 5 = 8$	

3 EXAMPLE Subtracting Rational Numbers

Simplify each expression.
a. $-4 - (-9)$

$\quad -4 - (-9) = -4 + 9 \qquad$ The opposite of -9 is 9.
$\qquad\qquad\qquad = 5 \qquad\qquad$ Add.

Need Help?
For help with simplifying and subtracting fractions, see Skills Handbook pp. 724 and 726.

b. $\frac{3}{4} - \left(-\frac{11}{12}\right)$

$\quad \frac{3}{4} - \left(-\frac{11}{12}\right) = \frac{3}{4} + \frac{11}{12} \qquad$ The opposite of $-\frac{11}{12}$ is $\frac{11}{12}$.
$\qquad\qquad\qquad = \frac{9}{12} + \frac{11}{12} \qquad$ Use common denominators.
$\qquad\qquad\qquad = \frac{20}{12} \qquad$ Add.
$\qquad\qquad\qquad = \frac{5}{3}$ or $1\frac{2}{3} \qquad$ Write $\frac{20}{12}$ in simplest form.

 Check Understanding **3** Find each difference.
a. $-6 - 2$ **-8** **b.** $8 - (-4)$ **12** **c.** $3.7 - (-4.3)$ **8.0** **d.** $-\frac{8}{9} - \left(-\frac{5}{6}\right)$ $-\frac{1}{18}$

OBJECTIVE
2 Applying Subtraction

Recall that when you simplify an expression, you work within grouping symbols first. Absolute value symbols are grouping symbols, so find the value of an expression within the absolute value symbols before finding the absolute value.

4 EXAMPLE Absolute Values

Simplify $|5 - 11|$.

$\quad |5 - 11| = |-6| \qquad$ Subtract within absolute value symbols.
$\qquad\qquad = 6 \qquad$ Find the absolute value.

 Check Understanding **4** Simplify each expression.
a. $|8 - 7|$ **1** **b.** $|7 - 8|$ **1** **c.** $|-10 - (-4)|$ **6** **d.** $|-4 - (-10)|$ **6**

Reaching All Students

Below Level Some students may find it helpful to discuss debt, and use money to show increasing or decreasing indebtedness or profit.	**Advanced Learners** Lead students in a discussion of the absolute value of zero.	**Tactile Learners** See note on page 34. **Error Prevention** See note on page 35.

 Professional Development

Math Background

Notice that the rules for subtraction essentially reduce the rules for combining real numbers to the rules for addition.

OBJECTIVE
1 Teaching Notes

2 EXAMPLE Connection to Language Arts

[NOTE: This activity is also referred to in Lesson 1-6 Objective 1 Teaching Notes Investigation]

On the board, write *I am healthy*. Then write *un* in front of *healthy*. Point out that the prefix *un* makes the word mean the opposite. Insert *not* to make the sentence read *I am not unhealthy*. Point out the negative word *not* and note how inserting it changes the meaning of the sentence. Cross out *not* and *un*. Lead students to understand that the two negative parts can be removed since, when used together, they do not change the meaning of the original statement. Now write $- (-5)$ on the board and cross out the two negative signs. Explain that, similarly, the two negative signs that are next to each other can be removed without changing the value of the expression.

Additional Examples

1 Find $-3 - 2$ using a number line. **-5**

2 Find $4 - (-2)$ using tiles. **6**

3 Simplify each expression.
a. $-11.6 - (-14)$ **2.4**
b. $\frac{2}{3} - \left(-\frac{4}{9}\right)$ **$1\frac{1}{9}$**

4 EXAMPLE Tactile Learners

Some students may need to be reminded that the absolute value of a number is its distance from 0. Make a number line on the floor with masking tape. Instruct students to begin at 0. Then walk, stepping on each number to 6, then to −6. Ask: *How many steps did you take for each move?* 6 *At the end of each move, how far away from zero were you?* 6 steps *Did it matter which direction you moved?* no Stress that distance is always positive. The sign just tells what direction you move.

Additional Examples

4 Simplify |−13 − (−21)|. 8

5 Evaluate $x - (-y)$ for $x = -3$ and $y = -6$. −9

6 The temperature in Montreal, Canada at 6:00 P.M. was −8°F. Find the temperature at 10:00 P.M. if it fell 7°F. −15°F

Closure

Ask students to explain the process of subtracting integers. To subtract an integer, add its opposite.

---

pages 34–36 Exercises

1. −1
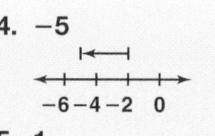

2. −2
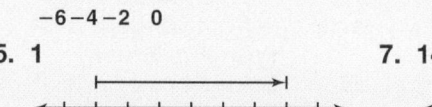

3. −6

4. −5

5. 1

You evaluate expressions that involve subtraction by substituting for the variable. Then simplify the expression.

5 EXAMPLE Evaluating Expressions

Evaluate $-a - b$ for $a = -3$ and $b = -5$.

$$
\begin{aligned}
-a - b &= -(-3) - (-5) && \text{Substitute −3 for } a \text{ and −5 for } b. \\
&= 3 - (-5) && \text{The opposite of −3 is 3.} \\
&= 3 + 5 && \text{To subtract −5, add its opposite, 5.} \\
&= 8 && \text{Add.}
\end{aligned}
$$

✓ **Check Understanding** 5 Evaluate each expression for $t = -2$ and $r = -7$.
a. $r - t$ −5　　b. $t - r$ 5　　c. $-t - r$ 9　　d. $-r - (-t)$ 5

You can write expressions to model real-world situations.

6 EXAMPLE Real-World Problem Solving

Stock Price Find the closing price of stock XYZ on Wednesday by subtracting the change in price from the closing price on Thursday.

$$
\begin{aligned}
17.37 - (-0.87) &= 17.37 + 0.87 && \text{Add the opposite.} \\
&= 18.24 && \text{Simplify.}
\end{aligned}
$$

The closing share price on Wednesday was $18.24.

		C3
STOCK PRICES		
	Thurs	
ge	Stock	Close	Change
6	ABC	32.79	0.32
2	PQR	14.23	-1.23
1	XYZ	17.37	-0.87

✓ **Check Understanding** 6 **Stock Price** Find the closing price of stocks ABC and PQR on Wednesday. ABC: $32.47; PQR: $15.46

EXERCISES

For more practice, see *Extra Practice*.

Practice and Problem Solving

1–8. See margin.

A Practice by Example

Examples 1, 2 (page 32)

Draw a number line or tiles to model each difference. Then find each difference.
1. $1 - 2$　　　2. $7 - 9$　　　3. $-4 - 2$　　　4. $-2 - 3$
5. $-5 - (-6)$　　6. $-3 - 8$　　7. $5 - (-9)$　　8. $-1 - (-4)$

Example 3 (page 33)

Simplify each expression.
9. $3 - 7$ −4　　10. $2 - (-9)$ 11　　11. $-4 - 6$ −10　　12. $-5 - (-1)$ −4
13. $6.2 - 8.3$ −2.1　14. $-7.4 - 1.8$ −9.2　15. $5.3 - (-8.4)$ 13.7　16. $-3.6 - (-7.1)$ 3.5
17. $\frac{1}{3} - \frac{1}{2}$ −$\frac{1}{6}$　18. $-\frac{2}{5} - \frac{7}{10}$ −1$\frac{1}{10}$　19. $\frac{2}{12} - \left(-\frac{3}{4}\right)$ $\frac{11}{12}$　20. $-\frac{5}{12} - \left(-\frac{1}{10}\right)$ −$\frac{19}{60}$

Example 4 (page 33)

21. $|5 - 2|$ 3　　22. $|-7 - 1|$ 8　　23. $|4 - 10|$ 6　　24. $|-3 - (-5)|$ 2
25. $|-6 - 7|$ 13　26. $|8 - 6|$ 2　　27. $|3 - 9|$ 6　　28. $|-11 - (-8)|$ 3

Example 5 (page 34)

Evaluate each expression for $x = 3$, $y = -4$, and $z = 6$.
29. $y - z$ −10　　30. $x - y$ 7　　31. $-y - x$ 1　　32. $-x - y$ 1
33. $z - x$ 3　　　34. $2x - z$ 0　　35. $x + y - z$ −7　　36. $-z + y - x$ −13

Example 6 (page 34)

37. On Friday, the closing price of a KJL company share was $51.72. It had risen $1.08 from the previous day. Find the closing price of KJL on Thursday. $50.64

4. −5
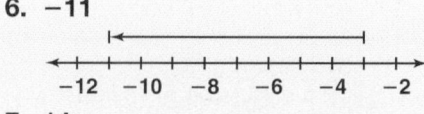

5. 1

6. −11
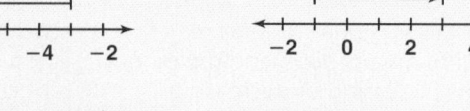

7. 14

8. 3

B **Apply Your Skills**

Evaluate each expression for $a = -2$, $b = 3.5$, and $c = -4$.

38. $a - b + c$ **−9.5** **39.** $-c - b + a$ **−1.5** **40.** $-|a|$ **−2** **41.** $|a| + |b|$ **5.5**

42. $|a + b|$ **1.5** **43.** $-|3 + a|$ **−1** **44.** $4b - a$ **16** **45.** $-4b - |a|$ **−16**

46. $|c + a - 5|$ **11** **47.** $|c + a + 5|$ **1** **48.** $|a - c| - |c|$ **−2** **49.** $|a| + |3b|$ **12.5**

50. Archaeology Archaeologists found a 1500-year-old ship at the bottom of the Black Sea. The ship is well preserved because oxygen could not make the ship decay. The ship is at a depth of 1000 ft below the surface. This is about 350 ft below the boundary between surface water, which has oxygen, and water below, which does not have oxygen. At what depth is the boundary? **650 ft**

51. Open-Ended Write two matrices with the same dimensions. Find the difference of the two matrices. **See margin.**

Decide if each statement is always true. If the statement is not always true, give a counterexample. **52–53. See left.**

52. The difference of two numbers is less than the sum of those two numbers.

53. The difference of two numbers is less than either of those two numbers.

54. A number minus its opposite is twice the number. **true**

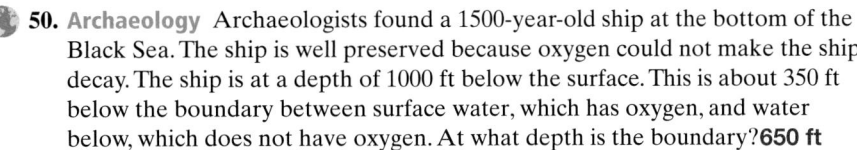

55. a. Sports Write the data in each table below as a matrix. **a–c. See left.**

Real-World Connection

Careers Archaeologists uncover and study the remains of ancient cultures. Archaeologists may look for remains in remote locations, underground, in caves, or underwater.

52. false; $-1 - (-7) = 6$, $-1 + (-7) = -8$

53. false; $2 - (-1) = 3$, $3 \not< 2$ or -1

55a. 1992:
$$\begin{bmatrix} 5.5 & 8.2 & 4.9 \\ 1.4 & 3.2 & 3.9 \\ 4.2 & 3.8 & 1.3 \\ 1.6 & 5.2 & 5.1 \end{bmatrix};$$

1997:
$$\begin{bmatrix} 6.8 & 7.9 & 4.9 \\ 1.0 & 1.8 & 1.7 \\ 5.6 & 4.1 & 1.3 \\ 1.8 & 4.9 & 2.9 \end{bmatrix}$$

b.
$$\begin{bmatrix} 1.3 & -0.3 & 0 \\ -0.4 & -1.4 & -2.2 \\ 1.4 & 0.3 & 0 \\ 0.2 & -0.3 & -2.2 \end{bmatrix}$$

c. Answers may vary. Sample: Invest in soccer; it is the only sport that has not lost any participants.

Participation in Sports Activities
(millions)

	Sport	Ages 7–11	Ages 12–17	Ages 18–24
	Basketball	5.5	8.2	4.9
1992	Tennis	1.4	3.2	3.9
	Soccer	4.2	3.8	1.3
	Volleyball	1.6	5.2	5.1

	Sport	Ages 7–11	Ages 12–17	Ages 18–24
	Basketball	6.8	7.9	4.9
1997	Tennis	1.0	1.8	1.7
	Soccer	5.6	4.1	1.3
	Volleyball	1.8	4.9	2.9

b. Subtract the 1992 matrix from the 1997 matrix to find the changes in participation in sports activities.

c. Writing Suppose you invest in sporting goods. In which sport would you invest? Use elements from your matrix to explain.

Subtract. 56–58. See margin.

56. $\begin{bmatrix} -3 & 4 \\ 0 & -1 \end{bmatrix} - \begin{bmatrix} -5 & 6 \\ 9 & -4 \end{bmatrix}$ **57.** $\begin{bmatrix} \frac{3}{8} & \frac{1}{5} & 4 \end{bmatrix} - \begin{bmatrix} \frac{5}{8} & \frac{2}{10} & 7 \end{bmatrix}$ **58.** $\begin{bmatrix} \frac{1}{4} \\ -3 \end{bmatrix} - \begin{bmatrix} \frac{2}{3} \\ -2 \end{bmatrix}$

59. Critical Thinking Use examples to illustrate your answers.
a. Is $|a - b|$ always equal to $|b - a|$? **a–b. See margin.**
b. Is $|a + b|$ always equal to $|a| + |b|$?

Lesson 1-5 Subtracting Real Numbers **35**

51. Answers may vary.
Sample:
$$\begin{bmatrix} 5 & 12 \\ -3 & 7 \end{bmatrix} - \begin{bmatrix} 4 & 6 \\ 5 & 10 \end{bmatrix} = \begin{bmatrix} 1 & 6 \\ -8 & -3 \end{bmatrix}$$

56. $\begin{bmatrix} 2 & -2 \\ -9 & 3 \end{bmatrix}$

57. $\begin{bmatrix} -\frac{1}{4} & 0 & -3 \end{bmatrix}$

58. $\begin{bmatrix} -\frac{5}{12} \\ -1 \end{bmatrix}$

Assignment Guide

1 Objective
Ⓐ Ⓑ Core 1–20, 52–54, 56–58
Ⓒ Extension 60–63

2 Objective
Ⓐ Ⓑ Core 21–51, 55, 59
Ⓒ Extension 64–66

Standardized Test Prep 67–71

Mixed Review 72–81

Error Prevention

Exercises 52–54 Suggest to students that they experiment with many combinations of positive and negative numbers.

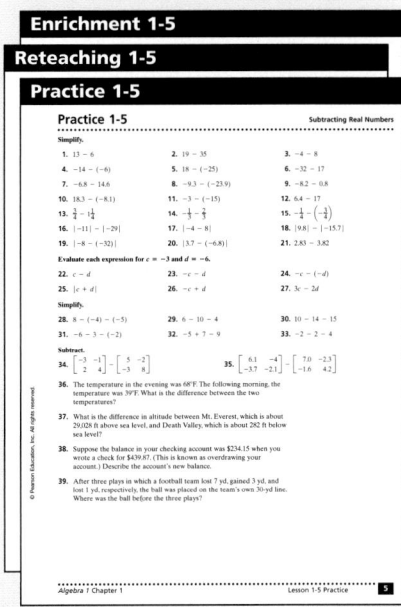

Enrichment 1-5
Reteaching 1-5
Practice 1-5

59a. Yes, answers may vary. Sample: n and $-n$ always have the same absolute value.

b. No, answers may vary. Sample:
$$|1| + |-1| \neq |1 + (-1)|, 2 \neq 0$$

35

Simplify each expression.

1. $7 - 12$ -5

2. $3 - (-8)$ 11

3. $-7 - 5$ -12

Evaluate each expression for $x = 3$ and $y = 4$.

4. $x - y$ -1

5. $|-y - x|$ 7

6. $\begin{bmatrix} -2 & x \\ y & 4 \end{bmatrix} - \begin{bmatrix} x & 8 \\ -5 & y \end{bmatrix}$

$\begin{bmatrix} -5 & -5 \\ 9 & 0 \end{bmatrix}$

Alternative Assessment

Have students work in groups of four. Using index cards, have each group write one number per card for each whole number from 1 to 10 (number cards). Using another set of ten cards, have each group write + on five cards and − on five cards (sign cards). Shuffle each set of cards separately and set them face down on the desk. In turn, the students turn over a sign card, a number card, another sign card, and another number card to form two integers. Each student mentally evaluates the difference between the two integers. Then, students compare answers.

Standardized Test Prep

 **Resources**

For additional practice with a variety of test item formats:
- Standardized Test Prep, p. 71
- Test-Taking Strategies, p. 66
- Test-Taking Strategies with Transparencies

Exercise 71 Point out to students that drawing a diagram is a good way to understand a problem. Suggest that they draw a number line to represent a thermometer and move their fingers along the number line to find the solution.

36

 **Challenge**

Simplify each expression.

60. $1 - \frac{1}{2} - \frac{1}{3} - \frac{1}{4} - \frac{1}{5} - \frac{1}{6}$ $-\frac{9}{20}$

61. $1 - \left(\frac{1}{2} - \left(\frac{1}{3} - \left(\frac{1}{4} - \left(\frac{1}{5} - \frac{1}{6}\right)\right)\right)\right)$ $\frac{37}{60}$

62. $5x - 7x + 6 - 2x - 5 + 8$ $-4x + 9$

63. $-8t - 5m + 3m - 7t - (-3t) + m$ $-12t - m$

64. $\frac{7r - 8}{4} - \left(\frac{-r + 3}{16}\right)$ $\frac{29r - 35}{16}$

65. $\frac{-5w - 2 + w - 1}{3} - \frac{w - 3w + 4w - 1 + w}{9}$ $\frac{-15w - 8}{9}$

66. Order $|x + y|, |x - y|, |x| - |y|$, and $x - y$ from least to greatest for $x = -8$ and $y = -10$. $|x| - |y|, |x - y|$ and $x - y, |x + y|$

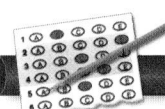

Standardized Test Prep

Multiple Choice

67. Evaluate $-|a - b| + |c|$ for $a = -3$, $b = 4$, and $c = -4$. **C**
  A. 11   B. 3   C. −3   D. −11

68. Which expression has a value different from the others? **F**
  F. $-7 - 12$ G. $17 - 12$ H. $12 - 7$ I. $12 + (-7)$

69. Find the next number in the pattern 11, 8, 5, 2, . . . **C**
  A. 1   B. 0   C. −1   D. −2

70. Use the bar graph at the right. Estimate the average hourly earnings of U.S. nonfarm workers in 2005. **H**

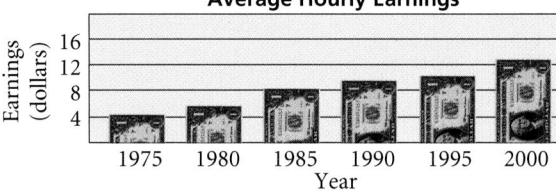

Average Hourly Earnings

  F. $12.00   G. $13.50   H. $15.00   I. $20.00

71. One January day, the temperature at noon is 8°F. During the afternoon, the temperature drops 5 degrees. By dawn, the temperature has fallen another 9 degrees. What is the temperature at dawn? **D**
  A. −22°F   B. 12°F   C. −4°F   D. −6°F

Take It to the NET
Online lesson quiz at
www.PHSchool.com
Web Code: aea-0105

Mixed Review

Lesson 1-4

Simplify each expression.

72. $6 + (-2)$ 4   **73.** $-5 + (-4)$ -9 **74.** $-3.4 + 2.7$ -0.7 **75.** $5.9 + (-10)$ -4.1

Simplify. 76–81. See margin.

76. $\begin{bmatrix} 3 & -8 \\ 2 & 11 \end{bmatrix} + \begin{bmatrix} 1 & 8 \\ -2 & 5 \end{bmatrix}$

77. $\begin{bmatrix} 1.3 \\ -6.7 \\ 7.1 \end{bmatrix} + \begin{bmatrix} -0.1 \\ 4.2 \\ -1.9 \end{bmatrix}$

78. $\begin{bmatrix} \frac{1}{2} & -1 \\ 6 & \frac{2}{3} \end{bmatrix} + \begin{bmatrix} -4 & \frac{1}{3} \\ \frac{1}{3} & -5 \end{bmatrix}$

Lesson 1-1

Define variables and write an equation to model each situation.

79. The total cost equals the number of pounds of pears times $1.19/lb.

80. You have $20. Then you buy a bouquet. How much do you have left?

81. You go out to lunch with five friends and split the check equally. What is your share of the check?

pages 34–36 **Exercises**

76. $\begin{bmatrix} 4 & 0 \\ 0 & 16 \end{bmatrix}$

77. $\begin{bmatrix} 1.2 \\ -2.5 \\ 5.2 \end{bmatrix}$

78. $\begin{bmatrix} -3\frac{1}{2} & -\frac{2}{3} \\ 6\frac{1}{3} & -4\frac{1}{3} \end{bmatrix}$

79–81. Choices of variables may vary.

79. t = total cost, p = pounds of pears, $t = 1.19p$

80. p = bouquet's price, m = money left, $m = 20 - p$

81. c = check ($), s = your share, $s = \frac{c}{6}$

1-6 Multiplying and Dividing Real Numbers

North Carolina Objectives

3.02 Operate (addition, subtraction, scalar multiplication) with matrices to solve problems.

Lesson Preview

What You'll Learn

 OBJECTIVE **1** To multiply real numbers

 OBJECTIVE **2** To divide real numbers

. . . And Why

To find the change in temperature with an increase in altitude, as in Example 3

 Check Skills You'll Need   (For help, go to Lessons 1-4 and 1-5.)

Simplify each expression.

1. $-2 + (-2) + (-2) + (-2)$ **−8**

2. $-5 + (-5) + (-5) + (-5) + (-5)$ **−25**

3. $-6 - 6 - 6 - 6$ **−24**

4. $-12 - 12 - 12 - 12 - 12 - 12$ **−72**

Write the next three numbers in each pattern.

5. $2, 4, 6, \blacksquare, \blacksquare, \blacksquare$ **8, 10, 12**

6. $6, 4, 2, \blacksquare, \blacksquare, \blacksquare$ **0, −2, −4**

7. $12, 9, 6, \blacksquare, \blacksquare, \blacksquare$ **3, 0, −3**

8. $-18, -12, -6, \blacksquare, \blacksquare, \blacksquare$ **0, 6, 12**

New Vocabulary

- Identity Property of Multiplication
- Multiplication Property of Zero
- Multiplication Property of −1
- Inverse Property of Multiplication
- multiplicative inverse   • reciprocal

OBJECTIVE

1 Multiplying Real Numbers

 iTEXT Interactive lesson includes instant self-check, tutorials, and activities.

Investigation: Multiplying Integers

1. Patterns Use patterns to complete each statement.

a. $2 \cdot 3 = \blacksquare$ 6
$2 \cdot 2 = \blacksquare$ 4
$2 \cdot 1 = \blacksquare$ 2
$2 \cdot 0 = \blacksquare$ 0
$2(-1) = \blacksquare$ −2
$2(-2) = \blacksquare$ −4
$2(-3) = \blacksquare$ −6

b. $3(-2) = \blacksquare$ −6
$2(-2) = \blacksquare$ −4
$1(-2) = \blacksquare$ −2
$0(-2) = \blacksquare$ 0
$-1(-2) = \blacksquare$ 2
$-2(-2) = \blacksquare$ 4
$-3(-2) = \blacksquare$ 6

2. Make a Conjecture From the patterns you found in Question 1, what seems to be the sign of the product of a positive number and a negative number? **neg.**

3. Make a Conjecture From the patterns you found in Question 1, what seems to be the sign of the product of two negative numbers? **pos.**

The product of a number and 1 is the original number. It does not matter whether the original number is positive or negative. The product of 0 and a number is 0. The product of −1 and a number is the opposite of the original number.

 Ongoing Assessment and Intervention

Before the Lesson
Diagnose prerequisite skills using:
- Check Skills You'll Need

During the Lesson
Monitor progress using:
- Check Understanding
- Additional Examples
- Standardized Test Prep

After the Lesson
Assess knowledge using:
- Lesson Quiz
- Computer Test Generator CD

1. Plan

Lesson Preview

 **Check Skills You'll Need**

Adding Real Numbers
Lesson 1-4: Example 2
Exercises 5–8
Extra Practice, p. 702

Subtracting Real Numbers
Lesson 1-5: Example 3
Exercises 9–12
Extra Practice, p. 702

Lesson Resources

Teaching Resources
Practice, Reteaching, Enrichment

Reaching All Students
Practice Workbook 1-6
Spanish Practice Workbook 1-6
Technology Activities 15
Basic Algebra Planning Guide 1-6

Presentation Assistant Plus!
Transparencies
- Check Skills You'll Need 1-6
- Additional Examples 1-6
- Student Edition Answers 1-6
- Lesson Quiz 1-6
PH Presentation Pro CD 1-6

PRENTICE HALL ASSESSMENT SYSTEM

Computer Test Generator CD

 Technology
Resource Pro® CD-ROM
Computer Test Generator CD
Prentice Hall Presentation Pro CD

www.PHSchool.com
Student Site
- Teacher Web Code: aek-5500
- Reasoning & Puzzles pp. 18, 19
- Self-grading Lesson Quiz
Teacher Center
- Lesson Planner
- Resources

Plus **iTEXT**

2. Teach

Professional
Development

Math Background

The rules for multiplying and dividing integers are really conventions. They are used because they keep the number system consistent—they 'make sense.' Using patterns to establish such rules is a powerful tool in mathematics.

OBJECTIVE
1 **Teaching Notes**

Investigation (Optional)

Some students have a difficult time understanding how the product or quotient of two negative numbers can be a positive number. Patterns such as the one in the Investigation can help convince these students. Refer to the example, *I am healthy* and *I am not unhealthy,* given in the Teachers' Edition on p. 33. It shows how two negative parts cancel each other. Likewise, two negative signs in a multiplication or division expression cancel each other.

1 EXAMPLE **Error Prevention**

Students may confuse the sign rules for addition, subtraction, and multiplication. Have students suggest a pair of integers with the same sign and a pair of integers with different signs. For each pair, have students find the sum, difference, and product. Then, have students discuss the signs of the results.

 Key Concepts

Property	Identity Property of Multiplication

For every real number n, $1 \cdot n = n$.

Examples $1 \cdot 5 = 5$ $1 \cdot (-5) = -5$

Property	Multiplication Property of Zero

For every real number n, $n \cdot 0 = 0$.

Examples $35 \cdot 0 = 0$ $-35 \cdot 0 = 0$

Property	Multiplication Property of -1

For every real number n, $-1 \cdot n = -n$.

Examples $-1 \cdot 5 = -5$ $-1 \cdot (-5) = 5$

From the examples for the properties above, you can see a pattern for multiplying positive and negative numbers.

Multiplying Numbers With the Same Sign

$$1 \cdot 5 = 5$$
positive · positive = positive

$$-1 \cdot (-5) = 5$$
negative · negative = positive

Multiplying Numbers With Different Signs

$$1 \cdot (-5) = -5$$
positive · negative = negative

$$-1 \cdot 5 = -5$$
negative · positive = negative

This pattern also holds true when multiplying by numbers other than 1 and -1.

Key Concepts

Rule	Multiplying Numbers With the Same Sign

The product of two positive numbers or two negative numbers is positive.

Examples $5 \cdot 2 = 10$ $-5(-2) = 10$

Rule	Multiplying Numbers With Different Signs

The product of a positive number and a negative number, or a negative number and a positive number, is negative.

Examples $3(-6) = -18$ $-3 \cdot 6 = -18$

1 EXAMPLE **Multiplying Numbers**

Simplify each expression.

a. $-9(-4) = 36$ The product of two negative numbers is positive.

b. $5\left(-\frac{2}{3}\right) = -\frac{10}{3}$ The product of a positive number and a negative number is negative.

$= -3\frac{1}{3}$ Write $-\frac{10}{3}$ as a mixed number.

✓**Check Understanding** **1** Simplify each expression.
   a. $4(-6)$ **−24**   **b.** $-10(-5)$ **50**   **c.** $-4.9(-8)$ **39.2**   **d.** $-\frac{2}{3}\left(\frac{3}{4}\right)$ **$-\frac{1}{2}$**

38   Chapter 1 Tools of Algebra

👥 Reaching All Students

Below Level Suggest that, when multiplying three or more real numbers, students verify the sign of each product as they multiply each *pair* of real numbers.	**Advanced Learners** Ask students to evaluate $2x + \frac{x-1}{y+2}$ for $x = -1$ and $y = -1$.	**Visual Learners** See note on page 39. **Error Prevention** See note on page 38.

You can evaluate expressions involving multiplication. To simplify expressions with three or more negative numbers, you must be careful to account for all of the negative signs as you multiply.

2 EXAMPLE **Evaluating Expressions**

Evaluate $-2xy$ for $x = -20$ and $y = -3$.

$-2xy = -2(-20)(-3)$ Substitute -20 for x and -3 for y.

$\quad\quad = -120$ $-2(-20)$ results in a positive number, 40. $40(-3)$ results in a negative number, -120.

✓ **Check Understanding** **2** Evaluate each expression for $c = -8$ and $d = -7$.

a. $-(cd)$ **−56**   **b.** $(-2)(-3)(cd)$ **336**   **c.** $c(-d)$ **−56**

You can use expressions involving multiplication to model real-world situations.

3 EXAMPLE **Real-World**  **Problem Solving**

Temperature You can use the expression $-5.5\left(\frac{a}{1000}\right)$ to calculate the change in temperature in degrees Fahrenheit for an increase in altitude a, measured in feet. A hot-air balloon starts on the ground and then rises 8000 ft. Find the change in temperature at the altitude of the balloon.

$-5.5\left(\frac{a}{1000}\right) = -5.5\left(\frac{8000}{1000}\right)$ Substitute 8000 for a.

$\quad\quad\quad\quad = -5.5(8)$ Divide within parentheses.

$\quad\quad\quad\quad = -44$ Multiply.

The change in temperature is -44 degrees.

8000 ft

✓ **Check Understanding** **3 a.** Find the change in temperature if a balloon rises 4500 ft from the ground. **−24.75°F**

b. Suppose the temperature is 40°F at ground level. What is the approximate air temperature at the altitude of the balloon? **15.25°F**

The expression -3^4 means the opposite of 3^4. The exponent 4 applies to the base 3. The negative sign is not part of the base. In the expression $(-3)^4$, the negative sign is part of the base -3. The exponent 4 applies to the base -3.

4 EXAMPLE **Simplifying Exponential Expressions**

Use the order of operations to simplify each expression.

a. -3^4

$-3^4 = -(3 \cdot 3 \cdot 3 \cdot 3)$ Write as repeated multiplication.

$\quad\quad = -81$ Simplify.

b. $(-3)^4$

$(-3)^4 = (-3)(-3)(-3)(-3)$ Write as repeated multiplication.

$\quad\quad = 81$ Simplify.

✓ **Check Understanding** **4** Simplify each expression.

a. -4^3 **−64**   **b.** $(-2)^4$ **16**   **c.** $(-0.3)^2$ **0.09**   **d.** $-\left(\frac{3}{4}\right)^2$ **$-\frac{9}{16}$**

2 EXAMPLE **Alternative Method**

Since the product of any two negative numbers is positive, have students count the number of negative signs in the expression that contains the substituted numbers. If there is an even number of negative signs, the result is positive. If there is an odd number of negative signs, the result is negative. Ask: *Will the product of seventeen negative numbers be positive or negative?* **negative**

3 EXAMPLE **Connection to Science**

There are two reasons air temperature decreases as altitude increases: 1) There is less heat radiation from the Earth's surface, 2) As air that is heated by the Earth's surface rises, it expands (less air pressure) and it cools.

4 EXAMPLE **Visual Learners**

Tell students to think of the parentheses in part b as a pair of hands holding the $-$ and the 3 together. They cannot be separated, so the exponent 4 must apply to both of them. In part a, there are no parentheses, so they can be separated. The exponent applies only to the 3 in this situation.

Additional Examples

1 Simplify each expression.

a. $-3(-11)$ **33**

b. $-6\left(\frac{3}{4}\right)$ **$-4\frac{1}{2}$**

2 Evaluate $5rs$ for $r = -18$ and $s = -5$. **450**

3 Use the expression $-5.5\left(\frac{a}{1000}\right)$ to calculate the change in temperature for an increase in altitude a of 7200 ft. **−39.6°F**

4 Use the order of operations to simplify each expression.

a. -0.2^4 **−0.0016**

b. $(-0.2)^4$ **0.0016**

5 EXAMPLE **Teaching Tip**

Show students how the sign rules for multiplying and dividing are the same. Have students rewrite the multiplication sentence $-4 \cdot 3 = -12$ as its related division sentences $\frac{-12}{-4} = 3$ **and** $\frac{-12}{3} = -4$. Have students carefully examine the signs and how they relate to the division rules.

6 EXAMPLE **Teaching Tip**

To reinforce that a fraction bar indicates division, have students reduce the fraction $\frac{20}{4}$ $\left(\frac{20 \div 4}{4 \div 4} = \frac{5}{1} = 5\right)$, and then calculate $20 \div 4$.

7 EXAMPLE **Math Tip**

Some students do not understand why dividing by 0 is undefined. They want to say that the result of dividing by 0 is 0. Write the following equations:

$\frac{6}{2} = 3$, so $3 \cdot 2 = 6$

$\frac{6}{0} = 0$, so $0 \cdot 0 = 6$

Ask: *Is the second statement true?* **no** *Why not?* $0 \cdot 0 = 0$, not 6.

Additional Examples

5 Simplify each expression.
a. $70 \div (-5)$ **−14**
b. $-54 \div (-9)$ **6**

6 Evaluate $-\frac{x}{y} - 4z^2$ for $x = 4, y = -2$, and $z = -4$. **−62**

7 Evaluate $\frac{p}{r}$ for $p = \frac{3}{2}$ and $r = -\frac{3}{4}$. **−2**

Closure

Ask students to state the rules for multiplying and dividing real numbers in their own words. When you multiply or divide numbers that have the same sign, the product or quotient is positive. When you multiply or divide numbers that do not have the same sign, the product or quotient is negative.

The rules for finding the sign when dividing real numbers are the same as the rules for finding the sign when multiplying real numbers.

Key Concepts

Rule	**Dividing Numbers With the Same Sign**

The quotient of two positive numbers or two negative numbers is positive.

Examples $6 \div 3 = 2$ $-6 \div (-3) = 2$

Rule	**Dividing Numbers With Different Signs**

The quotient of a positive number and a negative number, or a negative number and a positive number, is negative.

Examples $-6 \div 3 = -2$ $6 \div (-3) = -2$

You can use the rules for dividing numbers to simplify expressions.

5 EXAMPLE **Dividing Numbers**

Simplify each expression.

a. $12 \div (-4) = -3$ The quotient of a positive number and a negative number is negative.

b. $-12 \div (-4) = 3$ The quotient of a negative number and a negative number is positive.

✓ Check Understanding **5** Simplify each expression.
a. $-42 \div 7$ **−6**   **b.** $-8 \div (-2)$ **4**   **c.** $8 \div (-8)$ **−1**   **d.** $-39 \div (-3)$ **13**

You can evaluate expressions that involve division.

Reading Math

You can indicate division using a fraction bar.

$\frac{15}{5}$ means $15 \div 5$.

6 EXAMPLE **Evaluating Expressions**

Evaluate $\frac{-x}{-4} + 2y \div z$ for $x = -20, y = 6$, and $z = -1$.

$\frac{-x}{-4} + 2y \div z = \frac{-(-20)}{-4} + 2(6) \div (-1)$ **Substitute −20 for *x*, 6 for *y*, and −1 for *z*.**

$\phantom{\frac{-x}{-4} + 2y \div z} = -5 + (-12)$ **Divide and multiply.**

$\phantom{\frac{-x}{-4} + 2y \div z} = -17$ **Add.**

✓ Check Understanding **6** Evaluate each expression for $x = 8, y = -5$, and $z = -3$.
a. $3x \div 2z + y \div 10$ **−4½**   **b.** $\frac{2z + x}{2y}$ **−⅕**   **c.** $3z^2 - 4y \div x$ **29½**

A number and its multiplicative inverse have a special relationship.

Key Concepts

Property	**Inverse Property of Multiplication**

For every nonzero real number a, there is a **multiplicative inverse** $\frac{1}{a}$ such that $a\left(\frac{1}{a}\right) = 1$.

Examples $5\left(\frac{1}{5}\right) = 1$ $-5\left(-\frac{1}{5}\right) = 1$

The **multiplicative inverse,** or **reciprocal,** of a nonzero rational number $\frac{a}{b}$ is $\frac{b}{a}$. Zero does not have a reciprocal. Division by zero is undefined.

Need Help?

For help with dividing fractions, see Skills Handbook p. 727.

7 EXAMPLE Division Using the Reciprocal

Evaluate $\frac{x}{y}$ for $x = -\frac{3}{4}$ and $y = -\frac{5}{2}$.

$\frac{x}{y} = x \div y$ Rewrite the expression.

$\quad = -\frac{3}{4} \div \left(-\frac{5}{2}\right)$ Substitute $-\frac{3}{4}$ for x and $-\frac{5}{2}$ for y.

$\quad = -\frac{3}{4}\left(-\frac{2}{5}\right)$ Multiply by $-\frac{2}{5}$, the reciprocal of $-\frac{5}{2}$.

$\quad = \frac{3}{10}$ Simplify.

✔ **Check Understanding**   **7** Evaluate the expression in Example 7 for $x = 8$ and $y = -\frac{4}{5}$. **−10**

EXERCISES

Practice and Problem Solving

For more practice, see *Extra Practice*.

A Practice by Example

Example 1 (page 38)

Simplify each expression.

1. $3(-5)$ **−15**   **2.** $5(-3)$ **−15**   **3.** $3(5)$ **15**

4. $-3(-5)$ **15**   **5.** $8(-4.3)$ **−34.4**   **6.** $9\left(-\frac{5}{18}\right)$ **−2½**

7. $10(-12)$ **−120**   **8.** $7(-15)$ **−105**   **9.** $-4(20)$ **−80**

10. $-20(-4)$ **80**   **11.** $13(-6)$ **−78**   **12.** $-9(-9)$ **81**

Example 2 (page 39)

Evaluate each expression for $m = -4$, $n = 3$, and $p = -1$.

13. mn **−12**   **14.** $-mn$ **12**   **15.** $3m - n$ **−15**

16. $-5p$ **5**   **17.** $2m$ **−8**   **18.** $7p - 2n$ **−13**

19. $8p \cdot (-2n)$ **48**   **20.** $p \cdot (m + n)$ **1**   **21.** mnp **12**

22. $m \cdot (3 + p)$ **−8**   **23.** $4n^3 \cdot m$ **−432**   **24.** $m \cdot p + (-n)$ **1**

Example 3 (page 39)

Evaluate each expression for $x = -12$ and $y = 4$.

25. $xy - 4y$ **−64**   **26.** $2xy + 9$ **−87**   **27.** $x + 4y$ **4**

28. $-x + 3y$ **24**   **29.** $3y - 2x$ **36**   **30.** $6y + x$ **12**

 31. Weather The expression $-39 + \frac{3}{2}t$, where t is the actual air temperature, gives the approximate wind chill temperature when the wind speed is 20 mi/h. Find the approximate wind chill temperature for the given air temperatures with a 20 mi/h wind.

    a. $10°F$ **−24°F**   **b.** $-24°F$ **−75°F**   **c.** $-8°F$ **−51°F**   **d.** $5°F$ **−31.5°F**

Example 4 (page 39)

Simplify each expression.

32. $(-1)^5$ **−1**   **33.** $-(-2)^3$ **8**   **34.** -5^2 **−25**   **35.** $(-9)^2$ **81**

36. -9^2 **−81**   **37.** $3(-4)^3$ **−192**   **38.** $-5(-1)^4$ **−5**   **39.** $-5^2(-3)^3$ **675**

---

3. Practice

Assignment Guide

1 Objective
   A B Core 1–39, 64–75, 80–87, 89–98
   C Extension 99–104

2 Objective
   A B Core 40–63, 76–79, 88
   C Extension 105–108

Standardized Test Prep 109–113

Mixed Review 114–127

Exercises 1–12 Suggest to students that they first predict the sign of the result, and then calculate.

Careers

Exercise 31 Weather forecasters use the given formula to calculate wind chill temperatures and then broadcast these approximations. Ask: *Why do you think this is important?* Answers may vary. Sample: Wind chill temperature is colder than air temperature and is what people feel.

Enrichment 1-6

Reteaching 1-6

Practice 1-6

Exercises 90–95 Suggest to students that they check to see that the answer matrix has the same number of rows and columns as the exercise matrix.

Error Prevention

Exercise 96b Point out that the roller coaster has reached the bottom when $h = 0$. If students get values of h that are less than 0, they have used values of t that are too large.

Example 5
(page 40)

Simplify each expression.

40. $\frac{6}{-3}$ **−2**   **41.** $\frac{-36}{9}$ **−4**   **42.** $\frac{3-14}{-2}$ **$5\frac{1}{2}$**   **43.** $-18 \div (-3)$ **6**

44. $-121 \div 11$ **−11**   **45.** $-64 \div (-5)$ **$12\frac{4}{5}$** **46.** $2^3 \div (-4)$ **−2**   **47.** $-56 \div (4 + 3)$
−8

Example 6
(page 40)

Evaluate each expression for $x = -2, y = 3,$ and $z = 3.5$.

48. $(y + 3x) \div y$ **−1**   **49.** $4z \div x$ **−7**

50. $4x^3 - \frac{2z}{x}$ **$-28\frac{1}{2}$**   **51.** $(3x + 2y) \div (2x + 3y)$ **0**

52. $(2z + 7) \div y$ **$4\frac{2}{3}$**   **53.** $8 + 6x \div (4y) - \frac{3z}{y}$ **$3\frac{1}{2}$**

Example 7
(page 41)

Evaluate each expression.

54. $\frac{x}{y}$, for $x = \frac{2}{5}$ and $y = \frac{3}{10}$ **$1\frac{1}{3}$**   **55.** $\frac{-3m}{t}$, for $m = \frac{5}{6}$ and $t = \frac{1}{6}$ **−15**

56. $\frac{r}{-3s}$, for $r = -\frac{1}{8}$ and $s = \frac{3}{4}$ **$\frac{1}{18}$**   **57.** $\frac{3x}{5y}$, for $x = \frac{1}{5}$ and $y = -\frac{1}{2}$ **$-\frac{6}{25}$**

B **Apply Your Skills**

Simplify each expression.

58. $\frac{10}{-5}$ **−2**   **59.** $-3(-6)$ **18**   **60.** $\frac{2}{3} \div (-\frac{4}{3})$ **$-\frac{1}{2}$**

61. $\frac{2}{3}(-\frac{4}{5})$ **$-\frac{8}{15}$**   **62.** -5^3 **−125**   **63.** $2.25 \div 3$ **0.75**

64. $(-3)^3$ **−27**   **65.** $-7.2(-3.1)$ **22.32**   **66.** $|4 + 8(-6)|$ **44**

67. $|-6(-9)| \div (-2)$ **−27** **68.** $(-6)(-2)(-5)$ **−60**   **69.** $(-2)(5)(-3)$ **30**

70. d. No; answers may vary. Sample: The sign of the product is not affected by the number of pos. factors, only by the number of neg. factors.

70. a. Find each product.
    i. $(-1)(-2)$ **2**   **ii.** $(-1)(-2)(-3)$ **−6**
    iii. $(-1)(-2)(-3)(-4)$ **24**   **iv.** $(-1)(-2)(-3)(-4)(-5)$ **−120**
  b. **Patterns** For an even number of negative factors, the product will be ? .**pos.**
  c. For an odd number of negative factors, the product will be ? . **neg.**
  d. **Writing** For a product that includes negative and positive factors, do the positive factors affect the sign of the product? Explain. **See left.**

71. Suppose a and b are integers.
  a. When is the product ab positive? **When a and b are both neg. or both pos.**
  b. When is the product ab negative? **When a is neg. and b is pos., or when**
                         a is pos. and b is neg.

Evaluate each expression for $a = -\frac{3}{4}, b = \frac{1}{3},$ and $c = -\frac{2}{5}$.

72. $a - 2b$ **$-1\frac{5}{12}$**   **73.** $b \div c$ **$-\frac{5}{6}$**   **74.** $\frac{a}{c}$ **$1\frac{7}{8}$**   **75.** $-2abc$ **$-\frac{1}{5}$**

Evaluate each expression for the given value(s).

76. $\frac{3}{4}w - 7$, for $w = 1\frac{1}{3}$ **−6**   **77.** $\frac{x}{2y}$, for $x = 3.6$ and $y = -0.4$ **$-4\frac{1}{2}$**

78. $\frac{n}{m}$, for $n = -\frac{4}{5}$ and $m = 8$ **$-\frac{1}{10}$**   **79.** $\frac{3a}{b} + c$, for $a = -2, b = -5,$ and $c = -\frac{11}{5}$

Open-Ended Use $a = -3, b = 2,$ and $c = -5$ to write an algebraic expression that has each value. **80–84. Answers may vary. Samples are given.**

80. 17 $ac + b$ **81.** 0 $b - a + c$ **82.** −1 $ab - c$ **83.** 1 $-ab + c$ **84.** 7 $-bc + a$

85. **History** A toll bridge in Maine in the early 1900s charged 2¢ per person and $6\frac{1}{4}$¢ for a dozen sheep. How much would the toll for 3 people and 4 dozen sheep have been? **31¢**

86. Yes; whatever the signs of a and b, $|ab|$, $|a|$, and $|b|$ are pos., and $|ab| = |a| \cdot |b|$.

89. The opposite of a nonzero number n is $-n$ while the multiplicative inverse is $\frac{1}{n}$.

97a.
$$\begin{bmatrix} 180 & 210 & 200 \\ 170 & 230 & 190 \end{bmatrix}$$

b.
$$\begin{bmatrix} 5.8 & 6.8 & 6.4 \\ 5.5 & 7.4 & 6.1 \end{bmatrix}$$

c.
$$\begin{bmatrix} 198 & 231 & 220 \\ 187 & 253 & 209 \end{bmatrix}$$

155 ft

	Dept. Sales		
March	180	210	200
October	170	230	190

86. Reasoning Does $|ab|$ always equal $|a| \cdot |b|$? Explain. **See left.**

87. a. Simplify each expression.
$(-2)^2$ **4** $(-2)^3$ **−8** $(-2)^4$ **16** $(-2)^5$ **−32**
$(-3)^2$ **9** $(-3)^3$ **−27** $(-3)^4$ **81** $(-3)^5$ **−243**
   b. Make a Conjecture Do you think a negative number raised to an even power will be positive or negative? Explain. **b–c. See margin.**
   c. What is the sign of a negative number raised to an odd power? Explain.

88. Is -10 or 0.1 the multiplicative inverse of 10? Explain. **See margin.**

89. Explain why the reciprocal of a nonzero number is *not* the same as the opposite of the number. **See left.**

In *scalar multiplication,* **you multiply the elements in a matrix by a number, called a** *scalar.* **Find each product. 90–95. See margin.**

Sample $3\begin{bmatrix} 4 & -1.5 \\ \frac{1}{2} & -6 \end{bmatrix}$ $= \begin{bmatrix} 3 \cdot 4 & 3 \cdot (-1.5) \\ 3 \cdot \frac{1}{2} & 3 \cdot (-6) \end{bmatrix}$ **Multiply each entry by the scalar.**

$= \begin{bmatrix} 12 & -4.5 \\ \frac{3}{2} & -18 \end{bmatrix}$ **Simplify.**

90. $-2\begin{bmatrix} 11 & -5 \\ -9 & 6 \\ -4 & 3 \end{bmatrix}$

91. $\frac{3}{5}\begin{bmatrix} -25 & 35 \\ \frac{10}{9} & -15 \end{bmatrix}$

92. $-0.1\begin{bmatrix} -47 & 13 & -7.9 \\ 0.2 & -64 & 0 \end{bmatrix}$

93. $-4\begin{bmatrix} 3 & \frac{2}{3} \end{bmatrix}$

94. $2\begin{bmatrix} -4 & -5.3 & 2 \\ 3.1 & 0 & 6 \end{bmatrix}$

95. $\frac{1}{4}\begin{bmatrix} -1 & \frac{3}{4} \\ \frac{8}{9} & 0 \end{bmatrix}$

96. Entertainment As riders plunge down the hill of a roller coaster, you can approximate the height h, in feet, above the ground of their roller-coaster car. Use the formula $h = 155 - 16t^2$ where t is the number of seconds since the start of the descent. **a. 139 ft; 91 ft**
   a. How far is a rider from the bottom of the hill after 1 second? 2 seconds?
   b. Critical Thinking Does it take more than or less than 4 seconds to reach the bottom? Explain. **See margin.**

97. a. Sales The table at the left shows the monthly sales in March and October for three departments of a clothing store. Organize the data into a matrix.
   b. Use a scalar to find the matrix for each month's average daily sales. Assume the store is open every day. Round to the nearest tenth.
   c. Each department hopes sales in March and October increase by 10% next year. Find the matrix that shows the projected sales for these months.
   a–c. See above left.

98. Temperature Scales The formula $C = \frac{5}{9}(F - 32)$ changes a temperature reading from the Fahrenheit scale F to the Celsius scale C. What is the temperature measured in Celsius if the Fahrenheit temperature is $-10°$ degrees? Round to the nearest degree. **−23°C**

C Challenge Evaluate each expression for $b = -\frac{1}{2}$.
   99. b^3 $-\frac{1}{8}$ **100.** b^4 $\frac{1}{16}$ **101.** b^5 $-\frac{1}{32}$ **102.** b^6 $\frac{1}{64}$ **103.** $-b^6$ $-\frac{1}{64}$

104. What is the greatest integer n for which $(-n)^3$ is positive and the value of the expression has a 2 in the ones place? **−8**

pages 41–44 **Exercises**

87b. Pos.; the expression will involve an even number of neg. factors.
   c. Neg.; the expression will involve an odd number of neg. factors.

88. 0.1 is the multiplicative inverse of 10 because $0.1(10) = 1$. (-10 is the opposite of 10.)

Lesson Quiz 1-6

Simplify.
1. $-8(-7)$ **56**
2. $-6(-7 + 10) - 4$ **−22**

Evaluate each expression for $m = -3$, $n = 4$, and $p = -1$.
3. $\frac{8m}{n} + p$ **−7**
4. $(mp)^3$ **27**
5. mnp **12**
6. Evaluate $2a \div 4b - c$ for $a = -2$, $b = -\frac{1}{3}$, and $c = -\frac{1}{2}$. $3\frac{1}{2}$

Alternative Assessment

Have students make posters displaying the rules for multiplying and dividing real numbers using only signs. For example:

$$ + \times + = + $$

To make their posters clear, students may wish to color code or put boxes around the positive and negative symbols. Ask students to write an example for each rule.

90. $\begin{bmatrix} -22 & 10 \\ 18 & -12 \\ 8 & -6 \end{bmatrix}$

91. $\begin{bmatrix} -15 & 21 \\ \frac{2}{3} & -9 \end{bmatrix}$

92. $\begin{bmatrix} 4.7 & -1.3 & 0.79 \\ -0.02 & 6.4 & 0 \end{bmatrix}$

93. $\begin{bmatrix} -12 & -2\frac{2}{3} \end{bmatrix}$

94. $\begin{bmatrix} -8 & -10.6 & 4 \\ 6.2 & 0 & 12 \end{bmatrix}$

95. $\begin{bmatrix} -\frac{1}{4} & \frac{3}{16} \\ \frac{2}{9} & 0 \end{bmatrix}$

96b. Less than 4 s; for $t = 4$, $h = 155 - 16t^2 = -101$, so $h = 0$ for some value less than 4 (about 3.1).

43

Standardized Test Prep

Resources

For additional practice with a variety of test item formats:
- Standardized Test Prep, p. 71
- Test-Taking Strategies, p. 66
- Test-Taking Strategies with Transparencies

Exercise 112 Tell students to read the exercise carefully. Point out that the problem shows repeated addition of the same number. Remind them that an exponent means repeated multiplication of the same number.

Rewrite each expression using the symbol ÷. Then find each quotient.

Sample $\dfrac{\frac{-7}{12}}{4} = \dfrac{-7}{12} \div 4$ Rewrite as $\dfrac{-7}{12} \div 4$.

$= \dfrac{-7}{12} \cdot \left(\dfrac{1}{4}\right)$ Multiply by $\frac{1}{4}$, the reciprocal of 4.

$= -\dfrac{7}{48}$

105. $\dfrac{\frac{5}{4}}{\frac{9}{}}$ **$\frac{45}{4}$, or $11\frac{1}{4}$**   **106.** $\dfrac{\frac{3}{8}}{\frac{-2}{3}}$ **$-\frac{9}{16}$**   **107.** $\dfrac{\frac{-5}{6}}{8}$ **$-\frac{5}{48}$**   **108.** $\dfrac{\frac{-2}{5}}{\frac{-4}{5}}$ **$\frac{1}{2}$**

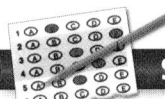

Standardized Test Prep

Multiple Choice

109. Simplify $(-3)(-3)(2)(2)(-1)$. **A**
   A. -36 B. -6 C. 6   D. 36

110. Evaluate $-ac + bc$ for $a = -2$, $b = 6$, and $c = -3$. **F**
   F. -24 G. -6 H. 6   I. 24

111. A Mach number M indicates the speed of a supersonic airplane. You can find an airplane's speed a in miles per hour using the formula $a = Ms$ where s is the speed of sound at the altitude of the airplane. Find an airplane's speed in miles per hour if the airplane travels at Mach 2.5 at an altitude where the speed of sound is 710 mi/h. **C**
   A. 177.5 mi/h   B. 284 mi/h   C. 1775 mi/h   D. 2840 mi/h

112. Which expression does NOT have the same value as $-11 + (-11) + (-11) + (-11)$? **H**
   F. -44 G. $4(-11)$ H. $(-11)^4$ I. $33 - 77$

113. Use the table below. What was the average temperature for the week? **B**

Day	Mon.	Tues.	Wed.	Thur.	Fri.	Sat.	Sun.
Temperature	$-3°F$	$4°F$	$-2°F$	$-5°F$	$-3°F$	$1°F$	$1°F$

   A. $-7°F$ B. $-1°F$ C. $1°F$ D. $4°F$

Take It to the NET
Online lesson quiz at
www.PHSchool.com
Web Code: aea-0106

Mixed Review

Lesson 1-5   **Subtract.**

114. $6 - 8$ **-2**   **115.** $-3 - 17$ **-20**   **116.** $-2.3 - (-3.1)$ **0.8**

117. $7 - (-2.8)$ **9.8**   **118.** $1\frac{3}{4} - \left(-\frac{1}{2}\right)$ **$2\frac{1}{4}$**   **119.** $-\frac{7}{8} - \left(-\frac{8}{9}\right)$ **$\frac{1}{72}$**

Lesson 1-3   **Find each absolute value.**

120. $|4.95|$ **4.95**   **121.** $|-56|$ **56**   **122.** $|-4.59|$ **4.59**   **123.** $\left|-\frac{3}{4}\right|$ **$\frac{3}{4}$**

Lesson 1-2   **Evaluate each expression for $a = 4$ and $b = 7$.**

124. $a^2 + b$ **23**   **125.** $(a + b)^2$ **121**   **126.** ab^2 **196**

127. A sweater costs \$32.95. The sales tax rate is 6%. Find the total cost. **\$34.93**

Technology

Matrices

For Use With Lesson 1-6

You can use a graphing calculator to add and subtract matrices and to multiply a matrix by a number, or scalar.

Take It to the NET
Graphing Calculator
procedures online at
www.PHSchool.com
Web Code: aee-2113

1 EXAMPLE **Matrix Operations**

Let $A = \begin{bmatrix} 3 & 7 & 1 \\ 2 & -4 & 9 \end{bmatrix}$ and $B = \begin{bmatrix} 5 & 0 & -8 \\ 6 & 2 & 2 \end{bmatrix}$. Find $A + B$ and $5A$.

A calculator names the matrices using brackets [A] and [B] to remind you that you are working with matrices.

Step 1 To enter the first matrix, access the **MATRX** feature of your calculator. Use the arrow keys to highlight **EDIT** at the top of the screen. Press ENTER . Matrix A is a 2×3 matrix, so revise the numbers at the top of the screen, if necessary. Press ENTER to access the first entry of the matrix. Enter the values given for matrix A. Use (-) for negative.

Step 2 To enter the second matrix, access the matrix screen again. Use the arrow keys to highlight **EDIT**. Use the arrow keys to move down to [B]. Press ENTER . Change the dimensions and enter the values for matrix B.

Step 3 To find $A + B$, use the **NAMES** list on the matrix screen to select [A] or [B]. The calculator will display the matrix sum as shown at the right.

Step 4 To find $5A$, press 5, select [A] from the **NAMES** list, and ENTER . The result is also shown at the right.

```
[A] + [B]
            [[8  7  -7]
             [8 -2 11]]
5[A]
            [[15  35  5 ]
             [10 -20 45]]
```

EXERCISES

For $A = \begin{bmatrix} 4 & -2 \\ 8 & 6 \end{bmatrix}$, $B = \begin{bmatrix} -5 & 12 \\ 0 & 3 \end{bmatrix}$, and $C = \begin{bmatrix} 3 & 15 \\ 9 & -10 \end{bmatrix}$, **find each of the following.**
1–9. See margin.

1. $A + B$ **2.** $B + C$ **3.** $C - A$

4. $A + C$ **5.** $B - C$ **6.** $3B$

7. $-4C$ **8.** $2A + B$ **9.** $-2B + C + A$

For $A = \begin{bmatrix} 4 & 7 & 3 \\ 8 & 2 & 1 \\ -7 & 5 & -2 \end{bmatrix}$, $B = \begin{bmatrix} -1 & 0 & 6 \\ 2 & -3 & 4 \\ 1 & 15 & 8 \end{bmatrix}$, and $C = \begin{bmatrix} 2 & 0 & 0 \\ 0 & -3 & 6 \\ 4 & 6 & 9 \end{bmatrix}$, **find each of the following.**
10–15. See margin.

10. $A + 2B$ **11.** $C + B - A$ **12.** $2A + 5B - C$

13. $-4A + 5C$ **14.** $-4A - 5C$ **15.** $A + B - 2C$

Technology Matrices **45**

Technology

Matrices

Students use a graphing calculator to add and subtract matrices and to multiply a matrix by a number, or scalar. This activity will prepare students for using a graphing calculator and matrices to solve systems of equations in chapter 7.

Resources

Students may use any graphing calculator.

Teaching Notes

This activity helps students see the importance of correctly determining matrix size. They will be immediately notified by an error message should they attempt to add matrices of unlike size.

Error Prevention

Briefly discuss the placement of the subtraction key and the negative key. Students sometimes use the incorrect one and get an error message.

11. $\begin{bmatrix} -3 & -7 & 3 \\ -6 & -8 & 9 \\ 12 & 16 & 19 \end{bmatrix}$

12. $\begin{bmatrix} 1 & 14 & 36 \\ 26 & -8 & 16 \\ -13 & 79 & 27 \end{bmatrix}$

13. $\begin{bmatrix} -6 & -28 & -12 \\ -32 & -23 & 26 \\ 48 & 10 & 53 \end{bmatrix}$

14. $\begin{bmatrix} -26 & -28 & -12 \\ -32 & 7 & -34 \\ 8 & -50 & -37 \end{bmatrix}$

15. $\begin{bmatrix} -1 & 7 & 9 \\ 10 & 5 & -7 \\ -14 & 8 & -12 \end{bmatrix}$

page 45 Technology

1. $\begin{bmatrix} -1 & 10 \\ 8 & 9 \end{bmatrix}$

2. $\begin{bmatrix} -2 & 27 \\ 9 & -7 \end{bmatrix}$

3. $\begin{bmatrix} -1 & 17 \\ 1 & -16 \end{bmatrix}$

4. $\begin{bmatrix} 7 & 13 \\ 17 & -4 \end{bmatrix}$

5. $\begin{bmatrix} -8 & -3 \\ -9 & 13 \end{bmatrix}$

6. $\begin{bmatrix} -15 & 36 \\ 0 & 9 \end{bmatrix}$

7. $\begin{bmatrix} -12 & -60 \\ -36 & 40 \end{bmatrix}$

8. $\begin{bmatrix} 3 & 8 \\ 16 & 15 \end{bmatrix}$

9. $\begin{bmatrix} 17 & -11 \\ 17 & -10 \end{bmatrix}$

10. $\begin{bmatrix} 2 & 7 & 15 \\ 12 & -4 & 9 \\ -5 & 35 & 14 \end{bmatrix}$

45

The Distributive Property

Students use algebra tiles to explore the Distributive Property.

Resources

Algebra tiles

Teaching Notes

You may wish to extend the investigation by introducing the red, negative *x* tile. Students can represent and simplify expressions such as $2(-x + 4)$, $3(-2x - 1)$, etc.

Error Prevention

Students sometimes mistakenly think that the *x* tile has a value of 5 since 5 unit tiles lined up are almost exactly the same length as the *x* tile. Remind students that the *x* tile represents a variable, which means it can have any value.

Alternative Method

Students can represent the variables with written *x*'s and represent the integers with tick marks or Arabic numerals. Have them use a red pen or pencil for negatives.

page 46   Investigation

4.
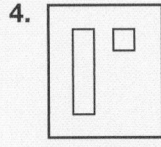

5.
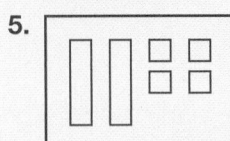

6.
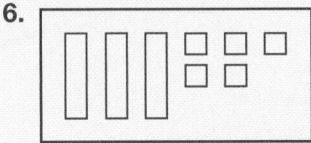

Investigation — The Distributive Property

FOR USE WITH LESSON 1-7

From Lesson 1-5, you know that ▯ represents +1 and ■ represents −1. The tile ▮ represents a variable.

You can use tiles to represent an expression like $x + 5$.

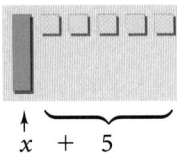

Write the expression represented by each group of tiles.

1.  $x - 3$

2. 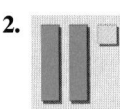 $2x + 1$

3. 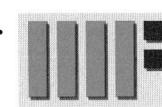 $4x - 2$

Represent each expression using tiles. 4–6. See margin.

4. $x + 1$

5. $2x + 4$

6. $3x - 5$

The expression $2(x + 5)$ indicates two groups of tiles, as shown below on the left. You can add the variable tiles together and the unit tiles together to simplify the expression, as shown below on the right.

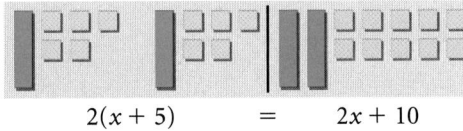

$$2(x + 5) \quad = \quad 2x + 10$$

The tiles show that the product $2(x + 5)$ equals $2x + 10$. This illustrates the Distributive Property.

Write an equation for each model.

7.
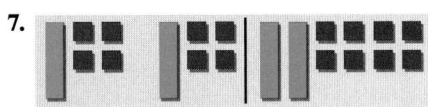

$2(x - 4) = 2x - 8$

8.
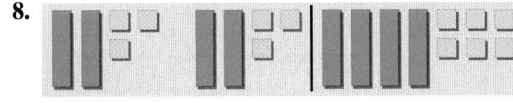

$2(2x + 3) = 4x + 6$

9.

$3(x - 3) = 3x - 9$

Use tiles to rewrite each expression without grouping symbols.

10. $3(x + 1)$ $3x + 3$

11. $2(x + 4)$ $2x + 8$

12. $3(2x - 1)$ $6x - 3$

13. **Critical Thinking** Does $5(2x - 3)$ equal $10x - 3$ or $10x - 15$? Explain. **See margin.**

13. $10x - 15$; there are 5 groups of 3 red tiles each, representing −15.

The Distributive Property

North Carolina Objectives 1.01 Write equivalent forms of algebraic expressions to solve problems. a) Apply the laws of exponents.

Lesson Preview

What You'll Learn

OBJECTIVE 1 To use the Distributive Property

OBJECTIVE 2 To simplify algebraic expressions

. . . And Why

To calculate costs when shopping, as in Example 2

✔ Check Skills You'll Need

(For help, go to Lessons 1-2 and 1-6.)

Use the order of operations to simplify each expression.

1. $3(4 + 7)$ **33**

2. $-2(5 + 6)$ **−22**

3. $-1(-9 + 8)$ **1**

4. $-0.5(8 - 6)$ **−1**

5. $\frac{1}{2}t(10 - 4)$ **3t**

6. $m(-3 - 1)$ **−4m**

New Vocabulary

• Distributive Property • term • constant • coefficient • like terms

---

1. Plan

Lesson Preview

✔ **Check Skills You'll Need**

Order of Operations
Lesson 1-2: Example 4
Exercises 15–20
Extra Practice, p. 702

Multiplying Real Numbers
Lesson 1-6: Example 1
Exercises 1–12
Extra Practice, p. 702

Lesson Resources

📁 **Teaching Resources**
Practice, Reteaching, Enrichment

👥 **Reaching All Students**
Practice Workbook 1-7
Spanish Practice Workbook 1-7
Hands-On Activities 3
Basic Algebra Planning Guide 1-7

⏰ **Presentation Assistant Plus!**
Transparencies
• Check Skills You'll Need 1-7
• Additional Examples 1-7
• Student Edition Answers 1-7
• Lesson Quiz 1-7
PH Presentation Pro CD 1-7

PRENTICE HALL ASSESSMENT SYSTEM

Computer Test Generator CD

💾 **Technology**
Resource Pro® CD-ROM
Computer Test Generator CD
Prentice Hall Presentation Pro CD

💻 **www.PHSchool.com**
Student Site
• Teacher Web Code: aek-5500
• Reasoning & Puzzles p. 28
• Self-grading Lesson Quiz
Teacher Center
• Lesson Planner
• Resources

Plus iTEXT

OBJECTIVE 1 — **Using the Distributive Property**

iTEXT Interactive lesson includes instant self-check, tutorials, and activities.

You can use the Distributive Property to multiply a sum or difference by a number.

🔑 **Key Concepts**

Property	Distributive Property

For every real number a, b, and c,

$$a(b + c) = ab + ac \qquad (b + c)a = ba + ca$$
$$a(b - c) = ab - ac \qquad (b - c)a = ba - ca$$

Examples
$$5(20 + 6) = 5(20) + 5(6) \qquad (20 + 6)5 = 20(5) + 6(5)$$
$$9(30 - 2) = 9(30) - 9(2) \qquad (30 - 2)9 = 30(9) - 2(9)$$

You can use the Distributive Property to multiply some numbers using mental math. For instance, you can think of 102 as $100 + 2$ and 98 as $100 - 2$.

1 EXAMPLE Simplifying a Numerical Expression

Use the Distributive Property to simplify $34(102)$.

$34(102) = 34(100 + 2)$ **Rewrite 102 as 100 + 2.**

$\quad\quad\quad = 34(100) + 34(2)$ **Use the Distributive Property.**

$\quad\quad\quad = 3400 + 68$ **Simplify.**

$\quad\quad\quad = 3468$

✔ **Check Understanding** ① Simplify each expression.

a. $13(103)$ **1339**

b. $21(101)$ **2121**

c. $24(98)$ **2352**

d. $15(99)$ **1485**

Ongoing Assessment and Intervention

Before the Lesson
Diagnose prerequisite skills using:
• Check Skills You'll Need

During the Lesson
Monitor progress using:
• Check Understanding
• Additional Examples
• Standardized Test Prep

After the Lesson
Assess knowledge using:
• Lesson Quiz
• Computer Test Generator CD

2. Teach

Math Background

The Distributive Property is the only property that combines multiplication and addition. The multiplier of an expression in parentheses must be *distributed* to every term in the parentheses and multiply each one.

OBJECTIVE 1 Teaching Notes

1 EXAMPLE Teaching Tip

Another way to show the usefulness of the Distributive Property is in simplifying the expression $6(\frac{1}{2} + \frac{1}{3})$. Write the following on the board:

$$6(\tfrac{1}{2} + \tfrac{1}{3}) = 6(\tfrac{1}{2}) + 6(\tfrac{1}{3})$$
$$= 3 + 2$$
$$= 5$$

If you add first, the fractions have to be rewritten with common denominators. Since each denominator is a factor of 6, it is easier to distribute the 6 to the fractions before adding.

2 EXAMPLE Alternative Method

Ask students to explain how to use mental math to calculate the costs. Ask them how to decide what numbers to put inside the parentheses.

Additional Examples

1 Use the Distributive Property to simplify 26(98). **2548**

2 Find the total cost of 4 CDs that cost $12.99 each. **$51.96**

OBJECTIVE 2 Teaching Notes

3 EXAMPLE Visual Learners

Some students may forget to multiply 2(3). Encourage students to draw arrows from the 2 to each term inside the parentheses.

48

$2.99 each

You can also use the Distributive Property and mental math to calculate costs.

2 EXAMPLE Real-World Problem Solving

Shopping Find the total cost of 8 sandwiches that cost $2.99 each.

$$8(2.99) = 8(3 - 0.01) \qquad \text{Rewrite 2.99 as } 3 - 0.01.$$
$$= 8(3) - 8(0.01) \qquad \text{Use the Distributive Property.}$$
$$= 24 - 0.08 \qquad \text{Simplify.}$$
$$= 23.92$$

● The total cost of 8 sandwiches is $23.92.

✓ Check Understanding **2** Find the total cost of 6 pairs of socks that cost $2.95 per pair. **$17.70**

OBJECTIVE 2 Simplifying Algebraic Expressions

You can use the Distributive Property to simplify an algebraic expression. An algebraic expression in simplest form has no grouping symbols.

3 EXAMPLE Simplifying an Expression

Simplify each expression.

a. $2(5x + 3)$
$$2(5x + 3) = 2(5x) + 2(3) \qquad \text{Use the Distributive Property.}$$
$$= 10x + 6 \qquad \text{Simplify.}$$

b. $(3b - 2)\left(\frac{1}{3}\right)$
$$(3b - 2)\left(\tfrac{1}{3}\right) = 3b\left(\tfrac{1}{3}\right) - 2\left(\tfrac{1}{3}\right) \qquad \text{Use the Distributive Property.}$$
$$= b - \tfrac{2}{3} \qquad \text{Simplify.}$$

✓ Check Understanding **3** Simplify each expression.

a. $6(m + 5)$ **b.** $2(3 - 7t)$ **c.** $(0.4 + 1.1c)(3)$
6m + 30   **6 − 14t**   **1.2 + 3.3c**

To simplify an expression like $-(6x + 4)$, rewrite the expression as $-1(6x + 4)$, using the Multiplication Property of -1.

4 EXAMPLE Using the Multiplication Property of −1

Simplify $-(6x + 4)$.

$$-(6x + 4) = -1(6x + 4) \qquad \text{Rewrite the expression using } -1.$$
$$= -1(6x) + (-1)(4) \qquad \text{Use the Distributive Property.}$$
$$= -6x - 4 \qquad \text{Simplify.}$$

✓ Check Understanding **4** Simplify each expression.

a. $-(2x + 1)$ **b.** $-(7 - 5b)$ **c.** $(3 - 8a)(-1)$
−2x − 1   **−7 + 5b**   **−3 + 8a**

48   Chapter 1   Tools of Algebra

Reaching All Students

Below Level Demonstrate how students can use algebra tiles to simplify algebraic expressions. Explain that the number of matching tiles equals the sum of the coefficients.	**Advanced Learners** Encourage students to find a counterexample for the expression $a(b + c) = ab + c$.	**Visual Learners** See note on page 48. **Tactile Learners** See note on page 49.

In an algebraic expression, a **term** is a number, a variable, or the product of a number and one or more variables.

$$6a^2 - 5ab + 3b - 12 \leftarrow \text{A \textbf{constant} is a term that has no variable.}$$

A **coefficient** is a numerical factor of a term.

Think of $3b - 12$ as $3b + (-12)$ to determine that the constant is -12.

Like terms have exactly the same variable factors.

Like Terms	Not Like Terms
$3x$ and $-2x$	$8x$ and $7y$
$-5x^2$ and $9x^2$	$5y$ and $2y^2$
xy and $-xy$	$4y$ and $5xy$
$-7x^2y^3$ and $15x^2y^3$	x^2y and xy^2

An algebraic expression in simplest form has no like terms. You can use the Distributive Property to combine like terms when simplifying an expression. Think of the Distributive Property as $ba + ca = (b + c)a$.

Need Help?

Identity Property of multiplication:
$c = 1 \cdot c$ or $1c$

5 EXAMPLE Combining Like Terms

Simplify each expression.

a. $3x^2 + 5x^2$

$3x^2 + 5x^2 = (3 + 5)x^2$ Use the Distributive Property.

$= 8x^2$ Simplify.

b. $-5c + c$

$-5c + c = -5c + 1c$ Rewrite c as 1c.

$= (-5 + 1)c$ Use the Distributive Property.

$= -4c$ Simplify.

✓ **Check Understanding** ⑤ Simplify each expression.

a. $7y + 6y$ **b.** $3t - t$ **c.** $-9w^3 - 3w^3$ **d.** $8d + d$
   13y **2**t **−12**w^3 **9**d

You can write an expression from a verbal phrase. The word *quantity* indicates that two or more terms are within parentheses.

6 EXAMPLE Writing an Expression

Write an expression for "3 times the quantity x minus 5."

Relate   3   times   the quantity x minus 5

Write   3   · $(x - 5)$

$3(x - 5)$

✓ **Check Understanding** ⑥ Write an expression for each phrase.
   a. -2 times the quantity t plus 7   **−2(**t **+ 7)**
   b. the product of 14 and the quantity 8 plus w **14(8 +** w**)**

49

---

4 EXAMPLE Math Tip

Ask students: *What is the product of a number and 1?* **the number** *What happens when you multiply a number by −1?* **The sign of the number changes, but the absolute value stays the same.** *Since a negative sign in front of parentheses means to multiply by −1, what happens to the numbers inside the parentheses when you multiply?* **The sign of each number inside the parentheses changes, but the absolute value of each number stays the same.**

5 EXAMPLE Tactile Learners

Give each group of 3 or 4 students a bag of different colored tokens. Ask the students to write a sentence describing exactly the amount of each color of token in their bag. Have students represent the tokens with an algebraic expression, for example $3r + 2b + 4g$. Ask: *What did you do first?* Lead students to realize that the most logical process is to "collect like tokens" first.

6 EXAMPLE Visual Learners

Tell students to replace the word *quantity* with a left parenthesis, just as they would replace *of* with a multiplication sign. Tell them to remember that an operation must occur inside the parentheses before the right parenthesis can be written.

Additional Examples

③ Simplify $3(4m - 7)$. $12m - 21$

④ Simplify $-(5q - 6)$. $-5q + 6$

⑤ Simplify $-2w^2 + w^2$. $-w^2$

⑥ Write an expression for "the product of -6 and the quantity 7 minus m." $-6(7 - m)$

Closure

Ask students to describe an everyday situation in which using the distributive property and mental math would be helpful. **Answers may vary. Sample: Buying 3 pounds of apples at $1.19 per pound.**

49

Assignment Guide

1 Objective
Ⓐ Ⓑ Core 1–14, 49–54, 85–87

2 Objective
Ⓐ Ⓑ Core 15–48, 55–84
Ⓒ Extension 88–96

Standardized Test Prep
97–104

Mixed Review 105–123

Error Prevention

Exercises 9–12 If students are having difficulty finding each price mentally, encourage them to first rewrite each exercise using the Distributive Property.

Exercises 15–34 Tell students to pay close attention to the signs. A negative number in front of parentheses changes the sign of both terms in the parentheses.

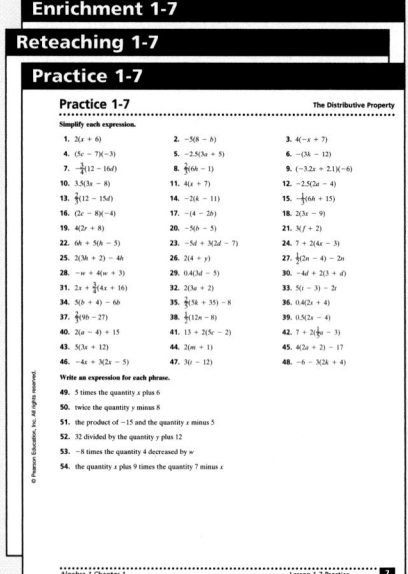

EXERCISES

For more practice, see *Extra Practice*.

Practice and Problem Solving

Ⓐ **Practice by Example**

Example 1
(page 47)

Simplify each expression using the Distributive Property.

1. 12(201) **2412**   **2.** 51(13) **663**   **3.** 11(499) **5489**   **4.** 8(306) **2448**

5. 7(98)**686**   **6.** 3(999) **2997**   **7.** 41(502) **20,582**   **8.** 24(1020) **24,480**

Example 2
(page 48)

Mental Math Use the Distributive Property to find each price.

9. 4($.99) **$3.96**   **10.** 6($1.97) **$11.82** **11.** 5($5.91) **$29.55** **12.** 7($29.93) **$209.51**

13. The school librarian got money to buy new reference works. She bought three new CD-ROMs for $32.99 each. How much did she spend in all? **$98.97**

14. You stopped on your way to basketball practice and bought four cans of fruit punch for $.69 each. How much did you spend in all? **$2.76**

Example 3
(page 48)

Simplify each expression. 24, 26. See left. 30–34. See margin.

15. $7(t - 4)$ **7t − 28**   **16.** $-2(n - 6)$ **−2n + 12**   **17.** $3(m + 4)$ **3m + 12**

18. $(5b - 4)\frac{1}{5}$ **b − $\frac{4}{5}$**   **19.** $-2(x + 3)$ **−2x − 6**   **20.** $\frac{2}{3}(6y + 9)$ **4y + 6**

24. **−4.5b + 13.5**

26. **−36 + 16n**

21. $0.25(6q + 32)$ **1.5q + 8** **22.** $(3n - 7)(6)$ **18n − 42** **23.** $(8 - 3r)\frac{5}{16}$ **$\frac{5}{2}$ − $\frac{15}{16}$r**

24. $-4.5(b - 3)$ **25.** $\frac{2}{5}(5w + 10)$ **2w + 4**   **26.** $(9 - 4n)(-4)$

Example 4
(page 48)

27. $-(x + 3)$**−x − 3** **28.** $-(x - 3)$**−x + 3** **29.** $-(3 + x)$**−3 − x** **30.** $-(3 - x)$

31. $-(6k + 5)$ **32.** $-(7x - 2)$ **33.** $-(2 - 7x)$ **34.** $(4 - z)(-1)$

Example 5
(page 49)

35. $4t - 7t$ **−3t**   **36.** $12k^2 + 8k^2$ **20k²** **37.** $9x - 2x$ **7x**   **38.** $w + 23w$ **24w**

39. $-18v^2 + 23v^2$ **5v²** **40.** $7m - m$ **6m**   **41.** $13q - 30q$ **−17q** **42.** $x - 46x$ **−45x**

Example 6
(page 49)

Write an expression for each phrase.

43. 3 times the quantity m minus 7 **3(m − 7)**

44. -4 times the quantity 4 plus w **−4(4 + w)**

45. twice the quantity b plus 9 **2(b + 9)**

46. the product of -11 and the quantity n minus 8 **−11(n − 8)**

47. 2 times the quantity 3 times c plus 9 **2(3c + 9)**

48. the quantity 3 plus r times the quantity r minus 7 **(3 + r)(r − 7)**

Ⓑ **Apply Your Skills**

Simplify each expression.

49. 9(4998) **44,982**   **50.** 8(299) **2392**   **51.** 7(2.003) **14.021**

52. 12(7.001) **84.012**   **53.** 6(1.97) **11.82**   **54.** 4(3.998) **15.992**

55. $7(4.3 + x)$ **30.1 + 7x** **56.** $\frac{10}{14}d(8 - 10h)$ **57.** $2(6.4 - 0.5n)$ **12.8 − n**

58. **135b + 128**

59. **18.6 + 15m**

60. $\frac{5}{8}$**d − 42**

61. **−8.4 − 300g + 512h**

62. **−12k − 5m + 62**

58. $144\left(\frac{15}{16}b + \frac{8}{9}\right)$ **59.** $3(6.2 + 5m)$ **$\frac{40}{7}$d − $\frac{50}{7}$dh**   **60.** $\frac{7}{8}\left(\frac{10}{14}d - 48\right)$

61. $-(8.4 + 300g - 512h)$ **62.** $-(12k + 5m - 62)$

63. $\frac{2}{5}p(15 - 35q + 75w)$ **6p − 14q + 30w**   **64.** $9(4x + 1.2y - 8.1)$ **36x + 10.8y − 72.9**

pages 50–53 **Exercises**

30. **−3 + x**

31. **−6k − 5**

32. **−7x + 2**

33. **−2 + 7x**

34. **−4 + z**

Write an expression for each phrase.

65. $2\frac{1}{4}$ times the quantity $5\frac{1}{2}$ minus k $2\frac{1}{4}\left(5\frac{1}{2} - k\right)$

66. $6\frac{7}{100}$ times the quantity 8 plus $\frac{4}{3}p$ $6\frac{7}{100}\left(8 + \frac{4}{3}p\right)$

67. the product of $\frac{11}{20}$ and the quantity b minus $\frac{13}{30}$ $\frac{11}{20}\left(b - \frac{13}{30}\right)$

68. 17 divided by the quantity z minus 34 $\frac{17}{z - 34}$

69. $4\frac{1}{3}$ times the quantity x minus $\frac{11}{12}$ $4\frac{1}{3}\left(x - \frac{11}{12}\right)$

70. Geometry Write an expression for the perimeter of the figure below. Simplify the expression. **$8x + 38$**

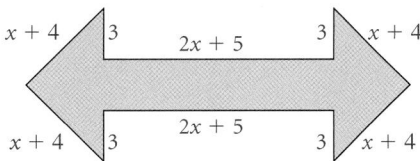

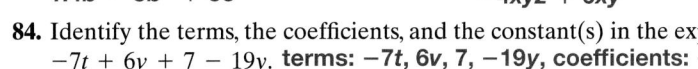

$x + 4$ 3 $2x + 5$ 3 $x + 4$

$x + 4$ 3 $2x + 5$ 3 $x + 4$

Problem Solving Hint

For Exercise 71, test positive and negative values of a and b as well as zero before writing your conclusion.

71. Writing Does $2ab = 2a \cdot 2b$? Explain. **No; $2a \cdot 2b = 4ab$.**

72. Error Analysis A student rewrote $4(3x + 10)$ as $12x + 10$. Explain the student's error. **See margin.**

73. Open-Ended Write a variable expression that you could simplify using the Distributive Property. Then simplify your expression.
Answers may vary. Sample: $2(x + 5) = 2x + 10$

Simplify each expression.

74. $4.78d + 0d$ **$4.78d$**

75. $-21p - 76p^2 - 9 + p$ $-76p^2 - 20p - 9$

76. $3.3t^2 + 8.7t - 9.4t^2 + 5t$

77. $1.5m - 4.2m - 12.5v + 4.2m$

78. $\frac{6}{7}n + n^3 - \left(-\frac{5}{6}n\right)$ **$\frac{71}{42}n + n^3$**

79. $-\frac{16}{15}k + \frac{3}{20}h + \frac{7}{40}k - \frac{107}{120}k + \frac{3}{20}h$

80. $8m^2 - 5mz + 4mz - m^2 + 4$

81. $9 - 4t + 6y - 3t + 10$

82. $1.4b - 3b^2 + 4c - 2b^2 + c$ **$1.4b - 5b^2 + 5c$**

83. $8xyz + 4xy - 12yzx + 2xy$ $-4xyz + 6xy$

76. $-6.1t^2 + 13.7t$

77. $1.5m - 12.5v$

80. $7m^2 - mz + 4$

81. $19 - 7t + 6y$

84. Identify the terms, the coefficients, and the constant(s) in the expression $-7t + 6v + 7 - 19y$. **terms: $-7t$, $6v$, 7, $-19y$, coefficients: -7, 6, -19, constant: 7**

85. Sports A high school basketball court is 84 ft long by 50 ft wide. A college basketball court is 10 ft longer than a high school court but has the same width.

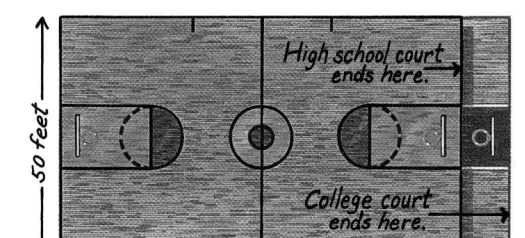

a. Write an expression using parentheses for the area of a college basketball court. **$(84 + 10)50$ ft^2**

b. Simplify your expression. **4700 ft^2**

Real-World Connection

Basketball is one of the ten most popular sports activities in the United States, based on participation.

Teaching Tip

Exercises 74–82 Encourage students to assign a different noun to each variable, such as *mango* for m and *van* for v.

Exercise 83 Remind students that by the Commutative Property of Multiplication, xyz is equivalent to yzx.

72. The student did not mult. the second number in parentheses, 10, by 4 to get the correct answer, $12x + 40$.

Lesson Quiz 1-7

Simplify each expression.

1. 11(299) **3289**

2. 4(x + 8) **4x + 32**

3. −3(2y − 7) **−6y + 21**

4. −(6 + p) **−6 − p**

5. 1.3a + 2b − 4c + 3.1b − 4a
−2.7a + 5.1b − 4c

6. Write an expression for the product of $\frac{4}{7}$ and the quantity b minus $\frac{3}{5}$.
$\frac{4}{7}(b − \frac{3}{5})$

Alternative Assessment

Group students in pairs. Have each student write an expression containing a variable and numbers less than 5 using the distributive property. Have students exchange expressions and model each one using tiles.

86. A student searched the pockets of his jeans before doing laundry and found the following numbers of coins: 4 pennies, 2 nickels, and a quarter; 3 quarters and 6 pennies; 1 dime and 5 nickels. How many of each type of coin does the student have? **10 pennies, 7 nickels, 4 quarters, 1 dime**

🌐 **87. Shopping** Suppose you buy 4 cans of tomatoes at $1.02 each, 3 cans of tuna for $.99 each, and 3 boxes of pasta at $.52 each. Write an expression to model this situation. Then use the Distributive Property to find the total cost.
4(1.02) + 3(0.99) + 3(0.52) = t; $8.61

C Challenge

Simplify each expression.

88. 9(5 + t) − 6(t + 3) **27 + 3t**

89. 4(r + 8) − 5(2r − 1) **−6r + 37**

90. −(m + 3) − 2(m + 3) **−3m − 9**

91. a[2 + b(2 + c)] **2a + 2ab + abc**

92. 7b[8 + 6(b − 1)] **14b + 42b²**

93. −[−5(y + 2z) − 3z] **5y + 13z**

94. Critical Thinking If y = 3x − 10, what is the value of $\frac{y}{3}$? $\frac{3x − 10}{3}$

95a. 2; 2

c. Yes; the two expressions are equal for the values of a, b, and c in parts (a) and (b).

96a. 30; −8

95. a. Evaluate (a + b) ÷ c and a ÷ c + b ÷ c for a = −10, b = 6, and c = −2.
b. Evaluate each expression for a = −9, b = −3, and c = 6. **−2; −2**
c. Reasoning Does it appear that (a + b) ÷ c = a ÷ c + b ÷ c? Explain.

96. a. Evaluate a ÷ (b + c) and a ÷ b + a ÷ c for a = −60, b = 3, and c = −5.
b. Evaluate each expression for a = −24, b = −4, and c = 2. **12, −6**
c. Reasoning Does it appear that a ÷ (b + c) = a ÷ b + a ÷ c? Explain.
No; parts (a) and (b) show the expressions are not equal.

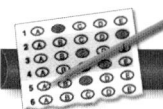

Standardized Test Prep

Multiple Choice

97. Which expression is another form of 14x − 21x? **D**
A. −7x² **B.** 7x²(2 − 3x) **C.** 7x(2x − 3) **D.** −7x

98. Which expression is another form of −6(k − 5)? **G**
F. −6k² − 30k **G.** −6k + 30 **H.** −6k² − 5 **I.** −6k² + 5

Use the table below for Exercises 99–102.

Competitors in the Ultra-Marathon 2000

Category	130-Mile Race		350-Mile Race	
	Number Started	Number Finished	Number Started	Number Finished
Bicycle	51	41	24	16
Foot	43	37	11	9
Ski	9	6	3	3

99. Which category had the most competitors in each race? **A**
A. bicycle **B.** foot **C.** ski **D.** all of them

100. What percent of the competitors on bicycles completed the 350-mile race? **F**
F. 67% **G.** 75% **H.** 80% **I.** 82%

101. What percent of the competitors completed the 130-mile race? **D**
A. 67% **B.** 75% **C.** 80% **D.** 82%

102. Rocky Reifenstuhl won the 130-mile race on his bicycle. He finished in 11 hours and 45 minutes. What was his average speed in miles per hour? **H**
  F. 11.8   **G.** 11.4   **H.** 11.1   **I.** 10.8

103. Simplify $7q + 8pq - 4qp - 9q$. **C**
  A. $-2q + 12pq$ **B.** $16q + 4pq$
  C. $-2q + 4pq$ **D.** $16q + 12pq$

104. A notebook costs \$1.89 at the school store. How much would notebooks for a class of 30 students cost? **I**
  F. \$59.70   **G.** \$59.67   **H.** \$57.30   **I.** \$56.70

Take It to the NET
Online lesson quiz at
www.PHSchool.com
Web Code: aea-0107

Standardized Test Prep

📁 **Resources**
For additional practice with a variety of test item formats:
- Standardized Test Prep, p. 71
- Test-Taking Strategies, p. 66
- Test-Taking Strategies with Transparencies

Exercises 97, 98 Alert students to the fact that nearly all incorrect answer choices involve common mistakes. Students should review their answers and check their work for common mistakes.

Mixed Review

Lessons 1-5, 1-6   **Simplify each expression.**

105. $8(-7) + 4(-3)$ **−68**   **106.** $8 + (-4) \cdot 3$ **−4**   **107.** $(-3)^2 + (-5)$ **4**

108. $(9^2 - 60) \div 3$ **7**   **109.** $\dfrac{-7 + 5}{-7 - 5}$ $\frac{1}{6}$ **110.** $\dfrac{7 - 2}{-12 + 8}$ $-\frac{5}{4}$

111. $\dfrac{1 + (-4)}{21 - 6}$ $-\frac{1}{5}$ **112.** $\dfrac{8 - 5}{16 - 17}$ **−3**   **113.** $-3^4 \div 9 - 4 \cdot 2$ **−17**

Lesson 1-4   **Simplify each expression.**

114. $6.034 + (-8.42)$ **−2.386**   **115.** $9.73 + 2.397$ **12.127**   **116.** $-54.1 + 99.4$ **45.3**

117. $|-28.2| + 17.5$ **45.7**   **118.** $-6.45 + |-9.02|$ **2.57**   **119.** $3.02 + (-2.1)$ **0.92**

120. $-5.7 + (-3.9)$ **−9.6**   **121.** $-12.5 + 4.8$ **−7.7**   **122.** $14.7 + |-8.3|$ **23**

Lesson 1-1   **123. a.** Write an expression for the phrase "4 more than the quotient of m and 3."   **a.** $4 + \frac{m}{3}$
    b. Evaluate your expression for $m = 9, m = 3$, and $m = 12$. **7; 5; 8**

A Point in Time

2000 B.C.   1000   0   1000   2000

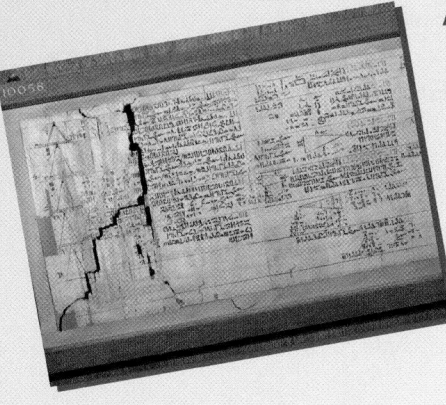

A papyrus scroll discovered in Egypt shows that Egyptians were using symbols for "plus," "minus," "equals," and "unknown quantity" more than 3500 years ago. Named for the scribe who copied it, the Ahmes Papyrus is 18 ft long and 1 ft wide. It is also known as the Rhind Papyrus, after the British Egyptologist who bought the papyrus. It is a practical handbook containing 85 problems that include work with rational numbers. In the Ahmes Papyrus, rational numbers are written as sums of unit fractions. A unit fraction has 1 as its numerator. Here are some examples.

$$\frac{3}{4} = \frac{1}{2} + \frac{1}{4} \qquad \frac{3}{8} = \frac{1}{4} + \frac{1}{8} \qquad \frac{21}{30} = \frac{1}{6} + \frac{1}{5} + \frac{1}{3}$$

Take It to the NET For more information about the Ahmes Papyrus, go to **www.PHSchool.com**.
Web Code: aee-2032

Lesson 1-7 The Distributive Property   **53**

1. Plan

Lesson Preview

 **Check Skills You'll Need**

Adding Real Numbers
Lesson 1-4: Example 2
Exercises 5–24
Extra Practice, p. 702

Multiplying Real Numbers
Lesson 1-6: Example 1
Exercises 1–12
Extra Practice, p. 702

Lesson Resources

📁 **Teaching Resources**
Practice, Reteaching, Enrichment
Checkpoint Quiz 2

Reaching All Students
Practice Workbook 1-8
Spanish Practice Workbook 1-8
Reading and Math Literacy 1C
Spanish Reading & Literacy 1C
Spanish Checkpoint Quiz 2
Basic Algebra Planning Guide 1-8

Presentation Assistant Plus!
Transparencies
• Check Skills You'll Need 1-8
• Additional Examples 1-8
• Student Edition Answers 1-8
• Lesson Quiz 1-8
PH Presentation Pro CD 1-8

PRENTICE HALL ASSESSMENT SYSTEM

Checkpoint Quiz 2
Computer Test Generator CD

Technology
Resource Pro® CD-ROM
Computer Test Generator CD
Prentice Hall Presentation Pro CD

💻 **www.PHSchool.com**
Student Site
• Teacher Web Code: aek-5500
• Reasoning & Puzzles p. 28
• Graphing Calculator,
  Procedure 2
• Self-grading Lesson Quiz
Teacher Center
• Lesson Planner
• Resources

Plus

54

1-8

Properties of Real Numbers

Lesson Preview

What You'll Learn

OBJECTIVE 1 To identify properties

OBJECTIVE 2 To use deductive reasoning

. . . And Why

To use mental math when buying multiple items, as in Example 2

✓ Check Skills You'll Need   (For help, go to Lessons 1-4 and 1-6.)

Simplify each expression.

1. $8 + (9 + 2)$ **19**
2. $3 \cdot (-2 \cdot 5)$ **−30**
3. $7 + 16 + 3$ **26**
4. $-4(7)(-5)$ **140**
5. $-6 + 9 + (-4)$ **−1**
6. $0.25 \cdot 3 \cdot 4$ **3**
7. $3 + x - 2$ **1 + x**
8. $2t - 8 + 3t$ **5t − 8**
9. $-5m + 2m$ **−4m −7m**

New Vocabulary   • deductive reasoning

OBJECTIVE 1

Identifying and Using Properties

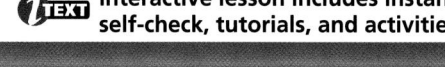 **Interactive lesson includes instant self-check, tutorials, and activities.**

The properties of real numbers allow you to write equivalent expressions and simplify expressions. The summary below reviews properties of real numbers that apply to both addition and multiplication.

🔑 **Key Concepts**

Property	Properties of Real Numbers
For every real number a, b, and c,	
Commutative Property of Addition $a + b = b + a$	**Example** $3 + 7 = 7 + 3$
Commutative Property of Multiplication $a \cdot b = b \cdot a$	**Example** $3 \cdot 7 = 7 \cdot 3$
Associative Property of Addition $(a + b) + c = a + (b + c)$	**Example** $(6 + 4) + 5 = 6 + (4 + 5)$
Associative Property of Multiplication $(a \cdot b) \cdot c = a \cdot (b \cdot c)$	**Example** $(6 \cdot 4) \cdot 5 = 6 \cdot (4 \cdot 5)$
Identity Property of Addition $a + 0 = a$	**Example** $9 + 0 = 9$
Identity Property of Multiplication $a \cdot 1 = a$	**Example** $6 \cdot 1 = 6$
Inverse Property of Addition For every a, there is an additive inverse $-a$ such that $a + (-a) = 0$.	**Example** $5 + (-5) = 0$
Inverse Property of Multiplication For every a ($a \neq 0$), there is a multiplicative inverse $\frac{1}{a}$ such that $a\left(\frac{1}{a}\right) = 1$.	**Example** $5 \cdot \frac{1}{5} = 1$

Ongoing Assessment and Intervention

Before the Lesson Diagnose prerequisite skills using:	**During the Lesson** Monitor progress using:	**After the Lesson** Assess knowledge using:
• Check Skills You'll Need	• Check Understanding • Additional Examples • Standardized Test Prep	• Lesson Quiz • Computer Test Generator CD • Chapter Checkpoint 2 (p. 58)

The following summary reviews some additional properties of real numbers.

 Key Concepts

Property	**Properties of Real Numbers**

For every real number a, b, and c,

Distributive Property	**Examples**
$a(b + c) = ab + ac$	$5(4 + 2) = 5 \cdot 4 + 5 \cdot 2$
$a(b - c) = ab - ac$	$5(4 - 2) = 5 \cdot 4 - 5 \cdot 2$

Multiplication Property of Zero

For every real number n, $n \cdot 0 = 0$. $-35 \cdot 0 = 0$

Multiplication Property of -1

For every real number n, $-1 \cdot n = -n$. $-1 \cdot (-5) = 5$

1 EXAMPLE **Identifying Properties**

Name the property that each equation illustrates. Explain.

a. $9 + 7 = 7 + 9$ — Commutative Property of Addition, because the order of the addends changes

b. $(d \cdot 4) \cdot 3 = d \cdot (4 \cdot 3)$ — Associative Property of Multiplication, because the grouping of the factors changes

c. $t + 0 = t$ — Identity Property of Addition, because the sum of a number and zero is the number

d. $-q = -1q$ — Multiplication Property of -1, because the opposite of a value is the same as -1 times the value

 Check Understanding **1** Name the property that each equation illustrates. Explain. **a–f. See back of book.**
a. $1m = m$ **b.** $(-3 + 4) + 5 = -3 + (4 + 5)$ **c.** $3(8 \cdot 0) = (3 \cdot 8)0$
d. $2 + 0 = 2$ **e.** $np = pn$ **f.** $p + q = q + p$

You can also use the properties to reorganize the order of numbers in sums or products so that you can calculate more easily.

2 EXAMPLE **Real-World Problem Solving**

Shopping Suppose you buy the school supplies shown at the left. Find the total cost of the supplies.

$0.85 + 2.50 + 5.15 = 2.50 + 0.85 + 5.15$ **Commutative Property of Addition**
$= 2.50 + (0.85 + 5.15)$ **Associative Property of Addition**
$= 2.50 + 6$ **Add within parentheses first.**
$= 8.50$ **Simplify.**

The total cost of the supplies is $8.50.

Check Understanding **2** **Shopping** At the supermarket, you buy a package of cheese for $2.50, a loaf of bread for $2.15, a cucumber for $.65, and some tomatoes for $3.50. Find the total cost of the groceries. **$8.80**

Reaching All Students

Below Level Have students write down their own examples for each property of real numbers. Then write the algebraic example beneath each of their own examples.	**Advanced Learners** Have students write complicated expressions, and then have a partner simplify the expression.	**Error Prevention** See note on page 55.

---

2. Teach

Math Background

The Commutative and Associative Properties do not apply to subtraction and multiplication unless these operations are expressed as addition and multiplication by using the inverse properties.

OBJECTIVE
1 **Teaching Notes**

1 EXAMPLE **Error Prevention**

Relate *commute* with changing locations going from home to work. Relate *associate* with associating with different groups of people.

2 EXAMPLE **Teaching Tip**

Have students add the numbers in the order they are written. Then have them find the sum using the Commutative Property. Ask: *Why is it helpful to add 0.85 and 5.15 first?* Their sum is the whole number 6. It is easier to add whole numbers than decimals.

Additional Examples

1 Name the property each equation illustrates.
a. $3 \cdot a = a \cdot 3$
Comm. Prop. of Mult.
b. $p \cdot 0 = 0$ Mult. Prop. of Zero
c. $6 + (-6) = 0$ Inv. Prop. of Add.

2 Suppose you buy a shirt for $14.85, a pair of pants for $21.95, and a pair of shoes for $25.15. Find the total amount you spent. $61.95

OBJECTIVE
2 **Teaching Notes**

Additional Example

3 Simplify $3x - 4(x - 8)$. Justify each step. $-x + 32$

Closure

Have students write their own expressions and simplify them, justifying each step. Instruct them to repeat the process until they have used at least 5 of the properties discussed in this lesson.

55

3. Practice

Assignment Guide

1 Objective

A B Core 1–16, 31–39

2 Objective

A B Core 17–30, 40–46

C Extension 47–52

Standardized Test Prep 53–58

Mixed Review 59–74

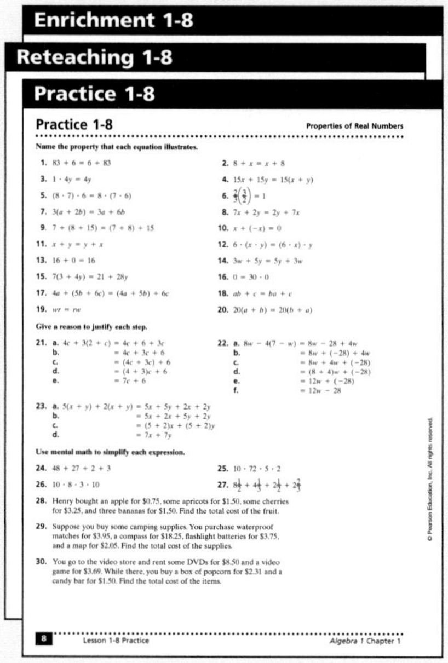
Enrichment 1-8

Reteaching 1-8

Practice 1-8

Practice 1-8 — Properties of Real Numbers

Name the property that each equation illustrates.

1. $83 + 6 = 6 + 83$
2. $8 + x = x + 8$
3. $1 \cdot 4y = 4y$
4. $15x + 15y = 15(x + y)$
5. $(8 \cdot 7) \cdot 6 = 8 \cdot (7 \cdot 6)$
6. $\frac{2}{3}\left(\frac{3}{2}\right) = 1$
7. $3(a + 2b) = 3a + 6b$
8. $7x + 2y = 2y + 7x$
9. $7 + (8 + 15) = (7 + 8) + 15$
10. $x + (-x) = 0$
11. $x + y = y + x$
12. $6 \cdot (x \cdot y) = (6 \cdot x) \cdot y$
13. $16 + 0 = 16$
14. $3w + 5y = 5y + 3w$
15. $7(3 + 4y) = 21 + 28y$
16. $0 = 30 \cdot 0$
17. $4a + (5b + 6c) = (4a + 5b) + 6c$
18. $ab + c = ba + c$
19. $wr = rw$
20. $20(a + b) = 20(b + a)$

Give a reason to justify each step.

21. a. $4c + 3(2 + c) = 4c + 6 + 3c$
 b. $= 4c + 3c + 6$
 c. $= (4c + 3c) + 6$
 d. $= (4 + 3)c + 6$
 e. $= 7c + 6$

22. a. $8w - 4(7 - w) = 8w - 28 + 4w$
 b. $= 8w + (-28) + 4w$
 c. $= 8w + 4w + (-28)$
 d. $= (8 + 4)w + (-28)$
 e. $= 12w + (-28)$
 f. $= 12w - 28$

23. a. $5(x + y) + 2(x + y) = 5x + 5y + 2x + 2y$
 b. $= 5x + 2x + 5y + 2y$
 c. $= (5 + 2)x + (5 + 2)y$
 d. $= 7x + 7y$

Use mental math to simplify each expression.

24. $48 + 27 + 2 + 3$
25. $10 \cdot 72 \cdot 5 \cdot 2$
26. $10 \cdot 8 \cdot 3 \cdot 10$
27. $8\frac{1}{2} + 4\frac{1}{3} + 2\frac{1}{2} + 2\frac{2}{3}$
28. Henry bought an apple for $0.75, some apricots for $1.50, some cherries for $3.25, and three bananas for $1.50. Find the total cost of the fruit.
29. Suppose you buy some camping supplies. You purchase waterproof matches for $3.95, a compass for $18.25, flashlight batteries for $3.75, and a map for $2.05. Find the total cost of the supplies.
30. You go to the video store and rent some DVDs for $8.50 and a video game for $3.69. While there, you buy a box of popcorn for $2.31 and a candy bar for $1.50. Find the total cost of the items.

8 Lesson 1-8 Practice — Algebra 1 Chapter 1

OBJECTIVE 2

Using Deductive Reasoning

Deductive reasoning is the process of reasoning logically from given facts to a conclusion. Using deductive reasoning, you justify each step in simplifying an expression with reasons such as properties, definitions, or rules.

3 EXAMPLE Justifying Steps

Simplify each expression. Justify each step.

a. $-4b + 9 + b$

Step	Reason
$-4b + 9 + b = -4b + 9 + 1b$	Identity Property of Multiplication
$= -4b + 1b + 9$	Commutative Property of Addition
$= (-4 + 1)b + 9$	Distributive Property
$= -3b + 9$	addition

b. $7z - 5(3 + z)$

Step	Reason
$7z - 5(3 + z) = 7z - 15 - 5z$	Distributive Property
$= 7z + (-15) + (-5z)$	definition of subtraction
$= 7z + (-5z) + (-15)$	Commutative Property of Addition
$= [7 + (-5)]z + (-15)$	Distributive Property
$= 2z + (-15)$	addition
$= 2z - 15$	definition of subtraction

Need Help?
To use the Commutative Property of Addition, write subtraction as addition of the opposite.

Check Understanding 3 Simplify each expression. Justify each step. **a–b. See margin.**

a. $5a + 6 + a$ **b.** $2(3t - 1) + 2$

EXERCISES

For more practice, see *Extra Practice*.

Practice and Problem Solving

A Practice by Example

Example 1 (page 55)

Name the property that each equation illustrates. Explain. **1–9. See margin p. 57.**

1. $-\frac{6}{7} + 0 = -\frac{6}{7}$ **2.** $8 + 43 = 43 + 8$ **3.** $1 \cdot \frac{21}{23} = \frac{21}{23}$

4. $(-7 + 4) + 1 = -7 + (4 + 1)$ **5.** $-0.3 + 0.3 = 0$

6. $9(7.3) = 7.3(9)$ **7.** $5(12 - 4) = 5(12) - 5(4)$

8. $8(9 \cdot 11) = (8 \cdot 9) \cdot 11$ **9.** $-0.5 \cdot (-2) = 1$

Example 2 (page 55)

Mental Math **Simplify each expression.**

10. $47 + 39 + 3 + 11$ **100** **11.** $25 \cdot 74 \cdot 2 \cdot 2$ **7400** **12.** $4.75 + 2.95 + 1.25 + 6$ **14.95**

13. $10 \cdot 6 \cdot 7 \cdot 10$ **4200** **14.** $2(5 - 3.5) - 8$ **−5** **15.** $6\frac{1}{2} + 4\frac{1}{3} + 1\frac{1}{2} + \frac{2}{3}$ **13**

16. Shopping You buy 3 grapefruits for $1.50, a pound of apples for $.79, some grapes for $2.50, and some bananas for $1.21. Find the total cost of the fruit. **$6.00**

page 56 Check Understanding

3a. $5a + 6 + a$
$= 5a + a + 6$ Comm. Prop. of Add.
$= (5a + a) + 6$ Assoc. Prop. of Add.
$= (5a + 1a) + 6$ Ident. Prop. of Mult.
$= (5 + 1)a + 6$ Dist. Prop.
$= 6a + 6$ addition

b. $2(3t - 1) + 2$
$= 6t - 2 + 2$ Dist. Prop.
$= 6t + (-2) + 2$ def. of subtr.
$= 6t + [(-2) + 2]$ Assoc. Prop. of Add.
$= 6t + 0$ Inv. Prop. of Add.
$= 6t$ Ident. Prop. of Add.

pages 56–58 Exercises

1. Ident. Prop. of Add.; 0, the identity for addition, is added.
2. Comm. Prop. of Add.; the order of the terms changes.
3. Ident. Prop. of Mult.; 1, the identity for multiplication, is multiplied.
4. Assoc. Prop. of Add.; the grouping of the terms changes.

Example 3
(page 56)

17a. def. of subtr.
  b. Dist. Prop.
  c. addition

Give a reason to justify each step. 18a. Comm. Prop. of Mult.

17. **a.** $3y - 5y = 3y + (-5y)$ _?_
    b. $= [3 + (-5)]y$ _?_
    c. $= -2y$ _?_

18. **a.** $3 \cdot (12 \cdot 10) = 3 \cdot (10 \cdot 12)$ _?_
    b. $= (3 \cdot 10) \cdot 12$ _?_
    c. mult. $= 30 \cdot 12$ _?_
    d. mult. $= 360$ _?_

18b. Assoc. Prop. of Mult.

Simplify each expression. Justify each step. 19–24. See back of book.

19. $25 \cdot 1.7 \cdot 4$
20. $-5(7y)$
21. $8 + 9m + 7$

22. $12x - 3 + 6x$
23. $29c + (-29c)$
24. $43\left(\frac{1}{43}\right) + 1$

B Apply Your Skills

25. $2 + g\left(\frac{1}{g}\right) = 2 + 1$
    Inv. Prop. of Mult.
    $= 3$ add.

26. $36jkm - 36mjk$
    $= 36jkm + (-36)mjk$
    def. of subtr.
    $= 36jkm + (-36)jmk$
    Comm. Prop. of
    Mult.
    $= 36jkm + (-36)jkm$
    Comm. Prop. of
    Mult.
    $= [36 + (-36)]jkm$
    Dist. Prop.
    $= (0)jkm$ Inv. Prop.
    of Add.
    $= 0$
    Mult. Prop. of Zero

Simplify each expression. Justify each step. 27–30. See back of book.

25. $2 + g\left(\frac{1}{g}\right)$
26. $36jkm - 36mjk$
27. $(3^2 - 2^3)(8759)$

28. $(7^6 - 6^5)(8 - 8)$
29. $4 + 6(8 - 3m)$
30. $5\left(w - \frac{1}{5}\right) - w(9)$

31. **Shopping** Suppose you are buying soccer equipment: a pair of cleats for $31.50, a soccer ball for $14.97, and shin guards for $6.50. Use mental math to find the total cost. **$52.97**

Tell whether the expressions in each pair are equivalent.

32. $6m + 1$ and $1 \cdot 6 + m$ **no**
33. $9y$ and $9 + y$ **no**

34. $mp + nq$ and $mq + np$ **no**
35. $-(5 - 9)$ and $9 - 5$ **yes**

36. $8 - 4c$ and $4c - 8$ **no**
37. $3(5 + z)$ and $15 + z$ **no**

38. $6t - 4$ and $2[(2 + 1)t - 2]$ **yes**
39. $vwx \cdot yz$ and $v \cdot w \cdot zxy$ **yes**

Reasoning Explain your answer to each question. 40–43. See back of book.

40. Is subtraction commutative?
41. Is subtraction associative?

42. Is division commutative?
43. Is division associative?

44. Give a reason to justify each step.
    a. $5t + 6 + 3(t + 2) = 5t + 6 + 3t + 6$ _?_ Dist. Prop.
    b. $= 5t + 3t + 6 + 6$ _?_ Comm. Prop. of Add.
    c. $= 5t + 3t + (6 + 6)$ _?_ Assoc. Prop. of Add.
    d. $= 5t + 3t + 12$ _?_ add.
    e. $= (5 + 3)t + 12$ _?_ Dist. Prop.
    f. $= 8t + 12$ _?_ add.

45. By the Comm. Prop.
of Mult.,
$(b + c)a = a(b + c)$.
By the Dist. Prop.,
$a(b + c) = ab + ac$.
By the Comm. Prop.
of Mult.,
$ab + ac = ba + ca$,
so $(b + c)a = ba + ca$.

C Challenge

45. **Reasoning** The Distributive Property states that $a(b + c) = ab + ac$. Use this and the other properties to explain why $(b + c)a = ba + ca$ is also true. **See left.**

46. **Writing** Suppose you make a peanut butter and jelly sandwich. Do you think it tastes the same regardless of whether the jelly is on top or the peanut butter is on top? Relate your answer to one of the properties of real numbers.
                                                     See back of book.

Critical Thinking The *closure properties* for a set of numbers assure that the sum and product of two numbers in a given set of numbers are also in the set of numbers. Determine whether each set of numbers is closed for addition, for multiplication, or for both. If not, give a counterexample.

47. rational numbers **both**
48. integers **both**
49. whole numbers **both**

50. negative numbers
not mult.; $(-2)(-3) = 6$
51. odd numbers
not add.; $1 + 3 = 4$
52. even numbers
both

5. Inv. Prop. of Add.; a number and its inverse are added.

6. Comm. Prop. of Mult.; the order of the factors changes.

7. Dist. Prop.; a number outside parentheses is distributed to the two terms inside the parentheses.

8. Assoc. Prop. of Mult.; the grouping of the factors changes.

9. Inv. Prop. of Mult.; a number and its mult. inverse are multiplied.

4. Assess

Name the property that each equation illustrates.

1. $1m = m$ Iden. Prop. of Mult.

2. $(-3 + 4) + 5 = -3 + (4 + 5)$
   Assoc. Prop. of Add.

3. $-14 \cdot 0 = 0$
   Mult. Prop. of Zero

4. Give a reason to justify each step.
   a. $3x - 2(x + 5)$
       $= 3x - 2x - 10$
   Distributive Property
   b. $= 3x + (-2x) + (-10)$
   Definition of Subtraction
   c. $= [3 + (-2)]x + (-10)$
   Distributive Property
   d. $= 1x + (-10)$
   Addition
   e. $= 1x - 10$
   Definition of Subtraction
   f. $= x - 10$
   Identity Property of Multiplication

Alternative Assessment

Have students write descriptions of each property in their own words, and provide an example of each.

✓ Chapter Checkpoint 2

To check understanding of Lessons 1-5 to 1-8:

Checkpoint Quiz 2 (p. 58)

📁 **Teaching Resources**

Checkpoint Quiz 2 (also in Prentice Hall Assessment System)

Reaching All Students

Reading and Math Literacy 1C

Spanish versions available

---

page 58   Checkpoint Quiz 2

10a. $9t + 3(t + 4)$
$= 9t + 3t + 12$
   Dist. Prop.
$= (9t + 3t) + 12$
   Assoc. Prop. of Add.
$= (9 + 3)t + 12$
   Dist. Prop.
$= 12t + 12$ add.

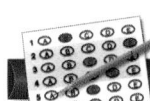

Standardized Test Prep

Multiple Choice

53. Simplify $-4 + 17 - 29 + 4 + 29 - 3$. **A**
  A. 14   B. 20   C. 22   D. 72

54. Which of the following has the same result as dividing a number by $\frac{5}{2}$ and then multiplying by $\frac{1}{2}$? **I**
  F. multiplying by 2   G. dividing by 2
  H. multiplying by 5   I. dividing by 5

55. In the formula $A = \pi r^2$, if the value of r is doubled, then what is the value of A multiplied by? **D**
  A. $\frac{1}{4}$ B. $\frac{1}{2}$ C. 2   D. 4

56. The variable a is an integer. Which of the following could NOT equal a^3? **G**
  F. -27 G. -16 H. 8   I. 64

57. What is the total cost if you buy 3 goldfish for $1.90 each, 3 angelfish for $6.10 each, and 12 neon tetras for $1.53 each? **B**
  A. $39.36   B. $42.36   C. $60.36   D. $66.36

58. Simplify $-2h - (5 - 3h)$. **F**
  F. $h - 5$ G. $-5h - 5$ H. h I. $-4h$

 Take It to the NET
Online lesson quiz at
www.PHSchool.com
Web Code: aea-0108

Mixed Review

Lesson 1-7   **Simplify each expression.**

59. $5(1.2 + k)$ **6 + 5k**   **60.** $\frac{1}{3}\left(33 - b\right)$ **11 − $\frac{1}{3}$b**   **61.** $-2.5(4p + 14)$
                                                                                                                −10p − 35
62. $4(7 - n)$ **63.** $-(-7.4m + 0.05)$ **64.** $(3v - 5.2)(-6)$
     28 − 4n   **7.4m − 0.05**   **−18v + 31.2**

Lesson 1-6   **Write an expression for each phrase.**

65. 7 + [m + (−17)]   **65.** 7 plus the sum of m and -17 **66.** 8 minus the quantity 9 minus t
66. 8 − (9 − t)   **67.** one half of the quotient of b and 4   **68.** one third of the sum of x and 5.1
                          $\frac{1}{2}\left(\frac{b}{4}\right)$ $\frac{1}{3}(x + 5.1)$

Lesson 1-4   **Simplify.**

69. $12 + (-5)$ **7**   **70.** $9.2 + (-27.5)$ **−18.3**   **71.** $\frac{5}{8} + \left(-\frac{7}{8}\right)$ **−$\frac{1}{4}$**

72. $-4\frac{6}{10} + 3\frac{2}{5}$ **−1$\frac{1}{5}$**   **73.** $-11 + (-124)$ **−135**   **74.** $|-2.4| + |6.8|$ **9.2**

✓ Checkpoint Quiz 2   Lessons 1-5 through 1-8

TEXT Instant self-check quiz online and on CD-ROM

5. −12 − 9w

Simplify each expression.

1. $7 + 4t + 6 + t$ **13 + 5t**   **2.** $(5 \cdot 16) \cdot 2$ **160**   **3.** $(5 + 16)2$ **42**

4. $(-4)^3 + (-3)(-5)$ **−49**   **5.** $-3(4 + w) - 6w$ **6.** $-(-5 - 4m)$ **5 + 4m**

7. $|43.7 + (-45.2)|$ **8.** $9 \div (-3) - 4 \div (-8)$ **9.** $3x + 6y - 8x - y$
     1.5   **−2.5**   **−5x + 5y**

10. a. Simplify the expression $9t + 3(t + 4)$. Justify each step. **See margin.**
    b. Evaluate the expression for $t = -3$. **−24**

58   Chapter 1   Tools of Algebra

Graphing Data on the Coordinate Plane

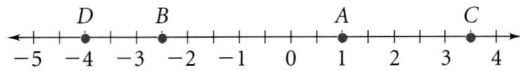
North Carolina Objectives   3.03   Create linear models for sets of data to solve problems.

Lesson Preview

What You'll Learn

 OBJECTIVE 1
To graph points on the coordinate plane

 OBJECTIVE 2
To analyze data using scatter plots

. . . And Why

To analyze car age and price data, as in Example 5

✔ Check Skills You'll Need

(For help, go to Lesson 1-3.)

Graph each number on a number line. 1–4. See back of book.

1. 6   **2.** −5   **3.** 2.7   **4.** 0

Write the coordinate of each point on the number line below.

```
        D     B              A         C
  ◄─┼──┼──┼──┼──┼──┼──┼──┼──┼──┼──┼──┼──┼──┼──►
    −5  −4  −3  −2  −1   0   1   2   3   4
```

5. A 1   **6.** B −2.5   **7.** C 3.5   **8.** D −4

New Vocabulary

- coordinate plane   • x-axis   • y-axis   • origin
- quadrants   • ordered pair   • coordinates
- x-coordinate   • y-coordinate   • scatter plot
- positive correlation   • negative correlation
- no correlation   • trend line

---

1. Plan

Lesson Preview

✔ **Check Skills You'll Need**

Exploring Real Numbers
Lesson 1-3: Examples 4, 5
Exercises 24–41
Extra Practice, p. 702

Lesson Resources

📁 **Teaching Resources**
Practice, Reteaching, Enrichment

👥 **Reaching All Students**
Practice Workbook 1-9
Spanish Practice Workbook 1-9
Basic Algebra Planning Guide 1-9

🕐 **Presentation Assistant Plus!**
Transparencies
- Check Skills You'll Need 1-9
- Additional Examples 1-9
- Student Edition Answers 1-9
- Lesson Quiz 1-9
PH Presentation Pro CD 1-9

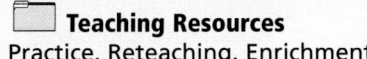
PRENTICE HALL
ASSESSMENT SYSTEM

Computer Test Generator CD

💰 **Technology**
Resource Pro® CD-ROM
Computer Test Generator CD
Prentice Hall Presentation Pro CD

💻 **www.PHSchool.com**
Student Site
- Teacher Web Code: aek-5500
- Reasoning & Puzzles pp. 61, 62
- Graphing Calculator, Procedure 20
- Self-grading Lesson Quiz
Teacher Center
- Lesson Planner
- Resources

Plus

OBJECTIVE

1 Graphing Points on the Coordinate Plane

Real-World 🌐 Connection

To find a street on a map, you look in a region between grid lines. To locate a point on a coordinate plane, you look at the intersection of grid lines.

 iTEXT Interactive lesson includes instant self-check, tutorials, and activities.

Two number lines that intersect at right angles form a **coordinate plane.** The horizontal axis is the **x-axis** and the vertical axis is the **y-axis.** The axes intersect at the **origin** and divide the coordinate plane into four sections called **quadrants.**

```
                    B    ↑ y-axis
            (−2, 4) •
        Quadrant II │  Quadrant I
    ◄───────────────┼───────────────►  x-axis
              origin │
        Quadrant III │  Quadrant IV
                     ↓
```

An **ordered pair** of numbers identifies the location of a point. These numbers are the **coordinates** of the point on the graph. Point B has coordinates (−2, 4).

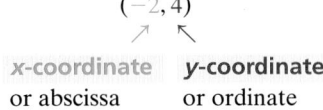
$$(-2, 4)$$
x-coordinate   y-coordinate
or abscissa   or ordinate

The x-coordinate tells you how far to move right (positive) or left (negative) from the origin. The y-coordinate tells you how far to move up (positive) or down (negative) from the origin.

⏱ Ongoing Assessment and Intervention

Before the Lesson	During the Lesson	After the Lesson
Diagnose prerequisite skills using:	**Monitor progress using:**	**Assess knowledge using:**
• Check Skills You'll Need	• Check Understanding	• Lesson Quiz
	• Additional Examples	• Computer Test Generator CD
	• Standardized Test Prep	

Math Background

In the conventional coordinate plane, a background grid is formed of rectangles—usually squares. However, it is possible to form a coordinate system with axes that are not perpendicular; the background grid is then formed of parallelograms.

OBJECTIVE
1 Teaching Notes

1 EXAMPLE Teaching Tip

Show students a road map. Direct their attention to the edges of the map. Explain how the numbers and letters form a grid. Give students different coordinates and have them find places that fit the description of each coordinate.

2 EXAMPLE Visual Learners

Some students may graph $(3, -4)$ as $(-4, 3)$. Help students make these visual relationships: An *x* is similar to a cross, so the *x*-coordinate represents movement that goes across to the left or to the right; A *y* has a tail that goes up and down, so a *y*-coordinate represents movement that goes up or down.

3 EXAMPLE Tactile Learners

Use masking tape to make a coordinate grid on the floor. Give each student a different coordinate. Have students start at the origin and move along the grid lines to find each given coordinate. Then have students say which quadrants they are standing in. Point out that the points on the axes are not in any quadrant. Ask: *If you are standing on a fence separating two yards, which yard are you in?* **neither yard**

---

1 EXAMPLE Identifying Coordinates

Name the coordinates of point *Z* in the graph.

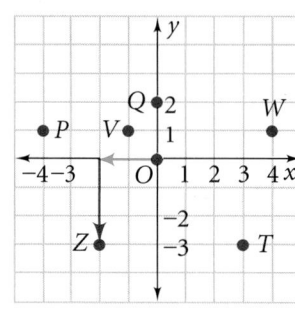

Move 2 units to the left of the origin. Then move 3 units down.

● The coordinates of *Z* are $(-2, -3)$.

✓ **Check Understanding** ① Name the coordinates of each point in the graph above.

a. *T* **(3, −3)**   b. *V* **(−1, 1)**   c. *W* **(4, 1)**   d. *Q* **(0, 2)**

2 EXAMPLE Graphing Points

Graph the point $A(3, -4)$ on the coordinate plane.

2. a–d.

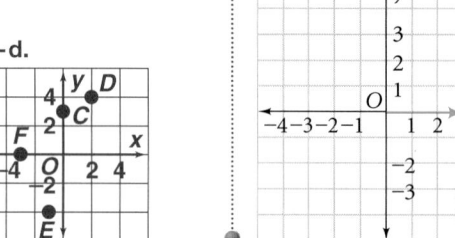

Move 3 units to the right of the origin. Then move 4 units down.

✓ **Check Understanding** ② Graph the points on the same coordinate plane.   **a–d. See left.**

a. $C(0, 3)$ b. $D(2, 4)$ c. $E(-1, -4)$ d. $F(-3, 0)$

You can determine which quadrant a point is in by graphing the point or by considering the signs of the *x*- and *y*-coordinates. A point that is on an axis is not considered to be in a quadrant.

3 EXAMPLE Identifying Quadrants

In which quadrant or on which axis would you find each point?

a. $(-1, 5)$ b. $(0, 3)$

Since the *x*-coordinate is negative   Since the *x*-coordinate is 0,
and the *y*-coordinate is positive,   the point is on the *y*-axis.
the point is in Quadrant II.

✓ **Check Understanding** ③ In which quadrant or on which axis would you find each point?

a. $(-2, 0)$ *x*-axis   b. $(4, -1)$ **IV**   c. $(-3, -5)$ **III**   d. $(2.7, 3.6)$ **I**

👥 Reaching All Students

Below Level Ask students what type of correlation is shown in Example 4. Then ask what it would mean about television and test scores if the plot showed a different type of correlation.	**Advanced Learners** Challenge students to give examples of data that could be plotted on a scatter plot in quadrants other than Quadrant I.	**English Learners** See note on page 66. **Visual Learners** See note on page 60.

A **scatter plot** is a graph that relates two groups of data. To make a scatter plot, plot the two groups of data as ordered pairs. Most scatter plots are in the first quadrant of a coordinate plane, because the data are usually positive numbers.

4 EXAMPLE Making a Scatter Plot

Data Collection The table at the left shows data students collected on their test scores and the number of hours they watched television the previous day. Make a scatter plot of the data.

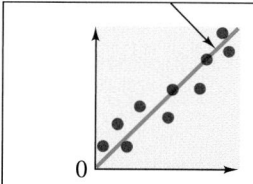
Television and Tests

Hours Watched	Test Score	Hours Watched	Test Score
0	92	2	80
0	100	2.5	65
0.5	89	2.5	70
1	82	3	68
1	90	3.5	60
1	95	4	65
1.5	85	4.5	55
2	70	5	60

For 2 hours of television watched and a test score of 80, plot (2, 80).

The highest score is 100. So a reasonable scale on the vertical axis is 0 to 100 with every 20 points labeled.

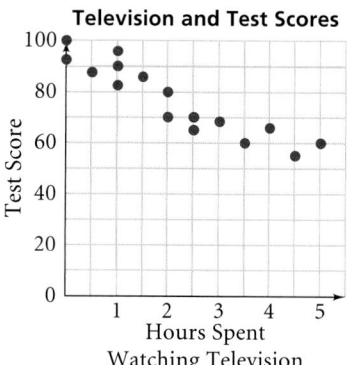
Television and Test Scores

✔ **Check Understanding** **4** Use the data in the table at the right. Make a scatter plot of the data. See margin.

Media in the United States

Year	Daily Newspaper Circulation (millions)	Number of Households With Television (millions)
1950	54	4
1960	59	46
1970	62	59
1980	62	76
1990	62	92
2000*	55	101

*estimated

You can use scatter plots to look for trends in data. The three scatter plots below show the types of relationships two sets of data may have.

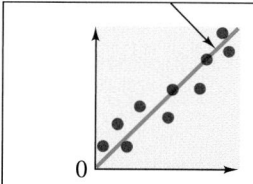
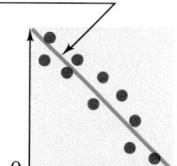
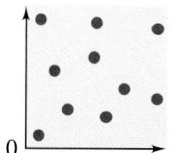

Positive correlation
In general, both sets of data increase together.

Negative correlation
In general, one set of data decreases as the other set increases.

No correlation
Sometimes data sets are not related.

→ A **trend line** on a scatter plot shows a correlation more clearly.

Lesson 1-9 · Graphing Data on the Coordinate Plane **61**

Additional Examples

1 Name the coordinates of point A in the graph. (−2, 3)

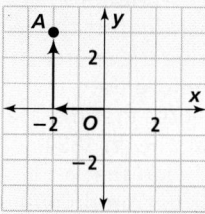

2 Graph the point B(−4, −2) on the coordinate plane.

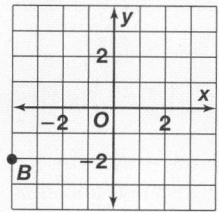

3 In which quadrant or on which axis would you find each point?
a. (2, −5) IV   **b.** (6, 0) x-axis

OBJECTIVE
2 **Teaching Notes**

4 EXAMPLE Technology Tip

Allow students to use graphing calculators to make the scatter plot.

page 61   Check Understanding

4.
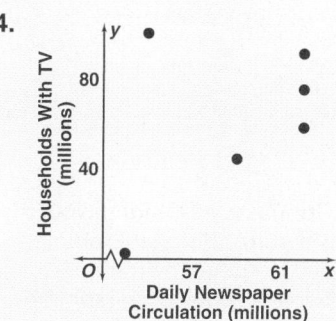

Even though correlations do not necessarily show cause, they can be useful. Using correlations, public health investigators can sometimes describe the source of a disease years before the organism that causes that disease is found. For example, in 1854, John Snow concluded that a cholera epidemic in London was originating in the water from one well. It was years later that the organism causing the cholera was identified.

📖 Additional Examples

④ The table below shows the number of hours worked and the amount of money each person earned. Make a scatter plot of the data.

Name	Hours worked	Amount earned
Janel	6	$25.50
Roscoe	12	$51.00
Victoria	11	$46.75
Alex	9	$38.25
Jordan	15	$63.75
Jennifer	10	$42.50

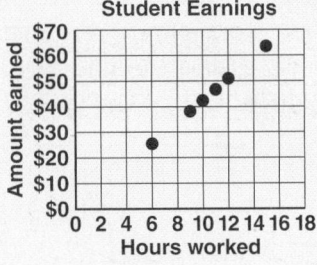

Student Earnings

⑤ Use the scatter plot in your answer for Additional Example 4 to answer the following question: Is there a *positive correlation, a negative correlation,* or *no correlation* between the number of hours worked and the amount earned? Explain. **Positive correlation; both sets of data increase.**

Closure

Ask: *How would you explain the process for graphing a point on a coordinate plane to a student who was absent today?*
Sample: A point is named by two

62

---

⑤ **EXAMPLE** Real-World 🌐 Problem Solving

Cars Use the scatter plot below. Is there a *positive correlation*, a *negative correlation*, or *no correlation* between the age of a used car and the asking price of the car?

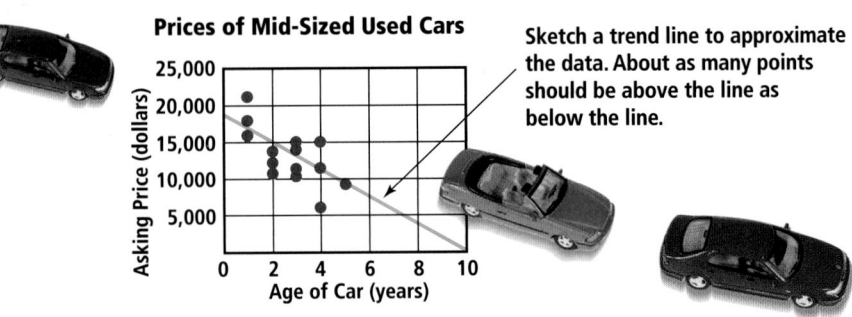

Sketch a trend line to approximate the data. About as many points should be above the line as below the line.

As the age of a car increases, the asking price generally decreases. There is a negative correlation between the age and asking price of a car.

✓ **Check Understanding** ⑤ a. **Critical Thinking** In the graph above, what does the data point at (4, 14,900) represent? **4-year-old car with an asking price of $14,900**
b. Use the graph to predict the asking price of a 7-year-old car. **$5000**

EXERCISES

For more practice, see *Extra Practice*.

Practice and Problem Solving

Ⓐ **Practice by Example**

Example 1
(page 60)

Name the coordinates of each point on the graph at the right.

1. A **(4, 5)**   **2.** F **(2, −2)**

3. D **(−5, 0)**   **4.** I **(5, 4)**

Example 2
(page 60)

Graph the points on the same coordinate plane. **5–8. See margin p. 63.**

5. (3, 0)   **6.** (−1, 8)

7. (−2, −3)   **8.** (7, −7)

Example 3
(page 60)

In which quadrant or on which axis would you find each point?

9. (−10, 6) **II**   **10.** (−12, 0) **x-axis**   **11.** (8, −18) **IV**   **12.** (0, 30) **y-axis**

Complete each statement.

13. If the x-coordinate and the y-coordinate of an ordered pair are positive, the ordered pair is in Quadrant _?_. **I**

14. If the x-coordinate of an ordered pair is negative, and the y-coordinate is positive, the ordered pair is in Quadrant _?_. **II**

15. The x-coordinate is 0 and the y-coordinate is negative. Is the point in Quadrant III? Explain. **No; the point is on the y-axis, not in Quadrant III.**

numbers, the x-coordinate and the y-coordinate. To graph the point, you start at the origin where the x-axis and y-axis meet. First, you move along the x-axis the number of units of the x-coordinate. If the x-coordinate

is positive, you move to the right. If the x-coordinate is negative, you move to the left. From that position, you move the number of units of the y-coordinate. If the y-coordinate is positive, you move up. If it is negative, you

move down. Now, you can mark the point on the graph.

Example 4
(page 61)

16. Make a scatter plot of the data below. **See back of book.**

Gasoline Purchases

Dollars Spent	10	11	9	10	13	5	8	4
Gallons Bought	6.3	6.1	5.6	5.5	8.3	2.9	5.2	2.7

Example 5
(page 62)

Describe the trend in each scatter plot below.

17.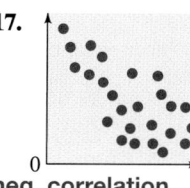
neg. correlation

18.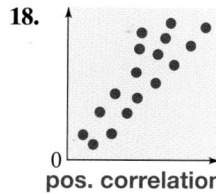
pos. correlation

19.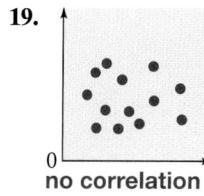
no correlation

B **Apply Your Skills**

Mental Math **Write the coordinates of each point.**

20. the point 3 units to the left of the y-axis and 4 units above the x-axis $(-3, 4)$

21. the point 5 units to the right of the y-axis and on the x-axis $(5, 0)$

22. the point 6 units to the right of the y-axis and 6 units below the x-axis $(6, -6)$

23. What are the coordinates of the points on the calculator screen at the right? Assume tick marks on the axis are separated by one unit.
$(-3, -2), (1, 3), (2, -4)$

24a. Answers may vary. Sample: $(-1, 1)$, $(-2, 2)$, $(10, -10)$

24. Open-Ended Write the coordinates of three points that satisfy each condition. **24a. See left.**
 a. The x-coordinate is the opposite of the y-coordinate.
 b. The x-coordinate and the y-coordinate have the same absolute value.
Answers may vary. Sample: $(1, 1), (-2, 2), (-10, -10)$

Geometry **Graph and connect the points in the order given. Connect the last point to the first. Describe the figure.** **25–28. See back of book.**

25. $(4, 4), (-1, 1), (2, -4), (7, -1)$ **26.** $(-3, 0), (0, 5), (3, 0), (0, -5)$

27. $(-2, 1), (2, 4), (5, 0)$ **28.** $(5, -3), (2, -7), (-6, -1), (-3, 3)$

Critical Thinking **Would you expect a *positive correlation*, a *negative correlation*, or *no correlation* between the two data sets? Explain why.**
29–32. See back of book.

29. the amount of free time you have and the number of classes you take

30. the air pollution levels for a city and the number of cars registered in that city

31. length of a baby at birth and the month in which the baby was born

32. the number of calories burned and the time spent exercising

33. Open-Ended Describe three situations: one that shows a positive correlation, one that shows a negative correlation, and one that shows no correlation. **See back of book.**

34. a. Think about the weather and its effect on voters. What correlation would you expect between the amount of precipitation and voter turnout? Explain. **See margin.**
 b. Reasoning Should candidates in an election be concerned about the weather forecast? Explain. **See margin.**

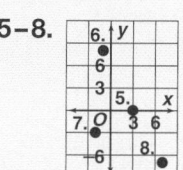

RAIN, HEAVY AT TIMES
CHANCE OF SNOW
HIGH: 38 LOW: 30
FULL REPORT ON PAGE 20

63

Assignment Guide

1 Objective
 Ⓐ Ⓑ Core 1–15, 20–28
 Ⓒ Extension 37–38

2 Objective
 Ⓐ Ⓑ Core 16–19, 29–36
 Ⓒ Extension 39–40

Standardized Test Prep 41–46

Mixed Review 47–57

Error Prevention

Exercises 1–8 Some students may confuse the order of the coordinates. Stress that alphabetically, x comes before y. Accordingly, in an ordered pair, the x-coordinate also comes before the y-coordinate.

Exercise 36b Point out that a correlation between two sets of data does not necessarily mean that there is a causal relationship between the two sets of data.

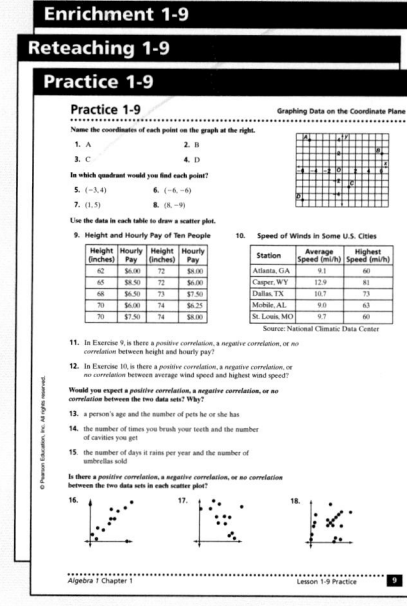

pages 62–65 Exercises

5–8.

34a. Neg. correlation; rain or snow makes travel more difficult or inconvenient, so voters would be less likely to go to the polls.

b. Answers may vary. Sample: In general, the weather has the same effect on both sides, but candidates usually want as many votes as possible, so they should be concerned.

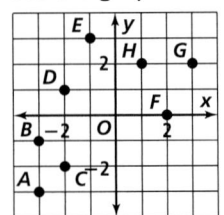

4. Assess

Lesson Quiz 1-9

Use the graph for 1–6.

Name the coordinates of each point.

1. A (−3, −3) **2.** D (−2, 1)

3. F (2, 0) **4.** G (3, 2)

5. In which quadrant is point E? **II**

6. Describe the trend.
positive correlation

Alternative Assessment

Have each student draw a coordinate plane and label the quadrants. Then have students write the signs of the coordinates in each quadrant. For example, (−, +) should be written in Quadrant II. Instruct students to randomly place ten points on their planes and then describe the trend, if any.

pages 62–65   Exercises

35b. Answers may vary. Sample: No; it is generally not reasonable to conclude that correlation between two trends implies cause.

36a, b.

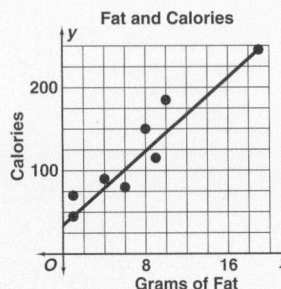

Fat and Calories

35. During one month at a local deli, the number of pounds of ham sold decreased as the number of pounds of turkey sold increased.
  a. Is this an example of a *positive correlation*, *negative correlation*, or *no correlation*? **neg. correlation**
  b. Reasoning Is it reasonable to conclude that fewer pounds of ham were sold because the deli sold more pounds of turkey? Explain. **See margin.**

Real-World Connection

Careers Nutritionists help people plan their diet and exercise.

36. a. Nutrition Draw a scatter plot of the data below. Graph the grams of fat on the *x*-axis and the number of calories on the *y*-axis. **See margin.**

Calories Per Serving of Some Common Foods

Food	Grams of Fat	Number of Calories	Food	Grams of Fat	Number of Calories
Whole Milk	8	150	Eggs	6	80
Chicken	4	90	Ham	19	245
Corn	1	70	Broccoli	1	45
Ground Beef	10	185	Cheese	9	115

  b. Draw a trend line on the scatter plot. Describe the correlation, if any, between calories and grams of fat. **pos. correlation**

  c. Writing Write a statement describing the relationship between calories and grams of fat. **See margin.**
  d. A serving of ice cream has 14 grams of fat. Predict the number of calories a serving of ice cream has. **Answers may vary. Sample: about 200 cal**

C Challenge **37.** Geometry Find the perimeter and area of a rectangle whose vertices have coordinates (4, 1), (−3, 1), (−3, −2), and (4, −2). **20 units; 21 square units**

38. Geometry Find the area of a triangle whose vertices have coordinates (−1, 2), (−1, −1), and (−6, 2). **7.5 square units**

39. Points with the coordinates (0, 3), (2, 5), (4, 3), and (2, 1) lie on a circle with center (2, 3). Find another circle with center (2, 3), such that there are at least eight points on the circle with integers for the *x*- and *y*- coordinates. What are the coordinates of the eight points? **See margin.**

40a. the distance a car traveled on the Indiana toll road and the toll charged
 b. The points have the same *x*-coordinate, that is, they lie on the same vertical line.
 c. The points have the same *y*-coordinate, that is, they lie on the same horizontal line.
 d. Pos. correlation; in general, as distance increases, the toll increases.

40. a. Transportation In the scatter plot below, what does a point on the scatter plot represent? **a–d. See left.**

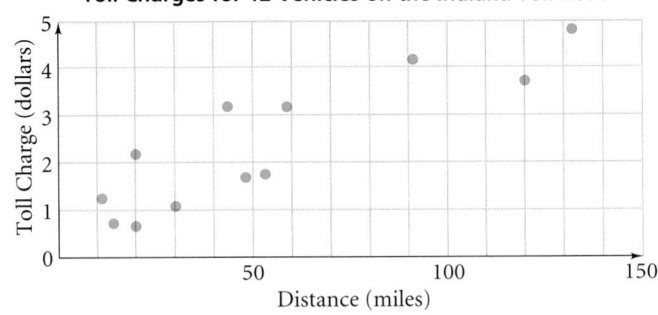

Toll Charges for 12 Vehicles on the Indiana Toll Road

SOURCE: Indiana Department of Highways

  b. How can you tell if some vehicles traveled the same distance?
  c. How can you tell which vehicles paid the same toll charge?
  d. Is there a correlation between distance traveled and toll charges? Explain.

64   Chapter 1 Tools of Algebra

c. In general, it appears that the greater the number of grams of fat in a serving of food, the greater the number of calories.

39. Answers may vary. Sample: There is a circle with radius 5 and center (2, 3) that contains the points (−1, −1), (−2, 0), (−2, 6), (−1, 7), (5, 7),

(6, 6), (6, 0), and (5, −1). (It also contains the points (−3, 3), (2, 8), (7, 3), and (2, −2).)

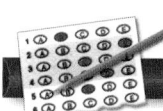

Multiple Choice

41. In which quadrant on the coordinate plane is $(-3, -1)$? **C**
   A. I   **B.** II   **C.** III   **D.** IV

42. What are the coordinates of the point that is on the y-axis 6 units above the x-axis? **G**
   F. $(0, -6)$ **G.** $(0, 6)$ **H.** $(6, 0)$ **I.** $(-6, 0)$

43. The point (q, r) is in Quadrant II. The value of q must be __?__. The value of r must be __?__. **D**
   A. positive, negative   **B.** negative, negative
   C. positive, positive   **D.** negative, positive

44. The coordinates of three vertices of a rectangle are $(-2, -1)$, $(2, -5)$, and $(9, 2)$. What are the coordinates of the fourth vertex? **G**
   F. $(4, 3)$ **G.** $(5, 6)$ **H.** $(5, 5)$ **I.** $(6, 6)$

45. Suppose you take a survey of all the schools in your state. What would you expect the relationship between the number of students and the number of teachers in each school to be? **A**
   A. positive correlation   **B.** negative correlation
   C. no correlation   **D.** none of the above

46. Which sets of data would most likely have a negative correlation? **H**
   F. the population of Detroit over a 10-year period and the population of Kansas over the same 10-year period
   G. the height of a person and that person's shoe size
   H. the number of times a car stops to fill its gas tank and the amount of gas the tank can hold
   I. the size of an animal and the amount of food it needs each day

Take It to the NET
Online lesson quiz at
www.PHSchool.com
Web Code: aea-0109

Mixed Review

Lesson 1-8

Simplify each expression. Justify each step. 47–50. See margin.

47. $x - 4(2x + 1) - 3$

48. $5(8t) + 4(9 - t) - 37$

49. $8b + 7a - 4b - 9a$

50. $3m^2 - (10m + 3m^2)$

Lessons 1-4, 1-5

Find each sum or difference.

51. $\begin{bmatrix} 9 & -13 \\ 19 & -1 \end{bmatrix}$

51. $\begin{bmatrix} 3 & -5 \\ 4 & -1 \end{bmatrix} + \begin{bmatrix} 6 & -8 \\ 15 & 0 \end{bmatrix}$

52. $[12 \quad -27 \quad 0 \quad -3] - [-4.5 \quad 2 \quad -1 \quad 6.5]$

$[16.5 \quad -29 \quad 1 \quad -9.5]$

53. $\begin{bmatrix} -2.9 & 5 & 17 \\ 0 & -4.7 & 3.9 \\ 1 & -8 & 15 \end{bmatrix} - \begin{bmatrix} -6 & 5.7 & -4 \\ 4.9 & 0 & 6 \\ 2 & -1 & 7 \end{bmatrix}$

See margin.

54. $\begin{bmatrix} \frac{1}{2} & -\frac{3}{5} \\ 6 & -9 \\ 4 & 16 \end{bmatrix} + \begin{bmatrix} -12 & \frac{1}{10} \\ \frac{9}{2} & -8 \\ 1 & 14 \end{bmatrix}$

See margin.

Lesson 1-3

Decide whether each statement is *true* or *false*. If the statement is false, give a counterexample.

55. All positive integers are natural numbers. **true**

56. A number cannot have a value equal to its square. **false;** $1 = 1^2$

57. All integers are rational numbers. **true**

Lesson 1-9 Graphing Data on the Coordinate Plane   **65**

47. $x - 4(2x + 1) - 3$
$= x - 8x - 4 - 3$
   Dist. Prop.
$= 1x - 8x - 4 - 3$
   Ident. Prop. of Mult.
$= 1x + (-8x) + (-4) + (-3)$
   def. of subtr.
$= [1x + (-8x)] + [(-4) + (-3)]$
   Assoc. Prop. of Add.
$= [1 + (-8)]x + (-4) + (-3)$
   Dist. Prop.
$= -7x + (-4) + (-3)$ **add.**
$= -7x + (-7)$ **add.**
$= -7x - 7$ **def. of subtr.**

48. $5(8t) + 4(9 - t) - 37$
$= 40t + 36 - 4t - 37$
   Dist. Prop.
$= 40t + 36 + (-4t) + (-37)$
   def. of subtr.
$= 40t + (-4t) + 36 + (-37)$
   Comm. Prop. of Add.

Standardized Test Prep

📁 **Resources**
For additional practice with a variety of test item formats:
- Standardized Test Prep, p. 71
- Test-Taking Strategies, p. 66
- Test-Taking Strategies with Transparencies

Exercises 41–44 Tell students it is always helpful to draw a coordinate plane when answering questions about graphing. Suggest that each student draw a coordinate plane in ink and use a pencil or erasable pen to write in the information from each exercise.

$= [40t + (-4t)] + [36 + (-37)]$
   Assoc. Prop. of Add.
$= [40 + (-4)]t + [36 + (-37)]$
   Dist. Prop.
$= 36t + (-1)$ **add.**
$= 36t - 1$ **def. of subtr.**

49. $8b + 7a - 4b - 9a$
$= 8b + 7a + (-4b) + (-9a)$
   def. of subtr.
$= 8b + (-4b) + 7a + (-9a)$
   Comm. Prop. of Add.
$= [8b + (-4b)] + [7a + (-9a)]$
   Assoc. Prop. of Add.
$= [8 + (-4)]b + [7 + (-9)]a$
   Dist. Prop.
$= 4b + (-2)a$ **add.**
$= 4b - 2a$ **def. of subtr.**

50. $3m^2 - (10m + 3m^2)$
$= 3m^2 - 1(10m + 3m^2)$
   Mult. Prop. of -1
$= 3m^2 - 10m - 3m^2$
   Dist. Prop.
$= 3m^2 + (-10m) + (-3m^2)$
   def. of subtr.
$= 3m^2 + (-3m^2) + (-10m)$
   Comm. Prop. of Add.
$= [3 + (-3)]m^2 + (-10m)$
   Dist. Prop.
$= 0m^2 + (-10m)$
   Inv. Prop. of Add.
$= 0 + (-10m)$
   Mult. Prop. of Zero
$= -10m$
   Ident. Prop. of Add.

53. $\begin{bmatrix} 3.1 & -0.7 & 21 \\ -4.9 & -4.7 & -2.1 \\ -1 & -7 & 8 \end{bmatrix}$

54. $\begin{bmatrix} -11\frac{1}{2} & -\frac{1}{2} \\ 10\frac{1}{2} & -17 \\ 5 & 30 \end{bmatrix}$

Writing Gridded Responses

Writing Gridded Responses

Some assessment tests now require students to grid in numbers for the answers.

Resources

PRENTICE HALL
ASSESSMENT SYSTEM

Test-Taking Strategies with Transparencies
• Transparency 1
• Practice sheet p. 1
• Blank Sheet of Grids p. vi

Teaching Notes

Use the transparency for more instruction on answering gridded-response questions.

Assign the worksheet to give student more practice answering gridded-response questions.

English Learners

Always write your answer in the spaces on top, being careful to write each numeral in the correct column. Double-check to make sure you have gridded your responses in the correct columns.

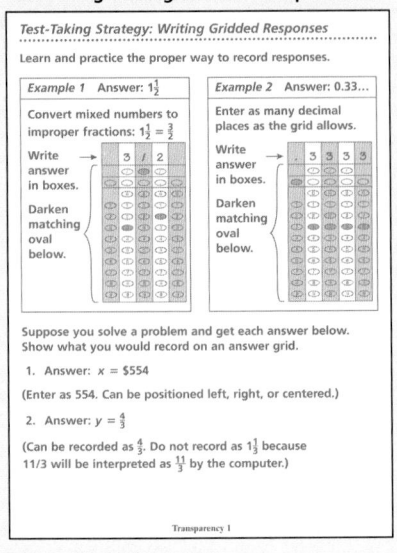

Some standardized test questions require you to enter a number answer on a grid. The number can be a fraction or a decimal.

1 EXAMPLE

What is $\frac{1}{2} + \frac{3}{4}$?

The sum can be written as $\frac{10}{8}$, $\frac{5}{4}$, or 1.25. Write your answer in the spaces at the top, and fill in the corresponding bubbles below. These three forms of the answer are shown at the right.

Note:

• Write a mixed number as an improper fraction. For example, do not put the mixed number $1\frac{1}{4}$ in the grid because the test-scoring computer will read "1 1/4" as $\frac{11}{4}$.

• Fractions do not have to be simplified.

2 EXAMPLE

How many feet are in $\frac{1}{7}$ mile? Round to the nearest foot.
There are 5280 feet in a mile, so there are $5280 \div 7 \approx 754.3$ feet in $\frac{1}{7}$ mile.
Rounded to the nearest foot, the answer is 754 feet. Enter 754 on the grid.
Do not enter the units.

EXERCISES

Which number should you grid for each answer?

1. What is 14% of 0.4? **C**

   A. 0.56   **B.** 0.006   **C.** 0.056   **D.** 0.05

2. What part of a mile is 2200 feet? Round to the nearest hundredth of a mile. **I**

   F. 0.40   **G.** $\frac{40}{100}$ **H.** 0.41   **I.** 0.42

3. What is the value of $\frac{(x + 2)^2}{x + 3}$ when $x = 1$? **D**

   A. 0.75   **B.** 1.25   **C.** $\frac{3}{4}$ **D.** $\frac{9}{4}$

4. What is the value of x^3 when $x = 0.2$? **I**

   F. 8   **G.** 0.8   **H.** 0.6   **I.** 0.008

Chapter Review

Vocabulary

absolute value (p. 20)
additive inverse (p. 24)
algebraic expression (p. 4)
base (p. 9)
coefficient (p. 49)
constant (p. 49)
coordinate plane (p. 59)
coordinates (p. 59)
counterexample (p. 18)
deductive reasoning (p. 56)
element (p. 27)
equation (p. 5)
evaluate (p. 10)
exponent (p. 9)
inequality (p. 19)

integers (p. 17)
irrational numbers (p. 18)
like terms (p. 49)
matrix (p. 27)
multiplicative inverse (p. 41)
natural numbers (p. 17)
negative correlation (p. 61)
no correlation (p. 61)
open sentence (p. 5)
opposites (p. 20)
ordered pair (p. 59)
order of operations (p. 10)
origin (p. 59)
positive correlation (p. 61)
power (p. 9)

quadrants (p. 59)
rational numbers (p. 17)
real numbers (p. 18)
reciprocal (p. 41)
scatter plot (p. 61)
simplify (p. 9)
term (p. 49)
trend line (p. 61)
variable (p. 4)
whole numbers (p. 17)
x-axis (p. 59)
x-coordinate (p. 59)
y-axis (p. 59)
y-coordinate (p. 59)

Reading Math
Understanding
Vocabulary

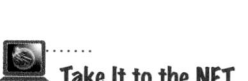

Take It to the NET
Online vocabulary quiz
at www.PHSchool.com
Web Code: aej-0151

Choose the term that correctly completes each sentence.

1. A (constant, term) is a number, a variable, or the product of a number and one or more variables. **term**

2. You (evaluate, simplify) an algebraic expression by substituting a given number for each variable. **evaluate**

3. A mathematical phrase that uses numbers, variables, and operation symbols is an (algebraic expression, equation). **algebraic expression**

4. The number $-\frac{5}{8}$ belongs to the set of (irrational, rational) numbers. **rational**

5. The (absolute value, opposite) of a number is its distance from 0 on a number line. **absolute value**

6. A (coordinate plane, matrix) is a rectangular arrangement of numbers in rows and columns. **matrix**

7. Dividing by a nonzero number is the same as multiplying by its (coefficient, reciprocal). **reciprocal**

8. You express the fraction of a pizza you have eaten using a(n) (rational number, integer). **rational number**

9. In an ordered pair, the first number is the (x-coordinate, y-coordinate), which tells how far to move to the left or right of the origin as you graph the point represented by the ordered pair. **x-coordinate**

10. A (coordinate plane, scatter plot) is a graph that relates data from two different sets. **scatter plot**

11. When one set of data increases while another set of data decreases, there is a (positive correlation, negative correlation) between the two sets of data. **neg. correlation**

12. You simplify a(n) (power, exponent) by multiplying the base by itself the indicated number of times. **power**

21. real numbers, rational numbers

22. real numbers, irrational numbers

23. real numbers, rational numbers

24. real numbers, rational numbers, natural numbers, whole numbers, integers

25. real numbers, rational numbers, natural numbers, whole numbers, integers

Skills and Concepts

1-1 and 1-2 Objectives

▼ To model relationships with variables (p. 4)

▼ To model relationships with equations and formulas (p. 5)

▼ To simplify and evaluate expressions and formulas (p. 9)

▼ To evaluate expressions containing grouping symbols (p. 11)

A **variable** represents one or more numbers. To **evaluate** a variable expression, you substitute a given number for each variable. Then you simplify the expression using the **order of operations.**

Order of Operations

1. Perform any operation(s) inside grouping symbols.

2. Simplify powers.

3. Multiply and divide in order from left to right.

4. Add and subtract in order from left to right.

Define a variable and write an expression for each phrase.

13. the sum of 5 and three times a number **Let n = the number, $5 + 3n$.**

14. 30 minus a number **Let n = the number, $30 - n$.**

15. the quotient of 7 and a number **Let n = the number, $\frac{7}{n}$.**

16. the product of a number and 12 **Let n = the number, $n(12)$.**

Evaluate each expression for $a = 3, b = 2,$ and $c = 1.$

17. $2a^2 - (4b + c)$ **18.** $9(a + 2b) + c$ **19.** $\frac{2a + b}{2}$ **4** **20.** $4a - b^2$ **8**

   9   64

1-3 Objectives

▼ To classify numbers (p. 17)

▼ To compare numbers (p. 19)

Real numbers can be classified as either rational numbers or irrational numbers. A **rational number,** like $\frac{5}{8}$, is a ratio of two integers. An **irrational number,** like π or $\sqrt{2}$, cannot be written as a ratio of integers. Rational numbers include **natural numbers** $(1, 2, 3, \dots)$, **whole numbers** $(0, 1, 2, 3, \dots)$, and **integers** $(\dots, -2, -1, 0, 1, 2, \dots)$.

Name the set(s) of numbers to which each number belongs. 21–25. See margin.

21. -3.21 **22.** $\sqrt{7}$ **23.** $-\frac{1}{2}$ **24.** 18 **25.** $\frac{35}{5}$

1-4, 1-5, and 1-6 Objectives

▼ To add real numbers using models and rules (p. 24)

▼ To apply addition (p. 26)

▼ To subtract real numbers (p. 32)

▼ To apply subtraction (p. 33)

▼ To multiply real numbers (p. 37)

▼ To divide real numbers (p. 40)

To add two real numbers with the same sign, add their absolute values. The sum has the same sign as the addends. To add two real numbers with different signs, find the difference of their absolute values. The sum has the sign of the addend with the greater absolute value. To subtract a real number, add its opposite.

The product or quotient of two real numbers that have the same sign is positive. The product or quotient of two real numbers with different signs is negative.

Simplify each expression.

26. $(-13) + (-4)$ **−17** **27.** $-12 - (-7)$ **−5** **28.** $-12.4 + 22.3$ **9.9**

29. $|54.3 - 29.4|$ **24.9** **30.** $5 - 17$ **−12** **31.** $-3^2 + (-3)^2$ **0**

32. $4 - 3(-2)$ **10** **33.** $5(4)(-2)$ **−40** **34.** $\left(\frac{5}{6}\right)\left(-\frac{2}{3}\right)$ **$-\frac{5}{9}$**

35. $\frac{4 - (-2)}{3}$ **2** **36.** $\frac{5}{6} \div \left(-\frac{2}{3}\right)$ **$-\frac{5}{4}$** **37.** $\frac{5}{6} + \left(-\frac{2}{3}\right)^2$ **$\frac{23}{18}$**

1-7 Objectives

▼ To use the Distributive Property (p. 47)

▼ To simplify algebraic expressions (p. 48)

Terms with exactly the same variable factors are **like terms.** You can combine like terms and use the Distributive Property to simplify expressions.

Distributive Property For all real numbers a, b, and c, $a(b + c) = ab + ac$ and $a(b - c) = ab - ac$.

Simplify each expression. 38–45. See margin.

38. $9m - 5m + 3$ **39.** $2b + 8 - b + 2$ **40.** $-5(w - 4)$ **41.** $9(4 - 3j)$

42. $-(3 - 10y)$ **43.** $-2\left(r - \frac{1}{2}\right)$ **44.** $(7b + 1)(5)$ **45.** $7 - 16v - 9v$

46. $\frac{3}{5}(15t - 2)$ **9t** $-\frac{6}{5}$ **47.** $(6 - 3m)(-3)$ **48.** $-(4 - x)$ **49.** $0.5(20g + 3)$
$\qquad\qquad\qquad\qquad\quad -18 + 9m \qquad\qquad -4 + x \qquad\quad 10g + 1.5$

1-8 Objectives

▼ To identify properties (p. 54)

▼ To use deductive reasoning (p. 56)

50. Assoc. Prop. of Add.

51. Ident. Prop. of Add.

52. Comm. Prop. of Mult.

53. Dist. Prop.

Use properties of real numbers to simplify expressions. Use the Commutative Property to change order. Use the Associative Property to change grouping.

Which property does each equation illustrate? 50–53. See left.

50. $62 + 15 + 38 = 62 + (15 + 38)$ **51.** $62 + 0 + (15 + 38) = 62 + (15 + 38)$

52. $50 \cdot 17 \cdot 2 = 50 \cdot 2 \cdot 17$ **53.** $9(2^3 - 4^2) = 9(2^3) - 9(4^2)$

Simplify each expression. Justify each step. 54–57. See margin.

54. $19 + 56\left(\frac{1}{56}\right)$ **55.** $-12p + 45 - 7p$ **56.** $24abc - 24bac$ **57.** $4 \cdot 13 \cdot 25 \cdot 1$

1-9 Objectives

▼ To graph points on the coordinate plane (p. 59)

▼ To analyze data using scatter plots (p. 61)

62.

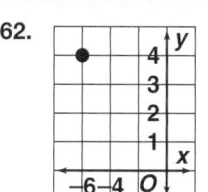

63.

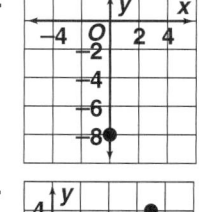

64.

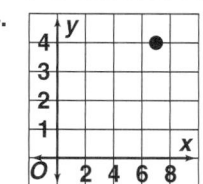

A **coordinate plane** is formed by the intersection of two number lines. The **x-axis** and the **y-axis** divide the coordinate plane into four **quadrants.** An **ordered pair** gives the coordinates of a point. The **x-coordinate** shows how far to move left or right from the origin. The **y-coordinate** shows how far to move up or down from the origin.

A **scatter plot** is a graph that relates two sets of data.

Write the coordinates of each point.

58. $R (-4, 1)$ **59.** $S (2, -2)$ **60.** $T (3, 0)$ **61.** U $(-1, -1)$

Graph each point on the coordinate plane. 62–64. See left.

62. $J(-6, 4)$ **63.** $K(0, -8)$ **64.** $L(7, 4)$

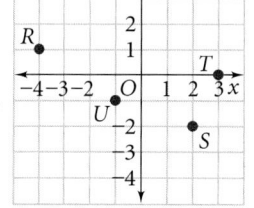

65. a. Make a scatter plot of the data below. **See margin.**

Height (meters)	1.5	1.8	1.7	2.0	1.7	2.1	1.6	1.9	1.9
Arm Span (meters)	1.4	1.7	1.7	1.9	1.6	2.0	1.6	1.8	1.9

b. Is there a *positive correlation*, a *negative correlation*, or *no correlation* between the sets of data? **pos. correlation**

38. $4m + 3$ **42.** $-3 + 10y$

39. $b + 10$ **43.** $-2r + 1$

40. $-5w + 20$ **44.** $35b + 5$

41. $36 - 27j$ **45.** $7 - 25v$

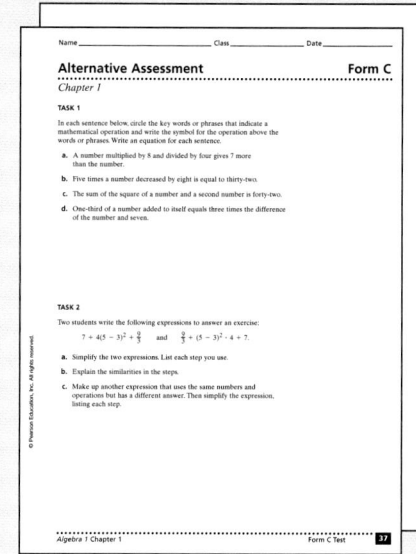

54. $19 + 56\left(\frac{1}{56}\right)$
$= 19 + 1$
Inv. Prop. of Mult.
$= 20$ add.

55. $-12p + 45 - 7p$
$= -12p + 45 + (-7p)$
def. of subtr.
$= -12p + (-7p) + 45$
Comm. Prop. of Add.
$= [-12 + (-7)]p + 45$
Dist. Prop.
$= -19p + 45$ add.

56. $24abc - 24bac$
$= 24abc - 24abc$
Comm. Prop. of Mult.
$= 0$
Inv. Prop. of Add.

57. $4 \cdot 13 \cdot 25 \cdot 1$
$= 4 \cdot 25 \cdot 13 \cdot 1$
Comm. Prop. of Mult.
$= (4 \cdot 25) \cdot (13 \cdot 1)$
Assoc. Prop. of Mult.
$= 100 \cdot 13$ mult.
$= 1300$ mult.

65a.

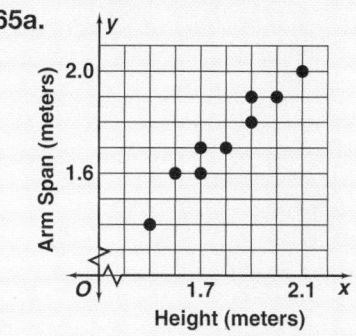

Take It to the NET
Online chapter test at
www.PHSchool.com
Web Code: aea-0152

Resources

 **Teaching Resources**
Ch. 1 Test, Forms A & B
Ch. 1 Alternative Assessment,
Form C

Reaching All Students
Spanish Ch. 1 Test, Forms A & B
Spanish Ch. 1 Alternative
Assessment, Form C
Basic Algebra Ch. 1 Test,
Forms D & E

 **PRENTICE HALL
ASSESSMENT SYSTEM**

Assessment Masters
• Ch. 1 Test, Forms A & B
• Ch. 1 Alternative Assessment,
  Form C
Computer Test Generator CD
• Ch. 1 pre-made Test
• Make your own Ch. 1 test

 **www.PHSchool.com**
Student Site
• Self-grading Chapter 1 Test
Teacher Center
• Resources

Plus **iTEXT**

Chapter Test — Form B

Chapter Test — Form A

| Chapter Test | Form A |
| Chapter 1 | |

Write an equation to model the relationship in each table.

Simplify.
3. $4 + 8 \div 2 + 6 \times 2$ 4. $12 - (-3)$
5. $-6(-3) + -2$ 6. $(-8)^2 + (-2)$

Evaluate each expression.
7. $5x + 4$ for $x = 5$ 8. $y^2 + z$ for $y = -12$ and $z = -9$
9. $|6 - 2m|$ for $m = -7$ 10. $-3(2s - 3)$ for $s = -5.2$ and $t = 1.9$
11. $\frac{8}{9}$ for $a = \frac{3}{8}$ and $b = -\frac{4}{5}$ 12. $\frac{2d-1}{-5}$ for $d = 9$

Find the sum or difference.
13.

Is each statement true or false? If the statement is false, give a counterexample.
15. All real numbers are rational numbers.
16. The absolute value of a negative number is positive.

Simplify each expression.
17. $-\frac{1}{3}(4 - 6a)$ 18. $-2(-3 + 2a)$

Write an expression for each phrase.
19. 4 minus the sum of a number and 6
20. 1 more than the quotient of n and 2

Simplify each expression. Justify each step.
21. $\frac{1}{4}(4x - 8) + 3x$ 22. $(a^2 - 2^3)(1^3 - 3^2)$

Algebra 1 Chapter 1 | Form A Test | 33

---

page 70   Chapter Test
1. n = number, c = cost,
   $c = 2.3n$

Define variables and write an equation to model the relationship in each table. 1–2. See margin.

1.
Number	Cost
1	$2.30
2	$4.60
3	$6.90

2.
Payment	Change
$1	$9
$2	$8
$3	$7

Simplify each expression.

3. $3 + 5 - 4$ **4**
4. $8 - 2^4 \div 2$ **0**
5. $\frac{2 \cdot 3 - 1}{3^2}$ **$\frac{5}{9}$**
6. $36 - (4 + 5 \cdot 4)$ **12**

Evaluate each expression for $x = 3$, $y = -1$, and $z = 2$.

7. $2x + 3y + z$ **5**
8. $-xyz$ **6**
9. $-3x - 2z - 7$ **−20**
10. $-z^3 - 2z + z$ **−10**
11. $\frac{xy - 3z}{-5}$ **$1\frac{4}{5}$**
12. $x^2 + (-x)^2$ **18**

Find each sum or difference.

13. $\begin{bmatrix} 3 & 2 \\ -1 & 5 \end{bmatrix} + \begin{bmatrix} 8 & -5 \\ 3 & 0 \end{bmatrix}$ $\begin{bmatrix} 11 & -3 \\ 2 & 5 \end{bmatrix}$

14. $\begin{bmatrix} 1 & 9 & -4 \\ 5 & 2 & -1 \\ -6 & -2 & -1 \end{bmatrix} - \begin{bmatrix} 2 & -6 & 7 \\ -8 & 3 & -3 \\ 4 & -7 & 9 \end{bmatrix}$ $\begin{bmatrix} -1 & 15 & -11 \\ 13 & -1 & 2 \\ -10 & 5 & -10 \end{bmatrix}$

Explain why each statement is true or false.

15. All rational numbers are integers. **See margin.**

16. The absolute value of a number is always positive.
    False, since $|0| = 0$, which is not pos.

Simplify each expression.

17. $(7 - 42a)\left(-\frac{3}{7}\right)$ **−3 + 18a**
18. $6(2d - 5)$ **12d − 30**

Simplify each expression. Justify each step.
19–20. See back of book.

19. $10x + 3\left(\frac{1}{3} - x\right)$
20. $(3^3 - 3^3)(1 - 2^2)$

Write an expression for each phrase.

21. negative ten times the quantity two minus eleven
    −10(2 − 11)
22. five divided by the quantity m plus six **$\frac{5}{m + 6}$**
23. the quantity p minus five eighths times the quantity
    one fourth plus p $\left(p - \frac{5}{8}\right)\left(\frac{1}{4} + p\right)$

Simplify each expression.

24. $-7\frac{7}{8} + \left(-2\frac{1}{2}\right) - 10\frac{3}{8}$
25. $-1.8 + 12.1 + (-7.6)$ **2.7**

26. **Writing** Tell whether each of the subtraction sentences will *always*, *sometimes*, or *never* be true. Support your answer with two examples. **See margin.**
   a. $(+) - (+) = (+)$ b. $(+) - (-) = (-)$
   c. $(-) - (-) = (-)$ d. $(-) - (+) = (+)$

27. **Open-Ended** Write four rational numbers. Use a number line to order them from least to greatest. **See back of book.**

In which quadrant or on which axis would you find each point?

28. $(0, -2)$ **y-axis**
29. $(-3, -6)$ **Quadrant III**

30. **Geometry** Find the area of a trapezoid whose vertices have coordinates $(-2, 1)$, $(2, 1)$, $(5, -3)$, and $(-5, -3)$. **28 square units**

31. On four plays, a football team gained 22 yd, lost 18 yd, gained 8 yd, and lost 14 yd. What is the total number of yards gained or lost on the four plays? **2 yd lost**

32. **Banking** Marcus had $163 in his checking account. On Monday, he wrote a check for $315. How much does Marcus need to deposit into his account to prevent the account balance from dipping below the minimum of $25? **$177**

33. **Sales** A CD costs $17.95 plus tax. The sales tax rate is 7.5%. Find the total cost of the CD. **$19.30**

Use the scatter plot below for Exercises 34–35.

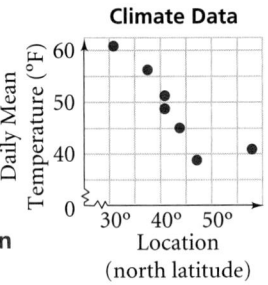

Climate Data

34. Is there a *positive correlation, negative correlation,* or *no correlation* between daily mean temperature and latitude? **neg. correlation**

35. What is the daily mean temperature for the location at latitude 58° N? **about 41°F**

36. **Writing** Explain why $\left|\frac{a}{b}\right| = \frac{a}{b}$ is *not* always true.
    If a and b have different signs, $\left|\frac{a}{b}\right|$ is positive and $\frac{a}{b}$ is negative.

---

2. p = payment,
   c = change,
   $c = 10 - p$

15. False, since $\frac{1}{2}$ is a
    rational number but is
    not an integer.

26a. Sometimes;
     $5 - 3 = 2$, but
     $3 - 5 = -2$.

b. Never;
   $3 - (-2) = 5$ and
   $8 - (-10) = 18$.

c. Sometimes;
   $-8 - (-3) = -5$, but
   $-3 - (-8) = 5$.

d. Never;
   $-3 - (8) = -11$ and
   $-7 - (10) = -17$.

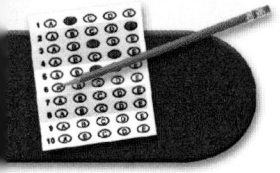

Standardized Test Prep

Standardized Test Prep

Reading Comprehension Read the passage below, and then answer the questions on the basis of what is *stated* or *implied* in the passage.

Travel Math Often one of the biggest complications of visiting a foreign country is doing the math. Things that would cause no problem at home are suddenly challenging because the units are different. Consider a quarter-pound hamburger. At 2.2 pounds (lbs) per kilogram (kg), what is the mass of a quarter-pound hamburger in the metric system?

Once you have ordered lunch, you have to pay for it. Let's see . . . one U.S. dollar is worth 1.53 Canadian dollars, 0.70 British pounds, or 1.07 European euros. So how much does a quarter-pound hamburger cost in other countries?

Then there is figuring out the temperature. Even if you can remember the formula Fahrenheit $= \frac{9}{5} \cdot$ Celsius $+ 32$, you must do some work to find whether 20°C is a beach day or a ski day.

Fortunately, it doesn't have to be quite so hard. If you look for some simple approximations, you can usually get around foreign countries without having to pack a calculator. As with many other aspects of travel, the trick is to think ahead, anticipate what might be coming, and have a plan for dealing with it. Before you go, figure out which formulas you will be using and come up with some simple approximations. Then you can leave your calculator home.

---

1. About how many kilograms are there in 10 lb? **D**
   A. 25 kg   B. 20 kg
   C. 11 kg   D. 5 kg

2. How many kilograms correspond to a quarter pound? **G**
   F. 0.1 kg   G. 0.5 kg
   H. 5 kg   I. 8.8 kg

3. Based on the article, which could you use to estimate an exchange of Canadian dollars and United States dollars? **C**
   A. 1 U.S. Dollar $= \frac{1}{2}$ Canadian Dollar
   B. 1 U.S. Dollar $= \frac{2}{3}$ Canadian Dollar
   C. 2 U.S. Dollar $= 3$ Canadian Dollars
   D. 3 U.S. Dollars $= 2$ Canadian Dollars

4. Suppose you pay $3.00 for a hamburger in Canada. How much is this in United States currency? **F**
   F. $1.95   G. $3.00
   H. $4.53   I. $4.59

5. According to the article, about how many euros could you get for 5 U.S. dollars? **D**
   A. 0.20 euros   B. 1.50 euros
   C. 4.20 euros   D. 5.50 euros

6. Suppose you are traveling in France. You see a T-shirt for 40 euros. Is this a reasonable price? Justify your answer. **See back of book.**

7. A taxicab ride in London costs you 15 pounds. How much is this in United States currency?
   See back of book.

8. The formula Fahrenheit $= 2 \cdot$ Celsius $+ 30$ gives a good estimate of the temperature in degrees Fahrenheit when you know the temperature in degrees Celsius. Is 20°C a beach day? Justify your answer. **See back of book.**

9. A foreign exchange student could use the formula Celsius $= \frac{5}{9}$(Fahrenheit $- 32$) to find the temperature in degrees Celsius when he knows the temperature in degrees Fahrenheit. Write a formula the student could use to get a good estimate of the Celsius temperature.
   See back of book.

Students must be able to extract information from reading passages, answer multiple choice questions, and construct responses in order to be successful on current state and national assessments.

To answer the questions, students apply skills and concepts from this chapter and previous chapters.
Multiple Choice: Items 1–5
Extended Response: Items 6–9

Resources

 **Teaching Resources**
Cumulative Review

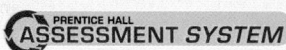 **Reaching All Students**
Spanish Cumulative Review

 PRENTICE HALL ASSESSMENT SYSTEM

Standardized Test Prep
• Ch. 1 Standardized Test Practice
Assessment Masters
• Cumulative Review
Computer Test Generator CD
• Standardized Test Practice

 **www.PHSchool.com**
• Standardized Test Practice
• Resources

Plus **iTEXT**

Cumulative Review

Solving Equations

Chapter at a Glance

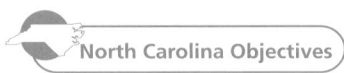
North Carolina Objectives

2-1	Solving One-Step Equations	1.02
NCTM 2, 3, 6, 7, 10	▼ Solving Equations Using Addition and Subtraction ▼ Solving Equations Using Multiplication and Division	

2-2	Solving Two-Step Equations	1.02
NCTM 2, 7, 8, 10	▼ Solving Two-Step Equations ▼ Using Deductive Reasoning	

2-3	Solving Multi-Step Equations	1.02
NCTM 2, 7, 9, 10	▼ Using the Distributive Property to Combine Like Terms ▼ Using the Distributive Property to Solve Equations	

2-4	Equations With Variables on Both Sides	1.02
NCTM 2, 3, 6, 7, 8	▼ Solving Equations With Variables on Both Sides ▼ Special Cases: Identities and No Solutions	

2-5	Equations and Problem Solving	1.02
NCTM 2, 3, 4, 6, 9, 10	▼ Defining Variables ▼ Distance-Rate-Time Problems	

2-6	Formulas	1.02
NCTM 2, 3, 4, 10	▼ Transforming Literal Equations	

2-7	Using Measures of Central Tendency	
NCTM 1, 2, 5, 9, 10	▼ Finding Mean, Median, and Mode ▼ Stem-and-Leaf Plots	

NCTM STANDARDS 2000

1	Number and Operations	6	Problem Solving
2	Algebra	7	Reasoning and Proof
3	Geometry	8	Communication
4	Measurement	9	Connections
5	Data Analysis and Probability	10	Representation

Pacing Options

This chart suggests pacing only for the lessons and their parts. It is provided as a possible guide. It will help you determine how much time you have in your schedule to cover other components, such as the features, Chapter Review, and Chapter Test.

Day	Traditional 45 min.	Two-Year 45 min.	Block 90 min.
1	2-1 ▼ ▼	2-1 ▼	2-1 ▼ ▼ 2-2 ▼ ▼
2	2-2 ▼	2-1 ▼	2-2 ▼ ▼ 2-3 ▼
3	2-2 ▼	2-2 ▼	2-3 ▼
4	2-3 ▼	2-2 ▼ ▼	2-4 ▼ ▼
5	2-3 ▼	2-2 ▼	2-5 ▼ ▼
6	2-4 ▼	2-3 ▼	2-6 ▼
7	2-4 ▼	2-3 ▼ ▼	2-7 ▼ ▼
8	2-5 ▼ ▼	2-3 ▼	
9	2-6 ▼	2-4 ▼	
10	2-7 ▼ ▼	2-4 ▼ ▼	
11		2-4 ▼	
12		2-5 ▼	
13		2-5 ▼	
14		2-6 ▼	
15		2-6 ▼	
16		2-7 ▼	
17		2-7 ▼	

NAEP Correlation (National Assessment of Educational Progress 2000 Mathematics Objectives)

2-1	2-2	2-3	2-4	2-5	2-6	2-7
N4f; A5a, c	N4f; A5a, c	N3d; A5a, c	N4f, G5, A5c	A5a, c	A5a, b	D2, D4, D6b

N = Number Sense, Properties, and Operations; **M** = Measurement; **G** = Geometry and Spatial Sense; **D** = Data Analysis, Statistics, and Probability; **A** = Algebra and Functions

Math Background

Chapter Overview

Students apply the tools of Algebra that were presented in Chapter 1, and the formal definitions of the addition, subtraction, multiplication, and division properties of equality to solving equations. First, students solve equations by isolating the variable and applying properties of equality to undo what has been done to the variable. This procedure is extended to include simplifying by first applying the Distributive Property and then collecting terms. Students proceed to solve equations with variable terms on both sides, and to solve literal equations for a specified variable. Skills are developed to solve problems using formulas such as those for rate and for measurement. Finally students find measures of central tendency and organize data into stem-and-leaf plots.

Solving One-Step Equations   2-1

Although many one-step equations can be solved using mental math, it is important to ask students to write the step that shows which property of equality they are using. First, it reinforces the structure of mathematics in which validity results from careful reasoning and justified procedures. Second, it prepares students for the more complex procedures that will be needed for solving equations (and inequalities, in Chapter 3) that cannot be solved simply by inspection. Third, it helps students avoid errors in calculation. For example, students using only mental math may look at $x - 7 = 17$ and incorrectly subtract 7 from 17. Writing the middle step that shows adding 7 to each side may prevent this type of error.

The use of the reciprocal in Example 5 is a particular case of solving $ax = b$ by multiplying by $\frac{1}{a}$.

$$\frac{1}{a} \cdot ax = \frac{1}{a} \cdot b$$

$$x = \frac{b}{a}$$

Some students may know that the subtraction and division properties of equality can be understood as part of the addition and multiplication properties. Other students may be helped by reviewing the definitions of subtraction and division, and seeing, for example, that solving $x - 3 = 4$ as

$$x + (-3) = 4$$

$$x + (-3) - (-3) = 4 - (-3)$$

gives the same solution as

$$x - 3 + 3 = 4 + 3.$$

Solving Two-Step Equations   2-2

Point out to students that solving two-step equations involves reversing the order of operations. Tell students to think of the process as undoing what has been done to the variable. Students will also learn to see patterns in situations that on the surface appear quite different. These patterns will lead them to realize that a solution method from one problem situation can be applied to other situations.

Solving Multi-Step Equations and Equations with Variables on Both Sides   2-3, 2-4

To solve more complex equations, students combine previously learned skills. Students who still simplify $4x - 3 + 2x$ as $4x - x$ need to review collecting like terms by using the distributive property. Students sometimes think that the variable must be written on the left. Help them to see that this is only a convention, and that the solution $7 = x$ is the same, and just as acceptable, as $x = 7$ because of the Symmetric Property of equality (if $a = b$, then $b = a$).

Problem Solving and Formulas   2-5, 2–6

Once students have learned to see the algebraic patterns in literal equations, they will be aware that common equations such as $A = \ell w$ and $d = rt$ are algebraically the same. Although these two formulas express relationships in very different situations, the same methods can be used to solve for any variable. Some students may know common formulas using different variable names. For example, for a rectangle, the formula for the area may be $A = \ell w$ if students are used to calling the dimensions of a rectangle length and width. Another version of the same formula is $A = bh$ if the dimensions of the rectangle are called base and height.

Using Measures of Central Tendency   2-7

Students investigate some guidelines that can help decide whether the mean, the median, or the mode may be the best way to represent the data set as a whole. For example, the mode may be the best representative for non-numeric data, such as the most preferred color of automobile, and for data that has numbers that tend to be discrete and grouped, as in clothing sizes, or student ages in a certain grade. Students are probably familiar with the average, or mean. They use it here to find the median of an even number of data. Later they will use it to find the coordinates of the midpoint of a segment. Most students will be unfamiliar with stem-and-leaf plots. They may find it helpful to compare them with line plots.

 # Ongoing Assessment and Intervention

Tools for Monitoring Student Progress

The Prentice Hall *Algebra 1* program provides you with many options for assessment in the Student Edition, the Teacher's Edition and the teaching resources. From these options you may choose instructional materials and techniques that are appropriate for your students and support your district's curriculum requirements.

Instant Check System™ in Chapter 2

Allows students to check their own learning before, during, and after each lesson.

Diagnosing Readiness before the chapter (p. 72)

Check Skills You'll Need exercises in each lesson (pp. 74, 81, 88, 96, 103, 111, 118)

Check Understanding questions with each Example (pp. 75, 76, 77, 82, 83, 88, 89, 90, 97, 98, 103, 104, 105, 106, 107, 111, 112, 113, 119, 120, 121)

Checkpoint Quiz (pp. 94, 115)

Test Prep in Chapter 2

Teaches students strategies and gives them practice with all the test item formats they will encounter on state tests and standardized national exams.

Standardized Test Prep exercises in each lesson (pp. 80, 86, 93, 101, 110, 115, 123)

Test-Taking Strategies (p. 124: Answering Short-Responses)

Standardized Test Prep (p. 129: Cumulative Review)

 PRENTICE HALL ASSESSMENT *SYSTEM*

All your assessment needs in one place!

Program Assessment

Assess student progress throughout the *Algebra 1* text with blackline masters and CD-ROM.

Assessment Resources

- Checkpoint Quizzes 1 & 2
- Chapter Test, Forms A & B
- Chapter Alternative Assessment

Spanish versions available. Tests for Basic Algebra also available.

 Computer Test Generator

- Unlimited questions of varying difficulty for every lesson objective.
- Create your own practice sheets, quizzes, and tests, or use the pre-made Chapter Tests.
- Diagnose readiness with questions on prerequisite skills.
- Prepare students by making tests based on standardized test objectives.
- Access Algebra 1, Geometry, and Algebra 2 content—all on one CD-ROM.

Test Preparation

A three-step approach to preparing students for high stakes, national, and state exams.

❶ Diagnose & Prescribe

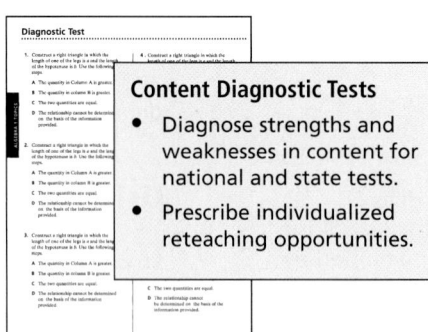

Content Diagnostic Tests

- Diagnose strengths and weaknesses in content for national and state tests.
- Prescribe individualized reteaching opportunities.

❷ Review & Reteach

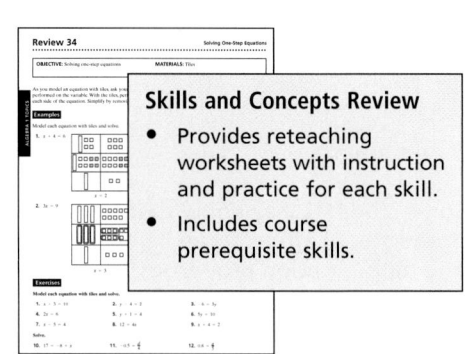

Skills and Concepts Review

- Provides reteaching worksheets with instruction and practice for each skill.
- Includes course prerequisite skills.

❸ Practice & Assess

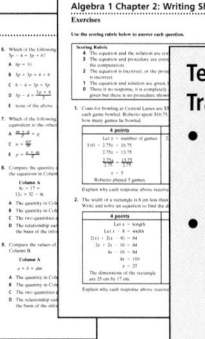

Test Preparation

- Features practice tests for End-of-Course and SAT/ACT exams.
- Includes standardized test practice by chapter for ongoing review.

Teacher's Guide with answers and correlations.

Test-Taking Strategies with Transparencies

- Support the Test-Taking Strategies pages in the Student Edition.
- Provide a teaching transparency and a practice worksheet for each strategy.

 **Reaching All Students**

Support in the Student Text and Additional Resources

The textbook, the iText, and other technology components provide numerous opportunities to reach students of various ability levels and learning styles. Each Teacher's Edition lesson suggests how you can help *all* your students be successful and understand the mathematics in Chapter 2.

Below Level

Student Edition
- Diagnosing Readiness*: p. 72
- Check Skills You'll Need*: pp. 74, 81, 88, 96, 103, 111, 118

Reteaching
Chapter 2 Support File: pp. 8–14

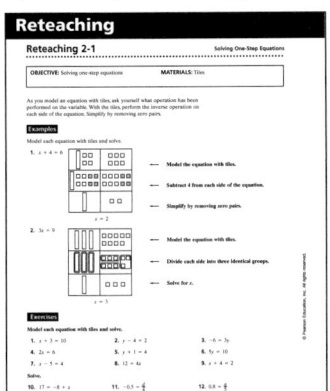

Basic Algebra Planning Guide
Chapter 2 Lesson Plans: pp. 10–16
Chapter 2 Tests: pp. 93–96

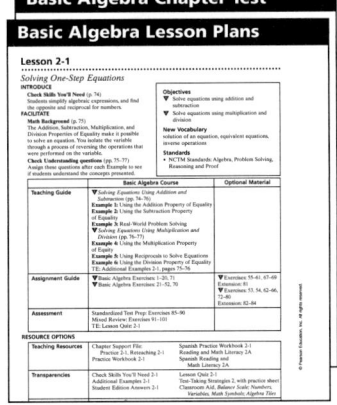

* Can be used with all ability levels to ensure mastery of prerequisite skills.

Advanced Learners

Student Edition
- Challenge exercises: pp. 79, 80, 86, 93, 100, 109, 110, 114, 123
- Extension, p. 116

Enrichment
Chapter 2 Support File: pp. 15–21

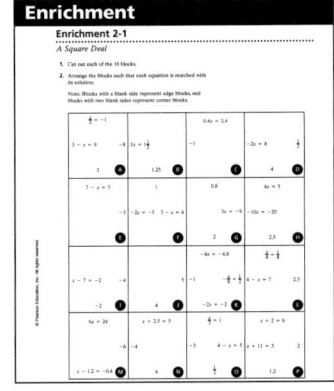

Reading and Math Literacy

Student Edition
- Vocabulary: pp. 73, 125, *plus* in every Lesson Preview
- Reading Math: pp. 75, 85, 87, 106, 125
- Illustrated Glossary: pp. 757–785

Reading and Math Literacy Masters
Chapter 2: pp. 5–8

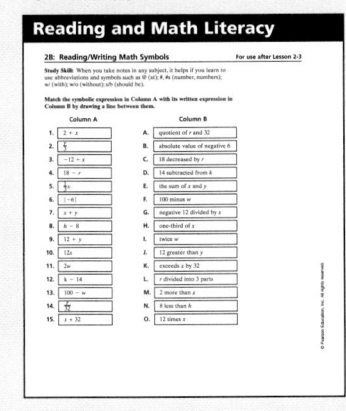

English Learners

Student Edition
- English/Spanish Illustrated Glossary: pp. 757–785

Workbook and Masters
Spanish Practice Workbook: pp. 10–16
Spanish Reading and Math Literacy Masters: pp. 5–8

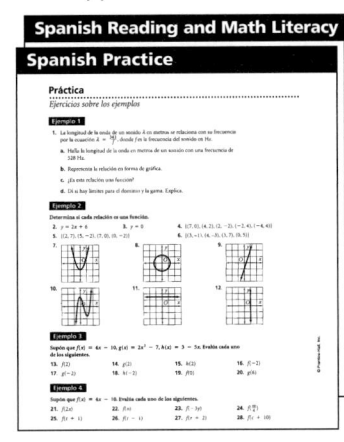

Learning Styles

Student Edition
- Investigation: pp. 95, 96, 111
- Technology: pp. 100, 102
- Writing: pp. 79, 85, 92, 100, 109, 114, 122, 128
- DK Activities: pp. 130–131

Activity Masters
Hands-On Activities: 4, 5, 6
Technology Activities: 16

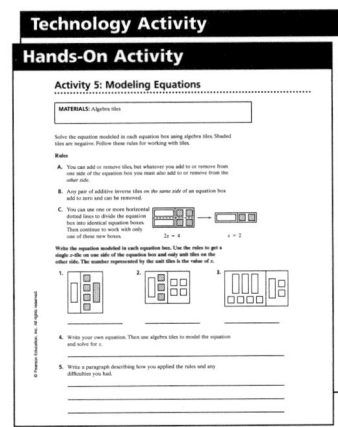

Program Resources

	Teaching Resources in Grab & Go™ Files				Resources for Reaching All Students				Spanish Resources			Transparencies				Presentation Assistant Plus!
	Practice	Reteach	Enrich	Checkpoint Quiz	Reading & Math Literacy	Technology Activities	Hands-On Activities	Basic Algebra Lesson Plans	Practice	Reading & Math Literacy	Checkpoint Quiz	Skills Check	Additional Examples	Answers to Exercises	Lesson Quiz	Prentice Hall Presentation Pro CD-ROM
2-1	■	■	■		■		■	■	■	■		■	■	■	■	■
2-2	■	■	■					■	■			■	■	■	■	■
2-3	■	■	■	■	■			■	■		■	■	■	■	■	■
2-4	■	■	■			■	■	■	■			■	■	■	■	■
2-5	■	■	■					■	■			■	■	■	■	■
2-6	■	■	■	■	■		■	■	■		■	■	■	■	■	■
2-7	■	■	■					■	■			■	■	■	■	■
For the chapter	Chapter Tests, Alternative Assessment, Cumulative Review, Cumulative Assessment				Basic Algebra Chapter Tests				Spanish Chapter Tests, Alternative Assessment, Cumulative Review, Cumulative Assessment			Classroom Aid Transparencies				

Also available for use with the chapter:

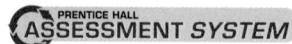 PRENTICE HALL ASSESSMENT SYSTEM   *See page 72C.*

- Practice Workbook
- Solution Key

- For teacher support and access to student Web site materials, use Web Code aek-5500.
- For additional online and technology resources, see below.

Technology

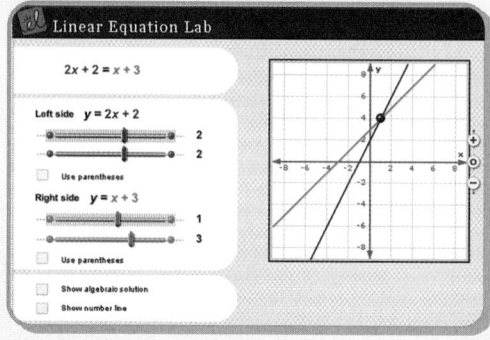

iTEXT Online and on CD-ROM

Complete Interactive Student Text online and on CD-ROM—with instant feedback assessment, tutorial help, dynamic activities, instructional and real-world videos, audio, and additional practice.

 www.PHSchool.com For Students

Use **Web codes** for easy access to online activities, chapter projects, self-grading lesson quizzes and chapter tests, vocabulary quizzes, updated data sources, graphing calculator procedures, and more.

PH SuccessNet For Teachers

Online lesson planning with built-in state correlations, all the teaching resources, complete reference library, your own calendar and Teacher Web page, professional development, and more.

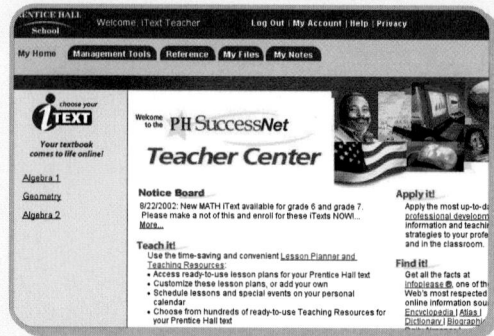

Presentation Assistant Plus!

The Prentice Hall *Presentation Assistant Plus!* provides you with the material you need to teach a lesson from beginning to end. Two easy-to-use formats—Transparencies and CD-ROM—allow you to present a lesson the way you are most comfortable.

 ## Transparencies

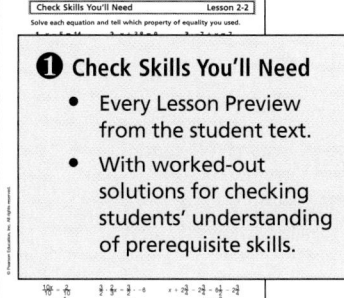

❶ Check Skills You'll Need
- Every Lesson Preview from the student text.
- With worked-out solutions for checking students' understanding of prerequisite skills.

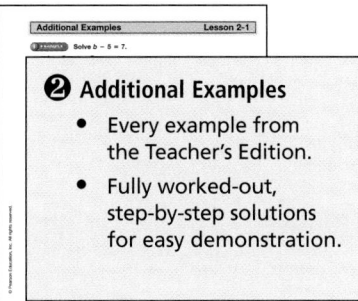

❷ Additional Examples
- Every example from the Teacher's Edition.
- Fully worked-out, step-by-step solutions for easy demonstration.

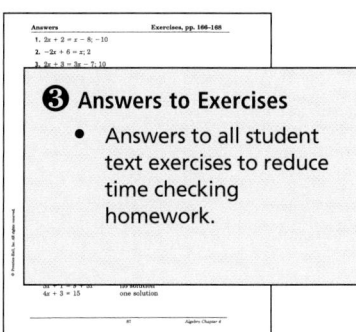

❸ Answers to Exercises
- Answers to all student text exercises to reduce time checking homework.

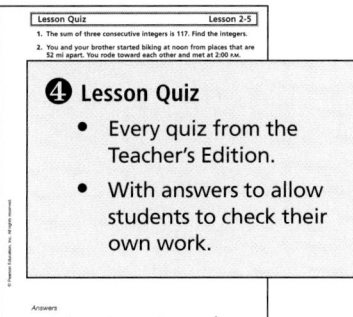

❹ Lesson Quiz
- Every quiz from the Teacher's Edition.
- With answers to allow students to check their own work.

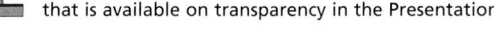

 ## Prentice Hall Presentation Pro CD-ROM

- Includes all Transparencies.
- Conveniently organized by lesson so you can easily ❶ Introduce, ❷ Teach, ❸ Check Homework, and ❹ Assess each lesson.
- Animated examples allow step-by-step instruction at your own pace.
- Easy to edit so you can create custom presentations.

Teaching Chapter 2 Using Presentation Assistant Plus!

	❶ Introduce	❷ Teach	❸ Check Homework	❹ Assess
	Check Skills You'll Need	Additional Examples	Student Edition Answers	Lesson Quiz
2-1	p. 10	pp. 13–14	✔	p. 94
2-2	p. 11	pp. 15–16	✔	p. 94
2-3	p. 12	pp. 17–19	✔	p. 95
2-4	p. 13	pp. 20–21	✔	p. 95
2-5	p. 14	pp. 22–26	✔	p. 96
2-6	p. 15	pp. 27–28	✔	p. 96
2-7	p. 16	pp. 28–30	✔	p. 97

 Throughout the Teacher's Edition, this symbol indicates material that is available on transparency in the Presentation Assistant Plus!

 ### Prentice Hall Presentation Pro

CD-ROM with dynamic PowerPoint® presentations for every lesson. Helps you introduce and develop concepts, check homework, and assess progress. Part of Presentation Assistant Plus! *(See above.)*

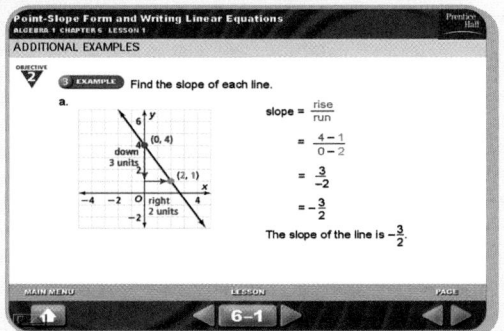

 ### Computer Test Generator

CD-ROM to create practice sheets and tests for course objectives and standardized tests. Includes Instant Chapter Tests™, online testing, and student reports. Part of the PH Assessment System. *(See page 72C.)*

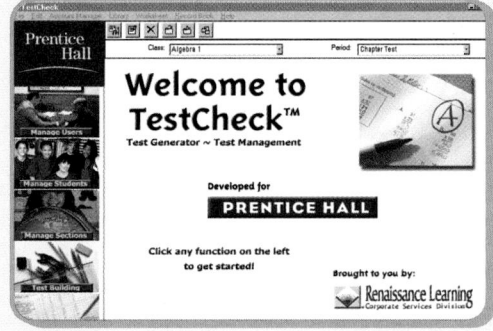

Resource Pro® with Planning Express®

CD-ROM with a lesson planning tool that allows you to import state and local objectives. Includes electronic versions of all the teaching resources.

Solving Equations

 Diagnosing Readiness

Students will find answers to these exercises in the back of their textbooks.

For intervention, direct students to:

Writing Equations
Lesson 1-1: Example 3
Exercises 17–19
Extra Practice, p. 702

Using Order of Operations
Lesson 1-2: Example 2
Exercises 7–12
Extra Practice, p. 702

Adding and Subtracting Rational Numbers
Lesson 1-4: Example 2
Exercises 6–12
Lesson 1-5: Example 3
Exercises 9–18
Extra Practice, p. 702

Multiplying and Dividing Rational Numbers
Lesson 1-6: Examples 1, 4, 5
Exercises 59–64
Extra Practice, p. 702

Combining Like Terms
Lesson 1-7: Example 5
Exercises 35–39
Extra Practice, p. 702

Where You've Been

- In previous courses, you learned to solve simple equations.

- In Chapter 1, you extended your ability to do arithmetic operations to include rational numbers.

- Also in Chapter 1, you used variables to write expressions and equations that represent real-world situations.

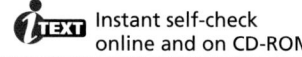 Instant self-check online and on CD-ROM

 **Diagnosing Readiness** (For help, go to the Lesson in green.)

Writing an Equation (Lesson 1-1)

Write an equation to model each situation.

1. The total cost of n cartons of milk is $3.60. Each carton costs $.45. **$0.45n = 3.60$**

2. The perimeter of an equilateral triangle is 3 times the length of a side s. The perimeter of an equilateral triangle is 124 in. **$3s = 124$**

Using the Order of Operations (Lesson 1-2)

Evaluate each expression for $a = 4$, $b = 13$, and $c = 2$.

3. $2a + cb$ **34** **4.** $cb - a^2$ **10** **5.** $5c + 2a - b$ **5** **6.** $38 - a^2 \div c$ **30**

Adding and Subtracting Integers (Lessons 1-4 and 1-5)

Simplify each expression.

7. $6 + (-3)$ **3** **8.** $-4 - 6$ **−10** **9.** $-5 - (-13)$ **8** **10.** $-7 + (-1)$ **−8**

11. $-4.51 + 11.65$ **7.14** **12.** $8.5 - (-7.9)$ **16.4** **13.** $\frac{3}{10} - \frac{3}{4}$ **$-\frac{9}{20}$** **14.** $\frac{1}{5} + \left(-\frac{2}{3}\right)$ **$-\frac{7}{15}$**

Multiplying and Dividing Rational Numbers (Lesson 1-6)

Simplify each expression.

15. $-85 \div (-5)$ **17** **16.** $7\left(-\frac{6}{14}\right)$ **−3** **17.** $4^2(-6)^2$ **576** **18.** $22 \div (-8)$ **−2.75**

Combining Like Terms (Lesson 1-7)

Simplify each expression.

19. $14k^2 - (-2k^2)$ **$16k^2$** **20.** $4xy + 9xy$ **$13xy$** **21.** $6t + 2 - 4t$ **$2t + 2$** **22.** $9x - 4 + 3x$ **$12x - 4$**

Solving Equations

Where You're Going

- In this chapter, you will solve equations, including equations with variables on both sides, using properties of equality.

- You will develop the ability to solve problems by defining variables, relating them to one another, and writing an equation.

- You will use measures of central tendency to describe a set of data.

Real-World Snapshots Applying what you learn, you will do an activity involving bicycle gears, on pages 130–131.

LESSONS

2-1   Solving One-Step Equations

2-2   Solving Two-Step Equations

2-3   Solving Multi-Step Equations

2-4   Equations With Variables on Both Sides

2-5   Equations and Problem Solving

2-6   Formulas

2-7   Using Measures of Central Tendency

Key Vocabulary

- consecutive integers (p. 104)
- equivalent equations (p. 75)
- identity (p. 98)
- inverse operations (p. 75)
- literal equation (p. 111)
- mean (p. 118)
- measures of central tendency (p. 118)
- median (p. 118)
- mode (p. 118)
- outlier (p. 118)
- range (p. 120)
- solution of an equation (p. 75)
- uniform motion (p. 104)

73

Chapter 2 Overview

Students solve equations, progressing from one-step equations to those that have the variable on both sides. They apply these skills to using formulas and to solving literal equations for one of the variables. Students calculate three measures of central tendency, mean, median, and mode, and evaluate which to use as the most representative of a set of data. They also organize data into useful information by making a stem-and-leaf plot.

Reading Math
Reading for Problem Solving, p. 87

Vocabulary
A complete list of terms, plus vocabulary exercises, appears in the Chapter Review, p. 125.

Illustrated Glossary
Examples for each vocabulary term, plus definitions in both English and Spanish, appear starting on p. 757.

Test-Taking Strategies
Answering Short-Response Questions, p. 124

Real-World Snapshots
See pages 130–131 for a real-world application of Applying Variations that utilizes Dorling Kindersley's (DK) unique graphic presentation.

Real-World Connections
Some of the applications you will find in this chapter are catalog purchasing (2-2), construction (2-3), recreation (2-4), and travel (2-5).

www.PHSchool.com
Internet support for this chapter includes:
- Self-grading Vocabulary and Chapter 2 Tests
- Chapter Project
- Chapter Planner
- Chapter 2 Resources

Plus

2-1

North Carolina Objectives 1.02

1. Plan

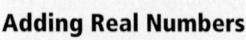

Lesson Preview

✓ **Check Skills You'll Need**

Adding Real Numbers
Lesson 1-4: Example 2
Exercises 5–24

Subtracting Real Numbers
Extra Practice p. 702
Lesson 1-5: Example 3
Exercises 9–20

Multiplying and Dividing Real Numbers
Extra Practice p. 702
Lesson 1-6: Examples 1, 5
Exercises 1–12, 40–43

Lesson Resources

📁 **Teaching Resources**
Practice, Reteaching, Enrichment

👥 **Reaching All Students**
Practice Workbook 2-1
Spanish Practice Workbook 2-1
Reading and Math Literacy 2A
Spanish Reading & Literacy 2A
Hands-On Activities 4
Basic Algebra Planning Guide 2-1

⏱ **Presentation Assistant Plus!**
Transparencies
• Check Skills You'll Need 2-1
• Additional Examples 2-1
• Student Edition Answers 2-1
• Lesson Quiz 2-1
PH Presentation Pro CD 2-1

PRENTICE HALL ASSESSMENT SYSTEM

Computer Test Generator CD

💿 **Technology**
Resource Pro® CD-ROM
Computer Test Generator CD
Prentice Hall Presentation Pro CD

🖥 **www.PHSchool.com**
Student Site
• Teacher Web Code: aek-5500
• Reasoning & Puzzles pp. 38–42
• Self-grading Lesson Quiz
Teacher Center
• Lesson Planner
• Resources

Plus iTEXT

2-1

Solving One-Step Equations

North Carolina Objectives
1.02 Use formulas and algebraic expressions, including iterative and recursive forms, to model and solve problems.

Lesson Preview

What You'll Learn

OBJECTIVE 1
To solve equations using addition and subtraction

OBJECTIVE 2
To solve equations using multiplication and division

. . . And Why

To model a geometric problem, as in Example 2

✓ **Check Skills You'll Need** (For help, go to Lessons 1-4, 1-5, and 1-6.)

Simplify each expression.

1. $x - 2 + 2x$ **2.** $n + 2 - 2n$ **3.** $\frac{c}{5} \cdot 5c$ **4.** $\frac{7m}{7} m$

For each number, state its opposite and its reciprocal.

5. $2 \ -2, \frac{1}{2}$ **6.** $-2 \ 2, -\frac{1}{2}$ **7.** $\frac{3}{5} \ -\frac{3}{5}, \frac{5}{3}$ **8.** $-\frac{3}{5} \ \frac{3}{5}, -\frac{5}{3}$

New Vocabulary   • solution of an equation   • equivalent equations
                      • inverse operations

Interactive lesson includes instant self-check, tutorials, and activities.

OBJECTIVE 1
Solving Equations Using Addition and Subtraction

An equation is like a balance scale because it shows that two quantities are equal. Look at the scales and equations below. The scales remain balanced when the same weight is added to each side.

$3 = 3$

$2 + 3 = 2 + 3$

Similarly, the scales remain balanced when the same weight is taken away from each side. This demonstrates the addition and subtraction properties of equality.

Key Concepts

Property	**Addition Property of Equality**
For every real number a, b, and c, if $a = b$, then $a + c = b + c$.	
Example $8 = 5 + 3$, so $8 + 4 = 5 + 3 + 4$.	

Property	**Subtraction Property of Equality**
For every real number a, b, and c, if $a = b$, then $a - c = b - c$.	
Example $8 = 5 + 3$, so $8 - 2 = 5 + 3 - 2$.	

74   Chapter 2   Solving Equations

Ongoing Assessment and Intervention

Before the Lesson
Diagnose prerequisite skills using:
• Check Skills You'll Need

During the Lesson
Monitor progress using:
• Check Understanding
• Additional Examples
• Standardized Test Prep

After the Lesson
Assess knowledge using:
• Lesson Quiz
• Computer Test Generator CD

Reading Math

The word *equivalent* is related to the word *equal*.

To solve an equation containing a variable, you find the value (or values) of the variable that make the equation true. Such a value is a **solution of the equation.** To find a solution, you can use properties of equality to form equivalent equations. **Equivalent equations** are equations that have the same solution (or solutions).

One way to solve an equation is to get the variable alone on one side of the equal sign. You can do this using **inverse operations,** which are operations that undo one another. Addition and subtraction are inverse operations.

1 EXAMPLE Using the Addition Property of Equality

Solve $x - 3 = -8$.

$x - 3 + 3 = -8 + 3$	Add 3 to each side to get the variable alone on one side of the equal sign.
$x = -5$	Simplify.
Check $\quad x - 3 = -8$	Check your solution in the original equation.
$-5 - 3 \stackrel{?}{=} -8$	Substitute -5 for x.
$-8 = -8$ ✓	

✓ **Check Understanding** ❶ Solve each equation. Check your answer.

 a. $m - 10 = 2$ **12** **b.** $y - 7.6 = 4$ **11.6** **c.** $-9 = b - 5$ **-4**

When you solve an equation involving addition, subtract the same number from each side of the equation.

2 EXAMPLE Using the Subtraction Property of Equality

Reading Math

$\overline{AB}$ represents a segment with endpoints A and B. AB represents the length of $\overline{AB}$.

Geometry The triangle below is isosceles with sides $\overline{AB}$ and $\overline{BC}$ congruent. Find the value of a.

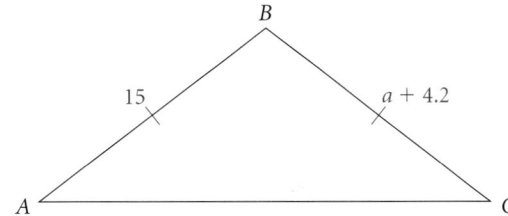

$AB = BC$	The lengths of congruent sides are equal.
$15 = a + 4.2$	Substitute.
$15 - 4.2 = a + 4.2 - 4.2$	Subtract 4.2 from each side.
$10.8 = a$	Simplify.
Check $\quad 15 = a + 4.2$	
$15 \stackrel{?}{=} 10.8 + 4.2$	Substitute 10.8 for a.
$15 = 15$ ✓	

✓ **Check Understanding** ❷ Solve each equation. Check your answer.

 a. $x + 5 = 6$ **1** **b.** $\frac{2}{3} + y = \frac{1}{4}$ **$-\frac{5}{12}$** **c.** $-18 = 6 + w$ **-24**

 Lesson 2-1 Solving One-Step Equations **75**

2. Teach

Professional Development

Math Background

The fundamental process of solving equations always involves writing equivalent equations. The use of graphs can help illustrate the relationship between two equations that are equivalent.

OBJECTIVE

▼ 1 Teaching Notes

❶ EXAMPLE English Learners

Some students may not understand the meaning of *balance*. To help these students feel the difference between balanced and *unbalanced* instruct them to stand on one foot while holding both arms out from their sides. After students are balanced, place a heavy book in one hand to show unbalanced. They must do something to compensate for the weight change to stay balanced. Let students use identical objects to achieve balance on a pan balance. Point out that when they add a weight to one side of a balance, they must add a like weight to the other side to keep the two sides in balance.

❷ EXAMPLE Connection to Geometry

Tick marks on geometric figures show congruence, or *having the same shape and size*. The parts of figures that have the same tick marks are congruent.

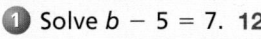 Additional Examples

❶ Solve $b - 5 = 7$. **12**

❷ Find the value of a. **5**

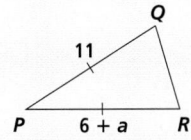

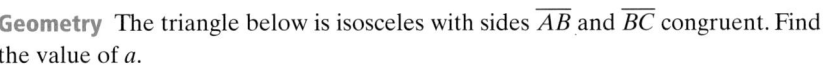
🫂 Reaching All Students

| **Below Level** Ask students to explain when they would use addition or subtraction, or multiplication or division on each side of an equation. | **Advanced Learners** Some students quickly grasp how to solve equations. Challenge students to work one-step equations mentally. | **English Learners** See note on page 75. **Auditory Learners** See note on page 78. |

Additional Examples

③ Together, you and your puppy weigh 128 lb. If you alone weigh 115 lb, how much does your puppy weigh? **13 lb**

② Teaching Notes

④ EXAMPLE   Math Tip

Students may be confused by how to handle the negative sign in $-\frac{r}{4}$. Remind students that $-\frac{r}{4}$ means $(-1)\frac{r}{4}$. Since $\frac{r}{4}$ is already being multiplied by (-1), when you multiply $-r$ by $\frac{1}{4}$ the result is the same as multiplying r by $-\frac{1}{4}$.

⑤ EXAMPLE   Teaching Tip

Some students may need to write 9 as $\frac{9}{1}$, then multiply by $\frac{4}{3}$ and simplify.

Additional Examples

④ Solve $-\frac{t}{6} = -9.3$. **55.8**

⑤ Solve $\frac{2}{5}y = -10$. **−25**

⑥ Solve $6m = -42$. **−7**

Closure

Ask: *When solving equations, what type of operations must you use to get the variable alone on one side of the equal sign?* **inverse operations**

You can write and solve equations describing real-world situations. Use estimation to check whether your solution is reasonable.

③ EXAMPLE   <u>Real-World</u>  **Problem Solving**

Weighing a Baby A mother holds her baby and steps on a scale as shown at the left. Alone, the mother weighs 129 lb. How much does the baby weigh?

Relate   baby's weight plus mother's weight   equals   scale reading

Define   Let w = the baby's weight.

Write w +   129   =   147

$$w + 129 = 147$$
$$w + 129 - 129 = 147 - 129 \quad \text{Subtract 129 from each side.}$$
$$w = 18 \quad \text{Simplify.}$$

The baby weighs 18 lb.

Check   Is the solution reasonable? The baby weighs about 20 lb, and the mother weighs about 130 lb. The baby's weight plus the mother's weight is about 150 lb, which is close to 147 lb. The answer is reasonable.

✓ **Check Understanding** **③ Banking** Brendan withdrew $25 from his bank account at an ATM. The transaction slip said his balance was then $243.19. Write and solve an equation to find Brendan's previous balance. **$268.19**

OBJECTIVE

② Solving Equations Using Multiplication and Division

Multiplication and division are inverse operations. When you multiply or divide to solve equations, you use the following properties.

 Key Concepts

Property	Multiplication Property of Equality

For every real number $a, b,$ and c, if $a = b$, then $a \cdot c = b \cdot c$.

Example $\frac{6}{2} = 3$, so $\frac{6}{2} \cdot 2 = 3 \cdot 2$.

Property	Division Property of Equality

For every real number $a, b,$ and c, with $c \neq 0$, if $a = b$, then $\frac{a}{c} = \frac{b}{c}$.

Example $3 + 1 = 4$, so $\frac{3+1}{2} = \frac{4}{2}$.

Multiplication and division are inverse operations. When you solve an equation involving division, multiply each side of the equation by the same number.

④ EXAMPLE   **Using the Multiplication Property of Equality**

Solve $-\frac{r}{4} = -10.4$.

$$-4\left(-\frac{r}{4}\right) = -4(-10.4) \quad \begin{array}{l}\text{Multiply each side by } -4 \text{ to get the variable alone}\\\text{on one side of the equal sign.}\end{array}$$
$$r = 41.6 \quad \text{Simplify.}$$

76   Chapter 2 Solving Equations

✓ Check Understanding ④ Solve each equation. Check your answer.

  a. $\frac{n}{6} = 5$ **30** **b.** $\frac{x}{-3} = 18$ **−54** **c.** $-\frac{a}{5} = -20$ **100**

In the next example, the coefficient of the variable is a fraction. You can use reciprocals to solve the equation.

⑤ **EXAMPLE** **Using Reciprocals to Solve Equations**

Solve $\frac{3}{4}x = 9$.

$\frac{4}{3}\left(\frac{3}{4}x\right) = \frac{4}{3}(9)$ **Multiply each side by $\frac{4}{3}$, the reciprocal of $\frac{3}{4}$.**

$x = 12$ **Simplify.**

Check $\frac{3}{4}x = 9$

$\frac{3}{4}(12) \overset{?}{=} 9$ **Substitute 12 for x.**

$9 = 9$ ✓

 Need Help?

To review reciprocals, see Lesson 1-6.

✓ Check Understanding ⑤ Solve each equation. Check your answer.

  a. $-\frac{1}{4}m = 8$ **−32** **b.** $\frac{3}{8}p = -15$ **−40** **c.** $\frac{8}{15} = \frac{2}{5}a$ **$1\frac{1}{3}$**

When you solve an equation involving multiplication, divide each side of the equation by the same number.

⑥ **EXAMPLE** **Using the Division Property of Equality**

Solve $4c = -96$.

$\frac{4c}{4} = \frac{-96}{4}$ **Divide each side by 4.**

$c = -24$ **Simplify.**

✓ Check Understanding ⑥ Solve each equation. Check your answer.

  a. $3a = 12$ **4** **b.** $20 = -2x$ **−10** **c.** $-8 = 5y$ **$-1\frac{3}{5}$**

EXERCISES

For more practice, see *Extra Practice*.

Practice and Problem Solving

Ⓐ **Practice by Example**

Example 1
(page 75)

Example 2
(page 75)

Solve each equation. Check your answer.

1. $x - 8 = 0$ **8** **2.** $n - 2 = -5$ **−3** **3.** $c - 4 = 9$ **13**

4. $23 = x - 17$ **40** **5.** $-3.5 = m - 2.5$ **−1** **6.** $x - \frac{2}{3} = 5$ **$5\frac{2}{3}$**

7. $x - \frac{4}{7} = \frac{3}{7}$ **1** **8.** $28.32 = p - 32.96$ **61.28** **9.** $c - 7.88 = 9.24$ **17.12**

10. $b + 5 = -13$ **−18** **11.** $x + 2 = 6$ **4** **12.** $23 + y = 16$ **−7**

13. $-31 = 26 + a$ **−57** **14.** $k + \frac{3}{11} = \frac{8}{11}$ **$\frac{5}{11}$** **15.** $4 = \frac{2}{3} + c$ **$3\frac{1}{3}$**

16. $x + 2.5 = 4.5$ **2** **17.** $5.25 + x = 3.75$ **−1.5** **18.** $73.35 = 4.37 + y$

  68.98

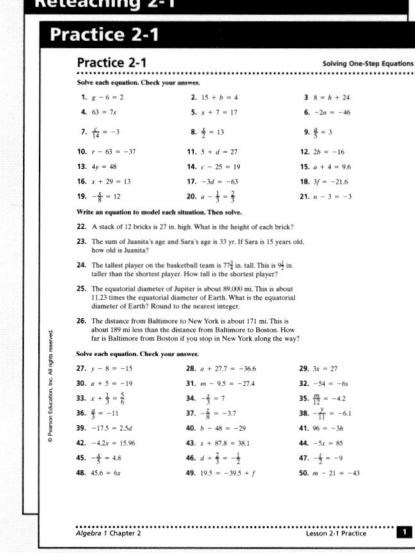

Example 3
(page 76)

Write an equation to model each situation. Then solve.

19. **Measurement** A physician's assistant measures a child and finds that his height is $41\frac{1}{2}$ in. At his last visit to the doctor's office, the child was $38\frac{3}{4}$ in. tall. How much did the child grow? $38\frac{3}{4} + g = 41\frac{1}{2}$; $2\frac{3}{4}$ **in.**

20. **Sales Tax** Sales tax charged by the state of Virginia is 4.5%. This is 2.5% less than the sales tax charged by the state of Rhode Island. What does Rhode Island charge for sales tax? **4.5 = t − 2.5; 7%**

Example 4
(page 76)

Solve each equation. Check your answer.

21. $\frac{y}{5} = 100$ **500**   22. $\frac{x}{2} = 98$ **196**   23. $\frac{m}{3} = -6$ **−18**   24. $\frac{w}{4} = -80$ **−320**

25. $28 = \frac{p}{7}$ **196**   26. $10 = \frac{a}{-2}$ **−20**   27. $-\frac{c}{7} = 35$ **−245**   28. $-\frac{r}{3} = -101$ **303**

Example 5
(page 77)

29. $-\frac{2}{3}x = 6$ **−9**   30. $\frac{2}{3}c = -18$ **−27**   31. $\frac{2}{5}a = -4$ **−10**   32. $\frac{3}{7}y = 1$ $2\frac{1}{3}$

33. $\frac{7}{8}w = 14$ **16**   34. $-\frac{2}{9}x = 10$ **−45**   35. $-\frac{1}{6}m = 12$ **−72**   36. $\frac{5}{11}n = 3$ $6\frac{3}{5}$

37. $\frac{5}{8}x = 8$ $12\frac{4}{5}$ 38. $-\frac{12}{17}y = 3$ $-4\frac{1}{4}$ 39. $\frac{4}{7}m = 8$ **14**   40. $\frac{3}{4}n = -\frac{3}{8}$ $-\frac{1}{2}$

Example 6
(page 77)

41. $5x = -75$ **−15**   42. $-7y = 28$ **−4**   43. $-8n = -64$ **8**   44. $6p = -120$ **−20**

45. $-6 = -3a$ **2**   46. $2 = -2m$ **−1**   47. $-4k = 52$ **−13**   48. $-3x = -48$ **16**

49. $-4 = 7x$ $-\frac{4}{7}$ 50. $9 = 11y$ $\frac{9}{11}$ 51. $-7m = 9$ $-1\frac{2}{7}$ 52. $9n = -5$ $-\frac{5}{9}$

 **Apply Your Skills**

53. **Estimation** Use estimation to check whether 96.26 is a reasonable solution for the equation $m - 62.74 = 159$. Explain. **No; 96.26 is close to 100 and 62.74 is close to 60, so the difference is close to 40.**

54. **Open-Ended** Write a word problem that you could solve using the equation $15n = 120$. **Answers may vary. Sample: CDs cost $15 each. How many CDs can you buy for $120?**

Solve each equation.

55. $14 + t = 16.1$ **2.1**   56. $\frac{2}{3}w = 12$ **18**   57. $b + 6\frac{1}{8} = 5\frac{3}{4}$ $-\frac{3}{8}$

58. $9\frac{2}{3} = a + 19$ $-9\frac{1}{3}$ 59. $\frac{x}{6} = -10$ **−60**   60. $y - 3.7 = 6.93$ **10.63**

61. $15.9 = r + 27.3$ **−11.4**   62. $-\frac{a}{7} = 2.5$ **−17.5**   63. $-3x = \frac{5}{6}$ $-\frac{5}{18}$

64. $\frac{x}{18} = 13.5$ **243**   65. $m - 1.2 = -2.09$ **−0.89**   66. $0.9x = 11.7$ **13**

67. $p + \frac{1}{4} = -3\frac{1}{2}$ $-3\frac{3}{4}$ 68. $6.1 + m = -11$ **−17.1**   69. $-1\frac{3}{4} = p - \frac{1}{2}$ $-1\frac{1}{4}$

Write an equation to model each situation. Then solve.

Average Annual Precipitation

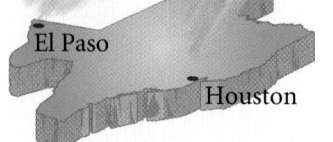

46 in.

?

El Paso

Houston

 70. **Weather** The average annual precipitation in Houston, Texas, is about 5.2 times that of El Paso, Texas. Use the information at the left to find the average annual precipitation in El Paso. Round to the nearest tenth. **5.2p = 46; 8.8 in.**

71. **Sports** In 1999, 189 physical therapists ran the New York City Marathon. This was 1048 fewer than the number of engineers who ran. How many engineers ran in the marathon? **189 = e − 1048; 1237 engineers**

72. **a. Tourism** Annual visits to Grand Canyon National Park increased from about 106,000 in 1915 to about 4,930,000 in 1999. What was the increase in the annual number of visits? **106,000 + i = 4,930,000; 4,824,000**

   b. Suppose $\frac{2}{5}$ of the park's visitors in 2000 were under the age of 18. If 1,928,000 visitors were under 18, what was the total number of visitors in 2000? $\frac{2}{5}v = 1,928,000$; **4,820,000**

73. Wages Suppose you work as a carpenter's apprentice. You earn $106.25 for working 17 hours. What is your hourly wage? **$17x = 106.25$, $6.25**

Use the cartoon for Exercises 74 and 75.

"Just a minute! Yesterday you said X equals two!"

74. Critical Thinking Explain what the student does *not* understand about using letters in algebra. **See left.**

74. Answers may vary. Sample: A letter only needs to represent the same value in related equations. If equations are not related, the values of the variable may be different.

75. What property of equality did the teacher use to solve the equation? **Subtr. Prop. of Eq.**

76. a. Error Analysis By using a calculator to solve the equation $-\frac{a}{6} = 11.2$, a student got the answer 672. What error (or errors) did the student make?

76a. The student forgot the neg. and used 112 instead of 11.2.

✎ **b. Writing** How could the student use estimation to catch the error? **See left.**

b. The student could have estimated by finding the product of -6 and 11, which is -66.

Geometry In each triangle, the measure of $\angle A$ = the measure of $\angle B$. Find the value of x.

77. 44

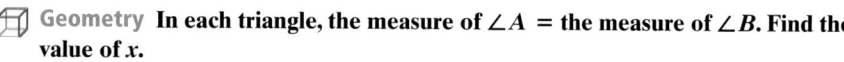

C, $52°$, $(x + 8)°$, A, B

78. A 14

$70°$, $(5x)°$, B, C

79. A $46°$ 92

$\left(\frac{x}{2}\right)°$, C, B

80. Labor Costs Your bill for a car repair is $166.50.
   a. One third of the bill is for labor. Write and solve an equation to find the cost for labor. **Let ℓ = cost of labor, $\frac{1}{3}(166.50) = \ell = \$55.50$**
   b. The mechanic worked on your car for 1.5 hours. What is the hourly charge for labor? **$37.00/h**

C Challenge

81. Geometry Two angles are supplementary if the sum of their measures is 180°. $\angle A$ and $\angle B$ are supplementary angles. The measure of $\angle A$ is 109°. What is the measure of $\angle B$? **71°**

82. a. Solve each equation.

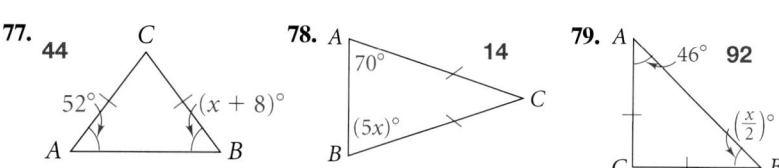

$22 = 23 + a$ $a = -1$ $\frac{s}{4} = \frac{1}{16}$ $s = \frac{1}{4}$

$-a = 0.1$ $a = -0.1$ $2T = -33$ $T = -16\frac{1}{2}$

$f + 10 = 11$ $f = 1$ $\frac{5}{8} + t = -\frac{1}{8}$ $t = -\frac{3}{4}$

$80h = -1288$ $h = -16.1$ $\frac{1}{5}u = 4$ $u = 20$

$9 + n = 33$ $n = 24$ $w - 1\frac{1}{6} = -1\frac{5}{6}$ $w = -\frac{2}{3}$

   b. Order the ten solutions from part (a) from least to greatest and use the letters used for variables to spell a word or phrase. **The phrase is "That was fun."**

▣ **Lesson Quiz 2-1**
Solve each equation.
1. $b - 8 = -2$ 6
2. $-12 = x + 9$ -21
3. $-\frac{y}{7} = 14$ -98
4. $28 = \frac{4}{5}x$ 35
5. $12r = -72$ -6

Alternative Assessment

Have students work in groups of four. Each member should write an equation that uses a different operation. Give each group enough algebra tiles to make models of each step of a solution. Have each group of students model the addition equation, then model each step of its solution. Repeat for the subtraction, multiplication, and division equations.

Careers

Exercise 83 A nutritionist is someone who studies, or is an expert on, nutrition. A nutritionist may also be referred to as a dietitian. Nutritionists help consumers make food choices to plan healthy diets. The recommended adequate intake of calcium is 1000 to 1200 mg per day. This may change because it is not known how much calcium is needed to prevent osteoporosis.

 83. Nutrition There are about 200 mg of calcium in 1 oz of cheddar cheese. This is only $\frac{2}{3}$ the amount of calcium in 1 c of skim milk. How many milligrams of calcium are in 1 c of skim milk? **300 mg**

84. a. For what value or values of x is $0 \cdot x = 0$? **all values of x**
   b. For what value or values of x is $0 \cdot x = 9$? **none**

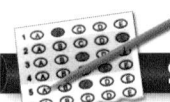

Standardized Test Prep

Multiple Choice

85. Solve $g + 7 = 28$. **D**
   A. -21 **B.** -4 **C.** 4   **D.** 21

86. Solve $\frac{2}{3}x = 18$. **H**
   F. 6   **G.** 12   **H.** 27   **I.** 36

87. During the first half of a basketball game, a team scored 38 points. They made only field goals, which are 2 points each. Which of the following equations could you use to find the number of field goals g the team scored? **D**
   A. $2 + g = 38$ **B.** $2 - g = 38$ **C.** $\frac{g}{2} = 38$ **D.** $2g = 38$

88. Jessica has $50.00 she wants to spend on CDs, which are on sale for $13.50 each. Which equation could you use to find out how many CDs she can afford to buy? **I**
   F. $c - 13.5 = 50$ **G.** $c + 13.5 = 50$ **H.** $50c = 13.5$ **I.** $13.5c = 50$

89. A meteorologist forecast that the high temperature would reach 34°F one afternoon. The low temperature for the day was −4°F. Which equation could you use to find out how many degrees d the temperature would need to rise to reach the predicted high temperature for the day? **B**
   A. $34 - 4 = d$ **B.** $-4 + d = 34$ **C.** $34 - d = 4$ **D.** $d - (-4) = 34$

90. Which of the following is an expression that represents "6 times the difference of a number n and 2"? **G**
   F. $6n - 2$ **G.** $6(n - 2)$ **H.** $6(n + 2)$ **I.** $6 \cdot 2 - n$

Take It to the NET
Online lesson quiz at
www.PHSchool.com
Web Code: aea-0201

Mixed Review

Lesson 1-9

Name the point in the coordinate plane with the given coordinates.

91. $(-2, 4)$ **A**   **92.** $(4, -2)$ **C**

93. $(4, 2)$ **B**   **94.** $(-2, -4)$ **D**

Lesson 1-8

Use the Distributive Property to simplify.

95. $5(a - 3)$ **5a − 15**   **96.** $(6 + y)(-2)$ **−12 − 2y**

97. $\frac{1}{2}(18 + m)$ **9 + $\frac{1}{2}$m**   **98.** $(4a - 5)(2c)$ **8ac − 10c**

Lesson 1-2

Simplify each expression.

99. $12 - 36 \div 6$ **6**   **100.** $5 \cdot 9 - 2^2$ **41**   **101.** $3 \cdot 2 + 13 - 4 \cdot 8$ **−13**

Solving Two-Step Equations

 North Carolina Objectives

1.02 Use formulas and algebraic expressions, including iterative and recursive forms, to model and solve problems.

Lesson Preview

What You'll Learn

OBJECTIVE 1 To solve two-step equations

OBJECTIVE 2 To use deductive reasoning

. . . And Why

To solve a problem involving ordering from a catalog, as in Example 2

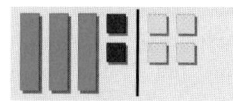 **Check Skills You'll Need**   (For help, go to Lesson 2-1.)

Solve each equation and tell which property of equality you used.

1. $x - 5 = 14$ **2.** $x + 3.8 = 9$ **3.** $-7 + x = 7$

4. $x - 13 = 20$ **5.** $\frac{x}{4} = 8$ **6.** $9 = 3x$

Solve each equation.

7. $10x = 2$ **8.** $\frac{2}{3}x = -6$ **9.** $x + 2\frac{3}{4} = 6\frac{1}{2}$

1–9. See back of book.

2-2 North Carolina Objectives 1.02

1. Plan

Lesson Preview

 **Check Skills You'll Need**

Solving One-Step Equations
Lesson 2-1: Examples 1–6
Exercises 1–52
Extra Practice, p. 703

Lesson Resources

Teaching Resources
Practice, Reteaching, Enrichment

Reaching All Students
Practice Workbook 2-2
Spanish Practice Workbook 2-2
Basic Algebra Planning Guide 2-2

Presentation Assistant Plus!
Transparencies
• Check Skills You'll Need 2-2
• Additional Examples 2-2
• Student Edition Answers 2-2
• Lesson Quiz 2-2
PH Presentation Pro CD 2-2

PRENTICE HALL ASSESSMENT SYSTEM

Computer Test Generator CD

Technology
Resource Pro® CD-ROM
Computer Test Generator CD
Prentice Hall Presentation Pro CD

www.PHSchool.com
Student Site
• Teacher Web Code: aek-5500
• Reasoning & Puzzles p. 43
• Self-grading Lesson Quiz
Teacher Center
• Lesson Planner
• Resources

Plus

OBJECTIVE 1 **Solving Two-Step Equations**

 **Interactive lesson** includes instant self-check, tutorials, and activities.

A two-step equation is an equation that involves two operations. Models can help you understand how to find the solution of a two-step equation.

 Need Help?

The zero pair

represents zero. Equal numbers of yellow and red tiles represent zeros.

$3x - 2 = 4$ 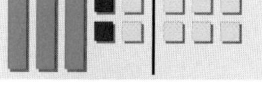   The tiles model the equation. A green tile represents *x*.

$3x - 2 + 2 = 4 + 2$    Add 2 to each side.

$3x = 6$ 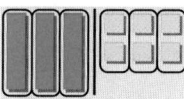   Simplify by removing zero pairs.

$\frac{3x}{3} = \frac{6}{3}$ Divide each side into three equal groups.

$x = 2$ Each green tile equals two yellow tiles, so *x* = 2.

 Key Concepts

Summary	**Solving Two-Step Equations**

Step 1 Use the Addition or Subtraction Property of Equality to get the term with a variable alone on one side of the equation.

Step 2 Use the Multiplication or Division Property of Equality to write an equivalent equation in which the variable has a coefficient of 1.

 Ongoing Assessment and Intervention

Before the Lesson
Diagnose prerequisite skills using:
• Check Skills You'll Need

During the Lesson
Monitor progress using:
• Check Understanding
• Additional Examples
• Standardized Test Prep

After the Lesson
Assess knowledge using:
• Lesson Quiz
• Computer Test Generator CD

Math Background

In isolating the variable, the order of operations is reversed, so that addition/subtraction is undone first before multiplication/division. The validity of the process of solving an equation is based on deductive reasoning, with each step justified by citing a property, or a theorem, or a definition, and so on.

OBJECTIVE

1 **Teaching Notes**

1 EXAMPLE **Teaching Tip**

Point out that since you use the *inverse* (opposite) operation to undo, you perform these operations in the *opposite* order from the order of operations. First, undo addition and subtraction. Then, undo multiplication and division.

2 EXAMPLE **Error Prevention**

Some students may want to divide by 0.75 first. Write $6a - 2 = -8$ in two places on the board. Solve one equation by adding 2 and then dividing by 6 on both sides. Solve the other as follows:

$$6a - 2 = -8$$
$$\frac{6a}{6} - \frac{2}{6} = -\frac{8}{6}$$
$$a - \frac{1}{3} = -\frac{4}{3}$$
$$a - \frac{1}{3} + \frac{1}{3} = -\frac{4}{3} + \frac{1}{3}$$
$$a = -\frac{3}{3}$$
$$a = -1$$

Ask: *Why is 2 divided by 6 in the first step?* **You must divide all terms in the equation by 6, not just some of them.** Lead students to see that the results are the same, but the traditional way is easier.

---

1 EXAMPLE **Solving a Two-Step Equation**

Solve $10 = \frac{m}{4} + 2$.

$10 - 2 = \frac{m}{4} + 2 - 2$	**Subtract 2 from each side.**
$8 = \frac{m}{4}$	**Simplify.**
$4 \cdot 8 = 4 \cdot \frac{m}{4}$	**Multiply each side by 4.**
$32 = m$	**Simplify.**

Check $10 = \frac{m}{4} + 2$

$10 \stackrel{?}{=} \frac{32}{4} + 2$	**Substitute 32 for *m*.**
$10 \stackrel{?}{=} 8 + 2$	
$10 = 10$ ✓	

✓ Check Understanding **1** Solve each equation. Check your answer.
a. $7 = 2y - 3$ **5**   **b.** $6a + 2 = -8$ **$-1\frac{2}{3}$**   **c.** $\frac{x}{9} - 15 = 12$ **243**

You can write two-step equations to model real-world situations. Some real-world situations require whole-number answers. So check that your answer is reasonable in the given situation.

2 EXAMPLE **Real-World 🌐 Problem Solving**

Retailing You are ordering tulip bulbs from a flower catalog. You have $14 to spend. Use the catalog page at the left to determine the number of bulbs you can order.

Relate | cost per tulip bulb | times | number of tulip bulbs | plus | shipping | equals | amount to spend |

Define Let b = number of bulbs you can order.

Write | 0.75 | · | b | + | 3 | = | 14 |

$0.75b + 3 = 14$	
$0.75b + 3 - 3 = 14 - 3$	**Subtract 3 from each side.**
$0.75b = 11$	**Simplify.**
$\frac{0.75b}{0.75} = \frac{11}{0.75}$	**Divide each side by 0.75.**
$b = 14.\overline{6}$	**Simplify.**

You can order 14 bulbs.

Check Is the solution reasonable? You can only order whole tulip bulbs. Since 15 bulbs would cost $15 \cdot \$0.75 = \$11.25$ plus $3 for handling, which is more than $14, you can only order 14 tulip bulbs.

✓ Check Understanding **2** Suppose tulips are on sale for $.60 per bulb. What number of bulbs can you order? **18 bulbs**

In some equations, the variable may have a negative sign in front of it, such as $-x = 3$. To help you solve these equations, recall that $x = 1 \cdot x$ and $-x = -1 \cdot x$. You can solve for x by multiplying or dividing by -1.

👫 Reaching All Students

Below Level Use the mnemonic: a number *down* in the *denominator* represents *division* by that number. Since 4 is in the denominator of Example 1, students must multiply by 4 to solve.	**Advanced Learners** Ask students to determine whether they will get the same answer to the equation in Example 3 if they first multiply both sides by -1, and then subtract 6.	**Alternative Method** See note on page 83. **Error Prevention** See note on page 82.

3 EXAMPLE Multiplying by Negative 1

Solve $-b + 6 = -11$.

$-b + 6 - 6 = -11 - 6$	Subtract 6 from each side.
$-b = -17$	Simplify.
$-1(-b) = -1(-17)$	Use the Multiplication Property of Equality. Multiply each side by -1.
$b = 17$	Simplify.

✔ **Check Understanding** ③ Solve each equation.

a. $-x + 7 = 12$ -5 **b.** $-a - 5 = -8$ 3 **c.** $4 = -c + 11$ 7

OBJECTIVE

2 Using Deductive Reasoning

To justify each step as you solve an equation, use deductive reasoning and the properties of equality.

Need Help?

For help with deductive reasoning see p. 56.

4 EXAMPLE Using Deductive Reasoning

Solve $1 = \frac{k}{12} + 5$. Justify each step.

Steps	Reasons
$1 = \frac{k}{12} + 5$	original equation
$1 - 5 = \frac{k}{12} + 5 - 5$	Subtraction Property of Equality
$-4 = \frac{k}{12}$	Subtract.
$(12)(-4) = (12)\frac{k}{12}$	Multiplication Property of Equality
$-48 = k$	Multiply.

✔ **Check Understanding** ④ Solve $\frac{3}{5}w + 9 = -1$. Justify each step. **See margin.**

Remember that an expression like $8 - 3y$ can be rewritten as $8 + (-3y)$ using the definition of subtraction.

5 EXAMPLE Using Deductive Reasoning

Solve $8 - 3y = 14$. Justify each step.

Steps	Reasons
$8 - 3y = 14$	original equation
$8 + (-3y) = 14$	definition of subtraction
$8 + (-3y) - 8 = 14 - 8$	Subtraction Property of Equality
$-3y = 6$	Subtract.
$\frac{-3y}{-3} = \frac{6}{-3}$	Division Property of Equality
$y = -2$	Divide.

✔ **Check Understanding** ⑤ Solve $-9 - 4m = 3$. Justify each step.

$-9 - 4m + 9 = 3 + 9$	Add. Prop. of Eq.
$-4m = 12$	Simplify.
$\frac{-4m}{-4} = \frac{12}{-4}$	Div. Prop. of Eq.
$m = -3$	Simplify.

Lesson 2-2 Solving Two-Step Equations   **83**

page 83   **Check Understanding**

4. $\frac{3}{5}w + 9 - 9 = -1 - 9$ **Subtr. Prop. of Eq.**

$\frac{3}{5}w = -10$ **Simplify.**

$\frac{3}{5}w \cdot \frac{5}{3} = -10 \cdot \frac{5}{3}$ **Mult. Prop. of Eq.**

$w = -16\frac{2}{3}$ **Simplify.**

3 EXAMPLE Alternative Method

Suggest to students that they read $-b = -17$ as "the *opposite* of b equals the opposite of 17."

Additional Examples

① Solve $13 = \frac{y}{3} + 5$. **24**

② You order iris bulbs from a catalog. Iris bulbs cost $.90 each. The shipping charge is $2.50. If you have $18.50 to spend, how many iris bulbs can you order? **17 iris bulbs**

③ Solve $-p + 8 = 21$. **−13**

OBJECTIVE

2 Teaching Notes

4 EXAMPLE Connection to Science

Point out that the scientific method requires all answers to be proved logically. The method uses both deductive and inductive logical reasoning.

Additional Examples

④ Solve $8 = \frac{c}{24} + 4$. Justify each step.

$8 - 4 = \frac{c}{24} + 4 - 4$

Subt. Prop. of Equality

$4 = \frac{c}{24}$ **Simplify.**

$(24)(4) = (24)(\frac{c}{24})$

Mult. Prop. of Equality

$96 = c$ **Simplify.**

⑤ Solve $3 - 5z = 18$. Justify each step.

$3 - 5z - 3 = 18 - 3$

Subt. Prop. of Equality

$-5z = 15$ **Simplify.**

$\frac{-5z}{-5} = \frac{15}{-5}$

Div. Prop. of Equality

$z = -3$ **Simplify.**

Closure

Ask: *What order of operations should you use to solve two-step equations?* First, undo any addition or subtraction. Then, undo the multiplication or division.

83

3. Practice

Assignment Guide

**Objective**

Ⓐ Ⓑ **Core** 1–35, 40–51, 56–69, 74

Ⓒ **Extension** 75–77

**Objective**

Ⓐ Ⓑ **Core** 36–39, 52–55, 70–73

Ⓒ **Extension** 78–80

Standardized Test Prep 81–85

Mixed Review 86–97

Exercise 19 Suggest to students that they first estimate the solution. Lead a discussion about how estimation can be used to evaluate whether a bill is reasonable.

Teaching Tip

Exercises 71, 72 Suggest to students that they first solve the exercise, and then compare their solution with that in the book.

Exercise 73 For students struggling to begin, suggest they model a hobby or activity that involves counting.

Enrichment 2-2
Reteaching 2-2
Practice 2-2

EXERCISES

For more practice, see *Extra Practice*.

Practice and Problem Solving

Ⓐ **Practice by Example**

Example 1
(page 82)

Solve each equation. Check your answer.

1. $1 + \frac{a}{5} = -1$ **-10** **2.** $2n - 5 = 7$ **6** **3.** $-1 = 3 + 4x$ **-1** **4.** $\frac{y}{2} + 5 = -12$ **-34**

5. $3b + 7 = -2$ **-3** **6.** $\frac{x}{3} - 9 = 0$ **27** **7.** $14 + \frac{h}{5} = 2$ **-60** **8.** $-10 = -6 + 2c$ **-2**

9. $\frac{m}{8} + 4 = 16$ **96** **10.** $\frac{a}{4} - 21 = 7$ **112** **11.** $3x - 1 = 8$ **3** **12.** $10 = 2n + 1$ **4½**

13. $35 = 3 + 5x$ **6⅖** **14.** $41 = \frac{2}{5}x - 7$ **120** **15.** $-3 + \frac{m}{3} = 12$ **45** **16.** $9 + \frac{n}{5} = 19$ **50**

Example 2
(page 82)

Define a variable and write an equation for each situation. Then solve.

17. Donations A library receives a large cash donation and uses the funds to double the number of books it owns. Then a book collector gives the library 4028 books. After this, the library has 51,514 books. How many books did the library have before the cash donation and the gift of books? **2n + 4028 = 51,514; 23,743 books**

18. Cooking Suppose you are helping to prepare a large meal. You can peel 2 carrots per minute. You need 60 peeled carrots. How long will it take you to finish if you have already peeled 18 carrots? **2m + 18 = 60; 21 min**

19. Cell Phones One cell phone plan costs $39.95 per month. The first 500 minutes of usage are free. Each minute thereafter costs $.35. For a bill of $69.70, how many minutes over 500 minutes was the cell phone in use? **39.95 + 0.35m = 69.70; 85 min**

Example 3
(page 83)

Solve each equation. Check your answer.

20. $-b + 5 = -16$ **21** **21.** $-p - 24 = -8$ **-16** **22.** $-7 = -c - 29$ **-22** **23.** $-y - 52 = 33$ **-85**

24. $-m + 2 = 11$ **-9** **25.** $-9 = -a + 16$ **25** **26.** $-x + 100 = 100$ **0** **27.** $-1 = -n - 3$ **-2**

28. $-y - 3 = 8$ **-11** **29.** $15 = -z + 8$ **-7** **30.** $-q + 5 = 10$ **-5** **31.** $-a + 9 = 25$ **-16**

32. $-x - 4 = 20$ **-24** **33.** $-y + 10 = 25$ **-15** **34.** $5 = -z - 3$ **-8** **35.** $9 = -x + 8$ **-1**

Examples 4, 5
(page 83)

Justify each step.

36.
$\frac{x}{5} + 9 = 11$	
$\frac{x}{5} + 9 - 9 = 11 - 9$	Subtr. Prop. of Eq.
$\frac{x}{5} = 2$	Simplify.
$5\left(\frac{x}{5}\right) = 5(2)$	Mult. Prop. of Eq.
$x = 10$	Simplify.

37.
$-y - 5 = 11$	
$-y - 5 + 5 = 11 + 5$	Add. Prop. of Eq.
$-y = 16$	Simplify.
$-1(-y) = -1(16)$	Mult. Prop. of Eq.
$y = -16$	Simplify.

38.
$18 - n = 21$	
$18 - n - 18 = 21 - 18$	Subtr. Prop. of Eq.
$-n = 3$	Simplify.
$-1(-n) = -1(3)$	Mult. Prop. of Eq.
$n = -3$	Simplify.

39.
$12 - 2h = 8$	
$12 - 2h - 12 = 8 - 12$	Subtr. Prop. of Eq.
$-2h = -4$	Simplify.
$\frac{-2h}{-2} = \frac{-4}{-2}$	Div. Prop. of Eq.
$h = 2$	Simplify.

Ⓑ **Apply Your Skills**

Solve each equation.

40. $\frac{5}{7}x + \frac{1}{7} = 3$ **4** **41.** $\frac{a}{5} + 15 = 30$ **75** **42.** $-\frac{1}{5}t - 2 = 4$ **-30** **43.** $-6 + 6z = 0$ **1**

44. $3.5 + 10m = 7.32$ **0.382** **45.** $7 = -2x + 7$ **0** **46.** $\frac{1}{2} = \frac{2}{5}c - 3$ **8¾** **47.** $10.7 = -d + 4.3$ **-6.4**

48. $0.4x + 9.2 = 10$ **2** **49.** $4x + 92 = 100$ **2** **50.** $-t - 0.4 = -3$ **2.6** **51.** $-10t - 4 = -30$ **2.6**

pages 84–86   Exercises

52.
$8 + \frac{c}{-4} - 8 = -6 - 8$	Subtr. Prop. of Eq.
$\frac{c}{-4} = -14$	Simplify.
$\frac{c}{-4}(-4) = -14(-4)$	Mult. Prop. of Eq.
$c = 56$	Simplify.

53.
$7 - 3k - 7 = -14 - 7$	Subtr. Prop. of Eq.
$-3k = -21$	Simplify.
$\frac{-3k}{-3} = \frac{-21}{-3}$	Div. Prop. of Eq.
$k = 7$	Simplify.

Solve each equation. Justify each step. 52–55. See margin p. 84.

52. $8 + \frac{c}{-4} = -6$ **53.** $7 - 3k = -14$ **54.** $14 = 6 - 2p$ **55.** $\frac{-y}{2} + 14 = -1$

Define a variable and write an equation for each situation. Then solve.

 56. Mining Beneath Earth's surface, the temperature increases 10°C every kilometer. Suppose that the surface temperature is 22°C, and the temperature at the bottom of a gold mine is 45°C. What is the depth of the gold mine? **$10k + 22 = 45$; 2.3 km**

57. Insurance One health insurance policy pays people for claims by multiplying the claim amount by 0.8 and then subtracting $500. If a person receives a check for $4650, how much was the claim amount? **$0.8c - 500 = 4650$; $6437.50**

58. Library The Library of Congress in Washington, D.C., is the largest library in the world. It contains nearly 125 million items. The library adds about 10,000 items to its collection daily. How many days will it take the library to reach about 150 million items? **$10{,}000d + 125{,}000{,}000 = 150{,}000{,}000$; about 2500 days**

Solve each equation. (*Hint:* As your first step, multiply each side by the denominator of the fraction.)

59. $\frac{x + 2}{9} = 5$ **43**   **60.** $\frac{y + 1}{3} = 2$ **5**   **61.** $\frac{a - 10}{-4} = 2$ **2**   **62.** $\frac{b - 7}{2} = 6$ **19**

63. $\frac{x - 5}{2} = 10$ **25**   **64.** $\frac{x - 3}{7} = 12$ **87**   **65.** $\frac{x + 4}{3} = -8$ **−28**   **66.** $\frac{x + 6}{4} = \frac{-7}{}$ **−34**

Geometry In each triangle, the measure of $\angle A$ = the measure of $\angle B$. **Find the value of x.**

67.

68. **15.5**

69. **31.5**

70. **x is the amount he needs to save each week; in 16 weeks he will save $16x$ dollars and have a total of $(40 + 16x)$ dollars. That amount should equal $129.**

70. Writing Miles has saved $40. He wants to buy a CD player for $129 in about four months. To find how much he should save each week, he wrote $40 + 16x = 129$. Explain his equation. **See left.**

Error Analysis What is the error in the work? Solve each equation correctly.

71.

$12 - 3y = 15$
$3y = 3$
$y = 1$

71. The neg. sign was dropped; −1.

72. −12 was divided by 3 instead of multiplied by 3; −36.

72.

$\frac{m}{3} - 9 = -21$
$\frac{m}{3} - 9 + 9 = -21 + 9$
$\frac{m}{3} = -12$
$m = -4$

73. Open-Ended Write a problem that you can model with a two-step equation. Write an equation and solve the problem. **Answers may vary.**

74. You can find the value of each variable in the matrices below by writing and solving equations. For example, to find the value of a, you solve the equation $2a + 1 = 11$. Find the values of a, x, y, and k.

$$\begin{bmatrix} 2a + 1 & -6 \\ -7 & -3k \end{bmatrix} = \begin{bmatrix} 11 & x - 5 \\ 5 - 2y & 27 \end{bmatrix}$$ **5; −1; 6; −9**

Reading Math
For help with reading and solving Exercise 56, see p. 87.

Real-World Connection

Since 1950, the size of the collections and the size of the staff of the Library of Congress have tripled.

4. Assess

Lesson Quiz 2-2

Solve each equation.

1. $3b + 8 = -10$ −6

2. $-12 = -3x - 9$ 1

3. $-\frac{c}{4} + 7 = 14$ −28

4. $-x - 13 = 35$ −48

5. What is the justification for the following step?

$12 - 2y = 46$

$12 - 2y - 12 = 46 - 12$

Subt. Prop. of Equality

Alternative Assessment

Instruct students to choose any problem from Exercises 1–16 that does not contain a fraction. Have each student draw a model of his or her chosen equation. Encourage students to use symbols such as squares and circles. Let one symbol represent the variable term and the other symbol represent the integers. Shade negative integers. For example $3b + 4 = -2$ can be drawn as 3 boxes and 4 unshaded circles equals 2 shaded circles. Instruct students to model the steps of the solution to the chosen equation and justify each step.

54. $14 - 6 = 6 - 2p - 6$ Subtr. Prop. of Eq.
$\quad\quad 8 = -2p$ Simplify.
$\quad\quad \frac{8}{-2} = \frac{-2p}{-2}$ Div. Prop. of Eq.
$\quad\quad -4 = p$ Simplify.

55. $\frac{-y}{2} + 14 - 14 = -1 - 14$ Subtr. Prop. of Eq.
$\quad\quad \frac{-y}{2} = -15$ Simplify.
$\quad\quad \frac{-y}{2}(-2) = -15(-2)$ Mult. Prop. of Eq.
$\quad\quad y = 30$ Simplify.

85

75. Critical Thinking If you multiply each side of $0.24r + 5.25 = -7.23$ by 100, the result is an equivalent equation. Explain why it might be helpful to do this. **This eliminates the decimals.**

Use the table at the right for Exercises 76 and 77.

 76. A formula for converting a temperature from Celsius C to Fahrenheit F is $F = 1.8C + 32$. Copy and complete the table. Round to the nearest degree.

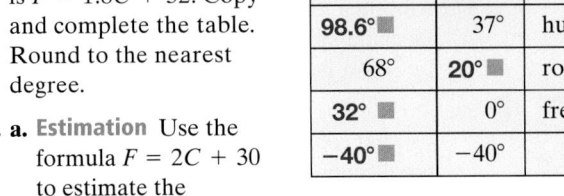

Fahrenheit	Celsius	Description of Temperature
212°	100°	boiling point of water
98.6°	37°	human body temperature
68°	20°	room temperature
32°	0°	freezing point of water
−40°	−40°	

77. a. Estimation Use the formula $F = 2C + 30$ to estimate the Fahrenheit temperatures not shown in the table. **104°F; 30°F; −50°F**

   b. Critical Thinking Compare your estimated values with the actual values. How good is your formula at estimating the actual temperatures? Explain.
   Answers may vary. Sample: The formula gives good estimates except for −40°C.

Solve the first equation for x. Then substitute your result into the second equation and solve for y.

78. $x + y = 8$ **$8 − y$; 5**
$2x + 3y = 21$

79. $x + 2y = 1$ **$1 − 2y$; 2**
$6x − y = −20$

80. $x + y = 12$ **$12 − y$; 7**
$2x + y = 17$

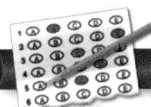

Standardized Test Prep

Gridded Response

$\frac{8}{5}$ **(or its equivalent)**
81. What is the value of the expression $-\frac{3}{5}x - 2$ when $x = -6$?

82. Dana has a photograph that is 4 in. wide and 5 in. long. She has the photo enlarged so that both dimensions are tripled. How many times larger than the original area will the area of the enlargement be? **9**

83. What is the value of the following expression? $\dfrac{3^2 \times 4 - (-5)^2}{(-2)^3 + 3 \times 4}$
2.75 (or its equivalent)

84. Last season, Everett scored 48 points. This is 6 less than twice the number of points Max scored. How many points did Max score? **27**

85. A cable television company charges $24.95 a month for basic cable service and $6.95 a month for each additional premium channel. If Sami's monthly bill is $45.80, how many premium channels is he receiving? **3**

Mixed Review

Lesson 2-1

Solve each equation.

86. $4s = 18$ **$4\frac{1}{2}$**   **87.** $x - 3 = 9$ **12**   **88.** $\frac{m}{5} = 3$ **15**   **89.** $-7 = n + 2$ **−9**

90. $7x = 42$ **6**   **91.** $3y = 99$ **33**   **92.** $5z = 57$ **$11\frac{2}{5}$**   **93.** $8a = 48$ **6**

Lessons 1-3, 1-4

Simplify.

94. $-2 + 6$ **4**   **95.** $9 + (-3)$ **6**   **96.** $-7 + (-4)$ **−11**   **97.** $16 + (-4)$ **12**

Reading for Problem Solving

Read through the problem below. Then follow along with what Maria thinks as she solves the problem. Check your understanding with the exercise at the bottom of the page.

Beneath Earth's surface, the temperature increases 10°C every kilometer. Suppose that the surface temperature is 22°C, and the temperature at the bottom of a gold mine is 45°C. What is the depth of the gold mine?

What Maria Thinks

I need to read the problem carefully so that I can understand it. I'll write down the important information.

The temperature increases 10 degrees for every kilometer I go down. This means I multiply. Now I can relate the temperature and the depth.

Since I am trying to find the depth of the gold mine, I'll let d be the depth in kilometers.

Now I can use the variable to write an equation.

I can solve the equation for d. First I subtract 22 from both sides. Then I divide each side by 10, to get d by itself.

I will state my answer in a sentence. Also, I need to remember to include the units.

What Maria Writes

The temperature at the surface is 22°C.
The temperature at the bottom is 45°C.
The temperature increases 10°C for every kilometer you go down.

$$\text{surface temperature} + 10 \text{ times depth} = \text{bottom temperature}$$

$d = $ depth, in kilometers

$$22 + 10d = 45$$

$$22 - 22 + 10d = 45 - 22$$
$$10d = 23$$
$$\frac{10d}{10} = \frac{23}{10}$$
$$d = 2.3$$

The gold mine is 2.3 km deep.

EXERCISE

The temperature at a ski slope decreases 2.5°F for every thousand feet of elevation above the base. The temperature at the base is 28°F and the temperature at the summit is 24°F. How many thousand feet above the base is the summit? **1.6**

Reading for Problem Solving

Students will read through a problem and follow the thinking of "another student." Not only do students see what the "other student" thought, but what relationships, variables, equations and calculations she did in order to solve the problem. Understanding how someone else thinks about and solves a problem should provide students strategies for solving problems on their own.

Teaching Notes

Have students tell you what words in the problem help them translate it into mathematical symbols. Ask: *What word or words indicate addition?* increases *What word or words indicate multiplication?* 10 degrees for *every* kilometer

Math Tip

Remind students that there are two things they should do when solving problems. The first is to **estimate** the answer. In this example, since 22 + 10 + 10 is 42 (42 is close to 45) and each 10 degrees represents a kilometer, the answer must be a little more than 2 kilometers. They should see that the answer of 2.3 is a reasonable answer. The second thing they should do is to **check** the answer. Is $2.3 \times 10 + 22 = 45$? Yes, it is. The answer checks.

Exercise

Have students work in pairs to solve a problem. Each will work independently to solve it and write an explanation and thinking (similar to the example). Then have the pairs exchange papers and discuss whether they understand and agree with the other's thinking and answers.

Lesson Preview

 Check Skills You'll Need

Order of Operations
Lesson 1-2: Example 2
Exercises 7–12
Extra Practice, p. 702

The Distributive Property
Lesson 1-7: Examples 3, 4
Exercises 15–34
Extra Practice, p. 702

Lesson Resources

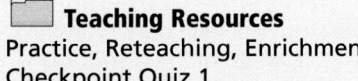 **Teaching Resources**
Practice, Reteaching, Enrichment
Checkpoint Quiz 1

Reaching All Students
Practice Workbook 2-3
Spanish Practice Workbook 2-3
Reading and Math Literacy 2B
Spanish Reading & Literacy 2B
Spanish Checkpoint Quiz 1
Basic Algebra Planning Guide 2-3

Presentation Assistant Plus!
Transparencies
• Check Skills You'll Need 2-3
• Additional Examples 2-3
• Student Edition Answers 2-3
• Lesson Quiz 2-3
PH Presentation Pro CD 2-3

 **PRENTICE HALL ASSESSMENT SYSTEM**

Checkpoint Quiz 1
Computer Test Generator CD

 **Technology**
Resource Pro® CD-ROM
Computer Test Generator CD
Prentice Hall Presentation Pro CD

www.PHSchool.com
Student Site
• Teacher Web Code: aek-5500
• Self-grading Lesson Quiz
Teacher Center
• Lesson Planner
• Resources

Plus

88

2-3

Solving Multi-Step Equations

North Carolina Objectives   1.02   Use formulas and algebraic expressions, including iterative and recursive forms, to model and solve problems.

Lesson Preview

What You'll Learn

OBJECTIVE 1 To use the Distributive Property when combining like terms

OBJECTIVE 2 To use the Distributive Property when solving equations

. . . And Why

To solve a problem involving building a fence, as in Example 2

 Check Skills You'll Need   (For help, go to Lessons 1-2 and 1-7.)

Simplify each expression.

1. $2n - 3n$ $-n$

2. $-4 + 3b + 2 + 5b$ $8b - 2$

3. $9(w - 5)$ $9w - 45$

4. $-10(b - 12)$ $-10b + 120$

5. $3(-x + 4)$ $-3x + 12$

6. $5(6 - w)$ $30 - 5w$

Evaluate each expression.

7. $28 - a + 4a$ for $a = 5$ **43**

8. $8 + x - 7x$ for $x = -3$ **26**

9. $(8n + 1)3$ for $n = -2$ **−45**

10. $-(17 + 3y)$ for $y = 6$ **−35**

OBJECTIVE 1

Using the Distributive Property to Combine Like Terms

IEXT Interactive lesson includes instant self-check, tutorials, and activities.

Need Help?

You use the Distributive Property whenever you add or subtract like terms.

$x + 4x = 1x + 4x$
$= (1 + 4)x$
$= 5x$

You can solve equations that require more than two steps. They are called multi-step equations. If there are like terms on one side of an equation, first use the Distributive Property to combine them. Then use the properties of equality to solve the equation.

1 EXAMPLE   **Combining Like Terms**

Solve each equation.

a. $2c + c + 12 = 78$

$2c + c + 12 = 78$

$3c + 12 = 78$ Combine like terms.

$3c + 12 - 12 = 78 - 12$ Subtract 12 from each side.

$3c = 66$ Simplify.

$\frac{3c}{3} = \frac{66}{3}$ Divide each side by 3.

$c = 22$ Simplify.

b. $4b + 16 + 2b = 46$

$4b + 16 + 2b = 46$

$4b + 2b + 16 = 46$ Use the Commutative Property of Addition.

$6b + 16 = 46$ Combine like terms.

$6b + 16 - 16 = 46 - 16$ Subtract 16 from each side.

$6b = 30$ Simplify.

$\frac{6b}{6} = \frac{30}{6}$ Divide each side by 6.

$b = 5$ Simplify.

Check Understanding **1** Solve each equation. Check your answer.

a. $3x - 4x + 6 = -2$ **8**

b. $7 = 4m - 2m + 1$ **3**

c. $-2y + 5 + 5y = 14$ **3**

d. $-3z + 8 + (-2z) = -12$ **4**

Ongoing Assessment and Intervention

Before the Lesson
Diagnose prerequisite skills using:
• Check Skills You'll Need

During the Lesson
Monitor progress using:
• Check Understanding
• Additional Examples
• Standardized Test Prep

After the Lesson
Assess knowledge using:
• Lesson Quiz
• Computer Test Generator CD
• Chapter Checkpoint 1 (p. 94)

You can model real-world situations using multi-step equations.

2. Teach

Math Background

You may need to illustrate Example 1 in greater detail by writing $2c + c = (2 + 1)c$. Students often lose sight of this use of the Distributive Property.

2 EXAMPLE Real-World 🌐 Problem Solving

Gardening A gardener is planning a rectangular garden area in a community garden. His garden will be next to an existing 12-ft fence. The gardener has a total of 44 ft of fencing to build the other three sides of his garden. How long will the garden be if the width is 12 ft?

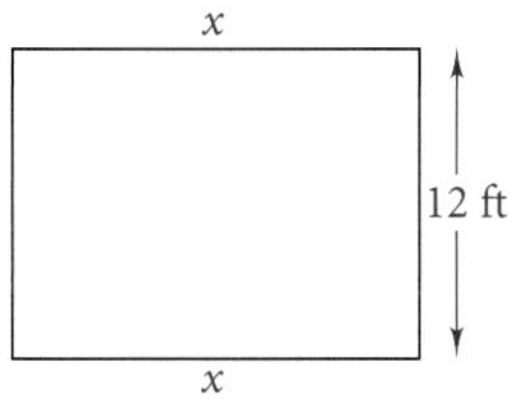

[Diagram: rectangle with x on top, x on bottom, and 12 ft on right side]

Relate	length of side	plus	12 ft	plus	length of side	equals	amount of fencing

Define Let x = length of a side adjacent to the fence.

Write	x	+	12	+	x	=	44

$x + 12 + x = 44$

$2x + 12 = 44$ Combine like terms on the left side of the equation.

$2x + 12 - 12 = 44 - 12$ Subtract 12 from each side.

$2x = 32$ Simplify.

$\frac{2x}{2} = \frac{32}{2}$ Divide each side by 2.

$x = 16$ Simplify.

• The garden will be 16 ft long.

Real-World 🌐 Connection

In the United States, there are approximately 10,000 cities with community gardens.

✔ **Check Understanding** ❷ A carpenter is building a rectangular fence for a playground. One side of the playground is the wall of a building 70 ft wide. He plans to use 340 ft of fencing material. What is the length of the playground if the width is 70 ft?

135 ft

OBJECTIVE 1 Teaching Notes

1 EXAMPLE Tactile Learners

Let students model and solve the equation with tiles to help them understand that $2c + c = 3c$.

2 EXAMPLE Diversity

Some students may not know what a community garden is. Let a student who has seen or participated in a community garden explain what one is and how it is run.

Additional Examples

❶ Solve $3a + 6 + a = 90$. **21**

❷ You need to build a rectangular pen in your back yard for your dog. One side of the pen will be against the house. Two sides of the pen have a length of x ft and the width will be 25 ft. What is the greatest length the pen can be if you have 63 ft of fencing? **19 ft**

OBJECTIVE 2

Using the Distributive Property to Solve Equations

In the equation $-2(b - 4) = 12$, the parentheses indicate multiplication. Use the Distributive Property to multiply each term within the parentheses by -2. Then use the properties of equality to solve the equation.

3 EXAMPLE Solving an Equation With Grouping Symbols

Solve $-2(b - 4) = 12$.

$-2b + 8 = 12$ Use the Distributive Property.

$-2b + 8 - 8 = 12 - 8$ Subtract 8 from each side.

$-2b = 4$ Simplify.

$\frac{-2b}{-2} = \frac{4}{-2}$ Divide each side by -2.

$b = -2$ Simplify.

✔ **Check Understanding** ❸ Solve each equation.
a. $3(k + 8) = 21$ **−1**   **b.** $15 = -3(x - 1) + 9$ **−1**

OBJECTIVE 2 Teaching Notes

3 EXAMPLE Auditory Learners

Have pairs of students take turns explaining the steps of this example to each other. Then, have them work together to solve the Check Understanding exercises.

Additional Examples

❸ Solve $2(x - 3) = 8$. **7**

👥 Reaching All Students

Below Level Remind students to multiply all terms within parentheses by the number before the parentheses. Also warn them to pay attention to the signs of the numbers.	**Advanced Learners** Challenge students to solve the equation in Example 5 by a different method than the one shown.	**Tactile Learners** See note on page 89. **Auditory Learners** See note on page 89.

4 EXAMPLE Math Tip

Review with students that they can use any common denominator to solve an equation. To demonstrate, tell students to solve the equation using a common denominator of 12.

5 EXAMPLE Math Tip

Remind students that decimals represent fractions that have powers of 10 as denominators. The number of decimal places is the same as the number of zeros in the power of 10.

Closure

Ask: *How can you clear an equation of fractions or decimals?* If an equation involves fractions, multiply each side of the equation by a common multiple of the denominators. If an equation involves decimals, multiply each side of the equation by a power of 10. The power equals the greatest number of digits to the right of any decimal point.

Reading Math

$\frac{x}{2}$ and $\frac{1}{2}x$ both represent $x \div 2$.

$\frac{2x}{3}$ and $\frac{2}{3}x$ both represent $2x \div 3$.

Need Help?

Powers of 10:

$10^1 = 10$

$10^2 = 100$

$10^3 = 1000$

$10^4 = 10{,}000$

You can solve an equation like $\frac{2x}{3} + \frac{x}{2} = 7$ by adding the fractions or by clearing the equation of fractions. To clear fractions, you multiply each side of the equation by a common multiple of the denominators.

4 EXAMPLE Solving an Equation That Contains Fractions

Solve $\frac{2x}{3} + \frac{x}{2} = 7$.

Method 1 Adding fractions

$$\frac{2x}{3} + \frac{x}{2} = 7$$

$\frac{2}{3}x + \frac{1}{2}x = 7$ Rewrite the equation with fractions as coefficients.

$\frac{4}{6}x + \frac{3}{6}x = 7$ Write the fractions with a denominator of 6.

$\frac{7}{6}x = 7$ Combine like terms.

$\frac{6}{7}\left(\frac{7}{6}x\right) = \frac{6}{7}(7)$ Multiply each side by $\frac{6}{7}$, the reciprocal of $\frac{7}{6}$.

$x = 6$ Simplify.

Method 2 Multiplying to clear fractions

$$\frac{2x}{3} + \frac{x}{2} = 7$$

$6\left(\frac{2x}{3} + \frac{x}{2}\right) = 6(7)$ Multiply each side by 6, a common multiple of 3 and 2.

$6\left(\frac{2x}{3}\right) + 6\left(\frac{x}{2}\right) = 6(7)$ Use the Distributive Property.

$4x + 3x = 42$ Multiply.

$7x = 42$ Combine like terms.

$\frac{7x}{7} = \frac{42}{7}$ Divide each side by 7.

$x = 6$ Simplify.

 Check Understanding **4** Solve each equation.

a. $\frac{m}{4} + \frac{m}{2} = \frac{5}{8}$ $\frac{5}{6}$

b. $\frac{2}{3}x - \frac{5}{8}x = 26$ **624**

You can clear an equation of decimals by multiplying by a power of 10. In the equation $0.5a + 8.75 = 13.25$, the greatest number of digits to the right of a decimal point is 2. To clear the equation of decimals, multiply each side of the equation by 10^2, or 100.

5 EXAMPLE Solving an Equation That Contains Decimals

Solve $0.5a + 8.75 = 13.25$.

$100(0.5a + 8.75) = 100(13.25)$ Multiply each side by 10^2, or 100.

$100(0.5a) + 100(8.75) = 100(13.25)$ Use the Distributive Property.

$50a + 875 = 1325$ Simplify.

$50a + 875 - 875 = 1325 - 875$ Subtract 875 from each side.

$50a = 450$ Simplify.

$\frac{50a}{50} = \frac{450}{50}$ Divide each side by 50.

$a = 9$ Simplify.

Check Understanding **5** Solve each equation.

a. $0.025x + 22.95 = 23.65$ **28**

b. $1.2x - 3.6 + 0.3x = 2.4$ **4**

Keep the steps in the summary below in mind as you solve equations that have variables on one side of the equation.

 Key Concepts

Summary	Steps for Solving a Multi-Step Equation

Step 1 Clear the equation of fractions and decimals.

Step 2 Use the Distributive Property to remove parentheses on each side.

Step 3 Combine like terms on each side.

Step 4 Undo addition or subtraction.

Step 5 Undo multiplication or division.

EXERCISES

Practice and Problem Solving

For more practice, see *Extra Practice*.

 A Practice by Example

Example 1 (page 88)

Solve each equation. Check your answer.

1. $4n - 2n = 18$ **9**
2. $y + y + 2 = 18$ **8**
3. $a + 6a - 9 = 30$ **$5\frac{4}{7}$**

4. $5 - x - x = -1$ **3**
5. $72 + 4 - 14c = 36$ **$2\frac{6}{7}$**
6. $13 = 5 - 13 + 3a$ **7**

7. $9 = -3 + n + 2n$ **4**
8. $7m - 3m - 6 = 6$ **3**
9. $-13 = 2b - b - 10$ **−3**

Example 2 (page 89)

Write an equation to model each situation. Solve your equation.

10. Two friends are renting an apartment. They pay the landlord the first month's rent. The landlord also requires them to pay an additional half of a month's rent for a security deposit. The total amount they pay the landlord before moving in is $1725. What is the monthly rent? $x + \frac{1}{2}x = 1725$; **$1150**

11. You are fencing a rectangular puppy kennel with 25 ft of fence. The side of the kennel against your house does not need a fence. This side is 9 ft long. Find the dimensions of the kennel. $x + 9 + x = 25$; **8 ft by 9 ft**

Example 3 (page 89)

Solve each equation. Check your answer.

12. $2(8 + p) = 22$ **3**
13. $5(a - 1) = 35$ **8**
14. $15 = -3(2q - 1)$ **−2**

15. $26 = 6(5 - a)$ **$\frac{2}{3}$**
16. $m + 5(m - 1) = 7$ **2**
17. $-4(x + 6) = -40$ **4**

18. $48 = 8(x + 2)$ **4**
19. $5(y - 3) = 19$ **$6\frac{4}{5}$**
20. $5(2 + y) = 77$ **$13\frac{2}{5}$**

Example 4 (page 90)

21. $\frac{a}{7} - \frac{5}{7} = \frac{6}{7}$ **11**
22. $x - \frac{5}{8} = \frac{7}{8}$ **$1\frac{1}{2}$**
23. $\frac{m}{6} - 7 = \frac{2}{3}$ **46**

24. $\frac{2}{3} + \frac{3k}{4} = \frac{71}{12}$ **7**
25. $4 + \frac{m}{8} = \frac{3}{4}$ **−26**
26. $\frac{a}{2} + \frac{1}{5} = 17$ **$33\frac{3}{5}$**

27. $\frac{1}{2} + \frac{7x}{10} = \frac{13}{20}$ **$\frac{3}{14}$**
28. $\frac{9y}{14} + \frac{3}{7} = \frac{9}{14}$ **$\frac{1}{3}$**
29. $\frac{1}{5} + \frac{3w}{15} = \frac{4}{5}$ **3**

Example 5 (page 90)

30. $3m + 4.5m = 15$ **2**
31. $7.8y + 2 = 165.8$ **21**
32. $3.5 = 12s - 5s$ **0.5**

33. $1.06y - 3 = 0.71$ **3.5**
34. $0.11p + 1.5 = 2.49$ **9**
35. $25.24 = 5y + 3.89$ **4.27**

36. $1.12 + 1.25y = 8.62$ **6**
37. $1.025x + 2.458 = 7.583$ **5**
38. $0.25m + 0.1m = 9.8$ **28**

Lesson 2-3 Solving Multi-Step Equations **91**

Assignment Guide

1 Objective
A B Core 1–11, 52, 54–56, 59–62

2 Objective
A B Core 12–51, 53, 57–58
C Extension 63–67

Standardized Test Prep 68–73

Mixed Review 74–95

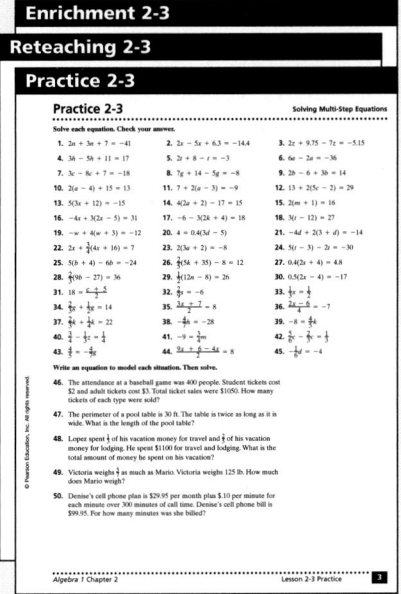

 **B** **Apply Your Skills**

Solve each equation.

39. $0.5t - 3t + 5 = 0$ **2**   **40.** $-(z + 5) = -14$ **9**   **41.** $\frac{a}{15} + \frac{4}{15} = \frac{9}{15}$ **5**

42. $0.5(x - 12) = 4$ **20**   **43.** $8y - (2y - 3) = 9$ **1**   **44.** $\frac{2}{3} + y = \frac{3}{4}$ $\frac{1}{12}$

45. $2 + \frac{a}{-4} = \frac{3}{5}$ $5\frac{3}{5}$ **46.** $\frac{1}{4}(m - 16) = 7$ **44**   **47.** $x + 3x - 7 = 29$ **9**

48. $4x + 3.6 + x = 1.2$ **−0.48**   **49.** $2(1.5c + 4) = -1$ **−3**   **50.** $26.54 - p = 0.5(50 - p)$ **3.08**

51. Error Analysis Explain the error in the student's work at the right. **The student forgot to multiply −1 by 8.**

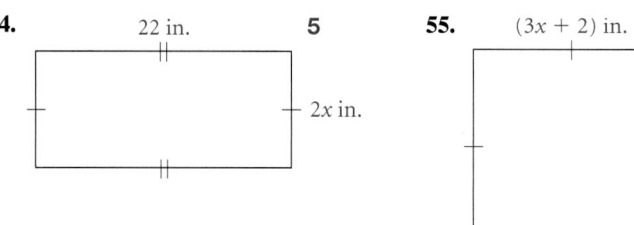

$$\frac{3}{8}x - 1 = 4$$
$$3x - 1 = 32$$
$$3x = 33$$
$$x = 11$$

52. Answers may vary. Sample: Combine −3m and 5m first to simplify the left side of the equation.

52. Critical Thinking Suppose you want to solve the equation $-3m + 4 + 5m = -6$. What would you do as your first step? **See left.**

 **53. Writing** To solve $-\frac{1}{2}(3x - 5) = 7$, you can use the Distributive Property, or you can multiply each side of the equation by −2. Which method do you prefer? Explain why.
Answers may vary. Sample: Multiply by −2 to eliminate fractions.

Geometry The perimeter of each rectangle is 64 in. Find the value of x.

54.

22 in. **5**

2x in.

55. $(3x + 2)$ in. $4\frac{2}{3}$

CANOE RENTAL
$5.00 per hour
$2.00 life jacket

Use an equation to solve each problem.

56. John and two friends rent a canoe at a park. Each person must rent a life jacket. If the bill for the rental of the canoe and life jackets is $41, for how many hours did they rent the canoe? **7 h**

57. Moving Costs The MacNeills rented a moving truck for $49.95 plus $.30 per mile. Before returning the truck, they filled the tank with gasoline, which cost $18.32. The total cost was $95.87. Find the number of miles the truck was driven. **92 mi**

58. Cell Phones Jane's cell phone plan is $40 per month plus $.15 per minute for each minute over 200 minutes of call time. If Jane's cell phone bill is $58.00, for how many extra calling minutes was she billed? **120 min**

59. Open-Ended Write an expression with four terms that can be simplified to an expression with two terms. **Answers may vary. Sample: 3x + 5 − 4x + 9**

Geometry Find the value of x. (*Hint:* The sum of the measures of the angles of a triangle is 180°.)

60. **64**

$x°$

66°   50°

61. **25**

$2x°$

$(x + 15)°$

62. **20**

$(2x + 16)°$

44° $4x°$

C Challenge

For Exercises 63–67, use an equation to solve each problem.

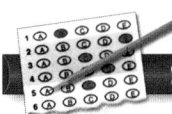

63. **Cars** You fill your car's gas tank when it is about $\frac{1}{2}$ empty. The next week, you fill the tank a second time when it is about $\frac{3}{4}$ empty. If you buy a total of $18\frac{1}{2}$ gal of gas on these two days, about how many gallons does the tank hold? **about 15 gal**

64. A work crew has two pumps, one new and one old. The new pump can fill a tank in 5 hours. The old pump can fill the same tank in 7 hours.
   a. How much of a tank can be filled in 1 hour with the new pump? With the old pump? $\frac{1}{5}$; $\frac{1}{7}$
   b. Write an expression for the number of tanks the new pump can fill in t hours. (*Hint:* Write the rate at which the new pump fills tanks as a fraction and then multiply by t.) $\frac{1}{5}t$
   c. Write an expression for the number of tanks the old pump can fill in t hours. $\frac{1}{7}t$
   d. Write and solve an equation for the time it will take the pumps to fill one tank if the pumps are used together. $\frac{1}{5}t + \frac{1}{7}t = 1$; $2\frac{11}{12}$ h

65. **Investing** Mr. Fairbanks invested half his money in land, a tenth in stock, and a twentieth in bonds. He put the remaining $35,000 in a savings account. What is the total amount of money that Mr. Fairbanks saved or invested? **$100,000**

66. **Business** A company buys a copier for $10,000. The value of the copier is $10,000(1 - \frac{n}{20})$ after n years. After how many years will the value of the copier be $6500? **7 years**

67. **Carpentry** Kate cut a board 2 m long into two pieces. One piece is 10 cm shorter than the other. How long is each piece? (*Note:* 1 m = 100 cm) **105 cm, 95 cm**

Standardized Test Prep

Multiple Choice

68. What is the value of the expression $-3r + 6 + r$ when $r = -2$? **C**
   A. -6 B. -2 C. 10   D. 14

69. Solve $8n + 5 - 2n = 41$.   **H**
   F. $3\frac{1}{2}$ G. $4\frac{1}{2}$ H. 6   I. $7\frac{2}{3}$

70. If a number is increased by 3 and that number is doubled, the result is -8. What was the original number? **A**
   A. -7 B. -5.5 C. 1   D. 6

71. The gas tank in Royston's car holds 12 gal of gasoline. The car averages 29 mi/gal. Royston filled up the tank and then drove 140 mi. About how many gallons of gasoline are left in the tank? **G**
   F. 6 gal   G. 7 gal   H. 8 gal   I. 9 gal

72. Josie's goal is to run 40 miles each week. This week she has already run distances of 5.3 miles, 6.5 miles, and 6.2 miles. If she wants to spread out the remaining miles evenly over the next 4 days, which equation can you use to find how many miles (m) per day she must run? **C**
   A. $5.3 + 6.5 + 6.2 + 40 = m$ B. $40 - 5.2 - 6.5 - 6.2 = m$
   C. $5.3 + 6.5 + 6.2 + 4m = 40$ D. $5.3 + 6.5 + 6.2 + m = \frac{40}{4}$

73. A cell phone company charges $.35 for the first minute but only $.10 every minute after that. Which equation can you use to find how many minutes m Eric talked if the bill for the call was $5.45? **F**
   F. $0.35 + 0.10(m - 1) = 5.45$ G. $0.35 + 0.10m = 5.45$
   H. $0.10 + 0.35(m - 1) = 5.45$ I. $0.10 + 0.35m = 5.45$

Take It to the NET
Online lesson quiz at
www.PHSchool.com
······· Web Code: aea-0203

Lesson 2-3 Solving Multi-Step Equations   **93**

To check understanding of Lessons 2-1 to 2-3:

Checkpoint Quiz 1 (p. 94)

📁 **Teaching Resources**
Checkpoint Quiz 1 (also in Prentice Hall Assessment System)

👥 **Reaching All Students**
Reading and Math Literacy 2B

Spanish versions available

Mixed Review

 Lesson 2-2   Solve each equation.

74. $2y + 4 = -6$ **−5** **75.** $3x - 15 = 33$ **16** **76.** $-4n + 20 = 36$ **77.** $-8 - c = 11$
                                                                      −4   **−19**
78. $3x + 5 = 12$ $2\frac{1}{3}$ **79.** $-4y - 3 = 15$ **80.** $8m - 4 = 8$ $1\frac{1}{2}$ **81.** $-p + 3 = 10$
                                             $-4\frac{1}{2}$ **−7**

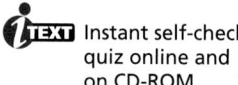 Lesson 1-8   **Mental Math** Simplify each expression.

82. $14 \cdot 4 \cdot 25$ **1400**   **83.** $16 + 28 + 34 + 72$ **150** **84.** $-8 + 15 + -9 + 2$ **0**

85. $3 \cdot 3 \cdot 10$ **90**   **86.** $2 \cdot 8 \cdot 5$ **80**   **87.** $27 + 46 - 17 - 16$ **40**

Lessons 1-4 through 1-6   **Simplify each expression.**

88. $2 - 6$ **−4**   **89.** $-9 \cdot (-3)$ **27**   **90.** $-7 + (-4)$ **−11** **91.** $16 \div (-4)$ **−4**

92. $-7 + (-3)$ **−10** **93.** $-5 - (-3)$ **−2**   **94.** $-5 \cdot 6$ **−30**   **95.** $-25 \div (-5)$ **5**

✔ Checkpoint Quiz 1   Lessons 2-1 through 2-3

TEXT Instant self-check quiz online and on CD-ROM

Solve and check.

1. $x - 7 = -6$ **1**   **2.** $\frac{w}{3} = 11$ **33**   **3.** $15 = 0.75v$ **20**

4. $2t - 1 = 4$ $2\frac{1}{2}$ **5.** $\frac{b}{3} - 20 = 20$ **120**   **6.** $-12 - 4x + 3 = -1$
                                                                        −2

7. $\frac{y}{8} + \frac{y}{12} = -4$ $-19\frac{1}{5}$ **8.** $9(n + 7) = -81$ **−16**   **9.** $\frac{1}{2} = \frac{2}{3}b + \frac{1}{6}b$ $\frac{3}{5}$

10. Sales A telemarketer makes calls from her home. She earns $240 per month plus a commission of 5% on her sales. Her employer also reimburses her for long distance telephone charges for calls made for the company. Last month she received a check for $256.65, which included a reimbursement of $8.95. What was the total of her sales? **$154.00**

Algebra at Work

⋯⋯⋯⋯⋯⋯⋯⋯⋯⋯⋯⋯⋯⋯ Airline Pilot

Airline pilots make many calculations before, during, and after a flight. Pilots study weather conditions to determine the safest altitude, route, and speed for a flight. Pilots calculate lift, which must equal the airplane's weight in pounds. An airplane's lift capabilities are calculated using the formula $L = \frac{1}{2}dv^2sa$, where L is the lift, d is the density of the air, v is the velocity of the aircraft in feet per second, s is the wing area of the aircraft in square feet, and a is a value determined by the type of airfoil the airplane has and the pitch angle of the airplane.

Take It to the NET For more information about a career as an airline pilot, go to **www.PHSchool.com**.
Web Code: aeb-2031

Modeling Equations

Models can help you understand how to solve equations that have variables on both sides.

EXAMPLE

Model and solve $3a - 2 = a + 4$.

$3a - 2 = a + 4$  The tiles model the equation.

$3a - 2 - a = a + 4 - a$
$2a - 2 = 4$ 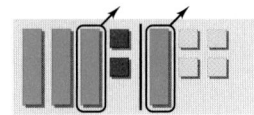 Use the Subtraction Property of Equality. Subtract a from each side to get the variable on one side of the equation.

$2a - 2 + 2 = 4 + 2$
$2a = 6$ 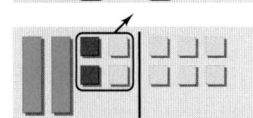 Use the Addition Property of Equality. Add 2 to each side. Remove zero pairs.

$\frac{2a}{2} = \frac{6}{2}$  Use the Division Property of Equality. Divide each side into two identical groups.

$a = 3$  Each green tile equals three yellow tiles, so $a = 3$.

EXERCISES

Write an equation for each model. Use tiles to solve each equation.

1.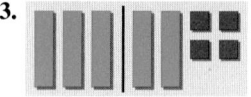
$2a + 4 = 4a - 4; 4$

2.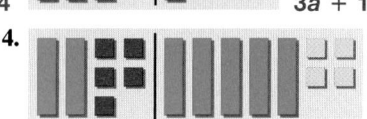
$3a + 1 = a - 5; -3$

3.
$3a = 2a - 4; -4$

4.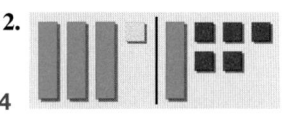
$2a - 5 = 5a + 4; -3$

Use tiles to model and solve each equation.

5. $4x + 2 = 2x + 6$ **2**

6. $2y - 2 = 4y + 2$ **−2**

7. $2a + 2 = a + 8$ **6**

8. $5b - 4 = 2b + 5$ **3**

9. $z - 8 = 2z - 1$ **−7**

10. $4(p + 1) = 2p - 2$ **−3**

11. $5n - 3 = 2(n + 3)$ **3**

12. $2(k + 1) = 5(k - 2)$ **4**

Modeling Equations

Students use algebra tiles to model equations with variables on both sides of the equal sign. In this lesson they will use the Addition, Subtraction and Division Properties of Equality to solve equations.

Resources

Algebra tiles

Teaching Notes

Using algebra tiles enables students to manipulate the equations in a way that makes sense to them. This physical model will help students build confidence in their abilities to solve equations.

Visual Learners

Visual learners may find it easier to make sense of an equation if they replace $3a - 2$ with $3a + -2$. It is easier for many students to think about adding two negative tiles to a balance scale than to think of subtracting two tiles.

Teaching Tip

Your students may incorrectly represent expressions such as $2(n + 3)$ in example 11 with tiles. Remind them that this expression means that they must represent $n + 3$ twice. This is a good opportunity to reinforce students' understanding of the distributive property since $n + 3$ represented twice results in the equivalent expression $2n + 6$.

Equations With Variables on Both Sides

1. Plan

Lesson Preview

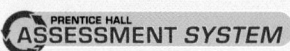 **Check Skills You'll Need**

Subtracting Real Numbers
Lesson 1-5: Examples 1, 2
Exercises 1–8
Extra Practice, p. 702

Solving Multi-Step Equations
Lesson 2-3: Example 1
Exercises 1–9
Extra Practice, p. 703

Lesson Resources

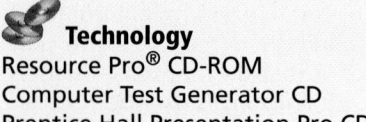 **Teaching Resources**
Practice, Reteaching, Enrichment

Reaching All Students
Practice Workbook 2-4
Spanish Practice Workbook 2-4
Technology Activities 16
Hands-On Activities 5
Basic Algebra Planning Guide 2-4

Presentation Assistant Plus!
Transparencies
• Check Skills You'll Need 2-4
• Additional Examples 2-4
• Student Edition Answers 2-4
• Lesson Quiz 2-4
PH Presentation Pro CD 2-4

ASSESSMENT SYSTEM

Computer Test Generator CD

Technology
Resource Pro® CD-ROM
Computer Test Generator CD
Prentice Hall Presentation Pro CD

www.PHSchool.com
Student Site
• Teacher Web Code: aek-5500
• Graphing Calculator, Procedures 7, 9
• Self-grading Lesson Quiz
Teacher Center
• Lesson Planner
• Resources

 Plus **iTEXT**

Lesson Preview

What You'll Learn

OBJECTIVE 1
To solve equations with variables on both sides

OBJECTIVE 2
To identify equations that are identities or have no solution

. . . And Why

To solve a problem involving renting in-line skates, as in Example 2

✓ Check Skills You'll Need

(For help, go to Lessons 1-5 and 2-3.)

Simplify.

1. $6x - 2x$ **4x**
2. $2x - 6x$ **−4x**
3. $5x - 5x$ **0**
4. $-5x + 5x$ **0**

Solve each equation.

5. $4x + 3 = -5$ **−2**
6. $-x + 7 = 12$ **−5**
7. $2t - 8t + 1 = 43$ **−7**
8. $0 = -7n + 4 - 5n$ **$\frac{1}{3}$**

New Vocabulary • identity

OBJECTIVE 1

iTEXT Interactive lesson includes instant self-check, tutorials, and activities.

Solving Equations With Variables on Both Sides

> ### Investigation: Using a Table to Solve an Equation
>
> Costs for a key chain business are $540 to get started plus $3 per key chain. The cost of producing k key chains is $(540 + 3k)$ dollars.
>
> Key chains sell for $7 each. The revenue for selling k key chains is $7k$ dollars. To make a profit, revenue must be greater than costs.
>
> 1. Copy and complete the following table.
>
> | Key Chains | Cost | Revenue |
> |:---:|:---:|:---:|
> | k | $540 + 3k$ | $7k$ |
> | 100 | 840 | 700 |
> | 110 | ■ 870 | ■ 770 |
> | 120 | ■ 900 | ■ 840 |
> | 130 | ■ 930 | ■ 910 |
> | 140 | ■ 960 | ■ 980 |
> | 150 | ■ 990 | ■1050 |
>
> 2. For 110 key chains, which is greater, the cost or the revenue? **cost**
> 3. When will the revenue be greater than the cost?
>   **between 130 and 140 key chains**
> 4. Use your table to estimate the solution of $540 + 3k = 7k$.
>   **about 135 key chains**
> 5. Explain how solving an equation can help you decide whether a business can make a profit or not. **See left.**

5. Answers may vary. Sample: An equation lets you determine how many items you must produce for revenue to cover cost. Then you can determine how many items you must produce to make a profit and whether that number is reasonable for you.

Ongoing Assessment and Intervention

Before the Lesson
Diagnose prerequisite skills using:
• Check Skills You'll Need

During the Lesson
Monitor progress using:
• Check Understanding
• Additional Examples
• Standardized Test Prep

After the Lesson
Assess knowledge using:
• Lesson Quiz
• Computer Test Generator CD

To solve an equation that has variables on both sides, use the Addition or Subtraction Properties of Equality to get the variables on one side of the equation.

① EXAMPLE Variables on Both Sides

Geometry Find the value of x in the diagram below.

$6x + 3 = 8x - 21$	Vertical angles are congruent.
$6x + 3 - 6x = 8x - 21 - 6x$	Subtract $6x$ from each side.
$3 = 2x - 21$	Combine like terms.
$3 + 21 = 2x - 21 + 21$	Add 21 to each side.
$24 = 2x$	Simplify.
$\frac{24}{2} = \frac{2x}{2}$	Divide each side by 2.
$x = 12$	Simplify.

$(6x + 3)°$

$(8x - 21)°$

● The value of x is 12.

Vertical angles are congruent, so their measures are equal.

✓ **Check Understanding** ① Solve each equation.
  a. $-6d = d + 4$ $-\frac{4}{7}$
  c. $m - 5 = 3m$ $-\frac{5}{2}$
  b. $2(c - 6) = 9c + 2$ -2
  d. $7k - 4 = 5k + 16$ **10**

② EXAMPLE Real-World 🌐 Problem Solving

Recreation You can buy used in-line skates from your friend for $40, or you can rent some. Either way, you must rent safety equipment. How many hours must you skate for the cost of renting and buying skates to be the same?

Relate | cost of friend's skates | plus | safety equipment rental | equals | skates plus equipment rental |

Define Let h = the number of hours you must skate.

Write | 40 | + | 1.5h | = | 3.5h |

$40 + 1.5h = 3.5h$	
$40 + 1.5h - 1.5h = 3.5h - 1.5h$	Subtract 1.5h from each side.
$40 = 2h$	Combine like terms.
$\frac{40}{2} = \frac{2h}{2}$	Divide each side by 2.
$20 = h$	Simplify.

You must skate for 20 hours for the cost to be the same.

Check Is the solution reasonable? Buying skates and renting safety equipment for 20 hours costs $40 + 1.5(20) = 70$, or $70. The cost of renting both skates and safety equipment for 20 hours is $3.5(20) = 70$, or $70. The answer is correct.

SKATE RENTALS
In-line skates and safety equipment
$3.50/hour
Safety equipment
$1.50/hour

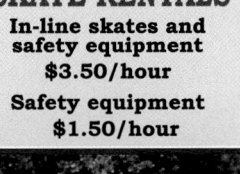

✓ **Check Understanding** ② **Business** A hairdresser is considering ordering a certain shampoo. Company A charges $4 per 8-oz bottle plus a $10 handling fee per order. Company B charges $3 per 8-oz bottle plus a $25 handling fee per order. How many bottles must the hairdresser buy to justify using Company B? **at least 15 bottles**

👥 **Reaching All Students**

| **Below Level** Reassure students that although some equations may appear intimidating at first, these equations can be solved by performing the steps they have learned, one at a time. | **Advanced Learners** Ask students how to construct an equation with no solution. | **Inclusion** See note on page 97. **English Learner** See note on page 98. |

---

2. Teach

Professional Development

Math Background

Students often think equations with no solutions are impractical. They will use this concept in Chapter 10 in solving Quadratic Equations.

OBJECTIVE
① Teaching Notes

Investigation (Optional) Technology Tip

Have students complete the table on a graphing calculator. Let x be the same as k, the number of key chains. Input $Y_1 = 540 + 3x$ and $Y_2 = 7x$. Press [2nd] [TABLE] to display the table. To find when the revenue and the cost are the same, scroll down until Y_1 and Y_2 are the same.

① EXAMPLE Error Prevention

Encourage students to add or subtract the variable term with the least coefficient. This always results in a positive coefficient for the new variable term. With no negative sign, there is one less chance of making a common sign mistake.

② EXAMPLE Inclusion

Some students may not have used in-line skates, possibly because of financial, physical, or availability limitations. Have a knowledgeable student explain the need for safety equipment.

⚒ Additional Examples

❶ The measure of an angle is $(5x - 3)°$. Its vertical angle has a measure of $(2x + 12)°$. Find the value of x. **5**

❷ You can buy a skateboard for $60 from a friend and rent the safety equipment for $1.50 per hour, or you can rent all items you need for $5.50 per hour. For how many hours must you use the skateboard to justify buying your friend's skateboard? **more than 15 hours**

97

3 **EXAMPLE** English Learners

Students may not understand the word *identity* in a mathematical context. Explain that *identity* means sameness. If the left and right sides of the equation can be simplified so that they are identical, or the same, the equation is an identity.

Additional Examples

3 Solve each equation.
a. $4 - 4y = -2(2y - 2)$ identity
b. $-6z + 8 = z + 10 - 7z$ no solution

Closure

Ask: *How is solving an equation with two variable terms on the same side of the equal sign different than solving an equation with variable terms on both sides of the equal sign?* When the variable terms are on the same side of the equal sign, you combine them using the given operation. When the variable terms are on both sides of the equal sign, you use an inverse operation and then combine them.

OBJECTIVE
2 **Special Cases: Identities and No Solutions**

An equation has no solution if no value of the variable makes the equation true. The equation $2x = 2x + 1$ has no solution. An equation that is true for every value of the variable is an **identity.** The equation $2x = 2x$ is an identity.

3 **EXAMPLE** Identities and Equations with No Solutions

a. Solve $10 - 8a = 2(5 - 4a)$.

$10 - 8a = 10 - 8a$	Use the Distributive Property.
$10 - 8a + 8a = 10 - 8a + 8a$	Add $8a$ to each side.
$10 = 10$	Always true!

This equation is true for every value of a, so the equation is an identity.

b. Solve $6m - 5 = 7m + 7 - m$.

$6m - 5 = 7m + 7 - m$	
$6m - 5 = 6m + 7$	Combine like terms.
$6m - 5 - 6m = 6m + 7 - 6m$	Subtract $6m$ from each side.
$-5 = 7$	Not true for any value of m!

This equation has no solution.

✓ **Check Understanding** **3** Determine whether each equation is an *identity* or whether it has *no solution*.
a. $9 + 5n = 5n - 1$ **no solution**   **b.** $9 + 5x = 7x + 9 - 2x$ **identity**

EXERCISES

For more practice, see *Extra Practice*.

Practice and Problem Solving

A Practice by Example

Example 1
(page 97)

Geometry **Find the value of x.**

1.
$(12x + 4)°$
$(13x - 5)°$ 9

2.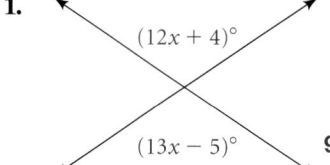
$(11x + 33)°$ $(15x + 5)°$ 7

Solve each equation. Check your answer.

3. $6x - 2 = x + 13$ **3**

4. $5y - 3 = 2y + 12$ **5**

5. $4k - 3 = 3k + 4$ **7**

6. $5m + 3 = 3m + 9$ **3**

7. $8 - x = 2x - 1$ **3**

8. $2n - 5 = 8n + 7$ **−2**

9. $3a + 4 = a + 18$ **7**

10. $6b + 14 = -7 - b$ **−3**

11. $5a - 14 = -5 + 8a$ **−3**

12. $3 + 4x = 3x + 6$ **3**

13. $30 - 7z = 10z - 4$ **2**

14. $8x - 3 = 7x + 2$ **5**

15. $-36 + 2w = -8w + w$ **4**

16. $4p - 10 = p + 3p - 2p$ **5**

Example 2
(page 97)

Write and solve an equation for each situation. Check the reasonableness of your solution.

17. Telephone Service One telephone company charges $16.95 per month and $.05 per minute for local calls. Another company charges $22.95 per month and $.02 per minute for local calls. For what number of minutes of local calls per month is the cost of the plans the same? **200 min**

18. Fitness One health club charges a $44 sign-up fee and $30 per month. Another health club charges a $99 sign-up fee and $25 per month. For what number of months is the cost the same? **11 months**

19. Carpentry Peter was building a porch. Placing boards of equal length from end to end, Peter found that 4 boards were 3 ft too long for the porch length, while 3 boards were 5 ft too short. How long was each board? **8 ft**

20. Flying You and a pilot friend decide to rent an airplane to do some sightseeing. One service charges $100 plus $80 per hour, while another charges $250 plus $70 per hour for the same airplane. At what number of hours is the cost the same? **15 h**

21a. Answers may vary.
Sample:
 0: 9 = 9
 3: −9 = −9
 −4: 33 = 33
 −6: 45 = 45

Example 3
(page 98)

21. a. Use the equation $9 - 6x = 3(3 - 2x)$. Substitute four different values for x and simplify. **See above left.**
  b. What kind of equation is $9 - 6x = 3(3 - 2x)$? **identity**

Determine whether each equation is an *identity* or whether it has *no solution*.

22. $14 - (2q + 5) = -2q + 9$ **identity** **23.** $6x + 1 = 6x - 8$ **no solution**

24. $-8x + 14 = -2(4x - 7)$ **identity** **25.** $y - 5 = -(5 - y)$ **identity**

26. $a - 4a = 2a + 1 - 5a$ **no solution** **27.** $9x + 3x - 10 = 3(3x + x)$ **no solution**

B Apply Your Skills

Solve each equation. If the equation is an identity, write *identity*. If it has no solution, write *no solution*.

28. $18x - 5 = 3(6x - 2)$ **no solution** **29.** $9 + 5a = 2a + 9$ **0**

30. $3(x - 4) = 3x - 12$ **identity** **31.** $6x = 4(x + 5)$ **10**

32. $\frac{3}{5}k - \frac{1}{10}k = \frac{1}{2}k + 1$ **no solution** **33.** $0.5y + 2 = 0.8y - 0.3y$ **no solution**

34. $5m - 2(m + 2) = -(2m + 15)$ **$-2\frac{1}{5}$** **35.** $\frac{7}{8}w = \frac{4}{8}w + \frac{6}{8}w$ **0**

36. $0 = 0.98b + 0.02b - b$ **identity** **37.** $6(6g - 2) + 8(1 - 5g) = 2g$ **$-\frac{2}{3}$**

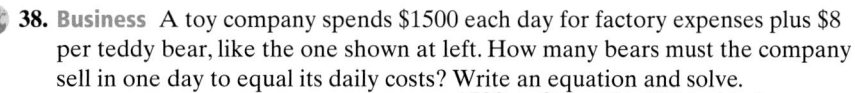

38. Business A toy company spends $1500 each day for factory expenses plus $8 per teddy bear, like the one shown at left. How many bears must the company sell in one day to equal its daily costs? Write an equation and solve. **$1500 + 8t = 12t$; 375 teddy bears**

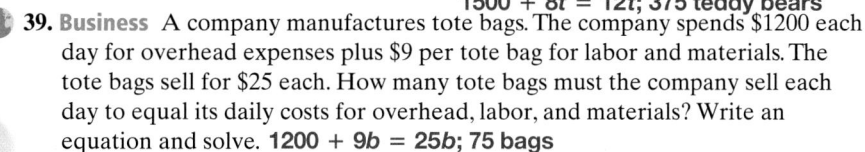

39. Business A company manufactures tote bags. The company spends $1200 each day for overhead expenses plus $9 per tote bag for labor and materials. The tote bags sell for $25 each. How many tote bags must the company sell each day to equal its daily costs for overhead, labor, and materials? Write an equation and solve. **$1200 + 9b = 25b$; 75 bags**

$12.00

Find the value of each variable.

40. $\begin{bmatrix} 2x + 1 & a - 1 \\ w - 4 & 9y \end{bmatrix} = \begin{bmatrix} -5x - 6 & 5a \\ 3w + 4 & -3y \end{bmatrix}$
$x = -1, a = -\frac{1}{4}, w = -4, y = 0$

41. $\begin{bmatrix} a + 1 & 4b \\ 2c + 3 & 5d - 3 \end{bmatrix} = \begin{bmatrix} 7 - a & 3b + 5 \\ 3c - 4 & 63 - d \end{bmatrix}$
$a = 3, b = 5, c = 7, d = 11$

Assignment Guide

1 Objective
 Ⓐ Ⓑ Core 1–20, 38–46
 Ⓒ Extension 55–56

2 Objective
 Ⓐ Ⓑ Core 21–37, 47–48
 Ⓒ Extension 49–54

Standardized Test Prep 57–63

Mixed Review 64–76

Exercises 42, 43 Remind students that if the matrices are equivalent, the corresponding entries are equal.

Exercise 47 Suggest to students that they ask themselves if they are able to graph either solution on a number line.

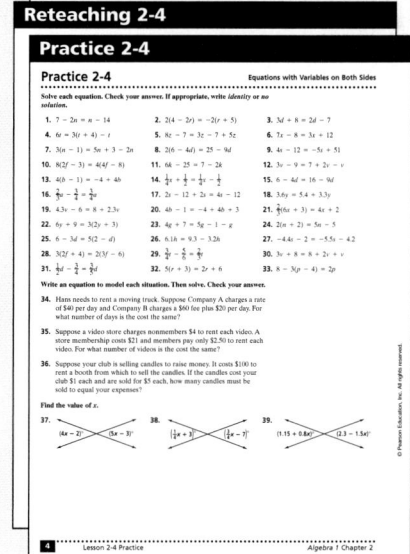

Alternative Assessment

Have students use the problem-solving technique *work backwards* to write three equations with variables on both sides to represent the three types of equations shown in this lesson. Make sure one equation has a unique solution, one has no solution, and one is an identity.

pages 98–101   Exercises

44. The student forgot a negative sign on the left side of the equation; −5.

45. The student subtracted y from both sides instead of adding y to both sides; 5.3.

47. No; an equation with a solution of 0 *has* a solution. An equation with no solution is not true for any value of the variable.

48b. 1 and 3; at 3, $4 - 3(x + 1)$ is greater than $5(x - 3)$, while at 1 the opposite is true. The value of x must be the same between 1 and 3.

Need Help?

If triangles are congruent, then their corresponding angles are congruent and their corresponding sides are congruent.

Find the value of each variable.

42. $\begin{bmatrix} 0.5x + 3 & w + 1.5 \\ 2.5y + 2.5 & a + 1 \end{bmatrix} = \begin{bmatrix} x + 0.5 & 2w - 1.5 \\ 5y - 2.5 & 19 - a \end{bmatrix}$ $x = 5, w = 3, y = 2, a = 9$

43. $\begin{bmatrix} \frac{1}{2} + a & \frac{1}{2}b + 2 \\ c - \frac{1}{3} & \frac{1}{3}d + \frac{2}{3} \end{bmatrix} = \begin{bmatrix} 6\frac{1}{2} - a & b - 1 \\ 4\frac{2}{3} & d + \frac{4}{9} \end{bmatrix}$ $a = 3, b = 6, c = 5, d = \frac{1}{3}$

Error Analysis Find the mistake in the solution of each equation. Explain the mistake and solve the equation correctly. 44–45. See margin.

44.
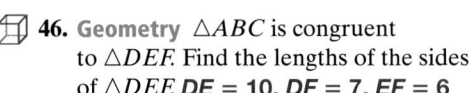
$$2x = 11x + 45$$
$$2x - 11x = 11x - 11x + 45$$
$$9x = 45$$
$$\frac{9x}{9} = \frac{45}{9}$$
$$x = 5$$

45.
$$4.5 - y = 2(y - 5.7)$$
$$4.5 - y = 2y - 11.4$$
$$4.5 - y - y = 2y - y - 11.4$$
$$4.5 = y - 11.4$$
$$4.5 + 11.4 = y - 11.4 + 11.4$$
$$15.9 = y$$

46. **Geometry** △ABC is congruent to △DEF. Find the lengths of the sides of △DEF. DE = 10, DF = 7, EF = 6

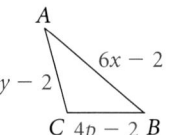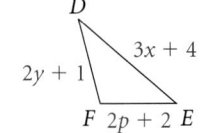

47. **Writing** Is an equation that has 0 for a solution the same as an equation with no solution? Explain. **See margin.**

48. **Spreadsheet** Don set up a spreadsheet to solve $5(x - 3) = 4 - 3(x + 1)$.
   a. Does Don's spreadsheet show a solution to the equation? **no**
   b. Between which two values of x is the solution to the equation? How do you know? **See margin.**
   c. For what values of x is $4 - 3(x + 1)$ less than $5(x - 3)$?
   for values of x greater than 2

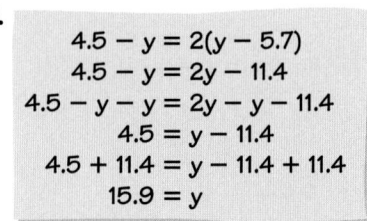

	A	B	C
1	x	$5(x - 3)$	$4 - 3(x + 1)$
2	−5	−40	16
3	−3	−30	10
4	−1	−20	4
5	1	−10	−2
6	3	0	−8

ⓒ Challenge

Open-Ended Write an equation with a variable on each side such that you get the solution described. 49–54. Answers may vary. Samples are given.

49. $x = 0$ $3x = 12x$

50. x is a positive number.
   $4x + 4 = 3x + 7$

51. x is a negative number. **See left.**

52. All values of x are solutions.
   $3x + 1 = 3\left(x + \frac{1}{3}\right)$

53. No values of x are solutions. **See left.**

54. $x = 1$ $7x - 2 = 5x$

51. $-\frac{x}{2} + 4 = 2x + 7$

53. $14x - 12 = 7(2x + 3)$

55. Use the equations below to find the length of the pipe. **18 units**

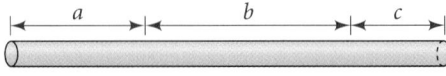

$a + b = 15$ $b - a = 3$ $a + b - 12 = c$

56. **Geometry** The perimeters of the rectangles at the right are equal. Find the length and width of each rectangle.

6 units, 2 units; 4 units, 4 units

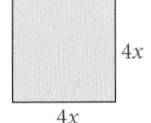

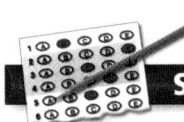

Standardized Test Prep

Standardized Test Prep

Resources

For additional practice with a variety of test item formats:
- Standardized Test Prep, p. 129
- Test-Taking Strategies, p. 124
- Test-Taking Strategies with Transparencies

Multiple Choice

57. Solve $2y = 3y - 20$. **D**

    A. -20 **B.** -4 **C.** 4 **D.** 20

58. Which of the following equations is NOT equivalent to the others? **G**

    F. $-2(y - 3) = -6y$ **G.** $-2y - 6 = -6y$

    H. $y = -\frac{3}{2}$ **I.** $4y = -6$

59. Ace Truck Rental charges $54.00 a day plus 9¢ per mile. Roni's Truck Rental charges $38.00 a day plus 13¢ per mile. For how many miles will the cost of renting a truck for one day at Ace equal the cost at Roni's? **C**

    A. 40 mi   **B.** 170 mi   **C.** 400 mi   **D.** 418 mi

60. Which equation is NOT equivalent to $3p - 2 = 6p + 4$? **H**

    F. $3p = 6p + 6$ **G.** $-6 = 3p$

    H. $3p = 6$ **I.** $-3p - 2 = 4$

61. A record store sells CDs for $12.00 each. A music club offers 5 free CDs and charges $15.00 for each additional CD. Which equation can you use to find the number of CDs x that would cost the same under both plans? **C**

    A. $15x - 5 = 12x$ **B.** $12x - 5 = 15x$

    C. $12x = 15(x - 5)$ **D.** $12(x - 5) = 15x$

62. Solve $2(y - 3) = 1.2 - y$. **I**

    F. -1.6 **G.** 1.4 **H.** 1.6 **I.** 2.4

63. The perimeters of the rectangle and the triangle below are equal. Find the value of x. **A**

    A. 6   **B.** 8   **C.** 10   **D.** 12

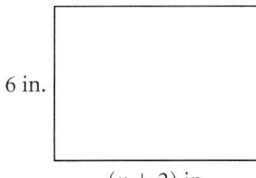
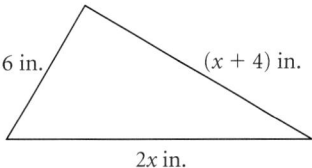

Take It to the NET
Online lesson quiz at
www.PHSchool.com
Web Code: aea-0204

Mixed Review

Lesson 2-3   **Solve each equation.**

64. $9 = -4y + 6y - 5$ **7**   **65.** $-2(a - 3) = 14$ **-4**   **66.** $0.5m + 2.8 = 3.64$ **1.68**

67. $\frac{1}{2}x + 4 = \frac{2}{3}$ **$-6\frac{2}{3}$**   **68.** $4.8 = 1.25(y - 17)$ **20.84**   **69.** $4\left(\frac{1}{4} + x\right) = 5$ **1**

Lesson 2-2   **70. Art** An art gallery owner is framing a painting. The width of the painting to be displayed is 30 in. He wants the width of the framed painting to be $38\frac{1}{2}$ in. How wide should each section of the frame be? **$4\frac{1}{4}$ in.**

Lesson 1-3   **Write the numbers in each group in order from least to greatest.**

71. $-\frac{3}{5}, -\frac{5}{8}, -\frac{4}{5}$ **$-\frac{4}{5}, -\frac{5}{8}, -\frac{3}{5}$**   **72.** $5.04, 5.009, 5.043$ **73.** $8.1, 8.02, 8.3$
                                       5.009, 5.04, 5.043   **8.02, 8.1, 8.3**

74. $-100, 93, -87, 500$ **75.** $0.45, -1.24, 2.24, 1.23$ **76.** $9.7, -9.8, 8.6, 0.9$
    $-100, -87, 93, 500$ **$-1.24, 0.45, 1.23, 2.24$**   **$-9.8, 0.9, 8.6, 9.7$**

Technology **Graphing to Solve Equations**

FOR USE WITH LESSON 2-4

Using Graphs to Solve and Check Equations

Students use their graphing calculators to graph each side of the equation separately to find the point of intersection of the two graphs. This is the solution of the equation.

Resources

Students may use any graphing calculator.

Teaching Notes

At first your students may find this method of solving equations time-consuming and cumbersome. However, if they are comfortable graphing linear equations using a graphing calculator, they will find this method especially handy when solving more complicated equations such as those containing fractions.

Teaching Tip

For students who do not understand why the intersection of two lines is the solution of the equation, refer to a balance scale. To solve an equation using a balance scale one can isolate the unknown on one side. This is the method that students use when they solve equations. However, they could also find the number that will make both sides balance. The point where the two lines cross is like finding the number that balances both sides of an equation without manipulating the original equation.

You can use a graphing calculator to check solutions of equations. One way to do this is to graph each side of the equation. The x-coordinate of the point where the graphs intersect gives the solution of the equation.

Take It to the NET
Graphing Calculator procedures online at **www.PHSchool.com**
Web Code: aee-2107

EXAMPLE

Solve $-\frac{1}{2}c = \frac{1}{2}c + 5$ using a graphing calculator.

Step 1 Press Y= to go to the equation screen. Delete any equation(s) that may appear on this screen by using the CLEAR and down arrow keys. Then for $Y_1 =$, enter $-\frac{1}{2}x$ by pressing ((−) 1 / 2) X,T,θ. For Y_2, enter $\frac{1}{2}x + 5$ by pressing (1 / 2) X,T,θ,n + 5.

Step 2 Graph the equations. Use a standard graphing window, which you can find using the ZOOM feature.

Step 3 Find the point where the graphs intersect. Access the CALC feature and press 5. Move the cursor near the point of intersection. Press ENTER three times to find the coordinates of the intersection point. The x-coordinate of the point is the solution of the equation. The solution of $-\frac{1}{2}c = \frac{1}{2}c + 5$ is -5.

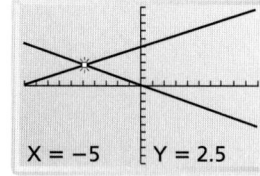
X = −5   Y = 2.5

EXERCISES

1. The graphing calculator screen at the right shows the solution of $2w - 1 = w + 1$.
   a. What two equations were graphed? **$y = 2x - 1$; $y = x + 1$**
   b. What is the x-coordinate of the point where the graphs intersect? **2**
   c. What is the solution of the equation? **2**

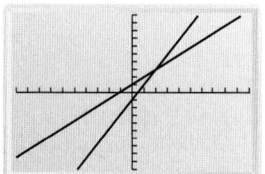

2. David solved $3(a + 1) = 5a + 4$. His solution was $-\frac{3}{2}$.
   Graph $y = 3(x + 1)$ and $y = 5x + 4$. Use the CALC feature to find the x-coordinate of the intersection of the two lines. Is David's solution correct? If not, what is the correct solution? **No; the solution is -0.5, or $-\frac{1}{2}$.**

Use your graphing calculator to solve each equation.

3. $2a + 5 = -a - 4$ **−3**

4. $4b - 10 = 2b$ **5**

5. $-5.4(2n + 5) = 1.8(6 + 3n)$ **−2.3̄**

6. $3p - 8 = -6 + p$ **1**

7. $4 - 7n = n + 4$ **0**

8. $5x - \frac{1}{2} = 4x + \frac{3}{4}$ **1.25**

Use your graphing calculator to check each solution. If the solution is incorrect, state the correct solution.

9. $5(q + 1) = q + 2; \frac{1}{4}$ **−0.75**

10. $2h - 9 = -3(h - 6); 5\frac{2}{5}$ **correct**

11. $b - 0 = -2(b + 1); 3\frac{2}{3}$ **−0.6̄**

12. $6(2n - 5) = -3(7 - 3n); 3$ **correct**

13. $8x + 5 = -(2x + 8) - 2; -2.5$ **−1.5**

Equations and Problem Solving

  1.02 Use formulas and algebraic expressions, including iterative and recursive forms, to model and solve problems.

1. Plan

Lesson Preview

What You'll Learn

 OBJECTIVE 1
To define a variable in terms of another variable

 OBJECTIVE 2
To model distance-rate-time problems

. . . And Why

To solve real-world problems involving distance, rate, and time, as in Examples 3–5

✓ Check Skills You'll Need

(For help, go to Lesson 1-1.)

Write a variable expression for each situation.

1. value in cents of q quarters **$25q$**
2. twice the length ℓ **2ℓ**
3. number of miles traveled at 34 mi/h in h hours **$34h$**
4. weight of 5 crates if each crate weighs x kilograms **$5x$**
5. cost of n items at $3.99 per item **$3.99n$**

New Vocabulary
• consecutive integers • uniform motion

Lesson Preview

✓ **Check Skills You'll Need**

Using Variables
Lesson 1-1: Example 1
Exercises 1–8
Extra Practice, p. 702

Lesson Resources

📁 **Teaching Resources**
Practice, Reteaching, Enrichment

👥 **Reaching All Students**
Practice Workbook 2-5
Spanish Practice Workbook 2-5
Basic Algebra Planning Guide 2-5

⏱ **Presentation Assistant Plus!**
Transparencies
• Check Skills You'll Need 2-5
• Additional Examples 2-5
• Student Edition Answers 2-5
• Lesson Quiz 2-5
PH Presentation Pro CD 2-5

PRENTICE HALL ASSESSMENT SYSTEM

Computer Test Generator CD

🖱 **Technology**
Resource Pro® CD-ROM
Computer Test Generator CD
Prentice Hall Presentation Pro CD

💻 **www.PHSchool.com**
Student Site
• Teacher Web Code: aek-5500
• Reasoning & Puzzles pp. 38, 39, 46
• Self-grading Lesson Quiz
Teacher Center
• Lesson Planner
• Resources

Plus

OBJECTIVE

1 Defining Variables

Some problems contain two or more unknown quantities. To solve such problems, first decide which unknown quantity the variable will represent. Then express the other unknown quantity or quantities in terms of that variable.

1 EXAMPLE Defining One Variable in Terms of Another

Geometry The length of a rectangle is 6 in. more than its width. The perimeter of the rectangle is 24 in. What is the length of the rectangle?

Relate The length is 6 in. more than the width.

Define Let w = the width. | The length is described in terms of the width. So define a variable for the width first.
Then $w + 6$ = the length.

Problem Solving Hint

For Example 1, drawing a diagram will help you understand the problem.

$$w + 6$$

w ☐

Write

$P = 2\ell + 2w$ Use the perimeter formula.

$24 = 2(w + 6) + 2w$ Substitute 24 for P and $w + 6$ for ℓ.

$24 = 2w + 12 + 2w$ Use the Distributive Property.

$24 = 4w + 12$ Combine like terms.

$24 - 12 = 4w + 12 - 12$ Subtract 12 from each side.

$12 = 4w$ Simplify.

$\dfrac{12}{4} = \dfrac{4w}{4}$ Divide each side by 4.

$3 = w$ Simplify.

The width of the rectangle is 3 in. The length of the rectangle is 6 in. more than the width. So the length of the rectangle is 9 in.

✓ **Check Understanding** ① The width of a rectangle is 2 cm less than its length. The perimeter of the rectangle is 16 cm. What is the length of the rectangle? **5 cm**

Ongoing Assessment and Intervention

Before the Lesson
Diagnose prerequisite skills using:
• Check Skills You'll Need

During the Lesson
Monitor progress using:
• Check Understanding
• Additional Examples
• Standardized Test Prep

After the Lesson
Assess knowledge using:
• Lesson Quiz
• Computer Test Generator CD

Math Background

Time-motion relationships occur in the real world in situations ranging from the atomic to the astronomic. Students will use the concepts of the lesson in much future work in mathematics.

1 **Teaching Notes**

1 EXAMPLE **Math Tip**

Defining the variable is a key step in interpreting the solution of the equation.

2 EXAMPLE **Visual Learners**

Make sure students understand *consecutive integers*. Have them look at 4 and 5 on a number line. Ask students to give their own definition of *consecutive integers* using the number line. *On a number line, consecutive integers do not have any other integers between them.* Ask students to name three consecutive integers. **Answers may vary. Sample: 7, 8, 9**

Consecutive integers differ by 1. The integers 50 and 51 are consecutive integers, and so are -10, -9, and -8. For consecutive integer problems, it may help to define a variable before describing the problem in words. Let a variable represent one of the unknown integers. Then define the other unknown integers in terms of the first one.

2 EXAMPLE **Consecutive Integer Problem**

The sum of three consecutive integers is 147. Find the integers.

Define Let n = the first integer.
Then $n + 1$ = the second integer,
and $n + 2$ = the third integer.

Relate	first integer	plus	second integer	plus	third integer	is	147
Write	n	$+$	$n + 1$	$+$	$n + 2$	$=$	147

$$n + n + 1 + n + 2 = 147$$

$3n + 3 = 147$ **Combine like terms.**

$3n + 3 - 3 = 147 - 3$ **Subtract 3 from each side.**

$3n = 144$ **Simplify.**

$\dfrac{3n}{3} = \dfrac{144}{3}$ **Divide each side by 3.**

$n = 48$ **Simplify.**

If $n = 48$, then $n + 1 = 49$, and $n + 2 = 50$. The three integers are 48, 49, and 50.

Check Is the solution correct? Yes; $48 + 49 + 50 = 147$.

✓ Check Understanding **2** The sum of three consecutive integers is 48.
a. Define a variable for one of the integers. **Let x = the first integer.**
b. Write expressions for the other two integers. **$x + 1$ is the second integer and $x + 2$ is the third integer.**
c. Write and solve an equation to find the three integers. **$3x + 3 = 48$; 15, 16, 17**

2 **Distance-Rate-Time Problems**

An object that moves at a constant rate is said to be in **uniform motion.** The formula $d = rt$ gives the relationship between distance d, rate r, and time t. Uniform motion problems may involve objects going the same direction, opposite directions, or round trips.

In the diagram below, the two vehicles are traveling the same direction at different rates. The distances the vehicles travel are the same.

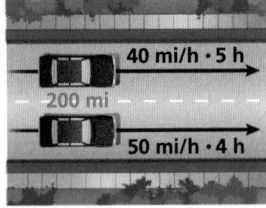

40 mi/h · 5 h

200 mi

50 mi/h · 4 h

Since the distances are equal, the products of rate and time for the two cars are equal. For the vehicles shown, $40 \cdot 5 = 50 \cdot 4$.

👥 Reaching All Students

Below Level Emphasize how helpful it is for students to organize the information from a distance-rate-time problem into a table before attempting to solve the problem.	**Advanced Learners** Remind students that the units of distance used to solve a problem must be consistent.	**Visual Learners** See note on page 104. **Tactile Learners** See note on page 105.

A table can also help you understand relationships in distance-rate-time problems.

3 EXAMPLE Same-Direction Travel

Engineering A train leaves a train station at 1 P.M. It travels at an average rate of 60 mi/h. A high-speed train leaves the same station an hour later. It travels at an average rate of 96 mi/h. The second train follows the same route as the first train on a track parallel to the first. In how many hours will the second train catch up with the first train?

Define Let $t =$ the time the first train travels.

Then $t - 1 =$ the time the second train travels.

Relate

Train	Rate	Time	Distance Traveled
1	60	t	$60t$
2	96	$t - 1$	$96(t - 1)$

Write

$60t = 96(t - 1)$	The distances traveled by the trains are equal.
$60t = 96t - 96$	Use the Distributive Property.
$60t - 60t = 96t - 96 - 60t$	Subtract $60t$ from each side.
$0 = 36t - 96$	Combine like terms.
$0 + 96 = 36t - 96 + 96$	Add 96 to each side.
$96 = 36t$	Simplify.
$\frac{96}{36} = \frac{36t}{36}$	Divide each side by 36.
$t = 2\frac{2}{3}$	Simplify.
$t - 1 = 1\frac{2}{3}$	Find the time the second train travels.

● The second train will catch up with the first train in $1\frac{2}{3}$ h.

✓ Check Understanding

3 A group of campers and one group leader left a campsite in a canoe. They traveled at an average rate of 10 km/h. Two hours later, the other group leader left the campsite in a motorboat. He traveled at an average rate of 22 km/h.
a. How long after the canoe left the campsite did the motorboat catch up with it? $3\frac{2}{3}$ h
b. How long did the motorboat travel? $1\frac{2}{3}$ h

For uniform motion problems that involve a round trip, it is important to remember that the distance going is equal to the distance returning.

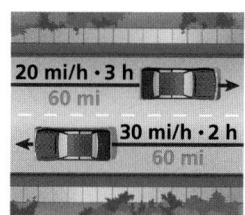

20 mi/h · 3 h
60 mi

30 mi/h · 2 h
60 mi

Since the distances are equal, the products of rate and time for traveling in both directions are equal. That is, $20 \cdot 3 = 30 \cdot 2$.

Lesson 2-5 Equations and Problem Solving **105**

Real-World Connection

High-speed trains that go from Boston to New York in less than 4 hours can reach a speed of 150 mi/h.

📖 Additional Examples

1 The width of a rectangle is 3 in. less than its length. The perimeter of the rectangle is 26 in. What is the width of the rectangle? **5 in.**

2 The sum of three consecutive integers is 72. Find the integers. **23, 24, 25**

OBJECTIVE
2 Teaching Notes

3 EXAMPLE Tactile Learners

Since each distance is represented by a different expression, some students may not understand how the distances can be the same. Have two students demonstrate. Both students stand at the same starting place. One student starts walking very slowly. The second student waits a few moments. Then the second student starts walking quickly to catch up with the first student. Show how they have traveled the same distance but at different speeds or rates.

📖 Additional Example

3 An airplane left an airport flying at 180 mi/h. A jet that flies at 330 mi/h left 1 hour later. The jet follows the same route as the airplane at a different altitude. How many hours will it take the jet to catch up with the airplane? $1\frac{1}{5}$ h

❹ Suppose you hike up a hill at 4 km/h. You hike back down at 6 km/h. Your hiking trip took 3 hours. How much time did it take you to hike up the hill? **1.8 h**

❺ Two jets leave Dallas at the same time and fly in opposite directions. One is flying west 50 mi/h faster than the other. After 2 hours, the jets are 2500 miles apart. Find the speed of each jet.
jet flying east: 600 mi/h;
jet flying west: 650 mi/h

4 EXAMPLE Error Prevention

Students may write $t - 2$ instead of $2 - t$. Ask: *Which is greater, the total travel time or the time to drive to the computer store?* **total travel time** *Which makes more sense, $t - 2$ or $2 - t$?* **$2 - t$**

5 EXAMPLE Tactile Learner

Make a number line on the floor with masking tape. Have two students stand beside each other at 0. Instruct the students to walk in opposite directions for 2 seconds. Have one student walk very slowly and one walk briskly. Lead students to note that the two distances are not equal, but combine to make a total distance walked.

Closure

Ask: *What are two ways to help set up distance problems like the ones in this lesson?* **Answers may vary. Sample: draw a diagram and use a table**

106

---

4 EXAMPLE Round-Trip Travel

Noya drives into the city to buy a software program at a computer store. Because of traffic conditions, she averages only 15 mi/h. On her drive home she averages 35 mi/h. If the total travel time is 2 hours, how long does it take her to drive to the computer store?

Define Let t = time of Noya's drive to the computer store.
$2 - t$ = the time of Noya's drive home.

Reading Math

The total travel time is for a round trip. If it takes x out of a 2-hour round trip to get to the store, then $2 - x$ is the time it will take for the drive home.

Relate

Part of Noya's Travel	Rate	Time	Distance
To the computer store	15	t	$15t$
Return home	35	$2 - t$	$35(2 - t)$

Noya drives $15t$ miles to the computer store and $35(2 - t)$ miles back.

Write

$15t = 35(2 - t)$	The distances traveled to and from the store are equal.
$15t = 70 - 35t$	Use the Distributive Property.
$15t + 35t = 70 - 35t + 35t$	Add $35t$ to each side.
$50t = 70$	Combine like terms.
$\dfrac{50t}{50} = \dfrac{70}{50}$	Divide each side by 50.
$t = 1.4$	Simplify.

● It took Noya 1.4 h to drive to the computer store.

✔ **Check Understanding** ❹ On his way to work from home, your uncle averaged only 20 miles per hour. On his drive home, he averaged 40 miles per hour. If the total travel time was $1\frac{1}{2}$ hours, how long did it take him to drive to work? **1 h**

For uniform motion problems involving two objects moving in opposite directions, you can write equations using the fact that the sum of their distances is the total distance.

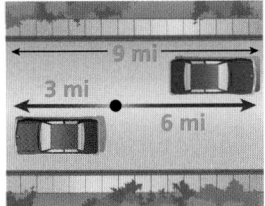

5 EXAMPLE Opposite-Direction Travel

Jane and Peter leave their home traveling in opposite directions on a straight road. Peter drives 15 mi/h faster than Jane. After 3 hours, they are 225 miles apart. Find Peter's rate and Jane's rate.

Define Let r = Jane's rate.
Then $r + 15$ = Peter's rate.

Relate

Person	Rate	Time	Distance
Jane	r	3	$3r$
Peter	$r + 15$	3	$3(r + 15)$

Jane's distance is $3r$. Peter's distance is $3(r + 15)$.

Write $3r + 3(r + 15) = 225$ The sum of Jane's and Peter's distances is the total distance, 225 miles.

$$3r + 3(r + 15) = 225$$

$3r + 3r + 45 = 225$	**Use the Distributive Property.**
$6r + 45 = 225$	**Combine like terms.**
$6r + 45 - 45 = 225 - 45$	**Subtract 45 from each side.**
$6r = 180$	**Simplify.**
$\frac{6r}{6} = \frac{180}{6}$	**Divide each side by 6.**
$r = 30$	**Simplify.**

● Jane's rate is 30 mi/h, and Peter's rate is 15 mi/h faster, which is 45 mi/h.

 **Check Understanding** ⑤ Sarah and John leave Perryville traveling in opposite directions on a straight road. Sarah drives 12 miles per hour faster than John. After 2 hours, they are 176 miles apart. Find Sarah's speed and John's speed. **John: 38 mi/h; Sarah: 50 mi/h**

EXERCISES

Practice and Problem Solving

For more practice, see *Extra Practice*.

A **Practice by Example**

Example 1
(page 103)

1. The length of a rectangle is 3 in. more than its width. The perimeter of the rectangle is 30 in.
   c. $2w + 2(w + 3) = 30; 6$
   a. Define a variable for the width. **Let w = width**
   b. Write an expression for the length in terms of the width. $\ell = w + 3$
   c. Write an equation to find the width of the rectangle. Solve your equation.
   d. What is the length of the rectangle? **9 in.** **See above.**

2. The length of a rectangle is 8 in. more than its width. The perimeter of the rectangle is 24 in. What are the width and length of the rectangle? **2 in.; 10 in.**

3. The width of a rectangle is one half its length. The perimeter of the rectangle is 54 cm. What are the width and length of the rectangle? **9 cm; 18 cm**

4. The length of a rectangular garden is 3 yd more than twice its width. The perimeter of the garden is 36 yd. What are the width and length of the garden?
   5 yd; 13 yd

Example 2
(page 104)

5. The sum of the two consecutive integers is -35. If $n = $ the first integer, which equation best models the situation? **C**
   A. $n(n + 1) = -35$
   B. $n + 2n = -35$
   C. $n + (n + 1) = -35$
   D. $n + (2n + 1) = -35$

6. The sum of two consecutive *even* integers is 118.
   a. Define a variable for the smaller integer. **Let n = the first integer.**
   b. What must you add to an even integer to get the next greater even integer? **2**
   c. Write an expression for the second integer. $n + 2$
   d. Write and solve an equation to find the two even integers.
   $n + n + 2 = 118; 58, 60$

7. The sum of two consecutive *odd* integers is 56.
   a. Define a variable for the smaller integer. **Let n = the first integer.**
   b. What must you add to an odd integer to get the next greater odd integer? **2**
   c. Write an expression for the second integer. $n + 2$
   d. Write and solve an equation to find the two odd integers.
   $n + n + 2 = 56; 27, 29$

8. The sum of three consecutive integers is 915. What are the integers?
   304, 305, 306

9. The sum of two consecutive *even* integers is -298. What are the integers?
   $-148, -150$

3. Practice

Assignment Guide

 Objective
Ⓐ Ⓑ **Core** 1–9, 16–20, 25, 28–31
Ⓒ **Extension** 32, 34

 Objective
Ⓐ Ⓑ **Core** 10–15, 21–24, 26–27
Ⓒ **Extension** 33

Standardized Test Prep 35–39

Mixed Review 40–50

Exercise 6 Suggest to students that they first think of any even whole number and the next greater even whole number for part b.

Enrichment 2-5

Reteaching 2-5

Practice 2-5

Practice 2-5   Equations and Problem Solving

Write and solve an equation for each situation.

1. A passenger train's speed is 60 mi/h, and a freight train's speed is 40 mi/h. The passenger train travels the same distance in 1.5 h less time than the freight train. How long does each train take to make the trip?

2. Lois rode her bike to visit a friend. She traveled at 10 mi/h. While she was there, it began to rain. Her friend drove her home in a car traveling at 25 mi/h. Lois took 1.5 h longer to go to her friend's than to return home. How many hours did it take Lois to ride to her friend's house?

3. May rides her bike the same distance that Leah walks. May rides her bike 10 km/h faster than Leah walks. If it takes May 1 h and Leah 3 h to travel that distance, how fast does each travel?

4. The length of a rectangle is 4 in. greater than the width. The perimeter of the rectangle is 24 in. Find the dimensions of the rectangle.

5. The length of a rectangle is twice the width. The perimeter is 48 in. Find the dimensions of the rectangle.

6. At 10:00 A.M., a car leaves a house at a rate of 60 mi/h. At the same time, another car leaves the same house at a rate of 50 mi/h in the opposite direction. At what time will the cars be 330 miles apart?

7. Maria begins walking at 3 mi/h toward the library. Her friend meets her at the halfway point and drives her the rest of the way to the library. The distance to the library is 4 miles. How many hours did Maria walk?

8. Fred begins walking toward John's house at 3 mi/h. John leaves his house at the same time and walks toward Fred's house on the same path at a rate of 2 mi/h. How long will it be before they meet if the distance between the houses is 4 miles?

9. A train leaves the station at 6:00 P.M. traveling west at 80 mi/h. On a parallel track, a second train leaves the station 3 hours later traveling west at 100 mi/h. At what time will the second train catch up with the first?

10. It takes 1 hour longer to fly to St. Paul at 200 mi/h than it does to return at 250 mi/h. How far away is St. Paul?

11. Find three consecutive integers whose sum is 126.

12. The sum of four consecutive odd integers is 216. Find the four integers.

13. A rectangular picture frame is to be 8 in. longer than it is wide. Dennis uses 84 in. of oak to frame the picture. What is the width of the frame?

14. Each of two congruent sides of an isosceles triangle is 8 in. less than twice the base. The perimeter of the triangle is 74 in. What is the length of the base?

Algebra 1 Chapter 2   Lesson 2-5 Practice   5

Exercise 10 Suggest to students that they use 0.75 instead of $\frac{3}{4}$ for the time.

Exercises 18, 19 Help students see that odd integers can be represented the same way as even integers here. Ask: *What is the difference between two consecutive odd integers?* **2** *What is the difference between two consecutive even integers?* **2**

Example 3
(page 105)

10. A moving van leaves a house traveling at an average rate of 35 mi/h. The family leaves the house $\frac{3}{4}$ hour later following the same route in a car. They travel at an average rate of 50 mi/h.
   a. Define a variable for the time traveled by the moving van. **Let t = time for the moving van.**
   b. Write an expression for the time traveled by the car. $t - \frac{3}{4}$
   c. Copy and complete the table.

Vehicle	Rate	Time	Distance Traveled
Moving van	■ 35	■ t	■ 35t
Car	■ 50	t ■ $\frac{3}{4}$	■ $50\left(t - \frac{3}{4}\right)$

   d. Write and solve an equation to find out how long it will take the car to catch up with the moving van. $35t = 50\left(t - \frac{3}{4}\right); t = 2\frac{1}{2}, 2\frac{1}{2} - \frac{3}{4} = 1\frac{3}{4}$ h

11. **Air Travel** A jet leaves the Charlotte, North Carolina, airport traveling at an average rate of 564 km/h. Another jet leaves the airport one half hour later traveling at 744 km/h in the same direction. How long will the second jet take to overtake the first? $1\frac{17}{30}$ h

Example 4
(page 106)

12b. $22x = 72 - 32x; 1\frac{1}{3}$ h

12. Juan drives to work. Because of traffic conditions, he averages 22 miles per hour. He returns home averaging 32 miles per hour. The total travel time is $2\frac{1}{4}$ hours.
   a. Define a variable for the time Juan takes to travel to work. Write an expression for the time Juan takes to return home. $x; 2\frac{1}{4} - x$
   b. Write and solve an equation to find the time Juan spends driving to work.

13. **Air Travel** An airplane flies from New Orleans, Louisiana, to Atlanta, Georgia, at an average rate of 320 miles per hour. The airplane then returns at an average rate of 280 miles per hour. The total travel time is 3 hours.
   a. Define a variable for the flying time from New Orleans to Atlanta. Write an expression for the travel time from Atlanta to New Orleans. $x; 3 - x$
   b. Write and solve an equation to find the flying time from New Orleans to Atlanta. $320x = 840 - 280x; 1\frac{2}{5}$ h

Example 5
(page 106)

14. John and William leave their home traveling in opposite directions on a straight road. John drives 20 miles per hour faster than William. After 4 hours they are 250 miles apart.
   $x; x - 20$
   a. Define a variable for John's rate. Write an expression for William's rate.
   b. Write and solve an equation to find John's rate. Then find William's rate.
   $4x + 4x - 80 = 250; 41\frac{1}{4}$ mi/h; $21\frac{1}{4}$ mi/h

15. Two bicyclists ride in opposite directions. The speed of the first bicyclist is 5 miles per hour faster than the second. After 2 hours they are 70 miles apart. Find their rates. **15 mi/h; 20 mi/h**

B **Apply Your Skills**

16 a. Which of the following numbers is not the sum of three consecutive integers? **61**
   I. 51　　　　**II.** 61　　　　**III.** 72　　　　**IV.** 81
   b. **Critical Thinking** What common trait do the other numbers share?
   They are all multiples of three.

17. **Geometry** The length of a rectangle is 8 cm more than twice the width. The perimeter of the rectangle is 34 cm. What is the length of the rectangle? **14 cm**

18. The sum of four consecutive *even* integers is 308. Write and solve an equation to find the four integers. $x + x + 2 + x + 4 + x + 6 = 308; 74, 76, 78, 80$

19. The sum of three consecutive *odd* integers is -87. What are the integers? $-27, -29, -31$

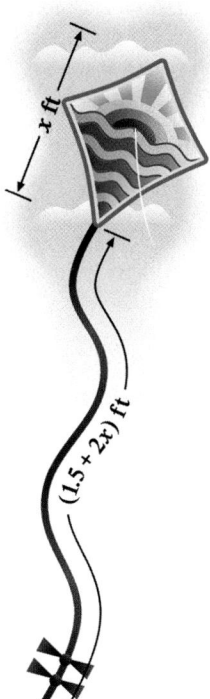

x ft

$(1.5 + 2x)$ ft

20. The tail of a kite is 1.5 ft plus twice the length of the kite. Together, the kite and tail are 15 ft 6 in. long.
  a. Write an expression for the length of the kite and tail together. $1.5 + 2x + x$
  b. Write 15 ft 6 in. in terms of feet. **15.5 ft**
  c. Write and solve an equation to find the length of the tail.
  $3x + 1.5 = 15.5$; $10\frac{5}{6}$ ft or 10 ft 10 in.

21. **Travel** A bus traveling at an average rate of 30 miles per hour left the city at 11:45 A.M. A car following the bus at 45 miles per hour left the city at noon. At what time did the car catch up with the bus? **12:30 P.M.**

22. Ellen and Kate raced on their bicycles to the library after school. They both left school at 3:00 P.M. and bicycled along the same path. Ellen rode at a speed of 12 miles per hour and Kate rode at 9 miles per hour. Ellen got to the library 15 minutes before Kate.
  a. How long did it take Ellen to get to the library? **45 min**
  b. At what time did Ellen get to the library? **3:45**

23. At 1:30 P.M., Tom leaves in his boat from a dock and heads south. He travels at a rate of 25 miles per hour. Ten minutes later, Mary leaves the same dock in her speedboat and heads after Tom. If she travels at a rate of 30 miles per hour, when will she catch up with Tom? **2:30 P.M.**

24. **Air Travel** Two airplanes depart from an airport traveling in opposite directions. The second airplane is 200 miles per hour faster than the first. After 2 hours they are 1100 miles apart. Find the speeds of the airplanes.
  175 mi/h; 375 mi/h

25. Three friends were born in consecutive years. The sum of their birth years is 5961. Find the year in which each person was born. **1986, 1987, 1988**

26. Two boats leave a ramp traveling in opposite directions. The second boat is 10 miles per hour faster than the first. After 3 hours they are 150 miles apart. Find the speeds of the boats. **first boat: 20 mi/h; second boat: 30 mi/h**

27. **Travel** A truck traveling 45 miles per hour and a train traveling 60 miles per hour cover the same distance. The truck travels 2 hours longer than the train. How many hours does each travel? **truck: 8 h; train: 6 h**

28. **Electricity** A group of ten 6- and 12-volt batteries are wired in series as shown at the right. The sum of their voltages is 84 volts. How many of each type of battery are used?

Batteries in Series

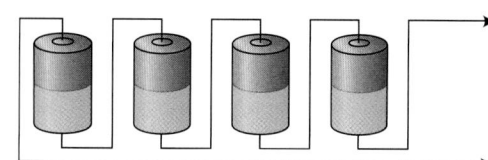

  6 6-V; 4 12-V

29. **Writing** Describe the steps you would use to solve consecutive integer problems. **See margin.**

31b. Yes; if n is the middle integer, $n - 1$ is the previous integer and $n + 1$ is the next integer. The three integers would be consecutive.

30. **Open-Ended** Write a word problem that could be solved using the equation $35(t - 1) = 20t$. **See margin.**

31. a. Write and solve an equation to find three consecutive integers with a sum of 126. Let n = the first integer. $n + n + 1 + n + 2 = 126$; **41, 42, 43**
  b. **Critical Thinking** In part (a), could you solve the problem by letting n = the middle integer, $n - 1$ = the smallest integer, and $n + 1$ = the largest integer? **See left.**

Challenge

32. **Geometry** A triangle has a perimeter of 165 cm. The first side is 65 cm less than twice the second side. The third side is 10 cm less than the second side. Write and solve an equation to find the length of each side of the triangle.
  $x + 2x - 65 + x - 10 = 165$; 60; **55 cm, 60 cm, 50 cm**

pages 107–110 Exercises

29. **Answers may vary. Sample:** Define a variable to represent the first integer. Use this variable to write expressions for the other integers. Write an equation that describes how the integers are related. Solve this equation to find the integers.

30. **Answers may vary. Sample:** Jeff and Anne both left school for the city at the same time. Jeff drove 35 mi/h and Anne drove 20 mi/h. Jeff arrived 1 h before Anne. How long did each drive?

⬛ **Lesson Quiz 2-5**

1. The sum of three consecutive integers is 117. Find the integers. 38, 39, 40

2. You and your brother started biking at noon from places that are 52 mi apart. You rode toward each other and met at 2:00 P.M. Your brother's average speed was 4 mi/h faster than your average speed. Find both speeds.
your speed: 11 mi/h; brother's speed: 15 mi/h

3. Joan ran from her home to the lake at 8 mi/h. She ran back home at 6 mi/h. Her total running time was 32 minutes. How much time did it take Joan to run from her home to the lake?
about 13.7 minutes

Alternative Assessment

Organize students in groups of 5. In each group, assign each student one of the examples from the lesson. Instruct each student to write a problem similar to the assigned example on a card. Have students in each group exchange cards and solve the problem given to them. Repeat until each student in a group has solved each problem. Have students compare answers and strategies.

Standardized Test Prep

Resources

For additional practice with a variety of test item formats:

- Standardized Test Prep, p. 129
- Test-Taking Strategies, p. 124
- Test-Taking Strategies with Transparencies

33. At 9:00 A.M., your friends begin hiking at 2 mi/h. You begin from the same place at 9:25 A.M. You hike at 3 mi/h.
   a. How long will you have hiked when you catch up with your friends? $\frac{5}{6}$ **h**
   b. At what time will you catch up with your friends? **10:15 A.M.**

34. Find five consecutive *odd* integers such that the sum of the first and the fifth is one less than three times the fourth. **−9, −7, −5, −3, −1**

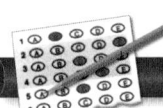

Standardized Test Prep

Multiple Choice

35. Solve $3n - 7 + 2n = 8n + 11$. **A**
   A. −6   **B.** $1\frac{1}{3}$ **C.** $3\frac{3}{5}$ **D.** 9

36. Which expression represents the sum of 3 odd integers of which n is the least integer? **H**
   F. $n + 3$ **G.** $3n + 3$
   H. $3n + 6$ **I.** $3n + 7$

37. Which equation does NOT have −2 as its solution? **B**
   A. $2x + 5 = 5x + 11$ **B.** $7n + 9 = 3 - 9n$
   C. $3k + 6 - 4k = k + 10$ **D.** $4 + 3q = 7q + 12$

38. A truck traveling at an average rate of 45 miles per hour leaves a rest stop. Fifteen minutes later a car traveling at an average rate of 60 miles per hour leaves the same rest stop traveling the same route. How long will it take for the car to catch up with the truck? **G**
   F. 15 minutes   **G.** 45 minutes
   H. 1 hour 15 minutes   **I.** 3 hours

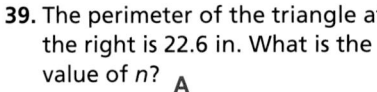

Take It to the NET
Online lesson quiz at **www.PHSchool.com**
Web Code: aea-0205

39. The perimeter of the triangle at the right is 22.6 in. What is the value of n? **A**
   A. 3.5   **B.** 4.6
   C. 7.8   **D.** 9.4

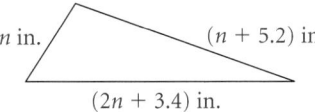
n in. $(n + 5.2)$ in. $(2n + 3.4)$ in.

Mixed Review

Lesson 2-4   **Solve each equation. If the equation is an identity, write *identity*. If it has no solution, write *no solution*.**

40. $2x = 7x + 10$ **−2**   **41.** $2q + 4 = 4 - 2q$ **0**

42. $0.5t + 3.6 = 4.2 - 1.5t$ **0.3**   **43.** $2x + 5 + x = 2(3x + 3)$ **$-\frac{1}{3}$**

44. $4 + x + 3x = 2(2x + 5)$ **no solution**   **45.** $8z + 2 = 2(z - 5) - z$ **$-1\frac{5}{7}$**

Lesson 2-3   **46.** Brendan earns $8.25 per hour at his job. He also makes $12.38 per hour for any number of hours over 40 that he works in one week. He worked 40 hours last week, plus some overtime, and made $385.71. How many overtime hours did he work? **$4\frac{1}{2}$ h**

Lesson 1-5   **Simplify.**

47. $-8 - 4$ **−12**   **48.** $2 - 12$ **−10**   **49.** $45 - (-9)$ **54**   **50.** $18 - 15$ **3**

Formulas

 North Carolina Objectives   1.02   Use formulas and algebraic expressions, including iterative and recursive forms, to model and solve problems.

Lesson Preview

What You'll Learn

OBJECTIVE 1 To transform literal equations

. . . And Why

To solve problems involving temperature, as in Example 4

✓ **Check Skills You'll Need**   (For help, go to Lessons 1-2, 1-4, and 1-6.)

Evaluate each formula for the values given.

1. distance: $d = rt$, when $r = 60$ mi/h and $t = 3$ h   **180 mi**

2. perimeter of a rectangle: $P = 2\ell + 2w$, when $\ell = 11$ cm, and $w = 5$ cm   **32 cm**

3. area of a triangle: $A = \frac{1}{2}bh$, when $b = 8$ m and $h = 7$ m   **28 m²**

New Vocabulary   • literal equation

 iTEXT   Interactive lesson includes instant self-check, tutorials, and activities.

OBJECTIVE

1   Transforming Literal Equations

Answers in m/min

d	r	t
1500 m	301	4.98 min
800 m	260	3.08 min
800 m	273	2.93 min
400 m	339	1.18 min

Investigation: Using a Transformed Formula

A track coach is calculating the average speed of each team member.

1. Using the formula $d = rt$, copy and complete the table at the left.

2. Now use the formula $r = \frac{d}{t}$ to find values for r.   **301 m/min; 260 m/min; 273 m/min; 339 m/min**

3. What do you notice about the two sets of values?   **They are the same.**

4. Which formula is easier to use when you need to find r? Explain. $r = \frac{d}{t}$; it is easier because the equation is solved for the unknown value r.

A **literal equation** is an equation involving two or more variables. Formulas are special types of literal equations. To transform a literal equation, you solve for one variable in terms of the others. This means that you get the variable you are solving for alone on one side of the equation.

1 EXAMPLE   **Transforming Geometric Formulas**

Geometry   Solve the formula for the area of a triangle $A = \frac{1}{2}bh$ for height h.

$A = \frac{1}{2}bh$

$2A = 2\left(\frac{1}{2}\right)bh$ Multiply each side by 2.

$2A = bh$ Simplify.

$\frac{2A}{b} = \frac{bh}{b}$ Divide each side by b, $b \neq 0$, to get h alone on one side of the equation.

$\frac{2A}{b} = h$ Simplify.

✓ **Check Understanding**   **1** Solve the formula for the perimeter of a rectangle $P = 2(\ell + w)$ for the width w. $w = \frac{P}{2} - \ell$

Lesson 2-6   Formulas   **111**

 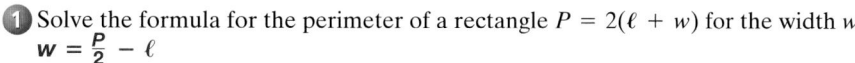

Ongoing Assessment and Intervention

Before the Lesson
Diagnose prerequisite skills using:
• Check Skills You'll Need

During the Lesson
Monitor progress using:
• Check Understanding
• Additional Examples
• Standardized Test Prep

After the Lesson
Assess knowledge using:
• Lesson Quiz
• Computer Test Generator CD
• Chapter Checkpoint 2 (p. 115)

---

1. Plan

Lesson Preview

✓ **Check Skills You'll Need**

Order of Operations
Lesson 1-2: Example 7
Exercises 35–40
Extra Practice, p. 702

Multiplying and Dividing Real Numbers
Lesson 1-6: Examples 2, 3
Exercises 13–30
Extra Practice, p. 702

Lesson Resources

📁 **Teaching Resources**
Practice, Reteaching, Enrichment
Checkpoint Quiz 2

👥 **Reaching All Students**
Practice Workbook 2-6
Spanish Practice Workbook 2-6
Reading and Math Literacy 2C
Spanish Reading & Literacy 2C
Spanish Checkpoint Quiz 2
Hands-On Activities 6
Basic Algebra Planning Guide 2-6

⏱ **Presentation Assistant Plus!**
Transparencies
• Check Skills You'll Need 2-6
• Additional Examples 2-6
• Student Edition Answers 2-6
• Lesson Quiz 2-6
PH Presentation Pro CD 2-6

PRENTICE HALL ASSESSMENT SYSTEM

Checkpoint Quiz 2
Computer Test Generator CD

💻 **Technology**
Resource Pro® CD-ROM
Computer Test Generator CD
Prentice Hall Presentation Pro CD

🖥 **www.PHSchool.com**
Student Site
• Teacher Web Code: aek-5500
• Self-grading Lesson Quiz
Teacher Center
• Lesson Planner
• Resources

Plus  **iTEXT**

111

Professional Development

Math Background

Many students will be familiar with most of the formulas used in this lesson. They will see some of the less familiar equations in other courses, for example, Engineering or Geometry.

OBJECTIVE

1 Teaching Notes

Investigation (Optional)
Alternative Method
Show students a parallel example using numbers for all the variables except the one for which the equation is to be solved.

1 EXAMPLE Error Prevention

Emphasize that the formula is completely transformed when the variable h is alone on one side of the equation.

Additional Examples

1 Solve the formula $V = \ell wh$ for width w. $w = \frac{V}{\ell h}$

2 Solve $y = 4x - 3$ for x. $x = \frac{y + 3}{4}$

3 Solve $z - br = p$ for b. $b = -\frac{p - z}{r}$

4 The formula $K = C + 273.15$ gives the Kelvin temperature K in terms of the Celsius temperature C. Transform the formula to find Celsius temperature in terms of Kelvin temperature. Then, find the Celsius temperature when the Kelvin temperature is 400°. $C = K - 273.15$; 126.85°C

Closure

Ask: *Given an equation that has x as a variable, what does "Solve for x." mean?* It means you should use the properties of equality to rewrite the equation so that one side of it is x.

2 EXAMPLE Transforming Equations

Solve $y = 5x + 7$ for x.

$y - 7 = 5x + 7 - 7$	Subtract 7 from each side.
$y - 7 = 5x$	Simplify.
$\frac{y - 7}{5} = \frac{5x}{5}$	Divide each side by 5.
$\frac{y - 7}{5} = x$	Simplify.

✓ **Check Understanding** **2** Solve $y - 4 = 3x - 8$ for x. $x = \frac{y + 4}{3}$

Sometimes an equation will only have variables. Transforming this type of equation is no different from transforming equations with numbers.

3 EXAMPLE Transforming Equations Containing Only Variables

Solve $ab - d = c$ for b.

$ab - d + d = c + d$	Add d to each side.
$ab = c + d$	Combine like terms.
$\frac{ab}{a} = \frac{c + d}{a}$	Divide each side by a, $a \neq 0$.
$b = \frac{c + d}{a}$	Simplify.

✓ **Check Understanding** **3** Solve $m - hp = d$ for p. $p = \frac{m - d}{h}; h \neq 0$

You can transform a formula so that it is in a convenient form for solving real-world problems.

4 EXAMPLE Real-World Problem Solving

Temperature The formula $C = \frac{5}{9}(F - 32)$ gives the Celsius temperature C in terms of the Fahrenheit temperature F. Transform the formula to find Fahrenheit temperature in terms of Celsius temperature. Then find the Fahrenheit temperature when the Celsius temperature is 30°.

Step 1 Solve for F.

$C = \frac{5}{9}(F - 32)$	
$\frac{9}{5} \cdot C = \frac{9}{5} \cdot \frac{5}{9}(F - 32)$	Multiply each side by $\frac{9}{5}$, the reciprocal of $\frac{5}{9}$.
$\frac{9}{5}C = F - 32$	Simplify.
$\frac{9}{5}C + 32 = F - 32 + 32$	Add 32 to each side.
$\frac{9}{5}C + 32 = F$	Simplify.

Step 2 Find F when $C = 30$.

$\frac{9}{5}(30) + 32 = F$	Substitute 30 for C.
$54 + 32 = F$	Simplify $\frac{9}{5}(30)$.
$86 = F$	

30°C is equivalent to 86°F.

112   Chapter 2   Solving Equations

Reaching All Students

| **Below Level** To help students keep track of variables when transforming literal equations, have them circle the variable for which they are solving. | **Advanced Learners** Have students check their answers to Examples 1–3 by substitution. | **Alternative Method** See note on page 112. **Error Prevention** See note on page 112. |

Check Understanding ④ You can use the number of chirps n a cricket makes in one minute to estimate the outside temperature F in degrees Fahrenheit. Transform the formula $F = \frac{n}{4} + 37$ to find the number of chirps in terms of temperature. How many chirps per minute can you expect if the temperature is 60°F? **$n = 4F - 148$; 92 chirps/min**

3. Practice

Assignment Guide

▼ **Objective**
ⒶⒷ Core 1–43
Ⓒ Extension 44–46

Standardized Test Prep 47–50

Mixed Review 51–55

EXERCISES

For more practice, see *Extra Practice*.

Practice and Problem Solving

Ⓐ **Practice by Example**

Example 1
(page 111)

Solve each formula in terms of the given variable. **3.** $\ell = \frac{P}{2} - w$ **4.** $B = \frac{S - L}{2}$

1. $C = 2\pi r$; r $r = \frac{C}{2\pi}$ **2.** $\pi = \frac{C}{d}$; d $d = \frac{C}{\pi}$ **3.** $P = 2\ell + 2w$; ℓ **4.** $S = L + 2B$; B

5. Volume of a rectangular prism
$V = \ell wh$; h $h = \frac{V}{\ell w}$

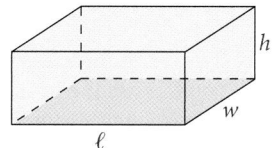

6. Perimeter of a square
$P = 4s$; s $s = \frac{P}{4}$

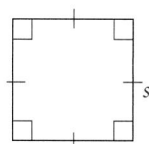

Problem Solving Hint

For Exercise 7, you can solve for b_1 by letting $(b_1 + b_2) = x$. Solve for x and then solve for b_1.

7. Area of a trapezoid $b_1 = \frac{2A}{h} - b_2$
$A = \frac{1}{2}h(b_1 + b_2)$; b_1

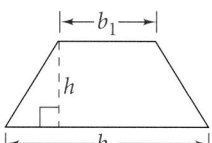

8. Volume of a cylinder $h = \frac{V}{\pi r^2}$
$V = \pi r^2 h$; h

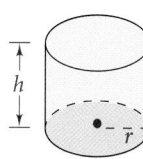

Example 2
(page 112)

Solve each equation for y. **9–16. See margin.**

9. $y + 2x = 5$ **10.** $y - 6x = -1$ **11.** $y + 4x = 3$ **12.** $2y + 4x = 8$

13. $3y - 5x = 9$ **14.** $4y + 3x = 7$ **15.** $5x + 4y = 4$ **16.** $2x + 7y = 4$

Example 3
(page 112)

Solve each equation for the variable in red. **17–24. See margin.**

17. $dx = c$ **18.** $c = \frac{d}{g}$ **19.** $z - a = y$ **20.** $ax + by = c$

21. $A = P + Prt$ **22.** $S = C + rC$ **23.** $\frac{m}{n} = \frac{p}{q}$ **24.** $\frac{y - b}{m} = x$

Example 4
(page 112)

25. Construction Bricklayers use the formula $N = 7LH$ to estimate the number of bricks N needed to build a wall of height H and length L.
a. Solve the equation for H. $H = \frac{N}{7L}$
b. What is the height of a wall that is 30 feet long and that requires 2310 bricks to build?   **11 ft**

26. Sports You can use the formula $a = \frac{h}{n}$ to find the batting average a of a batter who has h hits in n times at bat.
a. Solve the equation for h. $h = na$
b. If a batter has a batting average of .265 and has been at bat 200 times, how many hits does the batter have?   **53 hits**

Exercises 17–24 Suggest to students that they circle the red variable in each equation after writing it on their papers.

Exercise 27 Remind students that the principal is the original amount invested.

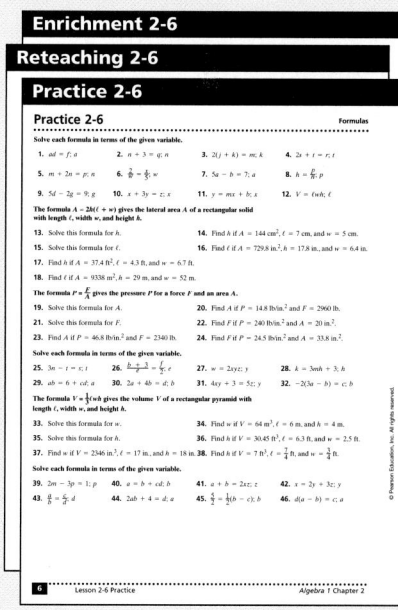

Enrichment 2-6
Reteaching 2-6
Practice 2-6

Lesson 2-6   Formulas   **113**

pages 113–115 Exercises

9. $y = -2x + 5$

10. $y = 6x - 1$

11. $y = -4x + 3$

12. $y = -2x + 4$

13. $y = \frac{5x + 9}{3}$

14. $y = \frac{-3x + 7}{4}$

15. $y = \frac{-5x + 4}{4}$

16. $y = \frac{-2x + 4}{7}$

17. $x = \frac{c}{d}$

18. $g = \frac{d}{c}$

19. $z = a + y$

20. $y = \frac{c - ax}{b}$

21. $t = \frac{A - P}{Pr}$

22. $r = \frac{S}{C} - 1$

23. $p = \frac{qm}{n}$

24. $y = mx + b$

Lesson Quiz 2-6

Solve each equation for the given variable.

1. $3x + 2y = z$; y $\quad y = \frac{1}{2}z - \frac{3}{2}x$

2. $\frac{a - b}{c} = \frac{d}{3}$; a $\quad a = \frac{cd}{3} + b$

3. $3x + 4 = 2(3 - y)$; y
   $\quad y = -\frac{3}{2}x + 1$

4. The formula $v^2 = \frac{GM}{r}$ can be used to find the constant speed v of a satellite revolving around the earth in a circular orbit of radius r. G is a number known as the gravitational constant and M is the mass of the earth. Transform this formula to find the mass of the Earth. $M = \frac{v^2 r}{G}$

Alternative Assessment

Have each student use index cards to form a literal equation on his or her desk. Students write each variable, sign, fraction bar, etc., on its own card. Give each student a counter. Instruct students to place the counter on the variable to be solved for. Have students move to a different desk and solve the equation at that desk by moving the index cards.

Standardized Test Prep

Resources

For additional practice with a variety of test item formats:
- Standardized Test Prep, p. 129
- Test-Taking Strategies, p. 124
- Test-Taking Strategies with Transparencies

Exercise 48 Suggest to students that they make a table to organize the data for each person.

$p = \frac{I}{rt}$

 **B** Apply Your Skills **27. a. Banking** The formula $I = prt$ gives the amount of simple interest I earned by principal p at an annual interest rate r over t years. Solve this formula for p.
   b. Find p if $r = 0.035, t = 4$, and $I = \$420$. **$3000**
   c. Writing What does the value p mean in your answer to part (b)?
   If the interest at 3.5% for 4 yr is $420, the principal is $3000.00.

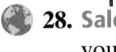 **28. Sales Commission** Suppose that you sell shoes and get a 5% commission on your sales. Last week, your paycheck included $24.71 in commissions.
   a. Solve the formula $C = 0.05s$ for s, where C is the amount of commission and s is the amount of sales. $s = \frac{C}{0.05}$
   b. Find your sales. **$494.20**

Solve each equation for the variable in red. 29–40. See margin.

29. $A = bh$ **30.** $y = \frac{2}{3}x + 8$ **31.** $ap - b = r$

32. $2(p + r) = 5$ **33.** $SA = 2\pi rh + 2B$ **34.** $2x + 10 = 5y - 4$

35. $\frac{a}{b} = \frac{c}{d}$ **36.** $\frac{m + k}{h} = w$ **37.** $V = \frac{1}{3}\pi r^2 h$

38. $3y + 2 = 9x - 4$ **39.** $y = 3(w - y)$ **40.** $3m = 2(4 + x)$

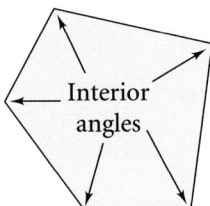
 41. Geometry To find S, the sum of the measures of the interior angles of a polygon with n sides, you can use the formula $S = (n - 2)180$. $n = \frac{S}{180} + 2$
   a. Transform the formula to find the number of sides in terms of the interior angle sum. Solve this equation for n.
   b. Complete the table at the right using your new formula.

Interior angles

S	n
540	■ 5
900	■ 7
360	■ 4
1260	■ 9

 42. Writing How is solving a literal equation similar to solving an equation that involves one variable? How is it different?
   See margin p. 115.

43. Open-Ended Write an equation using three variables. Solve the equation for each variable. Show all your steps. **Check students' work.**

 **C** Challenge **44. Geometry** To find the coordinate of the midpoint of a segment with endpoints that have coordinates a and b, you can use the formula $m = \frac{a + b}{2}$.
   a. Find the coordinate of the midpoint of a segment with endpoints 8.2 and 3.5. **5.85**
   b. Transform the formula to find b in terms of a and m. **$b = 2m - a$**
   c. A segment has midpoint 2.1. One endpoint is -1.7. Find the other endpoint. **5.9**

 45. Recreation The aspect ratio of a hang glider describes its ability to glide and soar. The formula $R = \frac{s^2}{A}$ gives the aspect ratio R for a glider with wingspan s and wing area A.
   a. Solve this formula for A. **$A = \frac{s^2}{R}$**
   b. Suppose you want to design a glider with a 9-ft wingspan and an aspect ratio of 3. Use the formula you found in part (a) to find the wing area. **27 ft^2**

Real-World Connection

Careers Aeronautical engineers may design simple aircraft, like hang gliders, or complex superjets. Every aspect of design, from wingspan to the size of fuel containers, requires engineers to know and use formulas.

 46. Health The volume of air an adult's lungs can hold decreases with age. The formula $V = 0.104h - 0.018a - 2.69$ estimates air volume V (in liters) of a person's lungs for someone of height h inches and age a years. Solve this formula for age a. $a = \frac{-V - 2.69 + 0.104h}{0.018}$

---

pages 113–115 **Exercises**

29. $b = \frac{A}{h}$

30. $x = \frac{3}{2}(y - 8)$

31. $p = \frac{r + b}{a}$

32. $p = \frac{S}{2} - r$

33. $h = \frac{5A - 2B}{2\pi r}$

34. $y = \frac{2x + 14}{5}$

35. $b = \frac{da}{c}$

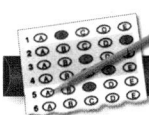

Multiple Choice

47. You can find the cost of renting a hot-air balloon at Tavares Balloon Rental using the formula $C = 85 + 36h$, where C is the total cost and h is the number of hours rented. Solve this equation for h. **B**

A. $h = C - 121$ B. $h = \dfrac{C - 85}{36}$ C. $h = C - 85$ D. $h = \dfrac{C - 36}{85}$

48. Kelly, Ted, and Lauren opened savings accounts. Kelly started with $80 and saves $30 per month. Ted started with $50 and saves twice as much as Kelly each month. Lauren started with twice as much as Kelly and saves one third as much as Ted each month. Let m represent the number of months each has been saving. Which expression represents the total amount of money saved by Kelly, Ted, and Lauren in m months? **I**

F. $290 + 270m$ G. $110 + 290m$ H. $270 + 290m$ I. $290 + 110m$

49. A rectangular table measures 36 in. by 48 in. A square game board that is 24 in. on each side is on the table. Which amount of the table's area is NOT covered by the game board? **B**

A. 264 in.²   B. 1152 in.²   C. 1704 in.²   D. 1728 in.²

50. The formula for the time that a traffic light remains yellow is $t = \frac{1}{8}s + 1$, where t is the time in seconds and s is the speed limit. If the light is yellow for 6 seconds, what is the speed limit in miles per hour? **G**

F. 56   G. 40   H. 10   I. 1.75

Take It to the NET
Online lesson quiz at
www.PHSchool.com
Web Code: aea-0206

Mixed Review

Lesson 2-5

51. The sum of three consecutive integers is 216. Find the integers. **71, 72, 73**

52. The perimeter of a rectangle is 116 cm. The length is 10 cm greater than twice the width. What is the length of the rectangle? **42 cm**

54. $\begin{bmatrix} 14 & -6.2 \\ \frac{1}{2} & -16 \end{bmatrix}$

Lesson 1-6

Multiply. 54–55. See left.

55. $\begin{bmatrix} -15.6 & 27 & 3 \\ 0 & 24 & -28.5 \end{bmatrix}$

53. $12\begin{bmatrix} -5 & \frac{3}{4} \end{bmatrix}$ **[−60 9]**   **54.** $2\begin{bmatrix} 7 & -3.1 \\ \frac{1}{4} & -8 \end{bmatrix}$

55. $-3\begin{bmatrix} 5.2 & -9 & -1 \\ 0 & -8 & 9.5 \end{bmatrix}$

 Checkpoint Quiz 2   **Lessons 2-4 through 2-6**

 TEXT Instant self-check quiz online and on CD-ROM

Solve each equation. 5. See left.

5. -13

1. $7x + 3 = 15x + 9$ $-\frac{3}{4}$ **2.** $\frac{3}{4}n + 5 = \frac{2}{5}n$ $-14\frac{2}{7}$ **3.** $-\frac{1}{5}x - 8 = 4x + 3$ $-2\frac{13}{21}$

4. $5(2w - 4) = 6w$ **5**   **5.** $2y - 8 = -\frac{1}{2}(3 - 5y)$ **6.** $0.3a + 0.7 = 0.5a - 0.1$ **4**

Solve each equation for y. 7–9. See left.

7. $y = \dfrac{35 - 2x}{7}$

8. $y = \dfrac{5x - 15}{2}$

9. $y = 12 - \dfrac{8}{9}x$

7. $2x + 7y = 35$ **8.** $5x - 2y = 15$ **9.** $\frac{2}{3}x + \frac{3}{4}y = 9$

10. Two cars are traveling on the same highway. The first car is traveling at an average rate of 44 mi/h. The second car leaves an hour later traveling at an average rate of 55 mi/h. How long will the cars have traveled when the second car catches up with the first car? **first car: 5 h, second car: 4 h**

Lesson 2-6   Formulas   **115**

42. Answers may vary. Sample: Both types of equations are transformed in the same way. In solving a literal equation, you must be concerned about dividing by a variable where the value of the variable might be zero.

Chapter Checkpoint 2

To check understanding of Lessons 2-4 to 2-6:

Checkpoint Quiz 2 (p. 115)

Teaching Resources
Checkpoint Quiz 2 (also in Prentice Hall Assessment System)

Reaching All Students
Reading and Math Literacy 2C

Spanish versions available

Developing Geometric Formulas

Students use what they know about the areas of familiar geometric shapes to develop formulas for the surface areas of various three-dimensional geometric figures. Students draw nets of three-dimensional figures to help them calculate surface area.

Resources

 Technology
Computer Test Generator CD-ROM, Chapter 0, Extension Topics

Teaching Notes

Drawing nets of various three-dimensional geometric figures will help students know what separate areas to calculate before adding them together to find the total surface area of the figure.

Tactile Learners

Tactile learners may benefit from taking a box such as a cereal box, opening it up to lie flat, and cutting off the overlap tabs. They can then measure the dimensions of the box to calculate the surface area. This will help them understand which edges have the same lengths.

Error Prevention

Students may confuse surface area and volume. Point out that the term *surface area* contains the word *face* and surface area is the sum of the areas of the faces of the figure.

You can develop formulas for the surface area of prisms and cylinders using what you know about the areas of geometric shapes. Making a net of a figure can help. A net is a two-dimensional figure that you could fold to make a three-dimensional figure.

1 EXAMPLE

The figure at the right is a rectangular prism. Write a formula for the surface area of a rectangular prism.

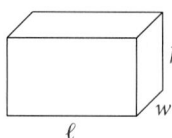

Draw a net.

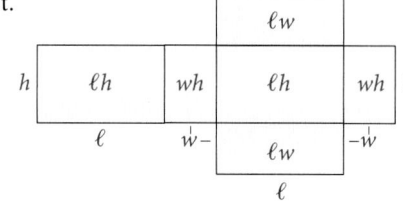

Add the areas of the six rectangles that form the net. The sum of the areas of all six faces of the net will give you the surface area SA of the prism.

$SA = \ell w + \ell w + \ell h + \ell h + hw + hw$

$= 2\ell w + 2\ell h + 2hw$ **Combine like terms.**

$= 2(\ell w + \ell h + hw)$ **Use the Distributive Property.**

The formula for the surface area is $SA = 2(\ell w + \ell h + hw)$.

EXERCISES

Use the net for each figure. Write a formula for the surface area of each figure.

1. cylinder $SA = 2\pi rh + 2\pi r^2$

2. square pyramid $SA = b^2 + 2b\ell$ or $b(b + 2\ell)$

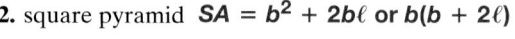

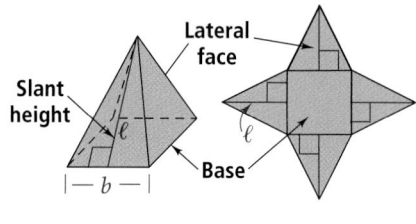

Use the formula in Example 1 and the formulas you wrote in Exercises 1 and 2 to find the surface area of each figure. Round answers to the nearest hundredth, if necessary.

3. rectangular prism with $\ell = 8$ in., $w = 5$ in., and $h = 10$ in. **340 in.²**

4. cylinder with $r = 3$ ft and $h = 10$ ft **245.04 ft²**

5. cylinder with $r = 8$ cm and $h = 100$ cm **5428.67 cm²**

6. square pyramid with $b = 12$ mm and $\ell = 10$ mm **384 mm²**

7. square pyramid with $b = 100$ m and $\ell = 90$ m **28,000 m²**

8. Write a formula for the surface area of a cube with edges of length s. **$A = 6s^2$**

In general, the formula for the volumes of rectangular prisms and cylinders is area of base × height. You make the formula more specific by including the formula for the area of the base in the formula for the volume.

2 EXAMPLE

Write a formula for the volume of a cylinder.

The base is a circle.
The area of a circle is πr^2.

The height of a cylinder takes into account "filling" the cylinder. So the volume of a cylinder is the area of the base times the height.

$V = \pi r^2 h$

EXERCISES

9. A rectangular prism is shown at the right. Write a formula for the volume of a rectangular prism. **$V = \ell wh$**

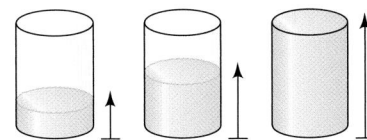

Find the volume of each figure.

10. rectangular prism with $\ell = 8$ in., $w = 5$ in., and $h = 10$ in. **400 in.³**

11. cylinder with $r = 3$ ft and $h = 10$ ft **282.74 ft³**

12.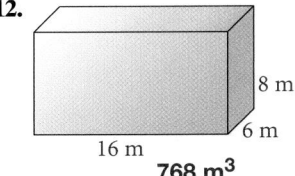

13. **1728 mm³**

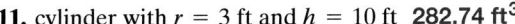

768 m³

14. a. The volume of a pyramid is $\frac{1}{3}$ the volume of a rectangular prism with the same base and height. Write a formula for the volume of a pyramid. **$V = \frac{1}{3}Bh$**
   b. Use your formula to find the volume of a rectangular pyramid with base length 7 cm, width 12 cm, and height 10 cm. **280 cm³**

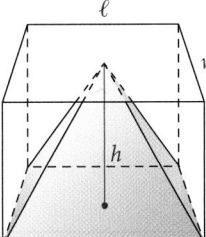

1. Plan

Lesson Preview

 **Check Skills You'll Need**

Adding Real Numbers
Lesson 1-4: Example 2
Exercises 5–24
Extra Practice, p. 702

Multiplying and Dividing Real Numbers
Lesson 1-6: Example 5
Exercises 40–47
Extra Practice, p. 702

Lesson Resources

Teaching Resources
Practice, Reteaching, Enrichment

Reaching All Students
Practice Workbook 2-7
Spanish Practice Workbook 2-7
Basic Algebra Planning Guide 2-7

Presentation Assistant Plus!
Transparencies
• Check Skills You'll Need 2-7
• Additional Examples 2-7
• Student Edition Answers 2-7
• Lesson Quiz 2-7
PH Presentation Pro CD 2-7

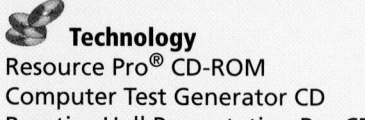

Computer Test Generator CD

Technology
Resource Pro® CD-ROM
Computer Test Generator CD
Prentice Hall Presentation Pro CD

www.PHSchool.com
Student Site
• Teacher Web Code: aek-5500
• Graphing Calculator, Procedure 21
• Self-grading Lesson Quiz
Teacher Center
• Lesson Planner
• Resources

Plus

 2-7

Using Measures of Central Tendency

Lesson Preview

What You'll Learn

OBJECTIVE 1 To find mean, median, and mode

OBJECTIVE 2 To make and use stem-and-leaf plots

. . . And Why

To analyze real-world employment data, as in Example 1

 Check Skills You'll Need (For help, go to Lessons 1-4 and 1-6.)

Write the numbers in each group in order from least to greatest. **2.** 58, 72, 98, 144, 195, 235

1. 2.4, 9.8, 3.6, 7.5, 1.9 **1.9, 2.4, 3.6, 7.5, 9.8** **2.** 144, 235, 98, 72, 58, 195

3. $-12, 14, -3, -8, 7, 0$
$-12, -8, -3, 0, 7, 14$

4. $2\frac{1}{2}, -3\frac{2}{3}, -4\frac{3}{8}, 6\frac{1}{4}, -2\frac{5}{8}, 4\frac{1}{2}$
$-4\frac{3}{8}, -3\frac{2}{3}, -2\frac{5}{8}, 2\frac{1}{2}, 4\frac{1}{2}, 6\frac{1}{4}$

Use mental math to simplify.

5. $\frac{3+4+5+6+7}{5}$ **5**

6. $\frac{5+6+8+9}{4}$ **7**

New Vocabulary
• measures of central tendency • mean • outlier
• median • mode • range • stem-and-leaf plot

 OBJECTIVE

1 Finding Mean, Median, and Mode

 Interactive lesson includes instant self-check, tutorials, and activities.

To understand a set of data, you need to organize and summarize the data using a measure of central tendency. Mean, median, and mode are all **measures of central tendency.**

You must decide which measure of central tendency best describes a set of data. Below is a review of mean, median, and mode, and where you would use each as the measure of central tendency.

Key Concepts

Review	Mean, Median, Mode

$$\text{Mean} = \frac{\text{sum of the data items}}{\text{total number of data items}}$$

Use the mean to describe the middle of a set of data that *does not* have an outlier. An **outlier** is a data value that is much higher or lower than the other data values in the set. The mean is often referred to as the average.

The **median** is the middle value in the set when the numbers are arranged in order. For a set containing an even number of data items, the median is the mean of the two middle data values.

Use the median to describe the middle of a set of data that *does* have an outlier.

The **mode** is the data item that occurs the most times. It is possible for a set of data to have no mode, one mode, or more than one mode.

Use the mode when the data are nonnumeric or when choosing the most popular item.

 Ongoing Assessment and Intervention

Before the Lesson
Diagnose prerequisite skills using:
• Check Skills You'll Need

During the Lesson
Monitor progress using:
• Check Understanding
• Additional Examples
• Standardized Test Prep

After the Lesson
Assess knowledge using:
• Lesson Quiz
• Computer Test Generator CD

 **EXAMPLE** Real-World  Problem Solving

Wages Find the mean, median, and mode of the data in the line plot below. Which measure of central tendency best describes the data?

Hourly Wages of Employees at a Local Restaurant

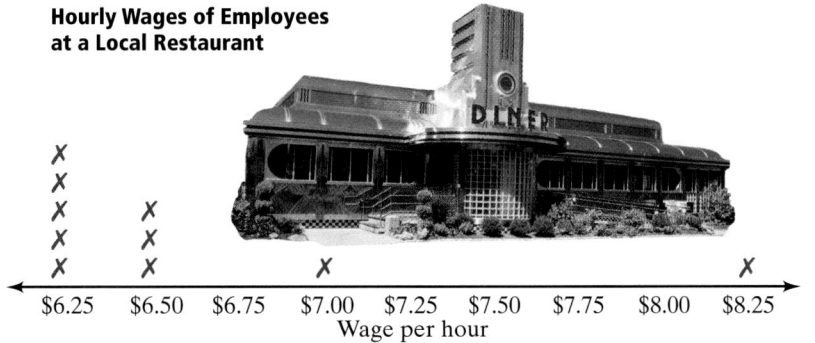

X							
X							
X	X						
X	X						
X	X	X				X	

$6.25 $6.50 $6.75 $7.00 $7.25 $7.50 $7.75 $8.00 $8.25
Wage per hour

↓ 5(6.25) is a shortcut for adding 6.25 + 6.25 + 6.25 + 6.25 + 6.25.

Mean: $\dfrac{5(6.25) + 3(6.50) + 7.00 + 8.25}{10} = 6.6$

↑ total number of employees

Median: 6.25 6.25 6.25 6.25 6.25 6.50 6.50 6.50 7.00 8.25   **List data in order. 6.25 and 6.50 are the two middle data values.**

$\dfrac{6.25 + 6.50}{2} = 6.375$ **The median of an even number of data items is the mean of the two middle data values.**

Mode: 6.25   **the data item that occurs most often**

The mean is $6.60, the median is about $6.38, and the mode is $6.25. The mean is greater than the salary of 8 workers. The mode is the salary of the 5 workers with the lowest salary. The median best describes the data.

✓ **Check Understanding** 1 **a.** about $6.53/h; about $6.38/h; $6.25/h

a. Wages The employee who earns $8.25 per hour resigns. She is replaced by an employee earning $7.50 per hour. Find the mean, median, and mode of the data.

b. Critical Thinking Which measure best describes the data? Explain why.
Median; the mean is still larger than 8 of 10 wages.

Students often ask, "What grade do I need on the next test to bring up my average?" The example below shows you how to solve that kind of problem.

2 **EXAMPLE** Solving an Equation

Suppose your grades on three history exams are 80, 93, and 91. What grade do you need on your next exam to have a 90 average on the four exams?

Mean (average): $\dfrac{80 + 93 + 91 + x}{4} = 90$ **Let x = the grade on the fourth exam.**

$\dfrac{264 + x}{4} = 90$ **Simplify the numerator.**

$4\left(\dfrac{264 + x}{4}\right) = 4(90)$ **Multiply each side by 4.**

$264 + x = 360$ **Simplify.**

$264 + x - 264 = 360 - 264$ **Subtract 264 from each side.**

$x = 96$ **Simplify.**

Your grade on the next exam must be 96 for you to have an average of 90.

---

2. Teach

Professional Development

Math Background

Students may know how to calculate mean, median, and mode, but they may not be familiar with the concept that each of these single numbers may be used to represent the central tendency of a collection of numbers, or data. They will encounter them in everyday surveys and samples, and must understand their limitations.

OBJECTIVE
1 **Teaching Notes**

1 **EXAMPLE** **Teaching Tip**

To determine which measure of central tendency best describes the data, you do not have to calculate any of them. Look at the frequency graph. There is an outlier at $8.25. The median is usually used to describe data that have an outlier.

Additional Examples

1 Find the mean, median, and mode of the data below. Which measure of central tendency best describes the data?
14 10 2 13 16 3 12 11
mean 10.125; median 11.5; mode none; The median best describes the data.

2 Suppose your grades on three science exams are 82, 94, and 89. What grade do you need on your next exam to have an average of 90? 95

👥 Reaching All Students

Below Level Challenge students to create a data set of seven consecutive integers where the median is equal to the mean and there is no mode.	**Advanced Learners** Lead students in a discussion of other situations where the mode, the median, or the mean would be the best measure of central tendency.	**English Learners** See note on page 120. **Error Prevention** See note on page 123.

3 Find the range and mean of each set of data. Use the range to compare the spread of the two sets of data.
45 47 34 36 38 and
56 35 27 47 35
1st set: range 13, mean 40;
2nd set: range 29, mean 40;
The first set clusters nearer the mean.

OBJECTIVE

2 **Teaching Notes**

4 EXAMPLE **English Learners**

Draw a stem and its leaves on the board and label the parts. Pronounce the words *stem, leaf,* and *leaves.* Ask: *Which is the main part?* the stem *Which is attached to the main part?* the leaves Relate the drawing to the stem-and-leaf plot.

■ **Additional Examples**

4 Make a stem-and-leaf plot for the data.
56 44 63 58 51 59 47 51 67 50 65 49 66 63

```
4 | 4 7 9
5 | 0 1 1 6 8 9
6 | 3 3 5 6 7
```

4 | 4 means 44

5 Find the mean of the city mileage and highway mileage for 16 new cars.

New Car Mileage (in mi/gal)

City		Highway
8 7	1	
6 4 1 0	2	2 4
8 6	3	0 0 2 3 8
	4	3

means 36 ← 6 | 3 | 0 → means 30
city: 25 mi/gal;
highway: 31.5 mi/gal

Closure

Ask: *When should the mean be used to describe data and when should the median be used?*
Use the mean when there is not an outlier. Use the median when there is an outlier.
What measure(s) are easy to find from a stem-and-leaf plot?
The mode is easiest to find.

120

✔ **Check Understanding** **2** **Critical Thinking** If 100 is the highest possible score on the fourth exam, is it possible to raise your average to 92? Explain.
No; you would need at least a 104 to have a 92 average.

The **range** of a set of data is the difference between the greatest and least data values. The range gives you a measure of the spread of the data.

3 EXAMPLE **Finding the Range and Mean of Data**

Find the range and mean of each set of data. Use the range to compare the spread of the two sets of data.

25 30 30 47 28

Range: $47 - 25 = 22$

Mean: $\dfrac{25 + 30 + 30 + 47 + 28}{5}$

$\dfrac{160}{5} = 32$

34 28 31 36 31

Range: $36 - 28 = 8$

Mean: $\dfrac{34 + 28 + 31 + 36 + 31}{5}$

$\dfrac{160}{5} = 32$

Both sets of data have a mean of 32. The range of the first set of data is 22, and the range of the second set of data is 8. The second set of data is less spread out.

✔ **Check Understanding** **3** For the first five days in February, the low temperatures in northern Maine were 7°F, 4°F, −3°F, −6°F, and 0°F. During the same time period, the low temperatures in northern Michigan were 24°F, 15°F, −2°F, −10°F, and −5°F. Find the mean and range of the temperatures. Compare the spreads of the temperature data.
See above left.

OBJECTIVE

2 **Stem-and-Leaf Plots**

You can use a stem-and-leaf plot to organize data. A **stem-and-leaf plot** is a display of data made by using the digits of the values. To make a stem-and-leaf plot, separate each number into a stem and a leaf. This is the stem and leaf for the number 1.54.

all digits to the left of last digit

last digit

→ 1.5 | 4

↑ stem   ↑ leaf

```
4. 0 | 2 8 8
   1 | 4
   2 | 6
   3 | 5
   4 | 3 3 5
   6 | 0
```

4 | 3 means 4.3

Gasoline Prices (cost /gallon)
$1.77
$1.55
$1.58
$1.73
$1.54
$1.83
$1.63
$1.67

4 EXAMPLE **Making a Stem-and-Leaf Plot**

Make a stem-and-leaf plot for the data at the left.

Use the first two digits for the "stems."

```
1.5 | 4 5 8
1.6 | 3 7
1.7 | 3 7
1.8 | 3
```

Use the corresponding last digits for the "leaves." Arrange the numbers in order.

1.8 | 3 means 1.83

✔ **Check Understanding** **4** Make a stem-and-leaf plot for the data below. **See above.**
4.5 4.3 0.8 3.5 2.6 1.4 0.2 0.8 4.3 6.0

3.
Maine: mean = 0.4°F;
            range = 13°F
Michigan: mean = 4.4°F;
            range = 34°F
On average, Maine was colder. The temperatures for Michigan were more spread out.

You can find the measures of central tendency of data displayed in a stem-and-leaf plot. The stem-and-leaf plot in the next example is a back-to-back stem-and-leaf plot. The stem is between the two bars, and the leaves are on each side. Leaves are in increasing order from the stems.

5 EXAMPLE Using a Stem-and-Leaf Plot

Find the mean of the city mileage and highway mileage for nine new cars.

New Car Mileage (mi/gal)

City		Highway
9	1	
9 8 3 3 0	2	7 8
4 1 1	3	0 2 2 7 8 8
	4	1

means 20 mi/gal ← 0 | 2 | 7 → means 27 mi/gal

Mean City Mileage: $\dfrac{19 + 20 + 23 + 23 + 28 + 29 + 31 + 31 + 34}{9} = 26.\overline{4}$ mi/gal

Mean Highway Mileage: $\dfrac{27 + 28 + 30 + 32 + 32 + 37 + 38 + 38 + 41}{9} = 33.\overline{6}$ mi/gal

✓ **Check Understanding** 5 a. Find the median of the city mileage and of the highway mileage.
b. Find the mode(s) of the city mileage and of the highway mileage.
c. Find the range of the city mileage and of the highway mileage.
a. city: 28 mi/gal; highway: 32 mi/gal
b. city: 23 mi/gal; 31 mi/gal; highway: 32 mi/gal; 38 mi/gal
c. city: 15 mi/gal; highway: 14 mi/gal

EXERCISES

For more practice, see *Extra Practice*.

Practice and Problem Solving

 **Practice by Example**

Find the mean, median, and mode. Which measure of central tendency best describes the data?

Example 1
(page 119)

1. weights of textbooks in ounces
12 10 9 15 16 10
12; 11; 10; median

2. ages of students on math team
14 14 15 15 16 15 15 16
15; 15; 15; any

3. time spent on Internet in min/day
75 38 43 120 65 48 52
63; 52; none; median

4. weights of channel catfish in pounds
4.8 5 2.3 4.5 4.8 5.2
4.4; 4.8; 4.8; median or mode

Example 2
(page 119)

Write and solve an equation to find the value of *x*. **5–8. See margin.**

5. 3.8, 4.2, 5.3, *x*; mean 4.8

6. 99, 86, 76, 95, *x*; mean 91

7. 100, 121, 105, 113, 108, *x*; mean 112

8. 31.7, 42.8, 26.4, *x*; mean 35

Example 3
(page 120)

Find the range.

9. 12 15 17 28 30 **18**

10. 5.3 6.2 3.1 4.8 7.3 **4.2**

11. −12 −15 5 3 −2 0 −7 **20**

12. $2\frac{1}{2}$ $3\frac{1}{3}$ $-5\frac{3}{4}$ $\frac{3}{8}$ $3\frac{5}{8}$ $9\frac{3}{8}$

13. For each list of data, find the range and the mean. Use the range to compare the spread of the data.

List 1	List 2
64 43 55 28 71	48 53 61 47 52

List 1—43; 52.2
List 2—14; 52.2
The second set of data is less spread out.

Lesson 2-7 Using Measures of Central Tendency **121**

5. $\dfrac{3.8 + 4.2 + 5.3 + x}{4} = 4.8$; 5.9

7. $\dfrac{100 + 121 + 105 + 113 + 108 + x}{6} = 112$; 125

6. $\dfrac{99 + 86 + 76 + 95 + x}{5} = 91$; 99

8. $\dfrac{31.7 + 42.8 + 26.4 + x}{4} = 35$; 39.1

Assignment Guide

▼ **1 Objective**
Ⓐ Ⓑ **Core** 1–13, 20–23, 25–28
Ⓒ **Extension** 30–31

Objective
Ⓐ Ⓑ **Core** 14–19, 24
Ⓒ **Extension** 29

Standardized Test Prep 32–36

Mixed Review 37–44

Exercises 1–4 Suggest to students that they look for an outlier.

Exercises 9–12 Suggest to students that they circle the greatest and the least data values if they do not put them in order.

Teaching Tip

Exercise 29 Point out to students that arranging the leaves in ascending order makes a stem-and-leaf plot easier to use.

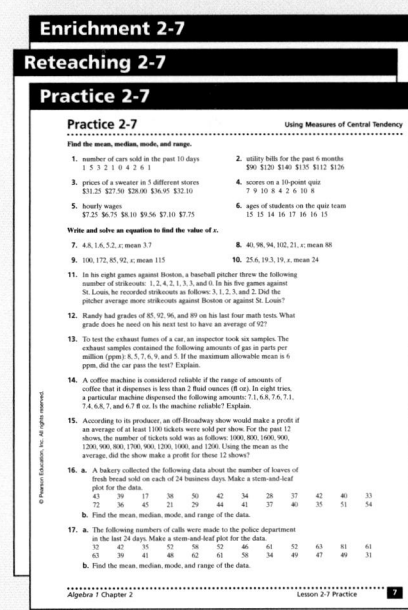

pages 121–123   Exercises

14.
```
1 | 0 5 5 8
2 | 2 5 8
3 | 5 6
```
1 | 0 means 10

15.
```
15 | 3 7
16 |
17 | 5 6
18 | 4 6
```
15 | 3 means 15.3

Example 4
(page 120)

Example 5
(page 121)

18. Class A—60.75, 59.5, 54, 35
Class B—60.35, 59, 52 and 79, 38

19. Type A—0.30, 0.31, 0.23 and 0.31, 0.18
Type B—0.42, 0.44, 0.31, 0.23

B Apply Your Skills

Make a stem-and-leaf plot for each set of data. 14–17. See margin.

14. 18 35 28 15 36 10 25 22 15   15. 18.6 18.4 17.6 15.7 15.3 17.5

16. 785 776 788 761 768 768 785   17. 0.8 0.2 1.4 3.5 4.3 4.5 2.6 2.2

Find the mean, median, mode, and range of each side of the stem-and-leaf plot.
18–19. See left.

18.

Time Spent on Homework (minutes/day)	
Class A	Class B
6 6 4 3	4	1 1 4 5 7
9 8 6 4 4 4	5	0 2 2 2 4
5 2 1 0	6	4 5 8 9
8 7 6 6 4 2	7	3 6 7 9 9 9

means 43 ← 3 | 4 | 1 → means 41

19.

Growth of Two Varieties of Tulip Plants (inches/day)	
Type A	Type B
6 3 3	2	
3 2 1 1	3	1 1 2
1	4	3 5 8
	5	2 4

means 0.33 ← 3 | 3 | 1 → means 0.31

Find the mean, median, mode, and range.

20. 9.8 7.2 6.3 8.7 5.8 9.4 5.1 6.2 **7.3125, 6.75, none, 4.7**

21. 3 −12 −1 −7 −2 0 −5 −1 −4 −2 **−3.1, −2, −1 and −2, 15**

22. 42.1 46.4 58.2 67.3 49.1 40.2 22.3 46.6 **46.525, 46.5, none, 45.0**

23. **Critical Thinking** The mean of a set of data is 7.8, the mode is 6.6, and the median is 6.8. What is the least possible number of data values? Explain.
See margin.

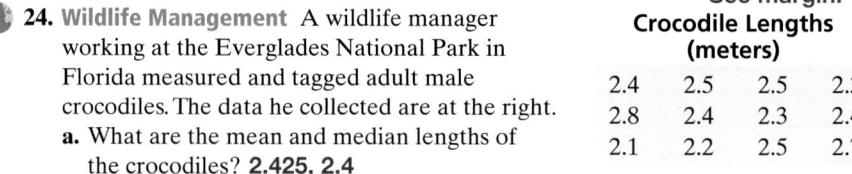

24. **Wildlife Management** A wildlife manager working at the Everglades National Park in Florida measured and tagged adult male crocodiles. The data he collected are at the right.
   a. What are the mean and median lengths of the crocodiles? **2.425, 2.4**
   b. The wildlife manager captured another crocodile. Its length was 3.3 m. What is the mean with this new piece of data? What is the median? Round to the nearest tenth. **2.5; 2.4**

Crocodile Lengths (meters)			
2.4	2.5	2.5	2.3
2.8	2.4	2.3	2.4
2.1	2.2	2.5	2.7

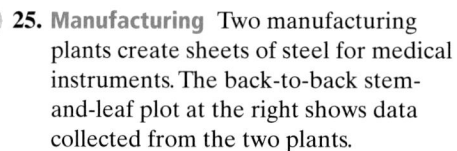

Real-World ⊕ Connection

Careers A wildlife manager collects data about the animal and plant life of an area. Using statistical measures, the wildlife manager can make predictions about the growth of plants and animals and the ecological health of the area.

25. **Manufacturing** Two manufacturing plants create sheets of steel for medical instruments. The back-to-back stem-and-leaf plot at the right shows data collected from the two plants.
   a. Find the mean, median, mode, and range of each set of data.
   b. Which measure of central tendency best describes each set of data? Explain.
   c. **Reasoning** Which plant has the better quality control? Explain.
   a–c. See margin p. 123.

Width of Steel (millimeters)	
Manufacturing Plant A	Manufacturing Plant B
	4	3 5 9
8 7 4 4 2	5	2 7
4 3 1	6	3 4
	7	2

means 6.1 ← 1 | 6 | 3 → means 6.3

26. **Open-Ended** Give an example of a set of data for which the mode best represents the data. Explain. **Answers may vary. Sample: 50, 62, 64, 64, 64, 65, 65, 85**

27. **Sports** The median height of the 21 players on a girls' soccer team is 5 ft 7 in. What is the greatest possible number of girls who are less than 5 ft 7 in. tall? **10**

28. **Writing** How does an outlier affect the mean of a set of data?
An outlier can skew the mean of a set of numbers enough that it is not a reliable measure of central tendency.

16.
```
76 | 1 8 8
77 | 6
78 | 5 5 8
```
76 | 1 means 761

17.
```
0 | 2 8
1 | 4
2 | 2 6
3 | 5
4 | 3 5
```
0 | 2 means 0.2

23. 5; two values are 6.6, one is 6.8, and two are greater than 6.8.

⊙ Challenge

29. Make a back-to-back stem-and-leaf plot of the data below. **See left.**

29.
July		April
7 2 0 0 0	0	
	0	1
8	2	
	3	
8 8 0	4	5 5
0	5	5 5
3 1	6	3 3 5 7
	7	
1	8	1 7 8
	9	4
	10	7 8

means 0.40 ← 0 | 4 | → 5 means 0.45

Daily Precipitation in Tropical Areas (centimeters)

First Two Weeks of July	First Two Weeks of April
0.28 0.48 0.02 0.63 0.81 0.10 0.40	1.08 0.94 0.88 1.07 0.45 0.45 0.65
0.07 0.61 0.50 0.48 0.00 0.00 0.00	0.67 0.55 0.87 0.63 0.81 0.55 0.63

30. Data Collection Record the high and low temperatures in your town for one week. Make a back-to-back stem-and-leaf plot with the data you collect. **Check students' work.**

31. During the first 6 hours of a trip, you average 44 mi/h. During the last 4 hours of your trip, you average 50 mi/h. What is your average speed for the whole trip? (*Hint:* First find the total number of miles traveled.) **46.4 mi/h**

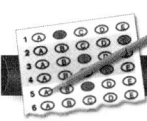

Standardized Test Prep

Gridded Response

32. You have a mean score of 84 after taking five 100-point tests. What do you need to score on the sixth 100-point test to have a mean score of 85? **90**

33. Five runners on the track team have the following times in seconds for the 100-meter dash. What is the difference between the mean and the median of the following times? **0.04**

10.2	10.6	11.9	9.9	10.6

34. The average speeds of the winners of the Daytona 500 from 1995 to 2000 are listed at the right. What is the mean in miles per hour of the given speeds rounded to the nearest tenth? **155.7**

35. Find the sum of the mean, the median, and the mode of the following data: 22, 18, 17, 18, 25, 24, 24, 18. **58.75**

36. The average low temperature for a 4-day period in January for the city of Orlando, Florida, was 58°F. After the fifth day, the 5-day average was 59°F. What was the low temperature on the fifth day? **63**

Daytona 500

Year	Average Speed
1995	141.7 mi/h
1996	154.3 mi/h
1997	148.3 mi/h
1998	172.7 mi/h
1999	161.6 mi/h
2000	155.7 mi/h

SOURCE: *2001 Sports Almanac*

Take It to the NET
Online lesson quiz at
www.PHSchool.com
Web Code: aea-0207

Mixed Review

Lesson 2-6

Solve each equation for *x*.

37. $y = x + 4$
$x = y - 4$

38. $y = -x + 3$
$x = 3 - y$

39. $y = 10x + 4$
$x = \frac{y - 4}{10}$

40. $y = 2x + 9$
$x = \frac{y - 9}{2}$

Lesson 2-1

Solve each equation.

41. $\frac{x}{8} = -18$
-144

42. $-15n = 210$
-14

43. $-a = \frac{2}{3}$
$-\frac{2}{3}$

44. $-\frac{y}{5} = -22$
110

25a. A—5.79, 5.75, 5.4, 1.2
B—5.56, 5.45, none, 2.9

b. A—mean. There are no outliers.
B—median. The mean is thrown off by high outliers.

c. Plant A has better quality control because there is a smaller range.

Writing Short Responses

This feature helps students understand that to get full credit for an answer, they may need to justify their reasoning and show how they solved the problem.

Resources

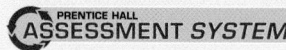
PRENTICE HALL
ASSESSMENT *SYSTEM*

Test-Taking Strategies with Transparencies
• Transparency 2
• Practice sheet p. 2

Teaching Notes

Help students understand that justifying their answers will help them to develop a better understanding of problem-solving.

Teaching Tip

Remind students to follow the rubric that is used to evaluate their answer.

Test-Taking Strategies with Transparencies

Test-Taking Strategy: Writing Short Responses

Della went to the carnival at the county fair. The admission to the carnival was $5.00 and the rides were $1.25 each. Della spent $20 at the carnival. Write and solve an equation to find out how many rides Della rode at the carnival.

Scoring Guide

2	The equation and solution are correct, AND all work is shown.
1	An incorrect equation is used, but the procedure for solving the equation is incorrect.
1	The correct equation or solution is given, but no work is shown.
0	No response, OR completely incorrect response with no work shown.

Answer earning 2 points	In the 2-point response, the student used the correct equation, found the correct answer, AND showed all the work.
$5 + 1.25x = 20$ $1.25x = 15$ $x = 12$ Della rode 12 rides.	

Answer earning 1 point	In this 1-point response, an incorrect equation is used, but the procedure is correct for the used equation.
$1.25x = 20$ $x = 16$ Della rode 16 rides	

Answer earning 1 point	In this 1-point response, the correct solution is given, but no work is shown.
Della rode 12 rides.	

Answer earning 0 points	In the 0-point response, the solution is incorrect, AND no work is shown.
15 rides	

Transparency 2

Short-response questions in this textbook are usually worth a maximum of 2 points. To get full credit you need to give the correct answer (including appropriate units, if applicable) and justify your reasoning or show your work.

EXAMPLE

The cost for using a phone card is 35 cents per call plus 25 cents per minute. A recent call cost $12.35. Write and solve an equation to find the length of the call.

The problem is asking you to do three things: (1) use a variable to set up an equation, (2) solve the equation, and (3) find the length of the call. Below is a rubric that shows the number of points awarded for different types of answers.

Scoring Rubric

[2]   The equation and the solution are correct. The call took 48 minutes.

[1]   There is no equation, but there is a method to show that the call took 48 minutes.

[1]   There is an equation and a solution, both of which may contain minor errors. The solution indicates the time, but does not show the units.

[0]   There is no response, it is completely incorrect, or it is a correct response, but no procedure is shown.

Three responses are below with the points each received.

2 points	1 point	0 points
Let n = number of minutes. $1235 = 35 + 25n$ $1200 = 25n$ $48 = n$ The call took 48 minutes.	$\dfrac{12.35 - 0.35}{0.25} = 48$ 48 minutes	48 minutes

EXERCISES

Use the rubric above to answer each question.

1. Explain why each response above received the indicated points. **See above.**

2. Write a 1-point response that begins with a correct equation. **See above.**

3. Write a 2-point response that includes the equation $0.35 + 0.25n = 12.35$. **See above.**

4. **Error Analysis** Suppose a student used the equation $25x + 35 = 12.35$. Explain why this equation is incorrect. **Left side is in cents; right side is in dollars.**

1. 2 points: The equation and solution are correct
   1 point: no equation
   0 points: no procedure

2. Answers may vary. Sample:
   $1235 = 35 + 25n$
   $1270 = 25n$
   $n \approx 51$
   51 minutes

3. Let n = number of minutes.
   $0.35 + 0.25n = 12.35$
   $0.25n = 12$
   $n = 48$
   The call took 48 min.

Chapter Review

Vocabulary

consecutive integers (p. 104)
equivalent equations (p. 75)
identity (p. 98)
inverse operations (p. 75)
literal equation (p. 111)

mean (p. 118)
measures of central tendency (p. 118)
median (p. 118)
mode (p. 118)
outlier (p. 118)

range (p. 120)
solution of an equation (p. 75)
stem-and-leaf plot (p. 120)
uniform motion (p. 104)

Reading Math
Understanding
Vocabulary

Take It to the NET
Online vocabulary quiz
at www.PHSchool.com
Web Code: aej-0251

Choose the term that correctly completes each sentence.

1. A(n) _?_ is true for all values of the variable. **identity**

2. A particular value of a variable that makes an equation true is called a(n) _?_ of the equation. **solution**

3. You use subtraction to undo addition, and division to undo multiplication. These are examples of _?_. **inverse operations**

4. _?_ have the same value. **Solutions of equivalent equations**

5. The difference between two _?_ is one. **consecutive integers**

Match the correct answer in Column II with the word in Column I.

Column I	Column II
6. mean **C**	**A.** the difference between the greatest and least items in a data set
7. mode **D**	**B.** the middle value in an ordered set of data
8. range **A**	**C.** the value of a data set most likely to be affected by an outlier
9. median **B**	**D.** the item in a data set that occurs most frequently

Skills and Concepts

2-1 Objectives

▼ To solve equations using addition and subtraction (p. 74)

▼ To solve equations using multiplication and division (p. 76)

The value of a variable that makes an equation true is a **solution of the equation.** To solve an equation you can use **inverse operations,** which are operations that undo one another. Addition and subtraction are inverse operations. So are multiplication and division.

To solve an addition or subtraction equation, subtract or add the same value to each side of the equation. To solve a multiplication or division equation, divide or multiply each side of the equation by the same nonzero value.

Solve each equation. Check your answer.

10. $y - 7 = 9$ **16**   **11.** $\frac{x}{12} = -3$ **−36**   **12.** $w + 23 = 54$ **31** **13.** $5d = 120$ **24**

14. $9 + t = 35$ **26**   **15.** $c + 0.25 = 4.5$ **4.25**   **16.** $7b = 84$ **12**   **17.** $\frac{z}{4} = \frac{1}{2}$ **2**

Resources

Student Edition
Extra Practice, Ch. 2, p. 703
English/Spanish Glossary, p. 757
Properties and Formulas, p. 752
Table of Symbols, p. 749

Reaching All Students
Reading and Math Literacy 2D
Spanish Reading and Math
Literacy 2D

ASSESSMENT SYSTEM

Standardized Test Prep
• Ch. 2 practice in standardized test formats

 **www.PHSchool.com**
Student Site
• Self-grading Vocabulary Test
Teacher Center
• Resources

Plus **iTEXT**

Spanish Reading and Math Literacy

Reading and Math Literacy

2D: Vocabulary   For use with Chapter Review

Study Skill: When you complete a puzzle such as a word search, remember to read the list of words carefully and completely. As you identify each word in the word search, circle it and then cross off the word from the list. Pay special attention to the spelling of each word.

Complete the word search.

base	coefficient	coordinates
equation	exponent	identity
inequality	integers	matrix
mean	median	mode
opposite	origin	outlier
power	quadrants	range
reciprocal	simplify	variable

```
C S W Z X D I F Y K A L R M P
T N E I C I F F E O C A P A Z
L I J T E M I G E D Y C U T N
S E D D A L E Q N T T O N R A
D R O E P N U D I W L R O I E
R M E M N A I L I C Y P U X M
T E I G T T A D B A E I T J A
N S W I E U I M R D N C L W T
E B O O Q T N T L O T E I U F
N N H E P Z N C Y N O R E O T
O P N E L B A I R A V C R O S
P I Q U A D R A N T S I R L N
X O P P O S I T E E G N A R M
E S U B A S E J M I D C S T U
G C N G W P C G N Z H L L X C
```

Reading and Math Literacy Masters   Algebra 1

▼ To solve two-step equations (p. 81)

▼ To use deductive reasoning (p. 83)

A two-step equation is an equation that has two operations. You can use tiles to model and solve a two-step equation. To solve a two-step equation, first add or subtract. Then multiply or divide.

Solve each equation. Check your answer.

18. $5x - 8 = 12$ **4**

19. $7t - 3 = 18$ **3**

20. $\frac{c}{5} - 4 = -3$ **5**

21. $-2q - 5 = -11$ **3**

22. $-3m + 8 = 2$ **2**

23. $11y + 9 = 130$ **11**

24. $8u + 2 = 6$ $\frac{1}{2}$

25. $10h - 4 = -94$ **-9**

26. $-z + 11 = -7$ **18**

27. $15 = -t + 3$ **-12**

28. $\frac{w}{3} + 2 = 5$ **9**

29. $-\frac{2}{5}x + 4 = 8$ **-10**

30. A state park charges admission of $6 per person plus $3 for parking. Jo paid $27 when her car entered the park. Write and solve an equation to find the number of people in Jo's car. Be sure to explain what your variable represents.
Let x = number of people; $6x + 3 = 27$; 4 people

Solve each equation. Justify each step. 31–33. See margin.

31. $314 = -n + 576$

32. $-\frac{1}{4}w - 1 = 6$

33. $3h - 4 = 5$

Solve each equation.

34. $10 = 35 + \frac{x}{5}$ **-125**

35. $0 = -8t + 48$ **6**

36. $31 = 3 - 4k$ **-7**

▼ To use the Distributive Property when combining like terms (p. 88)

▼ To use the Distributive Property when solving equations (p. 89)

▼ To solve equations with variables on both sides (p. 96)

▼ To identify equations that are identities or have no solution (p. 98)

You can combine like terms and use the Distributive Property to simplify expressions and solve equations. You can also use the properties of equality to solve an equation.

An equation has no solution if no value of the variable makes the equation true. An equation is an **identity** if every value of the variable makes the equation true.

Solve each equation. If the equation is an identity or if it has no solution, write *identity* or *no solution*.

37. $b + 4b = -90$ **-18**

38. $-x + 7x = 24$ **4**

39. $2(t + 5) = 9$ $-\frac{1}{2}$

40. $-(3 - 10y) = 12$ $\frac{3}{2}$

41. $x - (4 - x) = 0$ **2**

42. $4n - 6n = 2n$ **0**

43. $4 + 3n = 5n + 4$ **0**

44. $-2(r - \frac{1}{2}) = -2$ $\frac{3}{2}$

45. $9c + 4 = 3c - 8$ **-2**

46. $3(5x - 2) - 6x = 3(3x + 2)$ no solution

47. $3(2t - 6) = 2(3t - 9)$ identity

48. $\frac{3y}{4} - \frac{y}{2} = 5$ **20**

49. $0.36p + 0.26 = 3.86$ **10**

50. $2n + 3 + 4n = 5 + 6n - 2$ identity

51. $7s - (3s + 1) = 4(3 + s)$ no solution

52. Geometry The width of a rectangle is 6 cm less than the length. The perimeter is 72 cm. Write and solve an equation to find the width and the length of the rectangle.
$2x + 2(x - 6) = 72$; length = 21 cm, width = 15 cm

53. Costs for bowling at a certain bowling alley are $2.50 for shoes and $4.25 for each game bowled. Austin spent $15.25. Write and solve an equation to find how many games he bowled.
$4.25x + 2.50 = 15.25$; 3 games

31.
$$314 = -n + 576$$
$$314 - 576 = -n + 576 - 576 \quad \text{Subtr. Prop. of Eq.}$$
$$-262 = -n \quad \text{Simplify.}$$
$$-1(-262) = -1(-n) \quad \text{Mult. Prop. of Eq.}$$
$$262 = n \quad \text{Simplify.}$$

32.
$$-\tfrac{1}{4}w - 1 = 6$$
$$-\tfrac{1}{4}w - 1 + 1 = 6 + 1 \quad \text{Add. Prop. of Eq.}$$
$$-\tfrac{1}{4}w = 7 \quad \text{Simplify.}$$
$$-4(-\tfrac{1}{4}w) = -4(7) \quad \text{Mult. Prop. of Eq.}$$
$$w = -28 \quad \text{Simplify.}$$

2-5 and 2-6 Objectives

▼ To define a variable in terms of another variable (p. 103)

▼ To model distance-rate-time problems (p. 104)

▼ To transform literal equations (p. 111)

A **literal equation** is an equation that shows the relationship between two or more variables. A formula is a special type of literal equation. When you express one variable in terms of the others, you are solving the equation for that variable.

Solve each equation for the given variable.

54. $A = \frac{1}{2}bh; b$ $b = \frac{2A}{h}$ **55.** $y = mx + b; x$ $x = \frac{y - b}{m}$ **56.** $C = \pi d; d$ $d = \frac{C}{\pi}$

57. Science Ohm's Law states that in an electrical circuit $E = IR$, where E represents the potential in volts, I represents the current in amperes, and R represents the resistance in ohms.
  a. Solve this formula for I. $I = \frac{E}{R}$
  b. Find I if $E = 6$ volts and $R = 0.15$ ohms of resistance. **40 amperes**

Write and solve an equation for each situation.

58. The Great Seto Bridge in Japan is about 7.6 mi long. How long would it take you to cross the bridge if you were walking at 4 mi/h? **1.9 h or 1 h 54 min**

59. Botany A eucalyptus tree in New Guinea grew 10.5 meters in one year. How much will this tree grow in 3.5 years if it continues to grow at this rate? **36.75 m**

60. The sum of three consecutive integers is 582. Find the three integers.
  193, 194, 195

61. The sum of three consecutive *even* integers is −198. Find the three integers.
  −68, −66, −64

62. Ocean Travel A supertanker leaves port traveling north at an average speed of 10 knots. Two hours later a cruise ship leaves the same port heading south at an average speed of 18 knots. How many hours after the cruise ship sails will the two ships be 209 nautical miles apart? (*Hint:* 1 knot = 1 nautical mile per hour)
  6.75 h or 6 h 45 min

63. Recreation The handicap H of a bowler whose average is A is often found by using the formula $H = 0.8(200 - A)$. A bowler's final score for a game is the actual score plus the bowler's handicap. Find the handicap of a bowler whose average score is 135. **52**

2-7 Objectives

▼ To find mean, median, and mode (p. 118)

▼ To make and use stem-and-leaf plots (p. 120)

Mean, median, and **mode** are three measures of central tendency. The **range** of a data set is the difference between the greatest and least items. A stem-and-leaf plot is a display that organizes the data by showing each item in order.

Find the mean, median, and mode for each set of data.

64. 85, 87, 81, 92, 87, 80, 83 **85, 85, 87**   **65.** 24, 45, 33, 27, 24 **30.6, 27, 24**

66. 2.4, 2.3, 2.1, 2.5, 2.3, 2.2 **2.3, 2.3, 2.3**   **67.** 42, 18, 55, 37, 57, 37, 49, 47, 37
  42.1, 42, 37

Use the stem-and-leaf plot at the right for Exercises 68–71. It shows the number of kilometers walked during a benefit walk.

68. Find the range. **3.8 km**

69. How many data items are there? **19 items**

70. How many people walked more than 19 km? **6 people**

71. Find the mean, median, and mode. **18, 18.4, 19.9**

Benefit Walk
(km)

16	1 1 2 3 5 5
17	0 2 2
18	4 5 8 9
19	3 6 7 9 9 9

19 | 3 means 19.3

33.
$$3h - 4 = 5$$
$3h - 4 + 4 = 5 + 4$ Add. Prop. of Eq.
$3h = 9$ Simplify.
$\frac{3h}{3} = \frac{9}{3}$ Div. Prop. of Eq.
$h = 3$ Simplify.

Resources

Chapter Test — Form B

Chapter Test — Form A

Chapter Test	Form A
Chapter 2	

Solve each equation. Then check your answer.
1. $8f = 32$ 2. $b - 13 = -24$ 3. $\frac{x}{5} = 11$
4. $u + 7 = 4$ 5. $5n - 7 = 28$ 6. $-3x + 4 = -20$
7. $7y + 5 - 3y = -31$ 8. $-11.4x + 5.4x = 48$ 9. $8(t + 7) = 32$
10. $\frac{1}{4}(y + 2) = 12$ 11. $\frac{2h-4}{6} = \frac{x}{3}$ 12. $6(w - 5) - 3w = 12$
13. If $4x - 3 = -31$, what is the value of $-2x + 11$?
14. Solve $3x - 6 = -15$. Justify each step.

Solve each formula in terms of the given variable.
15. $x = \frac{y-c}{3}$ 16. $2b - 7c = 9; b$

Define a variable and write an equation to model each situation. Then solve.
17. The foreign language club began the year with $15.00 in its account. At the end of the candy sale, the club had $654.75 in its account. How much money did the club make?
18. An online music club sells compact discs for $13.95 each plus $1.95 shipping and handling per order. If Maria's total bill was $85.65, how many compact discs did Maria purchase?
19. Tickets to the county fair for four adults and five children cost $33.00. An adult's ticket costs $1.50 more than a child's ticket. Find the cost of an adult's ticket.

Solve. If the equation is an identity, write *identity*. If it has no solution, write *no solution*.
20. $18x + 6 = 3(6x + 1)$ 21. $8w - 18 = 12w + 14$
22. $4(2 - 4y) = 8y + 36$ 23. $3(x + 8) + 5x = 2(12 + 4x)$
24. **Open-Ended** Write a word problem that could be solved using the equation $2x + 8 = 12$.

Algebra 1 Chapter 2   *Form A Test*   **27**

Chapter 2

Chapter Test

💻 **Take It to the NET**
Online chapter test at
www.PHSchool.com
⋯⋯ Web Code: aea-0252

Solve each equation. Check your answers.

1. $5n = -20$ **−4**
2. $t + 7 = 4$ **−3**
3. $\frac{r}{3} = 21$ **63**
4. $u - 8 = -15$ **−7**
5. $-x + 4 = -7$ **11**
6. $-2z + 1 = -9$ **5**
7. $3w + 2 - w = -4$ **−3**
8. $\frac{1}{4}(k - 1) = 10$ **41**
9. $6(y + 3) = 24$ **1**
10. $\frac{5n + 1}{8} = \frac{1}{2}$ **$\frac{3}{5}$**
11. If $2t + 3 = -9$, what is the value of $-3t - 7$? **11**
12. Solve $2x - 4 = -7$. Justify each step. **See margin.**

Define a variable and write an equation to model each situation. Then solve. 13–15. See right.

13. Your chorus holds a car wash. They have $25.00 for making change. At the end of the car wash, they have $453.50. How much money did they make?

14. **Truck Rental** The rate to rent a certain truck is $55 per day and 20¢ per mile. Your family pays $80 to rent this truck for one day. How many miles did your family drive?

15. **Entertainment** Movie tickets for an adult and three children cost $20. An adult's ticket costs $2 more than a child's ticket. Find the cost of an adult's ticket.

Solve. If the equation is an identity, write *identity*. If it has no solution, write *no solution*.

16. $9j + 3 = 3(3j + 1)$ **identity**
17. $2(1 - 2y) = 4y + 18$ **−2**
18. $4v - 9 = 6v + 7$ **−8**
19. $4p - 5 + p = 7 + 5p + 2$ **no solution**

20. **Open-Ended** Describe a situation that you can model with the equation $\frac{m}{5} = 4$. **See margin.**

21. A taxicab company charges each person a flat fee of $1.85 plus an additional $.40 per quarter mile.
   a. Write a formula to find the total cost for each fare. **See margin.**
   b. Use this formula to find the cost for 1 person to travel 8 mi. **$14.65**
   c. **Writing** Is your answer for part (b) the same cost as for 2 people in the same taxi traveling 4 miles? Explain your reasoning.
   No, $1(1.85) + 0.40(32) \neq 2(1.85) + 0.40(16)$.

Use the table below for Exercises 22 and 23.

Percent of People Who Speak a Language Other Than English at Home	
State	**Percent**
Connecticut	15
Massachusetts	15
Maine	9
New Hampshire	9
New Jersey	20
New York	23
Pennsylvania	7
Rhode Island	17
Vermont	6

SOURCE: U.S. Census Bureau
Go to **www.PHSchool.com** for a data update.
Web Code: aeg-2041

22. Make a stem-and-leaf plot for the data. Find the range. **See margin p. 129.**

23. Find the mean, median, and mode for the data. **$13.\overline{4}\%$, 15%, 9% and 15%**

Define a variable and write an equation to model each situation. Then solve.

24. **Ticket Sales** Tickets for a high school play are $3.00 each for students and $4.00 each for all others. Find the total money collected from ticket sales if 315 student tickets are sold out of a total of 518 tickets. **Let S = ticket sales.**
   $3(315) + 4(518 - 315) = S$; $1757

25. Jan is one year younger than her brother Bill and one year older than her sister Sue. The sum of their ages is 57. How old is each family member? **See margin p. 129.**

26. **Labor Costs** Mr. Gomez paid a total of $267 for the repairs on his car. The cost of the labor was two thirds of the total charge. Find the charge for labor. **Let c = charge for labor. $c = \frac{2}{3}(267)$; $178**

27. **Travel** At noon, your family leaves Louisville on a trip to Memphis driving at 40 miles per hour. Your uncle leaves Memphis to come to Louisville 2 hours later. He is taking the same route and is driving 60 miles per hour. The two cities are 380 miles apart. At what time do the cars meet? **Let t = time for family car.**
   $40t + 60(t - 2) = 380$; 5:00 P.M.

13. Let x = money made at car wash.
   $x + 25.00 = 453.50$; $428.50

14. Let m = miles driven.
   $55 + 0.20m = 80$; 125 mi

15. Let c = cost of adult ticket.
   $c + 3(c - 2) = 20$; $6.50

---

page 128   Chapter Test

12.
$$2x - 4 = -7$$
$$2x - 4 + 4 = -7 + 4 \qquad \text{Add. Prop. of Eq.}$$
$$2x = -3 \qquad \text{Simplify.}$$
$$\frac{2x}{2} = \frac{-3}{2} \qquad \text{Div. Prop. of Eq.}$$
$$x = \frac{-3}{2} \qquad \text{Simplify.}$$

20. **Answers may vary. Sample:** The members of a club break up into committees of 5. There are 4 committees. How many members are there in the club?

21a. Let x = quarter miles, c = total cost
   $c = 1.85 + 0.40x$

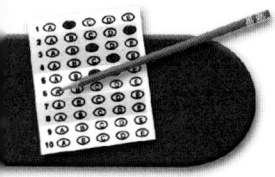

Standardized Test Prep

Standardized Test Prep

Multiple Choice

For Exercises 1–7, choose the correct letter.

1. Which equation is equivalent to
$3x + 5 - 4x = 7$? **D**
 A. $3x + 5 = 4x - 7$ **B.** $3x + 5 = 4x$
 C. $x = 2$ **D.** $x = -2$

2. Simplify the expression $15 - (6 + 3^2)$. **G**
 F. -66 **G.** 0
 H. 18 **I.** 36

3. Evaluate $-2xy$ for $x = 3$ and $y = 4$. **C**
 A. -234 **B.** -68
 C. -24 **D.** 24

4. Find the solution of the equation $-8k - 3 = 1$. **F**
 F. $-\frac{1}{2}$ **G.** $-\frac{1}{4}$
 H. $\frac{1}{4}$ **I.** $\frac{1}{2}$

5. Find the difference. **C**

$$\begin{bmatrix} 8 & -7 \\ 3 & -5 \end{bmatrix} - \begin{bmatrix} 4 & 0 \\ -2 & -4 \end{bmatrix}$$

 A. $\begin{bmatrix} 4 & 7 \\ 5 & 1 \end{bmatrix}$ **B.** $\begin{bmatrix} 4 & -7 \\ 1 & -1 \end{bmatrix}$

 C. $\begin{bmatrix} 4 & -7 \\ 5 & -1 \end{bmatrix}$ **D.** $\begin{bmatrix} 4 & -7 \\ 1 & -9 \end{bmatrix}$

6. Choose the pair of coordinates that lie on the graph shown. **I**

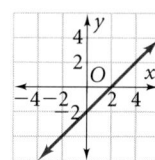

 F. $(-1, 1), (1, 3)$
 G. $(-1, 2), (1, -2)$
 H. $(-1, -3), (1, 1)$
 I. $(-1, -3), (1, -1)$

7. Which equation has -2 as its solution? **C**
 A. $4x + 2 = 5$
 B. $4x - 2 = 5$
 C. $4x - 2 = 5x$
 D. $4 - 2x = 5x$

8. Which expression *cannot* be simplified using the Distributive Property? **H**
 F. $3(2 + 8)$ **G.** $9(14 - 18)$
 H. $5(2 \cdot 3)$ **I.** $(18 - 25)7$

Gridded Response

9. Nice 'N' Clean Laundromat charges $1.50 to wash each load and $1.25 to dry each load. How much can a family with 8 loads expect to pay in dollars at this laundromat? **22**

10. The advertised price for salads at a local supermarket salad bar is $3.49 per pound. Find the price in dollars of a salad that weighs 10 oz. **2.18**

11. Sue's math class made the stem-and-leaf plot below. It shows each student's daily morning travel time to school. Find the mean of the data. **22.08**

Travel Time to School

```
0 | 3 5 8 8
1 | 0 0 0 1 1 2 2 5 6 8
2 | 1 2 3 7 7
3 | 0 5
4 | 5 9 9
5 |
6 |
7 | 5
```

7 | 5 means 75 minutes

12. Use the formula $P = 2(w + \ell)$ to find the perimeter in centimeters of a rectangle with length 4.45 cm and width 1.3 cm. **11.5**

13. Find the solution to the equation $3y = 6 - 2y$. **$\frac{6}{5}$, or 1.2**

14. Jon is in charge of ordering eggs to make pancake batter for his school's all-you-can-eat pancake breakfast fund-raiser. Jon figures that 594 eggs will be needed to make enough pancakes for the number of tickets sold. How many cartons of eggs should Jon order if each carton contains 1 dozen eggs? **50**

15. Four friends were born in consecutive years. The sum of their birth years is 7798. In what year was the oldest of the four friends born? **1951**

16. The Empire State Building is 1250 ft tall and it has 102 stories. It is 859 ft taller than the Park Row Building, the world's tallest building in 1900. What was the height in feet of the Park Row Building? **391**

22.
```
0 | 6 7 9 9
1 | 5 5 7
2 | 0 3
1 | 5        1 | 5 means 15%
          range: 17%
```

25. Let n = Sue's age.
$n + n + 1 + n + 2 = 57$
Sue is 18, Jan is 19, and
Bill is 20.

Resources

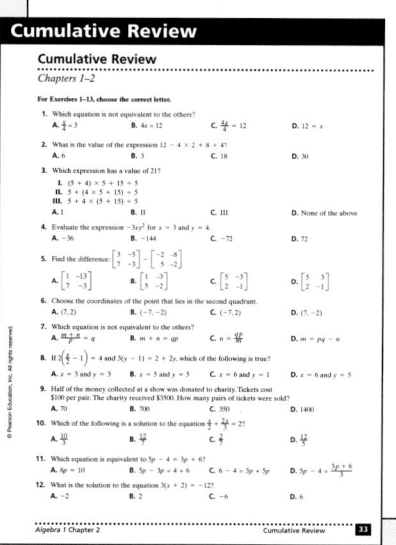

Item	Lesson	Item	Lesson
1	2-3	9	2-3
2	1-2	10	2-5
3	1-6	11	2-7
4	2-2	12	1-2
5	1-5	13	1-3
6	1-9	14	2-5
7	2-3	15	2-5
8	1-7	16	2-1

Shifting Gears

In these activities students apply their knowledge of variation, proportions, and the use of formulas.

Connecting to Prior Knowledge

Ask students to describe how bicycles that have no gear shift differ from those with shifting gears. Discuss what a rider can do on a mountain bike that is difficult on a child's bicycle, and how gears help a rider climb a steep hill.

Teaching Notes

Ask students to name examples of other machines that use gears. If possible, bring one or more examples of machines with gears to the classroom. Possible examples are can openers and pencil sharpeners. Ask students to conjecture how the gears allow the machines to do their work.

Teaching Tip

Have a volunteer read the introductory paragraph. Ask: *How many of you have changed gears while riding a bicycle?* Have students explain how they decide when to change gears.

Connection to Science

Discuss the gears in an automobile with a manual transmission. Ask: *Which gears are used by the driver of a car to climb or descend a very steep hill?* **Sample answer: The lower gears, such as first or second, are used to climb very steep hills. The highest gear is used for highway driving.**

English Learners

Make sure that students understand what is meant by the words *gear* and *sprocket*. Point out these items on the photo of the bicycle.

Real-World Snapshots

Shifting Gears

Applying Variation Gears and levers can make a job easier, but there is a trade-off for efficiency. For instance, the higher gears on a bicycle allow you to go farther with each rotation of the pedals, but the price you pay is pushing harder. Conversely, in first gear you don't have to push hard, but you also don't go very fast.

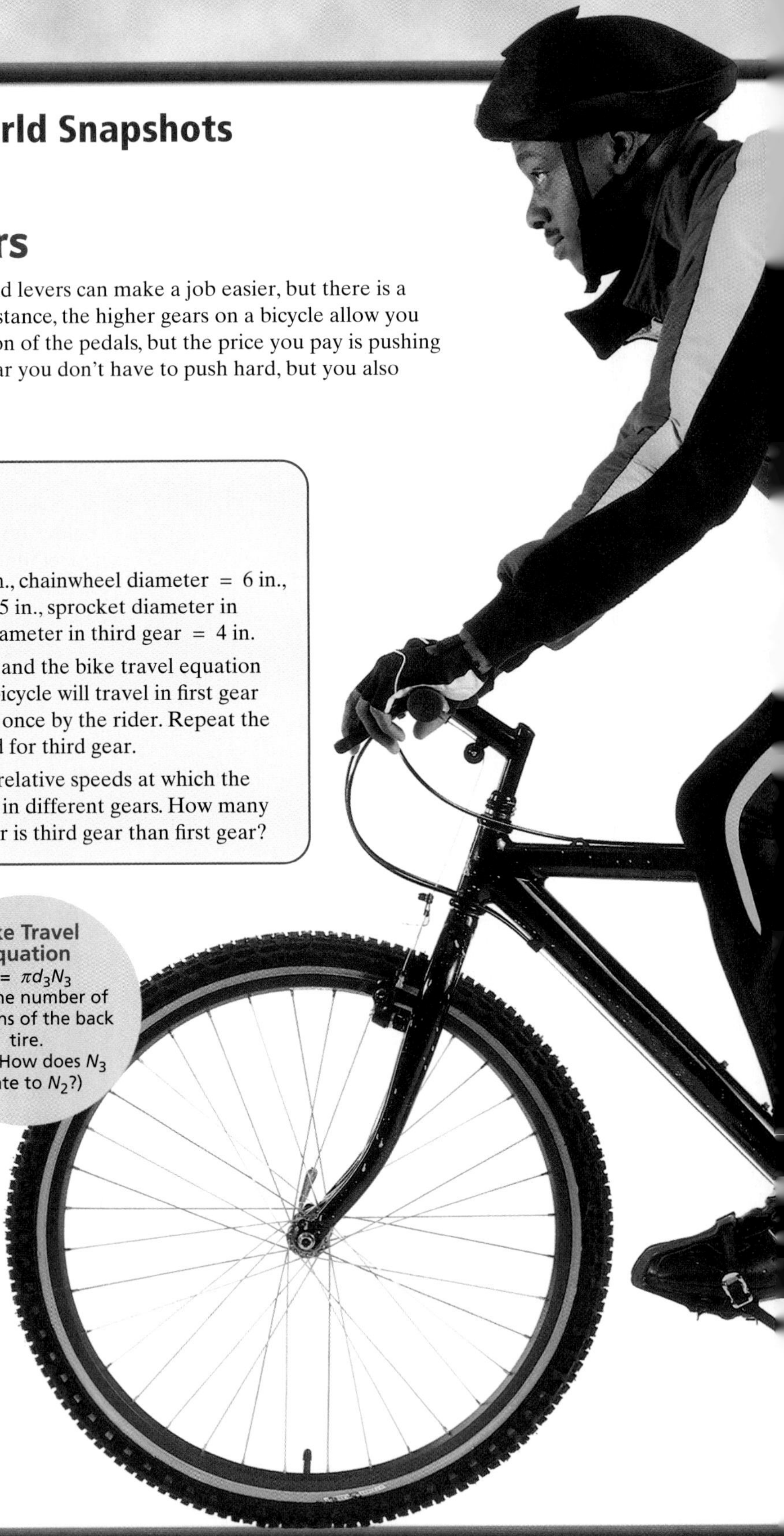

Activity 1

Materials: paper and pencil

Bicycle data: tire diameter = 26 in., chainwheel diameter = 6 in., sprocket diameter in first gear = 5 in., sprocket diameter in second gear = 4.5 in., sprocket diameter in third gear = 4 in.

a. Use the transmission equation and the bike travel equation below to find out how far the bicycle will travel in first gear when the chainwheel is turned once by the rider. Repeat the calculation for second gear and for third gear.

b. Your calculations indicate the relative speeds at which the bicycle moves in different gears. How many times faster is third gear than first gear?

Transmission Equation

$$\frac{d_1}{d_2} = \frac{N_2}{N_1}$$

N_1 and N_2 are the number of rotations of the chainwheel and the sprocket.

Bike Travel Equation

$L = \pi d_3 N_3$
N_3 is the number of rotations of the back tire.
(*Hint:* How does N_3 relate to N_2?)

d_1 = diameter of chainwheel
d_2 = diameter of sprocket
d_3 = diameter of back tire
L = distance bicycle travels

Shifting Gears

Some mountain bikes have gears you can shift with your thumb, allowing your other fingers to remain curled around the handlebars to maintain control.

pages 130–131 **Real-World Snapshots**

Activity 1

a. ≈98 in.; ≈109 in.; ≈123 in.

b. about 126 times as fast

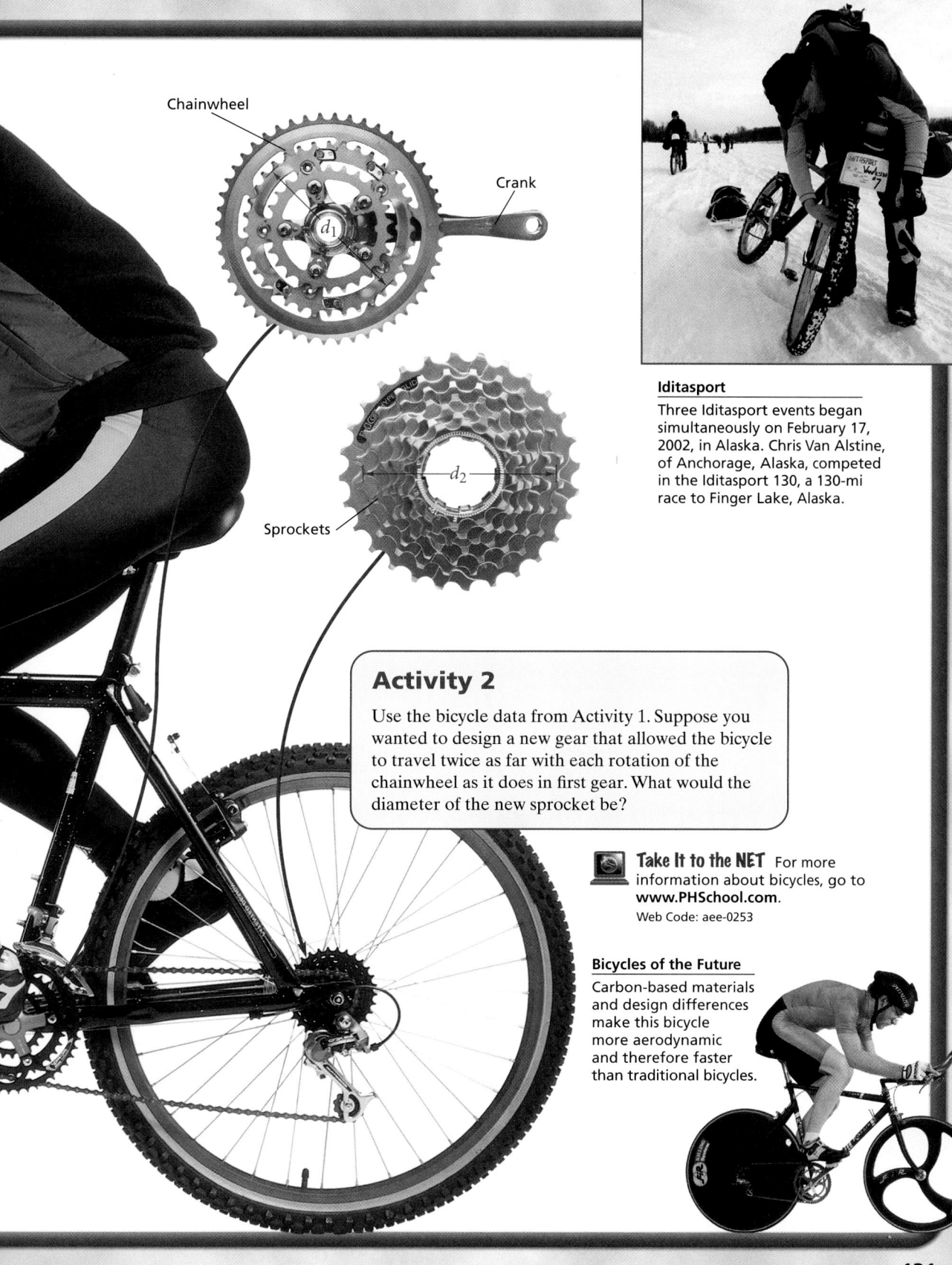

Chainwheel

Crank

d_1

Sprockets

d_2

Take It to the NET For more information about bicycles, go to **www.PHSchool.com**.
Web Code: aee-0253

Activity 2

Use the bicycle data from Activity 1. Suppose you wanted to design a new gear that allowed the bicycle to travel twice as far with each rotation of the chainwheel as it does in first gear. What would the diameter of the new sprocket be?

Bicycles of the Future
Carbon-based materials and design differences make this bicycle more aerodynamic and therefore faster than traditional bicycles.

Iditasport
Three Iditasport events began simultaneously on February 17, 2002, in Alaska. Chris Van Alstine, of Anchorage, Alaska, competed in the Iditasport 130, a 130-mi race to Finger Lake, Alaska.

131

Activity 2
2.5 in.

Solving Inequalities

Chapter at a Glance

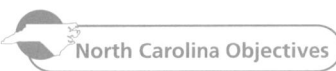

North Carolina Objectives

3-1	Inequalities and Their Graphs	4.01a

NCTM 1, 2, 9, 10	⋁ Identifying Solutions of Inequalities ⋎ Graphing and Writing Inequalities in One Variable

3-2	Solving Inequalities Using Addition and Subtraction	4.01a

NCTM 1, 2, 9, 10	⋁ Using Addition to Solve Inequalities ⋎ Using Subtraction to Solve Inequalities

3-3	Solving Inequalities Using Multiplication and Division	4.01a

NCTM 1, 2, 9, 10	⋁ Using Multiplication to Solve Inequalities ⋎ Using Division to Solve Inequalities

3-4	Solving Multi-Step Inequalities	4.01a

NCTM 1, 2, 6, 10	⋁ Solving Inequalities With Variables on One Side ⋎ Solving Inequalities With Variables on Both Sides

3-5	Compound Inequalities	4.01a

NCTM 1, 2, 6, 9, 10	⋁ Solving Compound Inequalities Containing *And* ⋎ Solving Inequalities Joined by *Or*

3-6	Absolute Value Equations and Inequalities	1.02

NCTM 1, 2, 6, 9, 10	⋁ Solving Absolute Value Equations ⋎ Solving Absolute Value Inequalities

NCTM STANDARDS 2000

1	Number and Operations	6	Problem Solving
2	Algebra	7	Reasoning and Proof
3	Geometry	8	Communication
4	Measurement	9	Connections
5	Data Analysis and Probability	10	Representation

Pacing Options

This chart suggests pacing only for the lessons and their parts. It is provided as a possible guide. It will help you determine how much time you have in your schedule to cover other components, such as the features, Chapter Review, and Chapter Test.

Day	Traditional 45 min.	Two-Year 45 min.	Block 90 min.
1	3-1 ⋁ ⋎	3-1 ⋁	3-1 ⋁ ⋎ 3-2 ⋁ ⋎
2	3-2 ⋁ ⋎	3-1 ⋎	3-3 ⋁ ⋎
3	3-3 ⋁ ⋎	3-2 ⋁	3-4 ⋁ ⋎ 3-5 ⋁
4	3-4 ⋁ ⋎	3-2 ⋎	3-5 ⋎
5	3-5 ⋁	3-3 ⋁	3-6 ⋁ ⋎
6	3-5 ⋎	3-3 ⋎	
7	3-6 ⋁	3-4 ⋁	
8	3-6 ⋎	3-4 ⋎	
9		3-5 ⋁	
10		3-5 ⋎	
11		3-6 ⋁	
12		3-6 ⋁ ⋎	
13		3-6 ⋎	

NAEP Correlation (National Assessment of Educational Progress 2000 Mathematics Objectives)

3-1	3-2	3-3	3-4	3-5	3-6
A1f, A3a	A1f, A5a	A1f, A2	N4f, A2, A5a	A2, A3a	A5a, d

N = Number Sense, Properties, and Operations; **M** = Measurement; **G** = Geometry and Spatial Sense;
D = Data Analysis, Statistics, and Probability; **A** = Algebra and Functions

Math Background

Chapter Overview

The tools of algebra presented in Chapter 1 and applied to solving equations in Chapter 2, are extended in this chapter to solving inequalities. The instructional sequence is the same as that used in the previous chapter for solving equations. Important exceptions to the similarities between solving equations and solving inequalities include the solution sets and the multiplication and division properties of inequality.

Inequalities and Their Graphs   3-1

The solution to an equation such as $x + 7 = 10$ is one value, $x = 3$, and the graph is one point on a number line. The solution can be checked by substituting it into the original equation and verifying that the equation is true. In contrast, the solution to an inequality such as $x + 7 < 10$ is an infinite number of values, $x < 3$. Its graph is an arrow on a number line, beginning with an open circle at 3 and continuing to the left. It would be impossible to check all solutions. However, an incomplete check can be done by substituting selected values from the solution set into the original inequality and verifying whether the resulting expression is true or not.

Solving Inequalities Using Addition, Subtraction, Multiplication, and Division   3-2, 3-3

The procedures for solving inequalities are parallel to those for solving equations. They consist of isolating the variable on one side by using inverse operations to undo what has been done to the variable. The addition and subtraction properties of inequality are applied in the same way as the addition and subtraction properties of equality.

The key difference in the properties between equalities and inequalities is in the multiplication and division properties. Multiplying or dividing both sides of an inequality by a negative number reverses the sense of the inequality.

Students may try to multiply and reverse the inequality sign in two separate steps. This leads to writing a false intermediate step. For example, a student might write $-3x \geq 12$, and then write $x \geq -4$, which is false. Emphasize that the multiplication or division and the reversal of the inequality sign must occur at the same time, in the same step. Even indicating the operation must include reversing the inequality, because $(-3x) \div (-3) \geq 12 \div (-3)$ is also a false statement.

Another important difference between equalities and inequalities occurs in the checking process. Students may think that checking one or two values from their solution set proves that their solution is correct. Checking sample values within the solution set helps

find errors, but does not confirm the validity of the entire solution set. Suggest that students also check a point outside the solution set to make sure that it does not make the inequality true.

Solving Multi-Step Inequalities   3-4

To solve these more complex inequalities, the student combines previously learned skills in the same sequence as that used for solving multi-step equations. The sequence begins with applying the Distributive Property to eliminate grouping symbols as necessary, and then collecting terms on each side of the inequality. Then the properties of inequality are applied to collect all the terms containing the variable on one side of the inequality, and all the numeric terms on the other side. Make sure that students do not confuse multiplying and dividing by a negative number with adding a negative number, and incorrectly reverse the inequality sign when collecting terms. The final step is to isolate the variable by using the multiplication and division properties of inequality.

Compound Inequalities   3–5

The material in this lesson may be new to the student, and the difference between *and* and *or* compound inequalities may be a source of some confusion. One way to clarify some of the confusion is to read the word *and* as "at the same time." So "$x < 3$ and $x > 1$" becomes "x is less than 3 and at the same time greater than 1." Writing this as $1 < x < 3$ also helps to clarify confusion, since this mirrors the graph of the solution set. Graph examples like "$x < 3$ or $x > 5$" to make it clear that no value can be both less than 3 and greater than 5 at the same time. Some students may know that the solution to "$x < 3$ and $x > 5$" is the empty set.

Absolute Value Equations and Inequalities   3-6

There is a natural tendency to say that there is something that is larger about -5 than -3, which is an intuitive way of saying that the absolute value, or distance from zero, of -5 is greater than that of -3. An expression such as $|x| > 5$ means "the distance of x from zero on a number line is greater than 5." Some students may understand that $|2x - 3| > 5$ can be read as "the distance of $2x$ from 3 is greater than 5." Understanding that a simple inequality such as $|x| > 5$ can be rewritten as the two separate inequalities $x > 5$ and $x < -5$ is fairly straightforward.

When x is replaced by a binomial such as $2x - 3$, solving an absolute value inequality becomes more complex. It may be helpful to sketch an intermediate graph. For example, to solve $|2x - 3| > 5$, begin by sketching a number line that shows $2x - 3$ is greater than 5 or less than -5. Then separate this first sketch into the two inequalities $2x - 3 > 5$ or $2x - 3 < -5$, each of which can be solved individually. Show the final solution set graphed on a number line as $x > 4$ or $x < -1$.

Ongoing Assessment and Intervention

Tools for Monitoring Student Progress

The Prentice Hall *Algebra 1* program provides you with many options for assessment in the Student Edition, the Teacher's Edition and the teaching resources. From these options you may choose instructional materials and techniques that are appropriate for your students and support your district's curriculum requirements.

Instant Check System™ in Chapter 3

Allows students to check their own learning before, during, and after each lesson.

Diagnosing Readiness before the chapter (p. 132)

Check Skills You'll Need exercises in each lesson (pp. 134, 140, 146, 153, 161, 167)

Check Understanding questions with each Example (pp. 134, 135, 136, 140, 141, 142, 147, 148, 149, 153, 154, 155, 161, 162, 163, 167, 168, 169)

Checkpoint Quiz (pp. 151, 166)

Test Prep in Chapter 3

Teaches students strategies and gives them practice with all the test item formats they will encounter on state tests and standardized national exams.

Standardized Test Prep exercises in each lesson (pp. 139, 145, 150, 151, 158, 159, 166, 171, 172)

Test-Taking Strategies (p. 174: Writing Extended Responses)

Standardized Test Prep (p. 179: Reading Comprehension)

All your assessment needs in one place!

Program Assessment

Assess student progress throughout the *Algebra 1* text with blackline masters and CD-ROM.

Assessment Resources

- Checkpoint Quizzes 1 & 2
- Chapter Test, Forms A & B
- Chapter Alternative Assessment

Spanish versions available. Tests for Basic Algebra also available.

Computer Test Generator

- Unlimited questions of varying difficulty for every lesson objective.
- Create your own practice sheets, quizzes, and tests, or use the pre-made Chapter Tests.
- Diagnose readiness with questions on prerequisite skills.
- Prepare students by making tests based on standardized test objectives.
- Access Algebra 1, Geometry, and Algebra 2 content—all on one CD-ROM.

Test Preparation

A three-step approach to preparing students for high stakes, national, and state exams.

❶ **Diagnose & Prescribe**

Content Diagnostic Tests
- Diagnose strengths and weaknesses in content for national and state tests.
- Prescribe individualized reteaching opportunities.

❷ **Review & Reteach**

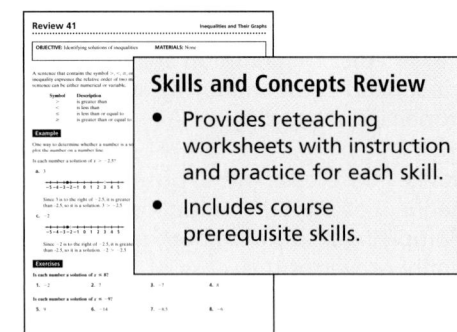

Skills and Concepts Review
- Provides reteaching worksheets with instruction and practice for each skill.
- Includes course prerequisite skills.

❸ **Practice & Assess**

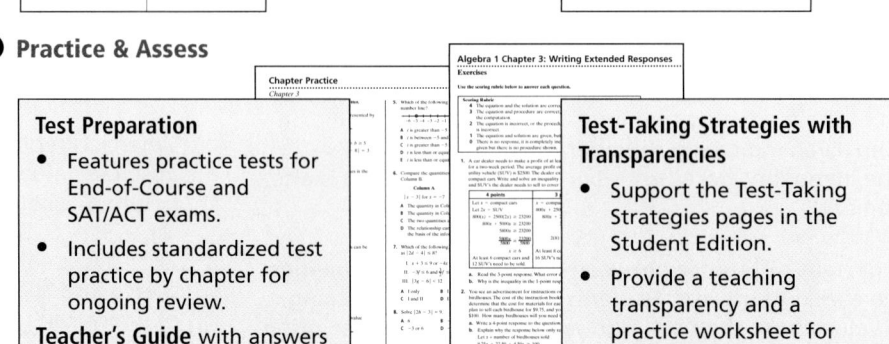

Test Preparation
- Features practice tests for End-of-Course and SAT/ACT exams.
- Includes standardized test practice by chapter for ongoing review.

Teacher's Guide with answers and correlations.

Test-Taking Strategies with Transparencies
- Support the Test-Taking Strategies pages in the Student Edition.
- Provide a teaching transparency and a practice worksheet for each strategy.

 # Reaching All Students

Support in the Student Text and Additional Resources

The textbook, the iText, and other technology components provide numerous opportunities to reach students of various ability levels and learning styles. Each Teacher's Edition lesson suggests how you can help *all* your students be successful and understand the mathematics in Chapter 3.

Below Level

Student Edition
- Diagnosing Readiness*: p. 132
- Check Skills You'll Need*: pp. 134, 140, 146, 153, 161, 167

Reteaching
Chapter 3 Support File: pp. 8–13

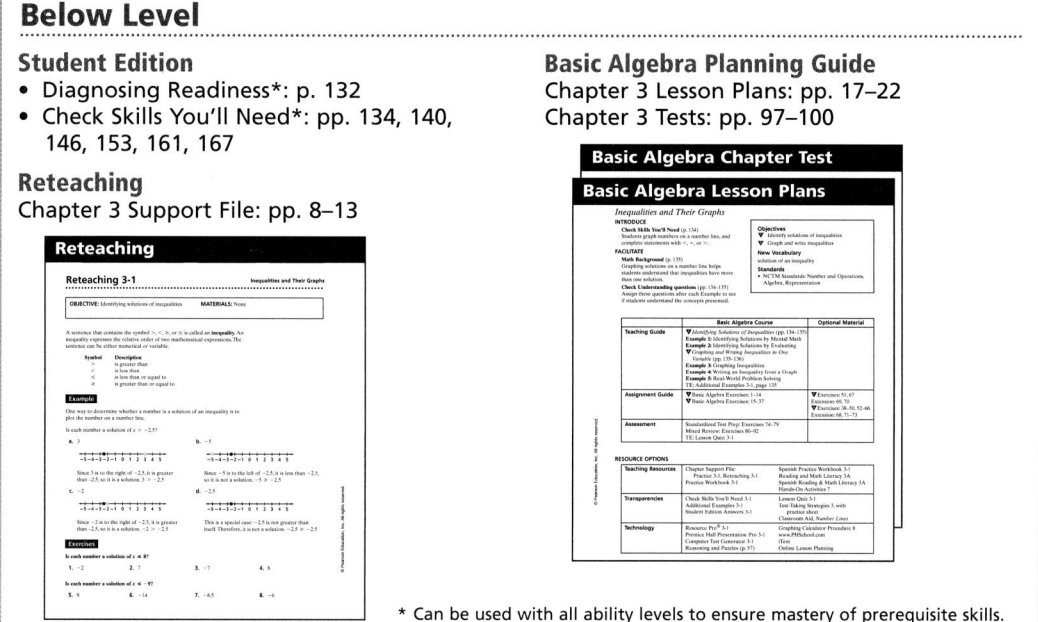

Basic Algebra Planning Guide
Chapter 3 Lesson Plans: pp. 17–22
Chapter 3 Tests: pp. 97–100

* Can be used with all ability levels to ensure mastery of prerequisite skills.

Advanced Learners

Student Edition
- Challenge exercises: pp. 138, 144, 150, 158, 165, 171
- Extension, pp. 160, 173

Enrichment
Chapter 3 Support File: pp. 14–19

Reading and Math Literacy

Student Edition
- Vocabulary: pp. 133, 175, *plus* in every Lesson Preview
- Reading Math: pp. 134, 135, 141, 150, 152, 161, 175
- Illustrated Glossary: pp. 757–785

Reading and Math Literacy Masters
Chapter 3: pp. 9–12

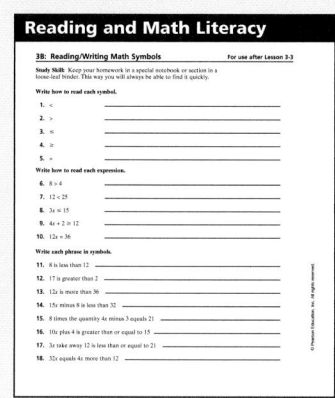

English Learners

Student Edition
- English/Spanish Illustrated Glossary: pp. 757–785

Workbook and Masters
Spanish Practice Workbook: pp. 17–22
Spanish Reading and Math Literacy Masters: pp. 9–12

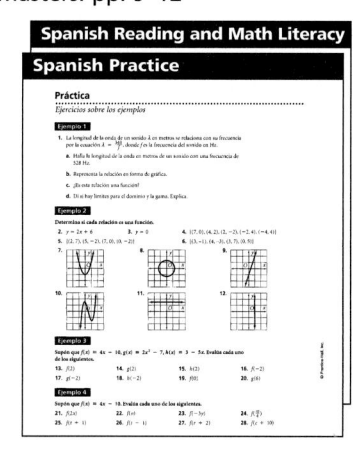

Learning Styles

Student Edition
- Investigation: p. 146
- Writing: pp. 137, 144, 150, 156, 164, 171, 178

Activity Masters
Hands-On Activities: 7, 8
Technology Activities: 17

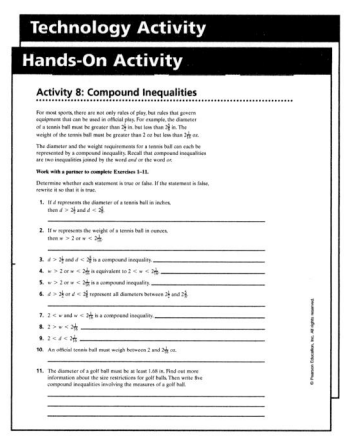

Program Resources

	Teaching Resources in Grab & Go™ Files				Resources for Reaching All Students				Spanish Resources			Transparencies				Presentation Assistant Plus!
	Practice	Reteach	Enrich	Checkpoint Quiz	Reading & Math Literacy	Technology Activities	Hands-On Activities	Basic Algebra Lesson Plans	Practice	Reading & Math Literacy	Checkpoint Quiz	Skills Check	Additional Examples	Answers to Exercises	Lesson Quiz	Prentice Hall Presentation Pro CD-ROM
3-1	■	■	■		■		■	■	■	■		■	■	■	■	■
3-2	■	■	■					■	■	■		■	■	■	■	■
3-3	■	■	■	■	■			■	■	■	■	■	■	■	■	■
3-4	■	■	■					■	■	■		■	■	■	■	■
3-5	■	■	■	■	■		■	■	■	■		■	■	■	■	■
3-6	■	■	■			■		■	■	■		■	■	■	■	■
For the chapter	Chapter Tests, Alternative Assessment, Cumulative Review, Cumulative Assessment				Basic Algebra Chapter Tests				Spanish Chapter Tests, Alternative Assessment, Cumulative Review, Cumulative Assessment			Classroom Aid Transparencies				

Also available for use with the chapter:

 PRENTICE HALL ASSESSMENT SYSTEM *See page 132C.*

- Practice Workbook
- Solution Key

- For teacher support and access to student Web site materials, use Web Code aek-5500.
- For additional online and technology resources, see below.

Technology

iTEXT Online and on CD-ROM

Complete Interactive Student Text online and on CD-ROM—with instant feedback assessment, tutorial help, dynamic activities, instructional and real-world videos, audio, and additional practice.

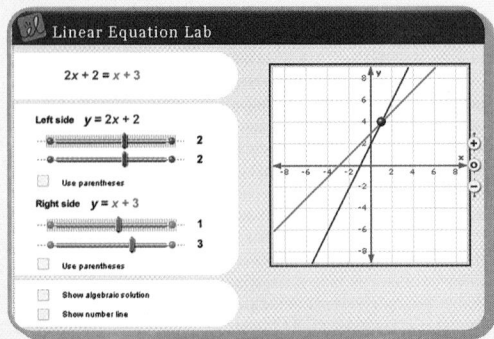

www.PHSchool.com For Students

Use **Web codes** for easy access to online activities, chapter projects, self-grading lesson quizzes and chapter tests, vocabulary quizzes, updated data sources, graphing calculator procedures, and more.

PH SuccessNet For Teachers

Online lesson planning with built-in state correlations, all the teaching resources, complete reference library, your own calendar and Teacher Web page, professional development, and more.

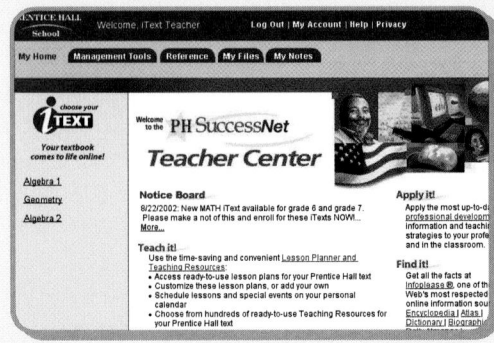

Presentation Assistant Plus!

The Prentice Hall *Presentation Assistant Plus!* provides you with the material you need to teach a lesson from beginning to end. Two easy-to-use formats—Transparencies and CD-ROM—allow you to present a lesson the way you are most comfortable.

Transparencies

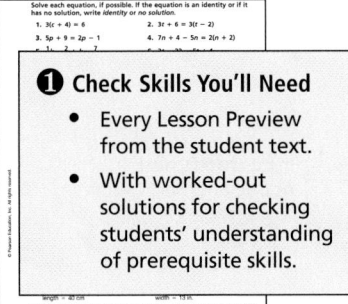

❶ Check Skills You'll Need
- Every Lesson Preview from the student text.
- With worked-out solutions for checking students' understanding of prerequisite skills.

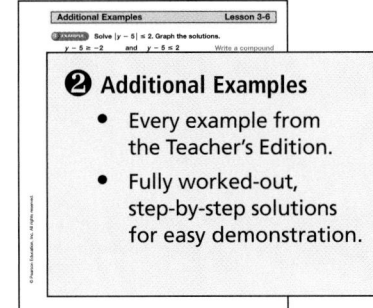

❷ Additional Examples
- Every example from the Teacher's Edition.
- Fully worked-out, step-by-step solutions for easy demonstration.

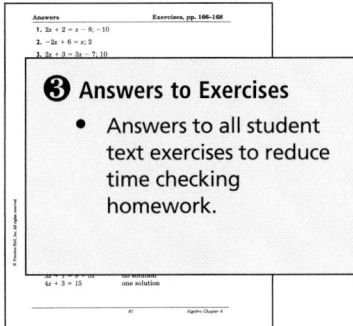

❸ Answers to Exercises
- Answers to all student text exercises to reduce time checking homework.

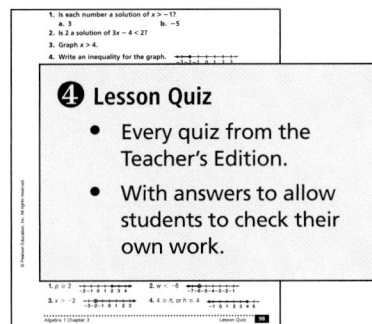

❹ Lesson Quiz
- Every quiz from the Teacher's Edition.
- With answers to allow students to check their own work.

 Throughout the Teacher's Edition, this symbol indicates material that is available on transparency in the Presentation Assistant Plus!

Prentice Hall Presentation Pro CD-ROM

- Includes all Transparencies.
- Conveniently organized by lesson so you can easily ❶ Introduce, ❷ Teach, ❸ Check Homework, and ❹ Assess each lesson.
- Animated examples allow step-by-step instruction at your own pace.
- Easy to edit so you can create custom presentations.

Teaching Chapter 3 Using Presentation Assistant Plus!

	❶ Introduce Check Skills You'll Need	❷ Teach Additional Examples	❸ Check Homework Student Edition Answers	❹ Assess Lesson Quiz
3-1	p. 17	pp. 31–32	✔	p. 98
3-2	p. 18	pp. 32–33	✔	p. 98
3-3	p. 19	pp. 34–35	✔	p. 99
3-4	p. 20	pp. 36–37	✔	p. 99
3-5	p. 21	pp. 38–40	✔	p. 100
3-6	p. 22	pp. 40–41	✔	p. 100

Prentice Hall Presentation Pro

CD-ROM with dynamic PowerPoint® presentations for every lesson. Helps you introduce and develop concepts, check homework, and assess progress. Part of Presentation Assistant Plus! *(See above.)*

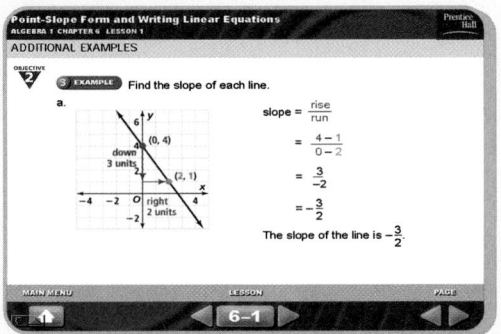

Computer Test Generator

CD-ROM to create practice sheets and tests for course objectives and standardized tests. Includes Instant Chapter Tests™, online testing, and student reports. Part of the PH Assessment System. *(See page 132C.)*

Resource Pro® with Planning Express®

CD-ROM with a lesson planning tool that allows you to import state and local objectives. Includes electronic versions of all the teaching resources.

Inequalities and Their Graphs

 Diagnosing Readiness

Students will find answers to these exercises in the back of their textbooks.

For intervention, direct students to:

Ordering Rational Numbers
Lesson 1-3: Example 4
Exercises 24–27
Extra Practice, p. 702

Absolute Value
Lesson 1-3: Example 5
Exercises 34–35
Extra Practice, p. 702

Solving One-Step Equations
Lesson 2-1: Examples 1, 2, 4 and 5
Exercises 1–12
Extra Practice, p. 703

Solving Two-Step Equations
Lesson 2-2: Examples 1, 4, and 5
Exercises 1–4
Extra Practice, p. 703

Solving Multi-Step Equations
Lesson 2–3: Examples 1, 3, 4, and 5
Exercises 1–4
Lesson 2-4: Example 1
Exercises 3–6
Extra Practice, p. 703

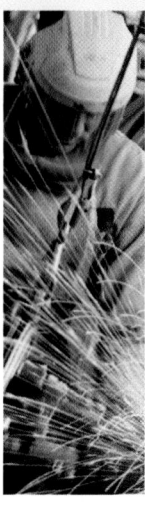

Where You've Been

- In Chapter 1 you learned about the real number system.

- In Chapter 1 you also learned how to add, subtract, multiply, and divide using rational numbers.

- In Chapters 1 and 2 you used this knowledge to evaluate variable expressions and solve equations.

 Instant self-check online and on CD-ROM

Diagnosing Readiness   (For help, go to the Lesson in green.)

Ordering Rational Numbers (Lesson 1-3)

Complete each statement with $<$, $=$, or $>$.

1. $-3 \; \overset{>}{\blacksquare} \; -5$ **2.** $7 \; \overset{=}{\blacksquare} \; \frac{14}{2}$ **3.** $-8 \; \overset{>}{\blacksquare} \; -8.4$ **4.** $-\frac{3}{2} \; \overset{<}{\blacksquare} \; -1$

Absolute Value (Lesson 1-3)

Simplify each expression.

5. $5 + |4 - 6|$ **7** **6.** $|30 - 28| - 6$ **−4** **7.** $|-7 + 2| - 4$ **1**

Solving One-Step Equations (Lesson 2-1)

Solve each equation. Check your solution.

8. $x - 4 = -2$ **2** **9.** $b + 4 = 7$ **3** **10.** $-\frac{3}{4}y = 9$ **−12** **11.** $\frac{m}{12} = 2.7$ **32.4**

12. $-8 + x = 15$ **23** **13.** $n - 7 = 22.5$ **29.5** **14.** $-\frac{12}{7}z = 48$ **−28** **15.** $\frac{5y}{4} = -15$ **−12**

Solving Two-Step Equations (Lesson 2-2)

Solve each equation. Check your solution.

16. $-5 + \frac{b}{4} = 7$ **48** **17.** $4.2m + 4 = 25$ **5** **18.** $-12 = 6 + \frac{3}{4}x$ **−24** **19.** $6 = -z - 4$ **−10**

20. $4m + 2.3 = 9.7$ **1.85** **21.** $\frac{5}{8}t - 7 = -22$ **−24** **22.** $-4.7 = 3y + 1.3$ **−2** **23.** $12.2 = 5.3x - 3.7$ **3**

Solving Multi-Step Equations (Lesson 2-3)

Solve each equation. Check your solution.

24. $4t + 7 + 6t = -33$ **−4** **25.** $2a + 5 = 9a - 16$ **3** **26.** $\frac{1}{3} + \frac{4y}{6} = \frac{2}{3}$ **$\frac{1}{2}$**

27. $6(y - 2) = 8 - 2y$ **$\frac{5}{2}$** **28.** $n + 3(n - 2) = 10.4$ **4.1** **29.** $\frac{1}{2}w + 3 = \frac{2}{3}w - 5$ **48**

Solving Inequalities

Where You're Going

- In this chapter you will learn how to graph inequalities.

- You will solve inequalities, noting the differences from the methods used for solving equations.

- You will write and solve compound inequalities by interpreting phrases that use *and* or *or*.

Real-World Connection Applying what you learn, you will solve problems involving quality control, on page 169.

LESSONS

3-1 Inequalities and Their Graphs

3-2 Solving Inequalities Using Addition and Subtraction

3-3 Solving Inequalities Using Multiplication and Division

3-4 Solving Multi-Step Inequalities

3-5 Compound Inequalities

3-6 Absolute Value Equations and Inequalities

Key Vocabulary

- compound inequalities (p. 161)
- equivalent inequalities (p. 140)
- solution to an inequality (p. 134)

Chapter 3 Overview

Students extend the skills of the previous chapter, related to solving various kinds of equations, to the solving of inequalities. Many of the procedures used are the same, reflecting the fact that the properties for inequalities are very similar to those for equations. Students solve and graph inequalities using addition, subtraction, multiplication, and division, progressing from one-step to multi-step inequalities, first with the variable on one side only, and then with variables on both sides. They also solve compound inequalities as well as equations and inequalities containing absolute values.

Reading Math
Reading to Analyze Errors, p. 152

Vocabulary
A complete list of terms, plus vocabulary exercises, appears in the Chapter Review, p. 175.

Illustrated Glossary
Examples for each vocabulary term, plus definitions in both English and Spanish, appear starting on p. 757.

Test-Taking Strategies
Answering Extended-Response Questions, p. 174

Real-World Connections
Some of the applications you will find in this chapter are air travel (3-1), safe loads (3-2), community service (3-3), and chemistry (3-5).

www.PHSchool.com
Internet support for this chapter includes:
- Self-grading Vocabulary and Chapter 3 Tests
- Chapter Project
- Chapter Planner
- Chapter 3 Resources

Plus *i*TEXT

1. Plan

Lesson Preview

 **Check Skills You'll Need**

Exploring Real Numbers
Lesson 1-3: Example 4
Exercises 24–27
Extra Practice, p. 702

Lesson Resources

📁 **Teaching Resources**
Practice, Reteaching, Enrichment

👥 **Reaching All Students**
Practice Workbook 3-1
Spanish Practice Workbook 3-1
Reading and Math Literacy 3A
Spanish Reading & Literacy 3A
Hands-On Activities 7
Basic Algebra Planning Guide 3-1

⏱ **Presentation Assistant Plus!**
Transparencies
• Check Skills You'll Need 3-1
• Additional Examples 3-1
• Student Edition Answers 3-1
• Lesson Quiz 3-1
PH Presentation Pro CD 3-1

PRENTICE HALL ASSESSMENT SYSTEM

Computer Test Generator CD

💿 **Technology**
Resource Pro® CD-ROM
Computer Test Generator CD
Prentice Hall Presentation Pro CD

📷 **www.PHSchool.com**
Student Site
• Teacher Web Code: aek-5500
• Reasoning & Puzzles, p. 57
• Graphing Calculator,
  Procedure 8
• Self-grading Lesson Quiz
Teacher Center
• Lesson Planner
• Resources

Plus 📱**iTEXT**

3-1 Inequalities and Their Graphs

North Carolina Objectives **4.01** Use linear functions or inequalities to model and solve problems; justify results. a) Solve using tables, graphs, and algebraic properties.

Lesson Preview

What You'll Learn

OBJECTIVE 1 To identify solutions of inequalities

OBJECTIVE 2 To graph and write inequalities

...And Why

To write inequalities for speed limits and starting salaries, as in Example 5

✓ Check Skills You'll Need

(For help, go to Lesson 1-3.)

Graph the numbers on the same number line.

1. 4   2. −3   3. $\frac{9}{3}$ 4. 0   5. 1.5

1–5. number line from −4 to 4

Complete each statement with <, =, or >.

6. $-3 \boxed{>} -5$ 7. $4.29 \boxed{<} 4.8$ 8. $(-3)(-4) \boxed{=} 12$

9. $-1-2 \boxed{=} 6-9$ 10. $-\frac{3}{4} \boxed{>} -\frac{4}{5}$ 11. $\frac{1}{3}+\frac{1}{3} \boxed{<} \frac{1}{2}+\frac{1}{2}$

New Vocabulary • solution of an inequality

📱**iTEXT** **Interactive lesson includes instant self-check, tutorials, and activities.**

OBJECTIVE 1 **Identifying Solutions of Inequalities**

Reading Math

Less than and *is less than* have different meanings. For example, *x less than 3* means $3 - x$; *x is less than 3* means $x < 3$.

A **solution of an inequality** is any number that makes the inequality true. For example, the solutions of the inequality $x < 3$ are all numbers that are less than 3.

1 EXAMPLE **Identifying Solutions by Mental Math**

Is each number a solution of $x \le 7$?

a. 9   No, $9 \le 7$ is not true.

b. −1   Yes, $-1 \le 7$ is true.

c. $\frac{14}{2}$ $\frac{14}{2} = 7$; yes, $\frac{14}{2} \le 7$ is true.

✓ **Check Understanding** ① Is each number a solution of $x \ge -4.1$?

a. −5 **no**   **b.** −4.1 **yes**   **c.** 8 **yes**   **d.** 0 **yes**

You can determine whether a value is a solution of an inequality by evaluating an expression.

2 EXAMPLE **Identifying Solutions by Evaluating**

Is each number a solution of $2 - 5x > 13$?

a. 3

$$2 - 5x > 13$$
$$2 - 5(3) > 13 \quad \leftarrow \text{Substitute for } x. $$
$$2 - 15 > 13 \quad \leftarrow \text{Simplify.}$$
$$-13 \not> 13 \quad \leftarrow \text{Compare.}$$

3 does not make the original inequality true, so 3 is not a solution.

b. −4

$$2 - 5x > 13$$
$$2 - 5(-4) > 13$$
$$2 + 20 > 13$$
$$22 > 13$$

−4 does make the original inequality true, so −4 is a solution.

Ongoing Assessment and Intervention

Before the Lesson	During the Lesson	After the Lesson
Diagnose prerequisite skills using:	**Monitor progress using:**	**Assess knowledge using:**
• Check Skills You'll Need	• Check Understanding	• Lesson Quiz
	• Additional Examples	• Computer Test Generator CD
	• Standardized Test Prep	

✓ **Check Understanding** ❷ Is each number a solution of $6x - 3 > 10$?

    a. 1 no   **b.** 2 no   **c.** 3 yes   **d.** 4 yes

OBJECTIVE

2   Graphing and Writing Inequalities in One Variable

Since the solution of an inequality is not just one number, you can use a graph to indicate all of the solutions.

📖 **Reading Math**

You normally read $-1 \geq a$ as "-1 is greater than or equal to a." The inequality symbol also indicates that a is less than or equal to -1.

Inequality	Graph	
$x < 3$	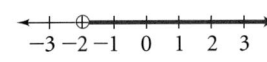	The open dot shows that 3 is *not* a solution. Shade to the left of 3.
$m \geq -2$	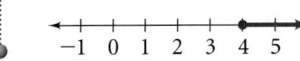	The closed dot shows that -2 is a solution. Shade to the right of -2.
$-1 \geq a$		The closed dot shows that -1 is a solution. Shade to the left of -1.

You can also write $-1 \geq a$ as $a \leq -1$.

❸ EXAMPLE   **Graphing Inequalities**

a. Graph $c > -2$.

     The solutions of $c > -2$ are all the points to the right of -2.

b. Graph $4 \leq m$.

     The solutions of $4 \leq m$ are 4 and all the points to the right of 4.

✓ **Check Understanding** ❸ Graph each inequality.

    a. $a < 1$ 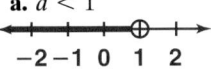   **b.** $n \geq -3$ 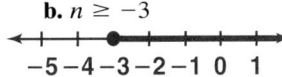   **c.** $2 > p$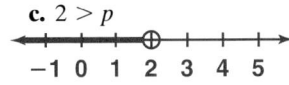

You can write an inequality for a graph.

❹ EXAMPLE   **Writing an Inequality From a Graph**

Write an inequality for each graph.

a. $x < -4$ Numbers less than -4 are graphed.

b. $x \leq 5$ Numbers less than or equal to 5 are graphed.

c. $x > \frac{1}{2}$ Numbers greater than $\frac{1}{2}$ are graphed.

d. $x \geq -1$ Numbers greater than or equal to -1 are graphed.

✓ **Check Understanding** ❹ Write an inequality for each graph. **Choice of variable may vary.**

    a. 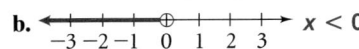 $x \geq 2$ **b.** $x < 0$

👥 **Reaching All Students**

Below Level Help students to understand that expressions such as $-1 \geq a$ and $a \leq -1$ have the same meaning. Review several examples of these expressions with the students.	**Advanced Learners** Ask students to discuss other situations that could be represented by an inequality and determine reasonable solutions.	**English Learners** See note on page 135. **Auditory Learners** See note on page 136.

---

2. Teach

Math Background

Graphing solutions on a number line helps students understand that inequalities have more than one solution.

OBJECTIVE

▼ 1   Teaching Notes

❶ EXAMPLE   **Math Tip**

The inequality sign replaces the equal sign in a math sentence. The equal sign is the mathematical way of writing *is*. Therefore, the inequality sign is the mathematical way of writing *is less than*.

❷ EXAMPLE   **English Learners**

Some students may be confused by the term *inequality*. Underline *in* in the word *inequality*. Have students find the definitions for *inactive, incorrect,* and *informal*. Ask: *What word do all the definitions have in common?* not Explain that *in* is a prefix meaning *not*.

 Additional Examples

❶ Is each number a solution of $x \geq 5$?
a. -2 no
b. 10 yes
c. $\frac{25}{5}$ yes

❷ Is each number a solution of $3 + 2x < 8$?
a. -2 yes
b. 3 no

OBJECTIVE

▼ 2   Teaching Notes

❸ EXAMPLE   **Error Prevention**

Tell students: *Write an inequality for Kyle is older than Jaime.* Kyle's age $>$ Jaime's age *Write this using a less than sign.* Jaime's age $<$ Kyle's age Lead students to understand the two inequalities have the same meaning.

135

You can describe real-world situations using an inequality.

5 EXAMPLE Real-World 🌐 Problem Solving

Define a variable and write an inequality for each situation.

a.

b.

Let s = a legal speed.
The sign indicates that $s \leq 65$.

Let p = pay per hour (in dollars).
The sign indicates that $p \geq 6.15$.

5a. No; speeds cannot be negative, so you can't use all real numbers.

b. No, answers may vary. Sample: Hourly wages are not likely to be in hundreds of dollars.

✔ **Check Understanding** 5 a. **Critical Thinking** In part (a) of Example 5, can the speed be *all* real numbers less than or equal to 65? Explain. **See left above.**

b. In part (b) of Example 5, are all real numbers greater than or equal to $6.15 reasonable solutions of the inequality? Explain. **See left above.**

EXERCISES

For more practice, see *Extra Practice.*

Practice and Problem Solving

A Practice by Example

Example 1
(page 134)

Mental Math Is each number following the inequality a solution of the given inequality?

1. $v \geq -5$; 4 **yes** **2.** $0.5 > c$; 2 **no** **3.** $b < 4$; -0.5 **yes** **4.** $d \leq \frac{17}{3}$; 5 **yes**

5. $g \leq \frac{12}{5}$; 3 **no** **6.** $k < 0$; -1 **yes** **7.** $a > 3.2$; 3 **no** **8.** $x \geq -2.5$; -2.5 **yes**

Example 2
(page 134)

Is each number a solution of the given inequality?

9. $3x - 7 > -1$ a. 2 **no** b. 0 **no** c. 5 **yes**

10. $4n - 3 \leq 5$ a. 2 **yes** b. 3 **no** c. -1 **yes**

11. $2y + 1 < -3$ a. 0 **no** b. -2 **no** c. 1 **no**

12. $\frac{4 - m}{m} \geq 5$ a. 0.5 **yes** b. 2 **no** c. -4 **no**

13. $n(n - 3) < 54$ a. 9 **no** b. 3 **yes** c. 10 **no**

14. $5(2q - 8) \geq 7$ a. -2 **no** b. $\frac{9}{2}$ **no** c. 6 **yes**

Example 3
(page 135)

Match each inequality with its graph.

15. $x < 4$ **C**   **16.** $x \geq 4$ **B**   **17.** $x > 4$ **D**   **18.** $x = 4$ **A**

A.

B.

C.

D.

pages 136–139 **Exercises**

19.

20.

21.

22.

23.

24.

25.

26.

Graph each inequality. 19–26. See margin p. 136.

19. $x > 1$ **20.** $s < -3$ **21.** $y \le -4$ **22.** $t \ge -1$

23. $-2 < d$ **24.** $-\frac{3}{2} \le b$ **25.** $7 \ge a$ **26.** $4.25 > c$

Example 4
(page 135)

Write an inequality for each graph. Choice of variable may vary.

27.
$x > -3$

28.
$x \le 7$

29.
$x \ge 1$

30.
$x < -6$

31.
$x \ge 4.5$

32.
$x < -0.5$

Example 5
(page 136)

Define a variable and write an inequality to model each situation.

33. A bus can seat at most 48 students. **Let s = number of students. $s \le 48$**

34. In many states, you must be at least 16 years old to obtain a driver's license. **Let a = age. $a \ge 16$**

35. It is not safe to use a light bulb of more than 60 watts in this light fixture. **Let w = number of watts. $w \le 60$**

36. At least 350 students attended the band concert Friday night. **Let s = number of students. $s \ge 350$**

37. Aviation The Navy's flying squad, the Blue Angels, makes more than 75 appearances each year. **Let a = number of appearances. $a > 75$**

B **Apply Your Skills**

Write each inequality in words. 38–46. See left. 47–49. See margin.

38. $n < 5$ **39.** $b > 0$ **40.** $7 \ge x$ **41.** $z \ge -5.6$

42. $4 > q$ **43.** $-1 \ge m$ **44.** $35 \ge w$ **45.** $g - 2 < 7$

46. $a \le 3$ **47.** $6 + r > -2$ **48.** $8 \le h$ **49.** $1.2 > k$

38. n is less than 5.

39. b is greater than 0.

40. 7 is greater than or equal to x, or x is less than or equal to 7.

Need Help?

For help with counterexamples see p. 18.

41. z is greater than or equal to -5.6.

42. q is less than 4, or 4 is greater than q.

43. -1 is greater than or equal to m, or m is less than or equal to -1.

44. 35 is greater than or equal to w, or w is less than or equal to 35.

45. g minus 2 is less than 7.

46. a is less than or equal to 3.

50. Writing Explain how you choose whether to draw an open or a closed dot when you graph an inequality. **Use an open dot for $<$ or $>$. Use a closed dot for $\le$ or $\ge$.**

51. Error Analysis A student claims that the inequality $3x + 1 > 0$ is always true because multiplying a number by three and then adding one to it makes the number greater than zero. Use a counterexample to show why the student is not correct. **Answers may vary. Sample: For $x = -1$, $3(-1) + 1 = -3 + 1 = -2$. $-2 \not> 0$.**

52. Critical Thinking Describe how you can display the solutions of the inequality $x \ne 3$ on a number line. **Put an open dot at 3 and color the rest of the number line.**

53. Open-Ended Describe a situation that you can represent using the inequality $x \ge 18$. **Answers may vary. Sample: Every class has at least 18 students.**

Rewrite each inequality so that the variable is on the left. Then graph the solutions. 54–57. See margin for graphs.

54. $2 < x$ $x > 2$ **55.** $-5 \ge b$ $b \le -5$ **56.** $0 \le r$ $r \ge 0$ **57.** $5 > a$ $a < 5$

Graph each inequality from the given description.

58. t is nonnegative.

59. x is positive.

60. k is no more than 3. **See margin.**

61. r is at least 2.

62. s is at most 4. **See margin.**

63. v is no less than 7. **See margin.**

64. Writing Explain how you interpret the phrases "at least" and "at most" in an inequality that models a real-world situation. **"At least" is translated as $\ge$. "At most" is translated as $\le$.**

47. 6 plus r is greater than -2.

48. 8 is less than or equal to h, or h is greater than or equal to 8.

49. 1.2 is greater than k, or k is less than 1.2.

54.

55.

56.

57.

60.

62.

63.

Assignment Guide

1 Objective

Ⓐ Ⓑ **Core** 1–14, 51, 67
Ⓒ **Extension** 69, 70

2 Objective

Ⓐ Ⓑ **Core** 15–50, 52–66
Ⓒ **Extension** 68, 71–73

Standardized Test Prep 74–79

Mixed Review 80–92

Error Prevention

Exercises 33–37 Some students may write $\ge$ for *at most* and $\le$ for *at least*. Make these terms relevant to the students' lives. Ask: *If 3 hours is at most the amount of time you want to study tonight, do you want to study more than 3 hours?* no *If you want to get at least $10 for an allowance, do you want less than $10?* no

Enrichment 3-1

Reteaching 3-1

Practice 3-1

Lesson Quiz 3-1

1. Is each number a solution of $x > -1$?
   a. 3 yes
   b. -5 no

2. Is 2 a solution of $3x - 4 < 2$? no

3. Graph $x > 4$.

   $-1\ 0\ 1\ 2\ 3\ 4\ 5$

4. Write an inequality for the graph. $p \le -2$

   $-3\ -2\ -1\ 0\ 1\ 2\ 3$

5. Graph each inequality.
   a. t is at most 2.

   $-3\ -2\ -1\ 0\ 1\ 2\ 3$

   b. w is at least 1.

   $-2\ -1\ 0\ 1\ 2\ 3\ 4$

Alternative Assessment

Make a number line on the floor out of masking tape. Have a student write an inequality on the board. Have another student demonstrate the inequality on the number line by standing on the appropriate number while holding their arms close to their sides or in a circle and then walking down the number line in the correct direction. If "or equal to" is part of the inequality, have students tuck their arms in close to their side. If there is no "or equal to," have students make a big circle with their arms. For example, to demonstrate $x > 2$, the student stands on 2, makes an arm circle, and walks in the positive direction.

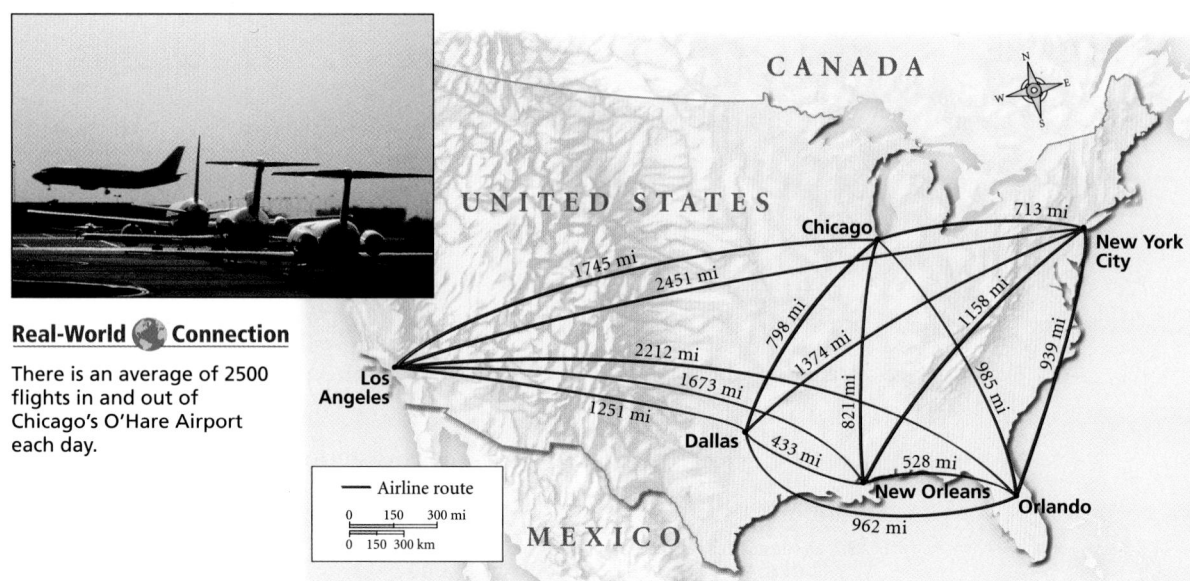

Real-World Connection

There is an average of 2500 flights in and out of Chicago's O'Hare Airport each day.

65. **Air Travel** You plan to go from New York City to Los Angeles. Let x be the distance in miles of any air-route between New York City and Los Angeles. The shortest route is a direct flight. Using the map, write a true statement about the mileage of any route from New York City to Los Angeles. $x \ge 2451$

66. **Air Travel** Your travel agent is making plans for you to go from Chicago to New Orleans. A direct flight costs too much. Option A consists of flights from Chicago to Dallas to New Orleans. Option B consists of flights from Chicago to Orlando to New Orleans. Write an inequality comparing the mileage of these two options. **Option A < Option B**

67. **Critical Thinking** Explain the difference between "4 greater than x" and "$4 > x$." **"4 greater than x" means $x + 4$; "$4 > x$" means 4 *is* greater than x.**

C Challenge

68. **Critical Thinking** Which is the correct graph of $-4 < -x$? Explain.

   A. $-3\ -2\ -1\ 0\ 1\ 2\ 3\ 4\ 5$

   B. $-5\ -4\ -3\ -2\ -1\ 0\ 1\ 2\ 3$

   C. $-3\ -2\ -1\ 0\ 1\ 2\ 3\ 4\ 5$

   D. $-5\ -4\ -3\ -2\ -1\ 0\ 1\ 2\ 3$

   C; the inequality is true for $x = 3$ but not true for $x = 5$, so C is correct.

69. **Reasoning** Give a counterexample for this statement. If $a < b$, then $a^2 < b^2$.
   Answers may vary. Sample: $a = -1$, $b = \frac{1}{2}$

70. **Reasoning** Describe the numbers a and b for which the following statement is true. If $a < b$, then $a^2 = b^2$.
   a is negative, and a and b are opposites.

Problem Solving Hint

In Exercise 70, make logical choices for values of a and b. Use positive and negative numbers as well as zero.

71. **Ticket Sales** Suppose your school plans a musical. The director's goal is ticket sales of at least $4000. Adult tickets are $5.00 and student tickets are $4.00. Let a represent the number of adult tickets and s represent the number of student tickets. Write an inequality that represents the director's goal. **$5a + 4s \ge 4000$**

Graph on a number line.

72. all values of x such that $x > -2$ and $x \le 2$
   $-3\ -2\ -1\ 0\ 1\ 2\ 3$

73. all values of x such that $x < -1$ or $x > 3$
   $-2\ -1\ 0\ 1\ 2\ 3\ 4\ 5$

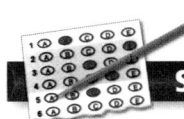
Standardized Test Prep

📁 **Resources**

For additional practice with a variety of test item formats:

• Standardized Test Prep, p. 179
• Test-Taking Strategies, p. 174
• Test-Taking Strategies with Transparencies

Multiple Choice

74. Which inequality has the same solutions as $n > 5$? **C**

    A. $n < -5$ **B.** $n < 5$ **C.** $5 < n$ **D.** $-n > -5$

75. What is the least whole-number solution of $k \geq -5$? **H**

    F. -5 **G.** -4 **H.** 0 **I.** 1

76. Employees must work at least 20 years in a company in order to receive full benefits upon retirement. Which inequality or graph does NOT describe this situation? **B**

    A. $y \geq 20$ **B.** $y > 20$

    C. $20 \leq y$ **D.** (number line: 0 5 10 15 20 25 with closed dot at 20, arrow right)

77. Which value makes the inequality $x^2 \geq x$ false? **H**

    F. $-\frac{1}{4}$ **G.** 0 **H.** $\frac{1}{4}$ **I.** 1

78. Fire codes require that no more than 150 persons occupy a conference room. Which graph includes a room count in possible violation of the fire codes? **B**

    A. (number line: 147 148 149 150 151)

    B. (number line: 147 148 149 150 151)

    C. (number line: 147 148 149 150 151)

    D. (number line: 147 148 149 150 151)

79. [2] (diagram: $12\frac{3}{5}$ total, labeled "completed" and "to be repaired")

Since $6\frac{3}{10}$ is half, $m > 6\frac{3}{10}$.

[1] incorrect inequality OR no diagram

Short Response

💻 **Take It to the NET**

Online lesson quiz at **www.PHSchool.com**

········ Web Code: aea-0301

79. A stretch of $12\frac{3}{5}$ mi of highway is being repaired. The project foreman reported that less than half of the job is complete. Draw a diagram to show the remaining miles to be repaired. Then write an inequality for the number of miles m that still need repair. **See above.**

Mixed Review

Lesson 2-7   **Solve for y in terms of x.**

80. $2x + 3y = 6$ $y = -\frac{2}{3}x + 2$ 81. $5x - y + 8 = 4$ $y = 5x + 4$

82. $-5y + 4x = 15$ $y = \frac{4}{5}x - 3$ 83. $2x + 4y = -20$ $y = -\frac{1}{2}x - 5$

Lesson 2-6   **Find each measure for the following data.**

         1   3   4   4   5   5   7   9   9   9   13

84. mean $6.\overline{27}$ 85. median **5**   86. mode **9**

Solve for the indicated variable.

87. $V = IR$; I $I = \frac{V}{R}$ 88. $P = 2\ell + 2w$; ℓ 89. $P = a + b + c$; b
                                  $\ell = \frac{P - 2w}{2}$ or $\ell = \frac{P}{2} - w$ $b = P - a - c$

Lesson 1-8   **Name the property that each equation demonstrates.**

90. $3(2 \cdot 7) = (3 \cdot 2)7$ 91. $5 \times 1 = 1 \times 5$ 92. $3 + 4 = 4 + 3$
Associative Property of Multiplication   **Commutative Property of Multiplication**   **Commutative Property of Addition**

1. Plan

✓ Check Skills You'll Need

Adding Real Numbers
Lesson 1-4: Example 2
Exercises 5–16
Extra Practice, p. 702

Solving One-Step Equations
Lesson 2-1: Example 1
Exercises 1–7
Extra Practice, p. 703

Lesson Resources

📁 **Teaching Resources**
Practice, Reteaching, Enrichment

👥 **Reaching All Students**
Practice Workbook 3-2
Spanish Practice Workbook 3-2
Basic Algebra Planning Guide 3-2

⏰ **Presentation Assistant Plus!**
Transparencies
• Check Skills You'll Need 3-2
• Additional Examples 3-2
• Student Edition Answers 3-2
• Lesson Quiz 3-2
PH Presentation Pro CD 3-2

PRENTICE HALL ASSESSMENT SYSTEM

Computer Test Generator CD

💿 **Technology**
Resource Pro® CD-ROM
Computer Test Generator CD
Prentice Hall Presentation Pro CD

🖥 **www.PHSchool.com**
Student Site
• Teacher Web Code: aek-5500x
• Reasoning & Puzzles, pp. 55, 56
• Self-grading Lesson Quiz
Teacher Center
• Lesson Planner
• Resources

Plus

3-2 Solving Inequalities Using Addition and Subtraction

North Carolina Objectives

4.01 Use linear functions or inequalities to model and solve problems; justify results. a) Solve using tables, graphs, and algebraic properties.

Lesson Preview

What You'll Learn

OBJECTIVE 1 To use addition to solve inequalities

OBJECTIVE 2 To use subtraction to solve inequalities

...And Why

To solve a problem involving safe loads, as in Example 4

✓ Check Skills You'll Need

(For help, go to Lessons 1-4 and 2-1.)

Complete each statement with <, =, or >.

1. $-3 + 4 \;\boxed{>}\; -5 + 4$ **2.** $-3 + 6 \;\boxed{>}\; 4 + 6$ **3.** $-3.4 + 2 \;\boxed{>}\; -3.45 + 2$

Solve each equation.

4. $x - 4 = 5$ **9**   **5.** $n - 3 = -5$ **-2**   **6.** $t + 4 = -5$ **-9**   **7.** $k + \frac{2}{3} = \frac{5}{6}$ **$\frac{1}{6}$**

New Vocabulary • equivalent inequalities

OBJECTIVE

🖥 **Interactive lesson includes instant self-check, tutorials, and activities.**

1 Using Addition to Solve Inequalities

Equivalent inequalities are inequalities with the same solutions. For example, $x + 4 < 7$ and $x < 3$ are equivalent inequalities.

$x + 4 < 7$ $x < 3$

You can add the same value to each side of an inequality, just as you did with equations.

🔑 **Key Concepts**

Property	**Addition Property of Inequality**

For every real number a, b, and c,
  if $a > b$, then $a + c > b + c$;   if $a < b$, then $a + c < b + c$.

Examples $3 > 1$, so $3 + 2 > 1 + 2$. $-5 < 4$, so $-5 + 2 < 4 + 2$.

This property is also true for $\geq$ and $\leq$.

Draw Diagram "number line"

1 EXAMPLE Using the Addition Property of Inequality

Solve $x - 3 < 5$. Graph the solution.

$x - 3 + 3 < 5 + 3$ **Add 3 to each side.**

   $x < 8$ **Simplify.**

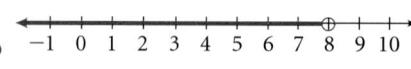
$-1\ 0\ 1\ 2\ 3\ 4\ 5\ 6\ 7\ 8\ 9\ 10$

✓ Check Understanding ① Solve $m - 6 > -4$. Graph your solution. $m > 2$;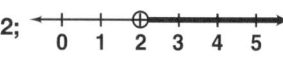
$0\ 1\ 2\ 3\ 4\ 5$

Ongoing Assessment and Intervention

Before the Lesson
Diagnose prerequisite skills using:
• Check Skills You'll Need

During the Lesson
Monitor progress using:
• Check Understanding
• Additional Examples
• Standardized Test Prep

After the Lesson
Assess knowledge using:
• Lesson Quiz
• Computer Test Generator CD

Reading Math

The word *infinite* indicates that the number of solutions is unlimited. The solutions cannot be listed or counted.

An inequality has an infinite number of solutions, so it is not possible to check all the solutions. You can check your computations and the direction of the inequality symbol. The steps below show how to check that $x < 8$ describes the solutions to Example 1.

Step 1 Check the computation. See if 8 is a solution to the equation $x - 3 = 5$.

$$x - 3 = 5$$
$$8 - 3 \overset{?}{=} 5 \quad \textbf{Substitute 8 for } x.$$
$$5 = 5 \checkmark$$

Step 2 Check the inequality symbol. Choose any number less than 8 and substitute it into $x - 3 < 5$. In this case, use 7.

$$x - 3 < 5$$
$$7 - 3 < 5 \quad \textbf{Substitute 7 for } x.$$
$$4 < 5 \checkmark$$

Since the computation and the direction of the inequality symbol are correct, $x - 3 < 5$ and $x < 8$ are equivalent inequalities. So the solution of $x - 3 < 5$ is $x < 8$.

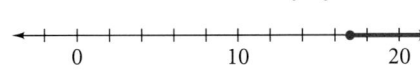 **Solving and Checking Solutions**

Solve $12 \leq x - 5$. Graph and check your solution.

$$12 + 5 \leq x - 5 + 5 \quad \textbf{Add 5 to each side.}$$
$$17 \leq x \quad\quad\quad\quad \textbf{Simplify.}$$

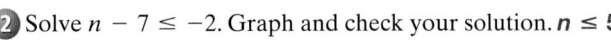

Check $12 = x - 5$ **Check the computation.**
$\quad\quad\quad 12 \overset{?}{=} 17 - 5$ **Substitute 17 for** x.
$\quad\quad\quad 12 = 12 \checkmark$

$\quad\quad\quad 12 \leq x - 5$ **Check the direction of the inequality.**
$\quad\quad\quad 12 \leq 18 - 5$ **Substitute 18 for** x.
$\quad\quad\quad 12 \leq 13 \checkmark$

 Check Understanding ❷ Solve $n - 7 \leq -2$. Graph and check your solution. $n \leq 5$;

OBJECTIVE

2 **Using Subtraction to Solve Inequalities**

You can subtract the same number from each side of an inequality to create an equivalent inequality.

 Key Concepts

Property	Subtraction Property of Inequality
For every real number a, b, and c, $\quad$ if $a > b$, then $a - c > b - c$; $\quad\quad$ if $a < b$, then $a - c < b - c$.	
Examples $3 > -1$, so $3 - 2 > -1 - 2$ $\quad\quad -5 < 4$, so $-5 - 2 < 4 - 2$	
This property is also true for $\geq$ and $\leq$.	

Lesson 3-2 Solving Inequalities Using Addition and Subtraction   **141**

Reaching All Students

Below Level Present students with several pairs of inequalities and their solutions. Have students take turns explaining what was done to each inequality to produce its solution.	**Advanced Learners** Have students discuss whether $x < 1$ is equivalent to $-x < -1$ and explain each step of their reasoning.	**Inclusion** See note on page 141. **Tactile Learners** See note on page 141.

---

2. Teach

 Professional Development

Math Background

Students may have used a balance scale to model equations. Here it may help them to solve inequalities if they refer to an unbalanced scale.

OBJECTIVE
1 Teaching Notes

1 EXAMPLE **Tactile Learners**

Let students use tiles to model the inequality. Have students write the inequality sign on an index card. Instruct them to place the card between the two sets of tiles. Then have them solve the inequality. When the solution is complete, students can check by substituting tiles for a value of x in the original model.

2 EXAMPLE **Inclusion**

Some students may have difficulty understanding the concept of infinity. Have students look at the number line in Example 2. Ask: *What integer is to the right of 20?* **21** Repeat the question for 21. **22** After repeating the question for several more successive integers, ask: *Will I ever have to stop asking what is the next number to the right because the numbers end?* **no** Explain that you can always add 1 more to whatever number you are given. Remind students that the dot and arrow in Example 2 means that 17 and all numbers to the right of 17 on the number line are solutions to the inequality.

141

① Solve $p - 4 < 1$. Graph the solution. $p < 5$

```
←—┼—┼—┼—┼—⊕—┼—┼—→
  0  1  2  3  4  5  6
```

② Solve $8 \geq d - 2$. Graph and check your solution. $10 \geq d$, or $d \leq 10$

```
←┼┼┼┼┼┼⊕┼┼┼┼┼→
 0      10      20
```

③ **EXAMPLE** Teaching Tip

Ask students why it is important to subtract the same amount from both sides of an inequality. Sample answer: If you subtract an amount from the greater side only, it may become less than the other side and change the inequality.

④ **EXAMPLE** Diversity

Some students may have lived in a shelter or may live in one now. Be sure other students are sensitive when discussing the Check Understanding question.

 **Additional Examples**

③ Solve $c + 4 > 7$. Graph the solution. $c > 3$

```
←┼—┼—┼—┼—┼—⊕—┼—→
 -1  0  1  2  3  4  5
```

④ In order to receive a B in your literature class, you must earn more than 350 points of reading credits. Last week you earned 120 points. This week you earned 90 points. How many more points must you earn to receive a B? **141 points**

Closure

Ask students to compare solving inequalities using addition and subtraction with solving equations using addition and subtraction. In both cases, you must add or subtract the same amount to or from both sides.

142

---

③ **EXAMPLE** Using the Subtraction Property of Inequality

Solve $y + 5 < -7$. Graph the solution.

$y + 5 - 5 < -7 - 5$ Subtract 5 from each side.

$\qquad y < -12$ Simplify.

```
  ⊕—┼—┼—┼—┼—┼—┼—┼—┼→
●  -12     -6      0      6
```

✓ **Check Understanding** ③ Solve $t + 3 \geq 8$. Graph and check your solution. $t \geq 5$;

```
←┼—┼—┼—┼—┼—┼—┼—●—┼→
 -1  0  1  2  3  4  5  6
```

You can use inequalities to model real-world situations.

④ **EXAMPLE** Real-World 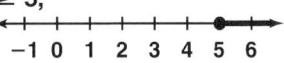 Problem Solving

Safe Load The maximum safe load of a chairlift like the one at the left is 680 lb. The weight of the person in the lift is 124 lb, and the weight of the bicycle is 32 lb. How much additional weight can the chairlift safely carry?

Relate | weight of a person and a bicycle | plus | additional weight | is at most | safe load |

Define Let w = the amount of weight that can be added to the chairlift.

Write $124 + 32 \qquad + \qquad w \qquad \leq \qquad 680$

$\qquad 124 + 32 + w \leq 680$

$\qquad 156 + w \leq 680$ Combine like terms.

$156 + w - 156 \leq 680 - 156$ Subtract 156 from each side.

$\qquad w \leq 524$ Simplify.

● The chairlift can safely carry an additional 524 lb.

Real-World Connection

The design of a chairlift allows for 170 lb per passenger, including equipment.

✓ **Check Understanding** ④ Your baseball team has a goal to collect at least 160 blankets for a shelter. Team members brought 42 blankets on Monday and 65 blankets on Wednesday. How many blankets must the team donate on Friday to make or exceed their goal? **at least 53 blankets**

EXERCISES

For more practice, see *Extra Practice*.

Practice and Problem Solving

Ⓐ **Practice by Example**

Examples 1, 2
(pages 140, 141)

State what number you would add to each side of the inequality to solve the inequality.

1. $d - 5 \geq -4$ **5**   **2.** $0 < c - 8$ **8**   **3.** $z - 4.3 \geq 1.6$ **4.3**

Solve each inequality. Graph and check your solution. 4–16. See margin.

4. $x - 1 > 10$ **5.** $t - 3 < -2$ **6.** $-5 > b - 1$ **7.** $7 \leq d - 3$

8. $s - 2 \geq -6$ **9.** $r - 9 \leq 0$ **10.** $8 < n - 2$ **11.** $-4 \geq w - 2$

12. $-1 < -4 + d$ **13.** $y - \frac{1}{2} \leq -5$ **14.** $-\frac{2}{3} > q - 4$ **15.** $x - 2 \geq 0.5$

16. $3.2 > -1.3 + r$ **17.** $-3.4 > m - 1.8$ **18.** $b - \frac{3}{8} < \frac{1}{8}$ **19.** $n - 2\frac{1}{2} > \frac{1}{2}$

17–19. See back of book.

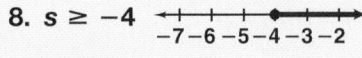

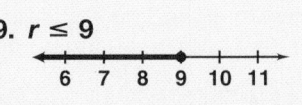

pages 142–145 **Exercises**

4. $x > 11$
```
←┼—┼—⊕—┼—┼—┼→
  9 10 11 12 13 14
```

5. $t < 1$
```
←┼—┼—┼—⊕—┼→
 -2 -1  0  1  2
```

6. $b < -4$
```
←┼—┼—┼—⊕—┼—┼→
-7 -6 -5 -4 -3 -2
```

7. $d \geq 10$
```
←┼—┼—●—┼—┼—┼→
 8  9 10 11 12 13
```

8. $s \geq -4$
```
←┼—┼—●—┼—┼—┼→
-7-6-5-4-3-2
```

9. $r \leq 9$
```
←┼—┼—┼—●—┼—┼→
  6  7  8  9 10 11
```

10. $n > 10$
```
←┼—┼—┼—⊕—┼→
-5  0  5 10 15
```

Example 3
(page 142)

State what number you would subtract from each side of the inequality to solve the inequality.

20. $w + 2 > -1$ **2**   **21.** $8 < \frac{5}{3} + r$ $\frac{5}{3}$ **22.** $5.7 \geq k + 3.1$ **3.1**

Solve each inequality. Graph and check your solution. 23–38. **See back of book.**

23. $w + 4 \leq 9$ **24.** $m + 5 > -3$ **25.** $1 < 8 + b$ **26.** $-2 \geq 4 + a$

27. $r + 1 \geq -5$ **28.** $k + 3 \leq 4$ **29.** $3 > 4 + x$ **30.** $-5 < 1 + p$

31. $\frac{3}{5} + z \geq -\frac{2}{5}$ **32.** $7.5 + y < 13$ **33.** $\frac{1}{2} < m + 2$ **34.** $2.7 \geq a + 3$

35. $-2.9 < 4.1 + p$ **36.** $\frac{1}{4} \geq h + \frac{3}{4}$ **37.** $5.3 + d > 3.8$ **38.** $t + \frac{3}{8} < -\frac{1}{8}$

Example 4
(page 142)

39. Vacation Budget Your brother has $2000 saved for a vacation. His airplane ticket is $637. Write and solve an inequality to find how much he can spend for everything else. $s + 637 \leq 2000$, $1363

40. Weekly Budget You have an allowance of $15.00 per week. You are in a bowling league that costs $6.50 each week, and you save at least $5.00 each week. Write and solve an inequality to show how much you have left to spend each week. $s + 6.50 + 5 \leq 15$, $3.50

41. Fund-Raising A school club is selling reflectors for Bicycle Safety Day. Each member is encouraged to sell at least 50 reflectors. You sell 17 on Monday and 12 on Tuesday. How many reflectors do you need to sell on Wednesday to meet your goal? $r + 17 + 12 \geq 50$, 21 reflectors

B Apply Your Skills

68c. Answers may vary. Sample: The = sign indicates that each side is equal, so the two sides may be interchanged. The < sign does not indicate equality. One side cannot be both greater than and less than the other side.

State what you must do to the first inequality in order to get the second.

42. $36 \leq -4 + y$; $40 \leq y$ **43.** $9 + b > 24$; $b > 15$ **44.** $m - \frac{1}{2} < \frac{3}{8}$; $m < \frac{7}{8}$
Add 4 to each side.   Subtract 9 from each side.   Add $\frac{1}{2}$ to each side.

Solve each inequality.

45. $w - 3 + 1 \geq 9$ $w \geq 11$ **46.** $\frac{1}{2} + c \leq 3\frac{1}{2}$ $c \leq 3$ **47.** $y - 0.3 < 2.8$ $y < 3.1$

48. $-6 > n - \frac{1}{5}$ $n < -5\frac{4}{5}$ **49.** $z + 4.1 < -5.6$ **50.** $-4.1 > y - 0.9$
                                               $z < -9.7$ $y < -3.2$
51. $\frac{2}{3} + t - \frac{5}{6} > 0$ $t > \frac{1}{6}$ **52.** $5 \leq v - 4 - 7$ $v \geq 16$ **53.** $3.6 + k \geq -4.5$
                                                                        $k \geq -8.1$
54. $6 + b - 7 < 5$ $b < 6$ **55.** $m + 2.3 \leq -1.2$ **56.** $4 \geq k - \frac{3}{4}$ $k \leq 4\frac{3}{4}$
                              $m \leq -3.5$
57. $h - \frac{1}{2} \geq -1$ $h \geq -\frac{1}{2}$ **58.** $-7.7 \geq x - 2$ $x \leq -5.7$ **59.** $-2 > 9 + 3 + w$
                                                              $w < -14$
60. $\frac{3}{2} + w \leq \frac{1}{3}$ $w \leq -1\frac{1}{6}$ **61.** $x + 4 - 7 < 13$ $x < 16$ **62.** $3.5 < m - 2$ $m > 5.5$

63. $9.4 \leq t - 3.5$ $t \geq 12.9$ **64.** $0 > k - 2\frac{3}{5}$ $k < 2\frac{3}{5}$ **65.** $5.3 > 1.6 + n - 2.3$
                                                                          $n < 6$
66. $-7\frac{3}{4} + m + \frac{1}{2} \leq -2\frac{1}{4}$ $m \leq 5$ **67.** $-1.4 + s + 2.1 > 11$ $s > 10.3$

68. a. If $45 + 47 = t$, does $t = 45 + 47$? **yes**
   b. If $45 + 47 < r$, is $r < 45 + 47$? **no**
   c. Discuss the differences between these two examples. **See above left.**

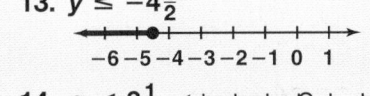

69. Gymnastics Suppose your sister wants to qualify for a regional gymnastics competition. At today's competition she must score at least 34.0 points. She scored 8.8 on the vault, 7.9 on the balance beam, and 8.2 on the uneven parallel bars. The event that remains is the floor exercise. **a–b. See back of book.**
   a. Write and solve an inequality that models the information.
   b. Explain what the solution means in terms of the original situation.
   c. Open-Ended Write three scores your sister could make that would allow her to qualify for the regional gymnastics competition. **Answers may vary. Sample: 9.1, 9.2, 9.3**

Real-World Connection

More than 71,000 athletes compete in gymnastic programs in the United States.

Lesson 3-2 Solving Inequalities Using Addition and Subtraction   **143**

11. $w \leq -2$
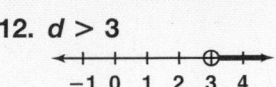
$-4 -3 -2 -1\ 0\ 1$

12. $d > 3$
$-1\ 0\ 1\ 2\ 3\ 4$

13. $y \leq -4\frac{1}{2}$
$-6 -5 -4 -3 -2 -1\ 0\ 1$

14. $q < 3\frac{1}{3}$
$0\ 1\ 2\ 3\ 4\ 5$

15. $x \geq 2.5$
$-1\ 0\ 1\ 2\ 3\ 4$

16. $r < 4.5$
$-1\ 0\ 1\ 2\ 3\ 4\ 5$

Assignment Guide

1 Objective
   A B Core 1–19, 42–54, 75–80
   C Extension 88–89

2 Objective
   A B 20–41, 55–74, 81–87
   C Extension 90–92

Standardized Test Prep 93–98

Mixed Review 99–120

Error Prevention

Exercises 4–19 Some students may have difficulty deciding in which direction to draw the graph of a solution. Point out that when the solution has the variable on the left, the graph points in the same direction as the inequality symbol. When the solution has the variable on the right, the graph points in the opposite direction of the inequality symbol.

Exercises 31–38 Suggest to students that they eliminate the fractions or decimals before solving.

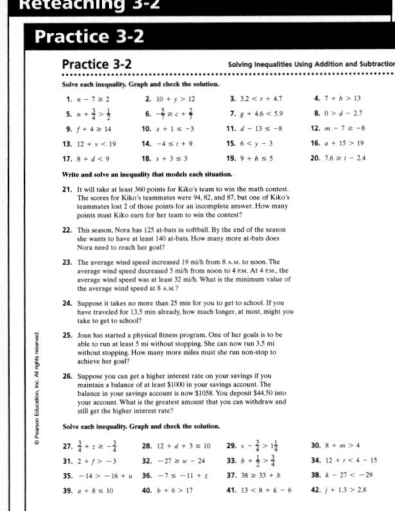

Enrichment 3-2
Reteaching 3-2
Practice 3-2

Alternative Assessment

Group students in pairs. Instruct
each student to model an
inequality using tiles and an index
card with the inequality sign
written on it. Have students
exchange inequalities with their
partners and find the solutions.
Encourage students to check their
solutions.

pages 142–145 Exercises

74b. Answers may vary.
Sample: Substituting
values does not work
because there is always
the possibility that the
solution lies between
values that make the
inequality true and a
value that does not.

Real-World Connection

In 1971, a computer chip
could hold 2300 transistors.
In 2000, a chip could hold
42,000,000 transistors.

88. not true; sample
counterexample:
for $a = 5$ and $b =$
-6, $5 - (-6) \not< 5 + (-6)$

91. not true; sample
counterexample:
for $a = 0$, $b = 1$, and $c =$
-2, $0 < 1$ and $0 \not< 1 + (-2)$

70. Computers Suppose your computer has nearly 64 megabytes (MB) of memory.
Its basic systems require 12.8 MB. How much memory is available for other
programs and functions? **nearly 51.2 MB**

71. Banking Your local bank offers free checking for accounts with a balance of at
least $500. Suppose you have a balance of $516.46 and you write a check for
$31.96. How much must you deposit to avoid being charged a service fee?
at least $15.50

72. To earn an A in Ms. Orlando's math class, students must score a total of at least
135 points on the three tests. On the first two tests, Amy's scores were 47 and
48. What is the minimum score she must get on the third test in order to earn
an A? **40 points**

73. a. Open-Ended Use each of the inequality symbols $<$, $\leq$, $>$, and $\geq$ to write
four addition or subtraction inequalities. **a–b. Answers may vary.**
  b. Solve each of the inequalities in part (a) and graph your solution.

74. a. Sam says that he can solve $z - 8.6 \geq 5.2$ by replacing z with 13, 14, and 15.
When $z = 13$, the inequality is false. When $z = 14$ and $z = 15$, the inequality is
true. So Sam says that the solution is $z \geq 14$. Is his reasoning correct? Justify
your answer. **No; the solution is $z \geq 13.8$, so $z \geq 14$ is not correct.**
  b. Critical Thinking Explain why substituting values into the inequality does
not guarantee that your solution is correct. **See margin.**

Solve each inequality.

75. $4x + 4 - 3x \geq 5$ $x \geq 1$

76. $-5n - 3 + 6n < 2$ $n < 5$

77. $7t - (6t - 2) \leq -1$ $t \leq -3$

78. $5k - 2(2k + 1) > 8$ $k > 10$

79. $3(r + 2) - 2r < 4$ $r < -2$

80. $4(r + 5) - 3r \geq 7$ $r \geq -13$

81. $3a + 6 - 2a \geq -19$ $a \geq -25$

82. $-5 \leq 3m - 10 - 2m$ $5 \leq m$

83. $-3d + 4(d + 3) > 4$ $d > -8$

84. $5(y - 2) - 4(y - 1) < 0$ $y < 6$

85. $-6(a + 2) + 7a \leq 12$ $a \leq 24$

86. $-2(a - 3) + 3(a + 2) < 4$ $a < -8$

87. Geometry The Triangle Inequality Theorem states that the sum of the lengths
of any two sides of a triangle is greater than the length of the third side.
Following are inequalities for sides of the triangle shown.

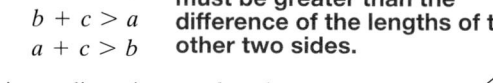
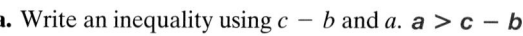

$a + b > c$
$b + c > a$
$a + c > b$

  d. The length of the third side
  must be greater than the
  difference of the lengths of the
  other two sides.

  a. Write an inequality using $c - b$ and a. **$a > c - b$**
  b. Write an inequality using $a - c$ and b. **$b > a - c$**
  c. Write an inequality using $b - a$ and c. **$c > b - a$**
  d. Writing Write a generalization about the length
  of the third side and the difference of the lengths of the other two sides.
  See above.

Challenge

Reasoning Decide if each inequality is true for all real numbers. If the inequality is
not true, give a counterexample.

88. $a - b < a + b$ **See above left.**

89. If $a \geq b$, then $a + c \geq b + c$. **true**

90. If $c > d$, then $a - c < a - d$. **true**

91. If $a < b$, then $a < b + c$.
See above left.

92. Reasoning Find real numbers x, y, z, and w for which it is true that $x > y$ and
$z > w$, but it is not true that $x - z > y - w$.
Answers may vary. Sample:
For $x = 2$, $y = 1$, $z = 4$, and $w = 3$, $2 > 1$ and $4 > 3$, but $2 - 4 \not> 1 - 3$.

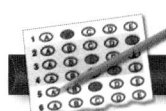

Standardized Test Prep

Standardized Test Prep

📁 **Resources**

For additional practice with a variety of test item formats:
- Standardized Test Prep, p. 179
- Test-Taking Strategies, p. 174
- Test-Taking Strategies with Transparencies

Exercise 95 Point out to students that they can quickly eliminate answer choices B and D, since these have open dots.

Multiple Choice

93. Solve $x + 5 < 13$. **B**
  A. $x > 8$ B. $x < 8$ C. $x > 18$ D. $x < 18$

94. Solve $-12 + n > 20$. **G**
  F. $n < 32$ G. $n > 32$ H. $n < 8$ I. $n > 8$

95. Which graph represents all real number solutions of $x + 4 \geq 8$? **A**

A.
```
←+—+—+—+—+—●—+—+→
  -1  0  1  2  3  4  5
```

B.
```
←—⊕—+—+—+—+—+—+→
 -5 -4 -3 -2 -1  0  1
```

C.
```
←+—+—+—+—+—●—+→
  -1  0  1  2  3  4  5
```

D.
```
←+—+—+—+—+—⊖—+—+→
   -3 -2 -1  0  1  2  3
```

98. [2] at least 33 points;
24(19.5) + x > 25(20)
  468 + x > 500
       x > 32
(OR equivalent explanation)
[1] incorrect answer OR no work or explanation

96. Which of the following is a solution for $5 < n - 0.1$? **I**
  F. 4.99   G. 5.01   H. 5.10   I. 5.11

97. Hector is flying his plane. To avoid a storm, he climbs 5,500 ft without going above his plane's maximum safe altitude of 35,000 ft. The inequality $a + 5,500 \leq 35,000$ represents his original altitude a in feet. Which of the following could have been the original altitude? **D**
  A. 40,500   B. 30,000 ft   C. 29,750 ft   D. 27,750 ft

Short Response

98. The leading scorer in your high school basketball's division finished the season with a game average of 20 points for 25 games. As the division's second leading scorer, you have a 19.5 point per game average for 24 games. You have your last game yet to play.

How many points must you score in the final game of the season to overtake the division's leading scorer? Show your work. **See above left.**

Take It to the NET

Online lesson quiz at **www.PHSchool.com**
.... Web Code: aea-0302

Mixed Review

Lesson 3-1

Define a variable and write an inequality to model each situation.

99. An octopus can be up to 10 ft long. **Let c = length of octopus in feet. $c \leq 10$**

100. A hummingbird migrates more than 1850 mi. **Let h = distance in miles a hummingbird migrates. $h > 1850$**

101. Your average in algebra class must be 90 or greater to receive an A for the term. **Let a = average. $a \geq 90$**

102. You must read at least 25 pages this weekend. **Let p = number of pages to read. $p \geq 25$**

Lessons 2-1 and 2-2

Solve each equation.

103. $n - 4 = 9$ **13**   **104.** $8 + w = 7$ **−1**   **105.** $c + 5 = -7$ **−12**

106. $7 - k = 3$ **4**   **107.** $4t = 52$ **13**   **108.** $-\frac{2x}{3} = 12$ **−18**

109. $\frac{k}{7} = -4$ **−28**   **110.** $18 = y - 4$ **22**   **111.** $40 = \frac{5}{8}q$ **64**

Lesson 1-2

Simplify.

112. $9^2 + 17$ **98**   **113.** $4(5 - 3)^2 - 3^2$ **7**   **114.** $0.2(4.2 - 3.4) + 0.4$ **0.56**

115. $3 \cdot 2 + 5^2$ **31**   **116.** $3 + 7^2 - 4$ **48**   **117.** $4^3 + 3^2$ **73**

118. $6(5 - 2)^2 + 4$ **58**   **119.** $2 + 8(6 + 2^2)$ **82**   **120.** $3^3 - 2^3 + 7$ **26**

3-3

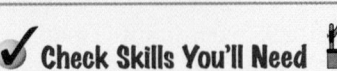1. Plan

Lesson Preview

✓ **Check Skills You'll Need**

Solving One-Step Equations
Lesson 2-1: Examples 4–6
Exercises 21–52
Extra Practice, p. 703

Inequalities and Their Graphs
Lesson 3-1: Example 4
Exercises 27–32
Extra Practice, p. 704

Lesson Resources

📁 **Teaching Resources**
Practice, Reteaching, Enrichment
Checkpoint Quiz 1

👥 **Reaching All Students**
Practice Workbook 3-3
Spanish Practice Workbook 3-3
Reading and Math Literacy 3B
Spanish Reading & Literacy 3B
Spanish Checkpoint Quiz 1
Basic Algebra Planning Guide 3-3

⏱ **Presentation Assistant Plus!**
Transparencies
• Check Skills You'll Need 3-3
• Additional Examples 3-3
• Student Edition Answers 3-3
• Lesson Quiz 3-3
PH Presentation Pro CD 3-3

PRENTICE HALL
ASSESSMENT SYSTEM

Checkpoint Quiz 1
Computer Test Generator CD

💿 **Technology**
Resource Pro® CD-ROM
Computer Test Generator CD
Prentice Hall Presentation Pro CD

🖥 **www.PHSchool.com**
Student Site
• Teacher Web Code: aek-5500
• Reasoning & Puzzles, p. 58
• Self-grading Lesson Quiz
Teacher Center
• Lesson Planner
• Resources

Plus

146

 **3-3**

Solving Inequalities Using Multiplication and Division

 North Carolina Objectives

4.01 Use linear functions or inequalities to model and solve problems; justify results. a) Solve using tables, graphs, and algebraic properties.

Lesson Preview

What You'll Learn

 OBJECTIVE 1
To use multiplication to solve inequalities

 OBJECTIVE 2
To use division to solve inequalities

. . . And Why

To find how much food can be purchased for a food bank, as in Example 4

✓ Check Skills You'll Need

(For help, go to Lessons 2-1 and 3-1.)

Solve each equation.

1. $8 = \frac{1}{2}t$ **16**

2. $14 = -21x$ $-\frac{2}{3}$

3. $\frac{x}{6} = -1$ **−6**

4. $5d = 32$ **6.4**

5. $\frac{2}{3}x = -12$ **−18**

6. $0.5n = 9$ **18**

Write an inequality for each graph.

7. $x \leq -1$
$-3 \ -2 \ -1 \ \ 0 \ \ 1 \ \ 2 \ \ 3$

8. $x > 3$
$-1 \ \ 0 \ \ 1 \ \ 2 \ \ 3 \ \ 4 \ \ 5$

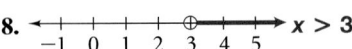 **iTEXT** Interactive lesson includes instant self-check, tutorials, and activities.

OBJECTIVE **1** Using Multiplication to Solve Inequalities

Investigation: Multiplying Each Side of an Inequality

Consider the inequality $4 > 1$.

1. Copy and complete each statement at the right by replacing each ■ with $<$, $>$, or $=$.

2. What happens to the inequality symbol when you multiply each side by a positive number?
There is no change in the inequality sign.

3. What happens to the inequality symbol when you multiply each side by zero?
The inequality becomes an equality: 0 = 0.

4. What happens to the inequality symbol when you multiply each side by a negative number?
The inequality sign is reversed.

$4 \cdot 3 \geq 1 \cdot 3$
$4 \cdot 2 \geq 1 \cdot 2$
$4 \cdot 1 \geq 1 \cdot 1$
$4 \cdot 0 \equiv 1 \cdot 0$
$4 \cdot -1 \leq 1 \cdot -1$
$4 \cdot -2 \leq 1 \cdot -2$
$4 \cdot -3 \leq 1 \cdot -3$

You can multiply each side of an inequality by the same number, just as you did with equations. When you multiply each side of an inequality by a positive number, the direction of the inequality symbol stays the same. When you multiply each side by a negative number, the direction of the inequality symbol reverses.

🔑 **Key Concepts**

Property	Multiplication Property of Inequality for *c* > 0

For every real number a and b, and for $c > 0$,

$\quad$ if $a > b$, then $ac > bc$; $\qquad\qquad$ if $a < b$, then $ac < bc$.

Examples $4 > -1$, so $4(5) > -1(5)$. $\qquad$ $-6 < 3$, so $-6(5) < 3(5)$.

This property is also true for $\geq$ and $\leq$.

Ongoing Assessment and Intervention

Before the Lesson	During the Lesson	After the Lesson
Diagnose prerequisite skills using:	**Monitor progress using:**	**Assess knowledge using:**
• Check Skills You'll Need	• Check Understanding	• Lesson Quiz
	• Additional Examples	• Computer Test Generator CD
	• Standardized Test Prep	• Chapter Checkpoint 1 (p. 151)

You can use the Multiplication Property of Inequality to solve inequalities that involve division.

1 EXAMPLE **Multiplying by a Positive Number**

Solve $\frac{x}{2} < -1$. Graph and check the solution.

$2\left(\frac{x}{2}\right) < 2(-1)$ **Multiply each side by 2. Do not reverse the inequality symbol.**

$x < -2$ **Simplify each side.**

<!-- number line from -5 to 5 with open circle at -2 -->
$$-5\ -4\ -3\ -2\ -1\ \ 0\ \ 1\ \ 2\ \ 3\ \ 4\ \ 5$$

Check $\frac{x}{2} = -1$ **Check the computation.**

$\frac{-2}{2} \stackrel{?}{=} -1$ **Substitute −2 for x.**

$-1 = -1 \checkmark$ **Simplify.**

$\frac{x}{2} < -1$ **Check the direction of the inequality.**

$\frac{-3}{2} < -1 \checkmark$ **Substitute −3 for x.**

 Check Understanding ① Solve each inequality. Graph and check your solution.

a. $\frac{b}{4} > \frac{1}{2}$ $b > 2$;

<!-- number line -1 to 3, open circle at 2 -->
$$-1\ \ 0\ \ 1\ \ 2\ \ 3$$

b. $\frac{d}{3} \geq \frac{5}{6}$ $d \geq 2\frac{1}{2}$;

<!-- number line -1 to 4, closed circle at 2.5 -->
$$-1\ \ 0\ \ 1\ \ 2\ \ 3\ \ 4$$

c. $\frac{y}{0.5} \leq -3$ $y \leq -1.5$;

<!-- number line -3 to 1, closed circle at -1.5 -->
$$-3\ -2\ -1\ \ 0\ \ 1$$

Key Concepts

Property	Multiplication Property of Inequality for $c < 0$

For every real number a and b, and for $c < 0$,

if $a > b$, then $ac < bc$;   if $a < b$, then $ac > bc$.

Examples $4 > -1$, so $4(-2) < -1(-2)$. $-6 < 3$, so $-6(-2) > 3(-2)$.

This property is also true for $\geq$ and $\leq$.

2 EXAMPLE **Multiplying by a Negative Number**

Solve $-\frac{2}{3}n \leq 2$. Graph and check the solution.

$\left(-\frac{3}{2}\right)\left(-\frac{2}{3}n\right) \geq \left(-\frac{3}{2}\right)2$ **Multiply each side by $-\frac{3}{2}$, the reciprocal of $-\frac{2}{3}$. Reverse the inequality symbol.**

$n \geq -3$ **Simplify.**

<!-- number line -6 to 4, closed circle at -3 -->
$$-6\ -5\ -4\ -3\ -2\ -1\ \ 0\ \ 1\ \ 2\ \ 3\ \ 4$$

? Need Help?

The reciprocal of a nonzero number $\frac{a}{b}$ is the number $\frac{b}{a}$.

Check $-\frac{2}{3}n = 2$ **Check the computation.**

$-\frac{2}{3}(-3) \stackrel{?}{=} 2$ **Substitute −3 for n.**

$2 = 2 \checkmark$

$-\frac{2}{3}n \leq 2$ **Check the direction of the inequality.**

$-\frac{2}{3}(-2) \leq 2$ **Substitute −2 for n.**

$\frac{4}{3} \leq 2 \checkmark$

2a.
<!-- number line -1 to 5, open circle at 4 -->
$$-1\ \ 0\ \ 1\ \ 2\ \ 3\ \ 4\ \ 5$$

b.
<!-- number line -3 to 2, open circle at -1 -->
$$-3\ -2\ -1\ \ 0\ \ 1\ \ 2$$

c.
<!-- number line -20 to 5, closed circle at -10 -->
$$-20\ \ -10\ \ \ 0\ \ 5$$

 Check Understanding ② Solve each inequality. Graph and check the solution. **See left for graphs.**

a. $-\frac{k}{4} > -1$ $k < 4$ **b.** $-t < \frac{1}{2}$ $t > -\frac{1}{2}$ **c.** $6 \leq -\frac{3}{5}w$ $w \leq -10$

👪 Reaching All Students

Below Level Have students pick integer solutions to Example 3 from the graph and substitute them in the original inequality to verify solutions.	**Advanced Learners** Draw a chart on the board similar to the one on p. 146. Begin with 4 ÷ 3. Help students decide which symbol replaces each box.	**Visual Learners** See note on page 148. **Error Prevention** See note on page 147.

Math Background

Given their great usefulness in developing insight, patterns should be discussed as often as possible.

OBJECTIVE
▼ ① Teaching Notes

Investigation (Optional)
Have students repeat the Investigation for an inequality that contains negative numbers only, such as $-3 < -1$. Then have them contrast and compare the answers for both inequalities. This will help students realize that the reversal of the inequality sign does not depend on positive or negative numbers in the inequality.

① EXAMPLE **Error Prevention**

Students may think that since a negative is part of the multiplication, they should reverse the inequality sign. Stress that you reverse the inequality sign only if the number by which you are multiplying or dividing both sides is negative.

② EXAMPLE **Alternative Method**

Show students that 0 is the easiest number to use to check a solution. Since 0 is part of the solution in Example 2, demonstrate how students can mentally replace n with 0, thus making the right side of the inequality 0. Two is greater than 0, so the solution is correct. Zero can be used whether it is part of the solution set or not. If it is not part of the solution set, then the checking process will end in a false statement.

In Example 3, substituting 0 for z leads to the false inequality $0 \leq -5$; so 0 is not in the solution set.

1 Solve $\frac{z}{3} > -2$. Graph and check the solution. $z > -6$

-8 -7 -6 -5 -4 -3 -2 -1 0 1 2

2 Solve $3 \le -\frac{3}{5}x$. Graph and check the solution.
$-5 \ge x$, or $x \le -5$

-8 -7 -6 -5 -4 -3 -2 -1 0 1 2

OBJECTIVE
2 **Teaching Notes**

3 EXAMPLE   Visual Learners

Have students solve the inequality with tiles. Give students 5 negative x-tiles and 25 positive unit tiles. Have them write "≥" on an index card and place it between the two sets of tiles. Students will have to exchange each set of tiles for the opposite color (opposite sign) as they solve. Students will need to rotate the card to reverse the inequality sign. This will help students see that the change in color (opposite sign) of the tiles on each side of the inequality also changes the direction of the inequality sign.

4 EXAMPLE   Teaching Tip

Instruct students to graph $c \le 15.71$. Tell them to place the dot on the left side close to, but not on, 16. Ask students if every number graphed can represent a case of food. Have them explain their answers. Only whole numbers can express the number of cases, because you can only buy a whole case, not part of one. Also, negative numbers cannot represent a number of cases.

 Additional Examples

3 Solve $-4c < 24$. Graph the solution. $c > -6$

-8 -7 -6 -5 -4 -3 -2 -1 0 1 2

4 Your family budgets $160 to spend on fuel for a trip. How many times can they fill the car's gas tank if it costs $25 each time?
6 times

OBJECTIVE
2   **Using Division to Solve Inequalities**

Solving inequalities using division is similar to solving inequalities using multiplication. Remember that division by zero is undefined.

Key Concepts

Property	Division Property of Inequality

For every real number a and b, and for $c > 0$,

if $a > b$, then $\frac{a}{c} > \frac{b}{c}$;   if $a < b$, then $\frac{a}{c} < \frac{b}{c}$.

Examples $6 > 4$, so $\frac{6}{2} > \frac{4}{2}$. $2 < 8$, so $\frac{2}{2} < \frac{8}{2}$.

For every real number a and b, and for $c < 0$,

if $a > b$, then $\frac{a}{c} < \frac{b}{c}$;   if $a < b$, then $\frac{a}{c} > \frac{b}{c}$.

Examples $6 > 4$, so $\frac{6}{-2} < \frac{4}{-2}$. $2 < 8$, so $\frac{2}{-2} > \frac{8}{-2}$.

This property also applies to $\ge$ and $\le$.

3 EXAMPLE   Dividing to Solve an Inequality

Solve $-5z \ge 25$. Graph the solution.

$\frac{-5}{-5}z \le \frac{25}{-5}$ **Divide each side by -5. Reverse the inequality symbol.**

$z \le -5$ **Simplify.**

-9 -8 -7 -6 -5 -4 -3 -2 -1 0 1

✓ **Check Understanding** **3** Solve the inequality. Graph and check your solution.
a. $-2t < -8$ $t > 4$;   **b.** $-3w \ge 12$ $w \le -4$;   **c.** $0.6 > -0.2n$ $n > -3$;

-2 0 2 4 6 8   -7 -6 -5 -4 -3 -2   -4 -3 -2 -1 0 1

There are times when you must think about which types of numbers are acceptable as solutions of inequalities that represent real-world situations.

4 EXAMPLE   Real-World Problem Solving

Community Service The student council votes to buy food for a local food bank. A case of 12 jars of spaghetti sauce costs $13.75. What is the greatest number of cases of sauce the student council can buy if they use at most $216 for this project?

Relate cost per case times the number of cases is at most total cost

Define Let c = the number of cases of spaghetti sauce.

Write   13.75   · c ≤   216

$13.75c \le 216$

$\frac{13.75c}{13.75} \le \frac{216}{13.75}$ **Divide each side by 13.75.**

$c \le 15.71$ **Simplify and round to the nearest hundredth.**

The student council does not have enough money to buy 16 cases, so they can buy at most 15 cases of sauce for the food bank.

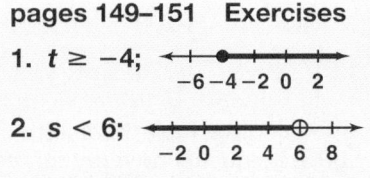

Real-World Connection

Careers The duties of a manager of a non-profit organization, such as a food bank, include organizing and supervising volunteers.

Closure

Have students state the main difference between solving inequalities using multiplication and division and solving equations using multiplication

and division. Both cases require the same operations. However, in solving inequalities in which you have to multiply or divide each side by a negative number, you must reverse the direction of the inequality.

pages 149–151 **Exercises**

1. $t \ge -4$;

-6 -4 -2 0 2

2. $s < 6$;

-2 0 2 4 6 8

✓ **Check Understanding** ④ Students in the school band are selling calendars. They earn $.40 on each calendar they sell. Their goal is to earn more than $327. Write and solve an inequality to find the fewest number of calendars they can sell and still reach their goal.
$0.4c > 327$; 818 calendars

EXERCISES

For more practice, see *Extra Practice*.

Practice and Problem Solving

A Practice by Example

Solve each inequality. Graph and check your solution. 1–28. See margin.

Examples 1, 2
(page 147)

1. $\frac{t}{4} \geq -1$ 2. $\frac{s}{6} < 1$ 3. $1 \leq -\frac{w}{2}$ 4. $2 < -\frac{p}{4}$

5. $-2 < \frac{y}{2}$ 6. $-\frac{v}{3} \geq 0.5$ 7. $4 > \frac{2}{3}x$ 8. $-5 \leq \frac{5}{2}k$

9. $0 < -\frac{7}{8}x$ 10. $\frac{4}{3}y \geq 0$ 11. $-\frac{5}{7}x > -5$ 12. $6 \geq -\frac{3}{2}d$

13. $-\frac{4}{9} < \frac{2}{3}c$ 14. $\frac{3}{4}b \geq -\frac{9}{8}$ 15. $-\frac{5}{3}u > \frac{5}{6}$ 16. $-\frac{5}{8} > -\frac{5}{6}n$

Example 3
(page 148)

17. $3t < -9$ 18. $4m \geq 8$ 19. $10 \leq -2w$ 20. $-20 > -5c$

21. $-27 \geq 3z$ 22. $-7b > 42$ 23. $18d < -12$ 24. $-3x \leq 16$

25. $-7 < 2q$ 26. $16 > 3.2h$ 27. $-1.5d < -6$ 28. $3.6 \leq -0.8m$

Example 4
(page 148)

29. **Fund-Raising** The science club charges $4.50 per car at their car wash. Write and solve an inequality to find how many cars they have to wash to earn at least $300. **$4.5c \geq 300$, 67 cars**

30. **Earnings** Suppose you earn $6.15 per hour working part time at a dry cleaner. Write and solve an inequality to find how many full hours you must work to earn at least $100. **$6.15h \geq 100$, 17 hours**

B Apply Your Skills

Write four solutions to each inequality. 31–38. Answers may vary. Samples given.

31. $\frac{x}{2} \leq -1$ 32. $\frac{r}{3} \geq -4$ 33. $-1 \geq \frac{t}{3}$ 34. $0.5 > \frac{1}{2}c$
   $-2, -3, -4, -5$ $-12, -10, -8, 0$ $-3, -4, -5, -6$ $\frac{1}{2}, 0, -1, -2$

35. $-\frac{3}{4}q > 4$ 36. $1 < -\frac{5}{7}s$ 37. $-4.5 \leq -0.9x$ 38. $-2.7w \geq 28$
   $-6, -7, -8, -9$ $-2, -3, -4, -5$ $5, 4, 3, 2$ $-10.4, -11, -12, -13$

39. Multiply each side by −4 and reverse the inequality symbol.

40. Multiply each side by 5.

41. Divide each side by 5.

42. Multiply each side by $\frac{4}{3}$.

43. Divide each side by 4.

44. Multiply each side by −1 and reverse the inequality symbol.

Tell what you must do to the first inequality in order to get the second. 39–44. See left.

39. $-\frac{c}{4} > 3$; $c < -12$ 40. $\frac{n}{5} \leq -2$; $n \leq -10$

41. $5z > -25$; $z > -5$ 42. $\frac{3}{4}b \leq 3$; $b \leq 4$

43. $-12 < 4a$; $-3 < a$ 44. $-b \geq 3.4$; $b \leq -3.4$

Replace each ▥ with the number that makes the inequalities equivalent.

45. ▥$s > 14$; $s < -7$ **−2**   46. ▥$x \geq 25$; $x \leq -5$ **−5**

47. $-8u \leq$ ▥; $u \geq -0.5$ **4**   48. $-2a >$ ▥; $a < -9$ **18**

49. $36 <$ ▥r; $r < -3.6$ **−10**   50. $-k \leq$ ▥; $k \geq -7.5$ **7.5**

Problem Solving Hint

For Exercise 51, drawing a graph may help you to understand the problem.

51. **Critical Thinking** If $x \geq y$ and $-x \geq -y$, what can you conclude about x and y?
x and y are equal.

Estimation Estimate the solution of each inequality. 52–55. Estimates may vary.

52. $-2.099r < 4$ 53. $3.87j > -24$ 54. $20.95 \geq \frac{1}{2}p$ 55. $-\frac{20}{39}s \leq -14$
   $r > -2$ $j > -6$ $p \leq 42$ $s \geq 28$

Lesson 3-3 Solving Inequalities Using Multiplication and Division   **149**

3. $w \leq -2$;
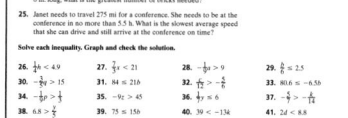
   −3−2−1 0 1

4. $p < -8$;
   −10−9−8−7−6−5

5. $y > -4$;
   −6 −5 −4 −3 −2 −1

6. $v \leq -1.5$;
   −3−2−1 0 1

7. $x < 6$;
   −2 0 2 4 6 8

8. $k \geq -2$;
   −3−2−1 0 1

9. $x < 0$;
   −3−2−1 0 1 2

10. $y \geq 0$;
   −2−1 0 1 2

11. $x < 7$;
   −2 0 2 4 6 8

12. $d \geq -4$;
   −6−4−2 0 2

13. $c > -\frac{2}{3}$;
   −1 0 1 2 3

14. $b \geq -1\frac{1}{2}$;
   −2−1 0 1 2

15. $u < -\frac{1}{2}$;
   −3−2−1 0 1

16–28. See margin pp. 150-151.

149

3. Practice

Assignment Guide

▼① Objective

Ⓐ Ⓑ Core 1–16, 31–36, 39–42, 54–55, 67–75

Ⓒ Extension 78–80

▼② Objective

Ⓐ Ⓑ Core 17–30, 37–38, 43–53, 56–66, 76–77

Ⓒ Extension 81–83

Standardized Test Prep 84–89

Mixed Review 90–106

Exercises 31–38 Encourage students to use some numbers that are not integers.

Exercise 77 Suggest to students that they begin by comparing the correct solution with Kia's solution.

Enrichment 3-3

Reteaching 3-3

Practice 3-3

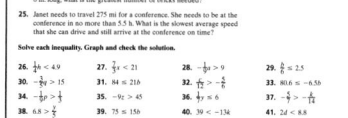

Alternative Assessment

Organize students into pairs. Have each pair complete Exercise 76. Then ask each pair to solve the inequalities written by another pair.

Standardized Test Prep

A sheet of blank grids is available in the Test-Taking Strategies with Transparencies booklet. Give this sheet to students for practice with filling in the grids.

Resources

For additional practice with a variety of test item formats:
- Standardized Test Prep, p. 179
- Test-Taking Strategies, p. 174
- Test-Taking Strategies with Transparencies

Exercise 89 Remind students to check for comparable units of measure. Be sure that the mile and the length of a can are converted to the same unit of measure.

pages 149–151   Exercises

16. $n > \frac{3}{4}$;

-1 0 1 2

17. $t < -3$;

-5-4-3-2-1 0 1

150

Real-World **Connection**

Depending on its size, an elevator at a construction site can have a maximum load from 900 lb to 20,000 lb.

77a. She should have divided each side by −15.

Reading Math

For help reading and solving Exercise 77, see page 152.

---

56. **Safe Load** An elevator like the one at the left can safely lift at most 4400 lb. A concrete block has an average weight of 42 lb. What is the maximum number of concrete blocks that the elevator can lift? **104 concrete blocks**

57. **Writing** Explain how solving the equation $-\frac{x}{3} = 4$ is similar to and different from solving the inequality $-\frac{x}{3} > 4$. **See margin p. 151.**

58. **Open-Ended** Write four different inequalities with $x > 3$ as their solution that you can solve using multiplication or division. **Answers may vary.**
   Sample: $2x > 6$, $\frac{4}{3}x > 4$, $-x < -3$, $-\frac{x}{5} < -\frac{3}{5}$

Solve each inequality.

59. $4d \leq -28$ $d \leq -7$
60. $\frac{u}{7} > 5$ $u > 35$
61. $2 < -8s$ $s < -\frac{1}{4}$
62. $\frac{3}{2}k \geq -45$ $k \geq -30$
63. $0.3y < 2.7$ $y < 9$
64. $9.4 \leq \frac{-4t}{}$ $t \leq -2.35$
65. $-h \geq 4$ $h \leq -4$
66. $\frac{5}{2}x > 5$ $x > 2$
67. $24 < -\frac{8}{3}x$ $x < -9$
68. $0 < -\frac{1}{6}b$ $b < 0$
69. $\frac{5}{6} > -\frac{1}{3}p$ $p > -2\frac{1}{2}$
70. $-0.2m \geq 9.4$ $m \leq -47$
71. $6 < -9g$ $g < -\frac{2}{3}$
72. $4n \geq 9$ $n \geq 2\frac{1}{4}$
73. $-3.5 < \frac{-m}{}$ $m < 3.5$
74. $\frac{2}{5}z \geq -1$ $z \geq -2\frac{1}{2}$

75. Michael solved the inequality $-2 > \frac{y}{-3}$ and got $6 < y$. Erica solved the same inequality and got $y > 6$. Are they both correct? Explain.
   Yes; in each case, y is greater than 6.

76. A friend calls you and asks you to meet at a location 3 miles from your home in 20 minutes. You set off on your bicycle after the telephone call. Write and solve an inequality to find the average rates in miles per minute you could ride to be at your meeting place within 20 minutes. $\frac{3}{20} < r$; $r > 0.15$

77. **a.** **Error Analysis** Kia solved $-15q \leq 135$ by adding 15 to each side of the inequality. What mistake did she make? **See left above.**
   b. Kia's solution was $q \leq 150$. She checked her work by substituting 150 for q in the original inequality. Why didn't her check let her know that she had made a mistake? **150 satisfies the original inequality $-15q \leq 135$.**
   c. **Open-Ended** Find a number that satisfies Kia's solution but does not satisfy the original inequality. **Answers may vary. Sample: −15**

 Challenge

Reasoning If a, b, and c are real numbers, for which values of a is each statement true?

78. If $c < 0$, then $ac < a$. $a > 0$
79. If $b > c$, then $ab > ac$. $a > 0$
80. If $b > c$, then $a^2b > a^2c$. $a \neq 0$
81. If $b > c$, then $\frac{b}{a} < \frac{c}{a}$. $a < 0$

82. **Packaging** Suppose you have a plastic globe that you wish to put into a gift box. The circumference of the globe is 15 in. The edges of cube-shaped boxes are either 3 in., 4 in., 5 in., or 6 in. Write and solve an inequality to find the boxes that will hold the globe. (*Hint:* circumference = $\pi \cdot$ diameter)
   $\pi d > 15$, 5-in. box or 6-in. box

83. **Tiling a Floor** The Sumaris' den floor measures 18 ft by 15 ft. They want to cover the floor with square tiles that are $\frac{9}{16}$ ft^2. Write and solve an inequality to find the least number of tiles they need to cover the floor. $\frac{9}{16}x \geq 18(15)$, 480 tiles

Standardized Test Prep

Gridded Response

84. Solve $\frac{2}{5}x = 16$. **40**

85. Mr. Houston expects to pay $16,800 in income taxes. This is no more than $\frac{1}{3}$ of his salary. What is his least possible earned income? **50,400**

18. $m \geq 2$;

-1 0 1 2 3 4

19. $w \leq -5$;

-8-6-4-2 0 2

20. $c > 4$;

-2 0 2 4 6 8

21. $z \leq -9$;

-12-10-8-6-4-2 0 2

22. $b < -6$;

-10-8-6-4-2 0 2

23. $d < -\frac{2}{3}$;

-3-2-1 0 1

24. $x \geq -5\frac{1}{3}$;

-6-5-4-3-2-1 0 1

86. Five boxes of tiles will cover 30 ft². What is the least number of boxes of tiles needed to tile 320 ft²? **54**

87. What is the greatest number of 34¢ stamps you can buy for $5.00? **14**

88. The length of a rectangle is 90 in. Its area is less than 380 in². What is the greatest possible width of the rectangle, to the nearest inch? **4**

89. The Environmental Club of City Middle School set a goal of collecting "one mile of cans." If the height of a typical 12 oz aluminum can is $4\frac{3}{4}$ in., what is the fewest number of cans needed to reach their goal? **13339**

Take It to the NET
Online lesson quiz at
www.PHSchool.com
.... Web Code: aea-0303

Mixed Review

Lesson 3-2 Solve each inequality.

90. $x + 3 \le -4$ **$x \le -7$**

91. $\frac{5}{8} > \frac{3}{4} + w$ **$w < -\frac{1}{8}$**

92. $t - 3.4 \ge 5.8$ **$t \ge 9.2$**

93. $0 < d - 4$ **$d > 4$**

94. $3.2 \ge m + 7.1$ **$-3.9 \ge m$**

95. $y - 2 < 6$ **$y < 8$**

96. $-3 > a - 4$ **$1 > a$**

97. $k + 12 \le 15$ **$k \le 3$**

Lesson 2-3 Solve each equation.

98. $3t + 5 - t = 9$ **$t = 2$**

99. $-3(2n + 1) = 9$ **$n = -2$**

100. $\frac{3x}{4} - \frac{1}{2} = \frac{1}{4}$ **$x = 1$**

Lesson 1-8 Name the property that each exercise illustrates. 101–106. See left.

101. Prop. of Opposites
102. Prop. of Reciprocals
103. Ident. Prop. of Add.
104. Ident. Prop. of Mult.
105. Assoc. Prop. of Mult.
106. Comm. Prop. of Mult.

101. $(-7) + 7 = 0$

102. $-3\left(-\frac{1}{3}\right) = 1$

103. $0 + 2 = 2$

104. $1x = x$

105. $4(2 \cdot 5) = (4 \cdot 2)5$

106. $4(2 \cdot 5) = 4(5 \cdot 2)$

Checkpoint Quiz 1   Lessons 3-1 through 3-3

 Instant self-check quiz online and on CD-ROM

Solve each inequality. Graph your solution. 1–6. See left for graphs.

1. $6 < c + 1$ **$c > 5$**

2. $5x < -30$ **$x < -6$**

3. $\frac{p}{3} \le -2$ **$p \le -6$**

4. $y - 4 \ge -2$ **$y \ge 2$**

5. $12 + g < 4$ **$g < -8$**

6. $-3b \ge 15$ **$b \le -5$**

7. Determine whether each of the following is a solution of $x + 7 \le 3$.
   a. -4 **yes**
   b. 0 **no**
   c. $-\frac{17}{4}$ **yes**
   d. -3.9 **no**

8. Determine whether each of the following is a solution of $-4x < -12$.
   a. 3 **no**
   b. 0 **no**
   c. $\frac{7}{3}$ **no**
   d. π **yes**

Write and solve an inequality that models each situation.

9. You plan to buy a bicycle that will cost at least $180. You have saved $38 and your parents have given you $50.
   a. Write an inequality to find how much more money m you need to save.
   b. Solve your inequality. **a. $m + 38 + 50 \ge 180$ b. $m \ge 92$**

10. Your local garden shop has plants on sale for $1.50 each. You are planning a vegetable garden. You have $20 to spend on tomato plants.
    a. Write an inequality to find the greatest number of plants p you can buy.
    b. How many plants can you buy? **a. $1.50p \le 20$ b. 13 plants**

1.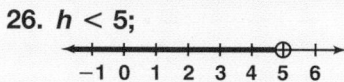
   $-5\ 0\ 5\ 10\ 15$

2. ↤—┼—┼—⊕—┼—┼—┼—┼→
   $-10\,-8\,-6\,-4\,-2\ 0\ \ 2$

3. ↤—┼—┼—●—┼—┼—┼—┼→
   $-10\,-8\,-6\,-4\,-2\ 0\ \ 2$

4. ↤—┼—┼—┼—┼—●—┼→
   $-1\ 0\ 1\ 2\ 3\ 4$

5. ↤—┼—┼—⊕—┼—┼—┼—┼—┼→
   $-12\,-10\,-8\,-6\,-4\,-2\ 0\ \ 2$

6. ↤●—┼—┼—┼—┼—┼→
   $-8\,-6\,-4\,-2\ 0\ \ 2$

Lesson 3-3 Solving Inequalities Using Multiplication and Division **151**

25. $q > -3\frac{1}{2}$;
    ↤—┼—┼○┼—┼—┼—┼—┼→
    $-5\,-4\,-3\,-2\,-1\ 0\ \ 1$

26. $h < 5$;
    ↤—┼—┼—┼—┼—┼—┼—┼—⊕┼→
    $-1\ 0\ 1\ 2\ 3\ 4\ 5\ 6$

27. $d > 4$; ↤—┼—┼—┼—⊕—┼—┼→
    $-2\ 0\ 2\ 4\ 6\ 8$

28. $m \le -4.5$;
    ↤—┼—●┼—┼—┼—┼—┼—┼→
    $-6\,-5\,-4\,-3\,-2\,-1\ 0\ \ 1$

57. For both the equation and the inequality, you multiply each side by -3. For the inequality, you must reverse the inequality symbol.

To check understanding of Lessons 3-1 to 3-3:

Checkpoint Quiz 1 (p. 151)

📁 **Teaching Resources**
Checkpoint Quiz 1 (also in Prentice Hall Assessment System)

👥 **Reaching All Students**
Reading and Math Literacy 3B

Spanish versions available

 **Reading Math** **Reading to Analyze Errors**

FOR USE WITH PAGE 150, EXERCISE 77

Reading to Analyze Errors

Students will read and analyze incorrect solutions to inequalities. They will demonstrate that although solved incorrectly, an answer may contain some correct solutions—but not all correct solutions. They will try to discover the error made by the person who solved it and show a number that is part of the incorrect solution set, but does not satisfy the original inequality.

Teaching Notes

Point out that there are two possible kinds of errors students may encounter as they analyze solutions of inequalities. One possible error is that the incorrect solution set contains some correct and some incorrect answers as in the example shown. The other possible error is that the incorrect solution set contains only correct answers but not all of them.

Alternative Method

Some students may find it useful to solve the inequality for themselves before analyzing someone else's solution. That way they have already gone through the thought processes to solve it, thus enabling them to better understand what the other person did differently and perhaps incorrectly.

Exercise

Have students work independently to analyze an incorrect solution. Then have students work in pairs to explain and discuss their error analyses with each other. If there is a disagreement between partners, have them each explain their thinking to the class. Then their classmates can help them by asking them questions and offering their own analyses.

Read the exercise below and the description of how Gina found Kia's mistake. Check your understanding with the exercise at the bottom of the page.

77. a. Error Analysis Kia solved $-15q \leq 135$ by adding 15 to each side of the inequality. What mistake did she make?

b. Kia's solution was $q \leq 150$. She checked her work by substituting 150 for q in the original inequality. Why didn't her check let her know that she had made a mistake?

c. Open-Ended Find a number that satisfies Kia's solution but does not satisfy the original inequality.

What Gina Thinks

The problem says Kia added 15 to each side of the inequality. Since q is being multiplied by -15, she should have divided both sides by -15.

I'll substitute 150 in the original inequality. Kia's check didn't let her know she was wrong because 150 makes the inequality true. Any positive number times -15 is negative, so for a positive number q, $-15q$ is less than 135.

Now, I need to find a number that satisfies Kia's solution but not the original inequality. First I'll solve the original inequality. The solution is $q \geq -9$. So I need a number that is less than 150, and is not greater than or equal to -9. I'll use a number less than -9. Let $q = -10$.

Yes, -10 works!

I'll write my answer as a sentence.

What Gina Writes

a. Kia's mistake was adding 15 to both sides. She should have divided both sides by -15.

b. Let $q = 150$.
$$-15q \leq 135$$
$$-15(150) \leq 135$$
$$-2250 \leq 135 \text{ True}$$

Kia's check didn't let her know she had made a mistake because her solution made the inequality true.

c. $-15q \leq 135$
$$q \geq \frac{135}{-15}$$
$$q \geq -9$$

Let $q = -10$
Kia's: $\qquad q \leq 150 \Rightarrow -10 \leq 150$ True
Original: $-15q \leq 135 \Rightarrow 150 \leq 135$ False

-10 satisfies Kia's solution but not the original inequality.

EXERCISE

a. To solve the inequality $-\frac{1}{2}k \geq -5$, Danny multiplied both sides by the reciprocal of $-\frac{1}{2}$. His solution was $k \geq 10$. What mistake did he make?   He forgot to change the direction of the inequality sign.

b. Danny checked his solution, but his check did not let him know that he had made an error. What number could he have substituted? **10**

c. Find a number that satisfies the original inequality but not Danny's solution. **Answers may vary. Sample: -2**

Solving Multi-Step Inequalities

North Carolina Objectives — 4.01 Use linear functions or inequalities to model and solve problems; justify results. a) Solve using tables, graphs, and algebraic properties.

Lesson Preview

What You'll Learn

 OBJECTIVE 1
To solve multi-step inequalities with variables on one side

 OBJECTIVE 2
To solve multi-step inequalities with variables on both sides

. . . And Why

To find the measurements of a banner, as in Example 2

 Check Skills You'll Need   (For help, go to Lessons 2-2 and 2-3.)

Solve each equation, if possible. If the equation is an identity or if it has no solution, write *identity* or *no solution*.

1. $3(c + 4) = 6$ **−2**

2. $3t + 6 = 3(t - 2)$ **no solution**

3. $5p + 9 = 2p - 1$ **−3$\frac{1}{3}$**

4. $7n + 4 - 5n = 2(n + 2)$ **identity**

5. $\frac{1}{2}k - \frac{2}{3} + k = \frac{7}{6}$ **1$\frac{2}{9}$**

6. $2t - 32 = 5t + 1$ **−11**

Find the missing dimension of each rectangle.

7. perimeter = 110 cm

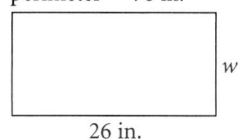
40 cm
15 cm
ℓ

8. perimeter = 78 in.
13 in.
w
26 in.

3-4

1. Plan

Lesson Preview

Check Skills You'll Need

Solving Two-Step Equations
Lesson 2-2: Example 1
Exercises 1–16
Extra Practice, p. 703

Solving Multi-Step Equations
Lesson 2-3: Examples 3, 4
Exercises 12–29
Extra Practice, p. 703

Lesson Resources

Teaching Resources
Practice, Reteaching, Enrichment

Reaching All Students
Practice Workbook 3-4
Spanish Practice Workbook 3-4
Basic Algebra Planning Guide 3-4

Presentation Assistant Plus!
Transparencies
• Check Skills You'll Need 3-4
• Additional Examples 3-4
• Student Edition Answers 3-4
• Lesson Quiz 3-4
PH Presentation Pro CD 3-4

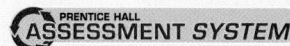
ASSESSMENT SYSTEM

Computer Test Generator CD

Technology
Resource Pro® CD-ROM
Computer Test Generator CD
Prentice Hall Presentation Pro CD

www.PHSchool.com
Student Site
• Teacher Web Code: aek-5500
• Self-grading Lesson Quiz
Teacher Center
• Lesson Planner
• Resources

Plus

OBJECTIVE

1 **Solving Inequalities With Variables on One Side**

Sometimes you need more than one step to solve an equation. The same is true when you solve inequalities. Just as with equations, you undo addition and subtraction first. Then undo multiplication and division.

1 EXAMPLE   **Using More Than One Step**

Solve $7 + 6a > 19$. Check the solution.

$7 + 6a - 7 > 19 - 7$ **Subtract 7 from each side.**

$6a > 12$ **Simplify.**

$\frac{6a}{6} > \frac{12}{6}$ **Divide each side by 6.**

$a > 2$ **Simplify.**

Check $7 + 6a = 19$ **Check the computation.**

$7 + 6(2) \overset{?}{=} 19$ **Substitute 2 for a.**

$19 = 19$ ✓

$7 + 6a > 19$ **Check the direction of the inequality.**

$7 + 6(3) > 19$ **Substitute 3 for a.**

$25 > 19$ ✓

✓ **Check Understanding** **1** Solve each inequality. Check your solution.

a. $-3x - 4 \le 14$ **$x \ge -6$**

b. $5 < 7 - 2t$ **$t < 1$**

c. $-8 < 5n - 23$ **$n > 3$**

d. $5k + 12 \le 2$ **$k \le -2$**

Lesson 3-4   Solving Multi-Step Inequalities   **153**

Ongoing Assessment and Intervention

Before the Lesson
Diagnose prerequisite skills using:
• Check Skills You'll Need

During the Lesson
Monitor progress using:
• Check Understanding
• Additional Examples
• Standardized Test Prep

After the Lesson
Assess knowledge using:
• Lesson Quiz
• Computer Test Generator CD

2. Teach

Math Background

Many real world examples are modeled by these more complex inequalities. Students should have several different ways of solving many exercises.

① Teaching Notes

① EXAMPLE Math Tip

Point out to students that they are performing the order of operations in reverse to isolate the variable on one side of the equation.

② EXAMPLE Teaching Tip

Ask students to list some reasonable widths for the banner and some unreasonable widths, such as 6 inches, that meet the criteria of the solution.

③ EXAMPLE Visual Learners

Some students may forget to distribute the factor 2 (outside the parentheses) to the 2 inside the parentheses, and some students may distribute it to the $3t$. Have students draw arrows from the factor 2 to both terms inside the parentheses.

Additional Examples

① Solve $5 + 4b < 21$. Check the solution. $b < 4$

② The band is making a rectangular banner that is 20 feet long with trim around the edges. What are the possible widths the banner can be if there is no more than 48 feet of trim? **4 feet or less**

③ Solve $3x + 4(6 - x) < 2$. $x > 22$

You can adapt familiar formulas like the formula for the perimeter of a rectangle to write inequalities. You determine which inequality symbol to use from the real-world situation.

② EXAMPLE Real-World 🌎 Problem Solving

Geometry The school band needs a banner to carry in a parade. The banner committee decides that the length of the banner should be 18 feet. A committee member drew the diagram at the left to help understand the problem. What are the possible widths of the banner if they can use no more than 48 feet of trim?

Relate Since the border goes around the edges of a rectangular banner, you can adapt the perimeter formula $P = 2\ell + 2w$.

twice the length	plus	twice the width	can be no more than	the length of trim

Write $\quad\quad 2(18) \quad\quad + \quad\quad 2w \quad\quad\quad \le \quad\quad\quad 48$

$2(18) + 2w \le 48$

$36 + 2w \le 48$ Simplify 2(18).

$36 + 2w - 36 \le 48 - 36$ Subtract 36 from each side.

$2w \le 12$ Simplify.

$\dfrac{2w}{2} \le \dfrac{12}{2}$ Divide each side by 2.

$w \le 6$ Simplify.

The banner's width must be 6 feet or less.

Check Is the solution reasonable? The trim is 48 feet long, so the greatest possible perimeter is 48 ft. For a length of 18 feet and a width of 6 feet, the perimeter is $2(18 + 6) = 2(24) = 48$, or 48 feet. So the width can be at most 6 feet. The answer is correct.

✓ **Check Understanding** ② To make a second banner, the committee decided to make the length 12 feet. They have 40 feet of a second type of trim. Write and solve an inequality to find the possible widths of the second banner.
$2(12) + 2w \le 40$, so the banner's width must be 8 feet or less.

Sometimes solving an inequality involves using the Distributive Property.

③ EXAMPLE Using the Distributive Property

Solve $2(t + 2) - 3t \ge -1$.

$2t + 4 - 3t \ge -1$ Use the Distributive Property.

$-t + 4 \ge -1$ Combine like terms.

$-t + 4 - 4 \ge -1 - 4$ Subtract 4 from each side.

$-t \ge -5$ Simplify.

$\dfrac{-t}{-1} \le \dfrac{-5}{-1}$ Divide each side by −1. Reverse the inequality symbol.

$t \le 5$ Simplify.

✓ **Check Understanding** ③ Solve each inequality. Check your solution.
   a. $4p + 2(p + 7) < 8$ **b.** $15 \le 5 - 2(4m + 7)$ **c.** $8 > 3(5 - b) + 2$
      $p < -1$ $m \le -3$ $b > 3$

👥 Reaching All Students

Below Level As the inequalities become more complex, reassure students that, just like multi-step equations, multi-step inequalities can be solved by performing one step at a time.	**Advanced Learners** Have students write a multi-step inequality with variables on both sides and that requires the Distributive Property. Let them exchange inequalities and solve.	**Visual Learners** See note on page 154. **Error Prevention** See note on page 156.

Solving Inequalities With Variables on Both Sides

Many inequalities have variables on both sides of the inequality symbol. You need to gather the variable terms on one side of the inequality and the constant terms on the other side.

4 EXAMPLE Gathering Variables on One Side of an Inequality

Solve $6z - 15 < 4z + 11$.

$6z - 15 - 4z < 4z + 11 - 4z$	To gather variables on the left, subtract **4z** from each side.
$2z - 15 < 11$	Combine like terms.
$2z - 15 + 15 < 11 + 15$	To gather the constants on the right, add **15** to each side.
$2z < 26$	Simplify.
$\dfrac{2z}{2} < \dfrac{26}{2}$	Divide each side by **2**.
$z < 13$	Simplify.

✓ Check Understanding ④ Solve $3b + 12 > 27 - 2b$. Check your solution. **b > 3**

5 EXAMPLE Multi-Step Inequalities

Solve $-3(4 - m) \geq 4(2m + 1)$.

$-12 + 3m \geq 8m + 4$	Use the Distributive Property.
$-12 + 3m - 8m \geq 8m + 4 - 8m$	Subtract **8m** from each side.
$-12 - 5m \geq 4$	Combine like terms.
$-12 - 5m + 12 \geq 4 + 12$	Add **12** to each side.
$-5m \geq 16$	Simplify.
$\dfrac{-5m}{-5} \leq \dfrac{16}{-5}$	Divide each side by **−5**. Reverse the inequality symbol.
$m \leq -3\frac{1}{5}$	Simplify.

✓ Check Understanding ⑤ Solve $-6(x - 4) \geq 7(2x - 3)$. Check your solution. $x \leq 2\frac{1}{4}$

④ EXAMPLE Alternative Method

Work the example a second way on the board by subtracting 6z from both sides. Lead students to see that division by a negative number is unnecessary if you choose the operation that results in a positive coefficient. Then, you do not have to remember to reverse the inequality sign.

Additional Examples

④ Solve $8z - 6 < 3z + 12$.
$z < 3\frac{3}{5}$

⑤ Solve $5(-3 + d) \leq 3(3d - 2)$.
$d \geq -2\frac{1}{4}$

Closure

Instruct students to write a multi-step inequality with variables on both sides that requires the use of the distributive property. Have students exchange inequalities and solve.

EXERCISES

For more practice, see *Extra Practice*.

Practice and Problem Solving

A Practice by Example

Solve each inequality. Check your solution.

Example 1
(page 153)

1. $4d + 7 \leq 23$ **d ≤ 4**   2. $5m - 3 > -18$ **m > −3**   3. $-4x - 2 < 8$ **x > −2½**

4. $5 - 3n \geq -4$ **n ≤ 3**   5. $8 \leq -12 + 5q$ **q ≥ 4**   6. $5 \leq 11 + 3h$ **h ≥ −2**

7. $-7 \leq 5 - 4a$ **a ≤ 3**   8. $10 > 29 - 3b$ **b > 6⅓**   9. $5 - 9c > -13$ **c < 2**

Example 2
(page 154)

Write and solve an inequality.

10. On a trip from Virginia to Florida, the Sampson family wants to travel at least 420 miles in 8 hours of driving. What must be their average rate of speed?
8t ≥ 420 and t ≥ 52.5, so the average rate of speed must be at least 52.5 mi/h.

3. Practice

Assignment Guide

 **Objective**

🅐 🅑 **Core** 1–12, 47–49,
52–59, 77–78

🅒 **Extension** 81–83

 **Objective**

🅐 🅑 13–46, 50–51,
60–76, 79–80

🅒 **Extension** 84–86

Standardized Test Prep 87–91

Mixed Review 92–104

Error Prevention

Exercises 1–9 Simple mistakes can be made while checking a solution, thus making you think your answer is incorrect when it is correct. Remind students that it is easiest to check an answer by substituting 0 for the variable in each solution.

Enrichment 3-4

Reteaching 3-4

Practice 3-4

Practice 3-4   Solving Multi-Step Inequalities

---

 11. Geometry The perimeter of an isosceles triangle is at most 27 cm. One side is 8 cm long. Find the possible lengths of the two congruent sides.
$27 \geq 2s + 8$ and $s \leq 9.5$, so the two equal sides must be no longer than 9.5 cm.

Example 3
(page 154)

12. You want to solve an inequality containing the expression $-3(2x - 3)$. The next line in your solution would rewrite this expression as ___?___. **$-6x + 9$**

Solve each inequality.

13. $2(j - 4) \geq -6$ **$j \geq 1$**   **14.** $-(6b - 2) > 0$ **$b < \frac{1}{3}$**   **15.** $-2(h + 2) < -14$ **$h > 5$**

16. $-3 \leq 3(5x - 16)$ **$x \geq 3$**   **17.** $25 > -(4y + 7)$ **$y > -8$** **18.** $4(w - 2) \leq 10w \leq 4\frac{1}{2}$

19. $-3(c + 4) - 2 > 7$ **$c < -7$**   **20.** $-2(r - 3) + 7 \geq 8$ **$r \leq 2\frac{1}{2}$**   **21.** $16 \leq 4 - 3(n - 13)$ **$n \leq 9$**

Example 4
(page 155)

22. $3w + 2 < 2w + 5$ **$w < 3$**   **23.** $3t + 7 \geq 5t + 9$ **$t \leq -1$** **24.** $4d + 7 \geq 1 + 5d$ **$d \leq 6$**

25. $5 - 2n \leq 3 - n$ **$n \geq 2$** **26.** $2k - 3 \leq 5k + 9$ **$k \geq -4$** **27.** $3s + 16 > 6 + 4s$ **$s < 10$**

28. $6p - 1 > 3p + 8$ **$p > 3$** **29.** $3x + 2 > -4x + 16$ **$x > 2$**   **30.** $2 - 3m < 4 + 5m$ **$m > -\frac{1}{4}$**

31. $4d + 5 < -4d - 3$ **$d < -1$**   **32.** $4 - 5y \geq 8 - y$ **$y \leq -1$** **33.** $2k + 6 \leq 4 + 5k$ **$k \geq \frac{2}{3}$**

Example 5
(page 155)

34. $-3(v - 3) \geq 5 - 4v$ **$v \geq -4$** **35.** $3q + 6 \leq -5(q + 2)$ **$q \leq -2$** **36.** $3(2 + r) \geq 15 - 2r$ **$r \geq 1\frac{4}{5}$**

37. $9 + x < 7 - 2(x - 3)$ **$x < 1\frac{1}{3}$**   **38.** $2(m - 8) < -8 + 3m$ **$m > -8$**   **39.** $2v - 4 \leq 2(3v - 6)$ **$v \geq 2$**

🅑 **Apply Your Skills**

Tell what you must do to the first inequality in order to get the second.

40. $8 - 4s > 16; -4s > 8$ **Subtract 8 from each side.**

41. $\frac{2}{3}g + 7 \geq 9; \frac{2}{3}g \geq 2$ **Subtract 7 from each side.**

42. Subtract y from each side and add 5 to each side.

42. $2y - 5 > 9 + y; y > 14$ **See left.**

43. $-8 > \frac{z}{-5} - 2; 30 < z$ **See left.**

43. Add 2 to each side, then multiply each side by −5, and reverse the inequality sign.

44. $4j + 5 \geq 23 + 3j; j \geq 18$ **See left.**

45. $2(q - 3) < 9 - 3q; q < 3$ **See left.**

44. Subtract 3j from each side and subtract 5 from each side.

46. a. Solve $5t + 4 \leq 8t - 5$ by gathering the variable terms on the left side and the constant terms on the right side of the inequality. **$-3t \leq -9, t \geq 3$**
b. Solve $5t + 4 \leq 8t - 5$ by gathering the constant terms on the left side and the variable terms on the right side of the inequality. **$9 \leq 3t, t \geq 3$**
c. Compare the results of parts (a) and (b). **The results are the same.**

45. Answers may vary. Sample: Multiply q − 3 by 2, add 3q to each side, add 6 to each side, and divide each side by 5.

Write and solve an inequality for each of the following statements.

Sample Four times the sum of x and 10 is less than 20.
$$4(x + 10) < 20$$
$$x + 10 < 5 \qquad \text{Divide each side by 4.}$$
$$x < -5 \qquad \text{Subtract 10 from each side.}$$

47. Six minus the sum of r and 3 is less than 15. **$6 - (r + 3) < 15, r > -12$**

48. One half the difference of t and six is less than or equal to four. **$\frac{1}{2}(t - 6) \leq 4, t \leq 14$**

49. Three times the quantity z plus 2 is greater than 12. **$3(z + 2) > 12, z > 2$**

50. Writing Suppose a friend is having difficulty solving $2.5(p - 4) > 3(p + 2)$. Explain how to solve the inequality, showing all necessary steps and identifying the properties you would use. **See margin.**

51. a. Mental Math Like equations, some inequalities are true for all values of the variable, and some inequalities are not true for any values of the variable. Determine whether each inequality is *always* true or *never* true. **See left.**
i. $4s + 6 \geq 6 + 4s$ **ii.** $3r + 5 > 3r - 2$ **iii.** $4(n + 1) < 4n - 3$
b. Critical Thinking How can you tell whether an inequality is always true or never true without solving? **See margin.**

51a. i. always true
ii. always true
iii. never true

?

Need Help?

Inequalities or equations that are always true are called *identities*. (See p. 98)

pages 155–159 Exercises

50. Answers may vary. Sample: To solve $2.5(p - 4) > 3(p + 2)$, first use the Distributive Property to simplify both sides. The result is $2.5p - 10 > 3p + 6$. Then use the Subtraction Property of Inequality. Subtract 6 from each side and 2.5p from each side. The result is $-16 > 0.5p$.

Then use the Division Property of Inequality. Divide each side by 0.5. The result is $-32 > p$. So the solution is $-32 > p$ or $p < -32$.

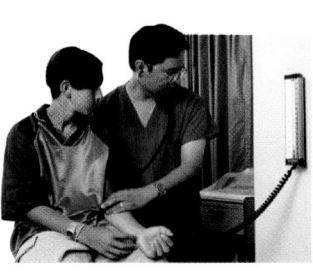

Real-World Connection

Normal blood pressure for teens is about 110/70.

52. For x = the number of guests, $(0.75)200 + 1.25x \geq 250$, $x \geq 80$, so at least 80 guests must attend.

🌐 **52. Expenses** The sophomore class is planning a picnic. The cost of a permit to use a city park is $250. To pay for the permit, there is a fee of $.75 for each sophomore and $1.25 for each guest who is not a sophomore. Two hundred sophomores plan to attend. Write and solve an inequality to find how many guests must attend for the sophomores to pay for the permit. **See left.**

🌐 **53. Health Care** Systolic blood pressure is the higher number in a blood pressure reading. It is measured as your heart muscle contracts. The formula $P \leq \frac{1}{2}a + 110$ gives the normal systolic blood pressure P based on age a.
  a. At age 20, does 120 represent a maximum or a minimum normal systolic pressure? **maximum**
  b. Find the normal systolic blood pressure for a 50-year-old person.
     no more than 135

Match each inequality with its graph below.

54. $-2x - 2 > 4$ **B**   **55.** $2 - 2x > 4$ **E**   **56.** $2x + 2 > 4$ **F**

57. $2x + 2 > 4x$ **A**   **58.** $2x - 2 > 4$ **D**   **59.** $-2(x - 2) > 4$ **C**

A. number line from -5 to 3, open circle at 1
B. number line from -5 to 3, open circle at -3
C. number line from -5 to 3, open circle at 0
D. number line from -3 to 5, open circle at 3
E. number line from -5 to 3, open circle at -1
F. number line from -3 to 5, open circle at 1

60. Open-Ended Write two different inequalities that you can solve by adding 5 and multiplying by -3. Solve each inequality. **Answers may vary.**
Samples: $-\frac{1}{3}x - 5 > 0$, $x < -15$; $-\frac{1}{3}x - 5 \leq 10$, $x \geq -45$

Solve each inequality.

61. $\frac{4}{3}r - 3 < r + \frac{2}{3} - \frac{1}{3}r$ $r < 5\frac{1}{2}$ **62.** $4 - 2m \leq 5 - m + 1$ $m \geq -2$

63. $-2(0.5 - 4s) \geq -3(4 - 3.5s)$ $s \leq 4.4$ **64.** $\frac{1}{2}n - \frac{1}{8} \geq \frac{3}{4} + \frac{5}{6}n$ $n \leq -2\frac{5}{8}$

65. $-(8 - s) < 0$ $s < 8$ **66.** $3.8 - k \leq 5.2 - 2k$ $k \leq 1.4$

67. $10 > 3(2n - 1) - 5(4n + 3)$ $n > -2$ **68.** $3(3r + 1) - (r + 4) \leq 13$ $r \leq 1\frac{3}{4}$

69. $2(3x + 7) > 4(7 - 2x)$ $x > 1$ **70.** $4(a - 2) - 6a \leq -9$ $a \geq \frac{1}{2}$

71. $4(3m - 1) \geq 2(m + 3)$ $m \geq 1$ **72.** $17 - (4k - 2) \geq 2(k + 3)$ $k \leq 2\frac{1}{6}$

73. $2n - 3(n + 3) \leq 14$ $n \geq -23$ **74.** $5x - \frac{1}{2}(3x + 8) \leq -4 + 3x$ $x \leq 0$

75. $5a - 2(a - 15) < 10$ $a < -6\frac{2}{3}$ **76.** $5c + 4(c - 1) \geq 2 + 5(2 + c)$ $c \geq 4$

77. For x = number of hours of work each month, $15x - (490 + 45 + 65) \geq 600$, so to make a profit he must work at least 80 h per month.

🌐 **77. Business** Mandela is starting a part-time word-processing business out of his home. He plans to charge $15 per hour. The table at the right shows his expected monthly business expenses. Write and solve an inequality to find the number of hours he must work in a month to make a profit of at least $600. **See left.**

Expense	Cost
Equipment rental	$490
Materials	$45
Business phone	$65

78. For x = amount of sales, $250 + 0.03x \geq 460$, so to reach her goal, she must have at least $7000 in sales.

🌐 **78. Commission** Joleen is a sales associate in a clothing store. Each week she earns $250 plus a commission equal to 3% of her sales. This week her goal is to earn no less than $460. Write and solve an inequality to find the dollar amount of the sales she must have to reach her goal. **See left.**

50b. If the coefficients of the only variable on each side of an inequality are the same, then the inequality will either be always true or never true.

Lesson 3-4 Solving Multi-Step Inequalities **157**

Connection to Geometry
Exercise 11 Some students may want to use the formula for the perimeter of a rectangle. Tell them there is no set formula for the perimeter of a triangle. Ask: *What is special about an isosceles triangle?* **Two sides are equal.** Instruct students to keep this in mind when they are writing their inequality.

Exercise 53 Normal systolic blood pressure for an adult is from 90 to 140.

Alternative Assessment

Have each student graph $x > -3$ on a number line. Instruct each student to work backwards from this inequality to write an inequality that can be solved using at least three steps.

79. Add $2x$ to each side rather than subtract $2x$, so $x \leq \frac{2}{5}$.

80. Distribute 4 to 2 as well as n, so $n > -7$.

C Challenge

Error Analysis Find and correct the mistake in each of the following. See left.

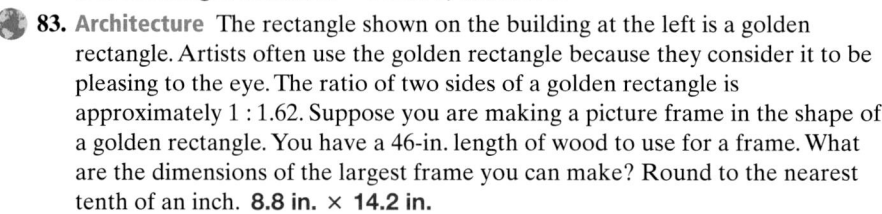

79.
$$3x + 3 \leq -2x + 5$$
$$3x \leq -2x + 2$$
$$x \leq 2$$

80.
$$4(n + 2) > 3n + 1$$
$$4n + 2 > 3n + 1$$
$$4n > 3n - 1$$
$$n > -1$$

81. **a.** Solve $ax + b > c$ for x, where a is positive. $x > \frac{c - b}{a}$
    b. Reasoning Solve $ax + b > c$ for x, where a is negative. $x < \frac{c - b}{a}$

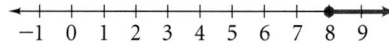

82. **Geometry** The base of a triangle is 10 in. Its height is $(x + 4)$ in. Its area is no more than 56 in.^{2}. What are the possible integer values of x?
    x **is an integer between -3 and 7, inclusive.**

83. **Architecture** The rectangle shown on the building at the left is a golden rectangle. Artists often use the golden rectangle because they consider it to be pleasing to the eye. The ratio of two sides of a golden rectangle is approximately 1 : 1.62. Suppose you are making a picture frame in the shape of a golden rectangle. You have a 46-in. length of wood to use for a frame. What are the dimensions of the largest frame you can make? Round to the nearest tenth of an inch. **8.8 in. × 14.2 in.**

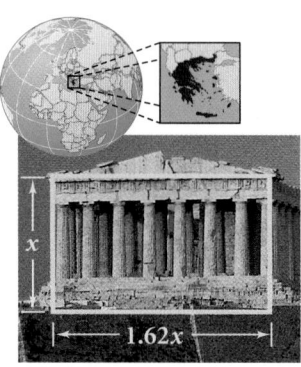

x

$\leftarrow\!\!-\!\!- 1.62x -\!\!-\!\!\rightarrow$

Real-World Connection

The Parthenon, an ancient Greek temple, has dimensions that form a golden rectangle.

84. **Critical Thinking** Find a value of a such that the number line below shows all the solutions of $ax + 4 \leq -12$. -2

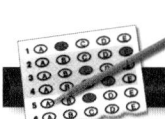

$-1\ \ 0\ \ 1\ \ 2\ \ 3\ \ 4\ \ 5\ \ 6\ \ 7\ \ 8\ \ 9$

85. **Earning** You can earn money by handing out flyers in the afternoon for $6.50 an hour and by typing a newsletter in the evening for $8 an hour. You have 20 hours available to work. What are the greatest number of hours you can spend handing out flyers and still make at least $145? **10 h**

86. **Freight Handling** The freight elevator of a building can safely carry a load of at most 4000 lb. A worker needs to move supplies in 50-lb boxes from the loading dock to the fourth floor of the building. The worker weighs 160 lb. The cart she uses weighs 95 lb.
    a. What is the greatest number of boxes she can move in one trip? **74 boxes**
    b. The worker must deliver 310 boxes to the fourth floor. How many trips must she make? **5 trips**

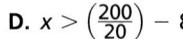

Standardized Test Prep

Multiple Choice

87. The Science Club hopes to collect at least 200 kg of aluminum cans for recycling this semester (21 weeks). The graph at the right shows the first week's results.

Let x represent the average mass of cans required per week for the remainder of the semester. Which inequality would you use to find x? **C**

A. $x \geq \frac{200}{21}$ B. $x \geq \frac{(200 - 8)}{21}$

C. $x \geq \frac{(200 - 8)}{20}$ D. $x > \left(\frac{200}{20}\right) - 8$

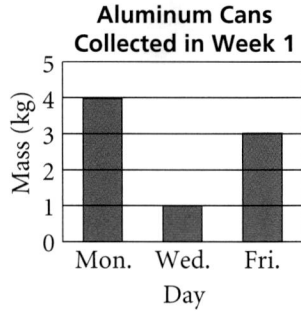

Aluminum Cans Collected in Week 1

Mass (kg) / Day (Mon., Wed., Fri.)

88. Solve $2x - 8 > 4x + 2$. **F**
   F. $x < -5$ G. $x > -5$ H. $x < 5$ I. $x > 5$

89. Solve $-5n + 16 \leq -7n$. **A**
   A. $n \leq -8$ B. $n \geq -8$ C. $n \leq 8$ D. $n \geq 8$

90. Great Gifts pays its supplier $65 for each box of 12 bells. The owner wants to determine the least amount x he can charge his customers per bell in order to make at least a 50% profit per box. Which inequality should he use? **F**
   F. $12x \geq 1.50(65)$ G. $65x \leq 1.50(12)$
   H. $0.50(12x) \geq 65$ I. $0.50(12x) \leq 65$

Short Response

91. Maxwell orders at least 30 bottles of flea shampoo per month for his pet-grooming business. His supplier charges $3 per quart bottle plus a $25 handling fee per order. A competing supplier offers a similar product for $4 per quart bottle plus a $5 handling fee per order. The salesman for the competitor shows Maxwell that 10 bottles from his company would cost only $45 compared to $55 from Maxwell's current supplier.

Which supplier would you advise Maxwell to use? Explain or show work to support your advice to Maxwell. **See margin.**

Take It to the NET
Online lesson quiz at
www.PHSchool.com
Web Code: aea-0304

Mixed Review

Lesson 3-3   **Solve each inequality.**

92. $-9m \geq 36$ **93.** $-24 \leq 3y$ $y \geq -8$ **94.** $\frac{x}{3} > -4$ $x > -12$ **95.** $-\frac{t}{3} \leq 1$ $t \geq -3$
$m \leq -4$

96. $\frac{2}{3}b < 18$ $b < 27$ **97.** $42 > -\frac{3}{7}w$ **98.** $56 < 42p$ $p > 1\frac{1}{3}$ **99.** $0.5d \geq 3.5$
$w > -98$ $d \geq 7$

Lesson 2-5   **100.** Your family leaves your town traveling at an average rate of 45 mi/h. Two hours later, your neighbor leaves your town along the same road at an average rate of 60 mi/h. How many hours will it take your neighbor to overtake you? **6 h**

Lesson 1-6   **Simplify each expression.**

101. -4^2 **−16**   **102.** $(-4)^2$ **16**   **103.** $(-2)^3(-3)$ **24**   **104.** -2^4 **−16**

Algebra at Work

•••••••••••••••••••••••••• **Marketing Director**

Marketing directors rely on equations and inequalities to predict the actions their companies must take to stay competitive. For example, the marketing director of a manufacturing company determines how much the cost of raw materials can increase before the company must raise the price of its finished goods or services. The director also predicts the effect of price changes on the quantity of goods and services sold by his company.

Take It to the NET For more information about a career in marketing, go to **www.PHSchool.com**.
Web Code: aeb-2031

Lesson 3-4 Solving Multi-Step Inequalities   **159**

Standardized Test Prep

Resources
For additional practice with a variety of test item formats:
• Standardized Test Prep, p. 179
• Test-Taking Strategies, p. 174
• Test-Taking Strategies with Transparencies

Exercise 87 Remind students to look for key words and phrases, such as *remainder of the semester.*

pages 155–159   Exercises

91. [2] Maxwell should continue ordering from the current supplier.

Let x = number of bottles Maxwell orders per month. The cost from the current supplier is $3x + 25$. The cost from the competitor is $4x + 5$. The inequality $4x + 5 \leq 3x + 25$ represents the number of bottles of shampoo for which the competitor will be less expensive. Since $x = 20$, the competitor will *not* be less expensive for orders of 30 bottles or more. (OR equivalent explanation)

[1] incorrect answer OR insufficient explanation

Interpreting Solutions

Interpreting Solutions

Students solve inequalities for the unknown in the usual manner. However, if there is a stated replacement set for the variable, they will need to examine the replacement set and select only those that satisfy the inequality.

Resources

Technology
Computer Test Generator CD-ROM, Chapter 0, Extension Topics

Teaching Notes

Help students understand that there may be an infinite number of solutions for an inequality, yet, depending on the replacement set, there may be no solutions, one solution, or many solutions. Students will have to examine the replacement set closely to see what part of it fits their solution.

English Learners

English learners may not know what to call this symbol { }. Explain that in mathematics we use three types of enclosure symbols: parentheses, brackets, and braces. These are called braces and they are used to designate sets of numbers.

Error Prevention

Remind students to reverse the inequality symbol when solving an inequality in which they divide or multiply both sides by a negative number. Many students will forget to do this because it is not intuitively evident to most students why this is true.

When you solve inequalities, the possible values for the variable make up the *replacement set*. Real numbers or integers can be replacement sets. The notation {3, 4, 5} indicates that 3, 4, and 5 is a replacement set. Your solution depends on the replacement set for the variable.

EXAMPLE

a. Solve $-5 < 2k$.

$-5 < 2k$

$\frac{-5}{2} < \frac{2k}{2}$ Divide by 2.

$-2\frac{1}{2} < k$ Simplify.

b. Graph the solutions for each replacement set.

i. the real numbers

ii. the integers

iii. $\{-5, -3, -2, 0, 3\}$

EXERCISES

Graph each inequality for the given replacement set.

1. $9v + 6 \leq 18$, for $\{-4, -2, 0, 2, 4\}$

2. $2n + 6 < 12$; integers

3. $-3(d - 1) \leq 4.5$; positive integers

4. $-2 < 2(c + 5)$; negative integers

5. $-4 \leq q + 1$; negative real numbers

6. $4 < 2 - 2m$; for $\{-2, -1, 0, 1, 2\}$

Write an inequality that represents each situation. Identify each replacement set. Solve and graph the solution on a number line.

 7. Geometry The length of a rectangle is 20 cm. For a perimeter of at most 48 cm, what is the width of the rectangle? **$2(20) + 2w \leq 48$, replacement set: positive real numbers;**

8. Grades Your grades on three tests are 85, 80, and 75. You will take one more 20-question test. Each question is worth 5 points. Your goal is to have a test average of at least 83. What grades on the fourth test will give you the average that you want? **See above.**

8. $\frac{85 + 80 + 75 + x}{4} \geq 83$; replacement set: multiples of 5 less than or equal to 100;

90 95 100

1.

$-5\ -4\ -3\ -2\ -1\ 0\ 1$

2.

$-1\ 0\ 1\ 2\ 3\ 4$

3.

$-1\ 0\ 1\ 2\ 3\ 4$

4.

$-7\ -6\ -5\ -4\ -3\ -2\ -1\ 0\ 1$

5.

$-6\ -5\ -4\ -3\ -2\ -1\ 0\ 1$

6.

$-3\ -2\ -1\ 0\ 1$

$-1\ 0\ 1\ 2\ 3\ 4\ 5$

Compound Inequalities

4.01 Use linear functions or inequalities to model and solve problems; justify results. a) Solve using tables, graphs, and algebraic properties.

1. Plan

North Carolina Objectives

Lesson Preview

What You'll Learn

OBJECTIVE 1 To solve and graph inequalities containing *and*

OBJECTIVE 2 To solve and graph inequalities containing *or*

. . . And Why

To solve a problem involving the chemistry of a swimming pool, as in Example 3

✓ Check Skills You'll Need

(For help, go to Lessons 1-1 and 3-1.)

Graph each pair of inequalities on one number line. 1–3. See below.

1. $c < 8$; $c \geq 10$ 2. $t \geq -2$; $t \leq -5$ 3. $m \leq 7$; $m > 12$

Use the given value of the variable to evaluate each expression.

4. $3n - 6$; 4 **6**   5. $7 - 2b$; 5 **−3**

6. $\dfrac{12 + 13 + y}{3}$; 17 **14**   7. $\dfrac{2d - 3}{5}$; 9 **3**

New Vocabulary
• compound inequality

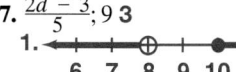
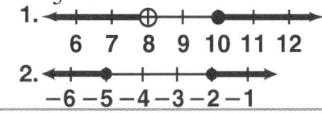

Lesson Preview

✓ Check Skills You'll Need

Using Variables
Lesson 1-2: Example 2
Exercises 7–12
Extra Practice, p. 702

Inequalities and Their Graphs
Lesson 3-1: Example 3
Exercises 19–26
Extra Practice, p. 704

Lesson Resources

📁 **Teaching Resources**
Practice, Reteaching, Enrichment
Checkpoint Quiz 2

👥 **Reaching All Students**
Practice Workbook 3-5
Spanish Practice Workbook 3-5
Reading and Math Literacy 3C
Spanish Reading & Literacy 3C
Spanish Checkpoint Quiz 2
Hands-On Activities 8
Basic Algebra Planning Guide 3-5

⏱ **Presentation Assistant Plus!**
Transparencies
• Check Skills You'll Need 3-5
• Additional Examples 3-5
• Student Edition Answers 3-5
• Lesson Quiz 3-5
PH Presentation Pro CD 3-5

ASSESSMENT SYSTEM

Checkpoint Quiz 2
Computer Test Generator CD

✏ **Technology**
Resource Pro® CD-ROM
Computer Test Generator CD
Prentice Hall Presentation Pro CD

🖥 **www.PHSchool.com**
Student Site
• Teacher Web Code: aek-5500
• Reasoning & Puzzles, p. 59
• Self-grading Lesson Quiz
Teacher Center
• Lesson Planner
• Resources

Plus **iTEXT**

OBJECTIVE 1

Solving Compound Inequalities Containing *And*

Two inequalities that are joined by the word *and* or the word *or* form a **compound inequality.**

You can write the compound inequality $x \geq -5$ and $x \leq 7$ as $-5 \leq x \leq 7$.

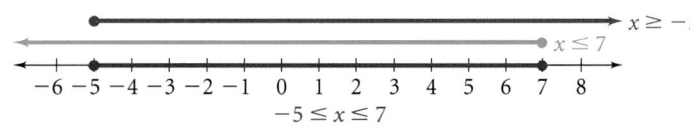

$$-5 \leq x \leq 7$$

📖 Reading Math

The word *inclusive* is related to the word *included*.

The graph above shows that a solution of $-5 \leq x \leq 7$ is in the overlap of the solutions of the inequality $x \geq -5$ and the inequality $x \leq 7$.

You can read $-5 \leq x \leq 7$ as "x is greater than or equal to -5 and less than or equal to 7." Another way to read it is "x is between -5 and 7, inclusive."

iTEXT Interactive lesson includes instant self-check, tutorials, and activities.

1 EXAMPLE   Writing a Compound Inequality

Write a compound inequality that represents each situation. Graph the solutions.

a. all real numbers that are at least -2 and at most 4
$n \geq -2$ and $n \leq 4$
$-2 \leq n \leq 4$

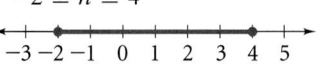

b. Today's temperatures will be above 32°F, but not as high as 40°F.
$32 < t$ and $t < 40$
$32 < t < 40$

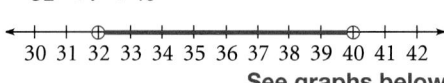

See graphs below.

✓ Check Understanding

1 Write a compound inequality that represents each situation. Graph your solution.
a. all real numbers greater than -2 but less than 9 $n > -2$ and $n < 9$ or $-2 < n < 9$
b. The books were priced between $3.50 and $6.00, inclusive. $3.50 \leq b \leq 6$

a.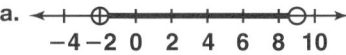

b.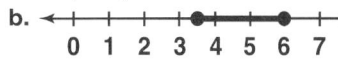

Ongoing Assessment and Intervention

Before the Lesson
Diagnose prerequisite skills using:
• Check Skills You'll Need

During the Lesson
Monitor progress using:
• Check Understanding
• Additional Examples
• Standardized Test Prep

After the Lesson
Assess knowledge using:
• Lesson Quiz
• Computer Test Generator CD
• Chapter Checkpoint 2 (p. 166)

Math Background

In logic, *and* means that a number or variable satisfies both conditions given. The word *or* means that only one condition must be satisfied. Mathematics uses these meanings from formal logic.

OBJECTIVE

1 Teaching Notes

2 EXAMPLE Alternative Method

Graph the example on the board using colored chalk. Use yellow chalk for one inequality and blue chalk for the other inequality. Shade where the two graphs overlap. Help students see that the solution for an inequality containing *and* is the area where the graphs overlap.

Additional Examples

1 Write a compound inequality that represents each situation. Graph the solutions.
a. all real numbers that are at least −1 and at most 3
$b \geq -1$ and $b \leq 3$
$-1 \leq b \leq 3$

$-5\ -4\ -3\ -2\ -1\ \ 0\ \ 1\ \ 2\ \ 3\ \ 4\ \ 5$

b. all real numbers that are less than 31, but greater than 25
$n < 31$ and $n > 25$
$25 < n < 31$

$23\ 24\ 25\ 26\ 27\ 28\ 29\ 30\ 31\ 32\ 33$

2 Solve $5 > 5 - f > 2$. Graph your solution. $0 < f < 3$

$-5\ -4\ -3\ -2\ -1\ \ 0\ \ 1\ \ 2\ \ 3\ \ 4\ \ 5$

3 Your test grades in science so far are 83 and 87. What possible grades can you make on your next test to have an average between 85 and 90, inclusive? **The third test grade must be between 85 and 100, inclusive.**

A solution of a compound inequality joined by *and* is any number that makes both inequalities true. One way you can solve a compound inequality is by writing two inequalities.

2 EXAMPLE Solving a Compound Inequality Containing *And*

Solve $-4 < r - 5 \leq -1$. Graph your solution.

Write the compound inequality as two inequalities joined by *and*.

$-4 < r - 5$	and	$r - 5 \leq -1$
$-4 + 5 < r - 5 + 5$		$r - 5 + 5 \leq -1 + 5$ **Solve each inequality.**
$1 < r$	and	$r \leq 4$ **Simplify.**

$$1 < r \leq 4$$

$-5\ -4\ -3\ -2\ -1\ \ 0\ \ 1\ \ 2\ \ 3\ \ 4\ \ 5$

✓ Check Understanding **2** Solve each inequality. Graph your solution.
a. $-6 \leq 3x \leq 15$
$-2 \leq x \leq 5;$

$-4\ -2\ 0\ \ 2\ \ 4\ \ 6$

b. $-3 < 2x - 1 < 7$
$-1 < x < 4;$

$-2\ -1\ 0\ \ 1\ \ 2\ \ 3\ \ 4\ \ 5$

c. $7 < -3n + 1 \leq 13$
c. $-4 \leq n < -2;$

$-5\ -4\ -3\ -2\ -1\ 0\ \ 1$

You could also solve an inequality like $-4 < r - 5 \leq -1$ by working on all three parts of the inequality at the same time. You work to get the variable alone between the inequality symbols.

3 EXAMPLE Real-World 🌐 Problem Solving

Chemistry The acidity of the water in a swimming pool is considered normal if the average of three pH readings is between 7.2 and 7.8, inclusive. The first two readings for a swimming pool are 7.4 and 7.9. What possible values for the third reading p will make the average pH normal?

Relate	7.2	is less than or equal to	the average	which is less than or equal to	7.8
Write	7.2	$\leq$	$\dfrac{7.4 + 7.9 + p}{3}$	$\leq$	7.8

$$7.2 \leq \frac{7.4 + 7.9 + p}{3} \leq 7.8$$

$$3(7.2) \leq 3\left(\frac{7.4 + 7.9 + p}{3}\right) \leq 3(7.8) \quad \textbf{Multiply by 3.}$$

$$21.6 \leq 15.3 + p \leq 23.4 \quad \textbf{Simplify.}$$

$$21.6 - 15.3 \leq 15.3 + p - 15.3 \leq 23.4 - 15.3 \quad \textbf{Subtract 15.3.}$$

$$6.3 \leq p \leq 8.1 \quad \textbf{Simplify.}$$

The value for the third reading must be between 6.3 and 8.1, inclusive.

Real-World 🌐 Connection

The lifeguard is checking the pH of swimming pool water. The pH of a substance is a measure of how acidic or basic it is. pH is measured on a scale from 1 to 14. Pure water is neutral, with a pH of 7.

✓ Check Understanding **3 a.** Suppose the first two readings for the acidity of water in a swimming pool are 7.0 and 7.9. What possible values for the third reading will make the average pH normal? $6.7 \leq p \leq 8.5$
b. Critical Thinking If two readings are 8.0 and 8.4, what possible values for the third reading will make the average pH normal? Are these third readings likely? Explain. $5.2 \leq p \leq 7$. **No; readings in this range are unlikely if the first readings are high.**

🎓 Reaching All Students

Below Level Have 3 students stand on a number line on the floor. Discuss how the middle student is "greater than" one student and "less than" the other at the same time.	**Advanced Learners** Ask students to explain how to write compound inequalities using *or* or *and* where solutions are all real numbers.	**English Learners** See note on page 163. **Error Prevention** See note on page 164.

Solving Compound Inequalities Joined by *Or*

A solution of a compound inequality joined by *or* is any number that makes either inequality true.

4 EXAMPLE Writing Compound Inequalities

Write a compound inequality that represents each situation. Graph the solution.

a. all real numbers that are less than -3 or greater than 7
  $x < -3$ or $x > 7$

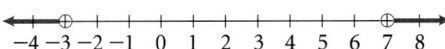

b. Discounted fares are available to children 12 and under or to adults at least 60 years of age.
  $n \le 12$ or $n \ge 60$; $n \ge 0$ because age cannot be negative.

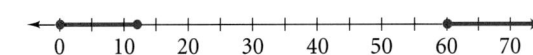

✓ **Check Understanding** **4** Write an inequality that represents all real numbers that are at most -5 or at least 3. Graph your solution. $n \le -5$ or $n \ge 3$;

For a compound inequality joined by *or*, you must solve each of the two inequalities separately.

5 EXAMPLE Solving a Compound Inequality Containing *Or*

Solve the compound inequality $4v + 3 < -5$ or $-2v + 7 < 1$. Graph the solution.

Need Help?

Remember to reverse the inequality symbol when you multiply or divide by a negative number.

$$
\begin{array}{ccc}
4v + 3 < -5 & \text{or} & -2v + 7 < 1 \\
4v + 3 - 3 < -5 - 3 & & -2v + 7 - 7 < 1 - 7 \\
4v < -8 & & -2v < -6 \\
\dfrac{4v}{4} < \dfrac{-8}{4} & & \dfrac{-2v}{-2} > \dfrac{-6}{-2} \\
v < -2 & \text{or} & v > 3
\end{array}
$$

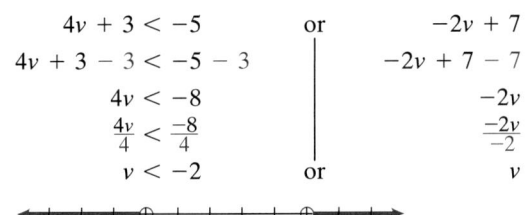

✓ **Check Understanding** **5** Solve the compound inequality $-2x + 7 > 3$ or $3x - 4 \ge 5$. Graph your solution. $x < 2$ or $x \ge 3$;

EXERCISES

For more practice, see *Extra Practice*.

Practice and Problem Solving

A Practice by Example

Example 1
(page 161)

Write a compound inequality that represents each situation. Graph your solution.

1. all real numbers that are between -4 and 6
  $-4 < x$ and $x < 6$ or $-4 < x < 6$;

2. all real numbers that are at least 2 and at most 9
  $2 \le n$ and $n \le 9$ or $2 \le n \le 9$;

3. The circumference of a baseball is between 23 cm and 23.5 cm.
  $23 < c < 23.5$;

4. **Tropical Storm** The wind speeds of a tropical storm are at least 40 mi/h but no more than 74 mi/h. $40 \le w \le 74$;

Lesson 3-5 Compound Inequalities   **163**

4 EXAMPLE English Learners

Some students may confuse *and* and *or*. Ask students wearing blue to stand and then sit. Ask students wearing yellow to stand and then sit. Then ask students wearing blue *and* yellow to stand. Point out that because you said *and* only some members of each group are now standing. Ask students wearing blue *or* yellow to stand. Note that all students in both groups are standing.

Additional Examples

4 Write an inequality that represents each situation. Graph the solution.
a. all real numbers that are less than 0 or greater than 3 $n < 0$ or $n > 3$

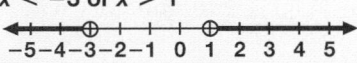

b. Discounted tickets are available to children under 7 years old or to adults 65 and older. $a < 7$ or $a \ge 65$; because age cannot be negative, $a \ge 0$

5 Solve the compound inequality $3x + 2 < -7$ or $-4x + 5 < 1$. Graph the solution. $x < -3$ or $x > 1$

Closure

Ask students to explain in their own words the difference between compound inequalities with *and* and those with *or*. Compound inequalities with *and* have solutions that satisfy every part of the inequality. Compound inequalities with *or* have solutions that satisfy at least one part of the inequality.

Assignment Guide

1 Objective

A B Core 1–19, 40–44, 47–54

C Extension 58–60

2 Objective

A B Core 20–39, 45–46

C Extension 55–57

Standardized Test Prep 61–63

Mixed Review 64–69

Connection To Geometry

Exercises 47–50 Point out that the length of the third side must be between the sum and the difference of the two given sides. Ask: *Can the length of the third side be 4 cm?* no *Why or Why not?* The sum of 3 and 7 is 10; the difference is 4. The length 4 is not between 10 and 4.

Error Prevention

Exercises 51–53 Students may have difficulty reading the graph. Ask questions about the high and low temperatures for each city to help students understand the different bars.

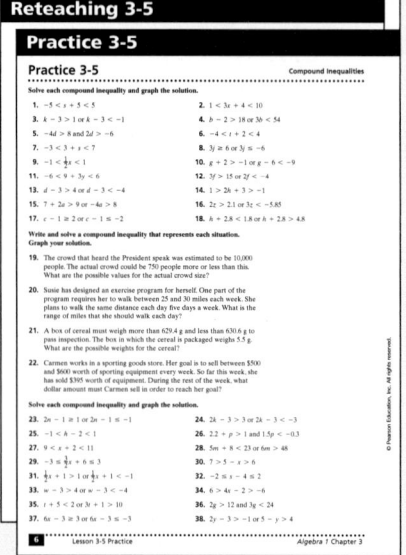

Examples 2, 3
(page 162)

Solve each compound inequality. Graph your solution. 5–19. See margin for graphs.

5. $-3 < j + 2 < 7$
$-5 < j < 5$

6. $3 \leq w + 2 \leq 7$
$1 \leq w \leq 5$

7. $2 < 3n - 4 \leq 14$
$2 < n \leq 6$

8. $7 \leq 3 - 2p < 11$
$-4 < p \leq -2$

9. $-2 < -3x + 7 < 4$
$1 < x < 3$

10. $1.5 < w + 3 \leq 6.5$
$-1.5 < w \leq 3.5$

11. $-16 < -3x + 8 < -7$
$5 < x < 8$

12. $-1 < 4m + 7 \leq 11$
$-2 < m \leq 1$

13. $-9 < -2s - 1 \leq -7$
$3 \leq s < 4$

14. $-\frac{1}{2} < \frac{1}{4}t - \frac{3}{4} < \frac{1}{8}$
$1 < t < 3\frac{1}{2}$

15. $3 \geq 4r - 5 \geq -1$
$1 \leq r \leq 2$

16. $3.2 \geq 2r + 0.2 > -3.8$
$-2 < r \leq 1.5$

17. $12 \leq \frac{14 + 17 + a}{3} \leq 16$
$5 \leq a \leq 17$

18. $\frac{1}{2} < \frac{3x - 1}{4} < 5$
$1 < x < 7$

19. $-2 \leq \frac{5 - x}{3} \leq 2$
$-1 \leq x \leq 11$

Example 4
(page 163)

For each situation write and graph an inequality.

20. all real numbers n that are at most -3 or at least 5
$n \leq -3$ or $n \geq 5$

21. all real numbers x that are less than 3 or greater than 7
$x < 3$ or $x > 7$

22. all real numbers h less than 1 or greater than 3
$h < 1$ or $h > 3$

23. all real numbers b less than 100 or greater than 300
$b < 100$ or $b > 300$

Example 5
(page 163)

Solve each compound inequality. Graph your solution. 24–33. See margin for graphs.

24. $3b - 1 < -7$ or $4b + 1 > 9$
$b < -2$ or $b > 2$

25. $4 + k > 3$ or $6k < -30$
$k < -5$ or $k > -1$

26. $3c + 4 \geq 13$ or $6c - 1 < 11$
$c < 2$ or $c \geq 3$

27. $6 - a < 1$ or $3a \leq 12$
$a \leq 4$ or $a \geq 5$

28. $7 - 3c \geq 1$ or $5c + 2 \geq 17$
$c \leq 2$ or $c \geq 3$

29. $5y + 7 \leq -3$ or $3y - 2 \geq 13$
$y \leq -2$ or $y \geq 5$

30. $2d + 5 \leq -1$ or $-2d + 5 \leq 5$
$d \leq -3$ or $d \geq 0$

31. $5z - 3 > 7$ or $4z - 6 < -10$
$z < -1$ or $z > 2$

32. $x - 5 \geq 0$ or $x + 1 < -2$
$x < -3$ or $x \geq 5$

33. $-3n < -9$ or $-2n > 10$
$n < -5$ or $n > 3$

B Apply Your Skills

Write a compound inequality that each graph could represent.

34. $-2 < x < 3$

35. $x < -3$ or $x \geq 2$

36. $x \leq 0$ or $x > 2$

37. $-4 \leq x \leq 3$

Solve each compound inequality.

38. $3q - 2 > 10$ or $3q - 2 \leq -10$
$q \leq -2\frac{2}{3}$ or $q > 4$

39. $3 - 2h > 17$ or $5h - 3 > 17$
$h < -7$ or $h > 4$

40. $1 \leq 0.25t \leq 3.5$
$4 \leq t \leq 14$

41. $25r < 400$ or $100 < 4r$
$r < 16$ or $r > 25$

42. $-20 \leq 3t - 2 < 1$
$-6 \leq t < 1$

43. $\frac{3x + 1}{4} - 4 > 3$ or $\frac{3 - 2x}{5} > 3$
$x < -6$ or $x > 9$

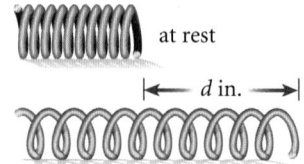
at rest

$|\leftarrow d$ in. $\rightarrow|$

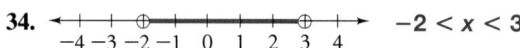
44. Physical Science The force exerted on a spring is proportional to the distance the spring stretches from its relaxed position. Suppose you stretch a spring distance d in inches by applying force F in pounds. For a certain spring, $\frac{d}{F} = 0.8$. You apply forces between 25 and 40 pounds, inclusive. Write a compound inequality describing the stretch of the spring. $20 \leq d \leq 32$

45. Reasoning Describe the solutions of $3x - 8 < 7$ or $2x - 9 > 1$.
all real numbers except 5

46. Writing Explain the difference between the words *and* and *or* in a compound inequality. **The word *and* means both statements must be true. The word *or* means that at least one of the statements must be true.**

pages 163–166 Exercises

5. $-10 -5 \ 0 \ 5 \ 10$

6. $-1 \ 0 \ 1 \ 2 \ 3 \ 4 \ 5 \ 6$

7. $-2 \ 0 \ 2 \ 4 \ 6 \ 8$

8. $-5 -4 -3 -2 -1 \ 0 \ 1$

9. $-1 \ 0 \ 1 \ 2 \ 3 \ 4$

10. $-2 -1 \ 0 \ 1 \ 2 \ 3 \ 4$

11. $4 \ 5 \ 6 \ 7 \ 8 \ 9$

12. $-3 -2 -1 \ 0 \ 1 \ 2$

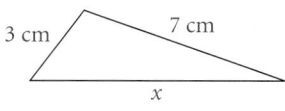

Geometry The sum of the lengths of any two sides of a triangle is greater than the length of the third side. The lengths of two sides of a triangle are given. Find the range of values for the possible lengths of the third side.

Sample 3 cm, 7 cm

Write inequalities for x as the longest side and for 7 cm as the longest side. The length 3 cm cannot be the longest side.

$x + 3 > 7$ and $3 + 7 > x$

$x > 4$ and $10 > x$ Solve each inequality.

$4 < x < 10$

The length of the third side is greater than 4 cm and less than 10 cm.

47. 2.5 in., 5 in.   **48.** 12 ft, 18 ft   **49.** 28 mm, 21 mm   **50.** 5 m, 16 m
2.5 < x < 7.5   **6 < x < 30**   **7 < x < 49**   **11 < x < 21**

Meteorology The graph below shows the average monthly high and low temperatures for Detroit, Michigan, and Charlotte, North Carolina.

51. Write a compound inequality for Charlotte's average temperature in June. **66 ≤ C ≤ 88**

52. Write a compound inequality for Detroit's average temperature in January. **15 ≤ D ≤ 30**

53. Write a compound inequality for the yearly temperature range for each city.

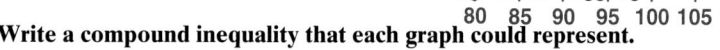
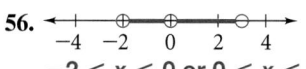

Monthly Average High and Low Temperatures

SOURCE: Statistical Abstract of the United States

Charlotte: 29 ≤ C ≤ 90
Detroit: 15 ≤ D ≤ 83

54. Open-Ended Describe a real-life situation that you could represent with the inequality $-2 < x < 8$. **Answers may vary. Sample: Elevation near a coastline varies between 2 m below and 8 m above sea level.**

C Challenge **55. Nursing** In nursing school, students learn temperature ranges for bath water. Tepid water is approximately 80°F to 93°F, warm water is approximately 94°F to 98°F, and hot water is approximately 110°F to 115°F. Model these ranges on one number line. Label each interval.

tepid   warm   hot
80 85 90 95 100 105 110 115

Write a compound inequality that each graph could represent.

56.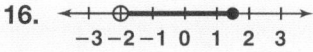
-4 -2   0   2   4
-2 < x < 0 or 0 < x < 3

57.
-2   0   2   4
n = 0 or n ≥ 3

58. Pulse Rates When you exercise, your pulse rate rises. Recommended pulse rates vary with age and physical condition. For vigorous exercise, such as jogging, the inequality $0.7(220 - a) \le R \le 0.85(220 - a)$ gives a target range for pulse rate R (in beats per minute), based on age a (in years).
   a. What is the target range for pulse rates for a person 35 years old? Round to the nearest whole number. **130 ≤ R ≤ 157**
   b. Your cousin's target pulse rate is in the range between 140 and 170 beats per minute. What is your cousin's age? **20 years old**

59. Find three consecutive even integers whose sum is between 48 and 60. **16, 18, 20**

60. Find three consecutive even integers such that one half of their sum is between 15 and 21. **10, 12, 14**

Real-World Connection

To estimate your pulse rate, count the number of beats you feel in 15 seconds at a pressure point. Multiply this number by 4.

13.
2 3 4 5

14.
-1 0 1 2 3 4 5

15.
-1 0 1 2 3 4

16.
-3 -2 -1 0 1 2 3

17.
0 5 10 15 20

18.
-2 0 2 4 6 8 10

19.
-2 0 2 4 6 8 10 12

24.
-3 -2 -1 0 1 2 3

25.
-6 -5 -4 -3 -2 -1 0 1

Lesson Quiz 3-5

1. Write two compound inequalities that represent the given situation. Graph the solution.

all real numbers that are at least 2 and at most 5
$b \ge 2$ and $b \le 5$,
$2 \le b \le 5$

-3 -2 -1 0 1 2 3 4 5 6 7

2. Write an inequality that represents the given situation. Graph the solution.

all real numbers that are less than -3 or greater than -1 $n < -3$ or $n > -1$

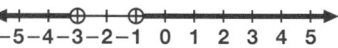
-5 -4 -3 -2 -1 0 1 2 3 4 5

3. Solve $-2 \le 2x - 4 < 6$. Graph the solution.
$1 \le x < 5$

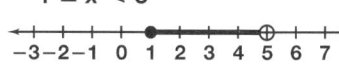
-3 -2 -1 0 1 2 3 4 5 6 7

4. Solve $3x - 2 < -8$ or $-2x + 5 \le 3$. Graph the solution. $x < -2$ or $x \ge 1$

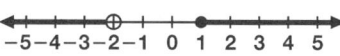
-5 -4 -3 -2 -1 0 1 2 3 4 5

Alternative Assessment

Organize students in groups of four and instruct them to sit in a circle. Instruct each student to write a real world problem similar to Example 3 on a piece of paper. Have students pass their problems to the student on their right. This student writes an inequality to represent the problem. Pass the problems to the right again. This student solves the inequality. Pass the problems to the right again. This student graphs the solutions.

26.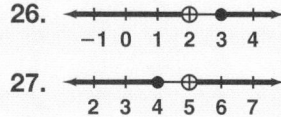
-1 0 1 2 3 4

27.
2 3 4 5 6 7

28.
0 1 2 3 4 5

29–33. See margin p. 166.

165

Resources

For additional practice with a variety of test item formats:
- Standardized Test Prep, p. 179
- Test-Taking Strategies, p. 174
- Test-Taking Strategies with Transparencies

Exercise 62 Suggest to students that they first solve each inequality.

Chapter Checkpoint 2

To check understanding of Lessons 3-4 to 3-5:

Checkpoint Quiz 2 (p. 166)

Teaching Resources

Checkpoint Quiz 2 (also in Prentice Hall Assessment System)

Reaching All Students

Reading and Math Literacy 3C

Spanish versions available

---

pages 163–166   Exercises

29.
$$-4\ -2\ \ 0\ \ 2\ \ 4\ \ 6\ \ 8$$

30.
$$-5\ -4\ -3\ -2\ -1\ \ 0\ \ 1\ \ 2$$

31.
$$-2\ -1\ \ 0\ \ 1\ \ 2\ \ 3$$

32.
$$-6\ -4\ -2\ \ 0\ \ 2\ \ 4\ \ 6$$

33.
$$-8\ -6\ -4\ -2\ \ 0\ \ 2\ \ 4\ \ 6$$

page 166   Checkpoint Quiz 2

1. $d < -3$
$$-5\ -4\ -3\ -2\ -1\ \ 0\ \ 1$$

2. $n \geq -2$
$$-3\ -2\ -1\ \ 0\ \ 1$$

3. $-2 \leq m \leq 1$
$$-3\ -2\ -1\ \ 0\ \ 1\ \ 2$$

4. $s < 2$
$$-1\ \ 0\ \ 1\ \ 2\ \ 3$$

166

Standardized Test Prep

Multiple Choice

63. [2] $35 \leq 10.4 + 0.0059g \leq 50$

$24.6 \leq 0.0059g \leq 39.6$

$4169 < g < 6712$

minimum consumption: 4169 gal

maximum consumption: 6712 gal

(OR equivalent explanation)

[1] incorrect answer OR insufficient explanation

Short Response

Take It to the NET

Online lesson quiz at **www.PHSchool.com**

Web Code: aea-0305

61. An emergency vehicle responding to a 911 call for a heart attack victim traveled 5 miles to the patient's home and then delivered him to the hospital 10 miles away. Which graph below represents the possible distances the emergency vehicle was from the hospital when the call was received? **B**

A.
$$0\ \ 2\ \ 4\ \ 6\ \ 8\ \ 10\ \ 12\ \ 14\ \ 16\ \ 18$$

B.
$$0\ \ 2\ \ 4\ \ 6\ \ 8\ \ 10\ \ 12\ \ 14\ \ 16\ \ 18$$

C.
$$0\ \ 2\ \ 4\ \ 6\ \ 8\ \ 10\ \ 12\ \ 14\ \ 16\ \ 18$$

D.
$$0\ \ 2\ \ 4\ \ 6\ \ 8\ \ 10\ \ 12\ \ 14\ \ 16\ \ 18$$

62. Which value below is a solution of neither $-3x - 7 \geq 8$ nor $-2x - 11 \leq -31$?
   F. –6   G. 0   H. 10   I. 16   **G**

63. The County Water Department charges a monthly administration fee of $10.40 plus $.0059 for each gallon g of water used, up to 7,500 gallons. Find the minimum and maximum water consumption (in gallons) for customers whose monthly charge is at least $35 but no more than $50. Express amounts to the nearest gallon. Show your work. **See left.**

Mixed Review

Lesson 3-4   **Solve each inequality.**

64. $5 < 6b + 3$ $b > \frac{1}{3}$ 65. $12n \leq 3n + 27$ $n \leq 3$ 66. $2 + 4r \geq 5(r - 1)$ $r \leq 7$

Lesson 2-4   **Solve. If the equation is an identity or if it has no solution, write *identity* or *no solution*.**

67. $x - 3 = 5x + 1$ $x = -1$ 68. $4(w + 3) = 10w$ $w = 2$ 69. $8p - 4 = 4(2p - 1)$ **identity**

Checkpoint Quiz 2   **Lessons 3-4 through 3-5**

Instant self-check quiz online and on CD-ROM

Solve each inequality. Graph the solution. 1–6. See margin.

1. $8d + 2 < 5d - 7$ 2. $2n + 1 \geq -3$ 3. $-1 \leq 4m + 7 \leq 11$

4. $5s - 3 + 1 < 8$ 5. $5(3p - 2) > 50$ 6. $3 - x \geq 7$ or $2x - 3 > 5$

Write an inequality that represents each situation.

7. A cat weighs less than 8 pounds. $c < 8$

8. We expect today's temperature to be between 65°F and 75°F, inclusive.
   $65 \leq t \leq 75$

9. **Geometry** The length of each side of a rectangular picture frame needs to be 15 in. You have only one 48 in. piece of wood to use for this frame. Write and solve an inequality that describes the possible widths for this frame.
   $2(15) + 2(w) \leq 48, w \leq 9$

10. Solve $-2x + 7 \leq 45$. $x \geq -19$

---

5. $p > 4$
$$-2\ \ 0\ \ 2\ \ 4\ \ 6\ \ 8$$

6. $x \leq -4$ or $x > 4$
$$-6\ -4\ -2\ \ 0\ \ 2\ \ 4\ \ 6$$

Absolute Value Equations and Inequalities

North Carolina Objectives

1.02 Use formulas and algebraic expressions, including iterative and recursive forms, to model and solve problems.

1. Plan

Lesson Preview

What You'll Learn

 OBJECTIVE 1
To solve equations that involve absolute value

 OBJECTIVE 2
To solve inequalities that involve absolute value

. . . And Why

To find a range of acceptable measurements for parts of an engine, as in Example 4

✓ Check Skills You'll Need
(For help, go to Lessons 1-3 and 1-4.)

Simplify.

1. $|15|$ **15** **2.** $|-3|$ **3** **3.** $|18 - 12|$ **6**

4. $-|-7|$ **−7** **5.** $|12 - (-12)|$ **24** **6.** $|-10 + 8|$ **2**

Complete each statement with <, =, or >.

7. $|3 - 7| \stackrel{=}{\blacksquare} 4$ **8.** $|-5| + 2 \stackrel{\geq}{\blacksquare} 6$ **9.** $|7| - 1 \stackrel{\leq}{\blacksquare} 8$

10. $\left|6 - 2\frac{1}{4}\right| \stackrel{>}{\blacksquare} 3\frac{5}{8}$ **11.** $\left|-4\frac{2}{3}\right| + 2\frac{1}{3} \stackrel{>}{\blacksquare} 2\frac{1}{2}$ **12.** $\left|-3\frac{1}{8} - 4\frac{1}{2}\right| \stackrel{=}{\blacksquare} 7\frac{5}{8}$

Lesson Preview

✓ Check Skills You'll Need

Exploring Real Numbers
Lesson 1-3: Example 5
Exercises 34–41
Extra Practice, p. 702

Adding Real Numbers
Lesson 1-4: Example 2
Exercises 5–24
Extra Practice, p. 702

Lesson Resources

📁 **Teaching Resources**
Practice, Reteaching, Enrichment

👥 **Reaching All Students**
Practice Workbook 3-6
Spanish Practice Workbook 3-6
Technology Activities 17
Basic Algebra Planning Guide 3-6

⏱ **Presentation Assistant Plus!**
Transparencies
• Check Skills You'll Need 3-6
• Additional Examples 3-6
• Student Edition Answers 3-6
• Lesson Quiz 3-6
PH Presentation Pro CD 3-6

PRENTICE HALL ASSESSMENT SYSTEM

Computer Test Generator CD

🐟 **Technology**
Resource Pro® CD-ROM
Computer Test Generator CD
Prentice Hall Presentation Pro CD

💻 **www.PHSchool.com**
Student Site
• Teacher Web Code: aek-5500
• Reasoning & Puzzles, pp. 52, 59
• Self-grading Lesson Quiz
Teacher Center
• Lesson Planner
• Resources

Plus

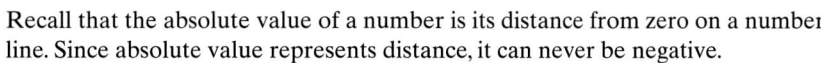

OBJECTIVE 1 Solving Absolute Value Equations

 Interactive lesson includes instant self-check, tutorials, and activities.

Recall that the absolute value of a number is its distance from zero on a number line. Since absolute value represents distance, it can never be negative.

The graph of $|x| = 3$ is below.

Need Help?
$|3| = 3$
$|-3| = 3$

3 units   3 units
−5 −4 −3 −2 −1 0 1 2 3 4 5

Find the numbers that are 3 units from 0.

The two solutions of the equation $|x| = 3$ are −3 and 3.

You can use the properties of equality to solve an absolute value equation.

---

1 EXAMPLE Solving an Absolute Value Equation

Solve $|x| + 5 = 11$.

$|x| + 5 - 5 = 11 - 5$ **Subtract 5 from each side.**

$|x| = 6$ **Simplify.**

$x = 6$ or $x = -6$ **Definition of absolute value.**

Check $|x| + 5 = 11$

$|6| + 5 \stackrel{?}{=} 11$ ← **Substitute 6 and −6 for x.** → $|-6| + 5 \stackrel{?}{=} 11$

$6 + 5 = 11$ ✓ $6 + 5 = 11$ ✓

✓ **Check Understanding** ① Solve each equation. Check your solution.

a. $|t| - 2 = -1$ **−1, 1** **b.** $3|n| = 15$ **−5, 5** **c.** $4 = 3|w| - 2$ **−2, 2**

d. Critical Thinking Is there a solution of $2|n| = -15$? Explain.
No; an absolute value cannot be negative.

Ongoing Assessment and Intervention

Before the Lesson
Diagnose prerequisite skills using:
• Check Skills You'll Need

During the Lesson
Monitor progress using:
• Check Understanding
• Additional Examples
• Standardized Test Prep

After the Lesson
Assess knowledge using:
• Lesson Quiz
• Computer Test Generator CD

Math Background

The rules for absolute value equations and inequalities all proceed from the definition of absolute value.

$$|x| = \begin{cases} x & x \geq 0 \\ -x & x < 0 \end{cases}$$

OBJECTIVE
1 **Teaching Notes**

1 EXAMPLE **Math Tip**

Stress to students that the absolute value term must be alone on one side of the equal sign before writing an absolute value equation as two separate equations.

2 EXAMPLE **Technology Tip**

Students can use a graphing calculator to check their solutions.

Additional Examples

1 Solve $|a| - 3 = 5$. $a = 8$ or $a = -8$

2 Solve $|3c - 6| = 9$. $c = 5$ or $c = -1$.

OBJECTIVE
2 **Teaching Notes**

3 EXAMPLE **Tactile Learners**

Some students may think that only -1 and 7 are solutions. Have students graph the solution on their own paper. Instruct students to place a finger on -1, and then run the finger along the number line to 7. Then have them write all integers that their finger touched. Stress that all of the integers they wrote and all the real numbers in between them are solutions of the inequality.

4 EXAMPLE **English Learners**

Some students may not be familiar with the word *piston*. Have a student who knows about internal combustion engines explain what a piston is and draw one on the board.

168

Some absolute value equations such as $|2p + 5| = 11$ have variable expressions within the absolute value symbols. The expression inside the absolute value symbols can be either positive or negative.

Key Concepts

Rule	**Solving Absolute Value Equations**
To solve an equation in the form $|A| = b$, where A represents a variable expression and $b > 0$, solve $A = b$ and $A = -b$.	

2 EXAMPLE **Solving an Absolute Value Equation**

Solve $|2p + 5| = 11$.

$2p + 5 = 11$	← Write two equations. →	$2p + 5 = -11$
$2p + 5 - 5 = 11 - 5$	← Subtract 5 from each side. →	$2p + 5 - 5 = -11 - 5$
$2p = 6$		$2p = -16$
$\dfrac{2p}{2} = \dfrac{6}{2}$	← Divide each side by 2. →	$\dfrac{2p}{2} = \dfrac{-16}{2}$
$p = 3$		$p = -8$

● The value of p is 3 or -8.

✓ Check Understanding **2** Solve each equation. Check your solution.
    a. $|c - 2| = 6$ **−4, 8**   **b.** $-5.5 = |t + 2|$ **no solution**   **c.** $|7d| = 14$ **−2, 2**

OBJECTIVE

2 **Solving Absolute Value Inequalities**

You can write absolute value inequalities as compound inequalities.

The graphs below show two absolute value inequalities.

$|n - 1| < 3$ $|n - 1| > 3$

3 units 3 units   3 units 3 units

$-3\ -2\ -1\ \ 0\ \ 1\ \ 2\ \ 3\ \ 4\ \ 5$ $-3\ -2\ -1\ \ 0\ \ 1\ \ 2\ \ 3\ \ 4\ \ 5$

$|n - 1| < 3$ represents all numbers whose distance from 1 is less than 3 units. So $-3 < n - 1 < 3$. $|n - 1| > 3$ represents all numbers whose distance from 1 is greater than 3 units. So $n - 1 < -3$ or $n - 1 > 3$.

Key Concepts

Rule	**Solving Absolute Value Inequalities**
To solve an inequality in the form $|A| < b$, where A is a variable expression and $b > 0$, solve $-b < A < b$.	
To solve an inequality in the form $|A| > b$, where A is a variable expression and $b > 0$, solve $A < -b$ or $A > b$.	
Similar rules are true for $|A| \leq b$ or $|A| \geq b$.	

168 Chapter 3 Solving Inequalities

👥 Reaching All Students

| **Below Level** Ask students to explain in their own words and also give an example of when to solve an absolute value inequality using *or* or *and* in the compound inequality. | **Advanced Learners** Ask students to write a real-world problem that can be modeled using an absolute value inequality. Have students exchange problems and discuss their answers. | **English Learners** See note on page 168. **Tactile Learners** See note on page 168. |

3 EXAMPLE Solving an Absolute Value Inequality

Solve $|v - 3| \geq 4$. Graph the solutions.

$v - 3 \leq -4$	or	$v - 3 \geq 4$	Write a compound inequality.
$v - 3 + 3 \leq -4 + 3$		$v - 3 + 3 \geq 4 + 3$	Add 3.
$v \leq -1$	or	$v \geq 7$	Simplify.

-2 -1 0 1 2 3 4 5 6 7 8

✔ **Check Understanding** **3 a.** Solve and graph $|w + 2| > 5$. **See below.**
   b. **Critical Thinking** What are the solutions of $|w + 2| > -5$? **all real numbers**

   a. $w < -7$ or $w > 3$,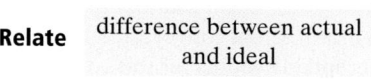
   -8 -6 -4 -2 0 2 4 6

To maintain quality, a manufacturer sets limits for how much an item can vary from its specifications. You can use an absolute value equation to model a quality-control situation.

4 EXAMPLE Real-World 🌐 Problem Solving

Manufacturing The ideal diameter of a piston for one type of car engine is 90.000 mm. The actual diameter can vary from the ideal by at most 0.008 mm. Find the range of acceptable diameters for the piston.

Relate | difference between actual and ideal | is at most | 0.008 mm |

Define Let d = actual diameter in millimeters of the cylindrical part.

Write $|d - 90.000|$ $\leq$ 0.008 mm

$$|d - 90.000| \leq 0.008$$

$-0.008 \leq$	$d - 90.000$	≤ 0.008	Write a compound inequality.
$-0.008 + 90.000 \leq d - 90.000 + 90.000 \leq 0.008 + 90.000$			Add 90.000.
$89.992 \leq$	d	≤ 90.008	Simplify.

The actual diameter must be between 89.992 mm and 90.008 mm, inclusive.

✔ **Check Understanding** **4** The ideal weight of one type of model airplane engine is 33.86 ounces. The actual weight may vary from the ideal by at most 0.05 ounce. Find the range of acceptable weights for this engine. **33.81 oz to 33.91 oz, inclusive**

Real-World 🌐 Connection

Careers A quality-control inspector inspects products to maintain quality. For engines produced on an assembly line, an inspector selects engines at random to check quality of materials and manufacturing.

For more practice, see *Extra Practice*.

EXERCISES

Practice and Problem Solving

A **Practice by Example**

Example 1
(page 167)

Solve each equation. If there is no solution, write *no solution*.

1. $|b| = 2$ **-2, 2**
2. $4 = |y|$ **-4, 4**
3. $|w| = \frac{1}{2}$ **$-\frac{1}{2}, \frac{1}{2}$**

4. $|n| + 2 = 8$ **-6, 6**
5. $7 = |s| + 4$ **-3, 3**
6. $|x| - 10 = -3$ **-7, 7**

7. $4|d| = 20$ **-5, 5**
8. $-3|m| = -6$ **-2, 2**
9. $|y| + 3 = 3$ **0**

10. $12 = -4|k|$
   no solution
11. $2|z| - 5 = 1$ **-3, 3**
12. $16 = 5|p| - 4$ **-4, 4**

Lesson 3-6 Absolute Value Equations and Inequalities **169**

Additional Examples

3 Solve $|y - 5| \leq 2$. Graph the solutions. **$3 \leq y \leq 7$**

-1 0 1 2 3 4 5 6 7 8 9 10

4 The ideal diameter of a piston for one type of car is 88.000 mm. The actual diameter can vary from the ideal by at most 0.007 mm. Find the range of acceptable diameters for the piston. **between 87.993 mm and 88.007 mm, inclusive**

Closure

Ask students to explain when to use *and* and when to use *or* in an absolute value inequality. Assuming that the absolute value expression is on the left side of the inequality, if the inequality reads *is less than* or *is less than or equal to*, use *and*. If it reads *is greater than* or *is greater than or equal to*, use *or*.

3. Practice

Assignment Guide

1 Objective
- **A B Core** 1–21, 37–42, 61–71
- **C Extension** 72–74

2 Objective
- **A B Core** 22–36, 45–60
- **C Extension** 75–80

Standardized Test Prep 81–86

Mixed Review 87–98

Error Prevention

Exercises 37–51 Remind students to isolate the absolute value before writing the two inequalities.

pages 169–172 Exercises

23. $k < -2.5$ or $k > 2.5$;

-4 -3 -2 -1 0 1 2 3 4

24. $-2 < w < 2$;

-3 -2 -1 0 1 2 3

25. $-8 < x < 2$;

-8 -6 -4 -2 0 2

Example 2
(page 168)

Solve each equation. If there is no solution, write *no solution*.

13. $|r - 8| = 5$ **3, 13**   14. $|c + 2| = 6$ **−8, 4**   15. $2 = |g + 1|$ **−3, 1**

16. $3 = |m + 2|$ **−5, 1**   17. $|v - 2| = 7$ **−5, 9**   18. $-3|y - 3| = 9$ **no solution**

19. $2|d + 3| = 8$ **−7, 1**   20. $-2|7d| = -14$ **−1, 1**   21. $1.2|5p| = 3.6$ **−0.6, 0.6**

Example 3
(page 169)

22. Complete each statement with *less than* or *greater than*.
   a. For $|x| < 5$, the graph includes all points whose distance is _?_ 5 units from 0. **less than**
   b. For $|x| > 5$, the graph includes all points whose distance is _?_ 5 units from 0. **greater than**

Solve each inequality. Graph your solution. 23–34. See margin.

23. $|k| > 2.5$ 24. $|w| < 2$ 25. $|x + 3| < 5$

26. $|n + 8| \geq 3$ 27. $|y - 2| \leq 1$ 28. $|p - 4| \leq 3$

29. $|2c - 5| < 9$ 30. $|2y - 3| \geq 7$ 31. $|3t + 1| > 8$

32. $|4x + 1| > 11$ 33. $|5t - 4| \geq 16$ 34. $|3 - r| < 5$

Example 4
(page 169)

35. **Manufacturing** The ideal diameter of a gear for a certain type of clock is 12.24 mm. An actual diameter can vary by 0.06 mm. Find the range of acceptable diameters. **between 12.18 mm and 12.30 mm, inclusive**

36. **Manufacturing** The ideal width of a certain conveyor belt for a manufacturing plant is 50 in. An actual conveyor belt can vary from the ideal by at most $\frac{7}{32}$ in. Find the acceptable widths for this conveyor belt. **between $49\frac{25}{32}$ in. and $50\frac{7}{32}$ in., inclusive**

B Apply Your Skills

Solve each equation or inequality.

37. $|2d| + 3 = 21$ **−9, 9**   38. $|-3n| - 2 = 7$ **−3, 3**   39. $|p| - \frac{2}{3} = \frac{5}{6}$ **$-1\frac{1}{2}, 1\frac{1}{2}$**

40. $|t| + 2.7 = 4.5$ **−1.8, 1.8**   41. $4|k + 1| = 16$ **−5, 3**   42. $-2|c - 4| = -8$ **0, 8**

43. $|3d| \geq 6$ **$d \leq -2$ or $d \geq 2$**   44. $|n| - 3 > 7$ **$n < -10$ or $n > 10$**   45. $9 < |c + 7|$ **$c < -16$ or $c > 2$**

46. $\frac{|v|}{-3} = -4.2$ **−12.6, 12.6**   47. $|6.5x| < 39$ **$-6 < x < 6$**   48. $4|n| = 32$ **−8, 8**

49. $\left|\frac{1}{2}a\right| + 1 = 5$ **−8, 8**   50. $|a| + \frac{1}{2} = 3\frac{1}{2}$ **−3, 3**   51. $4 - 3|m + 2| > -14$ **$-8 < m < 4$**

Write an absolute value inequality that represents each situation.

52. all numbers less than 3 units from 0 **$|n| < 3$**

53. all numbers greater than 7.5 units from 0 **$|n| > 7.5$**

54. all numbers more than 2 units from 6 **$|n - 6| > 2$**

55. all numbers at least 3 units from −1 **$|n + 1| \geq 3$**

56. **Manufacturing** A pasta manufacturer makes 16-ounce boxes of macaroni. The manufacturer knows that not every box weighs exactly 16 ounces. The allowable difference is 0.05 ounce. Write and solve an absolute value inequality that represents this situation. **$|w - 16| \leq 0.05$, $15.95 \leq w \leq 16.05$**

57. **Elections** In a poll for the upcoming mayoral election, 42% of likely voters said they planned to vote for Lucy Jones. This poll has a margin of error of ± 3 percentage points. Use the inequality $|v - 42| \leq 3$ to find the least and greatest percent of voters v likely to vote for Lucy Jones according to this poll. **39%, 45%**

Need Help?

10 ± 2 means
$10 + 2$ or $10 - 2$.

---

26. $n \leq -11$ or $n \geq -5$;

-12 -10 -8 -6 -4 -2 0 2

27. $1 \leq y \leq 3$;

-1 0 1 2 3 4 5

28. $1 \leq p \leq 7$;

-1 0 1 2 3 4 5 6 7 8

29. $-2 < c < 7$;

-4 -2 0 2 4 6 8

30. $y \leq -2$ or $y \geq 5$;

-4 -2 0 2 4 6

31. $t < -3$ or $t > 2\frac{1}{3}$;

-4 -3 -2 -1 0 1 2 3 4

58. Quality Control A box of one brand of crackers should weigh 454 g. The quality-control inspector randomly selects boxes to weigh. The inspector sends back any box that is not within 5 g of the ideal weight.
a. Write an absolute value inequality for this situation. $|w - 454| \le 5$
b. What is the range of allowable weights for a box of crackers?
between 449 g and 459 g, inclusive

59. Gears Acceptable diameters for one type of gear are from 6.25 mm to 6.29 mm. Write an absolute value inequality for the acceptable diameters for the gear. $|g - 6.27| \le 0.02$

60. Writing Explain why the absolute value inequality $|2c - 5| + 9 < 4$ has no solution. **The absolute value of a number cannot be less than zero.**

61. Open-Ended Write an absolute value equation using the numbers $5, 3, -12$. Then solve your equation. **sample:** $|5x - 12| = 3; 1\frac{4}{5}, 3$

Write an absolute value equation that has the given values as solutions.

Sample $8, 2$

$|x - 5| = 3$ **Since 8 and 2 are both 3 units from 5, write** $|x - 5| = 3$.

62. $2, 6$ $|x - 4| = 2$ **63.** $-2, 6$
$|x - 2| = 4$
64. $-3, 9$
$|x - 3| = 6$
65. $9, 16$
$|x - 12\frac{1}{2}| = 3\frac{1}{2}$
66. $-1, 7$ $|x - 3| = 4$ **67.** $3, 8$
$|x - 5\frac{1}{2}| = 2\frac{1}{2}$
68. $-15, -3$
$|x + 9| = 6$
69. $2, 10$
$|x - 6| = 4$

70. Banking The ideal weight of a nickel is 0.176 ounce. To check that there are 40 nickels in a roll, a bank weighs the roll and allows for an error of 0.015 ounce in the total weight. **See margin.**
a. What is the range of acceptable weights if the wrapper weighs 0.05 ounce?
b. Critical Thinking For any given roll of nickels, can you be certain that all the coins are acceptable? Explain.

71. a. Meteorology A meteorologist reported that the previous day's temperatures varied 14 degrees from the normal temperature of 25°F. What were the maximum and minimum temperatures possible on the previous day?
b. Write an absolute value equation for the temperature. $|t - 25| = 14$
a. 11°F, 39°F

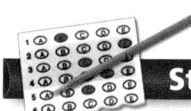 **Challenge**

Solve each equation. Check your solution.

72. $|x + 4| = 3x$ **2**   **73.** $|4x - 5| = 2x + 1$ $\frac{2}{3}, 3$ **74.** $\frac{4}{3}|2x + 3| = 4x$ **3**

Replace the ▪ with ≤, ≥, or =.

75. $|a + b| \underset{=}{\le} |a| + |b|$

76. $|a - b| \underset{=}{\ge} |a| - |b|$

77. $|ab| \underset{=}{=} |a| \cdot |b|$

78. $\left|\frac{a}{b}\right| \underset{=}{=} \frac{|a|}{|b|}, b \ne 0$

Write an absolute value inequality that each graph could represent.

79.
$-6\ -4\ -2\quad 0\quad 2\quad 4\quad 6$
$|x + 1| > 3$

80.
$-6\ -4\ -2\quad 0\quad 2\quad 4\quad 6$
$|x - 2| \le 4$

Standardized Test Prep

Multiple Choice

81. Which compound inequality has the same meaning as $|x + 4| < 8$? **A**
A. $-12 < x < 4$
B. $-12 > x > 4$
C. $x < -12$ or $x > 4$
D. $x > -12$ or $x < 4$

82. Which of the following values is a solution of $|2 - x| < 4$? **G**
F. -2 G. -1 H. 6 I. 7

Lesson 3-6   Absolute Value Equations and Inequalities   **171**

32. $x < -3$ or $x > 2.5$;
$-4\,-3\,-2\,-1\ 0\ 1\ 2\ 3$

33. $t \le -2.4$ or $t \ge 4$;
$-4\,-3\,-2\,-1\ 0\ 1\ 2\ 3\ 4\ 5$

34. $-2 < r < 8$;
$-4\,-2\ 0\ 2\ 4\ 6\ 8\ 10$

70a. between 7.075 oz and 7.105 oz, inclusive

b. No; the excess weight of some coins may be balanced by the lower weight of other coins.

Lesson Quiz 3-6
Solve.
1. $|a| + 6 = 9$ $a = 3$ or $a = -3$
2. $|2x + 3| = 7$ $x = 2$ or $x = -5$
3. $|p + 6| \le 1$ $-7 \le p \le -5$
4. $3|x + 4| > 15$ $x > 1$ or $x < -9$

Alternative Assessment

Have students make a list of the steps to follow in order to solve any absolute value inequality.
1. Isolate the absolute value.
2. If >, write as follows: expression < opposite number or expression > original number
3. If <, write as follows: opposite number < expression < original number.
4. Solve the compound inequality.

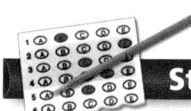
Hey! We're equal!   Absolutely!
$|8 - 5|$ $|2 - 5|$

171

Resources
For additional practice with a variety of test item formats:
- Standardized Test Prep, p. 179
- Test-Taking Strategies, p. 174
- Test-Taking Strategies with Transparencies

Error Prevention

Exercise 82 Suggest students rewrite $2 - x$ as $-x + 2$ before solving.

86a. [2]
15 20 25 30 35

86b. [2] The overlap of the three graphs is from 20 to 25, inclusive.

86a–b. [1] no graph OR insufficient explanation

Short Response

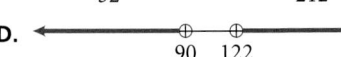
Take It to the NET
Online lesson quiz at
www.PHSchool.com
Web Code: aea-0306

83. The ideal diameter of a metal rod for a lamp is 1.25 inches with an allowable error of at most 0.005 inch. Which rod below would not be suitable? **D**
- **A.** a rod with diameter 1.249 inches
- **B.** a rod with diameter 1.251 inches
- **C.** a rod with diameter 1.253 inches
- **D.** a rod with diameter 1.355 inches

84. A delivery driver receives a bonus if he delivers pizza to a customer in 30 minutes plus or minus 5 minutes. Which inequality or equation represents the driver's allotted time to receive a bonus? **I**

- **F.** $|x - 30| < 5$
- **G.** $|x - 30| > 5$
- **H.** $|x - 30| = 5$
- **I.** $|x - 30| \le 5$

85. Water is in a liquid state if its temperature t, in degrees Fahrenheit, satisfies the inequality $|t - 122| < 90$. Which graph represents the temperatures described by this inequality? **A**

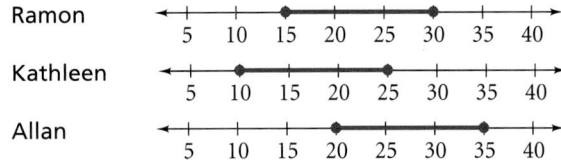

86. A bicycling club is planning a trip. The graphs below show the number of miles three people want to cycle per day.

Ramon
```
  5  10  15  20  25  30  35  40
```
Kathleen
```
  5  10  15  20  25  30  35  40
```
Allan
```
  5  10  15  20  25  30  35  40
```

a. Draw a graph showing a trip length that would be acceptable to all three bikers. **See above left.**
b. Explain how your graph relates to the graphs above. **See above left.**

Mixed Review

Lesson 3-5   **Write a compound inequality to model each situation.**

87. Elevation in North America is between the highest elevation of 20,320 ft above sea level at Mount McKinley, Alaska, and the lowest elevation of 282 ft below sea level at Death Valley, California. $-282 \le e \le 20{,}320$

88. Normal body temperature t is within 0.6 degrees of 36.6°C.
Let t = body temperature (°C), $36.0 \le t \le 37.2$.

Lesson 2-3   **Solve each equation.**

89. $3t + 4t = -21$ **−3**   **90.** $9(-2n + 3) = -27$ **3**   **91.** $k + 5 - 4k = -10$ **5**

92. $5x + 3 - 2x = -21$ **−8**   **93.** $5.4m - 2.3 = -0.5$ $\frac{1}{3}$ **94.** $3(y - 4) = 9$ **7**

Lesson 1-3   **Write each group of numbers from least to greatest.**

95. $3, -2, 0, -2.5, \pi$ $-2.5, -2, 0, 3, \pi$ **96.** $\frac{15}{2}, -1.5, -\frac{4}{3}, 7, -2$ $-2, -1.5, -\frac{4}{3}, 7, \frac{15}{2}$

97. $0.001, 0.01, 0.009, 0.011$ **98.** $-\pi, 2\pi, -2.5, -3, 3$
     $0.001, 0.009, 0.01, 0.011$ $-\pi, -3, -2.5, 3, 2\pi$

Algebraic Reasoning

You can use the properties you have studied along with the four properties below to prove algebraic relationships.

Reflexive, Symmetric, and Transitive Properties of Equality

For every real number a, b, and c:

Reflexive Property: $a = a$ **Example:** $5x = 5x$

Symmetric Property: If $a = b$, then $b = a$.   **Example:** If $15 = 3t$, then $3t = 15$.

Transitive Property: If $a = b$ and $b = c$, then $a = c$.   **Example:** If $d = 3y$ and $3y = 6$, then $d = 6$.

Transitive Property of Inequality

For all real numbers a, b, and c, if $a < b$ and $b < c$, then $a < c$.   **Example:** If $8x < 7$ and $7 < y^2$, then $8x < y^2$.

EXAMPLE

Prove each statement for all real numbers a, b, and c.

a. If $a = b$, then $ac = bc$.

$a = b$	Given
$ac = ac$	Reflexive Property
$ac = bc$	Substitute b for a.

b. If $c < 0$ and $a < b$, then $c < b - a$.

$c < 0$	Given
$a < b$	Given
$a - a < b - a$	Subtraction Property of Inequality
$a + (-a) < b - a$	Definition of subtraction
$0 < b - a$	Inverse Property of Addition
$c < b - a$	Transitive Property of Inequality

EXERCISES

Name the property that each exercise illustrates.

1. If $3.8 = z$, then $z = 3.8$.   **2.** If $x = \frac{1}{2}y$ and $\frac{1}{2}y = -2$, then $x = -2$.   **3.** $-r = -r$

4. If $k < m^2$ and $m^2 < 4$, then $k < 4$.   **5.** If $x = w^2$, then $w^2 = x$.

Supply the missing reasons to prove each statement.

6. $(a + b) + (-a) = b$

$(a + b) + (-a) = (b + a) + (-a)$	?
$= b + [a + (-a)]$	?
$= b + 0$	?
$= b$	?
$(a + b) + (-a) = b$	?

7. If $a < b$ and $c < d$, then $a + c < b + d$.

$a < b$	Given
$a + c < b + c$	?
$c < d$	Given
$b + c < b + d$	?
$a + c < b + d$	?

Answer key (sidebar)

1. Symmetric Prop. of Equality
2. Transitive Prop. of Equality
3. Reflexive Prop. of Equality
4. Transitive Prop. of Inequality
5. Symmetric Prop. of Equality

6. Comm. Prop. of Add.
Assoc. Prop. of Add.
Inverse Prop. of Add.
Identity Prop. of Add.
Transitive Prop. of Eq.

7. Add. Prop. of Ineq.
Add. Prop. of Ineq.
Transitive Prop. of Ineq.

Extension

Algebraic Reasoning

Students learn to identify and name four properties of numbers that will enable them to prove algebraic relationships.

Resources

Technology
Computer Test Generator
CD-ROM, Chapter 0, Extension Topics

Teaching Notes

Inclusion

To help students remember the names of the properties, have them use memory devices. They can make up their own or you can tell them these. For the reflexive property, have them think <u>re</u>peat/<u>re</u>flexive ($a = a$, a is <u>re</u>peated and they both begin with <u>re</u>). For the <u>trans</u>itive property they can think of <u>trans</u>fer as in a to b, b to c, c back to a. Sym<u>met</u>ric Property can be remembered that if a <u>met</u> b, then b most certainly <u>met</u> a and sym<u>met</u>ric contains <u>met</u>.

Writing Extended Responses

This feature helps students understand how answers to extended response questions are evaluated. This will encourage students to write complete solutions, answer all parts of a problem, label answers, and show the work they did to get the solutions.

Resources

PRENTICE HALL
ASSESSMENT SYSTEM

Test-Taking Strategies with Transparencies
- Transparency 3
- Practice sheet p. 3

Teaching Notes

Prior to this feature, give students several problems to do, and tell them to justify their answers. Write a four-point rubric. Have students use it to evaluate their work. Then have them re-write, if needed, until they feel their work is worth 4 points. Have pairs of students see if each agrees with their partner's self-assessment. Then encourage a class discussion.

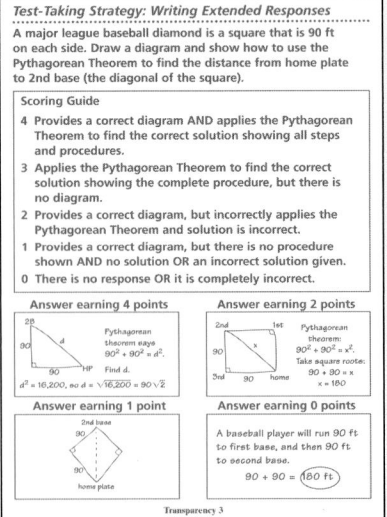

An extended-response question is usually worth a maximum of 4 points in this textbook. It sometimes has multiple parts. To get full credit, you need to answer each part and show all your work or justify your reasoning.

EXAMPLE

The Theatre Club needs to raise at least $440 to cover the cost of its children's play. The ticket prices are $14 for an adult and $2 for a child. The club expects that three times as many children as adults will attend the play. Write and solve an inequality to find how many adults and children have to buy tickets in order for the club to cover its costs.

Three responses are below with the points each received.

4 points	3 points	1 point
x = number of adults	x = number of adults	x = number of adults
$3x$ = number of children	$14(x) + 2(3x) \geq 440$	$x + 3x \geq 440$
$14(x) + 2(3x) \geq 440$	$14x + 5x \geq 440$	$4x \geq 440$
$14x + 6x \geq 440$	$19x \geq 440$	$x \geq 110$
$20x \geq 440$	$x \geq 23.2$	
$x \geq 22$	At least 24 adults	
$3x \geq 66$	and $3(24) = 72$	
At least 22 adults	children must	
and 66 children	attend the play.	
must attend the play.		

The 4-point response shows the work and gives a written answer to the problem. Note that it begins by identifying the variable before writing the inequality.

The 3-point response contains a computational error, but the student completed both parts.

The 1-point response shows an incorrect inequality, and it does not give the number of children who must attend to cover costs.

EXERCISES

Use the Example above to answer each question.

1. Read the 3-point response. What error did the student make? **computation error, $2(3x) = 6x$ not $5x$**

2. Write a 2-point response that begins by defining variables.
   x = **number of adults, $14(x) + 2(3x) \geq 440$, at least 24 adults and 72 children must attend.**

3. Error Analysis Why is the inequality in the 1-point response incorrect?
   The inequality does not include prices of tickets.

Chapter Review

Vocabulary

compound inequalities (p. 161)   equivalent inequalities (p. 140)   solution of an inequality (p. 134)

Reading Math
Understanding
Vocabulary

Write the letter of the choice that correctly completes each sentence.

1. A solution of an inequality is any number that makes the inequality _?_. **C**
  A. complete   **B.** reverse direction
  C. true   **D.** false

2. An inequality is equivalent to another inequality if the two inequalities have _?_. **B**
  A. the same number of terms   **B.** the same graphs
  C. real-number solutions   **D.** no solutions

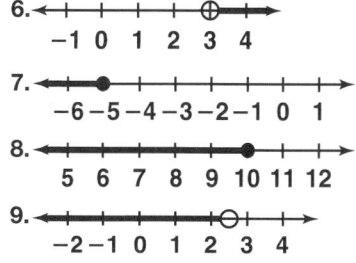

Take It to the NET
Online vocabulary quiz
at **www.PHSchool.com**
Web Code: aej-0351

3. Compound inequalities are joined by _?_. **A**
  A. either the word *and* or the word *or*   **B.** the word *or*
  C. the word *and*   **D.** equations

4. Write the expression "absolute value of x" as _?_. **C**
  A. $[x]$ **B.** $-x$ **C.** $|x|$ **D.** $a = x$

5. A number's distance from 0 on a number line is the number's _?_. **D**
  A. solution of an inequality   **B.** compound form
  C. equivalent form   **D.** absolute value

Skills and Concepts

3-1 Objectives

▼ To identify solutions of inequalities (p. 134)

▼ To graph and write inequalities (p. 135)

A **solution of an inequality** is any number that makes the inequality true. A graph can indicate all the solutions of an inequality. On the graph, a closed dot indicates that the number is a solution. An open dot indicates that the number is *not* a solution.

Graph each inequality.   6–9. See left.

6. $x > 3$ **7.** $m \le -5$ **8.** $10 \ge p$ **9.** $r < 2.5$

Write an inequality for each graph.

10. $n < -2$
−4 −3 −2 −1   0   1

11. $n \ge -3.5$
−5 −4 −3 −2 −1   0   1

12. $n > -6$
−10 −8 −6 −4 −2   0   2

13. $n \ge 2$
−2 −1   0   1   2   3   4

Define a variable and write an inequality to model each situation.

14. At least 600 people attended a school play. **Let p = number of people, $p \ge 600$.**

15. An elevator can carry at most 15 people. **Let n = number of people, $n \le 15$.**

16. The temperature was less than 32°F. **Let t = temperature in degrees Fahrenheit, $t < 32$.**

6.
−1 0 1 2 3 4

7.
−6 −5 −4 −3 −2 −1 0 1

8.
5 6 7 8 9 10 11 12

9.
−2 −1 0 1 2 3 4

Resources

Student Edition
Extra Practice, Ch. 3, p. 704
English/Spanish Glossary, p. 757
Properties and Formulas, p. 752
Table of Symbols, p. 749

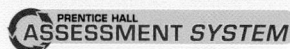 **Reaching All Students**
Reading and Math Literacy 3D
Spanish Reading and Math
Literacy 3D

 **PRENTICE HALL** **ASSESSMENT** *SYSTEM*

Standardized Test Prep
- Ch. 3 practice in standardized test formats

 **www.PHSchool.com**
Student Site
- Self-grading Vocabulary Test
Teacher Center
- Resources

Plus **i TEXT**

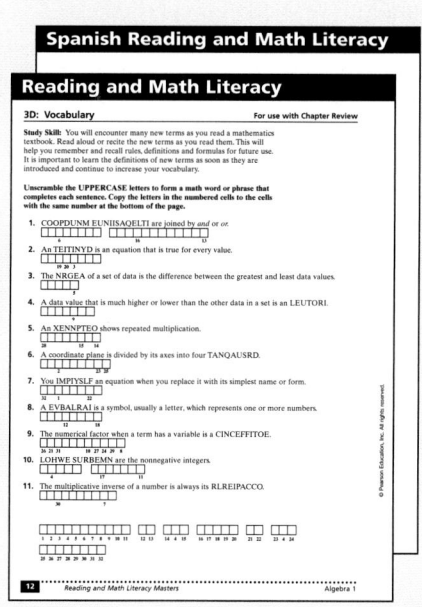

Spanish Reading and Math Literacy

Reading and Math Literacy

3D: Vocabulary   For use with Chapter Review

pages 175–177
Chapter Review

17. $h > -1$;

−3 −2 −1 0 1 2

18. $t < -5$;

−8 −7 −6 −5 −4 −3

19. $m \geq -3$;
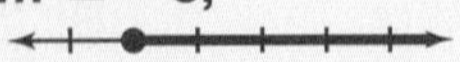
−4 −3 −2 −1 0 1

20. $w \geq -2$;

−4 −3 −2 −1 0 1

21. $q > -2.5$;
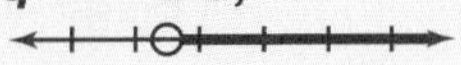
−4 −3 −2 −1 0 1

22. $y > -14$;

−15 −10 −5 0 5

23. $n \leq 15$;

−5 0 5 10 15 20

24. $d \geq 4$;
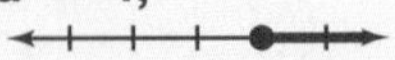
−2 0 2 4 6

25. $-2 \leq t$;

−6 −4 −2 0 2 4 6

26. $0 < c$;

−2 −1 0 1 2

27. $2.5 \geq u$;

−1 0 1 2 3 4

28. $-9 < p$;

−10 −8 −6 −4 −2 0 2

3-2 and 3-3 Objectives

- ▼ To use addition to solve inequalities (p. 140)
- ▼ To use subtraction to solve inequalities (p. 141)
- ▼ To use multiplication to solve inequalities (p. 146)
- ▼ To use division to solve inequalities (p. 148)

To solve inequalities, you may need to find a simpler, equivalent inequality. **Equivalent inequalities** have the same solution. You can add, subtract, multiply, or divide both sides of an inequality by the same number to find a simpler equivalent inequality. Multiplying or dividing by a negative number causes the direction of the inequality symbol to be *reversed.*

Properties of Inequality
For all real numbers a, b, and c:

- If $a > b$, then $a + c > b + c$ and $a - c > b - c$.
- If $a < b$, then $a + c < b + c$ and $a - c < b - c$.
- If $a > b$ and $c > 0$, then $ac > bc$ and $\frac{a}{c} > \frac{b}{c}$.
- If $a < b$ and $c > 0$, then $ac < bc$ and $\frac{a}{c} < \frac{b}{c}$.
- If $a > b$ and $c < 0$, then $ac < bc$ and $\frac{a}{c} < \frac{b}{c}$.
- If $a < b$ and $c < 0$, then $ac > bc$ and $\frac{a}{c} > \frac{b}{c}$.

These properties are also true for inequalities involving ≤ and ≥.

Solve each inequality. Graph and check the solution. **17–28. See margin.**

17. $h + 3 > 2$	**18.** $t - 4 < -9$	**19.** $8m \geq -24$	**20.** $-6w \leq 12$
21. $q + 0.5 > -2$	**22.** $y - 8 > -22$	**23.** $-\frac{3}{5}n \geq -9$	**24.** $\frac{5}{8}d \geq \frac{5}{2}$
25. $0 \leq 2 + t$	**26.** $0 < 4c$	**27.** $-0.3 \geq u - 2.8$	**28.** $3 > -\frac{1}{3}p$

29. Weekly Budget You have an allowance of \$12.00. You buy a discount movie ticket that costs at least \$3.50 and popcorn that costs \$2.75. Write and solve an inequality to find how much you have for other spending. **$3.50 + 2.75 + x \leq 12.00$, $x \leq 5.75$**

30. Jobs Suppose you earn \$7.25 per hour working part-time as a florist. Write and solve an inequality to find how many full hours you must work to earn at least \$200. **$7.25h \geq 200$, $h \geq 27.586$. You must work at least 28 h.**

3-4 Objectives

- ▼ To solve multi-step inequalities with variables on one side (p. 153)
- ▼ To solve multi-step inequalities with variables on both sides (p. 155)

When you solve equations, sometimes you need to use more than one step. The same is true for inequalities. Many inequalities have variables on both sides of the inequality symbol. You need to gather the variable terms on one side of the inequality and the constant terms on the other side.

Solve each inequality. Check your solution.

31. $3n + 5 > -1$ **$n > -2$**	**32.** $4k - 1 \leq -3$ **$k \leq -\frac{1}{2}$**	**33.** $\frac{5}{8}b < 25$ **$b < 40$**
34. $6(c - 1) \leq -18$ **$c \leq -2$**	**35.** $3m > 5m + 12$ **$m < -6$**	**36.** $t - 4t < -9$ **$t > 3$**
37. $0.5x - 2 \geq -4x + 7$ **$x \geq 2$**	**38.** $-\frac{6}{7}y - 6 \geq 42$ **$y \leq -56$**	**39.** $4 + \frac{x}{2} > 2x$ **$x < \frac{8}{3}$**

40. Commission Trenton sells electronic supplies. Each week he earns \$190 plus a commission equal to 4% of his sales. This week his goal is to earn no less than \$500. Write and solve an inequality to find the amount of sales he must have to reach his goal. **$190 + 0.04x \geq 500$, $x \geq 7750$**

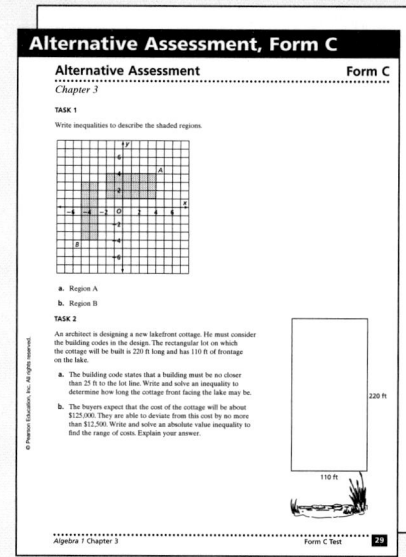
3-5 Objectives

▼ To solve and graph inequalities containing *and* (p. 161)

▼ To solve and graph inequalities containing *or* (p. 163)

Two inequalities that are joined by the word *and* or the word *or* are called **compound inequalities.** A solution of a compound inequality joined by *and* makes both inequalities true. A solution of a compound inequality joined by *or* makes either inequality true. A number sentence with two inequality symbols, such as $a < x < b$ represents the compound inequality $a < x$ and $x < b$.

Graph each compound inequality. 41–43. See margin.

41. $x > -3$ and $x < 2$ **42.** $m < -2$ or $m \geq 1$ **43.** $-3 \leq k < 4$

Solve each compound inequality and graph the solutions. 44–49. See margin.

44. $-3 \leq z - 1 < 3$ **45.** $-2 \leq d + \frac{1}{2} < 4\frac{1}{2}$ **46.** $0 < -8b \leq 12$

47. $2t \leq -4$ or $7t \geq 49$ **48.** $-1 \leq a - 3 < 2$ **49.** $-2 \leq 3a - 8 < 4$

50. Climate In Miami, Florida, July's average high temperature is 89°F. July's average low temperature is 75°F. Write a compound inequality to represent Miami's average temperature in July. **$75 \leq t \leq 89$**

3-6 Objectives

▼ To solve equations that involve absolute value (p. 167)

▼ To solve inequalities that involve absolute value (p. 168)

Recall that the absolute value of a number is its distance from 0 on a number line. Since absolute value represents distance, it can never be negative.

Solving Absolute Value Equations and Inequalities

- To solve an equation in the form $|A| = b$, where A represents a variable expression and $b > 0$, solve the equations $A = b$ or $A = -b$.
- To solve an inequality in the form $|A| < b$, where A represents a variable expression and $b > 0$, solve $-b < A < b$.
- To solve an inequality in the form $|A| > b$, where A represents a variable expression and $b > 0$, solve $A < -b$ or $A > b$.

Similar rules are true for $|A| \leq b$ and $|A| \geq b$.

Write an absolute value inequality that represents each set of numbers.

51. all numbers n that are more than 3 units from -2 $|n + 2| > 3$

52. all numbers n that are within 5 units of 12 $|n - 12| \leq 5$

Solve each equation or inequality. 53–64. See left.

53. 5 or −5
54. $n \leq -6$ or $n \geq 2$
55. $-3 \leq x \leq 3$
56. $-9.6 < m < 9.6$
57. $x < 3$ or $x > 4$
58. 6.5 or −12.5
59. 8
60. all real numbers
61. no solution
62. $k < -7$ or $k > -3$
63. −5 or 1
64. $z \leq -0.25$ or $z \geq 0.25$

53. $|y| = 5$ **54.** $|n + 2| \geq 4$ **55.** $|-5x| \leq 15$

56. $|\frac{1}{2}m| < 4.8$ **57.** $|2x - 7| - 1 > 0$ **58.** $|p + 3| = 9.5$

59. $|k - 8| = 0$ **60.** $|3x + 5| > -2$ **61.** $|6 - b| = -1$

62. $4|k + 5| > 8$ **63.** $4 + |r + 2| = 7$ **64.** $-2 + |3.6z| \geq -1.1$

65. Manufacturing The ideal diameter of a steel reinforcement rod is 2.8 cm. The actual diameter may vary from the ideal by at most 0.06 cm. Find the range of acceptable diameters for this steel rod. **$2.74 \leq d \leq 2.86$**

66. Manufacturing The ideal length of a certain nail is 20 mm. The actual length can vary from the ideal by at most 0.4 mm. Find the range of acceptable lengths of the nail. **$19.6 \leq \ell \leq 20.4$**

41.

42.

43.

44. $-2 \leq z < 4,$

45. $-\frac{5}{2} \leq d < 4,$

46. $-\frac{3}{2} \leq b < 0,$

47. $t \leq -2$ or $t \geq 7,$

48. $2 \leq a < 5,$

49. $2 \leq a < 4,$

Resources

Teaching Resources
Ch. 3 Test, Forms A & B
Ch. 3 Alternative Assessment,
Form C

Reaching All Students
Spanish Ch. 3 Test, Forms A & B
Spanish Ch. 3 Alternative
Assessment, Form C
Basic Algebra Ch. 3 Test,
Forms D & E

PRENTICE HALL ASSESSMENT SYSTEM

Assessment Masters
• Ch. 3 Test, Forms A & B
• Ch. 3 Alternative Assessment,
Form C
Computer Test Generator CD
• Ch. 3 pre-made Test
• Make your own Ch. 3 test

www.PHSchool.com
Student Site
• Self-grading Chapter 3 Test
Teacher Center
• Resources

Plus **iTEXT**

Chapter Test — Form B

Chapter Test — Form A

Chapter Test

Take It to the NET
Online chapter test at
www.PHSchool.com
Web Code: aea-0352

Determine whether each number is a solution of the given inequality.

1. $4z + 7 \geq 15$ a. -2 no b. 2 yes c. 5 yes

2. $-2g + 3 > 5$ a. -3 yes b. -1 no c. 4 no

Define a variable and write an inequality to model each situation.

3. A student can take at most 7 classes. $c \leq 7$

4. The school track team needs at least 5 runners to compete at Saturday's meet. $r \geq 5$

5. Elephants can drink up to 40 gallons of water at a time. $g \leq 40$

6. Your cousin's early-morning paper route has more than 32 homes. $h > 32$

Write an inequality for each graph.

7. $n < -7$

8. $n \leq 4.5$

9. $n \geq -5$

10. $n > 1.5$

Solve each inequality. Graph the solution.

11–24. See back of book.

11. $z + 7 \leq 9$ 12. $-16 \geq 4y$

13. $-\frac{1}{3}x < 2$ 14. $8 - u > 4$

15. $-5 + 4t \leq 3$ 16. $5w \geq -6w + 11$

17. $-\frac{7}{2}m < 14$ 18. $6y - 7 < -2y + 13$

19. $|x - 5| \geq 3$ 20. $|2h + 1| < 5$

21. $9 \leq 6 - b < 12$ 22. $-10 < 4q < 12$

23. $4 + 3n \geq 1$ or $-5n > 25$

24. $10k < 75$ and $4 - k \leq 0$

Solve each equation. Check your solution.

25. $3(d - 1) > -4$ $d > -\frac{1}{3}$ 26. $5(-2 + b) < 3b + 2$ $b < 6$

27. $3(m + 3) + 4 \leq 15$ $m \leq \frac{2}{3}$ 28. $0.5(x + 3) - 2.1 \geq -1$ $x \geq -0.8$

Write a compound inequality that each graph could represent.

29–30. Answers may vary. Samples are given:

29. $x \leq -6$ or $x > 2$

30. $-3 < x < 2$

Solve each equation. Check your solution.

31. $|4k - 2| = 11$ -2.25 or 3.25   32. $23 = |n + 10|$ -33 or 13

33. $|3c + 1| - 4 = 13$ -6 or $5\frac{1}{3}$ 34. $4|5 - t| = 20$ 0 or 10

35. **Writing** Explain why the solution to $ax - 1 < 3$ is not $x < \frac{4}{a}$. Use solutions of the inequality with different values of a to support your explanation. **See margin.**

36. **Open-Ended** Write an absolute value inequality that has 3 and -5 as two of its solutions. **Answers may vary. Sample: $|x| < 6$**

37. **Community Service** The chart below shows the number of cans of food collected by a club during the first four weeks of a food drive.

Food Drive

Week	Number of Cans
1	702
2	470
3	492
4	547

37. Let c = number of cans
$c + 702 + 470 + 492 + 547 \geq 3000$
$c \geq 789$

The goal is to collect at least 3000 cans in 5 weeks. Write and solve an inequality to find how many cans should be collected during Week 5 to meet or exceed the goal. **See above.**

38. **Safe Load** A freight elevator can safely hold no more than 2000 pounds. An elevator operator must take 55-pound boxes to a storage area. If he weighs 165 pounds, how many boxes can he safely move at one time? **33 boxes**

39. **Manufacturing** A manufacturer is cutting plastic sheets to make rectangles that are 11.125 in. by 7.625 in. Each rectangle's length and width must be within 0.005 in. of the desired size. Write and solve inequalities to find the acceptable range for the length ℓ and for the width w. **See margin.**

page 178 Chapter Test

35. Answers may vary. Sample: Depending on the sign of x, the inequality symbol may need to be reversed.

$a = 2$: $2x - 1 < 3$
$2x < 4$
$x < 2$
$a = -2$: $-2x - 1 < 3$
$-2x < 4$
$x > -2$

$2 < 3$
$(-4)(2)$ $(-4)(3)$
$-8 > -12$

$-3 < -2$
$(-4)(-3)$ $(-4)(-2)$
$12 > 8$

Standardized Test Prep

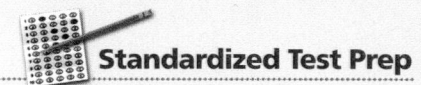

Reading Comprehension Read the passage below. Then answer the questions on the basis of what is *stated* or *implied* in the passage.

> **Geometry of Earth** Long before Columbus, a Greek scholar named Eratosthenes (274–194 B.C.) calculated the circumference of Earth by making some simple observations about shadows at noon and applying some insights from geometry.
>
> The size of Earth has been estimated and measured many times since then. The French Academy of Sciences tried to make an accurate measurement in the late 1700s in order to create a new unit of measure, the meter. They proposed to define the meter as one ten-millionth of the distance from the North Pole to the equator.
>
> Today we can measure Earth's circumference very accurately using data from satellites and making calculations on computers. The circumference at the equator is 24,901.55 miles. Earth is not a perfect sphere, however, because its rotation causes it to bulge a little at the equator. So the circumference from pole to pole is a bit smaller, about 24,859.82 miles.

1. How many centuries before the French Academy of Sciences measured the circumference of Earth did Eratosthenes live? **B**
   A. 22 centuries   B. 20 centuries
   C. 18 centuries   D. 16 centuries

2. How much greater is the circumference of Earth at the equator than the circumference at the poles? **G**
   F. about 20 miles
   G. about 40 miles
   H. about 80 miles
   I. about 200 miles

3. Earth is divided into 24 time zones. About how wide is each time zone at the equator? **C**
   A. 1031 miles
   B. 1036 miles
   C. 1038 miles
   D. 1042 miles

4. Which is the best estimate of the diameter of Earth measured from pole to pole? **I**
   F. 3960 miles
   G. 4530 miles
   H. 6300 miles
   I. 7920 miles

5. A geostationary satellite moves in an orbit 22,300 miles above the equator. The satellite moves at a rate such that it stays at the same point above Earth as Earth rotates on its axis. What is the approximate speed of the satellite? **B**
   A. 700 miles per hour
   B. 7000 miles per hour
   C. 10,000 miles per hour
   D. 14,000 miles per hour

6–7. See back of book.

6. a. One mile is equal to about 1610 meters. Write an equation expressing this relationship. Use the equation to calculate the approximate circumference of Earth from pole to pole in meters.
   b. Is the meter unit of measure you found close to the Academy of Sciences' original definition? Explain.

7. a. As Earth rotates, the line separating night from day moves west across Earth's surface. How fast is this line moving in miles per minute at the equator? Show your work.
   b. Does the day-night dividing line move more quickly or more slowly across your state than it does at the equator? Explain.

Students must be able to extract information from reading passages, answer multiple choice questions, and construct responses in order to be successful on current state and national assessments.

To answer the questions, students apply skills and concepts from this chapter and previous chapters.
Multiple Choice: Items 1–5
Extended Response: Items 6, 7

Resources

Teaching Resources
Cumulative Review
Quarter 1 Test, Forms A & B

Reaching All Students
Spanish Cumulative Review
Spanish Quarter 1 Test,
   Forms A & B

PRENTICE HALL
ASSESSMENT SYSTEM

Standardized Test Prep
• Ch. 3 Standardized Test Practice
Assessment Masters
• Cumulative Review
• Quarter 1 Test, Forms A & B
Computer Test Generator CD
• Standardized Test Practice

www.PHSchool.com
• Standardized Test Practice
• Resources

Plus **iTEXT**

---

39. Let ℓ = length
      w = width
   $|\ell - 11.125| \le 0.005$
   $|w - 7.625| \le 0.005$
     $11.120 \le \ell \le 11.130$
      $7.620 \le w \le 7.630$

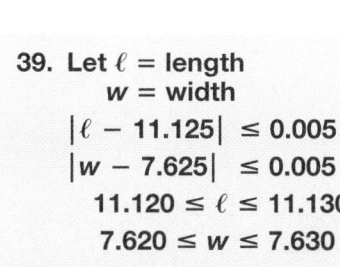

179

Chapter 4

Solving and Applying Proportions

Chapter at a Glance

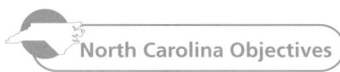 North Carolina Objectives

4-1 Ratio and Proportion   1.02

NCTM
1, 2, 4,
9, 10
   ⓥ Ratios and Rates
   ⓥ Solving Proportions

4-2 Proportions and Similar Figures   1.02

NCTM
2, 3, 4,
6
   ⓥ Similar Figures
   ⓥ Indirect Measurement and Scale Drawings

4-3 Proportions and Percent Equations   1.02

NCTM
1, 2, 6,
8
   ⓥ Applying Proportions to Percent Problems
   ⓥ Percent Equations

4-4 Percent of Change   1.02

NCTM
2, 3, 4,
6, 9
   ⓥ Percent of Change
   ⓥ Percent Error

4-5 Applying Ratios to Probability

NCTM
2, 5, 6,
7, 10
   ⓥ Theoretical Probability
   ⓥ Experimental Probability

4-6 Probability of Compound Events

NCTM
2, 5, 6,
7, 9
   ⓥ Finding the Probability of Independent Events
   ⓥ Finding the Probability of Dependent Events

NCTM STANDARDS 2000

1	Number and Operations	6	Problem Solving
2	Algebra	7	Reasoning and Proof
3	Geometry	8	Communication
4	Measurement	9	Connections
5	Data Analysis and Probability	10	Representation

Pacing Options

This chart suggests pacing only for the lessons and their parts. It is provided as a possible guide. It will help you determine how much time you have in your schedule to cover other components, such as the features, Chapter Review, and Chapter Test.

Day	Traditional 45 min.	Two-Year 45 min.	Block 90 min.
1	4-1 ⓥⓥ	4-1 ⓥ	4-1 ⓥⓥ 4-2 ⓥ
2	4-2 ⓥⓥ	4-1 ⓥ	4-2 ⓥ 4-3 ⓥ
3	4-3 ⓥⓥ	4-2 ⓥ	4-3 ⓥ 4-4 ⓥⓥ
4	4-4 ⓥⓥ	4-2 ⓥ	4-5 ⓥⓥ
5	4-5 ⓥ	4-3 ⓥ	4-6 ⓥⓥ
6	4-5 ⓥ	4-3 ⓥ	
7	4-6 ⓥⓥ	4-4 ⓥ	
8		4-4 ⓥ	
9		4-5 ⓥ	
10		4-5 ⓥⓥ	
11		4-5 ⓥ	
12		4-6 ⓥ	
13		4-6 ⓥⓥ	
14		4-6 ⓥ	

NAEP Correlation (National Assessment of Educational Progress 2000 Mathematics Objectives)

4-1	4-2	4-3	4-4	4-5	4-6
N5a, M6, M10	N5; M8, M9; G5; G6C	N5c, d, e	N5e; M7c, d	D10b, c; D11c	D11b, c

N = Number Sense, Properties, and Operations; **M** = Measurement; **G** = Geometry and Spatial Sense;
D = Data Analysis, Statistics, and Probability; **A** = Algebra and Functions

Math Background

Chapter Overview

This chapter takes one fundamental structure, a proportion that states the equality between two ratios, and uses it in many different applications. The methods for setting up and solving a proportion, once learned, can be used to solve problems involving percent, measurements in similar figures, indirect measurement, and probabilities. Students will use what they learn about ratio and proportions in this chapter when they tackle rational expressions and functions in Chapter 12.

Ratio and Proportion   4-1

The term ratio can be used as a clue that a ratio of two nonzero integers can be written as a rational number. The order of the parts of a ratio is extremely important: 2 : 3 is not the same as 3 : 2. Ratios represent multiplicative relationships. For example, if there are 7 students in a classroom, and the ratio of girls to boys is 4 : 3, the ratio is not maintained if one more girl and one more boy walk into the classroom. For the ratio to be maintained, some multiple of 4 boys and 3 girls must be added.

Dimensional analysis is especially useful when converting between units within the metric system. Students will probably have to use dimensional analysis to convert between units when they conduct experiments in their science classes.

Proportions and Similar Figures   4-2

Students probably know that similar figures have the same shape, but may have different sizes. Ratios and proportions are used to express the relationship between the corresponding sides of similar figures. When two geometric figures are similar, the lengths of their corresponding sides (as well as other measures such as the altitude or the median) are always in the same ratio. As with any proportion, several equivalent proportions can be written for pairs of corresponding parts.

Proportions and Percent Equations   4-3

Proportions provide a convenient structure for solving many kinds of problems. Essentially a proportion sets up two equivalent comparisons. When writing these comparisons, the two quantities being compared must be written in the same order. For example, a proportion that compares students to teachers on one side of the equation must also compare students to teachers on the other side, and not teachers to students.

Since any percent can easily be written as a ratio comparing a number to 100, proportions can be used to solve any kind of problem that involves percent. There may be some confusion about the vocabulary used with percent problems. For example, in the statement 50% of 16 is 8, 16 is the base, or whole, and 8 is often called the part. The base, or whole, is the value that is being multiplied by a percent, or rate. In this case, the percent is 50. In this example, 8 is the part because it is only part of a whole. However, be careful not to say that the part is less than the whole. Notice that 150% of 16 is 24, but 24 > 16.

Percent of Change   4-4

The percent of change is a ratio that compares the amount of the change (whether an increase or a decrease) to the original amount. In mathematical notation, this might be written as Δx, where the Δ, or delta, means "change in." Using this delta notation may help to avoid the common error of thinking that the percent of change is the ratio of the new amount to the original amount. Using the symbol delta to indicate change occurs frequently in higher mathematics.

The percent error in measurements and calculations is another important application of proportions. Students may tend to think of measurements as exact. It is important that they understand the difference between problems in abstract numbers, such as 12 inches = 1 foot, and the results of actual measurements, such as the length of the table = 12 inches. This latter statement should be interpreted as the length of the table is approximately 12 inches, within a margin of error that is one half of the measuring unit used.

Applying Ratios to Probability   4–5

Probability is another application of ratios, since probability is usually given as the ratio of favorable outcomes to all possible outcomes. As with measurements, there is a distinction between theoretical outcomes and those that result from actual events. Although the theoretical probability of an outcome of heads when tossing a coin is 1 : 2, it is perfectly possible that one can toss a coin 17 times and never have an outcome of heads. The principle that the experimental probability will approach the theoretical probability as the number of trials increases is sometimes called the Law of Large Numbers.

Probability of Compound Events   4-6

Discuss with students various compound probability events to make sure students understand the difference between dependent and independent events. When students look at compound probability problems, have them first look at whether the first event affects the second. For example, does rolling one number cube affect rolling a second? Does pulling a marble out of a bag affect pulling out a second? Once students determine whether the events are dependent or independent, they can select the appropriate equation. However, it is not always apparent whether events are independent, but it is certain that $P(A \text{ and } B) = P(A) \cdot P(B)$ if and only if A and B are independent events.

Ongoing Assessment and Intervention

Tools for Monitoring Student Progress

The Prentice Hall *Algebra 1* program provides you with many options for assessment in the Student Edition, the Teacher's Edition and the teaching resources. From these options you may choose instructional materials and techniques that are appropriate for your students and support your district's curriculum requirements.

 Instant Check System™ in Chapter 4

Allows students to check their own learning before, during, and after each lesson.

Diagnosing Readiness before the chapter (p. 180)

Check Skills You'll Need exercises in each lesson (pp. 182, 189, 197, 204, 211, 219)

Check Understanding questions with each Example (pp. 182, 183, 184, 185, 190, 191, 197, 198, 199, 200, 204, 205, 206, 212, 213, 220, 221)

Checkpoint Quiz (pp. 195, 217)

 Test Prep in Chapter 4

Teaches students strategies and gives them practice with all the test item formats they will encounter on state tests and standardized national exams.

Standardized Test Prep exercises in each lesson (pp. 188, 194, 195, 202, 209, 216, 217, 224)

Test-Taking Strategies (p. 226: Making Quantitative Comparisons)

Standardized Test Prep (p. 231: Cumulative Review)

All your assessment needs in one place!

Program Assessment

Assess student progress throughout the *Algebra 1* text with blackline masters and CD-ROM.

Assessment Resources

- Checkpoint Quizzes 1 & 2
- Chapter Test, Forms A & B
- Chapter Alternative Assessment

Spanish versions available. Tests for Basic Algebra also available.

 Computer Test Generator

- Unlimited questions of varying difficulty for every lesson objective.
- Create your own practice sheets, quizzes, and tests, or use the pre-made Chapter Tests.
- Diagnose readiness with questions on prerequisite skills.
- Prepare students by making tests based on standardized test objectives.
- Access Algebra 1, Geometry, and Algebra 2 content—all on one CD-ROM.

Test Preparation

A three-step approach to preparing students for high stakes, national, and state exams.

❶ **Diagnose & Prescribe**

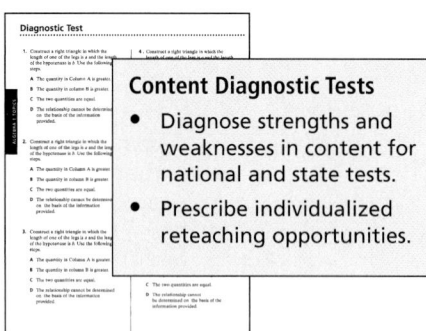

Content Diagnostic Tests
- Diagnose strengths and weaknesses in content for national and state tests.
- Prescribe individualized reteaching opportunities.

❷ **Review & Reteach**

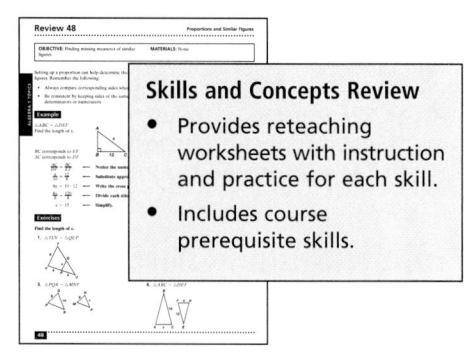

Skills and Concepts Review
- Provides reteaching worksheets with instruction and practice for each skill.
- Includes course prerequisite skills.

❸ **Practice & Assess**

Test Preparation
- Features practice tests for End-of-Course and SAT/ACT exams.
- Includes standardized test practice by chapter for ongoing review.

Teacher's Guide with answers and correlations.

Test-Taking Strategies with Transparencies
- Support the Test-Taking Strategies pages in the Student Edition.
- Provide a teaching transparency and a practice worksheet for each strategy.

 # Reaching All Students

Support in the Student Text and Additional Resources

The textbook, the iText, and other technology components provide numerous opportunities to reach students of various ability levels and learning styles. Each Teacher's Edition lesson suggests how you can help *all* your students be successful and understand the mathematics in Chapter 4.

Below Level

Student Edition
- Diagnosing Readiness*: p. 180
- Check Skills You'll Need*: pp. 182, 189, 197, 204, 211, 219

Reteaching
Chapter 4 Support File: pp. 8–13

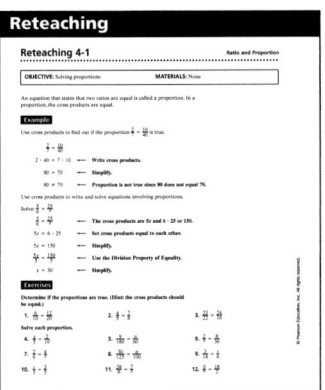

Basic Algebra Planning Guide
Chapter 4 Lesson Plans: pp. 23–28
Chapter 4 Tests: pp. 101–104

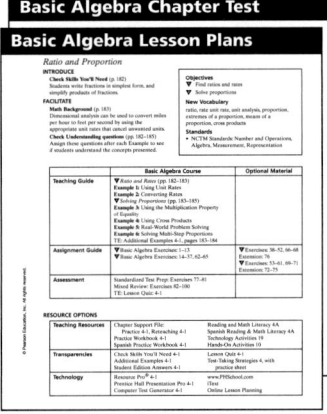

* Can be used with all ability levels to ensure mastery of prerequisite skills.

Advanced Learners

Student Edition
- Challenge exercises: pp. 187, 194, 202, 209, 216, 223
- Extension, p. 225

Enrichment
Chapter 4 Support File: pp. 14–19

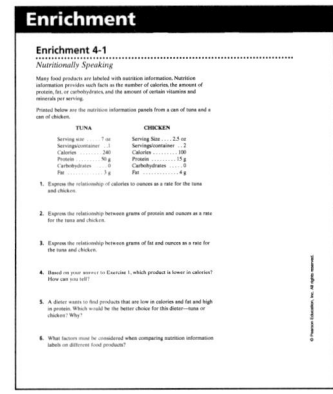

Reading and Math Literacy

Student Edition
- Vocabulary: pp. 181, 227, *plus* in every Lesson Preview
- Reading Math: pp. 184, 201, 203, 211, 212, 227
- Illustrated Glossary: pp. 757–785

Reading and Math Literacy Masters
Chapter 4: pp. 13–16

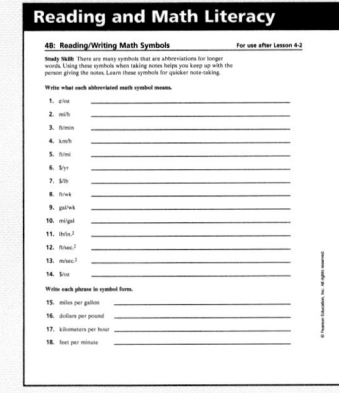

English Learners

Student Edition
- English/Spanish Illustrated Glossary: pp. 757–785

Workbook and Masters
Spanish Practice Workbook: pp. 23–28
Spanish Reading and Math Literacy Masters: pp. 13–16

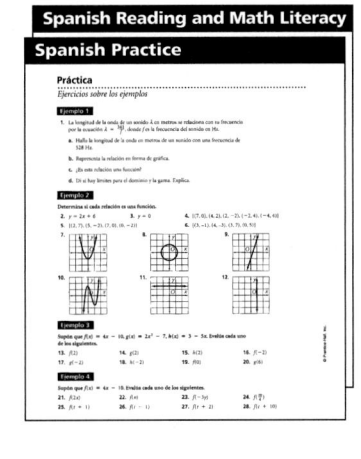

Learning Styles

Student Edition
- Investigation: pp. 189, 196, 210, 219
- Technology: p. 218
- Writing: pp. 187, 194, 201, 208, 215, 222, 229, 230
- DK Activities: pp. 232–233

Activity Masters
Hands-On Activities: 9, 10
Technology Activities: 18, 19

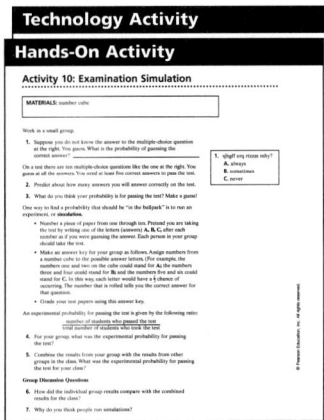

Program Resources

	Teaching Resources in Grab & Go™ Files				Resources for Reaching All Students				Spanish Resources			Transparencies				Presentation Assistant Plus!
	Practice	Reteach	Enrich	Checkpoint Quiz	Reading & Math Literacy	Technology Activities	Hands-On Activities	Basic Algebra Lesson Plans	Practice	Reading & Math Literacy	Checkpoint Quiz	Skills Check	Additional Examples	Answers to Exercises	Lesson Quiz	Prentice Hall Presentation Pro CD-ROM
4-1	■	■	■		■	■	■	■	■	■		■	■	■	■	■
4-2	■	■	■	■	■			■	■	■	■	■	■	■	■	■
4-3	■	■	■			■		■	■			■	■	■	■	■
4-4	■	■	■					■	■			■	■	■	■	■
4-5	■	■	■	■	■		■	■	■	■	■	■	■	■	■	■
4-6	■	■	■					■	■			■		■	■	■
For the chapter	Chapter Tests, Alternative Assessment, Cumulative Review, Cumulative Assessment				Basic Algebra Chapter Tests				Spanish Chapter Tests, Alternative Assessment, Cumulative Review, Cumulative Assessment			Classroom Aid Transparencies				

Also available for use with the chapter:

 *See page 180C.*

- Practice Workbook
- Solution Key

- For teacher support and access to student Web site materials, use Web Code aek-5500.
- For additional online and technology resources, see below.

Technology

 **Online and on CD-ROM**

Complete Interactive Student Text online and on CD-ROM—with instant feedback assessment, tutorial help, dynamic activities, instructional and real-world videos, audio, and additional practice.

 www.PHSchool.com For Students

Use **Web codes** for easy access to online activities, chapter projects, self-grading lesson quizzes and chapter tests, vocabulary quizzes, updated data sources, graphing calculator procedures, and more.

 **For Teachers**

Online lesson planning with built-in state correlations, all the teaching resources, complete reference library, your own calendar and Teacher Web page, professional development, and more.

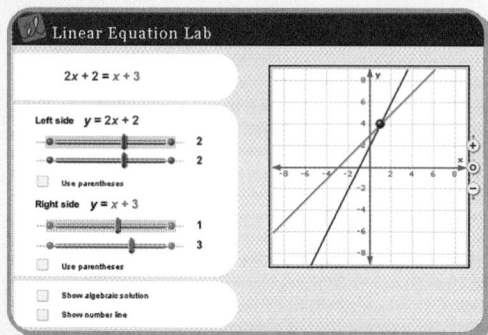
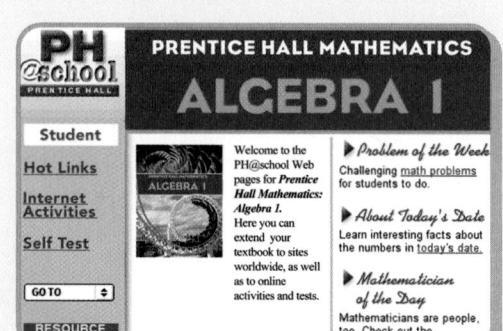
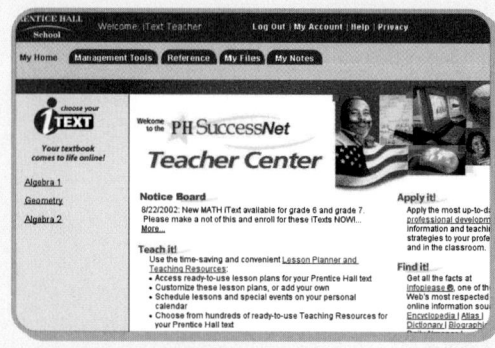

Presentation Assistant Plus!

The Prentice Hall *Presentation Assistant Plus!* provides you with the material you need to teach a lesson from beginning to end. Two easy-to-use formats—Transparencies and CD-ROM—allow you to present a lesson the way you are most comfortable.

 ## Transparencies

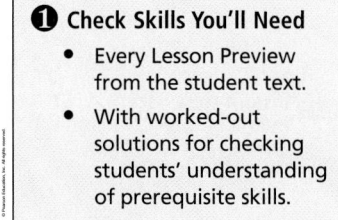

❶ Check Skills You'll Need
- Every Lesson Preview from the student text.
- With worked-out solutions for checking students' understanding of prerequisite skills.

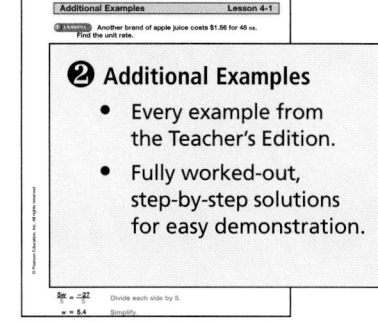

❷ Additional Examples
- Every example from the Teacher's Edition.
- Fully worked-out, step-by-step solutions for easy demonstration.

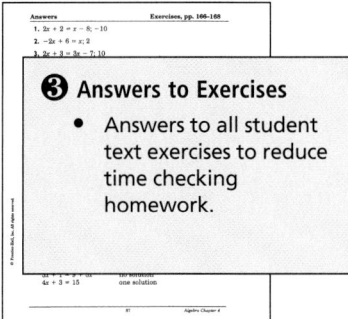

❸ Answers to Exercises
- Answers to all student text exercises to reduce time checking homework.

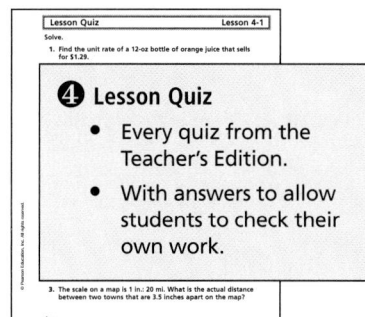

❹ Lesson Quiz
- Every quiz from the Teacher's Edition.
- With answers to allow students to check their own work.

 Throughout the Teacher's Edition, this symbol indicates material that is available on transparency in the Presentation Assistant Plus!

 ## Prentice Hall Presentation Pro CD-ROM

- Includes all Transparencies.
- Conveniently organized by lesson so you can easily ❶ Introduce, ❷ Teach, ❸ Check Homework, and ❹ Assess each lesson.
- Animated examples allow step-by-step instruction at your own pace.
- Easy to edit so you can create custom presentations.

Teaching Chapter 4 Using Presentation Assistant Plus!

	❶ Introduce	❷ Teach	❸ Check Homework	❹ Assess
	Check Skills You'll Need	Additional Examples	Student Edition Answers	Lesson Quiz
4-1	p. 23	pp. 42–43	✔	p. 101
4-2	p. 24	pp. 44–45	✔	p. 101
4-3	p. 25	pp. 45–47	✔	p. 102
4-4	p. 26	pp. 48–50	✔	p. 102
4-5	p. 27	pp. 51–52	✔	p. 103
4-6	p. 28	pp. 52–54	✔	p. 103

 Prentice Hall Presentation Pro

CD-ROM with dynamic PowerPoint® presentations for every lesson. Helps you introduce and develop concepts, check homework, and assess progress. Part of Presentation Assistant Plus! *(See above.)*

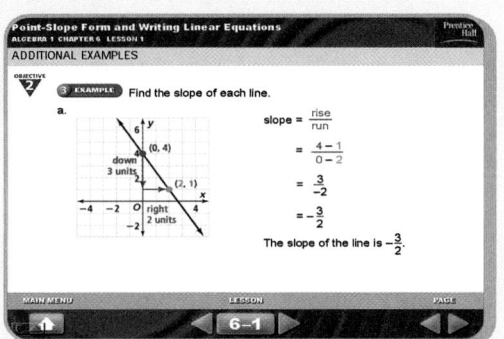

 Computer Test Generator

CD-ROM to create practice sheets and tests for course objectives and standardized tests. Includes Instant Chapter Tests™, online testing, and student reports. Part of the PH Assessment System. *(See page 180C.)*

Resource Pro® with Planning Express®

CD-ROM with a lesson planning tool that allows you to import state and local objectives. Includes electronic versions of all the teaching resources.

Chapter 4

Solving and Applying Proportions

 Diagnosing Readiness

Students will find answers to these exercises in the back of their textbooks.

For intervention, direct students to:

Multiplying and Dividing Fractions
Skills Handbook: p. 727
Examples 1–3, Exercises 1–30

Fractions, Decimals, and Percents
Skills Handbook: p. 728
Example 1, Exercises 1–12

Writing Expressions
Lesson 1-1: Example 1
Exercises 1–8
Extra Practice, p. 702

Using the Distributive Property
Lesson 1-7: Examples 3 and 4
Exercises 15–21
Extra Practice, p. 702

Solving One-Step Equations
Lesson 2-1: Examples 4, 5, and 6
Exercises 21, 29, 40, and 61
Extra Practice, p. 703

Where You've Been

- In Chapter 1 you used the distributive property to simplify variable expressions.

- In Chapter 2 you used the properties of equality to solve equations.

- In Chapter 3 you built on this knowledge to solve inequalities and absolute value equations.

 **Instant self-check** online and on CD-ROM

Diagnosing Readiness (For help, go to the Lesson in green.)

Multiplying and Dividing Fractions (Skills Handbook page 727)

Multiply or divide. Write your answers in simplest form.

1. $\frac{2}{3} \cdot \frac{3}{5}$ **$\frac{2}{5}$**   **2.** $4\frac{1}{2} \cdot \frac{1}{8}$ **$\frac{9}{16}$**   **3.** $2\frac{2}{5} \div \frac{3}{4}$ **$3\frac{1}{5}$**   **4.** $8 \div \frac{8}{3}$ **3**

Fractions, Decimals, and Percents (Skills Handbook page 728)

Write each number as a percent.

5. 0.75 **75%**   **6.** $\frac{5}{8}$ **62.5%**   **7.** 12.5 **1250%**   **8.** 0.002 **0.2%**   **9.** $\frac{105}{150}$ **70%**

Writing Expressions (Lessons 1-1 and 1-2)

Write an expression for each phrase.

10. a number n less 22 **$n - 22$**   **11.** A number p increased by 40 **$p + 40$**

12. 20 times a number m **$20m$**   **13.** 17 more than a number z **$z + 17$**

Using the Distributive Property (Lesson 1-7)

Simplify each expression.

14. $3(2 - n)$ **$6 - 3n$**   **15.** $0.4(t + 5)$ **$0.4t + 2$**   **16.** $-8(x - 1)$ **$-8x + 8$**

17. $25(a + 8)$ **$25a + 200$**   **18.** $-2.5(4 - c)$ **$-10 + 2.5c$**   **19.** $-(b + 12)$ **$-b - 12$**

Solving One-Step Equations (Lesson 2-1)

Solve each equation. Check your solution.

20. $\frac{t}{3} = 8$ **24**   **21.** $\frac{2}{5}w = -4$ **-10**   **22.** $7x = \frac{42}{5}$ **$1\frac{1}{5}$**   **23.** $\frac{4}{9}y = \frac{13}{3}$ **$9\frac{3}{4}$**

24. $-2k = \frac{5}{2}$ **$-1\frac{1}{4}$**   **25.** $20y = -2$ **$-\frac{1}{10}$**   **26.** $\frac{w}{2} = \frac{1}{3}$ **$\frac{2}{3}$**   **27.** $\frac{11}{3}x = 5$ **$1\frac{4}{11}$**

180 Chapter 4

Solving and Applying Proportions

Chapter 4

LESSONS

4-1 Ratio and Proportion

4-2 Proportions and Similar Figures

4-3 Proportions and Percent Equations

4-4 Percent of Change

4-5 Applying Ratios to Probability

4-6 Probability of Compound Events

Key Vocabulary

- complement of an event (p. 212)
- cross products (p. 183)
- dependent events (p. 221)
- event (p. 211)
- experimental probability (p. 212)
- greatest possible error (p. 205)
- independent events (p. 220)
- outcome (p. 211)
- percent error (p. 206)
- percent of change (p. 204)
- probability (p. 211)
- proportion (p. 183)
- rate (p. 182)
- ratio (p. 182)
- scale (p. 191)
- similar figures (p. 190)
- theoretical probability (p. 211)
- unit analysis (p. 182)
- unit rate (p. 182)

Chapter 4 Overview

The characteristics of ratio and proportion are discussed as are methods for solving proportions. The same structure and procedures are applied to a number of different applications. These include using proportions to find dimension for similar figures, solving percent problems, and finding the probability of both simple and compound events.

📖 **Reading Math**
Reading a Formula, p. 203

📖 **Vocabulary**
A complete list of terms, plus vocabulary exercises, appears in the Chapter Review, p. 227.

📖 **Illustrated Glossary**
Examples for each vocabulary term, plus definitions in both English and Spanish, appear starting on p. 757.

Test-Taking Strategies
Answering Quantitative Comparison Questions, p. 226

Real-World Snapshots
See pages 232–233 for a real-world application of probability that utilizes Dorling Kindersley's (DK) unique graphic presentation.

🌎 **Real-World Connections**
Some of the applications you will find in this chapter are bicycle racing (4-1), map distances (4-2), agriculture (4-3), and animal population (4-4).

💻 **www.PHSchool.com**
Internet support for this chapter includes:
- Self-grading Vocabulary and Chapter 4 Tests
- Chapter Project
- Chapter Planner
- Chapter 4 Resources

Plus 🅘**TEXT**

Where You're Going

- In this chapter, you will find ratios and rates to model real-world situations.

- You will use proportions to measure objects indirectly.

- You will solve problems that involve discounts, taxes, and interest.

Real-World Snapshots Applying what you learn, you will use ratios and probability to do activities related to baseball, on pages 232–233.

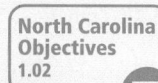

Lesson Preview

✔ **Check Skills You'll Need**

Simplifying Fractions
Skills Handbook: p. 724
Example 2, Exercises 23–34

Multiplying and Dividing Fractions
Skills Handbook: p. 727
Example 1, Exercises 1–5

Lesson Resources

📁 **Teaching Resources**
Practice, Reteaching, Enrichment

👥 **Reaching All Students**
Practice Workbook 4-1
Spanish Practice Workbook 4-1
Reading and Math Literacy 4A
Spanish Reading & Literacy 4A
Technology Activities 19
Hands-On Activities 9
Basic Algebra Planning Guide 4-1

🕐 **Presentation Assistant Plus!**
Transparencies
• Check Skills You'll Need 4-1
• Additional Examples 4-1
• Student Edition Answers 4-1
• Lesson Quiz 4-1
PH Presentation Pro CD 4-1

PRENTICE HALL
ASSESSMENT *SYSTEM*

Computer Test Generator CD

💿 **Technology**
Resource Pro® CD-ROM
Computer Test Generator CD
Prentice Hall Presentation Pro CD

💻 **www.PHSchool.com**
Student Site
• Teacher Web Code: aek-5500
• Self-grading Lesson Quiz
Teacher Center
• Lesson Planner
• Resources

Plus

4-1

Ratio and Proportion

1.02 Use formulas and algebraic expressions, including iterative and recursive forms, to model and solve problems.

Lesson Preview

What You'll Learn

OBJECTIVE **1** To find ratios and rates

OBJECTIVE **2** To solve proportions

. . . And Why

To use proportions for finding time, as in Example 5

✔ **Check Skills You'll Need** (For help, go to Skills Handbook pages 724 and 727.)

Write each fraction in simplest form.

1. $\frac{49}{84}$ $\frac{7}{12}$

2. $\frac{24}{42}$ $\frac{4}{7}$

3. $\frac{135}{180}$ $\frac{3}{4}$

Simplify each product.

4. $\frac{35}{25} \times \frac{40}{14}$ 4

5. $\frac{99}{144} \times \frac{96}{88}$ $\frac{3}{4}$

6. $\frac{21}{81} \times \frac{108}{56}$ $\frac{1}{2}$

New Vocabulary • ratio • rate • unit rate • unit analysis • proportion
• extremes of a proportion • means of a proportion
• cross products

🔵📄 **Interactive lesson includes instant self-check, tutorials, and activities.**

A **ratio** is a comparison of two numbers by division. The ratio of a to b is $a:b$ or $\frac{a}{b}$, where $b \neq 0$. If a and b represent quantities measured in different units, then the ratio of a to b is a **rate.** A **unit rate** is a rate with a denominator of 1. An example of a unit rate is $\frac{40 \text{ miles}}{1 \text{ hour}}$. You can write this rate as 40 miles per hour or 40 mi/h.

Price of Apple Juice

Price	Volume
$ .72	16 oz
$1.20	32 oz
$1.60	64 oz

1 **EXAMPLE** **Using Unit Rates**

Comparison Shopping The table at the left gives prices for different sizes of the same brand of apple juice. Find the unit rate (cost per ounce) for the 16-oz size.

cost ⟶ $\frac{\$.72}{16 \text{ oz}}$ = \$.045/oz **Divide the numerator and denominator by 16.**
ounces ⟶

The unit rate is 4.5¢/oz.

✔ **Check Understanding** **a.** Find the unit rates for the other two sizes. **3.75¢/oz, 2.5¢/oz**
b. Which of the three sizes has the lowest cost per ounce? **64-oz**

To change one unit of measure to another, you can use rates that equal 1. Since 60 min = 1 h, both $\frac{60 \text{ min}}{1 \text{ h}}$ and $\frac{1 \text{ h}}{60 \text{ min}}$ equal 1. You can use $\frac{60 \text{ min}}{1 \text{ h}}$ as a *conversion factor* to change hours into minutes. For example,

7 h = $\frac{7 \text{ h}}{1} \cdot \frac{60 \text{ min}}{1 \text{ h}}$ = 420 min **Divide the common unit, which is hours (h). The result is minutes.**

When converting from one unit to another, as in hours to minutes or minutes to hours, you must decide which conversion factor will produce the appropriate unit. This process is called **unit analysis,** or *dimensional analysis*.

 Ongoing Assessment and Intervention

Before the Lesson	**During the Lesson**	**After the Lesson**
Diagnose prerequisite skills using:	**Monitor progress using:**	**Assess knowledge using:**
• Check Skills You'll Need	• Check Understanding	• Lesson Quiz
	• Additional Examples	• Computer Test Generator CD
	• Standardized Test Prep	

2 EXAMPLE Converting Rates

Speed of Cheetah A cheetah ran 300 feet in 2.92 seconds. What was the cheetah's speed in miles per hour?

You need to convert feet to miles and seconds to hours.

$$\frac{300\text{ ft}}{2.92\text{ s}} \cdot \frac{1\text{ mi}}{5280\text{ ft}} \cdot \frac{60\text{ s}}{1\text{ min}} \cdot \frac{60\text{ min}}{1\text{ h}} \qquad \text{Use appropriate conversion factors.}$$

$$= \frac{300\text{ ft}}{2.92\text{ s}} \cdot \frac{1\text{ mi}}{5280\text{ ft}} \cdot \frac{60\text{ s}}{1\text{ min}} \cdot \frac{60\text{ min}}{1\text{ h}} \qquad \text{Divide the common units.}$$

$$\approx 70\text{ mi/h} \qquad \text{Simplify.}$$

Real-World Connection

The cheetah is the fastest land animal.

● The cheetah's speed was about 70 mi/h.

✓**Check Understanding** ② A sloth travels 0.15 miles per hour. Convert this speed to feet per minute. **13.2 ft/min**

OBJECTIVE

2 Solving Proportions

A **proportion** is an equation that states that two ratios are equal.

$$\frac{a}{b} = \frac{c}{d} \quad \text{for } b \neq 0 \text{ and } d \neq 0$$

You read this proportion as "*a* is to *b* as *c* is to *d*." For this proportion *a* and *d* are the **extremes of the proportion,** and *b* and *c* are the **means of the proportion.** Another way you may see this proportion written is $a:b = c:d$.

Need Help?

Multiplication Property of Equality:
For all numbers *a*, *b*, and *c*, if *a* = *b*, then *ac* = *bc*.

You can use the Multiplication Property of Equality to solve a proportion for a variable.

3 EXAMPLE Using the Multiplication Property of Equality

Solve $\frac{t}{9} = \frac{5}{6}$.

$$\frac{t}{9} \cdot 18 = \frac{5}{6} \cdot 18 \qquad \text{Multiply each side by the least common multiple of 9 and 6, which is 18.}$$

$$2t = 15 \qquad \text{Simplify.}$$

$$\frac{2t}{2} = \frac{15}{2} \qquad \text{Divide each side by 2.}$$

$$t = 7.5 \qquad \text{Simplify.}$$

✓**Check Understanding** ③ Solve each proportion.

a. $\frac{x}{8} = \frac{5}{6}$ **6$\frac{2}{3}$** **b.** $\frac{y}{12} = \frac{4}{7}$ **6$\frac{6}{7}$** **c.** $\frac{18}{50} = \frac{m}{15}$ **5.4**

You can use the Multiplication Property of Equality to prove an important property of proportions.

If $\frac{a}{b} = \frac{c}{d}$,

then $\frac{a}{b} \cdot bd = \frac{c}{d} \cdot bd$ **Multiplication Property of Equality**

$$\frac{ab^1d}{1^b} = \frac{cbd^1}{1^d} \qquad \text{Divide the common factors.}$$

and $ad = cb$ **Simplify.**

or $ad = bc$ **Commutative Property of Multiplication**

The products ad and bc are the **cross products** of the proportion $\frac{a}{b} = \frac{c}{d}$.

 Reaching All Students

Below Level Walk students through several examples of using the correct conversion factor when changing from one unit of measure to another.	**Advanced Learners** Ask students whether, if $\frac{a}{b} = \frac{c}{d}$, for $b \neq 0$, $c \neq 0$, and $d \neq 0$, then $\frac{a}{c} = \frac{b}{d}$. Have them explain their reasoning.	**Visual Learners** See note on page 184. **Error Prevention** See note on page 185.

---

2. Teach

Math Background

The process of canceling the units is really a shortcut for applying two basic properties, one that states that $a \div a$ is 1 and the other that states that 1 is the multiplicative identity.

OBJECTIVE
1 Teaching Notes

1 EXAMPLE Alternative Method

Some students may not understand why dividing 0.72 by 16 yields the unit rate. Stress that *unit* is singular. Therefore, to find the unit rate, you must convert 16 oz into 1 oz. Ask students what can be done to 16 that will result in 1. **divide by 16** Write the following on the board:

$$\frac{\$.72}{16\text{ oz}} = \frac{\frac{\$.72}{16\text{ oz}}}{\frac{16\text{ oz}}{16\text{ oz}}} = \frac{\$.45}{1\text{ oz}}$$

2 EXAMPLE Connection to Life Science

Speed helps many animals survive, either by escaping predators or by catching food. Here are some fast animal speeds in mi/h: peregrine falcon (168), pigeon (60), dolphin (37), barracuda (27), housefly (5).

 Additional Examples

① A brand of apple juice costs $1.56 for 48 oz. Find the unit rate. **3.25¢/oz**

② The fastest recorded speed for an eastern gray kangaroo is 40 mi/h. What was the kangaroo's speed in feet per second? **≈ 58.7 ft/s**

OBJECTIVE
2 Teaching Notes

3 EXAMPLE Math Tip

If a proportion has the variable in the numerator, the Multiplication Property of Equality is often more efficient than using cross products.

183

184

Key Concepts

Property	Cross Products of a Proportion

If $\frac{a}{b} = \frac{c}{d}$, then $ad = bc$.

Example $\frac{2}{3} = \frac{8}{12}$, so $2 \cdot 12 = 3 \cdot 8$.

Reading Math

The cross products property is also called the means-extremes property of proportions.

4 **EXAMPLE** **Using Cross Products**

Use cross products to solve the proportion $\frac{y}{2.5} = -\frac{3}{4}$.

$$\frac{y}{2.5} = -\frac{3}{4}$$

$y(4) = (2.5)(-3)$ **Write cross products.**

$4y = -7.5$ **Simplify.**

$\frac{4y}{4} = \frac{-7.5}{4}$ **Divide each side by 4.**

$y = -1.875$ **Simplify.**

✓ **Check Understanding** **4** Solve each proportion by using cross products.

   a. $\frac{x}{4} = \frac{25}{12}$ **8$\frac{1}{3}$**   **b.** $\frac{24}{5} = \frac{y}{7}$ **33.6**   **c.** $\frac{54}{d} = \frac{72}{64}$ **48**

You can use proportions to solve real-world problems. To write a correct proportion, form rates on each side that compare units in the same way such as $\frac{\text{kilometers}}{\text{hour}} = \frac{\text{kilometers}}{\text{hour}}$.

5 **EXAMPLE** **Real-World** 🌐 **Problem Solving**

Cycling In 2001, Lance Armstrong won the Tour de France, completing the 3454-km course in about 86.3 hours. Traveling at his average speed, how long would it take him to ride 185 km? Round the answer to the nearest tenth.

Define   Let t = time needed to ride 185 km.

Relate

	Tour de France average speed	equals	185-km trip average speed

Write $\begin{array}{c}\text{kilometers} \rightarrow \\ \text{hours} \longrightarrow\end{array}$ $\frac{3454}{86.3}$ $=$ $\frac{185}{t}$ $\begin{array}{c}\leftarrow \text{kilometers} \\ \longleftarrow \text{hours}\end{array}$

$$\frac{3454}{86.3} = \frac{185}{t}$$

$3454t = 86.3(185)$ **Write cross products.**

$t = \frac{(86.3)(185)}{(3454)}$ **Divide each side by 3454.**

$t \approx 4.6$ **Simplify. Round to the nearest tenth.**

Traveling at his average speed, it would take Lance approximately 4.6 hours to cycle 185 km.

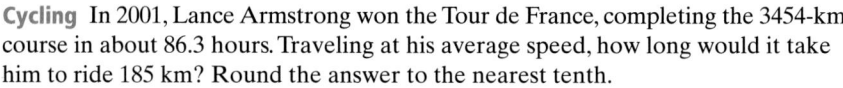

Real-World 🌐 **Connection**

Lance Armstrong has won the 21-day Tour de France several times.

✓ **Check Understanding** **5** Suppose you walk 2 miles in 35 minutes.

   a. Write a proportion to find how far you would walk in an hour if you were to continue at the same rate. $\frac{2}{35} = \frac{x}{60}$

   b. Solve the proportion. $\approx$**3.43 mi**

In Example 6, the ratios that form the proportion have variable expressions with more than one term. To solve for the variable, you will use cross products and the Distributive Property.

6 EXAMPLE Solving Multi-Step Proportions

Solve the proportion $\frac{x+4}{5} = \frac{x-2}{7}$

$$\frac{x+4}{5} = \frac{x-2}{7}$$

$(x+4)(7) = 5(x-2)$ **Write cross products.**

$7x + 28 = 5x - 10$ **Use the Distributive Property.**

$2x + 28 = -10$ **Subtract 5x from each side.**

$2x = -38$ **Subtract 28 from each side.**

$x = -19$ **Divide each side by 2.**

✓ **Check Understanding** **6** Solve each proportion.

a. $\frac{x+2}{14} = \frac{x}{10}$ **5**

b. $\frac{y-15}{y+4} = \frac{35}{7}$ **−8.75**

c. $\frac{3}{w+6} = \frac{5}{w-4}$ **−21**

d. $\frac{d-7}{4} = \frac{2d+1}{3}$ **−5**

EXERCISES

Practice and Problem Solving

For more practice, see *Extra Practice*.

A **Practice by Example**

Find each unit rate.

Example 1
(page 182)

1. $57 for 6 hours **$9.50/h**

2. $\frac{\$2}{5\,lb}$ **$.40/lb**

3. $\frac{524\ cars}{4\ weeks}$ **131 cars/week**

4. $\frac{600\ calories}{1.5\ h}$ **400 cal/h**

5. A 10-ounce bottle of shampoo costs $2.40. What is the cost per ounce? **$.24/oz**

6. A 12-ounce bottle of juice costs $1.08. What is the cost per ounce? **$.09/oz**

Example 2
(page 183)

Choose A or B for the correct conversion factor for each situation.

7. quarts to gallons **A**

    A. $\frac{1\ gal}{4\ qt}$ B. $\frac{4\ qt}{1\ gal}$

8. ounces to pounds **A**

    A. $\frac{1\ lb}{16\ oz}$ B. $\frac{16\ oz}{1\ lb}$

9. inches to yards **B**

    A. $\frac{36\ in.}{1\ yd}$ B. $\frac{1\ yd}{36\ in.}$

10. miles to feet **A**

    A. $\frac{5280\ ft}{1\ mi}$ B. $\frac{1\ mi}{5280\ ft}$

Complete each statement.

11. 8 h = ■ min **480**

12. 120 cm = ■ m **1.2**

13. 3 h = ■ s **10,800**

Examples 3, 4
(pages 183, 184)

Solve each proportion.

14. $\frac{5}{6} = \frac{c}{9}$ **7.5**

15. $\frac{3}{8} = \frac{x}{30}$ **11.25**

16. $\frac{2}{8} = \frac{n}{20}$ **5**

17. $\frac{7}{5} = \frac{k}{18}$ **25.2**

18. $\frac{3}{4} = \frac{x}{10}$ **7.5**

19. $\frac{4}{6} = \frac{m}{9}$ **6**

20. $\frac{8}{d} = \frac{-12}{30}$ **−20**

21. $\frac{5}{9} = \frac{8}{w}$ **14.4**

22. $\frac{2}{14} = \frac{m}{63}$ **9**

23. $-\frac{8}{11} = \frac{12}{v}$ **−16.5**

24. $\frac{4}{9} = \frac{b}{15}$ **$6\frac{2}{3}$**

25. $\frac{3}{k} = -\frac{20}{35}$ **−5.25**

26. $\frac{q}{42} = \frac{15}{7}$ **90**

27. $\frac{6}{8} = \frac{21}{x}$ **28**

28. $\frac{7}{n} = \frac{35}{88}$ **17.6**

29. $\frac{20}{18} = \frac{75}{w}$ **67.5**

Assignment Guide

1 Objective

   A B Core 1–13, 38–52, 66–68

   C Extension 76

2 Objective

   A B Core 14–37, 53–65, 69–71

   C Extension 72–75

Standardized Test Prep 77–81

Mixed Review 82–100

Exercises 5, 6 Help students make the connection that cost per ounce means cost divided by ounces.

Error Prevention

Exercises 11–13 Make sure students understand that more than one conversion is needed in each exercise.

Enrichment 4-1

Reteaching 4-1

Practice 4-1

Exercises 44–49 Remind students that 1 mi in 3 min is the same as $\frac{1 \text{ mi}}{3 \text{ min}}$.

Example 5
(page 184)

30. A canary's heart beats 200 times in 12 seconds. Use a proportion to find how many times its heart beats in 42 seconds. **700**

31. Suppose you traveled 66 kilometers in 1.25 hours. Moving at the same speed, how many kilometers would you cover in 2 hours? **105.6 km**

Example 6
(page 185)

Solve each proportion.

32. $\frac{x+3}{4} = \frac{7}{8}$ **0.5**

33. $\frac{a-6}{5} = \frac{7}{12}$ **$8\frac{11}{12}$**

34. $\frac{8}{9} = \frac{w-2}{6}$ **$7\frac{1}{3}$**

35. $\frac{1}{c+5} = \frac{2}{3}$ **$-3\frac{1}{2}$**

36. $\frac{8}{b+10} = \frac{4}{2b-7}$ **8**

37. $\frac{k+5}{10} = \frac{k-12}{9}$ **165**

 Apply Your Skills

Complete each statement.

38. $2/lb = ▥ ¢/oz **12.5**

39. $3/lb = ▥ ¢/oz **18.75**

40. 4¢/day = $ ▥/yr **14.60**

41. 5¢/day = $ ▥/yr **18.25**

42. 5 cm/min = ▥ m/week **504**

43. 1 qt/min = ▥ gal/week **2520**

Need Help?
5,280 ft = 1 mi

Express each rate in miles per hour.

44. 1 mi in 3 min **20 mi/h**

45. 1 mi in 4 min **15 mi/h**

46. 1 mi in 300 s **12 mi/h**

47. 10,560 ft in 2 h **1 mi/h**

48. 21,120 ft in 4 h **1 mi/h**

49. 270 ft in 10.8 min **about 0.28 mi/h**

50. You are riding your bicycle. It takes you 21 min to go 5 mi. If you continue traveling at the same rate, how long will it take you to go 12 mi? **50.4 min**

 51. Hair Human hair grows at a rate of about 0.35 mm per day. How much does it grow in 30 days? **10.5 mm**

52. Record Speed According to the *Guinness Book of World Records*, the peregrine falcon has a record diving speed of 168 miles per hour. Write this speed in feet per second. **246.4 ft/s**

Solve each proportion.

53. $\frac{m+12}{9m} = \frac{5}{9}$ **3**

54. $\frac{p}{20} = \frac{p-4}{5}$ **$5.\overline{3}$**

55. $\frac{n+12}{4} = \frac{n}{16}$ **−16**

56. $\frac{29}{24} = \frac{b+24}{b}$ **115.2**

57. $\frac{w}{15} = \frac{w-9}{12}$ **45**

58. $\frac{9}{3t-6} = \frac{6}{0.2t+4}$ **$4.\overline{4}$**

59. $\frac{n+2}{25} = \frac{n-4}{35}$ **−17**

60. $\frac{q-11}{q+13} = \frac{2}{3}$ **59**

61. $\frac{18+d}{14-d} = \frac{3}{7}$ **−8.4**

Data Analysis Below are the survey results of 60 students out of 1250 students in a school. These results are representative of the school population. Use the table for Exercises 62–64.

Real-World Connection

Enrollment in grades 9 through 12 has risen over 19% since 1990.

Question	Number Answering Yes
Do you work on weekends?	31
Do you spend 2 or more hours per night on homework?	36
Do you buy lunch in the school cafeteria?	48

62. Predict the number of students in the school who work on weekends. **about 646 students**

63. Predict the number of students in the school who spend 2 or more hours per night on homework. **about 750 students**

64. Predict the number of students in the school who buy lunch in the school cafeteria. **about 1000 students**

65. Answers may vary. Sample: Multiply the numerator of each side by the denominator of the other side. Set the products equal to each other and solve the equation.
$\frac{7}{5} = \frac{x}{15}$, $(7)(15) = 5x$, $x = 21$

67. 4 people/mi², 2485 people/mi², 78 people/mi²

70. Bonnie: $56.00, Tim: $32.00

 **Challenge**

 65. Writing Write an explanation telling an absent classmate how to use cross products to solve a proportion. Include an example. **See left.**

 66. Gasoline Cost Your car averages 34 miles per gallon on the highway. If gas costs $1.79 per gallon, how much does it cost in dollars per mile to drive your car on the highway? **$.05/mi**

 67. Demographics Population density is a unit rate describing the number of individuals per unit of area. An example of population density is 5 people per square mile. Use the diagram below. Find the population densities of Mongolia, Bangladesh, and the United States. Round your answers to the nearest integer. **See left.**

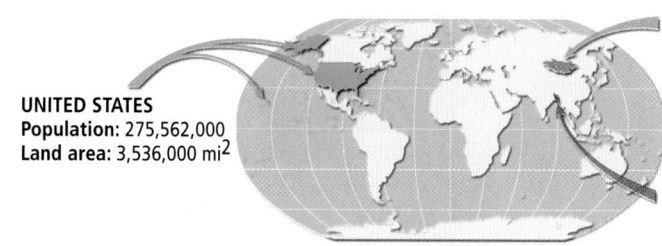

MONGOLIA
Population: 2,651,000
Land area: 604,000 mi²

UNITED STATES
Population: 275,562,000
Land area: 3,536,000 mi²

BANGLADESH
Population: 129,194,000
Land area: 52,000 mi²

68. Open-Ended Estimate your walking rate in feet per second. Write this rate in miles per hour. **Check students' work.**

69. a. Solve the proportions $\frac{x-1}{x} = \frac{6}{7}$ and $\frac{x-2}{x} = \frac{6}{7}$. **7, 14**
   b. Based on your answers to part (a), predict the answer for $\frac{x-3}{x} = \frac{6}{7}$. **21**
   c. Check your answer for $\frac{x-3}{x} = \frac{6}{7}$. **21**
   d. Critical Thinking For the ratio $\frac{x-a}{x} = \frac{6}{7}$, describe the relationship between a and x. **$x = 7a$**

70. Bonnie and Tim do some yardwork for their neighbor. The ratio comparing the amount of time each one works is $7:4$. The neighbor pays them $88. If Bonnie worked more, how much should each of them receive? **See left.**

 71. Engineering Transformers use coils of wire to increase or decrease voltage. The following proportion relates the number of turns of wire in the coils to the voltages. (*Note:* Each semi-circle in the diagram represents a turn of wire.)

primary coil   secondary coil

$$\frac{\text{primary turns}}{\text{secondary turns}} = \frac{\text{primary voltage}}{\text{secondary voltage}}$$

Suppose the primary-coil voltage is 120 volts. Use the proportion $\frac{5}{2} = \frac{120}{v}$ to find the secondary-coil voltage. **48 V**

72. Find y if $\frac{12}{72} = \frac{x}{24}$ and $\frac{x}{36} = \frac{y}{81}$. **9**

Solve each proportion.

73. $\frac{x^2 - 3}{5x + 2} = \frac{x}{5}$ **−7.5**   **74.** $\frac{w^3 + 7}{w} = \frac{9w^2 + 7}{9}$ **9**   **75.** $\frac{m^2 - 8}{3m} = \frac{4m + 1}{12}$ **−32**

 76. Sports Long-distance runners usually refer to their speed in terms of pace, a rate measured in minutes per mile rounded to the nearest hundredth.
   a. Naoko Takahashi of Japan won the gold medal in the marathon at the 2000 Olympic games. She set an Olympic record, completing the 26.2-mile race in $2:23:14$ (2 hours, 23 minutes, 14 seconds). Find her pace. **5.47 min/mi**
   b. Tegla Loroupe of Kenya set the women's world record at the 1999 Berlin marathon. Her time was $2:20:43$. Find her pace. **5.37 min/mi**

4. Assess

Lesson Quiz 4-1

Solve.

1. Find the unit rate of a 12-oz bottle of orange juice that sells for $1.29. **10.75¢/oz**

2. If you are driving 65 mi/h, how many feet per second are you driving? **about 95.3 ft/s**

Solve each proportion.

3. $\frac{c}{6} = \frac{12}{15}$ **4.8**

4. $\frac{21}{12} = \frac{7}{y}$ **4**

5. $\frac{3+x}{7} = \frac{4}{8}$ **$\frac{1}{2}$**

6. $\frac{2+x}{x-4} = \frac{25}{35}$ **−17**

Alternative Assessment

Bring newspapers and magazines to class or take the class to the library. Challenge students to find a ratio or proportion in a newspaper or magazine article. Invite students to read the articles, or excerpts of the articles, to the class and explain how the ratio or proportion is used.

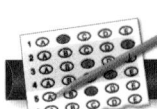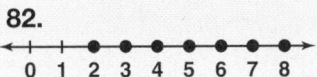

Resources

For additional practice with a variety of test item formats:
- Standardized Test Prep, p. 231
- Test-Taking Strategies, p. 226
- Test-Taking Strategies with Transparencies

Connection to Geometry

Exercise 81 Sometimes your vocabulary may be challenged in a math problem. *Concentric rings* are similar to *concentric circles* in geometry. They are circles in the same plane that have the same center, but have different radii.

pages 185–188 Exercises

81. [2] $\frac{12 \text{ in.}}{32 \text{ rings}} = \frac{20 \text{ in.}}{x \text{ rings}}$;

$x = 53\frac{1}{3}$, which is

$53\frac{1}{3}$ years OR

equivalent explanation

[1] incorrect proportion solved correctly OR correct proportion solved incorrectly

82.

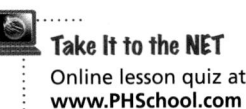

83.

84.

85.

86.

87. no solution

92.

93.

94.

Multiple Choice

77. Which ratio is greater than $\frac{3}{4}$? **D**

   A. $\frac{25}{35}$ **B.** $\frac{27}{36}$ **C.** $\frac{18}{25}$ **D.** $\frac{32}{42}$

78. To the nearest tenth of a cent, what is the unit cost of a 28-ounce bottle of dish detergent that is on sale for $2.50? **G**

   F. 8¢/ounce   **G.** 8.9¢/ounce   **H.** 11¢/ounce   **I.** 11.2¢/ounce

79. Trey works in a neighbor's yard from 8:00 A.M. to noon, cutting the lawn and trimming shrubs. After taking an hour off for lunch, he rakes the yard and sweeps the steps and walkways. He finishes at 3:00 P.M. Trey earned $24 for the work he did. Which unit rate indicates his hourly wage? **C**

   A. $12 in 3 hours   **B.** $6/hour

   C. $4/hour   **D.** $3/hour

80. Most mammals breathe about once every 4 heartbeats. A large dog's heart beats about 180 times in one minute. Which unit rate represents the number of times this dog breathes in 1 minute? **G**

   F. $\frac{40 \text{ breaths}}{\text{minute}}$ **G.** $\frac{45 \text{ breaths}}{\text{minute}}$ **H.** $\frac{180 \text{ breaths}}{4 \text{ minutes}}$ **I.** $\frac{720 \text{ breaths}}{\text{minute}}$

Short Response

Take It to the NET
Online lesson quiz at
www.PHSchool.com
Web Code: aea-0401

81. Many trees have concentric rings that can be counted to determine the tree's age. Each ring represents one year's growth. If a maple tree with a diameter of 12 inches has 32 rings, write a proportion to find the number of rings in a maple tree that has a diameter of 20 inches. Estimate the age of a maple tree with a 20-inch diameter. Show your work. **See margin.**

Mixed Review

Lessons 3-5, 3-6

Graph each inequality on a number line. Use positive integers as a replacement set. If there are no solutions, write *no solutions*. **82–87. See margin.**

82. $|r| > 1$ **83.** $|t - 9| > 2$

84. $-7 \le k \le 3$ **85.** $-3 < 2g + 1 < 7$

86. $e > 7$ or $e < -4$ **87.** $|8(b + 5)| < 16$

Define a variable and write an inequality to model each situation.

88. You are no more than 72 inches tall. $t =$ height (in.), $t \le 72$

89. At least 235 students attended the school dance. $s =$ students, $s \ge 235$

90. The car can travel up to 344 miles on a full tank of gas. $m =$ miles, $m \le 344$

91. A dog weighs more than 20 pounds. $w =$ weight (lb), $w > 20$

Graph each inequality from the given word descriptions. **92–94. See margin.**

92. g is at least 4   **93.** p is positive   **94.** v is no more than -2

Lesson 2-1

Solve and check each equation.

95. $15x = 90$ **6**   **96.** $34 = \frac{t}{4}$ **136**   **97.** $-35 = 7h$ **−5**

98. $4.3 - b = 9.8$ **−5.5**   **99.** $-\frac{3}{5}c = 54$ **−90**   **100.** $v + 7\frac{1}{6} = \frac{2}{3}$ **−6$\frac{1}{2}$**

4-2

Proportions and Similar Figures

 North Carolina Objectives

1.02 Use formulas and algebraic expressions, including iterative and recursive forms, to model and solve problems.

Lesson Preview

What You'll Learn

 OBJECTIVE 1
To find missing measures of similar figures

 OBJECTIVE 2
To use similar figures when measuring indirectly

...And Why

To apply proportions when finding distances represented on maps, as in Example 3

✓ **Check Skills You'll Need** (For help, go to the Skills Handbook and Lesson 4-1.)

Simplify each ratio.

1. $\frac{36}{42}$ $\frac{6}{7}$

2. $\frac{81}{108}$ $\frac{3}{4}$

3. $\frac{26}{52}$ $\frac{1}{2}$

Solve each proportion.

4. $\frac{x}{12} = \frac{7}{30}$ $2\frac{4}{5}$

5. $\frac{y}{12} = \frac{8}{45}$ $2\frac{2}{15}$

6. $\frac{w}{15} = \frac{12}{27}$ $6\frac{2}{3}$

7. $\frac{9}{a} = \frac{81}{10}$ $1\frac{1}{9}$

8. $\frac{25}{75} = \frac{z}{30}$ 10

9. $\frac{n}{9} = \frac{n+1}{24}$ $\frac{3}{5}$

New Vocabulary • similar figures • scale drawing • scale

OBJECTIVE 1 Similar Figures

 Interactive lesson includes instant self-check, tutorials, and activities.

Real-World Connection

The triangles in the quilt are the same shape, so they are *similar*.

Investigation: Proportions in Triangles

The figure below shows $\triangle ACB$ and $\triangle DCE$.

$AB = 8.5$ cm, $CA = 7.6$ cm,
$CB = 5.6$ cm, $CD = 3.5$ cm,
$CE = 2.6$ cm, $DE = 3.9$ cm

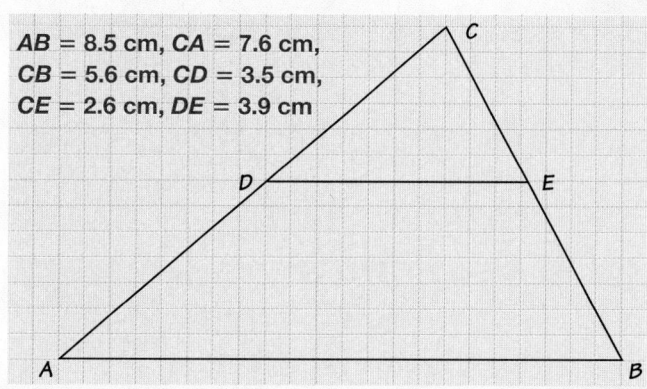

1. Measure AB, CA, CB, CD, CE, and DE using a metric ruler. **See above.**

2. Find each ratio.
   a. $\frac{DE}{AB}$ 0.46
   b. $\frac{CE}{CB}$ 0.46
   c. $\frac{CD}{CA}$ 0.46

3. Tell whether each statement is true.
   a. $\frac{DE}{AB} = \frac{CE}{CB}$ true
   b. $\frac{CD}{CA} = \frac{CE}{CB}$ true
   c. $\frac{AB}{DE} = \frac{CA}{CD}$ true

4. Using the lengths you have measured, write two ratios that equal $\frac{CB}{CE}$. $\frac{CA}{CD}, \frac{AB}{DE}$

Lesson 4-2 Proportions and Similar Figures **189**

4-2

 North Carolina Objectives 1.02

1. Plan

Lesson Preview

✓ **Check Skills You'll Need**

Simplifying Fractions
Skills Handbook: p. 724
Example 2, Exercises 23–34

Ratio and Proportion
Lesson 4-1: Example 4
Exercises 14–29
Extra Practice, p. 705

Lesson Resources

📁 **Teaching Resources**
Practice, Reteaching, Enrichment
Checkpoint Quiz 1

👥 **Reaching All Students**
Practice Workbook 4-2
Spanish Practice Workbook 4-2
Reading and Math Literacy 4B
Spanish Reading & Literacy 4B
Spanish Checkpoint Quiz 1
Basic Algebra Planning Guide 4-2

⏰ **Presentation Assistant Plus!**
Transparencies
• Check Skills You'll Need 4-2
• Additional Examples 4-2
• Student Edition Answers 4-2
• Lesson Quiz 4-2
PH Presentation Pro CD 4-2

 **PRENTICE HALL ASSESSMENT SYSTEM**

Checkpoint Quiz 1
Computer Test Generator CD

💿 **Technology**
Resource Pro® CD-ROM
Computer Test Generator CD
Prentice Hall Presentation Pro CD

🖥️ **www.PHSchool.com**
Student Site
• Teacher Web Code: aek-5500
• Self-grading Lesson Quiz
Teacher Center
• Lesson Planner
• Resources

Plus

189

2. Teach

Math Background

Not only the corresponding sides, but also the medians, altitudes, and other corresponding lengths of similar figures are all in the same proportion. This relationship can be used to measure indirectly the height of a flagpole or the distance across a body of water.

OBJECTIVE

1 Teaching Notes

Investigation (Optional)
Visual Learners

Draw a scalene triangle for the overhead projector. Project the image onto the chalkboard. Trace the triangle on the board. Move the projector closer to the board so that the image gets smaller. Trace the triangle again. Ask students to compare the triangles. **same shape, different sizes**

1 EXAMPLE English Learners

Some students may not understand the term *corresponding*. Have a student look up the definition in a dictionary and read it aloud to the class. In figures, corresponding parts are in matching places. For example, $\overline{AB}$ corresponds to $\overline{FG}$ because they are between pairs of congruent angles in similar triangles.

Additional Examples

1 In the figure below, $\triangle ABC \sim \triangle DEF$. Find AB. **12 mm**

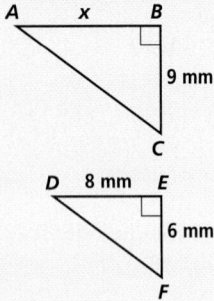

190

In the diagram below, $\triangle ABC$ and $\triangle FGH$ are similar. **Similar figures** have the same shape but not necessarily the same size. The symbol $\sim$ means "is similar to".

In similar triangles, corresponding angles are congruent and corresponding sides are in proportion. The order of the letters indicates the corresponding angles. If $\triangle ABC \sim \triangle FGH$, then the following is true.

Need Help?

Congruent angles have equal measures. The symbol $\cong$ means "is congruent to."

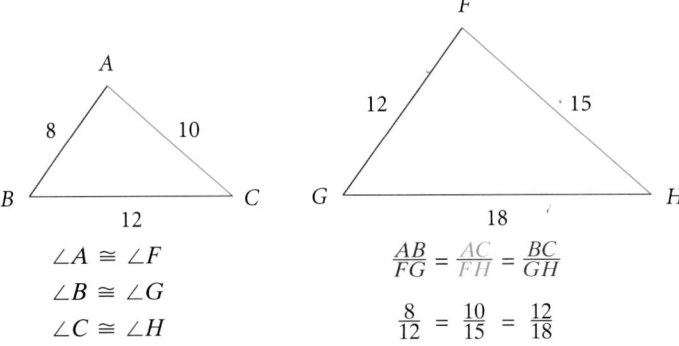

$$\angle A \cong \angle F$$
$$\angle B \cong \angle G$$
$$\angle C \cong \angle H$$

$$\frac{AB}{FG} = \frac{AC}{FH} = \frac{BC}{GH}$$

$$\frac{8}{12} = \frac{10}{15} = \frac{12}{18}$$

1 EXAMPLE Finding the Length of a Side

Geometry In the figure below, $\triangle ABC \sim \triangle DFE$. Find DE.

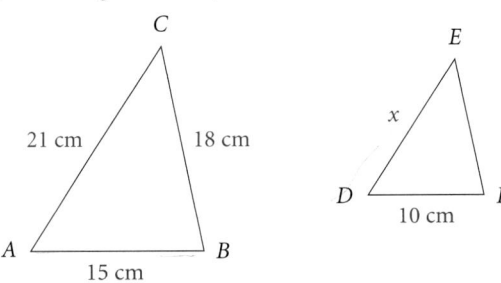

Relate $\dfrac{AB}{DF} = \dfrac{AC}{DE}$ — Write a proportion comparing the lengths of corresponding sides.

Define Let $x = DE$.

Write $\dfrac{15}{10} = \dfrac{21}{x}$ — Substitute 15 for AB, 10 for DF, 21 for AC, and x for DE.

$15x = 10(21)$ — Write cross products.

$\dfrac{15x}{15} = \dfrac{210}{15}$ — Divide each side by 15.

$x = 14$ — Simplify.

● DE is 14 cm.

✓ Check Understanding **1** In the figure below, $\triangle FGH \sim \triangle KLM$. Find LM. **15 cm**

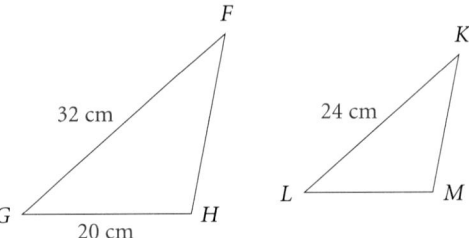

👥 Reaching All Students

| **Below Level** Suggest that before students write a proportion involving similar figures, they point to and say to themselves the names of the corresponding sides. | **Advanced Learners** Challenge students to write as many proportions as possible that can be used to solve the problem in Example 1. | **English Learners** See note on page 190.
Inclusion See note on page 191. |

You can use proportions to find the dimensions of objects that are difficult to measure directly.

2 EXAMPLE **Applying Similarity**

Indirect Measurement A tree casts a shadow 7.5 ft long. A woman 5 ft tall casts a shadow 3 ft long. The triangle shown for the tree and its shadow is similar to the triangle shown for the woman and her shadow. How tall is the tree?

$\frac{3}{7.5} = \frac{5}{x}$ **Corresponding sides of similar figures are in proportion.**

$3x = 7.5 \cdot 5$ **Write cross products.**

$3x = 37.5$ **Simplify.**

$x = 12.5$ **Divide each side by 3.**

3 ft   7.5 ft

● The tree is 12.5 ft tall.

✓ Check Understanding **2** **a.** A tree casts a 26-ft shadow. A boy standing nearby casts a 12-ft shadow. His height is 4.5 ft. How tall is the tree? **9.75 ft**
b. A house casts a 56-ft shadow. A girl standing nearby casts a 7.2-ft shadow. Her height is 5.4 ft. What is the height of the house? **42 ft**

A **scale drawing** is an enlarged or reduced drawing that is similar to an actual object or place. Floor plans, blueprints, and maps are all examples of scale drawings. The ratio of a distance in the drawing to the corresponding actual distance is the **scale** of the drawing.

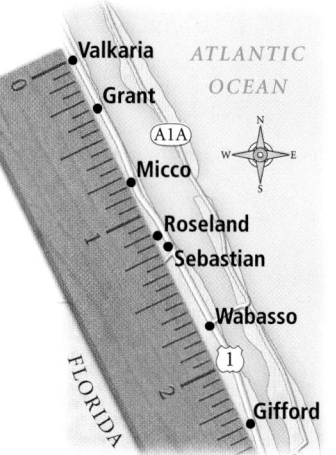

Valkaria ATLANTIC
Grant   OCEAN
(A1A)
Micco
Roseland
Sebastian
Wabasso
(1)
FLORIDA
Gifford

3 EXAMPLE **Finding Distances on Maps**

The scale of the map at the left is 1 inch : 10 miles. Approximately how far is it from Valkaria to Wabasso?

Map distance = 1.75 in.   **Measure the map distance.**

map → $\frac{1}{10} = \frac{1.75}{d}$ ← map
actual →   ← actual   **Write a proportion.**

$1 \cdot d = 10 \cdot 1.75$ **Write cross products.**

$d = 17.5$ **Simplify.**

● Wabasso is about 17.5 mi from Valkaria.

✓ Check Understanding **3** **a.** On the map above, measure the map distance from Grant to Gifford. Find the actual distance. **about 21 mi**
b. **Critical Thinking** If another map showed the distance from Valkaria to Wabasso but had a scale of 1 inch : 5 miles, what would the map distance be between the two locations? **3.5 in.**

2 EXAMPLE **Connection to Geometry**

Some students may wonder why the two triangles are similar. One way to prove triangles are similar is the Angle-Angle Similarity Theorem. If you can prove two pairs of corresponding angles of two triangles are congruent, then the two triangles are similar. The angles formed by the sun's rays and the standing objects are the same. Each object is standing at a right angle with the ground.

3 EXAMPLE **Inclusion**

Some students may have difficulty measuring because of disabilities. Let students work in pairs.

Additional Examples

2 A flagpole casts a shadow 102 feet long. A man 6 ft tall casts a shadow 17 feet long. How tall is the flagpole? **36 ft**

3 The scale of a map is 1 inch : 10 miles. The map distance from Valkaria to Gifford is 2.25 inches. How far is the actual distance? **22.5 mi**

Closure

Ask: *How can you use proportions to find a distance that is difficult to measure?* You can use the shadow and height of a figure that you can measure and the shadow of the figure you cannot measure to write a proportion. Then you can solve the proportion.

Practice and Problem Solving

Assignment Guide

1 Objective

Ⓐ Ⓑ **Core** 1–8, 21, 23, 29–33

Ⓒ **Extension** 36

2 Objective

Ⓐ Ⓑ **Core** 9–20, 22, 24–28

Ⓒ **Extension** 34–35

Standardized Test Prep 37–40

Mixed Review 41–48

Visual Learners

Exercises 1–8 Suggest to students that they trace the figures onto their papers. They can then use colored pencils or markers to color code the corresponding parts.

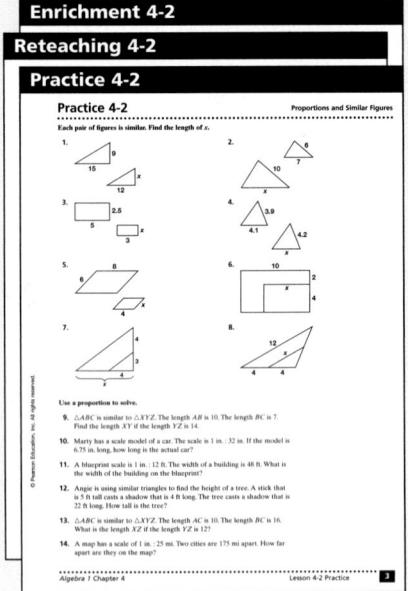

Enrichment 4-2
Reteaching 4-2
Practice 4-2

Ⓐ **Practice by Example**

Example 1
(page 190)

1. $\overline{AB} \cong \overline{PQ}$, $\overline{BC} \cong \overline{QR}$, $\overline{CA} \cong \overline{RP}$; $\angle A \cong \angle P$, $\angle B \cong \angle Q$, $\angle C \cong \angle R$

2. $\overline{DE} \cong \overline{HJ}$, $\overline{EF} \cong \overline{JK}$, $\overline{FD} \cong \overline{KH}$; $\angle D \cong \angle H$, $\angle E \cong \angle J$, $\angle F \cong \angle K$

The figures in each pair are similar. Identify the corresponding sides and angles.

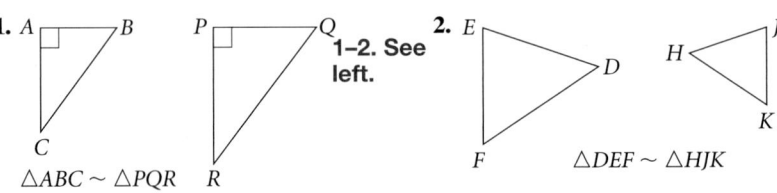

1. △ABC ~ △PQR   1–2. See left.

2. △DEF ~ △HJK

The figures in each pair are similar. Find the missing length.

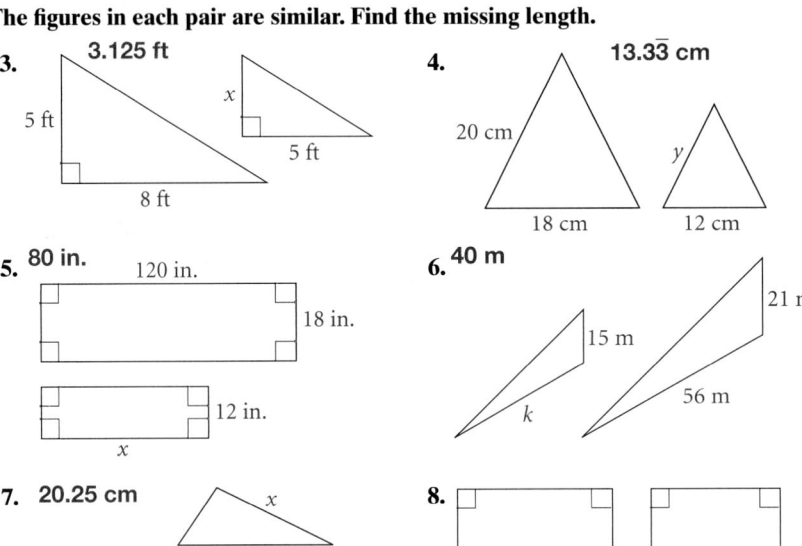

3. 3.125 ft, 5 ft, 8 ft, x, 5 ft

4. 13.33 cm, 20 cm, 18 cm, y, 12 cm

5. 80 in., 120 in., 18 in., 12 in., x

6. 40 m, 15 m, k, 21 m, 56 m

7. 20.25 cm, x, 24 cm, 27 cm, 32 cm

8. k, 6 ft, 6 ft, 5 ft, 7.2 ft

Example 2
(page 191)

The child in the figure is 3 ft tall.

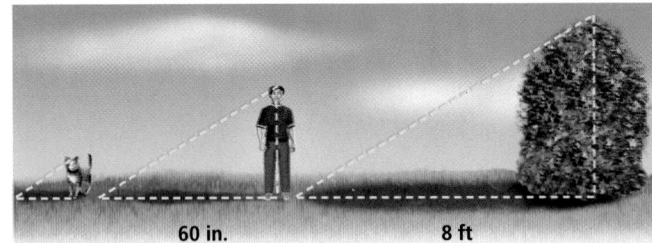

60 in.   8 ft

9. How tall is the tree? **4.8 ft**

10. The cat casts an 18-in. shadow. How tall is the cat? **12 in.**

Example 3
(page 191)

The scale of a map is 1 in. : 17.5 mi. Find the actual distance corresponding to each map distance.

11. 5 in. **87.5 mi**   **12.** 8.3 in. **145.25 mi**   **13.** 18.6 in. **325.5 mi**   **14.** 20 in. **350 mi**

Lincoln

San Paulo

Duncanville

SCALE
1 in. : 16 mi

B **Apply Your Skills**

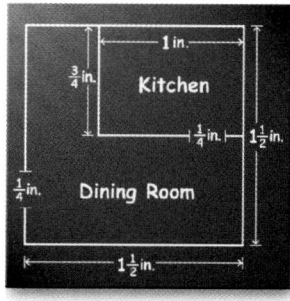

1 in.

$\frac{3}{4}$ in. **Kitchen**

$\frac{1}{4}$ in. $1\frac{1}{2}$ in.

$\frac{1}{4}$ in. **Dining Room**

$1\frac{1}{2}$ in.

23a. Answers may vary. Sample: *GK* and *RQ* are not corresponding sides.

30c. Yes, the ratio of the sides is equal to the ratio of perimeters in similar figures.

d. 2 m², 18 m²

15. a. Use a ruler and the map at the left. Find the distance from each town to the others. **See margin.**
   b. A student lives halfway between Lincoln and San Paulo and takes the shortest route to school in Duncanville. How far does the student travel each day to school? **26 mi**

16. The actual distance between two towns is 28 km. Suppose you measure the distance on your map and find that it is 3.5 cm. What is the scale of your map?
1 cm : 8 km

Using each of the following scales, find the dimensions in a blueprint of an 8 ft-by-12 ft room.

17. 1 in. : 2 ft
4 in. by 6 in.

18. 1 in. : 3 ft
$2\frac{2}{3}$ in. by 4 in.

19. 1 in. : 4 ft
2 in. by 3 in.

20. 1 in. : 2.5 ft
3.2 in. by 4.8 in.

21. Two rectangles are similar. The first is 4 in. wide and 15 in. long. The second is 9 in. wide. Find the length of the second rectangle. **33.75 in.**

22. Architecture A blueprint scale is 1 in. : 9 ft. On the plan, the room measures 2.5 in. by 3 in. What are the actual dimensions of the room? **22.5 ft by 27 ft**

23. Error Analysis The two figures are similar. Robert uses the proportion $\frac{GH}{PQ} = \frac{GK}{RQ}$ to find *RQ*.
   a. What is Robert's error?
   b. What proportion should he have used? $\frac{GH}{PQ} = \frac{HL}{RQ}$

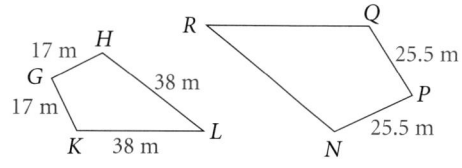

Architecture **A 2-in. length in the scale drawing represents an actual length of 24 ft.**

24. What is the scale of the drawing? **1 in. : 12 ft**

25. What are the actual dimensions of the kitchen? **9 ft by 12 ft**

26. Find the actual width of the doorways that lead into the kitchen and the dining room. **3 ft**

27. Find the actual area of the dining room. **216 ft²**

28. Can a table 7 ft long and 4 ft wide fit into the narrower section of the dining room? Explain your answer. **yes; because it is 6 ft wide and 9 ft long**

29. Two rectangles are similar. One is 5 cm by 12 cm. The longer side of the second rectangle is 8 cm greater than twice its shorter side. Find its length and width. **48 cm long by 20 cm wide**

30. Geometry Rectangle *ABCD* is similar to rectangle *KLMN*.
   a. What is the width *w* of rectangle *KLMN*? **6 m**
   b. What is the perimeter of each rectangle? **6 m, 18 m**
   c. Is the ratio of the perimeters of the rectangles (small : large) equal to the ratio of corresponding sides? Explain.
   d. What is the area of each rectangle?
   e. **Critical Thinking** Find the ratio of the areas (small : large). Explain how the ratio of the areas is related to the ratio of the corresponding sides.
   Answers may vary. Sample: The area ratio is the square of the side ratio.

31. Open-Ended Give some examples of similar figures found in everyday life. **See margin.**

Error Prevention

Exercises 9, 10 Students may have difficulty writing the proportion correctly. Have students write labels on each term as they write the proportion. For example:

$\frac{54 \text{ in. (child's shadow)}}{18 \text{ ft (tree's shadow)}} = \frac{3 \text{ ft (child's height)}}{x \text{ (tree's height)}}$

By seeing the matching words, students can determine if they wrote corresponding measurements in the same ratio.

Exercise 16 Let students know that a map scale is an instance of a unit rate.

Careers

Exercise 22 Architects draw buildings, houses, and landscapes to scale. These scale drawings must be exact so that the builders know exactly what size the building materials must be to fit together properly.

Exercise 23 Remind students that only corresponding sides of similar figures should be used to write proportions.

pages 192–195   Exercises

15a. Lincoln to
San Paulo = 16 mi
Lincoln to
Duncanville = 26 mi
San Paulo to
Duncanville = 18 mi

4. Assess

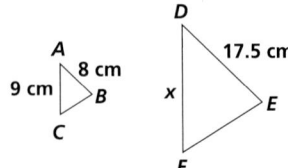

 32. a. Writing Are the two cubes similar? Explain your answer.
   b. Explain how the ratio of volumes (small : large) is related to the ratio of their sides (small : large).
   c. If the ratio of the sides of the two cubes is 3 : 1, what is the ratio of their volumes? **a-c See margin.**

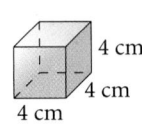 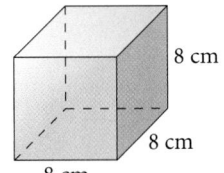

Problem Solving Hint

For Exercise 33, drawing a diagram can help you understand the problem.

33. Geometry The perimeter of a triangle with sides *a*, *b*, and *c* is 24 cm. Side *a* is 2 cm longer than side *b*. The ratio of the lengths of sides *b* and *c* is 3 : 5. What are the lengths of the three sides of the triangle? *a* = 8, *b* = 6, *c* = 10

 **Challenge**

34. The state of Alabama is about 335 mi long and 210 mi wide. What scale would you use to draw a map of Alabama on an $8\frac{1}{2}$ in.-by-11 in. paper to make the map as large as possible? **about 1 in. : 24.7 mi**

35. Astronomy You can block out the moon by holding a coin up at a distance from your eye that is 110 times the diameter of the coin. Using similar figures, $\frac{\text{coin diameter}}{\text{moon diameter}} = \frac{\text{coin distance}}{\text{moon distance}}$. The moon is roughly 3640 kilometers in diameter. How far away is it? **400,400 km**

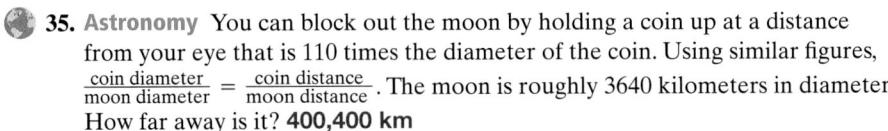

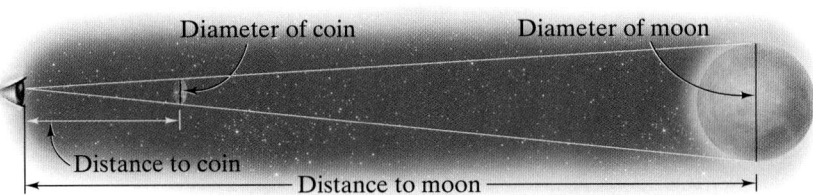
Not drawn to scale.

36. Geometry In the figure at the right, △*ABC* ~ △*ADE*.
   a. Substitute values from the diagram into the following proportion. $\frac{AD}{AB} = \frac{DE}{BC}$ $\frac{8}{8 + x} = \frac{5}{7}$ (*Hint:* $AB = AD + DB$.)
   b. Solve the proportion for *x*. **3.2**
   c. Find the length of *AB*. **11.2 in.**
   d. What is the area of △*ABC*? **39.2 in.²**

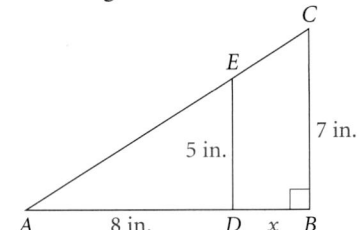

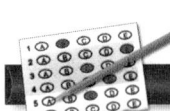

Standardized Test Prep

Multiple Choice

37. In the figure at the right, △*ABC* ~ △*XYZ*. Which proportion is incorrect? **B**

   A. $\frac{AB}{AC} = \frac{XY}{XZ}$
   B. $\frac{AB}{BC} = \frac{XY}{XZ}$
   C. $\frac{BC}{AC} = \frac{YZ}{XZ}$
   D. $\frac{AC}{XZ} = \frac{BC}{YZ}$

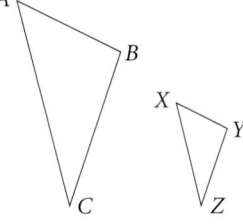

pages 192–195   **Exercises**

31. Answers may vary. Sample: doll house to regular house, model car to real car

32a. Yes; the sides are proportional.
   b. 1 : 8; 1 : 2; answers may vary. Sample: The

volume ratio is the cube of the side ratio.

   c. 27 : 1

38. A map of Kentucky is drawn with a scale of 1 cm : 11 km. The map distance between Louisville and Bowling Green is 14.5 cm. Which is the best estimate of the actual distance? **I**

    F. 1.3 km   **G.** 14 km   **H.** 100 km   **I.** 160 km

Short Response

39. You can paint a 6 ft-by-5 ft rectangular wall using 0.5 gallon of paint. How many gallons of paint will you need to cover a 10 ft-by-12 ft wall? Show your work. **See margin.**

Extended Response

40. Leonardo da Vinci's famous painting the Mona Lisa measures 77.5 cm by 55 cm. **See margin.**
    a. Explain how you know that a 16 cm-by-12 cm reproduction postcard is NOT similar to the original painting.
    b. What dimensions would make a postcard similar to the original painting? Approximate to the nearest tenth. Show your work or explain how you found your answer.

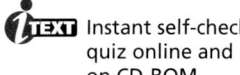
Take It to the NET
Online lesson quiz at
www.PHSchool.com
.... Web Code: aea-0402

Chapter Checkpoint 1

To check understanding of
Lessons 4-1 to 4-2:

Checkpoint Quiz 1 (p. 195)

Teaching Resources
Checkpoint Quiz 1 (also in Prentice Hall Assessment System)

Reaching All Students
Reading and Math Literacy 4B

Spanish versions available

Mixed Review

Lesson 4-1   Solve each proportion.

41. $\frac{x}{2} = \frac{9}{4}$ 4.5   **42.** $\frac{5}{n} = \frac{3}{10}$ $16\frac{2}{3}$ **43.** $\frac{-8}{m} = \frac{7}{20}$ $-22\frac{6}{7}$ **44.** $\frac{12}{30} = \frac{16}{v}$ 40

Lesson 3-3   Solve.

45. $5b < -20$ **46.** $\frac{4}{7}x \geq 4$ $x \geq 7$ **47.** $-3m > 12$ **48.** $-\frac{2}{3}h < 1$
     $b < -4$ $m < -4$ $h > -\frac{3}{2}$

Checkpoint Quiz 1   Lessons 4-1 through 4-2

Instant self-check quiz online and on CD-ROM

1. Complete the statement 2 days = ▇ minutes. **2880**

2. Write $48 for 8 hours as a unit rate. **$6.00/h**

Solve each proportion.

3. $\frac{x}{6} = \frac{7}{4}$ 10.5   **4.** $\frac{8}{k} = -\frac{12}{30}$ −20   **5.** $\frac{3}{5} = \frac{y+1}{9}$ 4.4

6. You are riding your bicycle. It takes you 12 min to go 2.5 mi. If you continue traveling at the same rate, how long will it take you to go 7 mi? **33.6 min**

The figures in each pair are similar. Find the missing length.

7.
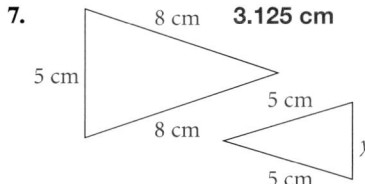
8 cm   **3.125 cm**

8.
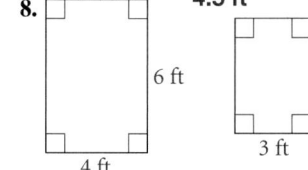
4.5 ft

9. A 3.5-ft child casts a 60-in. shadow. She is standing next to a telephone pole that casts a 50-ft shadow. How tall is the telephone pole? **35 ft**

10. The scale of a map is 3 in. : 20 mi. Find the actual distance if the map distance between two towns is 5.5 in. $36\frac{2}{3}$ **mi**

Lesson 4-2 Proportions and Similar Figures **195**

39. **[2]** smaller area: 6 · 5 = 30; 30 ft²; larger area: 10 · 12 = 120; 120 ft²;
$\frac{0.5}{30} = \frac{x}{120}$
0.5(120) = 30x
60 = 30x
2 = x

Two gallons of paint should cover a 10 ft × 20 ft wall.

[1] incorrect calculation for one area and proportion solved correctly OR correct area calculations but proportion set up incorrectly

40a. **[4]** $\frac{77.5}{16} \neq \frac{55}{12}$
77.5(12) ≠ 16(55)
930 ≠ 880

Since the cross products are not equal, the proportion is not true. So the postcard is not similar to the painting.

b. $\frac{77.5}{x} = \frac{55}{12}$ **OR**
$\frac{77.5}{16} = \frac{55}{y}$

The postcard should be 12 cm × 16.9 cm OR 11.4 cm × 16 cm.

[3] appropriate methods, but with one computational error OR found only one possible postcard size

[2] incorrect proportions solved correctly

[1] correct answer with no work shown

195

Modeling Percents

Students use the basic percent proportion to solve percent examples with various unknowns.

Resources

Using a calculator to do these problems is not recommended as it may lessen the incentive to make sense of percent problems. The impetus to find ways to simplify the proportion will also be lessened.

Teaching Notes

Before students write and solve a proportion in each example, you may want to ask them to explain the problem in their own words and predict a range for the answer. In the first example for instance, they may say that since 35 is more than half of 50, the answer should be more than 50%. In the second example, they may say that 60% of 100 is 60 and 60% of 200 is 120. Since 75 is between these two numbers, the answer is between 100 and 200. Continue in this way so that students become more confident using and thinking about percents.

Teaching Tip

Remind students that they should try to simplify the resulting fraction when solving a proportion. Students should be encouraged to suggest shortcuts when simplifying. For instance, in Example b, the 100 and the 60 can both be divided by 10 giving the same result as crossing out a zero in each.

Investigation

Modeling Percents

You can use a model to show relationships involving percents. The model at the right shows 60% of 80.

You can write this proportion for the model.

$$\begin{array}{c}\text{part} \rightarrow \\ \text{whole} \rightarrow\end{array} \quad \frac{60}{100} = \frac{n}{80}$$

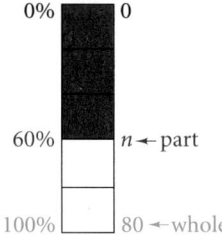

EXAMPLE

a. What percent of 50 is 35?

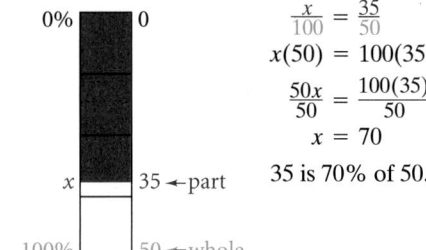

$\frac{x}{100} = \frac{35}{50}$ Write a proportion.

$x(50) = 100(35)$ Write cross products.

$\frac{50x}{50} = \frac{100(35)}{50}$ Divide each side by 50.

$x = 70$ Simplify.

35 is 70% of 50.

b. 75 is 60% of what number?

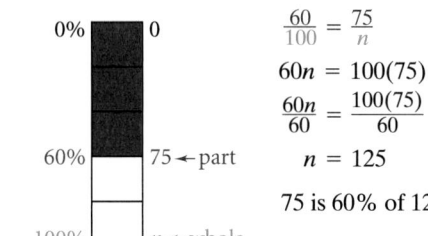

$\frac{60}{100} = \frac{75}{n}$ Write a proportion.

$60n = 100(75)$ Write cross products.

$\frac{60n}{60} = \frac{100(75)}{60}$ Divide each side by 60.

$n = 125$ Simplify.

75 is 60% of 125.

EXERCISES

Write and solve a proportion.

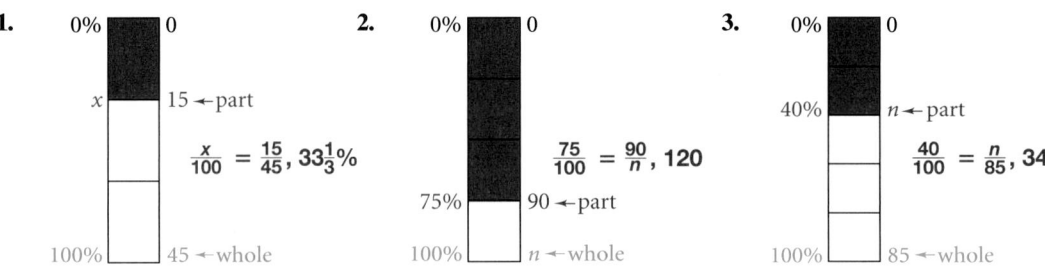

1. $\frac{x}{100} = \frac{15}{45}$, $33\frac{1}{3}\%$

2. $\frac{75}{100} = \frac{90}{n}$, 120

3. $\frac{40}{100} = \frac{n}{85}$, 34

Draw a model, write a proportion, and then solve.   4–9. See back of book.

4. What percent of 36 is 27?   **5.** What percent of 60 is 15?   **6.** 40 is 80% of what number?

7. 8 is 20% of what number?   **8.** 13 is 25% of what number?   **9.** What percent of 63 is 42?

4-3

Proportions and Percent Equations

 North Carolina Objectives

1.02 Use formulas and algebraic expressions, including iterative and recursive forms, to model and solve problems.

Lesson Preview

What You'll Learn

 OBJECTIVE 1
To use proportions when solving percent problems

 OBJECTIVE 2
To write and solve percent equations

. . . And Why

To calculate the total water supply of the United States, as in Example 3

✓ Check Skills You'll Need

(For help, go to Skills Handbook pages 727 and 728.)

Find each product.

1. $0.6 \cdot 9$ **5.4**   **2.** $3.8 \cdot 6.8$ **25.84**   **3.** $\frac{23}{60} \cdot \frac{20}{46}$ $\frac{1}{6}$ **4.** $\frac{17}{135} \cdot \frac{5}{34}$ $\frac{1}{54}$

Write each fraction as a decimal and as a percent.

5. $\frac{7}{10}$ **0.7, 70%**   **6.** $\frac{23}{100}$ **0.23, 23%**   **7.** $\frac{2}{5}$ **0.4, 40%**   **8.** $\frac{13}{20}$ **0.65, 65%**

9. $\frac{35}{40}$ **0.875, 87.5%**   **10.** $\frac{7}{16}$ **0.4375, 43.75%**   **11.** $\frac{4}{25}$ **0.16, 16%**   **12.** $\frac{170}{200}$ **0.85, 85%**

Lesson Preview

✓ Check Skills You'll Need

Multiplying Fractions
Skills Handbook: p. 727
Example 1, Exercises 1–5

Fractions, Decimals, and Percents
Skills Handbook: p. 728
Examples 1–2, Exercises 1–24

Lesson Resources

📁 **Teaching Resources**
Practice, Reteaching, Enrichment

👥 **Reaching All Students**
Practice Workbook 4-3
Spanish Practice Workbook 4-3
Technology Activities 18
Basic Algebra Planning Guide 4-3

⏱ **Presentation Assistant Plus!**
Transparencies
• Check Skills You'll Need 4-3
• Additional Examples 4-3
• Student Edition Answers 4-3
• Lesson Quiz 4-3
PH Presentation Pro CD 4-3

ASSESSMENT SYSTEM (PRENTICE HALL)

Computer Test Generator CD

💿 **Technology**
Resource Pro® CD-ROM
Computer Test Generator CD
Prentice Hall Presentation Pro CD

🖥 **www.PHSchool.com**
Student Site
• Teacher Web Code: aek-5500
• Self-grading Lesson Quiz
Teacher Center
• Lesson Planner
• Resources

Plus

 OBJECTIVE 1
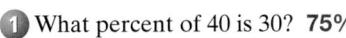 **Applying Proportions to Percent Problems**

 🍎TEXT **Interactive lesson includes instant self-check, tutorials, and activities.**

❓ **Need Help?**

For help with percent see Skills Handbook p. 728.

Recall that a percent is a ratio that compares a number to 100. For example, $23\% = \frac{23}{100}$. You can solve a percent problem by writing and solving a proportion.

$$\text{percent} \begin{cases} \dfrac{n}{100} = \dfrac{\text{part}}{\text{whole}} \end{cases}$$

1 EXAMPLE Finding the Percent

What percent of 80 is 18?

$$\text{percent} \begin{cases} \dfrac{n}{100} = \dfrac{18}{80} \quad \longleftarrow \text{part} \\ \qquad\qquad\quad \longleftarrow \text{whole} \end{cases}$$

$80n = 1800$ **Find the cross products.**

$n = 22.5$ **Divide each side by 80.**

22.5% of 80 is 18.

✓ **Check Understanding** ① What percent of 40 is 30? **75%**

You can use a proportion to find the part or the whole in a percent problem.

2 EXAMPLE Finding the Part

Find 75% of 320.

$$\dfrac{75}{100} = \dfrac{a}{320} \quad \longleftarrow \text{part} \\ \qquad\qquad\quad \longleftarrow \text{whole}$$

$24{,}000 = 100a$ **Find the cross products.**

$240 = a$ **Divide each side by 100.**

75% of 320 is 240.

✓ **Check Understanding** ② Find 30% of 40. **12**

 **Ongoing Assessment and Intervention**

Before the Lesson	During the Lesson	After the Lesson
Diagnose prerequisite skills using:	**Monitor progress using:**	**Assess knowledge using:**
• Check Skills You'll Need	• Check Understanding • Additional Examples • Standardized Test Prep	• Lesson Quiz • Computer Test Generator CD

2. Teach

Math Background

The usefulness of percents is one of the great advantages of our base 10 number system.

OBJECTIVE 1 Teaching Notes

1 EXAMPLE Visual Learners

Some students have difficulty remembering where to place the different parts of the percent proportion. Write the following:

$\frac{n}{100} = \frac{part}{whole}$

Since 100% = 1, 100% refers to a *whole* thing. Therefore, 100 and *whole* are in corresponding places in the percent proportion.

2 EXAMPLE Auditory Learners

Some students may not know whether 320 is the part or the whole. Have students repeat this sentence over and over: *Percent is part of whole.* Stress that the whole usually follows the word "of."

3 EXAMPLE Teaching Tip

Stress that *total* and *whole* mean the same. Since you are looking for the total water supply, *w* should be written in *whole's* place.

Additional Examples

1 What percent of 90 is 27? **30%**

2 Find 25% of 480. **120**

3 Water covers about 361,736,000 km², or about 70.8% of the earth's surface. Approximately what is the total surface area of the earth? **approximately 510,926,554 km²**

Real-World Connection

One million gallons of water would fill a 267 ft × 50 ft ×10 ft swimming pool.

3 EXAMPLE Finding the Whole

Water Supply According to the United States Geological Survey, surface water accounts for 77.6% of our country's total water supply. The surface water supply is about 264.4 billion gallons per day. Find the total water supply.

Relate 77.6% of total water supply is 264.4 billion gallons per day.

Define Let w = the total water supply.

Write $\frac{77.6}{100} = \frac{264.4}{w}$ ← part ← whole

$77.6w = 26{,}440$ **Find cross products.**

$w \approx 340.7$ **Divide each side by 77.6.**

● The total water supply is about 340.7 billion gallons per day.

✓ Check Understanding **3** Carlos worked 31.5 hours at a hospital as a volunteer. This represents 87.5% of his school's requirement for community service. How many hours does his school require for community service? **36 h**

Key Concepts

Summary	Percents and Proportions	
Finding the Percent	**Finding the Part**	**Finding the Whole**
What percent of 45 is 10?	What is 16% of 261?	71% of what number is 87?
$\frac{n}{100} = \frac{10}{45}$ ← part ← whole	$\frac{16}{100} = \frac{w}{261}$ ← part ← whole	$\frac{71}{100} = \frac{87}{v}$ ← part ← whole

The summary above illustrates the "three cases of percent": finding the percent, finding the part, and finding the whole.

OBJECTIVE 2 Percent Equations

You can also solve a percent problem by translating the words into an equation.

4 EXAMPLE Using a Percent Equation

What percent of 170 is 68?

Relate What percent | of | 170 | is | 68?

Define Let k = the decimal form of the percent.

Write k · 170 = 68

$170k = 68$

$k = 0.4$ **Divide each side by 170.**

$k = 40\%$ **Write the decimal as a percent.**

● 40% of 170 is 68.

✓ Check Understanding **4** Write and solve a percent equation for each problem.
a. What is 85% of 320? $\frac{85}{100} = \frac{x}{320}$, **272** **b.** 393 is 60% of what number? $\frac{60}{100} = \frac{393}{x}$, **655**

198 Chapter 4 Solving and Applying Proportions

👥 Reaching All Students

Below Level Ask students: *If you have 75 cents, what fraction of a dollar do you have?* $\frac{3}{4}$ Help students connect percent to the 100 cents in a dollar.	**Advanced Learners** Students take turns being a waiter or a customer. The waiter presents the bill, and checks the customer's estimate of a 15% tip.	**Visual Learners** See note on page 198. **Auditory Learners** See note on page 198.

Remember that percents can be greater than 100% and less than 1%.

5 EXAMPLE Percents Greater Than 100% and Less Than 1%

a. What percent of 90 is 135?

$n \cdot 90 = 135$

$90n = 135$ Write an equation.

$n = 1.5$ Divide each side by 90.

150% of 90 is 135.

b. What is 0.48% of 250?

$n = 0.0048 \cdot 250$ Write an equation. 0.48% = 0.0048

$= 1.2$ Simplify.

1.2 is 0.48% of 250.

✓ **Check Understanding** 5 Find each number or percent.
a. 105 is 125% of what number? **84**   b. What percent of 320 is 1.6? **0.5%**
c. 640 is what percent of 32? **2000%**   d. 0.13% of what number is 3900?
3,000,000

You can estimate some percents using fractions. You can use estimation to help check your calculations or in using mental math in real-world situations. For example, if you wanted to find 26.1% of a number, you could multiply $\frac{1}{4}$ times the number to estimate the answer. The table below gives the fraction equivalents of percents you should know.

Percents and Fractional Equivalents

Percent	5%	10%	20%	25%
Fraction	$\frac{1}{20}$	$\frac{1}{10}$	$\frac{1}{5}$	$\frac{1}{4}$
Percent	33.$\overline{3}$%	40%	50%	60%
Fraction	$\frac{1}{3}$	$\frac{2}{5}$	$\frac{1}{2}$	$\frac{3}{5}$
Percent	66.$\overline{6}$%	75%	80%	90%
Fraction	$\frac{2}{3}$	$\frac{3}{4}$	$\frac{4}{5}$	$\frac{9}{10}$

? Need Help?
Compatible numbers are numbers that are easy to divide mentally.

6 EXAMPLE Using Estimation

Estimate the number that is 32% of 241.

$32\% \approx \frac{1}{3}$ $\frac{1}{3} = 33\frac{1}{3}\%$. So $\frac{1}{3}$ is a good approximation of 32%.

$241 \approx 240$ 240 and 3 are compatible numbers.

$\frac{1}{3} \cdot 240 = 80$

80 is approximately 32% of 241.

✓ **Check Understanding** 6 Use fractions to estimate each answer.
a. 49% of 280 is what number? **140**   b. What is 65% of 334? **222**
c. What is 74.2% of 44? **33**   d. 11% of 521 is what number? **52**

Lesson 4-3 Proportions and Percent Equations   **199**

OBJECTIVE
2 Teaching Notes

4 EXAMPLE Alternative Method

Show students the percent T:

$$\frac{part}{percen\boxed{T}whole}$$

Show students how this is related to the percent equation part = percent · whole.
Ask: *What do you do with two numbers that are written side by side?* multiply *So if you know the percent and the whole, multiply to find the part. What do you do with numbers when one is written above the other?* divide *Since part is written above both percent and whole, if you know the part, you always divide it by the other known number.*

5 EXAMPLE Teaching Tip

Some students may have difficulty understanding that a part can be greater than a whole. Relate this situation to a savings account. Ask: *If 100% is the original amount put in a savings account, what percent is in the account after interest is added?* 100% + interest

6 EXAMPLE Math Tip

Ask students to divide 240 by 3. 80
Help students realize that they can just divide by the denominator if the numerator is 1.

7 EXAMPLE Error Prevention

Students may write 0.07% as 0.07. Remind them that the % symbol represents hundredths. To replace it they must add 2 decimal places. So .07% = .0007.

Additional Examples

4 What percent of 140 is 84? 60%

5 a. What percent of 60 is 114?
190%
b. What is 0.73% of 125? 0.9125

6 Estimate the number that is 19% of 323. 65

7 A candidate for mayor sent out surveys to 8056 people in his city. After two weeks, about 18% of the surveys were returned. Estimate the number of surveys that were returned. about 1450

Closure

Ask: *What are two ways to write percent problems?* You can use proportions or percent equations.

199

Assignment Guide

 **Objective**
- Ⓐ Ⓑ **Core** 1–19, 39–41
- Ⓒ **Extension** 59

 **Objective**
- Ⓐ Ⓑ **Core** 20–38, 42–58
- Ⓒ **Extension** 60

Standardized Test Prep 61–66

Mixed Review 67–74

Error Prevention

Exercises 26, 28 Remind students that when they find percents greater than 100, the % symbol represents 2 decimal places. For example, 160% = 1.60.

Real-World Connection

U.S. per capita consumption of milk is about 24 gallons per year. One gallon of milk weighs about 8.6 lb.

⑦ EXAMPLE Real-World 🌐 Problem Solving

Agriculture In 1997, the total production of milk in the United States was 156 billion pounds. The midwestern states of Michigan, Minnesota, Iowa, Wisconsin, and Illinois produced 25.2% of this total. Estimate the amount of milk produced in these five midwestern states.

| **Relate** | What | is | 25.2% | of | 156? |

Define Let n = the unknown number.

| **Write** | | n | $\approx$ | $\frac{1}{4}$ | $\cdot$ | 156 | Use $\frac{1}{4}$ to estimate 25.2%. |

$$n = \frac{1}{4} \cdot 156$$
$$n = 39 \text{ **Simplify.**}$$

The five midwestern states produced about 39 billion pounds of milk in 1997.

 **Check Understanding** ⑦ **Sales** A store advertises sneakers on sale for 33% off. The original price of sneakers is $56.
 a. Estimate the amount the sneakers have been marked down. **$18**
 b. Estimate the sale price of the sneakers. **$38**

EXERCISES

For more practice, see *Extra Practice*.

Practice and Problem Solving

Ⓐ **Practice by Example**

Example 1 (page 197)

Solve each problem using a proportion.

1. What percent of 40 is 20? **50%**
2. What percent of 80 is 20? **25%**
3. 15 is what percent of 45? **33⅓%**
4. What percent of 50 is 10? **20%**
5. What percent of 24 is 6? **25%**
6. 18 is what percent of 90? **20%**

Example 2 (page 197)

7. What is 40% of 20? **8**
8. What is 80% of 20? **16**
9. 30% of 70 is what number? **21**
10. What is 40% of 70? **28**
11. 8% of 125 is what number? **10**
12. 16% of 125 is what number? **20**

Example 3 (page 198)

Write a proportion and solve to find the whole. 13–18. See margin.

13. 20 is 40% of what number?
14. 20 is 80% of what number?
15. 15% of what number is 24?
16. 20% of what number is 48?
17. 60% of what number is 42?
18. 42 is 30% of what number?

19. Teresa worked 18 hours at a day-care center as a volunteer. This represents 60% of her school's requirement for community service. How many hours of community service does her school require? **30 h**

Example 4 (page 198)

Write an equation and solve.

20. 50 is 25% of what number?
 50 = 0.25x; 200
21. 25 is 50% of what number?
 25 = 0.50x; 50
22. 96 is what percent of 150?
 96 = n · 150; 64%
23. 45 is what percent of 60?
 45 = n · 60; 75%
24. What is 5% of 300?
 x = 0.05(300); 15
25. What is 5% of 200? x = 0.05(200); 10

pages 200–202 Exercises

13. $\frac{40}{100} = \frac{20}{x}$, 50
14. $\frac{80}{100} = \frac{20}{x}$, 25
15. $\frac{15}{100} = \frac{24}{x}$, 160
16. $\frac{20}{100} = \frac{48}{x}$, 240
17. $\frac{60}{100} = \frac{42}{x}$, 70
18. $\frac{30}{100} = \frac{42}{x}$, 140

200 Chapter 4 Solving and Applying Proportions

Example 5
(page 199)

Solve each percent problem.

26. What is 150% of 14? **21**

27. 28 is what percent of 14? **200%**

28. 18 is 450% of what number? **4**

29. 75 is what percent of 25? **300%**

30. What is 0.6% of 70? **0.42**

31. 2.1 is what percent of 700? **0.3%**

Examples 6, 7
(pages 199, 200)

Estimate each answer.

32. What is 51% of 400? **200**

33. 24.8% of 400 is what number? **100**

34. 67.18% of 33 is what number? **22**

35. What is 74% of 201? **150**

36. 9.8% of 680 is what number? **68**

37. What is 39% of 80.3? **32**

38. The freshman class of Mann High School has 1218 students. The graduation rate for the school is 82% of the freshman class. Estimate the number of students who will graduate. **about 960 students**

 **Apply Your Skills**

Write a proportion or an equation and find each answer. 39–44. See margin.

39. 3 is 75% of what number?

40. What percent of 75 is 300?

41. What is 0.2% of 900?

42. 1.8 is 2% of what number?

43. 988 is what percent of 1000?

44. 140% of 84 is what number?

Critical Thinking Use estimation to decide which number is closer to the exact answer. Explain your reasoning. 45–48. See margin.

45. 51.3% of 122; 60 or 62

46. 23.9% of 84; 20 or 22

47. 9.79% of 740; 73 or 75

48. 76.02% of 240; 175 or 185

49. **Sales Tax** Jane, who lives in Florida, plans to buy a car that costs $13,500. Her friend Julie lives in Georgia. She also plans to buy a car for $13,500. How much more will Jane pay in sales tax? **$297.00**

50. **Sales** Suppose you work in an electronics store and earn a 6% commission on every item you sell. How much do you earn if you sell a $545 sound system? **$32.70**

51. **Sales** Juan earns a 5.5% commission on his bicycle sales. In September, he earned $214.28 in commissions. What were his sales for the month? **$3896.00**

52. **Answers may vary. Sample: $1.20; take 10% and 5% of $8 and add them.**

52. **Writing** Estimate a 15% tip for a restaurant bill of $8.25. Explain your method. **See left.**

 53. **Finance** The formula for simple interest is $I = prt$, where I is the interest, p is the principal, r is the interest rate per year, and t is the time in years.

Reading Math

For more help with exercise 53b, go to page 203.

a. You invest $550 for three years. Find the amount of simple interest you earn with an annual interest rate of 4.5%. **$74.25**

b. Suppose you invested $900 for two years. You earned $67.50 in simple interest. What was the annual rate of interest? **3.75%**

c. You invest $812 with an annual interest rate of 6.5%. You earned $316.68 in simple interest. How many years was the money invested? **6 yr**

Finance Use the formula for simple interest, $I = prt$. Find each missing value.

54. $I = \blacksquare$, $p = \$340$, $r = 6\%$, $t = 3$ yr **$61.20**

55. $I = \$312.50$, $p = \blacksquare$, $r = 5\%$, $t = 5$ yr **$1250.00**

56. $I = \$392$, $p = \$1400$, $r = \blacksquare$, $t = 4$ yr **7%**

57. $I = \$1540$, $p = \$22,000$, $r = 3.5\%$, $t = \blacksquare$ **2 yr**

Alternative Assessment

Have students take surveys of the class, such as favorite color, favorite ice cream flavor, or favorite kind of music. Then have students find the related percents. Students may work alone or in small groups.

39-44. Prop. or eqs. may vary. Samples are given.

39. $\frac{75}{100} = \frac{3}{x}$, 4

40. $\frac{x}{100} = \frac{300}{75}$, 400%

41. $x = 0.002(900)$, 1.8

42. $0.02x = 1.8$, 90

43. $1000x = 988$, 98.8%

44. $1.4(84) = x$, 117.6

45. 62; 50% is 61 and 51.3% > 50%.

46. 20; 25% is 21 and 23.9% < 25%.

47. 73; 10% is 74 and 9.79% < 10%.

48. 185; 75% is 180 and 76.02% > 75%.

A sheet of blank grids is available in the Test-Taking Strategies with Transparencies booklet. Give this sheet to students for practice with filling in the grids.

Resources

For additional practice with a variety of test item formats:
- Standardized Test Prep, p. 231
- Test-Taking Strategies, p. 226
- Test-Taking Strategies with Transparencies

pages 200–202   Exercises

58. Answers may vary.
Sample: 33%; I sleep 8 h a day, and there are 24 h in a day, so $\frac{x}{100} = \frac{8}{24}$, $x = 33\frac{1}{3}$.

71. $b < -4$;

-7 -6 -5 -4 -3 -2

72. $x \geq 7$;

5 6 7 8 9 10

73. $h > -21$;

-22 -20 -18 -16 -14

74. $p < -\frac{1}{3}$;

-2 -1   0   1

58. **Open-Ended** What percent of your time do you spend sleeping? Describe the method you used to find this percent. **See margin.**

C Challenge

59. Since percent is a ratio that compares a number to 100, $a\% = \frac{a}{100} = 0.01a$.
   a. What is $n\%$ of $\frac{6}{n}$, $n \neq 0$? $\frac{3}{50}$ b. $2k$ is $k\%$ of what, $k \neq 0$? **200**
   c. What percent of $0.75x$ is $3x$, $x \neq 0$? **400%**

60. **Comparing Costs** At a store in Canada, Phillipe saw a CD he wanted to buy. It cost 16.99 Canadian dollars plus 15% sales tax. At the time, one Canadian dollar was approximately equal to 0.66 U.S. dollars. In the United States, Phillipe can buy the same CD for 13.99 U.S. dollars plus 6% tax. Is the CD less expensive in Canada? Explain.
Yes; 16.99(1.15)(0.66) < 13.99(1.06), 12.90 < 14.83.

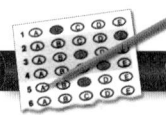

Standardized Test Prep

Reading Comprehension   **Read the passage below before doing Exercises 61 and 62.**

LUIS CORTES WINS LOCAL ELECTION

MIDDLETOWN, NOVEMBER 7
In local elections yesterday, Luis Cortes was elected mayor with 43% of the vote. His main opponent, Tom Morris, received 40% of the vote. The remaining 17% of the vote was split among three other candidates. Election officials noted that 62% of the registered voters took part in the election.

Gridded Response

61. If there were 43,931 registered voters in Middletown, how many people actually voted? **27237**

62. How many people actually voted for Cortes? **11712**

63. The U.S. Postal Service handles 170 billion pieces of mail each year. If this is 40% of the world's total, how many pieces, in billions, are mailed each year in the world? **425**

64. Pete chose a shirt from a sale rack. The ink on the price tag had smeared, and he couldn't read what the percent discount was. The original price was $35.00. When the clerk rang up the sale, the price before tax was $22.75. What percent was taken off the original price of the shirt? **35**

65. There were 580 students in ninth grade last year. If this year's ninth-grade class has 15% more students, how many ninth-graders are there this year? **667**

Take It to the NET
Online lesson quiz at
www.PHSchool.com
Web Code: aea-0403

66. Jessie plants sunflowers in $\frac{2}{5}$ of her garden area and daisies in 40% of her garden area. What percent is still available for planting? **20**

Mixed Review

Lesson 4-2   **The scale of a map is 3 in. : 40 mi. Find the actual distance for each map distance.**

67. 1 in. $13\frac{1}{3}$ mi   68. 4.5 in. **60 mi**   69. $6\frac{3}{4}$ in. **90 mi**   70. 8 in. $106\frac{2}{3}$ mi

Lesson 3-3   **Solve each inequality. Check your solutions. Graph each solution. 71–74. See margin.**

71. $5b < -20$ 72. $\frac{4}{7}x \geq 4$ 73. $-\frac{2}{3}h < 14$ 74. $3.4 < -10.2p$

Reading a Formula

FOR USE WITH PAGE 201, EXERCISE 53b

Read the exercise below and the explanation of how to interpret the formula. Check your understanding with the exercise at the bottom of the page.

Finance The formula for simple interest is $I = prt$, where I is the interest, p is the principal, r is the interest rate per year, and t is the time in years.

53b. Suppose you invested $900 for two years. You earned $67.50 in simple interest. What was the annual rate of interest?

Formulas represent mathematical relationships among quantities. When you're using formulas to solve problems, it's helpful to consider a few questions: What do the symbols mean? What does the formula mean? What information do I have?

What do the symbols mean?

Each symbol, or "variable," used in the formula represents one of the quantities. The quantities below are highlighted in colored boxes to help you see how the words relate to the variables. A different color is used for each variable.

I	$=$	p	$\times$	r	$\times$	t
simple Interest	$=$	principal amount	$\times$	interest rate (per year) in decimal form	$\times$	time (in years)

Another place to look for help is the Glossary. For simple interest, see page 779.

What does the formula mean?

Once you know what the variables represent, write the formula in your own words.

interest you earn on your money	$=$	amount of money you deposit in bank	$\times$	interest rate your money will earn	$\times$	number of years you leave money in bank

What information do I have?

Read the problem to identify the information given and the missing information.

The principal p is $900. The interest earned I is $67.50. The time t is 2 years. You have to find the annual rate of interest r. Substitute these values into the formula and solve for r.

$$I = p \times r \times t$$
$$67.5 = 900 \times r \times 2$$
$$67.5 = 1800\,r$$
$$0.0375 = r$$

The annual rate of interest was 3.75%.

Remember: Rate is a percent. Multiply your solution by 100%.

EXERCISE

You earned $110.25 in simple interest on money that you invested over three years. The interest rate was 5.25%. How much money did you invest? **$700**

Reading a Formula

Students interpret and use formulas to solve problems.

Teaching Notes

Students need to understand that each variable or symbol in a formula represents a quantity. They will need to read carefully to determine the various quantities before substituting them into the formula. Students must know what the symbols in the formula mean, what the formula itself means, and how to substitute the information they have into the formula.

English Learners

Explain that the word *principal* has several meanings in English. The principal of a school is the head or first in authority. In finances, principal is the amount of a debt or investment before interest is added to it. It is the amount of money upon which interest is computed.

Exercise

Present a scenario such as borrowing money to purchase a car. Have students look in a newspaper or check the Internet for current interest rates on car loans. Then have them decide whether they want a 3, 4, or 5 year loan. Have each student calculate the interest he/she would pay on the life of that loan. Then have students work in pairs to explain and justify their answers to each other. If there are disagreements, have the pair of students present the problem to the class and allow for a class discussion.

4-4

Lesson Preview

✓ **Check Skills You'll Need**

Proportions and Percent Equations
Lesson 4-3: Example 4
Exercises 20–25
Extra Practice, p. 705

Lesson Resources

📁 **Teaching Resources**
Practice, Reteaching, Enrichment

👥 **Reaching All Students**
Practice Workbook 4-4
Spanish Practice Workbook 4-4
Basic Algebra Planning Guide 4-4

⏱ **Presentation Assistant Plus!**
Transparencies
• Check Skills You'll Need 4-4
• Additional Examples 4-4
• Student Edition Answers 4-4
• Lesson Quiz 4-4
PH Presentation Pro CD 4-4

ASSESSMENT SYSTEM
PRENTICE HALL

Computer Test Generator CD

💿 **Technology**
Resource Pro® CD-ROM
Computer Test Generator CD
Prentice Hall Presentation Pro CD

💻 **www.PHSchool.com**
Student Site
• Teacher Web Code: aek-5500
• Self-grading Lesson Quiz
Teacher Center
• Lesson Planner
• Resources

Plus 📱TEXT

4-4

Percent of Change

North Carolina Objectives
1.02 Use formulas and algebraic expressions, including iterative and recursive forms, to model and solve problems.

Lesson Preview

What You'll Learn

OBJECTIVE 1 To find percent of change

OBJECTIVE 2 To find percent error

. . . And Why

To use percent of change in a real-world situation involving farming, as in Example 2

✓ **Check Skills You'll Need** (For help, go to Lesson 4-3.)

Write an equation for each problem and solve. $\frac{8}{20} = \frac{x}{100}$, 40%

1. What is 20% of 20? $\frac{x}{20} = \frac{20}{100}$, 4
2. 8 is what percent of 20?
3. 18 is 90% of what number?
4. 27 is 90% of what number?

Estimate each answer. $\frac{18}{x} = \frac{90}{100}$, 20 $\frac{27}{x} = \frac{90}{100}$, 30

5. 67.3% of 24 **16**
6. 65% of 48 **32**

New Vocabulary • percent of change • percent of increase
• percent of decrease • greatest possible error
• percent error

OBJECTIVE 1 Percent of Change

📱TEXT Interactive lesson includes instant self-check, tutorials, and activities.

Suppose the price of a $20 sweatshirt increases by $2. You can express the increase as a percent.

increase in price → $\frac{2}{20} = \frac{1}{10} = 10\%$
original price →

There was 10% increase in the price. This is an example of percent of change.
Percent of change is the ratio $\frac{\text{amount of change}}{\text{original amount}}$ expressed as a percent. When a value increases from its original amount, it is the **percent of increase**. When a value decreases from its original amount, it is the **percent of decrease**.

1 EXAMPLE Finding Percent of Change

The price of a sweater decreased from $29.99 to $24.49. Find the percent of decrease.

percent of decrease = $\frac{\text{amount of change}}{\text{original amount}}$

$= \frac{29.99 - 24.49}{29.99}$ **Subtract to find the amount of change. Substitute the original amount.**

$= \frac{5.50}{29.99}$ **Simplify the numerator.**

≈ 0.18 or 18% **Write as a decimal and then as a percent.**

● The price of the sweater decreased by about 18%.

✓ **Check Understanding** **1 a.** Find the percent of change if the price of a CD increases from $12.99 to $13.99. Round to the nearest percent. **8%**
b. Find the percent of change if the CD is on sale, and its price decreases from $13.99 to $12.99. Round to the nearest percent. **7%**

---

204 Chapter 4 Solving and Applying Proportions

✓ **Ongoing Assessment and Intervention**

Before the Lesson Diagnose prerequisite skills using:	During the Lesson Monitor progress using:	After the Lesson Assess knowledge using:
• Check Skills You'll Need	• Check Understanding • Additional Examples • Standardized Test Prep	• Lesson Quiz • Computer Test Generator CD

2 EXAMPLE Real-World Problem Solving

Farming In 1990, there were 1330 registered alpacas in the United States. By the summer of 2000, there were 29,856. What was the percent of increase in registered alpacas?

$$\text{percent of increase} = \frac{\text{amount of change}}{\text{original amount}}$$

$$= \frac{29,856 - 1330}{1330} \qquad \textbf{Substitute.}$$

$$= \frac{28,526}{1330} \qquad \textbf{Simplify the numerator.}$$

$$\approx 21.448 \text{ or } 2145\% \qquad \textbf{Write as a decimal and then as a percent.}$$

● The number of registered alpacas increased by nearly 2145%.

Real-World Connection

Alpacas produce 5 to 8 pounds of fleece per year, which sells for $32 to $128 per pound.

✔ **Check Understanding** ② The number of alpaca owners increased from 146 in 1991 to 2919 in 2000. Find the percent of increase. Round to the nearest percent. **1899%**

OBJECTIVE

2 Percent Error

Think about the last time you used a ruler. You probably measured to the nearest inch, half-inch, centimeter, or millimeter. Because no measurement is exact, you always measure to the nearest "something." The **greatest possible error** in a measurement is one half of that measuring unit.

3 EXAMPLE Finding the Greatest Possible Error

You use a beam balance to find the mass of a rock sample for a science lab. You read the scale as 3.8 g. What is your greatest possible error?

The rock's mass was measured to the nearest 0.1 g, so the greatest possible error is one half of 0.1 g, or 0.05 g.

✔ **Check Understanding** ③ You measure a picture for the yearbook and record its height as 9 cm. What is your greatest possible error? **0.5 cm**

4 EXAMPLE Finding Maximum and Minimum Areas

You measure a room and make the diagram shown at the left. Use the greatest possible error to find the maximum and minimum possible areas.

13 ft

7 ft

Both measurements were made to the nearest whole foot, so the greatest possible error is 0.5 ft. The length could be as little as 12.5 ft or as great as 13.5 ft. The width could be as little as 6.5 ft or as great as 7.5 ft. Find the minimum and maximum areas.

Minimum Area	**Maximum Area**
12.5 ft $\times$ 6.5 ft = 81.25 ft^2	13.5 ft $\times$ 7.5 ft = 101.25 ft^2

● The minimum area is 81.25 ft^2, and the maximum area is 101.25 ft^2.

✔ **Check Understanding** ④ You measure a wall of your room as 8 ft high and 12 ft wide. Find the minimum and maximum possible areas of the wall. **86.25 ft^2, 106.25 ft^2**

👥 Reaching All Students

Below Level Emphasize to students that the percent of change is always a percent of the original amount. The new amount is only used to compute the amount of change.	**Advanced Learners** Discuss with students how a percent of decrease could be greater than 100%; for example, overdrawing a checking account.	**English Learners** See note on page 205. **Tactile Learners** See note on page 205.

---

2. Teach

Math Background

Percent of change, whether increase or decrease, and percent of error are two applications of proportion. Percent of change is another way of setting up a ratio between the part and the whole.

OBJECTIVE

1 Teaching Notes

1 EXAMPLE English Learners

Have students discuss and give examples of percent of change, percent of increase, and percent of decrease. Point out that percent of change is always based on the original amount, not on the new amount.

2 EXAMPLE Diversity

Many students will not know what an alpaca is. If a student has seen one, have that student describe the alpaca. An alpaca is a domesticated South American mammal of the camel family, related to the llama and similar in appearance. Even though they are South American mammals, they were brought to the United States to use as a source for wool.

🖐 Additional Examples

1 The price of a skirt decreased from $32.95 to $28.95. Find the percent of decrease. **about 12%**

2 Between 1940 and 1980, the federal budget increased from $9.5 billion to $725.3 billion. What was the percent of increase in the federal budget? **nearly 7535%**

OBJECTIVE

2 Teaching Notes

4 EXAMPLE Tactile Learners

Students may not understand why no measurement is exact. Have five students each measure the circumference of the same circular object to the nearest millimeter. Instruct each student to write the measurement on a piece of paper. Announce the measurements aloud.

205

3 You read the bathroom scale as 122 lb. What is your greatest possible error? **0.5 lb**

4 When a garden plot was measured, the dimensions were 156 in. × 84 in. Use the greatest possible error to find the minimum and maximum possible areas.
min: 12,984.25 in.²;
max: 13,224.25 in.²

5 Suppose you measure a library book and record its width as 17.6 cm. Find the percent of error in your measurement. **about 0.3%**

6 A small jewelry box measures 7.4 cm by 12.2 cm by 4.2 cm. Find the percent error in calculating its volume. **about 2%**

5 EXAMPLE Error Prevention

Some students may use 0.5 cm as half of 0.1 cm. Have students write 0.1 as $\frac{1}{10}$. Then write 0.5 as $\frac{1}{2}$. Ask: *Is $\frac{1}{2}$ half of $\frac{1}{10}$?* **no** *What is half of $\frac{1}{10}$?* $\frac{1}{10} \times \frac{1}{2} = \frac{1}{20}$ *How do you write $\frac{1}{20}$ as a decimal?* $\frac{1}{20} = \frac{5}{100}$, **so** $\frac{1}{20} = 0.05$.

6 EXAMPLE Technology Tip

Show students two ways to input this information into a graphing calculator. One way is to enter (12376 − 11859) / 11859 ENTER. Ask: *Why do you need to use parentheses?* **You need the calculator to perform the subtraction before the division.** The other way to input this information is to enter 12376 − 11859 ENTER / 11859 ENTER. Ask: *How is this method similar to the first method?* **The first ENTER has the calculator perform the subtraction, so parentheses are not needed. The second ENTER has the calculator perform the division.**

Closure

Have students describe the difference between finding percent and finding percent of change. **To find percent, divide the part by the whole. To find percent of change, divide the amount of change by the original amount.**

206

Percent error is another useful way to think of the error in a measurement. It is the ratio of the greatest possible error and the measurement.

$$\textbf{percent error} = \frac{\text{greatest possible error}}{\text{measurement}}$$

5 EXAMPLE Finding Percent Error

Suppose you measure a CD and record its diameter as 12.1 cm. Find the percent error in your measurement.

Since the measurement is to the nearest 0.1 cm, the greatest possible error is 0.05 cm.

percent error $= \dfrac{\text{greatest possible error}}{\text{measurement}}$	Use the percent error formula.
$= \dfrac{0.05}{12.1}$	Substitute.
≈ 0.0041322314	Divide.
$\approx 0.4\%$	Round and write as a percent.

● The percent error is about 0.4%.

✓ Check Understanding 5 a. You measure the length of a table as 168 inches. Find the percent error in this measurement. **about 0.3%**

b. You measure the length of a table as 168.0 inches. Find the percent error in this measurement. **about 0.03%**

6 EXAMPLE Finding Percent Error in Calculating Volume

The diagram at the left shows the dimensions of a cassette case. Find the percent error in calculating its volume.

The measurements are to the nearest 0.1 cm. The greatest possible error is 0.05 cm.

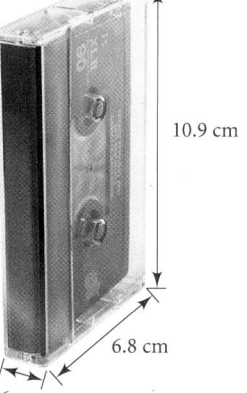

10.9 cm

6.8 cm

1.6 cm

as measured	maximum value	minimum value
$V = \ell \cdot w \cdot h$	$V = \ell \cdot w \cdot h$	$V = \ell \cdot w \cdot h$
$= 6.8 \cdot 1.6 \cdot 10.9$	$= 6.85 \cdot 1.65 \cdot 10.95$	$= 6.75 \cdot 1.55 \cdot 10.85$
$\approx 118.59 \text{ cm}^3$	$\approx 123.76 \text{ cm}^3$	$\approx 113.52 \text{ cm}^3$

Possible Error:	**maximum − measured**	**measured − minimum**
	$123.76 - 118.59 = 5.17$	$118.59 - 113.52 = 5.07$

Use the difference that shows the greatest possible error to find the percent error.

percent error $= \dfrac{\text{greatest possible error}}{\text{measurement}}$	Use the percent error formula.
$= \dfrac{123.76 - 118.59}{118.59}$	Substitute.
$= \dfrac{5.17}{118.59}$	Simplify the numerator.
≈ 0.0435955814	Write as a decimal.
$\approx 4\%$	Round and write as a percent.

● The percent error is about 4%.

✓ Check Understanding 6 Suppose you measured your math book and recorded the dimensions as 1 in. × 9 in. × 10 in. Find the percent error in calculating its volume. **about 66%**

pages 207–209   Exercises

1. 50%; increase

2. $33\frac{1}{3}$%; decrease

3. 25%; increase

4. 20%; decrease

5. $33\frac{1}{3}$%; increase

6. 25%; decrease

7. 25%; increase

8. 20%; increase

9. 84.4%; increase

10. 71.1%; increase

11. 60.7%; decrease

12. 14.4%; increase

19. 19.25 cm², 29.25 cm²

20. 48.75 mi², 63.75 mi²

EXERCISES

For more practice, see *Extra Practice*.

Practice and Problem Solving

A Practice by Example

Example 1
(page 204)

Find each percent of change. Describe the percent of change as an increase or decrease. If necessary, round to the nearest tenth. 1–12. See margin p. 206.

1. $2 to $3　　**2.** $3 to $2　　**3.** 4 ft to 5 ft　　**4.** 5 ft to 4 ft

5. 9 m to 12 m　**6.** 12 cm to 9 cm　**7.** 12 in. to 15 in.　**8.** 15 lb to 18 lb

9. 4.5 cm to 8.3 cm　**10.** $38 to $65　**11.** $12.20 to $4.80　**12.** 125 lb to 143 lb

Example 2
(page 205)

13. Physical Therapy Physical therapists measure strength on a dynamometer, which uses a unit called a foot-pound. Suppose you increase the strength in your elbow joint from 90 foot-pounds to 125 foot-pounds. Find the percent of increase to the nearest percent. **39%**

14. Environment From 1999 to 2000, the number of days of unhealthy air quality in Charlotte, North Carolina, dropped from 5 to 2. Find the percent of decrease in the number of days of unhealthy air. **60%**

Example 3
(page 205)

Find the greatest possible error for each measurement.

15. 14 ft **0.5 ft**　**16.** 3.5 cm **0.05 cm**　**17.** 56.38 g **0.005 g**　**18.** 17 in. **0.5 in.**

Example 4
(page 205)

Find the minimum and maximum possible areas for rectangles with the following measured areas. 19–24. See margin p. 206.

19. 4 cm × 6 cm　　**20.** 7 mi × 8 mi　　**21.** 6 in. × 9 in.

22. 12 km × 5 km　　**23.** 18 in. × 15 in.　　**24.** 23 km × 14 km

Example 5
(page 206)

Find the percent error of each measurement.

25. 2 cm **25%**　**26.** 0.2 cm **25%**　**27.** 4 cm **12.5%**　**28.** 0.4 cm **12.5%**

Example 6
(page 206)

29. The table below shows the measured dimensions of the prism and the maximum and minimum possible values based on the greatest possible error.

Dimensions	ℓ	w	h
Measured	8	3	2
Maximum	8.5	3.5	2.5
Minimum	7.5	2.5	1.5

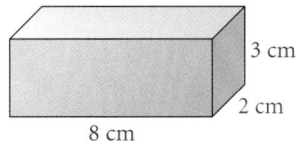

3 cm

2 cm

8 cm

74.375 cm³

a. Find the measured volume. **48 cm³**　　**b.** Find the maximum volume.
c. Find the minimum volume. **28.125 cm³**　**d.** Find the greatest possible error.
e. What is the percent error? Round to the nearest percent. **55%**　**d.** 26.375 cm³

B Apply Your Skills

Find each percent of change. Describe the percent of change as an increase or decrease. Round to the nearest percent. 30–38. See margin.

30. 26 to 20　　　**31.** $4.95 to $3.87　　**32.** 21 in. to 54 in.

33. 2 ft to $5\frac{1}{2}$ ft　**34.** $24,000 to $25,000　**35.** 18 to $17\frac{1}{2}$

36. 8.99 to 3.99　　**37.** 132 lb to 120 lb　　**38.** $42.69 to $49.95

Lesson 4-4 Percent of Change **207**

21. 46.75 in.², 61.75 in.²
22. 51.75 km², 68.75 km²
23. 253.75 in.², 286.75 in.²
24. 303.75 km²; 340.75 km²
30. 23%; decrease

31. 22%; decrease
32. 157%; increase
33. 175%; increase
34. 4%; increase
35. 3%; decrease

36. 56%; decrease
37. 9%; decrease
38. 17% increase

3. Practice

Assignment Guide

1 Objective
Ⓐ Ⓑ Core 1–14, 30–40, 42–44, 48
Ⓒ Extension 54

2 Objective
Ⓐ Ⓑ Core 15–29, 41, 45–47, 49–52
Ⓒ Extension 53, 55

Standardized Test Prep 56–59

Mixed Review 60–68

Connection to Physics
Exercise 13 A *foot-pound* is a unit of work equal to the work done by lifting a mass of one pound vertically against gravity through a distance of one foot.

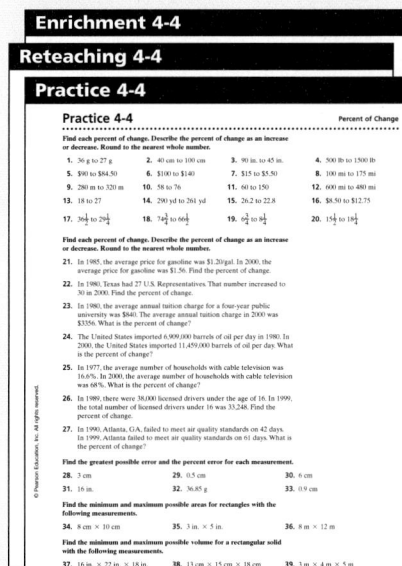

207

Lesson Quiz 4-4

Find each percent of change. Describe the percent of change as an increase or decrease.

1. $6 to $9 **50% increase**

2. 15 cm to 12 cm **20% decrease**

Find the greatest possible error.

3. 13.2 m **0.05 m**

4. 34.62 g **0.005 g**

5. Find the percent error for the measurement 6 cm. **about 8.3%**

6. Find the minimum and maximum possible areas for a rectangle measured as 3 m × 7 m. **min: 16.25 m²; max: 26.25 m²**

Alternative Assessment

Organize students in pairs. Have them choose two numbers and then use them to do the following:

a. Find the percent of increase between the two numbers.

b. Find the maximum and minimum areas of a rectangle using the two numbers as dimensions.

c. Find the percent error using one of the numbers as a measurement.

Hurricane Dennis
NOAA-14 1 km AVHRR HRPT
Multi-spectral False Color Image
August 30, 1999 @ 1957 UTC

Real-World Connection

Atlantic cyclones can be tropical depressions, tropical storms, or hurricanes.

44. **Answers may vary. Sample:** Joan bought shoes for $10. Sarah bought the same shoes 3 days later for $7. What was the percent change? **30% decrease**

51. **Answers may vary. Sample:** Determine measuring unit and use greatest possible error to find max. dimensions. Find the difference between the area using the max. and the measured dimensions; then divide by area using measured dimensions and write as a percent.

---

39. **Sports** In the 1988 Olympics, Florence Griffith-Joyner of the United States won the women's 100-meter run in 10.54 seconds. In 2000, Marion Jones, also of the United States, won with a time of 10.75 seconds. Find the percent of change in the winning times. Round to the nearest percent. **2%**

40. **Meteorology** In 1999, the National Oceanographic and Atmospheric Administration reported a total of 16 Atlantic cyclones. In 2000, there were 19 Atlantic cyclones. Find the percent of change in the number of cyclones from 1999 to 2000. Round to the nearest percent. **19%**

41. If you want accuracy of 0.5 mm, what measuring unit should you use? **1 mm**

42. **Critical Thinking** An item costs $64. The price is increased by $10, then reduced by $10. Is the percent of increase equal to the percent of decrease? Explain your answer. **no; 16% increase but a 14% decrease**

43. **Critical Thinking** An item costs $64. The price is increased by 10%, then reduced by 10%. Is the final price equal to the original price? Explain. **no; increases to $70.40 but decreases to $63.36**

44. **Open-Ended** Write a word problem involving percent of change. Include your solution. **See left.**

Find the minimum and maximum possible areas for rectangles with the following measured dimensions. Round to the nearest tenth.

45. 4.1 cm × 6.1 cm **24.5 cm², 25.5 cm²**

46. 7.0 mi × 8.4 mi **58 mi², 59.6 mi²**

47. 6.01 in. × 9.02 in. **54.1 in.², 54.3 in.²**

48. **Sales** Suppose that you are selling sweatshirts for a class fund-raiser. The wholesaler charges you $8 for each sweatshirt.

 a. You charge $16 for each sweatshirt. Find the percent of increase. **100%**

 b. Generalize your answer to part (a). Doubling a price is the same as a __?__ percent of increase. **100%**

 c. After the fund-raiser is over, you reduce the price on the remaining sweatshirts to $8. Find the percent of decrease. **50%**

 d. Generalize your answer to part (c). Cutting a price in half is the same as a __?__ percent of decrease. **50%**

Find the percent error in calculating the volume of each rectangular prism. Round to the nearest percent.

49. **11%**

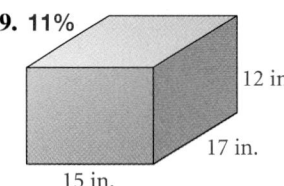

12 in.
17 in.
15 in.

50. **34%**

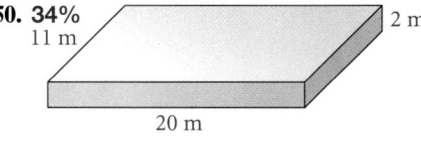

11 m
2 m
20 m

51. **Writing** Explain how to find the percent error when calculating the area of a rectangle. **See left.**

52. **Error Analysis** Jorge found the percent of change from $15 to $10 to be 50%. What error did he make? **Jorge found the change of $5 but divided by the final price instead of the original price.**

C Challenge

53. Suppose you measure two cubes. The smaller one measures 18 cm on each side. The larger one measures 45 cm on each side.
  a. Find the percent error of the volume of each cube. Round to the nearest percent. **9%, 3%**
  b. **Critical Thinking** Explain why using the same measuring unit did not yield the same percent error for the two cubes. **See margin.**

54. **Data Analysis** A reporter states, "From 1980 to 1996, the number of female physicians more than tripled." A second reporter states, "From 1980 to 1996, the number of female physicians increased about 205%." Can both reports be correct? Explain. **See margin.**

Year	U.S. Female Physicians
1980	48,700
1990	96,100
1996	148,300

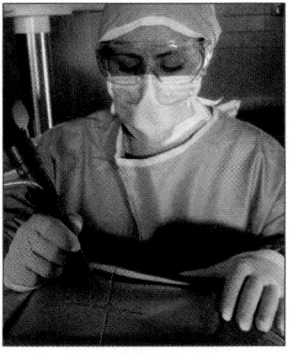

Real-World 🌐 **Connection**

Careers Students who want to become physicians must take calculus, physics, biology, and chemistry before going to medical school.

55. a. The sides of a 12 cm × 12 cm square are all increased in length by 10%. Find the percent of increase in the area. **21%**
  b. The sides of a 14 cm × 14 cm square are all increased in length by 10%. Find the percent of increase in the area. **21%**
  c. Predict the percent of increase in the area if the sides of a 16 cm × 16 cm square are all increased by 10%. Explain your prediction and check.
  21%; answers may vary. Sample: Relationship between % increase of side and area of the square doesn't depend on the side length. $1.1a \cdot 1.1a = 1.21a^2$, which is 21% greater than $a \cdot a = a^2$.

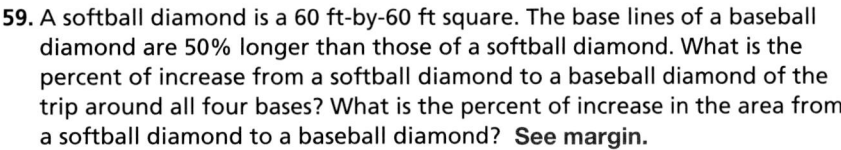

Standardized Test Prep

Multiple Choice

56. Which percent of change best reflects a price increase from $32 to $36? **C**
  A. 4%   **B.** 8%   **C.** 12%   **D.** 89%

57. A carpenter measured a rectangle as 5 in. by 8 in. Which number is the maximum possible area? **I**
  F. 33.75 in.^{2} **G.** 38.25 in.^{2} **H.** 40 in.^{2} **I.** 46.75 in.^{2}

58. A student records the measured length of an object as 24.7 cm. What is the greatest possible error in this measurement? **A**
  A. 0.05 cm   **B.** 0.2 cm   **C.** 0.5 cm   **D.** 1.0 cm

Short Response

Take It to the NET
Online lesson quiz at **www.PHSchool.com**
····· Web Code: aea-0404

59. A softball diamond is a 60 ft-by-60 ft square. The base lines of a baseball diamond are 50% longer than those of a softball diamond. What is the percent of increase from a softball diamond to a baseball diamond of the trip around all four bases? What is the percent of increase in the area from a softball diamond to a baseball diamond? **See margin.**

Mixed Review

Lesson 4-3

Write a proportion or an equation for each problem and solve. Round to the nearest tenth or to the nearest percent. 60–65. **See margin.**

60. 5 is what percent of 67?
61. What percent of 15 is 13?
62. 79 is 44% of what number?
63. 96 is what percent of 32?
64. What is 0.2% of 834?
65. 266% of 14 is what?

Lesson 3-4

Solve each inequality.

66. $5 - 7n > 4 + 8n$
  $n < \frac{1}{15}$
67. $8(q - 9) \le 12q - 4$
  $q \ge -17$
68. $4x + 17 - 2x \ge -15x$
  $x \ge -1$

📄 **Resources**
For additional practice with a variety of test item formats:
• Standardized Test Prep, p. 231
• Test-Taking Strategies, p. 226
• Test-Taking Strategies with Transparencies

Exercise 58 Help students see that the greatest possible error is always a 5 in the next place value to the right of the given number. They should write 0 in all place values between the decimal and the 5.

pages 207–209   Exercises

53b. Answers may vary. Sample: The larger a measure, the smaller is the percent error.

54. Yes; 148.3 > 3 (48.7) = 146.1, and $\frac{148.3 - 48.7}{48.7} \approx$ 205%.

59. [2] perimeter of softball diamond: 4(60) = 240, perimeter 240 ft, side of baseball diamond: 1.5(60) = 90, side 90 ft, perimeter of baseball diamond: 4(90) = 360, perimeter 360 ft, % of increase = $\frac{360 - 240}{240}$ = 50%; area of softball diamond: 60(60) = 3600, area 3600 ft^2. area of baseball diamond: 90(90) = 8100, area 8100 ft^2, percent of increase = $\frac{8100 - 3600}{3600}$ = 125% OR computation that gives same results

  [1] appropriate methods, but with one computational error OR finds only one % of increase

60–65. Equations may vary.

60. $\frac{x}{100} = \frac{5}{67}$, 7%
61. $\frac{x}{100} = \frac{13}{15}$, 87%
62. $\frac{44}{100} = \frac{79}{x}$, 179.5
63. $\frac{x}{100} = \frac{96}{32}$, 300%
64. $\frac{0.2}{100} = \frac{x}{834}$, 1.7
65. $\frac{266}{100} = \frac{x}{14}$, 37.2

209

Investigation

Understanding Probability

Understanding Probability

Students explore listing possible outcomes. They learn that the probability of an event is calculated by dividing the number of possible outcomes for the event by the total number of possible outcomes.

Teaching Notes

Encourage students to find an organized way to list all possible outcomes. Tables and tree diagrams are just two possible ways. Once results are organized, students can answer an assortment of related probability questions. In the first example, students can count the outcomes on their chart to find how many results are divisible by three (12) and the total number of outcomes (36) to find that the probability of rolling a number divisible by 3 is $\frac{12}{36}$ or $\frac{1}{3}$.

Tactile Learners

Tactile learners have more confidence in their results when they manipulate number cubes to explore different outcomes. They can leave one cube showing a 1 and turn the other to show the six possible outcomes. They can continue in this way until they have all possible outcomes.

Teaching Tip

To assess understanding of the concepts in this lesson, pose an unfair game with number cubes. Have students decide whether the game is fair or unfair and defend their answers. You will be able to assess their understanding by listening to their explanations. Here is an example of an unfair game. Say: *If I roll 6, 7, 8, or 9, I get a point. If I roll a 2, 3, 4, 5, 10, 11, or 12 you get a point. Who is more likely to win this game? Why?* **The teacher; the probabilities are $\frac{20}{36} = \frac{5}{9}$ for the teacher, and $\frac{4}{9}$ for the student.**

When you toss a number cube, there are a variety of possible results. You can find the probabilities of these results by first listing all the possible results.

1. List all the possible results of tossing a number cube like those at the right. **1, 2, 3, 4, 5, 6**

2. How many possible results are there? **6**

3. List all the possible results that are divisible by 3. **3, 6**

4. Use the ratio below to find the probability of tossing a number divisible by 3. $\frac{1}{3}$

$$\frac{\text{number of possible results that are divisible by 3}}{\text{total number of possible results}}$$

The table at the right shows all the possible results of tossing a red and blue number cube.

5. How many results are there? **36**

6. a. List the results that have a sum of 1. **none**
   b. What is the probability of a sum of 1? **0**

7. a. List the results that have a sum of 4. **(1, 3), (2, 2), (3, 1)**
   b. What is the probability of a sum of 4? $\frac{1}{12}$

8. a. List the results that have a sum of 11. **(5, 6), (6, 5)**
   b. What is the probability of a sum of 11? $\frac{1}{18}$

9. Find another sum that has the same probability of occurring as 11. **3**

10. **Reasoning** Are the sums 2–12 equally likely? Explain. **No; probabilities range from $\frac{1}{36}$ up to $\frac{1}{6}$.**

11. Are the probabilities of getting an even sum or an odd sum equal? **yes**

Sample Space for Two Number Cubes

(1, 1)	(1, 2)	(1, 3)	(1, 4)	(1, 5)	(1, 6)
(2, 1)	(2, 2)	(2, 3)	(2, 4)	(2, 5)	(2, 6)
(3, 1)	(3, 2)	(3, 3)	(3, 4)	(3, 5)	(3, 6)
(4, 1)	(4, 2)	(4, 3)	(4, 4)	(4, 5)	(4, 6)
(5, 1)	(5, 2)	(5, 3)	(5, 4)	(5, 5)	(5, 6)
(6, 1)	(6, 2)	(6, 3)	(6, 4)	(6, 5)	(6, 6)

The photo at the right shows two regular tetrahedrons. Assume you are tossing a pair of regular tetrahedrons with the numbers 1 through 4 printed on the faces, like those at the right. The same number appears at the bottom of each face, and this number is the result of the toss.

12. Construct a table that shows all the possible results. **See below.**

13. How many results are there? **16**

14. a. List the results that have a sum of 4. **(1, 3), (2, 2), (3, 1)**
    b. What is the probability of a sum of 4? $\frac{3}{16}$

15. **Critical Thinking** Is the probability of a sum of 4 with two regular tetrahedrons the same as the probability of a sum of 4 with two cubes? Explain. **No; each has the same number of outcomes for 4, but a cube has a greater number of total outcomes.**

12.

(1, 1)	(2, 1)	(3, 1)	(4, 1)
(1, 2)	(2, 2)	(3, 2)	(4, 2)
(1, 3)	(2, 3)	(3, 3)	(4, 3)
(1, 4)	(2, 4)	(3, 4)	(4, 4)

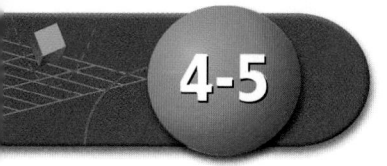

4-5 Applying Ratios to Probability

Lesson Preview

What You'll Learn

OBJECTIVE 1 To find theoretical probability

OBJECTIVE 2 To find experimental probability

...And Why

To analyze a manufacturing situation, as in Example 3

✔ **Check Skills You'll Need**   (For help, go to Skills Handbook page 728.)

Rewrite each decimal or fraction as a percent.

1. 0.32 **32%**   **2.** 0.09 **9%**   **3.** $\frac{45}{200}$ **22.5%**   **4.** $\frac{9}{50}$ **18%**

New Vocabulary
- probability
- outcome
- event
- sample space
- theoretical probability
- complement of an event
- experimental probability

OBJECTIVE 1 Theoretical Probability

 Reading Math

Read *P*(event) as "the probability of an event."

 Interactive lesson includes instant self-check, tutorials, and activities.

The **probability** of an event, or *P*(event), tells you how likely it is that something will occur. An **outcome** is the result of a single trial, like one roll of a number cube. An **event** is any outcome or group of outcomes. The **sample space** is all of the possible outcomes.

Here is how these terms apply to finding the probability of rolling an even number on a number cube.

event	sample space	favorable outcome
↓	↓	↓
rolling an even number	1, 2, 3, 4, 5, 6	2, 4, 6

The possible outcomes of rolling a fair number cube are *equally likely* to occur. When all possible outcomes are equally likely, you can find the theoretical probability of an event using the following formula.

theoretical probability $P(\text{event}) = \dfrac{\text{number of favorable outcomes}}{\text{number of possible outcomes}}$

$$P(\text{rolling an even number}) = \frac{3}{6} = \frac{1}{2}$$

You can write the probability of an event as a fraction, a decimal, or a percent. The probability of an event ranges from 0 to 1.

Probability

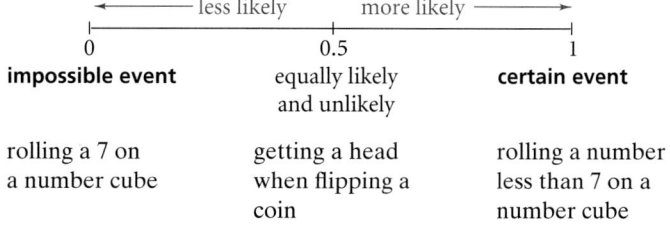

← less likely	more likely →
0	0.5	1
impossible event	equally likely and unlikely	**certain event**
rolling a 7 on a number cube	getting a head when flipping a coin	rolling a number less than 7 on a number cube

---

Ongoing Assessment and Intervention

Before the Lesson
Diagnose prerequisite skills using:
- Check Skills You'll Need

During the Lesson
Monitor progress using:
- Check Understanding
- Additional Examples
- Standardized Test Prep

After the Lesson
Assess knowledge using:
- Lesson Quiz
- Computer Test Generator CD
- Chapter Checkpoint 2 (p. 217)

Professional Development

Math Background

Probability is an application of ratios that compares the number of successful outcomes to the total number of possible outcomes. Probability is used for quality control in manufacturing, by sampling for defects.

OBJECTIVE

▼1 Teaching Notes

1 EXAMPLE Error Prevention

Explain that the term *favorable outcome* refers to the event you are studying at the moment, whether it is good or bad. In a study of the probability that a team loses under certain conditions, the team losing is a favorable outcome.

2 EXAMPLE English Learners

Explain that a *complement* helps *complete* a set while *compliment* means to praise.

▣ Additional Examples

1 A bowl contains 12 slips of paper, each with a different name of a month. Find the theoretical probability that a slip selected at random from the bowl has a the name of a month that ends with "ber." $\frac{1}{3}$

2 For a number cube, find the the probability of not rolling a number divisible by 3. $\frac{2}{3}$

---

1 EXAMPLE Finding Theoretical Probability

A bowl contains 12 slips of paper, each with a different name of a month. Find the theoretical probability that a slip selected at random from the bowl has a name of a month that starts with the letter J.

$$P(\text{event}) = \frac{\text{number of favorable outcomes}}{\text{number of possible outcomes}}$$

$$= \frac{3}{12} \quad \textbf{There are 3 months out of 12 that begin with the letter J: January, June, and July.}$$

$$= \frac{1}{4} \quad \textbf{Simplify.}$$

● The probability of picking a month that begins with the letter J is $\frac{1}{4}$.

✓ **Check Understanding** ① Suppose you write the names of days of the week on identical pieces of paper. Find the theoretical probability of picking a piece of paper at random that has the name of a day that starts with the letter T. $\frac{2}{7}$

Reading Math

An event and its *complement* represent the *complete* set of possible outcomes.

The **complement of an event** consists of all the outcomes not in the event.

possible outcomes for rolling a number cube	outcomes for rolling an even number	complement of rolling an even number
↓	↓	↓
1, 2, 3, 4, 5, 6	2, 4, 6	1, 3, 5

The sum of the probabilities of an event and its complement is 1.

$$P(\text{event}) + P(\text{not event}) = 1$$

or

$$P(\text{not event}) = 1 - P(\text{event})$$

2 EXAMPLE Finding the Complement of an Event

Games On a popular television game show, a contestant must choose one of five envelopes. One envelope contains the grand prize, a car. Find the probability of not choosing the car.

$$P(\text{car}) = \frac{\text{number of favorable outcomes}}{\text{number of possible outcomes}} = \frac{1}{5}$$

$$P(\text{not choosing the car}) = 1 - P(\text{car}) \quad \textbf{Use the complement formula.}$$

$$= 1 - \frac{1}{5} = \frac{4}{5} \quad \textbf{Simplify.}$$

● The probability of not choosing the car is $\frac{4}{5}$.

✓ **Check Understanding** ② **Critical Thinking** In Example 2, what happens to $P(\text{not choosing the car})$ as the number of envelopes increases? **increases**

OBJECTIVE

▼2 Experimental Probability

Probability based on data collected from repeated trials is experimental probability. You can find the experimental probability of an event using this formula.

experimental probability $\quad P(\text{event}) = \dfrac{\text{number of times an event occurs}}{\text{number of times the experiment is done}}$

212 Chapter 4 Solving and Applying Proportions

👪 Reaching All Students

Below Level Have students collect their own data by picking colored marbles or crayons out of a bag. Then help them calculate the experimental probability using their data.	**Advanced Learners** Students may wish to do further research on the Law of Large Numbers and how scientists use it when collecting experimental data.	**English Learners** See note on page 212. **Tactile Learners** See note on page 213.

Real-World Connection

More than 100,000 skateboards are manufactured each month.

✔ **Check Understanding**

✔ **Check Understanding**

3 EXAMPLE Finding Experimental Probability

Quality Control After receiving complaints, a skateboard manufacturer inspected 1000 skateboards at random. The manufacturer found no defects in 992 skateboards. What is the probability that a skateboard selected at random had no defects? Write the probability as a percent.

$$P(\text{no defects}) = \frac{\text{number of times an event occurs}}{\text{number of times the experiment is done}}$$

$$= \frac{992}{1000} \quad \textbf{Substitute.}$$

$$= 0.992 \quad \textbf{Simplify.}$$

$$= 99.2\% \quad \textbf{Write as a percent.}$$

● The probability that a skateboard has no defects is 99.2%.

3 The manufacturer decides to inspect 2500 skateboards. There are 2450 skateboards that have no defects. Find the probability that a skateboard selected at random has no defects. **98%**

You can use experimental probability to make a prediction. Predictions are not exact, so round your results.

4 EXAMPLE Using Experimental Probability

Quality Control The same manufacturer has 8976 skateboards in its warehouse. If the probability that a skateboard has no defect is 99.2%, predict how many skateboards are likely to have no defect.

$$\text{number with no defects} = P(\text{no defects}) \cdot \text{number of skateboards}$$

$$= 0.992 \times 8976 \quad \textbf{Substitute. Use 0.992 for 99.2\%.}$$

$$= 8904.192 \quad \textbf{Simplify.}$$

● Approximately 8900 boards are likely to have no defect.

4 A manufacturer inspects 700 light bulbs. She finds that the probability that a light bulb works is 99.6%. There are 35,400 light bulbs in the warehouse. Predict how many light bulbs are likely to work. **about 35,260 light bulbs**

How does the experimental probability of flipping a fair coin compare to the theoretical probability? Below are the results of flipping a coin 10, 100, and 1000 times.

number of times a coin is flipped	10	100	1000
number of times the coin is heads	7	58	498
experimental probability of heads	$\frac{7}{10}$	$\frac{58}{100}$	$\frac{498}{1000}$

The table above shows that the more times the coin is flipped, the closer the experimental probability comes to the theoretical probability, $\frac{1}{2}$. In general, as the amount of data you use to find an experimental probability increases, the closer the experimental probability will be to the theoretical probability. This is called the *Law of Large Numbers*.

OBJECTIVE

2 Teaching Notes

3 EXAMPLE Error Prevention

Students may think that a theoretical probability close to 1 somehow guarantees that a specific event is going to occur. Ask students to describe an event that was considered very likely, but did not happen.

4 EXAMPLE Tactile Learners

Let students conduct their own coin tossing experiment. Have them use their results from 10, 50, and 100 tosses, to find the experimental probability that the toss yields tails. Help students understand that a theoretical probability measures the likelihood of the occurrence, not the actual occurrence. For large numbers of events, the theoretical and experimental probabilities should be very close; for single or small numbers of events, they may not match.

Additional Examples

3 Quality control inspected 500 belts at random. They found no defects in 485 belts. What is the probability that a belt selected at random will pass quality control? **97%**

4 If the belt manufacturer from Additional Example 3 has 6258 belts, predict how many belts are likely to have no defects. **about 6070 belts**

Closure

Have students explain the difference between theoretical probability and experimental probability. Theoretical probability is what should happen and experimental probability is what actually happens.

Assignment Guide

▼1 Objective

Ⓐ Ⓑ **Core** 1–14, 23–32, 37, 39–45

▼2 Objective

Ⓐ Ⓑ **Core** 15–22, 33–36, 38

Ⓒ **Extension** 46–49

Standardized Test Prep 50–54

Mixed Review 55–70

Exercises 15–20 Suggest to students that they use a proportion.

Math Tip

Exercises 27–32 Tell students to find how many three-digit numbers there are by subtracting 999 − 99. The greatest three-digit number is 999, and 99 of the numbers less than 999 do not have three digits.

Enrichment 4-5

Reteaching 4-5

Practice 4-5

Practice 4-5   Applying Ratios to Probability

A driver collected data on how long it takes to drive to work.

Time in minutes	20	25	30
Number of trips	4	8	2

1. Find P(the trip will take 25 min).
2. Find P(the trip will take 20 min).
3. Find P(the trip will take at least 25 min).

Use the data in the line plot to find each probability.

Student Birth Months

4. P(June)   5. P(October)   6. P(first six months of year)
7. P(May)   8. P(not December)   9. P(last three months of year)

A cereal manufacturer selects 100 boxes of cereal at random. Ninety-nine of the boxes are the correct weight. Find each probability.

10. P(the cereal box is the correct weight)
11. P(the cereal box is not the correct weight)
12. There are 24,000 boxes of cereal. Predict how many of the boxes are the correct weight.
13. One letter is chosen at random from the word ALGEBRA. Find each probability.
   a. P(the letter is A)   b. P(the letter is a vowel)
14. Patrice has a 40% chance of making a free throw. What is the probability that she will miss the free throw?
15. A box of animal crackers contains five hippos, two lions, three zebras, and four elephants. Find the probability of one animal cracker is chosen at random.
   a. P(a hippo)   b. P(not an elephant)
   c. P(an elephant or a lion)
16. Anthony is making a collage for his art class by picking shapes randomly. He has five squares, two triangles, two ovals, and four circles. Find each probability.
   a. P(circle is chosen first)   b. P(a square is not chosen first)
   c. P(a triangle or a square is chosen first)

Lesson 4-5 Practice   Algebra 1 Chapter 4

Ⓐ **Practice by Example**

For Exercises 1–13, use the spinner at the right. Find the theoretical probability of landing on the given section(s) of the spinner.

Example 1 (page 212)

1. $P(\text{purple})\ \frac{1}{2}$ 2. $P(\text{green})\ \frac{1}{3}$ 3. $P(5)\ \frac{1}{6}$
4. $P(\text{even})\ \frac{1}{2}$ $\frac{2}{3}$ 5. $P(\text{purple or white})$ 6. $P(8)\ 0$
$\frac{1}{3}$ 7. $P(\text{greater than }4)$ 8. $P(\text{even or odd})\ 1$ 9. $P(1\text{ or }6)\ \frac{1}{3}$

Example 2 (page 212)

10. $P(\text{not white})\ \frac{5}{6}$ 11. $P(\text{not }2)\ \frac{5}{6}$ 12. $P(\text{not purple})\ \frac{1}{2}$ 13. $P(\text{not }8)\ 1$

14. Suppose the probability that you will be picked for a committee at school is 20%. What is the probability that you will not be picked? **80%**

Examples 3, 4 (page 213)

The results of a survey of 100 randomly selected students at a 2000-student high school are below. Find the experimental probability that a student selected at random makes the given response.

15. $P(\text{community college})\ $ **24%**

16. $P(\text{4-year college})\ $ **43%**

17. $P(\text{trade school})\ $ **15%**

18. $P(\text{not trade school})\ $ **85%**

19. $P(\text{trade school or community college})\ $ **39%**

20. $P(\text{community or 4-year college})\ $ **67%**

Plans for After Graduation

Response	Number of Respondents
Go to community college	24
Go to 4-year college	43
Take a year off before college	12
Go to trade school	15
Do not plan to go to college	6

21. A forest contains about 500 trees. You randomly pick 67 trees and find that 27 of them are oaks. **a. about 40%**
   a. What is the experimental probability that a tree in the forest is an oak?
   b. Predict how many oak trees there are in the forest. **about 200 oak trees**

22. Suppose 12 out of 30 families on your street have a cat or a dog as a pet.
   a. What is the experimental probability that a randomly selected family in your neighborhood will have a cat or a dog as a pet? **40%**
   b. Based on P(cat or dog) from part (a), predict how many cat- or dog-owning families you can expect among 57 families in your neighborhood.
   about 23 families

Ⓑ **Apply Your Skills**

Suppose you roll a number cube. Find each probability.

23. $P(5)\ \frac{1}{6}$ 24. $P(7)\ 0$ 25. $P(3\text{ or }4)\ \frac{1}{3}$ 26. $P(\text{not }5)\ \frac{5}{6}$

Suppose you select a 3-digit number at random from the set of all positive 3-digit numbers. Find each probability. (*Hint:* First find how many positive 3-digit numbers there are.)

27. $P(\text{odd number})\ \frac{1}{2}$ 28. $P(\text{number less than }900)\ \frac{8}{9}$

29. $P(243\text{ or }244)\ \frac{1}{450}$ 30. $P(\text{number less than }100)\ 0$

31. $P(\text{number is a multiple of }30)\ \frac{1}{30}$ 32. $P(\text{number less than }500)\ \frac{4}{9}$

Real-World Connection

About 10,700 people celebrate their sixteenth birthday each day.

33. Birthdays Each day in the United States, about 753,000 people have a birthday. Use the information at the left to find the probability that someone celebrating a birthday today will turn 16. Round to the nearest percent. **1%**

34. Land Area The United States has a land area of about 3,536,278 mi². Illinois has a land area of about 57,918 mi². What is the probability that a location in the United States chosen at random is in Illinois? **1.6%**

35. Open-Ended Suppose your teacher chooses a student at random from your algebra class. **Answers may vary. Sample: 20 students,**
a. What is the probability that you are selected? **12 girls and 8 boys: 5%**
b. What is the probability that a boy is not selected? **60%**
c. How did you find your answer to part (b)? Describe another way to find the probability that a boy is not selected. **Answers may vary. Sample: Subtract P(picking a boy) from 1.**

36. Data Analysis The population of the United States is about 275,000,000. Use the pie graph at the right to answer the following questions. Round to the nearest percent.
a. What is the probability of selecting at random a person whose age is between 10 and 19? **15%**
b. What is the probability of selecting at random a person whose age is between 40 and 49? **15%**

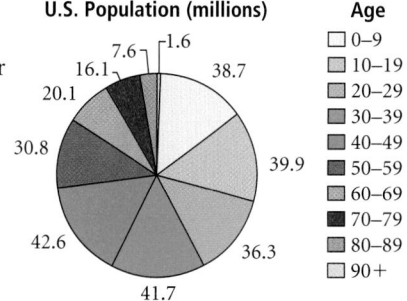

U.S. Population (millions)

Age
☐ 0–9
☐ 10–19
☐ 20–29
☐ 30–39
☐ 40–49
☐ 50–59
☐ 60–69
☐ 70–79
☐ 80–89
☐ 90+

SOURCE: U.S. Census Bureau

37. Radio A disc jockey makes music selections for a radio program. For his first selection, he can choose from eight alternative rock songs, three hip-hop dance mixes, five country-western ballads, and four rhythm-and-blues songs. Assume that all selections have equal chances of being chosen.
a. What is the probability that he does not choose a ballad? $\frac{3}{4}$
b. What is the probability that he chooses a rock song? $\frac{2}{5}$
c. What is the probability that he chooses a hip-hop dance mix? $\frac{3}{20}$

38. Writing Explain the difference between theoretical probability and experimental probability. **See left.**

38. Answers may vary. Sample: For theoretical probability, all possible outcomes are equally likely to happen, but experimental probability is based on observed outcomes.

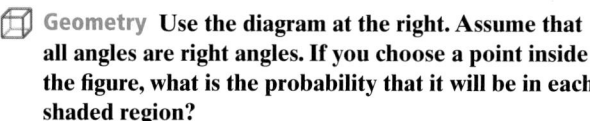
Geometry Use the diagram at the right. Assume that all angles are right angles. If you choose a point inside the figure, what is the probability that it will be in each shaded region?

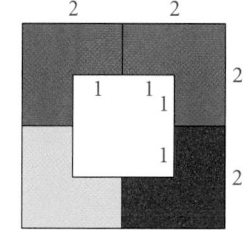

39. $P(\text{red})$ $\frac{3}{16}$ **40.** $P(\text{purple})$ $\frac{3}{8}$

41. $P(\text{yellow or white})$ $\frac{7}{16}$ **42.** $P(\text{not purple})$ $\frac{5}{8}$

For Exercises 43 and 44, use the spinner at the left. Use the formula below to find the odds in favor of an event.

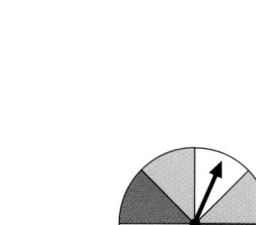

odds in favor $= \dfrac{\text{number of favorable outcomes}}{\text{number of unfavorable outcomes}}$

43. Find the odds in favor of the spinner stopping on green. $\frac{1}{3}$

44. Find the odds in favor of the spinner not stopping on white. $\frac{5}{3}$

45. Critical Thinking Explain how you can use odds to find probability. Include an example. **Answers may vary. Sample: You can add the numerator and denominator and make the sum the denominator, keeping the numerator the same.**

Lesson 4-5 Applying Ratios to Probability   **215**

Math Tip

Exercise 33 Remind students that a probability can be a percent. They should use *part ÷ whole* to find the probability of someone celebrating a 16th birthday today.

Teaching Tip

Exercises 46–48 Suggest to students that they review stem-and-leaf plots in Lesson 2-7.

Alternative Assessment

Have students work in small groups to find experimental probabilities for four tosses of a coin. Repeat the experiment with twenty and fifty tosses. Have students write a paragraph comparing the actual tosses to the theoretical probabilities. Have groups compare results.

Standardized Test Prep

Resources

For additional practice with a variety of test item formats:
- Standardized Test Prep, p. 231
- Test-Taking Strategies, p. 226
- Test-Taking Strategies with Transparencies

pages 214–217 Exercises

53. [4] a. theoretical $P(\text{red}) = \frac{1}{5}$ OR 20%

    b. experimental $P(\text{red}) = \frac{55}{280}$ OR about 19.6%

    c. For the red beads, the manufacturer's claim seems to be true. However, the experimental

216

C Challenge **Data Analysis** The stem-and-leaf plot at the right shows the difference between the points scored by the winning and losing teams in the Super Bowl from 1980 to 2000.

46. Find the probability that the winning team won by less than 10 points. $\frac{1}{4}$

47. Find the probability that the winning team won by 10 to 15 points. $\frac{3}{10}$

48. Find the probability that the winning team won by more than 20 points. $\frac{3}{10}$

Difference Between Winning and Losing Super Bowl Scores
0 | 1 4 5 7 7
1 | 0 0 2 3 4 5 7 7 9
2 | 2 3 9
3 | 2 6
4 | 5
Key: 1|0 means 10 points

Real-World Connection

The greatest total score of both teams in a Super Bowl was 75, in 1994.

49b.

1	2	3	4	5	6
2	4	6	8	10	12
3	6	9	12	15	18
4	8	12	16	20	24
5	10	15	20	25	30
6	12	18	24	30	36

49. **Data Collection** Roll a pair of number cubes and record the product of the results. Repeat 30 times.

    a. Use your data to find the following experimental probabilities: $P(5)$, $P(6)$, $P(12)$, $P(36)$. **Check students' work.**

    b. Make a chart to find the sample space for the product of two cubes. **See left.**

    c. Find the theoretical probabilities for $P(5)$, $P(6)$, $P(12)$, $P(36)$. $\frac{1}{18}, \frac{1}{9}, \frac{1}{9}, \frac{1}{36}$

    d. Are your experimental probabilities exactly the same as the theoretical probabilities? **no**

    e. Suppose you roll the number cubes 1000 times. Would you expect the experimental probabilities and the theoretical probabilities to be about the same? Explain. **Answers may vary. Sample: Yes; the more you roll, the closer you get to the theoretical probability.**

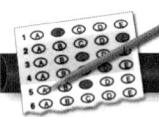

Standardized Test Prep

Multiple Choice

50. Suppose you roll a number cube with the numbers 1–6 on it. Which has the same probability as $P(1 \text{ or prime})$? **A**

    A. $P(\text{factor of 6})$ B. $P(1 \text{ or } 2)$
    C. $P(\text{less than 3})$ D. $P(\text{not odd})$

51. Of 150 widgets inspected, 142 passed inspection. Out of 2855 widgets, about how many would you predict would fail an inspection? **G**

    F. 140   G. 150   H. 2700   I. 2850

52. There are 28 right-handed students in a class of 31. What is the probability that a student chosen at random will be left-handed? **D**

    A. $\frac{31}{28}$ B. $\frac{28}{31}$ C. $\frac{3}{28}$ D. $\frac{3}{31}$

Extended Response

53. A "Bag-of-Beads" for crafts contains five different colors of beads. The company that makes them claims that each bag contains the same number of each color. **a–c. See margin.**

    a. If this claim is true, what is the theoretical probability of picking a red bead at random?

    b. Rosheeda purchased a bag to test the company's claim. She recorded the number of each color. Based on the results in the table to the right, what is the experimental probability of picking a red bead out of the bag?

    c. How does the experimental probability compare with the theoretical probability in Rosheeda's experiment? Explain why her results do or do not support the company's claim.

Color	Number
red	55
blue	53
green	64
yellow	47
purple	61

probabilities of the other colors are not as close to 20%, so Rasheeda's experiment does not support the manufacturer's claim.

[3] one computational error with complete explanation OR correct computation with weak explanation

[2] correct computation but no conclusion

[1] error(s) in computation and no conclusion

Short Response

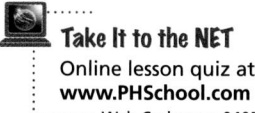
Take It to the NET
Online lesson quiz at
www.PHSchool.com
Web Code: aea-0405

54. An inspector for an office-supply company checked a batch of 350 staplers. He found that 18 of them were defective. What is the experimental probability of getting a defective stapler in this batch? Production must be stopped when the percent of defective staplers exceeds 4%. Should the inspector stop production? Explain. **See margin.**

Mixed Review

Lesson 4-4

Find each percent of change. Describe each percent of change as an increase or decrease. **55–60. See margin.**

55. 8 ft to 10 ft

56. 4 m to 6 m

57. 25 in. to 35 in.

58. $22 to $11

59. 16 cm to 12 cm

60. 80 ft to 70 ft

Lesson 3-5

Solve the following compound inequalities. Graph the solutions. **61–66. See margin.**

61. $-3 \le t \le 4$

62. $8 < b + 3 < 10$

63. $7h < 14 \text{ or } 4h > 20$

64. $5 < 7 - 2w \le 11$

65. $1 - 3x > -5 \text{ or } -x \le -4$

66. $-2 \le 4k - 6 \le 6$

Lesson 2-7

Find the mean, median, and mode of each set of numbers.

67. 3 4 5 5 8 12 **6.17, 5, 5**

68. 1 8 9 11 22 35 35 **17.29, 11, 35**

Make a stem-and-leaf plot for each set of data. **69–70. See margin.**

69. 34 37 39 41 49 65 71

70. 12 14 16 23 27 47 68 79

Checkpoint Quiz 2   Lessons 4-3 through 4-5

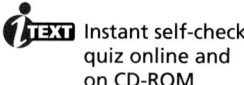 Instant self-check
quiz online and
on CD-ROM

Solve each percent problem.

1. What is 60% of 200? **120**

2. 4 is what percent of 5? **80%**

3. 18 is 75% of what number? **24**

4. What is 175% of 40? **70**

Find the percent of increase or decrease.

5. $20 to $25 **25%**

6. $20 to $30 **50%**

7. What are the minimum and maximum possible areas for a rectangle that you measure as 3 ft by 5 ft? **11.25 ft², 19.25 ft²**

8. Suppose you measure the length of a pencil as 5 in. What is the percent error in this measurement? **10%**

9. Suppose you write the days of the week on identical pieces of paper. You mix them in a bowl and choose one at random. What is the probability that the day you select will have the letter e in it? $\frac{2}{7}$

10. A manufacturer inspects 100 bicycles at random. She finds that 98 of them have no defects. There are 2400 bicycles in the warehouse. Predict how many bicycles are likely to be free of defects. **2352 bicycles**

Lesson 4-5 Applying Ratios to Probability   **217**

54. [2] P(defective stapler) = $\frac{18}{350} \approx 5.1\%$; production should be stopped because $5.1\% > 4\%$.

[1] correct calculation with no conclusion OR incorrect calculation but correct reasoning based on incorrect calculation

---

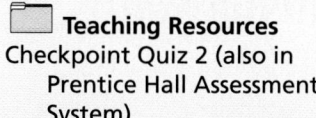 **Chapter Checkpoint 2**

To check understanding of Lessons 4-3 to 4-5:

Checkpoint Quiz 2 (p. 217)

📁 **Teaching Resources**
Checkpoint Quiz 2 (also in Prentice Hall Assessment System)

👥 **Reaching All Students**
Reading and Math Literacy 4C

Spanish versions available

---

55. 25%; increase

56. 50%; increase

57. 40%; increase

58. 50%; decrease

59. 25%; decrease

60. 12.5%; decrease

61. $-3 \le t \le 4$;

$-4\ -3\ -2\ -1\ 0\ 1\ 2\ 3\ 4$

62. $5 < b < 7$;

$4\ 5\ 6\ 7\ 8$

63. $h < 2 \text{ or } h > 5$;

$0\ 1\ 2\ 3\ 4\ 5\ 6$

64. $-2 \le w < 1$;

$-2\ -1\ 0\ 1\ 2$

65. $x < 2 \text{ or } x \ge 4$;

$0\ 1\ 2\ 3\ 4\ 5\ 6$

66. $1 \le k \le 3$;

$0\ 1\ 2\ 3\ 4$

69. 3 | 4 7 9
      4 | 1 9
      6 | 5
      7 | 1

70. 1 | 2 4 6
      2 | 3 7
      4 | 7
      6 | 8
      7 | 9

Technology

Conducting a Simulation

Students use their graphing calculators to generate random numbers that will represent or model a real situation or simulation. They learn to define, conduct, and interpret a simulation.

Resources

Students may use any graphing calculator to generate random numbers for a simulation.

Teaching Notes

Remind students that they may have different answers depending on the random number generated by their calculator. You will want to discuss why the answers differ and how the quantity of random numbers selected affects the results. The more numbers in the random sample, the more accurate the results.

Teaching Tip

Remind students that the numbers 1–9 should be thought of as 01, 02, 03, . . . so that both digits can be used for the simulation in Example 1. Also review with students that to calculate the expected probability, they should take all pairs of combinations in which both digits are 0, 1, 2, or 3 and divide that by the total number of random numbers that were generated. You may want them to do the same simulation again with a new set of random numbers so that they can compare, contrast, and discuss their answers. Suggest that in a third round, they generate one hundred random numbers. Ask what observations or conclusions they have after doing the simulations.

Technology

Conducting a Simulation

FOR USE WITH LESSON 4-5

A *simulation* is a model of a real-life situation. One way to do a simulation is to use random numbers generated by a graphing calculator or a computer program.

On a graphing calculator, the command randInt generates random integers. To create a list of random integers, press MATH ◁ 5. You will see randInt(. After the parenthesis, press 0 ❭ 99, and press ENTER repeatedly to create 1- and 2-digit random numbers.

Take It to the NET
Graphing Calculator procedures online at
www.PHSchool.com
Web Code: aee-2115

1 EXAMPLE

According to the American Red Cross, 40% of the people in the United States have type A blood. Find the probability that the next two people who donate blood have type A blood.

To simulate this problem, use 2-digit numbers to represent groups of 2 people. Use your calculator to generate 40 random numbers.

Define how the simulation will be done.

Since 40% of people have type A blood, let 40%, or 4 out of 10 digits, represent people in this group. Using numbers from the random number table, let 0, 1, 2, 3 represent people with type A blood. Let 4, 5, 6, 7, 8, 9 represent people who do not have type A blood.

Interpret the simulation

The six numbers in red represent "these two people have type A blood." Each of the other groups has at least one person with a different blood type.

P(next two people have type A blood) =

$\dfrac{\text{number of times an event happens}}{\text{number of times the experiment is done}} = \dfrac{6}{40} = 0.15 = 15\%$

25	71	47	46
66	13	63	36
01	59	27	07
83	25	72	24
73	52	59	81
14	09	40	64
81	72	02	38
21	09	92	10
93	34	36	45
53	18	23	75

● The probability that the next two people will have type A blood is about 15%.

EXERCISES

1. For this simulation, could you use 4, 5, 6, and 7 to represent donors who have type A blood? Explain. **Answers may vary. Sample: Yes, as long as they are 40% of the data, any 4 numbers will suffice.**

2. **Blood Types** In the United States, about 50% of people have type O blood. Use the random number table above to find the probability that the next two donors have type O blood. **25%**

3. **a.** Use a graphing calculator to find another set of 40 random numbers. Use these random numbers to answer Exercise 2 again. **Check students' work.**
   b. Are the results exactly the same as in Exercise 2? **no**
   c. Suppose you were to do this experiment with 400 random numbers. Which set of results would be more reliable, one with 40 random numbers or one with 400? Explain. **The one with 400 numbers would be more reliable; the results would more closely approach the theoretical probability.**

Probability of Compound Events

Lesson Preview

What You'll Learn

 OBJECTIVE 1 To find the probability of independent events

 OBJECTIVE 2 To find the probability of dependent events

... And Why

To use probability in a game, as in Example 2

✓ Check Skills You'll Need   (For help, go to Lesson 4-5.)

Find each probability for one roll of a number cube.

1. P(multiple of 3) $\frac{1}{3}$ 2. P(greater than 4) $\frac{1}{3}$

3. P(greater than 5) $\frac{1}{6}$ 4. P(greater than 6) 0

Simplify.

5. $\frac{2}{14} \cdot \frac{7}{6}$ $\frac{1}{6}$ 6. $\frac{15}{24} \cdot \frac{12}{30}$ $\frac{1}{4}$ 7. $\frac{6}{55} \cdot \frac{44}{3}$ $1\frac{3}{5}$

New Vocabulary   • independent events   • dependent events

Lesson Preview

✓ Check Skills You'll Need

Applying Ratios to Probability
Lesson 4-5: Example 1
Exercises 1–9
Extra Practice, p. 705

Lesson Resources

📁 **Teaching Resources**
Practice, Reteaching, Enrichment

👥 **Reaching All Students**
Practice Workbook 4-6
Spanish Practice Workbook 4-6
Basic Algebra Planning Guide 4-6

⏰ **Presentation Assistant Plus!**
Transparencies
• Check Skills You'll Need 4-6
• Additional Examples 4-6
• Student Edition Answers 4-6
• Lesson Quiz 4-6
PH Presentation Pro CD 4-6

PRENTICE HALL ASSESSMENT *SYSTEM*

Computer Test Generator CD

💿 **Technology**
Resource Pro® CD-ROM
Computer Test Generator CD
Prentice Hall Presentation Pro CD

💻 **www.PHSchool.com**
Student Site
• Teacher Web Code: aek-5500
• Self-grading Lesson Quiz
Teacher Center
• Lesson Planner
• Resources

Plus

OBJECTIVE 1 ▼ Finding the Probability of Independent Events

 Interactive lesson includes instant self-check, tutorials, and activities.

Investigation: Compound Events

Suppose you draw cards at random from the following collection.

| R | R | A | N | N | N | D | O | M | M |

1. You draw an R card and replace it. What is the probability that the next card you draw will be an R card? $\frac{1}{5}$

2. You draw an R card and do *not* replace it. What is the probability that the next card you draw will be an R card? $\frac{1}{9}$

3. Copy and complete each table.

Probability With Replacement

First Card		Second Card Matches	
P(R) = ▦		P(R) = ▦	
P(A) = ▦		P(A) = ▦	
P(N) = ▦		P(N) = ▦	
P(D) = ▦		P(D) = ▦	
P(O) = ▦		P(O) = ▦	
P(M) = ▦		P(M) = ▦	

Probability Without Replacement

First Card		Second Card Matches	
P(R) = ▦		P(R) = ▦	
P(A) = ▦		P(A) = ▦	
P(N) = ▦		P(N) = ▦	
P(D) = ▦		P(D) = ▦	
P(O) = ▦		P(O) = ▦	
P(M) = ▦		P(M) = ▦	

4. For each letter, the probability of drawing the first card is the same with replacement and without replacement. Explain why the probability of drawing the second card is not the same. **Answers may vary. Sample: If you don't replace it, then you take away that possibility.**

3.

Probability With Replacement

First card	Second Card Matches
P(R) $= \frac{1}{5}$	P(R) $= \frac{1}{5}$
P(A) $= \frac{1}{10}$	P(A) $= \frac{1}{10}$
P(N) $= \frac{3}{10}$	P(N) $= \frac{3}{10}$
P(D) $= \frac{1}{10}$	P(D) $= \frac{1}{10}$
P(O) $= \frac{1}{10}$	P(O) $= \frac{1}{10}$
P(M) $= \frac{1}{5}$	P(M) $= \frac{1}{5}$

Probability Without Replacement

First card	Second Card Matches
P(R) $= \frac{1}{5}$	P(R) $= \frac{1}{9}$
P(A) $= \frac{1}{10}$	P(A) $= 0$
P(N) $= \frac{3}{10}$	P(N) $= \frac{2}{9}$
P(D) $= \frac{1}{10}$	P(D) $= 0$
P(O) $= \frac{1}{10}$	P(O) $= 0$
P(M) $= \frac{1}{5}$	P(M) $= \frac{1}{9}$

 **Ongoing Assessment and Intervention**

Before the Lesson
Diagnose prerequisite skills using:
• Check Skills You'll Need

During the Lesson
Monitor progress using:
• Check Understanding
• Additional Examples
• Standardized Test Prep

After the Lesson
Assess knowledge using:
• Lesson Quiz
• Computer Test Generator CD

Math Background

It is not always logically apparent whether or not events are independent. The mathematical test that $P(A \text{ and } B) = P(A) \cdot P(B)$ is definitive.

OBJECTIVE

▼ Teaching Notes

Investigation (Optional)
Tactile Learners

Some students may not understand how *not* replacing the card affects the probability. Have a student make cards matching the ones in the Investigation. Then let a student count the M cards and total cards for each situation.

1 EXAMPLE Careers

Air quality inspectors have to predict when there will be an ozone action day. They combine the probabilities of various independent conditions to make their predictions on air quality.

2 EXAMPLE Alternative Method

Students may not understand why the two probabilities are multiplied rather than added. Draw a tree diagram of two independent events, such as tossing a coin and then rolling a number cube.

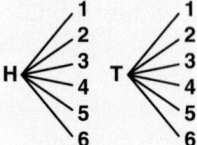

Show students that there are 12 outcomes (2×6), not 8 ($2 + 6$).

220

The diagram at the right shows the results of randomly choosing a checker, putting it back, and choosing again. The probability of getting a red on either pick is $\frac{1}{2}$. The first pick, or first event, does not affect the second event. The events are independent.

Independent events are events that do not influence one another.

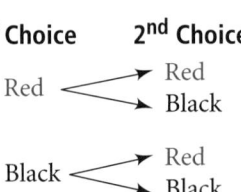

**Key Concepts**

Rule	Probability of Two Independent Events

If A and B are independent events,

$$P(A \text{ and } B) = P(A) \cdot P(B).$$

1 EXAMPLE **Independent Events**

Suppose you roll a red number cube and a blue number cube. What is the probability that you will roll a 3 on the red cube and an even number on the blue cube?

$$P(\text{red } 3) = \frac{1}{6} \qquad \text{There is one way to get a 3 out of six numbers.}$$

$$P(\text{blue even}) = \frac{3}{6} = \frac{1}{2} \qquad \text{There are three even numbers out of six numbers.}$$

$$P(\text{red 3 and blue even}) = P(\text{red 3}) \cdot P(\text{blue even})$$
$$= \frac{1}{6} \cdot \frac{1}{2} \qquad \text{Substitute.}$$
$$= \frac{1}{12} \qquad \text{Simplify.}$$

The probability that you will roll a 3 on the red number cube and an even number on the blue cube is $\frac{1}{12}$.

✓ Check Understanding ❶ Suppose you roll a red number cube and a blue number cube. What is the probability that you will roll a 5 on the red cube and a 1 or 2 on the blue cube? $\frac{1}{18}$

2 EXAMPLE **Selecting With Replacement**

Games In a word game, you choose a tile from a bag containing the letter tiles shown. You *replace* the first tile in the bag and then choose again. What is the probability that you will choose an A and then an E?

Since you replace the first tile, the events are independent.

$$P(A) = \frac{4}{15} \qquad \text{There are 4 } A\text{'s in the 15 tiles.}$$

$$P(E) = \frac{3}{15} \qquad \text{There are 3 } E\text{'s in the 15 tiles.}$$

$$P(A \text{ and } E) = P(A) \cdot P(E)$$
$$= \frac{4}{15} \cdot \frac{3}{15} \qquad \text{Multiply.}$$
$$= \frac{12}{225} = \frac{4}{75}$$

The probability that you will choose an A and then an E is $\frac{4}{75}$.

✓ Check Understanding ❷ Find the probability of picking a U and then an I after replacing the first tile. $\frac{4}{225}$

👥 Reaching All Students

Below Level Have a student demonstrate the example of choosing either a red or black checker illustrated on p. 220, but this time as dependent events.	**Advanced Learners** Ask students to determine which has the greater probability, the event in Example 2 or the event in Example 3, and to explain why this is reasonable.	**Tactile Learners** See note on page 220. **Auditory Learners** See note on page 221.

When you select one tile from a bag of 15 tiles and you do *not* replace it, there are only 14 tiles when you make your second selection. These events are dependent.

Dependent events are events that influence each other. The occurrence of one event affects the probability of a second event.

 Key Concepts

Rule	Probability of Two Dependent Events

If A and B are dependent events,

$$P(A \text{ then } B) = P(A) \cdot P(B \text{ after } A).$$

3 EXAMPLE **Selecting Without Replacement**

Games Suppose you choose a tile from the letter tiles shown in Example 2. Without replacing the tile, you select a second tile. What is the probability that you will choose an *A* and then an *E*?

$P(A) = \frac{4}{15}$ — **There are 4 *A*'s in the 15 tiles.**

$P(E \text{ after } A) = \frac{3}{14}$ — **There are 3 *E*'s in the 14 remaining tiles.**

$P(A \text{ then } E) = P(A) \cdot P(E \text{ after } A)$

$\qquad = \frac{4}{15} \cdot \frac{3}{14}$ — **Multiply.**

$\qquad = \frac{12}{210} = \frac{2}{35}$

● The probability that you will choose an *A* and then an *E* is $\frac{2}{35}$.

✓ **Check Understanding** **3** Find the probability that you will choose a *U* and then an *O* without replacing the first tile. $\frac{4}{105}$

4 EXAMPLE **Real-World** 🌐 **Problem Solving**

Selecting Representatives Suppose a teacher must select 2 high school students to represent their school at a conference. The teacher randomly picks names from a hat that contains the names of 3 freshmen, 2 sophomores, 4 juniors, and 4 seniors. What is the probability that a sophomore and then a freshman are chosen?

$P(\text{sophomore}) = \frac{2}{13}$ — **There are 2 sophomores among 13 students.**

$P(\text{freshman after sophomore}) = \frac{3}{12}$ — **There are 3 freshmen among the 12 remaining students.**

$P(\text{sophomore then freshman}) = P(\text{sophomore}) \cdot P(\text{freshman after sophomore})$

$\qquad\qquad = \frac{2}{13} \cdot \frac{3}{12}$ — **Substitute.**

$\qquad\qquad = \frac{1}{26}$ — **Simplify.**

● The probability that the teacher chooses a sophomore and then a freshman is $\frac{1}{26}$.

✓ **Check Understanding** **4 a.** What is the probability that the teacher chooses a sophomore and then a junior? $\frac{2}{39}$
b. What is the probability that the teacher chooses a junior and then a sophomore? $\frac{2}{39}$
c. **Critical Thinking** Does the probability of choosing without replacement change if the order of the events is reversed? Explain. **No; according to the Comm. Prop. of Mult., the order of the terms does not change the result.**

Closure

Ask: *How does finding the probability of independent events compare to finding the probability of dependent events?* For independent events, the total number of outcomes (the denominator) is the same for each event. For dependent events, the denominator decreases for each successive event.

Right sidebar:

Additional Examples

① Suppose you roll two number cubes. What is the probability that you will roll an odd number on one cube and a multiple of 3 on the other cube? $\frac{1}{6}$

② Suppose you have 3 quarters and 5 dimes in your pocket. You take out one coin, and then put it back. Then you take out another coin. What is the probability that you take out a dime and then a quarter? $\frac{15}{64}$

OBJECTIVE

2 **Teaching Notes**

3 EXAMPLE **Error Prevention**

Some students may interpret $P(A \text{ then } E)$ as the probability that either event *A* or event *E* occurs. Make sure students understand that $P(A \text{ then } E)$ means that event *A* happens, and then event *E* happens without replacing the tile chosen for event *A*.

4 EXAMPLE **Auditory Learners**

Lead a class discussion on ways people confuse independent and dependent events. Some examples to spark discussion are: bad luck comes in threes; lightning never strikes twice; and, if you roll a 6 on a number cube, you are more likely to roll some other number the next time.

Additional Examples

③ Suppose you have 3 quarters and 5 dimes in your pocket. You take out one coin from your pocket. Without replacing the coin, you select a second coin. What is the probability of first taking out a dime and then a quarter? $\frac{15}{56}$

④ A teacher must select 2 students for a conference. The teacher randomly picks names from among 3 freshman, 2 sophomores, 4 juniors, and 4 seniors. What is the probability that a junior and then a senior are chosen? $\frac{4}{39}$

Assignment Guide

1 Objective

Ⓐ Ⓑ **Core** 1–14, 33
Ⓒ **Extension** 43, 44

2 Objective

Ⓐ Ⓑ **Core** 15–32, 34–42
Ⓒ **Extension** 45

Standardized Test Prep 46–49

Mixed Review 50–59

Exercises 15–20 Tell students that for these exercises, the letters *a, e, i, o, u,* and *y* are considered vowels.

Exercises 15–20 Help students see that the numerator also decreases by 1.

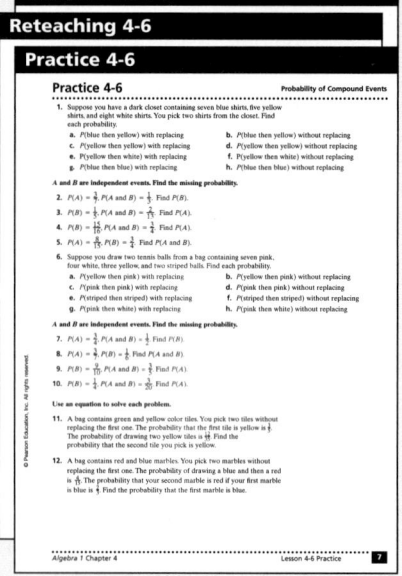

EXERCISES

For more practice, see *Extra Practice*.

Practice and Problem Solving

Ⓐ **Practice by Example**

Example 1
(page 220)

You roll a blue number cube and a green number cube. Find each probability.

1. P(blue 1 and green 1) $\frac{1}{36}$

2. P(blue 1 and green 1 or 2) $\frac{1}{18}$

3. P(blue 1 or 2 and green 1) $\frac{1}{18}$

4. P(blue 1 or 2 and green 1 or 2) $\frac{1}{9}$

5. P(blue even and green even) $\frac{1}{4}$

6. P(blue and green both less than 6) $\frac{25}{36}$

7. P(blue and green less than 7) **1**

8. P(blue 6 and green 7) **0**

Example 2
(page 220)

Suppose you choose a tile from a bag containing 2 A's, 3 B's, and 4 C's. You *replace* the first tile in the bag and then choose again. Find each probability.

9. P(A and A) $\frac{4}{81}$

10. P(A and B) $\frac{2}{27}$

11. P(B and B) $\frac{1}{9}$

12. P(C and C) $\frac{16}{81}$

13. P(B and C) $\frac{4}{27}$

14. P(C and B) $\frac{4}{27}$

Example 3
(page 221)

You select a card at random from those below. Without replacing the card, you choose a second card. Find each probability. Consider Y to be a vowel.

P R O B A B I L I T Y

15. P(vowel then vowel) $\frac{2}{11}$

16. P(consonant then consonant) $\frac{3}{11}$

17. P(*I* then *I*) $\frac{1}{55}$

18. P(consonant then vowel) $\frac{3}{11}$

19. P(*A* then *A*) **0**

20. P(letter then letter) **1**

Example 4
(page 221)

21. Four girls and three boys volunteer to represent their class at a school assembly. The teacher selects one name and then another from a bag containing the seven students' names. What is the probability that both representatives will be girls? $\frac{2}{7}$

22. A refrigerator contains 11 drinks: 5 lemon drinks, 3 apple drinks, and 3 orange drinks. Abby is first in line for drinks. Telly is second. What is the probability that Abby will get a lemon drink and Telly will get an orange drink, if they are given drinks at random? $\frac{3}{22}$

Ⓑ **Apply Your Skills**

You pick two marbles from the bag at the left. You pick the second one without replacing the first one. Find each probability.

23. P(red then blue) $\frac{1}{6}$

24. P(two blues) $\frac{2}{9}$

25. P(blue then green) $\frac{1}{9}$

26. P(two reds) $\frac{1}{15}$

27. P(green then yellow) **0**

28. P(two greens) $\frac{1}{45}$

Are the two events dependent or independent? Explain.

29–30. See margin p. 223.

29. Toss a penny and a nickel.

30. Pick a name from a hat. Without replacement, pick a different name.

31. Pick a ball from a basket of both yellow and pink balls. Return the ball and pick again. **Indep.; the data set hasn't changed.**

 32. Writing Use your own words to explain the difference between independent and dependent events. Give an example of each. **See margin p. 223.**

33. a. Agriculture An acre of land in Indiana is chosen at random. What is the probability that it is cropland? **0.58**
  b. An acre of land is chosen at random from each of the three states listed. What is the probability that all three acres will be cropland? **0.003248**

Percent of Cropland	
Alabama	8%
Florida	7%
Indiana	58%

34. Open-Ended Find the number of left-handed students in your class. Suppose your teacher randomly picks two students to work on a problem at the board. **a–c. Check students' work.**
  a. Find the probability that they are both left-handed.
  b. Find the probability that they are both right-handed.
  c. Find the probability that the first student is right-handed and the second student is left-handed.

 35. Quality Control The probability that a new spark plug is defective is 0.06. You need two new spark plugs for a motorcycle. What is the probability that both spark plugs you buy are defective? **0.0036**

You have three $1 bills, two $5 bills, and a $20 bill in your pocket. You choose two bills without looking. Find each probability.

36. $P(\$5 \text{ then } \$1)$ with replacing $\frac{1}{6}$

37. $P(\$1 \text{ then } \$20)$ without replacing $\frac{1}{10}$

38. $P(\$20 \text{ then } \$1)$ with replacing $\frac{1}{12}$

39. $P(\$1 \text{ then } \$1)$ without replacing $\frac{1}{5}$

40. $P(\$5 \text{ then } \$20)$ without replacing $\frac{1}{15}$

41. $P(\$20 \text{ then } \$5)$ with replacing $\frac{1}{18}$

42. A class has 12 girls and 10 boys. A hat contains the names of all the students in the class. To select representatives of the class to attend a meeting, the teacher draws two names from the hat without replacing the first name.
  a. Find $P(\text{two girls})$. $\frac{2}{7}$
  b. Find $P(\text{two boys})$. $\frac{15}{77}$
  c. Find $P(\text{boy then girl})$. $\frac{20}{77}$
  d. Find $P(\text{girl then boy})$. $\frac{20}{77}$
  e. Predict the sum of the probabilities in parts (a)–(d). Check to see that the sum agrees with your prediction. **See left.**

42e. Answers may vary. Sample: $1; \frac{2}{7} + \frac{15}{77} + \frac{20}{77} + \frac{20}{77} = 1$

C Challenge

43. a. You take a five-question multiple-choice quiz. You guess on all of the questions, selecting one of five answers randomly each time. What is the probability you will get a perfect score? $\frac{1}{3125}$
  b. What is the probability that you would get a perfect score if there were six questions on the quiz? $\frac{1}{15,625}$
  c. Find the ratio of $P(\text{perfect score on five-question quiz})$ to $P(\text{perfect score on six-question quiz})$. **5**

44. Suppose you roll a red number cube and a yellow number cube.
  a. Find $P(\text{red 1 and yellow 1})$. $\frac{1}{36}$
  b. Find $P(\text{red 2 and yellow 2})$. $\frac{1}{36}$
  c. Find the probability of rolling any matching pair of numbers. (*Hint:* Add the probabilities of each of the six matches.) $\frac{1}{6}$

45. A two-digit number is formed by randomly selecting from the digits 1, 2, 3, and 5 without replacement.
  a. How many different two-digit numbers can be formed? **12**
  b. What is the probability that a two-digit number contains a 2 or a 5? $\frac{5}{6}$
  c. What is the probability that a two-digit number is prime? $\frac{1}{3}$

Lesson 4-6 Probability of Compound Events **223**

Lesson Quiz 4-6

You roll two number cubes. Find each probability.

1. $P(\text{odd and even})$ $\frac{1}{4}$

2. $P(1 \text{ or } 2 \text{ and less than } 5)$ $\frac{2}{9}$

You select letters from the following:
A A B B B C D D E F G G G
and do not replace them. Find each probability.

3. $P(A \text{ then } B)$ $\frac{1}{26}$

4. $P(\text{vowel then } G)$ $\frac{3}{52}$

Alternative Assessment

Have students write four probability problems, two involving independent events and two involving dependent events, but not necessarily in that order. Ask each student to exchange problems with another student and find the probabilities of each event.

pages 222–224 Exercises

29. Indep.; you still have 2 choices for each coin with or without the other coin.

30. Dep.; with one name gone the data set changes.

32. Answers may vary. Sample: For dep. events, the outcome of the first event affects the outcome of the second (example: picking a marble out of a bag, and then picking a second marble without replacing the first one). For independent events, the outcomes do not affect each other (example: picking the second marble after replacing the first).

Standardized Test Prep

Resources
For additional practice with a variety of test item formats:
- Standardized Test Prep, p. 231
- Test-Taking Strategies, p. 226
- Test-Taking Strategies with Transparencies

Exercise 47 Help students see that there are three probabilities to be multiplied.

pages 222–224   Exercises

49. [2] P(green, green) = $\frac{3}{9} \cdot \frac{2}{8} = \frac{6}{72} = \frac{1}{12}$, P(red, red) = $\frac{4}{9} \cdot \frac{3}{8} = \frac{12}{72} = \frac{1}{6}$, P(r, r) is twice as likely as P(g, g).

[1] correct calculations for both probabilities but incorrect statement OR correct calculations for one probability and correct statement based on that answer

Standardized Test Prep

Multiple Choice

46. You roll a pair of number cubes. What is the probability of getting even numbers on both cubes? **C**

   A. 1   B. $\frac{1}{2}$ C. $\frac{1}{4}$ D. $\frac{1}{6}$

47. You take a three-question true or false quiz. You guess on all the questions. What is the probability that you will get a perfect score? **F**

   F. $\frac{1}{8}$ G. $\frac{3}{8}$ H. $\frac{1}{2}$ I. $\frac{3}{2}$

Take It to the NET
Online lesson quiz at **www.PHSchool.com**
Web Code: aea-0406

48. A standard domino set has 28 dominoes. Seven of these are called "doubles" since they have the same number on both ends or are blank on both ends. The first and second player each take a domino at random. What is the probability that they will both draw a double? **B**

   A. $\frac{1}{16}$ B. $\frac{1}{18}$ C. $\frac{3}{56}$ D. $\frac{13}{756}$

Short Response

49. You have a bag containing 3 green marbles, 4 red marbles, and 2 yellow marbles. You select 2 marbles randomly, without replacement. How does the probability that they will both be green compare to the probability that they will both be red? Show your work. **See margin.**

Mixed Review

Lesson 4-5

Suppose you select a two-digit number at random from 10 to 30 (including 10 and 30). Find each probability.

50. P(number is even) $\frac{11}{21}$ 51. P(number is a multiple of 6) $\frac{4}{21}$

52. P(number is prime) $\frac{2}{7}$ 53. P(number is less than 18) $\frac{8}{21}$

Lesson 3-6

Solve each equation or inequality. If there is no solution, explain why.

54. $|6g| + 7 = 31$ **4, −4**   55. $|-p + 2| = 0$ **2**   56. $|4a| > -3$ **all real numbers**

57. $|5 - y| - 2 < -9$
   No solution; abs. value can't be negative.

58. $|8w| + 9 < -7$
   No solution; abs. value can't be negative.

59. $16 < |26 - t| + 7$
   $t < 17$ or $t > 35$

Algebra at Work

.... Cartographer

A cartographer, or mapmaker, makes measurements of the area being mapped. The cartographer uses these dimensions to create the scale of the map, showing the ratio of map distance to actual distance. Knowing the scale of a map means that you can use a proportion to calculate any distance on the map.

Take It to the NET For more information about a career in cartography, go to **www.PHSchool.com**.
Web Code: aeb-2031

Sampling

FOR USE WITH LESSON 4-6

Suppose you want to gather data about the kinds of music teenagers in the United States prefer. It would not be possible to survey all 40 million teenagers in the United States. You could select a sample of teenagers and study their preferences. A *population* is a group of objects, plants, animals, or people. A *sample* is part of a population.

To gather data that reflect characteristics of the population, you need a random sample. When a *random sample* is being chosen, all members of a population have equal chances of being selected.

1 EXAMPLE Choosing a Random Sample

You want to find out how many videos or DVDs students at your school rent in a month. State whether each survey plan describes a good sample.

a. Interview every tenth teenager you see at a mall.

This sample will probably include students who do not go to your school. It is not a good sample because it is not taken from the population you want to study.

b. Interview every third student from your school that you see in a video store.

Teenagers in a video store are likely to be renting a video or DVD. This is not a good sample because it is not random.

c. Interview every tenth student leaving a school assembly.

This is a good sample. It is selected at random from the population you want to study.

EXERCISES

For Exercises 1 and 2, state whether each plan describes a good sample. Explain.

1. You want to know how often teens get haircuts. You plan to survey customers in a barbershop or salon. **Not good; not everyone in a barber shop or salon is a teenager.**

2. You want to know about peoples' favorite foods. You plan to survey every fifth person leaving the post office. **Good sample; it is a random sample from the population you want to study.**

3. You survey every tenth person leaving a sporting goods store. Of those surveyed, 83% support the mayor's proposal for bike paths. You are writing an article for the school newspaper. Do you report that there is overwhelming support for the mayor's proposal? Explain why or why not. **No; the sample was biased toward athletic activities such as biking.**

4. Critical Thinking You review the results of survey questions given to two random samples of registered voters in your city. Why are the results not the same? **Answers may vary.**

	Yes	No	**Sample: They are different because the word *reckless* was biased against skateboarders.**
Do you think that reckless skateboarders should be restricted in public playgrounds?	72%	28%	
Do you think that skateboarders should be banned from public places?	42%	58%	

Sampling

Students learn that a *sample* is a selected subgroup of a population. When doing surveys, students know that it is not possible to survey everyone, and therefore they need to select a part of the population. When each member of a population has an equal chance of being selected, the sample is called a random sample. Students learn to identify a random sample from a biased sample.

Resources

 Technology
Computer Test Generator CD-ROM, Chapter 0, Extension Topics

Teaching Notes

Some students may need help in clarifying why Example 1b is not a random sample. Point out that persons at a video store are more likely to rent DVDs, because they are in the store. A better sample might be to ask the question about DVDs at a fast food restaurant. Similarly, they shouldn't select a sample from a fast food restaurant to find out how many times a week students eat at a fast food restaurant.

Math Tip

When a sample is not random, as in Example 1b, students in the video store are less likely to say zero times than the general student population. The average may be skewed to a higher number because of this. Suggest that students do a survey that they know is biased, that is, one that doesn't use a random sample and then do the same survey with a random sample. Ask students to compare and contrast the results.

Making Quantitative Comparisons

This feature helps students develop strategies for comparing quantities.

Resources

PRENTICE HALL
ASSESSMENT *SYSTEM*

Test-Taking Strategies with Transparencies
• Transparency 4
• Practice sheet p. 4

Teaching Notes

Remind students not to jump to conclusions too quickly in this type of problem. The problems and answers are designed to be tricky and counter-intuitive. For example, it may seem logical that $x^2 < x^3$ because 2^2 is less than 2^3. Students must try numbers other than positive integers. If they try -1, 0, $\frac{1}{2}$, or 1, they will see why.

Teaching Tip

Suggest to students that it is best to try a positive integer, a negative integer, zero, one, and a positive and negative fraction before deciding on an answer

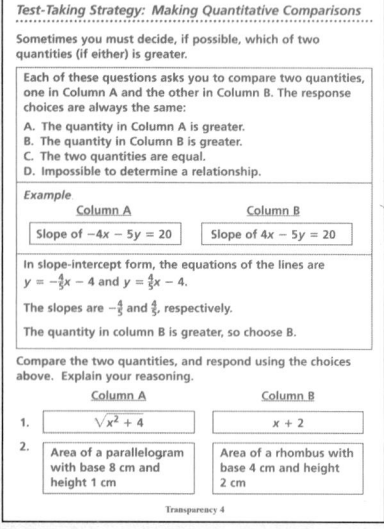

A Quantitative Comparison question asks you to determine the relationship between two quantities. Your answer is either A, B, C, or D.

• You pick A if the quantity in Column A is greater.
• You pick B if the quantity in Column B is greater.
• You pick C if the two quantities are always equal.
• You pick D if the relationship cannot be determined from the information given. If neither A nor B nor C is *always* true, then pick D.

Here are two strategies for answering quantitative comparison questions.

1 EXAMPLE Rewriting the Quantities

Column A	Column B
$\frac{1}{3}$	33%

Quantities are easier to compare if they have the same form. Rewrite $\frac{1}{3}$ as the decimal 0.3333 . . . and compare it to 33% or 0.33. Since $\frac{1}{3} > 33\%$, the answer is A.

2 EXAMPLE Evaluating a Variable

Column A	Column B
x^2	x^4

Substitute numbers for the variable. When you evaluate the variable, remember to include negative numbers as well as fractions. When $x = 2$, the quantity in column B is greater. However, when $x = \frac{1}{2}$, the quantity in column A is greater. The relationship cannot be determined because the value of x determines which quantity is greater. The answer is D.

EXERCISES

Refer to the Examples to answer each question.

1. Compare the quantities in Example 1 by writing the quantities as fractions with a common denominator. $\frac{100}{300} > \frac{99}{300}$

2. If values of x in Example 2 are between -1 and 0, which quantity in Example 2 is greater? x^2

3. Explain why an answer can never be D if the quantities in both boxes are numbers. **A real number is always less than, equal to, or greater than another real number.**

4. Answer the following Quantitative Comparison question using A, B, C, or D as described above. **D**

Column A	Column B
the value of x in the equation $x - 5 = 3x + 7$	the value of n in the equation $4n - 3 = 2(2n + 2) - 7$

Chapter Review

Vocabulary

complement of an event (p. 212)
cross products (p. 183)
dependent events (p. 221)
event (p. 211)
experimental probability (p. 212)
extremes of a proportion (p. 183)
greatest possible error (p. 205)
independent events (p. 220)

means of a proportion (p. 183)
outcome (p. 211)
percent error (p. 206)
percent of change (p. 204)
percent of decrease (p. 204)
percent of increase (p. 204)
probability (p. 211)
proportion (p. 183)
rate (p. 182)

ratio (p. 182)
sample space (p. 211)
scale (p. 191)
scale drawing (p. 191)
similar figures (p. 190)
theoretical probability (p. 211)
unit analysis (p. 182)
unit rate (p. 182)

Reading Math
Understanding
Vocabulary

Choose the correct term to complete each sentence.

1. To change one unit of measure to another you can use a (*proportion, rate*) that is equal to 1. **rate**

2. You can use (*cross products, unit analysis*) to solve a proportion that involves one variable. **cross products**

3. The ratio $\frac{\text{amount of change}}{\text{original amount}}$ is used to find (*percent of change, probability*).
percent of change

4. The (*greatest possible error, percent error*) in a measurement is one half of the measuring unit. **greatest possible error**

5. The result of a single trial, such as one toss of a coin, is (*an outcome, a sample space*). **an outcome**

6. (*Theoretical probability, Complement of an event*) is all the outcomes not in an event. **Complement of an event**

7. You select a card, replace it, then select another card. The events are (*dependent, independent*). **independent**

8. The (*probability, sample space*) for rolling a number cube is 1, 2, 3, 4, 5, and 6. **sample space**

Take It to the NET
Online vocabulary quiz
at **www.PHSchool.com**
Web Code: aej-0451

9. If you drive 210 miles in 3 hours, your (*scale, unit rate*) of travel is 70 miles per hour. **unit rate**

10. Last year, Taylor earned $4.50 per hour baby-sitting. This year she earns $5.25 per hour. The (*percent of decrease, percent of increase*) is about 17%.
percent of increase

Skills and Concepts

4-1 Objectives

▼ To find ratios and rates (p.182)

▼ To solve proportions (p.183)

A **ratio** is a comparison of two numbers by division. A **rate** is a ratio that compares quantities measured in different units. A **unit rate** is a rate with a denominator of 1.

A **proportion** is a statement that two ratios are equal. You can solve a proportion that involves one variable by finding the **cross products.**

Write in miles per hour. Round to the nearest hundredth.

11. 2.5 mi/min **150 mi/h**   **12.** 300 ft/min **3.41 mi/h**   **13.** 4 in./s **0.23 mi/h**

Resources

Student Edition
Extra Practice, Ch. 4, p. 705
English/Spanish Glossary, p. 757
Properties and Formulas, p. 752
Table of Symbols, p. 749

Reaching All Students
Reading and Math Literacy 4D
Spanish Reading and Math
    Literacy 4D

ASSESSMENT SYSTEM
PRENTICE HALL

Standardized Test Prep
● Ch. 4 practice in standardized
   test formats

www.PHSchool.com
Student Site
● Self-grading Vocabulary Test
Teacher Center
● Resources

Plus **iTEXT**

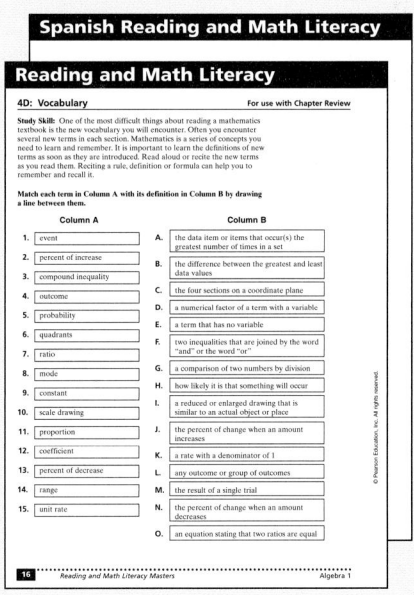

Solve each proportion.

14. $\frac{4}{12} = \frac{c}{6}$ **2**   **15.** $\frac{t}{5} = \frac{23}{50}$ **2.3**   **16.** $\frac{-9}{m} = \frac{3}{2}$ **−6**

17. $\frac{x}{8} = \frac{x-5}{6}$ **20**   **18.** $\frac{12}{r} = \frac{4}{0.5r-1}$ **6**   **19.** $\frac{d-2}{d+9} = \frac{3}{14}$ **5**

4-2 Objectives

▼ To find missing measures of similar figures (p. 189)

▼ To use similar figures when measuring indirectly (p. 191)

Similar figures have the same shape but not necessarily the same size. If two figures are **similar,** then corresponding angles are congruent, and corresponding sides are in proportion.

A scale drawing is an enlarged or reduced drawing of an object. The ratio of the length of the drawing to the actual length of the object is the **scale** of the drawing. You can use proportions to solve problems involving scale drawings. A map is an example of a scale drawing.

In the figure at the right, $\triangle DEF \sim \triangle QRS$.

20. Find RS. **7.5 m**   **21.** Find QR. **19.5 m**

22. Hobbies A certain model airplane is $\frac{1}{48}$ of the airplane's actual size. The length of the model airplane's wing is $\frac{3}{4}$ ft. How long is the airplane's wing? **36 ft**

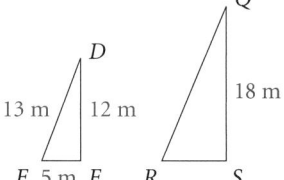

4-3 Objectives

▼ To use proportions when solving percent problems (p. 197)

▼ To write and solve percent equations (p. 198)

Below is a summary of how to solve problems involving percents by using proportions and by writing equations.

Finding the Percent	**Finding the Part**	**Finding the Whole**
What percent of 45 is 10?	What is 16% of 261?	71% of what number is 87?
$\frac{n}{100} = \frac{10}{45}$ ← **part** ← **whole**	$\frac{16}{100} = \frac{n}{261}$ ← **part** ← **whole**	$\frac{71}{100} = \frac{87}{n}$ ← **part** ← **whole**
$n \cdot 45 = 10$	$n = 0.16 \cdot 261$	$0.71n = 87$

Solve each percent problem.

23. What is 15% of 86? **12.9**   **24.** 1.8 is 72% of what number? **2.5**

25. What percent of 5 is 40? **800%**   **26.** 4% of what number is 34? **850**

27. In one high school, 30 of the school's 800 students work on the school paper. What percent of the students work on the paper? **3.75%**

28. Finance You invest $2000 in a bank account. Find the amount of simple interest you earn in two years for an annual interest rate of 5.5%. Use the formula for simple interest $I = p \cdot r \cdot t$, where I is the interest, p is the principal, r is the annual interest rate, and t is the time in years. **$220**

4-4 Objectives

▼ To find percent of change (p. 204)

▼ To find percent error (p. 205)

The **percent of change** $= \frac{\text{amount of change}}{\text{original amount}}$. If a value increases from its original amount, the percent of change is the **percent of increase.** If a value decreases from its original amount, the percent of change is the **percent of decrease.**

The greatest possible error in a measurement is one half of the measuring unit. The percent error is $\frac{\text{greatest possible error}}{\text{measurement}}$.

For Exercises 29–31, find each percent of change. Where necessary, round to the nearest percent. Describe the percent of change as a percent of increase or percent of decrease.

29. $75,000 to $85,000
about 13%; increase

30. 20 feet to 15 feet
25%; decrease

31. 60 hours to 40 hours
about 33%; decrease

32. Answers may vary. Sample: It costs a restaurant $.11 to make a cup of tea, which it sells for $.75. The percent of increase is about 582%.

32. Open-Ended Describe a situation that involves a percent of increase that is more than 100%. **See left.**

33. Suppose you measure a box. Its dimensions are 32 in. × 28 in. × 25 in. Find the percent error in calculating its volume. Round to the nearest tenth of a percent. **about 5.4%**

4-5 Objectives

▼ To find theoretical probability (p. 211)

▼ To find experimental probability (p. 212)

The **probability** of an event, or *P*(event), tells you how likely it is that something will occur. An **outcome** is the result of a single trial. An **event** is any outcome or group of outcomes. The **sample space** is all of the possible outcomes.

theoretical probability $P(\text{event}) = \dfrac{\text{number of favorable outcomes}}{\text{number of possible outcomes}}$

experimental probability $P(\text{event}) = \dfrac{\text{number of times an event occurs}}{\text{number of times the experiment is done}}$

Find each probability for one roll of a number cube.

34. $P(\text{number} \geq 7)$ **0**   **35.** $P(\text{not } 5)$ $\frac{5}{6}$ **36.** $P(2 \text{ or } 6)$ $\frac{1}{3}$ **37.** $P(3)$ $\frac{1}{6}$

38. Suppose you toss a coin 4 times.
  a. What is the probability that you toss exactly 3 heads? $\frac{1}{4}$
  b. Explain what *P*(not 3 heads) means. **See left.**

38b. Sample: *P*(not 3 heads) means the chances of getting 0, 1, 2, or 4 heads.

39. Science An astronomer calculates that the probability that a visible meteor shower will occur in May is $\frac{3}{14}$. What is the probability that a visible meteor shower will not occur in May? $\frac{11}{14}$

pages 227–229   Chapter Review

42. Answers may vary. Sample: In probability, two events are dependent if the outcome of one influences the outcome of the other. In everyday language, if one person is dependent on another, the first person relies on the second for support.

4-6 Objectives

▼ To find the probability of independent events (p. 219)

▼ To find the probability of dependent events (p. 221)

Independent events do not affect one another. When the outcome of one event affects the outcome of a second event, the events are **dependent events.**

For independent events *A* and *B*:   For dependent events *A* and *B*:

$P(A \text{ and } B) = P(A) \cdot P(B).$ $P(A \text{ and } B) = P(A) \cdot P(B \text{ after } A).$

For Exercises 40 and 41, suppose you choose two numbers from a box containing the numbers 1–10. State whether the two events are independent or dependent. Then find each probability.

40. $P(6 \text{ and an even number})$ without replacing the card **dependent;** $\frac{2}{45}$

41. $P(1 \text{ and an odd number})$ with replacing the card **independent;** $\frac{1}{20}$

42. Writing Explain what the word *dependent* means in probability and what it means in everyday language. **See margin.**

44. Dep.; once you select one sock, there are fewer socks when you make the second selection.

Are the two events dependent or independent? Explain.

43. Roll a red and a blue number cube. **Indep.; the result of one number cube does not affect the other.**

44. Randomly select a green sock and then another green sock to wear to school. **See left.**

Chapter 4   Chapter Review   **229**

Chapter

4

Chapter Test

Take It to the NET
Online chapter test at
www.PHSchool.com
Web Code: aea-0452

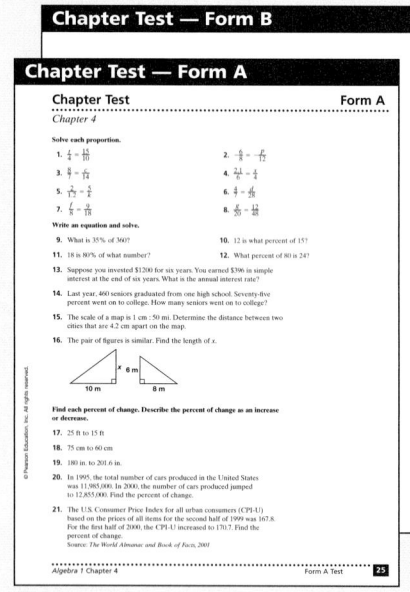

11. 11.$\overline{1}$%; increase

12. 25%; decrease

Solve each proportion.

1. $\frac{3}{4} = \frac{c}{20}$ **15**

2. $\frac{8}{15} = \frac{4}{w}$ **7.5**

3. $\frac{w}{6} = \frac{6}{15}$ **2.4**

4. $\frac{5}{t} = \frac{25}{100}$ **20**

Solve an equation to answer each question.

5. What is 16% of 250? **40**

6. 8 is what percent of 12.5? **64%**

7. 19 is 95% of what? **20**

8. The ratio of the length of a side of one square to that of another square is 3:4. A side of the smaller square is 9 cm. Find the length of a side of the larger square. **12 cm**

9. Finance You invest $500 for three years and receive $60 in simple interest. What is the annual interest rate? Use the formula for simple interest $I = p \cdot r \cdot t$, where I is the interest, p is the principal, r is the annual interest rate, and t is the time in years. **4%**

10. Suppose a person contributes 6% of her salary to her retirement account. She works 20 hours per week at $6.50 per hour. Find her weekly contribution. **$7.80**

Calculate the percent of change. If necessary, round to the nearest tenth. Describe each as a percent of increase or a percent of decrease. 11–14. See margin.

11. $4.50/h to $5/h

12. 60 km/h to 45 km/h

13. 150 lb to 135 lb

14. $18 to $24

15. Survey A random survey of 60 students showed that 36 students used calculators for computation. What is the probability that a student chosen at random used a calculator for computation? $\frac{3}{5}$

16. A softball player made a hit 34 times in the last 170 times at bat. Find the probability that the softball player will get a hit the next time at bat. $\frac{1}{5}$

Complete each statement.

17. 14¢/oz = $■ /lb **2.24**

18. 7 gal/wk = ■ qt/h $\frac{1}{6}$

19. 35 mi/h = ■ ft/min **3080**

20. 120 ft/day = ■ in./min
1

---

21. A scale on a map is 1 in.:25 mi. You measure 6.5 inches. How many miles is the actual distance?
162.5 mi

22. A boy 5 ft tall casts a shadow 8 ft long. He stands next to a monument that has a shadow 20 ft long. How tall is the monument? **12.5 ft**

23. Suppose you have a bag containing 3 red, 4 blue, 5 white, and 2 black marbles. One marble is selected at random. Find the theoretical probability of choosing each of the following.
a. P(not white) $\frac{9}{14}$
b. P(red or blue) $\frac{1}{2}$
c. P(orange) **0**

24. Comparison Shopping A bouquet of 12 carnations costs $6.99, while a bouquet of 8 carnations costs $4.99. Which is the better buy?
12 carnations for $6.99

25. Open-Ended Write and solve a probability problem involving dependent events. **See margin.**

26. The game Monopoly™ was introduced in 1935. The table shows how much some amounts in the game should have increased to have kept up with inflation.

Category	Money Values	
	in 1935	in 2000
Total money in game	$15,140	$188,203
Amount each player starts the game with	$1500	$18,646
Park Place rent with no houses	$35	$435
Money collected when passing GO	$200	$2486

a. Estimate the percent of inflation from 1935 to 2000 by finding the percent of increase in any one of the dollar amounts. **about 1143%**

b. Writing Describe the steps you used to calculate your answer to part (a). **See margin.**

27. You have 8 red checkers and 8 black checkers in a bag. You choose two checkers. Find each probability.
a. P(red and red) with replacing $\frac{1}{4}$
b. P(red and black) without replacing $\frac{4}{15}$
c. P(black and red) with replacing $\frac{1}{4}$

---

13. 10%; decrease

14. 33.$\overline{3}$%; increase

25. Answers may vary. Sample: Four cards have one letter each: A, B, C, or D. What is the probability that the first card you select is A and the second is B, if you don't replace the first card before selecting the second card? $\frac{1}{12}$

26b. Sample: Use the second row. Subtract the amount in the first column from the amount in the second column. Divide the result by the amount in the first column and multiply by 100.

Standardized Test Prep

Multiple Choice

For Exercises 1–10, choose the correct letter.

1. Tamara's teacher allows students to decide whether to use the mean, median, or mode for their test averages. Tamara will receive the highest average if she uses the mean. Which set of test scores are Tamara's? **B**
   A. 95, 82, 76, 95, 96   B. 79, 80, 91, 83, 80
   C. 65, 84, 75, 74, 65   D. 100, 87, 94, 94, 81

2. A store owner has a bicycle priced at $100. She raises the price 10%. During a sale, she then lowers the price 10%. What is the new price of the bicycle? **H**
   F. $101   G. $100   H. $99   I. $98

3. A bag contains 10 red marbles and 20 white marbles. You draw a marble, keep it, and draw another. What is the probability of drawing two red marbles? **B**
   A. $\frac{1}{10}$ B. $\frac{3}{29}$ C. $\frac{1}{9}$ D. $\frac{1}{3}$

4. Which equation does NOT have the same solution as $\frac{7}{y} = \frac{31}{36}$? **I**
   F. $\frac{7}{31} = \frac{y}{36}$ G. $7 \cdot 36 = 31y$
   H. $\frac{y}{36} = \frac{7}{31}$ I. $\frac{36}{31} = \frac{7}{y}$

5. The number of subscribers to a magazine fell from 210,000 to 190,000. Find the approximate percent of decrease. **B**
   A. 5%   B. 10%   C. 20%   D. 90%

6. Find the value of n if $3n - 5 = 7$. **H**
   F. 6   G. 5   H. 4   I. 3

7. The sum of four consecutive integers is 190. What is the third integer? **D**
   A. 45   B. 46   C. 47   D. 48

8. Evaluate $\frac{4a^2}{2b - 3}$ for $a = 3$ and $b = 6$. **G**
   F. 3   G. 4   H. 6   I. 16

9. Which ordered pair is graphed below? **B**
   A. $(-2, 3)$
   B. $(-3, 2)$
   C. $(-2, -3)$
   D. $(-3, -2)$

10. Which are solutions of $3(x - 4) \leq 18$ and $2(x - 1) \geq 6$? **F**
    I. 9   II. 12   III. 15
    F. I only   G. II only
    H. I and III   I. II and III

Quantitative Comparison

Compare the boxed quantity in Column A with the boxed quantity in Column B. Choose the best answer.

A. The quantity in Column A is greater.
B. The quantity in Column B is greater.
C. The two quantities are equal.
D. The relationship cannot be determined from the information given.

	Column A	Column B
D 11.	$-x - 1$	$x + 1$

A number cube is rolled.

	Column A	Column B
C 12.	the probability of rolling a number 5 or greater	the probability of rolling a number 2 or less

Compare the quantities for $x \neq 0$.

	Column A	Column B
B 13.	$-|x|$	$|-x|$

Gridded Response

Find each answer.

14. A CD player that normally costs $225 would cost an employee $180. What is the percent of the employee's discount? **20**

15. Solve $\frac{3}{5}(2m - 3) = -6$. $-\frac{7}{2}$

Short Response

Show your work. 16–17. See back of book.

16. **Art** In 1996, an exhibit in Washington, D.C., showed 21 paintings by Jan Vermeer. This is about $\frac{3}{5}$ of his known paintings. About how many of his paintings are known to exist?

17. Suppose you earn $80 a week at your summer job. Your employer offers you a $20 raise or a 20% raise. Which should you take? Explain why.

Resources

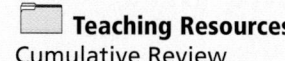

Teaching Resources
Cumulative Review

Reaching All Students
Spanish Cumulative Review

ASSESSMENT SYSTEM

Standardized Test Prep
• Ch. 4 Standardized Test Practice
Assessment Masters
• Cumulative Review
Computer Test Generator CD
• Standardized Test Practice

www.PHSchool.com
• Standardized Test Practice
• Resources

Plus **iTEXT**

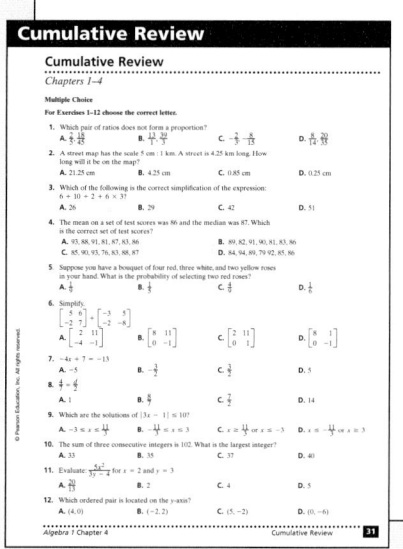

Item	Lesson	Item	Lesson
1	2-7	10	1-9
2	4-4	11	1-7
3	4-5	12	4-5
4	4-1	13	1-5
5	4-4	14	4-3
6	2-2	15	2-3
7	2-5	16	4-1
8	1-2	17	4-3
9	3-3		

A Swing of the Bat

In these activities students apply their knowledge of areas, proportions, probabilities, and simulations.

Connecting to Prior Knowledge

Ask students whether they have either played or watched a game of baseball or softball. If the general rules and events in a baseball game are unfamiliar to any student, ask volunteers to explain the big picture. Have a student use the baseball bat, and a cardboard model of home plate, to demonstrate a typical swing using a mock pitch without an actual ball.

Teaching Notes

Discuss what happens when a player hits a ball with the bat. Elicit the fact that one small area on the bat hits an equal area on the ball.

Teaching Tip

Have a volunteer read the introductory paragraph. Make sure students realize that a player's batting average for a given game may not be the same as the cumulative lifetime batting average for that player.

Tactile Learners

Let students handle the bat and have them point out the part of the bat that is held in the hands and the part that is most likely to hit the ball.

English Learners

Verify that students understand what is meant by the words *pitch* and *swing* by having them pantomime these actions while explaining them.

A Swing of the Bat

Applying Probability One of the most difficult athletic feats is also the one attempted most often in the United States—hitting a baseball with a baseball bat. A good batting average is .280 or better, which means that the batter gets a hit at least 28% of the time. The last major-league player with a season batting average above .400 was Ted Williams of the Boston Red Sox, who hit .406 in 1941. How do real batting averages compare with the probability of getting a hit?

Borders Cracks the Barrier
In 1997, Ila Borders, a left-handed pitcher with the St. Paul Saints, became the first woman to start and win a professional baseball game since the 1940s.

Activity 1

Materials: baseball bat, tape measure or ruler, pencil and paper

Suppose you are standing at the plate, ready to swing at a ball. Use the assumptions below.

• Every pitch will be in the strike zone.

• The timing of your swing will be correct so that the ball and bat are over the plate at the same time.

a. Use the given information to estimate the area of your strike zone.

b. Measure the bat and estimate the area that passes through the strike zone.

c. Use your answers to parts (a) and (b) to estimate the probability of making contact with the ball during a given swing.

Activity 2

a. Use your estimate from Activity 1 to calculate the probability of missing the ball during a given swing.

b. Use your answer to part (a) to estimate the probability of missing the ball three times in a row, or striking out.

c. Use your answer to part (b) to calculate the probability of not striking out.

KEY
● strikes ● balls ▪ strike zone

Chin music; brushback

High inside strike

Up and away ●
At the letters

Right down the pipe; down the middle; right down Broadway

High and tight

Outside
Inside

Caught the corner

Down and in

Down and away ●
At the knees

The Strike Zone
Vertically, the strike zone extends from the hollow just below the batter's knee cap to a point midway between the top of the batter's belt and top of the batter's shoulders.

Horizontally, the strike zone is the width of home plate, which is 17 in., plus twice the diameter of the ball, or 5.8 in.

232

pages 232–233   **Real-World Snapshots**

Activities 1 and 2

Check students' work.

Power Hitter
The bat bends from the power of Mark McGwire's swing during the 1992 All-Star Game.

Activity 3

a. Having the bat make contact with the ball doesn't always mean that you get a hit. Estimate the percentage of contacts with the ball that result in a hit, either through interviewing baseball players in your school or by researching baseball statistics.

b. Use your answer to part (a) and your results from Activity 2 to estimate the batting average you could expect to have if you kept your eyes closed.

Anatomy of a Hit
Begin with your feet about shoulders-width apart. As you swing the bat, your hips turn and your hands follow your hips. As the bat makes contact with the ball, snap your wrists and watch the ball soar.

Heavy Hitter
Ted Williams of the Boston Red Sox watches the ball sail over the crowd.

Take It to the NET
For more information about baseball, go to **www.PHSchool.com**.
Web Code: aee-0453

233

Teaching Tip
You may want to assign part a of Activity 3 several days before you plan to teach this snapshot. Have students work in pairs or in small groups to complete the activities. Have each team read through all three activities before beginning to work so that they understand that each activity uses the results from the previous one.

Activity 1

Materials baseball bat, tape measure, yard stick or ruler, pencil and paper

Teaching Tip
Ask students to suggest steps that will lead to an estimate of the area of the strike zone for a particular student.

Activity 2

Materials paper and pencil

Teaching Tip
Verify that the estimates of Activity 1 are reasonable before students use these results in Activity 2.

Activity 3

Materials paper and pencil

Teaching Tip
Have students report the sources they used to gather the information for estimating the percentage of contacts that result in a hit.

Scoring Rubric

This scoring rubric applies to both activities. Share this scoring rubric with students before they begin work.

4 Calculations are correct and estimates are reasonable. Steps are neat, accurate, and clearly show the mathematics.
3 Calculations are mostly correct, with some minor errors. Steps are neat and mostly accurate.
2 Calculations contain both major and minor errors.
1 Correct answer, but no work is shown.

233

Chapter 5

Graphs and Functions

Chapter at a Glance

 North Carolina Objectives

5-1	Relating Graphs to Events	
NCTM 2, 4, 5, 6, 9, 10	▼ Interpreting, Sketching, and Analyzing Graphs	

5-2	Relations and Functions	4.01a
NCTM 2, 7, 8, 10	▼ Identifying Relations and Functions ▼ Evaluating Functions	

5-3	Function Rules, Tables, and Graphs	4.01a
NCTM 2, 7, 8, 10	▼ Modeling Functions	

5-4	Writing a Function Rule	4.01a
NCTM 2, 6, 8, 9, 10	▼ Writing Function Rules	

5-5	Direct Variation	1.03, 4.01
NCTM 2, 5, 6, 8,10	▼ Writing the Equation of a Direct Variation ▼ Ratios, Proportions, and Direct Variations	

5-6	Describing Number Patterns	1.02
NCTM 2, 5, 6, 7	▼ Inductive Reasoning and Number Patterns ▼ Writing Rules for Arithmetic Sequences	

NCTM STANDARDS 2000

1	Number and Operations	6	Problem Solving
2	Algebra	7	Reasoning and Proof
3	Geometry	8	Communication
4	Measurement	9	Connections
5	Data Analysis and Probability	10	Representation

Pacing Options

This chart suggests pacing only for the lessons and their parts. It is provided as a possible guide. It will help you determine how much time you have in your schedule to cover other components, such as the features, Chapter Review, and Chapter Test.

Day	Traditional 45 min.	Two-Year 45 min.	Block 90 min.
1	5-1 ▼	5-1 ▼	5-1 ▼ 5-2 ▼ ▼
2	5-2 ▼ ▼	5-1 ▼	5-3 ▼ 5-4 ▼
3	5-3 ▼	5-2 ▼	5-5 ▼ ▼
4	5-4 ▼	5-2 ▼	5-6 ▼ ▼
5	5-5 ▼ ▼	5-3 ▼	
6	5-6 ▼ ▼	5-3 ▼	
7		5-4 ▼	
8		5-4 ▼	
9		5-5 ▼	
10		5-5 ▼	
11		5-6 ▼	
12		5-6 ▼	

NAEP Correlation (National Assessment of Educational Progress 2000 Mathematics Objectives)

5-1	5-2	5-3	5-4	5-5	5-6
D1a	A1, Ab5, A11	A1b, A1f, A3c	D1a, A1c	D1a; A1e, f	N6b, A1, A8b

N = Number Sense, Properties, and Operations; **M** = Measurement; **G** = Geometry and Spatial Sense;
D = Data Analysis, Statistics, and Probability; **A** = Algebra and Functions

Math Background

Chapter Overview

This chapter focuses on a fundamental idea in mathematics—functions. The functional relationship relates the value of one variable, such as *y*, to the value of another variable, such as *x*. Functional relationships can be represented visually by graphs. Students begin by graphing situations and interpreting the situations represented by a graph. They then use the vocabulary and mathematical notation for functions, and model functions with rules, tables, and graphs. They examine the particular function called a direct variation, and further examine the special patterns in arithmetic sequences.

Relating Graphs to Events   5-1

This lesson will help students see how they can use mathematics to make a general representation of a specific relationship that occurs in their daily lives. Through graphing, students explore the idea of change, such as changes in speed, altitude, etc. In addition to change, students investigate relationships between quantities by using graphs.

Relations and Functions   5-2

Students should learn to correctly read *f*(*x*), as "*f* of *x*." This will help them distinguish function notation from the more familiar notation used to show the multiplication of two variables, such as *ab* or *a*(*b*). Explain that the context usually makes the difference clear, and certain letters, such as *f, g, h,* and *k* are most commonly used for function notation.

Function Rules, Tables, and Graphs   5-3

Help students see that the rule $f(x) = x + 3$ represents an infinite number of points, each of which can be written as an ordered pair in the form $(x, x + 3)$. Similarly, the straight line that is the graph of $y = x + 3$ includes all these points, since the line extends forever. However, a table represents only a sample of points from this solution set—enough to determine and check the straight line that contains all the points in the solution set.

Make sure students understand that graphs represent the relationship between two quantities. While in this lesson, the quantities are abstract variables in equations, remind students that in Lesson 1, they learned that graphs can represent the relationship between two real quantities such as speed and time. Help students think of real world situations that could be

represented by the graph of a quadratic equation, such as the flight of a projectile.

Writing a Function Rule   5-4

When students write a rule for a table of values, they must make sure that the apparent pattern does indeed hold true for each pair of points listed in the table. While two points are enough to determine a line, at least a third point should be used as a check, to find and correct errors in calculation.

The fact that two points determine a line may not at first be obvious to students until they try to find a second and different line that includes the same two points.

Direct Variation   5-5

In direct variation, as the absolute value of one variable increases, the absolute value of the second variable also increases proportionally. Thus, for example in $y = -2x$, as *x* increases from 10 to 20, the absolute value of *y* increases from 20 to 40. This means that the ratio of *y* to *x* remains equal to the constant, *k*, or $\frac{y}{x} = k$. Another way to express this direct relationship is with the proportion $\frac{y_1}{x_1} = \frac{y_2}{x_2}$. So, in this example, $\frac{-20}{10} = \frac{-40}{20}$.

Discuss briefly the fact that there are other kinds of variation, such as inverse variation. One example of inverse variation is the relation between the number of gallons of hot water remaining in the tank of a water heater and the minutes used to take a shower. In inverse variation (see Chapter 12) the product of the two variables, rather than the quotient, remains constant.

Describing Number Patterns   5-6

An inductive argument reasons from observations of particular instances (for example, this crow is black, that crow is black) to a generality (all crows are black). Not all conclusions reached in this way are correct, but this kind of reasoning is very often used in daily life, and is often effective.

Students can use inductive reasoning to identify patterns, or sequences, in sets of numbers. An arithmetic sequence is formed by adding a specific number to each term after the first. Another type of sequence, the geometric sequence, will be introduced in Chapter 8. Later, deductive reasoning, using formal logic, will confirm or discredit their conclusions.

 # Ongoing Assessment and Intervention

Tools for Monitoring Student Progress

The Prentice Hall *Algebra 1* program provides you with many options for assessment in the Student Edition, the Teacher's Edition and the teaching resources. From these options you may choose instructional materials and techniques that are appropriate for your students and support your district's curriculum requirements.

Instant Check System™ in Chapter 5

Allows students to check their own learning before, during, and after each lesson.

Diagnosing Readiness before the chapter (p. 234)

Check Skills You'll Need exercises in each lesson (pp. 236, 241, 247, 254, 261, 268)

Check Understanding questions with each Example (pp. 236, 237, 241, 242, 243, 248, 249, 254, 255, 262, 263, 264, 268, 269, 270)

Checkpoint Quiz (pp. 246, 267)

 Test Prep in Chapter 5

Teaches students strategies and gives them practice with all the test item formats they will encounter on state tests and standardized national exams.

Standardized Test Prep exercises in each lesson (pp. 240, 245, 246, 251, 252, 258, 259, 266, 272, 273)

Test-Taking Strategies (p. 274: Using a Variable)

Standardized Test Prep (p. 279: Reading Comprehension)

All your assessment needs in one place!

Program Assessment

Assess student progress throughout the *Algebra 1* text with blackline masters and CD-ROM.

Assessment Resources

- Checkpoint Quizzes 1 & 2
- Chapter Test, Forms A & B
- Chapter Alternative Assessment

Spanish versions available. Tests for Basic Algebra also available.

 Computer Test Generator

- Unlimited questions of varying difficulty for every lesson objective.
- Create your own practice sheets, quizzes, and tests, or use the pre-made Chapter Tests.
- Diagnose readiness with questions on prerequisite skills.
- Prepare students by making tests based on standardized test objectives.
- Access Algebra 1, Geometry, and Algebra 2 content—all on one CD-ROM.

Test Preparation

A three-step approach to preparing students for high stakes, national, and state exams.

❶ Diagnose & Prescribe

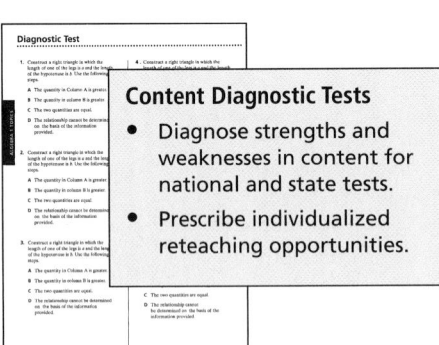

Content Diagnostic Tests
- Diagnose strengths and weaknesses in content for national and state tests.
- Prescribe individualized reteaching opportunities.

❷ Review & Reteach

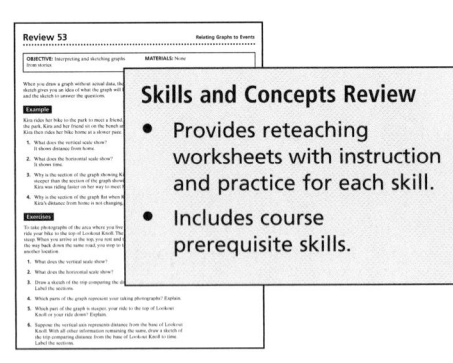

Skills and Concepts Review
- Provides reteaching worksheets with instruction and practice for each skill.
- Includes course prerequisite skills.

❸ Practice & Assess

Test Preparation
- Features practice tests for End-of-Course and SAT/ACT exams.
- Includes standardized test practice by chapter for ongoing review.

Teacher's Guide with answers and correlations.

Test-Taking Strategies with Transparencies
- Support the Test-Taking Strategies pages in the Student Edition.
- Provide a teaching transparency and a practice worksheet for each strategy.

✿ Reaching All Students

Support in the Student Text and Additional Resources

The textbook, the iText, and other technology components provide numerous opportunities to reach students of various ability levels and learning styles. Each Teacher's Edition lesson suggests how you can help *all* your students be successful and understand the mathematics in Chapter 5.

Below Level

Student Edition
- Diagnosing Readiness*: p. 234
- Check Skills You'll Need*: pp. 236, 241, 247, 254, 261, 268

Reteaching
Chapter 5 Support File: pp. 8–13

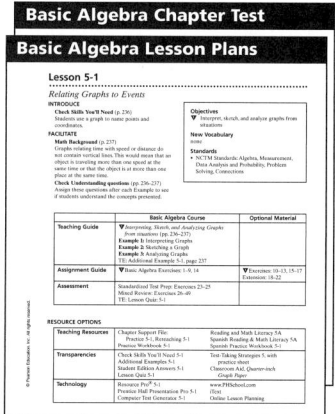

Basic Algebra Planning Guide
Chapter 5 Lesson Plans: pp. 29–34
Chapter 5 Tests: pp. 105–108

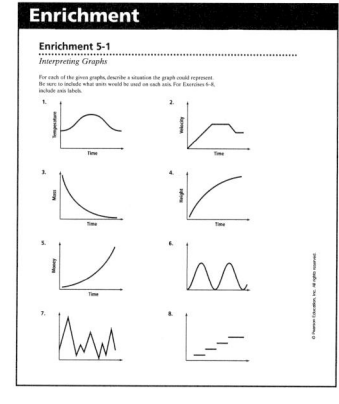

* Can be used with all ability levels to ensure mastery of prerequisite skills.

Advanced Learners

Student Edition
- Challenge exercises: pp. 239, 240, 245, 251, 258, 266, 272

Enrichment
Chapter 5 Support File: pp. 14–19

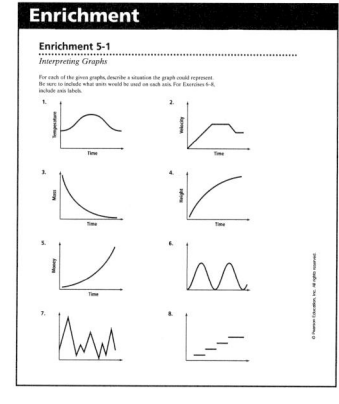

📖 Reading and Math Literacy

Student Edition
- Vocabulary: pp. 235, 275, *plus* in every Lesson Preview
- Reading Math: pp. 243, 260, 262, 268, 275
- Illustrated Glossary: pp. 757–785

Reading and Math Literacy Masters
Chapter 5: pp. 17–20

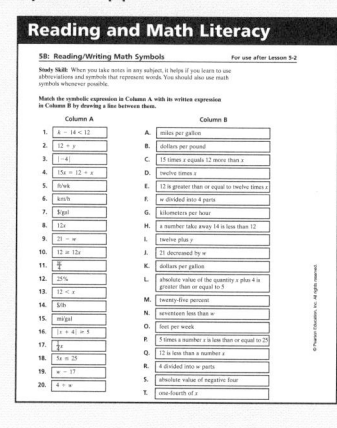

English Learners

Student Edition
- English/Spanish Illustrated Glossary: pp. 757–785

Workbook and Masters
Spanish Practice Workbook: pp. 29–34
Spanish Reading and Math Literacy Masters: pp. 17–20

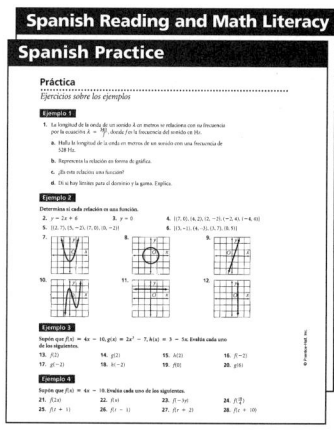

Learning Styles

Student Edition
- Investigation: pp. 247, 261
- Technology: p. 253
- Writing: pp. 239, 245, 250, 257, 265, 270, 278

Activity Masters
Hands-On Activities: 11, 12
Technology Activities:

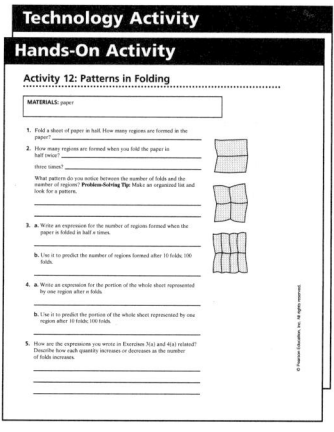

Program Resources

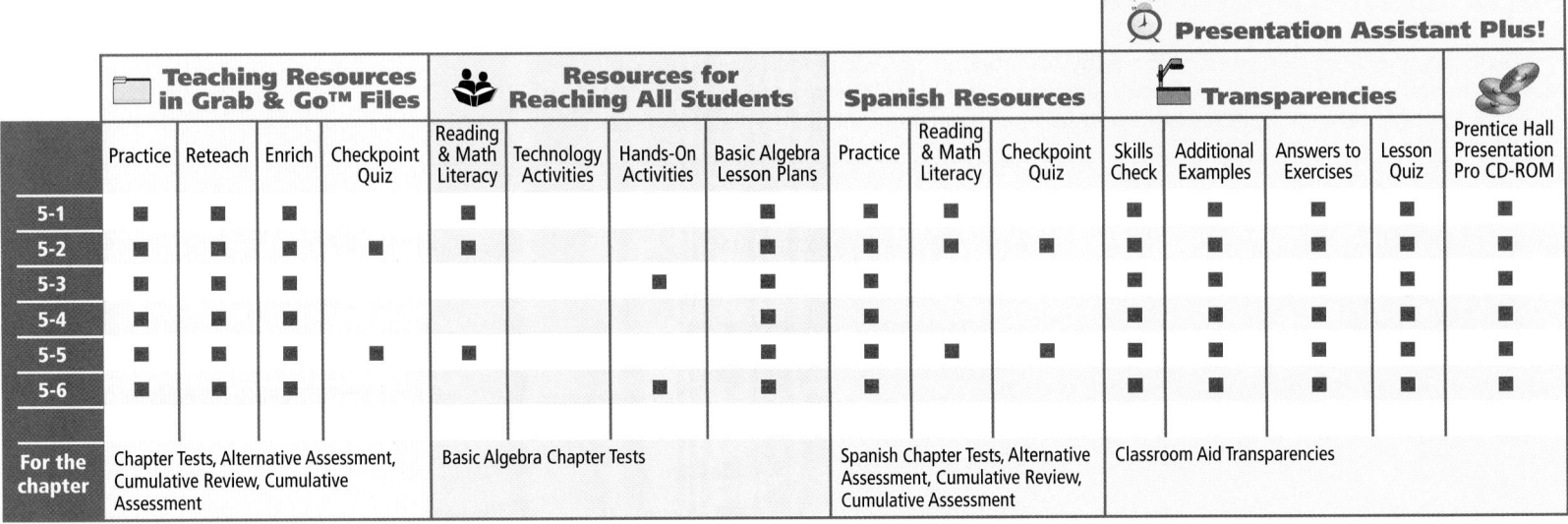

	Teaching Resources in Grab & Go™ Files				Resources for Reaching All Students				Spanish Resources			Transparencies				Presentation Assistant Plus!
	Practice	Reteach	Enrich	Checkpoint Quiz	Reading & Math Literacy	Technology Activities	Hands-On Activities	Basic Algebra Lesson Plans	Practice	Reading & Math Literacy	Checkpoint Quiz	Skills Check	Additional Examples	Answers to Exercises	Lesson Quiz	Prentice Hall Presentation Pro CD-ROM
5-1	■	■	■		■			■	■	■		■	■	■	■	■
5-2	■	■	■	■	■			■	■	■	■	■	■	■	■	■
5-3	■	■	■				■	■	■			■	■	■	■	■
5-4	■	■	■					■	■			■	■	■	■	■
5-5	■	■	■	■	■			■	■	■	■	■	■	■	■	■
5-6	■	■	■		■		■	■	■				■	■	■	■
For the chapter	Chapter Tests, Alternative Assessment, Cumulative Review, Cumulative Assessment				Basic Algebra Chapter Tests				Spanish Chapter Tests, Alternative Assessment, Cumulative Review, Cumulative Assessment			Classroom Aid Transparencies				

Also available for use with the chapter:

 *See page 234C.*

- Practice Workbook
- Solution Key

- For teacher support and access to student Web site materials, use Web Code aek-5500.
- For additional online and technology resources, see below.

 ## Technology

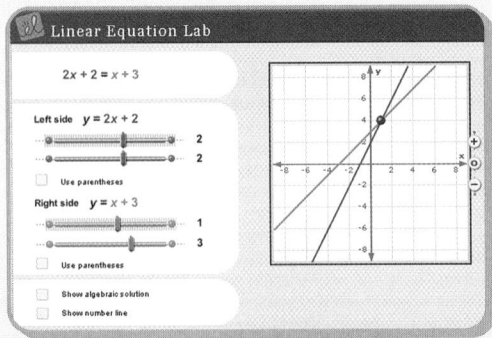

iTEXT Online and on CD-ROM

Complete Interactive Student Text online and on CD-ROM—with instant feedback assessment, tutorial help, dynamic activities, instructional and real-world videos, audio, and additional practice.

 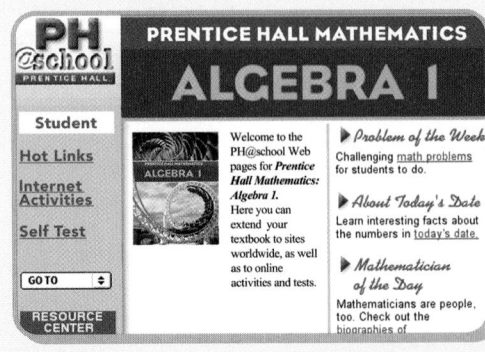

www.PHSchool.com For Students

Use **Web codes** for easy access to online activities, chapter projects, self-grading lesson quizzes and chapter tests, vocabulary quizzes, updated data sources, graphing calculator procedures, and more.

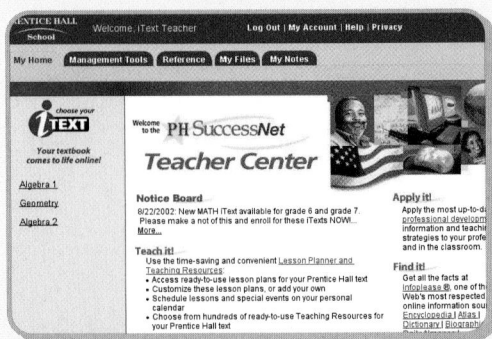

PH SuccessNet For Teachers

Online lesson planning with built-in state correlations, all the teaching resources, complete reference library, your own calendar and Teacher Web page, professional development, and more.

Presentation Assistant Plus!

The Prentice Hall *Presentation Assistant Plus!* provides you with the material you need to teach a lesson from beginning to end. Two easy-to-use formats—Transparencies and CD-ROM—allow you to present a lesson the way you are most comfortable.

Transparencies

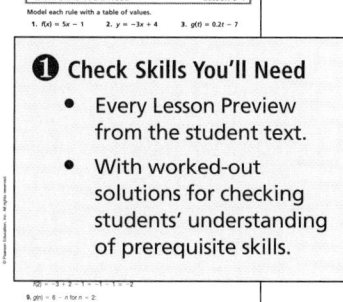

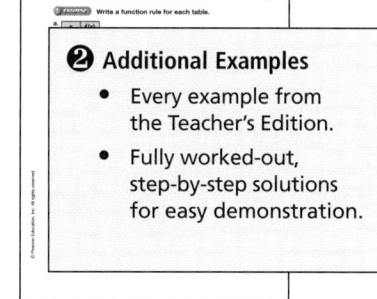

❶ **Check Skills You'll Need**
- Every Lesson Preview from the student text.
- With worked-out solutions for checking students' understanding of prerequisite skills.

❷ **Additional Examples**
- Every example from the Teacher's Edition.
- Fully worked-out, step-by-step solutions for easy demonstration.

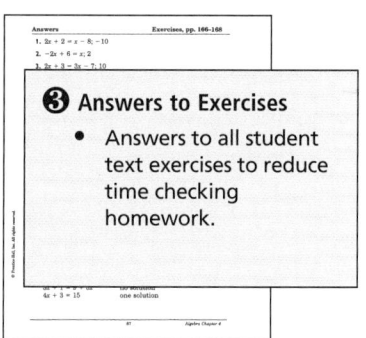

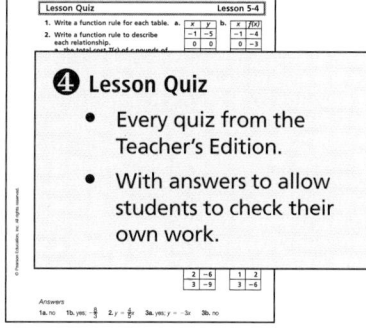

❸ **Answers to Exercises**
- Answers to all student text exercises to reduce time checking homework.

❹ **Lesson Quiz**
- Every quiz from the Teacher's Edition.
- With answers to allow students to check their own work.

 Throughout the Teacher's Edition, this symbol indicates material that is available on transparency in the Presentation Assistant Plus!

Prentice Hall Presentation Pro CD-ROM

- Includes all Transparencies.
- Conveniently organized by lesson so you can easily ❶ Introduce, ❷ Teach, ❸ Check Homework, and ❹ Assess each lesson.
- Animated examples allow step-by-step instruction at your own pace.
- Easy to edit so you can create custom presentations.

Teaching Chapter 5 Using Presentation Assistant Plus!

	❶ Introduce	❷ Teach	❸ Check Homework	❹ Assess
	Check Skills You'll Need	Additional Examples	Student Edition Answers	Lesson Quiz
5-1	p. 29	pp. 55–56	✔	p. 104
5-2	p. 30	pp. 56–58	✔	p. 104
5-3	p. 31	pp. 59–60	✔	p. 105
5-4	p. 32	pp. 61–62	✔	p. 106
5-5	p. 33	pp. 63–65	✔	p. 106
5-6	p. 34	p. 66	✔	p. 107

Prentice Hall Presentation Pro

CD-ROM with dynamic PowerPoint® presentations for every lesson. Helps you introduce and develop concepts, check homework, and assess progress. Part of Presentation Assistant Plus! *(See above.)*

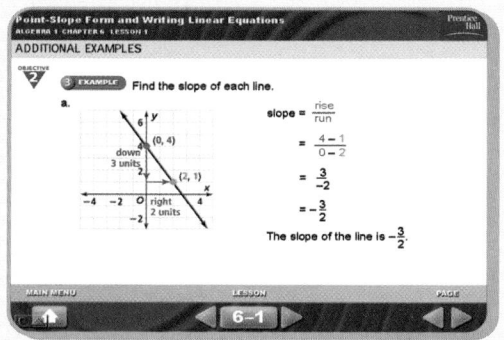

Computer Test Generator

CD-ROM to create practice sheets and tests for course objectives and standardized tests. Includes Instant Chapter Tests™, online testing, and student reports. Part of the PH Assessment System. *(See page 234C.)*

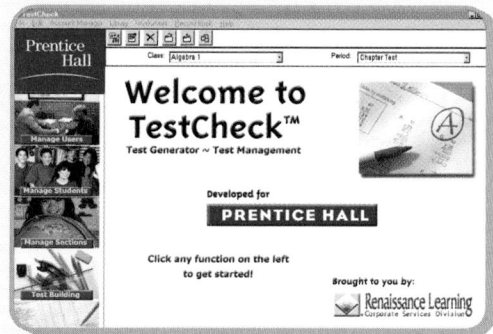

Resource Pro® with Planning Express®

CD-ROM with a lesson planning tool that allows you to import state and local objectives. Includes electronic versions of all the teaching resources.

Graphs and Functions

 Diagnosing Readiness

Students will find answers to these exercises in the back of their textbooks.

For intervention, direct students to:

Writing Equations
Lesson 1-1: Example 3
Exercises 17–20
Extra Practice, p. 702

Evaluating Expressions
Lesson 1-2: Examples 2 and 5
Exercises 11–12
Extra Practice, p. 702

Graphing on the Coordinate Plane
Lesson 1-9: Example 2
Exercises 5–8
Extra Practice, p. 702

Solving Absolute Value Equations
Lesson 3-6: Example 2
Exercises 16–21
Extra Practice, p. 704

Using Cross Products
Lesson 4-1: Example 4
Exercises 22–25
Extra Practice, p. 705

page 234 Diagnosing Readiness

8-11.
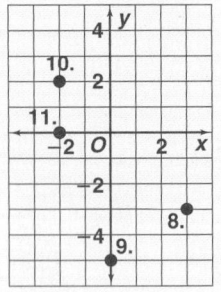

Where You've Been

- In Chapter 1, you learned to represent relationships using variables, and you reviewed graphing points on a coordinate plane.

- In Chapter 2, you learned the methods for solving equations in one variable. In Chapter 3, you applied those methods to solving inequalities and in Chapter 4, to solving proportions.

 Instant self-check online and on CD-ROM

Diagnosing Readiness (For help, go to the Lesson in green.)

Writing Equations (Lesson 1-1)

Define a variable and write an equation to model each situation.

1. The total price is the number of pens times $.59.
Let n = number of pens and t = total price; $t = 0.59n$.
2. The tower is 200 feet taller than the house.
Let h = height of house and t = height of tower; $t = h + 200$.
3. What is the perimeter of an equilateral triangle?
Let s = length of a side and p = perimeter; $p = 3s$.

Evaluating Expressions (Lesson 1-2)

Evaluate each expression.

4. $3x - 2y$, for $x = -1$ and $y = 2$ **−7**
5. $-w^2 + 3w$, for $w = -3$ **−18**
6. $\frac{3 + k}{k}$, for $k = 3$ **2**
7. $h - (h^2 - 1) \div 2$, for $h = -1$ **−1**

Graphing on the Coordinate Plane (Lesson 1-9)

Graph the points on the same coordinate plane. **8–11. See margin.**

8. $(3, -3)$ **9.** $(0, -5)$ **10.** $(-2, 2)$ **11.** $(-2, 0)$

Solving Absolute Value Equations (Lesson 3-6)

Solve each equation. If there is no solution, write *no solution*.

12. $|r + 2| = 2$ **−4, 0** **13.** $-3|d - 5| = -6$ **3, 7** **14.** $-3.2 = |8p|$ **no solution**

Using Cross Products (Lesson 4-1)

Solve the following proportions.

15. $\frac{4}{w} = \frac{5}{8}$ **$6\frac{2}{5}$** **16.** $\frac{c}{2.2} = \frac{3}{11}$ **0.6** **17.** $\frac{4}{0.5} = \frac{36}{p}$ **4.5** **18.** $-\frac{29}{2} = \frac{d}{4}$ **−58**

Graphs and Functions

Where You're Going

- In this chapter, you will move from the specific case of equations in one variable to the study of functions in two variables.

- You will learn about function rules, and model data using equations, tables, and graphs.

- You will learn how to use inductive reasoning for recognizing number patterns called sequences.

Real-World Connection Applying what you learn, you will solve a problem using sequences to describe a pattern relating the frequencies of musical notes, on page 271.

LESSONS

5-1 Relating Graphs to Events

5-2 Relations and Functions

5-3 Function Rules, Tables, and Graphs

5-4 Writing a Function Rule

5-5 Direct Variation

5-6 Describing Number Patterns

Key Vocabulary

- arithmetic sequence (p. 269)
- common difference (p. 269)
- conjecture (p. 268)
- constant of variation (p. 262)
- dependent variable (p. 248)
- direct variation (p. 262)
- domain (p. 241)
- function (p. 242)
- function notation (p. 243)
- function rule (p. 243)
- independent variable (p. 248)
- inductive reasoning (p. 268)
- range (p. 241)
- relation (p. 241)
- sequence (p. 269)
- term (p. 269)
- vertical-line test (p. 242)

Chapter 5 Overview

This chapter helps students build on their knowledge of equations by relating a graph to the story it tells and to the equation whose solutions it pictures. Students read and use functional notation as they model function rules with tables and graphs. They then identify direct variations and find constants of variation. The vocabulary of sequences is introduced. Students find the common difference for an arithmetic sequence and write rules for arithmetic sequences.

Reading Math
Reading a Graph, p. 260.

Vocabulary
A complete list of terms, plus vocabulary exercises, appears in the Chapter Review, p. 275.

Illustrated Glossary
Examples for each vocabulary term, plus definitions in both English and Spanish, appear starting on p. 757.

Test-Taking Strategies
Using a Variable, p. 274.

Real-World Connections
Some of the applications you will find in this chapter are cooking (5-1), business (5-2), water conservation (5-3), and weather (5-5).

www.PHSchool.com
Internet support for this chapter includes:
- Self-grading Vocabulary and Chapter 5 Tests
- Chapter Project
- Chapter Planner
- Chapter 5 Resources

Plus **iTEXT**

235

Lesson Preview

✓ **Check Skills You'll Need**

Graphing Data on the Coordinate Plane
Lesson 1-9: Example 1
Exercises 1–4
Extra Practice, p. 702

Lesson Resources

📁 **Teaching Resources**
Practice, Reteaching, Enrichment

👥 **Reaching All Students**
Practice Workbook 5-1
Spanish Practice Workbook 5-1
Reading and Math Literacy 5A
Spanish Reading & Literacy 5A
Basic Algebra Planning Guide 5-1

⏰ **Presentation Assistant Plus!**
Transparencies
• Check Skills You'll Need 5-1
• Additional Examples 5-1
• Student Edition Answers 5-1
• Lesson Quiz 5-1
PH Presentation Pro CD 5-1

ASSESSMENT SYSTEM

Computer Test Generator CD

💿 **Technology**
Resource Pro® CD-ROM
Computer Test Generator CD
Prentice Hall Presentation Pro CD

💻 **www.PHSchool.com**
Student Site
• Teacher Web Code: aek-5500
• Self-grading Lesson Quiz
Teacher Center
• Lesson Planner
• Resources

Plus 🔲**TEXT**

Lesson Preview

What You'll Learn

OBJECTIVE 1
To interpret, sketch, and analyze graphs from situations

. . . And Why

To use a sketch in showing a plane's altitude during a flight, as in Example 2

✓ **Check Skills You'll Need**
(For help, go to Lesson 1-9.)

Use the graph at the right.

Name the point with the given coordinates.

1. $(4, -2)$ **C**   **2.** $(4, 3)$ **D**

3. $(2, -4)$ **E**   **4.** $(-2, 1)$ **A**

Name the coordinates of each given point.

5. B **(0, 0)**   **6.** F **(−4, −2)**   **7.** G **(−3, 3)**

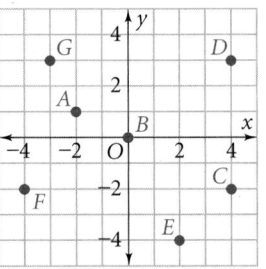

OBJECTIVE 1

🔲**TEXT** Interactive lesson includes instant self-check, tutorials, and activities.

Interpreting, Sketching, and Analyzing Graphs

You can use an equation, an inequality, or a proportion to make a statement about a variable. You can use a graph to show the relationship between two variables. For example, you can use a graph to show how a quantity changes over time.

1 EXAMPLE **Interpreting Graphs**

Commute One student walks and takes a bus to get from school to home each day. The graph at the right shows the student's commute by relating the time the student spends commuting and the distance he travels.

Describe what the graph shows by labeling each part.

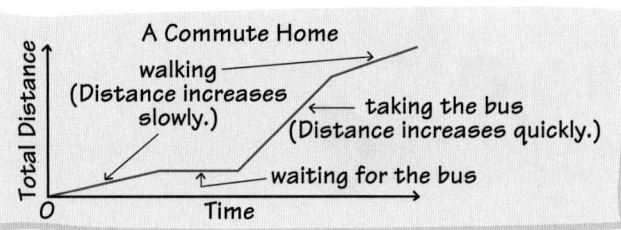

✓ **Check Understanding** **1** The graph at the right shows a trip from home to school and back. The trip involves walking and getting a ride from a neighbor. Copy the graph and label each section. **See back of book.**

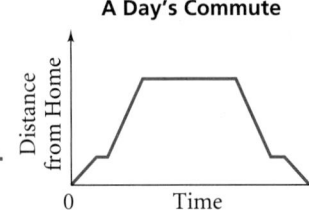

Ongoing Assessment and Intervention

Before the Lesson	During the Lesson	After the Lesson
Diagnose prerequisite skills using:	**Monitor progress using:**	**Assess knowledge using:**
• Check Skills You'll Need	• Check Understanding • Additional Examples • Standardized Test Prep	• Lesson Quiz • Computer Test Generator CD

Real-World Connection

The Statue of Liberty, in New York harbor, is 151 ft from base to torch. The clock tower, which is part of the Houses of Parliament in London, is 320 ft tall.

✔ **Check Understanding**

2.

Height While Jumping Rope

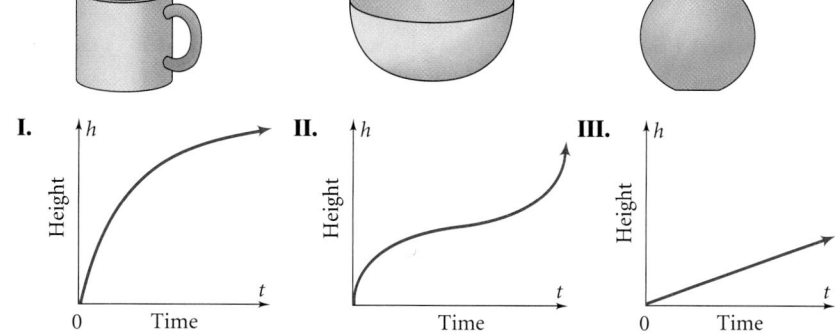

In Example 1, distance, which is on the vertical axis, depends on time, which is on the horizontal axis. When one quantity depends on another, show the dependent quantity on the vertical axis.

2 EXAMPLE Sketching a Graph

Travel A plane is flying from New York to London. Sketch a graph of the plane's altitude during the flight. Label each section.

2 Sketch a graph of the distance from a child's feet to the ground as the child jumps rope. Label each section. **See left.**

Most of the graphs in this lesson do not have numbers along the axes. You can analyze a graph based on the shape of the graph alone.

3 EXAMPLE Analyzing Graphs

A car travels at a steady speed. Which graph could you use to show the speed of the car, and which could you use to show the distance it has traveled? Explain.

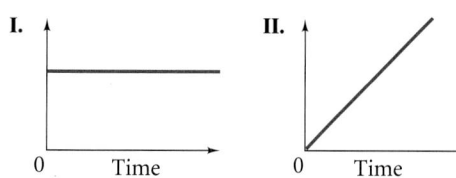

Graph I indicates a quantity that does not change with time. You could use it to indicate a car going at a steady speed. Graph II shows an increase over time. You could use it to indicate the distance a car travels at a steady speed over a given amount of time.

✔ **Check Understanding**

3. A. III
   B. I
   C. II

The height of the water in A will increase at a steady rate. The rate that the water rises in B will decrease steadily because it gets wider from the bottom to the top. The rate that the water rises in C will decrease as it gets wider and then increase as it gets narrower towards the top.

3 Suppose you pour water into each container below at a steady rate. Match each container with the graph that shows the change in the height of the liquid in the container over time. Explain your choices. **See left.**

Lesson 5-1 Relating Graphs to Events **237**

Professional Development

Math Background

Graphs relating time with speed or distance do not contain vertical lines. This would mean that multiple speeds are being traveled at the same time or that the object is at multiple distances at the one time. Neither of these are possible.

OBJECTIVE
1 Teaching Notes

1 EXAMPLE Teaching Tip

Ask students: *Could this graph contain a vertical line?* Explain. **No; a vertical line would mean traveling some distance in zero time.**

Additional Examples

1 Describe what this graph shows by labeling each part.

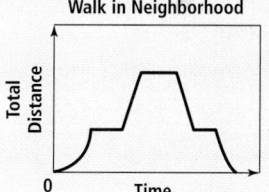

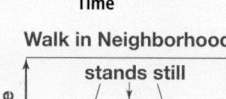

2 Sketch a graph of the altitude of a pelican, from take off from shore to diving to the water to catch a fish. Label each section.

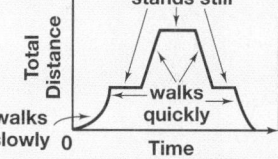

3 Describe the graph of a car that is parked. **The graph would be a horizontal line on the horizontal axis.**

Closure

Ask students to draw a graph representing their commutes from school to home.

237

👥 Reaching All Students

| **Below Level** To help students focus on what their graph will show in Check Understanding 2, make sure they label the axes and write the title of the graph before they begin drawing it. | **Advanced Learners** Have students redraw the graph from Check Understanding 1, but this time showing how the distance from school changes over time. | **English Learners** See note on page 238. **Error Prevention** See note on page 240. |

For more practice, see *Extra Practice*.

EXERCISES

Practice and Problem Solving

Assignment Guide

▼ 1 Objective
 Ⓐ Ⓑ Core 1–17
 Ⓒ Extension 18–22

Standardized Test Prep 23–25

Mixed Review 26–49

Exercises 5–8 Suggest to students that they ask themselves if the graph will return to zero, or ever be zero.

English Learners

Exercise 13 Help students not familiar with the English language understand the phrase "constant rate." You might show them how the second hand on a clock moves at a constant rate.

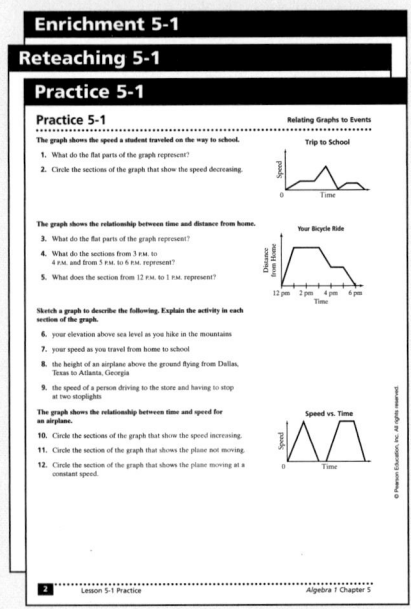

Ⓐ Practice by Example

Example 1
(page 236)

Copy each graph. Label each section of the graph. 1–4. See back of book.

1.
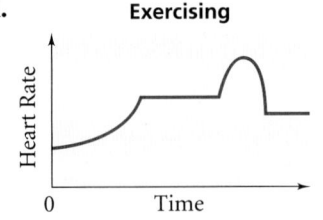

2.
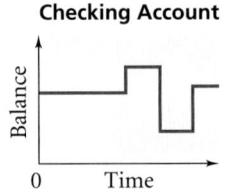

3.
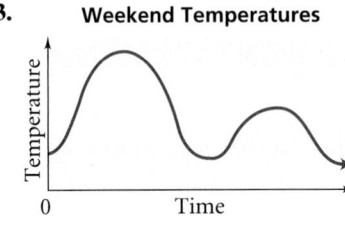

4.
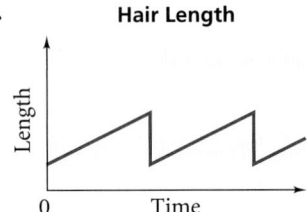

Example 2
(page 237)

Sketch a graph of each situation. Label each section. 5–8. See back of book.

5. hours of daylight over the course of one year

6. your distance from the ground as you ride a Ferris wheel for five minutes

7. your pulse rate as you watch a scary movie

8. your walking speed during five minutes between classes

Example 3
(page 237)

9. **Cooking** You turn on your oven to bake a casserole. Which graph best represents the oven temperature over time? Explain your choice. **See margin.**

A.
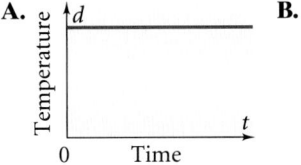

B.
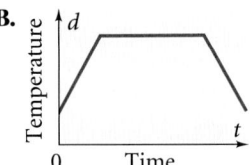

C.
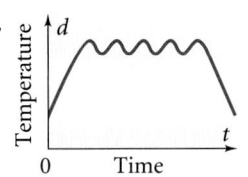

Ⓑ Apply Your Skills

10. The pressure dropped from 7 A.M. to 3 P.M., stayed about the same until 9 P.M., and then generally rose until 7 A.M. the next day.

 10. **Weather** The graph shows the barometric pressure in Pittsburgh, Pennsylvania, during a blizzard. Describe what happened to the pressure during the storm. **See left.**

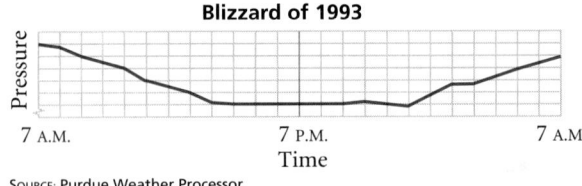

Blizzard of 1993

SOURCE: Purdue Weather Processor

11. Sketch graphs of each situation. Are the graphs the same? Explain.
 a. Your speed as you travel from the bottom of a ski slope to the top.
 b. Your speed as you travel from the top of a ski slope to the bottom.
 a–b. See back of book.

238 Chapter 5 Graphs and Functions

pages 238–240 Exercises

9. C; the temperature increases steadily and then alternates cooling and warming as the oven turns off and on during a cooking cycle.

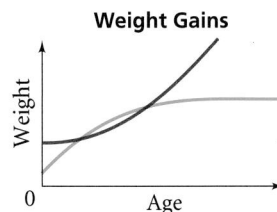

Weight Gains

12b. The baby weighs more at first and gains weight steadily for a number of years. The puppy's weight levels off at an earlier age.

14. It shows a person bicycling down and then up a hill because speed increases on the way down and decreases on the way up.

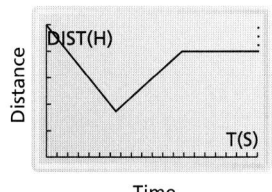

Time

16. A; one's growth rate is not steady, as shown in B. Also, as one gets older, one's height decreases slightly.

12. The graph at the left shows the weight of a baby and the weight of a puppy for their first two years.
  ✏ **a.** Which curve represents the puppy's weight? The baby's weight? **blue; red**
   b. Writing Describe the growth patterns of the baby and the puppy. **See left.**

13. You pour juice into a pitcher like the one shown in the photographs below. You pour the juice at a constant rate. Make a sketch to show the height of juice in the pitcher as you fill it. **See margin.**

14. Error Analysis The graph at the right shows a person's speed over the course of a bike ride. Your friend said that this graph describes a person bicycling up and then down a hill. Explain your friend's error. **See left.**

Speed on a Bike Ride

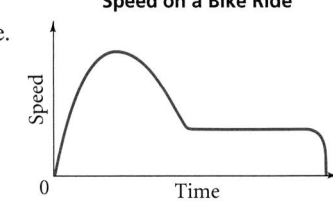

15. A student used a graphing calculator, a data collector, and a motion detector to make the graph at the left, which shows a classmate's distance from the motion detector.
   a. Copy the graph and label each section. **a–b. See margin.**
   b. During which section was the student walking toward the motion detector?
   c. During which section(s) was the student walking at a constant speed? **first 2 sections**

16. Which graph better represents a person's change in height from birth to age 80? Explain your choice. **See left.**

A. 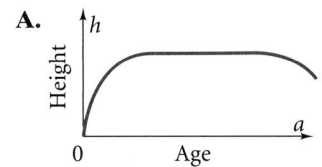   **B.**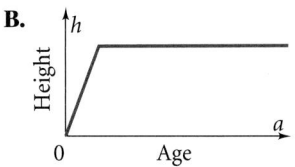

🌐 **17. a. Open-Ended** Sketch a graph of the daily high temperature over the course of one year for your town. **Check students' work.**
   b. Critical Thinking How would your graph be different if you lived at the equator? **A graph of temperatures at the equator would show little change for daily high temperatures.**

C **Challenge**

Use the graph at the right for Exercises 18–21.

Parking Garage Costs

18. How much does it cost to park for 2 hours? **$3**
19. How much does it cost to park for 121 minutes? **$6**
20. Suppose your mother pays $6 for parking. About how long was her car parked in the garage? **more than 2 h up to 4 h**
21. Vocabulary This graph is a *step graph*. Does this name make sense? Explain. **Answers may vary. Sample: Yes, the line segments make the graph look like steps.**

Lesson 5-1 Relating Graphs to Events   **239**

13. Answers may vary. Sample:

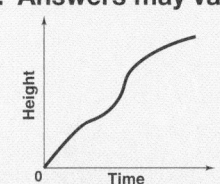

📝 **Lesson Quiz 5-1**

Person's Height

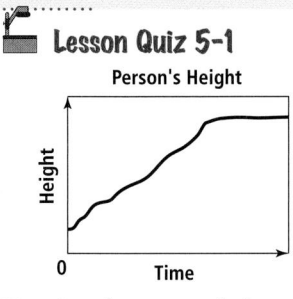

Use the above graph for questions 1–3.

1. Why does this graph not start at zero? **A person's height is not zero when born.**

2. Why is the graph not a straight slanted line? **A straight line represents a constant rate of growth and people do not grow that way.**

3. What does the flat part at the top of the graph represent? **The person has stayed the same height over a long period of time.**

4. Would a horizontal line, a straight slanted line, a curve, or a jagged curve best represent the calories you burn during the day? **a jagged curve**

Alternative Assessment

Group students in pairs. Have each student sketch a graph. Then have students exchange graphs with their partners. Instruct students to write a situation for the graph and label it accordingly.

15a.

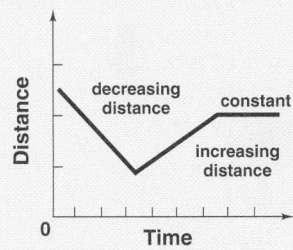

b. section showing the distance decreasing

239

Standardized Test Prep

Error Prevention

Exercise 25 Suggest to students that they first determine if the increase in height gets faster over time or slower over time. Then have students look at the hourglasses. I, II, and III are all wide at the bottom. IV is narrow at the bottom. Students should first determine if the hour glass that is least like the others will work.

pages 238–240 Exercises

22a. Answers may vary. Sample: The student started skating and got to cruising speed. After a while, the student sped up going downhill, lost control, and crashed. After getting up, the student decided not to go as fast.

b. Answers may vary. Sample:

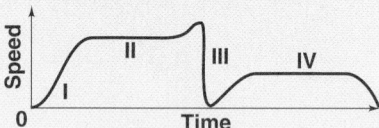

In-Line Skating After School

I–speeding up;
II–cruising; III–crash;
IV–slower speed

25. [2] IV; the graph rises sharply at first and then slows. This indicates that the container is narrow at the bottom and wide at the top.

[1] chooses correct graph but explanation is incomplete OR chooses the wrong graph but supports choice

 22. In-Line Skating a. Describe what the graph at the right shows about a student's in-line skating experience.
b. Label each section.
a–b. See margin.

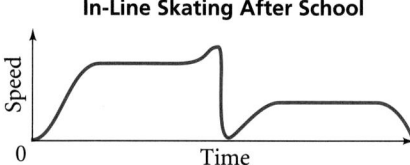
In-Line Skating After School

Standardized Test Prep

Multiple Choice

The graph at the right shows the distance Molly was from home throughout Tuesday. She spent about six hours at school, one hour at a friend's house, and about 30 minutes waiting for a bus. She also walked and rode the bus part of the day. Use the graph for Exercises 23–24.

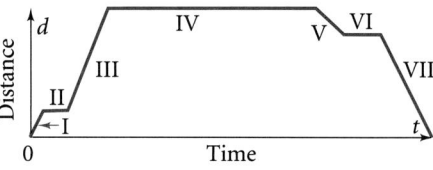

23. What section most likely represents walking to the bus stop? **D**
   A. I   **B.** II   **C.** IV   **D.** V

24. What section most likely represents spending time at a friend's house? **H**
   F. II   **G.** IV   **H.** VI   **I.** VII

Short Response

25. An hourglass has two compartments that hold sand. The graph at the right shows the height of the sand in the bottom container as it fills. Which hourglass does the graph represent? Explain your choice.
See margin.

      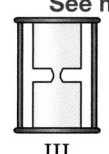   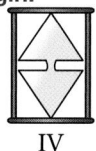
     I   II   III   IV

Take It to the NET
Online lesson quiz at
www.PHSchool.com
Web Code: aea-0501

Mixed Review

Lesson 4-6

You roll a red number cube and a blue number cube. Find each probability.

26. $P(\text{red 1 and blue 6})\ \frac{1}{36}$ **27.** $P(\text{red 3 and blue 5})\ \frac{1}{36}$ **28.** $P(\text{red} > 4 \text{ and blue 5})\ \frac{1}{18}$

29. $P(\text{red odd and blue 3})\ \frac{1}{12}$ **30.** $P(\text{red and blue even})\ \frac{1}{4}$ **31.** $P(\text{red and blue equal})\frac{1}{6}$

Lesson 3-4

Solve each inequality. 32–37. See left.

32. $x < 7$
33. $x < 8$
34. $x \geq -2$
35. $x > -4$
36. $x \leq -13$
37. $x < \frac{2}{3}$

32. $5x + 2 < 37$ **33.** $x + 4 > 2x - 4$ **34.** $8x + 4 - 3x \geq 3x$

35. $7 > -4x - 9$ **36.** $7(x + 1) \leq 6(x - 1)$ **37.** $-2 + 5x < 8 - 10x$

Lesson 2-1

Solve each equation.

38. $4t = 44$ **11**   **39.** $x - 8 = 9$ **17**   **40.** $\frac{d}{3} = 15$ **45**   **41.** $-9 = m + 6$ **−15**

42. $y + 18 = 2$ **−16** **43.** $\frac{k}{7} = 42$ **294**   **44.** $1.2q = 7.2$ **6**   **45.** $g + 22 = 25$ **3**

46. $-1 = p - 8$ **7**   **47.** $3x = 123$ **41**   **48.** $b - 78 = 101$ **179**   **49.** $2c = \frac{1}{2}$ **$\frac{1}{4}$**

Relations and Functions

 North Carolina Objectives   4.01   Use linear functions or inequalities to model and solve problems; justify results. a) Solve using tables, graphs, and algebraic properties.

Lesson Preview

What You'll Learn

OBJECTIVE **1**   To identify relations and functions

OBJECTIVE **2**   To evaluate functions

. . . And Why

To determine whether a relation is a function, as in Examples 2 and 3

✓ Check Skills You'll Need

(For help, go to Lessons 1-9 and 1-2.)

Graph each point on a coordinate plane. 1–4. See back of book.

1. $(2, -4)$ **2.** $(0, 3)$ **3.** $(-1, -2)$ **4.** $(-3, 0)$

Evaluate each expression.

5. $3a - 2$ for $a = -5$ **-17**   **6.** $\frac{x+3}{-6}$ for $x = 3$ **-1**   **7.** $3x^2$ for $x = 6$ **108**

New Vocabulary   • relation   • domain   • range   • function   • vertical-line test   • function rule   • function notation

---

OBJECTIVE

1   **Identifying Relations and Functions**

Real-World Connection

Adult giraffes have heights from 4.25 m to 5.5 m, or about 14 ft to 18 ft.

A **relation** is a set of ordered pairs. The (age, height) ordered pairs below form a relation.

Giraffes

Age (years)	Height (meters)
18	4.25
20	4.40
21	5.25
14	5.00
18	4.85

age   height
↓   ↓
(18,   4.25)
(20,   4.40)
(21,   5.25)
(14,   5.00)
(18,   4.85)

The **domain** of a relation is the set of first coordinates of the ordered pairs. The **range** is the set of second coordinates.

1 **EXAMPLE**   Finding Domain and Range

Find the domain and range of the ordered pairs listed for the giraffe data above.

domain: $\{14, 18, 20, 21\}$ **List the values in order. Do not repeat values.**
range: $\{4.25, 4.40, 4.85, 5.00, 5.25\}$

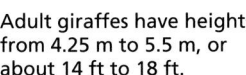 **Check Understanding**   ❶ Find the domain and range of the relation represented by the data in the table. **{−2, −1, 4}, {−2, 1, 3}**

Domain	Range
4	3
−2	1
−1	3
4	−2
−1	1

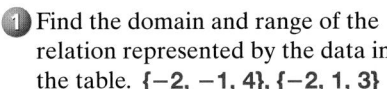 **Ongoing Assessment and Intervention**

Before the Lesson
Diagnose prerequisite skills using:
• Check Skills You'll Need

During the Lesson
Monitor progress using:
• Check Understanding
• Additional Examples
• Standardized Test Prep

After the Lesson
Assess knowledge using:
• Lesson Quiz
• Computer Test Generator CD
• Chapter Checkpoint 1 (p. 246)

Lesson Preview

✓ **Check Skills You'll Need**

Graphing Data on the Coordinate Plane
Lesson 1-9: Example 2
Exercises 5–8
Extra Practice, p. 702

Exponents and Order of Operations
Lesson 1-2: Example 2
Exercises 7–12
Extra Practice, p. 702

Lesson Resources

📁 **Teaching Resources**
Practice, Reteaching, Enrichment
Checkpoint Quiz 1

👥 **Reaching All Students**
Practice Workbook 5-2
Spanish Practice Workbook 5-2
Reading and Math Literacy 5B
Spanish Reading & Literacy 5B
Spanish Checkpoint Quiz 1
Basic Algebra Planning Guide 5-2

⏱ **Presentation Assistant Plus!**
Transparencies
• Check Skills You'll Need 5-2
• Additional Examples 5-2
• Student Edition Answers 5-2
• Lesson Quiz 5-2
PH Presentation Pro CD 5-2

PRENTICE HALL ASSESSMENT SYSTEM
Checkpoint Quiz 1
Computer Test Generator CD

💿 **Technology**
Resource Pro® CD-ROM
Computer Test Generator CD
Prentice Hall Presentation Pro CD

💻 **www.PHSchool.com**
Student Site
• Teacher Web Code: aek-5500
• Reasoning & Puzzles p. 89
• Self-grading Lesson Quiz
Teacher Center
• Lesson Planner
• Resources

Plus

241

2. Teach

Professional Development

Math Background

Functions and relations do not need to involve numbers. For example, the relationship that assigns a color to each pixel on a computer screen is a function.

OBJECTIVE

1 Teaching Notes

1 EXAMPLE Auditory Learners

Have students repeat the following, one sentence at a time: Alphabetically, *d* is before *r*, so *domain* is before *range*. Since *x* is before *y* alphabetically, *domain* corresponds to *x* and *range* corresponds to *y*. Therefore, *domain* refers to the first, or *x*-values, and *range* to the second, or *y*-values.

2 EXAMPLE Teaching Tip

Sketch the following graphs on the board or overhead projector. Then let student volunteers perform the vertical line test using a pencil or a yardstick.

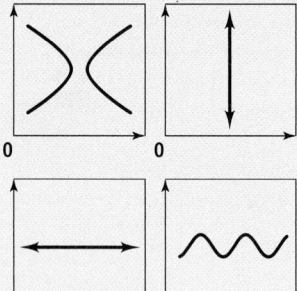

3 EXAMPLE Alternative Method

List all the *x*-values in Question a. Ask: *Do any x-values repeat?* no Repeat for Question b. yes Stress to students that if an *x*-value repeats and has a different *y*-value, there will be more than one point on the vertical line passing through the *x*-value. This violates the vertical-line test. Have students sketch each set of points so they can see the alignment of the points.

242

  Key Concepts

Definition	Function

A **function** is a relation that assigns exactly one value in the range to each value in the domain.

One way you can tell whether a relation is a function is to analyze the graph of the relation using the **vertical-line test.** If any vertical line passes through more than one point of the graph, the relation is not a function.

2 EXAMPLE Using the Vertical-Line Test

Determine whether the relation $\{(3, 0), (-2, 1), (0, -1), (-3, 2), (3, 2)\}$ is a function.

Step 1 Graph the ordered pairs on a coordinate plane.

Step 2 Pass a pencil across the graph as shown.

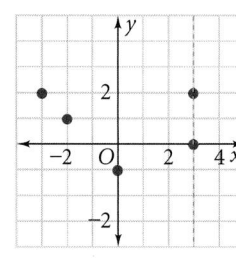 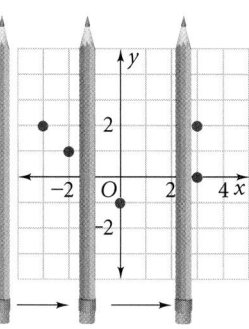

A vertical line would pass through both $(3, 0)$ and $(3, 2)$, so the relation is not a function.

✓ **Check Understanding** **2** Use the vertical-line test to determine whether each relation is a function.
  a. $\{(4, -2), (1, 2), (0, 1), (-2, 2)\}$ **b.** $\{(0, 2), (1, -1), (-1, 4), (0, -3), (2, 1)\}$
      function   not a function

Another way you can tell whether a relation is a function is by making a *mapping diagram*. List the domain values and the range values in order. Draw arrows from the domain values to their range values.

3 EXAMPLE Using a Mapping Diagram

Determine whether each relation is a function.
  a. $\{(11, -2), (12, -1), (13, -2), (20, 7)\}$ **b.** $\{(-2, -1), (-1, 0), (6, 3), (-2, 1)\}$

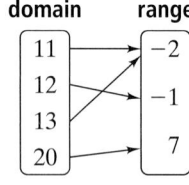 There is no value in the domain that corresponds to more than one value of the range.

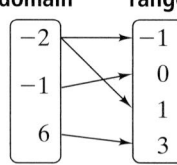 The domain value corresponds to two range values, −1 and 1.

? **Need Help?**

In a mapping diagram, functions have no more than one arrow starting from each value of the domain.

The relation is a function.

The relation is not a function.

✓ **Check Understanding** **3** Use a mapping diagram to determine whether each relation is a function.
  a. $\{(3, -2), (8, 1), (9, 2), (3, 3), (-4, 0)\}$ **b.** $\{(6.5, 0), (7, -1), (6, 2), (2, 6), (5, -1)\}$

      not a function   function

Chapter 5   Graphs and Functions

👪 Reaching All Students

Below Level Ask students to determine if the data in the two tables on p. 241 represent functions. Have them use the vertical-line test for one set of data and a mapping diagram for the other.	**Advanced Learners** Challenge students to find the meaning of $g(f(x))$.	**Auditory Learners** See note on page 242. **Error Prevention** See note on page 244.

242

A **function rule** is an equation that describes a function. You can think of a function rule as an input-output machine.

Words and Notations Used With a Function

Domain	Range
input	output
x	$f(x)$
x	y

The domain is the set of input values.

input

function rule

output

The range is the set of output values.

If you know the input values, you can use a function rule to find the output values. The output values depend on the input values.

$$y = 3x + 4$$

↑   ↑
output input

input values for x

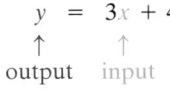

$3x + 4$

output values for y

Input	Output
x	y
1	7
2	10
3	13

Another way to write the function $y = 3x + 4$ is $f(x) = 3x + 4$. A function is in **function notation** when you use $f(x)$ to indicate the outputs. You read $f(x)$ as "f of x" or "f is a function of x." The notations $g(x)$ and $h(x)$ also indicate functions of x.

4 **EXAMPLE** **Evaluating a Function Rule**

a. Evaluate $f(n) = -3n - 10$ for $n = 6$. **b.** Evaluate $y = -2x^2 + 7$ for $x = -4$.

$f(n) = -3n - 10$

$f(6) = -3(6) - 10$ **Substitute 6 for n.**

$f(6) = -18 - 10$ **Simplify.**

$f(6) = -28$

$y = -2x^2 + 7$

$y = -2(-4)^2 + 7$ **Substitute −4 for x.**

$y = -2(16) + 7$ **Simplify the power.**

$y = -32 + 7$ **Simplify.**

$y = -25$

Reading Math

You can think of the notation $f(6)$ as "Replace n with 6 to find the value of $f(6)$."

✓ **Check Understanding** **4** Evaluate each function rule for $x = 2.1$.

a. $y = 2x + 1$ **b.** $f(x) = x^2 - 4$ **c.** $g(x) = -x + 2$
   5.2   **0.41**   **−0.1**

You can use a function rule and a given domain to find the range of the function. After computing the range values, write the values in order from least to greatest.

5 **EXAMPLE** **Finding the Range**

Evaluate the function rule $f(a) = -3a + 5$ to find the range of the function for the domain $\{-3, 1, 4\}$.

$f(a) = -3a + 5$

$f(-3) = -3(-3) + 5$

$f(-3) = 14$

$f(a) = -3a + 5$

$f(1) = -3(1) + 5$

$f(1) = 2$

$f(a) = -3a + 5$

$f(4) = -3(4) + 5$

$f(4) = -7$

The range is $\{-7, 2, 14\}$.

✓ **Check Understanding** **5** Find the range of each function for the domain $\{-2, 0, 5\}$.

a. $f(x) = x - 6$ **b.** $y = -4x$ **c.** $g(t) = t^2 + 1$
   {−8, −6, −1}   **{−20, 0, 8}**   **{1, 5, 26}**

Additional Examples

1 Find the domain and range of the ordered pairs.

age	weight
(14,	120)
(12,	110)
(18,	126)
(14,	125)
(16,	124)

domain: {12, 14, 16, 18}
range: {110, 120, 124, 125, 126}

2 Use the vertical-line test to determine whether the relation $\{(3, 2), (5, -1), (-5, 3), (-2, 2)\}$ is a function. **function**

3 Determine whether each relation is a function.
a. $\{(4, 3), (2, -1), (-3, -3), (2, 4)\}$
not a function
b. $\{(-4, 0), (2, 12), (-1, -3), (1, 5)\}$
function

5 **EXAMPLE** **Alternative Method**

Another way to find the values of the range is to input the function rule into the Y= function of the calculator. In TblSet, start at −3 and count by 1. Then press 2nd TABLE. Use the arrow keys to scroll up and down the table to find the necessary domain/range pairs.

Additional Examples

4 **a.** Evaluate $f(x) = -5x + 25$ for $x = -2$. **35**
b. Evaluate $y = 4x^2 + 2$ for $x = 3$. **38**

5 Evaluate the function rule $f(g) = -2g + 4$ to find the range for the domain $\{-1, 3, 5\}$.
$\{-6, -2, 6\}$

Closure

Have students explain the difference between a relation and a function. A relation is any set of ordered pairs. A function is a set of ordered pairs in which no x-value repeats with a different y-value.

243

Assignment Guide

 **Objective**

  Ⓐ Ⓑ **Core** 1–14, 27–31,
    33, 38–40

  Ⓒ **Extension** 47

 **Objective**

  Ⓐ Ⓑ **Core** 15–26, 32,
    34–37, 41–42

  Ⓒ **Extension** 43–46, 48

Standardized Test Prep 49–53

Mixed Review 54–66

Exercises 11–14 Suggest to
students that they check for
repeating *x*-values.

Error Prevention

Exercise 24 Remind students to
look at the values carefully. Since
the values are written in a list
with commas between them, they
may see −1.2 as −1, 2 if they are
not careful.

| Enrichment 5-2 |
| Reteaching 5-2 |
| Practice 5-2 |

Practice 5-2 .... Relations and Functions

EXERCISES

For more practice, see *Extra Practice*.

Practice and Problem Solving

Ⓐ **Practice by Example**

Example 1
(page 241)

Find the domain and range of each relation. 1–6. See margin.

1. $\{(4, 6), (6, 7), (4, 3), (5, 19), (5, 7)\}$ **2.** $\{(-3, 5), (-2, 8), (0, 7), (4, 22), (0, 5)\}$

3. $\{(2, -3), (-2, 3), (2, 3), (-2, -3), (3, -2)\}$ **4.** $\{(1, 0), (1, 5), (1, -7), (1, 6.1), (1, 10)\}$

5. $\{(1.2, 4), (-3.1, -5.2), (8.4, 0), (-3.1, 0)\}$ **6.** $\{(\frac{1}{2}, -1), (-\frac{2}{3}, -1), (4, \frac{3}{5}), (5, 0)\}$

Example 2
(page 242)

Use the vertical-line test to determine whether each relation is a function.

7. $\{(2, 5), (3, -5), (4, 5), (5, -5)\}$ **yes**   **8.** $\{(5, 0), (0, 5), (5, 1), (1, 5)\}$ **no**

9. $\{(3, -1), (-2, 3), (-1, -5), (3, 2)\}$ **no**   **10.** $\{(-2, 9), (3, 9), (-0.5, 9), (4, 9)\}$ **yes**

Example 3
(page 242)

Use a mapping diagram to determine whether each relation is a function.

11. $\{(3, 7), (3, 8), (3, -2), (3, 4), (3, 1)\}$ **no**   **12.** $\{(6, -7), (5, -8), (1, 4), (5, 5)\}$ **no**

13. $\{(0.04, 0.2), (0.2, 1), (1, 5), (5, 25)\}$ **yes**   **14.** $\{(4, 2), (1, 1), (0, 0), (1, -1), (4, -2)\}$ **no**

Example 4
(page 243)

Evaluate each function rule for $x = -3$.

15. $y = x + 7$ **4**   **16.** $y = 11x - 1$ **−34** **17.** $f(x) = x^2$ **9**   **18.** $f(x) = -4x$ **12**

19. $f(x) = 15 - x$ **18** **20.** $y = 3x + 2$ **−7**   **21.** $y = \frac{1}{4}x$ **$-\frac{3}{4}$**   **22.** $f(x) = -x + 2$ **5**

Example 5
(page 243)

Find the range of the function rule $y = 5x - 2$ for each domain.

23. $\{0.5, 11\}$
{0.5, 53}
     24. $\{-1.2, 0, 4\}$
{−8, −2, 18}
     25. $\{-5, -1, 0, 2, 10\}$
{−27, −7, −2, 8, 48}
     26. $\left\{-\frac{1}{2}, \frac{1}{4}, \frac{2}{5}\right\}$
$\left\{-4\frac{1}{2}, -\frac{3}{4}, 0\right\}$

Ⓑ **Apply Your Skills**

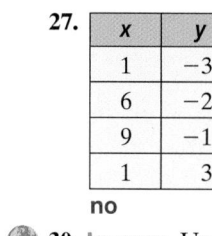

Iguanas

Age (years)	Length (inches)
2	30
4	37
3	31
5	45
4	40

Determine whether each relation is a function. If the relation is a function, state the domain and range.

27.

x	y
1	−3
6	−2
9	−1
1	3

no

28.

x	y
0	2
3	1
3	−1
5	3

no

29.

x	y
−4	−4
−1	−4
0	−4
3	−4

yes; {−4, −1, 0, 3}; {−4}

🌐 **30. Iguanas** Use the data in the table at the left. Is an iguana's length a function of its age? Explain. **No; two 4-year-old iguanas may have different lengths.**

31. Error Analysis A student thinks that the relation $\{(2, 1), (3, -2), (4, 5), (5, -2)\}$ is not a function because two values in the domain have the same range value. What is the student's error? **See margin.**

🌐 **32. a. Profit** A store bought a case of disposable cameras for $300. The store's profit *p* on the cameras is a function of the number *c* of cameras sold. Find the range of the function $p = 6c - 300$ when the domain is $\{0, 15, 50, 62\}$.
  b. Critical Thinking In this situation, what do the domain and range represent?
  a–b. See margin.

33. Open-Ended Create a data table for a relation that is *not* a function. Describe what your data might represent. **See margin p. 245.**

pages 244–246 Exercises

1. {4, 5, 6}, {3, 6, 7, 19}

2. {−3, −2, 0, 4}, {5, 7, 8, 22}

3. {−2, 2, 3}, {−3, −2, 3}

4. {1}, {−7, 0, 5, 6.1, 10}

5. {−3.1, 1.2, 8.4}, {−5.2, 0, 4}

6. $\left\{-\frac{2}{3}, \frac{1}{2}, 4, 5\right\}$, $\left\{-1, 0, \frac{3}{5}\right\}$

31. Answers may vary. Sample: A relation is not a function if two range values have the same domain value.

32a. {−300, −210, 0, 72}
  b. Domain is the number of cameras sold, and range is the profit.

Find the range of each function for the domain {−1, 0.5, 3.7}. 34–37. See left.

34. {−3, 3, 15.8}

35. {−13.8, −1, 5}

36. {−0.5, 0, 2.7}

37. {−0.75, 0, 12.69}

34. $f(x) = 4x + 1$ 35. $g(x) = -4x + 1$ 36. $y = |x| - 1$ 37. $s(t) = t^2 - 1$

Use the vertical-line test to determine whether each graph is the graph of a function.

38. 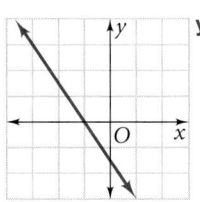 yes   39. 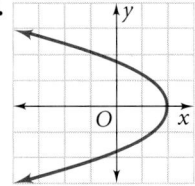 no   40. 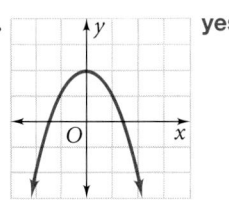 yes

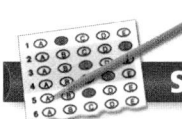

Real-World 🌐 **Connection**

A telecommunications device for the deaf (TDD) includes a keyboard and a visual display of the conversation. This lets a hearing-impaired person use a telephone.

41. **Telephone Bill** The cost of a long-distance telephone call c is a function of the time spent talking t in minutes. The rule $c(t) = 0.09t$ describes the function for one service provider. At the right, a student has calculated how much a 2-hour phone call would cost.

   a. **Writing** Why does the student's answer seem unreasonable? **a–b. See margin.**

   b. **Error Analysis** What mistake(s) did the student make?

   c. How much would it cost to make a 2-hour phone call? **$10.80**

   d. **Critical Thinking** What set of numbers is reasonable for the domain values? For the range values? **whole numbers; positive numbers**

$c = 0.09 \times 2$

$= 0.18$

$18 for 2 hours

42. **Physics** Light travels about 186,000 miles per second. The rule $d = 186,000t$ describes the relationship between distance d in miles and time t in seconds.

   a. How far does light travel in 20 seconds? **3,720,000 mi**

   b. How far does light travel in 1 minute? **11,160,000 mi**

🄲 **Challenge**

Use the functions $f(x) = 2x$ and $g(x) = x^2 + 1$ to find the value of each expression.

43. $f(3) + g(4)$ **23**   44. $g(3) + f(4)$ **18**   45. $f(5) - 2g(1)$ **6**   46. $f(g(3))$ **20**

47. Yes, it passes the vertical-line test; no, it doesn't pass the vertical-line test.

47. **Critical Thinking** Can the graph of a function be a horizontal line? A vertical line? Explain why or why not. **See left.**

48. The function $y = [x]$ is called the *greatest-integer function*. $[x]$ is the greatest integer less than or equal to x. For example, $[2.99] = 2$ and $[-2.3] = -3$.

   a. Evaluate the function for 0.5, −0.1, −1.99, and −5.2. **0, −1, −2, −6**

   b. The domain of $y = [x]$ is all real numbers. What is the range of $y = [x]$? **all integers**

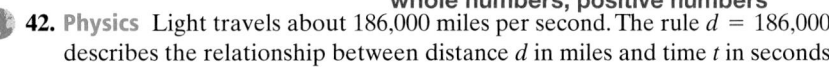
Standardized Test Prep

Gridded Response

49. Evaluate the function rule $f(x) = 7x$ for $x = 0.75$. **5.25**

50. Evaluate the function rule $f(x) = 9 - 0.2x$ for $x = 1.5$. **8.7**

51. What is the greatest value in the range of $y = x^2 - 7$ for the domain {−2, 0, 1}? **−3**

33. **Answers may vary. Sample:**

x	y
14	60
13	58
16	60
14	63

Data represent the ages (x) and heights (y) of 4 students.

41a. **Answers may vary. Sample: The cost**

appears to be far too little.

b. **Answers may vary. Sample: The student failed to convert hours to minutes.**

Lesson Quiz 5-2

1. a. Find the domain and range of the ordered pairs (1, 3), (−4, 0), (3, 1), (0, 4), (2, 3).
   domain: {−4, 0, 1, 2, 3}
   range: {0, 1, 3, 4}

   b. Use mapping to determine whether the relation is a function. **The relation is a function.**

2. Use the vertical-line test to determine whether each relation is a function.
   a. **no; b. yes**

   a.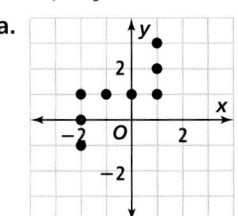

   b.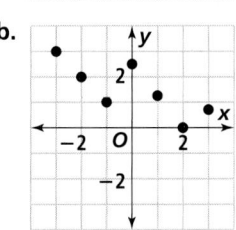

3. Find the range of the function $f(g) = 3g - 5$ for the domain {−1.5, 2, 4}. {−9.5, 1, 7}

Alternative Assessment

Organize students into groups of three. Have students draw a function machine such as the one shown in Lesson 5-2. One student writes a function rule on a sticky note and places it on the machine. Another student chooses a domain value, writes it on a sticky note and places it at the input. The third student finds the corresponding range value. Continue until each student has used a different domain value to find a range value. Repeat the whole process two more times, each time allowing a different student to write the function rule.

245

Standardized Test Prep

A sheet of blank grids is available in the Test-Taking Strategies with Transparencies booklet. Give this sheet to students for practice with filling in the grids.

 **Resources**

For additional practice with a variety of test item formats:
- Standardized Test Prep, p. 279
- Test-Taking Strategies, p. 274
- Test-Taking Strategies with Transparencies

Exercises 51, 52 Point out to students that since any number squared is positive, in Exercise 51 they should choose the domain value with the greatest absolute value. Since they are multiplying x by a positive number in Exercise 52, they should choose the domain value with the greatest value.

 **Chapter Checkpoint 1**

To check understanding of Lessons 5-1 to 5-2:

Checkpoint Quiz 1 (p. 246)

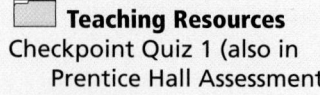 **Teaching Resources**
Checkpoint Quiz 1 (also in Prentice Hall Assessment System)

Reaching All Students
Reading and Math Literacy 5B

Spanish versions available

pages 244–246 Exercises

53. [2] Domain Range

65	→	58
74	→	69
80	→	72
93	→	84
98	→	91

(OR graph shown)
Yes, the data represent a function.

[1] shows calculation but no mapping diagram or graph

page 246 Checkpoint Quiz 1

1–3. Graphs may vary. Samples are given.

---

52. What is the greatest value in the domain of the function $f(x) = 3x - 5$ for the range $\{-2, 0, 4\}$? **3**

Short Response

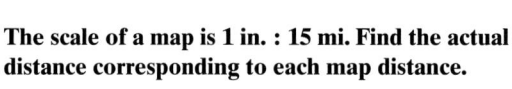 **Take It to the NET**
Online lesson quiz at
www.PHSchool.com
Web Code: aea-0502

53. Determine whether the data below are a function. Show your work.
See margin.

Mount Rushmore Temperatures (°F)

At Base of Mountain	At Top of Mountain
80	72
65	58
93	84
98	91
74	69

Mixed Review

Lesson 5-1

54. The graph shows distance from home as a family drives to the mountains for a vacation. Copy the graph. Label each section of the graph. **See back of book.**

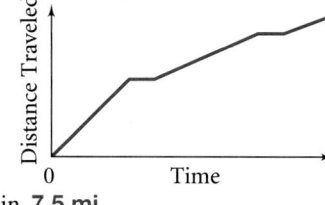
A Trip to the Mountains

Lesson 4-2

The scale of a map is 1 in. : 15 mi. Find the actual distance corresponding to each map distance.

55. 2 in. **30 mi**   **56.** 1.5 in. **22.5 mi**   **57.** 0.5 in. **7.5 mi**

58. 3.25 in. **48.75 mi** **59.** 5.5 in. **82.5 mi**   **60.** 7.25 in. **108.75 mi**

Lesson 2-7

Find the mean, median, mode, and range. 61–64. See left.

61. 33.5, 33.5, none, 3
62. $-\frac{1}{5}$, 0, −2 and 1, 4
63. $\frac{52}{9}$, 5, 5, 11
64. $\frac{117}{8}$, 14, 13, 11

61. 34 33 35 33 32 35 34 32

62. 1 −2 0 −1 1 −2 2 0 1 −2

63. 4 5 3 7 1 12 6 9 5

64. 15 13 19 20 9 13 15 13

65. −4 −8 −7 −7 −4 −7 −1 −9
$-\frac{47}{8}$, −7, −7, 8

66. 43 45 51 42 48 48 43 52
46.5, 46.5, 43 and 48, 10

 **Checkpoint Quiz 1**   **Lessons 5-1 through 5-2**

iTEXT Instant self-check quiz online and on CD-ROM

Sketch a graph of each situation. Label each section. 1–3. See margin.

1. the height of a plant that grows at a steady rate

2. the temperature in a classroom after the heater is turned on

3. a child's height above the ground while on a swing

4. Is the graph at the right the graph of a function? Explain.
   Yes; it passes the vertical-line test.

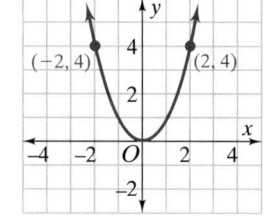

Evaluate each function rule for $x = 0.6$.

5. $f(x) = -4x$ **−2.4**   6. $g(x) = x + 1.53$ **2.13**

7. $y = 2 - 0.5x$ **1.7**   8. $y = 3x^2$ **1.08**

9. $f(x) = 34 - x$ **33.4** 10. $g(x) = -3 + 2x$ **−1.8**

246   Chapter 5 Graphs and Functions

1.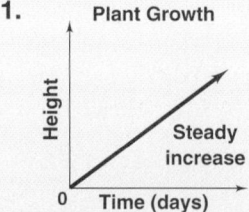
Plant Growth — Steady increase

2.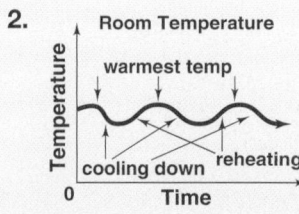
Room Temperature — warmest temp, cooling down, reheating

3.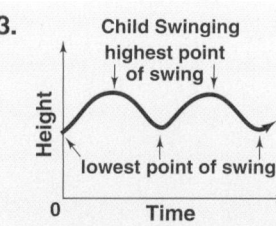
Child Swinging — highest point of swing, lowest point of swing

Function Rules, Tables, and Graphs

North Carolina Objectives

4.01 Use linear functions or inequalities to model and solve problems; justify results. a) Solve using tables, graphs, and algebraic properties.

Lesson Preview

What You'll Learn

OBJECTIVE 1
To model functions using rules, tables, and graphs

...And Why

To find the cost of making CDs, as in Example 2

 Check Skills You'll Need (For help, go to Lesson 5-2.)

Graph the data in each table. 1–3. See back of book.

1.
x	y
−3	−7
−1	−1
0	2
2	8

2.
x	y
−3	4
−2	0
0	−2
2	4

3.
x	y
−4	−3
0	−2
2	−1.5
4	−1

New Vocabulary • independent variable • dependent variable

---

1. Plan

Lesson Preview

 **Check Skills You'll Need**

Relations and Functions
Lesson 5-2: Example 2
Exercises 7–10
Extra Practice, p. 706

Lesson Resources

 **Teaching Resources**
Practice, Reteaching, Enrichment

 **Reaching All Students**
Practice Workbook 5-3
Spanish Practice Workbook 5-3
Hands-On Activities 11
Basic Algebra Planning Guide 5-3

Presentation Assistant Plus!
Transparencies
• Check Skills You'll Need 5-3
• Additional Examples 5-3
• Student Edition Answers 5-3
• Lesson Quiz 5-3
PH Presentation Pro CD 5-3

PRENTICE HALL ASSESSMENT SYSTEM

Computer Test Generator CD

 Technology
Resource Pro® CD-ROM
Computer Test Generator CD
Prentice Hall Presentation Pro CD

 **www.PHSchool.com**
Student Site
• Teacher Web Code: aek-5500
• Reasoning & Puzzles pp. 86, 88
• Graphing Calculator, Procedures 4, 6
• Self-grading Lesson Quiz
Teacher Center
• Lesson Planner
• Resources

Plus **iTEXT**

OBJECTIVE 1 Modeling Functions

TEXT Interactive lesson includes instant self-check, tutorials, and activities.

2a.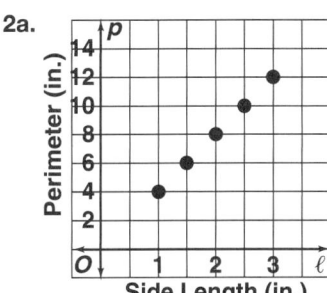

2b.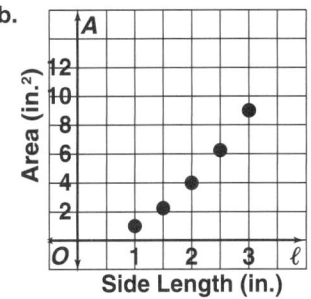

3. the graphs of side length and perimeter

4. Answers may vary. Sample:
Perimeter: $p = 4\ell$
Area: $A = \ell^2$

Investigation: Functions

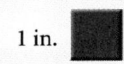 1 in.    $1\frac{1}{2}$ in.   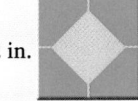 2 in.

1. Copy and complete the table for squares.

Side length (in.)	Perimeter (in.)	Area (in.²)
1	4	1
$1\frac{1}{2}$	6	$2\frac{1}{4}$
2	■ 8	■ 4
$2\frac{1}{2}$	■ 10	■ $6\frac{1}{4}$
3	■ 12	■ 9

2–4. See left.

2. a. Make a graph of side length ℓ and perimeter p for ordered pairs (ℓ, p).
   b. Make a graph of side length ℓ and area A for ordered pairs (ℓ, A).

3. For which of the two graphs could you join the points to form a line?

4. Write two rules, one for finding the perimeter of a square with side length ℓ, and one for finding the area A of a square.

You can model functions using rules, tables, and graphs. A function rule shows how the variables are related. A table identifies specific input and output values of the function. A graph gives a visual picture of the function.

Ongoing Assessment and Intervention

Before the Lesson
Diagnose prerequisite skills using:
• Check Skills You'll Need

During the Lesson
Monitor progress using:
• Check Understanding
• Additional Examples
• Standardized Test Prep

After the Lesson
Assess knowledge using:
• Lesson Quiz
• Computer Test Generator CD

Math Background

Graphs that contain the absolute value of x typically have a V-shape made up of two lines meeting at the vertex.

OBJECTIVE

1 **Teaching Notes**

Investigation (Optional)
Inclusion

Pair students who do not have good eye-hand coordination with other students to help them draw the squares in this Investigation.

1 EXAMPLE **Teaching Tip**

Ask students: *Why do you join the points to form a line?* You can choose any real number for the *x*-values. A linear graph includes all real numbers in its domain.

3 EXAMPLE **Visual Learners**

To help students know the general shape of absolute value and quadratic function graphs, write the following on the board:

absolute $\vee$ alue

$_{x}$ sq $\vee$ ared

Additional Examples

1 Model the function rule $y = \frac{1}{3}x + 2$ using a table of values and a graph. Sample:

x	$y = \frac{1}{3}x + 2$	(x, y)
−3	$y = \frac{1}{3}(-3) + 2 = 1$	(−3, 1)
0	$y = \frac{1}{3}(0) + 2 = 2$	(0, 2)
3	$y = \frac{1}{3}(3) + 2 = 3$	(3, 3)

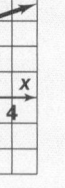

The inputs are values of the **independent variable**. The outputs are the corresponding values of the **dependent variable**.

Graph the independent variable on the horizontal axis.

Graph the dependent variable on the vertical axis.

Use the input and output values as ordered pairs to plot points.

Join the points with a line or smooth curve to give a general picture of the function.

1 EXAMPLE **Three Views of a Function**

Model the function rule $y = \frac{1}{2}x + 3$ using a table of values and a graph.

Step 1 Choose input values for x. Evaluate to find y.

Step 2 Plot points for the ordered pairs.

Step 3 Join the points to form a line.

x	$y = \frac{1}{2}x + 3$	(x, y)
−4	$y = \frac{1}{2}(-4) + 3 = 1$	(−4, 1)
0	$y = \frac{1}{2}(0) + 3 = 3$	(0, 3)
2	$y = \frac{1}{2}(2) + 3 = 4$	(2, 4)

✓ **Check Understanding** **1** Model the rule $f(x) = 3x + 4$ with a table of values and a graph. **See back of book.**

When you draw a graph for a real-world situation, choose appropriate intervals for the units on the axes. Be sure the intervals are equal. Also, if the data are positive numbers, use only the first quadrant.

2 EXAMPLE **Real-World** **Problem Solving**

Recording Costs Suppose your group recorded a CD. Now you want to copy and sell it. One company charges $250 for making a master CD and designing the art for the cover. There is also a cost of $3 to burn each CD. The total cost $P(c)$ depends on the number of CDs c burned. Use the function rule $P(c) = 250 + 3c$ to make a table of values and a graph.

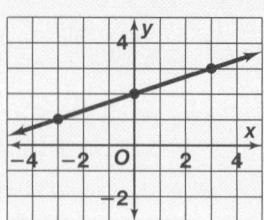

Real-World **Connection**

Careers Recording engineers record singers and instruments separately. The sounds are mixed later to achieve the desired effect.

c	P(c) = 250 + 3c	(c, P(c))
100	250 + 3(100) = 550	(100, 550)
200	250 + 3(200) = 850	(200, 850)
300	250 + 3(300) = 1150	(300, 1150)
500	250 + 3(500) = 1750	(500, 1750)

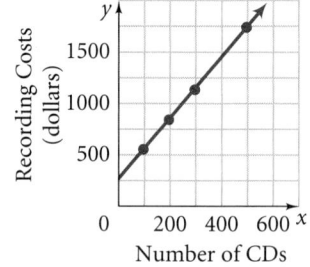

✓ **Check Understanding** **2** **a.** Another company charges $300 for making a master and designing the art. It charges $2.50 for burning each CD. Use the function rule $P(c) = 300 + 2.5c$. Make a table of values and a graph. **See back of book.**

b. Critical Thinking Compare your graph from part (a) to the graph in Example 2. For what number of CDs is the studio in the Example less expensive? **as many as 99 CDs**

Reaching All Students

Below Level Ask students to explain why the graph for Example 2 is only in Quadrant I.	**Advanced Learners** Ask students to explain why specific variables were graphed on the x-axis and others were graphed on the y-axis in the graphs in Examples 1 and 2.	**Inclusion** See note on page 248. **Visual Learners** See note on page 248.

Some functions have graphs that are not straight lines. You can graph a function as long as you know its rule. After you have graphed the ordered pairs that you have calculated from a rule, join the points with a smooth line or curve.

3 EXAMPLE Graphing Functions

a. Graph the function $y = |x| + 1$.

Make a table of values.

x	$y = |x| + 1$	(x, y)
-3	$|-3| + 1 = 4$	$(-3, 4)$
-1	$|-1| + 1 = 2$	$(-1, 2)$
0	$|0| + 1 = 1$	$(0, 1)$
1	$|1| + 1 = 2$	$(1, 2)$
3	$|3| + 1 = 4$	$(3, 4)$

Then graph the data.

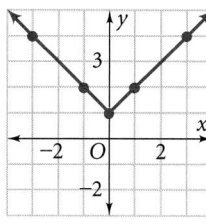

b. Graph the function $f(x) = x^2 + 1$.

Make a table of values.

x	$f(x) = x^2 + 1$	$(x, f(x))$
-2	$4 + 1 = 5$	$(-2, 5)$
-1	$1 + 1 = 2$	$(-1, 2)$
0	$0 + 1 = 1$	$(0, 1)$
1	$1 + 1 = 2$	$(1, 2)$
2	$4 + 1 = 5$	$(2, 5)$

Then graph the data.

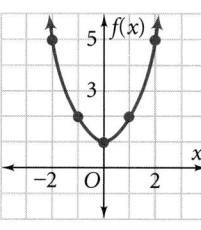

✔ Check Understanding **3** Make a table of values and graph each function.
a. $f(x) = |x| - 1$ **b.** $y = x^2 - 1$
a–b. See back of book.

EXERCISES

For more practice, see *Extra Practice*.

Practice and Problem Solving

 Practice by Example

Example 1
(page 248)

Match each graph with its rule.

1. $f(x) = 2x$ **C**   **2.** $f(x) = \frac{1}{2}x$ **A**   **3.** $f(x) = x + 2$ **B**

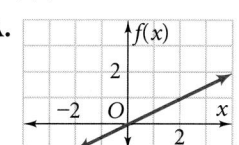

A.   B.   C.

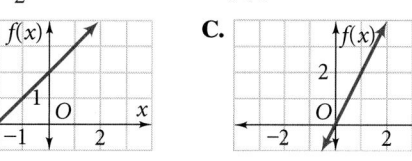

Model each rule with a table of values and a graph. **4–12. See back of book.**

4. $f(x) = -3x$ **5.** $f(x) = -3x + 1$ **6.** $f(x) = -3x - 2$

7. $y = 2x - 7$ **8.** $f(x) = 8 - x$ **9.** $y = 5 + 4x$

10. $f(x) = \frac{1}{4}x$ **11.** $y = 4x$ **12.** $y = x + 4$

2 At the local video store you can rent a video game for $3. It costs you $5 a month to operate your video game player. The total monthly cost $C(v)$ depends on the number of video games v you rent. Use the function rule $C(v) = 5 + 3v$ to make a table of values and a graph.

v	$C(v) = 5 + 3v$	$(v, C(v))$
0	$C(v) = 5 + 3(0) = 5$	$(0, 5)$
1	$C(v) = 5 + 3(1) = 8$	$(1, 8)$
2	$C(v) = 5 + 3(2) = 11$	$(2, 11)$

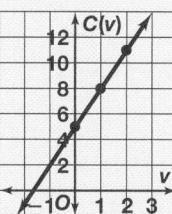

3 a. Graph the function $y = |x| + 2$.

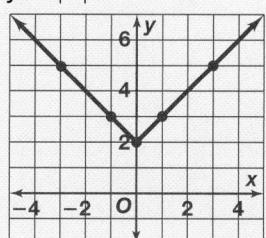

b. Graph the function $f(x) = x^2 + 2$.

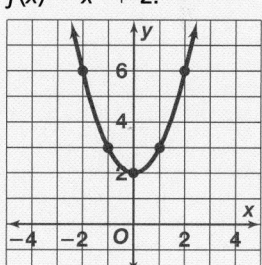

Closure

Have students brainstorm for advantages and disadvantages of representing functions using rules, tables, and graphs.
Answers may vary. Sample: A graph can show trends.

Assignment Guide

1 Objective

Ⓐ Ⓑ **Core** 1–43
Ⓒ **Extension** 44–46

Standardized Test Prep 47–52

Mixed Review 53–76

Exercises 1–3 Suggest to students that they substitute 0 and 2 for x in each rule. This will show that the graph for Exercise 3 does not pass through (0, 0) and that the graph for Exercise 1 has a greater y-value for an x-value of 2 than does Exercise 2.

Error Prevention

Exercises 10, 26 Suggest to students that if they use multiples of 4 for x they will be dealing only with whole numbers.

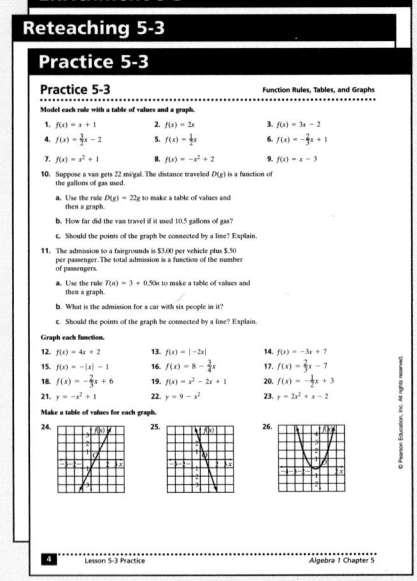

Enrichment 5-3
Reteaching 5-3
Practice 5-3

Example 2
(page 248)

13. Earnings Juan charges $3.50 per hour for baby-sitting.
　a. Write a rule to describe how the amount of money M earned is a function of the number of hours h spent baby-sitting. $M = 3.5h$
　b. Make a table of values. **See margin.**
　c. Graph the values and join the points with a line. **See back of book.**
　d. Estimation Use the graph to estimate how long it will take Juan to earn $30.
　　　　　　　　　　　　　　　　　　　　　　　　　See margin.

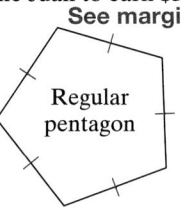

14. Geometry The figure at the right is a regular pentagon. The function $P(\ell) = 5\ell$ describes the perimeter of a regular pentagon with side length ℓ.
　a. Make a table of values for $\ell = 1, 2, 3,$ and 4.
　b. Graph the function. **a–b. See margin.**

Regular pentagon

Example 3
(page 249)

Graph each function. 15–23. See back of book.

15. $y = |x|$　**16.** $y = |x| + 2$　**17.** $y = x^2$

18. $f(x) = x^2 - 1$　**19.** $f(x) = |x| + 3$　**20.** $y = x^2 + 3$

21. $y = |x| - 4$　**22.** $f(x) = -x^2 - 1$　**23.** $f(x) = -x^2 + 2$

Ⓑ Apply Your Skills

24. a. Make a table for the perimeters of the rectangles formed by each set of blue tiles.
　b. The perimeter $P(t)$ is a function of the number of tiles t. Write a rule for the data in your table and graph the function.
　　　　　　　　　See margin p. 251.

Fig. 1　Fig. 2　Fig. 3　Fig. 4

24a.

Tiles	Perimeter
1	4
2	6
3	8
4	10

25. Writing Describe the steps you would use to graph the function rule $f(x) = 3x - 2$. **See margin p. 251.**

Graph each function. 26–37. See back of book.

26. $f(x) = \frac{3}{4}x + 7$　**27.** $y = x^2 - 4x + 4$　**28.** $y = |2x|$

29. $y = x + \frac{1}{2}$　**30.** $f(x) = 7 - 5x$　**31.** $f(x) = \left|\frac{1}{2}x\right|$

32. $f(x) = \left|\frac{1}{2}x\right| + 1$　**33.** $y = 1 - x^2$　**34.** $f(x) = -5x^2$

35. $y = 2x - 3$　**36.** $y = \left|\frac{1}{3}x\right|$　**37.** $f(x) = -|x + 2|$

39b. Input is to output as domain is to range.

38. Conserving Water The equation $w = 6m$ models the gallons of water w used by a standard shower head for a shower that takes m minutes. The function $w = 3m$ models the water-saving shower head. **a–b. See back of book.**
　a. Suppose you take a 6-minute shower using a water-saving shower head. How much water do you save compared to an average shower with a standard shower head?
　b. Graph both functions on the same coordinate plane.
　c. Open-Ended How much water did you use during your last shower? **c–d. Check students' work.**
　d. How did you find your answer?

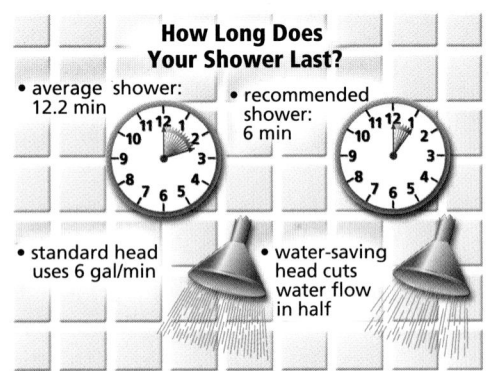

How Long Does Your Shower Last?

• average shower: 12.2 min
• recommended shower: 6 min
• standard head uses 6 gal/min
• water-saving head cuts water flow in half

Source: Opinion Research Corp.

39. a. Language Arts Copy and complete the analogy: "Input value is to output value as independent variable is to _?_." **dependent variable**
　b. Write an analogy using *input, output, domain,* and *range.* **See above left.**

pages 249–252 **Exercises**

13b-d. Answers may vary. Samples are given.

b.

h	M
0	$0.00
$\frac{1}{2}$	$1.75
1	$3.50
2	$7.00
3	$10.50

d. about 8.5 h

14a.

ℓ	$P(\ell)$
1	5
2	10
3	15
4	20

40. a.

ℓ	$A(\ell)$
1	0.5
2	2
3	4.5
4	8

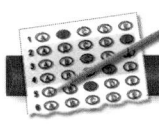

Need Help?

To review reflections, see Skills Handbook page 733.

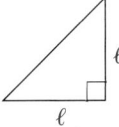 **40. a. Geometry** The function $A(\ell) = \frac{1}{2}\ell^2$ describes the area of an isosceles right triangle with leg ℓ. Make a table of values for $\ell = 1, 2, 3,$ and 4. **See left.**
   b. Graph the function. **See back of book.**

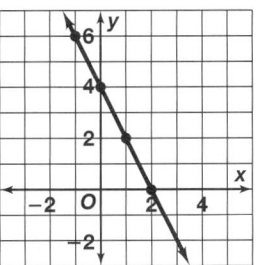

ℓ
Isosceles
right triangle

41. Calling Costs For one calling plan, the cost $C(a)$ of a call from Sacramento, California, to Salt Lake City, Utah, is a function of the number of additional minutes a after the first minute. The rule $C(a) = 0.27 + 0.11(a - 1)$ models the cost.
   a. How much will a 5-minute call cost? **$.71**
   b. How many minutes can you talk for $1.50? **about 12 min**

See back of book.

42. a. Graph $y = |x|$ and $y = -|x|$ on the same coordinate plane.
   b. The graph of $y = -|x|$ is the reflection of the graph of $y = |x|$. Over which axis is the graph of $y = |x|$ reflected? **x-axis**
   c. Write an equation of the reflection of the graph of $y = |x| + 1$ over the same axis. $y = -|x| - 1$

43. Which is the graph of the function $f(x) = \frac{1}{2}x^2 + x$? **B**

A. 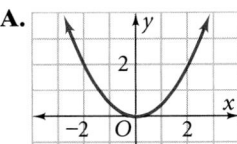   **B.** 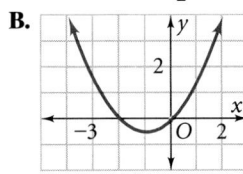   **C.**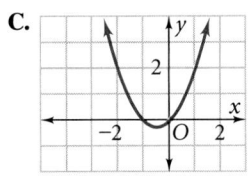

Challenge

45a.

44. a. Graph each function on the same coordinate plane. **See back of book.**
   i. $f(x) = |x| + 2$ **ii.** $f(x) = |x| + 4$ **iii.** $f(x) = |x| - 3$
   b. Critical Thinking In the function $y = |x| + b$, how does changing the value of b change the graph of the function? **It changes the y-intercept.**

45. a. Graph each function on the same coordinate plane. **See left.**
   i. $f(x) = |2x|$ **ii.** $f(x) = |0.5x|$ **iii.** $f(x) = |3x|$
   b. Critical Thinking In the function $y = |ax|$, how does changing the value of a change the graph of the function? **It makes the graph wider or narrower.**

46c. Tables may vary. Sample:

x	y
-4	-1
-2	-1
0	0
2	1
4	1

46. The function $s(x)$, sometimes called the signum function, is defined as
$$s(x) = \begin{cases} 1 \text{ if } x > 0 \\ 0 \text{ if } x = 0 \\ -1 \text{ if } x < 0 \end{cases}$$
For example, $s(17) = 1, s(0) = 0,$ and $s(-32) = -1$.
   a. Evaluate $s(3.77), s(0.003), s(-1.5),$ and $s(-2300)$. **1, 1, -1, -1**
   b. The domain of the function is all real numbers. What is the range? **{-1, 0, 1}**
   c. Make a table of values and graph the function. **See left.**
   d. Make a Conjecture Do you think $s(a + b) = s(a) + s(b)$? First, test some values of a and b. If your answer is *yes*, justify your answer. If your answer is *no*, give a counterexample.
   No; s(3 + 5) = s(8) = 1 and s(3) + s(5) = 1 + 1 = 2; 1 ≠ 2.

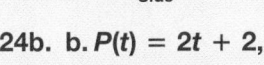

Standardized Test Prep

Multiple Choice

47. Suppose you hire an electrician to install several electrical outlets in your home. The electrician charges $68 for materials plus $40 per hour (or fraction of an hour). How much will the electrician charge you if the job takes $2\frac{1}{4}$ hours? **C**
   A. $148   **B.** $158   **C.** $188   **D.** $208

Lesson 5-3   Function Rules, Tables, and Graphs   **251**

14b.
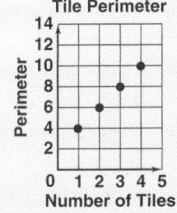

24b. b. $P(t) = 2t + 2,$

Tile Perimeter
[graph]

25. Answers may vary. Sample: Make a table to find values for $f(x)$ when $x = -2, 0,$ and 2. Then graph the ordered pairs $(x, f(x))$ and join the graphed points with a line.

Lesson Quiz 5-3

1. Model $y = -2x + 4$ with a table of values and a graph.

x	$y = -2x + 4$	(x, y)
-1	$y = -2(-1) + 4 = 6$	(-1, 6)
0	$y = -2(0) + 4 = 4$	(0, 4)
1	$y = -2(1) + 4 = 2$	(1, 2)
2	$y = -2(2) + 4 = 0$	(2, 0)

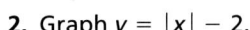

2. Graph $y = |x| - 2$.

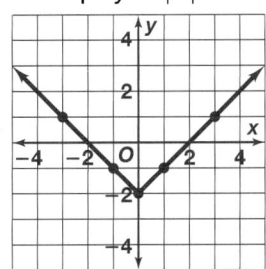

3. Graph $f(x) = 2x^2 - 2$.

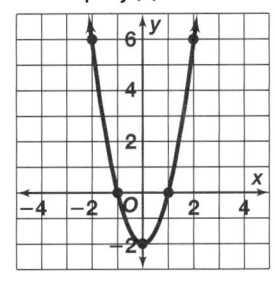

Alternative Assessment

Organize students into groups of three. Have each student write a function rule on a piece of paper. Then have students pass their papers to the student on their right. This student makes a table of values for the rule. Students pass the paper to the right again. Now students graph using each table. Have all students in each group review the results to determine if they are correct.

251

For additional practice with a variety of test item formats:
- Standardized Test Prep, p. 279
- Test-Taking Strategies, p. 274
- Test-Taking Strategies with Transparencies

Exercise 48 Suggest to students that they substitute 0 into the function rule to determine where the graph crosses the *y*-axis. This will eliminate two graphs. Then they can substitute the *x*-value of the point where the line crosses the *x*-axis for the two remaining graphs and determine which graph is the correct one.

pages 249–252 Exercises

51. [2]

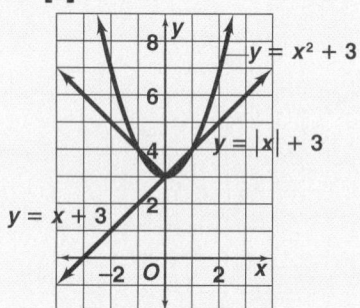

The graphs of all equations go through the point (0, 3). $y = x + 3$ and $y = x^2 + 3$ share points on the right side of the *y*-axis. Both sides of the graphs $y = x^2 + 3$ and $y = |x| + 3$ go upward, but $y = |x| + 3$ has straight lines and $y = x^2 + 3$ has curved lines.

[1] at least two of the graphs drawn correctly

52. [4] a. Tables may vary.
Sample:

x	f(x)
−4	1
−2	−1
−1	−2
0	−1
2	1

48. Which is the graph of the function rule $f(x) = \frac{1}{2}x - 2$? **F**

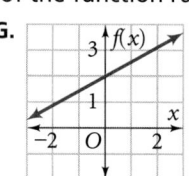 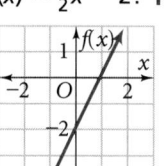 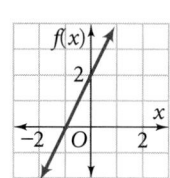

49. Which function is modeled by the table at the right? **B**
- **A.** $f(x) = x - 2$
- **B.** $f(x) = 2x + 1$
- **C.** $f(x) = -x + 1$
- **D.** $f(x) = \frac{1}{2}x - 1$

x	f(x)
−3	−5
0	1
2	5
3	7

50. Which points are on the graph of the function rule $f(x) = 10 - 4x$? **I**
- **F.** (18, −2), (10, 0), (2, 2)
- **G.** (−18, 2), (−10, 0), (−2, −2)
- **H.** (2, −18), (0, −10), (−2, −2)
- **I.** (−2, 18), (0, 10), (2, 2)

Take It to the NET
Online lesson quiz at
www.PHSchool.com
Web Code: aea-0503

Short Response

51. Graph the equations $y = x + 3$, $y = x^2 + 3$, and $y = |x| + 3$ on the same coordinate plane. Describe the similarities and differences in the graphs. **See margin.**

Extended Response

52. a. Make a table of values for the function rule $f(x) = |x + 1| - 2$.
b. Graph $f(x) = |x + 1| - 2$. **See margin.**

Mixed Review

Lesson 5-2

Find the range of each function for the domain {−2, 0, 3.5}. **53–61. See margin.**

53. $f(x) = 3x + 1$
54. $g(x) = 3x - 5$
55. $f(s) = -3s + 4$
56. $g(v) = |v| - 5$
57. $h(n) = 12 - n$
58. $g(w) = 5(w - 2)$
59. $p(n) = 6n + 1$
60. $f(x) = 0.5x - 8$
61. $k(n) = -11n + 9$

Lesson 3-6

Solve each equation. If there is no solution, explain.

63. No sol.; $9 = 10 - 1$ and $|b|$ cannot be −1.

62. $|x| + 7 = 11$ **4, −4**
63. $9 = 10 + |b|$
64. $5|t| = 18$ **−3.6, 3.6**
65. $-2|k| = -14$ **−7, 7**
66. $20 = 4|c| - 8$ **−7, 7**
67. $3 = |z - 1|$ **4, −2**
68. $|r + 11| = 4$ **−7, −15**
69. $|m - 0.5| = 1$ **1.5, −0.5**
70. $3|w + 4| = 9$ **−1, −7**

Lesson 4-2

The scale of a map is 1 cm : 16 km. Find the actual distance corresponding to each map distance.

71. 3 cm **48 km**
72. 2.5 cm **40 km**
73. 6.3 cm **100.8 km**
74. 8.5 cm **136 km**
75. 10.2 cm **163.2 km**

76. Architecture The Lyndon Johnson Presidential Library has a model of the Oval Office in the White House. The model in the Johnson Library is $\frac{7}{8}$ the size of the original. Write and solve a proportion to find each dimension in the Johnson Library given the following actual Oval Office dimensions.
a. greatest width: 29 ft $\frac{7}{8} = \frac{x}{29}$, **25.375 ft**
b. greatest length: 35 ft 10 in.
c. height: 18 ft 6 in.

b. $\frac{7}{8} = \frac{x}{35.833}$, **31.35 ft**

c. $\frac{7}{8} = \frac{x}{18.5}$, **16.1875 ft**

b.
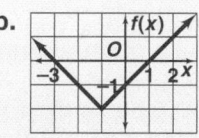

[3] appropriate methods but one calculation error

[2] correct table but an error in graph
[1] table with no graph OR graph with no table

53. {−5, 1, 11.5}
54. {−11, −5, 5.5}
55. {−6.5, 4, 10}
56. {−5, −3, −1.5}
57. {8.5, 12, 14}

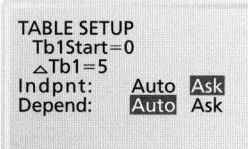

Technology

Function Rules, Tables, and Graphs

FOR USE WITH LESSON 5-3

You can use a graphing calculator to explore the relationship among a function rule, a table, and a graph. When you use the table feature, the calculator computes the values for y based on the values of x that you enter.

Take It to the NET
Graphing Calculator procedures online at **www.PHSchool.com**
Web Code: aee-2104

1 EXAMPLE

For the function $y = -2x + 5$, find the range when the domain is $\{-12, 2, 0, 3, 8\}$.

Access the **TBLSET** feature. Use the arrow key to shade the **Ask** to the right of **Indpnt**.

Press **ENTER**.

Press **Y=** . Enter the function. Access the **TABLE** feature. Enter values for x.

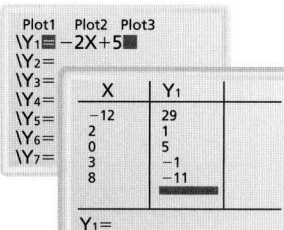

● The range is $\{29, 1, 5, -1, -11\}$.

To graph an equation, use the **GRAPH** feature. You can use the **TRACE** feature to find x- and y- values. If you graph and trace the equation in Example 1, you will see that the x- and y- values are generally given as 8-digit numbers. To see values for x that are given in tenths, press **ZOOM** 4 and then **TRACE** .

2 EXAMPLE

Graph $y = -0.5x - 2$. Where does the graph cross each axis?

Press **Y=** . Enter the function rule. Then press **GRAPH** .

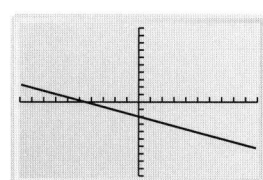

Press **ZOOM** 4 and then **TRACE** to find where the graph crosses the axes.

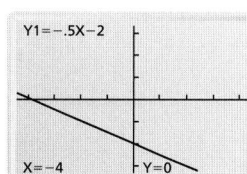

● The graph crosses the y-axis at -2 and the x-axis at -4.

EXERCISES

Find the range of each function for the given domain.

1. $y = 3x + 6; \{-5, 0, 3, 7\}$ **{−9, 6, 15, 27}**

2. $y = 0.4x - 5.1; \{-2.1, 1.35, 5.7\}$
{−5.94, −4.56, −2.82}

Determine where each graph crosses the y-axis and the x-axis.

3. $y = -2x + 3$ **$y = 3, x = 1.5$**   **4.** $y = -0.25x - 1$
$y = -1, x = -4$

5. $y = 1.2x + 2.16$
$y = 2.16, x = -1.8$

6. Open-Ended Graph $y = -0.2x + 6$. Using the **WINDOW** screen, experiment with values for Xmin, Xmax, Ymin, and Ymax until you can see the graph crossing both axes. What values did you use for Xmin, Xmax, Ymin, and Ymax? **Answers may vary. Sample: −10, 35, −10, 10**

58. $\{-20, -10, 7.5\}$

59. $\{-11, 1, 22\}$

60. $\{-9, -8, -6.25\}$

61. $\{-29.5, 9, 31\}$

Technology

Function Rules, Tables, and Graphs

Students use the table feature of their graphing calculators to find the range of a given function with a given domain. They will also use the calculator to graph functions and determine the intersection of the graphs with the x- and y-axes.

Resources

Students may use any graphing calculator to explore graphs and functions.

Teaching Notes

Technology Tip
Remind students that before they begin a new problem using a graphing calculator, it is best to reset the calculator. Resetting erases all previously entered data. The steps to clear the data are: [ON], 2nd, **MEM**, 7, ENTER .

Inclusion
Students with impaired vision may want to increase the contrast on their calculators. Help them adjust their settings.

1. Plan

Lesson Preview

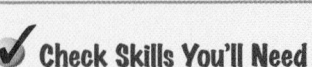
✓ Check Skills You'll Need

Function Rules, Tables, and Graphs
Lesson 5-3: Example 1
Exercises 4–12
Extra Practice, p. 706

Lesson Resources

📁 **Teaching Resources**
Practice, Reteaching, Enrichment

👥 **Reaching All Students**
Practice Workbook 5-4
Spanish Practice Workbook 5-4
Basic Algebra Planning Guide 5-4

⏰ **Presentation Assistant Plus!**
Transparencies
• Check Skills You'll Need 5-4
• Additional Examples 5-4
• Student Edition Answers 5-4
• Lesson Quiz 5-4
PH Presentation Pro CD 5-4

ⒶSSESSMENT SYSTEM
Computer Test Generator CD

🔧 **Technology**
Resource Pro® CD-ROM
Computer Test Generator CD
Prentice Hall Presentation Pro CD

💻 **www.PHSchool.com**
Student Site
• Teacher Web Code: aek-5500
• Self-grading Lesson Quiz
Teacher Center
• Lesson Planner
• Resources

Plus iTEXT

254

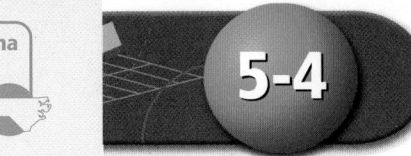
5-4

Writing a Function Rule

4.01   Use linear functions or inequalities to model and solve problems; justify results. a) Solve using tables, graphs, and algebraic properties.

Lesson Preview

What You'll Learn

OBJECTIVE
1 To write a function rule given a table or a real-world situation

. . . And Why

To write a function rule for finding profit, as in Example 3

✓ **Check Skills You'll Need**   (For help, go to Lesson 5-3.)

Model each rule with a table of values. 1–6. See back of book.

1. $f(x) = 5x - 1$ **2.** $y = -3x + 4$ **3.** $g(t) = 0.2t - 7$

4. $y = 4x + 1$ **5.** $f(x) = 6 - x$ **6.** $c(d) = d + 0.9$

Evaluate each function rule for $n = 2$.

7. $A(n) = 2n - 1$ **3**   **8.** $f(n) = -3 + n$ **-1 -2**   **9.** $g(n) = 6 - n$ **4**

🅣TEXT **Interactive lesson includes instant self-check, tutorials, and activities.**

OBJECTIVE
▽**1**   **Writing Function Rules**

You can write a rule for a function by analyzing a table of values. Look for a pattern relating the independent and dependent variables.

1 **EXAMPLE**   **Writing a Rule from a Table**

Write a function rule for each table.

a.

x	f(x)
1	5
2	6
3	7
4	8

Ask yourself, "What can I do to 1 to get 5, to 2 to get 6, . . . ?"

You add 4 to each x-value to get the $f(x)$ value.

Relate	$f(x)$	equals	x	plus	4
Write	$f(x)$	$=$	x	$+$	4

A rule for the function is $f(x) = x + 4$.

b.

x	y
1	1
3	9
6	36
9	81

Ask yourself, "What can I do to 3 to get 9, to 6 to get 36, . . . ?"

You multiply each x-value times itself to get the $f(x)$ value.

Relate	y	equals	x times itself
Write	y	$=$	x^2

A rule for the function is $y = x^2$.

✓ **Check Understanding** **①** Write a function rule for each table.

a.

x	f(x)
1	−1
2	0
3	1
4	2

$f(x) = x - 2$

b.

x	y
1	2
2	4
3	6
4	8

$y = 2x$

c.

x	y
1	3
2	4
3	5
4	6

$y = x + 2$

Ongoing Assessment and Intervention

Before the Lesson
Diagnose prerequisite skills using:
• Check Skills You'll Need

During the Lesson
Monitor progress using:
• Check Understanding
• Additional Examples
• Standardized Test Prep

After the Lesson
Assess knowledge using:
• Lesson Quiz
• Computer Test Generator CD

Real-World  **Connection**

The Museum of Science in Boston, Massachusetts, has an exhibit called The Walk Through Computer™ 2000.

2 EXAMPLE Real-World 🌐 Problem Solving

Scale Model The exhibit at the left is a scale model of a desktop computer. It is about 20 times the size of a normal-sized desktop computer.

a. Write a function rule to describe this relationship.

Relate larger is 20 times normal

Define Let n = length of normal-sized computer.

Let $L(n)$ = length of larger size shown in museum exhibit.

Write $L(n)$ = 20 · n

The function rule $L(n) = 20n$ describes the relationship between the size of the computer in the exhibit and a normal-sized computer.

b. A space bar on a normal-sized computer is $4\frac{3}{8}$ in long. About how long is the space bar in the exhibit?

$L(n) = 20 \cdot n$

$L(n) = 20 \cdot 4\frac{3}{8}$ **Substitute $4\frac{3}{8}$ for n.**

$L(n) = 87\frac{1}{2}$ **Simplify.**

The space bar in the exhibit is about $87\frac{1}{2}$ in. long.

✓ **Check Understanding** **2 a. Carpentry** A carpenter buys finishing nails by the pound. Each pound of nails costs $1.19. Write a function rule to describe this relationship. **$C(x) = 1.19x$**
b. How much do 12 lb of finishing nails cost? **$14.28**

When you write a function, the dependent variable is defined in terms of the independent variable. In Example 3 below, profit depends on the number of lawns mowed, so profit is a function of the number of lawns mowed.

3 EXAMPLE Real-World 🌐 Problem Solving

Earnings Suppose you borrow money from a relative to buy a lawn mower that costs $245. You charge $18 to mow a lawn. Write a rule to describe your profit as a function of the number of lawns mowed.

Relate total profit is $18 times lawns mowed minus cost of mower

Define Let n = number of lawns mowed.

Let $P(n)$ = total profit.

Write $P(n)$ = 18 · n − 245

The function rule $P(n) = 18n - 245$ describes your profit as a function of the number of lawns mowed.

✓ **Check Understanding** **3 Earnings** Suppose you buy a word-processing software package for $199. You charge $15 per hour for word processing. Write a rule to describe your profit as a function of the number of hours you work. **$p(n) = 15n - 199$**

Lesson 5-4 Writing a Function Rule **255**

---

2. Teach

Professional Development

Math Background

The function $t = \frac{n}{4} + 40$ is an example of a function in nature. It gives the temperature, t, in terms of n, the number of chirps per minute that a cricket makes.

OBJECTIVE

▼**1** **Teaching Notes**

1 EXAMPLE **Math Tip**

Some students may not look past the first row of coordinates when looking for the function rule. Stress to students that there are usually two ways to answer the question "What can I do. . . " for the first row, so they must continue with more rows to find the pattern. Have students write the following:

$1 \rightarrow 5$ $\times 5$ or $+ 4$
$2 \rightarrow 6$ $\times 3$ or $+ 4$
$3 \rightarrow 7$ $+ 4$
$4 \rightarrow 8$ $\times 2$ or $+ 4$

Ask: *What do they all have in common?* +4

Additional Examples

1 Write a function rule for each table.

a.

x	f(x)
2	8
4	10
6	12
8	14

b.

x	y
1	2
2	5
3	10
4	17

a. $f(x) = x + 6$ b. $y = x^2 + 1$

👭 **Reaching All Students**

Below Level Have students check the functions for Example 1 by substituting an ordered pair from the table or graph into the function. Each ordered pair should satisfy the function.	**Advanced Learners** Ask students which variables are dependent and which are independent in Examples 2 and 3. Have them explain their answers.	**English Learners** See note on page 258. **Error Prevention** See note on page 257.

255

2 The journalism class makes $25 per page of advertising in the yearbook. If the class sells p pages of advertising, how much money will it earn?
a. Write a function rule to describe this relationship.
$A(p) = 25p$
b. The class sold 6 pages of advertising. How much money did the class make? **$150**

3 The choir spent $100 producing audio tapes of its last performance and will sell the tapes for $5.50 each. Write a rule to describe the choir's profit as a function of the number of tapes sold t. $P(t) = 5.5t - 100$

Closure

Ask: *What question can you ask yourself when using a table to write a function rule?* **What can I do to _____ to get _____?**

EXERCISES

For more practice, see *Extra Practice*.

Practice and Problem Solving

A Practice by Example

Example 1
(page 254)

Match each table with its rule.

1. $y = 4x$ **B**   **2.** $y = x - 4$ **A**   **3.** $y = -4 - x$ **C**

A.

x	y
-2	-6
-1	-5
0	-4
1	-3

B.

x	y
-1	-4
-2	-8
-3	-12
-4	-16

C.

x	y
-1	-3
0	-4
1	-5
2	-6

Write a function rule for each table.

4. $f(x) = 3x$

x	$f(x)$
1	3
2	6
3	9
4	12

5. $f(x) = x - 0.5$

x	$f(x)$
1	0.5
2	1.5
3	2.5
4	3.5

6. $f(x) = 0.5x$

x	$f(x)$
1	0.5
2	1
3	1.5
4	2

7. $f(x) = -3x$

x	$f(x)$
1	-3
2	-6
3	-9
4	-12

8. $y = 4x$

x	y
-2	-8
-1	-4
0	0
1	4

9. $y = x^2$

x	y
-8	64
-4	16
0	0
4	16
8	64

Example 2
(page 255)

Write a function rule for each situation.

10. the total cost $t(c)$ of c ounces of cinnamon if each ounce costs $.79 $t(c) = 0.79c$

11. the total distance $d(n)$ traveled after n hours at a constant speed of 45 miles per hour $d(n) = 45n$

12. $f(h) = \frac{1}{12}h$

13. $e(n) = 6.37n$

12. the height $f(h)$ of an object in feet when you know the height h in inches

13. a worker's earnings $e(n)$ for n hours when the worker's hourly wage is $6.37

14. the area $A(n)$ of a square when you know the length n of a side $A(n) = n^2$

15. the volume $V(n)$ of a cube when you know the length n of a side $V(n) = n^3$

16. the area $A(r)$ of a circle with radius r $A(r) = \pi r^2$

Example 3
(page 255)

17. Food Costs At a supermarket salad bar, the price of a salad depends on its weight. Salad costs $.19 per ounce.
a. Write a rule to describe the function. $f(x) = 0.19x$
b. How much would an 8-ounce salad cost? **$1.52**

18. Postage In 2002, the price of mailing a letter was $.34 for the first ounce or part of an ounce and $.21 for each ounce or part of an ounce after the first ounce.
a. Write a rule to describe the function. $f(x) = 0.34 + 0.21(x - 1)$
b. How much did it cost to mail a 4-ounce letter? **$.97**

B Apply Your Skills

Write a function rule for each table.

19.

Distance (km)	Distance (m)
0.5	500
1.0	1000
1.5	1500
2.0	2000

$f(x) = 1000x$

20.

Inches	Centimeters
1	2.54
2	5.08
3	7.62
4	10.16

$f(x) = 2.54x$

  Math in the Media **Use the advertisement at the left for Exercises 21–22.**

BOOK EXPRESS!

Get your first **6** books for $1.00

Buy additional books at our regular low Club price of $10.00 per book. To become a Book Express member, just buy 2 additional books within the first year. You may resign your membership at any time.

23. **Answers may vary. Sample: The input values you need may not be in the table.**

24a. **gal of water, number of loads**

    b. $w(n) = 34n$

Reading Math

For help reading the graph and solving Exercise 25, see page 260.

21. **a.** Write a rule to find the total cost $C(a)$ for all the books a person buys through Book Express. Let a represent the number of additional books bought (after the first 6 books). $C(a) = 10a + 1$
   b. Suppose a person buys 9 books in all. Find the total cost. **$31**
   c. Evaluate the function for $a = 6$. What does the output represent?
       61; the total cost of 12 books
22. A bookstore sells the same books for an average price of $6 each.
   a. Write a function rule to model the total cost $C(b)$ of books bought at the bookstore. Let b represent the number of books bought. $C(b) = 6b$
   b. Evaluate your function for $b = 12$. What does the output represent? **See below.**
   c. You plan to buy 12 books. What is your average cost per book as a member of Book Express? **about $5.08**   **b. 72; the total cost of 12 books**
   d. Is it less expensive to buy 12 books through the club or at the bookstore? Explain. **Club; $61 is less than $72.**

23. **Writing** What advantage(s) can you see of having a function rule instead of a table of values for a function? **See left.**

 **Water Used for Laundry**

1 load	34 gallons
2 loads	68 gallons
3 loads	102 gallons
4 loads	136 gallons

24. **Water Usage** Use the function in the table at the right.
   a. Identify the dependent and **a-b. See left.** independent variables.
   b. Write a rule to describe the function.
   c. How many gallons of water would you use for 7 loads of laundry? **238 gal**
   d. **Critical Thinking** In one month, you used 442 gallons of water for laundry. How many loads did you wash? **13 loads**

Make a table of values for each graph. Use the table to write a function rule.

25. 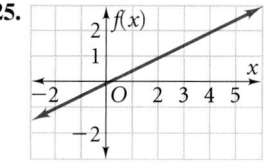   25–28. See margin.

26.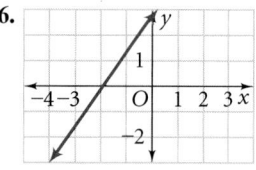

27.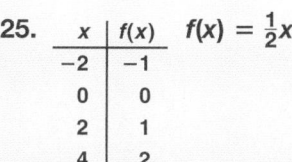

28.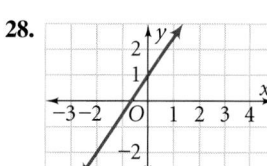

Lesson 5-4 Writing a Function Rule   **257**

---

pages 256–259 Exercises

25–28. **Tables may vary. Samples are given.**

25.
x	f(x)
−2	−1
0	0
2	1
4	2

$f(x) = \frac{1}{2}x$

26.
x	y
−4	−3
−2	0
0	3

$y = \frac{3}{2}x + 3$

27.
x	y
−1	3
0	2
1	1
2	0
3	−1

$y = -x + 2$

28.
x	y
−2	−2
−1	−\frac{1}{2}
0	1

$y = \frac{3}{2}x + 1$

Assignment Guide

1 Objective
   A B Core 1–30
   C Extension 31–35

Standardized Test Prep 36–41

Mixed Review 42–54

Error Prevention

Exercises 10–16 Suggest to students that they write each exercise on their papers and then relate each phrase to an equation. For example, in Exercise 10 students might write, *Total cost equals unit cost times number of units* or $T(c) = .79 \times c$.

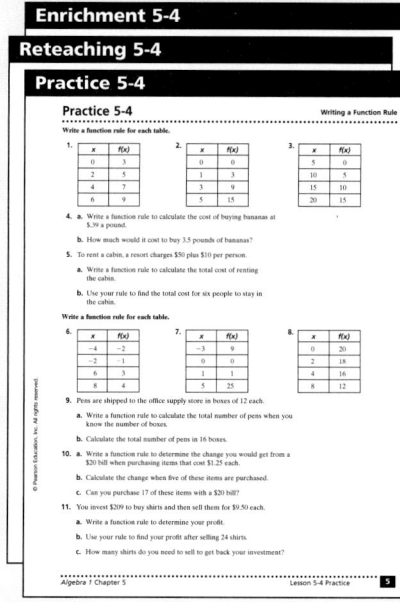

Enrichment 5-4
Reteaching 5-4
Practice 5-4

Exercise 30 Many waitpersons do not receive minimum wage, but rely on their tips to make most of their income. The average tip is 15% of the total bill. Challenge students to find ways to easily estimate a 15% tip. Some examples are:

1) Round to the nearest dollar. Find 10%, and then halve that to get 5%. Add the two amounts.

2) If your city's sales tax is near 7% or 8%, just double the tax.

English Learners

Exercise 35 Some students may be unfamiliar with the terms "pickling salt" and "brine." Bring a jar of pickles, or other pickled vegetables, to class. Let volunteers taste them and describe the flavors.

29. Answers may vary.
Sample: $f(x) = 60x$;
$f(3) = 180$, 180 mi in
3 h, the distance
you can travel at a
constant speed of
60 mi/h

 Challenge

Real-World 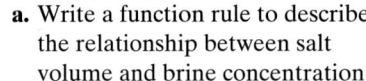 **Connection**

Pickling preserves vegetables by inhibiting the growth of bacteria. Pickling requires salt and acids, such as vinegar.

29. Open-Ended Write a function rule that models a real-world situation. Evaluate your function for an input value and explain what the output represents.
See left.

30. Tipping You go out to dinner and decide to leave a 15% tip for the server.
   a. The bill for your meal is b. Write an expression for the amount of the tip in terms of b. **0.15b**
   b. The total cost $c(b)$ of your meal is the original bill plus the tip. Write a function rule to model this situation. **$c(b) = 1.15b$**
   c. Suppose the original bill is $18. Find the cost of your meal with a 15% tip.
$20.70

Write a function rule for each table.

31.

x	$f(x)$
1	1
2	8
3	27
4	64

$f(x) = x^3$

32.

x	$f(x)$
-1	1
-2	8
-3	27
-4	64

$f(x) = -x^3$

33.

x	$f(x)$
-1	0
-2	7
-3	26
-4	63

$f(x) = -x^3 - 1$

34. Truck Rental A truck rental company charges $44 per day for renting a medium-sized truck. There is also a charge of $.38 per mile.
   a. Write a function rule $c(m)$ to model the cost of renting a truck for a day and driving m miles. **$c(m) = 44 + 0.38m$**
   b. Evaluate your function rule for $m = 70$ and $m = 120$. **$70.60, $89.60**
   c. You return the truck to the rental company and pay $58.44 (excluding tax). How far did you drive? **38 mi**
   d. Suppose you need to rent a truck for two days. You plan to drive 150 miles each day. How much will this cost? **$202**

35. Making Pickles The table at the right shows the relationship between the amount of pickling salt added to a gallon of water and the brine concentration, which is the percent of salt by weight. **$B(v) = 6.93v$**
   a. Write a function rule to describe the relationship between salt volume and brine concentration.
   b. Write a function rule to describe the relationship between salt weight and brine concentration.
$B(w) = \frac{7}{10}w$

Brine Strength

Salt Volume (cup)	Salt Weight (oz)	Brine Concentration (percent salt)
$\frac{1}{3}$	3.3	2.31
$\frac{1}{2}$	4.95	3.465
$\frac{2}{3}$	6.6	4.62
$\frac{3}{4}$	7.425	5.1975
1	9.9	6.93

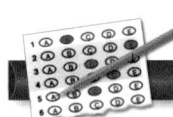 **Standardized Test Prep**

Multiple Choice

36. What is the function rule for the total cost $T(b)$ of b books, if each book costs $11.95? **A**
   A. $T(b) = 11.95b$ B. $T(b) = b + 11.95$
   C. $T(b) = 11.95 - b$ D. $T(b) = b - 11.95$

37. What is the function rule for the amount of change $C(x)$ you receive from a $50 bill if you buy x pounds of dog food at $1.60 a pound? **H**
   F. $C(x) = 1.6x - 50$ G. $C(x) = 50x - 1.6$
   H. $C(x) = 50 - 1.6x$ I. $C(x) = 160 - 50x$

258   Chapter 5 Graphs and Functions

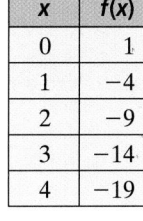

38. What is the function rule for the table at the right? **D**
   A. $f(x) = x - 5$
   B. $f(x) = -5x - 4$
   C. $f(x) = 5x - 1$
   D. $f(x) = -5x + 1$

x	f(x)
0	1
1	-4
2	-9
3	-14
4	-19

Quantitative Comparison Compare the boxed quantity in Column A with the boxed quantity in Column B. Choose the best answer.
   A. The quantity in Column A is greater.
   B. The quantity in Column B is greater.
   C. The two quantities are equal.
   D. The relationship cannot be determined from the information given.

Column A	Column B
B 39. $f(3)$ when $f(x) = 4x - 12$	$f(0)$ when $f(x) = x + 1$
C 40. $f(-3)$ when $f(x) = x^2 - 4$	$f(-2)$ when $f(x) = -2x + 1$

Short Response   **41.** The recommended dosage D in milligrams of a certain medicine depends on a person's body mass w in kilograms. The function rule $D = 0.1w^2 + 5w$ describes the relationship of the dosage to body mass. Evaluate the function for a person who has a mass of 60 kilograms. Show your work. **See margin.**

Take It to the NET
Online lesson quiz at
www.PHSchool.com
Web Code: aea-0504

Mixed Review

Lesson 5-3 **Model each rule with a table of values and a graph. 42–47. See back of book.**

42. $f(x) = x - 3$ **43.** $y = 5 - x$ **44.** $g(x) = -x + 3$

45. $f(x) = 2x - 3$ **46.** $y = |2x| - 3$ **47.** $y = 2x^2 - 3$

Lesson 4-4 **Find each percent of change. Describe the percent of change as an increase or decrease. Round to the nearest percent. 48–53. See margin.**

48. 12 cm to 14 cm   **49.** 98 oz to 100 oz   **50.** 65 ml to 60 ml

51. 6 ft to 1 ft   **52.** 1.4 m to 1.8 m   **53.** $1\frac{1}{2}$ in. to $\frac{7}{8}$ in.

Lesson 4-1 **54.** **Measurement** The figure at the right shows how much juice you can get from some fruits.
   a. What is the minimum number of oranges needed to make a cup of orange juice? What is the maximum number of oranges needed? (*Hint:* 16 tablespoons = 1 cup) **2 oranges; 3 oranges**
   b. Suppose you buy a bag of 6 lemons and a bag of 5 limes. What is the most juice you can expect to get from these bags of fruit? **28 tbsp**

How Much Juice in an Average Fruit?

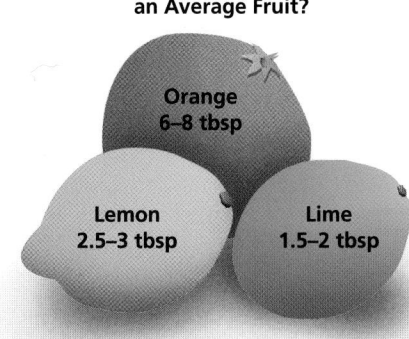

Orange
6–8 tbsp

Lemon
2.5–3 tbsp

Lime
1.5–2 tbsp

Lesson 5-4 Writing a Function Rule   **259**

---

pages 256–259   Exercises

41. [2] $D = 0.1w^2 + 5w$
    $D = 0.1(60)^2 + 5(60)$
    $D = 0.1(3600) + 300$
    $D = 660$
    The dosage is 660 mg.

[1] correctly substitutes 60 for w but makes a minor calculation error

48. 17%; increase

49. 2%; increase

50. 8%; decrease

51. 83%; decrease

52. 29%; increase

53. 42%; decrease

259

Reading a Graph

Reading a Graph

Students will identify coordinates of points on a graph and list them in a table. They will rearrange the x- and y-coordinates, if necessary, so that the x-coordinates are in order from least to greatest. They will look for a pattern that will enable them to write the function rule that fits the points from the table.

Teaching Notes

Ask students if they notice a relationship between the differences in the y values in the table and the coefficient of the x in their equation. Encourage them to try several other equations and to make a conjecture about the relationship.

Math Tip

In order for a pattern to emerge, students should select the x values for points on the graph in order and at equal intervals. For example, if they select $(-1, y_1)$ first, then they could select $(0, y_2)$, $(1, y_3)$ . . .

Tactile Learner

Direct students to select x values at intervals of 1 on the graph. Then tell them to draw steps from one point on the graph to the next (up and over, up and over . . .). Students can trace a path *up the stairs* with their fingers. They should notice that they are going up the same amount each step and that amount matches the coefficient of x when they write the equation.

Exercise

Have students write a simple linear equation and make a table of x- and y-coordinates. Then have them trade just the tables with their partners. Then they try to figure out what the other partner's equation is. When they think they have the answer, they can check with each other.

The problem below will help you recognize patterns in numerical data. These data describe the coordinates of points on the graph of a line. Read and solve the problem as you follow along. Check your understanding with the exercise at the bottom of the page.

Make a table of values for the graph. Use the table to write a function rule.

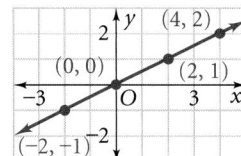

To create a table from a graph, identify the coordinates of points on the graph. For each point, list the x-value in the left column, and the corresponding $f(x)$-value (or y-value) in the right column.

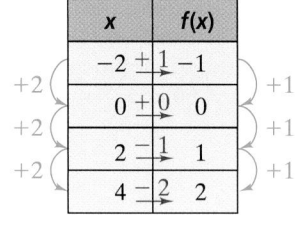

- Look for patterns between x-values and their corresponding y-values.

- Look for patterns between consecutive x-values and between consecutive y-values

To write a function rule from a table, you need to find a pattern among the data. You can ask yourself,

What do I need to do to x to get $f(x)$?

Make a guess using one pair of data points. Then try your guess with another pair to see if it works. The numbers in red in the table show that the difference between x and $f(x)$ values are not the same. So you cannot add the same number to an x value to get the corresponding $f(x)$ value.

As you go down the table, you can see that as x-values increase by 2, the corresponding y-values increase by 1. Notice that if you multiply –2 by $\frac{1}{2}$ you get –1, and $(-2, -1)$ is an (x, y) pair in the table. Using mental math, you can see that $\frac{1}{2}$ times any x-value gives the corresponding y-value.

$f(x)$ equals x multiplied by $\frac{1}{2}$. Relate.

$f(x) = \frac{1}{2}x$ Write.

EXERCISE

Make a table of values for the graph. Use the table to write a function rule.

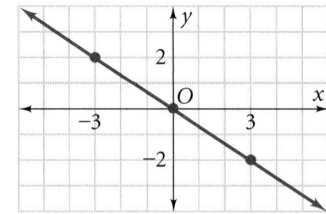

Tables may vary.
Sample:

x	y
-3	2
0	0
3	-2

function rule $y = -\frac{2}{3}x$

Direct Variation

North Carolina Objectives

1.03 Model and solve problems using direct variation.
4.01 Use linear functions or inequalities to model and solve problems; justify results.

Lesson Preview

What You'll Learn

 OBJECTIVE 1 To write an equation of a direct variation

 OBJECTIVE 2 To use ratios and proportions with direct variations

. . . And Why

To write a direct variation relating to weather, as in Example 3

 Check Skills You'll Need (For help, go to Lessons 2-6 and 4-1.)

Solve each equation for the given variable.

$y = -\dfrac{ax}{b}$

1. $nq = m; q$ $q = \dfrac{m}{n}$ **2.** $d = rt; r$ $r = \dfrac{d}{t}$ **3.** $ax + by = 0; y$

Solve each proportion.

4. $\dfrac{5}{8} = \dfrac{x}{12}$ 7.5   **5.** $\dfrac{4}{9} = \dfrac{n}{45}$ 20   **6.** $\dfrac{25}{15} = \dfrac{y}{3}$ 5

7. $\dfrac{7}{n} = \dfrac{35}{50}$ 10   **8.** $\dfrac{8}{d} = \dfrac{20}{36}$ 14.4   **9.** $\dfrac{14}{18} = \dfrac{63}{n}$ 81

New Vocabulary • direct variation • constant of variation

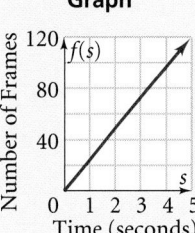 **Interactive lesson** includes instant self-check, tutorials, and activities.

OBJECTIVE 1

Writing the Equation of a Direct Variation

Investigation: Direct Variation

As you watch a movie, 24 individual pictures, or frames, flash on the screen each second. Here are three ways you can model the relationship between the number of frames $f(s)$ and the number of seconds s.

Table

s number of seconds	$f(s)$ number of frames
1	24
2	48
3	72
4	96
5	120

Graph

Number of Frames vs. Time (seconds), line through origin with steep positive slope; vertical axis labeled $f(s)$ from 0 to 120, horizontal axis labeled s from 0 to 5.

Function Rule

$f(s) = 24s$

1. As the number of seconds doubles, what happens to the number of frames? **The number of frames doubles.**

2. Find the ratio $\dfrac{\text{number of frames}}{\text{number of seconds}}$ for each pair of data in the table. $\dfrac{24}{1}$

3. For every increase of 1 second on the horizontal axis of the graph, what is the increase on the vertical axis? **24 frames**

4. What do you notice about your answers to Questions 2 and 3 and the coefficient of s in the function rule? **They are all the same.**

5. a. What number of frames corresponds to $s = 0$? **0**
    b. What is the ordered pair on the graph for the seconds and number of frames when $s = 0$? **(0, 0)**

 Ongoing Assessment and Intervention

Before the Lesson	During the Lesson	After the Lesson
Diagnose prerequisite skills using:	**Monitor progress using:**	**Assess knowledge using:**
• Check Skills You'll Need	• Check Understanding	• Lesson Quiz
	• Additional Examples	• Computer Test Generator CD
	• Standardized Test Prep	• Chapter Checkpoint 2 (p. 267)

1. Plan

Lesson Preview

 **Check Skills You'll Need**

Formulas
Lesson 2-6: Example 3
Exercises 17–24
Extra Practice, p. 703

Ratio and Proportion
Lesson 4-1: Example 4
Exercises 14–29
Extra Practice, p. 705

Lesson Resources

Teaching Resources
Practice, Reteaching, Enrichment
Checkpoint Quiz 2

Reaching All Students
Practice Workbook 5-5
Spanish Practice Workbook 5-5
Reading and Math Literacy 5C
Spanish Reading & Literacy 5C
Spanish Checkpoint Quiz 2
Basic Algebra Planning Guide 5-5

Presentation Assistant Plus!
Transparencies
• Check Skills You'll Need 5-5
• Additional Examples 5-5
• Student Edition Answers 5-5
• Lesson Quiz 5-5
PH Presentation Pro CD 5-5

PRENTICE HALL ASSESSMENT SYSTEM

Checkpoint Quiz 2
Computer Test Generator CD

 Technology
Resource Pro® CD-ROM
Computer Test Generator CD
Prentice Hall Presentation Pro CD

www.PHSchool.com
Student Site
• Teacher Web Code: aek-5500
• Updated Data
• Reasoning & Puzzles p. 87
• Self-grading Lesson Quiz
Teacher Center
• Lesson Planner
• Resources

Plus

261

2. Teach

Math Background

The concept of direct variation can be stated in a number of ways: $y = kx$; the straight line that has a slope of k and passes through the origin; y varies directly as x; and y is directly proportional to x.

Investigation (Optional)

Teaching Tip

Students may need help understanding that the table, graph, and function rule all represent the same relationship. Have students point to a row in the table, find the point with those coordinates on the graph, and then substitute the coordinates into the function rule. Repeat for each row in the table.

OBJECTIVE

1 Teaching Notes

1 EXAMPLE English Learners

The term "constant of variation" seems to be an oxymoron, and thus may be confusing to some students. Explain that this term means that the amount of change (variation) in y-values is constantly the same when x-values change by a constant amount. You may wish to introduce the term *oxymoron* to the class and have a student look up its definition and read it aloud.

2 EXAMPLE Error Prevention

Some students may think $-\frac{3}{4} = k$ is the equation and stop there. Remind students that an x and a y need to be in the equation. They have found only what k equals and must substitute that value into k's place in the direct variation formula.

262

When a film is projected the number of frames doubles as the number of seconds doubles. The number of frames is proportional to the number of seconds; that is, the number of frames varies directly with the number of seconds.

 Key Concepts

Definition	Direct Variation
A function in the form $y = kx$, where $k \neq 0$, is a **direct variation.** The **constant of variation** k is the coefficient of x. The variables y and x are said to vary directly with each other.	

 Reading Math

Constant means *remaining the same.* Constant of variation means changing at the *same rate.*

For $y = kx$, y is a function of x. If $x = 0$, then $y = 0$, so the graph of a direct variation is a line that passes through $(0, 0)$. To tell whether an equation represents a direct variation, solve for y. If the equation can be written in the form $y = kx$, it represents a direct variation.

1 EXAMPLE Is an Equation a Direct Variation?

Is each equation a direct variation? If it is, find the constant of variation.

a. $5x + 2y = 0$

$\qquad 2y = -5x$ **Subtract 5x from each side.**

$\qquad y = -\frac{5}{2}x$ **Divide each side by 2.**

The equation has the form $y = kx$, so the equation is a direct variation. The constant of variation is $-\frac{5}{2}$.

b. $5x + 2y = 9$

$\qquad 2y = 9 - 5x$ **Subtract 5x from each side.**

$\qquad y = \frac{9}{2} - \frac{5}{2}x$ **Divide each side by 2.**

The equation cannot be written in the form $y = kx$. It is not a direct variation.

✔ **Check Understanding** ❶ Is each equation a direct variation? If it is, find the constant of variation.
a. $7y = 2x$ **yes;** $\frac{2}{7}$ **b.** $3y + 4x = 8$ **no**   **c.** $y - 7.5x = 0$ **yes; 7.5**

To write an equation for a direct variation, you first find the constant of variation k using a point other than the origin that lies on the graph of the equation. Then use the value of k to write an equation.

2 EXAMPLE Writing an Equation Given a Point

Write an equation of the direct variation that includes the point $(4, -3)$.

$\qquad y = kx$ **Start with the function form of a direct variation.**

$\qquad -3 = k(4)$ **Substitute 4 for x and −3 for y.**

$\qquad -\frac{3}{4} = k$ **Divide each side by 4 to solve for k.**

$\qquad y = -\frac{3}{4}x$ **Write an equation. Substitute $-\frac{3}{4}$ for k in $y = kx$.**

An equation of the direct variation is $y = -\frac{3}{4}x$.

✔ **Check Understanding** ❷ Write an equation of the direct variation that includes the point $(-3, -6)$.
$y = 2x$

262   Chapter 5   Graphs and Functions

 **Reaching All Students**

Below Level Use stamps and money to show how stamp cost varies directly with the number bought. Ask students to identify the independent variable, and then write a table and an equation.	**Advanced Learners** Students may wish to explore whether there is direct variation in the lengths of sides of similar geometric figures.	**English Learners** See note on page 262. **Inclusion** See note on page 265.

You can use a direct variation to describe a real-world situation in which the dependent variable varies directly with the independent variable.

3 EXAMPLE Real-World 🌐 Problem Solving

Weather Your distance from lightning varies directly with the time it takes you to hear thunder. If you hear thunder 10 seconds after you see lightning, you are about 2 miles from the lightning. Write an equation for the relationship between time and distance.

Relate The distance varies directly with the time. When $x = 10$, $y = 2$.

Define Let x = the number of seconds between your seeing lightning and your hearing thunder.

Let y = your distance in miles from the lightning.

Write

$y = kx$	Use the general form of a direct variation.
$2 = k(10)$	Substitute 10 for x and 2 for y.
$\frac{1}{5} = k$	Divide each side by 10 to solve for k.
$y = \frac{1}{5}x$	Write an equation. Substitute $\frac{1}{5}$ for k in $y = kx$.

The equation $y = \frac{1}{5}x$ relates the time x in seconds it takes you to hear the thunder to the distance y in miles you are from the lightning.

Real-World 🌐 Connection

The total energy released by a single flash of lightning could power an ordinary light bulb for a few months.

✓ **Check Understanding** ❸ A recipe for a dozen corn muffins calls for 1 cup of flour. The number of muffins varies directly with the amount of flour you use. Write a direct variation for the relationship between the number of cups of flour and the number of muffins.
$y = 12x$

OBJECTIVE

2 Ratios, Proportions, and Direct Variations

You can rewrite a direct variation $y = kx$ as $\frac{y}{x} = k$. When two sets of data vary directly, the ratio $\frac{y}{x}$ is the constant of variation. It is the same for each data pair.

4 EXAMPLE Direct Variations and Tables

For each table, use the ratio $\frac{y}{x}$ to tell whether y varies directly with x. If it does, write an equation for the direct variation.

a.

x	y	$\frac{y}{x}$
-3	2.25	$\frac{2.25}{-3} = -0.75$
1	-0.75	$\frac{-0.75}{1} = -0.75$
4	-3	$\frac{-3}{4} = -0.75$
6	-4.5	$\frac{-4.5}{6} = -0.75$

b.

x	y	$\frac{y}{x}$
2	-1	$\frac{-1}{2} = -0.5$
4	1	$\frac{1}{4} = 0.25$
6	3	$\frac{3}{6} = 0.5$
9	4.5	$\frac{4.5}{9} = 0.5$

Yes, the constant of variation is -0.75. The equation is $y = -0.75x$.

No, the ratio $\frac{y}{x}$ is not the same for all pairs of data.

4 For each table, use the ratio $\frac{y}{x}$ to tell whether y varies directly with x. If it does, write an equation for the direct variation.

a.

x	y	$\frac{y}{x}$
-2	1	$\frac{1}{-2} = -0.5$
2	-1	$\frac{-1}{2} = -0.5$
4	-2	$\frac{-2}{4} = -0.5$

a. yes; $y = -0.5x$

b.

x	y	$\frac{y}{x}$
-1	2	$\frac{2}{-1} = -2$
1	2	$\frac{2}{1} = 2$
2	-4	$\frac{-4}{2} = -2$

b. no

5 Suppose a windlass requires 0.75 lb of force to lift an object that weighs 48 lb. How much force would you need to lift 210 lb? **about 3.3 lb of force**

Closure

Have students state the form of a direct variation rule. $y = kx$ Ask what k represents? **constant of variation**

pages 264–267 Exercises

29. $y = \frac{1}{6}x$

30. $y = -20x$

31. $y = -\frac{36}{25}x$

32. $y = 6x$

33. $y = 9x$

34. $y = -\frac{1}{32}x$

35. $y = -\frac{15}{52}x$

36. $y = \frac{27}{64}x$

37a. The ratio $\frac{y}{x}$ is the same for each pair of values.

   b. A line through the origin that is neither vertical nor horizontal is the graph of a direct variation.

38. True; a line that is neither horizontal nor vertical can pass through $(0, 0)$ and $(-2, 4)$.

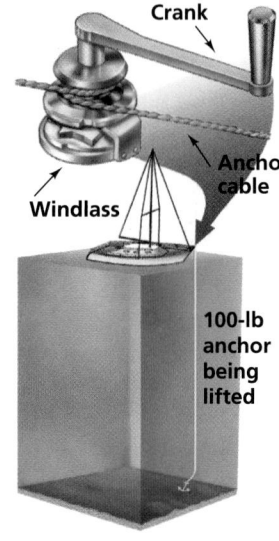

Crank

Anchor cable

Windlass

100-lb anchor being lifted

A windlass is a winch turned by a crank. It is used in a water well and to raise an anchor on a boat.

✓ Check Understanding **4** For the data in each table, tell whether y varies directly with x. If it does, write an equation for the direct variation.

a.

x	y
-2	3.2
1	2.4
4	1.6

no

b.

x	y
4	6
8	12
10	15

yes; $y = 1.5x$

In a direct variation, the ratio $\frac{y}{x}$ is the same for all pairs of data where $x \neq 0$. So the proportion $\frac{y_1}{x_1} = \frac{y_2}{x_2}$ is true for the ordered pairs (x_1, y_1) and (x_2, y_2), where neither x_1 nor x_2 are zero.

5 EXAMPLE **Real-World**  **Problem Solving**

Physics The force you must apply to lift an object varies directly with the object's weight. You would need to apply 0.625 lb of force to a windlass to lift a 28-lb weight. How much force would you need to lift 100 lb?

Relate A force of 0.625 lb lifts 28 lb. What force lifts 100 lb?

Define Let n = the force you need to lift 100 lb.

Write $\dfrac{\text{force}_1}{\text{weight}_1} = \dfrac{\text{force}_2}{\text{weight}_2}$ **Use a proportion.**

$\dfrac{0.625}{28} = \dfrac{n}{100}$ **Substitute 0.625 for force₁, 28 for weight₁, and 100 for weight₂.**

$0.625(100) = 28n$ **Use cross products.**

$n \approx 2.2$ **Solve for n.**

● You need about 2.2 lb of force to lift 100 lb.

✓ Check Understanding **5** **Physics** Suppose a second windlass requires 0.5 lb of force to lift an object that weighs 32 lb. How much force would you need to lift 160 lb? **2.5 lb**

EXERCISES

For more practice, see *Extra Practice*.

Practice and Problem Solving

A **Practice by Example**

Example 1
(page 262)

Is each equation a direct variation? If it is, find the constant of variation.

1. $2y = 5x + 1$ **no**
2. $8x + 9y = 10$ **no**
3. $-12x = 6y$ **yes; -2**
4. $y + 8 = -x$ **no**
5. $5x - 6y = 0$ **yes; $\frac{5}{6}$**
6. $-4 + 7x + 4 = 3y$ **yes; $\frac{7}{3}$**
7. $-x = 10y$ **yes; $-\frac{1}{10}$**
8. $0.7x - 1.4y = 0$ **yes; 0.5**
9. $\frac{1}{2}x + \frac{1}{3}y = 0$ **yes; $-\frac{3}{2}$**

Example 2
(page 262)

Write an equation of the direct variation that includes the given point.

10. $(1, 5)$ $y = 5x$
11. $(5, 1)$ $y = \frac{1}{5}x$
12. $(-8, 10)$ $y = -\frac{5}{4}x$
13. $(-5, -9)$ $y = \frac{9}{5}x$
14. $(-2, 3)$ $y = -\frac{3}{2}x$
15. $(-6, 1)$ $y = -\frac{1}{6}x$
16. $(3, -4)$ $y = -\frac{4}{3}x$
17. $(6, -8)$ $y = -\frac{4}{3}x$
18. $(-6, 8)$ $y = -\frac{4}{3}x$
19. $(-5, -10)$ $y = 2x$
20. $(12, -8)$ $y = -\frac{2}{3}x$
21. $(35, 7)$ $y = \frac{1}{5}x$

39. False; the line through $(0, 3)$ and $(0, 0)$ is vertical, so it is not a function and is therefore not a direct variation.

40. True; for the equation $y = kx$, if one side is multiplied by 3, then the other side must be multiplied by 3.

41. 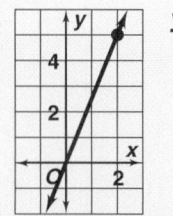 $y = \frac{5}{2}x$

22–23. **Choices of variables may vary.**

Example 3 (page 263)

Define the variables. Then write a direct variation to model each relationship.

22. Geometry The perimeter of a regular octagon varies directly with the length of one side of the octagon. $P(\ell) = 8\ell$

23. Earnings When you have a job that pays an hourly wage, the amount you earn varies directly with the number of hours you work. Suppose you earn $7.10/hour working at the library. $E(h) = 7.10h$

Example 4 (page 263)

For the data in each table, tell whether y varies directly with x. If it does, write an equation for the direct variation.

24.

x	y
3	5.4
7	12.6
12	21.6

yes; $y = 1.8x$

25.

x	y
−2	1
3	6
8	11

no

26.

x	y
−6	9
1	−1.5
8	−12

yes; $y = -1.5x$

Example 5 (page 264)

27. Physics The maximum weight you can lift with a lever varies directly with the amount of force you apply. Suppose you can lift a 50-lb weight by applying 20 lb of force to a certain lever.
 a. What is the ratio of weight to force for the lever? $\frac{50}{20}$ or $\frac{5}{2}$
 b. Write a proportion and find the force you need to lift a friend weighing 130 lb. $\frac{50}{20} = \frac{130}{x}$, 52 lb

28. Bicycling A bicyclist traveled at a constant speed during a timed practice period. Write a proportion to find the distance the cyclist traveled in 30 min. $\frac{10}{3} = \frac{30}{x}$, 9 mi

A Bicyclist's Practices

Elapsed Time	Distance
10 min	3 mi
25 min	7.5 mi

B **Apply Your Skills**

Write an equation of the direct variation that includes the given point. 29–36. See margin p. 264.

29. $\left(3, \frac{1}{2}\right)$ **30.** $\left(\frac{1}{4}, -5\right)$ **31.** $\left(\frac{-5}{6}, \frac{6}{5}\right)$ **32.** $(1.2, 7.2)$

33. $(0.5, 4.5)$ **34.** $\left(-2, \frac{1}{16}\right)$ **35.** $(5.2, -1.5)$ **36.** $\left(-\frac{8}{3}, -\frac{9}{8}\right)$

37. a. Writing How can you tell whether two sets of data vary directly?
 b. How can you tell if a line is the graph of a direct variation?
 a–b. See margin p. 264.

Critical Thinking Is each statement true or false? Explain. 38–40. See margin p. 264.

38. The graph of a direct variation may pass through $(-2, 4)$.

39. The graph of a direct variation may pass through $(0, 3)$.

40. If you triple an x-value of a direct variation, the y-value also triples.

Graph the direct variation that includes the given point. Write an equation of the line. 41–44. See margin p. 264.

41. $(2, 5)$ **42.** $(-2, 5)$ **43.** $(2, -5)$ **44.** $(-2, -5)$

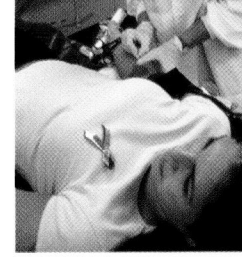

Real-World **Connection**

You must be at least 17 years old and weigh at least 110 pounds to give blood.

45. Biology The amount of blood in a person's body varies directly with body weight. A person who weighs 160 lb has about 5 qt of blood.
 a. Find the constant of variation. $\frac{1}{32}$
 b. Write an equation relating quarts of blood to weight. $b = \frac{1}{32}w$
 c. Open-Ended Estimate the number of quarts of blood in your body. **Check students' work.**

Lesson 5-5 Direct Variation **265**

 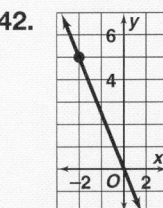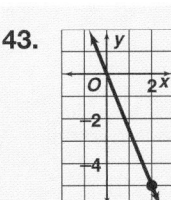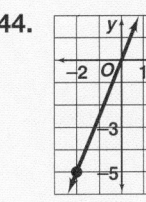
3. Practice

Assignment Guide

1 Objective
 Ⓐ Ⓑ Core 1–23, 29–44
 Ⓒ Extension 53

2 Objective
 Ⓐ Ⓑ Core 24–28, 45, 46
 Ⓒ Extension 47–52

Standardized Test Prep 54–59

Mixed Review 60–72

Connection to Geometry
Exercise 22 Suggest to students that they first write the formula for the perimeter of a regular polygon, $P = n\ell$, where n is the number of sides of the polygon and ℓ is the length of a side.

Connection to Physics
Exercise 27 Demonstrate to students that a lever is a rigid bar that pivots about a point, the fulcrum, and is used to move or lift a load at one end by applying force to the other end.

Inclusion
Exercise 45c Students who are self-conscious about weight may be uncomfortable with this exercise. As an alternative, assign weight amounts.

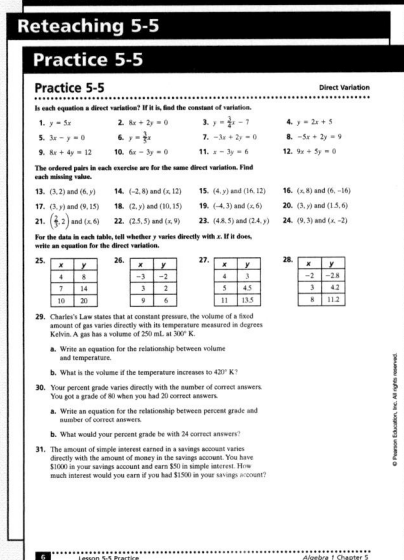

Lesson Quiz 5-5

1. Is each equation a direct variation? If it is, find the constant of variation.

  a. $x + 5y = 10$ **no**

  b. $3y + 8x = 0$ **yes;** $-\frac{8}{3}$

2. Write an equation of the direct variation that includes the point $(-5, -4)$. $y = \frac{4}{5}x$

3. For each table, tell whether y varies directly with x. If it does, write an equation for the direct variation.

a.

x	y
−1	3
−0	0
2	−6
3	−9

b.

x	y
−1	−2
0	0
1	2
3	−6

a. yes;   **b. no**
$y = -3x$

Alternative Assessment

Organize students into groups of five. Have each student write a coordinate pair in a table. Students pass their tables to the left. Students find k for the coordinate pair. Pass the tables to the left again. Students write the direct variation. Pass the tables to the left again. Students extend the table to include four coordinate pairs. Pass the tables to the left again. Students graph the direct variation.

Standardized Test Prep

Resources

For additional practice with a variety of test item formats:
• Standardized Test Prep, p. 279
• Test-Taking Strategies, p. 274
• Test-Taking Strategies with Transparencies

266

---

 46. Electricity Ohm's Law $V = I \times R$ relates the voltage, current, and resistance of a circuit. V is the voltage measured in volts. I is the current measured in amperes. R is the resistance measured in ohms.

  a. Find the voltage of a circuit that has a current of 24 amperes and resistance of 2 ohms. **48 volts**

  b. Find the resistance of a circuit that has a current of 24 amperes and a voltage of 18 volts. **0.75 ohms**

C Challenge   **The ordered pairs in each exercise are for the same direct variation. Find each missing value.**

47. $(3, 4)$ and $(9, y)$ **12**   **48.** $(-1, 2)$ and $(4, y)$ **−8**   **49.** $(-5, 3)$ and $(x, -4.8)$ **8**

50. $(1, y)$ and $\left(\frac{3}{2}, -9\right)$ **−6**   **51.** $(2, 5)$ and $(x, 12.5)$ **5**   **52.** $(-2, 5)$ and $(x, -5)$ **2**

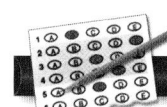
Problem Solving Hint

For Exercise 53, start with the relationship of miles and gallons:
$\frac{m}{g} = 24$.

53. Gas Mileage A car gets 24 miles per gallon. The number of gallons g of gas used varies directly with the number of miles m traveled.

  a. Suppose the price of gas is \$1.83 per gallon. Write a function relating the cost c for g gallons of gas. Is this a direct variation? $c = 1.83g$**; yes**

  b. Write a direct variation relating the cost of gas to the miles traveled.
$c = \frac{1.83}{24}m$ **or** $c = 0.07625m$

Standardized Test Prep

Multiple Choice

54. Which equation is a direct variation? **A**

  A. $y = -0.7x$ **B.** $y = \frac{21}{x}$ **C.** $y - x = 4$ **D.** $y = 3x + 2$

55. A direct variation includes the point $(-8, 2)$. Which is an equation of the direct variation? **H**

  F. $-8y = x + 2$ **G.** $2y = -8x$ **H.** $y = \frac{x}{-4}$ **I.** $y = -4x$

Quantitative Comparison

Compare the boxed quantity in Column A with the boxed quantity in Column B. Choose the best answer.

  A. The quantity in Column A is greater.

  B. The quantity in Column B is greater.

  C. The two quantities are equal.

  D. The relationship cannot be determined from the information given.

Use this statement for Exercises 56–58.

A direct variation includes the point $(5, -4)$.

	Column A	Column B
A 56.	constant of variation of the equation	y-value, when $x = 3$
B 57.	y-value, when $x = 5$	y-value, when $x = -5$
C 58.	y-value, when $x = 0$	0

Take It to the NET
Online lesson quiz at
www.PHSchool.com
Web Code: aea-0505

Short Response

59. Write an equation of the direct variation that includes the point $(-1, -4)$. Show your work. **See margin.**

266   Chapter 5   Graphs and Functions

pages 264–267 Exercises

59. [2] $y = kx$
$\quad -4 = k(-1)$
$\quad\quad 4 = k$
$\quad\quad y = 4x$

  [1] correct answer but no work shown

Lesson 5-4

Write a function rule for each table.

60.

Number of People	Total Bill
1	$3.00
2	$6.00
3	$9.00
4	$12.00

$y = 3x$

61.

Amount Earned	Amount Spent
$15	$5
$30	$10
$45	$15
$60	$20

$y = \frac{1}{3}x$

64. $r > -18$
65. $c \le -1.8$
66. $m < -3$
67. $a \ge 16.6$
68. $n < -80$
69. $t \ge 3.04$
70. $v \ge -\frac{5}{2}$
71. $b > \frac{1}{2}$

62.

Number of Days	Supplies Remaining
0	12 lb
2	10 lb
4	8 lb
6	6 lb

$y = 12 - x$

63.

Weight on Earth (lb)	Weight on Moon (lb)
96	16
123	20.5
144	24
171	28.5

$y = \frac{1}{6}x$

Lessons 3-2, 3-3

Solve each inequality. 64–71. See left above.

64. $r + 6 > -12$ 65. $5 + c \le 3.2$ 66. $7m < -21$ 67. $a - 4.5 \ge 12.1$

68. $\frac{n}{4} < -20$ 69. $3t \ge 9.12$ 70. $\frac{v}{-5} \le \frac{1}{2}$ 71. $b + 4\frac{2}{3} > 5\frac{1}{6}$

Lesson 1-6   72. **Shipping** For the ships that pass through the Panama Canal, the average toll is $45,000 per ship. The canal authority earned about $700 million in the year 2000. About how many ships passed through the canal that year? Round to the nearest hundred. **15,600 ships**

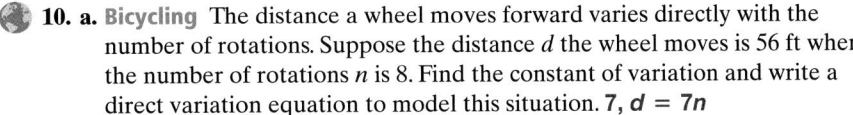
✓ Checkpoint Quiz 2 Lessons 5-3 through 5-5

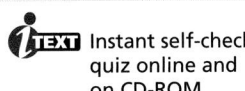 Instant self-check quiz online and on CD-ROM

Model each rule with a table of values and a graph. If the rule describes a direct variation, state the constant of variation. 1–4. See margin.

1. $y = 4x + 1$ 2. $y = \frac{1}{2}x$ 3. $f(x) = -3x$ 4. $y = -3x + 2$

Write a function rule for each situation.

5. the total cost $t(p)$ of p pounds of potatoes at $.79 per pound $t(p) = 0.79p$

6. the total distance $d(n)$ traveled in n hours at a constant speed of 60 mi/h
$d(n) = 60n$

Write an equation for the direct variation that includes the given point.

7. $(7, -2)$ $y = -\frac{2}{7}x$ 8. $(-3, -6)$ $y = 2x$ 9. $(-4, -5)$ $y = \frac{5}{4}x$

🌐 10. a. **Bicycling** The distance a wheel moves forward varies directly with the number of rotations. Suppose the distance d the wheel moves is 56 ft when the number of rotations n is 8. Find the constant of variation and write a direct variation equation to model this situation. **7, $d = 7n$**
   b. Use the direct variation you wrote for part (a) to find the distance the wheel moves in 20 rotations. **140 ft**

Lesson 5-5 Direct Variation **267**

✓ Chapter Checkpoint 2

To check understanding of Lessons 5-3 to 5-6:

Checkpoint Quiz 2 (p. 267)

📁 **Teaching Resources**
Checkpoint Quiz 2 (also in Prentice Hall Assessment System)

👥 **Reaching All Students**
Reading and Math Literacy 5C

Spanish versions available

page 267 Checkpoint Quiz 2

1.

x	y
-1	-3
0	1
1	5

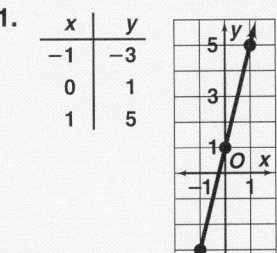

2.

x	y
-2	-1
0	0
2	1

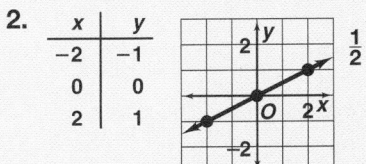 $\frac{1}{2}$

3.

x	f(x)
-1	3
0	0
1	-3

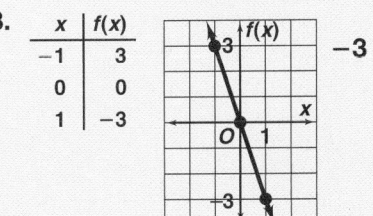 -3

4.

x	y
-1	5
0	2
1	-1

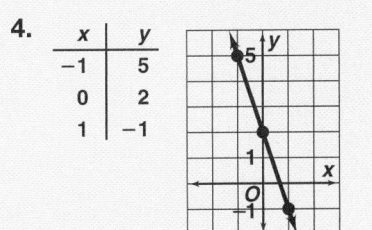

1. Plan

Lesson Preview

✓ Check Skills You'll Need

Exponents and Order of Operations
Lesson 1-2: Example 2
Exercises 7–12
Extra Practice, p. 702

Subtracting Real Numbers
Lesson 1-5: Example 3
Exercises 9–16
Extra Practice, p. 702

Lesson Resources

📁 Teaching Resources
Practice, Reteaching, Enrichment

👥 Reaching All Students
Practice Workbook 5-6
Spanish Practice Workbook 5-6
Hands-On Activities 12
Basic Algebra Planning Guide 5-6

⏱ Presentation Assistant Plus!
Transparencies
• Check Skills You'll Need 5-6
• Additional Examples 5-6
• Student Edition Answers 5-6
• Lesson Quiz 5-6
PH Presentation Pro CD 5-6

ASSESSMENT SYSTEM
Computer Test Generator CD

💿 Technology
Resource Pro® CD-ROM
Computer Test Generator CD
Prentice Hall Presentation Pro CD

🖥 www.PHSchool.com
Student Site
• Teacher Web Code: aek-5500
• Self-grading Lesson Quiz
Teacher Center
• Lesson Planner
• Resources

Plus 🔲 iTEXT

5-6

Describing Number Patterns

North Carolina Objectives

1.02 Use formulas and algebraic expressions, including iterative and recursive forms, to model and solve problems.

Lesson Preview

What You'll Learn

OBJECTIVE 1
To use inductive reasoning in continuing number patterns

OBJECTIVE 2
To write rules for arithmetic sequences

. . . And Why

To predict the next numbers in a pattern, as in Example 1

✓ Check Skills You'll Need

(For help, go to Lesson 1-2 and 1-5.)

Evaluate each expression for $x = 2, 3, 4$.

1. $9 + 3(x - 1)$ **12, 15, 18** **2.** $8 + 7(x - 1)$ **15, 22, 29** **3.** $0.4 - 3(x - 1)$
−2.6, −5.6, −8.6

Subtract.

4. $8 - (-6)$ **14** **5.** $-7 - 10$ **−17** **6.** $1.5 - 3.4$ **−1.9**

New Vocabulary • inductive reasoning • conjecture • sequence • term
• arithmetic sequence • common difference

🔲 iTEXT **Interactive lesson includes instant self-check, tutorials, and activities.**

OBJECTIVE 1
Inductive Reasoning and Number Patterns

Suppose you are in a city and notice that the first three streets you pass are 10th Street, 11th Street, and 12th Street. You would probably conclude that the next street would be 13th Street. You would be basing your conclusion on inductive reasoning.

Inductive reasoning is making conclusions based on patterns you observe. A conclusion you reach by inductive reasoning is a **conjecture.**

1a. "Multiply the previous term by 3"; 243, 729.

b. "Add 6 to the previous term"; 33, 39.

c. "Multiply the previous term by −2"; 32, −64.

Reading Math

You read ". . ." at the end of a sequence as "and so on."

1 EXAMPLE Extending Number Patterns

Use inductive reasoning to describe each pattern. Then find the next two numbers in each pattern.

a.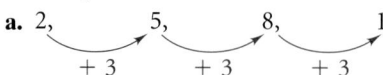

The pattern is "add 3 to the previous term." To find the next two numbers, you add 3 to each previous term: $11 + 3 = 14$ and $14 + 3 = 17$.

b.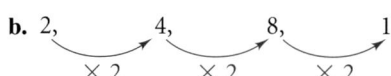

The pattern is "multiply the previous term by 2." To find the next two numbers, you multiply each previous term by 2: $16 \times 2 = 32$ and $32 \times 2 = 64$.

c. $1, 4, 9, 16, \ldots$

The pattern is "square consecutive integers": $1^2, 2^2, 3^2, 4^2$. To find the next two numbers, square the next two consecutive integers: $5^2 = 25$ and $6^2 = 36$.

✓ Check Understanding

1 Use inductive reasoning to describe each pattern. Then find the next two numbers in each pattern. **a–c. See left.**

a. $3, 9, 27, 81, \ldots$ **b.** $9, 15, 21, 27, \ldots$ **c.** $2, -4, 8, -16, \ldots$

268 Chapter 5 Graphs and Functions

🔲 Ongoing Assessment and Intervention

Before the Lesson
Diagnose prerequisite skills using:
• Check Skills You'll Need

During the Lesson
Monitor progress using:
• Check Understanding
• Additional Examples
• Standardized Test Prep

After the Lesson
Assess knowledge using:
• Lesson Quiz
• Computer Test Generator CD

A number pattern is also called a **sequence.** Each number in a sequence is a **term** of the sequence.

One kind of number sequence is an arithmetic sequence. You form an **arithmetic sequence** by adding a fixed number to each previous term. This fixed number is the **common difference.**

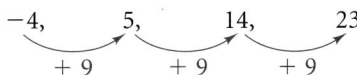

$$-4, \quad 5, \quad 14, \quad 23$$
$$\quad +9 \quad +9 \quad +9$$

2 EXAMPLE **Finding the Common Difference**

Find the common difference of each arithmetic sequence.

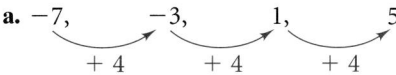
a. $-7, \quad -3, \quad 1, \quad 5$
$\quad +4 \quad +4 \quad +4$

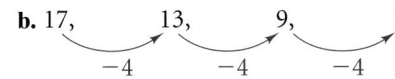
b. $17, \quad 13, \quad 9, \quad 5$
$\quad -4 \quad -4 \quad -4$

The common difference is 4.   The common difference is -4.

✓ **Check Understanding** **2** Find the common difference of each sequence.
a. $11, 23, 35, 47, \ldots$ **12**   **b.** $8, 3, -2, -7, \ldots$ **−5**

Consider the sequence $7, 11, 15, 19, \ldots$ Think of each term as the output of a function. Think of the term number as the input.

term number	1	2	3	4	← input
term	7	11	15	19	← output

You can use the common difference of the terms of an arithmetic sequence to write a function rule for the sequence. For the sequence $7, 11, 15, 19, \ldots$, the common difference is 4.

Let $n =$ the term number in the sequence.

Let $A(n) =$ the value of the nth term of the sequence.

$A(1) = 7$
$A(2) = 7 + 4 = 7 + 1 \cdot 4$
$A(3) = 7 + 4 + 4 = 7 + 2 \cdot 4$
$A(4) = 7 + 4 + 4 + 4 = 7 + 3 \cdot 4$
$A(n) = 7 + 4 + 4 + 4 + \ldots + 4 = 7 + (n - 1)4$

4 is the common difference.
Note that the number in red is one less than the term number, which is in blue.

For an arithmetic sequence, you can use the first term, the term number, and the common difference to find the value of any given term.

Key Concepts

Rule	Arithmetic Sequence
$A(n) = a + (n - 1)d$	
nth term / first term / term number / common difference	

Lesson 5-6 Describing Number Patterns **269**

---

2. Teach

Professional Development

Math Background

A sequence is a set of countable elements ordered in some specific way. In a finite sequence, there is a last term. There is no last term in an infinite sequence.

OBJECTIVE
1 **Teaching Notes**

1 EXAMPLE **Technology Tip**

Have students input the pattern into a spreadsheet. In cell A1, input 2. In cell A2, input =A1+3 ENTER. Highlight cell A2. Grab the bottom right corner of the cell and drag downward to fill the column as far as wanted. Show students how they can find the 23rd number in the pattern by looking at the 23rd row.

Additional Examples

1 Use inductive reasoning to describe each pattern. Then find the next two numbers in each pattern.
a. $1, 5, 9, \ldots$ **add 4 to the previous term; 13, 17**
b. $1, 3, 9, \ldots$ **multiply the previous term by 3; 27, 81**
c. $1, 9, 25, 49, \ldots$ **square of consecutive odd integers; 81, 121, 169**

OBJECTIVE
2 **Teaching Notes**

2 EXAMPLE **Error Prevention**

Students may think the common difference must be a positive number since the definition of arithmetic sequence says you *add* a fixed number. Point out that the common difference is a negative number if the sequence decreases.

👥 **Reaching All Students**

Below Level Help students find the first term, term number, and common difference for the arithmetic sequences in Example 2.	**Advanced Learners** Challenge students to discover that, for an arithmetic sequence, each term after the first is the mean (average) of the two adjacent terms.	**Visual Learners** See note on page 270. **Error Prevention** See note on page 269.

269

3 EXAMPLE   Finding Terms of a Sequence

Find the first, fifth, and tenth terms of the sequence that has the rule $A(n) = 12 + (n − 1)(−2)$.

first term: $A(1) = 12$

fifth term: $A(5) = 12 + (5 − 1)(−2) = 12 + 4(−2) = 4$

tenth term: $A(10) = 12 + (10 − 1)(−2) = 12 + 9(−2) = −6$

✓ **Check Understanding** **3** Find the first, sixth, and twelfth terms of each sequence.
a. $A(n) = −5 + (n − 1)(3)$ **−5, 10, 28**   **b.** $A(n) = 6.3 + (n − 1)(5)$
6.3, 31.3, 61.3

EXERCISES

For more practice, see *Extra Practice*.

Practice and Problem Solving

A Practice by Example

Example 1
(page 268)

Use inductive reasoning to describe each pattern. Then find the next two numbers in each pattern. **1–12. See margin.**

1. 4, 6, 8, 10, . . .   **2.** 4, 6, 9, $13\frac{1}{2}$, . . .   **3.** 4, 6, 9, 13, . . .

4. 3, 3.04, 3.08, 3.12, . . .   **5.** 3, 3.3, 3.63, 3.993, . . .   **6.** 3, 1, −1, −3, . . .

7. 1.1, 2.2, 3.3, 4.4, . . .   **8.** 0.001, 0.01, 0.1, 1, . . .   **9.** 2, 8, 32, 128, . . .

10. 1, $\frac{1}{4}$, $\frac{1}{9}$, $\frac{1}{16}$, . . .   **11.** 9, −5, −19, −33, . . .   **12.** 1.5, 7.5, 37.5, 187.5, . . .

Example 2
(page 269)

Find the common difference of each arithmetic sequence.

13. −5, −2, 1, 4, . . . **3**   **14.** −6, −10, −14, −18, . . . **−4** **15.** 18, 7, −4, −15, . . . **−11**

16. 8, 21, 34, 47, . . . **13**   **17.** $\frac{1}{2}$, $\frac{1}{3}$, $\frac{1}{6}$, 0, . . . **$-\frac{1}{6}$**   **18.** 0.7, 1.5, 2.3, 3.1, . . . **0.8**

19. 8, 6, 4, 2, . . . **−2**   **20.** 10, 22, 34, 46, . . . **12**   **21.** −9, −4, 1, 6, . . . **5**

Example 3
(page 270)

Find the second, fifth, and ninth terms of each sequence.

26. 3.5, 12.5, 24.5

29. −7.1, −22.1, −42.1

31. 17, 5, −11

32. −8, −17, −29

33. −0.8, −3.8, −7.8

22. $A(n) = 2 + (n − 1)(3)$ **5, 14, 26**   **23.** $A(n) = −9 + (n − 1)(6)$ **−3, 15, 39**

24. $A(n) = −7 + (n − 1)(4)$ **−3, 9, 25**   **25.** $A(n) = 8 + (n − 1)(9)$ **17, 44, 80**

26. $A(n) = 0.5 + (n − 1)(3)$ **27.** $A(n) = −5 + (n − 1)(7)$ **2, 23, 51**

28. $A(n) = 9 + (n − 1)(−6)$ **3, −15, −39** **29.** $A(n) = −2.1 + (n − 1)(−5)$

30. $A(n) = 65 + (n − 1)(−7)$ **58, 37, 9**   **31.** $A(n) = 21 + (n − 1)(−4)$

32. $A(n) = −5 + (n − 1)(−3)$ **33.** $A(n) = 0.2 + (n − 1)(−1)$

B Apply Your Skills

35. $3\frac{1}{4}$, $3\frac{1}{2}$

39. 31, 40

42. $\frac{4}{27}$, $-\frac{4}{81}$

Find the next two terms in each sequence.

34. 20, 14, 8, 2, . . . **−4, −10** **35.** 2, $2\frac{1}{4}$, $2\frac{1}{2}$, $2\frac{3}{4}$, 3, . . .   **36.** 2, 5, 10, 17, . . . **26, 37**

37. 12, 4, $1\frac{1}{3}$, $\frac{4}{9}$, . . . **$\frac{4}{27}$, $\frac{4}{81}$** **38.** 0, 3, 8, 15, 24, . . . **35, 48** **39.** −5, 4, 13, 22, . . .

40. 40, 20, 10, 5, . . . **2.5, 1.25** **41.** 7, $7\frac{1}{4}$, $7\frac{1}{2}$, $7\frac{3}{4}$, . . . **8, $8\frac{1}{4}$** **42.** 12, −4, $\frac{4}{3}$, $-\frac{4}{9}$, . . .

43. a. Writing Explain the difference between inductive and deductive reasoning.
   b. Open-Ended Give an example of inductive reasoning and of deductive reasoning. **a. See margin.**
   b. Answers may vary. Check students' work.

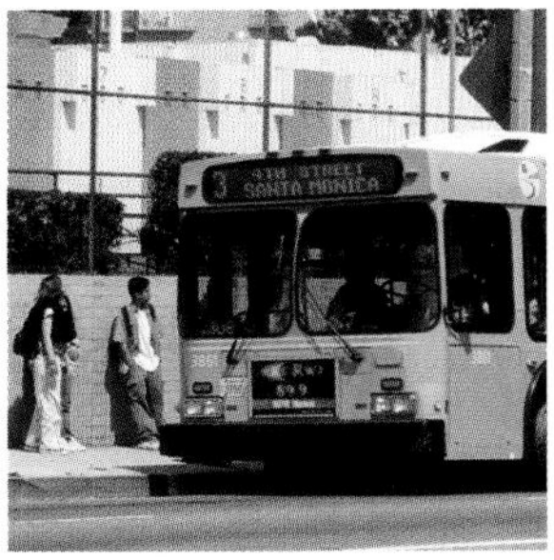

Real-World Connection

About 15% of all trips on mass transit are students going to or from school.

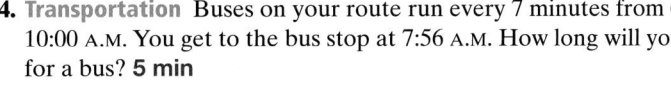

44. Transportation Buses on your route run every 7 minutes from 6:30 A.M. to 10:00 A.M. You get to the bus stop at 7:56 A.M. How long will you have to wait for a bus? **5 min**

45. Open-Ended Write a function rule for a sequence that has −30 as the eighth term. **Answers may vary. Sample: $A(n) = 2 - 4n$**

For Exercises 46 and 47, write the first five terms in each sequence. Explain what the fifth term means in the context of the situation. **46–47. See margin.**

46. A baby's birth weight is 7 lb 4 oz. The baby gains 5 oz each week.

47. The balance of a car loan starts at \$4,500 and decreases \$150 each month.

48. Use the sequence 1, 2, 4, . . .

a. Find the difference between consecutive terms in the sequence. Use inductive reasoning to make a conjecture about the next term in the sequence. **a–c. See left.**

b. Find the quotient of consecutive terms in the sequence. Use inductive reasoning to make a conjecture about the next term in the sequence.

c. Critical Thinking Explain why having more than three terms in a sequence can help you make a conjecture that is more likely to be correct.

48a. 1 2 4; 7 (differences 1, 2)

b. $\frac{2}{1} = 2$; $\frac{4}{2} = 2$; 8

c. When there are more than three terms, you can test the pattern to make sure it is reasonable.

Is each given sequence arithmetic? Justify your answer. **49–54. See margin.**

49. 0.3, 3, 30, 300, . . . **50.** −3, −7, −11, −15, . . . **51.** 1, 8, 27, 64, . . .

52. 2, 4, 8, 16, 32, . . . **53.** 46, 31, 16, 1, . . . **54.** 0.2, −0.6, −1.4, −2.2, . . .

55. The first five rows of Pascal's Triangle are at the right. **1, 5, 10, 10, 5, 1**

a. Predict the numbers in the sixth row.

b. Find the sum of the numbers in each of the first five rows. Predict the sum of the numbers in the sixth row. **1, 2, 4, 8, 16; 32**

1
1 1
1 2 1
1 3 3 1
1 4 6 4 1

Find the second, fourth, and eighth terms of each sequence.

56. $A(n) = 11 + (n - 1)\left(\frac{1}{3}\right)$ **$11\frac{1}{3}$, 12, $13\frac{1}{3}$**

57. $A(n) = 9 + (n - 1)(-4.5)$ **4.5, −4.5, −22.5**

58. $A(n) = -2 + (n - 2)(-1.6)$ **−2, −5.2, −11.6**

59. $A(n) = \frac{1}{5} + (n - 1)\left(\frac{4}{5}\right)$ **1, $2\frac{3}{5}$, $5\frac{4}{5}$**

60. a. Complete the table at the right for an arithmetic sequence.

b. Graph the ordered pairs (term number, term) on a coordinate plane. **a–c. See left.**

c. What do you notice about the points on your graph?

x	y
1	5
2	8
3	■
4	■

60a. 11, 14

b.

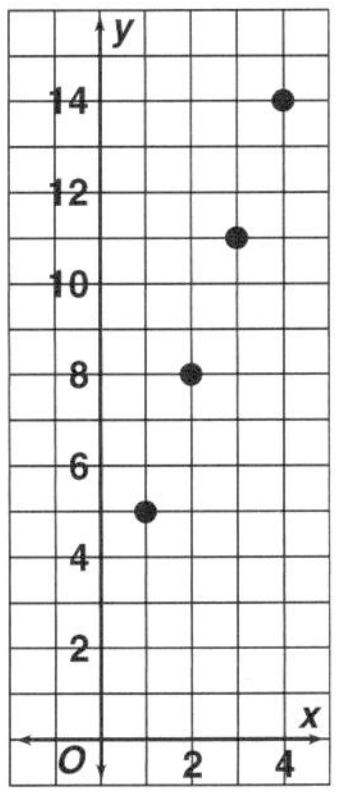

y
14
12
10
8
6
4
2
x
O
2
4

c. The points lie on a line.

61. Music There are 52 white keys on a piano. The frequency produced when a key is struck is the number of vibrations per second the key's string makes.

a. Reasoning Is this relation a function? Explain.

b. Writing Describe the pattern in the relation.

61a. Yes; for each input there is only one output value.

b. For every increase of 7 in the key position, the frequency doubles.

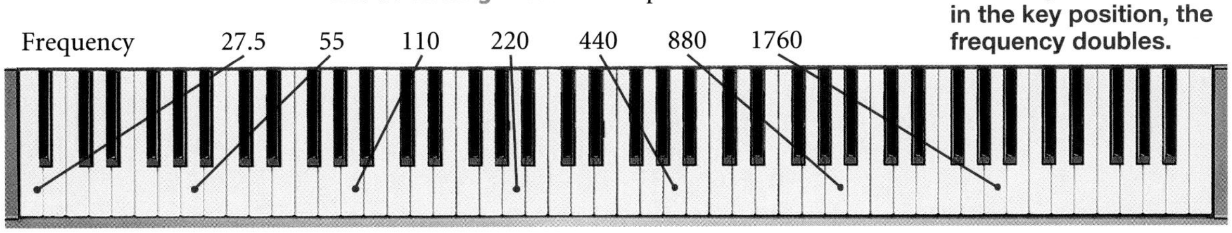

Frequency
27.5
55
110
220
440
880
1760

3. Practice

Assignment Guide

1 Objective

A B Core 1–12, 34–44, 49–55

C Extension 69, 70, 72

2 Objective

A B Core 13–33, 45–48, 56–68

C Extension 71, 73

Standardized Test Prep 74–81

Mixed Review 82–96

Exercises 13–21 Remind students that if the terms of a sequence increase in value, the common difference is positive. If the terms decrease in value, the common difference is negative.

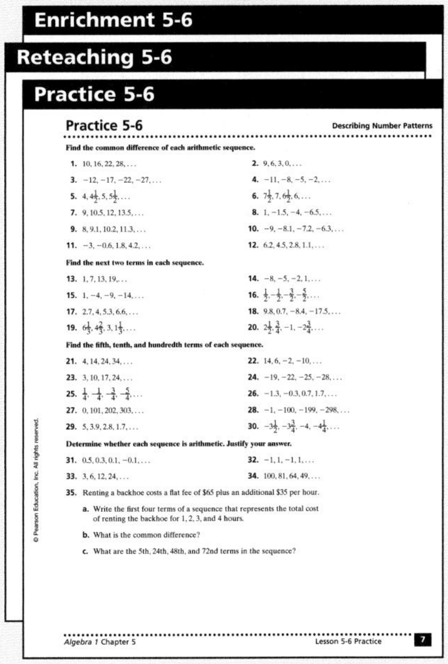
Enrichment 5-6

Reteaching 5-6

Practice 5-6

Practice 5-6 Describing Number Patterns

Find the common difference of each arithmetic sequence.

1. 10, 16, 22, 28, . . .
2. 9, 6, 3, 0, . . .
3. −12, −17, −22, −27, . . .
4. −11, −8, −5, −2, . . .
5. 4, $4\frac{1}{2}$, 5, $5\frac{1}{2}$, . . .
6. $7\frac{1}{2}$, 7, $6\frac{1}{2}$, 6, . . .
7. 9, 10.5, 12, 13.5, . . .
8. 1, −1.5, −4, −6.5, . . .
9. 8, 9.1, 10.2, 11.3, . . .
10. −9, −8.1, −7.2, −6.3, . . .
11. −3, −0.6, 1.8, 4.2, . . .
12. 6.2, 4.5, 2.8, 1.1, . . .

Find the next two terms in each sequence.

13. 1, 7, 13, 19, . . .
14. −8, −5, −2, 1, . . .
15. 1, −4, −9, −14, . . .
16. $\frac{1}{2}$, $-\frac{1}{2}$, $-\frac{3}{2}$, $-\frac{5}{2}$, . . .
17. 2.7, 4, 5.3, 6.6, . . .
18. 9.8, 0.7, −8.4, −17.5, . . .
19. $6\frac{1}{3}$, $4\frac{2}{3}$, 3, $1\frac{1}{3}$, . . .
20. $2\frac{1}{2}$, $\frac{3}{4}$, −1, $-2\frac{3}{4}$, . . .

Find the fifth, tenth, and hundredth terms of each sequence.

21. 4, 14, 24, 34, . . .
22. 14, 6, −2, −10, . . .
23. 3, 10, 17, 24, . . .
24. −19, −22, −25, −28, . . .
25. $\frac{1}{4}$, $-\frac{1}{4}$, $-\frac{3}{4}$, $-\frac{5}{4}$, . . .
26. −1.3, −0.3, 0.7, 1.7, . . .
27. 0, 101, 202, 303, . . .
28. −1, −100, −199, −298, . . .
29. 5, 3.9, 2.8, 1.7, . . .
30. $-3\frac{1}{2}$, $-3\frac{3}{4}$, −4, $-4\frac{1}{4}$, . . .

Determine whether each sequence is arithmetic. Justify your answer.

31. 0.5, 0.3, 0.1, −0.1, . . .
32. −1, 1, −1, 1, . . .
33. 3, 6, 12, 24, . . .
34. 100, 81, 64, 49, . . .
35. Renting a backhoe costs a flat fee of \$65 plus an additional \$35 per hour.
 a. Write the first four terms of a sequence that represents the total cost of renting the backhoe for 1, 2, 3, and 4 hours.
 b. What is the common difference?
 c. What are the 5th, 24th, 48th, and 72nd terms in the sequence?

Algebra 1 Chapter 5 Lesson 5-6 Practice 7

46. 7 lb 4 oz, 7 lb 9 oz, 7 lb 14 oz, 8 lb 3 oz, 8 lb 8 oz; the baby's weight at the end of the 4th week

47. \$4500, \$4350, \$4200, \$4050, \$3900; the balance after 4 payments

49. No; there is no common difference.

50. Yes; the common difference is −4.

51. No; there is no common difference.

52. No; there is no common difference.

53. Yes; the common difference is −15.

54. Yes; the common difference is −0.8.

272

Connection to Geometry

Exercise 55 Have a student volunteer research Pascal's Triangle in a geometry book and report to the class about the special pattern.

pages 270–273 **Exercises**

63. value of new term = value of previous term + 6

64. value of new term = value of previous term · 1.5

65. value of new term = value of previous term − 2.5

66. value of new term = value of previous term + 4

67. value of new term = value of previous term ÷ 7

68. value of new term = value of previous term · (−2.5)

Need Help?

Recursive formulas can include operations other than addition.

C **Challenge**

72b. Blue; the colors rotate red, blue, and purple. Every third figure is purple. Since 21 is divisible by 3, the 21st figure is purple. The figure just before a purple figure is blue.

c. 12 sides; the figures show this pattern for number of sides.

Figure		Number of Sides
1–3	→	3
4–6	→	4
7–9	→	5
10–12	→	6
13–15	→	7
16–18	→	8
19–21	→	9
22–24	→	10
25–27	→	11
28	→	12

62. **Number Theory** The Fibonacci sequence is $1, 1, 2, 3, 5, 8, 13, \ldots$ After the first two numbers, each number is the sum of the two previous numbers.
   a. What is the next term of the sequence? **21**
   b. What is the eleventh term of the sequence? **89**
   c. **Open-Ended** Choose two other numbers to start a Fibonacci-like sequence. Write the first seven terms of your sequence.
   Answers may vary. Sample: 3, 3, 6, 9, 15, 24, 39

A *recursive formula* relates a new term of a sequence to the previous term of the sequence. Describe each of the sequences using a recursive formula.

Sample $3, 7, 11, 15, \ldots$ **63–68. See margin.**
   value of new term = value of previous term + 4

63. $12, 18, 24, 30, \ldots$ 64. $12, 18, 27, 40.5, \ldots$ 65. $54, 51.5, 49, 46.5, \ldots$

66. $1.1, 5.1, 9.1, 13.1, \ldots$ 67. $98, 14, 2, \frac{2}{7}, \ldots$ 68. $-8, 20, -50, 125, \ldots$

Find the common difference of each sequence. Then find the next term.

69. $4, x + 4, 2x + 4, 3x + 4, \ldots$ **x; $4x + 4$**

70. $a + b + c, 4a + 3b + c, 7a + 5b + c, \ldots$ **$3a + 2b$; $10a + 7b + c$**

71. Use the sequence $10, 4, -2, -8, \ldots$
   a. What is the first term of the sequence? **10**
   b. What is the common difference of the sequence? **−6**
   c. Write a function rule $A(n)$ for the sequence. **$A(n) = 10 + (n - 1)(-6)$**

72. a. Draw the next figure in the pattern.

   b. **Reasoning** What is the color of the 20th figure? Explain. **See left.**
   c. How many sides does the 28th figure have? Explain. **See left.**

73. Use the arithmetic sequence $-5, 1, 7, 13, \ldots$
   a. What is the first term? **−5**
   b. What is the common difference? **6**
   c. Use your answers from parts (a) and (b) to write a rule for the sequence.
   $A(n) = -5 + (n - 1)(6)$

Standardized Test Prep

Multiple Choice

74. What is the seventh term of the sequence 24, 12, 6, 3, … ? **C**
   A. 0   B. 0.25   C. 0.375   D. 1.5

75. What is the common difference of the arithmetic sequence **F**
   9, −1, −11, −21, … ?
   F. −10   G. −9   H. 9   I. 10

76. What is the common difference of the arithmetic sequence $\frac{1}{5}, \frac{6}{5}, \frac{11}{5}, \frac{16}{5}, \ldots$? **A**
   A. 1   B. $1\frac{1}{5}$ C. $\frac{21}{5}$ D. 5

77. What is the seventh term of the sequence $A(n) = -9 + (n - 1)0.5$? **H**
   F. −7   G. −6.5   H. −6   I. −5.5

78. What is the first term of the sequence $A(n) = (n-1)(-3)$? **C**
   A. -3 **B.** -2 **C.** 0 **D.** 1

79. What is the next term in the sequence $x - 4, x - 2, x, x + 2, \ldots$? **H**
   F. $2x$ **G.** $x + 3$ **H.** $x + 4$ **I.** $2x + 2$

Short Response

Extended Response

80. Explain how to find the seventh term of the sequence 24, 21, 18, 15, . . . See margin.

81. Marta started to work at a company in the year 2001. Her yearly salary was $26,500. At the beginning of the next year she received a $2,880 raise. Assume that she receives the same raise each year.
   a. Write a function $f(n)$ to find Marta's salary n years after 2001.
   b. Find Marta's salary in 2008. Show your work. **a–b. See margin.**

Take It to the NET
Online lesson quiz at
www.PHSchool.com
Web Code: aea-0506

Mixed Review

Lesson 5-5

Write an equation of the direct variation that includes the given point.
                                                        84–87. See left.
82. $(4, -5)$ $y = -\frac{5}{4}x$ **83.** $(0.5, 12)$ $y = 24x$ **84.** $(-1, 14)$ **85.** $(10, 1.4)$

84. $y = -14x$

85. $y = 0.14x$

86. $(1.1, -3.1)$ **87.** $(11, -3.1)$ **88.** $(2, -3)$ $y = -\frac{3}{2}x$ **89.** $\left(\frac{1}{2}, \frac{1}{3}\right)$ $y = \frac{2}{3}x$

86. $y = -\frac{31}{11}x$ Lesson 5-2

87. $y = -\frac{31}{110}x$

Find the range of each function for the domain $\{-2, 1, 5\}$. **91, 92, 95. See left.**

90. $f(x) = -4x$ $\{-20, -4, 8\}$ **91.** $g(x) = 1 - 4x$ **92.** $y = 3x + 4$

91. $\{-19, -3, 9\}$

92. $\{-2, 7, 19\}$ Lesson 4-3

93. $y = 2|x|$ $\{2, 4, 10\}$ **94.** $h(x) = |2x|$ $\{2, 4, 10\}$ **95.** $f(x) = \frac{3}{4}x - 5$

95. $\left\{-6\frac{1}{2}, -4\frac{1}{4}, -1\frac{1}{4}\right\}$

96. **Time Zones** In 2001, people in some counties of Indiana did not set clocks forward in the spring to use daylight saving time. There are 92 counties in the state. Of those, 77 counties used eastern time without daylight saving. Five counties used eastern time with daylight saving. Ten counties were on central time with daylight saving. **a. about 84%**
   a. About what percent of Indiana's counties did *not* use daylight saving time?
   b. About what percent of the counties used central time? **about 11%**

········ **A Point in Time**

1500   1600   1700   1800   1900   2000

In 1971, Romana Acosta Bañuelos became the first Mexican American woman to hold the office of United States Treasurer. Before her appointment to this post by President Nixon, she founded and managed her own multimillion-dollar food enterprise and established the Pan American National Bank of East Los Angeles. As a highly successful businesswoman, she had to work on a daily basis with interest rates, balance sheets, investments, and other activities required in the corporate world.

Take It to the NET For more information about the office of United States Treasurer, go to **www.PHSchool.com**.
Web Code: aee-2032

Lesson 5-6   Describing Number Patterns   **273**

80. **[2]** The common difference is -3. The seventh term is $24 + (7 - 1)(-3) = 6$.
   [1] explanation incomplete

81. **[4] a.** $f(n) = 26,500 + 2880n$
   b. 2008 is 7 years after 2001.
   $f(7) = 26,500 + (2880)(7)$
   $= 46,660$
   Marta's 2008 salary is $46,660.

   [3] function and salary found but work not shown
   [2] minor computation error in finding salary
   [1] function shown but salary not found

---

4. Assess

Lesson Quiz 5-6

1. Use inductive reasoning to describe each pattern. Then find the next two numbers in each pattern.
   a. 1, 2.5, 4, . . . add 1.5 to the previous term; 5.5, 7
   b. $\frac{1}{2}, \frac{1}{4}, \frac{1}{8}, \ldots$ multiply the previous term by $\frac{1}{2}$; $\frac{1}{16}, \frac{1}{32}$

2. Find the common difference of each arithmetic sequence.
   a. $-1, -\frac{2}{3}, -\frac{1}{3}, 0, \ldots$ $\frac{1}{3}$
   b. 46, 34, 22, 10, . . . -12

3. Find the second, sixth, and ninth terms of the sequence that has the rule $A(n) = -3 + (n - 1)(6)$.
   3, 27, 45

4. Is $-2, 3, 8, 10, \ldots$ an arithmetic sequence? Explain. **No; the difference between the first two terms is 5, but the difference between the fourth and third terms is 2.**

Alternative Assessment

Write a rule for an arithmetic sequence on the board or overhead. Call on one student to say the first term. Go down the rows having students say the next number in the sequence. Change the rule after 6 or so terms.

Standardized Test Prep

📁 **Resources**
For additional practice with a variety of test item formats:
• Standardized Test Prep, p. 279
• Test-Taking Strategies, p. 274
• Test-Taking Strategies with Transparencies

Exercise 81 It may be students' first response to give short answers to these questions. Stress that the exercise is labeled as "Extended Response," so students should explain as much as possible about every step needed for writing the function and finding the salary.

273

Test-Taking Strategies

Using a Variable

This feature helps students understand the advantages of representing the unknown with a variable and writing an equation that accurately reflects the given information. When students solve the equation, the answer will match the unknown quantity. This strategy is particularly useful when *estimation* and *guess and check* strategies would take too long.

Resources

PRENTICE HALL
ASSESSMENT SYSTEM

Test-Taking Strategies with Transparencies
- Transparency 5
- Practice sheet p. 5

Teaching Notes

Help students understand that in most standardized tests, the more problems completed correctly, the better the score. It is not enough just to be able to figure out the answer, but how quickly and efficiently you can get the correct answer. Thus, guess and test is a strategy that will work, but it is not the most efficient strategy.

Test-Taking Strategies with Transparencies

Test-Taking Strategy: Using a Variable

Sometimes you can use a variable to solve a problem.

Example   A taxi ride costs a flat fee of $1.75 plus $.80 per mile. What is the fare for traveling 5 miles?

   A. $4.00   B. $1.75   C. $5.75   D. $41.75

Choose variables: Let *m* = miles traveled and *c* = cost.

Describe the situation in words:

   Cost = flat fee + cost for traveling *m* miles

Use variables to express the cost: *c* = 1.75 + 0.80*m*

Substitute *m* = 5: *c* = 1.75 + 0.80(5)

   = 1.75 + 4

   = $5.75

The answer is $5.75, or choice C.

Use a variable to find the answer. Explain your reasoning.

1. The measures of the angles of a triangle are in the ratio 2 : 4 : 6. Find the measure of the smallest angle.

   A. 15°   B. 20°   C. 30°   D. 60°

2. One side of a rectangle is 3 times the other side. The perimeter is 16 cm. How long is the long side?

   F. 8 cm   G. 2 cm   H. 3 cm   I. 16 cm

Solutions

1. C

2. I

Transparency 5

274

Test-Taking Strategies

Using a Variable

You can solve many problems by using a variable to represent an unknown quantity. Try to let the variable be the quantity that you are looking for. Then use the variable to write an equation or inequality.

1 EXAMPLE

A brand of cereal comes in two sizes. The 12-oz size costs $4.35. At that rate, how much should the 20-oz box cost?

The problem is asking for the cost of a 20-oz box. Let the variable x be the cost of the 20-oz box. Write and solve a proportion to answer the question.

$\frac{12}{20} = \frac{4.35}{x}$ **Write a proportion.**

$12x = 20(4.35)$ **Find the cross products.**

$12x = 87.00$ **Simplify.**

$x = 7.25$ **Divide each side by 12.**

● The 20-oz box should cost about $7.25.

2 EXAMPLE

One house painter charges an initial fee of $25, plus $15 per hour. A second painter charges $25 per hour. Find out how many hours a job takes for the charge of the second painter to be the same as the charge of the first painter.

Let h = number of hours each painter must work for the charges to be the same. Then write an equation that expresses the charges for each painter.

First painter   Second painter

$25 + 15h$ = $25h$

$25 = 10h$ **Subtract 15*h* from each side.**

$2.5 = h$ **Divide each side by 10.**

● The charges are the same when both painters have worked 2.5 hours.

EXERCISES

1. Another way to solve the problem in Example 2 is to try values and test them until you find the correct answer. What is the advantage of using a variable?

2. The pressure of water varies directly with the depth. At 98 meters, the pressure is 10.21 atmospheres. **a–b. See margin.**
   a. Let x be the depth where the pressure is 5 atmospheres. Use this variable to write and solve an equation to find that depth.
   b. Let x be the pressure at a depth of 150 meters. Use this variable to write and solve an equation to find the pressure.

> The trial and error method is very time consuming. Also, the results are impossible to guess if the answer is not a rational number.

274   Test-Taking Strategies   Using a Variable

page 274   Test-Taking Strategies

2a. $\frac{98}{10.21} = \frac{x}{5}$

$490 = 10.21x$

$x \approx 48.0$

The depth is about 48.0 m.

b. $\frac{98}{10.21} = \frac{150}{x}$

$98x = 1531.5$

$x \approx 15.6$

The pressure is about 15.6 atmospheres.

274

Chapter Review

Vocabulary

arithmetic sequence (p. 269)
common difference (p. 269)
conjecture (p. 268)
constant of variation (p. 262)
dependent variable (p. 248)
direct variation (p. 262)

domain (p. 241)
function (p. 242)
function notation (p. 243)
function rule (p. 243)
independent variable (p. 248)
inductive reasoning (p. 268)

range (p. 241)
relation (p. 241)
sequence (p. 269)
term (p. 269)
vertical-line test (p. 242)

Reading Math
Understanding
Vocabulary

Match the vocabulary term in the column on the left with the most specific description in the column on the right.

1. direct variation **C**

2. inductive reasoning **D**

3. independent variable **A**

4. function **E**

5. range **B**

6. sequence **G**

7. conjecture **F**

A. *x*-coordinate

B. *y*-coordinate

C. a function that can be expressed in the form $y = kx$, where $k \neq 0$

D. drawing conclusions based on observed patterns

E. a relation with exactly one value of the dependent variable for each value of the independent variable

F. a conclusion based on inductive reasoning

G. a number pattern

Take It to the NET
Online vocabulary quiz
at **www.PHSchool.com**
Web Code: aej-0551

Skills and Concepts

5-1 Objective

▼ To interpret, sketch, and analyze graphs from situations (p. 236)

8. Answers may vary. Sample: A computer rental costs $2.50/h. If you start with a fixed amount of money, the longer you work on the computer, the less money you will have left.

10. Answers may vary. Sample: An elevator is on the second floor. Someone gets in, goes to the 11th floor, and gets off.

A graph shows a visual representation of the relationship between two sets of data.

Describe a situation for each graph. 8 & 10. See left. 9. See margin.

8.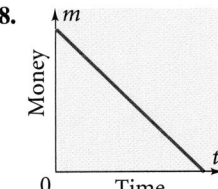

9.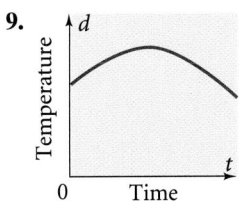

10.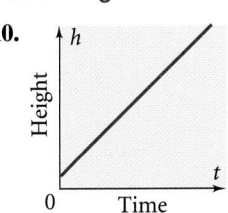

Sketch a graph of each situation. Label each section. 11–14. See back of book.

11. the height of a sunflower over a summer

12. the number of customers in a restaurant each hour of one day

13. the number of vehicles that enter a school parking lot during one day

14. the number of bags of peanuts sold during a 2-hour baseball game

Resources

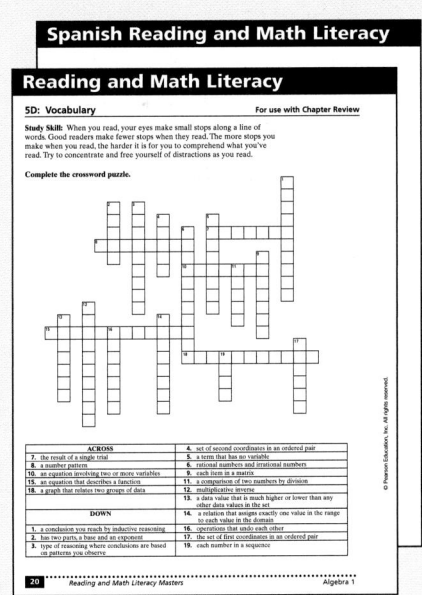

pages 275–277   Chapter Review

9. Answers may vary. Sample: A residential thermostat senses when the temperature in the room falls below the set level. The heater is turned on until the temperature is 3°F above the set level. The heater is then turned off.

The graph shows the air temperature rising while the heater is working, and falling after the heater is turned off.

24–27. Tables may vary. Samples are given.

24.

x	f(x)
−1	−2
0	−3
1	−2

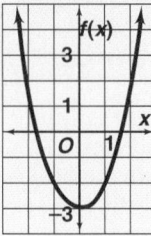

25.

x	f(x)
−2	−2
0	−3
2	−4

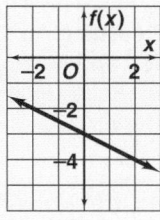

26.

x	y
−2	−5
−1	−6
0	−7
1	−6
2	−5

27.

x	y
−2	−3
−1	−1
0	1
1	3

5-2 Objectives

▼ To identify relations and functions (p. 241)

▼ To evaluate functions (p. 243)

A **relation** is a set of ordered pairs. The **domain** of a relation is the set of first coordinates of the ordered pairs. The **range** is the set of second coordinates.

A **function** is a relation that assigns exactly one value in the range to each value in the domain. A **function rule** is an equation that describes a function. A function is in **function notation** when it uses $f(x)$ for the outputs.

Find the range of each function when the domain is {−4, 0, 1, 5}.

15. $y = 4x - 7$ **16.** $m = 0.5n + 3$ **17.** $p = q^2 + 1$ **18.** $w = 5 - 3z$
{−23, −7, −3, 13}   {1, 3, 3.5, 5.5}   {1, 2, 17, 26}   {−10, 2, 5, 17}

Determine whether each relation is a function.

19. no

x	y
0	1
1	2
2	3
1	4

20. yes

x	y
0	−2
2	0
−2	−4
4	2

21. yes

x	y
2	−3
−1	−3
0	−3
5	−3

22. Use the vertical-line test to determine if the graph at the right is a function. **no**

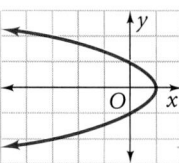

23. Writing When is a relation also a function?
A relation is a function when each value of the domain corresponds to exactly one value of the range.

5-3 and 5-4 Objectives

▼ To model functions using rules, tables, and graphs (p. 247)

▼ To write a function rule given a table or a real-world situation (p. 254)

When you graph data, put the **independent variable** on the horizontal axis and the **dependent variable** on the vertical axis. The dependent variable depends on the independent variable. You can model functions using rules, tables, and graphs.

Model each rule with a table of values and a graph. **24–27. See margin.**

24. $f(x) = x^2 - 3$ **25.** $f(x) = -\frac{1}{2}x - 3$ **26.** $y = |x| - 7$ **27.** $y = 2x + 1$

Write a function rule for each table of values.

28.

x	f(x)
2	3
4	5
6	7
8	9

$f(x) = x + 1$

29.

x	f(x)
−3	3
0	0
3	−3
6	−6

$f(x) = -x$

30.

x	f(x)
3.0	6.5
3.5	7.0
4.0	7.5
4.5	8.0

$f(x) = x + 3.5$

31. Weather The table at the right compares inches of snow to the corresponding amounts of rain. Write a function rule that models the data. **S(r) = 0.1r**

Precipitation

Snow (in.)	Rain (in.)
3	0.3
5	0.5
10	1.0
7.5	0.75

32. Campaign Advertising Brad wants to buy plain balloons and personalize them with his name to promote his campaign for class president. Each plain balloon costs $.07. Personalizing costs an initial setup fee of $27.00 plus $.13 for each plain balloon that is imprinted. Write a function rule to show the total cost of Brad's personalized campaign balloons. **c = 27 + 0.2b**

5-5 Objectives

▼ To write the equation of a direct variation (p. 261)

▼ To use ratios and proportions with direct variations (p. 263)

A function is a **direct variation** if it has the form $y = kx$, where $k \neq 0$. The coefficient k is the **constant of variation.**

Is each equation a direct variation? If it is, find the constant of variation.

33. $f(x) = -3x$ **34.** $y = x - 3$ **no**   **35.** $y = 2x + 5$ **no**   **36.** $y = \frac{2}{5}x$ **yes; $\frac{2}{5}$**
yes; -3

Write an equation of the direct variation that includes the given point.

37. $(5, 1)$ $y = \frac{1}{5}x$ **38.** $(-2, -2)$ $y = x$ **39.** $(1, 2)$ $y = 2x$ **40.** $(-2, 6)$ $y = -3x$

For the data in each table, tell whether y varies directly with x. If it does, write an equation for the direct variation.

41.

x	y
-7	14
-5	10
-3	6
-1	2

yes; $y = -2x$

42.

x	y
-6	-2
-3	-1
3	2
6	1

no

43.

x	y
24	4
18	3
-12	-2
-6	-1

yes: $y = \frac{1}{6}x$

44. Biology The number of kilograms of water w in a human body varies directly with the total body mass b. A person with a mass of 75 kg contains 54 kg of water. How many kilograms of water are there in a person with a mass of 95 kg? **68.4 kg**

45. Science The weight V of an object on Venus varies directly with its weight E on Earth. A person weighing 120 lb on Earth would weigh 106 lb on Venus. How much would a person weighing 150 lb on Earth weigh on Venus? **132.5 lb**

5-6 Objectives

▼ To use inductive reasoning in continuing number patterns (p. 268)

▼ To write rules for arithmetic sequences (p. 269)

46. "Add -9 to the previous term"; 63, 54, 45.

47. "Add 3 to the previous term"; 17, 20, 23.

48. "Add 11 to the previous term"; 56, 67, 78.

Inductive reasoning is the process of making conclusions or **conjectures** based on patterns you observe. A number pattern is called a **sequence,** and each number in the sequence is a **term.**

An **arithmetic sequence** is formed by adding a fixed number, the **common difference,** to each previous term.

Use inductive reasoning to describe each pattern. Then find the next three numbers in each pattern. 46–48. See left.

46. $99, 90, 81, 72, \ldots$ **47.** $5, 8, 11, 14, \ldots$ **48.** $12, 23, 34, 45, \ldots$

Find the common difference in each arithmetic sequence. Then find the next three terms.

49. $9, 8\frac{1}{2}, 8, 7\frac{1}{2}, \ldots$ **50.** $6, 4, 2, 0, -2, \ldots$ **51.** $1, 14, 27, 40, \ldots$
$-\frac{1}{2}; 7, 6\frac{1}{2}, 6$ $-2; -4, -6, -8$ **13; 53, 66, 79**

Find the third, eighth, and tenth terms of each sequence.

52. $A(n) = -1 + (n - 1)2$ **3, 13, 17**   **53.** $A(n) = 4 + (n - 1)3$ **10, 25, 31**

54. $A(n) = 1.5 + (n - 1)1.5$ **4.5, 12, 15**   **55.** $A(n) = 4 + (n - 1)(-3)$
                                                      $-2, -17, -23$

Determine whether each sequence is arithmetic. If it is, find the next three terms.

56. $14, 21, 28, 35, \ldots$ **yes; 42, 49, 56**   **57.** $16, -8, 4, -2, \ldots$ **no**

Chapter 5   Chapter Review   **277**

Resources

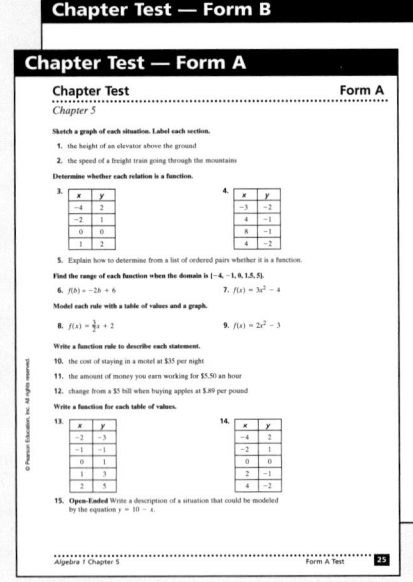

Chapter 5

Chapter Test

📡 **Take It to the NET**
Online chapter test at
www.PHSchool.com
Web Code: aea-0552

Sketch a graph of each situation. Label each section.

1. the speed of a bicycle during an afternoon ride
See back of book.
2. the amount of milk in your container over one
lunch period **See back of book.**

Determine whether each relation is a function. If the relation is a function, state the domain and range.

3.

x	y
−2	5
8	6
3	12
5	6

4. no

x	y
9	6
3	8
4	9.5
9	2

yes; domain: {−2, 3, 5, 8}; range: {5, 6, 12}

5. Writing Explain how to use the vertical-line test to determine whether a graph is a graph of a function. **See margin.**

Find the range of each function when the domain is {−3, −1.5, 0, 1, 4}.

6. $r = 4t^2 + 5$
{5, 9, 14, 41, 69}

7. $m = −3n − 2$
{−14, −5, −2, 2.5, 7}

Model each rule with a table of values and a graph.

8. $f(x) = 1.5x − 3$
8–9. See back of book.

9. $f(x) = −x^2 + 4$

Write a function rule to describe each statement.
10–12. Choice of variables may vary.

10. the cost in dollars of printing dollar bills when it costs 3.8¢ to print a dollar bill $c(d) = 0.038d$

11. the amount of money you earn mowing lawns at $15 per lawn $m(n) = 15n$

12. the profit you make selling flowers at $1.50 each when each flower costs you $.80 $p(n) = 0.7n$

Write a function rule for each table of values.

13.

x	y
0	1
1	3
2	5
−3	−5

$y = 2x + 1$

14.

x	f(x)
0	0
1	−4.5
−1	4.5
2	−9

$f(x) = −4.5x$

15. Open-Ended Describe a situation that could be modeled by the equation $y = 5x$.
Answers may vary. Sample: x = number of cars washed at $5 each and y = money earned.

16. Purchasing The price of turkey depends on its weight. Suppose turkeys sell for $.59 per lb.
a. Write a rule to describe the function. $p(t) = 0.59t$
b. What is the price of a 14-lb turkey? $8.26
c. If you had $10 to buy a turkey, how big a turkey could you buy? **about 16.9 lb**

Write an equation of the direct variation that includes the given point.

17. $(2, 2)$ **18.** $(−8, −4)$ **19.** $(3, −1)$ **20.** $(−5, 3)$
$y = x$ $y = \frac{1}{2}x$ $y = −\frac{1}{3}x$ $y = −\frac{3}{5}x$

Determine whether each of the following graphs shows a direct variation. Write an equation for each direct variation. **21. yes; $y = 3x$**

21.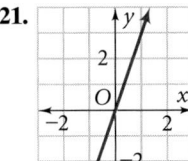

22. 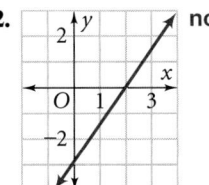 no

Find the constant of variation for each direct variation.

23. $10y = 13x$ $\frac{13}{10}$ **24.** $f(x) = 4.5x$ **4.5** **25.** $x + y = 0$ **−1**

26. Plumbing The total amount of water dripping from a leaky faucet varies directly with time. If water drips at the rate of 5 mL/min, how much water drips in 30 min? **150 mL**

Find the common difference for each arithmetic sequence. Then find the next three terms.

27. $−55, −50, −45, −40, \ldots$ **28.** $1.7, 2.7, 3.7, 4.7, \ldots$
5; −35, −30, −25   **1; 5.7, 6.7, 7.7**

Find the fifth term of each arithmetic sequence.

29. $A(n) = 2 + (n − 1)(−2.5)$ **−8**

30. $A(n) = −9 + (n − 1)3$ **3**

Is each sequence arithmetic? Justify your answer.
31–32. See margin.
31. $128, 64, 32, 16, \ldots$ **32.** $3, 3.25, 3.5, 3.75, \ldots$

33. Write a function rule for the cost of catfish shown in the table below. $C(p) = 3p$

Weight (lb)	1	2	3	4	5
Cost (dollars)	3	6	9	12	15

page 278 Chapter Test

5. If any vertical line crosses the graph in two or more places, the graph does not represent a function.

31. No; there is no common difference.

32. Yes; the common difference is 0.25.

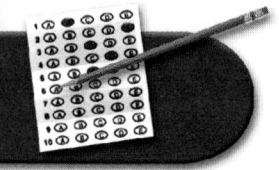

Standardized Test Prep

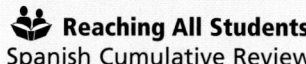

Reading Comprehension Read the passage below. Then answer the questions on the basis of what is *stated* or *implied* in the passage.

Train Math Amtrak's Acela regional train has taken more than an hour off the old five-hour train trip from Boston to New York City. The faster Acela Express makes the 231-mile run in about 3.5 hours. The Express goes from New York to Washington, D.C., in about 2.75 hours.

A train's speed depends on how secure the track is and how well banked the curves are. On the best stretches, the Express can go as fast as 150 miles an hour.

For the New York–Washington, D.C., run, Amtrak carries 70% of the passengers traveling by either train or air. For the Boston–New York run, Amtrak carries only 30% of the passengers. The average number of riders that Amtrak carries in one month on the Boston–New York run is 100,404. The average number of riders in a month on the New York–Washington, D.C., run is 771,900. Amtrak hopes the new, faster train will increase ridership between Boston and New York.

---

1. Which is closest to the average speed for the old five-hour Boston–New York run? **B**
   A. 30 miles per hour
   B. 40 miles per hour
   C. 80 miles per hour
   D. 1000 miles per hour

2. How much longer was the old five-hour Boston–New York run than the same trip on the Acela Express? **G**
   F. 0.75 hour
   G. 1.5 hours
   H. 2.25 hours
   I. 2.5 hours

3. Which is closest to the average speed of the Boston–New York run for the Acela Express? **B**
   A. 57 miles per hour
   B. 70 miles per hour
   C. 85 miles per hour
   D. 114 miles per hour

4. What is the percent of change between the Acela and Acela Express Boston–New York trip times? **H**
   F. 12.5%   G. 20%
   H. 30%   I. 70%

5. If the Acela Express could make the entire trip from Boston to New York at 150 miles an hour, how long would it take? **B**
   A. 1 hour
   B. $1\frac{1}{2}$ hours
   C. $2\frac{1}{5}$ hours
   D. 3 hours

6. If you took the Acela Express train from Boston to Washington, D.C., what portion of your travel time would be spent on the part of the trip between Boston and New York? **G**
   F. $\frac{11}{14}$ G. $\frac{14}{25}$
   H. $\frac{14}{11}$ I. $\frac{25}{14}$

7. Providence, Rhode Island, is on the Boston–New York run. It is about 180 miles from New York City. If the Acela travels at a constant speed, what portion of its Boston–New York run is spent on the Boston–Providence section?
   See margin.

8. If the number of passengers on the Boston–New York run doubled, would the percent of passengers on the Boston–New York run also double? Justify your answer. **See back of book.**

Students must be able to extract information from reading passages, answer multiple choice questions, and construct responses in order to be successful on current state and national assessments.

To answer the questions, students apply skills and concepts from this chapter and previous chapters.
Multiple Choice: Items 1–6
Extended Response: Items 7, 8

Resources

Teaching Resources
Cumulative Review

 Reaching All Students
Spanish Cumulative Review

ASSESSMENT SYSTEM
Standardized Test Prep
• Ch. 5 Standardized Test Practice
Assessment Masters
• Cumulative Review
Computer Test Bank CD-ROM
• Standardized Test Practice

 **www.PHSchool.com**
• Standardized Test Practice
• Resources

Plus **iTEXT**

---

page 279   Standardized Prep Test

7. [2] distance from Boston to Providence:
   230 − 180 = 50

$$\frac{\text{Boston} - \text{Providence}}{\text{Boston} - \text{New York}} = \frac{50}{230}$$
$$\approx \frac{1}{5}$$

$\frac{1}{5}$ of distance is
from Boston to Providence.
If the train travels at a
constant speed, $\frac{1}{5}$ of
the time is on this section.

[1] correct ratio, but no conclusion

Cumulative Review

Cumulative Review
Chapters 1–5

For Exercises 1–9, choose the correct letter.

1. Which of the following are true for the given data? 3, 4, 4, 5, 6, 7, 7, 8, 8, 8
   I. mode > median   II. mean < mode
   III. mean < median   IV. median > mode
   A. I and III   B. II, III and IV   C. I and II   D. I, II, and III

2. A bag contains a total of 24 red and green peppers. The probability of reaching into the bag and choosing a red pepper is $\frac{1}{3}$. How many peppers of each color are in the bag?
   A. 2 red, 3 green   B. 16 red, 8 green   C. 12 red, 12 green   D. 9 red, 15 green

3. Which pair of matrices has a difference of $\begin{bmatrix} 3 & -2 \\ 0 & 4 \end{bmatrix}$?

4. What is the range of the function $y = 2x^2 - 5$ when the domain is {−3, 0, 2, 4}?
   A. {−13, −5, 3, 28}   B. {−3, 0, 2, 4}   C. {13, −5, 3, 27}   D. {31, −5, 11, 59}

5. The number of students who are active in the computer club has jumped from 7 to 19. What is the percent increase?
   A. 171%   B. 17.1%   C. 271%   D. 36.8%

6. Solve the literal equation $\frac{2x-4}{5} = 1$ for x.

7. The number line shows the graph of all the solutions of an inequality. Which could not be that inequality?
   A. 4 > −2x   B. −3x < 6   C. 5x < −10   D. x > −2

8. Find $f(-3)$ when $f(x) = x^2 - 4x$.
   A. 21   B. 3   C. −3   D. −21

9. Which of the following relations is not a function?

Algebra 1 Chapter 5   Cumulative Review   **31**

Linear Equations and Their Graphs

Chapter at a Glance  North Carolina Objectives

6-1	Rate of Change and Slope	4.01

NCTM
2, 3, 4,
9, 10
- ▼ Finding Rates of Change
- ▼ Finding Slope

6-2	Slope-Intercept Form	4.01b

NCTM
2, 4, 9,
10
- ▼ Writing Linear Equations
- ▼ Graphing Linear Equations

6-3	Standard Form	4.01b

NCTM
2, 6, 8,
9, 10
- ▼ Graphing Equations Using Intercepts
- ▼ Writing Equations in Standard Form

6-4	Point-Slope Form and Writing Linear Equations	4.01b

NCTM
2, 6, 8,
9, 10
- ▼ Using Point-Slope Form
- ▼ Writing Linear Equations Using Data

6-5	Parallel and Perpendicular Lines	2.02

NCTM
2, 3, 4
6, 9, 10
- ▼ Parallel Lines
- ▼ Perpendicular Lines

6-6	Scatter Plots and Equations of Lines	3.03b

NCTM
2, 3, 4,
5, 6
- ▼ Writing an Equation for a Trend Line
- ▼ Writing an Equation for a Line of Best Fit

6-7	Graphing Absolute Value Equations

NCTM
1, 2, 3,
7, 10
- ▼ Translating Graphs of Absolute Value Equations

NCTM STANDARDS 2000

1	Number and Operations	6	Problem Solving
2	Algebra	7	Reasoning and Proof
3	Geometry	8	Communication
4	Measurement	9	Connections
5	Data Analysis and Probability	10	Representation

Pacing Options

This chart suggests pacing only for the lessons and their parts. It is provided as a possible guide. It will help you determine how much time you have in your schedule to cover other components, such as the features, Chapter Review, and Chapter Test.

Day	Traditional 45 min.	Two-Year 45 min.	Block 90 min.
1	6-1 ▼	6-1 ▼	6-1 ▼ ▼
2	6-1 ▼	6-1 ▼	6-2 ▼ ▼ 6-3 ▼ ▼
3	6-2 ▼ ▼	6-2 ▼	6-4 ▼ ▼
4	6-3 ▼ ▼	6-2 ▼	6-5 ▼ ▼
5	6-4 ▼	6-3 ▼	6-6 ▼ ▼
6	6-4 ▼	6-3 ▼	6-7 ▼
7	6-5 ▼	6-4 ▼	
8	6-5 ▼	6-4 ▼	
9	6-6 ▼ ▼	6-5 ▼	
10	6-7 ▼	6-5 ▼	
11		6-6 ▼	
12		6-6 ▼	
13		6-7 ▼	
14		6-7 ▼	

NAEP Correlation (National Assessment of Educational Progress 2000 Mathematics Objectives)

6-1	6-2	6-3	6-4	6-5	6-6	6-7
G9a, D1b, A1f	D1a, A1f, A5b	D1a, A5b	D1a, A5b	D1a, A5b	D1a, D2b, D5c, D7	G3b, D1a, A3d

N = Number Sense, Properties, and Operations; **M** = Measurement; **G** = Geometry and Spatial Sense;
D = Data Analysis, Statistics, and Probability; **A** = Algebra and Functions

Math Background

Chapter Overview

In the previous chapter, students learned the connection between a function and its graph. This chapter establishes the essential connection between a linear equation and its graph. This broad topic is introduced first by a discussion of rate of change that leads to the definition of the slope of a line. The idea of slope is then expanded to include the slope-intercept form of a linear equation, and the use of this form to graph an equation. Writing a linear equation in standard form leads to graphing and to writing linear equations given various kinds of information about a line. Writing equations and interpreting graphs are extended to include using these skills to solve problems. A discussion of the characteristics of the slopes and graphs of both parallel and perpendicular lines follows. The preceding skills are applied by students as they write the equation of a trend line and a line of best fit. Graphing a linear equation is extended to graphing and translating absolute value equations.

Rate of Change and Slope   6-1

The steepness of a road going up a hill and the pitch of a roof can both be expressed as the ratio of the rise over the run, or the slope. Remind students that they studied ratios in Chapter 4. Students may at first confuse the order of this ratio, since they are accustomed to putting x first when writing the coordinates of an ordered pair. This may lead them to place the difference in x-values, or run, incorrectly in the numerator.

Slope-Intercept Form   6-2

In Chapter 5, students learned that a function in the form of $y = kx$ is a direct variation. Have students compare $y = kx$ to $y = mx + b$. Lead students to understand that the slope of a linear function through the origin is a constant of variation.

Students may find it helpful to express slope as $\frac{\Delta y}{\Delta x}$ where Δ (delta) means "change in," as "the change in y divided by the change in x."

Standard Form   6-3

Suggest to students that an efficient way to create a table of values for an equation is by substituting 0 for x and finding the corresponding y-value, then substituting 0 for y and finding the corresponding x-value. If more points are needed, it may be convenient to evaluate the equation using 1 for x and then for y.

Point-Slope Form and Writing Linear Equations   6-4

Using the point-slope form of a linear equation is a generalization of the more specific slope-intercept form, in which the point is specifically designated to be the y-intercept. Students can use the point-slope form to write equations that model sets of data.

Parallel and Perpendicular Lines   6-5

Two lines in the same plane that have the same slope must either be parallel or coincide. In the latter case, the two equations are equivalent, as, for example $x + 1 = y$ and $3x = 3y - 3$. (Students may not realize that this is just another case of equivalent equations having exactly the same solution set). The family of lines with a given slope, $m = 5$, for example, consists of infinitely many lines, all parallel. Discuss with students the slopes of a family of lines with one common point.

Scatter Plots and Equations of Lines   6-6

Real-world data, when graphed, rarely falls exactly along a line. Data are classified as linear if the points approximate a line on a graph. When this is the case, there are techniques to approximate an equation for a line of "best fit." The graphing calculator makes this task easy by correlating equations of "best fit" to actual entered data.

Because real-world data is not linear, the range (the difference between the value of the greatest point and the least) is called a measure of scatter. Measures of scatter indicate whether the measurements in a distribution are bunched together or scattered apart. Other measures of scatter include deviation, variance, and standard deviation.

Graphing Absolute Value Equations   6-7

Translation is one of three commonly used transformations: translation or slide, rotation or turn, and reflection or flip. These three transformations are called isometries, or rigid motions, because the size and shape of the figure remain unchanged. Dilation, such as enlarging a figure using a copying machine, is another transformation, but it is not a rigid motion, because distances within the figure are changed. Students learn that graphs of various absolute value equations can be thought of as translations of the equation $y = |x|$.

Ongoing Assessment and Intervention

Tools for Monitoring Student Progress

The Prentice Hall *Algebra 1* program provides you with many options for assessment in the Student Edition, the Teacher's Edition and the teaching resources. From these options you may choose instructional materials and techniques that are appropriate for your students and support your district's curriculum requirements.

Instant Check System™ in Chapter 6

Allows students to check their own learning before, during, and after each lesson.

Diagnosing Readiness before the chapter (p. 280)

Check Skills You'll Need exercises in each lesson (pp. 282, 291, 298, 304, 311, 318, 325)

Check Understanding questions with each Example (pp. 283, 284, 285, 292, 293, 299, 300, 305, 306, 307, 311, 312, 313, 319, 320, 325, 326, 327)

Checkpoint Quiz (pp. 303, 324)

Test Prep in Chapter 6

Teaches students strategies and gives them practice with all the test item formats they will encounter on state tests and standardized national exams.

Standardized Test Prep exercises in each lesson (pp. 289, 297, 303, 309, 317, 323, 324, 329)

Test-Taking Strategies (p. 330: Drawing a Diagram)

Standardized Test Prep (p. 335: Cumulative Review)

All your assessment needs in one place!

Program Assessment

Assess student progress throughout the *Algebra 1* text with blackline masters and CD-ROM.

Assessment Resources

- Checkpoint Quizzes 1 & 2
- Chapter Test, Forms A & B
- Chapter Alternative Assessment

Spanish versions available. Tests for Basic Algebra also available.

Computer Test Generator

- Unlimited questions of varying difficulty for every lesson objective.
- Create your own practice sheets, quizzes, and tests, or use the pre-made Chapter Tests.
- Diagnose readiness with questions on prerequisite skills.
- Prepare students by making tests based on standardized test objectives.
- Access Algebra 1, Geometry, and Algebra 2 content—all on one CD-ROM.

Test Preparation

A three-step approach to preparing students for high stakes, national, and state exams.

❶ Diagnose & Prescribe

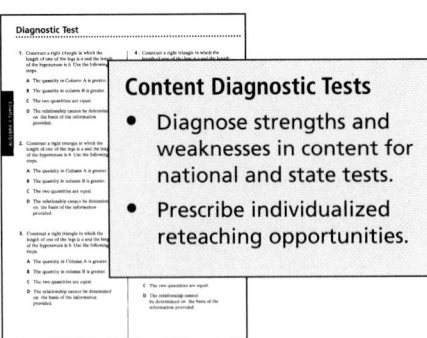

Content Diagnostic Tests

- Diagnose strengths and weaknesses in content for national and state tests.
- Prescribe individualized reteaching opportunities.

❷ Review & Reteach

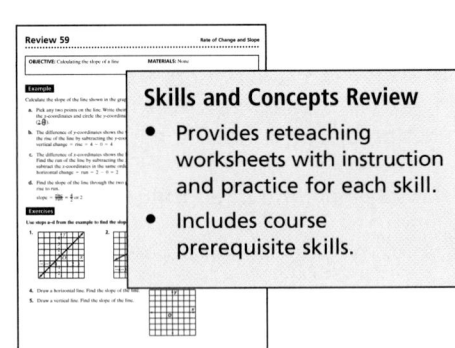

Skills and Concepts Review

- Provides reteaching worksheets with instruction and practice for each skill.
- Includes course prerequisite skills.

❸ Practice & Assess

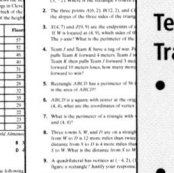

Test Preparation

- Features practice tests for End-of-Course and SAT/ACT exams.
- Includes standardized test practice by chapter for ongoing review.

Teacher's Guide with answers and correlations.

Test-Taking Strategies with Transparencies

- Support the Test-Taking Strategies pages in the Student Edition.
- Provide a teaching transparency and a practice worksheet for each strategy.

 # Reaching All Students

Support in the Student Text and Additional Resources

The textbook, the iText, and other technology components provide numerous opportunities to reach students of various ability levels and learning styles. Each Teacher's Edition lesson suggests how you can help *all* your students be successful and understand the mathematics in Chapter 6.

Below Level

Student Edition
- Diagnosing Readiness*: p. 280
- Check Skills You'll Need*: pp. 282, 291, 298, 304, 311, 318, 325

Reteaching
Chapter 6 Support File: pp. 8–14

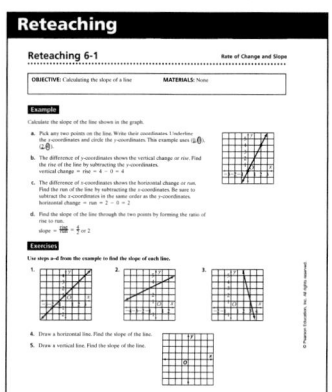

Basic Algebra Planning Guide
Chapter 6 Lesson Plans: pp. 35–41
Chapter 6 Tests: pp. 109–112

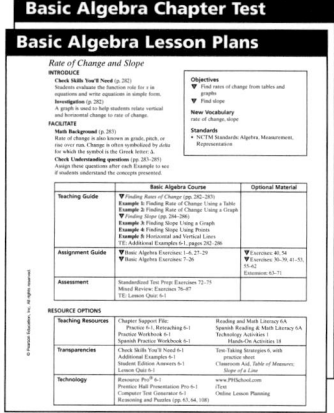

Advanced Learners

Student Edition
- Challenge exercises: pp. 289, 296, 302, 309, 316, 323, 328, 329

Enrichment
Chapter 6 Support File: pp. 15–21

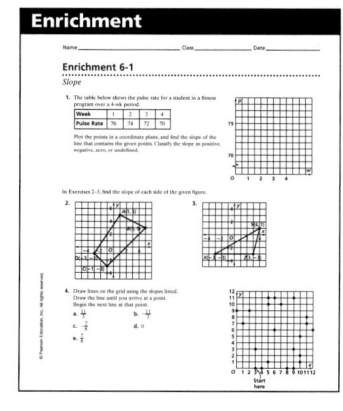

Reading and Math Literacy

Student Edition
- Vocabulary: pp. 281, 331, *plus* in every Lesson Preview
- Reading Math: pp. 284, 285, 305, 307, 310, 331
- Illustrated Glossary: pp. 757–785

Reading and Math Literacy Masters
Chapter 6: pp. 21–24

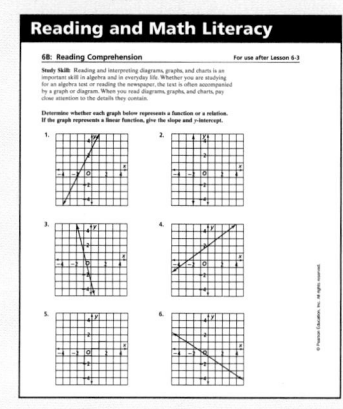

English Learners

Student Edition
- English/Spanish Illustrated Glossary: pp. 757–785

Workbook and Masters
Spanish Practice Workbook: pp. 35–41
Spanish Reading and Math Literacy
Masters: pp. 21–24

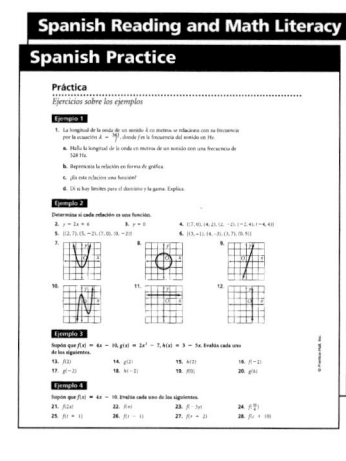

Learning Styles

Student Edition
- Investigation: pp. 282, 298
- Technology: pp. 290, 296, 319, 322, 323, 324, 329, 333, 334
- Writing: pp. 288, 296, 302, 303, 316, 322, 328
- DK Activities: pp. 336–337

Activity Masters
Hands-On Activities: 13, 14, 15
Technology Activities: 1, 2, 3, 6, 20

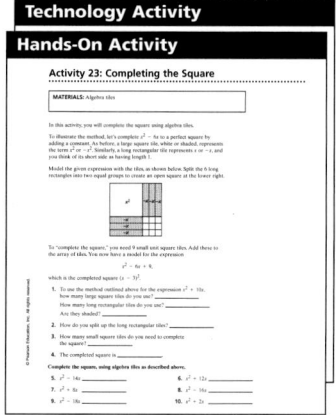

Program Resources

	Teaching Resources in Grab & Go™ Files				Resources for Reaching All Students				Spanish Resources			Transparencies				Presentation Assistant Plus!
	Practice	Reteach	Enrich	Checkpoint Quiz	Reading & Math Literacy	Technology Activities	Hands-On Activities	Basic Algebra Lesson Plans	Practice	Reading & Math Literacy	Checkpoint Quiz	Skills Check	Additional Examples	Answers to Exercises	Lesson Quiz	Prentice Hall Presentation Pro CD-ROM
6-1	■	■	■		■		■	■	■	■		■	■	■	■	■
6-2	■	■	■				■	■	■			■	■	■	■	■
6-3	■	■		■	■			■	■	■	■	■	■	■	■	■
6-4	■	■	■			■		■	■			■	■	■	■	■
6-5	■	■	■					■	■			■	■	■	■	■
6-6	■	■		■	■		■	■	■	■	■	■	■	■	■	■
6-7								■				■				■
For the chapter	Chapter Tests, Alternative Assessment, Cumulative Review, Cumulative Assessment				Basic Algebra Chapter Tests				Spanish Chapter Tests, Alternative Assessment, Cumulative Review, Cumulative Assessment			Classroom Aid Transparencies				

Also available for use with the chapter:

 **ASSESSMENT SYSTEM** *See page 280C.*

- Practice Workbook
- Solution Key

- For teacher support and access to student Web site materials, use Web Code aek-5500.
- For additional online and technology resources, see below.

 ## Technology

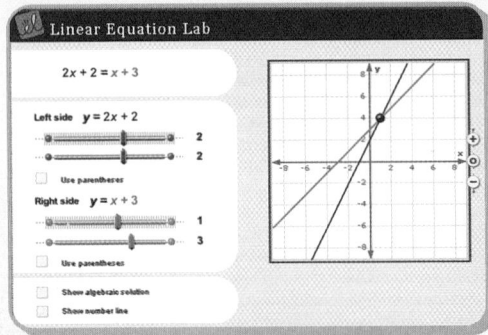 **Online and on CD-ROM**

Complete Interactive Student Text online and on CD-ROM—with instant feedback assessment, tutorial help, dynamic activities, instructional and real-world videos, audio, and additional practice.

 **www.PHSchool.com For Students**

Use **Web codes** for easy access to online activities, chapter projects, self-grading lesson quizzes and chapter tests, vocabulary quizzes, updated data sources, graphing calculator procedures, and more.

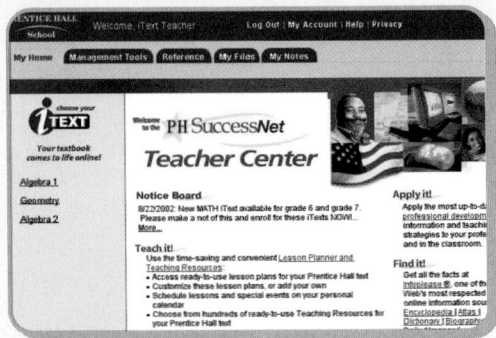 **PH SuccessNet For Teachers**

Online lesson planning with built-in state correlations, all the teaching resources, complete reference library, your own calendar and Teacher Web page, professional development, and more.

Presentation Assistant Plus!

The Prentice Hall *Presentation Assistant Plus!* provides you with the material you need to teach a lesson from beginning to end. Two easy-to-use formats—Transparencies and CD-ROM—allow you to present a lesson the way you are most comfortable.

 ## Transparencies

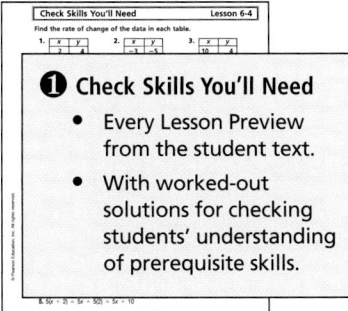

❶ Check Skills You'll Need
- Every Lesson Preview from the student text.
- With worked-out solutions for checking students' understanding of prerequisite skills.

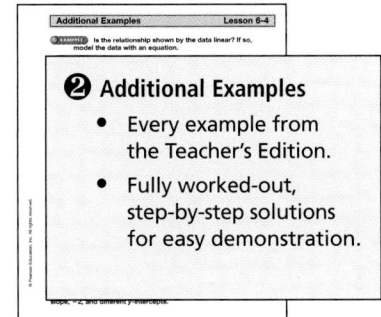

❷ Additional Examples
- Every example from the Teacher's Edition.
- Fully worked-out, step-by-step solutions for easy demonstration.

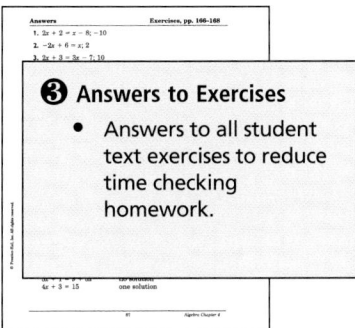

❸ Answers to Exercises
- Answers to all student text exercises to reduce time checking homework.

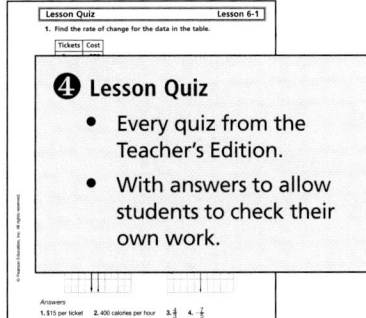

❹ Lesson Quiz
- Every quiz from the Teacher's Edition.
- With answers to allow students to check their own work.

 Throughout the Teacher's Edition, this symbol indicates material that is available on transparency in the Presentation Assistant Plus!

 ## Prentice Hall Presentation Pro CD-ROM

- Includes all Transparencies.
- Conveniently organized by lesson so you can easily ❶ Introduce, ❷ Teach, ❸ Check Homework, and ❹ Assess each lesson.
- Animated examples allow step-by-step instruction at your own pace.
- Easy to edit so you can create custom presentations.

Teaching Chapter 6 Using Presentation Assistant Plus!

	❶ Introduce	❷ Teach	❸ Check Homework	❹ Assess
	Check Skills You'll Need	Additional Examples	Student Edition Answers	Lesson Quiz
6-1	p. 35	pp. 67–71	✔	p. 108
6-2	p. 36	p. 72	✔	p. 109
6-3	p. 37	pp. 73–75	✔	p. 110
6-4	p. 38	pp. 75–78	✔	p. 111
6-5	p. 39	pp. 78–80	✔	p. 112
6-6	p. 40	pp. 81–82	✔	p. 113
6-7	p. 41	pp. 83–84	✔	p. 114

 ### Prentice Hall Presentation Pro

CD-ROM with dynamic PowerPoint® presentations for every lesson. Helps you introduce and develop concepts, check homework, and assess progress. Part of Presentation Assistant Plus! *(See above.)*

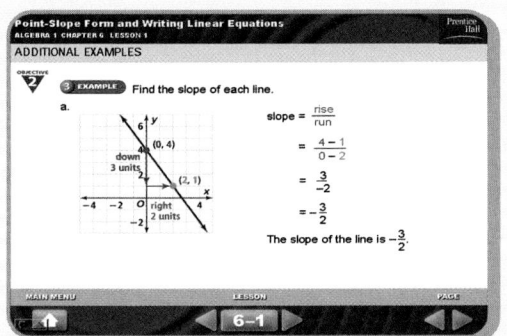

 ### Computer Test Generator

CD-ROM to create practice sheets and tests for course objectives and standardized tests. Includes Instant Chapter Tests™, online testing, and student reports. Part of the PH Assessment System. *(See page 280C.)*

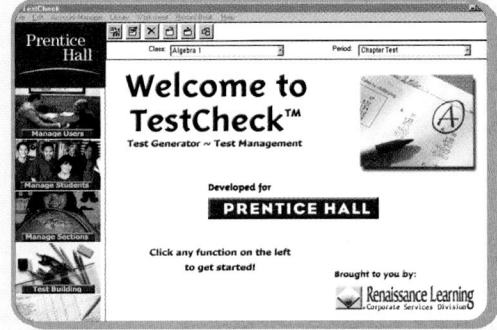

 ### Resource Pro® with Planning Express®

CD-ROM with a lesson planning tool that allows you to import state and local objectives. Includes electronic versions of all the teaching resources.

Chapter 6

Linear Equations and Their Graphs

 Diagnosing Readiness

Students will find answers to these exercises in the back of their textbooks.

For intervention, direct students to:

Adding and Subtracting Real Numbers Lesson 1-4: Example 2; Exercises 9–12
Lesson 1-5: Examples 3, 4
Exercises 9–12, 21–24
Extra Practice, p. 702

Analyzing Data Using Scatter Plots Lesson 1-9: Example 4
Exercise 16
Extra Practice, p. 702

Solving Equations
Lesson 2-4: Example 1
Exercises 6–9
Extra Practice, p. 703

Transforming Equations
Lesson 2-6: Example 2
Exercises 10–13
Extra Practice, p. 703

Graphing Functions
Lesson 5-3: Example 1
Exercises 7–10
Extra Practice, p. 706

page 280 Diagnosing
Readiness

6.   Average Life Span
of American Currency

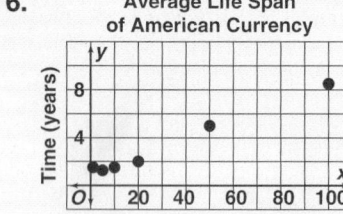

13–15. Table values may vary. Samples are given.

280

Where You've Been

● In Chapter 1, you used integers to graph points in the coordinate plane.

● In Chapters 2, 3, and 4, you solved multi-step problems, including equations, inequalities, and proportions, and applied this skill to solving a formula for a given variable.

● In Chapter 5, you graphed functions by making a table of values.

 *i*TEXT Instant self-check online and on CD-ROM

✓ **Diagnosing Readiness**   (For help, go to the Lesson in green.)

Adding and Subtracting Real Numbers (Lessons 1-4 and 1-5)

Simplify each expression.

1. $-5 + 7$ **2**   **2.** $2 - (-3)$ **5**   **3.** $-\frac{3}{4} + \frac{5}{6}$ $\frac{1}{12}$ **4.** $11 + (-4)$ **7**   **5.** $|1 - 8|$ **7**

Analyzing Data Using Scatter Plots (Lesson 1-9)

Make a scatter plot of the data below. **See margin.**

6.   **Average Life Span of American Currency**

Value of Currency ($)	1	5	10	20	50	100
Time (years)	1.5	1.25	1.5	2	5	8.5

Solving Equations (Lesson 2-4)

Solve each equation. Check your solution.

7. $3x + 4x = 8 - x$ **1**   **8.** $12 - 3d = d$ **3**   **9.** $6x - 8 = 7 + x$ **3**

Transforming Equations (Lesson 2-6)

Solve each equation for y.

10. $2y - x = 4$ $y = \frac{1}{2}x + 2$ **11.** $3x = y + 2$ $y = 3x - 2$ **12.** $-2y - 2x = 4$ $y = -x - 2$

Graphing Functions (Lesson 5-3)

Make a table of values and graph each function. **13–15. See margin.**

13. $y = -\frac{2}{3}x$ **14.** $y = 2x + 1$ **15.** $y = x - 5$

13.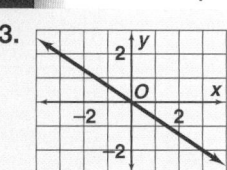

x	y
−3	2
0	0
3	2

14.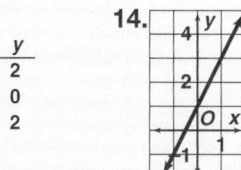

x	y
−1	−1
0	1
1	3

15.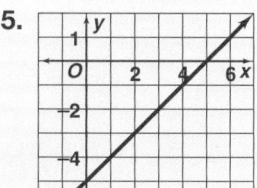

x	y
0	−5
2	−3
4	−1

Linear Equations and Their Graphs

Where You're Going

- In this chapter, you will learn how to write linear equations and recognize their different forms.

- By working with the rate of change, you will understand how the slope of a line can be interpreted in real-world situations.

- You will determine whether the graphs of two linear equations are parallel or perpendicular.

 **Real-World Snapshots** Applying what you learn, you will do activities involving pyramids, on pages 336–337.

LESSONS

6-1   Rate of Change and Slope

6-2   Slope-Intercept Form

6-3   Standard Form

6-4   Point-Slope Form and Writing Linear Equations

6-5   Parallel and Perpendicular Lines

6-6   Scatter Plots and Equations of Lines

6-7   Graphing Absolute Value Equations

Key Vocabulary

- absolute value equation (p. 325)
- correlation coefficient (p. 319)
- line of best fit (p. 319)
- linear equation (p. 291)
- negative reciprocal (p. 312)
- parallel lines (p. 311)
- perpendicular lines (p. 312)
- point-slope form (p. 304)
- rate of change (p. 282)
- slope (p. 284)
- slope-intercept form (p. 292)
- standard form (p. 298)
- translation (p. 325)
- x-intercept (p. 298)
- y-intercept (p. 291)

281

Chapter 6 Overview

This chapter introduces rates of change and defines slope of a line as the ratio of the vertical change to the horizontal change. This leads to graphing a linear equation and writing the equation of a line in three different forms, using the slope, intercepts, or points on the line. From there, the characteristics of parallel and perpendicular lines are examined. All of these topics are applied together to find trend lines and lines of best fit. Finally, the skills for graphing linear equations are extended to drawing the graph of an absolute value equation.

Reading Math
Reading Numerical Data, p. 260

Vocabulary
A complete list of terms, plus vocabulary exercises, appears in the Chapter Review, p. 331.

Illustrated Glossary
Examples for each vocabulary term, plus definitions in both English and Spanish, appear starting on p. 757.

Test-Taking Strategies
Drawing a Diagram, p. 330

Real-World Snapshots
See pages 336–337 for a real-world application of Measuring Force that utilizes Dorling Kindersley's (DK) unique graphic presentation.

Real-World Connections
Some of the applications you will find in this chapter are plant growth (6-1), commission (6-2), health and fitness (6-3), and urban planning (6-5).

 **www.PHSchool.com**
Internet support for this chapter includes:
- Self-grading Vocabulary and Chapter 6 Tests
- Chapter Project
- Chapter Planner
- Chapter 6 Resources

Plus **iTEXT**

6-1

North Carolina
Objectives
4.01

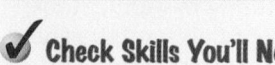

Lesson Preview

✓ **Check Skills You'll Need**

Relations and Functions
Lesson 5-2: Example 4
Exercises 15–22
Extra Practice, p. 706

Subtracting Real Numbers
Lesson 1-5: Example 3
Exercises 9–16
Extra Practice, p. 702

Lesson Resources

📁 **Teaching Resources**
Practice, Reteaching, Enrichment

👥 **Reaching All Students**
Practice Workbook 6-1
Spanish Practice Workbook 6-1
Reading and Math Literacy 6A
Spanish Reading & Literacy 6A
Technology Activities 1
Hands-On Activities 13
Basic Algebra Planning Guide 6-1

⏱ **Presentation Assistant Plus!**
Transparencies
• Check Skills You'll Need 6-1
• Additional Examples 6-1
• Student Edition Answers 6-1
• Lesson Quiz 6-1
PH Presentation Pro CD 6-1

PRENTICE HALL
ASSESSMENT SYSTEM

Computer Test Generator CD

💿 **Technology**
Resource Pro® CD-ROM
Computer Test Generator CD
Prentice Hall Presentation Pro CD

🖥 **www.PHSchool.com**
Student Site
• Teacher Web Code: aek-5500
• Reasoning & Puzzles pp. 63, 64, 108
• Graphing Calculator, Procedure 5
• Self-grading Lesson Quiz
Teacher Center
• Lesson Planner
• Resources

Plus 🄸TEXT
282

6-1

Rate of Change and Slope

North Carolina Objectives

4.01   Use linear functions or inequalities to model and solve problems; justify results.

Lesson Preview

What You'll Learn

 OBJECTIVE 1
To find rates of change from tables and graphs

 OBJECTIVE 2
To find slope

. . . And Why

To find the rate of change of an airplane's altitude, as in Example 2

New Vocabulary   • rate of change   • slope

✓ **Check Skills You'll Need**   (For help, go to Lessons 5-2 and 1-5.)

Evaluate each function rule for $x = -5$.

1. $y = x - 7$ −12

2. $y = 7 - x$ 12

3. $y = 2x + 5$ −5

4. $y = -\frac{2}{5}x + 3$ 5

Write in simplest form.

5. $\frac{7-3}{3-1}$ 2

6. $\frac{3-5}{6-0}$ $-\frac{1}{3}$

7. $\frac{8-(-4)}{3-7}$ −3

8. $\frac{-1-2}{0-5}$ $\frac{3}{5}$

9. $\frac{-6-(-4)}{-2-6}$ $\frac{1}{4}$

10. $\frac{0-1}{1-0}$ −1

OBJECTIVE
1 **Finding Rates of Change**

🄸TEXT **Interactive lesson includes instant self-check, tutorials, and activities.**

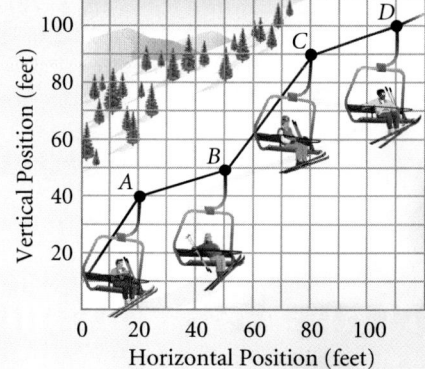

Investigation: Exploring Rate of Change

The diagram at the right shows the side view of a ski lift.

1. What is the vertical change from A to B? From B to C? From C to D? **10; 40; 10**

2. What is the horizontal change from A to B? From B to C? From C to D? **30; 30; 30**

3. Find the ratio of the vertical change to the horizontal change for each section of the ski lift. $\frac{1}{3}$; $\frac{4}{3}$; $\frac{1}{3}$

4. Which section is the steepest? Explain. **B to C; it has the highest ratio.**

? Need Help?
A rate is a comparison of two quantities measured in different units.

In the graph above, $\overline{AB}$ and $\overline{BC}$ have different rates of change.

✗ **Rate of change** allows you to see the relationship between two quantities that are changing. If one quantity depends on the other, then the following is true.

$$\text{rate of change} = \frac{\text{change in the dependent variable}}{\text{change in the independent variable}}$$

 **Ongoing Assessment and Intervention**

Before the Lesson
Diagnose prerequisite skills using:
• Check Skills You'll Need

During the Lesson
Monitor progress using:
• Check Understanding
• Additional Examples
• Standardized Test Prep

After the Lesson
Assess knowledge using:
• Lesson Quiz
• Computer Test Generator CD

Cost of Renting a Computer	
Number of Days	Rental Charge
1	$60
2	$75
3	$90
4	$105
5	$120

1 EXAMPLE Finding Rate of Change Using a Table

model

Business For the data at the left, is the rate of change for each pair of consecutive days the same? What does the rate of change represent?

$$\text{rate of change} = \frac{\text{change in cost}}{\text{change in number of days}}$$ **Cost depends on the number of days.**

$$\frac{75 - 60}{2 - 1} = \frac{15}{1} \qquad\qquad \frac{90 - 75}{3 - 2} = \frac{15}{1}$$

$$\frac{105 - 90}{4 - 3} = \frac{15}{1} \qquad\qquad \frac{120 - 105}{5 - 4} = \frac{15}{1}$$

The rate of change for each consecutive pair of days is $\frac{15}{1}$. The rate of change is the same for all the data. It costs $15 for each day a computer is rented after the first day.

✓ **Check Understanding** **1** **a.** Find the rate of change using Days 5 and 2. **15**

b. Critical Thinking Does finding the rate of change for just one pair of days mean that the rate of change is the same for all the data? Explain. **No; the rate of change for each consecutive pair of days does not have to be the same.**

GP

The graphs of all the ordered pairs (number of days, cost) in Example 1 lie on a line as shown at the right. So, the data are linear.

You can use a graph to find a rate of change. Recall that the independent variable is plotted on the horizontal axis and the dependent variable is plotted on the vertical axis.

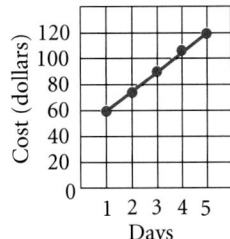

$$\text{rate of change} = \frac{\text{vertical change}}{\text{horizontal change}} = \frac{\text{change in the dependent variable}}{\text{change in the independent variable}}$$

2 EXAMPLE Finding Rate of Change Using a Graph

Model

Airplane Altitude The graph shows the altitude of an airplane as it comes in for a landing. Find the rate of change. Explain what this rate of change means.

$$\frac{\text{rate of}}{\text{change}} = \frac{\text{vertical change}}{\text{horizontal change}} \quad \leftarrow \text{change in altitude} \\ \leftarrow \text{change in time}$$

$$= \frac{1000 - 0}{60 - 180} \quad \textbf{Use two points.}$$

$$= \frac{1000}{-120} \quad \textbf{Divide the vertical change by the horizontal change.}$$

$$= -8\frac{1}{3} \quad \textbf{Simplify.}$$

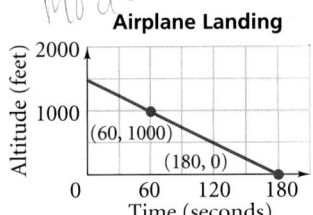

The rate of change is $-8\frac{1}{3}$. The airplane descends $8\frac{1}{3}$ feet each second.

✓ **Check Understanding** **2** Find the rate of change of the data in the graph.

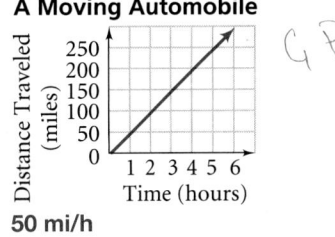

50 mi/h

2. Teach

 Professional Development

Math Background

Rate of change is also known as grade or pitch, or rise over run. Change is often symbolized in mathematics by *delta* for which the symbol is this Greek letter: Δ. Some calculators use Δ in their TABLE menu.

OBJECTIVE

1 **Teaching Notes**

Investigation (Optional)
Since the segments are neither vertical nor horizontal, some students may need help understanding the phrases *vertical change* and *horizontal change*.

2 EXAMPLE English Learners

Many students confuse the two terms *vertical* and *horizontal*. Tell students that when you look off into the distance, the boundary that you see between the sky and water or flat land is called the *horizon*. Relate this to *horizontal*.

Additional Examples

1 For the data in the table, is the rate of change for each pair of consecutive mileage amounts the same? **Yes**

Fee for Miles Driven

Miles	Fee
100	$30
150	$42
200	$54
250	$66

👫 Reaching All Students

Below Level Students may be confused about which point to label (x_1, y_1) when using the slope formula. Recalculate the slopes in Example 3 to show that labeling does not affect the slope.	**Advanced Learners** Draw a horizontal line on a grid. Lead students in a discussion of how the slope of that line changes as it is rotated 360° counterclockwise.	**English Learners** See note on page 283. **Visual Learners** See note on page 284.

283

Additional Examples

2 Below is a graph of the distance traveled by a motorcycle from its starting point. Find the rate of change. Explain what this rate of change means. **20 m/s; the motorcycle travels 20 meters each second**

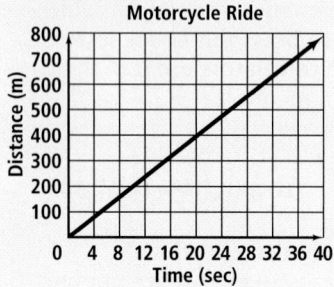

3 **EXAMPLE** **Math Tip**

The idea of a rise being negative is difficult for some students to understand. Point out that a fall is a negative rise.

4 **EXAMPLE** **Visual Learners**

Some students may have difficulty writing the coordinates in the correct place in the formula. Have them circle the *x*-coordinates, and box the *y*-coordinates. Then draw arrows going the same direction between the *x*-coordinates and between the *y*-coordinates to help keep the order correct. Use the following as an example:

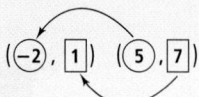

Some roads are steeper than others. A steeper road has a greater rate of change.

Real-World 🌐 Connection

The grade of a road is the ratio of rise to run expressed as a percent. For example, a road with 100% grade is at a 45° angle with level ground.

The slope of a line is its rate of change.

$$\text{slope} = \frac{\text{vertical change}}{\text{horizontal change}} = \frac{\text{rise}}{\text{run}}$$

3 **EXAMPLE** **Finding Slope Using a Graph**

Find the slope of each line.

a.
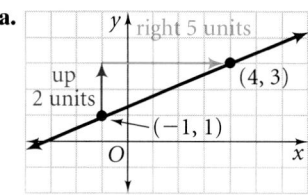

$$\text{slope} = \frac{\text{rise}}{\text{run}}$$

$$= \frac{3 - 1}{4 - (-1)}$$

$$= \frac{2}{5}$$

The slope of the line is $\frac{2}{5}$.

b.
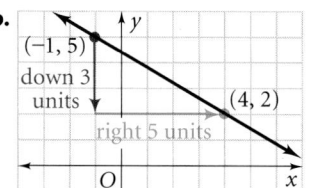

$$\text{slope} = \frac{\text{rise}}{\text{run}}$$

$$= \frac{2 - 5}{4 - (-1)}$$

$$= \frac{-3}{5} = -\frac{3}{5}$$

The slope of the line is $-\frac{3}{5}$.

✔ **Check Understanding** **3** Find the slope of each line.

a.
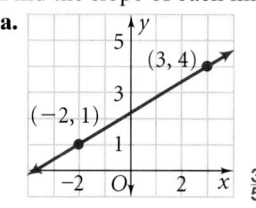
$\frac{3}{5}$

b.
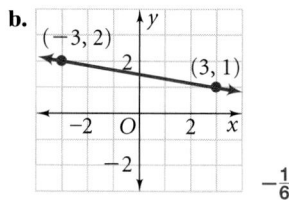
$-\frac{1}{6}$

📖 **Reading Math**

You read the coordinates (x_1, y_1) as "*x* sub 1, *y* sub 1."

You can use any two points on a line to find its slope. You use subscripts to distinguish between two points. In the diagram, (x_1, y_1) are the coordinates of P, and (x_2, y_2) are the coordinates of Q. To find the slope of $\overleftrightarrow{PQ}$, you can use the following formula.

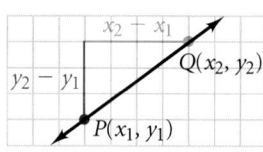

🔑 **Key Concepts**

Formula	Slope
$\text{slope} = \dfrac{\text{rise}}{\text{run}} = \dfrac{y_2 - y_1}{x_2 - x_1}$, where $x_2 - x_1 \neq 0$	

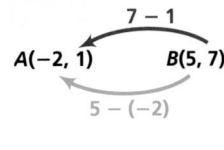

Reading Math

To set up the subtraction in the slope formula, think of moving from the coordinates of *B* to the coordinates of *A*.

$$7 - 1$$
$$A(-2, 1) \quad B(5, 7)$$
$$5 - (-2)$$

Keep in mind that the *x*-coordinate you use first in the denominator must belong to the same ordered pair as the *y*-coordinate you use first in the numerator.

4 EXAMPLE Finding Slope Using Points

Find the slope of the line through $A(-2, 1)$ and $B(5, 7)$.

$$\text{slope} = \frac{y_2 - y_1}{x_2 - x_1}$$

$$= \frac{7 - 1}{5 - (-2)} \quad \text{Substitute (5, 7) for } (x_2, y_2) \text{ and } (-2, 1) \text{ for } (x_1, y_1).$$

$$= \frac{6}{7} \quad \text{Simplify.}$$

• The slope of $\overleftrightarrow{AB}$ is $\frac{6}{7}$.

model

✓ **Check Understanding** **4** Find the slope of the line through each pair of points.
   a. $C(2, 5)$ and $D(4, 7)$ **1**   **b.** $P(-1, 4)$ and $Q(3, -2)$ $-\frac{3}{2}$ **c.** $M(a, b)$ and $N(c, d)$ $\frac{d - b}{c - a}$

GP

You can also analyze the graphs of horizontal and vertical lines. The next example shows why the slope of a horizontal line is 0, and the slope of a vertical line is undefined.

5 EXAMPLE Horizontal and Vertical Lines

Find the slope of each line.

a.
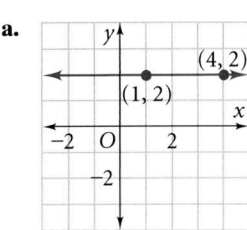

$$\text{slope} = \frac{y_2 - y_1}{x_2 - x_1}$$

$$= \frac{2 - 2}{4 - 1} \quad \text{Substitute (4, 2) for } (x_2, y_2) \text{ and (1, 2) for } (x_1, y_1).$$

$$= \frac{0}{3} \quad \text{Simplify.}$$

$$= 0$$

The slope of the horizontal line is 0.

model

b.
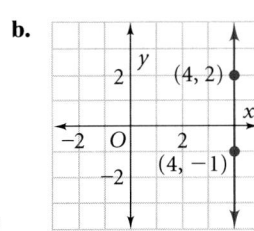

$$\text{slope} = \frac{y_2 - y_1}{x_2 - x_1}$$

$$= \frac{2 - (-1)}{4 - 4} \quad \text{Substitute (4, 2) for } (x_2, y_2) \text{ and (4, -1) for } (x_1, y_1).$$

$$= \frac{3}{0} \quad \text{Simplify.}$$

Division by zero is undefined. So, the slope of the vertical line is undefined.

✓ **Check Understanding** **5** Find the slope of each line.

GP

a. **0**
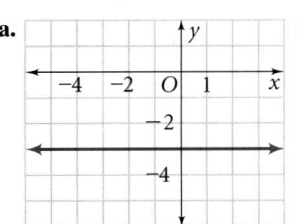

b. **undefined**
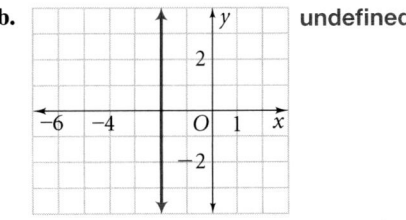

Lesson 6-1 Rate of Change and Slope **285**

3 Find the slope of each line.
a. $-\frac{3}{2}$; b. 2

a.
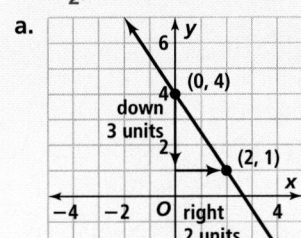

b.
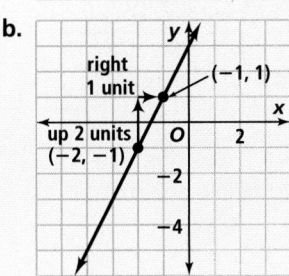

4 Find the slope of the line through $E(3, -2)$ and $F(-2, -1)$.
$-\frac{1}{5}$

5 Find the slope of each line.
a. 0; b. undefined

a.
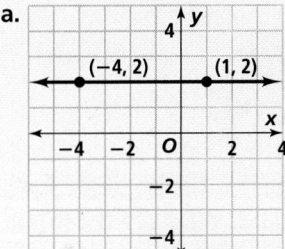

b.
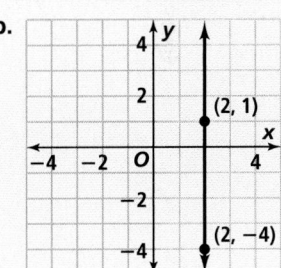

Closure

Ask: *What are two ways to find the slope of a line?* You can count the units of rise and run between two points on a graph of the line. Or you can find the difference of the *y*-coordinates, and, in the same order, the difference of the *x*-coordinates. Then write the quotient of the difference of the *y*-coordinates divided by the difference of the *x*-coordinates.

3. Practice

Assignment Guide

1 Objective
 Ⓐ Ⓑ Core 1–6, 27–29, 40, 54

2 Objective
 Ⓐ Ⓑ Core 7–26, 30–39, 41–53, 55–62
 Ⓒ Extension 63–71

Standardized Test Prep 72–75

Mixed Review 76–87

Teaching Tip

Exercises 1–6 Discuss with students which is the independent variable and which is the dependent variable.

Error Prevention

Exercise 6 Students may think the rate of change is $\frac{1}{2}$. Caution them to look carefully at the scales of the graph.

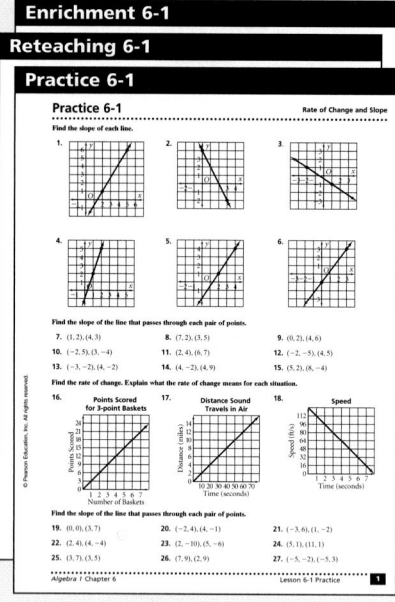

The following summarizes what you have learned about slope.

 **Key Concepts**

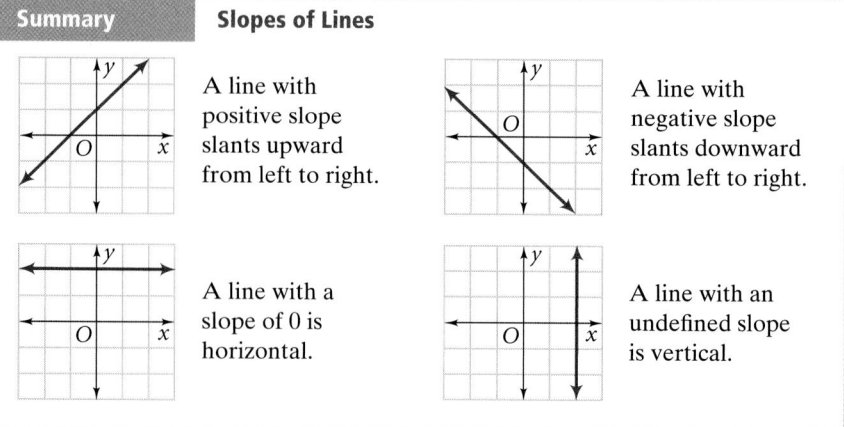

Summary	Slopes of Lines

A line with positive slope slants upward from left to right.

A line with negative slope slants downward from left to right.

A line with a slope of 0 is horizontal.

A line with an undefined slope is vertical.

EXERCISES

For more practice, see *Extra Practice*.

Practice and Problem Solving

Ⓐ Practice by Example

 Examples 1, 2
 (page 283)

The rate of change is constant in each table and graph. Find the rate of change. Explain what the rate of change means for each situation.

1.

Time (hours)	Temperature (°F)
1	−2
4	7
7	16
10	25
13	34

3; the temperature increases 3°F each hour.

2.

People	Cost (dollars)
2	7.90
3	11.85
4	15.80
5	19.75
6	23.70

3.95; the cost per person is $3.95.

3. A Tank of Gas $-\frac{1}{15}$ gal/mi

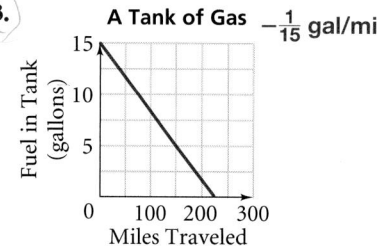

4. Emissions: Generating Electricity for TV Use

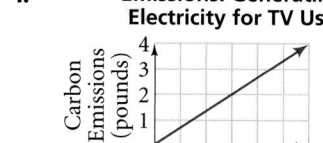

$\frac{2}{3}$; there are 2 lb of carbon emissions for every 3 h of television use.

5. Descent of a Skydiver

$-16\frac{2}{3}$; the skydiver descends $16\frac{2}{3}$ ft/s.

6. Price of Oregano

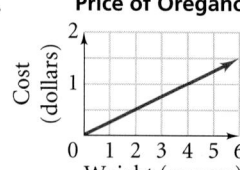

$\frac{1}{4}$; the cost of oregano is $1 for 4 ounces.

Real-World Connection

A jump from 11,000 feet gives a skydiver about 60 seconds of free fall at more than 100 mi/h.

286   Chapter 6   Linear Equations and Their Graphs

Example 3
(page 284)

Find the slope of each line.

7.
$\frac{1}{2}$
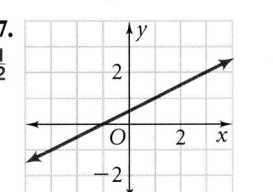

8.
-3
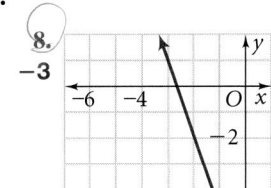

9.
$\frac{2}{3}$
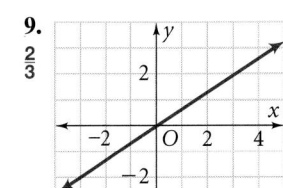

Example 4
(page 285)

Find the slope of the line that passes through each pair of points.

10. $(3, 2), (5, 6)$ **2**

11. $(5, 6), (3, 2)$ **2**

12. $(4, 8), (8, 11)$ $\frac{3}{4}$

13. $(-4, 4), (2, -5)$ $-\frac{3}{2}$

14. $(-2, 1), (1, -2)$ -1

15. $(-3, 1), (3, -5)$ -1

16. $(-8, 0), (1, 5)$ $\frac{5}{9}$

17. $(0, 0), (3, 5)$ $\frac{5}{3}$

18. $(-4, -5), (-9, 1)$ $-\frac{6}{5}$

19. $(5, 0), (0, 2)$ $-\frac{2}{5}$

20. $(-7, 1), (7, 8)$ $\frac{1}{2}$

21. $(0, -1), (1, -6)$ -5

Example 5
(page 285)

State whether the slope is zero or undefined.

22. **0**
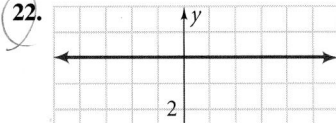

23. **undefined**
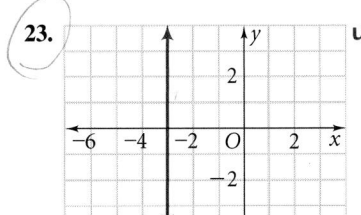

24. $(3, 4), (-3, 4)$
0

25. $(4, 3), (4, -3)$
undefined

26. $\left(-5, \frac{1}{2}\right), (-5, 3)$
undefined

B **Apply Your Skills**

Find the rate of change for each situation.

27. A baby is 18 in. long at birth and 27 in. long at ten months. $\frac{9}{10}$ in./month

28. The cost of group museum tickets is $48 for four people and $78 for ten people.
$5/person

29. You drive 30 mi in one hour and 120 mi in four hours. **30 mi/hr**

Find the slope of the line passing through each pair of points.

30. $(-7, 1), (7, 8)$ $\frac{1}{2}$

31. $\left(4, 1\frac{2}{3}\right), \left(-2, \frac{2}{3}\right)$ $\frac{1}{6}$

32. $(0, 3.5), (-4, 2.5)$ $\frac{1}{4}$

33. $\left(\frac{1}{2}, 8\right), (1, -2)$ **−20**

34. $\left(-5, \frac{1}{2}\right), (-5, 3)$
undefined

35. $(0.5, 6.25), (3, -1.25)$
−3

Through the given point, draw the line with the given slope. 36–39. See margin.

36. $K(3, 5)$
slope -2

37. $M(5, 2)$
slope $-\frac{1}{2}$

38. $Q(-2, 3)$
slope $\frac{3}{5}$

39. $R(2, -3)$
slope $-\frac{4}{3}$

40. a. Biology Which line in the graph at the left is the steepest? **C**
   b. During the 6-week period, which plant had the greatest rate of change? The least rate of change? How do you know? **C greatest; A least; the slope**

41. a. Find the slope of the line through $A(4, -3)$ and $B(1, -5)$ using A for (x_2, y_2) and B for (x_1, y_1). $\frac{2}{3}$
   b. Find the slope of the line in part (a) using B for (x_2, y_2) and A for (x_1, y_1). $\frac{2}{3}$
   c. Critical Thinking Explain why it does not matter which point you use for (x_2, y_2) and which point you use for (x_1, y_1) when you calculate a slope.
   See margin.

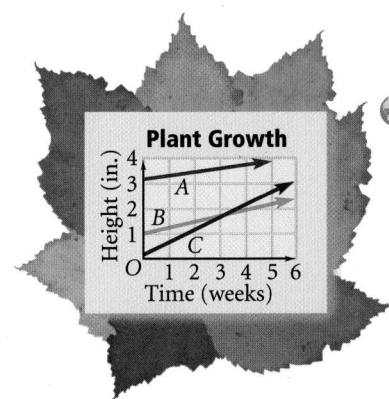
Plant Growth

Careers
Exercise 42 Encourage students to find other ways construction workers use slope, such as pitch of a roof or slant of a driveway. Ask students why construction workers need to know the slope of these items in order to build them.

pages 286–289   Exercises

36.
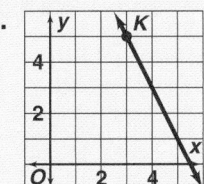

37.
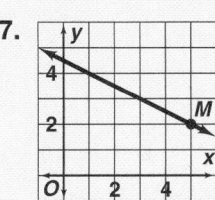

38.
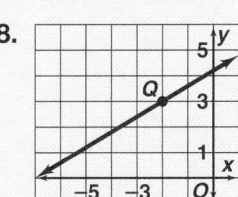

39.
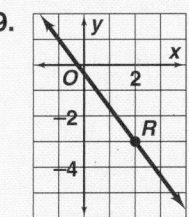

**41c. Answers may vary.
Sample:**
$$\frac{y_2 - y_1}{x_2 - x_1} = \frac{y_1 - y_2}{x_2 - x_1}$$

4. Assess

Lesson Quiz 6-1

1. Find the rate of change for the data in the table. **$15 per ticket**

Tickets	Cost
5	$75
6	$90
7	$105
8	$120

2. Find the rate of change for the data in the graph. **400 calories per hour**

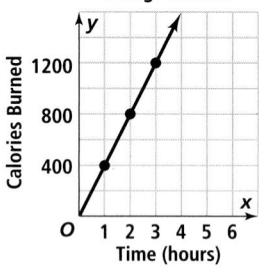

Calories Burned doing Aerobics

3. Find the slope of the line. **$\frac{4}{3}$**

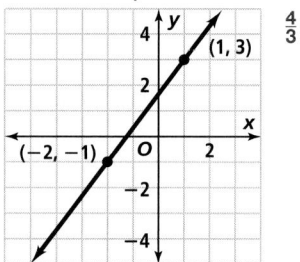

4. Find the slope of the line through $(3, -2)$ and $(-2, 5)$. **$-\frac{7}{5}$**

5. State whether the slope is zero or undefined. **a. undefined; b. 0**

a.

b.

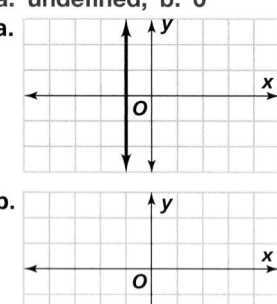

Need Help?

For help with direct variation and the constant of variation see p. 262.

47a. Answers may vary. Sample: $(0, 0)$, $\left(1, \frac{3}{4}\right)$

b. Answers may vary. Sample: $(0, 0)$, $\left(1, -\frac{1}{2}\right)$

Real-World Connection

On a carousel, the outer horses cover more distance than the inner horses, giving them a faster speed.

---

42. Construction An extension ladder has a label that says, "Do not place base of ladder less than 5 ft from the vertical surface." What is the greatest slope possible if the ladder can safely extend to reach a height of 12 ft? Of 18 ft? **$2\frac{2}{5}$; $3\frac{3}{5}$**

43. Writing If two points on a line have positive coordinates, is the slope necessarily positive? Explain. **See margin.**

Geometry Find the slope of the sides of each figure.

44. 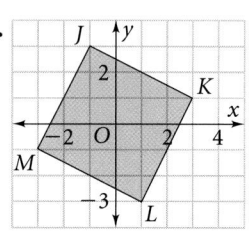 **PQ: $\frac{1}{2}$; QR: 0; RS: 5; SP: −1**

45. **JK: $-\frac{1}{2}$; KL: 2; ML: $-\frac{1}{2}$; MJ: 2**

46. a. Graph the direct variation $y = -\frac{2}{3}x$. **See margin.**
 b. What is the constant of variation? **$-\frac{2}{3}$**
 c. What is the slope? **$-\frac{2}{3}$**
 d. What is the relationship between the constant of variation and the slope? **equal**

47. a. Open-Ended Name two points on a line with a slope of $\frac{3}{4}$. **See left.**
 b. Name two points on a line with a slope of $-\frac{1}{2}$.

Each pair of points lies on a line with the given slope. Find x or y.

48. $(2, 4), (x, 8)$; slope $= -2$ **0**

49. $(2, 4), (x, 8)$; slope $= -\frac{1}{2}$. **−6**

50. $(4, 3), (x, 7)$; slope $= 2$ **6**

51. $(x, 3), (2, 8)$; slope $= -\frac{5}{2}$ **4**

52. $(-4, y), (2, 4y)$; slope $= 6$ **12**

53. $(3, 5), (x, 2)$; undefined slope **3**

Reasoning In Exercises 54–60, tell whether each statement is *true* or *false*. If false, give a counterexample. 54–60. Counterexamples may vary.

54. A rate of change must be either positive or zero. **False; it can be neg. or undefined.**

55. All horizontal lines have the same slope. **true**

56. A line with slope 1 always passes through the origin. **false; $y = x + 2$**

57. Two lines may have the same slope. **true**

58. The slope of a line that passes through Quadrant III must be negative. **false; $y = x$**

59. A line with slope 0 never passes through point $(0, 0)$. **false; $y = 0x$**

60. Two points with the same x-coordinate are always on the same vertical line. **true**

61. Business The graph shows how much it costs to rent carousel equipment.
 a. Estimate the slope of the line. What does that number mean? **111; $111/h**
 b. Customers pay $2 for a ride. What is the average number of customers needed to cover the rental costs? **about 56 customers per hour**

62. Error Analysis A friend says the slope of a line passing through $(1, 7)$ and $(3, 9)$ is equal to the ratio $\frac{1-3}{7-9}$. What is your friend's error? **Friend found $\frac{\text{run}}{\text{rise}}$ instead of $\frac{\text{rise}}{\text{run}}$.**

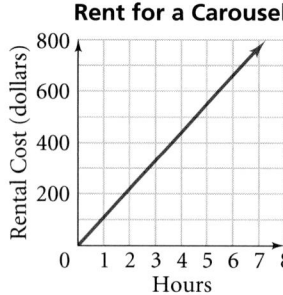

Rent for a Carousel

---

288 Chapter 6 Linear Equations and Their Graphs

pages 286–289 Exercises

43. No; for example, the line passing through the points such as $(1, 6)$ and $(2, 5)$ has a slope of -1.

46a.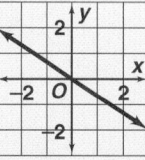

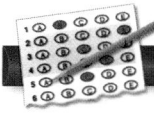

Challenge

66. Yes; $\overleftrightarrow{AB}$ and $\overleftrightarrow{BC}$ have the same slope.

67. Yes; $\overleftrightarrow{GH}$ and $\overleftrightarrow{HI}$ have the same slope.

68. No; $\overleftrightarrow{DE}$ and $\overleftrightarrow{EF}$ do not have the same slope.

69. No; $\overleftrightarrow{PQ}$ and $\overleftrightarrow{QR}$ do not have the same slope.

Find the slope of the line passing through each pair of points.

63. $(a, -b), (-a, -b)$ **0**   64. $(-m, n), (3m, -n)$ $-\frac{n}{2m}$ 65. $(2a, b), (c, 2d)$ $\frac{2d - b}{c - 2a}$

For 66–69, see left.

Do the points in each set lie on the same line? Explain your answer.

66. $A(1, 3), B(4, 2), C(-2, 4)$
67. $G(3, 5), H(-1, 3), I(7, 7)$
68. $D(-2, 3), E(0, -1), F(2, 1)$
69. $P(4, 2), Q(-3, 2), R(2, 5)$
70. $G(1, -2), H(-1, -5), I(5, 4)$
71. $S(-3, 4), T(0, 2), X(-3, 0)$

Yes; $\overleftrightarrow{GH}$ and $\overleftrightarrow{HI}$ have the same slope.

No; $\overleftrightarrow{ST}$ and $\overleftrightarrow{TX}$ do not have the same slope.

Standardized Test Prep

Multiple Choice

72. A line has slope $\frac{4}{3}$. Through which two points could this line pass? **C**
   A. (24, 19), (8, 10)
   B. (10, 8), (16, 0)
   C. (28, 10), (22, 2)
   D. (4, 20), (0, 17)

73. A horizontal line passes through (5, 22). Which other point does the line contain? **G**
   F. (5, 2)   G. (0, 22)   H. (22, 5)   I. (0, 5)

Short Response

74. The steepness, or grade, of a road is expressed as a percent. If a road rises 3 feet for every 24 horizontal feet, what is the slope of the road? What percent grade is this? Show your work. [2] $\frac{3}{24} = \frac{1}{8}$; the slope is $\frac{1}{8}$. $\frac{1}{8} = 12.5\%$; the grade is 12.5%. [1] finds grade only

Quantitative Comparison

Compare the quantity in Column A with the quantity in Column B. Choose the best answer.
   A. The quantity in Column A is greater.
   B. The quantity in Column B is greater.
   C. The two quantities are equal.
   D. The relationship cannot be determined from the information given.

Column A	Column B
75. **A** the slope of the line through the points $(-3, 4)$ and $(-2, 5)$	the slope of the line through the points $(3, 4)$ and $(2, 5)$

Take It to the NET
Online lesson quiz at
www.PHSchool.com
Web Code: aea-0601

Mixed Review

Lesson 5-6

Write a function rule for each situation.

76. the total cost of renting a movie for n days if it costs \$3.50/day $c = 3.5n$

77. the total profit if supplies and wages cost \$232, and each item q sells for \$4.95
   $p = 4.95q - 232$

Lesson 4-5

Find each probability based on one roll of a number cube.

78. $P(10)$ **0**   79. P(even number) $\frac{1}{2}$ 80. P(3 or 5) $\frac{1}{3}$ 81. P(integer) **1**

Lesson 2-3

Solve.

82. $x + 3 + 2x = -6$ **−3**   83. $3(2t + 5) = -9$ **−4**   84. $9 = y + 2(4y - 5)$ $\frac{19}{9}$

85. $4n - 7(n - 9) = 42$ **7**   86. $2(7 - q) - 4 = 0$ **5**   87. $\frac{2}{5}(p + 10) = 0$ **−10**

Give each student a laminated coordinate plane and a piece of uncooked spaghetti. Instruct students to place the spaghetti on the graph to represent a line, and then to find the slope of the line. Repeat.

Standardized Test Prep

Resources
For additional practice with a variety of test item formats:
- Standardized Test Prep, p. 335
- Test-Taking Strategies, p. 330
- Test-Taking Strategies with Transparencies

Math Tip
Exercise 73 You may want to point out that on a horizontal line, all the points are the same distance from the *x*-axis. So all the *y*-coordinates are the same.

Technology

Investigating
$y = mx + b$

Students use graphing calculators to explore equations of the form $y = mx + b$ and the corresponding graphs of those equations. Students will begin to make predictions about the effects on the graphs of the equations of changing the values of m and b.

Resources

Students may use any graphing calculator to graph equations in the form of $y = mx + b$.

Teaching Notes

Encourage students to use mathematical language when discussing patterns that they observe in the exercises.

Teaching Tip

After students have worked independently on the exercises, ask them to make a *conjecture* about how close a graph will be to having the same slope as the *x*- or *y*-axis. If students suggest that the lesser the value of *m* in the equation of the form $y = mx + b$, the closer to the *x*-axis the graph will be, ask if anyone can find a *counter-example* to that conjecture. If no one suggests one, have them look at their answers to Exercise 4. Then ask students if anyone would like to *revise* the original conjecture. Suggest that they use the term *absolute value* in their revised conjecture.

Technology
Investigating $y = mx + b$

FOR USE WITH LESSON 6-2

You can use a graphing calculator to explore the graph of an equation in the form $y = mx + b$. For this Investigation, use a standard screen by pressing ZOOM 6.

1. Graph these equations on the same screen. Then complete each statement.

$$y = x + 1 \qquad y = 2x + 1 \qquad y = \tfrac{1}{2}x + 1$$

   a. The graph of __?__ is closest to the *y*-axis. **$y = 2x + 1$**
   b. The graph of __?__ is closest to the *x*-axis. **$y = \tfrac{1}{2}x + 1$**

2. Match each equation with the best choice for its graph.
   A. $y = \tfrac{1}{5}x - 1$ **II**   **B.** $y = 5x - 1$ **III**   **C.** $y = x - 1$ **I**

   I. 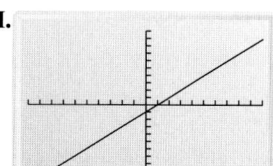   **II.** 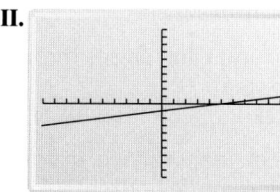   **III.**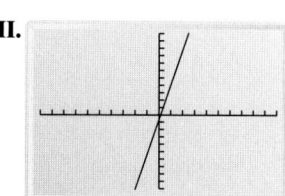

3. How does changing *m* affect the graph of an equation in the form $y = mx + b$?
   Answers may vary. Sample: Changing *m* affects the slope of the graph.
4. Graph these equations on the same screen.

$$y = 2x + 1 \qquad y = -2x + 1$$

   How does the sign of *m* affect the graph of an equation?
   Positive *m*, graph slants up from left to right; negative *m*, graph slants down from left to right.
5. Graph these equations on the same screen.

$$y = 2x + 1 \qquad y = 2x - 2 \qquad y = 2x + 2$$

   Where does the graph of each equation cross the *y*-axis? (*Hint:* Use the ZOOM feature to better see the points of intersection.) **1; −2; 2**

6. Match each equation with the best choice for its graph.
   A. $y = \tfrac{1}{2}x - 5$ **III**   **B.** $y = \tfrac{1}{2}x$ **I**   **C.** $y = \tfrac{1}{2}x + 3$ **II**

   I. 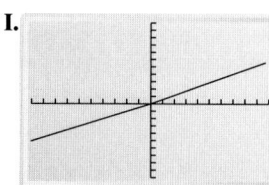   **II.** 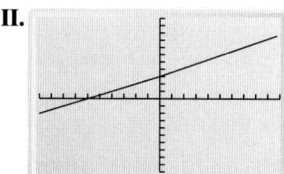   **III.**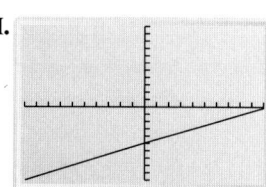

7. How does changing the value of *b* affect the graph of an equation in the form $y = mx + b$? **Answers may vary. Sample: Changing *b* affects the *y*-intercept.**

8. You can change the appearance of a graph by changing its scale in the WINDOW screen. Describe how the graph of $y = 2x + 1$ changes from its appearance on a standard screen using the following values for Xmin, Xmax, Ymin, and Ymax.

   a. Xmin = –5 Ymin = –10
      Xmax = 5 Ymax = 10
      The graph appears less steep.

   b. Xmin = –10 Ymin = –5
      Xmax = 10 Ymax = 5
      The graph appears steeper.

290   Technology   Investigating $y = mx + b$

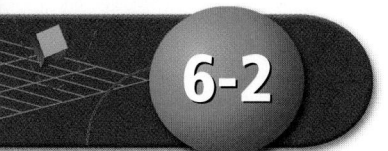

Slope-Intercept Form

4.01 Use linear functions or inequalities to model and solve problems; justify results. b) Interpret constants and coefficients in the context of the problem.

Lesson Preview

What You'll Learn

 OBJECTIVE 1 To write equations in slope-intercept form

 OBJECTIVE 2 To graph linear equations

. . . And Why

To use a graph for relating total earnings to sales, as in Example 5

✓ **Check Skills You'll Need**   (For help, go to Lessons 1-6 and 2-6.)

Evaluate each expression.

1. $6a + 3$ for $a = 2$ **15**

2. $-2x - 5$ for $x = 3$ **−11**

3. $\frac{1}{4}x + 2$ for $x = 16$ **6**

4. $0.2x + 2$ for $x = 15$ **5**

Solve each equation for y.

5. $y - 5 = 4x$ $y = 4x + 5$ **6.** $y + 2x = 7$ $y = -2x + 7$ **7.** $2y + 6 = -8x$
$y = -4x - 3$

New Vocabulary • linear equation • y-intercept • slope-intercept form

 Interactive lesson includes instant self-check, tutorials, and activities.

OBJECTIVE 1 **Writing Linear Equations**

An equation whose graph is a line is a **linear equation.** Since a function rule is an equation, a function can also be linear. Here are some examples of linear equations.

$$y = 2x + 5 \qquad f(x) = \frac{3x}{5} + 4$$

Not all equations are linear. Here are some examples of equations that are not linear.

$$y = x^2 \qquad f(x) = 2x^3 + x + 1$$

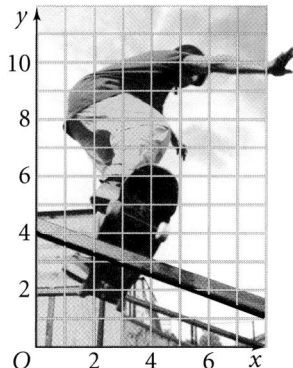

Real-World ⊕ Connection

The skateboarder performs a rail slide on a bar that has slope $-\frac{3}{8}$.

The **y-intercept** is the y-coordinate of the point where a line crosses the y-axis. The line shown at the right crosses the y-axis at $(0, 4)$. The y-intercept is 4. The slope of the line is $-\frac{3}{8}$.

If you know the slope of a line and its y-intercept, you can write the equation of the line. The letter m refers to the *slope*.

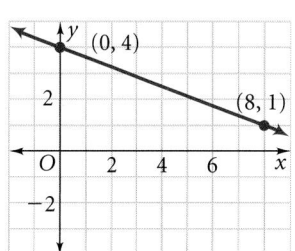

$\dfrac{y_2 - y_1}{x_2 - x_1} = m$ **Start with the slope formula.**

$\dfrac{y - 4}{x - 0} = -\dfrac{3}{8}$ **Substitute $(0, 4)$ for (x_1, y_1), (x, y) for (x_2, y_2), and $-\frac{3}{8}$ for m.**

$\dfrac{y - 4}{x} = -\dfrac{3}{8}$ **Simplify $x - 0$.**

$y - 4 = -\dfrac{3}{8}x$ **Multiply each side by x.**

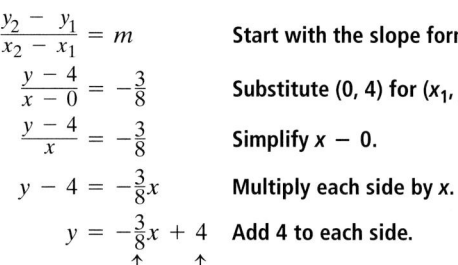

$y = -\dfrac{3}{8}x + 4$ **Add 4 to each side.**

⬆ slope   ⬆ y-intercept

The slope and y-intercept appear in the equation!

Lesson 6-2 Slope-Intercept Form   **291**

Ongoing Assessment and Intervention

Before the Lesson
Diagnose prerequisite skills using:
• Check Skills You'll Need

During the Lesson
Monitor progress using:
• Check Understanding
• Additional Examples
• Standardized Test Prep

After the Lesson
Assess knowledge using:
• Lesson Quiz
• Computer Test Generator CD

 North Carolina Objectives 4.01b

1. Plan

Lesson Preview

✓ **Check Skills You'll Need** 🖥

Multiplying and Dividing
Lesson 1-6: Example 2
Exercises 13–24
Extra Practice, p. 702

Formulas
Lesson 2-6: Example 2
Exercises 9–16
Extra Practice, p. 703

Lesson Resources

📁 **Teaching Resources**
Practice, Reteaching, Enrichment

👥 **Reaching All Students**
Practice Workbook 6-2
Spanish Practice Workbook 6-2
Technology Activities 2
Hands-On Activities 14
Basic Algebra Planning Guide 6-2

⏱ **Presentation Assistant Plus!**
Transparencies
• Check Skills You'll Need 6-2
• Additional Examples 6-2
• Student Edition Answers 6-2
• Lesson Quiz 6-2
PH Presentation Pro CD 6-2

ASSESSMENT SYSTEM (PRENTICE HALL)

Computer Test Generator CD

💿 **Technology**
Resource Pro® CD-ROM
Computer Test Generator CD
Prentice Hall Presentation Pro CD

💻 **www.PHSchool.com**
Student Site
• Teacher Web Code: aek-5500
• Reasoning & Puzzles p. 64
• Self-grading Lesson Quiz
Teacher Center
• Lesson Planner
• Resources

Plus **TEXT**

291

2. Teach

Math Background

In upper level mathematics, lines are considered curves. If the slope of a curve is constant, it is a line. Constant slope is the defining characteristic of a line.

OBJECTIVE

1 Teaching Notes

1 EXAMPLE **English Learners**

Students may wonder why m is used to represent *slope*. There really is no reason other than custom, but students may find it helpful to relate m to <u>m</u>ountain slope.

2 EXAMPLE **Error Prevention**

The point where a line crosses the y-axis is always of the form $(0, y)$. Some students may want to write the y-intercept as these coordinates. Explain to students that only the y-coordinate of the above point is defined as the y-intercept.

Additional Examples

1 What are the slope and y-intercept of $y = 2x - 3$?
Slope is 2; y-intercept is -3

2 Write an equation of the line with slope $\frac{2}{5}$ and y-intercept 4.
$y = \frac{2}{5}x + 4$

3 Write the equation for the line. $y = -\frac{2}{3}x + 1$

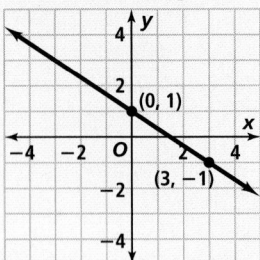

292

Key Concepts

Definition	Slope-Intercept Form of a Linear Equation

The **slope-intercept form** of a linear equation is $y = mx + b$.

$$\uparrow \qquad \uparrow$$
slope y-intercept

1 EXAMPLE **Identifying Slope and y-Intercept**

What are the slope and y-intercept of $y = 3x - 5$?

$y = mx + b$ **Use the slope-intercept form.**

$y = 3x + (-5)$ **Think of $y = 3x - 5$ as $y = 3x + (-5)$.**

The slope is 3; the y-intercept is -5.

✓ **Check Understanding** ① Find the slope and y-intercept of each equation.

a. $y = -2x + 1$ **b.** $y = \frac{7}{6}x - \frac{3}{4}$ **c.** $y = -\frac{4}{5}x$

$m = -2; b = 1$ $m = \frac{7}{6}; b = -\frac{3}{4}$ $m = -\frac{4}{5}; b = 0$

You can write an equation of a line when you know its slope and y-intercept.

2 EXAMPLE **Writing an Equation**

Write an equation of the line with slope $\frac{3}{8}$ and y-intercept 6.

$y = mx + b$ **Use the slope-intercept form.**

$y = \frac{3}{8}x + 6$ **Substitute $\frac{3}{8}$ for m and 6 for b.**

✓ **Check Understanding** ② Write an equation of a line with slope -3 and y-intercept 4. $y = -3x + 4$

You can write an equation from a graph. Use two points to find the slope. Then use the slope and the y-intercept to write the equation.

3 EXAMPLE **Writing an Equation From a Graph**

Write the equation of the line.

Step 1 Find the slope. Two points on the line are $(0, 2)$ and $(4, -1)$.

$\text{slope} = \frac{-1 - 2}{4 - 0}$

$= -\frac{3}{4}$

Step 2 Write an equation in slope-intercept form. The y-intercept is 2.

$y = mx + b$

$y = -\frac{3}{4}x + 2$ **Substitute $-\frac{3}{4}$ for m and 2 for b.**

✓ **Check Understanding** ③ Write the equation of the line.
$y = \frac{1}{2}x + 1$

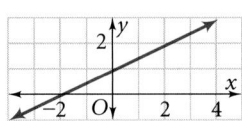

Reaching All Students

Below Level In Example 5, help students relate the slope and y-intercept to what they represent in the problem.	**Advanced Learners** Challenge students to arrange the following linear equations in order from steepest to least steep. $y = \frac{1}{2}x + 3$, $y = \frac{2}{3}x + 3$, $y = 2x + 3$	**English Learners** See note on page 292. **Auditory Learners** See note on page 294.

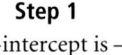

OBJECTIVE 2 — Graphing Linear Equations

Each point on the graph of an equation is an ordered pair that makes the equation true. The graph of a linear equation is a line that indicates all the solutions of the equation. You can use the slope and *y*-intercept to graph a line.

4 EXAMPLE — Graphing Equations

Graph $y = 3x - 1$.

Step 1
The y-intercept is –1. So plot a point at $(0, -1)$.

Step 2
The slope is 3, or $\frac{3}{1}$. Use the slope to plot a second point.

Step 3
Draw a line through the two points.

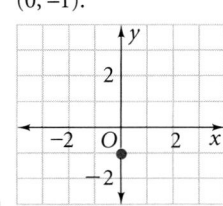
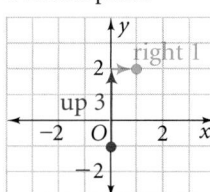
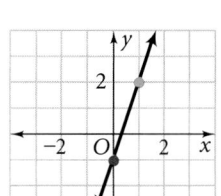

4.

✓ **Check Understanding** ④ Graph $y = \frac{3}{2}x - 2$. **See left.**

When you graph equations for real-world situations, use scales on the *x*- and *y*-axes that are reasonable for the situation. Recall that you can avoid having a large blank space in a graph by using a zigzag line to show a break in a scale.

5 EXAMPLE — Real-World Problem Solving

Commission The base pay of a water-delivery person is $210 per week. He also earns 20% commission on any sale he makes. The equation $t = 210 + 0.2s$ relates total earnings *t* to sales *s*. Graph the equation.

Step 1 Identify the slope and *y*-intercept.

$$t = 210 + 0.2s$$

$$t = 0.2s + 210 \qquad \text{Rewrite the equation in slope-intercept form.}$$

↑ slope   ↑ *y*-intercept

Step 2 Plot two points. First plot $(0, 210)$, the *y*-intercept. Then use the slope to plot a second point.

The slope is 0.2, which equals $\frac{2}{10}$, or $\frac{20}{100}$. Plot a second point 20 units above and 100 units to the right of the *y*-intercept.

Step 3 Draw a line through the points.

Weekly Earnings for a Water-Delivery Person

✓ **Check Understanding** ⑤ Suppose the base pay of the delivery person is $150, and his commission on each sale is 30%. The equation relating his total earnings *t* to sales *s* is $t = 150 + 0.3s$. Graph the equation. **See back of book.**

Real-World Connection

Between 1990 and 1999, the sales of bottled water in the United States increased 107.6%, which means that sales more than doubled.

Additional Examples

④ Graph $y = \frac{1}{3}x - 2$.

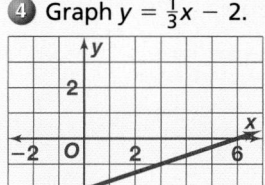

⑤ The base pay for a used car salesperson is $300 per week. The salesperson also earns 15% commission on sales made. The equation $t = 300 + 0.15s$ relates total earnings *t* to sales *s*. Graph the equation.

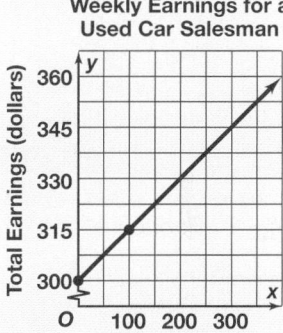

Weekly Earnings for a Used Car Salesman

Closure

Ask: *How does changing the value of m affect the graph of a line?* Changing *m* changes the slope, or slant, of a line. *How does changing the value of b affect the graph of a line?* Changing *b* changes the *y*-intercept.

Practice and Problem Solving

Assignment Guide

▼ **1 Objective**

A B Core 1–27, 41–49, 56–65, 68–74

C Extension 78–80

▼ **2 Objective**

A B Core 28–40, 50–55, 66, 67, 75–77

C Extension 81, 82

Standardized Test Prep 83–86

Mixed Review 87–91

Teaching Tip

Exercises 22–27 Suggest that students use both intercepts to determine the slope whenever possible.

Auditory Learners

Exercises 28–39 Some students may confuse the slope and *y*-intercept when graphing. Tell them to *begin* at *b*, and then *move m* (using rise and run).

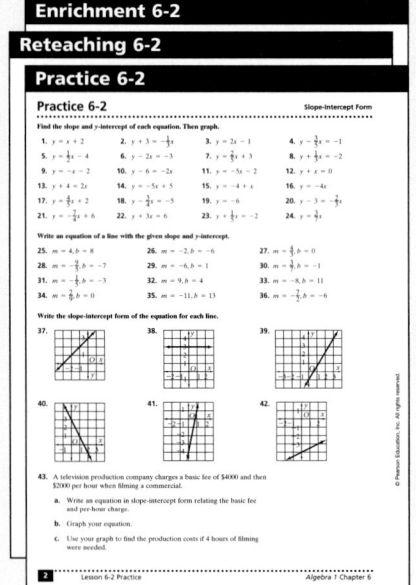

A Practice by Example

Example 1
(page 292)

Find the slope and *y*-intercept of each equation.

1. $y = -2x + 1$ −2; 1   **2.** $y = -\frac{1}{2}x + 2$ −$\frac{1}{2}$; 2   **3.** $y = x - \frac{5}{4}$ 1; −$\frac{5}{4}$

4. $y = 5x + 8$ 5; 8   **5.** $y = \frac{2}{3}x + 1\frac{2}{3}$; 1   **6.** $y = -4x$ −4; 0

7. $y = -x - 7$ −1; −7   **8.** $y = -0.7x - 9$ −0.7; −9   **9.** $y = -\frac{3}{4}x - 5$ −$\frac{3}{4}$; −5

Example 2
(page 292)

Write an equation of a line with the given slope and *y*-intercept. 10–21. See margin.

10. $m = \frac{2}{9}, b = 3$ **11.** $m = 3, b = \frac{2}{9}$ **12.** $m = \frac{9}{2}, b = 3$

13. $m = 0, b = 1$ **14.** $m = -1, b = -6$ **15.** $m = -\frac{2}{3}, b = 5$

16. $m = 0.3, b = 4$ **17.** $m = 0.4, b = 0.6$ **18.** $m = -7, b = \frac{1}{3}$

19. $m = -\frac{1}{5}, b = -\frac{2}{5}$ **20.** $m = -\frac{1}{4}, b = \frac{5}{4}$ **21.** $m = \frac{8}{3}, b = \frac{2}{3}$

Example 3
(page 292)

Write the slope-intercept form of the equation for each line. 22–27. See left.

22. $y = -\frac{2}{3}x + 1$

23. $y = \frac{3}{4}x + 2$

24. $y = 2x - 2$

25. $y = \frac{1}{2}x + \frac{1}{2}$

26. $y = -\frac{2}{5}x + 2.8$

27. $y = \frac{5}{4}x - \frac{1}{2}$

22. 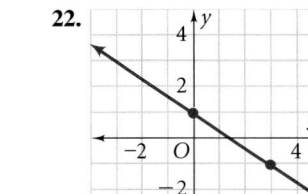 **23.** 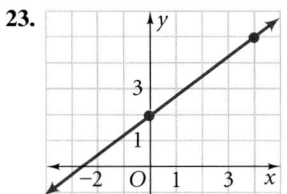 **24.**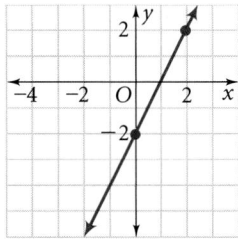

25. 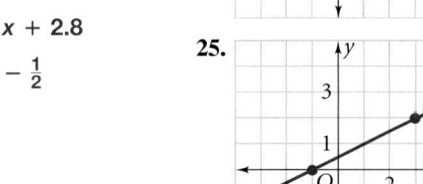 **26.** 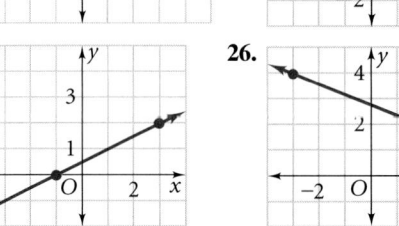 **27.**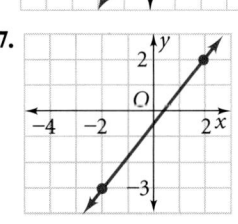

Example 4
(page 293)

Use the slope and *y*-intercept to graph each equation. 28–39. See margin.

28. $y = \frac{1}{2}x + 4$ **29.** $y = \frac{2}{3}x - 1$ **30.** $y = -5x + 2$ **31.** $y = 2x + 5$

32. $y = x + 4$ **33.** $y = -x + 2$ **34.** $y = 4x - 3$ **35.** $y = -\frac{3}{2}x$

36. $y = \frac{2}{5}x - 3$ **37.** $y = -\frac{2}{3}x + 2$ **38.** $y = -\frac{4}{5}x + 4$ **39.** $y = -0.5x + 2$

Example 5
(page 293)

40. Retail Sales A music store is offering a coupon promotion on its CDs. The regular price for CDs is $14. With the coupon, customers are given $4 off the total purchase. The equation $t = 14c - 4$, where *c* is the number of CDs and *t* is the total cost of the purchase, models this situation.
a. Graph the equation. **See margin p. 296.**
b. Find the total cost for a sale of 6 CDs. **$80**

B Apply Your Skills

Find the slope and *y*-intercept of each equation.

41. $y - 2 = -3x$ −3; 2   **42.** $y + \frac{1}{2}x = 0$ −$\frac{1}{2}$; 0   **43.** $y - 9x = \frac{1}{2}$ 9; $\frac{1}{2}$

44. $y = 3x - 9$ 3; −9   **45.** $2y - 6 = 3x$ $\frac{3}{2}$; 3   **46.** $-2y = 6(5 - 3x)$ 9; −15

47. $y - d = cx$ c; d   **48.** $y = (2 - a)x + a$ 2 − a; a   **49.** $2y + 4n = -6x$ −3; −2n

---

pages 294–296   Exercises

10. $y = \frac{2}{9}x + 3$

11. $y = 3x + \frac{2}{9}$

12. $y = \frac{9}{2}x + 3$

13. $y = 1$

14. $y = -x - 6$

15. $y = -\frac{2}{3}x + 5$

16. $y = 0.3x + 4$

17. $y = 0.4x + 0.6$

18. $y = -7x + \frac{1}{3}$

19. $y = -\frac{1}{5}x - \frac{2}{5}$

20. $y = -\frac{1}{4}x + \frac{5}{4}$

21. $y = \frac{8}{3}x + \frac{2}{3}$

Use the slope and *y*-intercept to graph each equation. 50–53. See margin.
pp. 296–297.

50. $y = 7 - 3x$ **51.** $2y + 4x = 0$ **52.** $3y + 6 = -2x$

53. $y + 2 = 5x - 4$ **54.** $4x + 3y = 2x - 1$ **55.** $-2(3x - 4) + y = 0$
54–55. See back of book.

56. The slope was used for the *y*-int., and the *y*-int. was used for the slope.

56. Error Analysis Fred drew the graph at the right for the equation $y = -2x + 1$. What error did he make? **See left.**

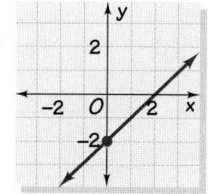

57. a. A candle begins burning at time $t = 0$. Its original height is 12 in. After 30 min the height of the candle is 8 in. Draw a graph showing the change in the height of the candle. **See back of book.**
b. Write an equation that relates the height of a candle to the time it has been burning. $h = -\frac{2}{15}t + 12$
c. How many minutes after the candle is lit will it burn out? **90 min**

Real-World Connection

Careers Airport ground crews direct airplanes to and from their gates.

58. Airplane Fuel The graph shows the relationship between the number of gallons of fuel in the tank of an airplane and the weight of the airplane. The equation $y = 6x + 2512$, where x is the number of gallons of fuel and y is the weight of the airplane, models this situation.
a. What does the slope represent?
b. Use the equation to predict the weight of the plane when the tank contains 25 gallons of fuel. **2662 lb**

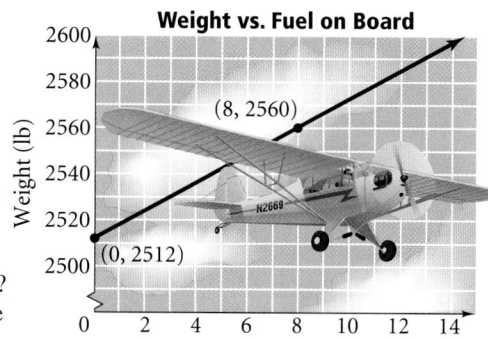

Weight vs. Fuel on Board

(8, 2560)

(0, 2512)

Weight (lb)

Fuel (gal)

a. Slope represents the weight of a gallon of fuel.

Is the ordered pair on the graph of the given equation?

59. $(-3, 4); y = -2x + 1$ **60.** $(-6, 5); y = -\frac{1}{2}x + 2$ **61.** $(0, -1); y = x - \frac{5}{4}$
no   yes   no

Match the equation with its graph. Each mark on the scale indicates one unit.

62. $y = x + 5$ III **63.** $y = -\frac{5}{2}x + 5$ I **64.** $y = -\frac{1}{2}x + 5$ II

I. 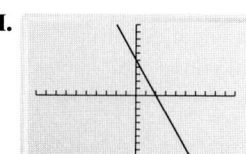 **II.** 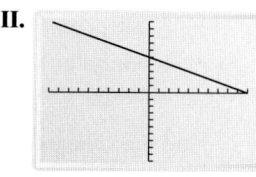 **III.**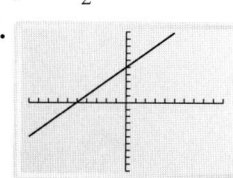

65. a. Math in the Media Write an equation relating the data in the cartoon. $d = 7p$
b. How many dog years are 12 human years? **84 dog years**

mother Goose and Grimm

Lesson 6-2 Slope-Intercept Form **295**

28. 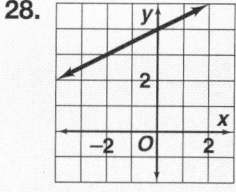 $y = \frac{1}{2}x + 4$ **29.** 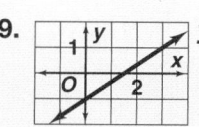 $y = \frac{2}{3}x - 1$ **30.** 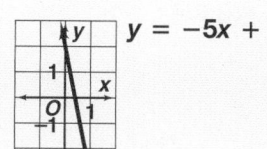 $y = -5x + 2$

Math Tip
Exercises 51–55 Remind students to begin by solving for *y*.

31. 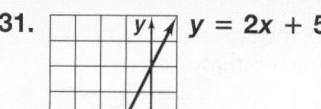 $y = 2x + 5$

32. 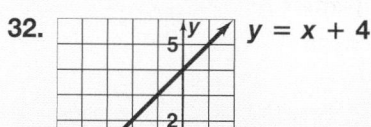 $y = x + 4$

33. 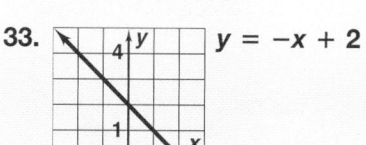 $y = -x + 2$

34. 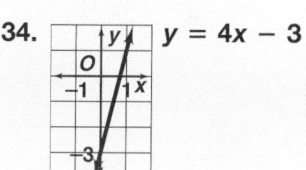 $y = 4x - 3$

35. 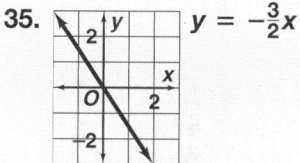 $y = -\frac{3}{2}x$

36. 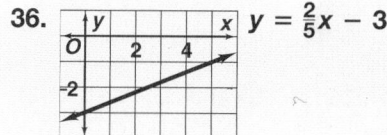 $y = \frac{2}{5}x - 3$

37. 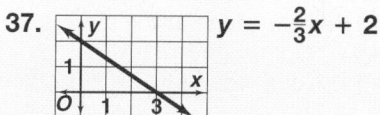 $y = -\frac{2}{3}x + 2$

38. 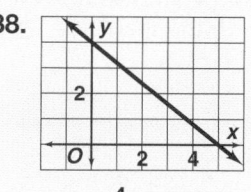 $y = -\frac{4}{5}x + 4$

39. 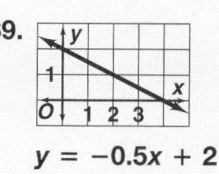 $y = -0.5x + 2$

295

Lesson Quiz 6-2

Find the slope and y-intercept of each equation.

1. $y = \frac{3}{4}x - 3$ $m = \frac{3}{4}; b = -3$

2. $y = -2x$ $m = -2; b = 0$

Write an equation of a line with the given slope and y-intercept.

3. $m = -\frac{3}{5}, b = -4$
   $y = -\frac{3}{5}x - 4$

4. $m = 0.5, b = 1$ $y = 0.5x + 1$

5. Write an equation for the line. $y = \frac{1}{2}x - 3$

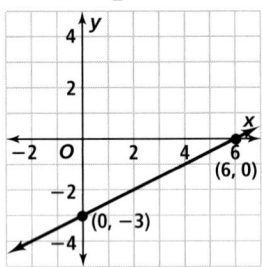

6. Graph $y = -x + 3$.

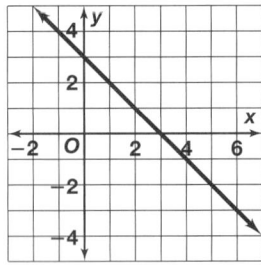

Alternative Assessment

Give each student a laminated coordinate plane and a piece of uncooked spaghetti. Instruct each student to write an equation for a line whose y-intercept is an integer, and then model the equation with the spaghetti. Repeat.

Real-World 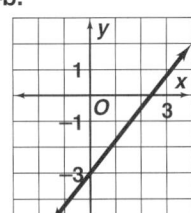 **Connection**

In the United States, although 35% of households have pet cats and 37% have pet dogs, there are about 25% more pet cats than pet dogs.

75a–b.

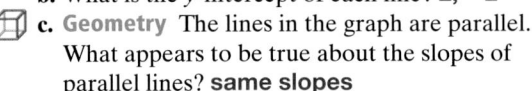

82b.

$r = -15d + 265$

66. **Pet Care** When the Bryants leave town for a vacation, they put their dog Tyco in a kennel. The kennel charges $15 for a first-day flea bath and $5 per day. The equation $t = 15 + 5d$ relates the total charge t to the number of days d.
    a. Rewrite the equation in slope-intercept form. $t = 5d + 15$
    b. Graph the equation. **See margin.**
    c. Explain why the line you graph should lie only in Quadrant I. **See margin.**

67. **Writing** Explain the steps you would use to graph $y = \frac{3}{4}x + 5$. **See margin.**

68. **Critical Thinking** Which graphed line has the greater slope? Explain.

A. 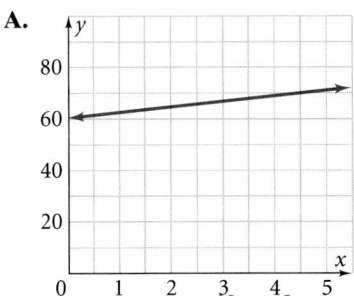   B.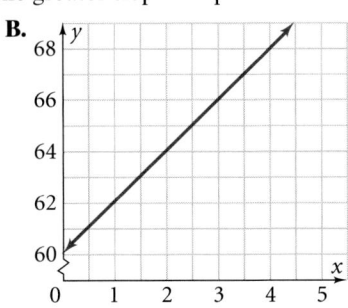

A; slope in A $= \frac{10}{4.5} > \frac{8}{4} = 2 =$ slope in B.

Given two points on a line, write the equation of the line in slope-intercept form.

69. $(3, 5), (5, 9)$ $y = 2x - 1$
70. $(5, -13), (2, -1)$ $y = -4x + 7$
71. $(-4, 10), (6, 5)$ $y = -\frac{1}{2}x + 8$
72. $(8, 7), (-12, 2)$ $y = \frac{1}{4}x + 5$
73. $(-7, 4), (11, -14)$ $y = -x - 3$
74. $(-1, -9), (2, 0)$ $y = 3x - 6$

75. **Graphing Calculator** Suppose you want to graph the equation $y = \frac{5}{4}x - 3$. Enter each key sequence and display the graph. **a–b. See left.**
    a. [Y=] 5 [÷] 4 [X,T,θ,n] [−] 3   b. [Y=] [(] 5 [÷] 4 [)] [X,T,θ,n] [−] 3
    c. Which equation gives you the graph of $y = \frac{5}{4}x - 3$? Explain. **Both; check students' work.**

76. a. What is the slope of each line? $\frac{1}{4}; \frac{1}{4}$
    b. What is the y-intercept of each line? 2; −2
    c. **Geometry** The lines in the graph are parallel. What appears to be true about the slopes of parallel lines? **same slopes**

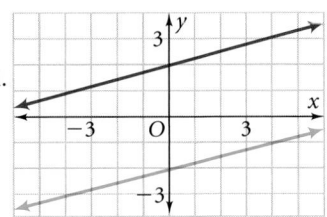

77. **Open-Ended** Write a linear equation. Identify the slope and y-intercept. Then graph your equation. **Check students' work.**

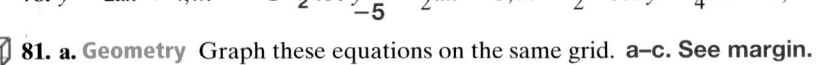

C Challenge

Find the value of a such that the graph of the equation has the given slope.

78. $y = 2ax + 4; m = -1$ $-\frac{1}{2}$
79. $y = -\frac{1}{2}ax - 5; m = \frac{5}{2}$ -5
80. $y = \frac{3}{4}ax + 3; m = \frac{9}{16}$ $\frac{3}{4}$

81. a. **Geometry** Graph these equations on the same grid. **a–c. See margin.**
       $y = 3$ $y = -3$ $x = 2$ $x = -2$
    b. Which geometric figure did you draw? Justify your answer.
    c. Draw a diagonal of the figure. What is the equation of this line? Explain.

82. **Recreation** A group of mountain climbers begin an expedition with 265 lb of food. They plan to eat a total of 15 lb of food per day.
    a. Write an equation in slope-intercept form relating the remaining food supply r to the number of days d. $r = -15d + 265$
    b. Graph your equation. **See left.**
    c. The group plans to eat the last of their food the day their expedition ends. Use your graph to find how many days they expect the expedition to last. **18 days**

pages 294–296 Exercises

40a. $t = 14c - 4$

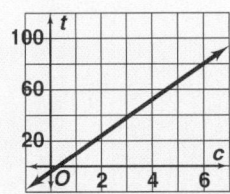

50.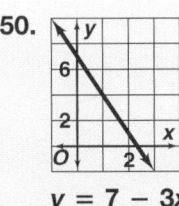
$y = 7 - 3x$

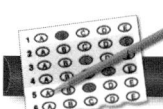

Multiple Choice

83. Which equation has the same y-intercept as $y = 4x - 3$? **D**

    A. $y - 3 = x$ **B.** $y = 8x + 3$ **C.** $3 - y = 4x$ **D.** $y = -3 + 8x$

84. Which of the following is the equation of the line that has the same slope as $y = -\frac{3}{2}x + 2$ and the same y-intercept as $y = 3x - 2$? **G**

    F. $y - 2 = -\frac{3}{2}x$ **G.** $-\frac{3}{2}x = y + 2$

    H. $y + 2 = -\frac{3}{2}$ **I.** $-\frac{3}{2}x = y + 3$

85. A software company started with 2 employees. In 6 months, the company had 7 employees. The number of employees increased at a steady rate. Which equation models the relationship between the number of employees n and the number of months m since the company started? **A**

    A. $n = \frac{5}{6}m + 2$ **B.** $m = 2n + \frac{5}{6}$

    C. $n = \frac{6}{5}m + 2$ **D.** $m = \frac{5}{6}n + 2$

Short Response

86. A line passes through the points (0, 3) and (1, 5). Graph this line and find an equation for the line in slope-intercept form. Show your work. **See margin.**

Take It to the NET Online lesson quiz at www.PHSchool.com Web Code: aea-0602

Mixed Review

Lesson 6-1   **Find the slope of the line that passes through each pair of points.**

87. $(-2, 8), (5, -1) -\frac{9}{7}$ **88.** $(0, 0), (-6, 5) -\frac{5}{6}$ **89.** $(4, 6), (2, -3) \frac{9}{2}$ **90.** $(1, 2), (2, 1) -1$

Lesson 4-3   **91.** The greeting card industry sells over 6 billion cards annually. Women purchase 80% of all greeting cards sold. How many cards do women purchase annually? **4.8 billion**

On August 30, 1984, Astronaut Judith A. Resnik became the second American woman in space, on the shuttle *Discovery*'s first voyage. Resnik was an electrical engineer with a Ph.D. from the University of Maryland. Prior to her mission, she helped to design and develop a remote manipulator system. This required skill in writing linear equations. Her job during *Discovery*'s six-day voyage was to manipulate a robotic arm and to extend and retract the shuttle's solar power array. Resnik died tragically in the *Challenger* disaster in 1986.

Take It to the NET For more information about astronauts, go to **www.PHSchool.com**. Web Code: aee-2032

Lesson 6-2   Slope-Intercept Form   **297**

51.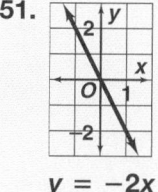

$y = -2x$

52.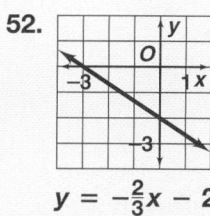

$y = -\frac{2}{3}x - 2$

53. 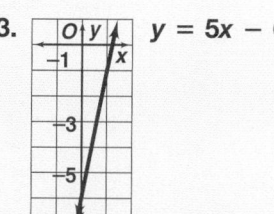 $y = 5x - 6$

📁 **Resources**

For additional practice with a variety of test item formats:
- Standardized Test Prep, p. 335
- Test-Taking Strategies, p. 330
- Test-Taking Strategies with Transparencies

Exercise 83 Suggest to students that they first check for equations that have already been solved for y.

66b. 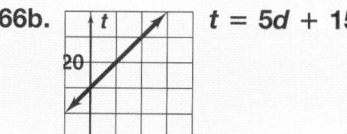 $t = 5d + 15$

  c. Answers may vary. Sample: no neg. charges and no neg. number of days

67. Answers may vary. Sample: Plot point (0, 5), then move up 3 and right 4. Plot (4, 8) and connect the two points.

81a.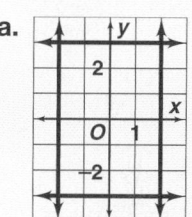

$x = -2; x = 2$
$y = 3; y = -3$

  b. Rectangle; check students' work.

  c. $y = \frac{3}{2}x$ OR $y = -\frac{3}{2}x$; explanations may vary.

86. [2]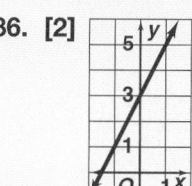

slope: $\frac{5-3}{1-0} = 2$
y-intercept: 3
equation: $y = 2x + 3$

[1] correct graph and minor error in finding function

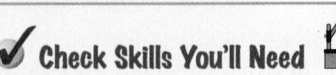
1. Plan

Lesson Preview

✓ **Check Skills You'll Need**

Solving Multi-Step Equations
Lesson 2-3: Example 5
Exercises 30–38
Extra Practice, p. 703

Formulas
Lesson 2-6: Example 2
Exercises 9–16
Extra Practice, p. 703

Lesson Resources

📁 **Teaching Resources**
Practice, Reteaching, Enrichment
Checkpoint Quiz 1

👫 **Reaching All Students**
Practice Workbook 6-3
Spanish Practice Workbook 6-3
Reading and Math Literacy 6B
Spanish Reading & Literacy 6B
Spanish Checkpoint Quiz 1
Basic Algebra Planning Guide 6-3

⏰ **Presentation Assistant Plus!**
Transparencies
• Check Skills You'll Need 6-3
• Additional Examples 6-3
• Student Edition Answers 6-3
• Lesson Quiz 6-3
• PH Presentation Pro CD 6-3

PRENTICE HALL ASSESSMENT SYSTEM

Checkpoint Quiz 1
Computer Test Generator CD

💿 **Technology**
Resource Pro® CD-ROM
Computer Test Generator CD
Prentice Hall Presentation Pro CD

🖥 **www.PHSchool.com**
Student Site
• Teacher Web Code: aek-5500
• Graphing Calculator,
  Procedure 5
• Self-grading Lesson Quiz
Teacher Center
• Lesson Planner
• Resources

Plus

6-3

Standard Form

North Carolina Objectives

4.01 Use linear functions or inequalities to model and solve problems; justify results. b) Interpret constants and coefficients in the context of the problem.

Lesson Preview

What You'll Learn

OBJECTIVE 1 To graph equations using intercepts

OBJECTIVE 2 To write equations in standard form

. . . And Why

To use an equation to model a real-world situation that involves exercise, as in Example 5

✓ **Check Skills You'll Need** (For help, go to Lessons 2-3 and 2-6.)

Solve each equation for y.

1. $3x + y = 5$ $y = -3x + 5$ **2.** $y - 2x = 10$ $y = 2x + 10$ **3.** $x - y = 6$ $y = x - 6$

4. $20x + 4y = 8$ $y = -5x + 2$ **5.** $9y + 3x = 1$ $y = -\frac{1}{3}x + \frac{1}{9}$ **6.** $5y - 2x = 4$ $y = \frac{2}{5}x + \frac{4}{5}$

Clear each equation of decimals.

7. $6.25x + 8.5 = 7.75$ $625x + 850 = 775$ **8.** $0.4 = 0.2x - 5$ $4 = 2x - 50$ **9.** $0.9 - 0.222x = 1$ $900 - 222x = 1000$

New Vocabulary • standard form of a linear equation • x-intercept

---

🖥 Interactive lesson includes instant self-check, tutorials, and activities.

OBJECTIVE 1

Graphing Equations Using Intercepts

1. Answers may vary.
Sample:

x	y
0	4
3	6
6	8
9	10

2.
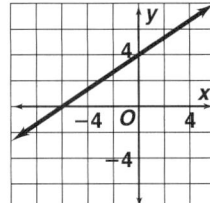

Investigation: Intercepts

1. Make a table of values for the equation $3y - 2x = 12$. **See left.**

2. Use the table of values to graph $3y - 2x = 12$. **See left.**

3. What is the y-intercept? **4**

4. What is the value of x when the line crosses the x-axis? **−6**

5. In the equation $3y - 2x = 12$, what is the value of y when $x = 0$? What is the value of x when $y = 0$? **4; −6**

6. Using your answers to 3, 4, and 5, explain how you can make a graph of $3y - 2x = 12$ without making a table.
Answers may vary. Sample: Find x- and y-intercepts, and then connect the two points.

The slope-intercept form is just one form of a linear equation. Another form is standard form, which is useful in making quick graphs.

🔑 **Key Concepts**

Definition	Standard Form of a Linear Equation

The **standard form of a linear equation** is $Ax + By = C$, where A, B, and C are real numbers, and A and B are not both zero.

You can use the x- and y-intercepts to make a graph. The **x-intercept** is the x-coordinate of the point where a line crosses the x-axis. To graph a linear equation in standard form, you can find the x-intercept by substituting 0 for y and solving for x. Similarly, to find the y-intercept, substitute 0 for x and solve for y.

Ongoing Assessment and Intervention

Before the Lesson
Diagnose prerequisite skills using:
• Check Skills You'll Need

During the Lesson
Monitor progress using:
• Check Understanding
• Additional Examples
• Standardized Test Prep

After the Lesson
Assess knowledge using:
• Lesson Quiz
• Computer Test Generator CD
• Chapter Checkpoint 1 (p. 303)

1 EXAMPLE Finding *x*- and *y*-Intercepts

Find the *x*- and *y*-intercept of $3x + 4y = 8$.

Step 1 To find the *x*-intercept, substitute 0 for *y* and solve for *x*.

$$3x + 4y = 8$$
$$3x + 4(0) = 8$$
$$3x = 8$$
$$x = \frac{8}{3}$$

The *x*-intercept is $\frac{8}{3}$.

Step 2 To find the *y*-intercept, substitute 0 for *x* and solve for *y*.

$$3x + 4y = 8$$
$$3(0) + 4y = 8$$
$$4y = 8$$
$$y = 2$$

The *y*-intercept is 2.

✓ **Check Understanding** ① Find the *x*- and *y*-intercepts of $4x - 9y = -12$. $-3; \frac{4}{3}$

If the *x*- and *y*-intercepts are integers, you can use them to make a quick graph.

2 EXAMPLE Graphing Lines Using Intercepts

Graph $2x + 3y = 12$ using intercepts.

Step 1 Find the intercepts.

$$2x + 3y = 12$$
$$2x + 3(0) = 12 \quad \textbf{Substitute 0 for } y.$$
$$2x = 12 \quad \textbf{Solve for } x.$$
$$x = 6$$

$$2(0) + 3y = 12 \quad \textbf{Substitute 0 for } x.$$
$$3y = 12 \quad \textbf{Solve for } y.$$
$$y = 4$$

Step 2 Plot $(0, 4)$ and $(6, 0)$.
Draw a line through the points.

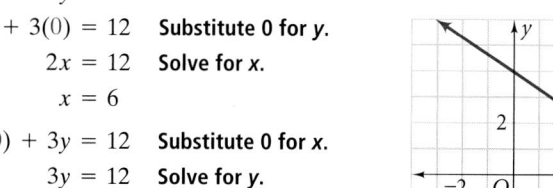

2.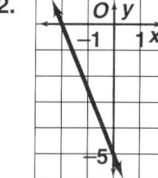

✓ **Check Understanding** ② Graph $5x + 2y = -10$ using the *x*- and *y*-intercepts. **See left.**

In the standard form of an equation $Ax + By = C$, either *A* or *B*, but not both, *may* be zero. If *A* or *B* is zero, the line is either horizontal or vertical.

?

Need Help?

The slope of a horizontal line is 0, and the slope of a vertical line is undefined.

3 EXAMPLE Graphing Horizontal and Vertical Lines

a. Graph $y = -3$.

$$0x + 1y = -3 \quad \leftarrow \textbf{Write in standard form.} \rightarrow$$
For all values of $x, y = -3$.

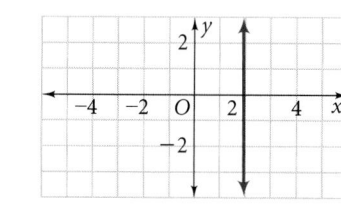

b. Graph $x = 2$.

$$1x + 0y = 2$$
For all values of $y, x = 2$.

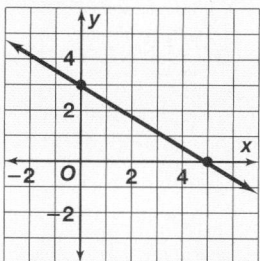

✓ **Check Understanding** ③ Graph each equation. **a–d. See back of book.**

a. $y = 5$ **b.** $y = 0$ **c.** $x = -4$ **d.** $x = 0$

👥 Reaching All Students

Below Level Students may confuse the coefficients of *x* and *y* with the *x*- and *y*-intercepts. Use the linear equation in Example 1 to illustrate the difference.	**Advanced Learners** Challenge students to develop the equations for horizontal lines and for vertical lines from the standard form $Ax + By = C$.	**Tactile Learners** See note on page 299. **Diversity** See note on page 300.

---

2. Teach

Professional Development

Math Background

François Viète, a French mathematician of the sixteenth century, was the first to use letters as coefficients before variables. He also he introduced the + and − signs, although he never used the = sign.

OBJECTIVE

▼ 1 Teaching Notes

Investigation (Optional)
Suggest that students rewrite the equation as $y = \frac{2}{3}x + 4$ to make a table of values. Since the values substituted for *x* are divided by 3, suggest students choose only multiples of 3 for *x*.

1 EXAMPLE Tactile Learners

To find the *x*-intercept, have students cover the *y* term with a finger, then solve the remaining equation for *x*. Repeat to find the *y*-intercept by covering the *x* term. Ask students why this works. Covering the term represents the 0 value of the term when 0 is substituted for the variable.

📖 Additional Examples

① Find the *x*- and *y*-intercepts of $2x + 5y = 6$. $x = 3, y = \frac{6}{5}$

② Graph $3x + 5y = 15$ using intercepts.

3 a. Graph $y = 4$.

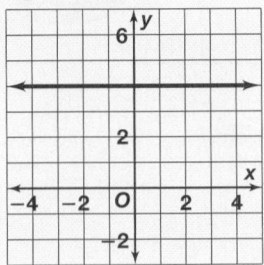

b. Graph $x = -3$.

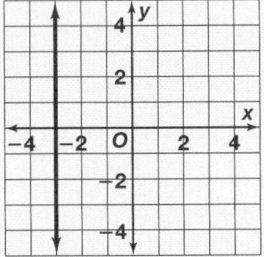

4 EXAMPLE Teaching Tip

Show students how the equation in standard form could also be $3x - 4y = -8$. Encourage skeptical students to rewrite this equation in y-intercept form and compare it to the equation given in the example.

5 EXAMPLE Diversity

Some students may not be familiar with swimming laps. Ask a student who is experienced in swimming laps to describe the activity. Ask the student to estimate the average amount of time it would take a person to swim a lap in a pool.

Additional Examples

4 Write $y = \frac{2}{3}x + 6$ in standard form using integers. $-2x + 3y = 18$ or $2x - 3y = -18$

5 Using the table below, write an equation in standard form to find the number of hours you would need to work at mowing lawns and delivering newspapers to make a total of $130. $12x + 5y = 130$

Job	Amount paid per hour
Mowing lawns	$12
Delivering newspapers	$5

300

You can change an equation from slope-intercept form to standard form. If the equation contains fractions or decimals, multiply to write the equation using integers.

4 EXAMPLE Transforming to Standard Form

Write $y = \frac{3}{4}x + 2$ in standard form using integers.

$$y = \frac{3}{4}x + 2$$
$$4y = 4\left(\frac{3}{4}x + 2\right) \quad \text{Multiply each side by 4.}$$
$$4y = 3x + 8 \quad \text{Use the Distributive Property.}$$
$$-3x + 4y = 8 \quad \text{Subtract } 3x \text{ from each side.}$$

● The standard form of $y = \frac{3}{4}x + 2$ is $-3x + 4y = 8$.

✓ **Check Understanding** **4** Write $y = -\frac{2}{5}x + 1$ in standard form using integers. $2x + 5y = 5$

You can write equations for real-world situations using standard form.

5 EXAMPLE Real-World 🌐 Problem Solving

Data Analysis Write an equation in standard form to find the minutes someone who weighs 150 lb would need to bicycle and swim laps in order to burn 300 calories. Use the data below.

Activity by a 150-lb Person	Calories Burned per Minute
Bicycling	10
Bowling	4
Hiking	7
Running 5.2 mi/h	11
Swimming, laps	12
Walking 3.5 mi/h	5

Define Let x = the minutes spent bicycling.
Let y = the minutes spent swimming laps.

Relate $10 \cdot$ minutes bicycling plus $12 \cdot$ minutes swimming laps equals 300 calories

Write $10x$ + $12y$ = 300

● The equation in standard form is $10x + 12y = 300$.

✓ **Check Understanding** **5** **Data Analysis** Write an equation in standard form to find the minutes someone who weighs 150 lb would need to bowl and walk to burn 250 calories. $4x + 5y = 250$

Real-World 🌐 Connection

Doctors recommend 30 minutes of exercise each day.

Closure

Ask: *How do you find the x- and y-intercepts of a linear equation?* To find the x-intercept, substitute 0 for y, then solve for x. To find the y-intercept, substitute 0 for x,

then solve for y. Write $y = 4 - \frac{1}{3}x$ in standard form. $x + 3y = 12$

pages 301–303 **Exercises**

13.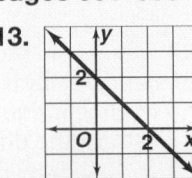

EXERCISES

Practice and Problem Solving

For more practice, see *Extra Practice*.

 Practice by Example

Example 1
(page 299)

Find the *x*- and *y*-intercepts of each equation.

1. $x + 2y = 18$ **18; 9**　　**2.** $3x - y = 9$ **3; −9**　　**3.** $-5x + y = 30$ **−6; 30**

4. $-6x + 3y = -9$ **$\frac{3}{2}$; −3**　**5.** $4x + 12y = -18$ **$-\frac{9}{2}$; $-\frac{3}{2}$** **6.** $9x - 6y = -72$ **−8; 12**

7. $-2x - 3y = -12$ **6; 4**　**8.** $7x - 2y = 4$ **$\frac{4}{7}$; −2**　**9.** $-8x + 10y = 40$ **−5; 4**

Example 2
(page 299)

Match each equation with its graph.

10. $2x - 5y = 10$ **B**　　**11.** $-2x + 5y = 10$ **C**　　**12.** $2x + 5y = 10$ **A**

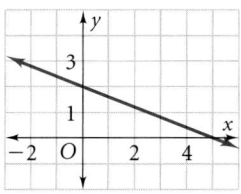　　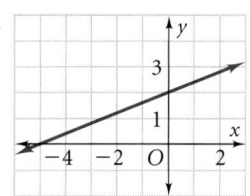

A.　　　**B.**　　　**C.**

Graph each equation using *x*- and *y*-intercepts. **13–18. See margin.**

13. $x + y = 2$　　　**14.** $x + y = -5$　　　**15.** $x - y = -7$

16. $-3x + y = 6$　　**17.** $-2x + y = -6$　　**18.** $5x - 3y = 15$

Example 3
(page 299)

For each equation, tell whether its graph is a horizontal or a vertical line.

19. $y = -1$　　**20.** $x = 4$　　**21.** $y = 2\frac{1}{2}$　　**22.** $x = -3.75$

　horizontal　　　vertical　　　horizontal　　　vertical

Graph each equation. **23–26. See back of book.**

23. $y = 3$　　**24.** $x = -7$　　**25.** $y = -1.5$　　**26.** $x = 4.5$

Example 4
(page 300)

Write each equation in standard form using integers.

27. $y = 3x + 1$ **−3x + y = 1** **28.** $y = 4x - 7$ **4x − y = 7** **29.** $y = \frac{1}{2}x - 3$ **x − 2y = 6**

30. $y = \frac{2}{3}x + 5$　　　**31.** $y = -\frac{3}{4}x - 4$　　　**32.** $y = -\frac{4}{5}x - 7$
　　$-2x + 3y = 15$　　　$-3x - 4y = 16$　　　$-4x - 5y = 35$

33. $y = \frac{7}{2}x + \frac{1}{4}$　　　**34.** $y = -\frac{2}{5}x + \frac{1}{10}$　　　**35.** $y = -3x$
　　$-14x + 4y = 1$　　　$4x + 10y = 1$　　　$3x + y = 0$

Example 5
(page 300)

36. Fund-Raising The sophomore class holds a car wash to raise money. A local merchant donates all of the supplies. A wash costs \$5 per car and \$6.50 per van or truck.

36a. Answers may vary. Sample: x = no. of cars; y = no. of vans or trucks

　a. Define a variable for the number of cars. Define a different variable for the number of vans or trucks. **See left.**

　b. Write an equation in standard form to relate the number of cars and vans or trucks the students must wash to raise \$800. **5x + 6.5y = 800**

37a. Answers may vary. Sample: x = time walking; y = time running

37. Fitness Larry runs at an average rate of 8 mi/h. He walks at an average rate of 3 mi/h.

　a. Define a variable for time spent walking. Define a different variable for time spent running. **See left.**

　b. Write an equation in standard form to relate the times he could spend running and walking if he travels a distance of 15 mi. **3x + 8y = 15**

Assignment Guide

▼1 Objective

Ⓐ Ⓑ **Core** 1–26, 38–46, 49–57

Ⓒ **Extension** 64, 65

▼2 Objective

Ⓐ Ⓑ **Core** 27–37, 47, 48, 58–62

Ⓒ **Extension** 63

Standardized Test Prep 66–69

Mixed Review 70–78

Technology Tip

Exercise 49–54 Suggest that studets press `ZOOM` 5 so the tick marks will be evenly spaced and the figure is not distorted.

Enrichment 6-3

Reteaching 6-3

Practice 6-3

---

14. 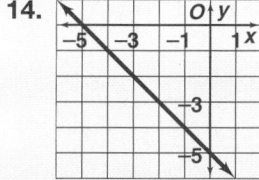　**15.** 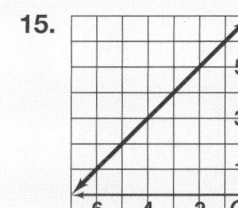　**16.** 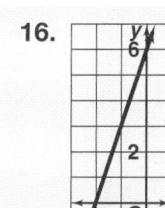　**17.** 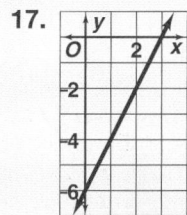　**18.**

301

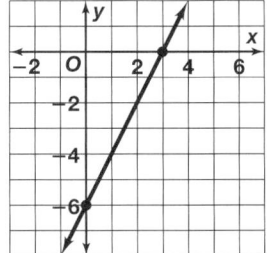

Lesson Quiz 6-3

Find the *x*- and *y*-intercepts of each equation.

1. $3x + y = 12$ $x = 4, y = 12$
2. $-4x - 3y = 9$ $x = -\frac{9}{4}$, $y = -3$
3. Graph $2x - y = 6$ using *x*- and *y*-intercepts.

For each equation, tell whether its graph is horizontal or vertical.

4. $y = 3$ **horizontal**
5. $x = -8$ **vertical**
6. Write $y = \frac{5}{2}x - 3$ in standard form using integers.
   $-5x + 2y = -6$
   or $5x - 2y = 6$

Alternative Assessment

Organize students into groups of four. Instruct each student to write an equation in slope-intercept form on a piece of paper, and then pass the paper to the student to the right. The next student rewrites the equation in standard form, then passes the paper to the right again. Now each student finds the *x*- and *y*-intercepts of the equation and passes the paper to the right again. Students graph the equations using the intercepts. Some intercepts may be approximations. If the intercepts coincide at the origin, they need to find an additional point.

Standardized Test Prep

Resources

For additional practice with a variety of test item formats:
• Standardized Test Prep, p. 335
• Test-Taking Strategies, p. 330
• Test-Taking Strategies with Transparencies

302

 **Apply Your Skills**

Graph each equation. 38–45. See margin.

38. $-3x + 2y = -6$ 39. $x + y = 1$ 40. $2x - 3y = 18$
41. $y - x = -4$ 42. $y = 2x + 5$ 43. $y = -3x - 1$
44. $2 - y = x - 6$ 45. $9 + y = 8 - x$ 46. $6x = y$
   See back of book.

 47. **Nutrition** Suppose you are preparing a snack mix. You want the total protein from peanuts and granola to equal 28 grams. Peanuts have 7 grams of protein per ounce, and granola has 3 grams of protein per ounce.
   a. Write an equation for the protein content of your mix. $3x + 7y = 28$
   b. Graph your equation. Use your graph to find how many ounces of granola you should use if you use 1 ounce of peanuts. **See back of book.**

48. You are sent to the store to buy sliced meat for a party. You are told to get roast beef and turkey, and you are given $30. Roast beef is $4.29/lb and turkey is $3.99/lb. Write an equation in standard form to relate the pounds of each kind of meat you could buy at the store with $30. $4.29x + 3.99y = 30$

Graphing Calculator Write each equation in slope-intercept form. Then use a graphing calculator to graph each equation. Make a sketch of the graph. Include the *x*- and *y*-intercepts. 49–54. See back of book.

49. $8x - 10y = -100$ 50. $-6x + 7y = 21$ 51. $12x + 15y = -45$
52. $-5x + 9y = -15$ 53. $16x + 11y = -88$ 54. $3x - 27y = 18$

55. **Writing** Two of the forms of a linear equation are slope-intercept form and standard form. Explain when each is the more useful. **See margin.**

56. **Critical Thinking** The definition of standard form states that *A* and *B* can't both be zero. Explain why. **Answers may vary. Sample: 0x + 0y = 0, no linear equation exists.**

57. **Error Analysis** A student says that the equation $3x + 2y = 6$ is a standard form of the equation $y = \frac{3}{2}x + 3$. What is the student's error? **−3x instead of 3x**

Write an equation for each line on the graph.

58. *a* $y = 2$ 59. *b* $y = -2$ 60. *c* $x = 1$ 61. *d* $x = -2$

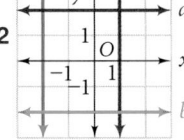

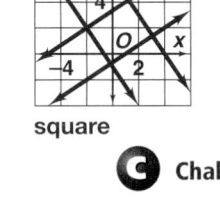
64.

square

Fund-Raising
 62. a. **Fund-Raising** Suppose your school is having a talent show to raise money for new music supplies. You estimate that 200 students and 150 adults will attend. You estimate $200 in expenses. Write an equation to find what ticket prices you should set to raise $1000. **200s + 150a = 1200**
   b. **Open-Ended** Graph your equation. Choose three possible prices you could set for students' and adults' tickets. Which is the best choice? Explain.
   See back of book.

Challenge

63. Write an equation of a line that has the same slope as the line $3x - 5y = 7$ and the same *y*-intercept as the line $2y - 9x = 8$. $y = \frac{3}{5}x + 4$

64. **Geometry** Graph each of the four lines below on the same graph. What figure do the four lines form? **See left above.**
   $-2x + 3y = 10$ $3x + 2y = -2$ $-2x + 3y = -3$ $3x + 2y = 11$

65c. Answers may vary. Sample: The *x*- and *y*-intercepts of $2x + 3y = 18$ are three times those of $2x + 3y = 6$.

65. a. Graph $2x + 3y = 6$ and $2x + 3y = 18$. **See margin.**
   b. What is the slope of each line? $-\frac{2}{3}$; $-\frac{2}{3}$
   c. Compare the *x*-intercepts of the two lines. How are they related? How are the *y*-intercepts related? **See left.**

302 Chapter 6 Linear Equations and Their Graphs

pages 301–303 Exercises

38.
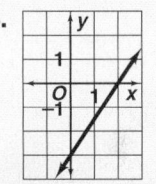

39.
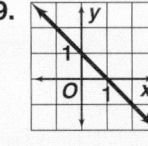

40.
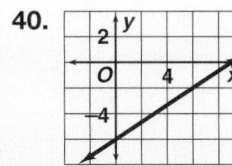

41.
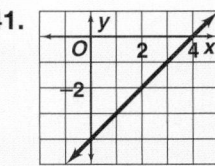

Real-World Connection

A peanut contains about 0.24 gram of protein.

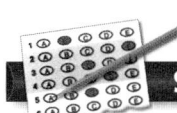

Multiple Choice

66. Which of the following is the standard form of $y = -\frac{2}{3}x + 6$ written using integers? **C**

    A. $\frac{2}{3}x + y = 6$ **B.** $-6 = -\frac{2}{3}x - y$ **C.** $2x + 3y = 18$ **D.** $-2x - 3y = 18$

67. Which is the slope of $Ax + By = C$? **H**

    F. $-\frac{B}{A}$ **G.** $\frac{C}{A}$ **H.** $-\frac{A}{B}$ **I.** $\frac{C}{B}$

Short Response

68. [2] $y = \frac{1}{4}x + 1$;
    $x - 4y = -4$
    [1] correct slope-
    intercept equation

68. A basket with 4 apples weighs 2 pounds. The same basket with 12 apples weighs 4 pounds. Write an equation in slope-intercept form for the weight y in terms of the number of apples x. Write an equation in standard form with integer coefficients that shows the relationship of the weight y and the number of apples x. **See left.**

Extended Response

69. A tire dealer sells Supreme tires for $48 each and Prestige tires for $56 each. During one week, the sales for both tires totaled $2008.
    a. Write an equation that you can use to determine the possible combinations of Supreme tires x and Prestige tires y sold.
    b. Graph your equation on a coordinate plane.
    c. Use your graph to list 3 possible combinations of Supreme and Prestige tires sold. **a–c. See back of book.**

Take It to the NET
Online lesson quiz at
www.PHSchool.com
········ Web Code: aea-0603

Mixed Review

Lesson 6-2

Determine whether the ordered pair is a solution of the equation.

70. $(2, -3)$; $y = -x - 1$ **71.** $(6, -1)$; $y = 2x - 15$ **72.** $(-5, -7)$; $y = -3x - 8$
    yes   **no**   **no**

Lesson 4-6

Find each probability for rolling a number cube.

73. P(rolling a 2, then a 4) $\frac{1}{36}$ **74.** P(rolling a 5, then an even number) $\frac{1}{12}$

Lesson 4-1

Solve each proportion.

75. $\frac{a}{5} = \frac{12}{15}$ **4**   **76.** $\frac{2}{8} = \frac{w}{9}$ **2.25**   **77.** $\frac{x + 2}{4} = \frac{3}{8}$ **−0.5** **78.** $\frac{14}{4m} = \frac{16}{5m + 9}$
                                                                  −21

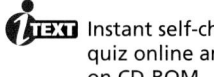
Checkpoint Quiz 1   **Lessons 6-1 through 6-3**

 Instant self-check
quiz online and
on CD-ROM

Find the slope of the line passing through each pair of points.

1. $(-1, 3)$, $(6, -2)$ $-\frac{5}{7}$ **2.** $(4, 5)$, $(0, 2)$ $\frac{3}{4}$ **3.** $(-2, -3)$, $(-1, -7)$ **−4**   **4.** $(4, -4)$, $(-5, 5)$ **−1**

5. Credit Cards In 1990, people charged $534 billion on the two most-used types of credit cards. In 1994, people charged $1.021 trillion on these same two types of credit cards. What was the rate of change? **$121.75 billion per year**

Graph each equation. 6–9. See margin.

6. $y = 4x - 1$ **7.** $y = -\frac{2}{5}x + 6$ **8.** $5x + 3y = -30$ **9.** $2x - 7y = 15$

10. Writing How are the graphs of $y = 3x + 5$, $y = \frac{2}{3}x + 5$, and $y = \frac{3}{5}x + 5$ alike? How are they different? **same y-intercepts; different slopes**

Lesson 6-3   Standard Form   **303**

42.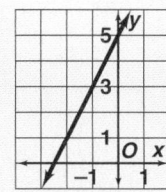

43.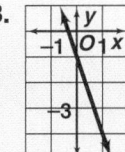

44.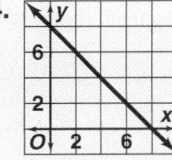

45.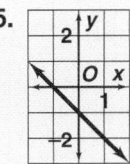

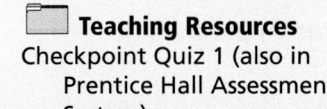
Chapter Checkpoint 1

To check understanding of Lessons 6-1 to 6-3:

Checkpoint Quiz 1 (p. 303)

📁 **Teaching Resources**
Checkpoint Quiz 1 (also in Prentice Hall Assessment System)

👫 **Reaching All Students**
Reading and Math Literacy 6B

Spanish versions available

55. Answers may vary. Sample: slope-intercept form when comparing the steepness of two lines; standard form when making quick graphs

65a.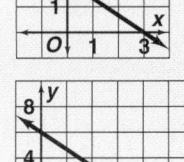

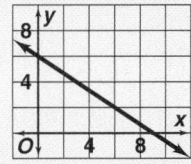

page 303   **Checkpoint Quiz 1**

6.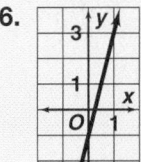

7.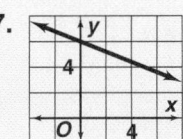

8.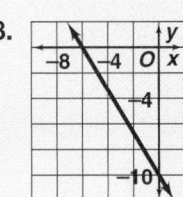

9.

303

Lesson Preview

 Check Skills You'll Need

Rate of Change and Slope
Lesson 6-1: Example 1
Exercises 1–6
Extra Practice, p. 707

The Distributive Property
Lesson 1-7: Example 3
Exercises 15–26
Extra Practice, p. 702

Lesson Resources

Teaching Resources
Practice, Reteaching, Enrichment

Reaching All Students
Practice Workbook 6-4
Spanish Practice Workbook 6-4
Technology Activities 6, 20
Basic Algebra Planning Guide 6-4

Presentation Assistant Plus!
Transparencies
• Check Skills You'll Need 6-4
• Additional Examples 6-4
• Student Edition Answers 6-4
• Lesson Quiz 6-4
PH Presentation Pro CD 6-4

PRENTICE HALL
ASSESSMENT SYSTEM

Computer Test Generator CD

Technology
Resource Pro® CD-ROM
Computer Test Generator CD
Prentice Hall Presentation Pro CD

 www.PHSchool.com
Student Site
• Teacher Web Code: aek-5500
• Self-grading Lesson Quiz
Teacher Center
• Lesson Planner
• Resources

Plus

304

6-4 Point-Slope Form and Writing Linear Equations

4.01 Use linear functions or inequalities to model and solve problems; justify results. b) Interpret constants and coefficients in the context of the problem.

Lesson Preview

What You'll Learn

OBJECTIVE 1 To graph and write linear equations using point-slope form

OBJECTIVE 2 To write a linear equation using data

. . . And Why

To write an equation relating altitude and the boiling point of water, as in Example 5

 Check Skills You'll Need   (For help, go to Lessons 6-1 and 1-7.)

Find the rate of change of the data in each table.

1. -2

x	y
2	4
5	-2
8	-8
11	-14

2. $\frac{1}{2}$

x	y
-3	-5
-1	-4
1	-3
3	-2

3. 2

x	y
10	4
7.5	-1
5	-6
2.5	-11

Simplify each expression.

4. $-3(x - 5)$ $-3x + 15$ **5.** $5(x + 2)$ $5x + 10$ **6.** $-\frac{4}{9}(x - 6)$
$-\frac{4}{9}x + \frac{8}{3}$

New Vocabulary   • point-slope form

OBJECTIVE

1 Using Point-Slope Form

iTEXT Interactive lesson includes instant self-check, tutorials, and activities.

Suppose you know that a line passes through the point $(3, 4)$ with slope 2. You can quickly write an equation of the line using the *x*- and *y*-coordinates of the point and using the slope.

$$y - 4 = 2(x - 3)$$

y-coordinate   slope   *x*-coordinate

You can use the definition of slope to verify that $y - 4 = 2(x - 3)$ is the equation of the line through the point $(3, 4)$ with slope 2.

$\dfrac{y_2 - y_1}{x_2 - x_1} = m$ **Use the definition of slope.**

$\dfrac{y - 4}{x - 3} = 2$ **Substitute (3, 4) for (x_1, y_1), (x, y) for (x_2, y_2), and 2 for *m*.**

$\dfrac{y - 4}{x - 3}(x - 3) = 2(x - 3)$ **Multiply each side by $x - 3$.**

$y - 4 = 2(x - 3)$ **Simplify the left side of the equation.**

The equation $y - 4 = 2(x - 3)$ is in point-slope form.

Key Concepts

Definition	Point-Slope Form of a Linear Equation

The **point-slope form** of the equation of a nonvertical line that passes through the point (x_1, y_1) with slope *m* is

$$y - y_1 = m(x - x_1)$$

Ongoing Assessment and Intervention

Before the Lesson
Diagnose prerequisite skills using:
• Check Skills You'll Need

During the Lesson
Monitor progress using:
• Check Understanding
• Additional Examples
• Standardized Test Prep

After the Lesson
Assess knowledge using:
• Lesson Quiz
• Computer Test Generator CD

1 **EXAMPLE** Graphing Using Point-Slope Form

Graph the equation $y - 5 = \frac{1}{2}(x - 2)$.

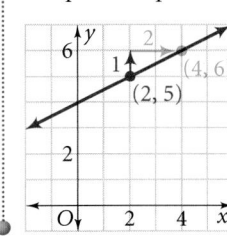

The equation shows that the line passes through (2, 5) with a slope $\frac{1}{2}$.

Start at (2, 5). Using the slope, go up 1 unit and right 2 units to (4, 6). Draw a line through the two points.

1.

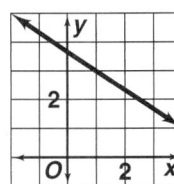

✔ **Check Understanding** **1** Graph the equation $y - 5 = -\frac{2}{3}(x + 2)$. **See left.**

Reading Math

Square brackets, [ ], are grouping symbols commonly used when parentheses, ( ), are inside.

2 **EXAMPLE** Writing an Equation in Point-Slope Form

Write the equation of the line with slope -3 that passes through the point $(-1, 7)$.

$y - y_1 = m(x - x_1)$ Use the point-slope form.

$y - 7 = -3[x - (-1)]$ Substitute $(-1, 7)$ for (x_1, y_1) and -3 for m.

$y - 7 = -3(x + 1)$ Simplify inside the grouping symbols.

✔ **Check Understanding** **2** Write the equation of the line with slope $\frac{2}{5}$ that passes through the point $(10, -8)$.
$y + 8 = \frac{2}{5}(x - 10)$

If you know two points on a line, first use them to find the slope. Then you can write an equation using either point.

3 **EXAMPLE** Using Two Points to Write an Equation

Write equations for the line in point-slope form and in slope-intercept form.

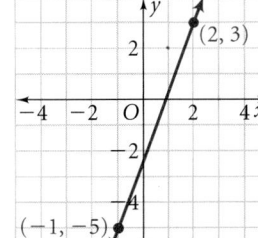

Step 1 Find the slope.

$\frac{y_2 - y_1}{x_2 - x_1} = m$

$\frac{-5 - 3}{-1 - 2} = \frac{8}{3}$

The slope is $\frac{8}{3}$.

?
Need Help?

For help with slope-intercept form see p. 292.

Step 2 Use either point to write the equation in point-slope form. Use (2, 3).

$y - y_1 = m(x - x_1)$

$y - 3 = \frac{8}{3}(x - 2)$

Step 3 Rewrite the equation from Step 2 in slope-intercept form.

$y - 3 = \frac{8}{3}(x - 2)$

$y - 3 = \frac{8}{3}x - 5\frac{1}{3}$

$y = \frac{8}{3}x - 2\frac{1}{3}$

✔ **Check Understanding** **3** **a.** Write an equation for the line in Example 3 in point-slope form using the point $(-1, -5)$. $y + 5 = \frac{8}{3}(x + 1)$
b. Write the equation you found in part (a) in slope-intercept form. $y = \frac{8}{3}x - 2\frac{1}{3}$
c. What is true about the equation you wrote in part (b) and the equation in Step 3 of Example 3? **They are the same.**

Lesson 6-4   Point-Slope Form and Writing Linear Equations   **305**

👥 **Reaching All Students**

Below Level In Step 2 of Example 4, have students write equations in point-slope form using each ordered pair in the table. Then ask them to show that all four equations are equivalent.	**Advanced Learners** Have students write the slope-intercept form of the linear equation found in Question 5 of Example 5. Ask them what the y-intercept in the equation represents.	**Auditory Learners** See note on page 305. **Error Prevention** See note on page 307.

Math Background

No matter what form a linear equation is written in, the coordinates of every point on the graph of the line satisfy its linear equation and, conversely, every pair of values that satisfy the equation represent a point on the graph.

OBJECTIVE
▼ 1 Teaching Notes

2 **EXAMPLE** Auditory Learners

Some students may confuse the signs in the point-slope equation. Suggest they rewrite the formula as $y + (-y_1) = m[x + (-x_1)]$ and read it as "the sum of y and the opposite of y_1 equals the slope times the sum of x and the opposite of x_1." Stress "the opposite of."

Additional Examples

1 Graph the equation $y - 2 = \frac{1}{3}(x - 1)$.

2 Write the equation of the line with slope -2 that passes through the point $(3, -3)$.
$y + 3 = -2(x - 3)$

3 Write equations for the line in point-slope form and in slope-intercept form.
$y - 4 = -\frac{1}{3}(x + 1)$
$y = -\frac{1}{3}x + 3\frac{2}{3}$

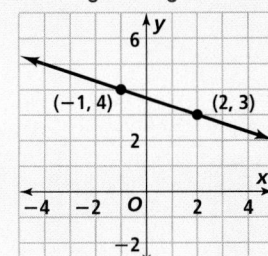

305

5 **EXAMPLE** Connection to Science

Boiling point is defined as the temperature at which the vapor pressure of a liquid slightly exceeds the pressure of the atmosphere above the liquid. Water at 1 atmosphere pressure boils at 212° F. If the pressure on a liquid is reduced, the boiling point is lowered. Air pressure is less at higher elevations. Denver, Colorado is 1 mile above sea level, so the boiling point of water there averages 201° F.

You can write a linear equation to model data in tables. Two sets of data have a linear relationship if the rate of change between consecutive pairs of data is the same. For data that have a linear relationship, the rate of change is the slope.

4 **EXAMPLE** Writing an Equation Using a Table

Is the relationship shown by the data linear? If so, model the data with an equation.

Step 1 Find the rate of change for consecutive ordered pairs.

x	y
−1	4
3	6
5	7
11	10

$4 \quad 2 \quad \frac{2}{4} = \frac{1}{2}$

$2 \quad 1 \quad \frac{1}{2} = \frac{1}{2}$

$6 \quad 3 \quad \frac{3}{6} = \frac{1}{2}$

Step 2 Use the slope and a point to write an equation.

$$y - y_1 = m(x - x_1)$$

Substitute (5, 7) for (x_1, y_1) and $\frac{1}{2}$ for m.

$$y - 7 = \frac{1}{2}(x - 5)$$

Additional Examples

4 Is the relationship shown by the data linear? If so, model the data with an equation. **yes;**
$y - 4 = 2(x - 2)$

x	y
3	6
2	4
−1	−2
−3	−6

✔ Check Understanding **4** Is the relationship shown by the data at the right linear? If so, model the data with an equation.

Yes; answers may vary. Sample:
$y - 5 = \frac{2}{5}(x - 19)$

x	y
−11	−7
−1	−3
4	−1
19	5

5 Is the relationship shown by the data linear? If so, model the data with an equation. **no**

x	y
−2	−2
−1	−1
1	0
2	1

5 **EXAMPLE** Real-World Problem Solving

Is the relationship shown by the data linear? If so, model the data with an equation.

Boiling Point of Water

Altitude (1000 ft)	Temperature (°F)
8	197.6
4.5	203.9
3	206.6
2.5	207.5

$-3.5 \quad 6.3$

$-1.5 \quad 2.7$

$-0.5 \quad 0.9$

Real-World Connection

At 5280 feet above sea level it takes 17 minutes to hard-boil an egg. This is more than 40% longer than it takes the same egg to cook at sea level.

Step 1 Find the rates of change for consecutive ordered pairs.

$$\frac{6.3}{-3.5} = -1.8 \qquad \frac{2.7}{-1.5} = -1.8 \qquad \frac{0.9}{-0.5} = -1.8$$

The relationship is linear. The rate of change is -1.8 degrees Fahrenheit per 1000 ft of altitude.

Step 2 Use the slope and a point to write an equation.

$$y - y_1 = m(x - x_1) \qquad \text{Use the point-slope form.}$$
$$y - 206.6 = -1.8(x - 3) \qquad \text{Substitute (3, 206.6) for } (x_1, y_1) \text{ and } -1.8 \text{ for } m.$$

The equation $y - 206.6 = -1.8(x - 3)$ relates altitude in thousands of feet x to the boiling point temperature in degrees Fahrenheit.

Closure

Ask students to write a set of data that is linear, and then model the data with an equation. Have them graph the data and the equation.

306 Chapter 6 Linear Equations and Their Graphs

pages 307–309 **Exercises**

10. $y + 4 = 6(x - 3)$

11. $y - 2 = -\frac{5}{3}(x - 4)$

12. $y - 2 = \frac{4}{5}(x)$

13. $y + 7 = -\frac{3}{2}(x + 2)$

14. $y = 1(x - 4)$

15. $y + 8 = -3(x - 5)$

16. $y - 2 = 0(x + 5)$ or $y = 2$

17. $y + 8 = -\frac{1}{5}(x - 1)$

18. $y - 1 = \frac{2}{3}(x + 6)$

19–30. **Answers may vary from the point indicated by the equation.**

19. $y = 1(x + 1)$; $y = x + 1$

20. $y - 5 = \frac{5}{3}(x - 3)$; $y = \frac{5}{3}x$

✓ Check Understanding ⑤ Is the relationship shown by the data in the table linear? If it is, model the data with an equation.
Yes; answers may vary. Sample:
$y - 3030 = -\frac{50}{3}(x - 68)$

Working Outdoors

Temperature	Calories Burned per Day
68°F	3030
62°F	3130
56°F	3230
50°F	3330

In Example 5 you could rewrite $y - 206.6 = -1.8(x - 3)$ as $y = -1.8x + 212$. This form gives you useful information about the y-intercept. For instance, 212°F is the boiling point of water at sea level.

Here are the three forms of linear equations you have studied.

 Key Concepts

 Reading Math

For more help with the three forms of a linear equation, see page 310.

Summary	Linear Equations	
Slope-Intercept Form	**Standard Form**	**Point-Slope Form**
$y = mx + b$	$Ax + By = C$	$(y - y_1) = m(x - x_1)$
m is the slope and b is the y-intercept.	A and B are not both 0.	(x_1, y_1) lies on the graph of the equation, and m is the slope.
Examples		
$y = -\frac{2}{3}x + \frac{5}{3}$	$2x + 3y = 5$	$y - 1 = -\frac{2}{3}(x - 1)$

EXERCISES

For more practice, see *Extra Practice*.

Practice and Problem Solving

Ⓐ **Practice by Example**

Graph each equation. 1–9. See back of book.

Example 1
(page 305)

1. $y - 2 = (x - 3)$ **2.** $y - 2 = 2(x - 3)$ **3.** $y - 2 = -\frac{3}{2}(x - 3)$

4. $y + 5 = -(x - 2)$ **5.** $y + 1 = \frac{2}{3}(x + 4)$ **6.** $y - 1 = -3(x + 2)$

7. $y + 3 = -2(x - 1)$ **8.** $y - 4 = (x - 5)$ **9.** $y - 2 = 3(x + 2)$

Example 2
(page 305)

Write an equation in point-slope form for the line through the given point with the given slope. 10–18. See margin.

10. $(3, -4); m = 6$ **11.** $(4, 2); m = -\frac{5}{3}$ **12.** $(0, 2); m = \frac{4}{5}$

13. $(-2, -7); m = -\frac{3}{2}$ **14.** $(4, 0); m = 1$ **15.** $(5, -8); m = -3$

16. $(-5, 2); m = 0$ **17.** $(1, -8); m = -\frac{1}{5}$ **18.** $(-6, 1); m = \frac{2}{3}$

Example 3
(page 305)

A line passes through the given points. Write an equation for the line in point-slope form. Then rewrite the equation in slope-intercept form. 19–30. See margin.

19. $(-1, 0), (1, 2)$ **20.** $(3, 5), (0, 0)$ **21.** $(4, -2), (9, -8)$

22. $(6, -4), (-3, 5)$ **23.** $(-1, -5), (-7, -6)$ **24.** $(-3, -4), (3, -2)$

25. $(2, 7), (1, -4)$ **26.** $(-2, 6), (5, 1)$ **27.** $(3, -8), (-2, 5)$

28. $\left(1, \frac{1}{2}\right), (3, 2)$ **29.** $\left(\frac{1}{2}, 2\right), \left(-\frac{3}{2}, 4\right)$ **30.** $(0.2, 1.1), (7, 3)$

Lesson 6-4 Point-Slope Form and Writing Linear Equations **307**

21. $y + 2 = -\frac{6}{5}(x - 4);$
$y = -\frac{6}{5}x + \frac{14}{5}$

22. $y + 4 = -1(x - 6);$
$y = -x + 2$

23. $y + 5 = \frac{1}{6}(x + 1);$
$y = \frac{1}{6}x - \frac{29}{6}$

24. $y + 4 = \frac{1}{3}(x + 3);$
$y = \frac{1}{3}x - 3$

25. $y - 7 = 11(x - 2);$
$y = 11x - 15$

26. $y - 6 = -\frac{5}{7}(x + 2);$
$y = -\frac{5}{7}x + 4\frac{4}{7}$

3. Practice

Assignment Guide

▼**1 Objective**
Ⓐ Ⓑ **Core** 1–30, 36–53, 56–59
Ⓒ **Extension** 61–63

▼**2 Objective**
Ⓐ Ⓑ **Core** 31–35, 54, 55, 60
Ⓒ **Extension** 64

Standardized Test Prep 65–69

Mixed Review 70–81

Error Prevention
Exercises 19–30 Suggest to students that they circle the x-coordinates and box the y-coordinates.

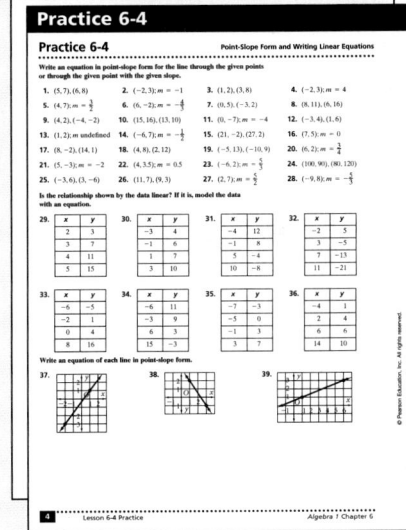

27. $y + 8 = -\frac{13}{5}(x - 3);$
$y = -\frac{13}{5}x - \frac{1}{5}$

28. $y - \frac{1}{2} = \frac{3}{4}(x - 1);$
$y = \frac{3}{4}x - \frac{1}{4}$

29. $y - 2 = -1\left(x - \frac{1}{2}\right);$
$y = -x + \frac{5}{2}$

30. $y - 1.1 = \frac{1.9}{6.8}(x - 0.2);$
$y = \frac{1.9}{6.8}x + \frac{7.1}{6.8}$

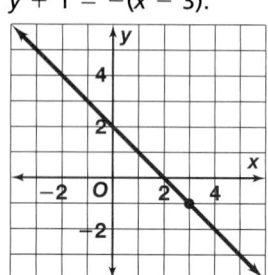

Lesson Quiz 6-4

1. Graph the equation $y + 1 = -(x - 3)$.

2. Write an equation of the line with slope $-\frac{2}{3}$ that passes through the point $(0, 4)$. $y - 4 = -\frac{2}{3}(x - 0)$, or $y = -\frac{2}{3}x + 4$

3. Write an equation for the line that passes through $(3, -5)$ and $(-2, 1)$ in point-slope form and slope-intercept form. $y + 5 = -\frac{6}{5}(x - 3)$; $y = -\frac{6}{5}x - \frac{7}{5}$

4. Is the relationship shown by the data linear? If so, model that data with an equation. yes; $y + 3 = \frac{2}{5}(x - 0)$

x	y
-10	-7
0	-3
5	-1
20	5

Alternative Assessment

Let students work in pairs. Instruct each student to write coordinates for two points, and then write an equation passing through those points in point-slope form. Have each pair exchange points and repeat. Then compare answers to check.

Example 4
(page 306)

31. Yes; answers may vary. Sample: $y - 9 = -2(x + 4)$

32. Yes; answers may vary. Sample: $y - 40 = 3(x - 5)$

Example 5
(page 306)

34. Yes; answers may vary. Sample: $y - 75 = 10(x - 10)$

B Apply Your Skills

Is the relationship shown by the data linear? If so, model the data with an equation.

31. See left.

x	y
-4	9
2	-3
5	-9
9	-17

32. See left.

x	y
-10	-5
-2	19
5	40
11	58

33. no

x	y
3	1
6	4
9	13
15	49

34. See left.

Speed Over Posted Speed (mi/h)	Fine ($)
10	75
12	95
15	125
19	165

35. no

Volume (gal)	Weight (lb)
0	0
2	16
4	33
6	50

Write an equation of each line in point-slope form. 36–53. Answers may vary from point indicated by the equation.

36.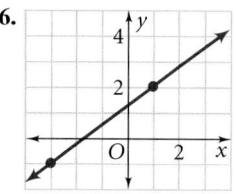
$y - 2 = \frac{3}{4}(x - 1)$

37.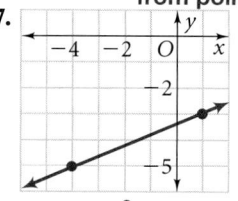
$y + 3 = \frac{2}{5}(x - 1)$

38.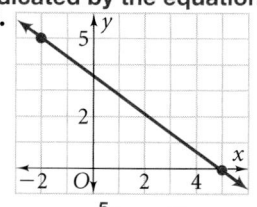
$y = -\frac{5}{7}(x - 5)$

Write one equation of the line through the given points in point-slope form and one in standard form using integers. 39–53. See margin.

39. $(1, 4), (-1, 1)$ 40. $(6, -3), (-2, -3)$ 41. $(0, 0), (-1, -2)$

42. $(0, 2), (-4, 2)$ 43. $(-6, 6), (3, 3)$ 44. $(2, 3), (-1, 5)$

45. $(5, -3), (3, 4)$ 46. $(2, 2), (-1, 7)$ 47. $(-7, 1), (5, -1)$

48. $(-8, 4), (-4, -2)$ 49. $(2, 4), (-3, -6)$ 50. $(5, 3), (4, 5)$

51. $(0, 1), (-3, 0)$ 52. $(-2, 4), (0, -5)$ 53. $(6, 2), (1, -1)$

54. **Science** At the surface of the ocean, pressure is 1 atmosphere. At 66 ft below sea level, the pressure is 3 atmospheres. The relationship of pressure and depth is linear.
   a. Write an equation for the data. $y = -\frac{1}{33}x + 1$
   b. Predict the pressure at 100 ft below sea level. **about 4 atmospheres**

55. **Environment** Worldwide carbon monoxide emissions are decreasing about 2.6 million metric tons each year. In 1991, carbon monoxide emissions were 79 million metric tons. Use a linear equation to model the relationship between carbon monoxide emissions and time. Let $x = 91$ correspond to 1991. $y = -2.6x + 315.6$

56. a. **Open-Ended** Write an equation in point-slope form that contains the point $(-4, -6)$. Explain your steps. **a–b. See margin.**
   b. How many equations could you write in part(a)? Explain.

57. **Critical Thinking** How would the graph of $y - 12 = 8(x - 2)$ change if all of the subtraction signs were changed to addition signs? **y-intercept changes.**

58. **Reasoning** Is $y - 5 = 2(x - 1)$ an equation of a line through $(4, 11)$? Explain. **Yes; the point satisfies the equation.**

A scuba diver can descend to about 131 feet.

The submersible *Alvin* can descend to about 2.5 miles.

In 1960, the submersible *Trieste* descended to a record depth of 6.8 miles.

PRESSURE INCREASES

---

pages 307–309 Exercises

39. $y - 4 = \frac{3}{2}(x - 1)$; $-3x + 2y = 5$

40. $y + 3 = 0(x - 6)$; $y = -3$

41. $y + 2 = 2(x + 1)$; $-2x + y = 0$

42. $y - 2 = 0(x - 0)$; $y = 2$

43. $y - 6 = -\frac{1}{3}(x + 6)$; $x + 3y = 12$

44. $y - 3 = -\frac{2}{3}(x - 2)$; $2x + 3y = 13$

45. $y + 3 = -\frac{7}{2}(x - 5)$; $7x + 2y = 29$

46. $y - 2 = -\frac{5}{3}(x - 2)$; $5x + 3y = 16$

59. Open-Ended Write an equation in each of the following forms.
  a. slope-intercept form $y = x + 1$
  b. standard form $-x + y = 1$
  c. point-slope form $y - 1 = 1(x - 0)$

59a-c. Answers may vary.
Sample is given.

60a. Answers may vary.
Sample:
$y - 332 = \frac{3}{5}(x - 0)$

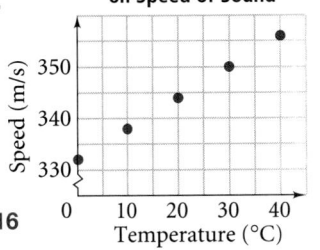

60. Science Use the scatter plot.
  a. Write an equation to model the data. **See left.**
  b. What is the speed of sound at 15°C? **341 m/s**
  c. Predict the speed of sound at 60°C. **368 m/s**

Effect of Air Temperature on Speed of Sound

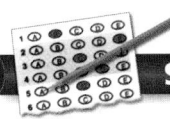 **Challenge**

Write an equation in slope-intercept form of each line described below.

61. The line contains the point $(-3, -5)$ and has the same slope as $y + 2 = 7(x + 3)$. $y = 7x + 16$

62. The line contains the point $(1, 3)$ and has the same y-intercept as $y - 5 = 2(x - 1)$. $y = 3$

63. The line contains the point $(2, -2)$ and has the same x-intercept as $y + 9 = 3(x - 4)$. $y = \frac{2}{5}x - \frac{14}{5}$

64. The table shows data that you can model using a linear function.
  a. Find the value of y when $x = 6$. **14.75**
  b. Find the value of y when $x = 120$. **57.5**
  c. Find the value of x when $y = 11$. **−4**
  d. Find the value of x when $y = 50$. **100**

x	y
4	14
8	15.5
12	17
16	18.5

Standardized Test Prep

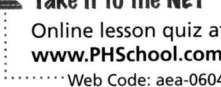

Gridded Response

65. What is the slope of the graph of $y - 8 = \frac{1}{2}(x + 2)$? $\frac{1}{2}$

66. Find the y-intercept of the line $y + 3 = 4(x + 3)$. **9**

67. What is the x-intercept of the line $y = 3x - 7$? $\frac{7}{3}$

68. When $y - 1 = -\frac{4}{5}(x - 3)$ is written in standard form using positive integers, what is the coefficient of x? **4**

Take It to the NET
Online lesson quiz at
www.PHSchool.com
Web Code: aea-0604

69. When $y = -\frac{5}{2}x + \frac{2}{3}$ is written in standard form using positive integers, what is the coefficient of y? **6**

Mixed Review

Lesson 6-3

Graph each line. **70–75. See margin.**

70. $6x + 7y = 14$
71. $-2x + 9y = -9$
72. $5x - 4y = 24$

73. $3x - 8y = 4$
74. $5x + 18y = 6$
75. $-7x + 4y = -21$

Lesson 5-5

Find the common difference of each sequence. Then write the next two terms.

76. $-12, -7, -2, \ldots$ **5; 3, 8**
77. $\frac{1}{2}, \frac{5}{6}, \frac{7}{6}, \ldots$ **$\frac{2}{6}; \frac{3}{2}, \frac{11}{6}$**
78. $2.45, 2.52, 2.59, \ldots$ **0.07; 2.66, 2.73**
79. $-3.2, -3.25, -3.3, \ldots$ **−0.05; −3.35, −3.4**
80. $18, 35, 52, \ldots$ **17; 69, 86**
81. $-7, -3, 1, \ldots$ **4; 5, 9**

Lesson 6-4 Point-Slope Form and Writing Linear Equations **309**

47. $y - 1 = -\frac{1}{6}(x + 7);$
  $x + 6y = -1$

48. $y - 4 = -\frac{3}{2}(x + 8);$
  $3x + 2y = -16$

49. $y - 4 = 2(x - 2);$
  $-2x + y = 0$

50. $y - 3 = -2(x - 5);$
  $2x + y = 13$

51. $y - 1 = \frac{1}{3}x; -x + 3y = 3$

52. $y - 4 = -\frac{9}{2}(x + 2);$
  $9x + 2y = -10$

53. $y - 2 = \frac{3}{5}(x - 6);$
  $-3x + 5y = -8$

Standardized Test Prep

A sheet of blank grids is available with the Test-Taking Strategies with Transparencies booklet. Give this sheet to students for practice with filling in the grids.

Resources
For additional practice with a variety of test item formats:
• Standardized Test Prep, p. 335
• Test-Taking Strategies, p. 330
• Test-Taking Strategies with Transparencies

56a. **Answers may vary.**
Sample:
$y + 6 = 2(x + 4)$;
chose slope and substituted into
$y - y_1 = m(x - x_1)$

b. **infinite; infinite number of slopes**

70.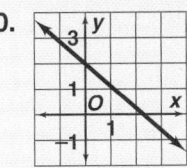

71.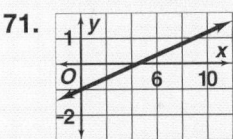

72.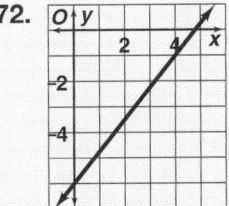

73.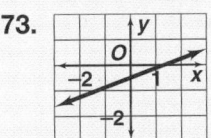

74.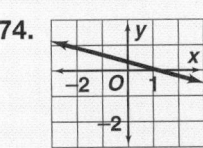

75.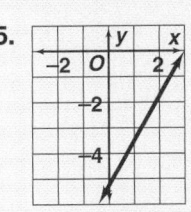

309

Reading Math Vocabulary

Reading Math Vocabulary

FOR USE WITH LESSON 6–4

Reading Math Vocabulary

Students see how the English meaning of some words relates to the mathematical meaning of the same words.

Teaching Notes

Visual Learners

Have students draw visual representations of the English and mathematical meanings of slope and point.

Exercise

Group students in pairs. Instruct each student to write a slope and y-intercept, a pair of x- and y-intercepts, and a point and slope. Partners exchange information. Then each student writes the three equations for the given information.

There are three forms of a linear equation that you have studied in this chapter:
- slope-intercept form
- standard form
- point-slope form

To understand and remember these forms, it may help you to connect the English words with their specialized meanings in mathematics.

English words often have specialized meanings in mathematics. Usually you can relate your understanding of a word to its mathematical meaning.

Word	English Meaning	Mathematical Meaning
Slope	An inclined surface (for example, the upward slope of a hill)	The rate of change that gives the steepness of a line $$\text{slope} = \frac{\text{vertical change}}{\text{horizontal change}} = \frac{\text{rise}}{\text{run}}$$
Intercept	To cut off from a path (for example, to intercept a football)	The values of the points at which x-axis or y-axis intersect (or cut) a line
Standard	Generally accepted	A general form for an equation
Point	A dot or speck (noun)	A fixed location on a coordinate plane. Every point has a unique x-value and y-value.

Slope-intercept form, standard form, and point-slope form all have their advantages.
- Knowing the slope and y-intercept makes an equation in slope-intercept form easy to graph.
- An equation in point-slope form is also easy to graph.
- You can model many real-world situations using the standard form. Also, it is easy to find the x- and y-intercepts of an equation in this form.

When you write an equation in each of these forms, think about what the values mean.

slope-intercept form
$y = 3x - 1$

The graph of this equation has y-intercept -1 and slope 3.

standard form
$5x - y = 100$

The graph of this equation intersects the y-axis at -100 and intersects the x-axis at 20.

point-slope form
$y - 2 = 3(x - 5)$

The graph of this equation passes through the point (5, 2), and its slope is 3.

EXERCISE

a. Find the slope and y-intercept of the graph of $y = 2x + 5$. **2, 5**
b. Find the x- and y- intercepts of the graph of $50x + 25y = 100$. **2, 4**
c. Find a point and the slope on the graph of $y - 4 = 2(x + 3)$. **(−3, 4), 2**

6-5 Parallel and Perpendicular Lines

2.02 Use the parallelism or perpendicularity of lines and segments to solve problems.

Lesson Preview

What You'll Learn

OBJECTIVE 1 To determine whether lines are parallel

OBJECTIVE 2 To determine whether lines are perpendicular

. . . And Why

To use parallel and perpendicular lines to plan a bike path, as in Example 4

 Check Skills You'll Need (For help, go to Lessons 1-6 and 6-2.)

What is the reciprocal of each fraction?

1. $\frac{1}{2}$ $\frac{2}{1}$ 2. $\frac{4}{3}$ $\frac{3}{4}$ 3. $-\frac{2}{5}$ $-\frac{5}{2}$ 4. $-\frac{7}{5}$ $-\frac{5}{7}$

What are the slope and y-intercept of each equation?

5. $y = \frac{5}{3}x + 4$ $\frac{5}{3}$; 4   6. $y = \frac{5}{3}x - 8$ $\frac{5}{3}$; -8 7. $y = 6x$ 6; 0   8. $y = 6x + 2$ 6; 2

New Vocabulary
- parallel lines
- perpendicular lines
- negative reciprocal

OBJECTIVE 1 Parallel Lines

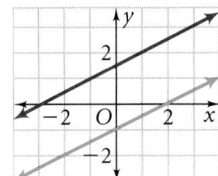

In the graph at the right, the red and blue lines are parallel. **Parallel lines** are lines in the same plane that never intersect. The equation of the red line is $y = \frac{1}{2}x + \frac{3}{2}$. The equation of the blue line is $y = \frac{1}{2}x - 1$.

Key Concepts

Property	Slopes of Parallel Lines

Nonvertical lines are parallel if they have the same slope and different y-intercepts. *Any* two vertical lines are parallel.

Example The equations $y = \frac{2}{3}x + 1$ and $y = \frac{2}{3}x - 3$ have the same slope, $\frac{2}{3}$, and different y-intercepts. The graphs of the two equations are parallel.

You can use slope-intercept form to determine whether the lines are parallel.

1 EXAMPLE Determining Whether Lines Are Parallel

Are the graphs of $y = -\frac{1}{3}x + 5$ and $2x + 6y = 12$ parallel? Explain.

Write $2x + 6y = 12$ in slope-intercept form. Then compare with $y = -\frac{1}{3}x + 5$.

$6y = -2x + 12$ **Subtract 2x from each side.**

$\frac{6y}{6} = \frac{-2x + 12}{6}$ **Divide each side by 6.**

$y = -\frac{1}{3}x + 2$ **Simplify.**

The lines are parallel. The equations have the same slope, $-\frac{1}{3}$, and different y-intercepts.

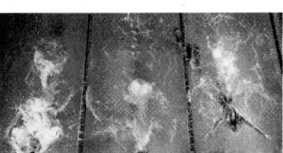

Real-World Connection

The lanes for competitive swimming are parallel.

 Check Understanding ➊ Are the graphs of $-6x + 8y = -24$ and $y = \frac{3}{4}x - 7$ parallel? Explain.
 yes; same slope, different y-intercept

Lesson 6-5 Parallel and Perpendicular Lines **311**

Ongoing Assessment and Intervention

Before the Lesson
Diagnose prerequisite skills using:
- Check Skills You'll Need

During the Lesson
Monitor progress using:
- Check Understanding
- Additional Examples
- Standardized Test Prep

After the Lesson
Assess knowledge using:
- Lesson Quiz
- Computer Test Generator CD

6-5

North Carolina Objectives 2.02

1. Plan

Lesson Preview

Check Skills You'll Need

Multiplying and Dividing
Lesson 1-6: Example 7
Exercises 54–57
Extra Practice, p. 702

Slope-Intercept Form
Lesson 6-2: Example 1
Exercises 1–9
Extra Practice, p. 707

Lesson Resources

Teaching Resources
Practice, Reteaching, Enrichment

Reaching All Students
Practice Workbook 6-5
Spanish Practice Workbook 6-5
Technology Activities 3
Basic Algebra Planning Guide 6-5

Presentation Assistant Plus!
Transparencies
- Check Skills You'll Need 6-5
- Additional Examples 6-5
- Student Edition Answers 6-5
- Lesson Quiz 6-5
PH Presentation Pro CD 6-5

ASSESSMENT SYSTEM
Computer Test Generator CD

Technology
Resource Pro® CD-ROM
Computer Test Generator CD
Prentice Hall Presentation Pro CD

www.PHSchool.com
Student Site
- Teacher Web Code: aek-5500
- Self-grading Lesson Quiz
Teacher Center
- Lesson Planner
- Resources

Plus **iTEXT**

311

Math Background

Vertical lines have an undefined, or infinite, slope because the denominator in the ratio is zero. This is why the Property of Slopes of Parallel Lines includes the word *nonvertical*.

OBJECTIVE
1 Teaching Notes

1 EXAMPLE Alternative Method

Write $y = 2x + 4$ and $y = 2x - 1$ on the board. Ask: *What number do the equations have in common?* 2 *What does this number represent in each equation?* the slope Have students find the *y*-coordinates of the point on each line when $x = 4$. Then find the difference between the *y*-coordinates. Tell students that the difference is the vertical distance between the two lines. Repeat for $x = 100$, $x = 50,000$ and $x = 100,000$. Compare the vertical distance between the lines for each pair of points. **The vertical distances are all the same.** Ask: *What geometric term describes lines that are always the same distance apart?* parallel *What might you conclude about lines that have the same slope?* Lines that have the same slope are parallel.

2 EXAMPLE Visual Learners

Some students confuse the terms *parallel* and *perpendicular*. Print *parallel* on the board using large, lower-case letters. Circle the two *l*'s near the middle of the word. Tell students to think of these two *l*'s as parallel lines.

Additional Examples

1 Are the graphs of $y = -2x - 1$ and $4x + 2y = 6$ parallel? yes

2 Write an equation for the line that contains $(-2, 3)$ and is parallel to $y = \frac{5}{2}x - 4$. $y = \frac{5}{2}x + 8$

312

You can use the fact that the slopes of parallel lines are the same to write the equation of a line parallel to a given line. To write the equation, you use the slope of the given line and the point-slope form of a linear equation.

2 EXAMPLE Writing Equations of Parallel Lines

Write an equation for the line that contains $(5, 1)$ and is parallel to $y = \frac{3}{5}x - 4$.

Step 1 Identify the slope of the given line.

$$y = \frac{3}{5}x - 4$$
$$\uparrow$$
slope

Step 2 Write the equation of the line through $(5, 1)$ using slope-intercept form.

$y - y_1 = m(x - x_1)$	point-slope form
$y - 1 = \frac{3}{5}(x - 5)$	Substitute $(5, 1)$ for (x_1, y_1) and $\frac{3}{5}$ for *m*.
$y - 1 = \frac{3}{5}x - \frac{3}{5}(5)$	Use the Distributive Property.
$y - 1 = \frac{3}{5}x - 3$	Simplify.
$y = \frac{3}{5}x - 2$	Add 1 to each side.

✓ **Check Understanding** **2** Write an equation for the line that contains $(2, -6)$ and is parallel to $y = 3x + 9$.
$y = 3x - 12$

OBJECTIVE
2 Perpendicular Lines

The lines at the right are perpendicular. **Perpendicular lines** are lines that intersect to form right angles. The equation of the red line is $y = -\frac{1}{4}x - 1$. The equation of the blue line is $y = 4x + 2$.

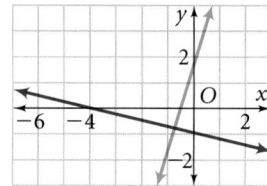

 **Key Concepts**

Property	**Slopes of Perpendicular Lines**

Two lines are perpendicular if the product of their slopes is -1. A vertical and a horizontal line are also perpendicular.

Example The slope of $y = -\frac{1}{4}x - 1$ is $-\frac{1}{4}$. The slope of $y = 4x + 2$ is 4. Since $-\frac{1}{4} \cdot 4 = -1$, the graphs of the two equations are perpendicular.

The product of two numbers is -1 if one number is the **negative reciprocal** of the other. Here is how to find the negative reciprocal of a number.

Start with a fraction: $-\frac{3}{5}$.	$\rightarrow$	Find its reciprocal: $-\frac{5}{3}$.	$\rightarrow$	Write the negative reciprocal: $\frac{5}{3}$.

Since $-\frac{3}{5} \cdot \frac{5}{3} = -1$, $\frac{5}{3}$ is the negative reciprocal of $-\frac{3}{5}$.

Start with an integer: 4.	$\rightarrow$	Find its reciprocal: $\frac{1}{4}$.	$\rightarrow$	Write its negative reciprocal: $-\frac{1}{4}$.

Since $4\left(-\frac{1}{4}\right) = -1$, $-\frac{1}{4}$ is the negative reciprocal of 4.

312 Chapter 6 Linear Equations and Their Graphs

Reaching All Students

Below Level To demonstrate that the signs of the slopes of parallel lines are the same, have students graph $y = \frac{1}{2}x - 1$. Then have them compare their graphs with the one on p. 311.	**Advanced Learners** Draw a square and its diagonals on a coordinate grid. Challenge students to prove that the diagonals are perpendicular.	**Visual Learners** See note on page 312. **Error Prevention** See note on page 313.

You can use the negative reciprocal of the slope of a given line to write an equation of a line perpendicular to that line.

3 EXAMPLE **Writing Equations for Perpendicular Lines**

Find an equation of the line that contains $(0, -2)$ and is perpendicular to $y = 5x + 3$.

Step 1 Identify the slope of the given line.

$$y = 5x + 3$$
$$\uparrow$$
$$\text{slope}$$

Step 2 Find the negative reciprocal of the slope.

The negative reciprocal of 5 is $-\frac{1}{5}$.

Step 3 Use the slope-intercept form to write an equation.

$$y = mx + b$$
$$y = -\frac{1}{5}x + (-2) \quad \textbf{Substitute } -\tfrac{1}{5} \textbf{ for } m, \textbf{ and } -2 \textbf{ for } b.$$
$$y = -\frac{1}{5}x - 2 \quad \textbf{Simplify.}$$

● The equation is $y = -\frac{1}{5}x - 2$.

✔ **Check Understanding** ❸ Write an equation of the line that contains $(1, 8)$ and is perpendicular to $y = \frac{3}{4}x + 1$.
$$y = -\tfrac{4}{3}x + 9\tfrac{1}{3}$$

You can use equations of parallel and perpendicular lines to solve some real-world problems.

4 EXAMPLE **Real-World 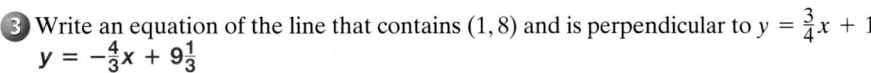 Problem Solving**

Urban Planning A bike path for a new city park will connect the park entrance to Park Road. The path will be perpendicular to Park Road. Write an equation for the line representing the bike path.

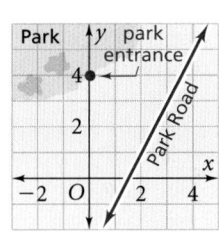

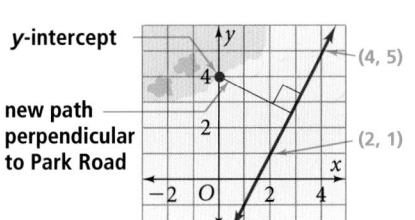

Real-World 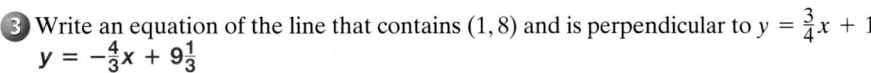 Connection

Careers Urban planners use mathematics to make decisions on community problems such as traffic congestion and air pollution.

Step 1 Find the slope m of Park Road.

$$m = \frac{y_2 - y_1}{x_2 - x_1} = \frac{5 - 1}{4 - 2} = \frac{4}{2} = 2 \quad \textbf{Points (2, 1) and (4, 5) are on Park Road.}$$

Step 2 Find the negative reciprocal of the slope.

The negative reciprocal of 2 is $-\frac{1}{2}$. So the slope of the bike path is $-\frac{1}{2}$. The y-intercept is 4.

● The equation for the bike path is $y = -\frac{1}{2}x + 4$.

✔ **Check Understanding** ❹ A second bike path is planned. It will be parallel to Park Road and will also contain the park entrance. Write an equation for the line representing this bike path. $y = 2x + 4$

3 EXAMPLE **Error Prevention**

Students may think that a negative reciprocal is always negative. Tell students that the phrase *negative reciprocal* actually means *the negative of the reciprocal*. So they are really just finding the opposite of the reciprocal.

▣ Additional Examples

❸ Find an equation of the line that contains $(6, 2)$ and is perpendicular to $y = -2x + 7$. $y = \frac{1}{2}x - 1$

❹ The line in the graph represents the street in front of a new house. The point is the front door. The sidewalk from the front door will be perpendicular to the street. Write an equation representing the sidewalk. $y = \frac{3}{2}x - 3$

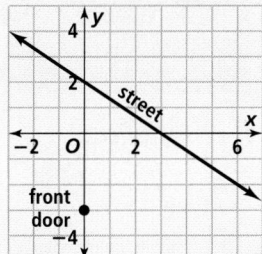

Closure

Ask: *Compare the equations of non-vertical parallel lines.* Parallel lines have the same slope, but different y-intercepts. *Compare the equations of perpendicular lines.* Perpendicular lines have slopes that are negative reciprocals of each other. They will have the same y-intercept only if that is where the two lines intersect.

3. Practice

Assignment Guide

1 ▼ **Objective**
Ⓐ Ⓑ **Core** 1–18, 42, 43, 46, 47, 53–62
Ⓒ **Extension** 68

2 ▼ **Objective**
Ⓐ Ⓑ **Core** 19–41, 44, 45, 48–52, 63–65
Ⓒ **Extension** 66–67, 69–72

Standardized Test Prep 73–79

Mixed Review 80–91

Exercise 4 Suggest to students that they graph the line $y = 6$.

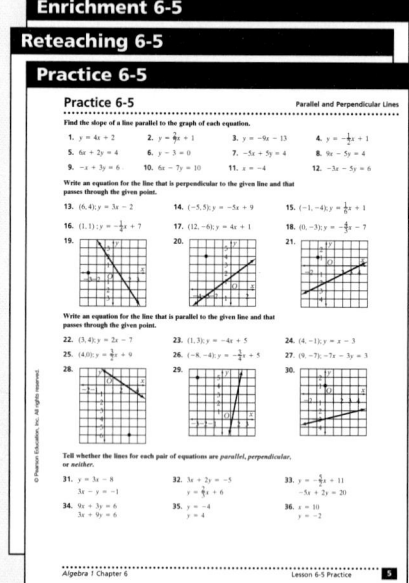

EXERCISES

For more practice, see *Extra Practice*.

Practice and Problem Solving

Ⓐ **Practice by Example**

Example 1
(page 311)

Find the slope of a line parallel to the graph of each equation.

1. $y = \frac{1}{2}x + 2.3$ $\frac{1}{2}$
2. $y = -\frac{2}{3}x - 1$ $-\frac{2}{3}$
3. $y = x$ **1**
4. $y = 6$ **0**
5. $3x + 4y = 12$ $-\frac{3}{4}$
6. $7x - y = 5$ **7**

Are the graphs of the lines in each pair parallel? Explain. **7–12. See margin.**

7. $y = 4x + 12$
   $-4x + 3y = 21$
8. $y = -\frac{3}{2}x + 2$
   $3x + 2y = 8$
9. $y = \frac{1}{3}x + 3$
   $x - 3y = 6$
10. $y = -\frac{1}{2}x + \frac{3}{2}$
    $5x - 10y = 15$
11. $y = -3x$
    $21x + 7y = 14$
12. $y = \frac{3}{4}x - 2$
    $-3x + 4y = 8$

Example 2
(page 312)

Write an equation for the line that is parallel to the given line and that passes through the given point. **13–18. See margin.**

13. $y = 6x - 2; (0, 0)$
14. $y = -3x; (3, 0)$
15. $y = -2x + 3; (-3, 5)$
16. $y = -\frac{7}{2}x + 6; (-4, -6)$
17. $y = 0.5x - 8; (8, -5)$
18. $y = -\frac{2}{3}x + 12; (5, -3)$

Example 3
(page 313)

Find the slope of a line perpendicular to the graph of each equation.

19. $y = 2x - \frac{1}{2}$
20. $y = -3x$ $\frac{1}{3}$
21. $y = \frac{7}{5}x - 2$ $-\frac{5}{7}$
22. $y = -\frac{x}{5} - 7$ **5**
23. $2x + 3y = 5$ $\frac{3}{2}$
24. $y = -8$ **undefined**

Write an equation for the line that is perpendicular to the given line and that passes through the given point.

25. $y = 2x + 7; (0, 0)$ $y = -\frac{1}{2}x$
26. $y = x - 3; (4, 6)$ $y = -x + 10$
27. $y = -\frac{1}{3}x + 2; (4, 2)$ $y = 3x - 10$
28. $3x + 5y = 7; (-1, 2)$ $y = \frac{5}{3}x + \frac{11}{3}$
29. $-10x + 8y = 3; (15, 12)$
    $y = -\frac{4}{5}x + 24$
30. $4x - 2y = 9; (8, -2)$ $y = -\frac{1}{2}x + 2$

Example 4
(page 313)

31. **Maps** A city's civil engineer is planning a new parking garage and a new street. The new street will go from the entrance of the parking garage to Handel St. It will be perpendicular to Handel St. What is the equation of the line representing the new street? $y = \frac{5}{4}x + 1$

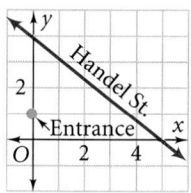

Ⓑ **Apply Your Skills**

Tell whether the lines for each pair of equations are *parallel*, *perpendicular*, **or** *neither*.

32. $y = 4x + \frac{3}{4}, y = -\frac{1}{4}x + 4$ **perpendicular**
33. $y = \frac{2}{3}x - 6, y = \frac{2}{3}x + 6$ **parallel**
34. $y = -x + 5, y = x + 5$ **perpendicular**
35. $y = 5x, y = -5x + 7$ **neither**
36. $y = \frac{x}{3} - 4, y = \frac{1}{3}x + 2$ **parallel**
37. $x = 2, y = 9$ **perpendicular**
38. $2x + y = 2, 2x + y = 5$ **parallel**
39. $3x - 5y = 3, -5x + 3y = 8$ **neither**
40. $4x - 3y = 36, 3x + 4y = 20$ **perpendicular**
41. $2x - 5y = 15, 2x + 5y = 10$ **neither**

42. **Critical Thinking** Explain how you can tell that the graphs of $7x - 3y = 5$ and $7x - 3y = 8$ are parallel without finding their slopes.
   Answers may vary. Sample: same *x* and *y* coefficients

7. no, different slopes
8. yes, same slopes and different *y*-intercepts
9. yes, same slopes and different *y*-intercepts

10. no, different slopes
11. yes, same slopes and different *y*-intercepts
12. yes, same slopes and different *y*-intercepts

13. $y = 6x$
14. $y = -3x + 9$
15. $y = -2x - 1$

16. $y = -\frac{7}{2}x - 20$
17. $y = 0.5x - 9$
18. $y = -\frac{2}{3}x + \frac{1}{3}$

Find the equation for each line.

43.

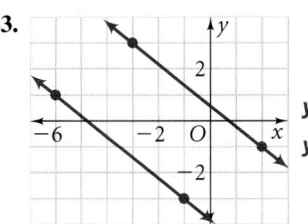

$y = -\frac{4}{5}x - \frac{19}{5}$;
$y = -\frac{4}{5}x + \frac{3}{5}$

44.

$y = \frac{1}{3}x + \frac{4}{3}$; $y = -3x + 7$

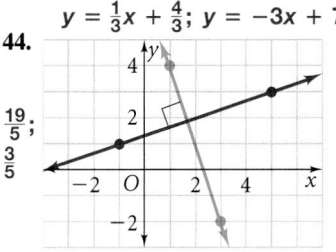

45.

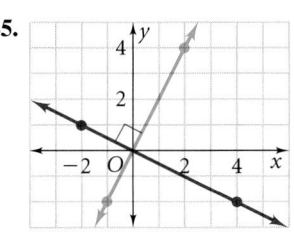

$y = -\frac{1}{2}x$;
$y = 2x$

46.

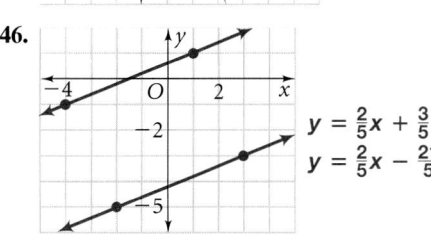

$y = \frac{2}{5}x + \frac{3}{5}$;
$y = \frac{2}{5}x - \frac{21}{5}$

47.

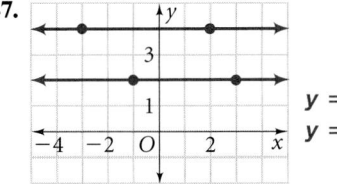

$y = 4$;
$y = 2$

48.

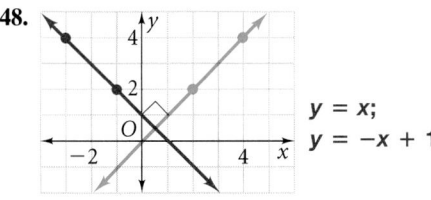

$y = x$;
$y = -x + 1$

🌐 **Maps** Use the map below for Exercises 49–51.

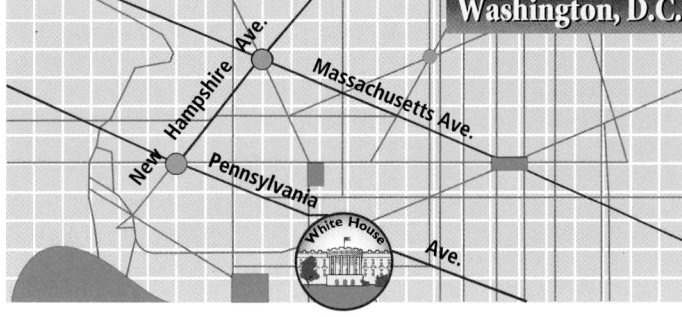

49. What is the slope of New Hampshire Avenue? **about $\frac{5}{4}$**

50. Show that the parts of Pennsylvania Avenue and Massachusetts Avenue near New Hampshire Avenue are parallel. **Answers may vary.**
Sample: same slope of $-\frac{1}{2}$

51. Show that New Hampshire Avenue is not perpendicular to Pennsylvania Avenue. **Answers may vary. Sample: $\frac{5}{4} \cdot \left(-\frac{1}{2}\right) \neq -1$**

52. a. The graphs of $y = x$ and $y = -x$ are shown on the standard screen at the right. The product of the slopes is -1. Explain why the lines do not appear to be perpendicular. **a–b. See margin.**

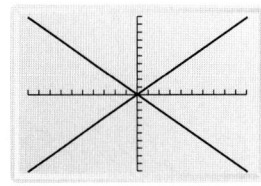

    📱 **b.** **Graphing Calculator** Graph $y = x$ and $y = -x$ on a graphing calculator. In the ZOOM feature, choose the square screen. What do you notice?

53. Open-Ended Write an equation for a line parallel to the graph of $4x - y = 1$.
Answers may vary. Sample: $y = 4x + 1$

Lesson 6-5 Parallel and Perpendicular Lines **315**

52a. The screen is not square.

  b. The lines appear perpendicular.

Teaching Tip

Exercises 32–41 Ask students to describe equations of lines that are neither parallel nor perpendicular. The slopes are neither the same nor negative reciprocals of each other.

Error Prevention

Exercise 66 Suggest that students first sketch a graph of the triangle to determine which two sides may be perpendicular.

4. Assess

📓 **Lesson Quiz 6-5**

1. Find the slope of a line parallel to $3x - 2y = 1$. $\frac{3}{2}$

2. Find the slope of a line perpendicular to $4x + 5y = 7$. $\frac{5}{4}$

Tell whether the lines for each pair of equations are *parallel*, *perpendicular*, or *neither*.

3. $y = 3x - 1$, $y = -\frac{1}{3}x + 2$ **perpendicular**

4. $y = 2x + 5$, $2x + y = -4$ **neither**

5. $y = -\frac{2}{3}x - 1$, $2x + 3y = 6$ **parallel**

6. Write an equation of the line that contains $(2, 1)$ and is perpendicular to $y = -\frac{1}{2}x + 3$. $y = 2x - 3$

Alternative Assessment

Write an equation in slope-intercept form on the board. Have students first write an equation of a line that is parallel to the given line, and then write an equation of a line that is perpendicular to the given equation. Let students compare their answers. Repeat.

pages 314–317 Exercises

56. yes; same slopes and different y-intercepts

60. The slopes of $\overleftrightarrow{AD}$ and $\overleftrightarrow{BC}$ are both undefined, so they are parallel. The slopes of $\overleftrightarrow{AB}$ and $\overleftrightarrow{CD}$ are both $\frac{2}{5}$, so they are parallel. The quadrilateral is a parallelogram.

61. The slope of $\overleftrightarrow{JK}$ is $\frac{1}{5}$. The slope of $\overleftrightarrow{KL}$ is -2. The slope of $\overleftrightarrow{LM}$ is $\frac{1}{6}$. The slope of $\overleftrightarrow{JM}$ is -4. The quadrilateral is not a parallelogram.

316

---

54. No; the slopes are not equal.

55. No; the slopes are not neg. reciprocals.

⋯⋯⋯⋯⋯⋯

Problem Solving Hint

For Exercises 57–59, sketch a graph to help you understand the statement in each exercise.

⋯⋯⋯⋯⋯⋯

57. False; the product of two positive numbers can't be -1.

58. True; $y = x + 2$ and $y = x + 3$ are parallel.

59. False; all direct variations go through the point $(0, 0)$. If they have the same slope, they are the same line, not parallel lines.

70. $y = -\frac{3}{8}x - \frac{17}{8}$; $y = \frac{8}{3}x + 7$

71. $y = \frac{1}{2}x - 3$; $y = -2x + 7$

---

54. Are the graphs of $2x + 7y = 6$ and $7y = 2x + 6$ parallel? Explain. **See left.**

55. Are the graphs of $8x + 3y = 6$ and $8x - 3y = 6$ perpendicular? Explain. **See left.**

✏️ 56. **Writing** Are all horizontal lines parallel? Explain. **See margin.**

Tell whether each statement is *true* or *false*. Explain your choice.

57–59. See below left.

57. Two lines with positive slopes can be perpendicular.

58. Two lines with positive slopes can be parallel.

59. The graphs of two different direct variations can be parallel.

📦 **Geometry** A quadrilateral with both pairs of opposite sides parallel is a parallelogram. Use slopes to determine whether each figure is a parallelogram.

60–62. See margin.

60. 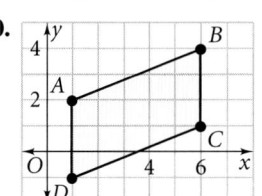 61. 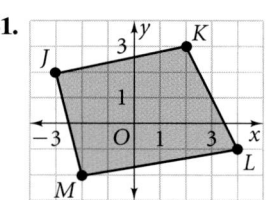 62.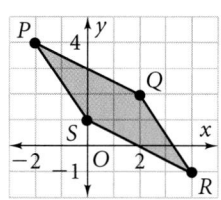

📦 **Geometry** A quadrilateral with four right angles is a rectangle. Use slopes to determine whether each figure is a rectangle. 63–65. See margin.

63. 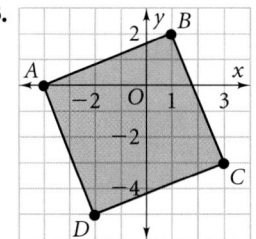 64. 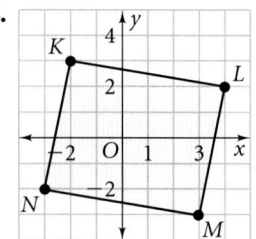 65.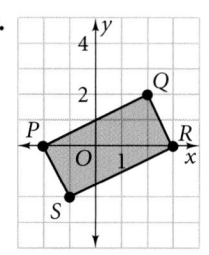

C **Challenge** 📦 66. **Geometry** A quadrilateral with two pairs of parallel sides and with diagonals that are perpendicular is a rhombus. Quadrilateral $ABCD$ has vertices $A(-2, 2)$, $B(1, 6)$, $C(6, 6)$, and $D(3, 2)$. Show that $ABCD$ is a rhombus. **See margin.**

📦 67. **Geometry** A triangle with two sides that are perpendicular to each other is a right triangle. Triangle PQR has vertices $P(3, 3)$, $Q(2, -2)$, and $R(0, 1)$. Determine whether PQR is a right triangle. Explain. **See margin.**

Tell whether the lines in each pair are *parallel*, *perpendicular*, or *neither*.

68. $ax - by = c$; $-ax + by = d$ **parallel**

69. $ax + by = c$; $bx - ay = d$ **perpendicular**

Assume the two lines are perpendicular. Find an equation for each line.

70–71. See left.

70. 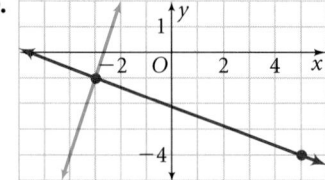 71.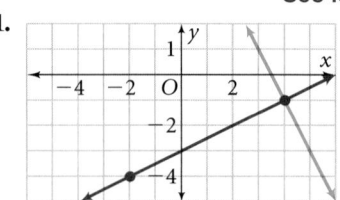

72. For what value of k are the graphs of $3x + 12y = 8$ and $6y = kx - 5$ parallel? Perpendicular? **-1.5; 24**

316 Chapter 6 Linear Equations and Their Graphs

62. The slopes of $\overleftrightarrow{PQ}$ and $\overleftrightarrow{RS}$ are both $-\frac{1}{2}$. The slopes of $\overleftrightarrow{QR}$ and $\overleftrightarrow{SP}$ are both $-\frac{3}{2}$. The quadrilateral is a parallelogram.

63. The slopes of $\overleftrightarrow{AB}$ and $\overleftrightarrow{CD}$ are both $\frac{2}{5}$. The slopes of $\overleftrightarrow{BC}$ and $\overleftrightarrow{AD}$ are both $-\frac{5}{2}$. The product is -1, so the quadrilateral is a rectangle.

64. The slopes of $\overleftrightarrow{KL}$ and $\overleftrightarrow{MN}$ are both $-\frac{1}{6}$. The slopes of $\overleftrightarrow{LM}$ and $\overleftrightarrow{KN}$ are both 5. The product is not -1, so the quadrilateral is not a rectangle.

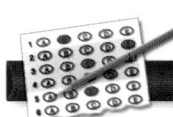

Standardized Test Prep

📁 **Resources**
For additional practice with a
variety of test item formats:
- Standardized Test Prep, p. 335
- Test-Taking Strategies, p. 330
- Test-Taking Strategies with
  Transparencies

Multiple Choice

73. Which equation has as its graph a line perpendicular to a line with a slope of $\frac{2}{3}$? **D**

A. $y = \frac{2}{3}x + 5$ B. $y = \frac{3}{2}x - 1$ C. $y = 3x - 2$ D. $3x + 2y = 8$

74. Which equation has as its graph a line parallel to the graph of $-2x - 4y = 3$? **F**

F. $y = -\frac{1}{2}x + 5$ G. $y = 2x - 6$ H. $y = -2x + 4$ I. $y = \frac{1}{2}x - 2$

75. A parallelogram has vertices $A(0, 2)$, $B(2, -1)$, $C(6, 3)$, and $D(p, q)$. Which of the following ordered pairs has possible values for (p, q)? **C**

A. $(0, 6)$ B. $(6, 1)$ C. $(4, 6)$ D. $(6, 4)$

Short Response

76. Suppose the line through points $(x, 6)$ and $(1, 2)$ is parallel to the graph of $2x + y = 3$. Find the value of x. Show your work. **See margin.**

Quantitative Comparison

Compare the equation in Column A with the equation in Column B. Choose the best answer.

A. The quantity in Column A is greater.
B. The quantity in Column B is greater.
C. The two quantities are equal.
D. The relationship cannot be determined from the information given.

	Column A	Column B
77. C	the slope of $y = -5x - 1$	the slope of $10x + 2y = -2$
78. A	the product of the slopes of $y = -\frac{4}{3}x + 5$ and $3x + 4y = 12$	-1
79. B	the slope of $6y = 3x + 10$	2

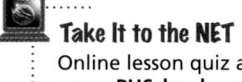
Take It to the NET
Online lesson quiz at
www.PHSchool.com
········ Web Code: aea-0605

Connection to Geometry
Exercise 75 Tell students that they can eliminate some possible answers by first sketching the three points in the exercise on a coordinate plane.

Mixed Review

Lesson 6-4

Write an equation for the line through the given point with the given slope.

80. $(0, 4); m = 3$ $y = 3x + 4$ **81.** $(-2, 0); m = -4$ $y = -4x - 8$

82. $(5, -3); m = \frac{3}{4}$ $y + 3 = \frac{3}{4}(x - 5)$ **83.** $(-1, -9); m = -\frac{2}{3}$ $y + 9 = -\frac{2}{3}(x + 1)$

84. $(-6, 4); m = -\frac{3}{5}$ $y - 4 = -\frac{3}{5}(x + 6)$ **85.** $(7, 11); m = \frac{1}{2}$ $y - 11 = \frac{1}{2}(x - 7)$

Lesson 5-6

Find the third, fifth, and seventh term in the sequence that has each given rule.

86. $A(n) = 2n + 1$ **7; 11; 15**   **87.** $A(n) = 3 - 4n$ **−9; −17; −25**

Lesson 5-2

Determine whether each relation is a function.

88. $\{(1, 1), (2, 2), (3, 3)\}$ **yes**   **89.** $\{(1, 3), (2, 5), (3, 5)\}$ **yes**

90. $\{(5, 1), (5, 2), (4, 3)\}$ **no**   **91.** $\{(1, 3), (2, 2), (3, 1)\}$ **yes**

65. The slopes of $\overleftrightarrow{PQ}$ and $\overleftrightarrow{RS}$ are both $\frac{1}{2}$. The slopes of $\overleftrightarrow{PS}$ and $\overleftrightarrow{QR}$ are both -2. The product is -1, so the quadrilateral is a rectangle.

66. $\overleftrightarrow{BC}$ and $\overleftrightarrow{AD}$ both have a slope of zero. $\overleftrightarrow{BC}$ and $\overleftrightarrow{AD}$ are parallel. $\overleftrightarrow{AB}$ and $\overleftrightarrow{CD}$ both have a slope of $\frac{4}{3}$. $\overleftrightarrow{AB}$ and $\overleftrightarrow{CD}$ are parallel. The diagonal

$\overleftrightarrow{BD}$ has a slope of -2. The diagonal $\overleftrightarrow{AC}$ has a slope of $\frac{1}{2}$. The diagonals are perpendicular. $\square ABCD$ is a rhombus.

67. $\overleftrightarrow{RP}$ has a slope of $\frac{2}{3}$. $\overleftrightarrow{RQ}$ has a slope of $-\frac{3}{2}$. $\overleftrightarrow{RP}$ is the neg. reciprocal of $\overleftrightarrow{RQ}$, so $\triangle PQR$ is a right triangle.

76. [2] Find slope of $2x + y = 3$:
$y = -2x + 3$,
therefore slope is -2.
Find x: $\frac{2 - 6}{1 - x} = -2$,
$\frac{-4}{1 - x} = -2$,
$-4 = -2 + 2x$,
$x = -1$
(OR equivalent explanation)

[1] correct value of x but no work OR minor computation error in work

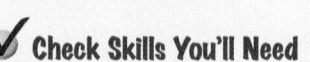

Lesson Preview

✓ Check Skills You'll Need

Data on the Coordinate Plane
Lesson 1-9: Example 4
Exercise 16
Extra Practice, p. 702

Lesson Resources

📁 **Teaching Resources**
Practice, Reteaching, Enrichment
Checkpoint Quiz 2

👥 **Reaching All Students**
Practice Workbook 6-6
Spanish Practice Workbook 6-6
Reading and Math Literacy 6C
Spanish Reading & Literacy 6C
Spanish Checkpoint Quiz 2
Hands-On Activities 19
Basic Algebra Planning Guide 6-6

🕐 **Presentation Assistant Plus!**
Transparencies
• Check Skills You'll Need 6-6
• Additional Examples 6-6
• Student Edition Answers 6-6
• Lesson Quiz 6-6
PH Presentation Pro CD 6-6

ASSESSMENT SYSTEM

Checkpoint Quiz 2
Computer Test Generator CD

💿 **Technology**
Resource Pro® CD-ROM
Computer Test Generator CD
Prentice Hall Presentation Pro CD

💻 **www.PHSchool.com**
Student Site
• Teacher Web Code: aek-5500
• Updated Data
• Graphing Calculator,
  Procedure 22
• Self-grading Lesson Quiz
Teacher Center
• Lesson Planner
• Resources

Plus *i*TEXT

318

6-6

Scatter Plots and Equations of Lines

North Carolina Objectives   3.03 Create linear models for sets of data to solve problems. b) Check the model for goodness-of-fit and use the model, where appropriate, to draw conclusions or make predictions.

Lesson Preview

What You'll Learn

OBJECTIVE 1 To write an equation for a trend line and use it to make predictions

OBJECTIVE 2 To write the equation for a line of best fit and use it to make predictions

. . . And Why

To use a trend line to make a prediction, as in Example 1

✓ Check Skills You'll Need   (For help, go to Lesson 1-9.)

Use the data in each table to draw a scatter plot. 1–2. See back of book.

1.
x	y
1	2
2	−3
3	8
4	9
5	−25

2.
x	y
1	21
2	15
3	12
4	9
5	7

New Vocabulary • line of best fit • correlation coefficient

🖥 *i*TEXT   Interactive lesson includes instant self-check, tutorials, and activities.

OBJECTIVE 1
Writing an Equation for a Trend Line

In Chapter 1 you used scatter plots to determine how two sets of data are related. You can now write an equation for a trend line.

1 EXAMPLE   **Trend Line**

Birds Make a scatter plot of the data at the left. Draw a trend line and write its equation. Use the equation to predict the wingspan of a hawk that is 28 in. long.

Length and Wingspan of Hawks

Type of Hawk	Length (in.)	Wing-span (in.)
Cooper's	21	36
Crane	21	41
Gray	18	38
Harris's	24	46
Roadside	16	31
Broad-winged	19	39
Short-tailed	17	35
Swanson's	19	46

Source: *Birds of North America*

Step 1 Make a scatter plot and draw a trend line. Estimate two points on the line.

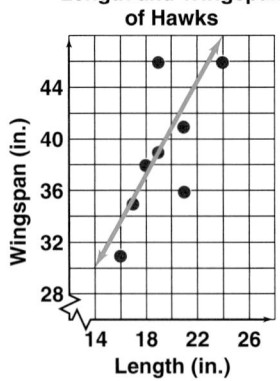

Length and Wingspan of Hawks

Two points on the trend line are (14, 30) and (19, 39).

Step 2 Write an equation of the trend line.

$$m = \frac{y_2 - y_1}{x_2 - x_1} = \frac{39 - 30}{19 - 14} = \frac{9}{5}$$

$y - y_1 = m(x - x_1)$ Use point-slope form.

$y - 30 = \frac{9}{5}(x - 14)$ Substitute $\frac{9}{5}$ for m and (14, 30) for (x_1, y_1).

Step 3 Predict the wingspan of a hawk that is 28 in. long.

$y - 30 = \frac{9}{5}(28 - 14)$ Substitute 28 for x.

$y - 30 = \frac{9}{5}(14)$ Simplify within the parentheses.

$y - 30 = 25.2$ Multiply.

$y = 55.2$ Add 30 to each side.

The wingspan of a hawk 28 in. long is about 55.2 in.

🔄 **Ongoing Assessment and Intervention**

Before the Lesson
Diagnose prerequisite skills using:
• Check Skills You'll Need

During the Lesson
Monitor progress using:
• Check Understanding
• Additional Examples
• Standardized Test Prep

After the Lesson
Assess knowledge using:
• Lesson Quiz
• Computer Test Generator CD
• Chapter Checkpoint 2 (p. 324)

1 Graph the data below and draw a trend line. Find an equation for the trend line. Estimate the number of calories in a fast-food that has 14g of fat. **See back of book.**

Calories and Fat in Selected Fast-Food Meals

Fat (g)	6	7	10	19	20	27	36
Calories	276	260	220	388	430	550	633

OBJECTIVE

2 **Writing an Equation for a Line of Best Fit**

The trend line that shows the relationship between two sets of data most accurately is called the **line of best fit.** A graphing calculator computes the equation of a line of best fit using a method called linear regression.

The graphing calculator also gives you the **correlation coefficient** r, which tells you how closely the equation models the data.

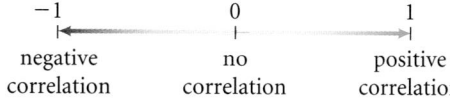

negative correlation   no correlation   positive correlation

When the data points cluster around a line, there is a strong correlation between the line and the data. So the nearer r is to 1 or -1, the more closely the data cluster around the line of best fit. In later chapters, you will learn how to find non-linear models which may better describe some data.

Graphing Calculator Hint

The equation of the line of best fit will be in one of these forms:

$y = ax + b$
↑ ↑
slope y-intercept

$y = a + bx$
↑ ↑
y-intercept slope

2 **EXAMPLE** **Line of Best Fit**

Recreation Use a graphing calculator to find the equation of the line of best fit for the data at the right. What is the correlation coefficient?

Step 1 Use the **EDIT** feature of the `STAT` screen on your graphing calculator. Let 93 correspond to 1993. Enter the data for years and then the data for costs.

Step 2 Use the **CALC** feature in the `STAT` screen. Find the equation for the line of best fit.

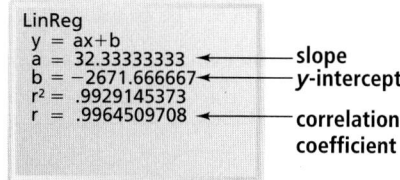

```
LinReg
  y = ax+b
  a = 32.33333333    ← slope
  b = -2671.666667   ← y-intercept
  r² = .9929145373
  r = .9964509708    ← correlation coefficient
```

Recreation Expenditures

Year	Dollars (billions)
1993	340
1994	369
1995	402
1996	430
1997	457
1998	489
1999	527
2000	574

SOURCE: *Statistical Abstract of the United States*. Go to **www.PHSchool.com** for a data update. Web Code: aeg-2041

Take It to the NET

Graphing Calculator procedures online at **www.PHSchool.com**
Web Code: aee-2122

The equation for the line of best fit is $y = 32.33x - 2671.67$ for values of a and b rounded to the nearest hundredth. The correlation coefficient is 0.9964509708.

👥 **Reaching All Students**

Below Level To better understand a correlation coefficient, draw and discuss scatter plots that show positive and negative correlations with varying correlation coefficients.

Advanced Learners Make several scatter plots with different correlation coefficients. Students match each scatter plot with its corresponding correlation coefficient.

Error Prevention See note on page 320.
English Learners See note on page 321.

2. Teach

Math Background

Lines of best fit can be used to determine whether slopes for two sets of data are approximately equal, indicating a similarity in the relationships.

OBJECTIVE

1 **Teaching Notes**

1 **EXAMPLE** **Math Tip**

Trend lines are not precise; they are similar to estimates. In drawing a trend line for data that seem to cluster near a line, you should try to have about as many points above the line as below the line.

 Additional Examples

1 Make a scatter plot to represent the data. Draw a trend line and write an equation for the trend line. Use the equation to predict the time needed to travel 32 miles on a bicycle. **See back of book.**

Speed on a Bicycle Trip

Miles	5	10	14	18	22
Time (min)	27	46	71	78	107

OBJECTIVE

2 **Teaching Notes**

 Additional Examples

2 Use a graphing calculator to find the equation of the line of best fit for the data below. What is the correlation coefficient?

U.S. Crime Rate (per 100,000 inhabitants)   See back of book.

Year	No. of Crimes
1995	5275.9
1996	5086.6
1997	4930.0
1998	4619.3
1999	4266.8

[Source: *Crime in the United States*, 1999, FBI, Uniform Crime Reports]

Closure

Ask: *What is the difference between a trend line and a line of best fit?* A trend line is an approximation for a line of best fit.

Assignment Guide

1 Objective

Ⓐ Ⓑ **Core** 1–6, 12–13, 15, 19

2 Objective

Ⓐ Ⓑ **Core** 7–11, 14, 16–18

Ⓒ **Extension** 20

Standardized Test Prep 21–23

Mixed Review 24–35

Error Prevention

Exercise 1–5 Some students may expect their trend lines to be exactly like those of their neighbors. Remind them that a trend line is not precise. Thus, their lines and equations may differ slightly.

Exercise 2 Ask students if these data have a strong correlation or a weak correlation.

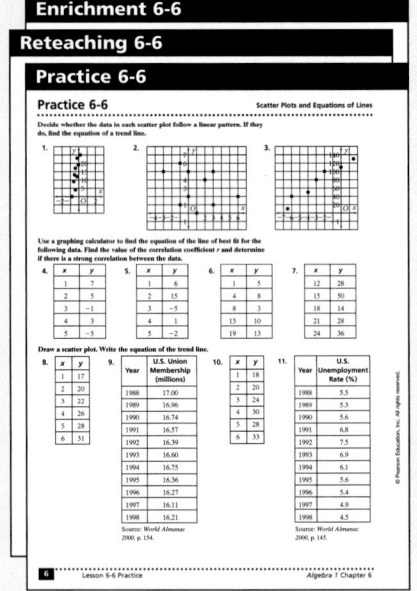

✓ **Check Understanding** ② Find the equation of the line of best fit. Let 91 correspond to 1991. What is the correlation coefficient? **2.** $y = 0.33x - 25.35$; 0.9751360069

Yearly Box Office Gross for Movies (billions)

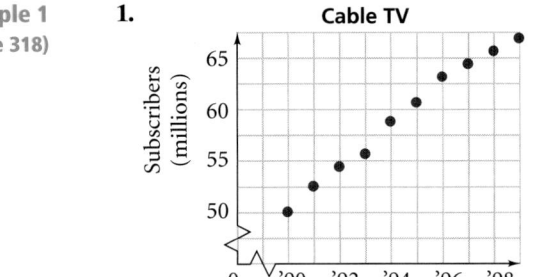

1991	1992	1993	1994	1995	1996	1997	1998	1999
$4.8	$4.9	$5.2	$5.4	$5.5	$6.0	$6.4	$7.0	$7.4

EXERCISES

For more practice, see *Extra Practice*.

Practice and Problem Solving

1–6. Trend lines may vary. Samples are given.

Ⓐ **Practice by Example**

Example 1 (page 318)

Find an equation of a reasonable trend line for each scatter plot.

1.

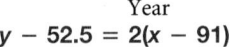
Cable TV

$y - 52.5 = 2(x - 91)$

2. Animal Longevity and Gestation

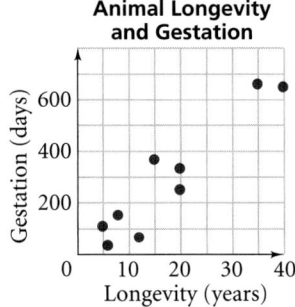

$y - 100 = 15.71(x - 5)$

3. NBA Players

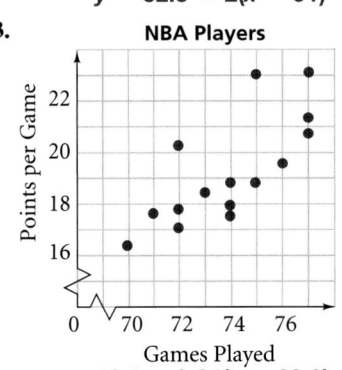

$y - 16.4 = 0.64(x - 69.9)$

4. Memory Test

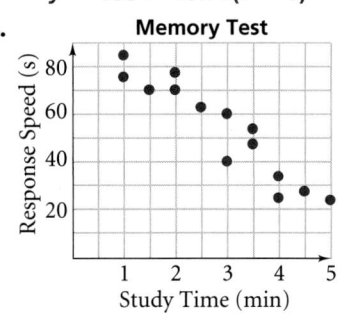

$y - 85 = -15.25(x - 1)$

5.

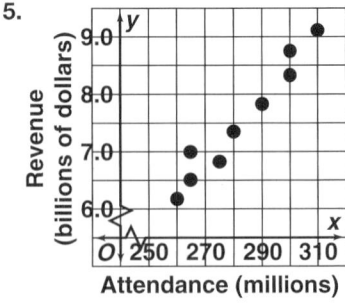
Attendance (millions)

$y - 5 = 0.06(x - 240)$

5. Graph the data in the table below for the attendance and revenue at theme parks. Find an equation for the trend line of the data. **See left.**

Attendance and Revenue at U.S. Theme Parks

Year	1991	1992	1993	1994	1995	1996	1997	1998	1999
Attendance (millions)	260	267	275	267	280	290	300	300	309
Revenue (billions of dollars)	6.1	6.5	6.8	7.0	7.4	7.9	8.4	8.7	9.1

SOURCE: International Association of Amusement Parks and Attractions.
Go to www.PHSchool.com for a data update.
Web Code: aeg-2041

Example 2
(page 319)

Graphing Calculator Use a graphing calculator to find the equation of the line of best fit for the data. Find the value of the correlation coefficient *r*.

6. Graph the data for the average July temperature and the annual precipitation of the cities in the table below. Find an equation for the line of best fit of the data. Estimate the average rainfall for a city with average July temperature of 75° F.

6.

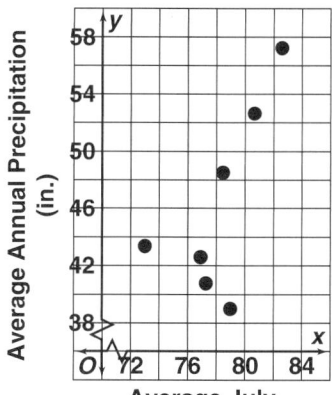

Average July Temperature (°F)

$y \approx 1.6x - 80$; 40 in.

Precipitation and Temperature in Selected Eastern Cities

City	Average July Temperature (°F)	Average Annual Precipitation (in.)
New York	76.4	42.82
Baltimore	76.8	41.84
Atlanta	78.6	48.61
Jacksonville	81.3	52.76
Washington, D.C.	78.9	39.00
Boston	73.5	43.81
Miami	82.5	57.55

SOURCE: Time *Almanac*

7. **Average Temperatures in Northern Latitudes**

Latitude (° N)	0	10	20	30	40	50	60	70	80
Temp. (°F)	79.2	80.1	77.5	68.7	57.4	42.4	30.0	12.7	1.0

$y = -1.06x + 92.31$; -0.9701709306

8. **Retail Department Store Sales (billions of dollars)**

Year	1980	1985	1990	1994	1995	1996	1997	1998
Sales	86	126	166	217	231	245	261	279

SOURCE: *Statistical Abstract of the United States.*
Go to **www.PHSchool.com** for an update.
Web Code: aeg-2041

$y = 10.60x - 772.66$; 0.990733298

9. **Olympic 500-Meter Men's Gold Medal Speed Skating Times**

Year	1980	1984	1988	1992	1994	1998
Time (seconds)	422	432	404	420	395	382

SOURCE: International Skating Union

$y = -2.29x + 613.93$; -0.8108238756

10. **Average Male Lung Power**

Respiration (breaths/min)	50	30	25	20	18	16	14
Heart Rate (beats/min)	200	150	140	130	120	110	100

SOURCE: Encyclopedia Britannica

$y = 2.64x + 70.51$; 0.9900170523

11. **Wind Chill Temperature for 15 mi/h Wind**

Air Temp. (°F)	35	30	25	20	15	10	5	0
Wind-Chill Temp. (°F)	16	9	2	−5	−11	−18	−25	−31

$y = 1.35x - 31.42$; 0.999808967

Real-World Connection

The 500-meter men's speed skating race has been an Olympic event since 1924.

English Learners

Exercises 7–11 Help students understand the term *correlation* by covering *cor* at the beginning of the word to reveal only the word *relation*. The *correlation coefficient* tells you how closely *related* the equation and the data are.

Connection to Geography

Exercise 7 Longitudes and latitudes make up a coordinate system used in designating the location of places on the surface of Earth. Latitude gives location north or south of the equator. It is expressed by angle measurements ranging from 0° at the equator to 90° at the poles.

Connection to Geometry

Exercise 12 The circumference of a circle divided by its diameter equals π.

pages 320–324 Exercises

12a.

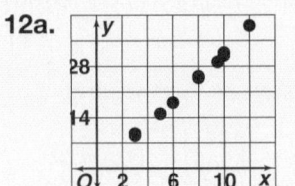

13a.

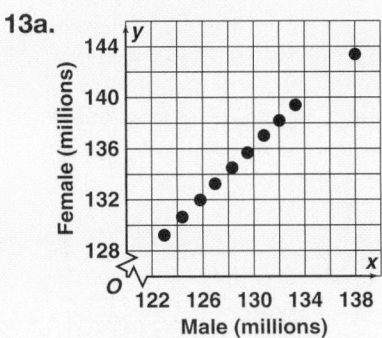

b. Answers may vary.
Sample:
$y = 0.939x + 13,800$

d. Answers may vary.
Sample: No, the year is too far in the future.

14a. Check students' work.

b. 1

18c. No, the correlation coefficient is not close to 1 or −1, so the equation does not closely model the data.

20a.

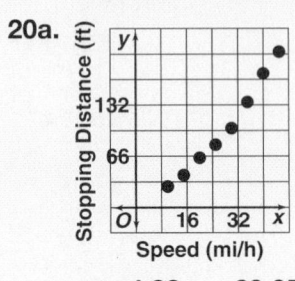

$y = 4.82x - 29.65$

B **Apply Your Skills**

12c. Answers may vary.
Sample: The slope is the approximate ratio of the circumference to the diameter.

Population Growth

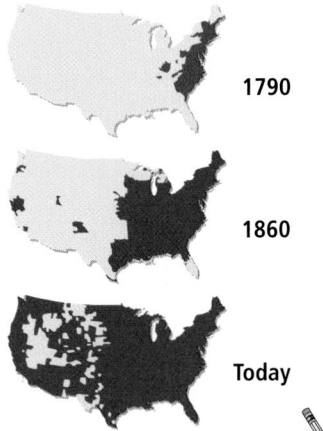

1790

1860

Today

■ More than 2 persons per square mile

15. Answers may vary.
Sample: Pos. slope; as temp. increases, more students are absent.

16a. $y = 0.61x + 35.31$

b. Answers may vary.
Sample: small set of data with weak correlation

---

12. Geometry Students measured the diameters and circumferences of the tops of a variety of cylinders. Below is the data that they collected.

Cylinder Tops

Diameter (cm)	3	3	5	6	8	8	9.5	10	10	12
Circumference (cm)	9.3	9.5	16	18.8	25	25.6	29.5	31.5	30.9	39.5

a. Graph the data. **See margin.** b. Find the equation of a trend line. $y = 3.25x - 1$
c. What does the slope of the equation mean? **See left.**
d. Find the diameter of a cylinder with a circumference of 45 cm. **14 cm**

13a–b. See margin.

13. Population Use the data at the right.
a. Graph the data for the male and female populations of the United States.
b. Find the equation of a trend line.
c. Use your equation to predict the number of females if the number of males were to increase to 138,476,000. **143,800,000**
d. **Critical Thinking** Would it be reasonable to predict the population in 2025 from these data? Explain. **See margin.**

14. a. Open-Ended Make a table of data for a linear function. Use a graphing calculator to find the equation of the line of best fit.
b. What is the correlation coefficient for your linear data? **a–b. See margin.**

15. Writing What kind of trend line do you think data for the following comparison would be likely to show? Explain. **See left.**
temperature and the number of students absent from school

Estimated Population of the United States (thousands)

Year	Male	Female
1991	122,956	129,197
1992	124,424	130,606
1993	125,788	131,995
1994	127,049	133,278
1995	128,294	134,510
1996	129,504	135,724
1997	130,783	137,001
1998	132,030	138,218
1999	133,277	139,414
2000	138,054	143,368

SOURCE: U.S. Census Bureau. Go to **www.PHSchool.com** for a data update. Web Code: aeg-2041

16. Graphing Calculator A school collected data on math and science grades of nine randomly selected students.

Student	1	2	3	4	5	6	7	8	9
Math	76	89	84	79	94	71	79	91	84
Science	82	94	89	89	94	84	68	89	84

a. Use a graphing calculator to find the equation of the line of best fit for the data. **a–b. See left.**
b. **Critical Thinking** Should the equation for the line of best fit be used to predict grades? Explain.

17. Graphing Calculator Use a graphing calculator to find the equation of the line of best fit for the data below. Predict sales of greeting cards in the year 2010.

Greeting Card Sales

Year	1989	1990	1991	1992	1993	1994	1995	1996	1997	1998
Sales (billions)	$4.2	$4.6	$5.0	$5.3	$5.6	$5.9	$6.3	$6.8	$7.3	$7.5

SOURCE: Greeting Card Association

$y = 0.37x - 28.66$; **$12.04 billion**

18. a. Data Collection Find two sets of data that you could display in a scatter plot, such as the number of boys and girls in each class in your school, or the population and the number of airports in some states. Then graph the data.
  b. Find the equation of a trend line.
  c. Use the equation to predict another value that could be on your scatter plot.
  d. What is the correlation coefficient? **a–d. Check students' work.**

19. Another way you can find a line of best fit is the *median-median method.* The graph below shows how this method works. The points in red indicate the original data.

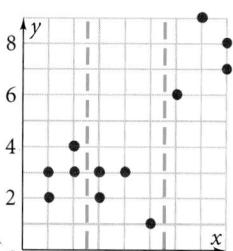 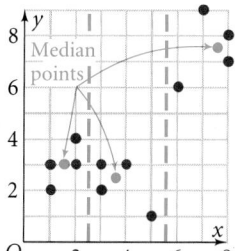 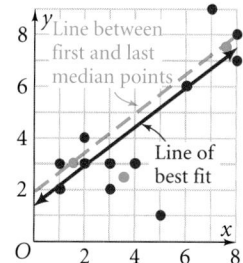

| Divide the data into three groups of equal size. | Find and plot the median point, (*x*-median, *y*-median). | Find the line parallel to the line between the first and last median points and $\frac{1}{3}$ of the way to the middle median point. |

  a. Estimate two coordinates on the purple line in the graph at the right above. Find the equation of the line of best fit. **(2, 3) and (6, 6); y = 0.75x + 1.5**
   b. Graphing Calculator You can use a graphing calculator to find the line of best fit with the median-median method. Below are the coordinates of the points graphed in red. Use the EDIT feature of the STAT screen on your graphing calculator. Use the Med-Med feature to find a line of best fit. **y = 0.75x + 1.21**
  $(1, 2), (1, 3), (2, 3), (2, 4), (3, 2), (3, 3), (4, 3), (5, 1), (6, 6), (7, 9), (8, 8), (8, 7)$

 Challenge

20. a. Make a scatter plot of the data below. Then find the equation of the line of best fit. **See margin.**

20c. The speed is much faster than those speeds used to find the equation of a trend line.

Car Stopping Distances

Speed (mi/h)	10	15	20	25	30	35	40	45
Stopping Distances (ft)	27	44	63	85	109	136	164	196

  b. Use your equation to predict the stopping distance at 90 mi/h. **404 ft**
  c. Critical Thinking The actual stopping distance at 90 mi/h is close to 584 ft. Why do you think this is not close to your prediction? **See left.**

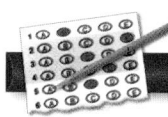

Standardized Test Prep

Multiple Choice

21. A horizontal line passes through $(5, -2)$. Which other point does it also pass through? **B**
  A. $(5, 2)$ **B.** $(-5, -2)$ **C.** $(-5, 2)$ **D.** $(5, 0)$

22. Which of the following equations contains the ordered pairs $(-3, 4)$ and $(1, -4)$? **H**
  F. $x + 2y = 8$ **G.** $2x - y = 4$ **H.** $2x + y = -2$ **I.** $x - 2y = -6$

 Lesson Quiz 6-6

Number of Households in the U.S.

Year	Households (millions)
1975	71.1
1980	80.8
1985	86.8
1990	93.3
1995	99.0

[Source: U.S. Census Bureau, *Current Population Reports.* From *Statistical Abstract of the United States, 2000*]

1. Graph the data in a scatter plot. Draw a trend line.

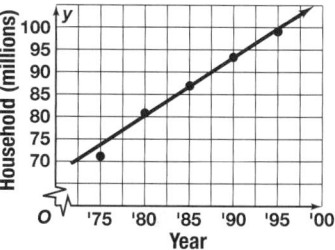

2. Write an equation for the trend line. **y − 86.8 = 1.3(x − 85)**

3. Predict the number of households in the U.S. in 2005. (Use 105 for *x*.) **about 112.8 million households**

4. Use a calculator to find the line of best fit for the data. **y = 1.366x − 29.91**

5. What is the correlation coefficient? **0.9943767027**

Alternative Assessment

Have students search for data that would be suitable for a scatter plot. Each student should graph the data, find a trend line, and then use a graphing calculator to find the line of best fit and the correlation coefficient.

For additional practice with a variety of test item formats:
- Standardized Test Prep, p. 335
- Test-Taking Strategies, p. 330
- Test-Taking Strategies with Transparencies

Alternative Method

Exercise 22 Many times there is more than one way to solve a problem. For Exercise 22, you can substitute both points into each equation or use the two points to find an equation.

✔ **Chapter Checkpoint 2**

To check understanding of Lessons 6-4 to 6-6:

Checkpoint Quiz 2 (p. 324)

📁 **Teaching Resources**
Checkpoint Quiz 2 (also in Prentice Hall Assessment System)

👥 **Reaching All Students**
Reading and Math Literacy 6C

Spanish versions available

---

pages 320–324   Exercises

23. [4] a.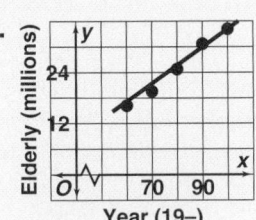
Year (19–)

b–c. Answers may vary. Samples:

b. Let 1960 = 60. Two points on line are (62, 18) and (90, 30). $y = 0.429x - 8.6$

c. $y = 0.429(105) - 8.6$; 36.4 million people

324

Extended Response

Take It to the NET
Online lesson quiz at **www.PHSchool.com**
Web Code: aea-0606

23. The table right shows the number of elderly in the United States from 1960 through 2000.
a. Graph the data and draw a trend line.
b. Write an equation for the trend line you drew.
c. Predict the elderly population in the United States in 2005. Show your work.
  a–c. See margin.

U.S. Elderly Population

Year	Elderly (millions)
1960	16.560
1970	19.980
1980	25.550
1990	31.235
2000	34.709

Source: *Statistical Abstract of the United States.*
Go to **www.PHSchool.com** for a data update.
Web Code: aeg-2041

Mixed Review

Lesson 6-5

24. $y + 3 = 5(x - 2)$
25. $y - 5 = -x$
26. $y - 4 = -\frac{2}{3}(x + 1)$

Write the equation for the line that is parallel to the given line and that passes through the given point. **24–26. See left**

24. $y = 5x + 1; (2, -3)$ **25.** $y = -x - 9; (0, 5)$ **26.** $2x + 3y = 9; (-1, 4)$

27. $y = -\frac{1}{2}x; (3, -4)$ **28.** $y = -2x + 3 (-2, -1)$ **29.** $y = \frac{2}{3}x + 7; (-1, 2)$
  $y + 4 = -\frac{1}{2}(x - 3)$ $y + 1 = -2(x + 2)$ $y - 2 = \frac{2}{3}(x + 1)$

Lesson 3-4

Solve each inequality. **30–32. See left**

30. $x > 1\frac{3}{4}$
31. $x < 5$
32. $x > -1$

30. $1 + 5x + 1 > x + 9$ **31.** $7x + 3 < 2x + 28$ **32.** $4x + 4 > 2 + 2x$

33. $4x + 3 \le 2x - 7$ **34.** $-x + 5 < 3x - 1$ **35.** $2x > 7x - 3 - 4x$
  $x \le -5$ $x > \frac{3}{2}$ $x < 3$

✔ Checkpoint Quiz 2

Lessons 6-4 through 6-6

1–3. See left.

 Instant self-check quiz online and on CD-ROM

Write an equation for the line through the given point with the given slope.

1. $(3, 4); m = -\frac{1}{4}$ **2.** $(0, -3); m = 18$ **3.** $(-7, -5); m = 0$

4. Write an equation for the line through the points $(2, -6)$ and $(-1, -4)$.
  $y + 6 = -\frac{2}{3}(x - 2)$

Write an equation of the line that is parallel to the given line and that passes through the given point.

5. $x + y = 3; (5, 4)$ $y - 4 = -(x - 5)$ **6.** $3x + 2y = 1; (-2, 6)$
  $y - 6 = -\frac{3}{2}(x + 2)$

Write an equation of a line that is perpendicular to the given line and that passes through the given point.

7. $y = -4x + 2; (0, 2)$ $y - 2 = \frac{1}{4}x$ **8.** $y = \frac{2}{3}x + 6; (-6, 2)$
  $y - 2 = -\frac{3}{2}(x + 6)$

1. $y - 4 = -\frac{1}{4}(x - 3)$
2. $y + 3 = 18x$
3. $y = -5$

9. Find the equation for a trend line for the data at the right.
  Answers may vary. Sample: $y = 5.33x + 1.34$

x	1	2	3	4	5	6	7
y	7	12	19	20	28	33	40

10. $y = -6.07x + 62.71$

 10. Graphing Calculator Use a graphing calculator to find the equation for the line of best fit for the data at the right.
See left.

x	1	2	3	4	5	6	7
y	54	52	45	40	33	27	18

324   Chapter 6   Linear Equations and Their Graphs

[3] appropriate methods but one computational error
[2] incorrect points used correctly OR points used incorrectly;

function written appropriately, given previous results.
[1] correct function, without work shown

Graphing Absolute Value Equations

Lesson Preview

What You'll Learn

OBJECTIVE 1
To translate the graph of an absolute value equation

. . . And Why

To graph an absolute value equation quickly, as in Examples 2 and 4

 Check Skills You'll Need   (For help, go to Lesson 1-5 and 5-3.)

Simplify each expression.

1. $|2 - 7|$ **5**   **2.** $|7 - 12|$ **5**   **3.** $|38 - 56|$ **18**   **4.** $|-24 + 12|$ **12**

Model each rule using a table of values. **5–7. See back of book.**

5. $y = 6 - x$ **6.** $y = |x| + 1$ **7.** $y = |x + 1|$

New Vocabulary • absolute value equation • translation

Lesson Preview

 Check Skills You'll Need

Subtracting real Numbers
Lesson 1-5: Example 4
Exercises 21–28
Extra Practice, p. 702

Function Rules, Tables, and Graphs
Lesson 5-3: Example 3
Exercises 15, 16, 19, 23, 26, 27
Extra Practice, p. 706

Lesson Resources

 Teaching Resources
Practice, Reteaching, Enrichment

Reaching All Students
Practice Workbook 6-7
Spanish Practice Workbook 6-7
Basic Algebra Planning Guide 6-7

 Presentation Assistant Plus!
Transparencies
• Check Skills You'll Need 6-7
• Additional Examples 6-7
• Student Edition Answers 6-7
• Lesson Quiz 6-7
PH Presentation Pro CD 6-7

ASSESSMENT SYSTEM

Computer Test Generator CD

Technology
Resource Pro® CD-ROM
Computer Test Generator CD
Prentice Hall Presentation Pro CD

 www.PHSchool.com
Student Site
• Teacher Web Code: aek-5500
• Self-grading Lesson Quiz
Teacher Center
• Lesson Planner
• Resources

 Plus

OBJECTIVE

1 **Translating Graphs of Absolute Value Equations**

 Interactive lesson includes instant self-check, tutorials, and activities.

? Need Help?

The absolute value of a number is its distance from 0 on a number line.

A V-shaped graph that points upward or downward is the graph of an **absolute value equation.** In Lesson 5-3, you graphed absolute value equations by making tables of values.

In this lesson you will graph by translating the graph of $y = |x|$. A **translation** is a shift of a graph horizontally, vertically, or both. The result is a graph of the same shape and size, but in a different position.

1 EXAMPLE **Vertical Translations**

Below are the graphs of $y = |x|$ and $y = |x| + 2$. Describe how the graphs are the same and how they are different.

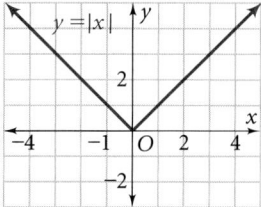   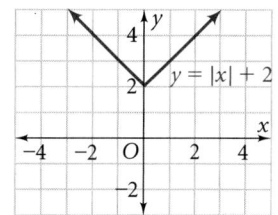

The graphs are the same shape. The y-intercept of the first graph is 0. The y-intercept of the second graph is 2.

✓ Check Understanding **1** Describe how each graph below is like $y = |x|$ and how it is different. **See left.**

1a. Answers may vary. Sample: same shape, different y-intercepts 0 and 3

b. Answers may vary. Sample: same shape, different y-intercepts 0 and −3

a. 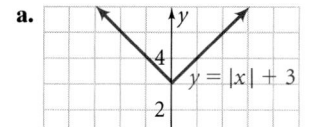   **b.**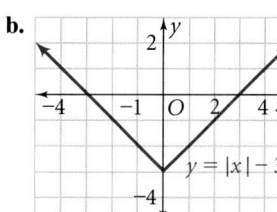

✓ Ongoing Assessment and Intervention

Before the Lesson
Diagnose prerequisite skills using:
• Check Skills You'll Need

During the Lesson
Monitor progress using:
• Check Understanding
• Additional Examples
• Standardized Test Prep

After the Lesson
Assess knowledge using:
• Lesson Quiz
• Computer Test Generator CD

Math Background

Absolute value is the distance from zero, without regard to direction. The distance between any two numbers, *a* and *b*, on a number line is $|a - b|$ which is equal to $|b - a|$.

OBJECTIVE

1 **Teaching Notes**

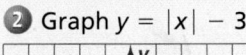

1 **EXAMPLE** **Auditory Learners**

Tell students that a trans*l*ation of a graph is a *sl*iding of the graph.

Additional Examples

1 Describe how the graphs of $y = |x|$ and $y = |x| + 1$ are the same and how they are different. Both graphs are v-shaped. The *y*-intercept of the first graph is 0. The *y*-intercept of the second graph is 1.

2 Graph $y = |x| - 3$.

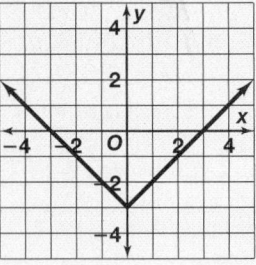

3 Write an equation for each translation of $y = |x|$.
a. 9 units down $y = |x| - 9$
b. 13 units up $y = |x| + 13$

4 Graph each equation by translating $y = |x|$. **See back of book.**
a. $y = |x + 2.5|$
b. $y = |x - 2.5|$

5 Write an equation for each translation of $y = |x|$.
a. 10 units left $y = |x + 10|$
b. 7 units right $y = |x - 7|$

Closure

Ask: *Explain the difference between the graph of $y = |x| + 3$ and the graph of $y = |x + 3|$.* The first graph is $y = |x|$ translated up 3 units. The second graph is $y = |x|$ translated to the left 3 units.

326

The graph of $y = |x| + k$ is a translation of $y = |x|$. Let k be a positive number. Then $y = |x| + k$ translates the graph of $y = |x|$ up k units, while $y = |x| - k$ translates the graph of $y = |x|$ down k units.

2 **EXAMPLE** **Graphing a Vertical Translation**

Graph $y = |x| - 1$.

Start with the graph of $y = |x|$. Translate the graph *down* 1 unit.

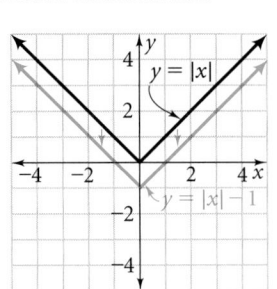

a.

b.

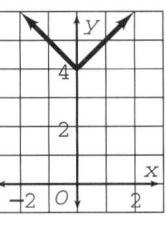

✓ **Check Understanding** **2** Graph each function by translating $y = |x|$.
a. $y = |x| + 4$ **b.** $y = |x| - 5$
a–b. See right above.

You can write an equation to describe a vertical translation.

3 **EXAMPLE** **Writing an Absolute Value Equation**

Write an equation for each translation of $y = |x|$.
a. 8 units down
   The equation is $y = |x| - 8$.
b. 6 units up
   The equation is $y = |x| + 6$.

✓ **Check Understanding** **3** For each translation of $y = |x|$, write an equation.
a. 2 units up $y = |x| + 2$ **b.** 5 units down $y = |x| - 5$

The following tables of values and graphs show what happens when you graph $y = |x - 3|$ and $y = |x + 3|$.

x	$y = |x|$	$y = |x - 3|$
-3	$|-3| = 3$	$|-3 - 3| = 6$
-2	$|-2| = 2$	$|-2 - 3| = 5$
-1	$|-1| = 1$	$|-1 - 3| = 4$
0	$|0| = 0$	$|0 - 3| = 3$
1	$|1| = 1$	$|1 - 3| = 2$
2	$|2| = 2$	$|2 - 3| = 1$
3	$|3| = 3$	$|3 - 3| = 0$

x	$y = |x|$	$y = |x + 3|$
-3	$|-3| = 3$	$|-3 + 3| = 0$
-2	$|-2| = 2$	$|-2 + 3| = 1$
-1	$|-1| = 1$	$|-1 + 3| = 2$
0	$|0| = 0$	$|0 + 3| = 3$
1	$|1| = 1$	$|1 + 3| = 4$
2	$|2| = 2$	$|2 + 3| = 5$
3	$|3| = 3$	$|3 + 3| = 6$

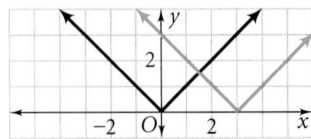

For the graph of $y = |x - 3|$, $y = |x|$ is translated 3 units to the right.

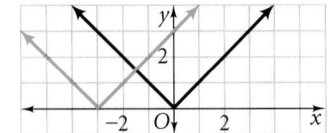

For the graph of $y = |x + 3|$, $y = |x|$ is translated 3 units to the left.

👥 Reaching All Students

Below Level To help students relate the sign of *h* to the direction of a horizontal translation, have them plot specific points for the equations in Example 4.	**Advanced Learners** Challenge students to write an absolute value equation that would translate the graph of $y = |x|$ both vertically and horizontally.	**Auditory Learners** See note on page 326. **Error Prevention** See note on page 327.

Real-World  Connection

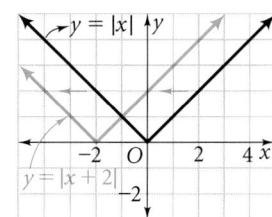

Moving this chess piece is a horizontal and vertical translation.

So for a positive number h, $y = |x + h|$ translates the graph of $y = |x|$ by h units to the left, and $y = |x - h|$ translates the graph of $y = |x|$ by h units to the right.

4 EXAMPLE Graphing a Horizontal Translation

Graph each equation by translating $y = |x|$.

a. $y = |x + 2|$ **b.** $y = |x - 2|$

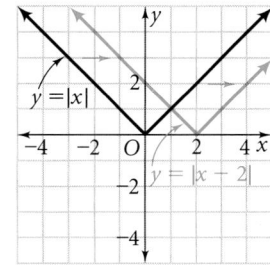

✓ Check Understanding

4 Graph each equation by translating $y = |x|$. **4a–b. See left.**

a. $y = |x - 4|$ **b.** $y = |x + 1|$

4a.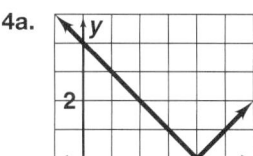

b.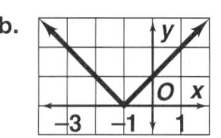

If you know the number of units that a function is to be translated and the direction of the translation, you can write an equation to describe the horizontal translation.

5 EXAMPLE Writing an Absolute Value Equation

Write an equation for each translation.

a. $y = |x|$, 8 units left   **b.** $y = |x|$, 6 units right
   The equation is $y = |x + 8|$.   The equation is $y = |x - 6|$.

✓ Check Understanding

5 Write an equation for each translation of $y = |x|$.

a. 5 units right $y = |x - 5|$ **b.** 7 units left $y = |x + 7|$

EXERCISES

For more practice, see *Extra Practice*.

Practice and Problem Solving

A Practice by Example

Example 1
(page 325)

Describe how each graph is like the graph of $y = |x|$ and how it is different.
1–3. See back of book.

1. 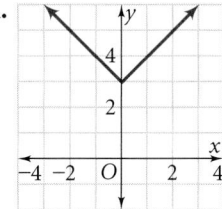   **2.** 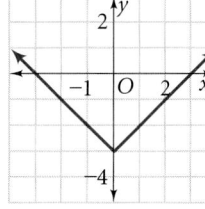   **3.**

Example 2
(page 326)

Graph each function by translating $y = |x|$. 4–9. See margin.

4. $y = |x| + 2$ **5.** $y = |x| - 4$ **6.** $y = |x| + 8$

7. $y = |x| + 1$ **8.** $y = |x| - 6$ **9.** $y = |x| - 2.5$

Lesson 6-7   Graphing Absolute Value Equations   **327**

pages 327–329   **Exercises**

4. 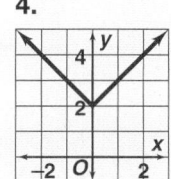   5. 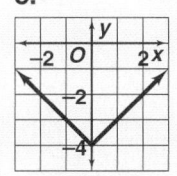   6. 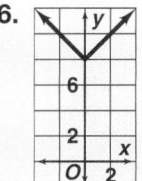   7. 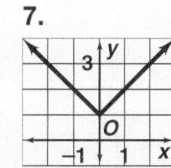   8. 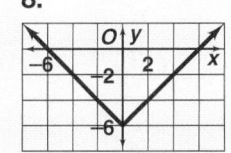   9.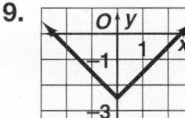

327

3. Practice

Assignment Guide

1 Objective
  Ⓐ Ⓑ Core   1–41
  Ⓒ Extension   42–43

Standardized Test Prep 44–48

Mixed Review 49–53

Error Prevention

Exercises 16–21 Some students may translate the graph the wrong direction. Stress that the formula is $y = |x - h|$ no matter what the sign of h.

Math Tip

Exercises 28–31 Point out to students that the graph of $y = -|x|$ is the reflection of $y = |x|$ over the x-axis.

Enrichment 6-7
Reteaching 6-7
Practice 6-7

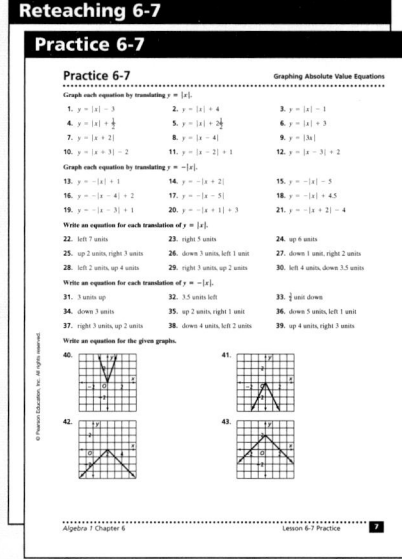

Lesson Quiz 6-7

1. Describe how the graphs of $y = |x|$ and $y = |x| - 9$ are the same and how they are different. **The graphs are the same shape. The y-intercept of the first graph is 0. The y-intercept of the second graph is -9.**

2. Graph $y = |x| - 2$ by translating $y = |x|$.

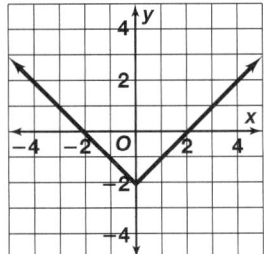

3. Write an equation for the translation of $y = |x|$, 1.5 units down. $y = |x| - 1.5$

4. Graph $y = |x - 5|$.

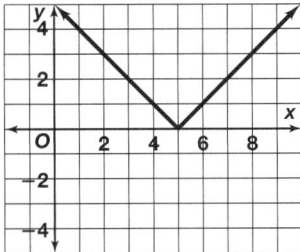

5. Write an equation for the translation of $y = |x|$, 7 units left. $y = |x + 7|$

Alternative Assessment

Group students in pairs. Have each partner graph an absolute value equation translation of $y = |x|$. Partners exchange graphs and write the equation for the graph. Next, each partner writes an absolute value equation translation of $y = |x|$. Partners exchange papers and graph the equation. Have the pairs do both a vertical translation and a horizontal translation.

Example 3
(page 326)

Write an equation for each translation of $y = |x|$.

10. 9 units up $y = |x| + 9$
11. 6 units down $y = |x| - 6$
12. 0.25 units up $y = |x| + 0.25$
13. $\frac{5}{2}$ units up $y = |x| + \frac{5}{2}$
14. 5.90 units up $y = |x| + 5.90$
15. 1 unit down $y = |x| - 1$

Example 4
(page 327)

Graph each function by translating $y = |x|$. 16–21. See margin.

16. $y = |x - 3|$
17. $y = |x + 3|$
18. $y = |x - 1|$
19. $y = |x + 5|$
20. $y = |x - 7|$
21. $y = |x + 2.5|$

Example 5
(page 327)

Write an equation for each translation of $y = |x|$.

22. left 9 units $y = |x + 9|$
23. right 9 units $y = |x - 9|$
24. right $\frac{5}{2}$ units $y = |x - \frac{5}{2}|$
25. left $\frac{3}{2}$ units $y = |x + \frac{3}{2}|$
26. left 0.5 unit $y = |x + 0.5|$
27. right 8.2 units $y = |x - 8.2|$

28–31. See back of book.

B **Apply Your Skills**

Problem Solving Hint

For Exercises 28–31, you can check your work by substituting ordered pairs from the graph into the corresponding equation.

At the right is the graph of $y = -|x|$. Graph each function by translating $y = -|x|$.

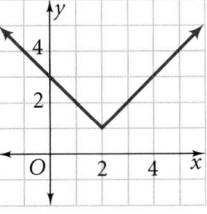

28. $y = -|x| + 3$
29. $y = -|x| - 3$
30. $y = -|x + 3|$
31. $y = -|x - 3|$

Write an equation for each translation of $y = -|x|$.

32. 2 units up $y = -|x| + 2$
33. 2.25 units left $y = -|x + 2.25|$
34. $\frac{3}{2}$ units down $y = -|x| - \frac{3}{2}$
35. 4 units right $y = -|x - 4|$

36. The graph at the right shows a translation of $y = |x|$ where there is both a vertical and a horizontal change. Which equation below is an equation for this graph? **B**
   A. $y = |x + 2| - 1$
   B. $y = |x - 2| + 1$
   C. $y = |x - 2| - 1$
   D. $y = |x + 2| + 1$

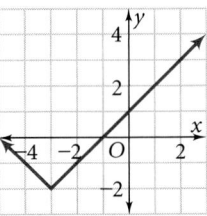

Graph each translation of $y = |x|$. 37–40. See margin.

Sample For $y = |x + 3| - 2$, the 3 indicates the translation of the graph 3 units left. The 2 indicates the translation of the graph 2 units down.

37. $y = |x - 1| + 2$
38. $y = |x + 2| - 1$
39. $y = |x - 3| - 4$
40. $y = |x + 3| + 4$

41. **a.** Graph $y = |x - 2| + 3$. (*Hint:* Read the sample above for Exercises 37–40.) **a–c. See margin.**
   b. The vertex of an absolute value function is the point at which the function changes direction. What is the vertex of $y = |x - 2| + 3$?
   c. What relationship do you see between the vertex and the equation?
   d. **Writing** Explain how you would graph any equation of the form $y = |x - a| + b$. Use (a, b) for the vertex. Graph $y = x$ and $y = -x$ above the vertex.

C **Challenge**

42. **a.** Graph $y = |2x|$ by making a table of values. **a–d. See back of book.**
   b. Translate $y = |2x|$ to graph $y = |2x| + 3$.
   c. Translate $y = |2x|$ to graph $y = |2(x - 1)|$.
   d. Translate $y = |2x|$ to graph $y = |2(x - 1)| + 3$.

pages 327–329
Exercises

16.
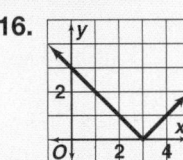

17.
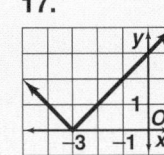

18.
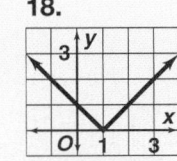

19.
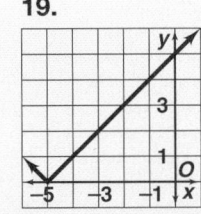

20.
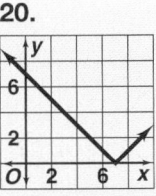

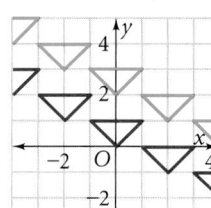

 43. Programming A computer programmer is plotting the triangles at the left. The pattern extends infinitely in both directions. She will use two equations for each triangle: some translation of $y = |x|$ and $y = c$ (c is a constant).
  a. What equations will the programmer use to plot the red triangle with vertices at $(0, 0), (-1, 1)$, and $(1, 1)$? **$y = |x|; y = 1$**
  b. What are the least and greatest values in the domain for the equations the programmer would use to plot the triangle with vertices $(0, 0), (-1, 1)$ and $(1, 1)$? **−1 and 1**
  c. What linear equation can the programmer use to find the lowest vertex on each red triangle? Each blue triangle? **$y = -\frac{1}{2}x$ or $y = -\frac{1}{2}x + 2$**

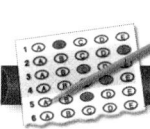

Standardized Test Prep

Multiple Choice

44. Which equation translates $y = |x|$ 8 units to the left? **B**
  A. $y = |x| + 8$ **B.** $y = |x + 8|$ **C.** $y = |x| - 8$ **D.** $y = |x - 8|$

45. What is the lowest point of the graph of $y = |x - 9|$? **H**
  F. $(0, -9)$ **G.** $(-9, 0)$ **H.** $(9, 0)$ **I.** $(0, 9)$

46. What point do the graphs of $y = |x - 3|$ and $y = |x + 5|$ have in common? **A**
  A. $(-1, 4)$ **B.** $(1, 4)$ **C.** $(4, 1)$ **D.** $(4, -1)$

47. The graph of which equation contains the point $(3, 5)$? **G**
  F. $y = |x + 3| + 5$ **G.** $y = |x - 3| + 5$
  H. $y = |x + 3| - 5$ **I.** $y = |x - 3| - 5$

Extended Response

 Take It to the NET
Online lesson quiz at
www.PHSchool.com
········· Web Code: aea-0607

48. a. Graph the equation $y = |x| - 4$ on a coordinate plane.
  b. Graph the equation $y = |x| + 4$ on the same coordinate plane.
  c. Describe the relationship of the ordered pairs in the graphs of $y = |x| - 4$ to the graph of $y = |x| + 4$. **a–c. See back of book.**

Mixed Review

Lesson 6-6 Graphing Calculator **The data below follow a linear pattern. Write an equation for a trend line or use a graphing calculator to find the equation of the line of best fit.**

49. $y = 5000x - 413,000$

50. $y = 4000x - 313,000$

49. 49–50. See left.

Year	Sales
1988	$27,000
1989	$32,000
1990	$37,000
1991	$42,000
1992	$47,000
1993	$52,000
1994	$57,000

50.

Year	Sales
1990	$47,000
1991	$51,000
1992	$55,000
1993	$59,000
1994	$63,000
1995	$67,000
1996	$71,000

Lesson 1-4 **Add the matrices. 51–53. See margin.**

51. $\begin{bmatrix} 5 & 3 \\ 1 & 2 \end{bmatrix} + \begin{bmatrix} 7 & 2 \\ 1 & 4 \end{bmatrix}$ **52.** $\begin{bmatrix} -3 & 2 \\ -7 & 4 \end{bmatrix} + \begin{bmatrix} 7 & -1 \\ 8 & 0 \end{bmatrix}$ **53.** $\begin{bmatrix} -5.6 & 9.8 \\ -4.2 & 3.2 \end{bmatrix} + \begin{bmatrix} 8.1 & 4.2 \\ 2.2 & 7.5 \end{bmatrix}$

Lesson 6-7 Graphing Absolute Value Equations **329**

21.

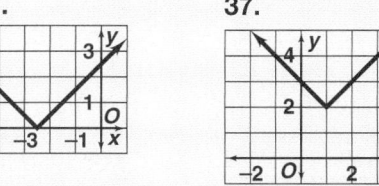

37.

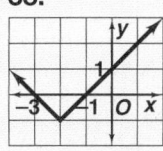

38.

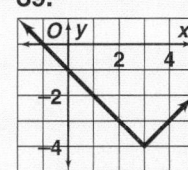

39.

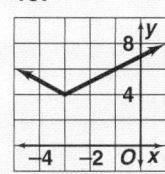

40.

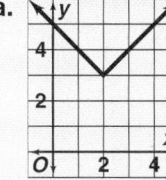

Standardized Test Prep

Resources
For additional practice with a variety of test item formats:
• Standardized Test Prep, p. 335
• Test-Taking Strategies, p. 330
• Test-Taking Strategies with Transparencies

Exercise 46 Since two answer choices contain the x-coordinate 4, substitute 4 into the equations first. This will either find the correct answer, or eliminate two choices at once.

41a.

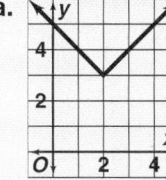

  b. (2, 3)

  c. Answers may vary. Sample: The x-coordinate is the horizontal translation, and the y-coordinate is the vertical translation.

51. $\begin{bmatrix} 12 & 5 \\ 2 & 6 \end{bmatrix}$

52. $\begin{bmatrix} 4 & 1 \\ 1 & 4 \end{bmatrix}$

53. $\begin{bmatrix} 2.5 & 14 \\ -2.0 & 10.7 \end{bmatrix}$

329

Drawing a Diagram

This feature helps students understand the advantages of drawing a diagram to help them solve a problem. A diagram enables students to organize and visualize multiple pieces of information. This also helps determine what information is extraneous and can be ignored. Once students can visualize the problem, a solution strategy will begin to emerge.

Resources

PRENTICE HALL
ASSESSMENT SYSTEM

Test-Taking Strategies with Transparencies
• Transparency 6
• Practice sheet p. 6

Teaching Notes

Remind students to label the parts of the diagram. This will help them use the diagram more effectively.

For some problems, it may help to draw a diagram of the given information if one is not provided.

1 EXAMPLE

The points R, S, and T lie on a line in order such that the length of $\overline{ST}$ is twice the length of $\overline{RS}$. The length of $\overline{RT}$ is 5 cm more than the length of $\overline{ST}$. Find the length of $\overline{RS}$ and $\overline{ST}$.

Draw $\overline{RST}$. Since $\overline{ST}$ is twice as long as $\overline{RS}$, let $RS = x$ and $ST = 2x$. Since the length of $\overline{RT}$ is 5 cm more than the length of $\overline{ST}$, let $RT = 5 + 2x$.

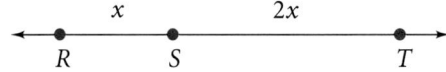

You can see from your diagram that $2x + x = 5 + 2x$. Solve this equation, and you find that $x = 5$. The length of $\overline{RS}$ is 5 cm and the length of $\overline{ST}$ is 10 cm.

2 EXAMPLE

The points $A(−8, 1)$, $B(−2, 7)$ and $C(4, −11)$ form a right triangle. Which two segments form the right angle of the triangle?

Two lines form a right angle if the product of their slopes is $−1$.

When you draw a diagram, you can see that the right angle cannot be at point C. You need to see if the product of the slopes of $\overline{AC}$ and $\overline{AB}$ or of $\overline{BC}$ and $\overline{AB}$ is $−1$. The slope of $\overline{AB}$ is 1, and the slope of $\overline{AC}$ is $−1$. Therefore $\overline{AB}$ and $\overline{AC}$ form the right angle.

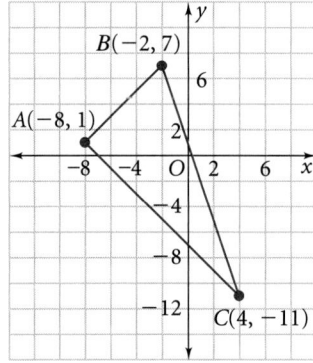

EXERCISES

Draw a diagram to solve each exercise.

1. The points $L(4, 0)$, $M(10, 0)$, and $N(7, 5)$ form $\triangle LMN$. What is the sum of the slopes of the three sides of the triangle?   **0**

2. Three towns A, B, and C lie on a straight road in that order. The distance from B to C is 6 miles more than twice the distance from A to B. The distance from A to C is 2 miles more than four times the distance from A to B. What is the distance from A to B?   **4 mi**

3. $P(1, 3)$ and $R(5, 5)$ are the endpoints of a diagonal of the rectangle $PQRS$. Which sides of the rectangle are parallel to the x-axis? To the y-axis? What is the perimeter of the rectangle?   **12**

Chapter Review

Vocabulary

absolute value equation (p. 325)
correlation coefficient (p. 319)
line of best fit (p. 319)
linear equation (p. 291)
negative reciprocal (p. 312)
parallel lines (p. 311)

perpendicular lines (p. 312)
point-slope form (p. 304)
rate of change (p. 282)
slope (p. 284)
slope-intercept form (p. 292)

standard form of a
   linear equation (p. 298)
translation (p. 325)
x-intercept (p. 298)
y-intercept (p. 291)

Reading Math
Understanding
Vocabulary

Take It to the NET
Online vocabulary quiz
at www.PHSchool.com
Web Code: aej-0651

Choose the vocabulary term that correctly completes the sentence.

1. Two lines are ___?___ if the product of their slopes is −1. **perpendicular lines**

2. Two lines in the same plane that never intersect are ___?___. **parallel lines**

3. A(n) ___?___ shifts a graph horizontally, vertically, or both. **translation**

4. The ratio of the vertical change to the horizontal change is called the ___?___. **slope**

5. The *y*-coordinate of the point at which the graph of a line crosses the vertical axis is called the ___?___. ***y*-intercept**

Skills and Concepts

6-1 Objectives

▼ To find rates of change from tables and graphs (p. 282)

▼ To find slope (p. 284)

Rate of change allows you to look at how two quantities change relative to each other.

$$\text{rate of change} = \frac{\text{change in the dependent variable}}{\text{change in the independent variable}}$$

Slope is the ratio of the vertical change to the horizontal change.

$$\text{slope} = \frac{\text{vertical change}}{\text{horizontal change}} = \frac{\text{rise}}{\text{run}}$$

Find the rate of change for each situation. 6. 8 oz/mo

6. A kitten grows from 5 oz at birth to 3 lb 5 oz at 6 months. (*Hint:* 1 lb = 16 oz)

7. A plant measures 0.5 in. at the end of Week 1 and 14 in. at the end of Week 5.
   3.375 in./wk

8. 5; the speed is 5 mi/h.

9. −1.25; gasoline decreases 1.25 gal for each hour of driving time.

10. 150; the height is at a constant level of 150 ft.

Find each rate of change. Explain what *rate of change* means in each situation.
8–10. See left.

8.
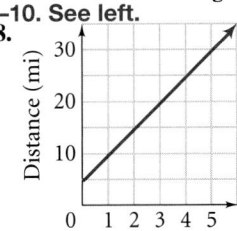

9.
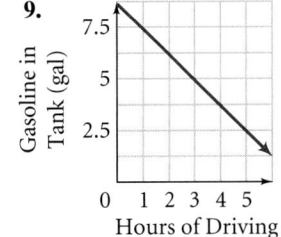

10.
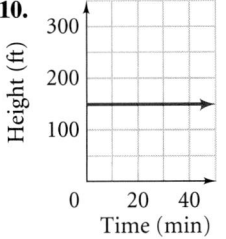

Find the slope of the line that passes through each pair of points.

11. (3, −2) and (−5, −4) $\frac{1}{4}$
12. (4.5, −1) and (4.5, 2.6)
   undefined
13. (2, 5) and (−5, −2) **1**

Resources

Student Edition
Extra Practice, Ch. 6, p. 707
English/Spanish Glossary, p. 757
Properties and Formulas, p. 752
Table of Symbols, p. 749

Reaching All Students
Reading and Math Literacy 6D
Spanish Reading and Math
   Literacy 6D

PRENTICE HALL ASSESSMENT SYSTEM

Standardized Test Prep
• Ch. 6 practice in standardized test formats

www.PHSchool.com
Student Site
• Updated Data
• Self-grading Vocabulary Test
Teacher Center
• Resources

Plus **iTEXT**

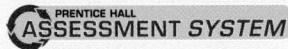

14. $y = -3$

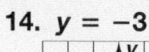

15. $y = -7x + \frac{1}{2}$

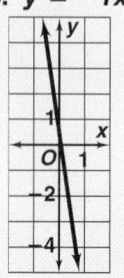

16. $y = \frac{2}{5}x$

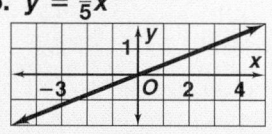

22. $y + 2 = 2(x - 1)$

23. $y + 2 = \frac{3}{4}(x - 1)$

24. $y + 2 = -3(x - 1)$

25. $y + 2 = 0$

26. $y - 3 = \frac{1}{3}(x - 4)$ or
$y - 1 = \frac{1}{3}(x + 2)$

27. $y + 4 = -\frac{6}{5}(x - 5)$ or
$y - 2 = -\frac{6}{5}x$

28. $y = \frac{1}{2}(x + 1)$ or
$y + 1 = \frac{1}{2}(x + 3)$

29b.

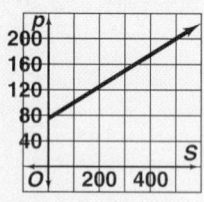

d. 75; weekly salary when no sales are made

6-2, 6-3, and 6-4 Objectives

▼ To write linear equations in slope-intercept form (p. 291)

▼ To graph linear equations (p. 293)

▼ To graph equations using intercepts (p. 298)

▼ To write equations in standard form (p. 300)

▼ To graph and write linear equations using point-slope form (p. 304)

▼ To write a linear equation using data (p. 306)

19. 2; 5

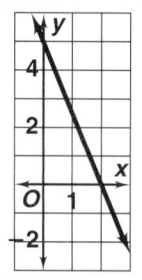

20. 8; −13

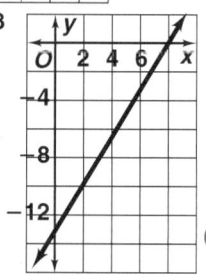

21. $-1; -\frac{1}{3}$

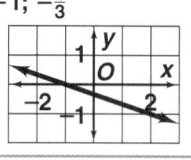

6-5 Objectives

▼ To determine whether lines are parallel (p. 311)

▼ To determine whether lines are perpendicular (p. 312)

The graph of a **linear equation** is a line. The **x-intercept** of a line is the x-coordinate of the point where the line crosses the x-axis, and the **y-intercept** is the y-coordinate of the point where the line crosses the y-axis. Following are three forms of linear equations.

- **slope-intercept form:** $y = mx + b$ where m is the slope and b is the y-intercept
- **standard form:** $Ax + By = C$, where A, B, and C are real numbers, and A and B are not both zero
- **point-slope form:** $y - y_1 = m(x - x_1)$, which passes through the point (x_1, y_1) with slope m

Write an equation of a line with the given slope and y-intercept. Then graph the equation. 14–16. See margin.

14. $m = 0, b = -3$ **15.** $m = -7, b = \frac{1}{2}$ **16.** $m = \frac{2}{5}, b = 0$

Write the slope-intercept form of the equation for each line.

17. 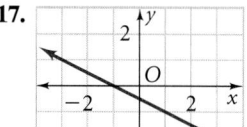 $y = -\frac{1}{2}x - \frac{1}{2}$ **18.** 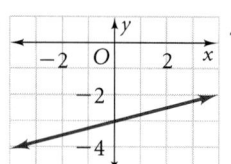 $y = \frac{1}{4}x - 3$

Find the x- and y-intercepts. Then graph each equation. 19–21. See left.

19. $5x + 2y = 10$ **20.** $6.5x - 4y = 52$ **21.** $x + 3y = -1$

Use point-slope form to write an equation of a line that passes through the point $(1, -2)$ with slope m. 22–25. See margin.

22. $m = 2$ **23.** $m = \frac{3}{4}$ **24.** $m = -3$ **25.** $m = 0$

Use the point-slope form to write an equation of a line through the given points. 26–28. See margin.

26. $(4, 3), (-2, 1)$ **27.** $(5, -4), (0, 2)$ **28.** $(-1, 0), (-3, -1)$

29. Earnings A job at a retail store pays \$75 each week plus 25% commission on total weekly sales. **a.** $p = 0.25s + 75$ **b. See margin.**
  a. Write an equation for the total weekly pay p for total weekly sales s.
  b. Use p as the vertical axis and s as the horizontal axis. Graph your equation.
  c. What is the total weekly pay if total weekly sales are \$800? **\$275**
  d. What is the p intercept? What does it mean in this situation? **See margin.**

Parallel lines are lines in the same plane that never intersect. Nonvertical lines are parallel if they have the same slope. Two lines are **perpendicular lines** if they intersect to form right angles. For perpendicular lines that are not horizontal and vertical, the product of their slopes is -1.

Write an equation for each of the following conditions.

30. parallel to $y = 5x - 2$, through $(2, -1)$ $y + 1 = 5(x - 2)$ or $y = 5x - 11$

31. perpendicular to $y = -3x + 7$, through $(3, 5)$ $y - 5 = \frac{1}{3}(x - 3)$ or $y = \frac{1}{3}x + 4$

32. parallel to $y = 9x$, through $(0, -5)$ $\quad y + 5 = 9x$ or $y = 9x - 5$

33. perpendicular to $y = 8x - 1$, through $(4, 10)$
$$y - 10 = -\tfrac{1}{8}(x - 4) \text{ or } y = -\tfrac{1}{8}x + 10\tfrac{1}{2}$$

6-6 Objectives

▼ To write an equation for a trend line and use it to make predictions (p. 318)

▼ To write the equation for a line of best fit and use it to make predictions (p. 319)

34a. Answers may vary.
   Sample:
   $y = 1.28x - 60.2$

b. For sample in (a):
   80.6 lb/person

You can find an equation to model the relationship between two sets of data in a scatter plot by sketching a trend line and using two points on the line to write an equation.

The **line of best fit** of a scatter plot is the most accurate trend line for the data. You can find the equation of a line of best fit using a graphing calculator. The **correlation coefficient** tells how well the equation of the line of best fit models the data.

34. Graphing Calculator The table shows the average consumption of poultry in the United States in pounds per person from 1970 to 2000.
   a. Find the equation of a trend line or use a graphing calculator to find the equation of the line of best fit. **a–b. See left.**
   b. Use your equation to **predict** how much poultry the average person will eat in 2010.

Years	Pounds
1970	33.8
1975	32.9
1980	40.8
1985	45.5
1990	56.3
1995	62.9
2000	68.4

Source: U.S. Department of Agriculture. Go to **www.PHSchool.com** for a data update.
Web Code: aeg-2041

6-7 Objective

▼ To translate the graph of an absolute value equation (p. 325)

The graph of an **absolute value equation** is a V-shaped graph that points upward or downward.

A **translation** shifts a graph either vertically, horizontally, or both. It results in a graph of the same shape and size in a different position.

Graph each equation by translating $y = |x|$. 35–36. See left.

35. $y = |x - 2|$

36. $y = |x| - 3$

Match each equation with one of the graphs below.

37. $y = |x| + 2$ **B**   **38.** $y = |x + 2|$ **D**   **39.** $y = -|x + 2|$ **C**   **40.** $y = -2|x|$ **A**

35.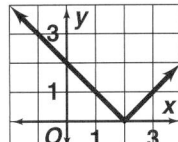

36.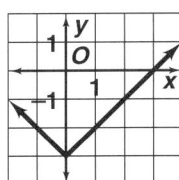

A.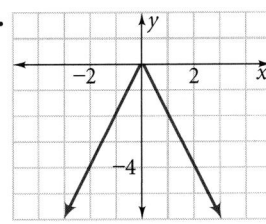

B.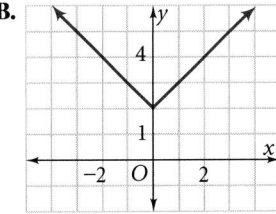

C.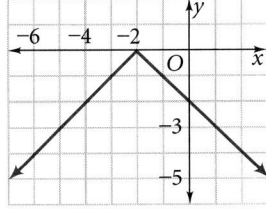

D.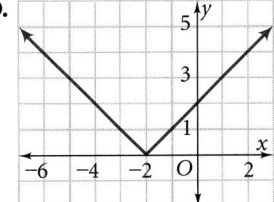

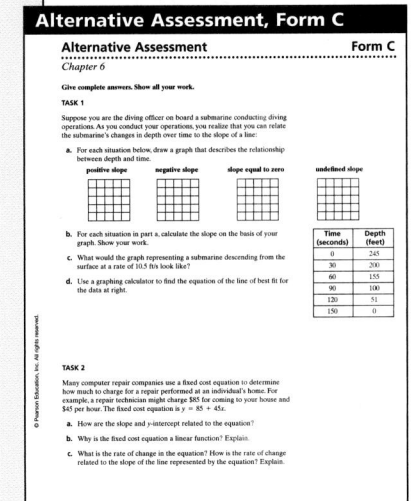

Chapter 6 Chapter Review **333**

Chapter Test

Take It to the NET
Online chapter test at
www.PHSchool.com
Web Code: aea-0625

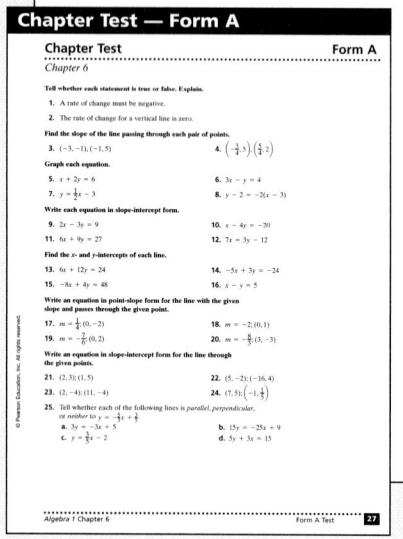
Tell whether each statement is *true* **or** *false*. **Explain.**
1–2. See margin.
1. A rate of change must be positive.

2. The rate of change for a vertical line is 0.

Find the slope of the line that passes through each pair of points.

3. $(4, 3), (3, 8)$ **−5**

4. $(-2, 1), (6, -1)$ **−$\frac{1}{4}$**

Graph each equation. 5–8. See back of book.

5. $x - 4y = 8$

6. $2x + 4y = -4$

7. $y = \frac{1}{3}x + 2$

8. $y - 1 = -3(x - 3)$

Write each equation in slope-intercept form.

9. $-7y = 8x - 3$
$y = -\frac{8}{7}x + \frac{3}{7}$
10. $x - 3y = -18$
$y = \frac{1}{3}x + 6$
11. $5x + 4y = 100$
$y = -\frac{5}{4}x + 25$
12. $9x = 2y + 13$
$y = \frac{9}{2}x - \frac{13}{2}$

Find the *x*- **and** *y*-**intercepts of each line.**

13. $3x + 4y = -24$ **−8; −6**
14. $-6x + 2y = -8$
$\frac{4}{3}; -4$
15. $-5x + 10y = 60$ **−12; 6**
16. $x + y = 1$ **1; 1**

Write an equation in point-slope form for the line with the given slope and through the given point.
17–20. See margin.
17. slope $= \frac{8}{3}, (-2, -7)$
18. slope $= 3, (4, -8)$

19. slope $= \frac{-1}{2}, (0, 3)$
20. slope $= -5, (9, 0)$

Write an equation in point-slope form for the line through the given points. Samples are given.
21–22. See margin.
21. $(4, 9), (-2, -6)$
22. $(-1, 0), (3, 10)$

23. $(5, -8), (-9, -8)$
$y + 8 = 0$
24. $(0, 7), (1, 5)$
$y - 7 = -2x$

25. Which of the following lines is *not* perpendicular to $y = -2.5x + 13$? **D**
A. $y = 0.4x - 7$
B. $-2x + 5y = 8$
C. $y = \frac{2}{5}x + 4$
D. $2y = 5x + 1.5$

Write an equation in slope-intercept form for a line that passes through the given point and is parallel to the given line.

26. $y = 5x; (2, -1)$
$y = 5x - 11$
27. $y = 5; (-3, 6)$
$y = 6$

Write an equation in slope-intercept form for a line that passes through the given point and that is perpendicular to the given line.

28. $y = -2x; (4, 0)$ $y = \frac{1}{2}x - 2$
29. $x = -7; (0, 2)$ $y = 2$

30. Open-Ended Write the equation of a line parallel to $y = 0.5x - 10$. **Answers may vary. Sample:**
$y = 0.5x + 2$
31. You start a pet-washing service. You spend $30 on supplies. You plan to charge $5 to wash each pet.
a. Write an equation to relate your income *y* to the number of pets *x* you wash. $y = 5x - 30$
b. Graph the equation. What are the *x*- and *y*-intercepts? **See back of book.**

Write an equation for each translation of $y = |x|$.

32. 2 units down $y = |x| - 2$
33. right $\frac{3}{4}$ unit
$y = |x - \frac{3}{4}|$

Graph each function by translating $y = |x|$.

34. $y = |x - 4|$
35. $y = |x| + 2$
34–35. See back of book.

Use the data below for Exercises 36 and 37.

Local Governments in the United States (thousands)

Year	Municipalities	School Districts
1967	18.0	21.8
1972	18.5	15.8
1977	18.9	15.2
1982	19.1	14.9
1987	19.2	14.7
1992	19.3	14.4
1997	19.4	13.7

SOURCE: *Statistical Abstract of the United States.*
Go to **www.PHSchool.com** for a data update.
Web Code: aeg-2041

36. a. Graphing Calculator Find an equation of a trend line or the line of best fit for the number of municipalities and the year. **a–b. See back of book.**
b. Predict the number of municipalities in 2010.

37. a. Graphing Calculator Find the equation of a trend line or the line of best fit for the number of school districts and the year. **a–b. See back of book.**
b. Predict the number of school districts in the year 2010.

page 334 Chapter Test

1. False; a rate of change could also be negative or 0.

2. False; a vertical line has an undefined rate of change.

17. $y + 7 = \frac{8}{3}(x + 2)$

18. $y + 8 = 3(x - 4)$

19. $y - 3 = -\frac{1}{2}x$

20. $y = -5(x - 9)$

21. $y - 9 = \frac{5}{2}(x - 4)$

22. $y = \frac{5}{2}(x + 1)$

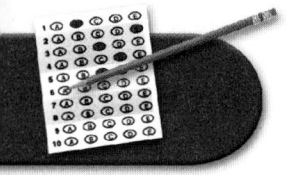

Standardized Test Prep

Standardized Test Prep

Multiple Choice

For Exercises 1–9, choose the correct letter.

1. Suppose you earn $74.25 for working 9 hours. How much will you earn for working 15 hours? **B**
   A. $120   B. $123.75
   C. $124.50   D. $127.25

2. Which is *not* a solution of $5x - 4 < 12$? **I**
   F. -2 G. 0   H. 3   I. 4

3. A line perpendicular to $y = 3x - 2$ passes through the point (0, 6). Which other point lies on the line? **A**
   A. (9, 3)   B. $(-9, 3)$
   C. $(9, -3)$ D. $(-9, -3)$

4. If *a*, *b*, and *c* are three consecutive positive integers, which of the following is true? **G**
   I. $a + c < 2b$ II. $a + b < c$
   III. $a + c > 2b$ IV. $b + c > a$
   F. I only   G. IV only
   H. I and II   I. III and IV

5. A scatter plot shows a positive correlation. Which of the following could be an equation of the line of best fit? **D**
   A. $y = -5x + 1$ B. $2x + 3y = 6$
   C. $x = 16$ D. $y = 2x - 1$

6. Which of the following is the solution of $6(4x - 3) = -54$? **G**
   F. -3 G. -1.5 H. 1.5   I. 3

7. Find $f(-2)$ when $f(x) = -3x + 4$. **D**
   A. -10 B. -2 C. 2   D. 10

8. Mariko runs 800 ft in one minute. What is her approximate speed in miles per hour? (*Hint:* 5280 ft = 1 mi) **H**
   F. 6   G. 8   H. 9   I. 12

9. Which of the following formulas correctly represent(s) the perimeter of the rectangle? **A**
   I. $p = c + c + d + d$
   II. $p = cd$
   III. $p = 2c + 2d$

   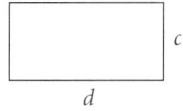
   c
   d

   A. I and III   B. II and III
   C. I only   D. II only

Quantitative Comparison

Compare the boxed quantity in Column A with the boxed quantity in Column B. Choose the best answer.

A. The quantity in Column A is greater.
B. The quantity in Column B is greater.
C. The two quantities are equal.
D. The relationship cannot be determined from the information given.

Column A	Column B
the *y*-intercept of the graph of $6y - 5x = 2$	the *y*-intercept of the graph of $x + 9y = 2$
the slope of the line through (2, −5) and (−3, 1)	the slope of the graph of $15y + 12x = 5$

10. **A**

11. **B**

Gridded Response

Find each answer.

12. A car rental company charges $19.95 per day plus $.15 per mile. Calculate the cost in dollars to travel 250 miles over a 2-day period. **77.40**

13. The ratio of crocus bulbs to tulip bulbs at a nursery is 5 to 2. The nursery has 175 crocus bulbs. How many crocus and tulip bulbs does the nursery have altogether? **245**

14. A train moving at a constant speed travels 260 miles in 5 hours. At this rate, how many miles does the train travel in 9 hours? **468**

Short Response

Show all of your work. 15–17. See back of book.

15. Write an equation in slope-intercept form of the line through (2, −1) and (3, 4).

16. Write an equation in slope-intercept form of the line through (2, −3) that is perpendicular to the line $y = \frac{2}{5}x - \frac{7}{8}$.

17. Solve $-3 \le 2x + 1 < 7$. Graph the solutions.

Resources

Teaching Resources
Cumulative Review
Quarter 2 Test, Forms A & B
Mid-Course Test, Forms A & B

Reaching All Students
Spanish Cumulative Review
Spanish Quarter 2 Test, Forms A & B
Spanish Mid-Course Test, Forms A & B
Basic Algebra Mid-Course Tests

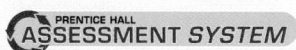
PRENTICE HALL
ASSESSMENT *SYSTEM*

Standardized Test Prep
• Ch. 6 Standardized Test Practice
Assessment Masters
• Cumulative Review
• Quarter 2 Test, Forms A & B
• Mid-Course Test, Forms A & B
Computer Test Generator CD
• Standardized Test Practice

www.PHSchool.com
• Standardized Test Practice
• Resources

Plus **TEXT**

Cumulative Review

Cumulative Review
Chapters 1–6

For Exercises 1–11, choose the correct letter.

1. Which of the following is true?
   A. The graph of $y = x$ is a circle.
   B. The graph of $y = |x - 10|$ is a U-shaped curve that opens down.
   C. The graph of $y = \frac{1}{2}x^2$ is a straight line.
   D. The graph of $y = x + 8$ is a straight line.

2. A mail order company sells boxes of worms for $26.95 per box. A charge of $8.95 is added to orders, regardless of the order size. Which of the following equations models the relationship between the number of boxes ordered and the total cost of the order?
   A. $c = 26.95w; w \ge 1$ B. $c = (26.95 + 8.95)w; w \ge 1$
   C. $8.95c = 26.95w; w \ge 1$ D. $c = 26.95w + 8.95; w \ge 1$

3. Which of the following is the correct simplification of the expression: $n^2 + 15 - 3 + 4 \times 3$?
   A. 63   B. 53   C. 29   D. 21

4. Which is *not* a solution of $3x - 5 < 17$?
   A. −4   B. 5   C. 7   D. 12

5. Which of the following statements is *not* true for the equation $5x + 3y = 12$?
   A. The *y*-intercept is 4.   B. The line has a positive slope.
   C. The *x*-intercept is 2.4.   D. The line contains the point $(2, \frac{2}{3})$.

6. Find the sum. $\begin{bmatrix} 4 & -4 \\ 3 & -1 \end{bmatrix} + \begin{bmatrix} -1 & 1 \\ -5 & 9 \end{bmatrix}$
   A. $\begin{bmatrix} 3 & -3 \\ -2 & 8 \end{bmatrix}$ B. $\begin{bmatrix} 2 & 3 \\ -2 & 8 \end{bmatrix}$ C. $\begin{bmatrix} -2 & 3 \\ 2 & -8 \end{bmatrix}$ D. $\begin{bmatrix} 3 & -3 \\ 2 & 8 \end{bmatrix}$

7. Find $f(-4)$ when $f(x) = -x^2 - 2x$.
   A. 24   B. 8   C. −8   D. −24

8. The Girl Scouts hoped to raise $1000 selling cookies. Instead, they raised $1050. What percent of their goal did they achieve?
   A. 115%   B. 105%   C. 100%   D. 95%

9. Which of the following is the solution of $3(5x - 6) = -63$?
   A. −5   B. 5   C. 3   D. 15

10. Evaluate $\frac{4x + 3y^2}{4x - 3y}$ for $x = 2$ and $y = 3$.
    A. −22   B. −8   C. 7.5   D. $\frac{42}{7}$

Algebra 1 Chapter 6   Cumulative Review   33

Item	1	2	3	4	5	6	7	8	9	10	11	12	13	14	15	16	17
Lesson	4-3	3-4	6-5	3-1	6-6	2-3	5-2	4-1	1-1	6-2	6-1	2-2	4-3	4-1	6-4	6-5	3-5

Mathematically Inclined

In this activity students apply their knowledge of rate of change, slope, graphing, and line of best fit.

Connecting to Prior Knowledge

Ask students to recall ramps they have seen that are used for access to public buildings. Ask them whether a steep ramp or a shallow ramp is easier to climb, whether walking or pushing a wheelchair.

Teaching Notes

Have a volunteer read the introductory paragraph. Explain that scientists have formulated theories to explain how these pyramids were built and then tested their theories. However, there is still much disagreement about exactly how the pyramids were built.

Teaching Tip

Have students work in pairs or in small groups to complete the activity. Have each team read through the activity before beginning to work.

Activity

Materials paper and pencil, yardstick, wooden plank, toy truck with a rubber band attached to the front axle

Teaching Tip

Have a set of books available to prop up one end of the plank. The height of the stack of books will be the distance *x*. The rubber band needs to be light enough to stretch significantly when pulling the truck, but sturdy enough to hold the weight of the truck without breaking. The toy vehicle needs to be heavy enough to cause the rubber band to stretch when pulled.

336

Mathematically Inclined

Measuring Force Although there are more than 80 pyramids in Egypt, the most famous are the three at Giza, near Cairo. Archaeologists think that the ancient Egyptians used ramps, either similar to the one below, or in a spiral around the perimeter of the pyramid, to lift the stone blocks into place. Moving heavy objects up a ramp requires a certain amount of effort, or force. The heavier the object, the more force is required.

Made of mud bricks, the ramp grew in height as layers were added to the pyramid.

Stone blocks were dragged on sleds with wooden rollers underneath.

Solidly Built
The Great Pyramid, around the Pharaoh's Chamber, is almost entirely solid. It contains more than 2,300,000 blocks, or 90 million ft^3 of stone. The same volume of brick and stone would build 40 Empire State Buildings.

Activity

Materials: paper and pencil, yardstick, wooden board at least 30 in. long, toy truck with a rubber band attached to the front axle

a. Raise one end of the plank to a height of 10 in. Hold the rubber band and pull the truck up the ramp. When your hand reaches the top, stop pulling, keeping the rubber band stretched. Hold the truck still while your partner records the height of the ramp (*x*) and the length of the rubber band (*y*).

b. **Data Collection** Raise the end of the ramp in 2-in. increments. Repeat part (a) until you have at least 10 (*x*, *y*) pairs of data. Record your data.

c. Graph your data and draw a line of best fit. Determine the equation of the line.

d. **Writing** The variable *y* represents the force required to move the toy truck. How does the height of the plank affect the force required?

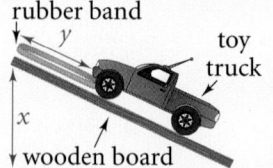
rubber band
y
toy truck
x
wooden board

The Pharaoh's Chamber lies almost in the center of the pyramid.

pages 336–337   Real-World Snapshots

Activity

a–c. Check students' work.

d. The force required to move the truck varies directly with the height of the plank.

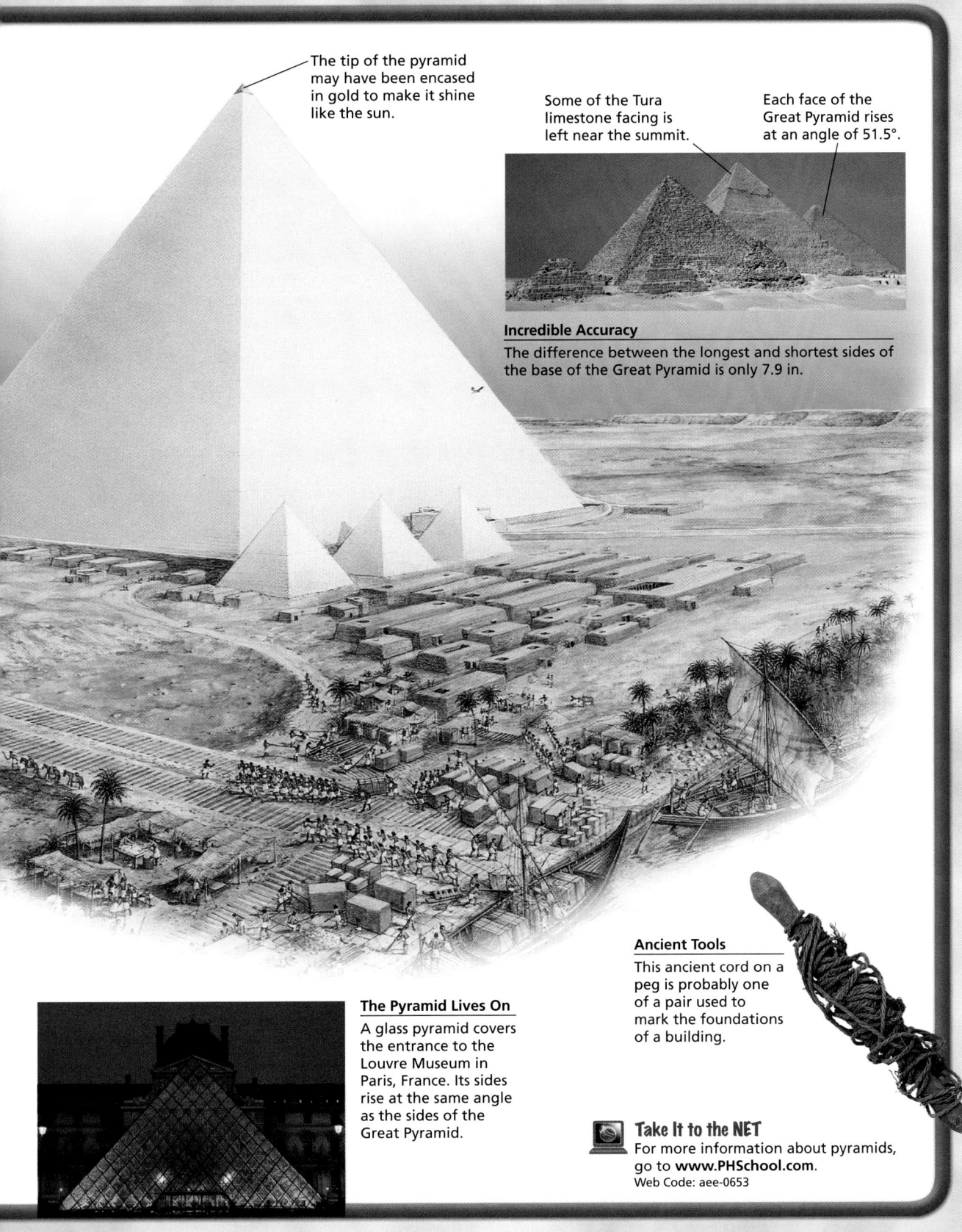

The tip of the pyramid may have been encased in gold to make it shine like the sun.

Some of the Tura limestone facing is left near the summit.

Each face of the Great Pyramid rises at an angle of 51.5°.

Incredible Accuracy

The difference between the longest and shortest sides of the base of the Great Pyramid is only 7.9 in.

The Pyramid Lives On

A glass pyramid covers the entrance to the Louvre Museum in Paris, France. Its sides rise at the same angle as the sides of the Great Pyramid.

Ancient Tools

This ancient cord on a peg is probably one of a pair used to mark the foundations of a building.

Take It to the NET

For more information about pyramids, go to **www.PHSchool.com**.
Web Code: aee-0653

Teaching Tip

Help students organize their data by drawing a table or T-chart on which they can record the ten or more sets of values for *x* and *y*.

English Learners

Make sure that students understand what is meant by the words *spiral* and *increments*. Have students record these terms for future reference.

Scoring Rubric

This scoring rubric applies to both activities. Share this scoring rubric with students before they begin work.

4 Data are accurately recorded; equations and calculations are correct; graphs are accurate and completely labeled. Steps are neat, accurate, and clearly show the mathematics. Written responses are clearly written and answer the question completely and accurately.

3 Equations, calculations, and graphs are mostly correct, with some minor errors. Steps are neat and mostly accurate. Answers are not completely accurate.

2 Equations, calculations, and graphs contain both major and minor errors.

1 Correct answer, but no work is shown.

Chapter at a Glance

North Carolina Objectives

7-1	Solving Systems by Graphing	4.03

**NCTM
2, 8, 10**
▽ Solving Systems by Graphing
▼ Analyzing Special Types of Systems

7-2	Solving Systems Using Substitution	4.03

**NCTM
2, 3, 8, 9, 10**
▽ Using Substitution

7-3	Solving Systems Using Elimination	4.03

**NCTM
1, 2, 8, 9, 10**
▽ Adding or Subtracting to Solve Systems
▼ Multiplying First to Solve Systems

7-4	Application of Linear Systems	4.03

**NCTM
1, 2, 8, 9, 10**
▽ Writing Systems of Linear Equations

7-5	Linear Inequalities	4.01a

**NCTM
1, 2, 6, 9,10**
▽ Graphing Linear Inequalities
▼ Modeling Real-World Situations

7-6	Systems of Linear Inequalities	4.03

**NCTM
1, 2, 6, 8, 9**
▽ Solving Systems of Linear Inequalities by Graphing
▼ Writing and Using Systems of Linear Inequalities

NCTM STANDARDS 2000

1	Number and Operations	6	Problem Solving
2	Algebra	7	Reasoning and Proof
3	Geometry	8	Communication
4	Measurement	9	Connections
5	Data Analysis and Probability	10	Representation

Pacing Options

This chart suggests pacing only for the lessons and their parts. It is provided as a possible guide. It will help you determine how much time you have in your schedule to cover other components, such as the features, Chapter Review, and Chapter Test.

Day	Traditional 45 min.	Two-Year 45 min.	Block 90 min.
1	7-1 ▽ ▼	7-1 ▽	7-1 ▽ ▼ 7-2 ▽
2	7-2 ▽	7-1 ▼	7-3 ▽ ▼
3	7-3 ▽	7-2 ▽	7-4 ▽
4	7-3 ▼	7-2 ▽	7-5 ▽ ▼
5	7-4 ▽	7-3 ▽	7-6 ▽ ▼
6	7-4 ▽	7-3 ▽ ▼	
7	7-5 ▽ ▼	7-3 ▼	
8	7-6 ▽	7-4 ▽	
9	7-6 ▼	7-4 ▽	
10		7-4 ▽	
11		7-4 ▽	
12		7-5 ▽	
13		7-5 ▼	
14		7-6 ▽	
15		7-6 ▽ ▼	
16		7-6 ▼	

NAEP Correlation (National Assessment of Educational Progress 2000 Mathematics Objectives)

7-1	7-2	7-3	7-4	7-5	7-6
A5b, A6a	N4f, A6b	N4f, A5d, A6b	A1f, A5a	A6a	A6a

N = Number Sense, Properties, and Operations; **M** = Measurement; **G** = Geometry and Spatial Sense; **D** = Data Analysis, Statistics, and Probability; **A** = Algebra and Functions

Math Background

Chapter Overview

This chapter examines systems of two linear equations or two linear inequalities. First students graph the two equations on a single coordinate system, then identify the common point, or intersection, to find the solution. When the solution to the system is not apparent graphically, algebraic methods, such as substitution and elimination, enable students to find the coordinates of the point of intersection. Students will learn that some systems may be easily solved by graphing, while other systems may need to be solved algebraically, or with a graphing calculator.

Make sure students understand that real-world situations can be modeled by systems of linear equations or inequalities. Examples include finding the time or location where two travelers will meet, or finding how many products must be sold in order to make a profit.

Solving Systems by Graphing   7-1

A solution of a system is a point that satisfies each equation of the system. For example, suppose one car leaves a rest area and accelerates to a speed of 60 mph. Later, a second car leaves the rest area going in the same direction as the first car, and accelerates to a speed of 70 mph. If you graph the trips of these two cars, the graphs will cross at the point at which the second car reaches the first car. This point is the solution that is common to the equations of both graphs.

Help students realize that systems of equations with no solutions result in false equations such as $7 = -2$, while systems with more than one solution will result in a universally true equation such as $3 + 2 = 5$.

Solving Systems Using
Substitution and Elimination   7-2, 7-3

In theory, any system of linear equations can be solved by graphing and then reading the coordinates of the point of intersection from the graph. However, unless the x- and y-values of the solution are integers, accurately determining the value of the coordinates may be difficult. The TRACE function of a graphing calculator can be used for an approximate solution.

Similarly, any system of linear equations can be solved by substitution, but the calculations may be quite difficult and lengthy when neither equation has a variable with a coefficient of 1 or -1. Dividing an equation by the coefficient of one of the variables (for example, rewriting $7x + 3y = 13$ as $x = -\frac{3}{7}y + \frac{13}{7}$) makes it possible to use substitution, but this is often not a very efficient method of solving the system. It is important for students to choose a method for solving a system of equations that is efficient.

As with the other methods, it is theoretically possible to solve any system of two linear equations by first multiplying to make the

coefficients of one of the variables into additive inverses, then using the elimination method. However, again, the calculations may be too cumbersome to make this the best approach, so remind students to choose an efficient method.

Applications of Linear Systems   7-4

Applications, such as the one in Example 2 in this lesson, that find the break-even point for a business enterprise, given expenses for producing items and the price at which each item is sold, can be very relevant for secondary school students. They can use this kind of application to determine selling prices that will be profitable.

There are some systems that can reasonably be solved by any one of the methods taught. For example, a student who is comfortable with using the graphing calculator may prefer that method. In Exercise 14 ($u = 4v$; $3u - 2v = 7$), one student might decide to use substitution while another might elect to multiply the second equation by –2 and use elimination. To use this latter method, first rewrite the two equations.

$$u - 4v = 0$$
$$3u - 2v = 7$$

Then multiply the second equation by -2 to give

$$u - 4v = 0$$
$$-6u + 4v = -14, \text{ so}$$
$$-5u = -14 \text{ and } u = \frac{14}{5} \text{ and } v = \frac{7}{10}.$$

Linear Inequalities   7-5

A linear inequality is different from a linear equality in two essential ways: first, the solution set is a region rather than a line and, second, when solving an inequality, the multiplication property of equality has no exact parallel. Instead, multiplying both sides of an inequality by a number less than zero reverses the sense of the inequality.

In general, when an inequality is written so that y is isolated on the left, the $<$ sign means that the solution region is below the boundary line and the $>$ sign means that the solution region is above the boundary line. However, it is always a good idea to check by testing one point in the solution set and another that is outside the solution set.

Systems of Linear Inequalities   7-6

When picturing the solution region for a system of linear inequalities, it is a good idea to use different colors to help make clear exactly which points make up the solution set. It is also important to make clear whether or not points on the various boundary lines of the regions are included in the solution set by using either solid or dashed lines. Because it is easy to forget to reverse the inequality sign when multiplying by a negative, it is particularly important to test a few points in the set. It is also possible to graph a set of linear inequalities on the graphing calculator, using the shaded areas to confirm test points.

Ongoing Assessment and Intervention

Tools for Monitoring Student Progress

The Prentice Hall *Algebra 1* program provides you with many options for assessment in the Student Edition, the Teacher's Edition and the teaching resources. From these options you may choose instructional materials and techniques that are appropriate for your students and support your district's curriculum requirements.

Instant Check System™ in Chapter 7

Allows students to check their own learning before, during, and after each lesson.

Diagnosing Readiness before the chapter (p. 338)

Check Skills You'll Need exercises in each lesson (pp. 340, 347, 353, 362, 370, 377)

Check Understanding questions with each Example (pp. 340, 341, 342, 348, 349, 353, 354, 355, 356, 363, 364, 365, 371, 372, 378, 379, 380)

Checkpoint Quiz (pp. 352, 376)

 Test Prep in Chapter 7

Teaches students strategies and gives them practice with all the test item formats they will encounter on state tests and standardized national exams.

Standardized Test Prep exercises in each lesson (pp. 345, 352, 359, 367, 368, 375, 384)

Test-Taking Strategies (p. 386: Finding Multiple Correct Answers)

Standardized Test Prep (p. 391: Reading Comprehension)

Program Assessment

Assess student progress throughout the *Algebra 1* text with blackline masters and CD-ROM.

Assessment Resources

- Checkpoint Quizzes 1 & 2
- Chapter Test, Forms A & B
- Chapter Alternative Assessment

Spanish versions available. Tests for Basic Algebra also available.

Computer Test Generator

- Unlimited questions of varying difficulty for every lesson objective.
- Create your own practice sheets, quizzes, and tests, or use the pre-made Chapter Tests.
- Diagnose readiness with questions on prerequisite skills.
- Prepare students by making tests based on standardized test objectives.
- Access Algebra 1, Geometry, and Algebra 2 content—all on one CD-ROM.

Test Preparation

A three-step approach to preparing students for high stakes, national, and state exams.

❶ Diagnose & Prescribe

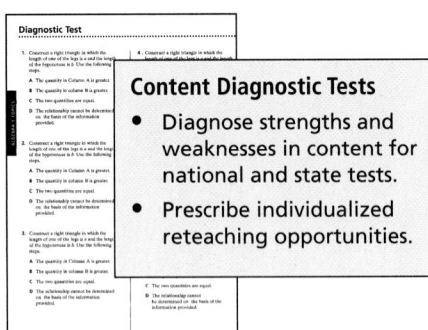

Content Diagnostic Tests
- Diagnose strengths and weaknesses in content for national and state tests.
- Prescribe individualized reteaching opportunities.

❷ Review & Reteach

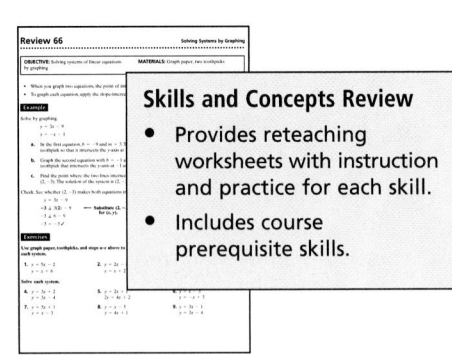

Skills and Concepts Review
- Provides reteaching worksheets with instruction and practice for each skill.
- Includes course prerequisite skills.

❸ Practice & Assess

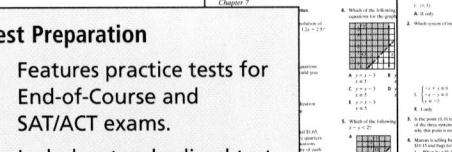

Test Preparation
- Features practice tests for End-of-Course and SAT/ACT exams.
- Includes standardized test practice by chapter for ongoing review.

Teacher's Guide with answers and correlations.

Test-Taking Strategies with Transparencies
- Support the Test-Taking Strategies pages in the Student Edition.
- Provide a teaching transparency and a practice worksheet for each strategy.

All your assessment needs in one place!

Reaching All Students

Support in the Student Text and Additional Resources

The textbook, the iText, and other technology components provide numerous opportunities to reach students of various ability levels and learning styles. Each Teacher's Edition lesson suggests how you can help *all* your students be successful and understand the mathematics in Chapter 7.

Below Level

Student Edition
- Diagnosing Readiness*: p. 338
- Check Skills You'll Need*: pp. 340, 347, 353, 362, 370, 377

Reteaching
Chapter 7 Support File: pp. 10–18

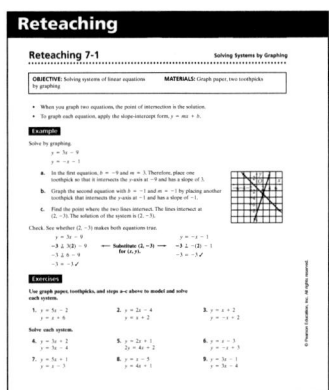

Basic Algebra Planning Guide
Chapter 7 Lesson Plans: pp. 42–47
Chapter 7 Tests: pp. 113–116

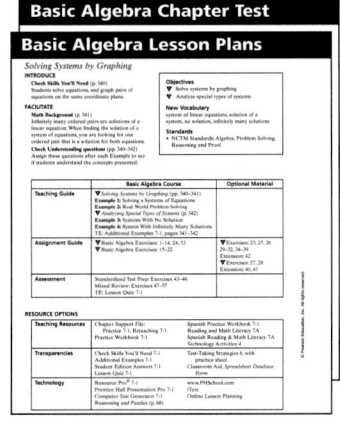

* Can be used with all ability levels to ensure mastery of prerequisite skills.

Advanced Learners

Student Edition
- Challenge exercises: pp. 345, 351, 358, 359, 367, 375, 383

Enrichment
Chapter 7 Support File: pp. 19–27

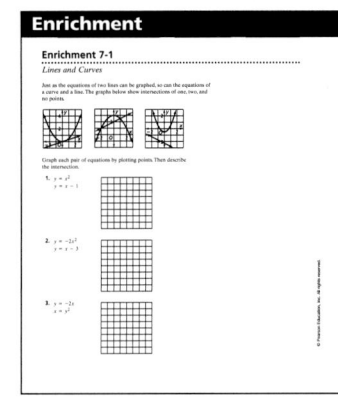

Reading and Math Literacy

Student Edition
- Vocabulary: pp. 339, 387, *plus* in every Lesson Preview
- Reading Math: pp. 342, 347, 359, 363, 366, 369, 387
- Illustrated Glossary: pp. 757–785

Reading and Math Literacy Masters
Chapter 7: pp. 25–28

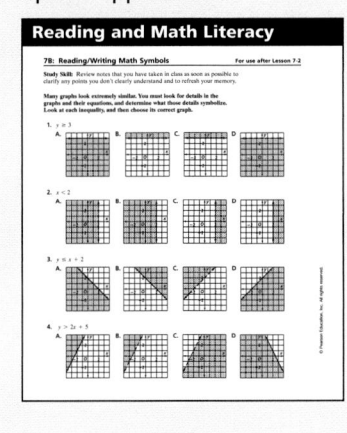

English Learners

Student Edition
- English/Spanish Illustrated Glossary: pp. 757–785

Workbook and Masters
Spanish Practice Workbook: pp. 42–47
Spanish Reading and Math Literacy Masters: pp. 25–28

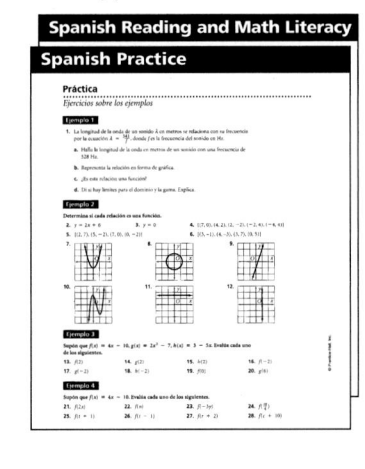

Learning Styles

Student Edition
- Investigation: pp. 346, 347, 370
- Technology: pp. 341, 343, 344, 360, 385
- Writing: pp. 344, 350, 358, 366, 374, 383, 386, 388, 390

Activity Masters
Hands-On Activities: 16, 17
Technology Activities: 4, 21

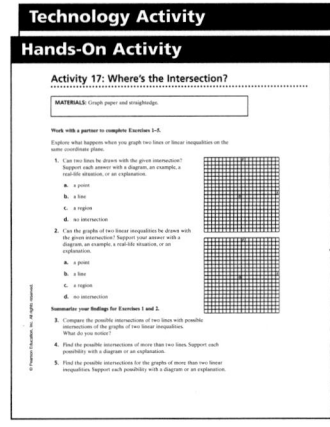

Program Resources

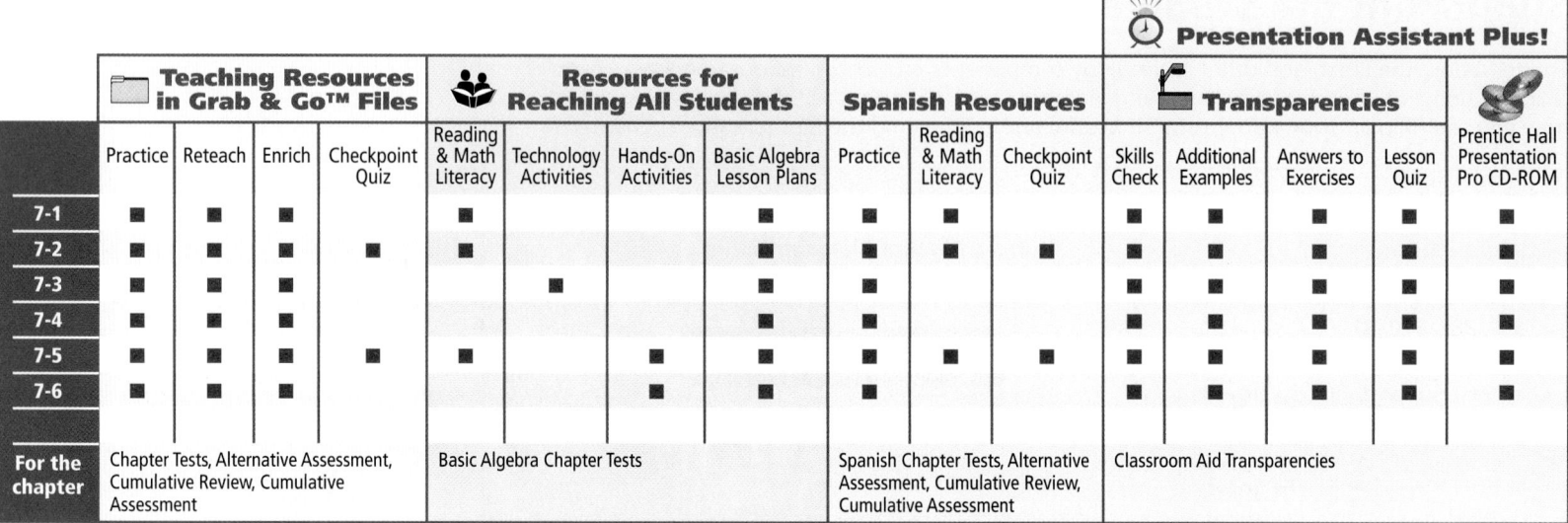

	Practice	Reteach	Enrich	Checkpoint Quiz	Reading & Math Literacy	Technology Activities	Hands-On Activities	Basic Algebra Lesson Plans	Practice	Reading & Math Literacy	Checkpoint Quiz	Skills Check	Additional Examples	Answers to Exercises	Lesson Quiz	Prentice Hall Presentation Pro CD-ROM
	Teaching Resources in Grab & Go™ Files				**Resources for Reaching All Students**				**Spanish Resources**			**Presentation Assistant Plus! Transparencies**				
7-1	■	■	■		■			■	■	■		■	■	■	■	■
7-2	■	■	■	■	■			■	■	■	■	■	■	■	■	■
7-3	■	■	■			■		■	■			■	■	■	■	■
7-4	■	■	■					■	■			■	■	■	■	■
7-5	■	■	■	■	■		■	■	■	■		■	■	■	■	■
7-6	■	■	■				■	■				■	■	■	■	■
For the chapter	Chapter Tests, Alternative Assessment, Cumulative Review, Cumulative Assessment				Basic Algebra Chapter Tests				Spanish Chapter Tests, Alternative Assessment, Cumulative Review, Cumulative Assessment			Classroom Aid Transparencies				

Also available for use with the chapter:

 **PRENTICE HALL ASSESSMENT SYSTEM** *See page 338C.*

- Practice Workbook
- Solution Key

- For teacher support and access to student Web site materials, use Web Code aek-5500.
- For additional online and technology resources, see below.

Technology

 Online and on CD-ROM

Complete Interactive Student Text online and on CD-ROM—with instant feedback assessment, tutorial help, dynamic activities, instructional and real-world videos, audio, and additional practice.

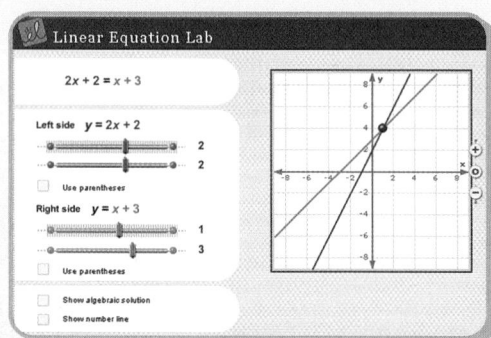

www.PHSchool.com For Students

Use **Web codes** for easy access to online activities, chapter projects, self-grading lesson quizzes and chapter tests, vocabulary quizzes, updated data sources, graphing calculator procedures, and more.

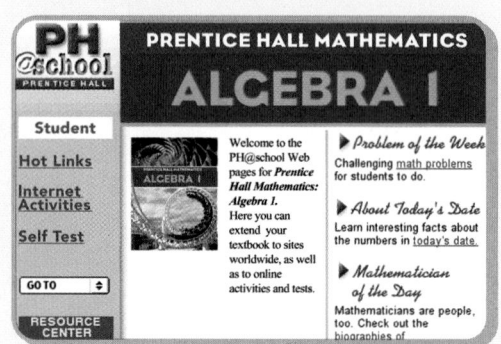

PH SuccessNet For Teachers

Online lesson planning with built-in state correlations, all the teaching resources, complete reference library, your own calendar and Teacher Web page, professional development, and more.

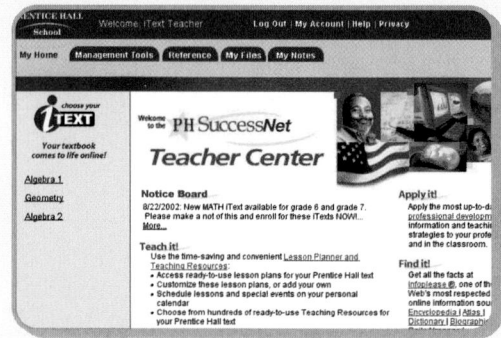

Presentation Assistant Plus!

The Prentice Hall *Presentation Assistant Plus!* provides you with the material you need to teach a lesson from beginning to end. Two easy-to-use formats—Transparencies and CD-ROM—allow you to present a lesson the way you are most comfortable.

Transparencies

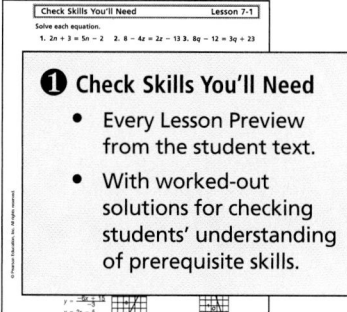

❶ Check Skills You'll Need
- Every Lesson Preview from the student text.
- With worked-out solutions for checking students' understanding of prerequisite skills.

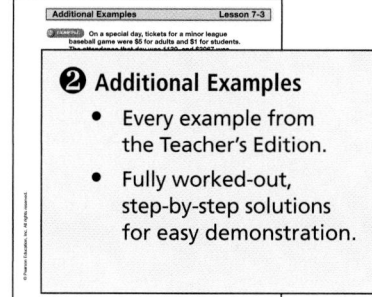

❷ Additional Examples
- Every example from the Teacher's Edition.
- Fully worked-out, step-by-step solutions for easy demonstration.

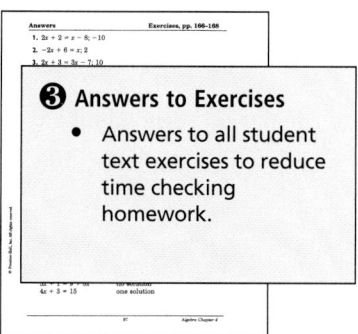

❸ Answers to Exercises
- Answers to all student text exercises to reduce time checking homework.

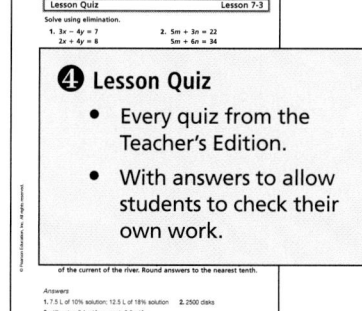

❹ Lesson Quiz
- Every quiz from the Teacher's Edition.
- With answers to allow students to check their own work.

 Throughout the Teacher's Edition, this symbol indicates material that is available on transparency in the Presentation Assistant Plus!

Prentice Hall Presentation Pro CD-ROM

- Includes all Transparencies.
- Conveniently organized by lesson so you can easily ❶ Introduce, ❷ Teach, ❸ Check Homework, and ❹ Assess each lesson.
- Animated examples allow step-by-step instruction at your own pace.
- Easy to edit so you can create custom presentations.

Teaching Chapter 7 Using Presentation Assistant Plus!

	❶ Introduce	❷ Teach	❸ Check Homework	❹ Assess
	Check Skills You'll Need	Additional Examples	Student Edition Answers	Lesson Quiz
7-1	p. 42	pp. 85–87	✔	p. 115
7-2	p. 43	pp. 88–90	✔	p. 115
7-3	p. 44	pp. 91–95	✔	p. 116
7-4	p. 45	pp. 96–98	✔	p. 116
7-5	p. 46	pp. 99–100	✔	p. 117
7-6	p. 47	pp. 101–103	✔	p. 118

 Prentice Hall Presentation Pro

CD-ROM with dynamic PowerPoint® presentations for every lesson. Helps you introduce and develop concepts, check homework, and assess progress. Part of Presentation Assistant Plus! *(See above.)*

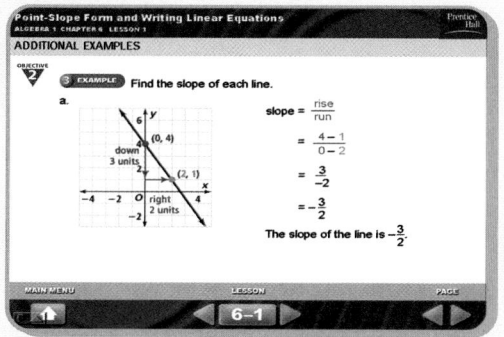

 Computer Test Generator

CD-ROM to create practice sheets and tests for course objectives and standardized tests. Includes Instant Chapter Tests™, online testing, and student reports. Part of the PH Assessment System. *(See page 338C.)*

 **Resource Pro® with Planning Express®**

CD-ROM with a lesson planning tool that allows you to import state and local objectives. Includes electronic versions of all the teaching resources.

Systems of Equations and Inequalities

 Diagnosing Readiness

Students will find answers to these exercises in the back of their textbooks.

For intervention, direct students to:

Solving Equations
Lesson 2-4: Examples 1 and 3
Exercises 3–5 and 32–39
Extra Practice, p. 703

Solving For a Variable
Lesson 2-6: Example 2
Exercises 9–12
Extra Practice, p. 703

Writing Compound Inequalities
Lesson 3-5: Example 1
Exercises 1–3 and 21–23
Extra Practice, p. 704

Writing A Function Rule
Lesson 5-4: Example 2
Exercises 17–18
Extra Practice, p. 706

Graphing Linear Equations
Lesson 6-2: Example 4
Exercises 34–38
Lesson 6-3: Example 2
Exercises 16–18
Lesson 6-4: Example 1
Exercises 1–3
Extra Practice, p. 707

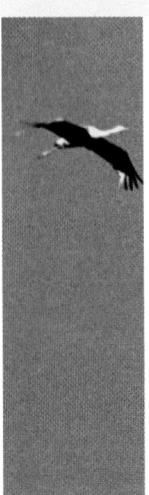

Where You've Been

- In Chapter 2, you solved multi-step equations, employing the Distributive Property and the properties of equality.

- In Chapter 3, you graphed one-variable inequalities and interpreted their solutions.

- In Chapters 5 and 6, you graphed linear equations and used them to model real-world situations.

*i*TEXT Instant self-check online and on CD-ROM

 **Diagnosing Readiness**   (For help, go to the Lesson in green.)

Solving Equations (Lesson 2-4)

Solve each equation. If the equation is an identity, write *identity*. If it has no solution, write *no solution*.

1. $3(2 - 2x) = -6(x - 1)$ **identity**   **2.** $3m + 1 = -m + 5$ **1**   **3.** $4x - 1 = 3(x + 1) + x$ **no solution**
4. $\frac{1}{2}(6x - 4) = 4 + x$ **3**   **5.** $5x = 2 - (x - 7)$ $\frac{3}{2}$ **6.** $x + 5 = x - 5$ **no solution**

Solving for a Variable (Lesson 2-6)

Solve for y in terms of x.

7. $3x - 2y = -2$ $y = \frac{3}{2}x + 1$ **8.** $10 = x + 5y$ $y = -\frac{1}{5}x + 2$ **9.** $2y = -2x - 8$ $y = -x - 4$

Writing Compound Inequalities (Lesson 3-5)

Write an inequality that represents each situation. Graph the solutions. **10–11. See margin.**

10. all real numbers that are between -10 and 3

11. Discounts are given to children under 12 and seniors over 60.

Writing a Function Rule (Lesson 5-4)

12. For every \$35 ticket, the box office charges a fee of \$4.50.
  a. Write a function rule that relates the total cost $C(t)$ to t, the number of tickets. **$C(t) = 39.50t$**
  b. What is the total cost for 3 tickets? **\$118.50**
  c. How many tickets were purchased if the total cost was \$237? **6**

Graphing Linear Equations (Lessons 6-2, 6-3, and 6-4)

Graph each line. **13. See margin. 14–15. See back of book.**

13. $2x + 4y = -8$ **14.** $y = -\frac{2}{3}x + 3$ **15.** $2x = y - 4$

page 338   **Diagnosing Readiness**

10. $-10 < x < 3$;

11. $x < 12$ or $x > 60$

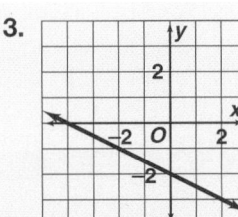

13.

Systems of Equations and Inequalities

Where You're Going

- In this chapter, you will extend your ability to solve equations to include solving a system of two equations with two variables.

- You will learn methods of solving a linear system, including graphing, substitution, and elimination, and how to determine which method is best for a given situation.

 Real-World Connection Applying what you learn about linear systems, you will solve a problem involving ultralight aircraft on page 367.

LESSONS

7-1 Solving Systems by Graphing

7-2 Solving Systems Using Substitution

7-3 Solving Systems Using Elimination

7-4 Applications of Linear Systems

7-5 Linear Inequalities

7-6 Systems of Linear Inequalities

Key Vocabulary

- elimination method (p. 353)
- infinitely many solutions (p. 342)
- linear inequality (p. 371)
- no solution (p. 342)
- solution of a system (p. 340)
- solution of a system of linear inequalities (p. 377)
- solutions of an inequality (p. 371)
- substitution method (p. 347)
- system of linear equations (p. 340)
- system of linear inequalities (p. 377)

Chapter 7 Overview

In this chapter, students find the solution of a system of linear equations by graphing. They learn the three possibilities for the solution of a system of two equations: parallel lines, lines that coincide, and lines that intersect. This leads to algebraic methods for solving a system of equations, and then to solving problems by writing a system of linear equations. Graphing linear equations is compared to graphing linear inequalities and solving systems of linear inequalities by graphing.

📖 **Reading Math**
Reading for Problem Solving, p. 369.

📖 **Vocabulary**
A complete list of terms, plus vocabulary exercises, appears in the Chapter Review, p. 387.

📖 **Illustrated Glossary**
Examples for each vocabulary term, plus definitions in both English and Spanish, appear starting on p. 757.

▦ **Test-Taking Strategies**
Finding Multiple Correct Answers, p. 386.

🌐 **Real-World Connections**
Some of the applications you will find in this chapter are agriculture (7-2), sales (7-3), metallurgy (7-4), and animal habitat (7-6).

💻 **www.PHSchool.com**
Internet support for this chapter includes:
- Self-grading Vocabulary and Chapter 7 Tests
- Chapter Project
- Chapter Planner
- Chapter 7 Resources

Plus

339

Lesson Preview

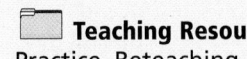
✓ Check Skills You'll Need

Equations with Variables on Both Sides
Lesson 2-4: Example 1
Exercises 1–16
Extra Practice, p. 703

Slope-Intercept Form
Lesson 6-2: Example 4
Exercises 28–39
Extra Practice, p. 707

Lesson Resources

📁 **Teaching Resources**
Practice, Reteaching, Enrichment

👥 **Reaching All Students**
Practice Workbook 7-1
Spanish Practice Workbook 7-1
Reading and Math Literacy 7A
Spanish Reading & Literacy 7A
Technology Activities 4
Basic Algebra Planning Guide 7-1

⏰ **Presentation Assistant Plus!**
Transparencies
• Check Skills You'll Need 7-1
• Additional Examples 7-1
• Student Edition Answers 7-1
• Lesson Quiz 7-1
PH Presentation Pro CD 7-1

PRENTICE HALL **ASSESSMENT SYSTEM**

Computer Test Generator CD

💿 **Technology**
Resource Pro® CD-ROM
Computer Test Generator CD
Prentice Hall Presentation Pro CD

🖥 **www.PHSchool.com**
Student Site
• Teacher Web Code: aek-5500
• Reasoning & Puzzles p. 68
• Self-grading Lesson Quiz
Teacher Center
• Lesson Planner
• Resources

Plus  TEXT

7-1

Solving Systems by Graphing

North Carolina Objectives

4.03 Use systems of linear equations or inequalities in two variables to model and solve problems. Solve using tables, graphs, and algebraic properties; justify results.

Lesson Preview

What You'll Learn

OBJECTIVE 1 To solve systems by graphing

OBJECTIVE 2 To analyze special types of systems

. . . And Why

To use graphs to compare growth of plants, as in Example 2

✓ Check Skills You'll Need

(For help, go to Lessons 2-4 and 6-2.)

Solve each equation.

1. $2n + 3 = 5n - 2$ $1\frac{2}{3}$ **2.** $8 - 4z = 2z - 13$ $3\frac{1}{2}$ **3.** $8q - 12 = 3q + 23$ **7**

Graph each pair of equations on the same coordinate plane. 4–7. See back of book.

4. $y = 3x - 6$
$y = -x + 2$

5. $y = 6x + 1$
$y = 6x - 4$

6. $y = 2x - 5$
$6x - 3y = 15$

7. $y = x + 5$
$y = -3x + 5$

New Vocabulary
• system of linear equations • solution of a system of linear equations • no solution • infinitely many solutions

---

ⓘTEXT **Interactive lesson includes instant self-check, tutorials, and activities.**

OBJECTIVE

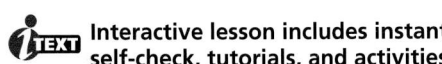
1 **Solving Systems by Graphing**

Two or more linear equations together form a **system of linear equations.** One way to solve a system of linear equations is by graphing each equation. Look for any point common to all the lines. Any ordered pair in a system that makes *all* the equations true is a **solution of the system of linear equations.**

? Need Help?

The slope-intercept form of a linear equation is

$y = mx + b$, where m = slope and b = y-intercept.

1 EXAMPLE **Solving a System of Equations**

Solve by graphing.
$y = 2x - 3$
$y = x - 1$

Graph both equations on the same coordinate plane.

$y = 2x - 3$ **The slope is 2. The y-intercept is −3.**
$y = x - 1$ **The slope is 1. The y-intercept is −1.**

Find the point of intersection.

The lines intersect at $(2, 1)$, so $(2, 1)$ is the solution of the system.

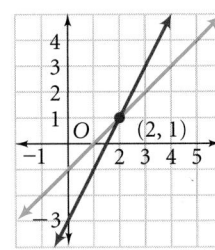
$(2, 1)$

Check See if $(2, 1)$ makes both equations true.

$y = 2x - 3$
$1 \stackrel{?}{=} 2(2) - 3$
$1 \stackrel{?}{=} 4 - 3$
$1 = 1$ ✓

←Substitute (2, 1) for (x, y).→

$y = x - 1$
$1 \stackrel{?}{=} 2 - 1$
$1 = 1$ ✓

✓ Check Understanding ① Solve by graphing. Check your solution. **a–b. See back of book.**

a. $y = x + 5$
$y = -4x$

b. $y = -\frac{1}{2}x + 2$
$y = -3x - 3$

⚡ Ongoing Assessment and Intervention

Before the Lesson
Diagnose prerequisite skills using:
• Check Skills You'll Need

During the Lesson
Monitor progress using:
• Check Understanding
• Additional Examples
• Standardized Test Prep

After the Lesson
Assess knowledge using:
• Lesson Quiz
• Computer Test Generator CD

② EXAMPLE Real-World Problem Solving

Plant Growth Suppose you are testing two fertilizers on bamboo plants A and B, which are growing under identical conditions. Plant A is 6 cm tall and growing at a rate of 4 cm/day. Plant B is 10 cm tall and growing at a rate of 2 cm/day. After how many days will the bamboo plants be the same height? What will their height be?

Define Let d = number of days.
Let $H(d)$ = the height of the plant after d days.

Relate plant height is initial height plus daily growth

Write Plant A: $H(d)$ = 6 + $4d$
Plant B: $H(d)$ = 10 + $2d$

Method 1 Using paper and pencil

$H(d) = 4d + 6$ **The slope is 4. The intercept on the vertical axis is 6.**
$H(d) = 2d + 10$ **The slope is 2. The intercept on the vertical axis is 10.**

Graph the equations.

$H(d) = 4d + 6$
$H(d) = 2d + 10$

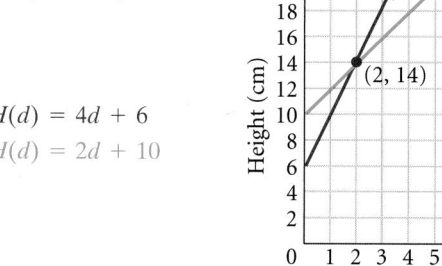

The lines intersect at (2, 14). After 2 days, both plants will be 14 cm tall.

Method 2 Using a graphing calculator

First rewrite the equations using x and y.

$H(d) = 4d + 6 \rightarrow y = 4x + 6$
$H(d) = 2d + 10 \rightarrow y = 2x + 10$

Then graph the equations using a graphing calculator.

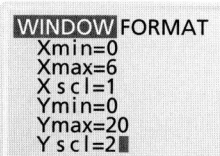
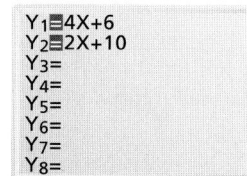
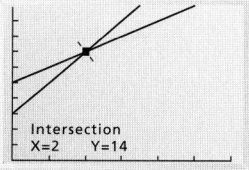

Set an appropriate range.   Then graph the equations.   Use CALC to find the coordinates of the intersection point.

● The lines intersect at (2, 14). After 2 days, both plants will be 14 cm tall.

✓ **Check Understanding** ❷ You are testing two fertilizers on bamboo plants C and D. Plant C is 5 cm tall and growing at a rate of 2 cm/day. Plant D is 11 cm tall and growing at a rate of 1 cm/day. After how many days will the bamboo plants be the same height? What will their heights be? **after 6 days; 17 cm**

Real-World Connection
Under ideal conditions, some bamboo shoots can grow 2 feet per day.

Graphing Calculator Hint
You can also use the **TABLE** feature to find the intersection point. The **ZOOM** and **TRACE** keys will only estimate the point of intersection.

Take It to the NET
Graphing Calculator procedures online at www.PHSchool.com
Web Code: aee-2109

2. Teach

Math Background

Infinitely many ordered pairs of numbers are solutions of a linear equation. When finding the solution of a system of two equations, you are looking for the one ordered pair of numbers that is a solution for both equations.

OBJECTIVE
① Teaching Notes

① EXAMPLE Careers

Economists use systems of linear equations to represent supply and demand. The x-axis represents quantity and the y-axis represents price. As supply rises (a positive slope), demand usually decreases (a negative slope). The point of intersection of the supply and demand graphs is called the *equilibrium point.*

② EXAMPLE Technology Tip

Students may use a calculator to graph the equations. Since the intersection will be in Quadrant I, set the window for each axis to min 0, max 16, scl 2. Grids will make it easier for students to see the point of intersection. Have students press 2nd ZOOM, and then highlight GridOn and press ENTER. Point out to students that **CALC** is the 2nd function of TRACE. To find the intersection point, have students press 2nd **CALC** 5 ENTER ENTER ENTER. The point of intersection is then displayed at the bottom of the screen.

Additional Examples

❶ Solve by graphing. Check your solution. **(2, 5)**
$y = 2x + 1$
$y = 3x - 1$

❷ Suppose you plan to start taking an aerobics class. Nonmembers pay $4 per class while members pay a $10 fee plus an additional $2 per class. After how many classes will the cost be the same? What is that cost?
5 classes; $20

Lesson 7-1 Solving Systems by Graphing **341**

👥 Reaching All Students

Below Level Remind students that a solution to a system of equations is an ordered pair. Ask them if writing the solution to the system in Example 1 as (1, 2) would still be correct.	**Advanced Learners** Have students graph $y = -x$ on the same grid as the other equations in Example 1, and translate $y = -x$ to create a solution to the system of three equations.	**Tactile Learners** See note on page 342. **Error Prevention** See note on page 342.

341

3 EXAMPLE Tactile Learners

Have students make a large coordinate grid on the floor using masking tape. Select two pairs of students. Give each pair a length of string long enough to reach across the room. Have each pair model one of the graphs. Ask the class: *Do you think these two lines will ever intersect?* no *What kinds of lines do not intersect?* parallel lines *Describe the equations of parallel lines.* They have the same slope but different y-intercepts.

4 EXAMPLE Error Prevention

Students may not be able to see that the two equations represent the same line. Have them rewrite $2x + 4y = 8$ in slope-intercept form, and then compare the equations.

Additional Examples

3 Solve by graphing. no solution
$y = 3x + 2$
$y = 3x - 2$

4 Solve by graphing. infinitely many solutions
$3x + 4y = 12$
$y = -\frac{3}{4}x + 3$

Closure

Ask students to write three systems of equations: a system with one solution, a system with no solution, and a system with infinitely many solutions.

page 342   Check Understanding

4. all the ordered pairs (x, y) such that $y = \frac{1}{5}x + 9$

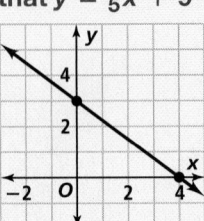

When two lines are parallel, there are no points of intersection. So a system of linear equations has **no solution** when the graphs of the equations are parallel.

3 EXAMPLE Systems With No Solution

Solve by graphing. $y = -2x + 1$
$y = -2x - 1$

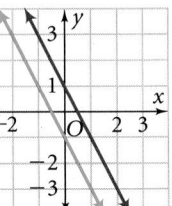

Graph both equations on the same coordinate plane.

$y = -2x + 1$ The slope is −2. The y-intercept is 1.
$y = -2x - 1$ The slope is −2. The y-intercept is −1.

● The lines are parallel. There is no solution.

✓ **Check Understanding** **3** Critical Thinking Without graphing, how can you tell if a system has no solution? Give an example.   If the slopes are the same, but the y-intercepts are different, the system will have no solution.

A system of linear equations has **infinitely many solutions** when the graphs of the equations are the same line. The coordinates of the points on the common line are all solutions of the system.

Reading Math

Infinitely many solutions is another way of saying that there are an infinite number of solutions of a system.

4 EXAMPLE Systems With Infinitely Many Solutions

Solve by graphing. $2x + 4y = 8$
$y = -\frac{1}{2}x + 2$

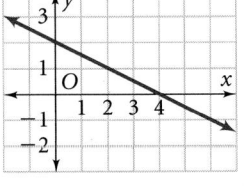

Graph both equations on the same coordinate plane.

$2x + 4y = 8$ The y-intercept is 2. The x-intercept is 4.
$y = -\frac{1}{2}x + 2$ The slope is $-\frac{1}{2}$. The y-intercept is 2.

● The graphs are the same line. The solutions are an infinite number of ordered pairs (x, y) such that $y = -\frac{1}{2}x + 2$.

✓ **Check Understanding** **4** Solve by graphing. $y = \frac{1}{5}x + 9$ See margin.
$5y = x + 45$

🔑 **Key Concepts**

Summary	Numbers of Solutions of Systems of Linear Equations	
different slopes	same slope different y-intercepts	same slope same y-intercept
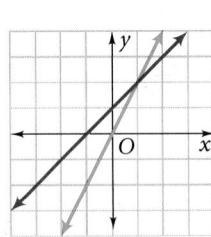	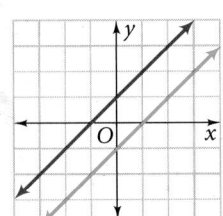	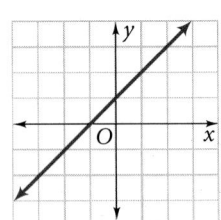
The lines intersect so there is one solution.	The lines are parallel so there are no solutions.	The lines are the same so there are infinitely many solutions.

pages 343–345   Exercises

1. Yes, (−1, 5) makes both equations true.

2. No, (−1, 5) makes only one equation true.

3. Yes, (−1, 5) makes both equations true.

4. Yes, (−1, 5) makes both equations true.

5. (0, 2);
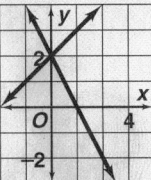

EXERCISES

For more practice, see *Extra Practice*.

Practice and Problem Solving

A Practice by Example

Example 1
(page 340)

Is $(-1, 5)$ a solution of each system? Explain. 1–4. See margin.

1. $x + y = 4$
$x = -1$

2. $y = -x + 4$
$y = -\frac{1}{5}x$

3. $y = 5$
$x = y - 6$

4. $y = 2x + 7$
$y = x + 6$

Solve by graphing. Check your solution. 5–12. See margin.

5. $y = x + 2$
$y = -2x + 2$

6. $y = x$
$y = 5x$

7. $y = 1$
$y = x$

8. $y = x + 4$
$y = 4x + 1$

9. $y = -\frac{1}{3}x + 1$
$y = \frac{1}{3}x - 3$

10. $y = \frac{1}{2}x + 1$
$y = -3x + 8$

11. $3x + 4y = 12$
$2x + 4y = 8$

12. $y = \frac{1}{2}x + 2$
$y = -x + 5$

Example 2
(page 341)

13. Suppose you have $20 in your bank account. You start saving $5 each week. Your friend has $5 in his account and is saving $10 each week. Assume that neither you nor your friend makes any withdrawals.
 a. After how many weeks will you and your friend have the same amount of money in your accounts? **3 weeks**
 b. How much money will each of you have? **$35**

14. Suppose you have $55 in your bank account. You start saving $10 each week. Your friend has $20 in her account and is saving $15 each week. When will you and your friend have the same amount of money in your accounts? **7 weeks**

Examples 3, 4
(page 342)

Graph each system. Tell whether the system has *no solution* or *infinitely many solutions*. 15–18. See margin.

15. $y = -2x + 1$
$y = -2x - 3$

16. $x + 2y = 10$
$2x + 4y = 10$

17. $y = 3x + 4$
$-12x + 4y = 16$

18. $y = 2x + 6$
$4x - 2y = 8$

B Apply Your Skills

19. no solution; same slope, different y-int.

20. inf. many solutions; equivalent equations

21. one solution; different slopes

22. inf. many solutions; equivalent equations

Without graphing, decide whether each system has *one solution*, *no solution*, or *infinitely many solutions*. Explain. 19–22. See left.

19. $y = 2x$
$y = 2x - 5$

20. $x + y = 4$
$2x + 2y = 8$

21. $y = -3x + 1$
$y = 3x + 7$

22. $3x - 5y = 0$
$y = \frac{3}{5}x$

 23. Which graphing calculator screen shows the solution of the system below? **A**
$y = -5x + 4$
$y = \frac{3}{4}x - 3$

A.
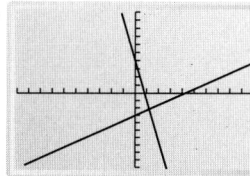

B.
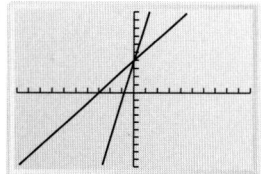

 24. Communications A communications company offers a variety of calling card options. Card A has a 30¢ connection fee and then costs 2¢ per minute. Card B has a 10¢ connection fee and then costs 6¢ per minute. Find the length of the call that would cost the same with both cards. **5 min**

Lesson 7-1 Solving Systems by Graphing **343**

6–12 and 15–18. See back of book for graphs.

6. (0, 0)

7. (1, 1)

8. (1, 5)

9. (6, −1)

10. (2, 2)

11. (4, 0)

12. (2, 3)

15. no solution

16. no solution

17. infinitely many solutions

18. no solution

Assignment Guide

 Objective
 A **B** Core 1–14, 23–26, 29–39
 C Extension 42

 **Objective**
 A **B** Core 15–22, 27, 28
 C Extension 40, 41

Standardized Test Prep 43–46

Mixed Review 47–57

Technology Tip

Exercises 9–12 If students use a graphing calculator, remind them to put parentheses around the fractional slopes.

Exercises 20, 22 Suggest to students that they first write the equations in slope-intercept form.

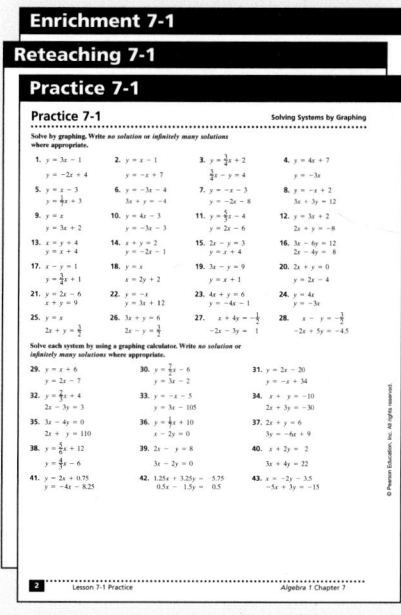

Alternative Assessment

Write *none, infinitely many,* or *one* on individual index cards. Make enough enough cards for each student to receive one card. Give each student a card. On a piece of paper, have each student write a system of equations that has the number of solutions specified on his or her card. Instruct students to exchange papers. Tell students to predict the number of solutions for the system and then find the solution of that system on their own papers. Repeat as often as necessary.

Diversity

Exercise 25 Soccer is an increasingly popular sport in the United States, often due to the arrival of people from other countries where soccer is the primary sport. Ask a student from such a country to share with the class how people view the teams and players.

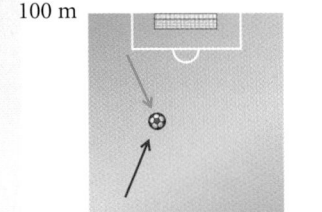

100 m

0 m   73 m

25. **Soccer** Jim and Tony are on opposing teams in a soccer match. They are running after the same ball. Jim's path is the line $y = 3x$. Tony's path is the line $y = -2x + 100$. Solve by graphing to find the coordinates of the ball.
See margin.

Open-Ended Write a system of two linear equations with the given characteristics.
26–28. See margin.

26. One solution; perpendicular lines

27. No solution; one equation is $y = 2x + 5$.

28. Infinitely many solutions; one equation has a *y*-intercept of 3.

Solve by graphing. Check your solution. 29–32. See margin.

29. $y = 4x + 12$
    $y = -2x + 24$

30. $y = 3x - 5$
    $y = 2x + 10$

31. $y = x + 18$
    $y = -\frac{1}{2}x + 36$

32. $y = 4x + 80$
    $y = \frac{1}{2}x + 10$

33. Below is a retelling of one of Aesop's fables. Read it and use the story to answer the questions below.

One day, the tortoise challenged the hare to a race. The hare laughed while bragging about how fast a runner he was. On the day of the race, the hare was so confident that he took a nap during the race. When he awoke, he ran as hard as he could, but he could not beat the slow-but-sure tortoise across the finish line.

a–c. See back of book.

a. The graph at the right shows the race of the tortoise and the hare. Which label should be on each axis?
b. **Writing** Which color indicates the tortoise? Which indicates the hare? Explain your answers.
c. What does the point of intersection mean?

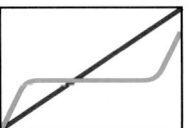

34. $(-12, -16)$

35. $(-2, 10)$

36. $(-30, -2.5)$

37. $(-0.9, 1.6)$

Graphing Calculator Find the solution of each system. If necessary, round answers to the nearest tenth. 34–37. See left.

34. $y = 1.5x + 2$
    $y = 2.5x + 14$

35. $y = -\frac{7}{3}x + \frac{16}{3}$
    $y = \frac{4}{3}x + \frac{38}{3}$

36. $y = 0.2x + 3.5$
    $y = 0.4x + 9.5$

37. $y = 3.2x + 4.5$
    $y = -8.7x - 6.1$

38. Use the spreadsheet to find the solution of the following system. **(2, 3)**

    $y = -4x + 11$
    $y = 3x - 3$

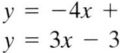

39. **Recording Music** Suppose you and your friends form a band. You want to record a demo. Studio A rents for $100 plus $50/hour. Studio B rents for $50 plus $75/hour.

	A	B	C
1	x	$y = -4x + 11$	$y = 3x - 3$
2	-1	15	-6
3	0	11	-3
4	1	7	0
5	2	3	3
6	3	-1	6

a. Solve the system by graphing. **a–b. See back of book.**
b. Explain what the solution of the system means in terms of renting a studio.

344   Chapter 7   Systems of Equations and Inequalities

pages 343–345   Exercises

25. **(20, 60); see back of book for graph.**

26. **Answers may vary. Sample:** $y = -1; x = 2$

27. **Answers may vary. Sample:** $y = 2x - 1,$ $y = 2x + 5$

28. **Answers may vary. Sample:** $x + y = 3,$ $3x + 3y = 9$

29–32. **See back of book for graphs.**

29. **(2, 20)**

30. **(15, 40)**

31. **(12, 30)**

32. **(−20, 0)**

C Challenge

40. a. Critical Thinking For what values of w and v does the system have exactly one solution? **no values**

$y = -5x + w$
$y = -5x + v$

b. For what values of w and v does the system have no solution? $\mathbf{w \neq v}$

c. For what values of w and v does the system have infinitely many solutions? $\mathbf{w = v}$

41. a. If $g \geq h$, the system at the right has no solution *always, sometimes,* or *never?* **sometimes**

$y = gx + 3$
$y = hx + 7$

b. If $g \leq h$, the system has infinitely many solutions *always, sometimes,* or *never?* **never**

42. The slope of the line joining point P to the origin is $\frac{2}{9}$. The slope of the line joining point P to $(-4, 3)$ is 1. Find the coordinates of point P. **$(-9, -2)$**

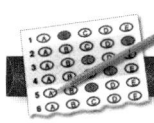

Standardized Test Prep

Multiple Choice

43. Which ordered pair is the solution of the system? **D**
$6x - 6y = 2$
$3x + 9y = -7$
A. $\left(\frac{2}{3}, -\frac{1}{3}\right)$
B. $\left(\frac{1}{3}, \frac{2}{3}\right)$
C. $\left(-\frac{2}{3}, \frac{1}{3}\right)$
D. $\left(-\frac{1}{3}, -\frac{2}{3}\right)$

44. Which value of b will make the graphs of $y = 2x + 3$ and $y = 2.5x + b$ intersect at $(2, 7)$? **F**
F. 2
G. 3
H. 5
I. 7

Short Response

45. The first equation in a system of two equations is $x - 2y = 10$. The graph of the second equation does not intersect the first.
a. Write a possible second equation for the system.
b. Explain your answer to part (a). **a–b. See margin.**

Extended Response

46. The advertisements at the right are for two jobs you are considering.
a. Write a system of equations that relates the amount of sales x to the money y earned in a week at each job.
b. How much would you need to sell in a week at each job to earn the same amount of money at both?
c. After talking with salespeople, you estimate weekly sales of about $600 at either job. At which job would you earn more money? **a–c. See margin.**

> **Sales Position**
> Salesperson Wanted
> Knowledge of Cellular Phones
> On-Site Sales
> $150/week + 20% commission

> **CAREER OPPORTUNITY**
> Sell Stereo Equipment in
> National Electronics Retail Chain!
> $200/week + 10% commission

Take It to the NET
Online lesson quiz at
www.PHSchool.com
Web Code: aea-0701

Mixed Review

Lesson 6-7

Graph each equation and describe its translation from $y = |x|$. **47–49. See margin.**

47. $y = |x| + 2$
48. $y = |x + 3|$
49. $y = |x - 2| + 5$

Lesson 4-4

Find each percent of change. Describe the percent of change as an increase or decrease. **50–53. See margin.**

50. 4 cm to 5 cm
51. 12 in. to 8 in.
52. $20 to $24
53. 10 ft to 25 ft

54. $9 to $6
55. 12 cm to 15 cm
56. 50 m to 55 m
57. $48 to $42

$33\frac{1}{3}$% decrease
25% increase
10% increase
12.5% decrease

45. [2] a. Answers may vary. Sample: $x - 2y = 6$

b. Since the lines do not intersect, the lines are parallel. Parallel lines have the same slope but different intercepts.

[1] incorrect equation OR incorrect explanation

46. [4] a. $y = 150 + 0.20x$
$y = 200 + 0.10x$

b. $500

c. cellular phone sales

Standardized Test Prep

📁 **Resources**

For additional practice with a variety of test item formats:
• Standardized Test Prep, p. 391
• Test-Taking Strategies, p. 386
• Test-Taking Strategies with Transparencies

Exercise 44 Point out that since (2, 7) is the intersection, these coordinates satisfy the equation of each line. Students can substitute 2 for x and 7 for y in the second equation to find b.

46. (cont.)
[3] appropriate methods but one computational error.
[2] incorrect system solved correctly OR correct system solved incorrectly
[1] no work shown

47.
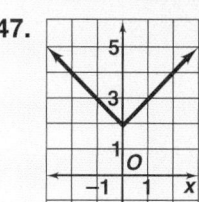
It is translated up 2 units.

48.
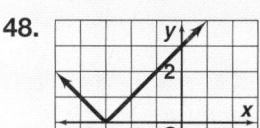
It is translated 3 units left.

49.
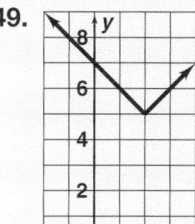
It is translated 5 units up and 2 units right.

50. 25% increase
51. $33\frac{1}{3}$% decrease
52. 20% increase
53. 150% increase

345

Investigation

Solving Systems Using Algebra Tiles

Solving Systems Using Algebra Tiles

Students use algebra tiles to model linear equations. They model the substitution method for solving systems of linear equations.

Resources

Students use algebra tiles to explore solving systems of equations. If algebra tiles are unavailable, students may draw a rectangle with an x on it to represent the variable, an unshaded square to represent $+1$, and a shaded square to represent -1.

Teaching Notes

Tactile Learners

Tactile learners may want to continue to use algebra tiles to solve systems of equations, because they feel more confident of their answers when they physically manipulate the tiles. Make the tiles available regularly, so that students will be free to use them as needed or desired.

Teaching Tip

Some students may find it helpful to have tiles that represent two variables. They could put stickers on the x-tiles to make them y-tiles. Then to model this system: $2x + y = 3$ and $x - y = -6$, they could place the correct tiles for each equation beneath each other and add. The y's will be a zero pair on the left and 3 positives and 3 negatives are zero pairs on the right. This leaves $3x = -3$ and $x = -1$.

You can model and solve some linear systems using algebra tiles.

Solve the following system.
$$2x + y = 5$$
$$y = x - 1$$

Model the value of y, which is $x - 1$.

To model the equation $2x + y = 5$, substitute the value of y, which is $x - 1$.

$$2x + y = 5$$
$$2x + x - 1 = 5$$
$$3x - 1 = 5$$

Using the Addition Property of Equality, add 1 to each side. Simplify the model by removing the zero pair.

$$3x - 1 + 1 = 5 + 1$$
$$3x = 6$$

Divide each side into three identical groups.

$$\frac{3x}{3} = \frac{6}{3}$$

Solve for x.

$$x = 2$$

To find y, substitute the value of x into the equation $y = x - 1$.
$$y = x - 1$$
$$= 2 - 1$$
$$= 1$$

The solution of the system is $(2, 1)$.

EXERCISES

Model and solve each system.

1. $y = x + 1$
   $2x + y = 10$ **(3, 4)**

2. $x + 4y = 1$
   $x = y - 4$ **(−3, 1)**

3. $y = 2x - 1$
   $y = x + 5$ **(6, 11)**

4. $x = 3y + 2$
   $2x = y + 9$ **(5, 1)**

5. $x - 4y = 2$
   $x = y + 1$ $\left(\frac{2}{3}, -\frac{1}{3}\right)$

6. $y = x + 3$
   $y = 2x + 6$ **(−3, 0)**

7. **Open-Ended** Let the equation $y = x + 2$ be part of a system. Write the second equation of the system such that the system could be solved using algebra tiles.
   Answers may vary. Sample: $x + 2y = 7$

7-2 Solving Systems Using Substitution

 North Carolina Objectives

4.03 Use systems of linear equations or inequalities in two variables to model and solve problems. Solve using tables, graphs, and algebraic properties; justify results.

Lesson Preview

What You'll Learn

OBJECTIVE 1 To solve systems using substitution

. . . And Why

To solve problems involving transportation, as in Example 3

✓ Check Skills You'll Need   (For help, go to Lessons 2-4 and 7-1.)

Solve each equation.

1. $m - 6 = 4m + 8$ $-4\frac{2}{3}$ 2. $4n = 9 - 2n$ $1\frac{1}{2}$ 3. $\frac{1}{3}t + 5 = 10$ 15

For each system, is the ordered pair a solution of both equations?

4. $(5, 1)$ $y = -x + 4$
          $y = x - 6$ **no**

5. $(2, 2.4)$ $4x + 5y = 20$
            $2x + 6y = 10$ **no**

New Vocabulary   • substitution method

OBJECTIVE 1 Using Substitution

 Interactive lesson includes instant self-check, tutorials, and activities.

1. Answers may vary. Sample: $(-2.5, 3.5)$

2. $3.5 \neq 3.6$; solutions did not agree.

3. No; it is too difficult to read an exact value when that value is not an integer.

4.
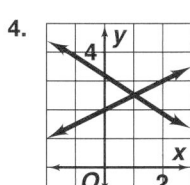

5–6. Answers may vary. Samples are given.

5. 2.5

6. $\frac{5}{6}$ or 1

Investigation: Estimating Solutions

1. Use the graph to estimate the solution of the following system.

   $y = x + 6.1$
   $y = -2x - 1.4$

2. Check your solution in both equations.

3. Can you use the graph to find the exact x-coordinate and y-coordinate of the solution of the system? Explain.

4. Graph the following system.

   $3x + 5y = 15$
   $-x + 2y = 4$

5. Use the graph to find the y-coordinate of the solution.

6. Substitute the y-coordinate into one of the equations to find the x-coordinate of the solution.

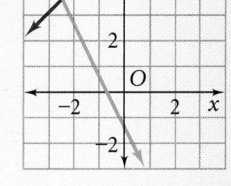

📖 Reading Math

Substitution means one value or expression is used in place of another.

You can solve a system of equations by graphing when the solution contains integers or when you have a graphing calculator. Another method for solving systems of equations is the **substitution method.** By replacing one variable with an equivalent expression containing the other variable, you can create a one-variable equation that you can solve using methods shown in chapter 2.

Lesson 7-2 Solving Systems Using Substitution   **347**

🔲 Ongoing Assessment and Intervention

Before the Lesson
Diagnose prerequisite skills using:
• Check Skills You'll Need

During the Lesson
Monitor progress using:
• Check Understanding
• Additional Examples
• Standardized Test Prep

After the Lesson
Assess knowledge using:
• Lesson Quiz
• Computer Test Generator CD
• Chapter Checkpoint 1 (p. 352)

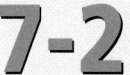 

7-2

North Carolina Objectives 4.03

1. Plan

Lesson Preview

✓ Check Skills You'll Need

Equations with Variables on Both Sides
Lesson 2-4: Example 1
Exercises 1–16
Extra Practice, p. 703

Solving Systems by Graphing
Lesson 7-1: Example 1
Exercises 1–4
Extra Practice, p. 708

Lesson Resources

📁 Teaching Resources
Practice, Reteaching, Enrichment
Checkpoint Quiz 1

👥 Reaching All Students
Practice Workbook 7-2
Spanish Practice Workbook 7-2
Reading and Math Literacy 7B
Spanish Reading & Literacy 7B
Spanish Checkpoint Quiz 1
Basic Algebra Planning Guide 7-2

⏰ Presentation Assistant Plus!
Transparencies
• Check Skills You'll Need 7-2
• Additional Examples 7-2
• Student Edition Answers 7-2
• Lesson Quiz 7-2
PH Presentation Pro CD 7-2

PRENTICE HALL ASSESSMENT SYSTEM

Checkpoint Quiz 1
Computer Test Generator CD

💿 Technology
Resource Pro® CD-ROM
Computer Test Generator CD
Prentice Hall Presentation Pro CD

🌐 www.PHSchool.com
Student Site
• Teacher Web Code: aek-5500
• Reasoning & Puzzles pp. 71, 72
• Self-grading Lesson Quiz
Teacher Center
• Lesson Planner
• Resources

 Plus 🔲TEXT

347

2. Teach

Math Background

Solving systems using substitution begins with the concept of evaluating variable expressions. Here a variable is replaced with its value in terms of the other variable.

OBJECTIVE

Teaching Notes

Investigation (Optional)
Point out that some systems of equations are very difficult to solve without a graphing calculator. This Investigation shows how to solve systems of equations using the substitution method.

 **EXAMPLE** **Error Prevention**

Some students may equate $51b$ with 51 buses. Point out that b represents the number of buses, and 51 represents the number of people each bus can hold.

Additional Examples

1 Solve using substitution.
$y = 2x + 2$
$y = -3x + 4$ **(0.4, 2.8)**

2 Solve using substitution.
$-2x + y = -1$
$4x + 2y = 12$ **(1.75, 2.5)**

3 A youth group with 26 members is going to the beach. There will also be five chaperones that will each drive a van or a car. Each van seats 7 persons, including the driver. Each car seats 5 persons, including the driver. How many vans and cars will be needed?
3 vans and 2 cars

Closure

Ask: *Why it is sometimes easier to solve equations using substitution rather than graphing?*
Sometimes the solution is a very large number or a decimal.

348

---

1 **EXAMPLE** **Using Substitution**

Solve using substitution. $y = -4x + 8$
$\qquad\qquad\qquad\qquad\qquad y = x + 7$

Step 1   Write an equation containing only one variable, and solve it.

$y = -4x + 8$	**Start with one equation.**
$x + 7 = -4x + 8$	**Substitute $x + 7$ for y.**
$5x + 7 = 8$	**Add $4x$ to each side.**
$5x = 1$	**Subtract 7 from each side.**
$x = 0.2$	**Divide each side by 5.**

Step 2   Solve for the other variable in either equation.

$y = 0.2 + 7$	**Substitute 0.2 for x in $y = x + 7$.**
$y = 7.2$	**Simplify.**

Since $x = 0.2$ and $y = 7.2$, the solution is $(0.2, 7.2)$.

Check	$7.2 \stackrel{?}{=} -4(0.2) + 8$	**Since $y = x + 7$ was used in step 2, see if (0.2, 7.2) solves $y = -4x + 8$.**
	$7.2 = 7.2$ ✓	**Simplify.**

✔ **Check Understanding** **1** Solve using substitution. Check your solution. $y = 2x$
$\qquad\qquad\qquad\qquad\qquad\qquad\qquad\qquad\qquad\qquad 7x - y = 15$ **(3, 6)**

To use the substitution method, you must have an equation that has already been solved for one of the variables. Solving for a variable that has a coefficient of 1 or -1 is a good place to start.

2 **EXAMPLE** **Using Substitution and the Distributive Property**

Solve using the substitution method. $3y + 2x = 4$
$\qquad\qquad\qquad\qquad\qquad\qquad\qquad\qquad -6x + y = -7$

Step 1   Solve the second equation for y because it has a coefficient of 1.

$-6x + y = -7$	
$y = 6x - 7$	**Add $6x$ to each side.**

Step 2   Write an equation containing only one variable and solve.

$3y + 2x = 4$	**Start with the other equation.**
$3(6x - 7) + 2x = 4$	**Substitute $6x - 7$ for y. Use parentheses.**
$18x - 21 + 2x = 4$	**Use the Distributive Property.**
$20x = 25$	**Combine like terms and add 21 to each side.**
$x = 1.25$	**Divide each side by 20.**

Step 3   Solve for the other variable in either equation.

$-6(1.25) + y = -7$	**Substitute 1.25 for x in $-6x + y = -7$.**
$-7.5 + y = -7$	**Simplify.**
$y = 0.5$	**Add 7.5 to each side.**

Since $x = 1.25$ and $y = 0.5$, the solution is $(1.25, 0.5)$.

✔ **Check Understanding** **2** Solve using substitution. Check your solution. $6y + 8x = 28$
$\qquad\qquad\qquad\qquad\qquad\qquad\qquad\qquad\qquad\qquad 3 = 2x - y$ **(2.3, 1.6)**

Reaching All Students

Below Level Remind students that they must check that a solution makes all equations in the system true in order for it to be a solution of the entire system.	**Advanced Learners** Part of the graphs of some systems form geometric figures. Have students write a system of three equations whose graph forms a triangle.	**Error Prevention** See note on page 348. **Inclusion** See note on page 350.

You can use substitution to solve systems that model real-world situations.

3 EXAMPLE   Real-World  Problem Solving

Transportation Your school committee is planning an after-school trip by 193 people to a competition at another school. There are eight drivers available and two types of vehicles, school buses and minivans. The school buses seat 51 people each, and the minivans seat 8 people each. How many buses and minivans will be needed?

Let b = number of school buses.
Let m = number of minivans.

drivers $b + m = 8$
people $51b + 8m = 193$

Solve using the substitution method.

Step 1 Write an equation containing only one variable.

$b + m = 8$ **Solve the first equation for m.**

$m = -b + 8$

Step 2 Write and solve an equation containing the variable b.

$51b + 8(-b + 8) = 193$ **Substitute −b + 8 for m in the second equation.**

$51b - 8b + 64 = 193$ **Solve for b.**

$43b + 64 = 193$

$43b = 129$

$b = 3$

Step 3 Solve for m in either equation.

$(3) + m = 8$ **Substitute 3 for b in b + m = 8.**

$m = 5$

Three school buses and five minivans will be needed to transport 193 people.

Check   Is the answer correct? Three buses, each transporting 51 people, carry $3(51)$, or 153, people. Five minivans, each transporting 8 people, carry $5(8)$, or 40, people. The total number of people transported by buses and minivans is $153 + 40$, or 193. The answer is correct.

Real-World  Connection

According to the U.S. Department of Transportation, every year about 440,000 public school buses transport 24 million students to and from school.

✓ **Check Understanding** ③ **Geometry** A rectangle is 4 times longer than it is wide. The perimeter of the rectangle is 30 cm. Find the dimensions of the rectangle. **3 cm by 12 cm**

Assignment Guide

▼ **Objective**
 Ⓐ Ⓑ **Core** 1–40
 Ⓒ **Extension** 41–46

Standardized Test Prep 47–50

Mixed Review 51–59

Exercises 1–4 Suggest to students that they first substitute the coordinate into the equation in each system that is easiest to work with, such as $x = y$ in Exercise 3.

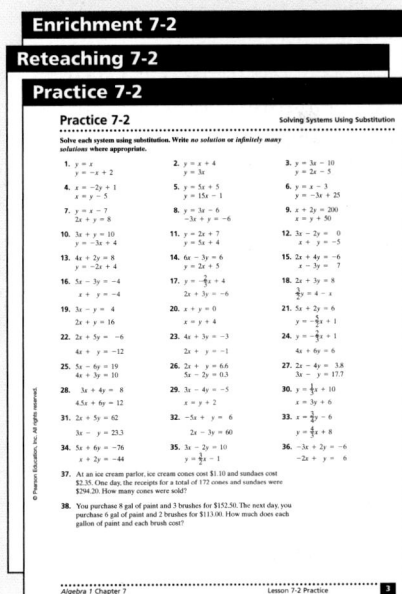

EXERCISES

Practice and Problem Solving

For more practice, see Extra Practice.

Ⓐ **Practice by Example**

Example 1
(page 348)

Mental Math **Match each system with its solution at the right.**

1. $y = x + 1$ **D**
$y = 2x - 1$

2. $y = \frac{1}{2}x + 4$ **C**
$2y + 2x = 2$

A. $(3, 2)$

3. $2y = x + 3$ **B**
$x = y$

4. $x - y = 1$ **A**
$x = \frac{1}{2}y + 2$

B. $(3, 3)$

C. $(-2, 3)$

D. $(2, 3)$

Error Prevention

Exercise 17 Some students may use $p = 34$ for the second equation. Explain to students that the expression for finding perimeter, $2\ell + 2w$, must be used so that the equations have the same variables.

Alternative Method

Exercise 18 Students may want to solve this problem by keeping two running balances like those used in bank account registers. Have them make side-by-side vertical lists to find when the numbers are the same.

Week	$28 + 18.25	$161 − 15
1	46.25	146.00
2	64.50	131.00
	etc.	etc.
	101.00	101.00

Inclusion

Exercise 45 If a student is having difficulty distinguishing the colors of the lines, draw the graph on the board with lines in two different thicknesses.

pages 349–352   Exercises

5–16. Coordinates given in alphabetical order.

5. **(9, 28)**

6. $\left(-\frac{1}{2}, -4\frac{1}{2}\right)$

7. $\left(6\frac{1}{3}, -\frac{1}{3}\right)$

8. $\left(2, 4\frac{1}{2}\right)$

9. **(4, 20)**

10. $\left(\frac{3}{4}, 9\frac{3}{8}\right)$

11. **(2, 0)**

12. $\left(7\frac{7}{17}, 11\frac{8}{17}\right)$

13. **(6, −2)**

14. **(3, −2)**

15. **(8, −7)**

16. **(−3, 9.4)**

31a. **Let n = number of nickels, let d = number of dimes. $n + d = 28$ $0.05n + 0.10d = 2.05$**

b. **Solve the first eq. for either var. Sub. the expression into the second eq. Solve this eq. for the other var., and then sub. its value into the first eq. and solve for the first var.**

Solve each system using substitution. Check your solution. 5–16. See margin.

5. $y = 4x - 8$
   $y = 2x + 10$

6. $C(n) = -3n - 6$
   $C(n) = n - 4$

7. $m = 5p + 8$
   $m = -10p + 3$

8. $y = -4x + 12\frac{1}{2}$
   $y = \frac{1}{4}x + 4$

9. $h = 6g - 4$
   $h = -2g + 28$

10. $a = \frac{2}{5}b - 3$
    $a = 2b - 18$

Example 2 (page 348)

11. $y = x - 2$
    $2x + 2y = 4$

12. $c = 3d - 27$
    $4d + 10c = 120$

13. $3x - 6y = 30$
    $y = -6x + 34$

14. $m = 4n + 11$
    $-6n + 8m = 36$

15. $7x - 8y = 112$
    $y = -2x + 9$

16. $t = 0.2s + 10$
    $4s + 5t = 35$

Example 3 (page 349)

17. **Geometry** The length of a rectangle is 5 cm more than twice the width. The perimeter of the rectangle is 34 cm. Find the dimensions of the rectangle. **4 cm by 13 cm**

18. Suppose you have $28.00 in your bank account and start saving $18.25 every week. Your friend has $161.00 in his account and is withdrawing $15 every week. When will your account balances be the same? **4 wk**

B **Apply Your Skills**

Solve each system by substitution. Check your solution.

19. $a - 1.2b = -3$
    $0.2b + 0.6a = 12$ **(15, 15)**

20. $0.5x + 0.25y = 36$
    $y + 18 = 16x$ **(9, 126)**

21. $y = 0.8x + 7.2$
    $20x + 32y = 48$ **(−4, 4)**

For Exercises 22–24, define variables and write a system of equations for each situation. Solve using substitution.

22. **Renting Videos** Suppose you want to join a video store. Big Video offers a special discount card that costs $9.99 for one year. With the discount card, each video rental costs $2.49. A discount card from Main Street Video costs $20.49 for one year. With the Main Street Video discount card, each video rental costs $1.79. After how many video rentals is the cost the same? **15 video rentals**

23. **Agriculture** A farmer grows only sunflowers and flax on his 240-acre farm. This year he wants to plant 80 more acres of sunflowers than of flax. How many acres of each crop does the farmer need to plant? **80 acres flax, 160 acres sunflowers**

24. **Buying a Car** Suppose you are thinking about buying one of two cars. Car A will cost $17,655. You can expect to pay an average of $1230 per year for fuel, maintenance, and repairs. Car B will cost about $15,900. Fuel, maintenance, and repairs for it will average about $1425 per year. After how many years are the total costs for the cars the same? **9 yr**

Real-World **Connection**

Sunflower seeds are sold as snacks and as bird food, and they are a source of cooking oil.

Estimation Graph each system to estimate the solution. Then use substitution to find the exact solution of the system. **25–30. See back of book.**

25. $y = 2x$
    $y = -6x + 4$

26. $y = \frac{1}{2}x + 4$
    $y = -4x - 5$

27. $x + y = 0$
    $5x + 2y = -3$

28. $y = 2x + 3$
    $y = 0.5x - 2$

29. $y = -x + 4$
    $y = 2x + 6$

30. $y = 0.7x + 3$
    $y = -1.5x - 7$

31. **a.** You have 28 coins that are all nickels and dimes. The value of the coins is $2.05. Define variables and write a system of equations for this situation.
    b. Writing Explain the steps necessary to solve the system in part (a).
    c. Solve the system. **(15, 13)**   **a–b. See margin.**

32. **Answers may vary. Sample:** $y = x$ and $y = -3x + 2; \left(\frac{1}{2}, \frac{1}{2}\right)$

32. **Open-Ended** Write a system of linear equations with exactly one solution. Use substitution to solve your system. **See left.**

33. a. Solve the system below using substitution. **(x, y) such that $y = 0.5x + 4$**

$$y = 0.5x + 4$$
$$-x + 2y = 8$$

b. Solve the system by graphing. **See back of book.**

c. Critical Thinking Make a general statement about the solutions you get when solving by graphing and the results you get when solving by substitution. **See margin.**

34. a. Solve the system below using substitution. **no solution**

$$6x - 2y = 10$$
$$y = 3x + 1$$

b. Solve by graphing. **See back of book.**

c. Critical Thinking Make a general statement about the solutions you get when solving by graphing and the results you get when solving by substitution. **See margin.**

Solve each system using substitution.

35. $y = 2x$
$6x - y = 8$ **(2, 4)**

36. $y = 3x + 1$
$x = 3y + 1$ $\left(-\frac{1}{2}, -\frac{1}{2}\right)$

37. $x - 3y = 14$
$x - 2 = 0$ **(2, −4)**

38. $2x + 2y = 5$
$y = \frac{1}{4}x$ $\left(2, \frac{1}{2}\right)$

39. $4x + y = -2$
$-2x - 3y = 1$ $\left(-\frac{1}{2}, 0\right)$

40. $3x + 5y = 2$
$x + 4y = -4$ **(4, −2)**

C Challenge

For Exercises 41–43, suppose you are solving a system of linear equations and get the given result. How many solutions must the system have?

41. a true statement, such as $2 = 2$
inf. many solutions

42. a false statement, such as $10 = 1$
no solution

43. a statement such as $x = 4$ **1 solution**

44. There are 1170 students in a school. The ratio of girls to boys is $23 : 22$. The system below describes relationships between the number of girls and the number of boys.

$$g + b = 1170 \qquad \frac{g}{b} = \frac{23}{22}$$

a. Solve the proportion for g. $g = \frac{23}{22}b$
b. Solve the system. **$(b, g) = (572, 598)$**
c. How many more girls are there than boys? **26**

 45. Sprinting The graph at the left represents the start of a 100-meter race between Joetta and Gail. The red line and blue line represent Joetta's and Gail's time and distance. Joetta averages 8.8 m/s. Gail averages 9 m/s but started 0.2 s after Joetta. At time 0.2, Gail's distance is 0 m. You can use point-slope form to write an equation that relates Gail's time t to her distance d.

$$y - y_1 = m(x - x_1)$$
$$d - 0 = 9(t - 0.2)$$
$$d = 9t - 1.8$$

Since Joetta started at $t = 0$, the equation $d = 8.8t$ relates her time and distance.
a. Solve the system using substitution. **$(t, d) = (9, 79.2)$**
b. Will Gail overtake Joetta before the finish line? **yes**

46. Use substitution to solve the following system. **$(r, s, t) = (7, 9, 4)$**

$$t + r + s = 20$$
$$r = t + 3$$
$$t + 5r + 10s = 129$$

Distance (meters)

Time (seconds)

33c. Graphing shows only one line. Substitution results in a true equation with no variables.

34c. Graphing shows 2 parallel lines. Substitution results in a false equation with no variables.

 Lesson Quiz 7-2

Solve each system using substitution.

1. $5x + 4y = 5$
$y = 5x$ **(0.2, 1)**

2. $3x + y = 4$
$2x - y = 6$ **(2, −2)**

3. $6m - 2n = 7$
$3m + n = 4$ **(1.25, 0.25)**

Alternative Assessment

Group students in pairs. Give each student a system of equations. You may wish to choose systems from the Extra Practice section in the back of the book. One partner solves the system using a graphing calculator. The other student uses substitution to solve the system. They compare answers to check. Have partners switch roles. Give each student another system of equations to solve.

Standardized Test Prep

A sheet of blank grids is available with the Test-Taking Strategies booklet. Give this sheet to students for practice with filling in the grids.

Resources
For additional practice with a variety of test item formats:
• Standardized Test Prep, p. 391
• Test-Taking Strategies, p. 386
• Test-Taking Strategies with Transparencies

Exercise 48 Point out to students that when two equations are written in slope-intercept form, they can set the right sides of the equations equal to each other and then solve for x.

To check understanding of Lessons 7-1 to 7-2:

Checkpoint Quiz 1 (p. 352)

📁 **Teaching Resources**
Checkpoint Quiz 1 (also in Prentice Hall Assessment System)

👥 **Reaching All Students**
Reading and Math Literacy 7B

Spanish versions available

---

pages 349–352   Exercises

50. [2] $7(-7) - 4(-2) \overset{?}{=} 29$
   $-49 + 8 \overset{?}{=} 29$
   $-41 \neq 29$
   No, $(-2, -7)$ must satisfy both equations to be a solution of the system.
   [1] no explanation given

51.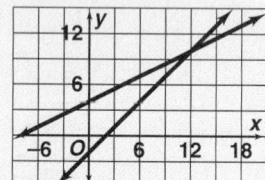

52.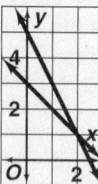

53.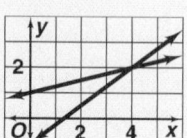

54.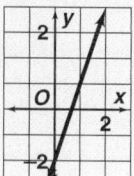

55.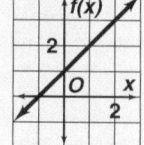

Gridded Response

47. Find the value of the *y*-coordinate of the solution to the given system.
   $5x + 5y = 179$
   $x = 5y - 143$ **29.8**

48. Find the value of the *y*-coordinate of the solution to the given system.
   $y = 9x + 3480$
   $y = 81x - 7104$ **4803**

 Take It to the NET
Online lesson quiz at
www.PHSchool.com
Web Code: aea-0702

49. Tina has $220 in her account. Cliff has $100 in his account. Starting in July, Tina adds $25 to her account on the first of each month, while Cliff adds $35 to his. How many dollars will they have in their accounts when the amounts are the same?   **520**

Short Response

50. Is $(-2, -7)$ the solution of the following system? Justify your answer.
   $7y - 4x = 29$ **See margin.**
   $x = y - 5$

 Mixed Review

Lesson 7-1   **Solve each system by graphing.   51–53. See margin for graphs.**

51. $y = x - 2$
   $y = \frac{1}{2}x + 4$ **(12, 10)**

52. $y = -2x + 5$
   $y = -x + 3$ **(2, 1)**

53. $y = \frac{3}{4}x - 1$
   $y = \frac{1}{4}x + 1$ **(4, 2)**

Lesson 5-3   **Graph each function.   54–55. See margin. 56–59. See back of book.**

54. $y = 3x - 2$

55. $f(x) = x + 1$

56. $f(x) = -2x$

57. $y = |x| + 5$

58. $y = -2|x|$

59. $y = |x + 3| - 1$

✓ **Checkpoint Quiz 1**   **Lessons 7-1 through 7-2**

📱 **TEXT** Instant self-check quiz online and on CD-ROM

Solve each system by graphing.   1–3. See margin for graphs.

1. $y = 3x - 4$
   $y = -2x + 1$ **(1, −1)**

2. $y = \frac{4}{3}x - 2$
   $y = \frac{2}{3}x$ **(3, 2)**

3. $y = \frac{1}{4}x - 1$
   $y = -2x - 10$
   (−4, −2)

Solve each system using substitution.

4. $y = 3x - 14$
   $y = x - 10$ **(2, −8)**

5. $y = 2x + 5$
   $y = 6x + 1$ **(1, 7)**

6. $x = y + 7$
   $y = 8 + 2x$
   (−15, −22)

7. $3x + 4y = 12$
   $y = -2x + 10 \left(\frac{28}{5}, -\frac{6}{5}\right)$

8. $4x + 9y = 24$
   $y = -\frac{1}{3}x + 2$ **(6, 0)**

In Exercises 9 and 10, write and solve a system of equations for each situation.

9. A rectangle is 3 times longer than it is wide. The perimeter is 44 cm. Find the dimensions of the rectangle. **2L + 2W = 44, 3W = L; 5.5 cm by 16.5 cm**

10. A farmer grows only pumpkins and corn on her 420-acre farm. This year she wants to plant 250 more acres of corn than of pumpkins. How many acres of each crop does the farmer need to plant? **p + c = 420, c = p + 250; 85 acres pumpkins, 335 acres corn**

page 352   Checkpoint Quiz 1.

1.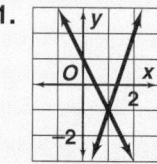

2.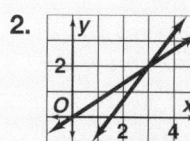

3.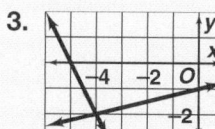

7-3

Solving Systems Using Elimination

 North Carolina Objectives

4.03 Use systems of linear equations or inequalities in two variables to model and solve problems. Solve using tables, graphs, and algebraic properties; justify results.

Lesson Preview

What You'll Learn

 OBJECTIVE 1 To solve systems by adding or subtracting

OBJECTIVE 2 To multiply first when solving systems

. . . And Why

To analyze a ticket-sales situation, as in Example 2

 Check Skills You'll Need (For help, go to Lesson 7-2.)

Solve each system using substitution.

1. $y = 4x - 3$
$y = 2x + 13$ **(8, 29)**

2. $y + 5x = 4$
$y = 7x - 20$ **(2, −6)**

3. $y = -2x + 2$
$3x - 17 = 2y$
(3, −4)

New Vocabulary • elimination method

 OBJECTIVE 1

Adding or Subtracting to Solve Systems

 Interactive lesson includes instant self-check, tutorials, and activities.

Need Help?

Addition Property of Equality:
If $a = b$,
then $a + c = b + c$.

Subtraction Property of Equality:
If $a = b$,
then $a - c = b - c$.

The Addition and Subtraction Properties of Equality can be extended to state,

If $a = b$ and $c = d$, then $a + c = b + d$. If $a = b$ and $c = d$, then $a - c = b - d$.

You can use the Addition and Subtraction Properties of Equality to solve a system by the **elimination method.** You can add or subtract equations to eliminate a variable.

1 EXAMPLE Adding Equations

Solve by elimination. $5x - 6y = -32$
$3x + 6y = 48$

Step 1 Eliminate y because the sum of the coefficients of y is zero.

$$5x - 6y = -32$$
$$\underline{3x + 6y = 48}$$
$$8x + 0 = 16 \quad \text{Addition Property of Equality}$$
$$x = 2 \quad \text{Solve for } x.$$

Step 2 Solve for the eliminated variable y using either of the original equations.

$$3x + 6y = 48 \quad \text{Choose the second equation.}$$
$$3(2) + 6y = 48 \quad \text{Substitute 2 for } x.$$
$$6 + 6y = 48 \quad \text{Simplify. Then solve for } y.$$
$$y = 7$$

Since $x = 2$ and $y = 7$, the solution is $(2, 7)$.

Check $5(2) - 6(7) \stackrel{?}{=} -32$ See if (2, 7) solves $5x - 6y = -32$.
$$10 - 42 \stackrel{?}{=} -32$$
$$-32 = -32 ✓$$

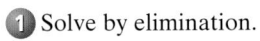 **Check Understanding** **1** Solve by elimination. $6x - 3y = 3$ **(2, 3)**
$-6x + 5y = 3$

Lesson 7-3 Solving Systems Using Elimination **353**

 **7-3**

 North Carolina Objectives 4.03

1. Plan

Lesson Preview

 **Check Skills You'll Need**

Solving Systems Using Substitution
Lesson 7-2: Example 1
Exercises 1–13
Extra Practice, p. 708

Lesson Resources

 Teaching Resources
Practice, Reteaching, Enrichment

 Reaching All Students
Practice Workbook 7-3
Spanish Practice Workbook 7-3
Technology Activities 21
Basic Algebra Planning Guide 7-3

⏱ **Presentation Assistant Plus!**
Transparencies
• Check Skills You'll Need 7-3
• Additional Examples 7-3
• Student Edition Answers 7-3
• Lesson Quiz 7-3
PH Presentation Pro CD 7-3

PRENTICE HALL **ASSESSMENT SYSTEM**

Computer Test Generator CD

 **Technology**
Resource Pro® CD-ROM
Computer Test Generator CD
Prentice Hall Presentation Pro CD

💻 **www.PHSchool.com**
Student Site
• Teacher Web Code: aek-5500
• Reasoning & Puzzles p. 69
• Self-grading Lesson Quiz
Teacher Center
• Lesson Planner
• Resources

Plus **iTEXT**

Ongoing Assessment and Intervention

Before the Lesson	During the Lesson	After the Lesson
Diagnose prerequisite skills using:	**Monitor progress using:**	**Assess knowledge using:**
• Check Skills You'll Need	• Check Understanding	• Lesson Quiz
	• Additional Examples	• Computer Test Generator CD
	• Standardized Test Prep	

353

Math Background

In Algebra 2, students will solve systems of equations that contain three equations in three variables. They will use the elimination method several times to solve one system.

OBJECTIVE

▼ ① Teaching Notes

① EXAMPLE English Learners

Explain to students that *elimination* is the process of getting rid of, or removing. Demonstrate the meaning by writing the system on the board. Cross out and then erase $-6y$ and $6y$, and write only $8x$ below the left side of the system. Explain that you *eliminated* the variable y because the sum of the coefficients is 0.

② EXAMPLE Error Prevention

When subtracting the second equation, some students may fail to subtract every term. Suggest to students that they write parentheses around the whole second equation and then write a subtraction sign in front of the parentheses.

🖐 Additional Examples

① Solve by elimination.
$2x + 3y = 11$
$-2x + 9y = 1$ **(4, 1)**

② On a special day, tickets for a minor league baseball game cost $5 for adults and $1 for students. The attendance that day was 1139, and $3067 was collected. Write and solve a system of equations to find the number of adults and the number of students that attended the game.
$a + s = 1139$
$5a + s = 3067$
482 adults and 657 students

354

Real-World 🌐 Connection

There are 181 basketball teams in 22 conferences in the National Wheelchair Basketball Association.

② EXAMPLE Real-World 🌐 Problem Solving

Ticket Sales Suppose your community center sells a total of 292 tickets for a basketball game. An adult ticket costs $3. A student ticket costs $1. The sponsors collect $470 in ticket sales. Write and solve a system to find the number of each type of ticket sold.

Define Let a = number of adult tickets.
Let s = number of student tickets.

Relate total number of tickets   total amount of sales
Write $a + s = 292$ $3a + 1s = 470$

Solve by elimination.

Step 1 Eliminate s because the difference of the coefficients of s is zero.

$$a + s = 292$$
$$\underline{3a + s = 470}$$
$$-2a + 0 = -178 \qquad \text{Subtraction Property of Equality}$$
$$a = 89 \qquad \text{Solve for } a.$$

Step 2 Solve for the eliminated variable using either of the original equations.

$a + s = 292$ **Choose the first equation.**
$89 + s = 292$ **Substitute 89 for a.**
$s = 203$ **Solve for s.**

There were 89 adult tickets sold and 203 student tickets sold.

Check Is the solution reasonable? The total number of tickets is $89 + 203$, or 292. The total sales is $\$3(89)$, or $\$267$, plus $\$1(203)$, or $\$203$, which is $\$470$. The solution is correct.

✓ **Check Understanding** ② Your class sells a total of 64 tickets to a play. A student ticket costs $1, and an adult ticket costs $2.50. Your class collects $109 in total ticket sales. How many adult tickets did you sell? How many student tickets did you sell? **30 adult; 34 student**

OBJECTIVE

◤ ② Multiplying First to Solve Systems

From examples 1 and 2 you can see that to eliminate a variable its coefficients must have a sum or difference of zero. Sometimes you may need to multiply one or both of the equations by a nonzero number first.

③ EXAMPLE Multiplying One Equation

Solve by the elimination method. $2x + 5y = -22$
                               $10x + 3y = 22$

Step 1 Eliminate one variable.

Start with the given system.	**To prepare for eliminating x, multiply the first equation by 5.**	**Subtract the equations to eliminate x.**
$2x + 5y = -22$ →	$5(2x + 5y = -22)$	→ $10x + 25y = -110$
$10x + 3y = 22$ →	$\underline{10x + 3y = 22}$	→ $\underline{10x + 3y = 22}$
		$0 + 22y = -132$

🤝 Reaching All Students

Below Level Help students understand that they can either add or subtract equations to solve a system by elimination. Have them examine the methods used in Examples 1 and 2.	**Advanced Learners** Have students solve by elimination then describe the solution. $2x + y = 4$ $-6x - 3y = -12$	**English Learners** See note on page 354. **Error Prevention** See note on page 354.

Step 2 Solve for y.

$$22y = -132$$
$$y = -6$$

Step 3 Solve for the eliminated variable using either of the original equations.

$$2x + 5y = -22 \quad \textbf{Choose the first equation.}$$
$$2x + 5(-6) = -22 \quad \textbf{Substitute } -6 \textbf{ for } y.$$
$$2x - 30 = -22 \quad \textbf{Solve for } x.$$
$$2x = 8$$
$$x = 4$$

● The solution is $(4, -6)$.

✔ **Check Understanding** ③ Solve by elimination. $\quad -2x + 15y = -32 \quad (1, -2)$
$$7x - 5y = 17$$

To solve problems that arise from real-world situations, you can also use the elimination method.

④ EXAMPLE   **Real-World 🌎 Problem Solving**

Sales Suppose your class sells gift wrap for $4 per package and greeting cards for $10 per package. Your class sells 205 packages in all and receives a total of $1084. Find the number of packages of gift wrap and the number of packages of greeting cards sold.

Define   Let w = number of packages of gift wrap sold.
         Let c = number of packages of greeting cards sold.

Relate   total number of packages   total amount of sales

Write $w + c = 205$ $4w + 10c = 1084$

Step 1 Eliminate one variable.

Start with the given system.	**To prepare for eliminating w, multiply the first equation by 4.**	**Subtract the equations to eliminate w.**
$w + c = 205 \quad \rightarrow$	$4(w + c = 205) \quad \rightarrow$	$4w + 4c = 820$
$4w + 10c = 1084 \quad \rightarrow$	$\underline{4w + 10c = 1084} \quad \rightarrow$	$\underline{4w + 10c = 1084}$
		$0 - 6c = -264$

Step 2 Solve for c.

$$-6c = -264$$
$$c = 44$$

Step 3 Solve for the eliminated variable using either of the original equations.

$$w + c = 205 \quad \textbf{Use the first equation.}$$
$$w + 44 = 205 \quad \textbf{Substitute 44 for } c.$$
$$w = 161 \quad \textbf{Solve for } w.$$

● The class sold 161 packages of gift wrap and 44 packages of greeting cards.

✔ **Check Understanding** ④ Suppose your younger brother's elementary school class sells a different brand of gift wrap, which costs $2 per package, and cards, which cost $5 per package. His class sells 220 packages in all and earns a total of $695. Find the number of each type of package sold. **85 cards, 135 gift wrap**

OBJECTIVE
▼2 **Teaching Notes**

③ EXAMPLE   **Teaching Tip**

Some students may be unsure of the number by which they should multiply the equation. Direct students' attention to the coefficients of each variable. Ask: *Is one coefficient a factor of the other coefficient for the same variable?* Yes, 2 is a factor of 10. Point out that the equation with the coefficient 2 can be multiplied by 5 so that the new coefficient becomes 10.

④ EXAMPLE   **Error Prevention**

Students commonly forget to multiply the constant on the right side of the equation. Remind them that the Multiplication Property of Equality requires that all terms on both sides must be multiplied to preserve equality.

📬 **Additional Examples**

③ Solve by elimination.
$$3x + 6y = -6$$
$$-5x - 2y = -14 \quad (4, -3)$$

④ Suppose the band sells cans of popcorn for $5 per can and cans of mixed nuts for $8 per can. The band sells a total of 240 cans and receives a total of $1614. Find the number of cans of popcorn and the number of cans of mixed nuts sold. **102 cans of popcorn, 138 cans of nuts**

5 EXAMPLE Math Tip

Encourage students to find the least common multiple of the coefficients of one variable, since working with lesser numbers tends to reduce the likelihood of errors.

 **Additional Examples**

5 Solve by elimination.
$3x + 5y = 10$
$5x + 7y = 10$ **(−5, 5)**

Closure

Ask students to explain when it is best to solve a system by using elimination, and when it is best to use substitution. **You should use elimination if the two coefficients of a variable are the same or opposites, or one is a multiple of the other. Use substitution if one equation is easy to solve, or is already solved, for one of the variables.**

pages 356–359   Exercises

3. (5, −17)

4. (−3, 4)

5. $\left(-9, \frac{1}{2}\right)$

6. $\left(-\frac{1}{2}, 10\right)$

15a. $30w + \ell = 17.65,$
$20w + 3\ell = 25.65$

  b. $0.39 for a wallet size, $5.95 for an 8 × 10

23–28. Choice of method may vary. Samples are given.

23. (−1, −2); substitution; both solved for *y*

24. (15, −10); elimination; equations not solved for *y*

25. (10, 2); substitution; one eq. solved for *x*

26. (−3, 11); elimination; eqs. not solved for a variable

27. (5, 1); substitution; one eq. solved for *x*

28. $\left(\frac{1}{3}, 2\frac{1}{3}\right)$; substitution; eqs. solved for *y*

356

To eliminate a variable, you may need to multiply both equations in a system by a nonzero number. Multiply each equation by values such that when you write equivalent equations, you can then add or subtract to eliminate a variable.

5 EXAMPLE   Multiplying Both Equations

Solve by elimination. $4x + 2y = 14$
$7x - 3y = -8$

Step 1   Eliminate one variable.

Start with the given system.	To prepare for eliminating *y*, multiply one equation by 3 and the other equation by 2.	Add the equations to eliminate *y*.
$4x + 2y = 14$ →	$3(4x + 2y = 14)$ →	$12x + 6y = 42$
$7x - 3y = -8$ →	$2(7x - 3y = -8)$ →	$14x - 6y = -16$
		$\overline{26x + 0 = 26}$

Step 2   Solve for *x*.
$$26x = 26$$
$$x = 1$$

Step 3   Solve for the eliminated variable *y* using either of the original equations.
$4x + 2y = 14$ **Use the first equation.**
$4(1) + 2y = 14$ **Substitute 1 for *x*.**
$2y = 10$
$y = 5$

• The solution is $(1, 5)$.

✓ **Check Understanding** **5** Solve by elimination. $15x + 3y = 9$ **(1, −2)**
$10x + 7y = -4$

When you solve systems using elimination, plan a strategy. A flowchart like the one below can help you to decide how to eliminate a variable.

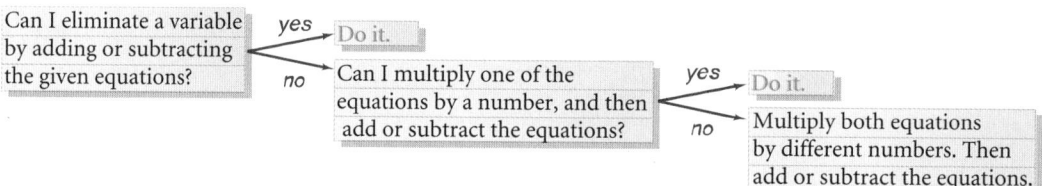

EXERCISES

For more practice, see *Extra Practice*.

Practice and Problem Solving

 **Practice by Example**   **Solve by elimination. 3–6. See margin.**

Example 1
(page 353)

1. $2x + 5y = 17$
$6x - 5y = -9$ **(1, 3)**

2. $7x + 2y = 10$
$-7x + y = -16$ **(2, −2)**

3. $2x - 3y = 61$
$2x + y = -7$

4. $8x + 11y = 20$
$5x - 11y = -59$

5. $2x + 18y = -9$
$4x + 18y = -27$

6. $20x + 3y = 20$
$-20x + 5y = 60$

356   Chapter 7   Systems of Equations and Inequalities

Example 2
(page 354)

7. The sum of two numbers is 20. Their difference is 4. $x + y = 20,$
    a. Write a system of equations that describes this situation. $x - y = 4$
    b. Solve by elimination to find the two numbers. **12 and 8**

8. Ticket Sales Your school sold 456 tickets for a high school play. An adult ticket cost $3.50. A student ticket cost $1. Total ticket sales equaled $1131. Let a equal the number of adult tickets sold, and let s equal the number of student tickets sold. **a.** $a + s = 456, 3.5a + s = 1131$
    a. Write a system of equations that relates the number of adult and student tickets sold to the total number of tickets sold and to the total ticket sales.
    b. Solve by elimination to find the number of each type of ticket sold.
                                      270 adult, 186 student

Example 3
(page 354)

Solve by elimination.

9. $3x - 10y = -25$
    $4x + 40y = 20$ **(−5, 1)**

10. $7x + 15y = 32$
    $x - 3y = 20$ **(11, −3)**

11. $x - 8y = 18$
    $-16x + 16y = -8$

12. $24x + 2y = 52$
    $6x - 3y = -36$ **(1, 14)**

13. $88x - 5y = 39$
    $-8x + 3y = -1$ $\left(\frac{1}{2}, 1\right)$

14. $2x + 4y = 8$ $\left(-2, -\frac{5}{2}\right)$
    $5x + y = -7$ **(−2, 3)**

Example 4
(page 355)

15. Sales A photo studio that takes school pictures offers several different packages. Let w equal the cost of a wallet-sized portrait, and let ℓ equal the cost of an 8×10 portrait.

Basic Package
30 wallet-sized photos
1 8" x 10" portrait
$17.65

Deluxe Package
20 wallet-sized photos
3 8" x 10" portraits
$25.65

    a. Write a system of equations that relates the cost of wallet-sized portraits and 8×10 portraits to the cost of the basic and deluxe packages.
    b. Find the cost of each type of portrait. **a–b. See margin.**

16. Two groups of students order burritos and tacos at a local restaurant. One order of 3 burritos and 4 tacos costs $11.33. The other order of 9 burritos and 5 tacos costs $23.56.

16a. $x =$ burritos,
    $y =$ tacos,
    $3x + 4y = 11.33,$
    $9x + 5y = 23.56$

    a. Write a system of equations that describes this situation. **See left.**
    b. Solve by elimination to find the cost of a burrito and the cost of a taco.
                          $1.79 for a burrito, $1.49 for a taco

Example 5
(page 356)

Solve by elimination.

17. $3x + 2y = -9$ **(−1, −3)**
    $-10x + 5y = -5$

18. $4x + 5y = 15$
    $6x - 4y = 11$ **(2.5, 1)**

19. $3x - 2y = 10$ **(2, −2)**
    $2x + 3y = -2$

20. $-2x + 5y = 20$
    $3x - 7y = -26$ **(10, 8)**

21. $10x + 8y = 2$
    $8x + 6y = 1$ $\left(-1, \frac{3}{2}\right)$

22. $9x + 5y = 34$
    $8x - 2y = -2$ **(1, 5)**

(B) Apply Your Skills

Solve each system using any method. Tell why you chose the method you used.
23–28. See margin.

23. $y = 2x$
    $y = x - 1$

24. $7x + 8y = 25$
    $9x + 10y = 35$

25. $x = 12y - 14$
    $3y + 2x = 26$

26. $-20x + 7y = 137$
    $4x + 5y = 43$

27. $5y = x$
    $2x - 3y = 7$

28. $y = x + 2$
    $y = -2x + 3$

Assignment Guide

1 Objective
  (A) (B) **Core** 1–8, 32, 39–41
  (C) **Extension** 43

2 Objective
  (A) (B) **Core** 9–31, 33–38
  (C) **Extension** 42, 44–46

Standardized Test Prep 47–50

Mixed Review 51–62

Exercises 23–28 Suggest to students that they first write the equations in standard form, making sure they align matching variables.

Exercises 33–38 Suggest to students that they first multiply by the least common denominator or the appropriate multiple of 10 to eliminate fractions and decimals.

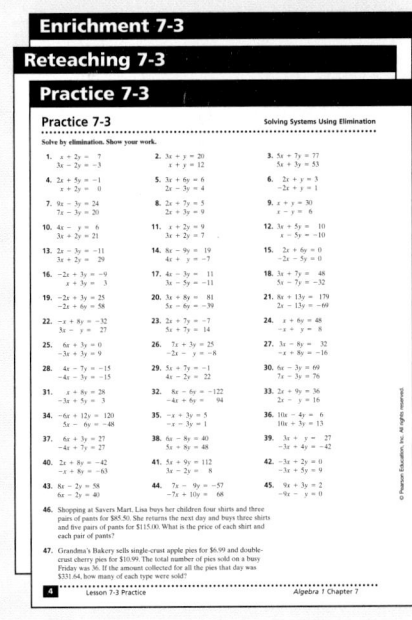

Alternative Assessment

Give students blue, red, green, and yellow counters. Let blue represent positive x and red represent negative x. Let green represent positive y and yellow represent negative y. Give students systems of equations in standard form to model and solve using the counters. Pairs of blue and red counters eliminate each other, as do pairs of green and yellow counters.

pages 356–359 Exercises

40. Answers may vary.
Sample: You solve a system using the elimination method by adding or subtracting the eqs. to eliminate one of the variables. This sum or difference is one eq. with one variable that can be solved.
Use addition:
$3x + 2y = 6$
$-x - 2y = 4$
Use subtraction:
$5x + 3y = 15$
$5x - 2y = 10$
Use multiplication:
$4x + 5y = 20$
$2x - y = 10$

One weekend for
$195
One week for
$650
(per person, double occupancy)

Beach
Bay
Hotel

32. Answers may vary.
Sample: $2x - 3y = 6$,
$x + 3y = 9$; $\left(5, \frac{4}{3}\right)$

 29. **Vacation** A weekend at the Beach Bay Hotel in Florida includes 2 nights and 4 meals. A week includes 7 nights and 10 meals. Let $n =$ the cost of 1 night and $m =$ the cost of 1 meal. Find the cost of 1 night and the cost of 1 meal. **one night: $81.25; one meal: $8.13**

30. a. **Business** A company sells brass and steel machine parts. One shipment contains 3 brass and 10 steel parts and costs $48. A second shipment contains 7 brass and 4 steel parts and costs $54. Find the cost of each type of machine part. **brass: $6; steel: $3**

   b. How much would a shipment containing 10 brass and 13 steel machine parts cost? **$99**

31. **Error Analysis** Beth is solving a system by elimination. Her work is shown below. What error did she make? **She forgot to multiply −8 by 6.**

$$4x - 6y = 1 \longrightarrow 20x - 30y = 5$$
$$3x + 5y = -8 \longrightarrow 18x + 30y = -8$$

32. **Open-Ended** Write a system of equations that can be solved by elimination. Solve your system. **See left.**

Solve by elimination.

33. $\frac{1}{2}x + y = -1$
   $16x - \frac{1}{2}y = 163$ **(10, −6)**

34. $\frac{1}{4}x - 6y = -70$
   $5x + \frac{3}{4}y = 49$ **(8, 12)**

35. $-0.2x + 4y = -1$
   $x + 0.5y = -15.5$
   (−15, −1)

36. $y = 0.5x + 2$
   $1.5x + y = 42$ **(20, 12)**

37. $\frac{1}{4}x + \frac{33}{2} = y$
   $y - 12 = -2x$ **(−2, 16)**

38. $\frac{2}{3}x - y = 70$
   $\frac{1}{3}x - \frac{2}{3}y = 43$
   (33, −48)

39. **Critical Thinking** Find a value of n such that the x-value of the solution of the system at right is 4. **9**
   $5x - 10y = 50$
   $nx + 10y = 6$

 40. **Writing** Explain how to solve a system using elimination. Give examples of when you use addition, subtraction, and multiplication. **See margin.**

41. **Electricity** Two batteries produce a total voltage of 4.5 volts ($B_1 + B_2 = 4.5$). The difference in their voltages is 1.5 volts ($B_1 - B_2 = 1.5$). Find the voltages of the two batteries. **$B_1 = 3$ volts; $B_2 = 1.5$ volts**

C Challenge

Solve by elimination.

42. $\frac{6}{x} - \frac{4}{y} = -4$
   $\frac{3}{x} + \frac{8}{y} = 3$ **(−3, 2)**

43. $ax + y = c$
   $ax + by = c$
   $\left(\frac{c}{a}, 0\right)$ $(a \neq 0, b \neq 1)$

44. $x + y + z = 41$
   $x - y + z = 15$
   $3x - z = 4$
   (8, 13, 20)

Problem Solving Hint

For Exercise 45, simplify each equation before solving by elimination.

45. **Music** Suppose your band wants to sell CDs and cassette tapes of your music. You use a production company that offers two different production packages.

	CDs	Tapes	Mastering	Artwork	Total Cost
Package #1	300	400	✓	✓	$2080
Package #2	500	600	✓	✓	$3120

Both companies charge $100 to master your original recording and $240 to create cover artwork. Find the average production cost of each CD and cassette tape. **CD: $3.40, cassette: $1.80**

Reading Math

Density is the ratio of mass to volume.

Since $d = \frac{m}{v}$, $m = dv$.

 46. Jewelry A ring is made out of gold and copper. Gold has a density of 19.3 g/cm³. Copper has a density of 9 g/cm³. Mass m, density d, and volume v are related by the formula $m = dv$. The ring has a volume of 8.4 cm³, and a mass of 104.44 g.

Let a = volume of gold.   mass of gold = $dv = 19.3a$
Let c = volume of copper.   mass of copper = $dv = 9c$

a. Solve the following system by elimination to find out how many grams of gold are in the ring. **2.8 g of gold**

$$a + c = 8.4$$
$$19.3a + 9c = 104.44$$

b. What is the percent of gold by mass? **about 2.7%**

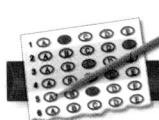

Standardized Test Prep

Multiple Choice

47. Which of the following systems does NOT have the same solution as the system at the right? **D**

$$7x - 4y = 5$$
$$6x + 7y = -11$$

A. $49x - 28y = 35$
$\quad 24x + 28y = -44$

B. $42x - 24y = 30$
$\quad 42x + 49y = -77$

C. $-14x + 8y = -10$
$\quad 12x + 14y = -22$

D. $21x + 12y = 15$
$\quad -24x - 28y = 44$

 **Take It to the NET**

Online lesson quiz at **www.PHSchool.com**

Web Code: aea-0703

48. Use the solution of the system below to find $x - y$. **H**

$$4x - 2y = 11$$
$$3x - 4y = -6$$

F. 11.3   **G.** 0.1   **H.** -0.1 **I.** -11.3

Short Response

49. Solve the following system by elimination. Show your work. **See margin.**

$$y - x = 13$$
$$7y + x = 11$$

Extended Response

50. A trapezoid is fomed by lines with the following equations.

$$2x + 4y = 16 \qquad x = 4 \qquad x = 0 \qquad y = 0$$

Find the area of the trapezoid. **See margin.**

Standardized Test Prep

 Resources

For additional practice with a variety of test item formats:
- Standardized Test Prep, p. 391
- Test-Taking Strategies, p. 386
- Test-Taking Strategies with Transparencies

49. [2] $y - x = 13$
$\quad\quad \underline{7y \pm x = 11}$
$\quad\quad\quad 8y = 24$
$\quad\quad\quad\quad y = 3$
$\quad\quad 3 - x = 13$
$\quad\quad\quad\quad x = -10 \; (-10, 3)$

[1] no work shown

50. [4]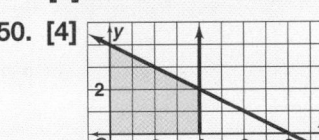

$A = \frac{1}{2}h(b_1 + b_2)$
$\quad = \frac{1}{2}(4)(4 + 2)$
$\quad = 2(6)$
$\quad = 12$

The area is 12 square units.

Mixed Review

Lesson 7-2

Solve using substitution. Give the solutions in alphabetical order.

51. $y = 4x + 2$
$\quad y = 6x - 10$ **(6, 26)**

52. $p = q - 5$
$\quad 3p + q = 1$ **(−1, 4)**

53. $w + a = 4$
$\quad w + 2a = 13$ **(9, −5)**

Lesson 4-6

You have a bag with two red marbles, three blue marbles, and five green marbles. You choose a marble at random. Without replacing the marble, you choose a second marble. Find each probability.

54. P(red then green) $\frac{1}{9}$ **55.** P(two greens) $\frac{2}{9}$ **56.** P(blue then red) $\frac{1}{15}$

Lesson 2-1

Solve and check each solution.

57. $c - 4 = 67$ **71**   **58.** $t + 27 = 9$ **−18**   **59.** $n - 12 = -56$ **−44**

60. $-9 + k = 13$ **22**   **61.** $x - 82 = 1$ **83**   **62.** $17 + b = 11$ **−6**

Multiplying Matrices and Solving Systems

Students use graphing calculators and the matrix functions to multiply matrices and solve systems of equations. They will need to know how to enter the dimensions of a matrix and how to use the calculator to find the inverse of a matrix.

Resources

Students may use any graphing calculator to explore operations with matrices.

Teaching Notes

Students may need to be reminded that they can only multiply matrix A by matrix B if the number of columns in A matches the number of rows in B. If they try to multiply A × B on their graphing calculators, and the number of columns in A does not match the number of rows in B, they will get the message: ERR:DIM MISMATCH. This means: error: dimensions mismatch.

Error Prevention

If students use the graphing calculator to find the solution to a system of equations, suggest that they check the solution in each equation to show that in fact the solution is correct.

In Chapter 1, you learned how to add and subtract two matrices. You can also multiply matrices. You multiply the elements in a row of the first matrix by the corresponding elements in a column of the second matrix. Then you add the products.

3 elements in a row →
$$\begin{bmatrix} 2 & 5 & -3 \\ 3 & 1 & 6 \end{bmatrix}\begin{bmatrix} 7 \\ 2 \\ 1 \end{bmatrix} = \begin{bmatrix} 2 \cdot 7 + 5 \cdot 2 + (-3 \cdot 1) \\ 3 \cdot 7 + 1 \cdot 2 + 6 \cdot 1 \end{bmatrix} = \begin{bmatrix} 21 \\ 29 \end{bmatrix}$$

↑
3 elements in a column

The second matrix can have more than one column.

$$\begin{bmatrix} 2 & 5 & -3 \\ 3 & 1 & 6 \end{bmatrix}\begin{bmatrix} 7 & 3 \\ 2 & 9 \\ 1 & 2 \end{bmatrix} = \begin{bmatrix} 2 \cdot 7 + 5 \cdot 2 + (-3 \cdot 1) & 2 \cdot 3 + 5 \cdot 9 + (-3 \cdot 2) \\ 3 \cdot 7 + 1 \cdot 2 + 6 \cdot 1 & 3 \cdot 3 + 1 \cdot 9 + 6 \cdot 2 \end{bmatrix} = \begin{bmatrix} 21 & 45 \\ 29 & 30 \end{bmatrix}$$

- first row and first column
- first row and second column
- second row and first column
- second row and second column

You can use a graphing calculator to multiply matrices. To enter matrices, you must know their dimensions. A matrix with two rows and three columns is a 2 × 3 matrix.

1 EXAMPLE

Use a graphing calculator to find $A \times B$ for

$$A = \begin{bmatrix} 2 & 5 & -3 \\ 3 & 1 & 6 \end{bmatrix} \qquad B = \begin{bmatrix} 7 & 3 \\ 2 & 9 \\ 1 & 2 \end{bmatrix}$$

Step 1 Use the **MATRX** feature. Edit the dimensions and enter the values of the elements. You have to quit the first matrix screen before using the **MATRX** feature to enter the second matrix.

Matrix A	Matrix B

```
Matrix [A]   2×3
[2        5       -3]
[3        1        6]




2,3=6
```

```
Matrix [B]   3×2
[7        3       ]
[2        9       ]
[1        2       ]



3, 2=2
```

Step 2 Use the **NAMES** list on the matrix screen. Select [A]. Then use the name list on the matrix screen to select [B]. Press ENTER.
- The product matrix will appear on the main screen.

```
[A] [B]

           [[21    45]
            [29    30]]
```

You can use matrices to solve systems of equations. Start with equations in standard form.

System of Equations

$$2x + 6y = 80$$
$$4x + 5y = -1$$

Matrices for the System

$$\begin{bmatrix} 2 & 6 \\ 4 & 5 \end{bmatrix} \begin{bmatrix} x \\ y \end{bmatrix} = \begin{bmatrix} 80 \\ -1 \end{bmatrix}$$
$$\quad A \quad \cdot \quad X \;\; = \;\; B$$

A is the matrix for the coefficients of the variables, X is a matrix for the variables, and B is a matrix for the constants. To solve the system you must use the inverse of A, which is A^{-1}. The product $A^{-1} \times B$ gives you X.

2 EXAMPLE

Solve the system at the right by using matrix multiplication.

$$A = \begin{bmatrix} 2 & 6 \\ 4 & 5 \end{bmatrix} \text{ and } B = \begin{bmatrix} 80 \\ -1 \end{bmatrix}$$

$$2x + 6y = 80$$
$$4x + 5y = -1$$

Step 1

Use the matrix feature. Edit the dimensions and enter the values of the elements for each matrix.

Step 2

Use the matrix feature. Select [A]. Then press $\boxed{x^{-1}}$. $[A]^{-1}$ will appear on the main screen.

Step 3

Use the matrix feature. Select [B]. Then press $\boxed{\text{ENTER}}$.

The values of matrix X will appear as shown at the right.

$\begin{matrix} [[-29] \\ [23]] \end{matrix}$ corresponds to $\begin{bmatrix} x \\ y \end{bmatrix}$, so $x = -29$ and $y = 23$.

● The solution of the system is $(-29, 23)$.

```
[A]⁻¹ [B]


              [[-29]
               [23]]
```

EXERCISES

Find each product. 2–3. See margin.

1. $[4 \quad 2 \quad 9] \begin{bmatrix} 3 \\ 1 \\ 7 \end{bmatrix}$ **[77]**

2. $\begin{bmatrix} 12 & 10 \\ 8 & -11 \end{bmatrix} \begin{bmatrix} 0 & 4 \\ 9 & -1 \end{bmatrix}$

3. $\begin{bmatrix} 44 & -12 \\ 27 & 35 \\ 25 & -16 \end{bmatrix} \begin{bmatrix} 21 & -41 \\ 25 & 17 \end{bmatrix}$

4. The table at the near right shows the number of three sizes of widgets made at a manufacturing plant on Monday and Tuesday. The table at the far right shows the production costs of each widget. Write each table as a matrix. Then multiply to find the total production cost each day. **See margin.**

Number of Widgets			
Day	**Size A**	**Size B**	**Size C**
Monday	212	318	175
Tuesday	185	292	221

Cost of Widgets	
Cost A	$.96
Cost B	$1.23
Cost C	$1.51

Solve each system using matrix multiplication.

5. $1x + 8y = 16$
$9x + 12y = 66$ **(5.6, 1.3)**

6. $29x + 7y = 1012$
$8x - 25y = 737$ **(39, −17)**

7. $76x + 18y = 86$
$189x + 47y = 132$ **(9.8, −36.6)**

Visual Learners

Students may be confused about whether they can multiply two particular matrices. Suggest that they write the dimensions of the two matrices as, for example, $(2 \times 3)(4 \times 3)$. The number of columns (3) of the first matrix does not match the number of rows (4) of the second matrix. Therefore there is no product. Consider $(2 \times 3)(3 \times 4)$; the 3s match so there is a product.

pages 360–361   Technology

2. $\begin{bmatrix} 90 & 38 \\ -99 & 43 \end{bmatrix}$

3. $\begin{bmatrix} 624 & -2008 \\ 1442 & -512 \\ 125 & -1297 \end{bmatrix}$

4. $\begin{bmatrix} 212 & 318 & 175 \\ 185 & 292 & 221 \end{bmatrix} \begin{bmatrix} 0.96 \\ 1.23 \\ 1.51 \end{bmatrix}$;

$858.91 Monday
$870.47 Tuesday

 North Carolina Objectives 4.03

1. Plan

Lesson Preview

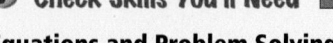 **Check Skills You'll Need**

Equations and Problem Solving
Lesson 2-5: Example 3
Exercise 10
Extra Practice, p. 703

Lesson Resources

 **Teaching Resources**
Practice, Reteaching, Enrichment

Reaching All Students
Practice Workbook 7-4
Spanish Practice Workbook 7-4
Basic Algebra Planning Guide 7-4

Presentation Assistant Plus!
Transparencies
- Check Skills You'll Need 7-4
- Additional Examples 7-4
- Student Edition Answers 7-4
- Lesson Quiz 7-4
PH Presentation Pro CD 7-4

 **PRENTICE HALL ASSESSMENT SYSTEM**

Computer Test Generator CD

Technology
Resource Pro® CD-ROM
Computer Test Generator CD
Prentice Hall Presentation Pro CD

 **www.PHSchool.com**
Student Site
- Teacher Web Code: aek-5500
- Self-grading Lesson Quiz
Teacher Center
- Lesson Planner
- Resources

Plus **iTEXT**

 7-4

Applications of Linear Systems

4.03 Use systems of linear equations or inequalities in two variables to model and solve problems. Solve using tables, graphs, and algebraic properties; justify results.

Lesson Preview

What You'll Learn

OBJECTIVE 1 To write systems of linear equations

. . . And Why

To find average wind speed during an airplane flight, as in Example 3

✓ Check Skills You'll Need

(For help, go to Lesson 2-5.)

1. Two trains run on parallel tracks. The first train leaves a city $\frac{1}{2}$ hour before the second train. The first train travels at 55 mi/h. The second train travels at 65 mi/h. How long does it take for the second train to pass the first train? **3.25 h**

2. Carl drives to the beach at an average speed of 50 mi/h. He returns home on the same road at an average speed of 55 mi/h. The trip home takes 30 min less. What is the distance from his home to the beach? **275 mi**

OBJECTIVE

 1 Writing Systems of Linear Equations

 Interactive lesson includes instant self-check, tutorials, and activities.

Below is a summary of the methods you have used to solve systems of equations. You must choose a method before you solve a word problem.

Key Concepts

Summary	Methods for Solving Systems of Linear Equations
Graphing	Use graphing for solving systems that are easily graphed. If the point of intersection does not have integers for coordinates, find the exact solution by using one of the methods below or by using a graphing calculator.
Substitution	Use substitution for solving systems when one variable has a coefficient of 1 or -1.
Elimination	Use elimination for solving any system.

---

1 EXAMPLE Real-World Problem Solving

Metallurgy A metalworker has some ingots of metal alloy that are 20% copper and others that are 60% copper. How many kilograms of each type of ingot should the metalworker combine to create 80 kg of a 52% copper alloy?

Define Let g = the mass of the 20% alloy.
Let h = the mass of the 60% alloy.

Relate mass of alloys   mass of copper

Write $g + h = 80$ $0.2g + 0.6h = 0.52(80)$

Solve using substitution.

Step 1 Choose one of the equations and solve for a variable.

$g + h = 80$ **Solve for g.**

$g = 80 - h$ **Subtract h from each side.**

Real-World Connection

The melting point of copper is 1083°C.

Ongoing Assessment and Intervention

Before the Lesson
Diagnose prerequisite skills using:
- Check Skills You'll Need

During the Lesson
Monitor progress using:
- Check Understanding
- Additional Examples
- Standardized Test Prep

After the Lesson
Assess knowledge using:
- Lesson Quiz
- Computer Test Generator CD

Step 2 Find h.

$$0.2g + 0.6h = 0.52(80)$$

$0.2(80 - h) + 0.6h = 0.52(80)$ **Substitute $80 - h$ for g. Use parentheses.**

$16 - 0.2h + 0.6h = 0.52(80)$ **Use the Distributive Property.**

$16 + 0.4h = 41.6$ **Simplify. Then solve for h.**

$$0.4h = 25.6$$

$$h = 64$$

Step 3 Find g. Substitute 64 for h in either equation.

$$g = 80 - 64$$

$$g = 16$$

To make 80 kg of 52% copper alloy, you need 16 kg of 20% copper alloy and 64 kg of 60% copper alloy.

✔ **Check Understanding** ❶ Suppose you combine ingots of 25% copper alloy and 50% copper alloy to create 40 kg of 45% copper alloy. How many kilograms of each do you need?
32 kg 50% alloy; 8 kg 25% alloy

Reading Math

In business, the point at which income equals expenses is called the break-even point.

When starting a business, people want to know the *break-even point*, the point at which their income equals their expenses. The graph at the right shows the break-even point for one business.

☐ Lose money   ▨ Make money

Notice that the values of y on the red line represent dollars spent on expenses, and the values of y on the blue line represent dollars received as income. So y is used to represent both expenses and income.

2 EXAMPLE   **Finding a Break-Even Point**

Publishing Suppose a model airplane club publishes a newsletter. Expenses are $.90 for printing and mailing each copy, plus $600 total for research and writing. The price of the newsletter is $1.50 per copy. How many copies of the newsletter must the club sell to break even?

Define   Let x = the number of copies.
        Let y = the amount of dollars of expenses or income.

Relate   Expenses are printing costs   Income is price
        plus research and writing.   times copies sold.

Write $y = 0.9x + 600$ $y = 1.5x$

Choose a method to solve this system. Use substitution since it is easy to substitute for y with these equations.

$y = 0.9x + 600$ **Start with one equation.**

$1.5x = 0.9x + 600$ **Substitute $1.5x$ for y.**

$0.6x = 600$ **Solve for x.**

$x = 1000$

To break even, the model airplane club must sell 1000 copies.

👥 Reaching All Students

| **Below Level** Before attempting to solve a word problem, students should list the information given, what they need to find, and any relationships that may help solve the problem. | **Advanced Learners** Have students write inequalities that illustrate when the model airplane club in Example 2 is making a profit and when it is losing money. | **English Learners** See note on page 363.
 Auditory Learners See note on page 363. |

---

2. Teach

Math Background

The Japanese mathematician Seki Kowa (1683) solved simultaneous linear equations by using bamboo rods placed in squares on a table, similar to the modern way of using matrices and determinants.

OBJECTIVE
❶ Teaching Notes

❶ EXAMPLE   **English Learners**

English Learners may understand the mathematical concepts in this chapter, but may find it difficult to translate the word problems of this lesson. Consider pairing these students with students who are proficient in English to help them interpret word problems.

❷ EXAMPLE   **Auditory Learners**

Encourage students to read the question quietly to themselves. Then have students ask themselves the following questions and write their answers mathematically.
• *What do I know?*
• *What am I trying to find?*
• *What can I find using the facts I have?*

Additional Examples

❶ A chemist has one solution that is 50% acid. She has another solution that is 25% acid. How many liters of each type of acid solution should she combine to get 10 liters of a 40% acid solution? **6 L of 50% solution, 4 L of 25% solution**

❷ Suppose you have a typing service. You buy a personal computer for $1750 on which to do your typing. You charge $5.50 per page for typing. Expenses are $.50 per page for ink, paper, electricity, and other expenses. How many pages must you type to break even? **350 pages**

Explain to students that *A* is the speed of the plane with no wind at all. Since a tailwind makes you go faster, you add the speed of the wind to the speed of the plane, using $A + W$ when traveling wih the wind. Since head winds decrease the speed of the plane, you subtract the speed of the wind from the speed of the plane, using $A - W$ when traveling against the wind.

Additional Examples

3 Suppose it takes you 6.8 hours to fly about 2800 miles from Miami, Florida to Seattle, Washington. At the same time, your friend flies from Seattle to Miami. His plane travels with the same average airspeed, but his flight takes only 5.6 hours. Find the average airspeed of the planes. Find the average wind speed. **airspeed: 455.9 mi/h; wind speed: 44.1 mi/h**

Closure

Ask students to tell what they found most difficult about writing a system of equations to solve a word problem.

✔ **Check Understanding**   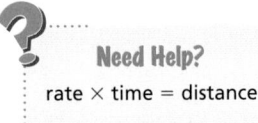 **2** Suppose an antique car club publishes a newsletter. Expenses are $.35 for printing and mailing each copy, plus $770 total for research and writing. The price of the newsletter is $.55 per copy. How many copies of the newsletter must the club sell to break even? **3850 copies**

? Need Help?

rate × time = distance

In Chapter 6, you modeled rate-time-distance problems using one variable. You can also model rate-time-distance problems using two variables. The steady west-to-east winds across the United States act as tail winds for planes traveling from west to east. The tail winds increase a plane's groundspeed. For planes traveling east to west, the head winds decrease a plane's groundspeed.

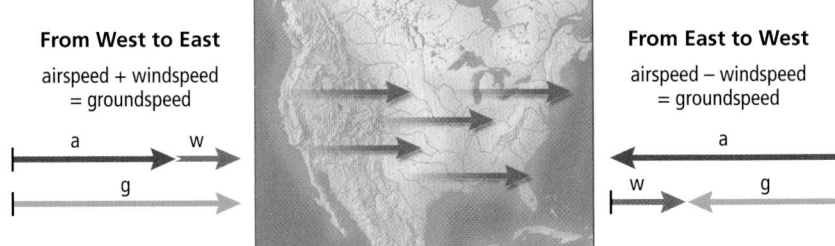

From West to East

airspeed + windspeed = groundspeed

From East to West

airspeed – windspeed = groundspeed

3 EXAMPLE Real-World 🌐 Problem Solving

Travel Suppose you fly from Miami, Florida, to San Francisco, California. It takes 6.5 hours to fly 2600 miles against a head wind. At the same time, your friend flies from San Francisco to Miami. Her plane travels at the same average airspeed, but her flight only takes 5.2 hours. Find the average airspeed of the planes. Find the average wind speed.

Define   Let A = the airspeed. Let W = the wind speed.

Relate   with tail wind   with head wind
          (rate)(time) = distance   (rate)(time) = distance
          $(A + W)$(time) = distance. $(A - W)$(time) = distance.

Write $(A + W)5.2 = 2600$ $(A - W)6.5 = 2600$

Step 1 Divide to get the variables of each equation with coefficients of 1 or −1.

    $(A + W)5.2 = 2600 \rightarrow A + W = 500$ **Divide each side by 5.2.**

    $(A - W)6.5 = 2600 \rightarrow A - W = 400$ **Divide each side by 6.5.**

Step 2 Eliminate W.

    $A + W = 500$
    $\underline{A - W = 400}$ **Add the equations to eliminate W.**
    $2A + 0 = 900$

Step 3 Solve for A.

    $A = 450$ **Divide each side by 2.**

Step 4 Solve for W using either of the original equations.

    $A + W = 500$ **Use the first equation.**

    $450 + W = 500$ **Substitute 450 for A.**

    $W = 50$ **Solve for W.**

● The average airspeed of the planes is 450 mi/h. The average wind speed is 50 mi/h.

 **Check Understanding** ③ A plane takes about 6 hours to fly 2400 miles from New York City to Seattle, Washington. At the same time, your friend flies from Seattle to New York City. His plane travels with the same average airspeed, but his flight takes 5 hours. Find the average airspeed of the planes. Find the average wind speed.

440 mi/h; 40 mi/h

EXERCISES

Practice and Problem Solving

For more practice, see *Extra Practice*.

Ⓐ **Practice by Example**

1. Tyrels and Dalia bought some pens and pencils. Tyrel bought 4 pens and 5 pencils, which cost him $6.71. Dalia bought 5 pens and 3 pencils, which cost her $7.12. Let *a* equal the price of a pen. Let *b* equal the price of a pencil.
  a. Write an equation that relates the number of pens and pencils Tyrel bought to the amount he paid for them. **$4a + 5b = 6.71$**
  b. Write an equation that relates the number of pens and pencils Dalia bought to the amount she paid for them. **$5a + 3b = 7.12$**
  c. Solve the system you wrote for parts (a) and (b) to find the price of a pen and the price of a pencil. **pen: $1.19, pencil: $.39**

Example 1
(page 362)

2. Suppose you have just enough money, in coins, to pay for a loaf of bread priced at $1.95. You have 12 coins, all quarter and dimes. Let *q* equal the number of quarters and *d* equal the number of dimes. Which system models the given information? **D**
  A. $q + d = 12$
  $q + d = 1.95$
  B. $25q + 10d = 195$
  $q + 12 = d$
  C. $10q + 25d = 12$
  $q + d = 1.95$
  D. $q + d = 12$
  $25q + 10d = 195$

3. Suppose you want to combine two types of fruit drink to create 24 kilograms of a drink that will be 5% sugar by weight. Fruit drink A is 4% sugar by weight, and fruit drink B is 8% sugar by weight.
  a. Copy and complete the table below.

	Fruit Drink A 4% Sugar	Fruit Drink B 8% Sugar	Mixed Fruit Drink 5% Sugar
Fruit Drink (kg)	▦ *a*	▦ *b*	▦ 24
Sugar (kg)	▦ $0.04a$	▦ $0.08b$	▦ $0.05(24)$

  b. Write a system of equations that relates the amounts of fruit drink A and fruit drink B to the total amount of drink needed and to the total amount of sugar needed. **$a + b = 24$; $0.04a + 0.08b = 1.2$**
  c. Solve the system to find how much of each type of fruit drink you need to use.
  18 kg A, 6 kg B

4. You have $22 in your bank account and deposit $11.50 each week. At the same time your cousin has $218 but is withdrawing $13 each week.
  a. When will your accounts have the same balance? **at 8 wk**
  b. How much money will each of you have after 12 weeks? **$160; $62**

Example 2
(page 363)

5. Business Suppose you invest $10,410 in equipment to manufacture a new board game. Each game costs $2.65 to manufacture and sells for $20. How many games must you make and sell before your business breaks even?
  600 games

3. Practice

Assignment Guide

① **Objective**
  Ⓐ Ⓑ Core 1–22
  Ⓒ Extension 23, 24

Standardized Test Prep 25–28

Mixed Review 29–43

Exercise 2 Tell students they can avoid decimal errors by writing the amounts in terms of cents, such as 195 instead of 1.95.

Alternative Method

Exercise 4 You can use a graphing calculator to determine when the balances are the same. Input each equation into the [Y=] function, and then press [2nd] [TABLE]. Use the arrows to scroll to find the row in which Y_1 and Y_2 are the same.

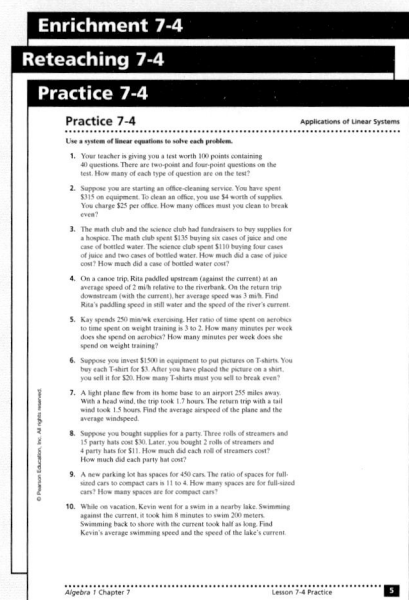

Error Prevention

Exercise 8 Some students may stop after solving for the first variable—the airspeed—and assume it is the complete answer to the problem. Remind students they should always go back and read the question again after they have done the algebraic work to make sure their answers are reasonable. It would not be reasonable for the wind's speed to be about 406 mi/h.

Exercises 9–14 Suggest to students that they read the key concepts at the beginning of this lesson and quickly review Lessons 7-1 through 7-3 to remind them when it is best to use each solution method.

pages 365–368   Exercises

9–14. Answers may vary. Samples are given.

9. Substitution; one eq. is solved for *t*.

10. Substitution; both eqs. are solved for *y*.

11. Elimination; subtract to eliminate *m*.

12. Substitution; both eqs. are solved for *y*.

13. Elimination; mult. first eq. by 3 and add to elim. *y*.

14. Substitution; one eq. is solved for *u*.

15a. $t = 99 - 3.5m$; $t = 0 + 2.5m$; $t = 41.25°$, $m = 16.5$ min

b. After 16.5 min, the temp. of either piece will be 41.25°C.

17. Answers may vary. Sample: You have 10 coins, all dimes and quarters. The value of the coins is $1.75. How many dimes do you have? How many quarters do you have? $q + d = 10$ $0.25q + 0.10d = 1.75$ You have 5 dimes and 5 quarters.

---

6. **Business** Several students decide to start a T-shirt company. After initial expenses of $280, they purchase each T-shirt wholesale for $3.99. They sell each T-shirt for $10.99. How many must they sell to break even? **40 shirts**

Example 3 (page 364)

7. **Travel** A family is canoeing downstream (with the current). Their speed relative to the banks of the river averages 2.75 mi/h. During the return trip, they paddle upstream (against the current), averaging 1.5 mi/h relative to the riverbank.
   a. Write an equation for the rate of the canoe downstream. **$s + c = 2.75$**
   b. Write an equation for the rate of the canoe upstream. **$s - c = 1.5$**
   c. Solve the system to find the family's paddling speed in still water. **2.125 mi/h**
   d. Find the speed of the current of the river. **0.625 mi/h**

8. **Travel** John flies from Atlanta, Georgia, to San Francisco, California. It takes 5.6 hours to travel 2100 miles against the head wind. At the same time Debby flies from San Francisco to Atlanta. Her plane travels with the same average airspeed but, with a tail wind, her flight takes only 4.8 hours.
   a. Write a system of equations that relates time, airspeed, and wind speed to distance for each traveler. **$(A + W)4.8 = 2100$, $(A - W)5.6 = 2100$**
   b. Solve the system to find the airspeed. **406.25 mi/h**
   c. Find the wind speed. **31.25 mi/h**

B Apply Your Skills

Open-Ended **Without solving, what method would you choose to solve each system: *graphing*, *substitution*, or *elimination*? Explain your reasoning.**

9–14. See margin.

9. $4s - 3t = 8$
   $t = -2s - 1$

10. $y = 3x - 1$
    $y = 4x$

11. $3m - 4n = 1$
    $3m - 2n = -1$

12. $y = -2x$
    $y = -\frac{1}{2}x + 3$

13. $2x - y = 4$
    $x + 3y = 16$

14. $u = 4v$
    $3u - 2v = 7$

15. **Chemistry** A piece of glass with an initial temperature of 99°C is cooled at a rate of 3.5 degrees Celsius per minute (°C/min). At the same time, a piece of copper with an initial temperature of 0°C is heated at a rate of 2.5°C/min. Let m = the number of minutes, and t = the temperature in degrees Celsius after m minutes.
   a. Write a system of equations that relates the temperature t of each material to the time m. Solve the system. **a–b. See margin.**
   b. **Writing** Explain what the solution means in this situation.

Real-World Connection

Glass can be drawn into optical fibers 16 km long. One fiber can carry 20 times as many phone calls as 500 copper wires.

16. **Geometry** The perimeter of the rectangle is 34 cm. The perimeter of the triangle is 30 cm. Find the values of m and n. **5 cm; 12 cm**

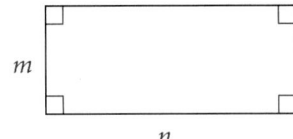 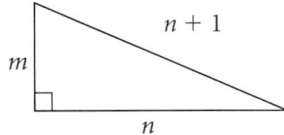

17. **Open-Ended** Write a problem for the total of two types of coins. Then solve the problem. **See margin.**

Reading Math

For help reading and solving Exercise 18, see page 369.

18. **Sales** A garden supply store sells two types of lawn mowers. Total sales of mowers for the year were $8379.70. The total number of mowers sold was 30. The small mower costs $249.99. The large mower costs $329.99. Find the number sold of each type of mower. **19 small mowers, 11 large mowers.**

Real-World  **Connection**

Ultralight aircraft like the one pictured above can weigh less than 400 lb.

20b. $g + b = 1908$
$g = \frac{19}{17}b$
901 boys, 1007 girls

24a. $2.50s + 4.00\ell = 10{,}000$
$\ell = \frac{5}{2}s$
800 small, 2000 large

19. Aviation Suppose you are flying an ultralight aircraft like the one pictured at the left. You fly to a nearby town, 18 miles away. With a tail wind, the trip takes $\frac{1}{3}$ hour. Your return flight with a head wind takes $\frac{3}{5}$ hour.
a. Find the average airspeed of the ultralight aircraft. **42 mi/h**
b. Find the average wind speed. **12 mi/h**

20. Suppose the ratio of girls to boys in your school is $19 : 17$. There are 1908 students altogether.
a. Solve the proportion $\frac{g}{b} = \frac{19}{17}$ for g. $g = \frac{19}{17}b$
b. Write and solve the system of equations to find the total number of boys b and girls g. **See left.**

21. Consumer Decisions Suppose you are trying to decide whether to buy ski equipment. Typically, it costs you $60 a day to rent ski equipment and buy a lift ticket. You can buy ski equipment for about $400. A lift ticket alone costs $35 for one day.
a. Find the break-even point. **16 days**
b. Critical Thinking If you expect to ski five days a year, should you buy the ski equipment? Explain. **See margin.**

22. Geometry Find the values of x and y. $x = 2$, $y = 4$

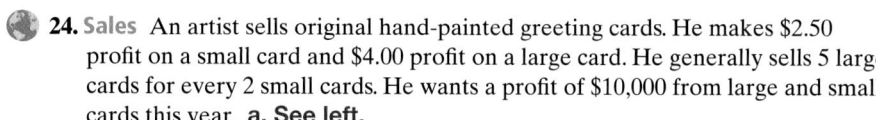

perimeter $= 14$

$3x$

y

$\frac{5}{4}y$

x

$\frac{5}{4}y$

perimeter $= 12$

 **Challenge**

23. You can represent the value of any two-digit number with the expression $10a + b$, where a is the tens' place digit and b is the ones' place digit. If a is 5 and b is 7, then the value of the number is $10(5) + 7$, or 57. **37**
Use a system of equations to find the two-digit number described below.

• The ones' place digit is one more than twice the tens' place digit.
• The value of the number is two more than five times the ones' place digit.

24. Sales An artist sells original hand-painted greeting cards. He makes $2.50 profit on a small card and $4.00 profit on a large card. He generally sells 5 large cards for every 2 small cards. He wants a profit of $10,000 from large and small cards this year. **a. See left.**
a. Find the quantity of each card the artist needs to sell to reach his goal.
b. The artist can create a card every 12 minutes. How many hours will he need to make enough to reach his profit target if he sells them all? **560 h**
c. What is the artist's hourly rate of pay? **$17.86/h**

Standardized Test Prep

Multiple Choice

25. Which system describes the following situation: The sum of two numbers is 20. The difference between three times the larger and twice the smaller is 40. **C**
A. $x + y = 20$
$3x + 2y = 40$
B. $x - y = 20$
$3x - 2y = 40$
C. $x + y = 20$
$3x - 2y = 40$
D. $x - y = 20$
$3x + 2y = 40$

Lesson 7-4 Applications of Linear Systems **367**

21b. **Answers may vary. Sample: If you plan to ski for many years, you should buy the equipment, since you will break even at 16 days.**

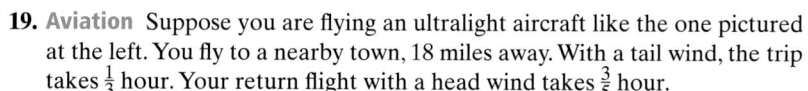

4. Assess

Lesson Quiz 7-4

1. One antifreeze solution is 10% alcohol. Another antifreeze solution is 18% alcohol. How many liters of each antifreeze solution should be combined to create 20 liters of antifreeze solution that is 15% alcohol?
7.5 L of 10% solution; 12.5 L of 18% solution

2. A local band is planning to make a compact disk. It will cost $12,500 to record and produce a master copy, and an additional $2.50 to make each sale copy. If they plan to sell the final product for $7.50, how many disks must they sell to break even? **2500 disks**

3. Suppose it takes you and a friend 3.2 hours to canoe 12 miles downstream (with the current). During the return trip, it takes you and your friend 4.8 hours to paddle upstream (against the current) to the original starting point. Find the average paddling speed in still water of you and your friend and the average speed of the current of the river. Round answers to the nearest tenth.
still water: 3.1 mi/h; current: 0.6 mi/h

Alternative Assessment

Organize students in groups of three. Let each group choose a word problem from the exercises. Assign each student a different method for solving the problem.

367

Standardized Test Prep

📁 **Resources**

For additional practice with a variety of test item formats:
- Standardized Test Prep, p. 391
- Test-Taking Strategies, p. 386
- Test-Taking Strategies with Transparencies

Exercise 27 Suggest to students that they first write "four more nickels than dimes" as $n = d + 4$.

26. The federal tax on a $12,000 salary was 8 times the state tax. If the combined taxes were $2700, find the state's share of taxes. **H**

   F. $400   **G.** $150

   H. $300   **I.** $350

27. Which system describes the following situation? Craig has 80¢ in nickels n and dimes d. He has four more nickels than dimes. **B**

   A. $d + n = 4$ **B.** $n - d = 4$

      $10d + 5n = 80$ $10d + 5n = 80$

   C. $d - n = 4$ **D.** $d + n = 4$

      $10d + 5n = 80$ $10d - 5n = 80$

Short Response

Take It to the NET
Online lesson quiz at
www.PHSchool.com
Web Code: aea-0704

28. A large group of students wants to go to the movies. If the students take 3 vans and 1 car, they can transport 22 people. If they take 2 vans and 4 cars, they can transport 28 people. Write and solve a system of equations to find the number of people that can be transported in a van. Show your work. **See margin.**

━━━━━━━━━━ **Mixed Review** ━━━━━━━━━━

Lesson 7-3   **Solve by elimination.**

29. $2x + 5y = 13$ **30.** $4x + 2y = -10$ **31.** $7x + 6y = 30$

     $3x - 5y = 7$ **(4, 1)** $-2x + 3y = 33$ **(−6, 7)** $9x - 8y = 15$ $\left(3, \frac{3}{2}\right)$

Lesson 6-1   **Find the slope of the line that passes through each pair of points.**

32. $(2, 4), (6, 10)$ $\frac{3}{2}$ **33.** $(-3, 1), (10, 14)$ **1**   **34.** $(8, -11), (5, -12)$ $\frac{1}{3}$

35. $(1.2, 7), (4.6, 0.2)$ **−2**   **36.** $\left(5, -\frac{1}{2}\right), \left(-6, 3\frac{1}{2}\right)$ $-\frac{4}{11}$ **37.** $(8, 0), (8, 5)$ **undefined**

Lesson 3-5   **Solve each inequality and graph the solutions. 38–43. See margin.**

38. $6 < y < 10$ **39.** $-8 < n \le 3$ **40.** $2 < k + 1 < 7$

41. $4 \le 4p \le 16$ **42.** $-13 < 3c + 2 \le 17$ **43.** $21 > 5w - 4 > 1$

Algebra at Work

·····Businessperson

Restriction Polygon

— Advertising
— Raw Materials
— Transportation
— Packaging
— Equipment
— Labor

Some of the goals of a business are to minimize costs and maximize profits. People in business use systems of linear inequalities to analyze data in order to achieve these goals. The illustration lists some of the variables involved in operating a small manufacturing company. To solve a problem, a businessperson must identify the variables and restrictions, and then search for the best of many possible solutions.

Take It to the NET For more information about a career in business, go to **www.PHSchool.com**.
Web Code: aeb-2031

pages 365–368 Exercises

28. **[2]** $3V + C = 22$ $12V + 4C = 88$

        $2V + 4C = 28$ $\Rightarrow$ $\underline{2V + 4C = 28}$

                         $10V = 60$

                           $V = 6$

   6 people/van

[1] 6 people/van, no work shown

38. $6 < y < 10$

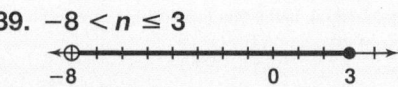

39. $-8 < n \le 3$

Reading Math

Reading for Problem Solving

FOR USE WITH PAGE 366, EXERCISE 18

Read the exercise below and then follow along with what Bill thinks and writes. Check your understanding by solving the exercise at the bottom of the page.

A garden supply store sells two types of lawn mowers. Total sales of mowers for the year were $8379.70. The total number of mowers sold was 30. The small mowers cost $249.99. The large mowers cost $329.99. Find the number of each type of mower sold.

What Bill Thinks

I'll read the problem and write down the important information.

Where should I start? Well, it's always helpful to write sentences based on the information I'm given. Total sales include the sales for both the small mowers and the large mowers.

Total number of mowers is the number of small mowers *plus* the number of large mowers.

Now I'll define some variables. The problem asks for the number of small mowers and the number of large mowers. I'll use 2 variables.

Now I can write 2 equations.

Since the first equation has large numbers, it's probably easier to rewrite the second equation and substitute into the first equation. I'll then solve for w and s.

I'll write my answer in a sentence.

What Bill Writes

Total sales = $8379.70
Total number of mowers = 30
Small mowers cost $249.99.
Large mowers cost $329.99.

Total sales = sales from small mowers + sales from large mowers

Total number of mowers = number of small mowers + number of large mowers

Number of small mowers = s
Number of large mowers = w

Total sales: $8379.70 = 249.99s + 329.99w$
Total number: $30 = s + w$

$s = 30 - w$
$8379.70 = (249.99)(30 - w) + 329.99w$
$8379.70 = 7499.70 + 80w$
$880 = 80w$
$11 = w; s = 30 - 11 = 19$

The store sold 19 small mowers and 11 large mowers.

EXERCISE

A nursery sells small apple trees for $19.99 and large apple trees for $35.99. Total sales for the year were $1907.27. The total number of apple trees sold was 73. Find the number of each type of apple tree sold. **45 small trees; 28 large trees**

40. $1 < k < 6$

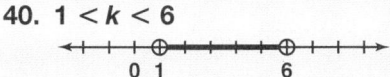

42. $-5 < c \leq 5$

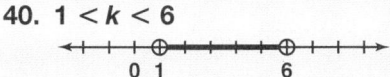

41. $1 \leq p \leq 4$

43. $5 > w > 1$

369

Lesson Preview

 **Check Skills You'll Need**

Standard Form
Lesson 6-3: Example 4
Exercises 27–35
Extra Practice, p. 707

Linear Inequalities
Lesson 3-1: Example 1
Exercises 1–8
Extra Practice, p. 704

Lesson Resources

📁 **Teaching Resources**
Practice, Reteaching, Enrichment
Checkpoint Quiz 2

👥 **Reaching All Students**
Practice Workbook 7-5
Spanish Practice Workbook 7-5
Reading and Math Literacy 7C
Spanish Reading & Literacy 7C
Spanish Checkpoint Quiz 2
Hands-On Activities 16
Basic Algebra Planning Guide 7-5

⏱ **Presentation Assistant Plus!**
Transparencies
• Check Skills You'll Need 7-5
• Additional Examples 7-5
• Student Edition Answers 7-5
• Lesson Quiz 7-5
PH Presentation Pro CD 7-5

PRENTICE HALL ASSESSMENT SYSTEM

Checkpoint Quiz 2
Computer Test Generator CD

💿 **Technology**
Resource Pro® CD-ROM
Computer Test Generator CD
Prentice Hall Presentation Pro CD

💻 **www.PHSchool.com**
Student Site
• Teacher Web Code: aek-5500
• Self-grading Lesson Quiz
Teacher Center
• Lesson Planner
• Resources

Plus 🄸TEXT

Linear Inequalities

North Carolina Objectives   4.01   Use linear functions or inequalities to model and solve problems; justify results. a) Solve using tables, graphs, and algebraic properties.

Lesson Preview

What You'll Learn

OBJECTIVE 1 To graph linear inequalities

OBJECTIVE 2 To write and use linear inequalities when modeling real-world situations

. . . And Why

To analyze possible purchases within a budget, as in Example 3

✔ **Check Skills You'll Need**   (For help, go to Lessons 3-1 and 6-2.)

Describe each statement as *always*, *sometimes*, or *never* true.

1. $-3 > -2$ never   **2.** $8 \le 8$ always   **3.** $4n \ge n$ sometimes

Write each equation in slope-intercept form.

4. $2x - 3y = 9$ $y = \frac{2}{3}x - 3$ **5.** $y + 3x = 6$ $y = -3x + 6$ **6.** $4y - 3x = 1$ $y = \frac{3}{4}x + \frac{1}{4}$

New Vocabulary   • linear inequality   • solutions of an inequality

---

🄸TEXT   Interactive lesson includes instant self-check, tutorials, and activities.

Graphing Linear Inequalities

Investigation: Graphing Inequalities

1. Graph $y = x + 4$ on a coordinate plane. **See back of book.**

2. Test three points that lie above the graph of $y = x + 4$. Substitute the coordinates of each of the points for (x, y) in the inequality $y > x + 4$. If the results are true statements, mark the points on your graph.
See back of book.

3. Test three points that lie below the graph of $y = x + 4$. Substitute the coordinates of each of the points for (x, y) in the inequality $y > x + 4$. If the results are true statements, mark the points on your graph.
See back of book.

4. **Critical Thinking** To graph $y > x + 4$, would you choose points above or below $y = x + 4$? **above**

5. Determine whether you would graph points above or below the graph of $y = x - 2$ to graph the inequality $y < x - 2$. **below**

Need Help?

To review graphing inequalities in one variable see p. 135.

Just as you have used inequalities to describe graphs on a number line, you can use inequalities to describe regions of a coordinate plane.

Number line
$x < 1$

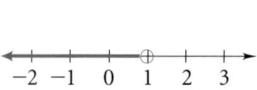

Coordinate plane
$x < 1$

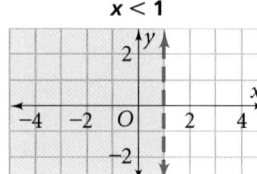

Ongoing Assessment and Intervention

Before the Lesson
Diagnose prerequisite skills using:
• Check Skills You'll Need

During the Lesson
Monitor progress using:
• Check Understanding
• Additional Examples
• Standardized Test Prep

After the Lesson
Assess knowledge using:
• Lesson Quiz
• Computer Test Generator CD
• Chapter Checkpoint 2 (p. 376)

A **linear inequality** describes a region of the coordinate plane that has a boundary line. The **solutions of an inequality** are the coordinates of the points that make the inequality true.

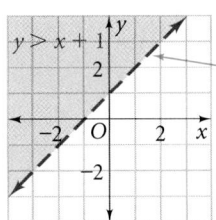

Each point on a *dashed* boundary line is not a solution.

Each point on a *solid* boundary line is a solution.

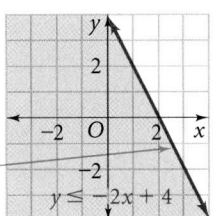

As you can see in the graphs above, you can tell from an inequality whether to shade above or below the boundary line. For an inequality written in the form of $y <$ or $y \leq$, shade below the boundary line. For an inequality written in the form of $y >$ or $y \geq$, shade above the boundary line.

1 **EXAMPLE** Graphing an Inequality

Graph $y < 2x + 3$.

First graph the boundary line $y = 2x + 3$.

The coordinates of points on the boundary line do not make the inequality true. So, use a dashed line.

Shade below the boundary line.

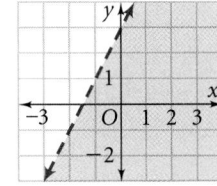

Check The point $(0, 0)$ is in the region of the graph of the inequality. See if $(0, 0)$ satisfies the inequality.

$y < 2x + 3$

$0 < 2(0) + 3$ **Substitute (0, 0) for (x, y).**

$0 < 3$ ✓

✓ **Check Understanding** ① Graph $y \geq 3x - 1$. **See left.**

1.

2.

In order to tell whether you shade above or below a boundary line, you may need to write the inequality in slope-intercept form.

2 **EXAMPLE** Rewriting to Graph an Inequality

Graph $3x - 5y \leq 10$.

Solve $3x - 5y \leq 10$ for y.

$3x - 5y \leq 10$

$-5y \leq -3x + 10$ **Subtract 3x from each side.**

$y \geq \frac{3}{5}x - 2$ **Divide each side by −5. Reverse the inequality symbol.**

Graph $y = \frac{3}{5}x - 2$.

The coordinates of points on the boundary line make the inequality true. So, use a solid line.

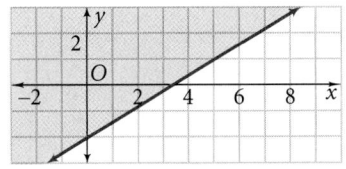

Since $y \geq \frac{3}{5}x - 2$, shade above the boundary line.

? Need Help?
Multiplying or dividing an inequality by a negative number reverses the order of the inequality.

✓ **Check Understanding** ② Graph $6x + 8y \geq 12$. **See above left.**

👥 Reaching All Students

| **Below Level** To help students decide if a solution region of an inequality is above or below a boundary line, have them always test a point on both sides of the boundary line or solve for y. | **Advanced Learners** Challenge students to graph $y \geq x$. | **Tactile Learners** See note on page 371. **Error Prevention** See note on page 371. |

Math Background

When inequalities are written with y isolated on the left, they are easier to compare. In this form, $<$ will indicate a region below or to the left of the line, while $>$ will indicate a region above or to the right of the line.

OBJECTIVE

1 Teaching Notes

Investigation (Optional)
Tactile Learners

Use masking tape or string to make a large coordinate grid on the floor. Have two students use string to model the equations related to simple inequalities, such as $y \geq 3$, $x < 1$, or $y \leq x$. Direct other students to move to the correct regions.

1 **EXAMPLE** Error Prevention

Students may confuse when to use dashed or solid lines as boundaries. Relate *dashed* lines to *open* circles and *solid* lines to *solid* circles used in graphing one-variable inequalities.

2 **EXAMPLE** Math Tip

Students may ask why the half-planes are above or below, instead of to the right or left, of the line. Either can be used. When an inequality is solved for y, it means the y-values in the solution half-plane are more or less than the corresponding y-values on the boundary line. Since the y-axis is vertical, we generally say the half-plane is above or below the line. Similarly, since the x-axis is horizontal, we say the half-plane is to the right or left of the line when an inequality is solved for x.

📋 Additional Examples

① Graph $y > -2x + 1$.

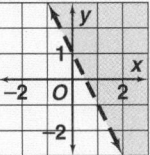

371

Additional Examples

② Graph $4x - 3y \geq 9$.

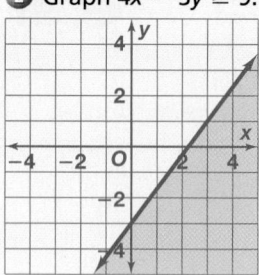

OBJECTIVE 2 Teaching Notes

③ EXAMPLE Alternative Method

Show the solution of this system of inequalities using an overhead projector. On one transparency draw the grid in black and the solution of $y \geq 80$ in red. On another transparency, draw the grid in black and the solution of $2x + 2y \leq 310$ in blue. Show each transparency separately and then show them superimposed. The area that is both red and blue (purple) represents the graph of the solution. If an overhead projector is not available, show the solutions on the board using two colors or different shading patterns.

Additional Examples

③ Suppose your budget allows you to spend no more than $24 for decorations for a party. Streamers cost $2 a roll and tablecloths cost $6 each. Use intercepts to graph the inequality that represents the situation. Find three possible combinations of streamers and tablecloths you can buy. **Sample answers:**
9 streamers and 1 tablecloth,
6 streamers and 2 tablecloths, and
4 streamers and 2 tablecloths

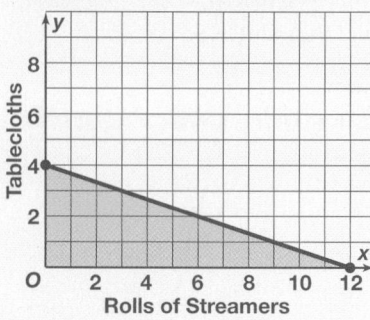

OBJECTIVE 2 Modeling Real-World Situations

Many situations are modeled by inequalities that have a boundary line of the form $Ax + By = C$. You can use the intercepts to graph the boundary line of the inequality. Choose a test point such as $(0, 0)$ to determine whether the solutions are above or below the boundary line.

③ EXAMPLE Real-World Problem Solving

Budget Suppose your budget for a party allows you to spend no more than $12 on peanuts and cashews. Peanuts cost $2/lb and cashews cost $4/lb. Find three possible combinations of peanuts and cashews you can buy.

Relate cost of peanuts plus cost of cashews is less than or equal to total budget

Define Let x = the number of pounds of peanuts.

Let y = the number of pounds of cashews.

Write $2x + 4y \leq 12$

Graph $2x + 4y = 12$ by graphing the intercepts, $(6, 0)$ and $(0, 3)$.

The coordinates of points on the boundary line make the inequality true. So, use a solid line.

Graph only in Quadrant I, since you cannot buy a negative amount of peanuts or cashews.

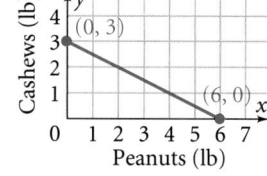

Test the point $(0, 0)$.

$2x + 4y \leq 12$
$2(0) + 4(0) \leq 12$ **Substitute (0, 0) for (x, y).**
$0 \leq 12$ **Since the inequality is true, (0, 0) is a solution.**

Shade the region containing $(0, 0)$. The graph below shows all the possible solutions of the problem.

Party Snacks

Since the boundary line is included in the graph, the intercepts are also solutions of the inequality. The solution $(2, 2)$ means that if you buy 2 lb of peanuts, you can buy 2 lb of cashews. Three solutions are $(2, 2)$, $(3, 1)$, and $(1, 2)$.

Real-World Connection

One ounce of peanuts has 9 g of protein. One ounce of cashews has 5.4 g of protein.

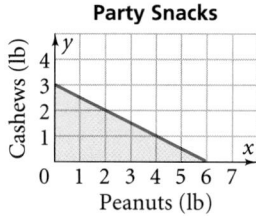

3. Answers may vary.
Sample:
6 lb hamburger and 2 lb chicken,
3 lb hamburger and 6 lb chicken,
5 lb hamburger and 3 lb chicken

✓ Check Understanding

③ Cooking Suppose you plan to spend no more than $24 on meat for a cookout. At your local market, hamburger costs $3.00/lb and chicken wings cost $2.40/lb. Find three possible combinations of hamburger and chicken wings you can buy. See left.

372 Chapter 7 Systems of Equations and Inequalities

Closure

Ask students to compare graphing linear inequalities with graphing linear equations. When you graph a linear equation, the graph is a solid line. When you graph a linear inequality, the boundary line may be dashed or solid, and you shade the region on one side of the line.

pages 373–376 Exercises

11.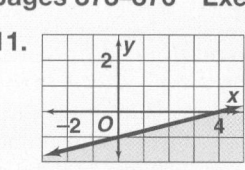

EXERCISES

For more practice, see *Extra Practice.*

Practice and Problem Solving

Ⓐ **Practice by Example**

Example 1
(page 371)

Determine whether point *P* is a solution of the linear inequality.

1. $y \leq -2x + 1; P(2, 2)$ no **2.** $x < 2; P(1, 0)$ yes **3.** $y \geq 3x - 2; P(0, 0)$ yes

4. $y > x - 1; P(0, 1)$ yes **5.** $y \geq -\frac{2}{5}x + 4; P(0, 0)$ no **6.** $y > \frac{5}{3}x - 4; P(0, 1)$ yes

Choose the linear inequality that describes each graph.

7.
A
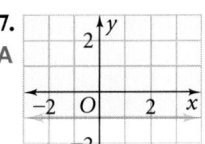
A. $y \geq -1$
B. $y \leq -1$

8.
B
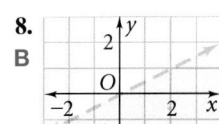
A. $y > \frac{1}{2}x$
B. $y < \frac{1}{2}x$

9.
B
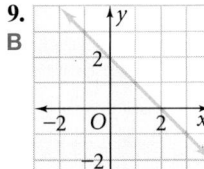
A. $y \geq -x + 2$
B. $y \leq -x + 2$

10.
A
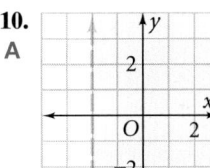
A. $x > -2$
B. $x < -2$

Graph each linear inequality. **11–17. See margin.**

11. $y \leq \frac{1}{4}x - 1$ **12.** $y \geq \frac{1}{4}x - 1$ **13.** $y < -4x - 1$ **14.** $y \geq 4x - 1$

15. $y < 5x - 5$ **16.** $y \leq \frac{2}{5}x - 3$ **17.** $y \leq -3x$ **18.** $y \geq -\frac{1}{2}x$

See back of book.

Example 2
(page 371)

Write each linear inequality in slope-intercept form. Then graph the inequality.
19–22. See back of book.

19. $2x - 3y \geq 7$ **20.** $5x - 3y \leq 6$ **21.** $4x - 6y \geq 16$ **22.** $-4y - 6x > 8$

Example 3
(page 372)

Real-World 🌐 Connection

The American Academy of
Orthopaedic Surgeons
suggest that a backpack's
weight should not be more
than 20% of a student's
body weight.

23. Budget Suppose you are shopping for crepe paper to decorate the school gym
for a dance. Gold crepe paper costs $5 per roll, and blue crepe paper costs $3
per roll. Your budget allows you to spend at most $48 for crepe paper. How many
rolls of gold and blue crepe paper can you buy without exceeding your budget?

  Let x = the number of rolls of blue crepe paper.
  Let y = the number of rolls of gold crepe paper.

  a. Write a linear inequality that describes the situation. $3x + 5y \leq 48$
  b. Graph the linear inequality. b–d. See back of book.
  c. Write three possible solutions to the problem.
  d. Critical Thinking The point $(-2, 5)$ is a solution of the inequality. Is it
  a solution of the problem? Explain.

24. Manufacturing A company makes nylon and canvas backpacks, as shown at
the left. The profit on a nylon backpack is $3 and the profit on a canvas
backpack is $10. How many backpacks must the company sell to make a profit
of more than $250?
  a. Write a linear inequality that describes the situation. $3n + 10c > 250$
  b. Graph the linear inequality. b–d. See back of book.
  c. Write three possible solutions to the problem.
  d. Critical Thinking Which values are reasonable for the domain and for
  the range? Explain.

Lesson 7-5 Linear Inequalities **373**

Assignment Guide

▼ 1 **Objective**
Ⓐ Ⓑ **Core** 1–22, 25–36,
38–43
Ⓒ **Extension** 46–47

▼ 2 **Objective**
Ⓐ Ⓑ **Core** 23, 24, 37,
44, 45
Ⓒ **Extension** 48–49

Standardized Test Prep 50–54

Mixed Review 55–70

Error Prevention
Exercises 11–18 Suggest to
students that they circle the
symbols $<$ and $>$ that do not
include "equals" to remind them
to use a dashed boundary line.

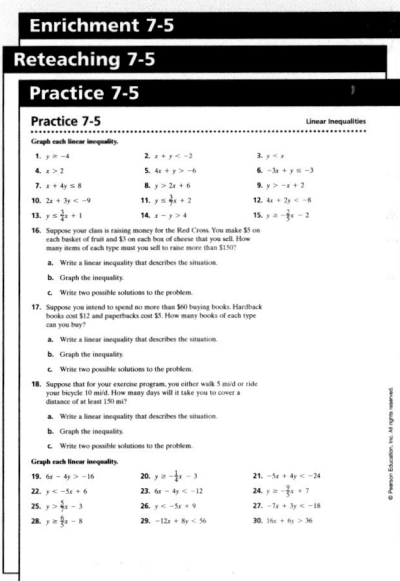

12.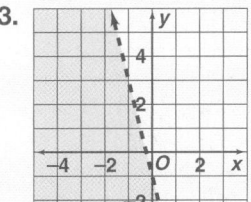

13.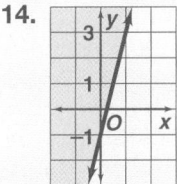

14.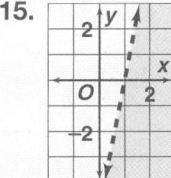

15.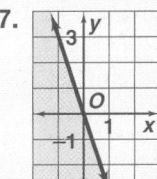

16.

17.

25.
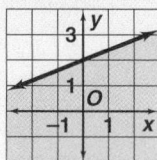

26.
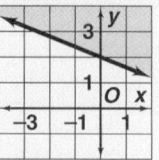

27.
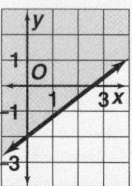

28.
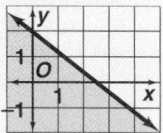

29.
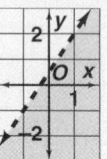

30.
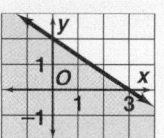

31.
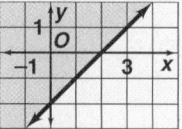

32.
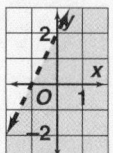

33. For an inequality written in the form $y <$ or $y \leq$, shade below the boundary line. For an inequality written in the form $y >$ or $y \geq$, shade above the boundary line.

374

 Apply Your Skills

Graph each linear inequality. 25–32. See margin.

25. $y \leq \frac{2}{5}x + 2$ **26.** $y \geq -\frac{2}{5}x + 2$ **27.** $4x - 5y \leq 10$ **28.** $4x + 5y \leq 10$

29. $4y < 6x + 2$ **30.** $2x + 3y \leq 6$ **31.** $4x - 4y \leq 8$ **32.** $y - 2x < 2$

33. Writing Explain how you can tell from a linear inequality whether you will shade above or below the graph of the boundary line. **See margin.**

Write the inequality shown in each graph.

34.
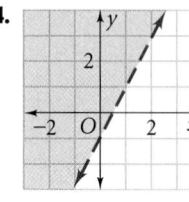
$y > 2x - 1$

35.
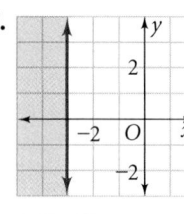
$x \leq -3$

36.
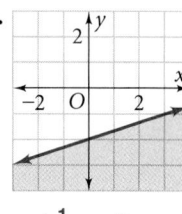
$y \leq \frac{1}{3}x - 2$

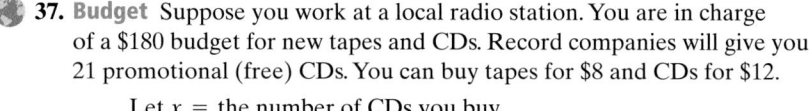

37. Budget Suppose you work at a local radio station. You are in charge of a $180 budget for new tapes and CDs. Record companies will give you 21 promotional (free) CDs. You can buy tapes for $8 and CDs for $12.

Let x = the number of CDs you buy.
Let y = the number of tapes you buy.

$12x + 8y \leq 180$

a. Write an inequality that shows the number of tapes and CDs you can buy.
b. Graph the inequality. **b–c. See margin.**
c. Is $(8, 9)$ a solution of the inequality? Explain what the solution means.
d. If you buy only tapes and you buy as many as possible, how many new recordings will the station get? **43**

Write the linear inequality described. Then graph the inequality. 38–41.
See margin.

38. x is positive.   **39.** y is negative.

40. y is not negative.   **41.** x is less than y.

42. Error Analysis Jan's graph of the inequality $4x + 6y > 12$ is shown below. What is wrong with the graph?

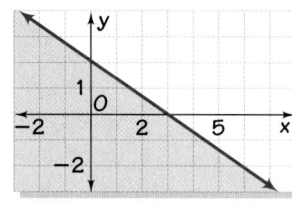

It should be shaded above the line, and the line should be dashed.

43. Critical Thinking Write an inequality that describes the entire part of the coordinate plane *not* included in the solution of $y \geq x + 2$. $y < x + 2$

44. Probability Suppose you play a carnival game. You toss one blue and one red number cube. If the number on the blue cube is greater than the number on the red cube, you win a prize. The graph at the left shows all the possible outcomes of tossing the cubes.
a. Copy and shade the graph to show the winning outcomes. **See margin p. 376.**
b. Write an inequality that describes the shaded region. $y > x$
c. What is the probability that you will win a prize? $\frac{5}{12}$

Comparing Cubes
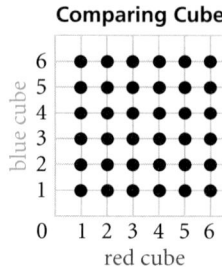

Real-World Connection

In 2000, there were about 12,900 licensed radio stations in the United States.

37b.
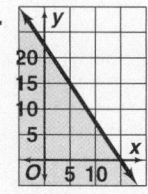

c. Yes; you can buy 8 CDs and 9 tapes.

Problem Solving Hint

For Exercise 45, draw a diagram of a possible garden.

45. Geometry You want to fence a rectangular area of your yard for a garden. You plan to use no more than 50 ft of fencing. **a–c. See margin p. 376.**
  a. Write and graph a linear inequality that describes this situation.
  b. **Open-Ended** What are two possible sizes for a square garden?
  c. Can you make the garden 12 ft by 15 ft? Justify your answer.

C Challenge

For Exercises 46–47, write the inequality that has the solution described.

46. The points $(0, -3)$ and $(8, 5)$ lie on the boundary line, but neither point is a solution. The point $(1, 1)$ is not a solution. $y < x - 3$

47. The points $(7, 12)$ and $(-3, -8)$ lie on the boundary line, and each point is a solution. The point $(1, 1)$ is also a solution. $y \geq 2x - 2$

48. a. Open-Ended Write and graph an inequality in the form $Ax + By > C$, where A, B, and C are all positive. **a–c. See margin p. 376.**
  b. Write and graph an inequality in the form $Ax + By < C$, where A, B, and C are all positive.
  c. **Reasoning** Both inequalities are in standard form. Make a conjecture about the inequality symbol and the region shaded.
  d. Would your conjecture in part (c) be different if B were negative? **yes**

49c. Answers may vary. Sample: (2, 3)

d.

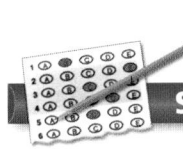

49. a. Is the point $(4, 5)$ a solution of the inequality $y > x - 1$? **yes**
  b. Is the point $(4, 5)$ a solution of the inequality $y < 3x$? **yes**
  c. Find one other point that is a solution of both inequalities.
  d. Draw a graph that shows all the points that are solutions of both inequalities. **c–d. See left.**

Standardized Test Prep

Multiple Choice

50. Which of the following is true of the graph of $y \geq -x + 1$? **A**
  A. The line is solid, and the shading is above the line.
  B. The line is dashed, and the shading is above the line.
  C. The line is solid, and the shading is below the line.
  D. The line is dashed, and the shading is below the line.

51. Which linear inequality describes the graph at the right? **H**
  F. $y < -\frac{2}{3}x - 4$ G. $y > -\frac{2}{3}x - 4$
  H. $y \leq -\frac{2}{3}x - 4$ I. $y \geq -\frac{2}{3}x - 4$

52. The graph of which of the following is shaded above the line? **D**
  A. $x + y < 9$ B. $x + y < -9$
  C. $y - x < 9$ D. $x - y < 9$

53. Which inequality below models the following situation?

You want to spend less than $20 on asparagus and bananas. Asparagus is $3.00 per pound and bananas are $.50 per pound. Let a represent the weight of the asparagus and b represent the weight of the bananas. **F**

Take It to the NET

Online lesson quiz at **www.PHSchool.com**

Web Code: aea-0705

  F. $3a + 0.5b < 20$ G. $3a + 0.5b > 20$
  H. $3a + 0.5b \leq 20$ I. $3a + 0.5b \geq 20$

Short Response

54. Explain how to graph $y \leq 3x - 4$. Then graph the inequality.
  See back of book.

38. $x > 0$;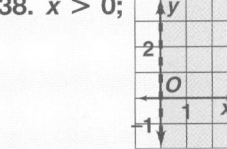

39. $y < 0$;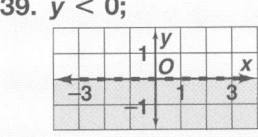

40. $y \geq 0$;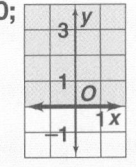

41. $x < y$;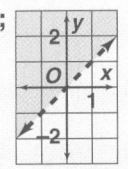

 Lesson Quiz 7-5

1. Determine whether $(4, 1)$ is a solution of $3x + 2y \geq 10$.
yes

Graph each inequality.

2. $x > -2$

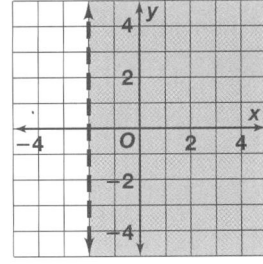

3. $5x - 2y > 10$

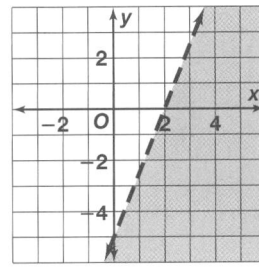

4. $2x + 6y \leq 0$

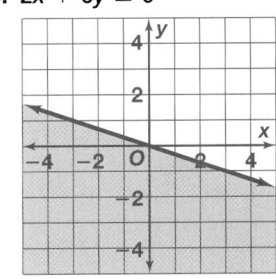

Alternative Assessment

Organize students into groups of three. Instruct each student to write a linear inequality on a piece of paper and give the paper to another student in the group. That student graphs the dashed or solid boundary line of the inequality and passes the paper on to the third student. The third student shades the appropriate region.

375

📁 **Resources**

For additional practice with a variety of test item formats:
- Standardized Test Prep, p. 391
- Test-Taking Strategies, p. 386
- Test-Taking Strategies with Transparencies

✓ **Chapter Checkpoint 2**

To check understanding of Lessons 7-3 to 7-5:

Checkpoint Quiz 2 (p. 376)

📁 **Teaching Resources**
Checkpoint Quiz 2 (also in Prentice Hall Assessment System)

Reaching All Students
Reading and Math Literacy 7C

Spanish versions available

---

pages 373–376   Exercises

44a.

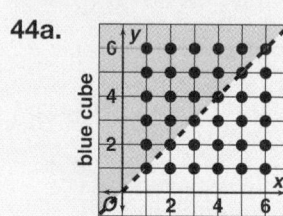

blue cube / red cube

45a. $2w + 2\ell \leq 50$;

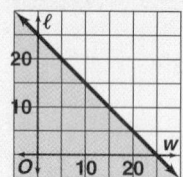

b. Answers may vary. Sample: 10 ft by 10 ft, 5 ft by 5 ft

c. No; (12, 15) is not in the shaded region and is not a sol. of the inequality.

48a. Answers may vary. Sample: $2x + y > 3$

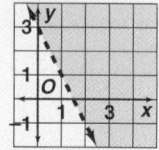

376

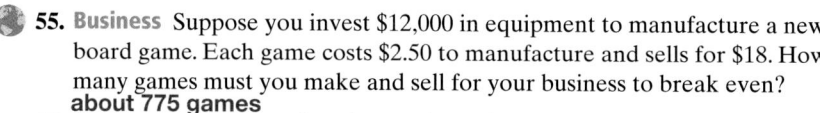
Mixed Review

Lesson 7-4   For Exercises 55–56, define the variables and write a system of equations for each situation. Solve by any method.

🌐 **55. Business** Suppose you invest $12,000 in equipment to manufacture a new board game. Each game costs $2.50 to manufacture and sells for $18. How many games must you make and sell for your business to break even? **about 775 games**

56. Suppose you are canoeing along a river with a steady current. Your average speed upstream is 2.5 mi/h. On the return trip you paddle with the current, and your average speed is 4 mi/h. Find the average speed of the current and your average speed if you were paddling in still water. **0.75 mi/h, 3.25 mi/h**

Lesson 5-6   Find the common difference of each arithmetic sequence.

57. $-8, -3, 2, \ldots$ **5**   **58.** $4, 11, 18, \ldots$ **7**   **59.** $13, 24, 35, \ldots$ **11**   **60.** $11, 5, -1, \ldots$ **-6**

Find the second and fourth terms of each sequence.

61. $A(n) = 3 + (n - 1)(5)$ **8, 18**   **62.** $A(n) = -9 + (n - 1)(2.3)$ **-6.7, -2.1**

Lesson 4-1   Solve each proportion.

63. $\frac{3}{4} = \frac{m}{16}$ **12**   **64.** $\frac{6}{7} = \frac{24}{8}$ **28**   **65.** $\frac{4}{w} = \frac{8}{22}$ **11**   **66.** $\frac{9}{10} = \frac{15}{a}$ **$16\frac{2}{3}$**

67. $\frac{x + 1}{3} = \frac{2}{9}$ **$-\frac{1}{3}$**   **68.** $\frac{n - 2}{5} = \frac{6}{15}$ **4**   **69.** $\frac{8}{r + 1} = \frac{4}{7}$ **13**   **70.** $\frac{9}{x + 3} = \frac{18}{19}$ **6.5**

✓ **Checkpoint Quiz 2** 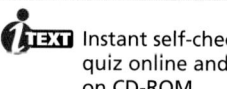 **Lessons 7-3 through 7-5**

📱**TEXT** Instant self-check quiz online and on CD-ROM

For Exercises 1–5, solve each system using elimination.

1. $2x + 5y = 2$
$3x - 5y = 53$ **(11, −4)**

2. $-8x - 3y = 69$
$8x + 7y = -65$ **(−9, 1)**

3. $4x + 2y = 34$
$10x - 4y = -5$ **(3.5, 10)**

4. $11x - 13y = 89$
$-11x + 13y = 107$ **no solution**

5. $3x + 6y = 42$
$-7x + 8y = -109$ **$\left(15, -\frac{1}{2}\right)$**

6. $n + d = 21$,
$0.05n + 0.10d = 1.70$;
8 nickels, 13 dimes

6. You have a total of 21 coins, all nickels and dimes. The total value is $1.70. Write and solve a system of equations to find the number of dimes d and the number of nickels n that you have. **See left.**

7. $y = 200 + 0.35x$,
$y = 1.20x$; about 236 ice cream cones

🌐 **7. Business** Suppose you start an ice cream business. You buy a freezer for $200. It costs you $.35 to make each single-scoop ice cream cone. You sell each cone for $1.20. Write and solve a system of equations to find the break-even point for your business. **See left.**

8. To go to a campsite 12 miles away, you paddle a canoe against the current of a river for 4 hours. During your return trip you paddle with the current, and you travel the same distance in 3 hours. Write and solve a system of equations to find your paddling speed in still water. Find the speed of the current of the river. $x + y = 4, x - y = 3$; **3.5 mi/h, 0.5 mi/h**

Graph each inequality. 9–10. See margin.

9. $y \geq 2x - 4$

10. $3x + 4y < 18$

48b. Answers may vary. Sample: $3x + y < 1$

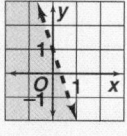

c. If an inequality is in standard form, where A, B, and C are all positive, you shade above the line for $>$ or $\geq$ and below the line for $<$ or $\leq$.

page 376   Checkpoint Quiz 2

9.

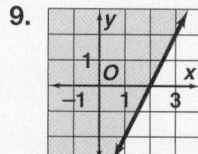

10.

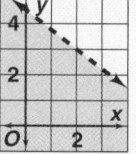

Systems of Linear Inequalities

North Carolina Objectives

4.03 Use systems of linear equations or inequalities in two variables to model and solve problems. Solve using tables, graphs, and algebraic properties; justify results.

Lesson Preview

What You'll Learn

 OBJECTIVE 1
To solve systems of linear inequalities by graphing

 OBJECTIVE 2
To model real-world situations using systems of linear inequalities

. . . And Why

To find the possible dimensions for a zoo habitat, as in Example 3

 Check Skills You'll Need   (For help, go to Lessons 7-1 and 7-5.)

Solve each system by graphing. 1–3. See back of book.

1. $y = 3x - 6$
$y = -x + 2$

2. $y = -\frac{1}{2}x + 4$
$y = -\frac{1}{2}x + 3$

3. $x + y = 4$
$2x - y = 8$

Graph each inequality. 4–6. See back of book.

4. $y > 5$

5. $y \leq \frac{2}{3}x - 1$

6. $4x - 8y \geq 4$

New Vocabulary
• system of linear inequalities
• solution of a system of linear inequalities

 Interactive lesson includes instant self-check, tutorials, and activities.

OBJECTIVE 1 Solving Systems of Linear Inequalities by Graphing

Two or more linear inequalities together form a **system of linear inequalities.** The system below describes the lavender-shaded region of the graph. Notice that there are two boundary lines.

System of Linear Inequalities

$x \geq 3$
$y < -2$

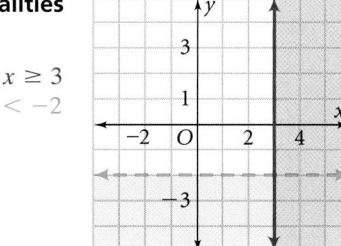

You can describe all the points of a quadrant with a system of linear inequalities.

$x < 0$
$y > 0$

$x > 0$
$y > 0$

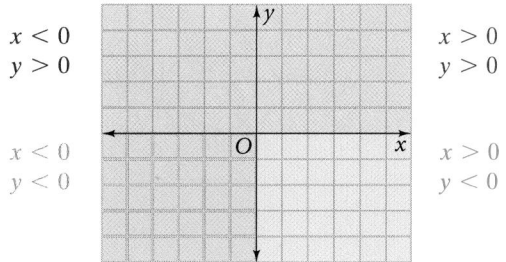

$x < 0$
$y < 0$

$x > 0$
$y < 0$

A **solution of a system of linear inequalities** makes each inequality in the system true. The graph of a system shows all of its solutions.

Lesson 7-6 Systems of Linear Inequalities **377**

 **Ongoing Assessment and Intervention**

Before the Lesson
Diagnose prerequisite skills using:
• Check Skills You'll Need

During the Lesson
Monitor progress using:
• Check Understanding
• Additional Examples
• Standardized Test Prep

After the Lesson
Assess knowledge using:
• Lesson Quiz
• Computer Test Generator CD

 7-6   North Carolina Objectives 4.03

1. Plan

Lesson Preview

 **Check Skills You'll Need**

Linear Inequalities
Lesson 7-5: Example 2
Exercises 19–22
Extra Practice, p. 708

Solving Systems by Graphing
Lesson 7-1: Examples 1, 3
Exercises 5–12, 14, 15, 17
Extra Practice, p. 708

Lesson Resources

 Teaching Resources
Practice, Reteaching, Enrichment

Reaching All Students
Practice Workbook 7-6
Spanish Practice Workbook 7-6
Hands-On Activities 17
Basic Algebra Planning Guide 7-6

 Presentation Assistant Plus!
Transparencies
• Check Skills You'll Need 7-6
• Additional Examples 7-6
• Student Edition Answers 7-6
• Lesson Quiz 7-6
PH Presentation Pro CD 7-6

PRENTICE HALL ASSESSMENT SYSTEM

Computer Test Generator CD

Technology
Resource Pro® CD-ROM
Computer Test Generator CD
Prentice Hall Presentation Pro CD

 **www.PHSchool.com**
Student Site
• Teacher Web Code: aek-5500
• Self-grading Lesson Quiz
Teacher Center
• Lesson Planner
• Resources

Plus **iTEXT**

Math Background

The various relations of inequality are binary relations that possess some, but not all, of the properties of equality. For example, 'is less than' is not a reflexive relation; $6 < 6$ is not true.

OBJECTIVE 1 Teaching Notes

1 EXAMPLE Visual Learners

Have students use one colored pencil or highlighting marker to graph the first inequality and another color to graph the second inequality. Tell students that the points in the region where the two colors overlap are the solutions. Any point in that region must satisfy both inequalities.

2 EXAMPLE Connection to Economics

Some problems involving allocation of goods or resources can be modeled by using systems of many inequalities. Linear programming is a process of analyzing these systems to maximize profits, minimize expenses, and so forth. It was initially developed after World War II to deal with problems like blending gasoline.

page 379 Check Understanding

3.

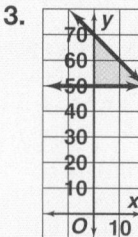

378

---

1 EXAMPLE Graphing a System of Inequalities

Solve by graphing.
$$y > 2x - 5$$
$$3x + 4y < 12$$

Graph $y > 2x - 5$ and $3x + 4y < 12$.

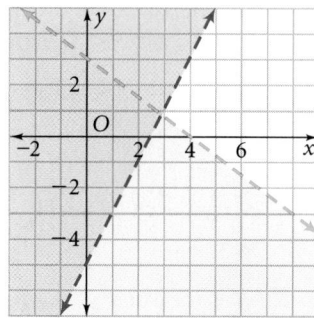

The coordinates of the points in the region where the graphs of the two inequalities overlap (shaded in lavender) are solutions of the system.

Check The point $(0, 0)$ is in the region graphed by both inequalities. See if $(0, 0)$ satisfies both inequalities.

$y > 2x - 5$ $3x + 4y < 12$
$0 > 2(0) - 5$ ⟵ Substitute (0, 0) for (x, y). ⟶ $3(0) + 4(0) < 12$
$0 > -5$ ✓ $0 < 12$ ✓

✓Check Understanding **1** Solve by graphing. $y \geq -x + 2$ **See left.**
$$2x + 4y < 4$$

1.
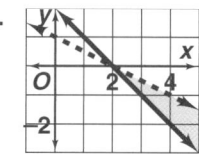

You can combine your knowledge of linear equations with your knowledge of inequalities to describe a graph using a system of inequalities.

2 EXAMPLE Writing a System of Inequalities From a Graph

Write a system of inequalities from each shaded region below.

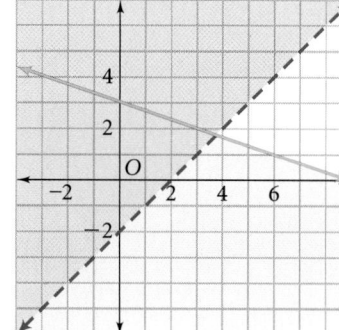

red region
boundary: $y = x - 2$
The region lies above the boundary line, so the inequality is $y > x - 2$.

blue region
boundary: $y = -\frac{1}{3}x + 3$
The region includes the boundary line and the points lying below the boundary line, so the inequality is $y \leq -\frac{1}{3}x + 3$.

system for the lavender region: $y > x - 2$
$$y \leq -\frac{1}{3}x + 3$$

378   Chapter 7   Systems of Equations and Inequalities

👐 **Reaching All Students**

| Below Level The intersection point of inequality boundary lines may or may not be a solution to the system. Have students examine the intersection point in Example 2. | Advanced Learners Ask students to describe the solution to the following system. $y > x + 1$ $y < x + 1$ | Visual Learners See note on page 378. Error Prevention See note on page 381. |

✓ Check Understanding

2 Write a system of inequalities for the lavender region in each of the following graphs.

a.

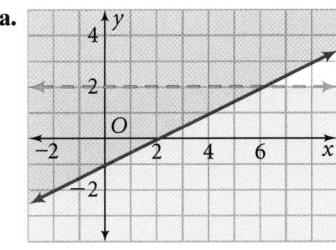

$y \geq \frac{1}{2}x - 1$ and $y < 2$

b.

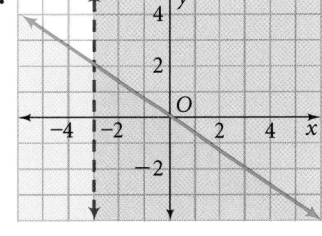

$y \leq -\frac{2}{3}x$ and $x > -3$

Writing and Using Systems of Linear Inequalities

You can model some real-world situations by graphing linear inequalities. When you graph real-world situations, you often need to plan how you will scale each axis. Use the values for the x- and y-intercepts to determine your scale.

3 **EXAMPLE** Real-World Problem Solving

Animal Habitat A zoo keeper wants to fence a rectangular habitat for goats. The length of the habitat should be at least 80 ft, and the distance around it should be no more than 310 ft. What are the possible dimensions of the habitat?

Relate | the length | is at least | 80 ft | the perimeter | is no more than | 310 ft |

Define Let x = width of the habitat.
Let y = length of the habitat.

Write | y | $\geq$ | 80 | $2x + 2y$ | $\leq$ | 310 |

Solve by graphing. $y \geq 80$
$2x + 2y \leq 310$.

$y \geq 80$
$m = 0$
$b = 80$

Shade above
$y = 80$.

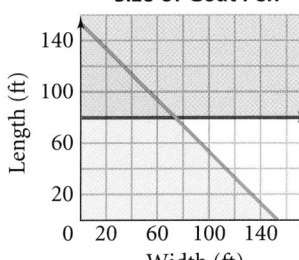

Size of Goat Pen

$2x + 2y \leq 310$

Graph the intercepts $(155, 0)$ and $(0, 155)$.

Test $(0, 0)$.
$2(0) + 2(0) \leq 310$
$0 \leq 310$

Shade below
$2x + 2y = 310$.

The solutions are the coordinates of the points that lie in the region shaded lavender and on the parts of the lines $y = 80$ and $2x + 2y = 310$ that border the lavender region.

✓ Check Understanding

3 Suppose you want to fence a rectangular garden plot. You want the length of the garden to be at least 50 ft and the perimeter to be no more than 140 ft. Solve by graphing to show all of the possible dimensions of the garden.

See margin.

Lesson 7-6 Systems of Linear Inequalities **379**

Real-World Connection

Careers A zoologist studies individual animals and the processes that sustain an animal within its group and its environment. To adapt an animal to a zoo habitat, a zoologist must research ways to help an animal adapt to a restricted environment.

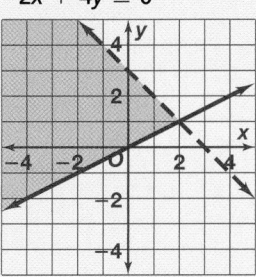
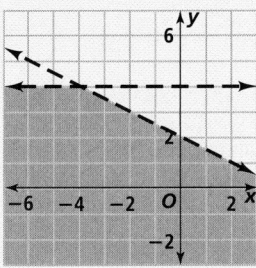
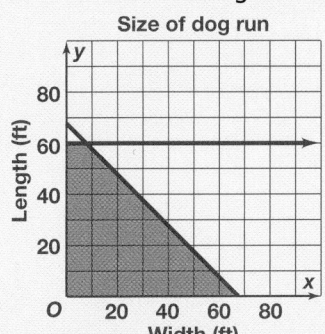

You may want to use this example as an opportunity to review solving word problems. Remind students they need to read carefully and think logically about what is needed before they begin solving any problem. In Example 4, the situation calls for only a subset of all the possible solutions. Point out that there cannot be fewer than zero stamps nor can partial stamps be used to mail a package. Therefore, the solutions will be whole numbers only.

Additional Examples

④ Suppose you have two jobs, babysitting, which pays $5 per hour, and sacking groceries, which pays $6 per hour. You can work no more than 20 hours each week, but you need to earn at least $90 per week. How many hours can you work at each job?

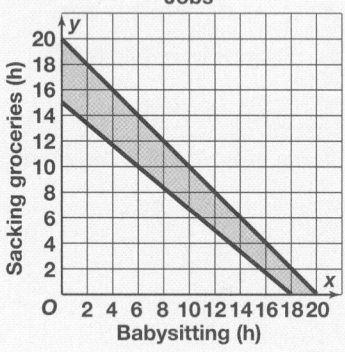

Jobs

Closure

Ask students to model the different outcomes of graphing a system of two inequalities with parallel boundary lines. **There are four possible outcomes: no solution, all points between the two lines, all points above the upper line, and all points below the lower line. The last three outcomes may also include one or both lines if there is an "equals" in the inequality.**

Some real-world situations have a domain and range that include only integers. In such cases, the solutions will be some, but not all, of the points in the region included in the graphs of both inequalities.

4 EXAMPLE Real-World 🌐 Problem Solving

Mailing Packages Suppose you need $2.40 in postage to mail a package to a friend. You have 9 stamps, some 20¢ and some 34¢. How many of each do you need to mail the package?

Relate | the number of 20¢ and 34¢ stamps | is less than or equal to | 9 | | the value of 20¢ and 34¢ stamps | is at least | 240¢ |

Define Let a = the number of 20¢ stamps.
Let b = the number of 34¢ stamps.

Write | $a + b$ | $\leq$ | 9 | | $20a + 34b$ | $\geq$ | 240 |

Solve by graphing.
$a + b \leq 9$
$20a + 34b \geq 240$

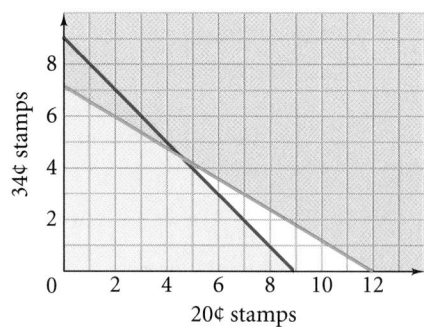

The solutions are all of the coordinates of points that are nonnegative integers lying in the region shaded lavender and on its boundary lines.

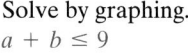

Real-World 🌐 Connection

In 1932, you would have needed a 3¢ stamp to mail a letter. To mail the same letter in 2001 would have cost 34¢.

4a. Answers may vary.
Sample:
2 20¢ stamps and
6 34¢ stamps;
4 20¢ stamps
and 5 34¢ stamps

✔ **Check Understanding**

④ **a.** Give two solutions from the graph in Example 4. **See left.**
b. Does either solution give you the exact postage needed to mail the package? **no**
c. Critical Thinking Why are the solutions to the problem only nonnegative integers?
You cannot have a negative or fractional number of stamps.

EXERCISES

For more practice, see *Extra Practice*.

Practice and Problem Solving

Ⓐ **Practice by Example**

Example 1
(page 378)

Is the given ordered pair a solution of the system?

1. $(1, 19)$
$y \leq 7x - 13$
$y > 3x + 6$ **no**

2. $(4, 10)$
$9x - y \geq 23$
$5x + 0.2y \geq 20$ **yes**

3. $(-2, 40)$
$y > -13x + 29$
$y \leq 9x + 11$ **no**

Solve each system by graphing. 4–10. See back of book. 11–15. See margin.

4. $y < 2x + 4$
$-3x - 2y \geq 6$

5. $y < 2x + 4$
$2x - y \leq 4$

6. $y > 2x + 4$
$2x - y \leq 4$

7. $y > \frac{1}{4}x$
$y \leq -x + 4$

8. $y < 2x - 3$
$y > 5$

9. $y \leq -\frac{1}{3}x + 7$
$y \geq -x + 1$

380 Chapter 7 Systems of Equations and Inequalities

pages 380–384 **Exercises**

11.
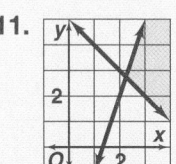

12.
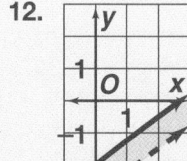

13.
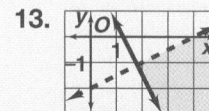

14.
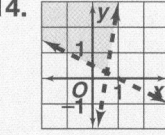

10. $x + 2y \le 10$
    $x + 2y \ge 9$

11. $y \ge -x + 5$
    $y \le 3x - 4$

12. $y \le 0.75x - 2$
    $y > 0.75x - 3$

13. $8x + 4y \ge 10$
    $3x - 6y > 12$

14. $2x - \frac{1}{4}y < 1$
    $4x + 8y > 4$

15. $6x - 5y < 15$
    $x + 2y \ge 7$

Example 2
(page 378)

Write a system of inequalities for each graph. 16–19. See margin.

16.
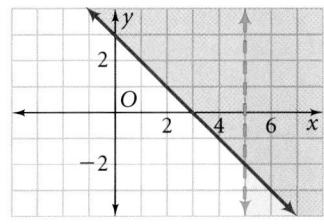

17.
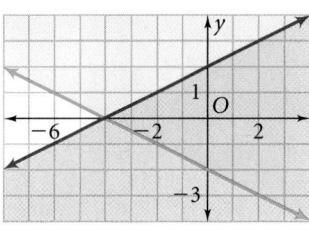

18.
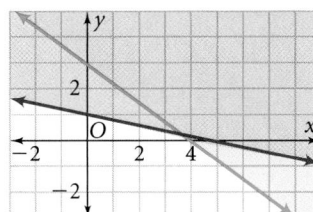

19.
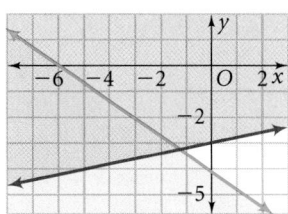

Example 3
(page 379)

20. **Budget** Suppose you buy flour and cornmeal in bulk to make flour tortillas and corn tortillas. Flour costs $1.50/lb. Cornmeal costs $2.50/lb. You want to spend less than $9.50 on flour and cornmeal, and you need at least 4 lb altogether.
   a. Write a system of inequalities that describes this situation.
   b. Graph the system to show all possible solutions. **a–b. See back of book.**

21. Suppose you want to fence a rectangular area for your dog. You will use the house as one of the four sides. Since the house is 40 ft wide, the length ℓ needs to be no more than 40 ft. You plan to use at least 150 ft of fencing. Graph the following system to find possible dimensions for the rectangle.
   See back of book.

   $$\ell \le 40$$
   $$\ell + 2w \ge 150$$

Example 4
(page 380)

22. Suppose you receive a $50 gift certificate to the Cityside Music and Books store. All CDs at the store cost $9.99, and all books cost $5.99. You want to buy some books and at least one CD.
   a. Write a system of inequalities for x books and y CDs that describes this situation. **$5.99x + 9.99y \le 50; x \ge 0, y \ge 1$**
   b. Graph the system to show all possible solutions. **b–c. See back of book.**
   c. What purchase does the ordered pair $(2, 6)$ represent? Is it a solution to your system? Explain.
   d. Find a solution in which you spend almost all of the gift certificate.
   Answers may vary. Sample: 3 books and 3 CDs for $47.94

15.
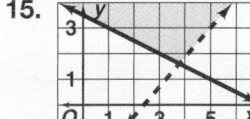

16. $x > 5$ and $y \ge -x + 3$

17. $y \ge -\frac{1}{2}x - 2$ and
    $y \le \frac{1}{2}x + 2$

18. $y > -\frac{1}{5}x + 1$ and
    $y > -\frac{3}{4}x + 3$

19. $y \le -\frac{2}{3}x - 4$ and
    $y \ge \frac{1}{6}x - 3$

Assignment Guide

▼1 Objective
   Ⓐ Ⓑ **Core** 1–19, 25–34, 36–42
   Ⓒ **Extension** 44–46

▼2 Objective
   Ⓐ Ⓑ **Core** 20–24, 35
   Ⓒ **Extension** 43, 47, 48

Standardized Test Prep 49–52

Mixed Review 53–70

Error Prevention

Exercises 4–15 Some students may have difficulty deciding which is the overlapping region to be shaded. Have them draw arrows from each boundary to show the shading of each individual inequality. Then have them shade the appropriate region.

Error Prevention

Exercise 21 Some students may want to use the complete perimeter formula. Have them sketch a drawing of the dog area and then trace over the lines that represent the fence.

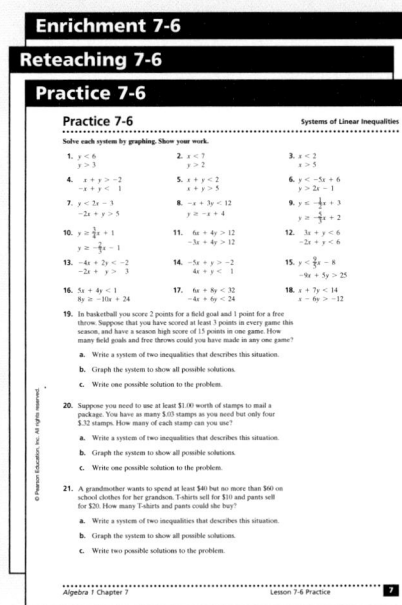

Connection to Geometry

Exercises 31–34 Review the definition of a trapezoid with students. A trapezoid is a quadrilateral with exactly one pair of parallel sides. The formula for the area of a trapezoid is $A = \frac{1}{2}h(b_1 + b_2)$.

Careers

Exercises 35, 43, and 48 Economists use systems of equations in the models. They also use systems of inequalities. The area of the system above the point of intersection and between the two graphs represents the area of surplus: more product is being sold than bought. The area of the system below the point of intersection and between the two graphs represents a shortage: more product is wanted than is being supplied.

Connection to Geometry

Exercise 48 Pose this problem to students: *You are making two heads for a cylindrical log drum that has a diameter of 14 in. The hide of each head must fall over the side of the drum by 2 inches all the way around in order to pull it taut. How can you find out how much hide you'll need for the drum heads?* **Find the area of the circle needed for each head and multiply by 2.** *What is an equation to find this?* **area of a circle:** $A = \pi r^2$; **area of both drum heads:** $2[3.14 \times (7 + 2)^2]$

pages 380–384   Exercises

24a. $x + y \le 12$,
$6x + 4y \ge 60$

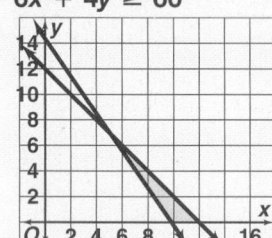

b. Answers may vary.
   Sample: (8, 3), (9, 1), (10, 0)

28. Answers may vary.
   Sample: $x \ge -2, x \le 4,$
   $y \le 1, y \ge -2$

B Apply Your Skills

Perch $4.00/lb

Salmon $3.00/lb

23. Business A seafood restaurant owner orders perch and salmon. He wants to buy at least 50 pounds of fish but cannot spend more than $180. Write and graph a system of inequalities to show the possible combinations of perch and salmon he could buy. **See back of book.**

24. Earnings Suppose you have a job in an ice cream shop that pays $6 per hour. You also have a babysitting job that pays $4 per hour. You want to earn at least $60 per week but would like to work no more than 12 hours per week.
   a. Graph and write a system of linear inequalities that describes this situation.
   b. Give three possible solutions to the system. **a–b. See margin.**

Write a system of inequalities for each of the following graphs. **See left.**

25. $x \le 3, x \ge -3, y \le 3,$
   $y \ge -3$

26. $y \ge 2, x < 5, y \le x$

27. $y \ge \frac{2}{3}x - 2, y < \frac{2}{3}x + 2$

28. $y \ge -x - 3, y \le -x + 3,$
   $y \le x + 3, y \ge x - 3$

25.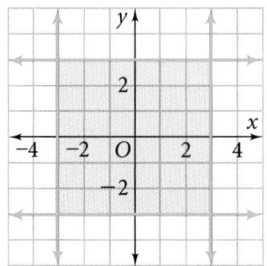

26.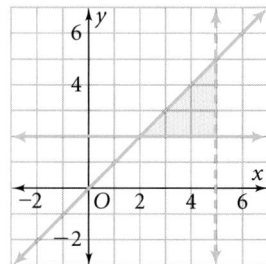

27.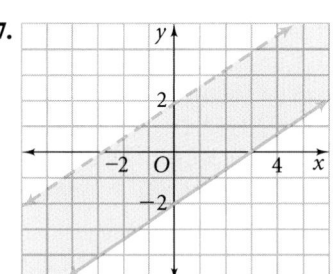

28.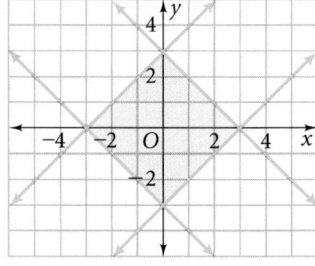

29. Open-Ended Write a system of four inequalities that describes a rectangle. Graph the system. **See margin.**

30. Geometry The following system of inequalities describes a right isosceles triangle.
   a. Find m. **−1**
   b. Find the area of the triangle. **8**

$x > 0$
$y > 0$
$y < mx + 4$

Geometry **The solution region of each system of linear inequalities below forms a figure. (a) Describe the shape. (b) Find the vertices. (c) Find the area.**
   31. See margin. 32–34. See back of book.

31. $y \ge \frac{1}{2}x + 1$
   $y \le 2$
   $x \ge -4$

32. $x \ge 1$
   $x \le 5$
   $y \ge -1$
   $y \le 3$

33. $x \ge 0$
   $x \le 2$
   $y \ge -4$
   $y \le -x + 2$

34. $x \ge 2$
   $y \ge -3$
   $x + y \le 4$

35. a. Business A clothing store has a going-out-of-business sale. They are selling pants for $10.99 and shirts for $4.99. You can spend as much as $45 and want to buy at least one pair of pants. Write and graph a system of inequalities that describes this situation. **See back of book.**
   b. Suppose you need to buy at least three pairs of pants. From your graph, find all the ordered pairs that are possible solutions. **(3, 0), (3, 1), (3, 2), (4, 0)**

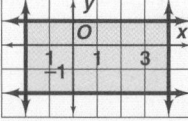

30a. triangle
   b. (2, 2), (−4, −1), (−4, 2)
   c. 9 units²

31a. square
   b. (1, −1), (5, −1), (1, 3), (5, 3)
   c. 16 units²

36. a.

36. a. Graph each inequality. $y > 4x + 1$ **See left.**
$y < 4x - 2$

✎ **b. Writing** Will the boundary lines $y = 4x + 1$ and $y = 4x - 2$ ever intersect? Explain. **No; they are parallel.**

c. Will the shaded regions you drew in part (a) overlap? **no**

d. Does the system of inequalities have any solutions? **no**

37. a. Graph the system of inequalities. $y > 3x - 5$
$y < 3x + 4$ **a–b. See back of book.**

b. Will the boundary lines $y = 3x - 5$ and $y = 3x + 4$ ever intersect? Explain.

c. Describe the shape of the overlapping region. **It is a strip between the lines.**

Open-Ended Write a system of linear inequalities with the given characteristics.
38–42. See margin.

38. $(0, 0)$ is a solution.

39. Solutions are only in Quadrant II.

40. There is no solution.

41. $(3, 7)$ is not a solution.

42. Solutions are only in Quadrant IV.

C **Challenge** 🌐 **43. Business** A jeweler plans to produce a ring made of silver and gold. The price of gold is approximately $10/g. The price of silver is approximately $.15/g. She considers the following in deciding how much gold and silver to use in the ring.

• The total mass must be more than 10 g but less than 20 g.
• The ring must contain at least 3 g of gold.
• The total cost of the gold and silver must be less than $60.

Let s = the mass of silver in grams and d = the mass of gold in grams.
a. Write and graph the four inequalities that describe this situation.
b. For one solution (s, d), find the mass of the ring and the cost of the gold and silver. **a–b. See back of book.**

44. Solve $|y| \geq x$. (*Hint:* Write two inequalities; then graph them.) **See margin.**

Write a system of linear inequalities with the given characteristics. See left.

45. Answers may vary.
$y > \frac{1}{2}x$
$y < 2x$

45. $(2, 5)$ and $(5, 2)$ are not solutions; $(5, 5)$ is a solution.

46. Answers may vary.
$y > x + 1$
$y > -x + 1$

46. $(-3, 2)$ and $(3, 2)$ are not solutions; $(-2, 6)$ is a solution.

🌐 **47. Sports** During part of the baseball season, a player had 120 hits in 305 at-bats. The ratio $\frac{120}{305}$ gave him a .393 batting average. (Batting averages are rounded to the nearest thousandth.) The inequality $\frac{120 + h}{305 + a} \geq .400$ gives the number of hits h needed during his next at-bats a to reach at least a .400 average. The inequality $h \leq a$ indicates the player cannot have more hits than at-bats.

a. Solve $\frac{120 + h}{305 + a} \geq .400$ for h. $h \geq 2 + 0.400a$

b. Graph the system. **See back of book.**

c. What does a solution mean in terms of the original problem?
Answers may vary. Sample: 5 hits, 6 at-bats

🌐 **48. Business** A drum maker sells two sizes of frame drums like the ones at the left. A 14-in. drum sells for $180 and an 18-in. drum sells for $240. He is trying to decide how many drums to build and considers the following:

• He wants to produce and sell at least $2700 worth of drums.
• He has materials to make no more than 17 drums.
• He plans to make more 14-in. drums than 18-in. drums.
• He wants to make at least four 18-in. drums.

a. Write and graph the four inequalities that describe this situation.
b. Give one possible solution to the system. **a–b. See back of book.**

38–42. Answers may vary.
Samples given.

38. $x \leq 1$ and $y \leq 2$

39. $x < 0$ and $y > 0$

40. $y > 5$ and $y < 3$

41. $x < 2$ and $y < 5$

42. $x > 0$ and $y < 0$

44.

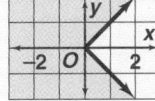

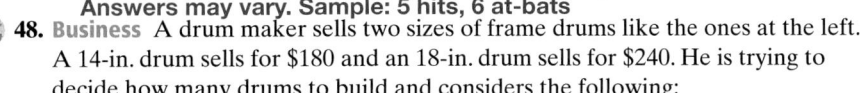

4. Assess

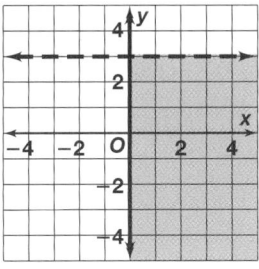

📖 **Lesson Quiz 7-6**

Solve each system by graphing.

1. $x \geq 0$
$y < 3$

2. $2x + 3y > 12$
$3x + 2y < 12$

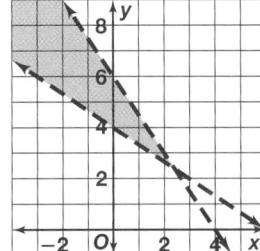

3. $y \geq \frac{2}{3}x - 3$
$2x - 3y \geq -9$

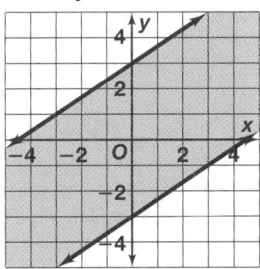

4. Write a system of inequalities for the following graph.

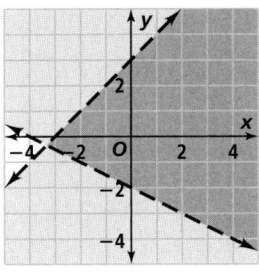

$y < x + 3$
$y > -\frac{1}{2}x - 2$

383

Alternative Assessment

Have each student work with a partner. Give each pair two different-colored transparencies and a printed coordinate plane. Instruct students to lay the transparencies on the coordinate plane so that they overlap. Have students write the system of inequalities they have modeled.

Standardized Test Prep

Resources

For additional practice with a variety of test item formats:
- Standardized Test Prep, p. 391
- Test-Taking Strategies, p. 386
- Test-Taking Strategies with Transparencies

Exercise 49 Suggest to students that instead of graphing both equations, they can use substitution to find the answer choice that satisfies both inequalities.

pages 380–384   Exercises

51. [2] all points on the line
    $3x + 4y = 12$

    [1] incorrect description given

52. [4]

    a. Let x = number of toppings, and
       y = cost of pizza.
       Maria's: $y = 0.50x + 8$
       Tony's: $y = 0.75x + 7$

    b. (4, 10)   With 4 toppings, the cost is $10 at either Tony's or Maria's.

    c. Answers may vary. Sample: Since I prefer more than 4 toppings, I will go to Maria's, because the pizza will be less expensive.

    [3] (a) and (b) only done correctly

    [2] (a) done correctly, but student makes a computational error in (b)

    [1] error in (a), but the system solved correctly

384

Standardized Test Prep

Multiple Choice

49. Which point is a solution of the following system? $y > x$
$y < 3x - 4$ **D**

    I. (1, 2)   **II.** (3, 4)   **III.** (3, 9)
    A. I only   **B.** I and II   **C.** I and III   **D.** II only

50. There are at most 12 bicycles and tricycles in a school playground. There are at least 17 wheels altogether. Let b equal the number of bicycles and t equal the number of tricycles. Which system describes this situation? **G**

  F. $b + t < 12$ **G.** $b + t \leq 12$
      $2b + 3t \geq 17$ $2b + 3t \geq 17$
  H. $b + t \leq 12$ **I.** $b + t \leq 12$
      $2b + 3t > 17$ $2b + 3t \leq 17$

Short Response

51. Describe the solution to the following system. $3x + 4y \geq 12$
See margin. $3x + 4y \leq 12$

Extended Response

52. Suppose you and your friends are going out for pizza. **a–b.** See margin.

    a. Write a system of equations for the cost of a large pizza at each restaurant, based on the information at the right.

    b. Solve the system. Interpret your results.

    c. Where will you go for pizza? Explain your reasons.

Take It to the NET
Online lesson quiz at
www.PHSchool.com
Web Code: aea-0706

	Tony's Pizza	Maria's Pizza
Large cheese	$7	$8
Each topping	$.75	$.50

Mixed Review

Lesson 7-5

Graph each linear inequality. 53–54. See margin. 55–58. See back of book.

53. $y > x - 5$ **54.** $y \leq -2x + 4$ **55.** $y > -3$

56. $y + x \leq 7$ **57.** $3y - x \geq 6$ **58.** $4y + 2x < 8$

Find the slope of a line parallel to the graph of each equation.

59. $5x - 2y = 8\frac{5}{2}$ **60.** $y - 17 = -3x - 3$ **61.** $0.5y - 10 + 4x = 0$
                                                                       −8

Lesson 6-5

Find the slope of a line perpendicular to the graph of each equation.

62. $y = 4x - \frac{1}{4}$ **63.** $y = 5x - 7 - \frac{1}{5}$ **64.** $y = \frac{3}{8}x + 19 - \frac{8}{3}$

65. $y = -\frac{9}{10}x - 3\frac{10}{9}$ **66.** $6y + 13x = 22\frac{6}{13}$ **67.** $-4x - 15y = 74\frac{15}{4}$

Lesson 5-4

Write a function rule for each table.

68.

x	f(x)
1	7
2	14
3	21
4	28
5	35

$f(x) = 7x$

69.

x	f(x)
1	7
2	8
3	9
4	10
5	11

$f(x) = x + 6$

70.

x	f(x)
−2	4
−1	1
0	0
1	1
2	4

$f(x) = x^2$

384   Chapter 7 Systems of Equations and Inequalities

53.
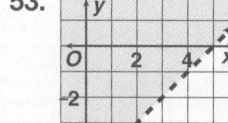

54.
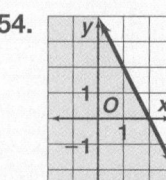

Technology

Graphing Linear Inequalities

FOR USE WITH LESSON 7-6

You can use a graphing calculator to show the solutions of an inequality or a system of inequalities. The symbol before each Y in the $\boxed{Y=}$ window indicates the graph style. You can use the graph style to shade above or below a line. The standard style, indicated by \\, shows only the line.

Take It to the NET
Graphing Calculator procedures online at **www.PHSchool.com**
Web Code: aee-2108

To change the graph style, select \\ and press $\boxed{\text{ENTER}}$ to rotate through the seven styles available. You can use ◤ to shade above the line and ◣ to shade below the line.

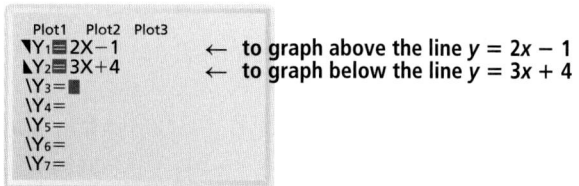

← to graph above the line $y = 2x - 1$
← to graph below the line $y = 3x + 4$

The graphing calculator does not make a distinction between a boundary line that is dotted ($y < 2x - 1$) and a boundary line that is solid ($y \leq 2x - 1$). You must decide whether a boundary line should be solid or dotted when you sketch the inequality.

1 EXAMPLE

Graph $y > -4x + 1$.

Enter the equation for the boundary line $y = -4x + 1$.
Select ◤ to shade above the boundary line.

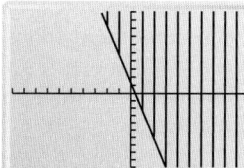

2 EXAMPLE

Graph the system: $y < -x + 4$
$\qquad\qquad\qquad\qquad y > 2x + 3$

Enter the equation of the first boundary line as Y_1.
Enter the equation of the second boundary line as Y_2.

Select ◣ to shade below $y = -x + 4$.
Select ◤ to shade above $y = 2x + 3$.

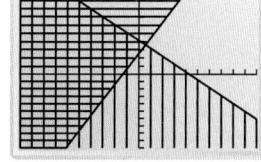

EXERCISES

Use a graphing calculator to graph each inequality. Sketch your graph. 1–4. See back of book.

1. $y < x$ **2.** $y > 2x - 3$ **3.** $y \geq -x + 3$ **4.** $y \leq 5$

Use a graphing calculator to graph each system of inequalities. Sketch your graph. 5–8. See margin.

5. $y \geq -1$
$\quad\ y \geq 2x$

6. $y \geq 0.5x - 2$
$\quad\ y \leq x + 2$

7. $y < x$
$\quad\ y \geq 1$

8. $y \geq -4x + 6$
$\quad\ y \geq -2x + 5$

Technology

Graphing Linear Inequalities

Students use graphing calculators to show the solution to an inequality or system of inequalities. When graphing an inequality, they will need to know how to graph it as an equation first and then decide whether to shade above or below the line.

Resources

Students may use any graphing calculator.

Teaching Notes

Students may need to be reminded that when graphing an inequality in the form $y > mx + b$ or $y < mx + b$, they must graph the corresponding equation $y = mx + b$ and then shade above the line for the symbol *is greater than* and below the line for the symbol *is less than*.

Technology Tip

Before students begin, remind them to press $\boxed{Y=}$ to see that all functions are deselected. Then press $\boxed{\text{ZOOM}}$ 6 to reset the screen to the standard viewing window.

Error Prevention

When students use a graphing calculator to find the solution to a system of inequalities, suggest that they choose several points in the shaded solution area on their graph and check to see if those points do in fact satisfy both inequalities.

page 385   Technology

5.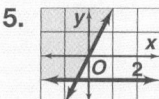

6.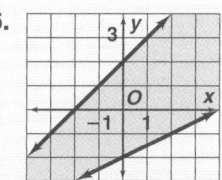

7.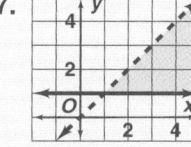

8.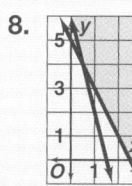

385

Finding Multiple Correct Answers

This feature helps students develop strategies for answering questions that have more than one correct solution. Students need to look at each statement and test it to see if it is true or false. They will discover that there are often several ways to determine the most inclusive answer containing true statements. This type of problem requires logical reasoning in addition to problem-solving skills.

Resources

**PRENTICE HALL
ASSESSMENT SYSTEM**

Test-Taking Strategies with Transparencies
• Transparency 7
• Practice sheet p. 7

Teaching Notes

Help students understand that they must choose the most inclusive answer with all true statements.

Teaching Tip

In Exercise 3, logical reasoning tells you that I is true since it appears in all three choices.

Test-Taking Strategies with Transparencies

Test-Taking Strategy: Finding Multiple Correct Answers

Examine each choice to see which one(s) are true.

Example Which of the following are true about the graph of the line $y = -4x - 5$?

I. The slope is 4.
II. The y-intercept is -5.
III. The point $(1, -9)$ is on the line.

A. None   B. II only   C. III only   D. II and III only

The line is in slope-intercept form: $y = mx + b$, so its slope is -4 and its y-intercept is -5.

So, choice I is false, and choice II is true.

Notice, $-9 = -4(1) - 5$, so choice III is true.

The answer is II and III only, or choice D.

Find the answer. Explain your reasoning.

1. If $3x + 4 < 5$, which of the following are true?
   I. $6x + 8 < 10$ II. $-6x - 8 < -10$ III. $-3x > -1$
   A. None   B. I only   C. III only   D. I and III only
2. Use the data: 3, 5, 7, 10, 15. Which of the following are true?
   I. The mean is 8.   II. The median is 7.   III. The range is 12.
   F. None   G. I and II only   H. II only   I. All

Solutions

1. D
2. I

Transparency 7

386

In multiple correct answer questions, you have to determine the truth or falsehood of a number of statements. As you test each statement, mark it as true or false. Then choose the option with all those that are true.

1 EXAMPLE

Which system(s) of inequalities represent(s) the shaded region below?

I. $y \geq x$
$y \geq -x$
$y \leq 1$

II. $x + y \geq 0$
$x - y \geq 0$
$y \leq 1$

III. $y \geq |x|$
$y \leq 1$

A. I only
B. I and III only
C. I and II only
D. I, II, and III

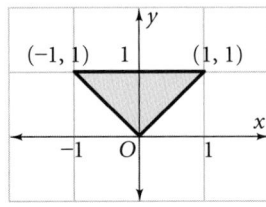

Method 1 Graph each system in I, II, and III to see which systems match the shaded region. The graph of the systems in I and III match the shaded region. Statements I and III are true; the correct answer is B.

Method 2 Choose a point, such as $(0, 0.5)$, inside the given shaded region. Test each of the three statements with the values $x = 0$ and $y = 0.5$. When $x = 0$ and $y = 0.5$, all the inequalities in I are true. The second inequality in II is $x - y = 0 - 0.5 \geq 0$, which is false. All the inequalities in III are true. Statements I and III are true; the correct answer is B.

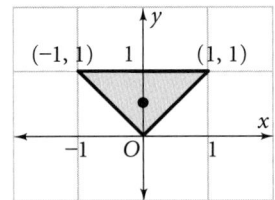

When you use Method 2, you should choose more than one point to test each system. This is because the point you choose may show a system to be true when it is really false. For example, if you choose to test the point $(1, 1)$, all the inequalities in II will be true, so you might think that II is true.

EXERCISES

1. Choose another point in the shaded region and test each of the three statements with the coordinates to determine which are true.

2. **Writing** The point $(0, 0)$ is in the shaded region. Test each of the three statements with its coordinates to determine which are true. Explain why this point is not a good choice with which to answer this question.

3. Louis is selling lemonade for $.25 per cup. He bought the lemonade mix for $8.40 and the cups for $.05 each. Which statement(s) must be true? **C**
   I. His break-even point is 42 cups.
   II. When he sells 20 cups, his income will be $13.40.
   III. His income is greater than his expenses when he sells 20 cups.
   A. I and II only
   B. I and III only
   C. I only
   D. III only

1. Answers may vary. Sample: $\left(0, \frac{3}{4}\right)$; when $x = 0$ and $y = \frac{3}{4}$, $y \geq x$, $y \geq -x$, and $y \leq 1$ are true, so I is true. $x + y \geq 0$ is true, but $x - y \geq 0$ is false, so II is false. $y \geq |x|$ and $y \leq 1$ are true, so III is true.

2. All of the inequalities in the three options are true. $(0, 0)$ is not a good choice because it is on the border of the region.

Chapter 7

Chapter Review

Vocabulary

elimination method (p. 353)
infinitely many solutions (p. 342)
linear inequality (p. 371)
no solution (p. 342)

solution of a system of linear
    equations (p. 340)
solution of a system of linear
    inequalities (p. 377)

solutions of an inequality (p. 371)
substitution method (p. 347)
system of linear equations (p. 340)
system of linear inequalities (p. 377)

Reading Math

Understanding Vocabulary

Take It to the NET

Online vocabulary quiz
at www.PHSchool.com
Web Code: aej-0751

Choose the vocabulary term that correctly completes each sentence.

1. _____?_____ is a method for solving a system of linear equations in which you multiply one or both equations by a nonzero number to get a variable term with coefficients that have a sum or difference of zero. **Elimination**

2. Any ordered pair that makes all equations in a system of equations true is a(n)_____?_____. **solution of a system of linear equations**

3. A(n)_____?_____ is formed by two or more linear inequalities. **system of linear inequalities**

4. Each point whose coordinates make an inequality true is a(n)_____?_____. **solution of the inequality**

5. _____?_____ is a method for solving a system of linear equations in which at least one equation must first be solved for a single variable. **Substitution**

Skills and Concepts

7-1 Objectives

▼ To solve systems by graphing (p. 340)

▼ To analyze special types of systems (p. 342)

Two or more linear equations form a **system of linear equations.** You can solve a system of linear equations by graphing. The point where all the lines intersect is the **solution of the system.**

6. Which graph shows the solution of the following system? **A** $y = x - 1$
$y = -x + 3$

A. 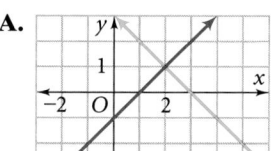   **B.**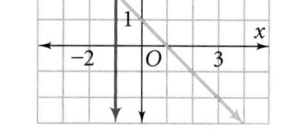

7. Is $(2, 5)$ a solution of the following system? Explain. $y = 2x + 1$
No; (2, 5) only satisfies one equation. $2x - y = 8$

8. How many solutions does the following system have? Explain. $y = -\frac{1}{2}x + 2$
Infinitely many; the equations are equivalent. $3x + 6y = 12$

9. Critical Thinking What kinds of systems would be hard to solve by graphing?
Answers may vary. Sample: systems with noninteger solutions.

Solve each system by graphing. 10–13. See margin p. 388 for graph.

10. $y = 3x - 1$
$y = -x + 3$ **(1, 2)**

11. $x - y = -3$
$3x + y = -1$ **(−1, 2)**

12. $-x + 2y = -2$
$y = \frac{1}{2}x + 3$ **no solution**

13. $y = -2x + 1$
$y = 2x - 3$ **(1, −1)**

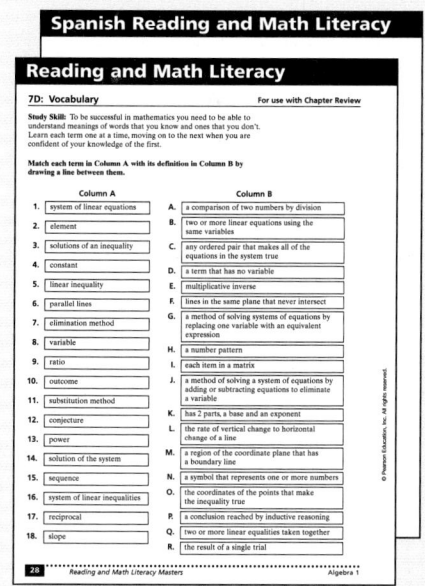

10.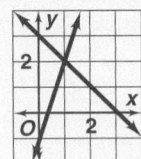

11.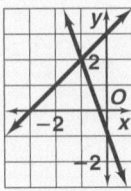

12.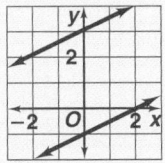

13.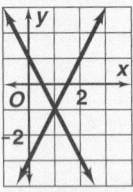

18. Answers may vary.
Sample: There is no
solution when you get a
false equation such as
0 = 2. There are infinitely
many solutions when you
get a true equation such
as 5 = 5.

30.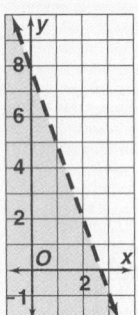

31.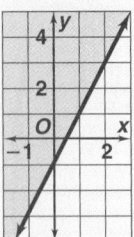

388

7-2 Objective

▼ To solve systems using substitution (p. 347)

You can also solve a system of linear equations using the **substitution method.** By replacing one variable with an equivalent expression containing the other variable, you create a one-variable equation to solve.

Solve each system using substitution.

14. $y = 3x + 11$
$y = -2x + 1$ **(−2, 5)**

15. $4x - y = -12$
$-6x + 5y = -3$
$\left(-4\frac{1}{2}, -6\right)$

16. $8x = -2y - 10$
$2x = 4y$
$\left(-1\frac{1}{9}, -\frac{5}{9}\right)$

17. $y = 5x - 8$
$5y = 2x + 6$
(2, 2)

18. Writing Explain how you determine if a system has no solution or infinitely many solutions when you solve a system using substitution. **See margin.**

19. There are 24 questions on a test. Each question is worth either 4 points or 5 points. The total is 100 points. **a. $x + y = 24$, $4x + 5y = 100$**
a. Write a system of equations to find the number of each type of question.
b. Solve the system by substitution. **(20, 4)**
c. How many questions of each type are on the test? **20 4-point, 4 5-point**

7-3 Objectives

▼ To solve systems by adding or subtracting (p. 353)

▼ To multiply first when solving systems (p. 354)

You can solve a system of linear equations using the **elimination method.** You add or subtract the equations to eliminate one variable. You can multiply one or both of the equations by a nonzero number before adding or subtracting.

Solve each system using elimination. Check your solution.

20. $y = -3x + 5$
$y = -4x - 1$
(−6, 23)

21. $2x - 3y = 5$
$x + 2y = -1$
(1, −1)

22. $x + y = 10$
$x - y = 2$
(6, 4)

23. $x + 4y = 12$
$2x - 3y = 6$
$\left(5\frac{5}{11}, 1\frac{7}{11}\right)$

24. Farming A farmer raises chickens and cows. There are 34 animals in all. The farmer counts 110 legs on these animals. Write a system of equations to find the number of each type of animal. Solve the system by elimination. How many of each animal does the farmer have?
$x + y = 34$, $2x + 4y = 110$; **13 chickens and 21 cows**

7-4 Objective

▼ To write systems of linear equations (p. 362)

You can use systems of linear equations to solve word problems. First, define variables. Then model the situation with a system of linear equations.

25. A furniture finish consists of turpentine and linseed oil. It contains twice as much turpentine as linseed oil. If you plan to make 16 fluid ounces of furniture finish, how much turpentine do you need? $10\frac{2}{3}$ **fl oz**

26. Geometry The difference between the measures of two complementary angles is 36°. Find both angle measures. (*Hint:* Two angles are complementary if the sum of their measures is 90°.) **63° and 27°**

27. Geometry The perimeter of a rectangle is 114 feet. Its length is three more than twice its width. Find the dimensions of the rectangle. **18 ft by 39 ft**

28. Supplies Marcella and Rupert bought some party supplies. Marcella bought 3 packages of balloons and 4 packages of favors for $14.63. Rupert bought 2 packages of balloons and 5 packages of favors for $16.03. Find the price of a package of balloons. **$1.29**

29. An airplane flew for 6 hours with a 22-km/h tail wind. The return flight against the same wind took 8 hours. Find the speed of the plane in still air. **154 km/h**

7-5 Objectives

▼ To graph linear inequalities (p. 370)

▼ To use linear inequalities when modeling real-world situations (p. 372)

A **linear inequality** describes a region of the coordinate plane. The **solutions of the inequality** are the coordinates of the points that make the inequality true.

Graph each linear inequality. 30–33. See margin.

30. $y < -3x + 8$ **31.** $y \geq 2x - 1$ **32.** $y \leq 0.5x + 6$ **33.** $y > -\frac{1}{4}x - 2$

Write the linear inequality shown in each graph.

34.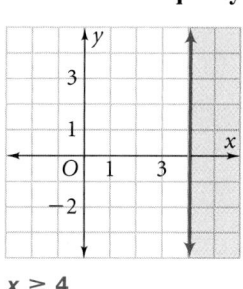

$x \geq 4$

35.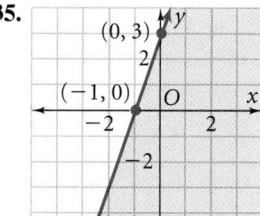

$y \leq 3x + 3$

36.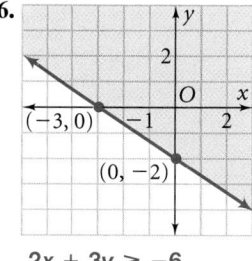

$2x + 3y \geq -6$

7-6 Objectives

▼ To solve systems of linear inequalities by graphing (p. 377)

▼ To model real-world situations using systems of linear inequalities (p. 379)

Two or more linear inequalities form a **system of linear inequalities.** To find the **solution of a system of linear inequalities,** graph each linear inequality. The solution region is where all the inequalities are true.

Solve each system of linear inequalities by graphing. 37–40. See margin.

37. $y \geq -4x + 1$
$y \leq \frac{5}{2}x - \frac{9}{2}$

38. $x - y < 10$
$x + y \leq 8$

39. $y \leq x - 3$
$y > x - 7$

40. $y < 5x$
$y \geq 0$

Write the system of inequalities shown in each graph. 41–44. See left.

41. $y \leq 3, y > x$

42. $y > -2x + 2, y > \frac{4}{5}x - 4$

43. $x > -1, y \leq x + 5$

44. $y \leq -\frac{3}{2}x + 3,$
$y \geq -\frac{1}{2}x - 1$

45. Answers may vary. Sample: $x \geq -1, y \leq 5,$
$x \leq 5, x + y \leq 7, y \geq -1$

41.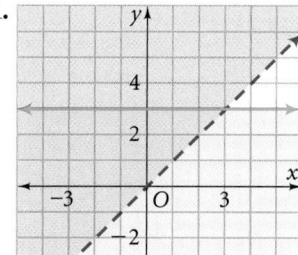

42.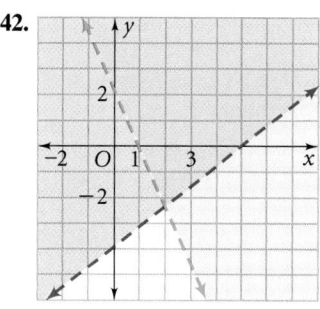

43.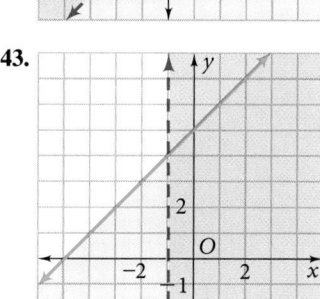

44.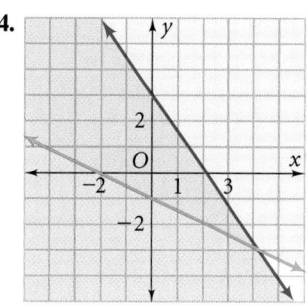

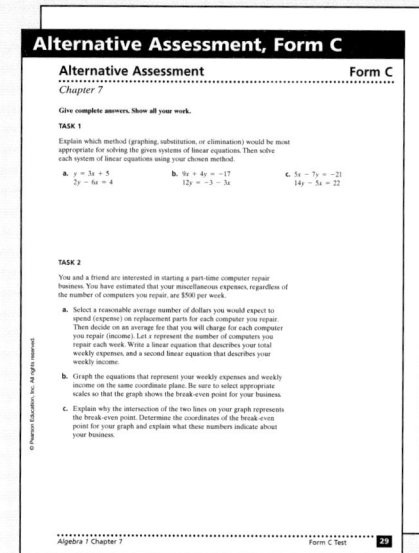
32.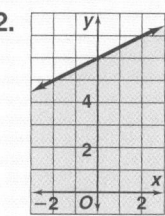

33.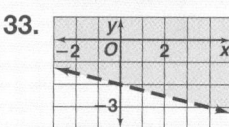

37.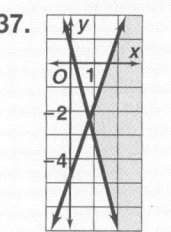

38.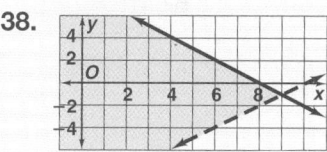

39.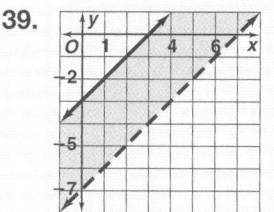

40.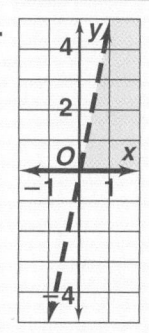

Resources

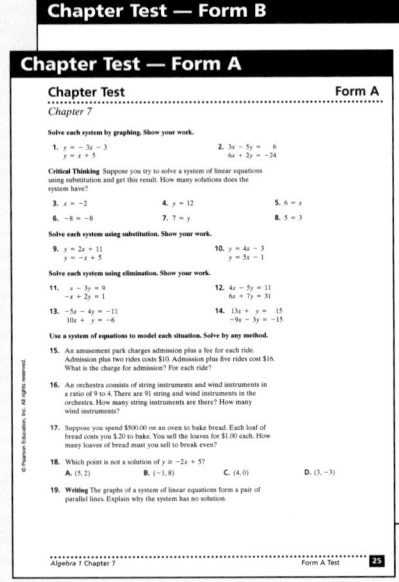

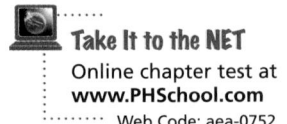
······
Take It to the NET
Online chapter test at
www.PHSchool.com
······· Web Code: aea-0752

Solve each system by graphing. 1–2. See back of book.

1. $y = 3x - 7$
$y = -x + 1$

2. $4x + 3y = 12$
$2x - 5y = -20$

Critical Thinking Suppose you try to solve systems of linear equations using substitution and get the results below. How many solutions does each system have?

3. $x = 8$ one sol.

4. $5 = y$ one sol.

5. $-7 = 4$ no sol.

6. $x = -1$ one sol.

7. $2 = y$ one sol.

8. $9 = 9$ inf. many sol.

Solve each system using substitution.

9. $y = 4x - 7$
$y = 2x + 9$ **(8, 25)**

10. $y = -2x - 1$
$y = 3x - 16$ **(3, -7)**

11. $8x + 2y = -2$
$y = -5x + 1$ **(2, -9)**

12. $y + 6 = 2x$
$4x - 10y = 4$ **(3.5, 1)**

Solve each system using elimination.

13. $4x + y = 8$
$-3x - y = 0$ **(8, -24)**

14. $2x + 5y = 20$
$3x - 10y = 37$
$\left(11, -\frac{2}{5}\right)$

15. $x + y = 10$
$-x - 2y = -14$ **(6, 4)**

16. $3x + 2y = -19$
$x - 12y = 19$
(-5, -2)

Write a system of equations to model each situation. Solve by any method.

17. Cable Service Your local cable television company offers two plans: basic service with one movie channel for $35 per month or basic service with two movie channels for $45 per month. What is the charge for the basic service and the charge for each movie channel? **See margin.**

18. Education A writing workshop enrolls novelists and poets in a ratio of 5 to 3. There are 24 people at the workshop. How many novelists are there? How many poets are there? **See margin.**

19. You have 15 coins in your pocket that are either quarters or nickels. They total $2.75. How many of each coin do you have? **See margin.**

✏️ **20. Writing** Compare solving a system of linear equations with solving a system of linear inequalities. What are the similarities? What are the differences? **See back of book.**

21. Which point is *not* a solution of $y < 3x - 1$? **C**
A. $(2, -4)$ **B.** $(5, 7)$ **C.** $(0, -1)$ **D.** $(-2, -9)$

Solve each system by graphing. 22–25. See back of book.

22. $y > 4x - 1$
$y \le -x + 4$

23. $y \ge 3x + 5$
$y > x - 2$

24. $x > -3$
$-3x + y \ge 6$

25. $2x - y \le 2$
$y \ge 4$

26. Open-Ended Write a system of two linear equations. Solve by any method. **See margin.**

27. Garage Sale Leo held a garage sale. He priced all the items at a dime or a quarter. His sales totaled less than $5. **a. See back of book.**
   a. Write a linear inequality that describes the situation. Graph the linear inequality.
   b. What is the maximum possible number of items that could have been sold for a dime? **49 items**
   c. What is the maximum possible number of items that could have been sold for a quarter? **19 items**

28. Gardening Mrs. Paulson bought chicken wire to enclose a rectangular garden. She is restricted to a width of no more than 30 ft. She would like to use at most 180 ft of chicken wire.
   a. Write a system of linear inequalities that describes this situation. **a–b. See back of book.**
   b. Graph the system to show all possible solutions.

29. A chemist needs to mix a solution containing 30% insecticide with a solution containing 50% insecticide to make 200 L of a solution that is 42% insecticide. How much of each solution should she use?
   a. Complete the table below.

	30% Insecticide	50% Insecticide	42% Insecticide
Liters of Solution	x	y	200
Liters of Insecticide	0.30x	0.50y	0.42(200)

   b. Write a system of equations that describes the situation. Solve the system. **See margin.**

page 390   Chapter Test

17. $b + m = 35$, $b + 2m = 45$;
$25; $10

18. $\frac{n}{p} = \frac{5}{3}$, $n + p = 24$;
15 novelists, 9 poets

19. $q + n = 15$,
$0.25q + 0.05n = 2.75$;
10 quarters, 5 nickels

26. Answers may vary.
Sample:
$y = x + 1$, $y = 3x - 5$;
(3, 4)

29b. $x + y = 200$,
$0.3x + 0.5y = 84$;
120 liters of 50%
insecticide and 80 liters
of 30% insecticide

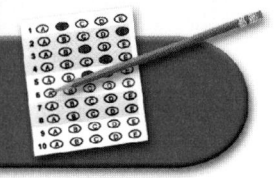

Standardized Test Prep

Reading Comprehension Read the passage below. Then answer the questions on the basis of what is *stated* or *implied* in the passage.

Music to Our Ears The way in which the music industry delivers music has changed dramatically since 1985. In that year, according to industry sources, there were 22.6 million CDs shipped. By 1990, the number of CDs shipped increased to 286.5 million. In 1999, shipments swelled to 938.9 million CDs, an increase of over 4000% from the number in 1985.

From 1985 to 1999, cassette shipments decreased from 339.1 million cassettes to 123.6 million, and record album shipments went from 167.0 million albums to 2.9 million. Clearly, CDs have replaced both cassettes and record albums as listeners' favorites.

---

1. What was the total number of CDs, cassettes, and record albums shipped in 1985? **B**
   A. 22.6 million
   B. 528.7 million
   C. 1065.4 million
   D. 1445 million

2. Which graph correctly illustrates data in the article above? **H**

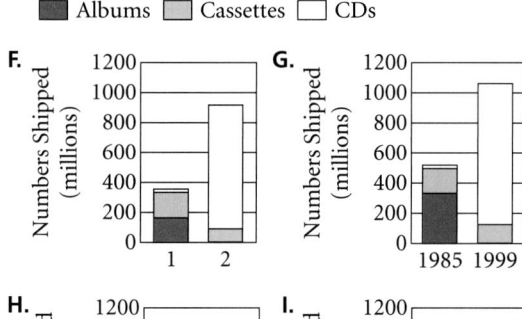

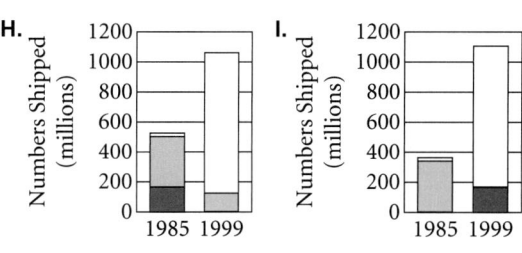

3. Which equation could you use to find the percent of change in the number of cassettes shipped from 1985 to 1999? **D**

   A. $\dfrac{339.1 + 123.6}{123.6}$ B. $\dfrac{339.1 - 123.6}{123.6}$

   C. $\dfrac{339.1 + 123.6}{339.1}$ D. $\dfrac{339.1 - 123.6}{339.1}$

4. Suppose a linear equation models record album shipments from 1985 to 1999. What is a correct interpretation of the slope of the model? **F**
   F. about 12 million fewer shipped each year
   G. 164.1 million fewer shipped in all
   H. about 12 million more shipped each year
   I. 164.1 million more shipped in all

5. Which of the following statements is true? **B**
   A. There is a positive correlation between the numbers of CDs and record albums shipped.
   B. There is a negative correlation between the numbers of CDs and record albums shipped.
   C. There is a positive correlation between the numbers of cassettes and CDs shipped.
   D. There is a negative correlation between the numbers of cassettes and record albums shipped.

6. Use percent of change to describe the change in the number of cassettes shipped between 1985 and 1999. **See margin.**

7. According to the article, the increase in CD shipments from 1985 to 1999 was over 4000%. Do you agree? Explain. **See back of book.**

8. Write a linear equation to model the number of CDs shipped from 1985 to 1999. Use the equation to predict the number of CDs shipped in 2010. **See back of book.**

9. Do you agree with the main conclusion stated in the article? Explain. **See margin.**

---

page 391   **Standardized Test Prep**

6. [2] $\dfrac{339.1 - 123.6}{339.1} = \dfrac{215.5}{339.1}$

   ≈ 0.6355

The percent of decrease was about 64%.

[1] minor calculation error

9. [2] Yes, in 1999 more CDs were sold than cassettes and albums.

[1] correct conclusion but no explanation

Students must be able to extract information from reading passages, answer multiple choice questions, and construct responses in order to be successful on current state and national assessments.

To answer the questions, students apply skills and concepts from this chapter and previous chapters.
Multiple Choice: Items 1–5
Extended Response: Items 6–9

Resources

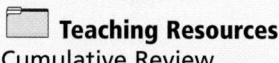 **Teaching Resources**
Cumulative Review

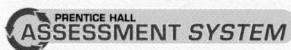 **Reaching All Students**
Spanish Cumulative Review

 PRENTICE HALL **ASSESSMENT SYSTEM**

Standardized Test Prep
• Ch. 7 Standardized Test Practice
Assessment Masters
• Cumulative Review
Computer Test Generator CD
• Standardized Test Practice

 **www.PHSchool.com**
• Standardized Test Practice
• Resources

Plus *i*TEXT

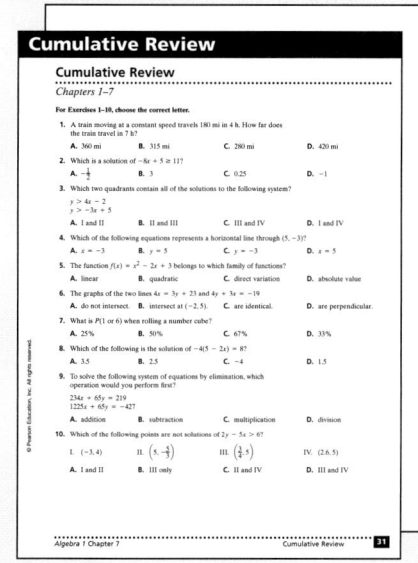

Exponents and Exponential Functions

Chapter at a Glance

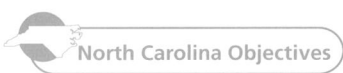 North Carolina Objectives

8-1   Zero and Negative Exponents   1.01a

NCTM
2, 4, 8, 10
- ▼ Zero and Negative Exponents
- ▽ Evaluating Exponential Expressions

8-2   Scientific Notation   1.01a

NCTM
1, 4, 8, 9, 10
- ▼ Writing Numbers in Scientific and Standard Notation
- ▽ Using Scientific Notation

8-3   Multiplication Properties of Exponents   1.01a

NCTM
1, 4, 8, 9, 10
- ▼ Multiplying Powers
- ▽ Working With Scientific Notation

8-4   More Multiplication Properties of Exponents   1.01a

NCTM
1, 2, 4, 6, 10
- ▼ Raising a Power to a Power
- ▽ Raising a Product to a Power

8-5   Division Properties of Exponents   1.01a

NCTM
1, 2, 4, 6, 10
- ▼ Dividing Powers With the Same Base
- ▽ Raising a Quotient to a Power

8-6   Geometric Sequences   1.02

NCTM
2, 3, 6, 9, 10
- ▼ Geometric Sequences
- ▽ Using a Formula

8-7   Exponential Functions   4.04

NCTM
2, 4, 5, 8, 10
- ▼ Evaluating Exponential Functions
- ▽ Graphing Exponential Functions

8-8   Exponential Growth and Decay   4.04

NCTM
2, 4, 5, 6, 8, 10
- ▼ Exponential Growth
- ▽ Exponential Decay

NCTM STANDARDS 2000

1	Number and Operations	6	Problem Solving
2	Algebra	7	Reasoning and Proof
3	Geometry	8	Communication
4	Measurement	9	Connections
5	Data Analysis and Probability	10	Representation

Pacing Options

This chart suggests pacing only for the lessons and their parts. It is provided as a possible guide. It will help you determine how much time you have in your schedule to cover other components, such as the features, Chapter Review, and Chapter Test.

Day	Traditional 45 min.	Two-Year 45 min.	Block 90 min.
1	8-1 ▼ ▽	8-1 ▼	8-1 ▼ ▽ 8-2 ▼ ▽
2	8-2 ▼ ▽	8-1 ▽	8-3 ▼ ▽
3	8-3 ▼	8-2 ▼	8-4 ▼ ▽
4	8-3 ▽	8-2 ▽	8-5 ▼ ▽ 8-6 ▼ ▽
5	8-4 ▼	8-3 ▼	8-7 ▼ ▽
6	8-4 ▽	8-3 ▼ ▽	8-8 ▼ ▽
7	8-5 ▼ ▽	8-3 ▽	
8	8-6 ▼ ▽	8-4 ▼	
9	8-7 ▼ ▽	8-4 ▼ ▽	
10	8-8 ▼	8-4 ▽	
11	8-8 ▽	8-5 ▼	
12		8-5 ▽	
13		8-6 ▼	
14		8-6 ▽	
15		8-7 ▼	
16		8-7 ▽	
17		8-8 ▼	
18		8-8 ▼ ▽	
19		8-8 ▽	

NAEP Correlation (National Assessment of Educational Progress 2000 Mathematics Objectives)

8-1	8-2	8-3	8-4	8-5	8-6	8-7	8-8
A5a	N2d, e; M1	A5a	A5a; A7a, b	A5a	N6b; A1a, c; A8b	A1a, A5a	N3a, A5a, A13

N = Number Sense, Properties, and Operations; **M** = Measurement; **G** = Geometry and Spatial Sense;
D = Data Analysis, Statistics, and Probability; **A** = Algebra and Functions

Math Background

Chapter Overview

Before beginning the chapter, ask students to recall the definitions of exponent and power. Make sure students understand that a power is a term with an exponent, and that the words are not interchangeable. Students may find the definitions and meanings of zero and negative exponents a little puzzling, so these are introduced by extending familiar number patterns to show that the definitions follow from the need to maintain a consistent system. The chapter then goes on to develop rules for combining powers and to relate these rules to applications and graphs. The arithmetic sequences introduced in Chapter 5 are now joined by geometric sequences. Finally the properties of exponents are applied in problems involving exponential growth and decay.

Zero and Negative Exponents   8-1

Thus far, students' exposure to the negative sign has been limited to subtraction (a binary operation) and to negative integers. In this lesson, students learn that negative exponents indicate the reciprocal of the base raised to the opposite of the exponent—which is an entirely different conceptual use of the negative symbol.

Scientific Notation   8-2

When a number is written in scientific notation, the exponent of 10 indicates roughly how big or how small the number is. Two numbers are of the same order of magnitude if they are the same power of 10 when written in scientific notation.

The power of 10 is also useful in making approximate comparisons between two numbers. For example, Earth weighs about 6×10^{27} grams, or alternatively 6.6×10^{21} tons. You can compare Earth's weight in grams with its weight in tons by comparing the second factors of the two weights. The first number is roughly 10^6 ($10^{27} \div 10^{21}$) times as large as the second, or approximately a million times as great.

Multiplication Properties of Exponents   8-3 and 8-4

Students who become confused when trying to remember the rules for multiplying powers, raising a power to a power, raising a product to a power, and other combinations of these instances should be encouraged to return to the basic definition of exponents. Practice in writing the base of an exponent as a factor the appropriate number of times for any of these instances should help to clarify the summary the rules provide.

Division Properties of Exponents   8-5

When dividing powers where the base is an integer, students may try to perform illegal operations, such as dividing the exponents. Thus, for example, $\frac{3^{10}}{3^2}$ may be incorrectly simplified as 3^5. Explain that the operation with the exponents (in this case subtracting) is how the operation of dividing the powers is performed, and any other division is redundant and meaningless.

Geometric Sequences   8-6

Recall that an arithmetic sequence is a number pattern in which a common difference is added to each term and a geometric sequence is a number pattern in which each term is multiplied by a common ratio. If two infinite sequences—one arithmetic and one geometric—are both increasing, the values of the terms of the geometric sequence will always overtake those of the arithmetic sequence, no matter how great a headstart the arithmetic sequence has at the beginning.

An interesting sequence that is neither arithmetic nor geometric was discovered by Leonardo of Pisa, also known as Fibonacci, an Italian mathematician of the thirteenth century. His greatest achievement was popularizing the Hindu-Arabic numerals in the Western world. The Fibonacci sequence looks like this: {1, 1, 2, 3, 5, 8, 13, 21, 34, 55, 89, 144, 233, . . .}. The first two terms are 1, and every term thereafter is the sum of the two preceding terms. Some students may enjoy researching some of the surprising real-world connections involving this sequence.

Exponential Functions   8-7

Comparing graphs such as $f(x) = 3x$ and $f(x) = x^3$ should help students better understand the implications of the phrase *exponential growth or decay*. The way in which the graph of an exponential function changes depends on the value of the base in the function. The slope of the graph either gets increasingly steeper as x increases, if the value of the base is greater than one, or the slope approaches zero as x increases if the value of the base is between zero and one. If the value of the base is 1, then the slope of the graph is zero.

Exponential Growth and Decay   8-8

There is an exponential function that models many phenomena in both the world of manufacturing and in the world of nature. This particular function has as its base the irrational number e, a constant (transcendental, as is the more familiar π) which is approximately equal to 2.7182818284 . . . , and is also the base for natural logarithms. This exponential function is $y = e^x$.

Ongoing Assessment and Intervention

Tools for Monitoring Student Progress

The Prentice Hall *Algebra 1* program provides you with many options for assessment in the Student Edition, the Teacher's Edition and the teaching resources. From these options you may choose instructional materials and techniques that are appropriate for your students and support your district's curriculum requirements.

Instant Check System™ in Chapter 8

Allows students to check their own learning before, during, and after each lesson.

Diagnosing Readiness before the chapter (p. 392)

Check Skills You'll Need exercises in each lesson (pp. 394, 400, 405, 411, 417, 424, 430, 437)

Check Understanding questions with each Example (pp. 395, 396, 400, 401, 402, 405, 406, 407, 412, 413, 418, 419, 424, 425, 426, 427, 430, 431, 432, 438, 439, 440, 441)

Checkpoint Quiz (pp. 416, 435)

Test Prep in Chapter 8

Teaches students strategies and gives them practice with all the test item formats they will encounter on state tests and standardized national exams.

Standardized Test Prep exercises in each lesson (pp. 399, 404, 409, 410, 415, 423, 429, 434, 435, 444)

Test-Taking Strategies (p. 446: Testing Multiple Choices)

Standardized Test Prep (p. 451: Exponential Growth and Decay)

All your assessment needs in one place!

Program Assessment

Assess student progress throughout the *Algebra 1* text with blackline masters and CD-ROM.

Assessment Resources

- Checkpoint Quizzes 1 & 2
- Chapter Test, Forms A & B
- Chapter Alternative Assessment

Spanish versions available. Tests for Basic Algebra also available.

Computer Test Generator

- Unlimited questions of varying difficulty for every lesson objective.
- Create your own practice sheets, quizzes, and tests, or use the pre-made Chapter Tests.
- Diagnose readiness with questions on prerequisite skills.
- Prepare students by making tests based on standardized test objectives.
- Access Algebra 1, Geometry, and Algebra 2 content—all on one CD-ROM.

Test Preparation

A three-step approach to preparing students for high stakes, national, and state exams.

❶ Diagnose & Prescribe

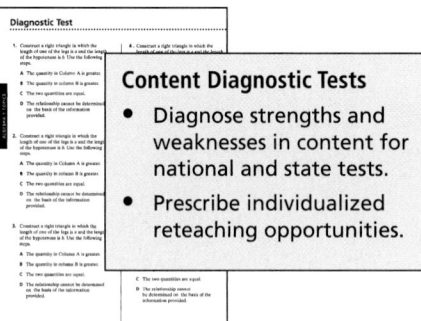

Content Diagnostic Tests
- Diagnose strengths and weaknesses in content for national and state tests.
- Prescribe individualized reteaching opportunities.

❷ Review & Reteach

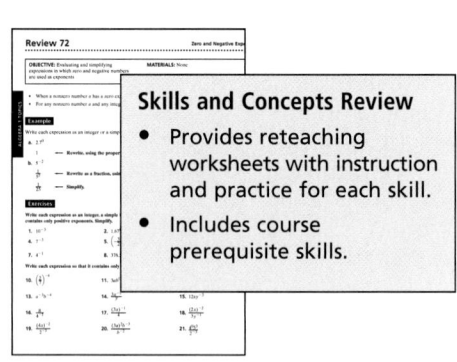

Skills and Concepts Review
- Provides reteaching worksheets with instruction and practice for each skill.
- Includes course prerequisite skills.

❸ Practice & Assess

Test Preparation
- Features practice tests for End-of-Course and SAT/ACT exams.
- Includes standardized test practice by chapter for ongoing review.

Teacher's Guide with answers and correlations.

Test-Taking Strategies with Transparencies
- Support the Test-Taking Strategies pages in the Student Edition.
- Provide a teaching transparency and a practice worksheet for each strategy.

 # Reaching All Students

Support in the Student Text and Additional Resources

The textbook, the iText, and other technology components provide numerous opportunities to reach students of various ability levels and learning styles. Each Teacher's Edition lesson suggests how you can help *all* your students be successful and understand the mathematics in Chapter 8.

Below Level

Student Edition
- Diagnosing Readiness*: p. 392
- Check Skills You'll Need*: pp. 394, 400, 405, 411, 417, 424, 430, 437

Reteaching
Chapter 8 Support File: pp. 10–17

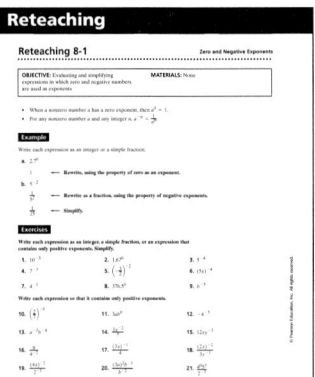

Basic Algebra Planning Guide
Chapter 8 Lesson Plans: pp. 48–55
Chapter 8 Tests: pp. 117–120

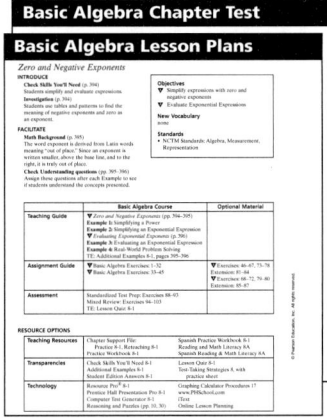

* Can be used with all ability levels to ensure mastery of prerequisite skills.

Advanced Learners

Student Edition
- Challenge exercises: pp. 399, 404, 409, 415, 422, 428, 429, 434, 443, 444

Enrichment
Chapter 8 Support File: pp. 18–25

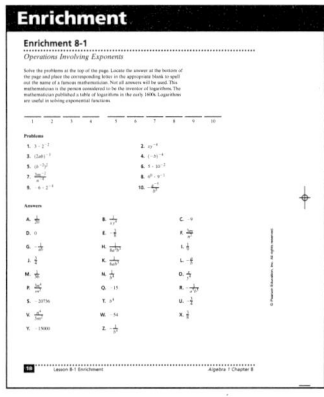

Reading and Math Literacy

Student Edition
- Vocabulary: pp. 393, 447, *plus* in every Lesson Preview
- Reading Math: pp. 395, 424, 443, 445, 447
- Illustrated Glossary: pp. 757–785

Reading and Math Literacy Masters
Chapter 8: pp. 29–32

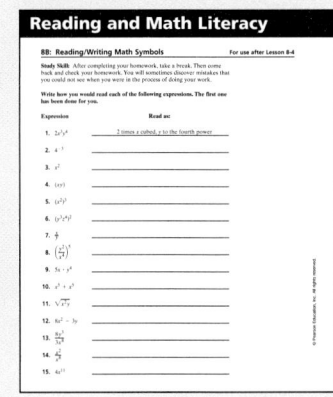

English Learners

Student Edition
- English/Spanish Illustrated Glossary: pp. 757–785

Workbook and Masters
Spanish Practice Workbook: pp. 48–55
Spanish Reading and Math Literacy Masters: pp. 29–32

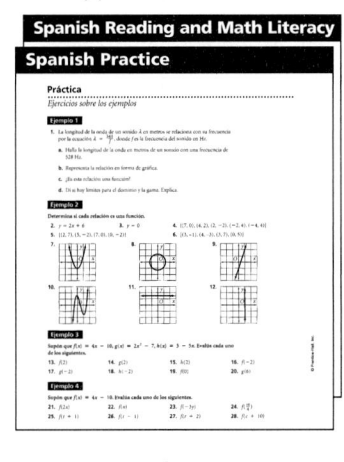

Learning Styles

Student Edition
- Investigation: p. 411
- Technology: pp. 400, 403, 415, 420, 434, 436, 438
- Writing: pp. 397, 403, 409, 415, 421, 427, 434, 443, 448, 450
- DK Activities: pp. 452–453

Activity Masters
Hands-On Activities: 18, 19
Technology Activities: 8, 22

Program Resources

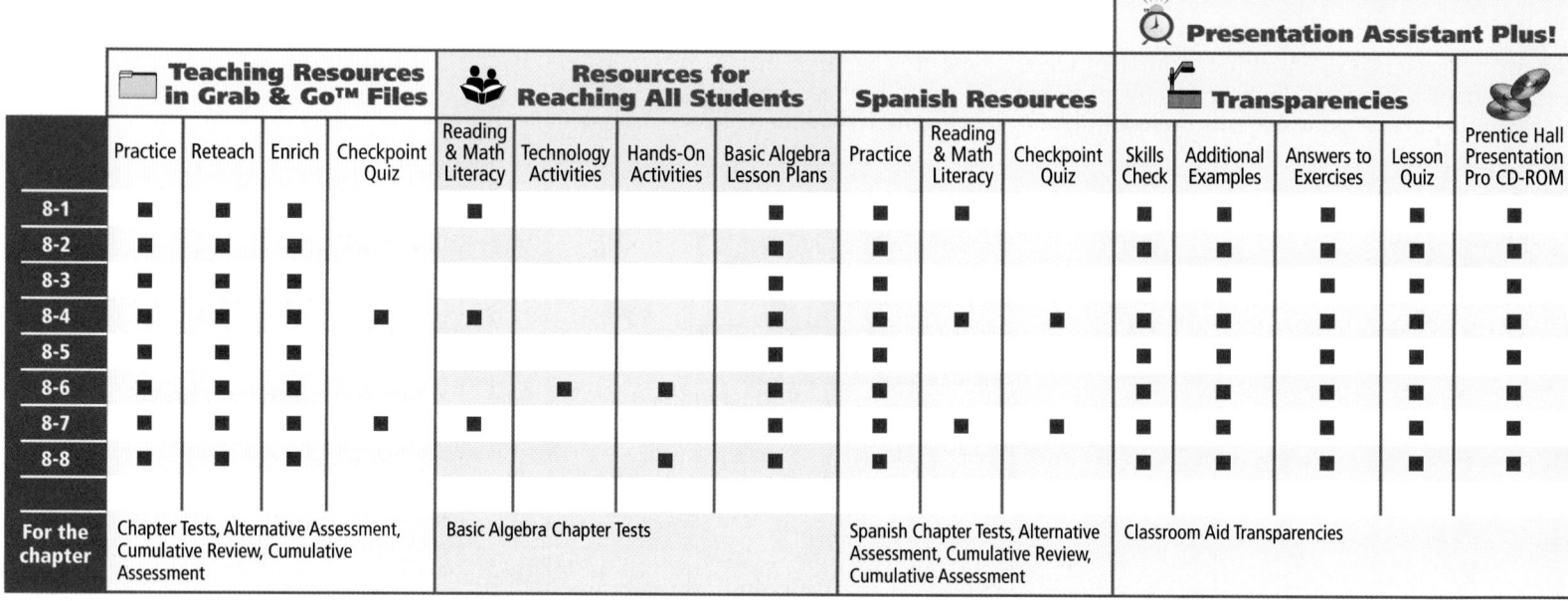

	Teaching Resources in Grab & Go™ Files				Resources for Reaching All Students				Spanish Resources			Transparencies				Presentation Assistant Plus!
	Practice	Reteach	Enrich	Checkpoint Quiz	Reading & Math Literacy	Technology Activities	Hands-On Activities	Basic Algebra Lesson Plans	Practice	Reading & Math Literacy	Checkpoint Quiz	Skills Check	Additional Examples	Answers to Exercises	Lesson Quiz	Prentice Hall Presentation Pro CD-ROM
8-1	■	■	■		■			■	■	■		■	■	■	■	■
8-2	■	■	■					■	■			■	■	■	■	■
8-3	■	■	■					■	■			■	■	■	■	■
8-4	■	■	■	■	■			■	■	■	■	■	■	■	■	■
8-5	■	■	■					■	■			■	■	■	■	■
8-6	■	■	■			■	■	■	■			■	■	■	■	■
8-7	■	■	■	■	■			■	■	■		■	■	■	■	■
8-8	■	■	■				■	■	■			■	■	■	■	■
For the chapter	Chapter Tests, Alternative Assessment, Cumulative Review, Cumulative Assessment				Basic Algebra Chapter Tests				Spanish Chapter Tests, Alternative Assessment, Cumulative Review, Cumulative Assessment			Classroom Aid Transparencies				

Also available for use with the chapter:

 *See page 392C.*

- Practice Workbook
- Solution Key

- For teacher support and access to student Web site materials, use Web Code aek-5500.
- For additional online and technology resources, see below.

Technology

iTEXT Online and on CD-ROM

Complete Interactive Student Text online and on CD-ROM—with instant feedback assessment, tutorial help, dynamic activities, instructional and real-world videos, audio, and additional practice.

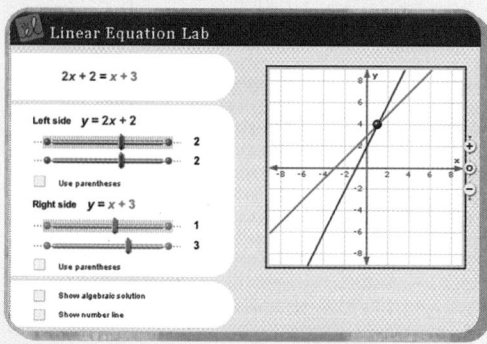

www.PHSchool.com For Students

Use **Web codes** for easy access to online activities, chapter projects, self-grading lesson quizzes and chapter tests, vocabulary quizzes, updated data sources, graphing calculator procedures, and more.

PH SuccessNet For Teachers

Online lesson planning with built-in state correlations, all the teaching resources, complete reference library, your own calendar and Teacher Web page, professional development, and more.

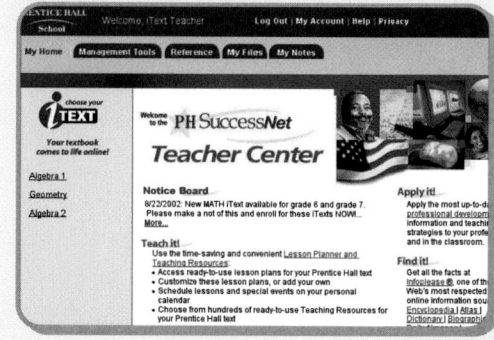

Presentation Assistant Plus!

The Prentice Hall *Presentation Assistant Plus!* provides you with the material you need to teach a lesson from beginning to end. Two easy-to-use formats—Transparencies and CD-ROM—allow you to present a lesson the way you are most comfortable.

Transparencies

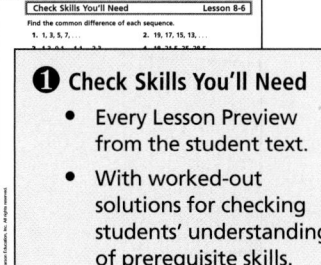

❶ **Check Skills You'll Need**
- Every Lesson Preview from the student text.
- With worked-out solutions for checking students' understanding of prerequisite skills.

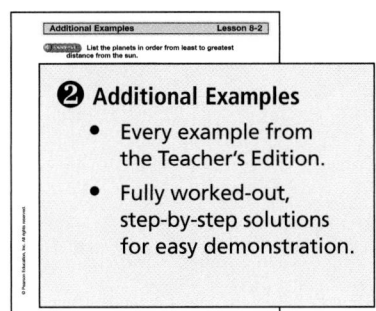

❷ **Additional Examples**
- Every example from the Teacher's Edition.
- Fully worked-out, step-by-step solutions for easy demonstration.

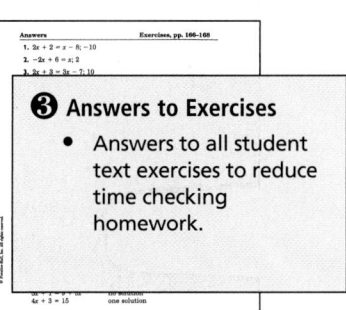

❸ **Answers to Exercises**
- Answers to all student text exercises to reduce time checking homework.

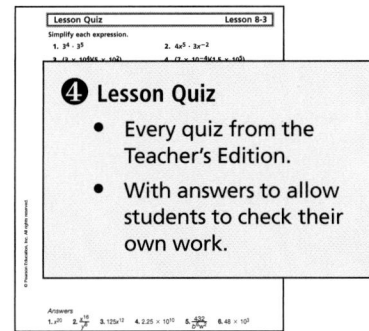

❹ **Lesson Quiz**
- Every quiz from the Teacher's Edition.
- With answers to allow students to check their own work.

 Throughout the Teacher's Edition, this symbol indicates material that is available on transparency in the Presentation Assistant Plus!

Prentice Hall Presentation Pro CD-ROM

- Includes all Transparencies.
- Conveniently organized by lesson so you can easily ❶ Introduce, ❷ Teach, ❸ Check Homework, and ❹ Assess each lesson.
- Animated examples allow step-by-step instruction at your own pace.
- Easy to edit so you can create custom presentations.

Teaching Chapter 8 Using Presentation Assistant Plus!

	❶ Introduce	❷ Teach	❸ Check Homework	❹ Assess
	Check Skills You'll Need	Additional Examples	Student Edition Answers	Lesson Quiz
8-1	p. 48	pp. 104–106	✔	p. 119
8-2	p. 49	pp. 106–109	✔	p. 119
8-3	p. 50	pp. 109–111	✔	p. 120
8-4	p. 51	pp. 112–113	✔	p. 120
8-5	p. 52	pp. 113–115	✔	p. 121
8-6	p. 53	pp. 116–118	✔	p. 122
8-7	p. 54	pp. 119–120	✔	p. 123
8-8	p. 55	pp. 121–124	✔	p. 124

Prentice Hall Presentation Pro

CD-ROM with dynamic PowerPoint® presentations for every lesson. Helps you introduce and develop concepts, check homework, and assess progress. Part of Presentation Assistant Plus! *(See above.)*

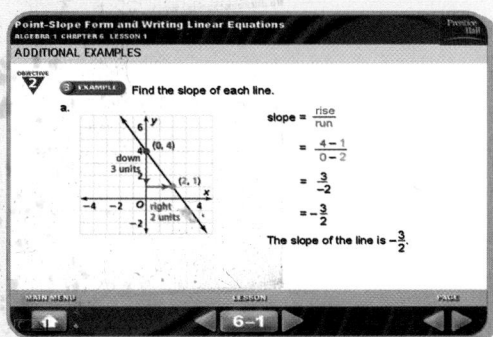

Computer Test Generator

CD-ROM to create practice sheets and tests for course objectives and standardized tests. Includes Instant Chapter Tests™, online testing, and student reports. Part of the PH Assessment System. *(See page 392C.)*

Resource Pro® with Planning Express®

CD-ROM with a lesson planning tool that allows you to import state and local objectives. Includes electronic versions of all the teaching resources.

Exponents and Exponential Functions

 Diagnosing Readiness

Students will find answers to these exercises in the back of their textbooks.

For intervention, direct students to:

Converting Fractions to Decimals
Skills Handbook, p. 725

Using Order of Operations
Lesson 1-2: Example 1
Exercises 2–5 and 22–25
Extra Practice, p. 702

Evaluating Expressions
Lesson 1-6: Example 2
Exercises 13–24
Extra Practice, p. 702

Calculating Simple Interest
Lesson 4-3: Example 2
Exercises 54–57
Extra Practice, p. 705

Understanding Domain and Range Lesson 5-2: Example 5
Exercises 23–25
Extra Practice, p. 706

Finding Terms of a Sequence
Lesson 5-6: Example 3
Exercises 34–39
Extra Practice, p. 706

Where You've Been

- In Chapter 1 you learned how to use the order of operations to simplify expressions containing exponents.

- In Chapter 5 you studied number patterns and learned to recognize an arithmetic sequence. You also wrote equations for function rules.

- In Chapter 6 you found a line of best fit for a set of data.

 **Diagnosing Readiness**

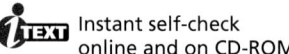 Instant self-check online and on CD-ROM

(For help, go to the Lesson in green.)

Converting Fractions to Decimals (Skills Handbook page 725)

Write as a decimal.

1. $\frac{7}{10}$ **0.7**   **2.** $6\frac{2}{5}$ **6.4**   **3.** $\frac{8}{1000}$ **0.008**   **4.** $\frac{7}{2}$ **3.5**   **5.** $\frac{3}{11}$ **0.$\overline{27}$**

Using the Order of Operations (Lesson 1-2)

Simplify each expression.

6. $(9 \div 3 + 4)^2$ **49**   **7.** $5 + (0.3)^3$ **5.027**   **8.** $3 - (1.5)^2$ **0.75**   **9.** $64 \div 2^4$ **4**

Evaluating Expressions (Lessons 1-4 to 1-6)

Evaluate each expression for $a = -2$ and $b = 5$.

10. $(ab)^2$ **100**   **11.** $(a - b)^2$ **49**   **12.** $a^3 + b^2$ **17**   **13.** $b - (3a)^2$ **−31**

Calculating Simple Interest (Lesson 4-3)

Use the formula for simple interest, $I = Prt$. Find each missing value.

14. $I = \blacksquare, p = \$1000, r = 3\%, t = 4$ yr **\$120**   **15.** $I = \$672, p = \blacksquare, r = 7\%, t = 12$ yr **\$800**

Understanding Domain and Range (Lesson 5-2)

Find the range of each function with domain $\{-2, 0, 3.5\}$.

16. $f(x) = -2x^2$
$\{-24.5, -8, 0\}$

17. $g(x) = 10 - x^3$
$\{-32.875, 10, 18\}$

18. $y = 5x - 1$
$\{-11, -1, 16.5\}$

Finding Terms of a Sequence (Lesson 5-6)

Find the next two terms of each sequence.

19. $1, 3, 5, 7, \ldots$ **9, 11**   **20.** $-1, 0, 2, 5, 9, \ldots$ **14, 20**   **21.** $7, 13, 19, 25, \ldots$ **31, 37**

Exponents and Exponential Functions

Where You're Going

- In this chapter you will extend your knowledge about exponents to include zero and negative exponents.

- You will learn the properties of exponents, and how exponents are used to write a geometric sequence.

- By making a table of values, you will graph exponential functions.

 **Real-World Snapshots** Applying what you learn, you will use functions and graphs to do activities related to animals, on pages 452–453.

LESSONS

8-1 **Zero and Negative Exponents**

8-2 **Scientific Notation**

8-3 **Multiplication Properties of Exponents**

8-4 **More Multiplication Properties of Exponents**

8-5 **Division Properties of Exponents**

8-6 **Geometric Sequences**

8-7 **Exponential Functions**

8-8 **Exponential Growth and Decay**

Key Vocabulary

- common ratio (p. 424)
- compound interest (p. 438)
- decay factor (p. 440)
- exponential decay (p. 440)
- exponential function (p. 430)
- exponential growth (p. 437)
- geometric sequence (p. 424)
- growth factor (p. 437)
- interest period (p. 438)
- scientific notation (p. 400)

Chapter 8 Overview

This chapter introduces using zero and negative exponents, and evaluating exponential equations. Scientific notation illustrates a common use for exponents. Problems using scientific notation and other exponential expressions illustrate multiplying and dividing powers, raising a power to a power, and raising products and quotients to a power. This leads to work with geometric sequences. Then students evaluate and graph exponential functions and apply this to modeling exponential growth and decay.

📖 **Reading Math**
Reading Graphs, p. 445.

📖 **Vocabulary**
A complete list of terms, plus vocabulary exercises, appears in the Chapter Review, p. 447.

📖 **Illustrated Glossary**
Examples for each vocabulary term, plus definitions in both English and Spanish, appear starting on p. 757.

📝 **Test-Taking Strategies**
Working Backward, p. 446.

DK **Real-World Snapshots**
See pages 452–453 for a real-world application of Velocity and Linear Equations that utilizes Dorling Kindersley's (DK) unique graphic presentation.

🌐 **Real-World Connections**
Some of the applications you will find in this chapter are population growth (8-1), astronomy (8-2), medicine (8-3), and recycling (8-5).

💻 **www.PHSchool.com**
Internet support for this chapter includes:
- Self-grading Vocabulary and Chapter 8 Tests
- Chapter Project
- Chapter Planner
- Chapter 8 Resources

Plus 🚶**TEXT**

1. Plan

✓ Check Skills You'll Need

Exponents
Lesson 1-2: Example 4
Exercises 21–28
Extra Practice, p. 702

Multiplying and Dividing
Lesson 1-6: Example 7
Exercises 54–57
Extra Practice, p. 702

Lesson Resources

📁 **Teaching Resources**
Practice, Reteaching, Enrichment

👥 **Reaching All Students**
Practice Workbook 8-1
Spanish Practice Workbook 8-1
Reading and Math Literacy 8A
Spanish Reading & Literacy 8A
Basic Algebra Planning Guide 8-1

⏰ **Presentation Assistant Plus!**
Transparencies
• Check Skills You'll Need 8-1
• Additional Examples 8-1
• Student Edition Answers 8-1
• Lesson Quiz 8-1
PH Presentation Pro CD 8-1

ASSESSMENT SYSTEM

Computer Test Generator CD

💻 **Technology**
Resource Pro® CD-ROM
Computer Test Generator CD
Prentice Hall Presentation Pro CD

🖥 **www.PHSchool.com**
Student Site
• Teacher Web Code: aek-5500
• Reasoning & Puzzles pp. 10, 30
• Graphing Calculator,
  Procedure 17
• Self-grading Lesson Quiz
Teacher Center
• Lesson Planner
• Resources

Plus

394

Zero and Negative Exponents

1.01 Write equivalent forms of algebraic expressions to solve problems. a) Apply the laws of exponents.

North Carolina Objectives

Lesson Preview

What You'll Learn

OBJECTIVE 1
To simplify expressions with zero and negative exponents

OBJECTIVE 2
To evaluate exponential expressions

. . . And Why

To find the size of a population, as in Example 4

✓ Check Skills You'll Need

(For help, go to Lessons 1-2 and 1-6.)

Simplify each expression.

1. 2^3 **8**

2. $\frac{1}{4^2}$ **$\frac{1}{16}$**

3. $4^2 \div 2^2$ **4**

4. $(-3)^3$ **−27**

5. -3^3 **−27**

6. $6^2 \div 12$ **3**

Evaluate each expression for $a = 2$, $b = -1$, and $c = 0.5$.

7. $\frac{a}{2a}$ **$\frac{1}{2}$**

8. $\frac{bc}{c}$ **−1**

9. $\frac{ab}{bc}$ **4**

---

iTEXT Interactive lesson includes instant self-check, tutorials, and activities.

OBJECTIVE 1 Zero and Negative Exponents

Investigation: Exponents

1. a. Copy the table below. Replace each blank with the value of the power in simplest form.

2^x	5^x	10^x	
$2^4 = \blacksquare$	$5^4 = \blacksquare$	$10^4 = \blacksquare$	16, 625, 10,000
$2^3 = \blacksquare$	$5^3 = \blacksquare$	$10^3 = \blacksquare$	8, 125, 1000
$2^2 = \blacksquare$	$5^2 = \blacksquare$	$10^2 = \blacksquare$	4, 25, 100

1b. In the first column, each term is $\frac{1}{2}$ the previous term. In the second column, each term is $\frac{1}{5}$ the previous term. In the third column, each term is $\frac{1}{10}$ the previous term.

b. Look at the values that you used to replace the blanks. What pattern do you see as you go down each column? **See left.**

2. Copy the table below. Use the pattern you described in Question 1 to complete the table.

2^x	5^x	10^x	
$2^1 = \blacksquare$	$5^1 = \blacksquare$	$10^1 = \blacksquare$	2, 5, 10
$2^0 = \blacksquare$	$5^0 = \blacksquare$	$10^0 = \blacksquare$	1, 1, 1
$2^{-1} = \blacksquare$	$5^{-1} = \blacksquare$	$10^{-1} = \blacksquare$	$\frac{1}{2}, \frac{1}{5}, \frac{1}{10}$
$2^{-2} = \blacksquare$	$5^{-2} = \blacksquare$	$10^{-2} = \blacksquare$	$\frac{1}{4}, \frac{1}{25}, \frac{1}{100}$

3. **Critical Thinking** What pattern do you notice in the row with 0 as an exponent? **The values are all 1.**

4. Copy and complete each expression.

a. $2^{-1} = \frac{1}{2^{\blacksquare}}$ **1**

b. $2^{-2} = \frac{1}{2^{\blacksquare}}$ **2**

c. $2^{-3} = \frac{1}{2^{\blacksquare}}$ **3**

Ongoing Assessment and Intervention

Before the Lesson
Diagnose prerequisite skills using:
• Check Skills You'll Need

During the Lesson
Monitor progress using:
• Check Understanding
• Additional Examples
• Standardized Test Prep

After the Lesson
Assess knowledge using:
• Lesson Quiz
• Computer Test Generator CD

Consider 3^3, 3^2, and 3^1. Decreasing the exponent by one is the same as dividing by 3. Continuing the pattern, 3^0 equals 1 and 3^{-1} equals $\frac{1}{3}$.

 Key Concepts

Property	Zero as an Exponent

For every nonzero number a, $a^0 = 1$.

Examples $\quad 5^0 = 1 \qquad (-2)^0 = 1 \qquad (1.02)^0 = 1 \qquad \left(\frac{1}{3}\right)^0 = 1$

Property	Negative Exponent

For every nonzero number a and integer n, $a^{-n} = \frac{1}{a^n}$.

Examples $\quad 6^{-4} = \frac{1}{6^4} \qquad (-8)^{-1} = \frac{1}{(-8)^1}$

Why can't you use 0 as a base? By the first property, $3^0 = 1$, $2^0 = 1$, and $1^0 = 1$, which implies $0^0 = 1$. However, the pattern $0^3 = 0$, $0^2 = 0$, and $0^1 = 0$ implies $0^0 = 0$. Since both 1 and 0 cannot be the answer, 0^0 is undefined. In the second property, using 0 as a base results in division by zero, which you know is undefined.

 Reading Math

Read 4^{-3} as "four to the negative three".

1 EXAMPLE **Simplifying a Power**

Simplify.

a. $4^{-3} = \frac{1}{4^3}$ $\qquad$ Use the definition of negative exponent.

$\qquad = \frac{1}{64}$ $\qquad$ Simplify.

b. $(-1.23)^0 = 1$ $\qquad$ Use the definition of zero as an exponent.

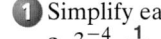 **Check Understanding** **1** Simplify each expression.

a. 3^{-4} $\frac{1}{81}$ $\qquad$ **b.** $(-7)^0$ **1** $\qquad$ **c.** $(-4)^{-3}$ $-\frac{1}{64}$ **d.** 7^{-1} $\frac{1}{7}$ $\qquad$ **e.** -3^{-2} $-\frac{1}{9}$

An algebraic expression is in simplest form when it is written with only positive exponents. If the expression is a fraction in simplest form, the only common factor of the numerator and denominator is 1.

2 EXAMPLE **Simplifying an Exponential Expression**

Simplify each expression.

a. $4yx^{-3} = 4y\left(\frac{1}{x^3}\right)$ $\qquad$ Use the definition of negative exponent.

$\qquad = \frac{4y}{x^3}$ $\qquad$ Simplify.

b. $\frac{1}{w^{-4}} = 1 \div w^{-4}$ $\qquad$ Rewrite using a division symbol.

$\qquad = 1 \div \frac{1}{w^4}$ $\qquad$ Use the definition of negative exponent.

$\qquad = 1 \cdot w^4$ $\qquad$ Multiply by the reciprocal of $\frac{1}{w^4}$, which is w^4.

$\qquad = w^4$ $\qquad$ Identity Property of Multiplication

Check Understanding **2** Simplify each expression.

Reaching All Students

Below Level In Example 4, suggest that students make a table to help keep track of what w represents in different situations.	Advanced Learners Have students simplify $\frac{1}{x^{-1}}$.	Inclusion See note on page 395. Auditory Learners See note on page 395.

Math Background

The word "exponent" is derived from Latin words meaning "out of place." Since an exponent is written smaller, above the base line, and to the right, it is truly out of place!

OBJECTIVE

1 **Teaching Notes**

Investigation (Optional)
Inclusion

Some students have writing difficulties that make it hard to copy this much material in a short time. Let these students just write their replacements for the blanks or work with a partner.

1 EXAMPLE **Teaching Tip**

Assure students that in Lesson 5 you will demonstrate another reason why $a^0 = 1$.

2 EXAMPLE **Auditory Learners**

Some students may forget to remove the negative sign from the exponent after the factor is moved. Students may find it useful to remember the phrase "move it, lose it," meaning that when they *move* the factor with the negative exponent, they should *lose* the negative sign.

Additional Examples

1 Simplify.

a. 3^{-2} $\frac{1}{9}$

b. $(-22.4)^0$ **1**

2 Simplify each expression.

a. $3ab^{-2}$ $\frac{3a}{b^2}$

b. $\frac{1}{x^{-3}}$ x^3

3 EXAMPLE Error Prevention

When students substitute -3 for t, they may incorrectly write -3^2 and multiply as "the negative of 3 times 3." Suggest that they write parentheses around their substitutions to help avoid confusion.

Additional Examples

3 Evaluate $4x^2y^{-3}$ for $x = 3$ and $y = -2$. $-4\frac{1}{2}$

4 In the lab, the population of a certain bacteria doubles every month. The expression $3000 \cdot 2^m$ models a population of 3000 bacteria after m months of growth. Evaluate the expression for $m = 0$ and $m = -2$. Describe what the value of the expression represents in each situation.
When $m = 0$, the value of the expression is 3000. This represents the initial population of the bacteria.
When $m = -2$, the value of the expression is 750. This represents the 750 bacteria in the population 2 months before the present population of 3000 bacteria.

Closure

Ask students to explain the meaning of a zero exponent and the meaning of a negative exponent. A nonzero base raised to a zero exponent is equal to 1. A nonzero base raised to a negative exponent is equal to the reciprocal of the base raised to the positive exponent.
Also ask what the first step is for simplifying an exponential expression that contains negative exponents. Use the definition of negative exponents to rewrite the expression with positive exponents only.

396

When you evaluate an exponential expression, you can write the expression with positive exponents before substituting values.

3 EXAMPLE Evaluating an Exponential Expression

Evaluate $3m^2t^{-2}$ for $m = 2$ and $t = -3$.

Method 1 Write with positive exponents first.

$3m^2t^{-2} = \dfrac{3m^2}{t^2}$ **Use the definition of negative exponent.**

$= \dfrac{3(2)^2}{(-3)^2}$ **Substitute 2 for m and -3 for t.**

$= \dfrac{12}{9} = 1\frac{1}{3}$ **Simplify.**

Method 2 Substitute first.

$3m^2t^{-2} = 3(2)^2(-3)^{-2}$ **Substitute 2 for m and -3 for t.**

$= \dfrac{3(2)^2}{(-3)^2}$ **Use the definition of negative exponent.**

$= \dfrac{12}{9} = 1\frac{1}{3}$ **Simplify.**

✓ Check Understanding **3** Evaluate each expression for $n = -2$ and $w = 5$.
a. $n^{-3}w^0$ $-\frac{1}{8}$ **b.** $\dfrac{n^{-1}}{w^2}$ $-\frac{1}{50}$ **c.** $\dfrac{w^0}{n^4}$ $\frac{1}{16}$ **d.** $\dfrac{1}{nw^{-2}}$ $-12\frac{1}{2}$

You can also evaluate exponential expressions that model real-world situations.

4 EXAMPLE 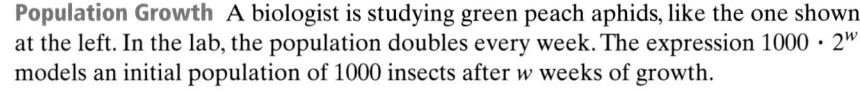 Real-World Problem Solving

Population Growth A biologist is studying green peach aphids, like the one shown at the left. In the lab, the population doubles every week. The expression $1000 \cdot 2^w$ models an initial population of 1000 insects after w weeks of growth.

a. Evaluate the expression for $w = 0$. Then describe what the value of the expression represents in the situation.

$1000 \cdot 2^w = 1000 \cdot 2^0$ **Substitute 0 for w.**

$= 1000 \cdot 1$ **Simplify.**

$= 1000$

The value of the expression represents the initial population of insects. This makes sense because when $w = 0$, no time has passed.

Real-World Connection

During the months of June and July, green peach aphids in a field of potato plants can double in population every three days.

b. Evaluate the expression for $w = -3$. Then describe what the value of the expression represents in the situation.

$1000 \cdot 2^w = 1000 \cdot 2^{-3}$ **Substitute -3 for w.**

$= 1000 \cdot \frac{1}{8}$ **Simplify.**

$= 125$

There were 125 aphids 3 weeks before the present population of 1000 insects.

✓ Check Understanding **4** A sample of bacteria triples each month. The expression $5400 \cdot 3^m$ models a population of 5400 bacteria after m months of growth. Evaluate the expression for $m = -2$ and $m = 0$. Describe what each value of the expression represents in the situation. **See margin.**

page 396   Check Understanding

4. 600; 5400; for $x = -2$, the population is 600, 2 months before the population is 5400. For $x = 0$, it is the population when time is 0.

EXERCISES

For more practice, see *Extra Practice*.

Practice and Problem Solving

A Practice by Example

Example 1
(page 395)

Simplify each expression.

1. $-(2.57)^0$ -1
2. 4^{-2} $\frac{1}{16}$
3. $(-5)^{-2}$ $\frac{1}{25}$
4. -5^{-2} $-\frac{1}{25}$

5. $(-4)^{-2}$ $\frac{1}{16}$
6. -3^{-4} $-\frac{1}{81}$
7. 2^{-6} $\frac{1}{64}$
8. -12^{-1} $-\frac{1}{12}$

9. $\frac{1}{2^0}$ 1
10. 78^{-1} $\frac{1}{78}$
11. $(-4)^{-3}$ $-\frac{1}{64}$
12. -4^{-3} $-\frac{1}{64}$

Example 2
(page 395)

Copy and complete each equation.

13. $4n^{\blacksquare} = \frac{4}{n^2}$ -2
14. $\frac{x^{\blacksquare}}{2y^{\blacksquare}} = \frac{1}{2x^{-3}y^4}$ $3; 4$
15. $\frac{a^{\blacksquare}}{3b^{\blacksquare}} = \frac{b^3}{3}$ $0; -3$
16. $3xy^{\blacksquare} = \frac{3x}{y^5}$ -5

Simplify each expression.

17. $3ab^0$ $3a$
18. $5x^{-4}$ $\frac{5}{x^4}$
19. $\frac{1}{x^{-7}}$ x^7
20. $\frac{1}{c^{-1}}$ c

21. $\frac{5^{-2}}{p}$ $\frac{1}{25p}$
22. $a^{-4}c^0$ $\frac{1}{a^4}$
23. $\frac{3x^{-2}}{y}$ $\frac{3}{x^2y}$
24. $\frac{7ab^{-2}}{3w}$ $\frac{7a}{3b^2w}$

25. $x^{-5}y^{-7}$ $\frac{1}{x^5y^7}$
26. $x^{-5}y^7$ $\frac{y^7}{x^5}$
27. $\frac{8}{2c^{-3}}$ $4c^3$
28. $\frac{7s}{5t^{-3}}$ $\frac{7st^3}{5}$

29. $\frac{6a^{-1}c^{-3}}{d^0}$ $\frac{6}{ac^3}$
30. $2^{-3}x^2z^{-7}$ $\frac{x^2}{8z^7}$
31. $9^0y^7t^{-11}$ $\frac{y^7}{t^{11}}$
32. $\frac{7s^0t^{-5}}{2^{-1}m^2}$ $\frac{14}{m^2t^5}$

Example 3
(page 396)

Evaluate each expression for $r = -3$ and $s = 5$.

33. s^{-2} $\frac{1}{25}$
34. r^{-2} $\frac{1}{9}$
35. $-r^{-2}$ $-\frac{1}{9}$
36. s^0 1

37. $3s^{-2}$ $\frac{3}{25}$
38. $(2s)^{-2}$ $\frac{1}{100}$
39. $r^{-4}s^2$ $\frac{25}{81}$
40. $\frac{1}{r^{-4}s^2}$ $\frac{81}{25}$

41. s^2r^{-3} $-\frac{25}{27}$
42. r^0s^{-2} $\frac{1}{25}$
43. $5r^3s^{-1}$ -27
44. $2^{-4}r^3s^{-2}$ $-\frac{27}{400}$

Example 4
(page 396)

45. a. Suppose your allowance doubles every week. This week you receive $2.56. How much will your allowance be three weeks from now? How much was your allowance three weeks ago? **$20.48; $0.32**

b. Critical Thinking From a parent's point of view, is doubling your allowance each week a good plan? Explain.
No; the value of the allowance rapidly becomes very great.

B Apply Your Skills

Mental Math Is the value of each expression *positive* or *negative*?

46. -2^2 neg.
47. $(-2)^2$ pos.
48. 2^{-2} pos.
49. $(-2)^3$ neg.
50. $(-2)^{-3}$ neg.

Write each number as a power of 10 using negative exponents.

51. $\frac{1}{10}$ 10^{-1}
52. $\frac{1}{100}$ 10^{-2}
53. $\frac{1}{1000}$ 10^{-3}
54. $\frac{1}{10,000}$ 10^{-4}
55. $\frac{1}{100,000}$ 10^{-5}

Write each expression as a decimal.

56. 10^{-3}
0.001
57. 10^{-6}
0.000001
58. $7 \cdot 10^{-1}$
0.7
59. $3 \cdot 10^{-2}$
0.03
60. $5 \cdot 10^{-4}$
0.0005

61. a. Patterns Complete the pattern using powers of 5.

$$\frac{1}{5^2} = \blacksquare 5^{-2} \quad \frac{1}{5^1} = \blacksquare 5^{-1} \quad \frac{1}{5^0} = \blacksquare 5^0 \quad \frac{1}{5^{-1}} = \blacksquare 5^1 \quad \frac{1}{5^{-2}} = \blacksquare 5^2$$

b. Write $\frac{1}{5^{-4}}$ using a positive exponent. 5^4

c. Rewrite $\frac{1}{a^{-n}}$ so that the power of a is in the numerator. $\frac{a^n}{1}$

62. In -3^0, 3 is raised to the zero power, and then the opposite is determined. In $(-3)^0$, the number -3 is raised to the zero power.

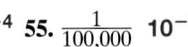

62. Writing Explain why the value of -3^0 is negative but the value of $(-3)^0$ is positive. **See left.**

Assignment Guide

1 Objective
A B Core 1–32, 46–67, 73–78
C Extension 81–84

2 Objective
A B Core 33–45, 68–72, 79–80
C Extension 85–87

Standardized Test Prep 88–93

Mixed Review 94–103

Error Prevention

Exercises 1–12 Remind students to look at each problem carefully to determine whether a negative sign is part of the base of an exponent.

Math Tip

Exercises 51–55 Remind students that the exponent for a power of 10 is the same as the number of zeros when the number is written in standard form.

397

Simplify each expression.

1. 3^{-4} $\frac{1}{81}$
2. $(-6)^0$ 1
3. $-2a^0b^{-2}$ $-\frac{2}{b^2}$
4. $\frac{k}{m^{-3}}$ km^3
5. $8000 \cdot 4^0$ 8000
6. $4500 \cdot 3^{-2}$ 500

Alternative Assessment

Call on a student to give you a number from 1 through 4. Write this number on the board or overhead transparency. Ask another student to give you a positive or negative exponent. Write that number as the exponent for the base number on the board. Ask a third volunteer to simplify the expression. Ask this last student to give the first number for the next expression. Repeat the process.

74b. They are reciprocals for $a \neq 0$; $\frac{1}{a^n} = a^{-n}$

and $\frac{1}{a^{-n}} = \frac{1}{\frac{1}{a^n}} = a^n$.

77. No; $3x^{-2} \cdot 3x^2 = 9 \cdot x^0$ $= 9$. The product of reciprocals should be 1.

78. The student multiplied b by zero instead of raising b to the zero power, which would equal 1.

Simplify each expression.

63. $45 \cdot (0.5)^0$ 45   **64.** $54 \cdot 3^{-2}$ 6   **65.** $\frac{5^{-2}}{10^{-3}}$ 40   **66.** $\frac{4^{-1}}{9^0}$ $\frac{1}{4}$ **67.** $\frac{(-3)^{-4}}{-3}$ $-\frac{1}{243}$

Evaluate each expression for $a = 3$, $b = 2$, and $c = -4$.

68. c^b 16   **69.** $a^{-b}b$ $\frac{2}{9}$ **70.** b^{-a} $\frac{1}{8}$ **71.** b^c $\frac{1}{16}$ **72.** $c^{-a}b^{ab}$ -1

73. Copy and complete the table below.

a	4	■$\frac{1}{3}$	■6	$\frac{7}{8}$	■2
a^{-1}	■$\frac{1}{4}$	3	$\frac{1}{6}$	■$\frac{8}{7}$	0.5

74. a. Critical Thinking Simplify $a^n \cdot a^{-n}$. 1
   b. What is the mathematical relationship of a^n and a^{-n}? Justify your answer. **See left.**

75. Which expressions equal $\frac{1}{4}$? **A, B, D**
   A. 4^{-1} **B.** 2^{-2} **C.** -4^1 **D.** $\frac{1}{2^2}$ **E.** 1^4 **F.** -2^{-2}

76. Open-Ended Choose a fraction to use as a value for the variable a. Find the values of a^{-1}, a^2, and a^{-2}. **Check students' work.**

77. Critical Thinking Are $3x^{-2}$ and $3x^2$ reciprocals? Explain. **See left.**

78. Error Analysis A student simplified an expression as shown at the right. What error did the student make?
   See left.

$$\frac{x^n}{a^{-n}b^0} = \frac{a^nx^n}{b^0}$$
$$= \frac{a^nx^n}{0} \text{ undefined}$$

 79. Probability Suppose your history teacher gives a multiple-choice quiz. There are four questions, each with five answer choices. The probability p of guessing the answer to a question correctly is $\frac{1}{5}$. The probability q of guessing the answer to each question incorrectly is $\frac{4}{5}$.
   a. The table has expressions to find the probability of correctly guessing a certain number of answers on this quiz. Copy and complete the table.

Multiple-Choice Quiz

Number Correct	Expression	Probability
0	p^0q^4	$\left(\frac{1}{5}\right)^0\left(\frac{4}{5}\right)^4 = 0.4096$
1	$4p^1q^3$	■0.4096
2	$6p^2q^2$	■0.1536
3	$4p^3q^1$	■0.0256
4	p^4q^0	■0.0016

   b. Which number of correct answers is most likely? **0 or 1**

80. Communication Suppose you are the only person in your class who knows a certain story. After a minute you tell a classmate. Every minute after that, every student who knows the story tells another student (sometimes the person being told already will have heard it). In a class of 30 students, the expression $\frac{30}{1 + 29 \cdot 2^{-t}}$ predicts the approximate number of people who will have heard the story after t minutes. About how many students will have heard your story after 2 min? After 5 min? After 10 min?
   about 4 students; about 16 students; about 29 students

C Challenge **Simplify each expression.**

81. $2^3(5^0 - 6m^2)$ **8 − 48m²** **82.** $(-5)^2 - (0.5)^{-2}$ **21**   **83.** $\frac{6}{m^2} + \frac{5m^{-2}}{3^{-3}}$ **$\frac{141}{m^2}$**

84. $(0.8)^{-3} + 19^0 - 2^{-6}$ **85.** $\frac{2r^{-5}y^3}{n^2} \div \frac{r^2y^5}{2n}$ **$\frac{4}{nr^7y^2}$**   **86.** $2^{-1} - \frac{1}{3^{-2}} + 5\left(\frac{1}{2^2}\right)$
2.9375   **$-7\frac{1}{4}$**

87. For what values of n is $n^{-3} = \left(\frac{1}{n}\right)^5$? **1 and −1**

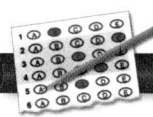

Standardized Test Prep

Gridded Response

88. Evaluate the expression xy^{-1} for $x = 2$ and $y = 3$. **$\frac{2}{3}$**

89. Simplify $\frac{3^{-2}b^2}{a^0b^2}$. **$\frac{1}{9}$**

Take It to the NET
Online lesson quiz at
www.PHSchool.com
Web Code: aea-0801

90. Evaluate the expression $(4cd)^{-2}$ for $c = 2$ and $d = 1$. **$\frac{1}{64}$**

91. Simplify $-6(-6)^{-1}$. **1**

92. Write $26 \cdot 10^{-2}$ as a decimal. **0.26**

93. Write $0.2584 \cdot 10^3$ as a decimal. **258.4**

Mixed Review

Lesson 7-6

Solve each system by graphing. 94–96. See margin.

94. $y > 3x + 4$
   $y \leq -3x + 1$

95. $y \leq -2x + 1$
   $y < 2x - 1$

96. $y \geq 0.5x$
   $y \leq x + 2$

Lesson 6-6

**97c. Answers may vary
slightly. Sample:
$y = 53x - 4328$
d. Answers may vary
slightly. Sample:
$1,237,000,000**

97. Hat Sales Use the data in the
table at the right.
a. Make a scatter plot of the
data. Use 87 for 1987. **a–b.**
b. Draw a trend line.**See margin.**
c. Write an equation for the
trend line. **See left.**
d. Use your trend line to
predict the retail sales of
women's hats in 2005.**See left.**

Lesson 6-2

**Write an equation of the line with
the given slope and y-intercept.**

98. $m = -1, b = 4$ **$y = -x + 4$**

99. $m = 5, b = -2$ **$y = 5x - 2$**

100. $m = \frac{2}{5}, b = -3$ **$y = \frac{2}{5}x - 3$**

$y = -\frac{3}{11}x - 17$ **101.** $m = -\frac{3}{11}, b = -17$

102. $m = \frac{5}{9}, b = \frac{1}{3}$ **$y = \frac{5}{9}x + \frac{1}{3}$**

103. $m = 1.25, b = -3.79$
   $y = 1.25x - 3.79$

Estimated Women's Retail Hat Sales

Year	Sales (millions of dollars)
1987	300
1988	345
1989	397
1990	457
1991	510
1992	587
1993	664
1994	700
1995	770
1996	792
1997	830
1998	872
1999	915

SOURCE: Headwear Information Bureau

Standardized Test Prep

A sheet of blank grids is available
in the Test-Taking Strategies with
Transparencies booklet. Give this
sheet to students for practice with
filling in grids.

 Resources
For additional practice with a
variety of test item formats:
- Standardized Test Prep, p. 451
- Test-Taking Strategies, p. 446
- Test-Taking Strategies with
  Transparencies

Math Tip
Exercises 92, 93 Remind students
that multiplying or dividing by 10
has the effect of 'moving' the
decimal. Here they are dividing by
10 twice, and multiplying by 10
three times.

pages 397–399   Exercises

94.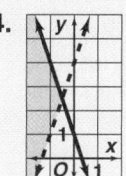

95.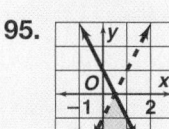

96.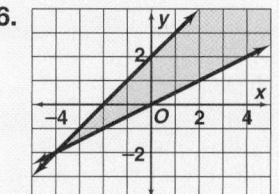

97a–b.
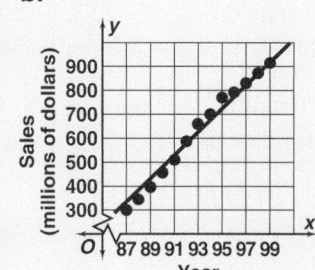

8-2

1. Plan

Lesson Preview

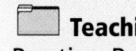 **Check Skills You'll Need**

Zero and Negative Exponents
Lesson 8-1: Example 4
Exercise 45
Extra Practice, p. 709

Lesson Resources

📁 **Teaching Resources**
Practice, Reteaching, Enrichment

👥 **Reaching All Students**
Practice Workbook 8-2
Spanish Practice Workbook 8-2
Basic Algebra Planning Guide 8-2

⏱ **Presentation Assistant Plus!**
Transparencies
- Check Skills You'll Need 8-2
- Additional Examples 8-2
- Student Edition Answers 8-2
- Lesson Quiz 8-2
PH Presentation Pro CD 8-2

(ASSESSMENT SYSTEM)

Computer Test Generator CD

💿 **Technology**
Resource Pro® CD-ROM
Computer Test Generator CD
Prentice Hall Presentation Pro CD

💻 **www.PHSchool.com**
Student Site
- Teacher Web Code: aek-5500
- Reasoning & Puzzles p. 13
- Graphing Calculator, Procedure 18
- Self-grading Lesson Quiz
Teacher Center
- Lesson Planner
- Resources

Plus 𝒊 TEXT

400

8-2

Scientific Notation

1.01   Write equivalent forms of algebraic expressions to solve problems. a) Apply the laws of exponents.

Lesson Preview

What You'll Learn

 OBJECTIVE 1
To write numbers in scientific and standard notation

 OBJECTIVE 2
To use scientific notation

. . . And Why

To order planets based on their masses, as in Example 4

✓ Check Skills You'll Need   (For help, go to Lesson 8-1.)

Simplify each expression.

1. $6 \cdot 10^4$ **60,000**   **2.** $7 \cdot 10^{-2}$ **0.07**   **3.** $8.2 \cdot 10^5$ **820,000**

4. $3 \cdot 10^{-3}$ **0.003**   **5.** $3.4 \cdot 10^1$ **34**   **6.** $5.24 \cdot 10^2$ **524**

7. Simplify $3 \times 10^2 + 6 \times 10^1 + 7 \times 10^0 + 8 \times 10^{-1}$. **367.8**

New Vocabulary   • scientific notation

Interactive lesson includes instant self-check, tutorials, and activities.

OBJECTIVE

1   **Writing Numbers in Scientific and Standard Notation**

Calculator Hint

The *E* on a calculator readout means exponentiation. The **EE** or **EXP** keys let you input an exponent for a power of 10. So to enter 4×10^6, you can enter 4 **EE** 6.

The planet Jupiter has an average radius of 69,111 km. What is Jupiter's volume?

Since Jupiter is a sphere, to answer this question you use the formula for the volume of a sphere.

$$V = \frac{4}{3}\pi r^3$$
$$= \frac{4}{3}\pi(69{,}111)^3 \qquad \text{Substitute 69,111 for } r.$$
$$\approx 1.382706933E15 \qquad \text{Use a calculator.}$$

In standard notation, you write the number above as 1,382,706,933,000,000. In scientific notation, you write the number as $1.382706933 \times 10^{15}$. Scientific notation is a shorthand way to write very large or very small numbers.

🔑 **Key Concepts**

Definition	Scientific Notation

A number in **scientific notation** is written as the product of two factors in the form $a \times 10^n$, where n is an integer and $1 \le a < 10$.

Examples 3.4×10^6 5.43×10^{13} 2.1×10^{-10}

---

1 **EXAMPLE**   **Recognizing Scientific Notation**

Is each number written in scientific notation? If not, explain.

a. 56.29×10^{12} No; 56.29 is greater than 10.

b. 0.84×10^{-3} No; 0.84 is less than 1.

c. 6.11×10^5 yes

 ✓ Check Understanding **1** Is each number written in scientific notation? If not, explain.
a. 3.42×10^{-7} **yes**   **b.** 52×10^4 **No; 52 > 10.**   **c.** 0.04×10^{-5} **No; 0.04 < 1.**

🔄 Ongoing Assessment and Intervention

Before the Lesson
Diagnose prerequisite skills using:
- Check Skills You'll Need

During the Lesson
Monitor progress using:
- Check Understanding
- Additional Examples
- Standardized Test Prep

After the Lesson
Assess knowledge using:
- Lesson Quiz
- Computer Test Generator CD

In scientific notation, you use positive exponents to write a number greater than 1. You use negative exponents to write a number between 0 and 1.

② EXAMPLE **Writing a Number in Scientific Notation**

Write each number in scientific notation.

a. 56,900,000

$56{,}900{,}000 = 5.69 \times 10^7$ **Move the decimal point 7 places to the left and use 7 as an exponent. Drop the zeros after the 9.**

b. 0.00985

$0.00985 = 9.85 \times 10^{-3}$ **Move the decimal point 3 places to the right and use −3 as an exponent. Drop the zeros before the 9.**

✓ Check Understanding **②** Write each number in scientific notation. a–d. See left.

a. 267,000   **b.** 46,205,000   **c.** 0.0000325   **d.** 0.000000009
e. Critical Thinking You express 1 billion as 10^9. Explain why you express 436 billion as 4.36×10^{11}. **436 is 436 times greater than 1, and 436 = 4.36 × 10². Then (4.36 × 10²) · 10⁹ = 4.36 × 10¹¹.**

2a. 2.67×10^5

b. 4.6205×10^7

c. 3.25×10^{-5}

d. 9.0×10^{-9}

③ EXAMPLE **Writing a Number in Standard Notation**

Physical Science Write each number in standard notation.

a. temperature at the sun's core: 1.55×10^6 kelvins

$1.55 \times 10^6 = 1.550000$ **A positive exponent indicates a number greater than 10. Move the decimal point 6 places to the right.**

$= 1{,}550{,}000$

b. lowest temperature recorded in a lab: 2×10^{-11} kelvin

$2 \times 10^{-11} = 000000000002.$ **A negative exponent indicates a number between 0 and 1. Move the decimal point 11 places to the left.**

$= 0.00000000002$

✓ Check Understanding **③** Write each number in standard notation.
a. 3.2×10^{12} **b.** 5.07×10^4 **c.** 5.6×10^{-4} **d.** 8.3×10^{-2}
3,200,000,000,000   **50,700**   **0.00056**   **0.083**

OBJECTIVE
2 **Using Scientific Notation**

Masses of Planets (kilograms)

Jupiter 3.7×10^{27}
Uranus 8.7×10^{25}
Neptune 1.0×10^{26}
Saturn 5.7×10^{26}

You can compare and order numbers in scientific notation. First compare the powers of 10, and then compare the decimals.

④ EXAMPLE **Real-World** **Problem Solving**

Astronomy List the planets in order from least to greatest mass.

Order the powers of 10. Arrange the decimals with the same power of 10 in order.

8.7×10^{25} 1.0×10^{26} 5.7×10^{26} 3.7×10^{27}
Uranus   Neptune   Saturn   Jupiter

From least to greatest mass, the order of the planets is Uranus, Neptune, Saturn, and Jupiter.

✓ Check Understanding **④** The following masses of parts of an atom are measured in grams. Order the parts of an atom from least to greatest mass.
neutron: 1.6749×10^{-24}, electron: 9.1096×10^{-28}, proton: 1.6726×10^{-24}
electron, proton, neutron

Lesson 8-2   Scientific Notation   **401**

👥 Reaching All Students

Below Level Comparing extremely small numbers in scientific notation may be confusing to some students. Explain why the numbers in Example 4, Question 4, are ordered as shown.	**Advanced Learners** Challenge students to express a googol (1 followed by 100 zeros) and a googolplex (10^{googol}) in scientific notation.	**Error Prevention** See note on page 403.

Additional Examples

4 List the planets in order of their distance from the sun from least to greatest.
Jupiter : 4.84×10^8 mi
Earth : 9.3×10^7 mi
Neptune : 2.8×10^9 mi
Mercury : 3.8×10^7 mi
Mercury, Earth, Jupiter, Neptune

5 Order 0.0063×10^5, 6.03×10^4, 6103, and 63.1×10^3 from least to greatest. **0.0063×10^5, 6103, 6.03×10^4, 63.1×10^3**

6 Simplify. Write each answer using scientific notation.
a. $6(8 \times 10^{-4})$ **4.8×10^{-3}**
b. $0.3(1.3 \times 10^3)$ **3.9×10^2**

Closure

Ask students to explain how to write a number in scientific notation. **Move the decimal to the right of the first non-zero digit. Count the number of places the decimal moved. This is the exponent. If the number in standard form was a number greater than or equal to 1, the exponent is positive. Otherwise, the exponent is negative.**

You can write numbers like 815×10^5 and 0.078×10^{-2} in scientific notation.
$$815 \times 10^5 = 81,500,000 = 8.15 \times 10^7 \qquad 0.078 \times 10^{-2} = 0.00078 = 7.8 \times 10^{-4}$$

The examples above show this pattern: When you move a decimal n places left, the exponent of 10 increases by n; when you move a decimal point n places right, the exponent of 10 decreases by n.

5 EXAMPLE **Using Scientific Notation to Order Numbers**

Order 0.052×10^7, 5.12×10^5, 53.2×10, and 534 from least to greatest.

Write each number in scientific notation.

$$0.052 \times 10^7 \quad 5.12 \times 10^5 \quad 53.2 \times 10 \quad 534$$
$$\downarrow \qquad\qquad \downarrow \qquad\qquad \downarrow \qquad\quad \downarrow$$
$$5.2 \times 10^5 \quad 5.12 \times 10^5 \quad 5.32 \times 10^2 \quad 5.34 \times 10^2$$

Order the powers of 10. Arrange the decimals with the same power of 10 in order.

$$5.32 \times 10^2 \quad 5.34 \times 10^2 \quad 5.12 \times 10^5 \quad 5.2 \times 10^5$$

Write the original numbers in order.

$$53.2 \times 10 \quad 534 \quad 5.12 \times 10^5 \quad 0.052 \times 10^7$$

Need Help?
Remember that 53.2×10 is 53.2×10^1.

✓ **Check Understanding** **5** Order 60.2×10^{-5}, 63×10^4, 0.067×10^3, and 61×10^{-2} from least to greatest.
60.2×10^{-5}, 61×10^{-2}, 0.067×10^3, 63×10^4

You can multiply a number that is in scientific notation by another number. If the product is less than one or greater than 10, rewrite the product in scientific notation.

6 EXAMPLE **Multiplying a Number in Scientific Notation**

Simplify. Write each answer using scientific notation.

a. $7(4 \times 10^5) = (7 \cdot 4) \times 10^5$ Use the Associative Property of Multiplication.
$= 28 \times 10^5$ Simplify inside the parentheses.
$= 2.8 \times 10^6$ Write the product in scientific notation.

b. $0.5(1.2 \times 10^{-3}) = (0.5 \cdot 1.2) \times 10^{-3}$ Use the Associative Property of Multiplication.
$= 0.6 \times 10^{-3}$ Simplify inside the parentheses.
$= 6 \times 10^{-4}$ Write the product in scientific notation.

✓ **Check Understanding** **6** Simplify. Write each answer using scientific notation.
a. $2.5(6 \times 10^3)$ **1.5×10^4**   **b.** $0.4(2 \times 10^{-9})$ **8×10^{-10}**

EXERCISES

For more practice, see *Extra Practice*.

Practice and Problem Solving

A Practice by Example

Example 1 (page 400)

Is each number written in scientific notation? If not, explain.
1. 55×10^4 **No; 55 > 10.**   **2.** 3.2×10^5 **yes**   **3.** 0.9×10^{-2} **No; 0.9 < 1.**
4. 7.3×10^{-5} **yes**   **5.** 1.12×10^1 **yes**   **6.** 46×10^7 **No; 46 > 10.**

Example 2
(page 401)

7. 9.04×10^9

8. 2.0×10^{-2}

Example 3
(page 401)

9. 9.3×10^6

10. 2.17×10^4

Examples 4, 5
(pages 401, 402)

15. 500

16. 0.05

17. 2040

18. 720,000

25.
$0.52 \times 10^{-3}, 50.1 \times 10^{-3},$
$4.8 \times 10^{-1}, 56 \times 10^{-2}$

B Apply Your Skills

Real-World Connection

Elephant calves weigh from 100 to 145 kilograms.

43. 2.796×10^{10}
instructions;
1.6776×10^{12}
instructions

Write each number in scientific notation. 7–10. See left.

7. 9,040,000,000   **8.** 0.02   **9.** 9.3 million   **10.** 21,700

11. 0.00325   **12.** 8,003,000   **13.** 0.00092   **14.** 0.0156
3.25×10^{-3} 8.003×10^6 9.2×10^{-4} 1.56×10^{-2}

Write each number in standard notation. 15–18. See left.

15. 5×10^2 **16.** 5×10^{-2} **17.** 2.04×10^3 **18.** 7.2×10^5

19. 8.97×10^{-1} **20.** 1.3×10^0 **21.** 2.74×10^{-5} **22.** 4.8×10^{-3}
0.897   1.3   0.0000274   0.0048

Order the numbers in each list from least to greatest.

23. $10^5, 10^{-3}, 10^0, 10^{-1}, 10^1$ $10^{-3}, 10^{-1}, 10^0, 10^1, 10^5$

24. $9 \times 10^{-7}, 8 \times 10^{-8}, 7 \times 10^{-6}, 6 \times 10^{-10}$ $6 \times 10^{-10}, 8 \times 10^{-8},$
    $9 \times 10^{-7}, 7 \times 10^{-6}$

25. $50.1 \times 10^{-3}, 4.8 \times 10^{-1}, 0.52 \times 10^{-3}, 56 \times 10^{-2}$ **See left.**

26. $0.53 \times 10^7, 5300 \times 10^{-1}, 5.3 \times 10^5, 530 \times 10^8$ $5300 \times 10^{-1}, 5.3 \times 10^5,$
    $0.53 \times 10^7, 530 \times 10^8$

27. Measuring instruments may have different degrees of precision. Instrument A is precise to 10^{-2} cm, Instrument B is precise to 5×10^{-2} cm, and Instrument C is precise to 8×10^{-3} cm. Order the instruments from most precise (least possible error) to least precise (greatest possible error). **C, A, B**

Simplify. Write each answer using scientific notation.

28. $8(7 \times 10^{-3})$ 5.6×10^{-2} **29.** $8(3 \times 10^{14})$ 2.4×10^{15} **30.** $0.2(3 \times 10^2)$ 6.0×10^1

31. $6(5.3 \times 10^{-4})$ **32.** $0.3(8.2 \times 10^{-3})$ **33.** $0.5(6.8 \times 10^5)$
3.18×10^{-3} 2.46×10^{-3} 3.4×10^5

For Exercises 34–39, find the missing value.

Selected Masses (kilograms)

		Standard Notation		Scientific Notation
34.	Elephant	■ 5400		5.4×10^3
35.	Adult human	70	7×10^1 ■	
36.	Dog	10	1×10^1 ■	
37.	Golf ball	0.046	4.6×10^{-2} ■	
38.	Paper clip	■ 0.0005		5×10^{-4}
39.	Oxygen atom	0.00000000000000000000000003	3×10^{-26} ■	

40. Critical Thinking Is the number 10^5 in scientific notation? Explain.
Yes; it can be written as 1×10^5.

41. Writing Explain how to write 48 million and 48 millionths in scientific notation.
See margin.

42. Health Care In 2005, the population in the United States will be about 2.87×10^8. Spending for health care will be about $5745 per person. About how much will the United States spend on health care in 2005? Use scientific notation.
about 1.65×10^{12}

43. Computers A computer can perform 4.66×10^8 instructions per second. How many instructions is that per minute? Per hour? Use scientific notation.

44. Open-Ended If you were writing a report about the national debt, would you use scientific notation or standard notation to express the debt amount? Explain why. **See margin.**

---

pages 402–404 Exercises

41. 48 million = 48 × 10^6. Write 48 in scientific notation; then add the powers of 10: $4.8 \times 10^1 \times 10^6 =$

4.8×10^7. 48 millionths = 48×10^{-6}. So $4.8 \times 10^1 \times 10^{-6} = 4.8 \times 10^{-5}$.

44. Answers may vary. Sample: Since the national debt is expressed in dollars, use standard notation, which most people will understand, rather than scientific notation, which is used mainly in science.

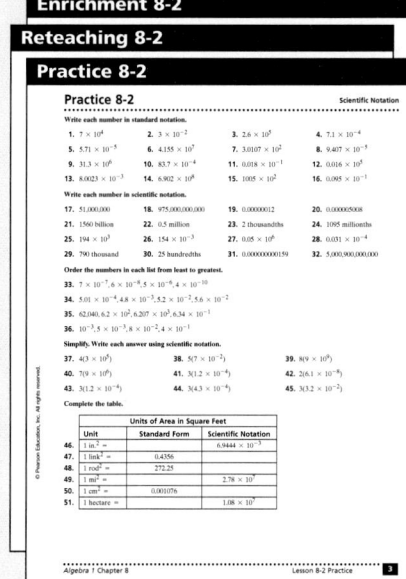

403

1. Write each number in scientific notation.
   a. 0.00627 6.27×10^{-3}
   b. 3,486,000 3.486×10^{6}

2. Write each number in standard form.
   a. 9.4×10^{4} 94,000
   b. 2.3×10^{-6} 0.0000023

3. Order the following numbers from least to greatest.
   0.98×10^{-1}, 1.6×10^{3}, 2.4×10^{-1}, 11×10^{0}
   0.98×10^{-1}, 2.4×10^{-1}, 11×10^{0}, 1.6×10^{3}

4. Simplify. Write the answer in scientific notation.
   $7(6.1 \times 10^{-2})$ 4.27×10^{-1}

Alternative Assessment

Organize students in groups of 4. Give each student a note card and have each write a number in standard form on the card. Instruct students to exchange cards with a member of their group. Students are to write the standard number in scientific notation on the reverse side of the card and place that side face-up on the desk. Instruct students to arrange the cards in order from least to greatest.

Standardized Test Prep

Resources

For additional practice with a variety of test item formats:
- Standardized Test Prep, p. 451
- Test-Taking Strategies, p. 446
- Test-Taking Strategies with Transparencies

pages 402–404 Exercises

52. [2] $(8 \times 10^{-4})(1000) =$ $0.0008 \times 1000 = 0.8$; the diameter is 0.8 mm

    [1] minor computational error

---

 45. Math in the Media Use the cartoon below.

FOX TROT by Bill Amend

a. Write 500 trillion in scientific notation. 5×10^{14}
b. Since the 10-second length of the movie is off by a factor of 500 trillion, what time span does the movie actually represent? **about 1.6×10^{8} years**

C Challenge **46. World Population** The world population in 2025 may reach 7.84×10^{9} persons. This is about 3 times the world population in 1950. What was the world population in 1950? **about 2.61×10^{9} people**

47. Astronomy Use a calculator to find the volume of each planet with the given radius. **a. 6.08×10^{10} km³ b. 1.09×10^{12} km³ c. 9.17×10^{14} km³**
a. Mercury: 2439 km b. Earth: 6378 km c. Saturn: 60,268 km

48. Write $\frac{1}{300}$ using scientific notation. $3.\overline{3} \times 10^{-3}$

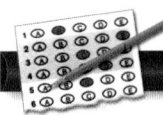

Standardized Test Prep

Multiple Choice **49.** Simplify $90(1.2 \times 10^{-5})$. Write the answer in scientific notation. **D**
A. 1.08×10^{-7} B. 108.0×10^{-5} C. 108.0×10^{-3} D. 1.08×10^{-3}

50. Which answer has the states in the table at the right ordered from least to greatest projected population? **G**
F. New York, Florida, Virginia, Vermont
G. Vermont, Virginia, New York, Florida
H. Vermont, Virginia, Florida, New York
I. Florida, New York, Virginia, Vermont

Projected Population in 2025	
State	**Population**
Florida	2.07×10^{7}
Virginia	8.47×10^{6}
Vermont	6.78×10^{5}
New York	1.98×10^{7}

Take It to the NET
Online lesson quiz at
www.PHSchool.com
Web Code: aea-0802

51. Which equals 275 million? **C**
A. 275×10^{5} B. 2.75×10^{6}
C. 2.75×10^{8} D. 275×10^{9}

Short Response **52.** A microscope set on 1000X makes an object appear 1000 times its actual size. If a bacterium is 8×10^{-4} millimeters in diameter, how large will it appear under this microscope? Use scientific notation. Show your work.
See margin.

Mixed Review

Lesson 8-1 **Simplify each expression.**
53. $4(1.8)^{0}$ 4 **54.** $12 \cdot 2^{-2}$ 3 **55.** $6 \cdot 3^{-2}$ $\frac{2}{3}$ **56.** $\frac{4^{3}}{7^{2}}$ $\frac{64}{49}$ **57.** $\frac{3^{-2}}{9^{0}}$ $\frac{1}{9}$

Lesson 7-5 **Graph each linear inequality. 58–60. See margin.**
58. $y < -\frac{1}{4}x + 2$ **59.** $y \geq \frac{2}{3}x$ **60.** $y < 3x - 4$

58. 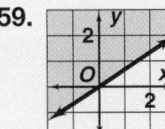 **59.** (graph) **60.**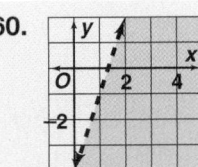

Multiplication Properties of Exponents

 North Carolina Objectives

1.01 Write equivalent forms of algebraic expressions to solve problems. a) Apply the laws of exponents.

Lesson Preview

1. Plan

What You'll Learn

 OBJECTIVE **1** To multiply powers

OBJECTIVE **2** To work with scientific notation

. . . And Why

To find the number of red blood cells in the human body, as in Example 5

✓ Check Skills You'll Need

(For help, go to Lesson 1-6.)

Rewrite each expression using exponents.

1. $t \cdot t \cdot t \cdot t \cdot t \cdot t \cdot t$ t^7

2. $(6-m)(6-m)(6-m)$ $(6-m)^3$

3. $(r+5)(r+5)(r+5)(r+5)(r+5)$ $(r+5)^5$

4. $5 \cdot 5 \cdot 5 \cdot s \cdot s \cdot s$ $5^3 s^3$

Simplify.

5. -5^4 -625 6. $(-5)^4$ 625 7. $(-5)^0$ 1 8. $(-5)^{-4}$ $\frac{1}{625}$

Lesson Preview

 Check Skills You'll Need

Multiplying and Dividing Real Numbers
Lesson 1-6: Example 4
Exercises 32–39
Extra Practice, p. 702

Lesson Resources

 **Teaching Resources**
Practice, Reteaching, Enrichment

Reaching All Students
Practice Workbook 8-3
Spanish Practice Workbook 8-3
Basic Algebra Planning Guide 8-3

Presentation Assistant Plus!
Transparencies
• Check Skills You'll Need 8-3
• Additional Examples 8-3
• Student Edition Answers 8-3
• Lesson Quiz 8-3
PH Presentation Pro CD 8-3

 ASSESSMENT SYSTEM

Computer Test Generator CD

 Technology
Resource Pro® CD-ROM
Computer Test Generator CD
Prentice Hall Presentation Pro CD

 **www.PHSchool.com**
Student Site
• Teacher Web Code: aek-5500
• Self-grading Lesson Quiz
Teacher Center
• Lesson Planner
• Resources

Plus **iTEXT**

OBJECTIVE
1 Multiplying Powers

iTEXT Interactive lesson includes instant self-check, tutorials, and activities.

You can write a power as a product of powers with the same base. Think of the power as the product of factors.

$$8^6 = \underbrace{8 \cdot 8 \cdot 8 \cdot 8}_{8^4} \cdot \underbrace{8 \cdot 8}_{8^2} \qquad\qquad 8^6 = \underbrace{8 \cdot 8 \cdot 8}_{8^3} \cdot \underbrace{8 \cdot 8 \cdot 8}_{8^3}$$

The work above shows that $8^6 = 8^4 \cdot 8^2$ and $8^6 = 8^3 \cdot 8^3$. Notice the pattern in the exponents. The sums $4+2$ and $3+3$ both equal 6, the exponent of 8^6.

 Key Concepts

Property	Multiplying Powers With the Same Base
	For every nonzero number a and integers m and n, $a^m \cdot a^n = a^{m+n}$.

Examples $3^5 \cdot 3^4 = 3^{5+4} = 3^9$ $h^2 \cdot h^9 = h^{2+9} = h^{11}$

1 EXAMPLE   Multiplying Powers

Rewrite each expression using each base only once.

a. $11^4 \cdot 11^3 = 11^{4+3}$ Add exponents of powers with the same base.

           $= 11^7$ Simplify the sum of the exponents.

b. $2^5 \cdot 2^2 \cdot 2^{-1} = 2^{5+2-1}$ Think of $5+2-1$ as $5+2+(-1)$ so you can add the exponents.

           $= 2^6$ Simplify the sum of the exponents.

c. $5^{-2} \cdot 5^2 = 5^{-2+2}$ Add exponents of powers with the same base.

           $= 5^0$ Simplify the sum of the exponents.

           $= 1$ Use the definition of zero as an exponent.

✓ **Check Understanding** **1** Rewrite each expression using each base only once.

   a. $5^3 \cdot 5^6$ 5^9 **b.** $2^4 \cdot 2^{-3}$ 2^1 **c.** $7^{-3} \cdot 7^2 \cdot 7^6$ 7^5

Lesson 8-3   Multiplication Properties of Exponents   **405**

Ongoing Assessment and Intervention

Before the Lesson	During the Lesson	After the Lesson
Diagnose prerequisite skills using:	**Monitor progress using:**	**Assess knowledge using:**
• Check Skills You'll Need	• Check Understanding	• Lesson Quiz
	• Additional Examples	• Computer Test Generator CD
	• Standardized Test Prep	

2. Teach

Math Background

In scientific notation, all zeros are meaningful. Thus the recorded weight of an elephant at 1.20×10^4 pounds means that the weight was measured to the nearest hundred pounds.

1 **Teaching Notes**

1 EXAMPLE Auditory Learners

Have a student say *11 to the power* _____, letting the student fill in the blank with a power from 1 to 10. Have a second student do the same. Then have a third student say the product of powers. For example, if the two students say 11^3 and 11^6, the third student should say 11^9. Repeat the process with various bases until you are comfortable that students understand the rule for multiplying powers.

3 EXAMPLE Visual Learners

Encourage students to rewrite the problems on paper. Then, they can use circles, squares, or underlines to identify factors with matching bases.

 Additional Examples

1 Rewrite each expression using each base only once.
a. $7^3 \cdot 7^2$ **7^5**
b. $4^4 \cdot 4^1 \cdot 4^{-2}$ **4^3**
c. $6^8 \cdot 6^{-8}$ **1**

2 Simplify each expression.
a. $p^2 \cdot p \cdot p^5$ **p^8**
b. $4x^6 \cdot 5x^{-4}$ **$20x^2$**

3 Simplify each expression.
a. $a^2 \cdot b^{-4} \cdot a^5$ **$\frac{a^7}{b^4}$**
b. $2q \cdot 3p^3 \cdot 4q^4$ **$24p^3q^5$**

2 **Teaching Notes**

5 EXAMPLE Diversity

Ask a student who has donated blood to describe the process. Make students aware of the need for blood donations.

406

Need Help?

Remember that $x = x^1$.

2 EXAMPLE Multiplying Powers in an Algebraic Expression

Simplify each expression.
a. $x \cdot x^2 \cdot x^4 = x^{1\,+\,2\,+\,4}$ Add exponents of powers with the same base.
     $= x^7$ Simplify.
b. $2n^5 \cdot 3n^{-2} = (2 \cdot 3)\left(n^5 \cdot n^{-2}\right)$ Commutative Property of Multiplication
     $= 6\left(n^{5\,+\,(-2)}\right)$ Add exponents of powers with the same base.
     $= 6n^3$ Simplify.

✔ **Check Understanding** **2** Simplify each expression.
a. $a \cdot a^5$ **a^6**   b. $n^2 \cdot n^3 \cdot 7n$ **$7n^6$**   c. $6y^2 \cdot 3y^3 \cdot 2y^{-4}$ **36y**

When variable factors have more than one base, be careful to combine only those powers with the same base.

3 EXAMPLE Multiplying Powers in an Algebraic Expression

Simplify each expression.
a. $c^4 \cdot d^{-3} \cdot c^2 = c^4 \cdot c^2 \cdot d^{-3}$ Commutative Property of Multiplication
     $= c^{4\,+\,2} \cdot d^{-3}$ Add exponents of powers with the same base.
     $= \frac{c^6}{d^3}$ Simplify.
b. $5x \cdot 2y^4 \cdot 3x^8 = (5 \cdot 2 \cdot 3)\left(x \cdot x^8\right)\left(y^4\right)$ Commutative and Associative Properties of Multiplication
     $= 30\left(x^1 \cdot x^8\right)\left(y^4\right)$ Multiply the coefficients. Write x as x^1.
     $= 30\left(x^{1\,+\,8}\right)\left(y^4\right)$ Add exponents of powers with the same base.
     $= 30x^9y^4$ Simplify.

✔ **Check Understanding** **3** Simplify each expression.
a. $a \cdot b \cdot a^5$ **a^6b**   b. $2y^3 \cdot 7x^2 \cdot 2y^4$ **$28x^2y^7$**   c. $m^2 \cdot n^{-2} \cdot 7m$ **$\frac{7m^3}{n^2}$**

OBJECTIVE

2 **Working With Scientific Notation**

In Lesson 8-2, you wrote numbers in scientific notation using patterns to move decimal points. You can now use the property for multiplying powers with the same base to write numbers and to multiply numbers in scientific notation.

4 EXAMPLE Multiplying Numbers in Scientific Notation

Simplify $(7 \times 10^2)(4 \times 10^5)$. Write the answer in scientific notation.

$(7 \times 10^2)(4 \times 10^5) = (7 \cdot 4)\left(10^2 \cdot 10^5\right)$ Commutative and Associative Properties of Multiplication
     $= 28 \times 10^7$ Simplify.
     $= 2.8 \times 10^1 \cdot 10^7$ Write 28 in scientific notation.
     $= 2.8 \times 10^{1\,+\,7}$ Add exponents of powers with the same base.
     $= 2.8 \times 10^8$ Simplify the sum of the exponents.

✔ **Check Understanding** **4** Simplify each expression. Write each answer in scientific notation.
a. $(2.5 \times 10^8)(6 \times 10^3)$ b. $(1.5 \times 10^{-2})(3 \times 10^4)$ c. $(9 \times 10^{-6})(7 \times 10^{-9})$
1.5×10^{12}   **4.5×10^2**   **6.3×10^{-14}**

406 Chapter 8 Exponents and Exponential Functions

 Reaching All Students

| **Below Level** Ask students to explain why the expression in Example 3b is not simplified if written as $15x^9 2y^4$. | **Advanced Learners** Challenge students to find the value of x that makes the expression $(4^x)(4^3) = 16$ true. | **English Learners** See note on page 409. **Visual Learners** See note on page 406. |

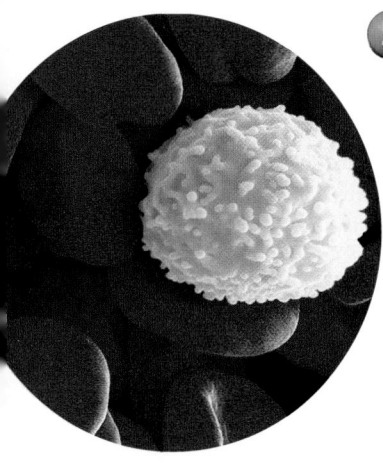

Real-World 🌐 **Connection**

The blood cells shown in the photo above are magnified 5×10^3 times their actual size.

5 EXAMPLE **Real-World** 🌐 **Problem Solving**

Biology A human body contains about 3.2×10^4 μL (microliters) of blood for each pound of body weight. Each microliter of blood contains about 5×10^6 red blood cells. Find the approximate number of red blood cells in the body of a 125-lb person.

$\text{red blood cells} = \text{pounds} \cdot \dfrac{\text{microliters}}{\text{pound}} \cdot \dfrac{\text{cells}}{\text{microliter}}$ Use dimensional analysis.

$= 125 \text{ lb} \cdot (3.2 \times 10^4) \dfrac{\mu L}{lb} \cdot (5 \times 10^6) \dfrac{\text{cells}}{\mu L}$ Substitute.

$= (125 \cdot 3.2 \cdot 5) \times (10^4 \cdot 10^6)$ Commutative and Associative Properties of Multiplication

$= (2000) \times (10^{4 \,+\, 6})$ Simplify.

$= 2000 \times 10^{10}$ Add exponents.

$= 2 \times 10^3 \cdot 10^{10}$ Write 2000 in scientific notation.

$= 2 \times 10^{13}$ Add the exponents.

• There are about 2×10^{13} red blood cells in a 125-lb person.

✓ **Check Understanding** ⑤ About how many red blood cells are in the body of a 160-lb soccer player?
about 2.56×10^{13} red blood cells

EXERCISES

For more practice, see *Extra Practice*.

Practice and Problem Solving

A **Practice by Example**

Example 1
(page 405)

Rewrite each expression using each base only once.

1. $2^6 \cdot 2^4$ **2^{10}**
2. $5^{-13} \cdot 10^5$ **$\dfrac{2^5}{5^8}$**
3. $10^{-6} \cdot 10^5 \cdot 10^1$ **1**
4. $(0.99)^3 \cdot (0.99)^0$ **$(0.99)^3$**
5. $6^6 \cdot 6^{-2} \cdot 6^5$ **6^9**
6. $(1.025)^2(1.025)^{-2}$ **1**

Example 2
(page 406)

Simplify each expression.

7. $c^{-2}c^7$ **c^5**
8. $3r \cdot r^4$ **$3r^5$**
9. $5t^{-2} \cdot 2t^{-5}$ **$\dfrac{10}{t^7}$**
10. $(7x^5)(8x)$ **$56x^6$**
11. $3x^2 \cdot x^2$ **$3x^4$**
12. $(-2.4n^4)(2n^{-1})$ **$-4.8n^3$**
13. $b^{-2} \cdot b^4 \cdot b$ **b^3**
14. $(-2m^3)(3.5m^{-3})$ **-7**
15. $(15a^3)(-3a)$ **$-45a^4$**

Example 3
(page 406)

16. $(x^5 y^2)(x^{-6} y)$ **$\dfrac{y^3}{x}$**
17. $(5x^5)(3y^6)(3x^2)$ **$45x^7 y^6$**
18. $(4c^4)(ac^3)(3a^5 c)$ **$12a^6 c^8$**
19. $x^6 \cdot y^2 \cdot x^4$ **$x^{10} y^2$**
20. $a^6 b^3 \cdot a^2 b^{-2}$ **$a^8 b$**
21. $-m^2 \cdot 4r^3 \cdot 12r^{-4} \cdot 5m$ **$-\dfrac{240m^3}{r}$**

Example 4
(page 406)

Simplify each expression. Write each answer in scientific notation. 22–24. See left.

22. $(2 \times 10^3)(3 \times 10^2)$
23. $(2 \times 10^6)(3 \times 10^3)$
24. $(4 \times 10^6) \cdot 10^{-3}$

22. 6×10^5
23. 6×10^9
24. 4×10^3

25. $(1 \times 10^3)(3.4 \times 10^{-8})$ **3.4×10^{-5}**
26. $(8 \times 10^{-5})(7 \times 10^{-3})$ **5.6×10^{-7}**
27. $(5 \times 10^7)(3 \times 10^{14})$ **1.5×10^{22}**

Example 5
(page 407)

Write each answer in scientific notation.

28. **Astronomy** The distance light travels in one year (one light-year) is about 5.88×10^{12} miles. The closest star to Earth (other than the sun) is Alpha Centauri, which is 4.35 light-years from Earth. About how many miles from Earth is Alpha Centauri? **about 2.5578×10^{13} mi**

Additional Examples

④ Simplify $(3 \times 10^{-3})(7 \times 10^{-5})$. Write the answer in scientific notation. **2.1×10^{-7}**

⑤ The speed of light is about 3×10^8 m/s. If there are 1×10^{-3} km in 1 m, and 3.6×10^3 s in 1 h, approximate the speed of light in km/h. **about 1.08×10^9 km/h**

Closure

Ask students to write an algebraic expression for multiplication. The expression must contain powers and at least two different variables. Then instruct students to simplify their expressions. Repeat with an expression containing two numbers in scientific notation.

3. Practice

Assignment Guide

1 Objective
  Ⓐ Ⓑ Core 1–21, 31–47,
    55–57, 65–70
  Ⓒ Extension 71–76

2 Objective
  Ⓐ Ⓑ Core 22–30, 48–54,
    58–64
  Ⓒ Extension 77–78

Standardized Test Prep 79–84

Mixed Review 85–99

Error Prevention

Exercises 26, 27 Some students may try to write the exponents in the answers as −8 and 21. Remind students that if the first factor of the answer is not between 0 and 10, they must 'move the decimal,' which will affect the exponents.

Enrichment 8-3

Reteaching 8-3

Practice 8-3

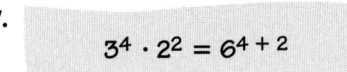

44. $-6x^6$

45. $12a^7$

46. x^{10}

47. $3^4 \cdot 2^2$

55b. Answers may vary.
  Sample: $y^{-1}y^9$;
  $y^{-2}y^{10}$; $y^{-3}y^{11}$;
  $y^{-4}y^{12}$

Calculator Hint

To simplify $(6.12 \times 10^5) \cdot (12.5 \times 10^8)$, press

6.12 [EE] 5 [ENTER]

[×] 12.5 [EE] 8 [ENTER].

Write each answer in scientific notation.

29. **Geology** Earth's crust contains approximately 120 trillion metric tons of gold. One metric ton of gold is worth about $9 million. What is the approximate value of the gold in Earth's crust? **1.08×10^{21} dollars**

30. **Astronomy** Light travels through space at a constant speed of about 3×10^5 km/s. Sunlight reflecting from the moon takes about 1.28×10^0 s to reach Earth. Find the distance from the moon to Earth. **about 3.84×10^5 km**

Ⓑ **Apply Your Skills**

Complete each equation.

31. $5^2 \cdot 5^{\blacksquare} = 5^{11}$ **9**   32. $5^7 \cdot 5^{\blacksquare} = 5^3$ **−4**   33. $2^{\blacksquare} \cdot 2^4 = 2^1$ **−3**

34. $c^{-5} \cdot c^{\blacksquare} = c^6$ **11**   35. $m^{\blacksquare} \cdot m^{-4} = m^{-9}$ **−5**   36. $a \cdot a \cdot a^3 = a^{\blacksquare}$ **5**

37. $a^{\blacksquare} \cdot a^4 = 1$ **−4**   38. $a^{12} \cdot a^{\blacksquare} = a^{12}$ **0**   39. $x^3 y^{\blacksquare} \cdot x^{\blacksquare} = y^2$ **2, −3**

⬚ **Geometry Find the area of each figure.**

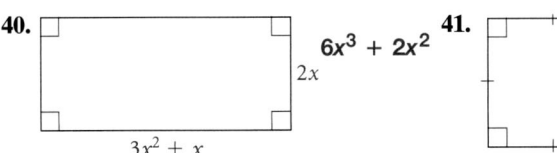

40.

41. $4x^4$
  $6x^3 + 2x^2$
  $2x$
  $3x^2 + x$
  $2x^2$

42. $4y^2$
  $y^3 + 2$
  $4y^5 + 8y^2$

43. $4c^4$
  $4c$
  $2c^3$

Error Analysis Correct each error. 44–47. See left.

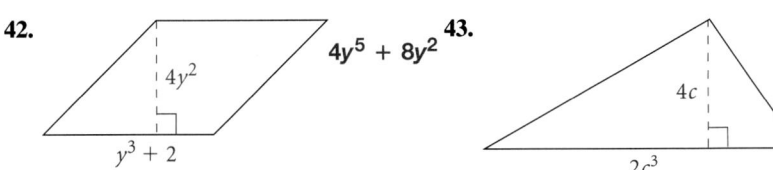

44.
$$(3x^2)(-2x^4) = 3(-2)x^{2 \cdot 4}$$
$$= -6x^8$$

45.
$$4a^2 \cdot 3a^5 = (4+3)a^{2+5}$$
$$= 7a^7$$

46.
$$x^6 \cdot x \cdot x^3 = x^{6+3}$$
$$= x^9$$

47.
$$3^4 \cdot 2^2 = 6^{4+2}$$

Simplify each expression. Write each answer in scientific notation.

48. $(9 \times 10^7)(3 \times 10^{-16})$ **2.7×10^{-8}**   49. $(8 \times 10^{-3})(0.1 \times 10^9)$ **8.0×10^5**

50. $(0.7 \times 10^{-12})(0.3 \times 10^8)$ **2.1×10^{-5}**   51. $(0.4 \times 10^0)(3 \times 10^{-4})$ **1.2×10^{-4}**

52. $(0.2 \times 10^5)(4 \times 10^{-12})$ **8.0×10^{-8}**   53. $(0.5 \times 10^{13})(0.3 \times 10^{-4})$ **1.5×10^8**

🌐 54. **Chemistry** The term *mole* can be used in chemistry to refer to 6.02×10^{23} atoms of a substance. The mass of a single hydrogen atom is approximately 1.67×10^{-24} gram. What is the mass of 1 mole of hydrogen atoms? **about 1.01 g**

55. a. **Open-Ended** Write y^8 as a product of two powers with the same base in four different ways. Use only positive exponents. **$y^1 y^7$; $y^2 y^6$; $y^3 y^5$; $y^4 y^4$**

  b. Write y^8 as a product of two powers with the same base in four different ways using negative or zero exponents in each. **See left.**

  c. **Reasoning** How many ways are there to write y^8 as the product of two powers? Explain your reasoning. **An infinite number; there are an infinite number of integer pairs with a sum of 8.**

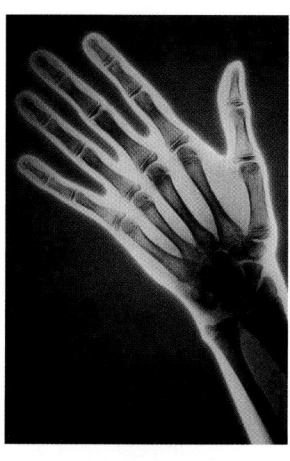

Real-World Connection

X-rays are absorbed more by dense objects such as bones, and less by soft tissue. So bones show up as darker than soft tissues.

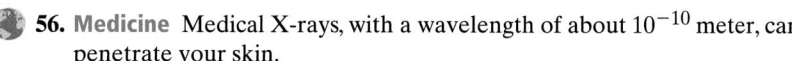

56. Medicine Medical X-rays, with a wavelength of about 10^{-10} meter, can penetrate your skin.
    a. Ultraviolet rays, which cause sunburn by penetrating only the top layers of skin, have a wavelength about 1000 times the wavelength of an X-ray. Find the wavelength of ultraviolet rays. **about 10^{-7} m**
    b. Critical Thinking The wavelengths of visible light are between 4×10^{-7} meters and 7.5×10^{-7} meters. Are these wavelengths longer or shorter than those of ultraviolet rays? Explain. **See margin.**

57. Writing Explain why $x^3 \cdot y^5$ cannot be written with fewer bases. **See margin.**

58. Technology A CD-ROM stores about 650 megabytes (6.5×10^8 bytes) of information along a spiral track. Each byte uses about 9 micrometers (9×10^{-6} m) of space along the track. Find the length of the track. **about 5.85×10^3 m**

Use a calculator. Simplify each expression. Write each answer in scientific notation.

59. $(6.12 \times 10^5)(12.5 \times 10^8)$ **7.65×10^{14}**   **60.** $(1.98 \times 10^{-3})(2.04 \times 10^{11})$
                                                                               4.0392×10^8
61. $(9.55 \times 10^7)(7.371 \times 10^{-15})$ **62.** $(6.934 \times 10^{-9})(2.579 \times 10^{-4})$
7.039305×10^{-7}   **$1.7882786 \times 10^{-12}$**

63. Measurement There are about 3.35×10^{25} molecules in a liter of water. Pine Lake, in New York, has about 2×10^8 liters of water. About how many molecules of water are in Pine Lake? **about 6.7×10^{33} molecules**

64. Measurement About 8.4×10^{11} drops of water flow over Niagara Falls each minute. Each drop of water contains about 1.7×10^{21} molecules of water. About how many molecules of water flow over the falls each minute? **1.428×10^{33} molecules**

Simplify each expression.

65. $\dfrac{1}{x^2 \cdot x^{-5}}$ **x^3**   **66.** $\dfrac{1}{a^3 \cdot a^{-2}}$ **$\dfrac{1}{a}$**   **67.** $\dfrac{5}{c \cdot c^{-4}}$ **$5c^3$**

68. $2a^2(3a + 5)$ **69.** $8m^3(m^2 + 7)$ **70.** $-4x^3(2x^2 - 9x)$
$6a^3 + 10a^2$ **$8m^5 + 56m^3$**   **$-8x^5 + 36x^4$**

C Challenge   **Simplify.**

71. $3^x \cdot 3^{2-x} \cdot 3^2$ **81**   **72.** $2^n \cdot 2^{n+2} \cdot 2$ **2^{2n+3}**   **73.** $3^x \cdot 2^y \cdot 3^2 \cdot 2^x$ **$2^{x+y} \cdot 3^{x+2}$**

74. $(a+b)^2(a+b)^{-3}$ **$\dfrac{1}{a+b}$**   **75.** $(t+3)^7(t+3)^{-5}$ **$(t+3)^2$**   **76.** $5^{x+1} \cdot 5^{1-x}$ **25**

77. a. Geometry Find the volume of a rectangular prism with length 1.3×10^{-3} km, width 1.5×10^{-3} km, and height 9.4×10^{-4} km. Write your answer in scientific notation. **1.833×10^{-9} km^3**
    b. What is the volume of the prism in cubic meters? **1.833 m^3**

78. Science An illustrator plans to draw a diagram of a protozoan for a science book. A protozoan is 1.1×10^{-4} meters long. The illustrator wants the diagram to be 7.7 centimeters long. The diagram will be how many times greater than the protozoan in size? **700 times**

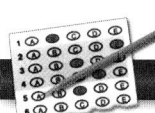

Standardized Test Prep

Multiple Choice

79. Simplify $(2x^2y^3)(4xy^{-2})$. **D**
    A. $6x^3y^5$ **B.** $6x^2y^6$ **C.** $8x^2y$ **D.** $8x^3y$

80. In the 2000 Olympics, the winning time for the women's 100-meter race was 1.79×10^{-1} min. Which is another way of expressing this time in minutes? **F**
    F. 0.179   **G.** 17.9   **H.** 179×10^1 **I.** 179×10^{-2}

Math Tip

Exercise 37 If students have difficulty with this problem, ask: *How can you write 1 as a power of a?* a^0

Connection to Chemistry

Exercise 54 *A mole is also called Avogadro's number.* It is named in honor of the Italian physicist Amedeo Avogadro, who postulated that equal volumes of gases, at equivalent temperatures and pressures, contain the same number of molecules. This theory, developed in 1811, was significant in the development of chemistry, but was not calculated until the later 19th century. At that time, the concept was extended to include all chemicals, not just gases. Avogadro's number holds true for all substances, whether in solid, liquid, or gaseous form.

English Learner

Exercise 58 Use a gesture to demonstrate the meaning of the term *spiral*, or draw a spiral on the board.

Connection to Geometry

Exercise 77 Students need to make sure they use the correct conversion factor when converting from cubic kilometers to cubic meters. You do not multiply cubic meters by 1000, but by 1000^3.

1 cu km = 1×10^9 cu m

pages 407–410   Exercises

56b. Longer; $1 < 4 < 7$ so $1 \times 10^{-7} < 4 \times 10^{-7} < 7 \times 10^{-7}$.

57. Answers may vary. Sample: The property of multiplying powers only applies when 2 terms have the same base.

Lesson Quiz 8-3

Simplify each expression.

1. $3^4 \cdot 3^5$ 3^9

2. $4x^5 \cdot 3x^{-2}$ $12x^3$

3. $(-2w^{-2})(-3w^2b^{-2})(-5b^{-3})$
$-\dfrac{30}{b^5}$

Write each product using scientific notation.

4. $(3 \times 10^4)(5 \times 10^2)$
1.5×10^7

5. $(7 \times 10^{-4})(1.5 \times 10^5)$
1.05×10^2

6. What is 2 trillion times 3 billion written in scientific notation?
6×10^{21}

Alternative Assessment

Write expressions such as $6x^2y^5$ and 1.4×10^{-6} on the board or on a transparency. Ask students to write expressions that can be simplified into the given expressions.

Standardized Test Prep

Resources

For additional practice with a variety of test item formats:
• Standardized Test Prep, p. 451
• Test-Taking Strategies, p. 446
• Test-Taking Strategies with Transparencies

pages 407–410 Exercises

84. [4] a. $4r^2$

b. $4(5)^2 = 4 \times 25 = 100$ in.^{2}

c. $144 = 4r^2$
$36 = r^2$ so $r = 6$
$d = 2r = 12$
12 in.

[3] radius found in (c) but not the diameter

[2] only two questions answered correctly

[1] only one question answered correctly

410

Quantitative Comparison

Compare the boxed quantity in Column A with the boxed quantity in Column B. Choose the best answer.
A. The quantity in Column A is greater.
B. The quantity in Column B is greater.
C. The two quantities are equal.
D. The relationship cannot be determined from the given information.

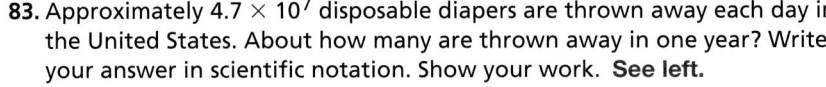

	Column A	Column B
A 81.	$(3.84 \times 10^{-2})(3.84 \times 10^2)$	$\frac{1}{12} \cdot (12)$
B 82.	the slope of $y = -\frac{1}{3}x + 7$	$3^5 \cdot 3^2 \cdot 3^{-9}$

Short Response

83. Approximately 4.7×10^7 disposable diapers are thrown away each day in the United States. About how many are thrown away in one year? Write your answer in scientific notation. Show your work. **See left.**

Extended Response

83. [2] $365 \times 4.7 \times 10^7 =$
$1715.5 \times 10^7 =$
1.7155×10^{10}:
about 1.7×10^{10}
diapers

[1] no work shown OR answer not written in scientific notation

Take It to the NET
Online lesson quiz at
www.PHSchool.com
Web Code: aea-0803

84. Sophie's Desserts packages its cheesecake in boxes with square bottoms, as shown below. Answer each of the following, showing all of your work.

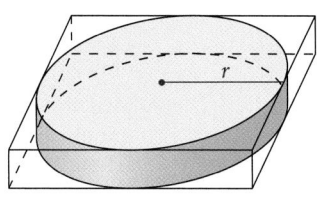

a. Write an expression for the area of the bottom of the box.

b. If the cheesecake has a radius of 5 in., what is the area of the bottom of the box? **a–c. See margin.**

c. The area of the bottom of a second box is 144 in.^{2}. What is the diameter of the largest cheesecake the box can hold?

Mixed Review

Lesson 8-2

Write each number in scientific notation.

85. 1,280,000
1.28×10^6

86. 0.0035
3.5×10^{-3}

87. 0.00009
9.0×10^{-5}

88. 6.2 million
6.2×10^6

Write each number in standard form.

89. 8.76×10^8
876,000,000

90. 1.052×10^{-3}
0.001052

91. 9.1×10^{11}
910,000,000,000

92. 2.9×10^{-4}
0.00029

Lesson 7-6

Solve each system by graphing. 93–95. See margin.

93. $y < 3x + 2$
$2x + y \geq 4$

94. $y < x + 6$
$x - 3y \leq 6$

95. $y > x + 4$
$x + 2y \leq 6$

Lesson 5-6

Find the third, seventh, and tenth terms of each sequence.

96. $A(n) = 10 + (n - 1)(4)$ 18; 34; 46

97. $A(n) = -5 + (n - 1)(2)$ −1; 7; 13

98. $A(n) = 12 + (n - 1)(-4)$
4; −12; −24

99. $A(n) = 1.2 + (n - 1)(-4)$
−6.8; −22.8; −34.8

93.

94.

95.

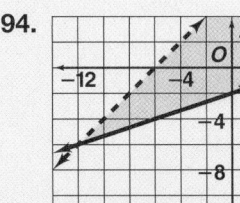

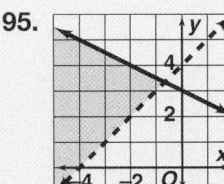

8-4

More Multiplication Properties of Exponents

  North Carolina Objectives
1.01 Write equivalent forms of algebraic expressions to solve problems. a) Apply the laws of exponents.

  North Carolina Objectives 1.01a

Lesson Preview

What You'll Learn

 OBJECTIVE 1 To raise a power to a power

 OBJECTIVE 2 To raise a product to a power

. . . And Why

To find the resting energy of an object, as in Example 5

 Check Skills You'll Need (For help, go to Lesson 8-3.)

Rewrite each expression using each base only once.

1. $3^2 \cdot 3^2 \cdot 3^2$ 3^6

2. $2^3 \cdot 2^3 \cdot 2^3 \cdot 2^3$ 2^{12}

3. $5^7 \cdot 5^7 \cdot 5^7 \cdot 5^7$ 5^{28}

4. $7 \cdot 7 \cdot 7$ 7^3

Simplify.

5. $x^3 \cdot x^3$ x^6

6. $a^2 \cdot a^2 \cdot a^2$ a^6

7. $y^{-2} \cdot y^{-2} \cdot y^{-2}$ $\frac{1}{y^6}$

8. $n^{-3} \cdot n^{-3}$ $\frac{1}{n^6}$

iTEXT Interactive lesson includes instant self-check, tutorials, and activities.

OBJECTIVE

1 Raising a Power to a Power

3. $2^{7 + 7 + 7 + 7} = 2^{7 \cdot 4} = 2^{28}$

5. $g^{4 + 4 + 4} = g^{4 \cdot 3} = g^{12}$

6. $c^{3 + 3 + 3 + 3} = c^{3 \cdot 4} = c^{12}$

7a. The power of the result is the product of the powers in the original expression.

Investigation: Powers of Powers

You can use what you learned in the previous lesson to find a shortcut for simplifying expressions with powers. Copy and complete each statement.

1. $(3^6)^2 = 3^6 \cdot 3^6 = 3^{\blacksquare + \blacksquare} = 3^6 \cdot \blacksquare = 3^{\blacksquare}$ $3^{6 + 6} = 3^{6 \cdot 2} = 3^{12}$

2. $(5^4)^3 = 5^4 \cdot 5^4 \cdot 5^4 = 5^{\blacksquare + \blacksquare + \blacksquare} = 5^4 \cdot \blacksquare = 5^{\blacksquare}$ $5^{4 + 4 + 4} = 5^{4 \cdot 3} = 5^{12}$

3. $(2^7)^4 = 2^7 \cdot 2^7 \cdot 2^7 \cdot 2^7 = 2^{\blacksquare + \blacksquare + \blacksquare + \blacksquare} = 2^7 \cdot \blacksquare = 2^{\blacksquare}$ See left.

4. $(a^3)^2 = a^3 \cdot a^3 = a^{\blacksquare + \blacksquare} = a^3 \cdot \blacksquare = a^{\blacksquare}$ $a^{3 + 3} = a^{3 \cdot 2} = a^6$

5. $(g^4)^3 = g^4 \cdot g^4 \cdot g^4 = g^{\blacksquare + \blacksquare + \blacksquare} = g^4 \cdot \blacksquare = g^{\blacksquare}$ See left.

6. $(c^3)^4 = c^3 \cdot c^3 \cdot c^3 \cdot c^3 = c^{\blacksquare + \blacksquare + \blacksquare + \blacksquare} = c^3 \cdot \blacksquare = c^{\blacksquare}$ See left.

7. **a.** Make a Conjecture What pattern do you see in your answers to Questions 1–6? See left.

   b. Use your pattern to simplify $(8^6)^3$. 8^{18}

Raising a power to a power is the same as raising the base to the product of the exponents.

 Key Concepts

Property	Raising a Power to a Power
For every nonzero number a and integers m and n, $(a^m)^n = a^{mn}$.	

Examples $(5^4)^2 = 5^{4 \cdot 2} = 5^8$ $(n^2)^5 = n^{2 \cdot 5} = n^{10}$

 ## Ongoing Assessment and Intervention

Before the Lesson
Diagnose prerequisite skills using:
• Check Skills You'll Need

During the Lesson
Monitor progress using:
• Check Understanding
• Additional Examples
• Standardized Test Prep

After the Lesson
Assess knowledge using:
• Lesson Quiz
• Computer Test Generator CD
• Chapter Checkpoint 1 (p. 416)

 # 8-4

  North Carolina Objectives 1.01a

1. Plan

Lesson Preview

 Check Skills You'll Need

Multiplication Properties of Exponents
Lesson 8-3: Examples 1, 2
Exercises 1–15
Extra Practice, p. 709

Lesson Resources

 Teaching Resources
Practice, Reteaching, Enrichment
Checkpoint Quiz 1

 Reaching All Students
Practice Workbook 8-4
Spanish Practice Workbook 8-4
Reading and Math Literacy 8B
Spanish Reading & Literacy 8B
Spanish Checkpoint Quiz 1
Basic Algebra Planning Guide 8-4

 **Presentation Assistant Plus!**
Transparencies
• Check Skills You'll Need 8-4
• Additional Examples 8-4
• Student Edition Answers 8-4
• Lesson Quiz 8-4
PH Presentation Pro CD 8-4

 PRENTICE HALL ASSESSMENT *SYSTEM*

Checkpoint Quiz 1
Computer Test Generator CD

 Technology
Resource Pro® CD-ROM
Computer Test Generator CD
Prentice Hall Presentation Pro CD

 **www.PHSchool.com**
Student Site
• Teacher Web Code: aek-5500
• Reasoning & Puzzles p. 78
• Self-grading Lesson Quiz
Teacher Center
• Lesson Planner
• Resources

Plus **iTEXT**

411

2. Teach

Math Background

The laws of exponents help to clarify why negative exponents, zero exponents, and fractional exponents are defined as they are. The laws of exponents describe what happens to positive integral exponents. Then the rules for other kinds of exponents are designed to be consistent with these laws.

OBJECTIVE
1 Teaching Notes

Investigation (Optional)
Teaching Tip
Remind students that they can read $(a^m)^n$ as the nth power of a^m.

1 EXAMPLE Tactile Learners

Encourage small groups of students to make class posters that describe what they have learned about using exponents. Have them include examples and leave space for additional material.

Additional Examples

1 Simplify $(a^3)^4$. a^{12}

2 Simplify $b^2(b^3)^{-2}$. $\frac{1}{b^4}$

OBJECTIVE
2 Teaching Notes

5 EXAMPLE Math Tip

Even though the expression in the example is very long, it actually just represents Einstein's famous $e = mc^2$. To help students make the connection, ask: *What part of the expression relates to m in Einstein's equation?* 10^{-3} *What part relates to c?* (3×10^8)

---

1 EXAMPLE Simplifying a Power Raised to a Power

Simplify $(x^3)^6$.

$(x^3)^6 = x^{3 \cdot 6}$ Multiply exponents when raising a power to a power.

$\quad\quad = x^{18}$ Simplify.

✓ **Check Understanding** **1** Simplify $(a^4)^7$ and $(a^{-4})^7$. a^{28}; $\frac{1}{a^{28}}$

Be sure to use the order of operations. Simplify expressions in parentheses that are being raised to a power before multiplying by expressions outside the parentheses.

2 EXAMPLE Simplifying an Expression With Powers

Simplify $c^5(c^3)^{-2}$.

$c^5(c^3)^{-2} = c^5 \cdot c^{3 \cdot (-2)}$ Multiply exponents in $(c^3)^{-2}$.

$\quad\quad = c^5 \cdot c^{-6}$ Simplify.

$\quad\quad = c^{5 + (-6)}$ Add exponents when multiplying powers with the same base.

$\quad\quad = c^{-1}$ Simplify.

$\quad\quad = \frac{1}{c}$ Write using only positive exponents.

✓ **Check Understanding** **2** Simplify each expression.
a. $(n^4)^3 \cdot n^5$ n^{17} **b.** $t^2(t^7)^{-2}$ $\frac{1}{t^{12}}$ **c.** $(a^4)^2 \cdot (a^2)^5$ a^{18}

OBJECTIVE
2 Raising a Product to a Power

You can use repeated multiplication to simplify expressions like $(5y)^3$.

$(5y)^3 = 5y \cdot 5y \cdot 5y$

$\quad\quad = 5 \cdot 5 \cdot 5 \cdot y \cdot y \cdot y$

$\quad\quad = 5^3 y^3$

$\quad\quad = 125y^3$

Notice that $(5y)^3 = 5^3 y^3$. This illustrates another property of exponents.

Key Concepts

Property	Raising a Product to a Power
For every nonzero number a and b and integer n, $(ab)^n = a^n b^n$.	
Example $(3x)^4 = 3^4 x^4 = 81x^4$	

3 EXAMPLE Simplifying a Product Raised to a Power

Simplify $(2x^2)^4$.

$(2x^2)^4 = 2^4(x^2)^4$ Raise each factor to the 4th power.

$\quad\quad = 2^4 x^8$ Multiply exponents of a power raised to a power.

$\quad\quad = 16x^8$ Simplify.

✓ **Check Understanding** **3** Simplify each expression.
a. $(2z)^4$ $16z^4$ **b.** $(4g^5)^{-2}$ $\frac{1}{16g^{10}}$ **c.** $(3t^0)^4$ 81

Reaching All Students

Below Level Students may be confused about when to multiply or when to add exponents. Have students write out the factors of $3^6 \cdot 3^2$ and of $(3^6)^2$, and then evaluate both expressions.	**Advanced Learners** Ask students whether 2^{10} or 2^6 is twice 2^5. Have them explain their answer.	**Tactile Learners** See note on page 412. **Error Prevention** See note on page 415.

Some expressions have more than one power raised to a power.

4 EXAMPLE Simplifying a Product Raised to a Power

Simplify $(x^{-2})^2(3xy^2)^4$.

$(x^{-2})^2(3xy^2)^4 = (x^{-2})^2 \cdot 3^4 x^4 (y^2)^4$ **Raise the three factors to the 4th power.**

$= x^{-4} \cdot 3^4 x^4 y^8$ **Multiply the exponents of a power raised to a power.**

$= 3^4 \cdot x^{-4} \cdot x^4 \cdot y^8$ **Use the Commutative Property of Multiplication.**

$= 3^4 x^0 y^8$ **Add exponents of powers with the same base.**

$= 81y^8$ **Simplify.**

✓ **Check Understanding** ④ Simplify each expression.
a. $(c^2)^3(3c^5)^4$ **81c²⁶**   **b.** $(2a^3)^5(3ab^2)^3$ **864a¹⁸b⁶**   **c.** $(6mn)^3(5m^{-3})^2$ $\frac{5400n^3}{m^3}$

You can use the property of raising a product to a power to solve problems involving scientific notation. For an expression like $(3 \times 10^8)^2$, raise both 3 and 10^8 to the second power.

5 EXAMPLE Real-World Problem Solving

Physical Science All objects, even resting ones, contain energy. A raisin has a mass of 10^{-3} kg. The expression $10^{-3} \cdot (3 \times 10^8)^2$ describes the amount of resting energy in joules the raisin contains. Simplify the expression.

$10^{-3} \cdot (3 \times 10^8)^2 = 10^{-3} \cdot 3^2 \cdot (10^8)^2$ **Raise each factor within parentheses to the second power.**

$= 10^{-3} \cdot 3^2 \cdot 10^{16}$ **Simplify $(10^8)^2$.**

$= 3^2 \cdot 10^{-3} \cdot 10^{16}$ **Use the Commutative Property of Multiplication.**

$= 3^2 \cdot 10^{-3+16}$ **Add exponents of powers with the same base.**

$= 9 \times 10^{13}$ **Simplify. Write in scientific notation.**

Real-World  Connection

Albert Einstein is famous for discovering the relationship $E = mc^2$, where E is energy (in joules), m is mass (in kg), and c is the speed of light (about 3×10^8 meters per second).

✓ **Check Understanding** ⑤ **Energy** An hour of television use consumes 1.45×10^{-1} kWh (kilowatt-hour) of electricity. Each kilowatt-hour of electric use is equivalent to 3.6×10^6 joules of energy.
a. Simplify the expression $(1.45 \times 10^{-1})(3.6 \times 10^6)$ to find how many joules a television uses in 1 hour.   **5.22 × 10⁵ joules**
b. Critical Thinking Suppose you could release the resting energy in a raisin. About how many hours of television use could be powered by that energy?
about 1.7 × 10⁸ h

EXERCISES

For more practice, see *Extra Practice*.

Practice and Problem Solving

Ⓐ Practice by Example

Examples 1, 2
(page 412)

Simplify each expression.

1. $(c^5)^2$ **c¹⁰**   **2.** $(c^2)^5$ **c¹⁰**   **3.** $(n^8)^4$ **n³²**   **4.** $(q^{10})^{10}$ **q¹⁰⁰**

5. $(c^5)^3 c^4$ **c¹⁹**   **6.** $(d^3)^5(d^3)^0$ **d¹⁵**   **7.** $(t^2)^{-2}(t^2)^{-5}$ $\frac{1}{t^{14}}$ **8.** $(x^3)^{-1}(x^2)^5$ **x⁷**

---

③ Simplify $(4x^3)^2$.   **16x⁶**

④ Simplify $(4xy^3)^2(x^3)^{-3}$. $\frac{16y^6}{x^7}$

⑤ An object has a mass of 10^2 kg. The expression $10^2 \cdot (3 \times 10^8)^2$ describes the amount of resting energy in joules the object contains. Simplify the expression.   **9 × 10¹⁸**

Closure

Ask students to tell what is meant by "simplifying a power to a power" and "simplifying a product to a power." When you simplify a *power to a power*, a power is the base of an exponent. When you simplify a *product to a power*, the different factors are each a base for the same exponent.

413

Assignment Guide

1 Objective

Ⓐ Ⓑ Core 1–8, 32–37, 52–56, 60–62

Ⓒ Extension 63–65

2 Objective

Ⓐ Ⓑ Core 9–31, 38–51, 57–59

Ⓒ Extension 66–68

Standardized Test Prep 69–73

Mixed Review 74–85

Alternate Method

Exercises 6, 7 Point out to students that the parentheses contain the same base, and so they may choose to first add exponents of the powers to the same base and then apply the Raising a Power to a Power Property.

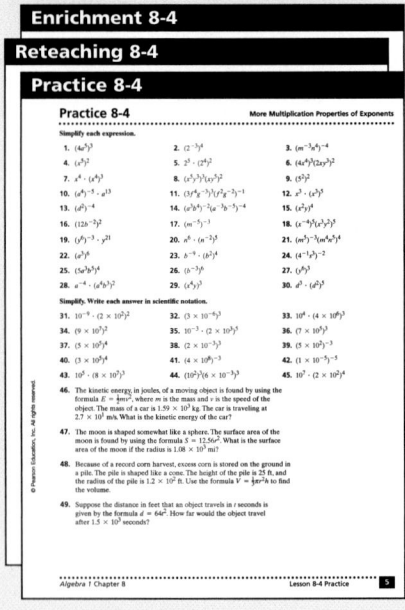

Example 3
(page 412)

Simplify each expression.

9. $(5y)^4$ $625y^4$ **10.** $(4m)^5$ $1024m^5$ **11.** $(7a)^2$ $49a^2$ **12.** $(12g^4)^{-1}$ $\frac{1}{12g^4}$

13. $(6y^2)^2$ $36y^4$ **14.** $(3n^6)^4$ $81n^{24}$ **15.** $(2y^4)^{-3}$ $\frac{1}{8y^{12}}$ **16.** $(2p^6)^0$ 1

Example 4
(page 413)

17. $(x^2)^5(x^3)^2$ x^{16} **18.** $(2xy)^3x^2$ $8x^5y^3$ **19.** $(mg^4)^{-1}(mg^4)$ 1

20. $(c^{-2})^3c^{-12}$ $\frac{1}{c^{18}}$ **21.** $(3b^{-2})^2(a^2b^4)^3$ $9a^6b^8$ **22.** $(2a^2c^4)^{-5}(c^{-1}a^7)^6$ $\frac{a^{32}}{32c^{26}}$

Example 5
(page 413)

Simplify. Write each answer in scientific notation. 23–26. See left.

23. $(4 \times 10^5)^2$ **24.** $(3 \times 10^5)^2$ **25.** $(2 \times 10^{-10})^3$ **26.** $(2 \times 10^{-3})^3$

23. 1.6×10^{11}

24. 9×10^{10}

25. 8×10^{-30}

26. 8×10^{-9}

27. $(7 \times 10^4)^2$ **28.** $(6 \times 10^{12})^2$ **29.** $(4 \times 10^8)^{-2}$ **30.** $(3.5 \times 10^{-4})^3$
4.9×10^9 3.6×10^{25} 6.25×10^{-18} 4.2875×10^{-11}

31. Geometry The length of one side of a cube is 9.5×10^{-4} m. What is the volume of the cube? 8.57375×10^{-10} m³

 Apply Your Skills

Complete each equation.

32. $(x^2)^\blacksquare = x^6$ **3**   **33.** $(m^\blacksquare)^3 = m^{-12}$ **−4**   **34.** $(b^2)^\blacksquare = b^8$ **4**

35. $(y^{-4})^\blacksquare = y^{12}$ **−3**   **36.** $(n^9)^\blacksquare = 1$ **0**   **37.** $7(c^1)^\blacksquare = 7c^8$ **8**

38. $(5x^\blacksquare)^2 = 25x^{-4}$ **−2**   **39.** $(3x^3y^\blacksquare)^3 = 27x^9$ **0**   **40.** $(m^2n^3)^\blacksquare = \frac{1}{m^6n^9}$ **−3**

41. Error Analysis One student simplified $x^5 + x^5$ to x^{10}. A second student simplified $x^5 + x^5$ to $2x^5$. Which student is correct? Explain.
The student who wrote $x^5 + x^5 = 2x^5$ is correct; x^5 times x^5 is x^{10}.
Simplify each expression.

42. $(4.1)^5 \cdot (4.1)^{-5}$ **1**   **43.** $3^2(3x)^3$ **$243x^3$**   **44.** $(b^5)^3b^2$ **b^{17}**

45. $(-5x)^2 + 5x^2$ **$30x^2$**   **46.** $(2x^{-3})^2 \cdot (0.2x)^2$ $\frac{0.16}{x^4}$ **47.** $(-2a^2b)^3(ab)^3$ **$-8a^9b^6$**

48. $(3^7)^2 \cdot (3^{-4})^3$ **49.** $(10^3)^4(4.3 \times 10^{-8})$ **50.** $(4xy^2)^4(-y)^{-3}$
9 4.3×10^4 $-256x^4y^5$

51. a. Geometry Write an expression for the surface area of each cube. **$24x^2$; $96x^2$**
b. How many times greater than the surface area of the small cube is the surface area of the large cube? **4 times**
c. Write an expression for the volume of each cube. **$8x^3$; $64x^3$**
d. How many times greater than the volume of the small cube is the volume of the large cube? **8 times**

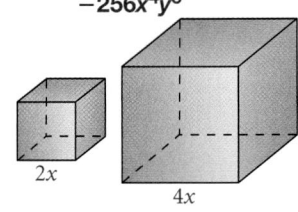
$2x$
$4x$

Write each expression with only one exponent. Use parentheses.

52. $m^4 \cdot n^4$ **$(mn)^4$**   **53.** $(a^5)(b^5)(a^0)$ **$(ab)^5$** **54.** $49x^2y^2z^2$ **$(7xyz)^2$** **55.** $\frac{12x^2}{3y^2}$ $\left(\frac{2x}{y}\right)^2$

56. Open-Ended Choose a value of n for the expression a^n. Express the power you wrote as a product of the form $(a^c)^d$ in four different ways.
Check students' work.

57. Measurement Write each answer as a power of 10.
a. How many cubic centimeters are in a cubic meter? **10^6**
b. How many cubic millimeters are in a cubic meter? **10^9**
c. How many cubic meters are in a cubic kilometer? **10^9**
d. How many cubic millimeters are in a cubic kilometer? **10^{18}**

58. Computers Write each answer as a power of 2.

    a. Computer capacity is often measured in bits and bytes. A bit is the smallest unit, a 1 or 0 in the computer's memory. A byte is 2^3 bits. A megabyte (MB) is 2^{20} bytes. How many bits are in a megabyte? **2^{23} bits**

    b. A gigabyte (GB) is 2^{10} megabytes. How many bytes are there in a gigabyte? How many bits are there in a gigabyte? **2^{30} bytes; 2^{33} bits**

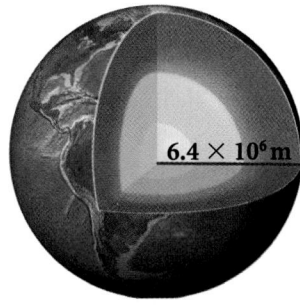 

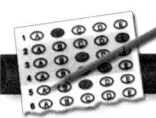 **59. a. Geography** Earth has a radius of about 6.4×10^6 m. Approximate the surface area of Earth using the formula for the surface area of a sphere, $S = 4\pi r^2$. **about 5.15×10^{14} m²**

    b. Earth's surface is about 70% water, almost all of it in oceans. About how many square meters of Earth's surface are covered with water? **See below.**

    c. The oceans have an average depth of 3795 m. Estimate the volume of water on Earth. **about 1.37×10^{18} m³**   **59b. about 3.60×10^{14} m²**

60. Which expression or expressions do *not* equal 64? **C**

    A. $2^5 \cdot 2$ **B.** 2^6 **C.** $2^2 \cdot 2^3$ **D.** $(2^3)^2$ **E.** $(2^2)(2^2)^2$

61. Writing Explain how you know when to add the exponents of powers and when to multiply the exponents. **Add exponents for products of powers as in $a^2 a^4$. Multiply exponents for powers of powers, as in $(a^2)^4$.**

C Challenge   **Solve each equation.**

  Sample $25^3 = 5^x$

            $(5^2)^3 = 5^x$ **Write 25 as a power of 5.**

              $5^6 = 5^x$ **Simplify $(5^2)^3$.**

                $6 = x$ **Since the bases are the same, the exponents must be equal.**

62. $5^6 = 25^x$ **3**   **63.** $8^2 = 2^x$ **6**   **64.** $3^x = 27^4$ **12**

65. $4^x = 2^6$ **3**   **66.** $3^{2x} = 9^4$ **4**   **67.** $2^x = \frac{1}{32}$ **−5**

68. Critical Thinking Simplify $(x^3)^4$ and x^{3^4}. Are the expressions equivalent? **x^{12}; x^{81}; no**

Standardized Test Prep

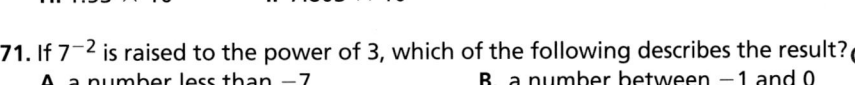

Multiple Choice

69. Which expression could you use for the area of the triangle at the right? **B**

    A. $3x$ **B.** $4.5x^2$

    C. $9x^2$ **D.** $22.5x^2$

70. Evaluate $3a^2$ for $a = 5.1 \times 10^{-5}$. **I**

    F. 1.53×10^{-10} **G.** 7.803×10^{-10}

    H. 1.53×10^{-9} **I.** 7.803×10^{-9}

71. If 7^{-2} is raised to the power of 3, which of the following describes the result? **C**

    A. a number less than -7 **B.** a number between -1 and 0

    C. a number between 0 and 1   **D.** a number greater than 1

Take It to the NET
Online lesson quiz at
www.PHSchool.com
·········· Web Code: aea-0804

72. Which expression does NOT equal $25n^{12}$? **H**

    F. $(5n^6)^2$ **G.** $(5n^3)(5n^9)$ **H.** $25(n^3)^9$ **I.** $5^2(n^2)^6$

Short Response

73. Does $(x^2 + 3y)^2$ equal $x^4 + 9y^2$? Substitute values for x and y to justify your answer. **See margin.**

Error Prevention

Exercises 9–22 Some students forget to raise the coefficient to the power. Suggest that they write out the expression to show distribution of the exponents to each factor of the base inside the corresponding parentheses for the exponent.

Error Prevention

Exercise 45 Some students may multiply $25x^2$ and $5x^2$. Point out that this exercise involves addition and requires the use of the rule for combining like terms.

pages 413–416   Exercises

73. [2] No,
$(x^2 + 3y)^2 \neq x^4 + 9y^2$;
for $x = 2$, $y = 4$
$(x^2 + 3y)^2 =$
$(4 + 12)^2 = 16^2 = 256$
$x^4 + 9y^2 = 2^4 + 9(4)^2$
$= 16 + 9 \cdot 16 = 160$
(OR equivalent
explanation)

[1] appropriate conclusion but no work to support conclusion

4. Assess

 Lesson Quiz 8-4

Simplify each expression.

1. $(x^4)^5$ x^{20}

2. $x(x^5y^{-2})^3$ $\frac{x^{16}}{y^6}$

3. $(5a^4)^3$ $125a^{12}$

4. $(1.5 \times 10^5)^2$ 2.25×10^{10}

5. $(2w^{-2})^4(3w^2b^{-2})^3$ $\frac{432}{w^2b^6}$

6. $(3 \times 10^{-5})(4 \times 10^4)^2$ 4.8×10^4

Alternative Assessment

Have students write their own expressions representing Examples 1–4 in this lesson. Then have the students give their expressions to other students to solve.

Standardized Test Prep

 Resources

For additional practice with a variety of test item formats:
- Standardized Test Prep, p. 451
- Test-Taking Strategies, p. 446
- Test-Taking Strategies with Transparencies

Exercise 73 Students have not learned the FOIL method, so they should be encouraged to apply the distributive property to $(x^2 + 3y)^2$.

 Chapter Checkpoint 1

To check understanding of Lessons 8-1 to 8-4:

Checkpoint Quiz 1 (p. 416)

 Teaching Resources
Checkpoint Quiz 1 (also in Prentice Hall Assessment System)

Reaching All Students
Reading and Math Literacy 8B

Spanish versions available

Mixed Review

Lesson 8-3 **Simplify each expression.**

74. $bc^{-6} \cdot b$ $\frac{b^2}{c^6}$ 75. $(a^2b^3)(a^6)$ a^8b^3 76. $9m^3(6m^2n^4)$ $54m^5n^4$ 77. $2t(-2t^4)$ $-4t^5$

Lesson 7-2 **Solve each system using substitution.**

78. $y = 3x + 5$ 79. $y = 0.5x - 1$ 80. $y = 5x - 9$ 81. $y = x + 4$
    $y = -4x + 12$ $y = 0.2x + 0.4$ $y = 3x + 5$ $y = -5$
    (1, 8) $\left(4\frac{2}{3}, 1\frac{1}{3}\right)$ **(7, 26)**   **(-9, -5)**

Lesson 6-1 **Find the slope of the line that passes through each pair of points.**

82. $(0, 3), (4, 0)$ $-\frac{3}{4}$ 83. $(2, -5), (3, 1)$ **6**   84. $(-3, 6), (1, 0)$ $-\frac{3}{2}$ 85. $(0, 0), (11, -9)$ $-\frac{9}{11}$

 Checkpoint Quiz 1   **Lessons 8-1 through 8-4**

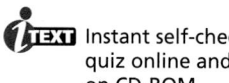 Instant self-check quiz online and on CD-ROM

Simplify each expression.

1. $5^{-1}(3^{-2})$ $\frac{1}{45}$ 2. $(r^{-5})^{-4}$ r^{20} 3. $(2x^5)(3x^{12})$ $6x^{17}$ 4. $\frac{mn^{-4}}{p^0q^{-2}}$ $\frac{mq^2}{n^4}$

5. $a^2b^0(a^{-3})$ $\frac{1}{a}$ 6. $(3^2)^{-1}(4m^2)^3$ $\frac{64m^6}{9}$ 7. $(2m^3)(3m^6)$ $6m^9$ 8. $(3t^2)^3(2t^0)^{-3}$ $\frac{27t^6}{8}$

9. A certain bacteria population doubles in size every day. Suppose a sample starts with 500 bacteria. The expression $500 \cdot 2^x$ models the number of bacteria in the sample after x days. Evaluate the expression for $x = 0, 2, 5$. **500; 2000; 16,000**

10. **Astronomy** The diameter of Mars is about 6800 km.
    a. Write this number in scientific notation. 6.8×10^3 km
    b. Approximate the surface area of Mars using the formula for the surface area of a sphere, $S = 4\pi r^2$. Write your answer in scientific notation. **about 1.45×10^8 k**
    c. Write your answer from part (b) in standard form. **145,000,000 km²**

Algebra at Work

············**Dr. Jewel Plummer Cobb**

Dr. Jewel Plummer Cobb was born in 1924 and obtained her master's and doctor's degrees in cell physiology from New York University. Dr. Cobb has concentrated on the study of normal and malignant skin cells and has published nearly 50 books, articles, and reports. Because the number of cancer cells grows exponentially, cell biologists often write cancer cell data in scientific notation.

 Take It to the NET For more information about a career in cancer research, go to **www.PHSchool.com**.
Web Code: aeb-2031

Division Properties of Exponents

 North Carolina Objectives

1.01 Write equivalent forms of algebraic expressions to solve problems. a) Apply the laws of exponents.

Lesson Preview

What You'll Learn

 OBJECTIVE 1 To divide powers with the same base

 OBJECTIVE 2 To raise a quotient to a power

. . . And Why

To find the amount of paper recycled per person in the United States, as in Example 2

✓ Check Skills You'll Need

(For help, go to Skills Handbook page 724.)

Write each fraction in simplest form.

1. $\frac{5}{20}$ $\frac{1}{4}$
2. $\frac{125}{25}$ 5
3. $\frac{60}{100}$ $\frac{3}{5}$
4. $\frac{124}{4}$ 31
5. $\frac{6}{15}$ $\frac{2}{5}$
6. $\frac{8}{30}$ $\frac{4}{15}$
7. $\frac{10}{35}$ $\frac{2}{7}$
8. $\frac{18}{63}$ $\frac{2}{7}$
9. $\frac{5xy}{15x}$ $\frac{y}{3}$
10. $\frac{6y^2}{3x}$ $\frac{2y^2}{x}$
11. $\frac{3ac}{12a}$ $\frac{c}{4}$
12. $\frac{24m}{6mn^2}$ $\frac{4}{n^2}$

Lesson Preview

 ✓ **Check Skills You'll Need**

Skills Handbook, Simplifying Fractions, page 724

Lesson Resources

 Teaching Resources
Practice, Reteaching, Enrichment

Reaching All Students
Practice Workbook 8-5
Spanish Practice Workbook 8-5
Basic Algebra Planning Guide 8-5

Presentation Assistant Plus!
Transparencies
• Check Skills You'll Need 8-5
• Additional Examples 8-5
• Student Edition Answers 8-5
• Lesson Quiz 8-5
PH Presentation Pro CD 8-5

 **ASSESSMENT SYSTEM**

Computer Test Generator CD

Technology
Resource Pro® CD-ROM
Computer Test Generator CD
Prentice Hall Presentation Pro CD

 www.PHSchool.com
Student Site
• Teacher Web Code: aek-5500
• Self-grading Lesson Quiz
Teacher Center
• Lesson Planner
• Resources

Plus

OBJECTIVE 1 Dividing Powers With the Same Base

You can use repeated multiplication to simplify fractions. Expand the numerator and the denominator using repeated multiplication. Then cancel like terms.

$$\frac{5^6}{5^2} = \frac{\cancel{5} \cdot \cancel{5} \cdot 5 \cdot 5 \cdot 5 \cdot 5}{\cancel{5} \cdot \cancel{5}} = 5^4$$

This illustrates the following property of exponents.

 Key Concepts

Property	Dividing Powers With the Same Base
	For every nonzero number a and integers m and n, $\frac{a^m}{a^n} = a^{m-n}$.
	Example $\frac{3^7}{3^3} = 3^{7-3} = 3^4$

Since division by zero is undefined, assume that no variable is equal to zero.

1 EXAMPLE Simplifying an Algebraic Expression

Simplify each expression.

a. $\frac{a^6}{a^{14}} = a^{6-14}$ — Subtract exponents when dividing powers with the same base.

$\quad = a^{-8}$ — Simplify the exponents.

$\quad = \frac{1}{a^8}$ — Rewrite using positive exponents.

b. $\frac{c^{-1}d^3}{c^5d^{-4}} = c^{-1-5}d^{3-(-4)}$ — Subtract exponents when dividing powers with the same base.

$\quad = c^{-6}d^7$ — Simplify.

$\quad = \frac{d^7}{c^6}$ — Rewrite using positive exponents.

 Interactive lesson includes instant self-check, tutorials, and activities.

Ongoing Assessment and Intervention

Before the Lesson
Diagnose prerequisite skills using:
• Check Skills You'll Need

During the Lesson
Monitor progress using:
• Check Understanding
• Additional Examples
• Standardized Test Prep

After the Lesson
Assess knowledge using:
• Lesson Quiz
• Computer Test Generator CD

Math Background

Pierre Hérigone, a Basque mathematician teaching in Paris, was writing forms such as $a4$ for a^4 in 1634. Descartes however, in 1637, wrote exponents in the same notation that is used today.

OBJECTIVE 1 ▼ Teaching Notes

1 EXAMPLE Math Tip

Reinforce that $x^0 = 1$, for $x \neq 0$, with the division rule for exponents. Use the following example.
Use division rules for exponents.

$\frac{x^3}{x^3} = x^{3-3} = x^0$

Also, any number divided by itself equals 1.

$\frac{x^3}{x^3} = 1$

Since $\frac{x^3}{x^3}$ equals *both* x^0 and 1, it follows that x^0 must equal 1.

2 EXAMPLE Technology Tip

Students can use a graphing calculator to divide in scientific notation. They must first set the [MODE] to SCI. Remind students to put each number in scientific notation in its own set of parentheses. In the result, the number following E is the exponent for 10.

🖱 Additional Examples

1 Simplify each expression.

a. $\frac{x^4}{x^9}$ $\frac{1}{x^5}$

b. $\frac{p^3 j^{-4}}{p^{-3} j^6}$ $\frac{p^6}{j^{10}}$

2 A small dog's heart beats about 64 million beats in a year. If there are 530 thousand minutes in a year, what is its average heart rate in beats per minute? **about 121 beats per min**

418

✔ Check Understanding **1** Simplify each expression.

a. $\frac{b^4}{b^9}$ $\frac{1}{b^5}$
b. $\frac{z^{10}}{z^5}$ z^5
c. $\frac{a^2 b}{a^4 b^3}$ $\frac{1}{a^2 b^2}$
d. $\frac{m^{-1} n^2}{m^3 n}$ $\frac{n}{m^4}$
e. $\frac{x^2 y^{-1} z^4}{x y^4 z^{-3}}$ $\frac{x z^7}{y^5}$

When you divide numbers that are in scientific notation, you can use the property of dividing powers with the same base. In real-world situations, decide whether to write the result in standard or scientific notation.

2 EXAMPLE   Real-World 🌐 Problem Solving

Recycling In 1998, the total amount of wastepaper and cardboard recycled in the United States was 35 million tons. The population of the United States in 1998 was 270.5 million. On average, how much paper did each person recycle?

$\frac{35 \text{ million tons}}{270.5 \text{ million people}} = \frac{3.5 \times 10^7 \text{ tons}}{2.705 \times 10^8 \text{ people}}$ **Write in scientific notation.**

$= \frac{3.5}{2.705} \times 10^{7-8}$ **Subtract exponents when dividing powers with the same base.**

$= \frac{3.5}{2.705} \times 10^{-1}$ **Simplify the exponent.**

$\approx 1.3 \times 10^{-1}$ **Divide. Round to the nearest tenth.**

$= 0.13$ **Write in standard notation.**

● There was about 0.13 ton of waste paper recycled per person in 1998.

Real-World 🌐 Connection

Worldwide, about 43% of the paper that is discarded is recovered for recycling.

✔ Check Understanding **2** Find each quotient. Write each answer in scientific notation.

a. $\frac{2 \times 10^3}{8 \times 10^8}$ 2.5×10^{-6}
b. $\frac{7.5 \times 10^{12}}{2.5 \times 10^{-4}}$ 3.0×10^{16}
c. $\frac{4.2 \times 10^5}{12.6 \times 10^2}$ $3.\overline{3} \times 10^2$

d. In 1998 the total amount of glass recycled in the United States was 3.2 million tons. The population of the United States in 1998 was 270.5 million people. On average, about how many tons of glass were recycled per person?
about 1.18×10^{-2} tons

OBJECTIVE 2 ▼ Raising a Quotient to a Power

You can use repeated multiplication to simplify the expression $\left(\frac{x}{y}\right)^3$.

$\left(\frac{x}{y}\right)^3 = \frac{x}{y} \cdot \frac{x}{y} \cdot \frac{x}{y}$

$= \frac{x \cdot x \cdot x}{y \cdot y \cdot y}$

$= \frac{x^3}{y^3}$

This illustrates another property of exponents.

🔩 Key Concepts

Property	**Raising a Quotient to a Power**

For every nonzero number a and b and integer n, $\left(\frac{a}{b}\right)^n = \frac{a^n}{b^n}$.

Example $\left(\frac{4}{5}\right)^3 = \frac{4^3}{5^3} = \frac{64}{125}$

👥 Reaching All Students

Below Level Some students may not see the progression in Example 1b from $c^{-6} d^7$ to $\frac{d^7}{c^6}$. Explain this step carefully, then show them other examples using similar expressions.	**Advanced Learners** Have students complete the expression $\frac{x^{\square}}{x^{\square}} = x^2$ in more than one way.	**English Learners** See note on page 421. **Error Prevention** See note on page 421.

3 EXAMPLE Raising a Quotient to a Power

Simplify $\left(\frac{4}{x^2}\right)^3$.

$$\left(\frac{4}{x^2}\right)^3 = \frac{4^3}{(x^2)^3}$$ **Raise the numerator and the denominator to the third power.**

$$= \frac{4^3}{x^6}$$ **Multiply the exponents in the denominator.**

$$= \frac{64}{x^6}$$ **Simplify.**

✓ **Check Understanding** ❸ Simplify each expression.

a. $\left(\frac{3}{x^2}\right)^2$ $\frac{9}{x^4}$

b. $\left(\frac{x}{y^2}\right)^3$ $\frac{x^3}{y^6}$

c. $\left(\frac{t^7}{2^3}\right)^2$ $\frac{t^{14}}{64}$

You can use what you know about exponents to write an expression in the form $\left(\frac{a}{b}\right)^{-n}$ using positive exponents.

$$\left(\frac{a}{b}\right)^{-n} = \frac{1}{\left(\frac{a}{b}\right)^n}$$ **Use the definition of negative exponent.**

$$= \frac{1}{\frac{a^n}{b^n}}$$ **Raise the quotient to a power.**

$$= \frac{1}{\frac{a^n}{b^n}} \cdot \frac{b^n}{b^n}$$ **Use the Identity Property of Multiplication to multiply by $\frac{b^n}{b^n}$.**

$$= \frac{b^n}{a^n}$$ **Simplify.**

$$= \left(\frac{b}{a}\right)^n$$ **Write the quotient using one exponent.**

So, $\left(\frac{a}{b}\right)^{-n} = \left(\frac{b}{a}\right)^n$.

4 EXAMPLE Simplifying an Exponential Expression

Simplify each expression.

a. $\left(\frac{3}{5}\right)^{-2} = \left(\frac{5}{3}\right)^2$ **Rewrite using the reciprocal of $\frac{3}{5}$.**

$$= \frac{5^2}{3^2}$$ **Raise the numerator and denominator to the second power.**

$$= \frac{25}{9} \text{ or } 2\frac{7}{9}$$ **Simplify.**

b. $\left(-\frac{2x}{y}\right)^{-4} = \left(-\frac{y}{2x}\right)^4$ **Rewrite using the reciprocal of $-\frac{2x}{y}$.**

$$= \left(\frac{-y}{2x}\right)^4$$ **Write the fraction with a negative numerator.**

$$= \frac{(-y)^4}{(2x)^4}$$ **Raise the numerator and denominator to the fourth power.**

$$= \frac{y^4}{16x^4}$$ **Simplify.**

✓ **Check Understanding** ❹ Simplify each expression.

a. $\left(\frac{3}{4}\right)^{-3}$ $\frac{64}{27}$

b. $\left(\frac{-1}{2}\right)^{-5}$ -32

c. $\left(\frac{2r}{s}\right)^{-1}$ $\frac{s}{2r}$

d. $\left(\frac{7a}{m}\right)^{-2}$ $\frac{m^2}{49a^2}$

Assignment Guide

 **Objective**
Ⓐ Ⓑ Core 1–20, 37–45
Ⓒ Extension 79–80

 **Objective**
Ⓐ Ⓑ Core 21–36, 46–78
Ⓒ Extension 81–83

Standardized Test Prep 84–90

Mixed Review 91–103

Exercise 36 Suggest to students that they always look carefully at how an exponent of 0 affects an expression before doing any simplifying.

| Enrichment 8-5 |
| Reteaching 8-5 |
| Practice 8-5 |

Practice 8-5 .... Division Properties of Exponents

pages 420–423 Exercises

37. 5^3 simplifies to 125.

38. y^{-2} contains a negative exponent.

39. Each term should be raised to the 4th power and simplified.

40. x^0 simplifies to 1.

41. The base d should appear only once.

420

EXERCISES
For more practice, see *Extra Practice*.

Practice and Problem Solving

Ⓐ **Practice by Example**

Example 1
(page 417)

Copy and complete each equation.

1. $\dfrac{5^9}{5^2} = 5^{\blacksquare}$ 7

2. $\dfrac{2^4}{2^3} = 2^{\blacksquare}$ 1

3. $\dfrac{3^2}{3^5} = 3^{\blacksquare}$ −3

4. $\dfrac{5^2 5^3}{5^3 5^2} = 5^{\blacksquare}$ 0

Simplify each expression.

5. $\dfrac{2^5}{2^7}$ $\dfrac{1}{4}$

6. $\dfrac{2^7}{2^5}$ 4

7. $\dfrac{c^{12}}{c^{15}}$ $\dfrac{1}{c^3}$

8. $\dfrac{m^{-2}}{m^{-5}}$ m^3

9. $\dfrac{3s^{-9}}{6s^{-11}}$ $\dfrac{s^2}{2}$

10. $\dfrac{x^{13}y^2}{x^{13}y}$ y

11. $\dfrac{c^2d^{-3}}{c^3d^{-1}}$ $\dfrac{1}{cd^2}$

12. $\dfrac{3^2m^3t^6}{3^5m^7t^{-5}}$ $\dfrac{t^{11}}{27m^4}$

Example 2
(page 418)

Simplify each quotient. Write each answer in scientific notation.

13. $\dfrac{6.5 \times 10^{15}}{1.3 \times 10^8}$ 5×10^7

14. $\dfrac{2.7 \times 10^{-8}}{9 \times 10^{-4}}$ 3×10^{-5}

15. $\dfrac{4.2 \times 10^8}{7 \times 10^5}$ 6×10^2

16. $\dfrac{8.4 \times 10^{-5}}{2 \times 10^{-8}}$ 4.2×10^3

17. $\dfrac{4.65 \times 10^{-4}}{3.1 \times 10^2}$ 1.5×10^{-6}

18. $\dfrac{3.5 \times 10^6}{5 \times 10^8}$ 7×10^{-3}

19. Television In 2000, people in the United States over age 2 watched television a total of 386 billion hours. The population of the United States over age 2 was about 265 million people.
   a. Write each number in scientific notation. 3.86×10^{11} h; 2.65×10^8 people
   b. Find the average number of hours of TV viewing per person older than age 2 for 2000. **about 1457 h**
   c. On average, how many hours per day did each person older than age 2 watch television in 2000? **about 4.0 h**

20. Computers The speed of computers is measured in number of calculations per picosecond. There are 3.6×10^{15} picoseconds per hour. What fraction of a second is a picosecond? 1×10^{-12} s

Example 3
(page 419)

Simplify each expression.

21. $\left(\dfrac{3}{5}\right)^2$ $\dfrac{9}{25}$

22. $\left(\dfrac{1}{x}\right)^3$ $\dfrac{1}{x^3}$

23. $\left(\dfrac{2x}{y}\right)^5$ $\dfrac{32x^5}{y^5}$

24. $\left(\dfrac{3a}{2b}\right)^4$ $\dfrac{81a^4}{16b^4}$

25. $\left(\dfrac{2^2}{5}\right)^3$ $\dfrac{64}{125}$

26. $\left(\dfrac{3^3}{3^4}\right)^2$ $\dfrac{1}{9}$

27. $\left(\dfrac{6}{n^6}\right)^2$ $\dfrac{36}{n^{12}}$

28. $\left(\dfrac{2p}{5}\right)^3$ $\dfrac{8p^3}{125}$

Example 4
(page 419)

29. $\left(\dfrac{2}{3}\right)^{-1}$ $\dfrac{3}{2}$

30. $\left(\dfrac{2}{3}\right)^{-2}$ $\dfrac{9}{4}$

31. $\left(-\dfrac{2}{3}\right)^{-2}$ $\dfrac{9}{4}$

32. $\left(-\dfrac{2}{3}\right)^{-3}$ $-\dfrac{27}{8}$

33. $\left(\dfrac{3x^4}{15}\right)^2$ $\dfrac{9x^8}{225}$

34. $\left(\dfrac{4n}{2n^2}\right)^3$ $\dfrac{8}{n^3}$

35. $\left(\dfrac{c^5}{c^9}\right)^3$ $\dfrac{1}{c^{12}}$

36. $\left(\dfrac{3b^2}{5}\right)^0$ 1

Ⓑ **Apply Your Skills**

Explain why each expression is *not* in simplest form. 37–41. See margin.

37. 5^3m^3

38. x^5y^{-2}

39. $(2c)^4$

40. x^0y

41. $\dfrac{d^7}{d}$

Simplify each expression.

42. $\dfrac{3^2 \cdot 5^0}{2^3}$ $\dfrac{9}{8}$

43. $\left(\dfrac{2m^5}{m^2}\right)^{-4}$ $\dfrac{1}{16m^{12}}$

44. $\dfrac{5x^3}{(5x)^3}$ $\dfrac{1}{25}$

45. $\dfrac{(2a^7)(3a^2)}{6a^3}$ a^6

46. $\left(\dfrac{7t^3}{21t}\right)^3$ $\dfrac{t^6}{27}$

47. $\left(\dfrac{n^4n}{n^{-2}}\right)^{-4}$ $\dfrac{1}{n^{28}}$

48. $\left(\dfrac{2k^3}{3k^{-2}}\right)^{-2}$ $\dfrac{9}{4k^{10}}$

49. $\dfrac{7^9 \cdot (10)^2}{7^7}$ 49

1920's

1950's

Today

51a. Answers may vary.
Sample: $\frac{c^4}{c^6}$ can be written as c^{4-6} or c^{-2}. $c^{-2} = \frac{1}{c^2}$.

61. Answers may vary.
Sample: You can raise the numerator and denominator to the power and then simplify, or simplify and then raise to the power.

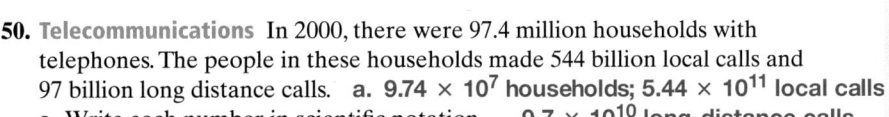

50. Telecommunications In 2000, there were 97.4 million households with telephones. The people in these households made 544 billion local calls and 97 billion long distance calls. **a. 9.74 × 10⁷ households; 5.44 × 10¹¹ local calls**

a. Write each number in scientific notation. **9.7 × 10¹⁰ long-distance calls**

b. What was the average number of local calls placed per household? Round to the nearest whole number. **about 5585 local calls**

c. What was the average number of long distance calls placed per household? Round to the nearest whole number. **about 996 long-distance calls**

51. a. Writing While simplifying the expression $\frac{c^4}{c^6}$, Kneale said, "I've found a property of exponents that's not in my algebra book!" Write an explanation of why Kneale's method works. **See left below.**

b. Open-Ended Apply Kneale's method to an example you create. **Check students' work.**

> Kneale
>
> $$\frac{c^4}{c^6} = \frac{1}{c^{6-4}} = \frac{1}{c^2}$$

Simplify each expression.

52. $\left(\frac{2ab^6}{a^3b}\right)^{-2}$ $\frac{a^4}{4b^{10}}$ **53.** $\frac{a^3b^2c^{-4}}{a^{-2}b^5c^{-9}}$ $\frac{a^5c^5}{b^3}$ **54.** $\frac{\left(\frac{1}{3}\right)^{-3}}{\left(\frac{1}{6}\right)^{-2}}$ $\frac{3}{4}$ **55.** $\frac{0.2^2 \cdot 0.2^3}{0.2^6}$ **5**

56. $\left(\frac{p^{-2}q^4r}{p^3q^5}\right)^5$ $\frac{r^5}{p^{25}q^5}$ **57.** $\left(\frac{(-3)^2}{(-2)^{-4}}\right)^2$ **20,736**   **58.** $\left(\frac{(3x)^2y}{x^2y^4}\right)^{-2}$ $\frac{y^6}{81}$ **59.** $\frac{(5a^2)(6b^3)}{(2a^3)(25b^{-2})}$ $\frac{3b^5}{5a}$

60. a. Census The 2000 census counted approximately 281 million people in the United States. About 65,000 of those were centenarians, which means their ages are 100 or greater. Centenarians are about what percent of the population? **about 0.02%**

b. About what percent of the population does not include people who are centenarians? **about 99.98%**

61. Critical Thinking Lena and Jared used different methods to simplify $\left(\frac{b^7}{b^3}\right)^2$. Why are both methods correct? **See left.**

> Lena
>
> $$\left(\frac{b^7}{b^3}\right)^2 = \frac{b^{14}}{b^6}$$
> $$= b^8$$

> Jared
>
> $$\left(\frac{b^7}{b^3}\right)^2 = (b^4)^2$$
> $$= b^8$$

62. a. Finance In 1990, The United States government owed $3.23 trillion to its creditors. The population of the United States was 248.7 million people. How much did the government owe per person in 1990? Round to the nearest dollar. **about $12,988**

b. about $20,733

b. In 1999 the debt had grown to $5.66 trillion, with a population of 273 million. How much did the government owe per person? Round to the nearest dollar.

c. What was the percent of increase in the average amount owed per person from 1990 to 1999? **about 60%**

63. a. Error Analysis What error did the student make in simplifying the expression at the right? **The student treated $\frac{5^4}{5}$ as $\left(\frac{5}{5}\right)^4$.**

b. What is the correct answer? **125**

> $$5^4 \div 5 = \frac{5^4}{5}$$
> $$= 1^4$$
> $$= 1$$

Simplify each expression

1. $\frac{a^8}{a^{-2}}$ a^{10}

2. $\frac{w^3}{w^7}$ $\frac{1}{w^4}$

3. $\frac{(3a)^4(2a^{-2})}{6a^2}$ 27

4. $\frac{1.6 \times 10^3}{4 \times 10^{-2}}$ 4×10^4

5. $\left(\frac{2^4}{5}\right)^2$ $10\frac{6}{25}$

6. $\left(\frac{4x^3}{3x^2}\right)^{-3}$ $\frac{27}{64x^3}$

Alternative Assessment

Group students in pairs. Give each pair four number cubes. Have students use the four numbers rolled to form a division expression with exponents and then simplify the expression. Repeat. Tell students to use at least one negative sign in every other expression.

Technology Tip

Exercise 72 Remind students they can calculate the number of seconds in a day by multiplying $60 \times 60 \times 24$. Tell them if they use a graphing calculator in SCI mode, the answer will already be in scientific notation.

Exercises 74–78 Suggest students simplify each expression, and write down each property used as they proceed.

Write each expression with only one exponent. You may need to use parentheses.

64. $\frac{3^5}{5^5}$ $\left(\frac{3}{5}\right)^5$

65. $\frac{m^7}{n^7}$ $\left(\frac{m}{n}\right)^7$

66. $\frac{d^8}{d^5}$ d^3

67. $\frac{10^7 \cdot 10^0}{10^{-3}}$ 10^{10}

68. $\frac{27x^3}{8y^3}$ $\left(\frac{3x}{2y}\right)^3$

69. $\frac{4m^2}{169m^4}$ $\left(\frac{2}{13m}\right)^2$

70. $\frac{49m^2}{25n^2}$ $\left(\frac{7m}{5n}\right)^2$

71. $\frac{125c^7}{216c^4}$ $\left(\frac{5c}{6}\right)^3$

74. def. of neg. exponent

75. dividing powers with the same base, def. of neg. exponent

76. raising a quotient to a power

77. mult. powers with the same base

78. raising a power to a power, dividing powers with the same base, def. of neg. exponents

 72. **Medicine** If you donate blood regularly, the American Red Cross recommends a 56-day waiting period between donations. One pint of blood contains about 2.4×10^{12} red blood cells. Your body normally produces about 2×10^6 red blood cells per second.
   a. At its normal rate, in how many seconds will your body replace the red blood cells lost by giving one pint of blood? **about 1.2×10^6 s**
   b. Convert your answer from part (a) to days. **about 13.9 days**

73. a. **Open Ended** Write three numbers in scientific notation. **Check students' work.**
   b. Divide each number by 2. **Check students' work.**
   c. **Critical Thinking** Is the power of 10 divided by 2 when you divide a number in scientific notation by 2? Explain.
   No, the power may remain the same or be one less.

Which property or properties of exponents would you use to simplify each expression? 74–78. See left.

74. 2^{-3}

75. $\frac{2^2}{2^5}$

76. $\left(\frac{1}{2}\right)^3$

77. $\frac{1}{2^{-4}2^7}$

78. $\frac{(2^4)^3}{2^{15}}$

 C **Challenge**

Simplify each expression.

79. $n^{x+2} \div n^x n^2$

80. $n^{5x} \div n^x n^{4x}$

81. $\left(\frac{x^m}{x^{m-2}}\right)^2 x^4$

82. $\frac{\left(\frac{n^5}{n^4}\right)}{n^3}$ $\frac{1}{n^2}$

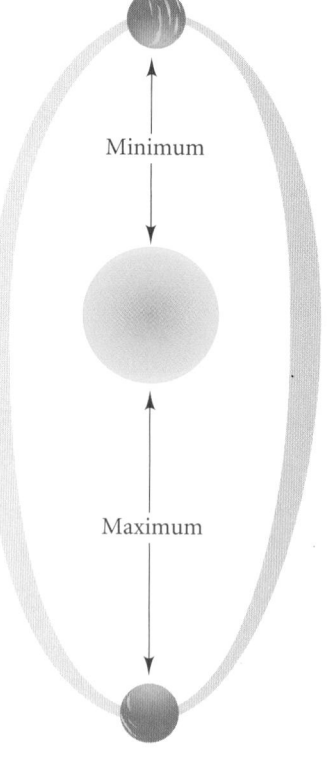

83. **Astronomy** The ratio of a planet's maximum to minimum distance from the sun is related to how circular its orbit is.
   a. Copy and complete the table below. Round decimals to the nearest hundredth. **See back of book.**
   b. **Reasoning** How can you use the ratio maximum : minimum to determine whether a planet's orbit is close to circular? **See below.**
   c. Which planet has the least circular orbit? The most circular orbit?
   Pluto, Venus

Minimum

Maximum

Distance From the Sun (kilometers)

Planet	Maximum	Minimum	Maximum : Minimum
Mercury	6.97×10^7	4.59×10^7	$\blacksquare : \blacksquare = \frac{6.97 \times 10^7}{4.59 \times 10^7} = \frac{6.97}{4.59} \approx 1.52$
Venus	1.089×10^8	1.075×10^8	$1.089 \times 10^8 : \blacksquare \approx \blacksquare$
Earth	1.521×10^8	1.471×10^8	$\blacksquare : 1.471 \times 10^8 \approx \blacksquare$
Mars	2.491×10^8	2.067×10^8	$\blacksquare : \blacksquare \approx \blacksquare$
Jupiter	8.157×10^8	7.409×10^8	$\blacksquare : \blacksquare \approx \blacksquare$
Saturn	1.507×10^9	1.347×10^9	$\blacksquare : \blacksquare \approx \blacksquare$
Uranus	3.004×10^9	2.735×10^9	$\blacksquare : \blacksquare \approx \blacksquare$
Neptune	4.537×10^9	4.457×10^9	$\blacksquare : \blacksquare \approx \blacksquare$
Pluto	7.375×10^9	4.425×10^9	$\blacksquare : \blacksquare \approx \blacksquare$

83b. **The closer the ratio is to 1, the more circular the orbit.**

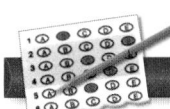

Multiple Choice

84. Simplify the expression $\frac{(-6)^5}{6^5}$. **B**

   A. -6^5 **B.** -1 **C.** 1 **D.** 6^7

85. Evaluate $\frac{-5x^3y^5}{15x^{-7}y^5z^{-2}}$ for $x = -1$, $y = 5$, and $z = 3$. **G**

   F. -9 **G.** -3 **H.** -1 **I.** 0

86. Which point on the number line below could be the graph of 2^n if n is a negative integer? **D**

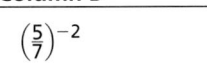

   A. W **B.** X **C.** Y **D.** Z

Quantitative Comparison

Compare the boxed quantity in Column A with the boxed quantity in Column B. Choose the best answer.
   A. The quantity in Column A is greater.
   B. The quantity in Column B is greater.
   C. The two quantities are equal.
   D. The relationship cannot be determined from the information given.

Column A	Column B
B 87. $\left(-\frac{7}{5}\right)^{-3}$	$\left(\frac{5}{7}\right)^{-2}$
C 88. $\left(\frac{-1}{2^2}\right)^{-2}$	$\left(\frac{2^2}{-1}\right)^2$
B 89. $\left(\frac{2 \cdot 5}{10^2}\right)^2$	$\left(\frac{2 \cdot 10}{5^2}\right)^{-2}$

Extended Response

Take It to the NET
Online lesson quiz at
www.PHSchool.com
Web Code: aea-0805

90. At its closest, Saturn is about 743,000,000 miles from Earth. A deep-space probe travels from Earth to Saturn at an average speed of 25,000 miles per hour. Assume that the probe can go straight from Earth to Saturn. How many hours will it take the probe to get from Earth to Saturn? About how many years will it take? Show your work. **See margin.**

Mixed Review

Lesson 8-4   **Simplify each expression.**

91. $(3y^2)^3$ $27y^6$ **92.** $(2m^{-7})^3$ $\frac{8}{m^{21}}$ **93.** $(r^2t^{-5})^{-4}$ $\frac{t^{20}}{r^8}$ **94.** $2(3s^{-2})^{-3}$ $\frac{2s^6}{27}$

95. $(2^3c^2)^{-1}$ $\frac{1}{8c^2}$ **96.** $(-3)^2(-r^3)^2$ $9r^6$ **97.** $(7^0n^{-3})^2(n^5)^2$ n^4 **98.** $(7^2y^{12})^0$ 1

Lesson 7-1   **Solve each system by graphing. 99–102. See margin.**

99. $y = 3x$ **100.** $y = 2x + 1$ **101.** $y = 5$ **102.** $y = 7$
   $y = -2x$ $y = x - 3$ $x = 3$ $y = 8$

Lesson 6-7   **103.** Graph $y = |x|$ and its translation $y = |x| + 3$. **See margin.**

Lesson 8-5   Division Properties of Exponents   **423**

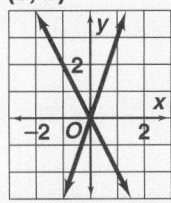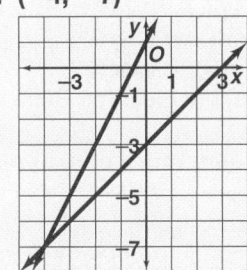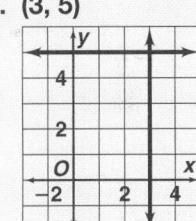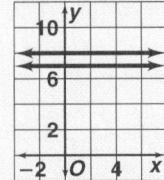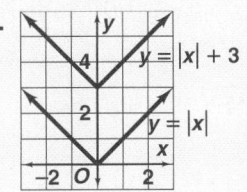
pages 420–423   Exercises

90. [4] $(7.43 \times 10^8) \div (2.5 \times 10^4) = 2.972 \times 10^4$
   29,720 h
   $\frac{29,720 \text{ hours}}{1} \cdot \frac{1 \text{ day}}{24 \text{ hours}} \cdot \frac{1 \text{ year}}{365 \text{ days}} \approx 3.4 \text{ years}$
   about 3.4 years (OR equivalent explanation)

[3] appropriate methods but one computational error

[2] error in conversion factor used or a missing conversion factor

[1] correct number of hours and years but no work shown

423

Lesson Preview

 Check Skills You'll Need

Describing Number Patterns
Lesson 5-6: Examples 1, 2
Exercises 1–21
Extra Practice, p. 706

Lesson Resources

 Teaching Resources
Practice, Reteaching, Enrichment

 Reaching All Students
Practice Workbook 8-6
Spanish Practice Workbook 8-6
Technology Activities 22
Hands-On Activities 18
Basic Algebra Planning Guide 8-6

 Presentation Assistant Plus!
Transparencies
• Check Skills You'll Need 8-6
• Additional Examples 8-6
• Student Edition Answers 8-6
• Lesson Quiz 8-6
PH Presentation Pro CD 8-6

 **ASSESSMENT SYSTEM**

Computer Test Generator CD

 Technology
Resource Pro® CD-ROM
Computer Test Generator CD
Prentice Hall Presentation Pro CD

 www.PHSchool.com
Student Site
• Teacher Web Code: aek-5500
• Self-grading Lesson Quiz
Teacher Center
• Lesson Planner
• Resources

Plus

 **8-6**

Geometric Sequences

1.02 Use formulas and algebraic expressions, including iterative and recursive forms, to model and solve problems.

 North Carolina Objectives

Lesson Preview

What You'll Learn

 OBJECTIVE 1 To form geometric sequences

 OBJECTIVE 2 To use formulas when describing geometric sequences

. . . And Why

To find the height of a ball after a number of bounces, as in Example 5

✔ **Check Skills You'll Need** (For help, go to Lesson 5-6.)

Find the common difference of each sequence.

1. $1, 3, 5, 7, \ldots$ **2**
2. $19, 17, 15, 13, \ldots$ **−2**
3. $1.3, 0.1, -1.1, -2.3, \ldots$ **−1.2**
4. $18, 21.5, 25, 28.5, \ldots$ **3.5**

Use inductive reasoning to find the next two numbers in each pattern.

5. $2, 4, 8, 16, \ldots$ **32, 64**
6. $4, 12, 36, \ldots$ **108, 324**
7. $0.2, 0.4, 0.8, 1.6, \ldots$ **3.2, 6.4**
8. $200, 100, 50, 25, \ldots$ **12.5, 6.25**

New Vocabulary • geometric sequence • common ratio

 Interactive lesson includes instant self-check, tutorials, and activities.

OBJECTIVE
1 Geometric Sequences

Recall that a number pattern is also called a sequence, and each number in a sequence is a term of the sequence.

In Chapter 5 you studied arithmetic sequences, where you found each new term by adding the same amount to each previous term. Another kind of number sequence is a geometric sequence. You form a **geometric sequence** by multiplying a term in the sequence by a fixed number to find the next term. The fixed number is the **common ratio.**

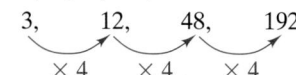 **Reading Math**
When you write a ratio of one term to the previous term in a geometric sequence, the ratios are equal. Thus the name is *common ratio*.

Term   2,   10,   50,   250
Common Ratio $\times 5$ $\times 5$ $\times 5$

1 EXAMPLE Finding the Common Ratio

Find the common ratio of each sequence.

a. $3, 12, 48, 192, \ldots$

3,   12,   48,   192
  $\times 4$ $\times 4$ $\times 4$

The common ratio is 4.

b. $80, 20, 5, \frac{5}{4}, \ldots$

80,   20,   5, $\frac{5}{4}$
  $\times \frac{1}{4}$ $\times \frac{1}{4}$ $\times \frac{1}{4}$

The common ratio is $\frac{1}{4}$.

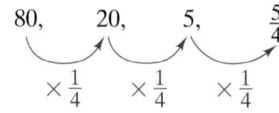 **Check Understanding** ❶ Find the common ratio of each sequence.
a. $750, 150, 30, 6, \ldots$ $\frac{1}{5}$ **b.** $-3, -6, -12, -24, \ldots$ **2** **c.** $4, 6, 9, 13.5, \ldots$ $\frac{3}{2}$

Ongoing Assessment and Intervention

Before the Lesson
Diagnose prerequisite skills using:
• Check Skills You'll Need

During the Lesson
Monitor progress using:
• Check Understanding
• Additional Examples
• Standardized Test Prep

After the Lesson
Assess knowledge using:
• Lesson Quiz
• Computer Test Generator CD

2 EXAMPLE **Finding the Next Terms in a Sequence**

Find the next three terms of the sequence $2, -6, 18, -54, \ldots$

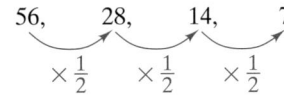

$$2, \quad -6, \quad 18, \quad -54$$
$$\times (-3) \quad \times (-3) \quad \times (-3)$$

The common ratio is -3. The next three terms are $-54(-3) = 162$, $162(-3) = -486$, and $-486(-3) = 1458$.

✓ **Check Understanding** **2** Find the next three terms of each sequence.
a. $1, 3, 9, 27, \ldots$ **b.** $120, -60, 30, -15, \ldots$ **c.** $1.1, 2.2, 4.4, 8.8, \ldots$
81, 243, 729 **7.5, −3.75, 1.875** **17.6, 35.2, 70.4**

You can find the common difference or common ratio to determine whether a sequence is arithmetic or geometric. If there is no common difference or common ratio, the sequence is neither arithmetic nor geometric.

3 EXAMPLE **Arithmetic or Geometric Sequence**

Determine whether each sequence is arithmetic or geometric.
a. $-7, -5, -3, -1, \ldots$

$$-7, \quad -5, \quad -3, \quad -1$$
$$+2 \quad +2 \quad +2$$

The sequence has a common difference. The sequence is arithmetic.

b. $56, 28, 14, 7, \ldots$

$$56, \quad 28, \quad 14, \quad 7$$
$$\times \tfrac{1}{2} \quad \times \tfrac{1}{2} \quad \times \tfrac{1}{2}$$

The sequence has a common ratio. The sequence is geometric.

✓ **Check Understanding** **3** Determine whether each sequence is arithmetic or geometric.
a. $2, 4, 6, 8, \ldots$ **arithmetic** **b.** $2, 4, 8, 16, \ldots$ **geometric c.** $1, 3, 5, 7, \ldots$ **arithmetic**

OBJECTIVE
2 **Using a Formula**

You can use the common ratio of a geometric sequence to write a function rule for the sequence. Consider the sequence $2, 6, 18, 54, \ldots$ Its common ratio is 3.

Let n = the term number in a sequence.

Let $A(n)$ = the value of the nth term of the sequence.

$A(1) = 2$

$A(2) = 2 \cdot 3 = 2 \cdot 3^1$

$A(3) = 2 \cdot 3 \cdot 3 = 2 \cdot 3^2$ **Note that each exponent is one less than its term number.**

$A(4) = 2 \cdot 3 \cdot 3 \cdot 3 = 2 \cdot 3^3$

$\vdots$

$A(n) = 2 \cdot 3 \cdot 3 \cdot 3 \cdot 3 \ldots \cdot 3 = 2 \cdot 3^{n-1}$

In general, you can write a function rule using the first term, the term number, and the common ratio. For the sequence above, the rule is $A(n) = 2 \cdot 3^{n-1}$.

Math Background

The common ratio of a geometric sequence can be found as the ratio of successive terms. Just as with arithmetic sequences, the sequence can be finite or infinite. The sum of the terms of a sequence, usually written by using sigma, Σ, is called a series.

OBJECTIVE
1 **Teaching Notes**

1 EXAMPLE **Alternative Method**

To find the common ratio, have students write each term over the term to its left and simplify. Start with writing the second term over the first term. Repeat for each term, checking to be sure all the ratios simplify to the same ratio. The simplified ratio is the *common ratio*.

2 EXAMPLE **Math Tip**

Point out to students that when the signs of the terms in a sequence alternate between positive and negative, the common ratio is negative.

Additional Examples

1 Find the common ratio of each sequence.
a. $3, -15, 75, -375, \ldots$ **−5**
b. $3, \frac{3}{2}, \frac{3}{4}, \frac{3}{8}, \ldots$ **$\frac{1}{2}$**

2 Find the next three terms of the sequence $5, -10, 20, -40, \ldots$
80, −160, 320

3 Determine whether each sequence is arithmetic or geometric.
a. $162, 54, 18, 6, \ldots$ **geometric**
b. $98, 101, 104, 107, \ldots$
arithmetic

Reaching All Students

Below Level Remind students that a sequence may have a pattern and still not be an arithmetic or geometric sequence. Discuss the sequence 1, 4, 9, 16, 25, . . . to illustrate this.	**Advanced Learners** Ask students how many bounces it will take the ball in Example 5 to bounce less than 1 cm.	**Alternative Method** See note on page 425. **Error Prevention** See note on page 427.

425

4 **EXAMPLE** **Technology Tip**

Have students input the sequence into a spreadsheet. In cell A1 input 5. In cell A2 input = A1 * −2, and press the "Enter" key. Highlight cell A2. Grab the bottom right corner of the cell and drag downward to fill the column. Show students how they can find any number term just by looking at the row labeled with that particular number.

5 **EXAMPLE** **Teaching Tip**

Explain to students that they should evaluate the rule for $n = 5$ because $n = 1$ represents the initial height of the ball before the first bounce.

 Additional Examples

4 Find the first, fifth, and tenth terms of the sequence that has the rule $A(n) = -3(2)^{n-1}$. −3, −48, −1536

5 Suppose you drop a tennis ball from a height of 2 meters. On each bounce, the ball reaches a height that is 75% of its previous height. Write a rule for the height the ball reaches on each bounce. In centimeters, what height will the ball reach on its third bounce? $A(n) = 200 \cdot 0.75^{n-1}$; 84.375 cm

Closure

Ask students to write a rule for a geometric sequence and a rule for an arithmetic sequence without looking in their books. Then have them label the parts of the rule with *nth term, first term, common ratio* or *difference*, and *term number*. They can compare their work with the diagram in the book.

 Key Concepts

Rule	Geometric Sequence

$$A(n) = a \cdot r^{n-1}$$

nth term $first$ term $common$ ratio term number

4 **EXAMPLE** **Finding Terms of a Sequence**

Find the first, fifth, and tenth terms of the sequence that has the rule $A(n) = 5(-2)^{n-1}$.

first term: $A(1) = 5$

fifth term: $A(5) = 5(-2)^{5-1} = 5(-2)^4 = 5(16) = 80$

tenth term: $A(10) = 5(-2)^{10-1} = 5(-2)^9 = 5(-512) = -2560$

✓ **Check Understanding** **4** Find the first, sixth, and twelfth terms of each sequence.
a. $A(n) = 4 \cdot 3^{n-1}$ 4; 972; 708,588 **b.** $A(n) = -2 \cdot 5^{n-1}$ −2; −6250; −97,656,250

You can write and evaluate a rule for a geometric sequence that models a real-world situation.

5 **EXAMPLE** **Real-World** 🌐 **Problem Solving**

Sports You drop a rubber ball from a height of 1 meter and it bounces back to lower and lower heights. Each curved path has 80% the height of the previous path. Write a rule for the height of each successive path. What height will the ball reach at the top of the fifth path?

Draw a diagram to help understand the problem.

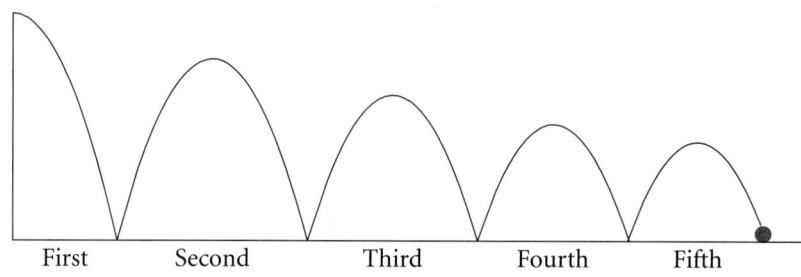

First   Second   Third   Fourth   Fifth

The height of the first path is 100 cm. So the height is 100 cm for the first term, with $n = 1$. The height of the fifth path is given by the term $n = 5$. The common ratio is 80%, or 0.8.

A rule for the sequence is $A(n) = 100 \cdot 0.8^{n-1}$.

$A(n) = 100 \cdot 0.8^{n-1}$	Use the sequence to find the height of the fifth path.
$A(5) = 100 \cdot 0.8^{5-1}$	Substitute 5 for n.
$= 100 \cdot 0.8^4$	Simplify exponents.
$= 100 \cdot 0.4096$	Evaluate powers.
$= 40.96$	Simplify.

The height of the fourth bounce will be 40.96 cm.

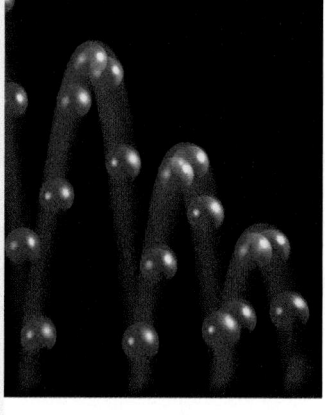

Real-World 🌐 **Connection**

Strobe-light photography is often used to highlight details of the motion of objects.

Check Understanding **5** **Basketball** You drop a basketball from a height of 2 meters. Each curved path has 56% of the height of the previous path. Using the height in centimeters, write a rule for the sequence. What height will the basketball reach at the top of the fourth path (when $n = 4$)? Round to the nearest tenth of a centimeter.

$A(n) = 200 \cdot 0.56^{n-1}$; 35.1 cm

EXERCISES

For more practice, see *Extra Practice*.

Practice and Problem Solving

A **Practice by Example**

Example 1
(page 424)

Find the common ratio of each sequence.

1. 2, 8, 32, 128, . . . **4**
2. −3, −12, −48, −192, . . . **4**
3. 70, 7, 0.7, 0.07, . . . **0.1**
4. 8, 20, 50, 125, . . . **2.50**
5. −80, 20, −5, 1.25, . . . **−0.25**
6. 0.45, 0.9, 1.8, 3.6, . . . **2**

Example 2
(page 425)

7. 40, 80, 160
8. 48, 96, 192
9. 20.25, 30.375, 45.5625

Find the next three terms of each sequence. **7–9. See left.**

7. 2.5, 5, 10, 20, . . .
8. 3, 6, 12, 24, . . .
9. 4, 6, 9, 13.5, . . .
10. −8, 4, −2, 1, . . .
   −0.5, 0.25, −0.125
11. 225, 45, 9, 1.8 . . .
   0.36, 0.072, 0.0144
12. −3, 6, −12, 24, . . .
   −48, 96, −192

Example 3
(page 425)

13. geometric
14. arithmetic
15. geometric

Determine whether each sequence is *arithmetic* or *geometric*. **13–15. See left.**

13. 2, 14, 98, 686, . . .
14. 12, 8, 4, 0, . . .
15. 9, −36, 144, −576, . . .
16. −5, −10, −15, −20, . . .
   arithmetic
17. 0.6, 1.3, 2, 2.7, . . .
   arithmetic
18. 9, 12, 16, $21\frac{1}{3}$, . . .
   geometric

Example 4
(page 426)

19. 5; 135; 10,935
20. −5; −135; −10,935
21. 5; −135; −10,935

Find the first, fourth, and eighth terms of each sequence. **19–21. See left.**

19. $A(n) = 5 \cdot 3^{n-1}$
20. $A(n) = -5 \cdot 3^{n-1}$
21. $A(n) = 5 \cdot (-3)^{n-1}$
22. $A(n) = 0.5 \cdot 3^{n-1}$
   0.5; 13.5, 1093.5
23. $A(n) = -2 \cdot 5^{n-1}$
   −2; −250; −156,250
24. $A(n) = -1.1 \cdot (-4)^{n-1}$
   −1.1; 70.4; 18,022.4

Example 5
(page 426)

25. $A(n) = 6 \cdot 0.5^{n-1}$; 0.375
26. $A(n) = -6 \cdot 2^{n-1}$; −3072
27. $A(n) = 7 \cdot (1.1)^{n-1}$; 9.317

Write a rule and find the given term in each geometric sequence described below.

25. What is the fifth term when the first term is 6 and the common ratio is 0.5?

26. What is the tenth term when the first term is −6 and the common ratio is 2?

27. What is the fourth term when the first term is 7 and the common ratio is 1.1?

28. What is the seventh term when the first term is 1 and the common ratio is −4?
   $A(n) = 1 \cdot (-4)^{n-1}$; 4096

29. You drop a handball from a height of 1 meter. Each curved path has 64% of the height of the previous path. **a.** $A(n) = 100 \cdot (0.64)^{n-1}$
   a. Write a rule for the sequence using centimeters. The initial height is when $n = 1$.
   b. What height will the ball reach at the top of the sixth path? **about 10.74 cm**

B **Apply Your Skills**

Find the next three terms of each sequence. Then write a rule for each sequence.

30. 216, 72, 24, 8, . . . $2\frac{2}{3}, \frac{8}{9}, \frac{8}{27};$
   $A(n) = 216 \cdot \left(\frac{1}{3}\right)^{n-1}$
31. 625, 125, 25, 5, . . .   1, 0.2, 0.04;
   $A(n) = 625 \cdot (0.2)^{n-1}$
32. 0.1, 0.9, 8.1, 72.9, . . .
   656.1, 5904.9, 53,144.1; $A(n) = 0.1 \cdot 9^{n-1}$
33. 16, −8, 4, −2, . . .   1, −0.5, 0.25; $A(n) = 16 \cdot (-0.5)^{n-1}$

34. **Open-Ended** Write four terms of a geometric sequence. Then write a rule for your sequence. **Check students' work.**

Problem Solving Hint

For Exercises 30 and 31, making a list of the terms of a sequence, and their factors, can help you write a rule.

35. **Writing** How can you determine whether a sequence is arithmetic or geometric? **If all consecutive terms have a common difference, the sequence is arithmetic. If all consecutive terms have a common ratio, the sequence is geometric.**

Lesson 8-6   Geometric Sequences   **427**

3. Practice

Assignment Guide

1 **Objective**
  A **B** Core 1–18, 30–35, 37–40
  C Extension 45–47

2 **Objective**
  A **B** Core 19–29, 36, 41–43
  C Extension 44, 48–50

Standardized Test Prep 51–54

Mixed Review 55–72

Error Prevention

Exercises 1–6 Suggest to students that they check their work by finding the ratio between more than two pairs of consecutive terms.

Exercises 13–18 Remind students that the difference between consecutive terms in an arithmetic sequence is constant.

Enrichment 8-6

Reteaching 8-6

Practice 8-6

Practice 8-6   Geometric Sequences

Find the next three terms of each sequence.

1. 4, 12, 36, 108, . . .
2. 2, −8, 32, −128, . . .
3. 18, 9, $\frac{9}{2}$, $\frac{9}{4}$, . . .
4. 1, $-\frac{1}{3}$, $\frac{1}{9}$, $-\frac{1}{27}$, . . .
5. −2, 20, −200, 2000, . . .
6. 30, −10, $\frac{10}{3}$, $-\frac{10}{9}$, . . .
7. $\frac{1}{3}$, $\frac{1}{6}$, $\frac{1}{12}$, $\frac{1}{24}$, . . .
8. 20, 4, $\frac{4}{5}$, $\frac{4}{25}$, . . .
9. −100, −40, −16, −6.4, . . .
10. 40, 20, 10, 5, . . .

Determine whether each sequence is arithmetic or geometric.

11. −8, −10, −12.5, −15.625, . . .
12. 5, 1, −3, −7, . . .
13. $1\frac{3}{5}, \frac{4}{5}, \frac{2}{25}$, . . .
14. −0.2, −0.02, −0.002, −0.0002, . . .
15. −10, −5, 0, 5, . . .
16. 6, −3, $\frac{3}{2}$, $-\frac{3}{4}$, . . .

Write a rule for each sequence.

17. 4, 12, 36, 108, . . .
18. 2, −8, 32, −128, . . .
19. 18, 9, $\frac{9}{2}$, $\frac{9}{4}$, . . .
20. 1, $-\frac{1}{3}$, $\frac{1}{9}$, $-\frac{1}{27}$, . . .
21. −2, 20, −200, 2000, . . .
22. 30, −10, $\frac{10}{3}$, $-\frac{10}{9}$, . . .
23. 3, 4, 16, 64, . . .
24. 6, 12, 24, 48, . . .
25. 125, 25, 5, 1, . . .
26. 50, 25, 12.5, 6.25, . . .

Find the first, fourth, and eighth terms of each sequence.

27. $A(n) = 2 \cdot 3^{n-1}$
28. $A(n) = 3 \cdot 4^{n-1}$
29. $A(n) = 3 \cdot 2^{n-1}$
30. $A(n) = -1 \cdot 5^{n-1}$
31. $A(n) = 4 \cdot 2^{n-1}$
32. $A(n) = \frac{1}{2} \cdot 2^{n-1}$
33. $A(n) = 0.1 \cdot 4^{n-1}$
34. $A(n) = -2.1 \cdot 3^{n-1}$
35. $A(n) = 10 \cdot 5^{n-1}$

Write a rule and find the given term in each geometric sequence described below.

36. What is the sixth term when the first term is 4 and the common ratio is 3?
37. What is the fifth term when the first term is −2 and the common ratio is $-\frac{1}{2}$?
38. What is the tenth term when the first term is 3 and the common ratio is 1.2?
39. What is the fourth term when the first term is 5 and the common ratio is 6?
40. Suppose a manufacturer invented a computer chip in 1976 that had a computational speed of x. The company improves its chips so that every 3 years, the chip doubles in speed. What would the chip's speed have been for the year 2002? Write your solution in terms of x.

Algebra 1 Chapter 8   Lesson 8-6 Practice   **7**

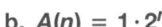

36. **Paper Folding** You can fold a sheet of paper in half, making 2 rectangles. If you fold the paper in half again, you divide the paper into 4 rectangles. Suppose you were to keep folding the paper and making more rectangles.
    a. Copy and complete the table at the right.
    b. Write a rule to model this situation.
    b. $A(n) = 1 \cdot 2^n$
    c. Suppose you could continue to fold the paper. How many rectangles would would there be if you could fold the paper 10 times?
    1024 rectangles

Number of Folds	Number of Rectangles
0	1
1	2
2	4
3	8 ■
4	16 ■
5	32 ■

Determine whether each sequence is *arithmetic, geometric,* or *neither.* Find the next three terms of each sequence.

37. $11, 9, 7, 5, \ldots$ arithmetic; $3, 1, -1$

38. $7, 6, 4, 1, \ldots$ neither; $-3, -8, -14$

39. $18, 9, 4.5, 2.25, \ldots$
    geometric; $1.125, 0.5625, 0.28125$

40. $12, 14, 16, 18, \ldots$
    arithmetic; $20, 22, 24$

41. **Physics** On the first swing, a pendulum swings through an arc of length 36 centimeters. On each successive swing, the length of the arc is 90% of the length of the previous swing.
    a. Write a rule to model this situation. $A(n) = 36 \cdot (0.9)^{n-1}$
    b. **Critical Thinking** What value of n would you use to find the length of the arc on the sixth swing? Explain. **See left below.**
    c. Find the length of the arc on the sixth swing, to the nearest tenth of a centimeter. **21.3 cm**

42. a. **Geometry** What fraction of each figure is shaded? **a–b. See below.**
    b. Rewrite each fraction from part (a) in the form $2^{■}$.
    c. Write a rule that relates the figure number n to the shaded rectangle r. $r = 2^{-n}$
    d. What portion of the square would be shaded in Figure 10? 2^{-10} or $\frac{1}{2^{10}}$

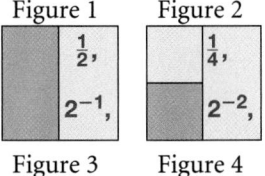
Figure 1 $\frac{1}{2},$ $2^{-1},$ Figure 2 $\frac{1}{4},$ $2^{-2},$

43. **Reasoning** Can zero be a term of a geometric sequence that has terms that are not zero? Explain. **See left below.**

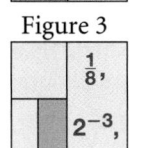 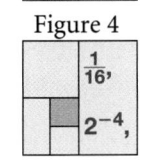
Figure 3 $\frac{1}{8},$ $2^{-3},$ Figure 4 $\frac{1}{16},$ $2^{-4},$

C Challenge

41b. 6; $n = 1$ corresponds to the first swing, because $A(1) = 36$.

43. No; if a term were 0, then all terms would be 0 because you multiply a term to get the next term.

44. **Fractal Geometry** The figures below show the first four steps in making Sierpinski's Triangle.

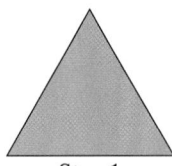 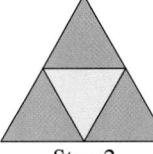 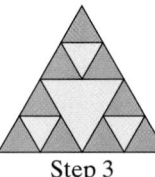 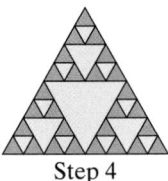
Step 1   Step 2   Step 3   Step 4

a. **Patterns** What fraction of each step is shaded? $1, \frac{3}{4}, \frac{9}{16}, \frac{27}{64}$
b. Use your answer from part (a) to write a rule that relates the step number n to the fraction r of the figure that is shaded. $r = 1 \cdot \left(\frac{3}{4}\right)^{n-1}$
c. What fraction of Step 6 would be shaded? $\frac{243}{1024}$
d. **Patterns** What fraction of each step is *not* shaded? $0, \frac{1}{4}, \frac{7}{16}, \frac{37}{64}$
e. Write a rule that relates the step number n to the fraction r of the figure that is *not* shaded. $r = \left[1 - 1 \cdot \left(\frac{3}{4}\right)^{n-1}\right]$
f. What fraction of Step 8 would *not* be shaded? $\frac{14,197}{16,384}$

428   Chapter 8   Exponents and Exponential Functions

45. x; x^5, x^6, x^7

46. $3x$; $27x^4$, $81x^5$, $243x^6$

47. xy^2; x^5y^9, x^6y^{11}, x^7y^{13}

48. ab; $2a^4b^2$, $2a^5b^3$, $2a^6b^4$

Find each common ratio. Then find the next three terms in each sequence.

45. $x, x^2, x^3, x^4, \ldots$

46. $\frac{1}{3}, x, 3x^2, 9x^3, \ldots$

47. $xy, x^2y^3, x^3y^5, x^4y^7, \ldots$

48. $\frac{2}{b^2}, \frac{2a}{b}, 2a^2, 2a^3b, \ldots$

49. $2 \times 10^7, 1.2 \times 10^6, 7.2 \times 10^4, 4.32 \times 10^3, \ldots$
6×10^{-2}; 2.592×10^2, 1.5552×10^1, 9.3312×10^{-1}

50. What term is 512 in the geometric sequence with the first term 2 and the common ratio 4? **5th**

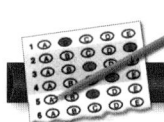

Standardized Test Prep

Multiple Choice

54. [2] Day 1   350
        Day 2   700
        Day 3   1400
        Day 4   2800
        Day 5   5600
        (OR equivalent
        explanation)

[1] answer with no
    work shown

Take It to the NET

Online lesson quiz at
www.PHSchool.com
Web Code: aea-0806

Short Response

51. Which set of numbers continues the pattern 27, 9, 3, 1, ...? **D**

A. $-3, -9, -27$

B. $-\frac{1}{3}, -\frac{1}{6}, -\frac{1}{9}$

C. $\frac{1}{3}, \frac{1}{6}, \frac{1}{9}$

D. $\frac{1}{3}, \frac{1}{9}, \frac{1}{27}$

52. Charlie is stacking cans at a grocery store. The picture shows the first four tiers. How many cans are there in 6 rows? **H**

F. 36 cans

G. 61 cans

H. 91 cans

I. 729 cans

53. Which equation could you use to find the next term in the pattern 3, 6, 12, 24, 48, ...? **B**

A. $A(n) = 3^{n-1}$

B. $A(n) = 3(2)^{n-1}$

C. $A(n) = 3 \cdot 2n$

D. $A(n) = 3n^2$

54. In a research laboratory, bacteria of a certain species double in number each day. If the number of bacteria at the beginning of a day is 350, how many bacteria will there be at the beginning of the 5th day? Show your work. **See left above.**

Mixed Review

Lesson 8-5

Simplify each expression.

55. $\left(\frac{a^2}{a^3}\right)^{-4}$ a^4

56. $\left(\frac{1}{2}\right)^{-4}$ 16

57. $\left(\frac{x^2z}{z^{-3}}\right)^{-5}$ $\frac{1}{x^{10}z^{20}}$

58. $\left(\frac{m^{-3}}{n^4}\right)^0$ 1

59. $\left(\frac{8}{9}\right)^{-2}$ $\frac{81}{64}$

60. $\left(\frac{m^4}{m^2}\right)^{-7}$ $\frac{1}{m^{14}}$

61. $\left(\frac{pq^0}{p^4}\right)^5$ $\frac{1}{p^{15}}$

62. $\left(\frac{c^2d^{-2}}{d^3}\right)^{-1}$ $\frac{d^5}{c^2}$

63. Write 0.002467 in scientific notation. 2.467×10^{-3}

Lesson 8-2

64. **Water Conservation** The Folsom Dam in California holds 1 million acre-feet of water in a reservoir. An acre-foot of water is the amount of water that covers an acre to the depth of one foot, or 326,000 gal. How many gallons are in the reservoir? Write your answer in scientific notation. 3.26×10^{11} **gal**

Lesson 5-5

Write an equation of the direct variation that includes the given point.

65. $(3, 8)$ $y = \frac{8}{3}x$

66. $(-5, 2)$ $y = -\frac{2}{5}x$

67. $(6, -7)$ $y = -\frac{7}{6}x$

68. $(-3, -5)$ $y = \frac{5}{3}x$

69. $(4, 7)$ $y = \frac{7}{4}x$

70. $(-16, 4)$ $y = -\frac{1}{4}x$

71. $(9, 5)$ $y = \frac{5}{9}x$

72. $(4, -2)$ $y = -\frac{1}{2}x$

Standardized Test Prep

 **Resources**

For additional practice with a variety of test item formats:
- Standardized Test Prep, p. 451
- Test-Taking Strategies, p. 446
- Test-Taking Strategies with Transparencies

Exercise 51 Ask students if the sequence is geometric or arithmetic. Point out that unless they are multiplying by a negative number, the terms will not be negative. Since the terms in the pattern are all powers of 3, the terms in the continuing pattern will also be powers of 3.

1. Plan

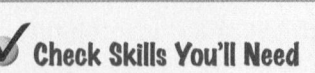

Lesson Preview

 **Check Skills You'll Need**

Slope-Intercept Form
Lesson 6-2: Example 4
Exercises 28–39
Extra Practice, p. 707

Zero and Negative Exponents
Lesson 8-1: Example 1
Exercises 1–12
Extra Practice, p. 709

Lesson Resources

📁 **Teaching Resources**
Practice, Reteaching, Enrichment
Checkpoint Quiz 2

👥 **Reaching All Students**
Practice Workbook 8-7
Spanish Practice Workbook 8-7
Reading and Math Literacy 8C
Spanish Reading & Literacy 8C
Spanish Checkpoint Quiz 2
Basic Algebra Planning Guide 8-7

⏲ **Presentation Assistant Plus!**
Transparencies
• Check Skills You'll Need 8-7
• Additional Examples 8-7
• Student Edition Answers 8-7
• Lesson Quiz 8-7
PH Presentation Pro CD 8-7

**PRENTICE HALL
ASSESSMENT SYSTEM**

Checkpoint Quiz 2
Computer Test Generator CD

💿 **Technology**
Resource Pro® CD-ROM
Computer Test Generator CD
Prentice Hall Presentation Pro CD

🖥 **www.PHSchool.com**
Student Site
• Teacher Web Code: aek-5500
• Self-grading Lesson Quiz
Teacher Center
• Lesson Planner
• Resources

Plus

430

Exponential Functions

4.04   Graph and evaluate exponential functions to solve problems.

 North Carolina Objectives

Lesson Preview

What You'll Learn

OBJECTIVE 1 To evaluate exponential functions

OBJECTIVE 2 To graph exponential functions

. . . And Why

To use an exponential model for a population of rabbits, as in Example 2

✓ **Check Skills You'll Need**   (For help, go to Lessons 6-2 and 8-1.)

Graph each function. 1–3. See back of book.

1. $y = 3x$ **2.** $y = 4x$ **3.** $y = -2x$

Simplify each expression.

4. 3^2 9   **5.** 5^{-3} $\frac{1}{125}$ **6.** $2 \cdot 3^4$ 162

7. $2 \cdot 3^{-2}$ $\frac{2}{9}$ **8.** $3 \cdot 2^{-1}$ $\frac{3}{2}$ **9.** $10 \cdot 3^2$ 90

New Vocabulary   • exponential function

🕮 **Interactive lesson includes instant self-check, tutorials, and activities.**

OBJECTIVE
1 Evaluating Exponential Functions

The rules you wrote in Lesson 8-6 to describe geometric sequences, such as $A(n) = 3 \cdot 4^{n-1}$, are examples of exponential functions.

🔑 **Key Concepts**

Definition	Exponential Function

An **exponential function** is a function in the form $y = a \cdot b^x$, where a is a nonzero constant, b is greater than 0 and not equal to 1, and x is a real number.

Examples $y = 0.5 \cdot 2^x$ $f(x) = -2 \cdot 0.5^x$

You can evaluate an exponential function for given values of the domain to find the corresponding values of the range.

1 EXAMPLE   **Evaluating an Exponential Function**

Evaluate each exponential function.

a. $y = 5^x$ for $x = 2, 3, 4$

b. $t(n) = 4 \cdot 3^n$ for the domain $\{-3, 6\}$

Need Help?
You can review domain and range in Lesson 5-2.

x	5^x	y
2	$5^2 = 25$	25
3	$5^3 = 125$	125
4	$5^4 = 625$	625

n	$4 \cdot 3^n$	$t(n)$
-3	$4 \cdot 3^{-3} = 4 \cdot \frac{1}{27} = \frac{4}{27}$	$\frac{4}{27}$
6	$4 \cdot 3^6 = 4 \cdot 729 = 2916$	2916

 ✓ **Check Understanding** **1** Evaluate each exponential function for the domain $\{-2, 0, 3\}$.

a. $y = 4^x$
$\frac{1}{16}$, 1, 64

b. $f(x) = 10 \cdot 5^x$
$\frac{2}{5}$, 10, 1250

c. $g(x) = -2 \cdot 3^x$
$-\frac{2}{9}$, -2, -54

430   Chapter 8 Exponents and Exponential Functions

⏱ **Ongoing Assessment and Intervention**

Before the Lesson	During the Lesson	After the Lesson
Diagnose prerequisite skills using:	**Monitor progress using:**	**Assess knowledge using:**
• Check Skills You'll Need	• Check Understanding	• Lesson Quiz
	• Additional Examples	• Computer Test Generator CD
	• Standardized Test Prep	• Chapter Checkpoint 2 (p. 435)

You can evaluate exponential functions to solve real-world problems.

2 EXAMPLE Real-World Problem Solving

Biology Suppose 20 rabbits are taken to an island. The rabbit population then triples every half year. The function $f(x) = 20 \cdot 3^x$, where x is the number of half-year periods, models this situation. How many rabbits would there be after 2 years?

$$f(x) = 20 \cdot 3^x$$
$$= 20 \cdot 3^4 \quad \text{In 2 years, there are 4 half years. Evaluate the function for } x = 4.$$
$$= 20 \cdot 81 \quad \text{Simplify powers.}$$
$$= 1620 \quad \text{Simplify.}$$

● After two years, there would be 1620 rabbits.

Real-World Connection

Rabbits were brought to Australia in 1860. Their numbers increased exponentially.

✓**Check Understanding** ② Suppose 10 animals are taken to an island, and then the population of these animals quadruples every year. Use the function $f(x) = 10 \cdot 4^x$. How many animals would there be after 6 years? **40,960 animals**

OBJECTIVE
2   **Graphing Exponential Functions**

Here are two graphs that show what exponential functions generally look like.

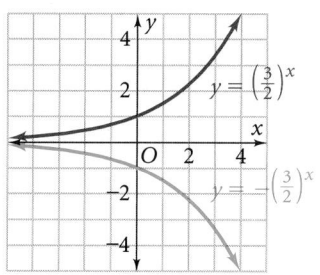   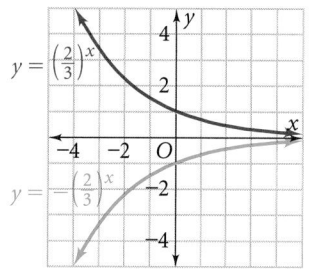

To graph an exponential function, make a table of values. Plot the points. Then join the points to form a smooth curve.

3 EXAMPLE Graphs of Exponential Functions

Graph $y = 3 \cdot 2^x$.

x	$3 \cdot 2^x$	(x, y)
−2	$3 \cdot 2^{-2} = \frac{3}{2^2} = \frac{3}{4}$	$\left(-2, \frac{3}{4}\right)$
−1	$3 \cdot 2^{-1} = \frac{3}{2^1} = 1\frac{1}{2}$	$\left(-1, 1\frac{1}{2}\right)$
0	$3 \cdot 2^0 = 3 \cdot 1 = 3$	$(0, 3)$
1	$3 \cdot 2^1 = 3 \cdot 2 = 6$	$(1, 6)$
2	$3 \cdot 2^2 = 3 \cdot 4 = 12$	$(2, 12)$

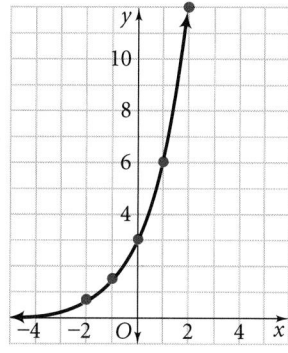

✓**Check Understanding** ③ Graph each exponential function. **a–c. See margin p. 432.**
a. $y = 0.5 \cdot 2^x$ **b.** $y = -0.5 \cdot 2^x$ **c.** $y = 2 \cdot (0.5)^x$

Lesson 8-7 Exponential Functions   **431**

👥 **Reaching All Students**

Below Level Ask students what $f(x)$ and x represent in the function $f(x) = 1.5^x$ in Example 4. Help them to see what effect the value of the base, 1.5, has on the graph of the function.	**Advanced Learners** Lead students in a discussion of the graph of $y = a^x$, when a is greater than or equal to 1 and when a is between 0 and 1.	**Error Prevention** See note on page 433.

2. Teach

Professional Development

Math Background

Exponential functions can model many naturally occurring phenomena, such as the growth of a colony of bacteria and the decay of radioactive polonium.

OBJECTIVE
1 **Teaching Notes**

Additional Examples

① Evaluate each exponential function.
a. $y = 3^x$ for $x = 2, 3, 4$ **9, 27, 81**
b. $p(q) = 3 \cdot 4^x$ for the domain $\{-2, 3\}$ $\frac{3}{16}$, **192**

② Suppose two mice live in a barn. If the number of mice quadruples every 3 months, how many mice will be in the barn after 2 years? **131,072**

OBJECTIVE
2 **Teaching Notes**

Additional Examples

③ Graph $y = 2 \cdot 3^x$. **See back of book.**

④ The function $f(x) = 1.25^x$ models the increase in size of an image being copied over and over at 125% on a photocopier. Graph the function. **See back of book.**

Closure

Ask students to explain why $y = x^4$ is not an exponential function. The exponent, not the base, must be a variable. Have students explain how the graphs of $y = x^4$ and $y = 4^x$ differ. The graph of $y = x^4$ is a u-shape in which the y-values increase on both sides of the y-axis as you move away from the y-axis. The graph of $y = 4^x$ is a smooth curve in which the y-values increase quickly as you move to the right side of the y-axis and decrease slowly as you move to the left of the y-axis.

431

Assignment Guide

1 Objective
  Ⓐ Ⓑ **Core** 1–11, 25–34, 36–42
  Ⓒ **Extension** 44–47

2 Objective
  Ⓐ Ⓑ **Core** 12–24, 35, 43
  Ⓒ **Extension** 48–50

Standardized Test Prep 51–55

Mixed Review 56–65

Careers

Exercises 9–11 A financial planner helps people plan how to manage and invest their money to pay for present and future needs. Investments may be used to earn money for a business venture, to buy property, to save for retirement, or to pay for any large purchase.

Enrichment 8-7
Reteaching 8-7
Practice 8-7

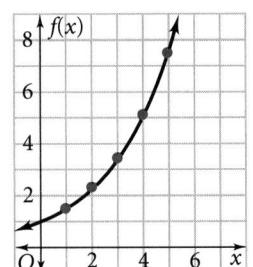

You can graph exponential functions to model real-world situations.

4 **EXAMPLE** **Real-World** 🌐 **Problem Solving**

Photocopying Many photocopiers allow you to choose how large you want an image to be. The function $f(x) = 1.5^x$ models the new size of an image being copied over and over at 150%, where x is the number of enlargements. Graph the function.

x	1.5^x	(x, f(x))
1	$1.5^1 = 1.5$	(1, 1.5)
2	$1.5^2 = 2.25 \approx 2.3$	(2, 2.3)
3	$1.5^3 = 3.375 \approx 3.4$	(3, 3.4)
4	$1.5^4 = 5.0625 \approx 5.1$	(4, 5.1)
5	$1.5^5 = 7.59375 \approx 7.6$	(5, 7.6)

✓ **Check Understanding** **4** **a.** You can also make images that are smaller than the original on a photocopier. The function $y = 0.9^x$ models the new size of an image being copied over and over at 90%. Graph the function. **See margin.**

  b. **Critical Thinking** In both models, what does $f(0)$ represent?
  $f(0) = 1$, so copies are made at the same size as the original, or at 100%.

EXERCISES

For more practice, see *Extra Practice*.

Practice and Problem Solving

Ⓐ **Practice by Example**

Example 1
(page 430)

Evaluate each function rule for the given value.

1. $f(x) = 6^x$ for $x = 3$ **216**

2. $g(t) = 2 \cdot 3^t$ for $t = -2$ **$\frac{2}{9}$**

3. $y = 20 \cdot (0.5)^x$ for $x = 3$ **2.5**

4. $h(w) = 0.5 \cdot 4^w$ for $w = 3$ **32**

5. $y = 50 \cdot (0.3)^x$ for $x = 2$ **4.5**

6. $f(x) = 1.8 \cdot 2^x$ for $x = 6$ **115.2**

7. $y = 100 \cdot \left(\frac{1}{2}\right)^x$ for $x = -4$ **1600**

8. $y = 9 \cdot \left(\frac{5}{2}\right)^x$ for $x = -3$ **0.576**

Example 2
(page 431)

9. **Finance** Suppose an investment of $10,000 doubles in value every 13 years. How much is the investment worth after 52 years? After 65 years? **See left.**

9. $160,000; $320,000

10. **Finance** Suppose an investment of $500 doubles in value every 15 years. How much is the investment worth after 30 years? After 45 years? **See left.**

10. $2000; $4000

11. **Finance** Suppose an investment of $2000 doubles in value every 8 years. How much is the investment worth after 24 years? After 32 years? **$16,000, $32,000**

Example 3
(page 431)

Match each table with the function that models the data.

12. $y = 3x$ **A**

13. $y = x^3$ **C**

14. $y = 3^x$ **B**

A.

x	y
1	3
2	6
3	9
4	12

B.

x	y
1	3
2	9
3	27
4	81

C.

x	y
1	1
2	8
3	27
4	64

432 Chapter 8 Exponents and Exponential Functions

pages 431–432
Check Understanding

3a.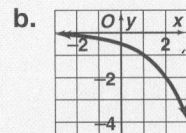

b.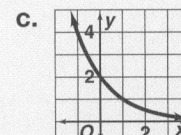

c. (graph)

4a.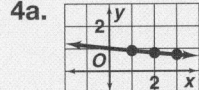

Match each function rule with the graph of the function.

15. $y = 2^x$ **B**   **16.** $y = -(2^x)$ **D**   **17.** $y = \left(\frac{1}{2}\right)^x$ **C**   **18.** $y = -\left(\frac{1}{2}\right)^x$ **A**

A.
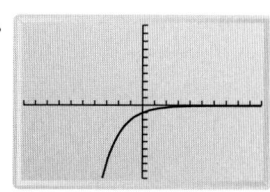

B.
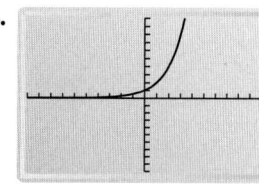

C.
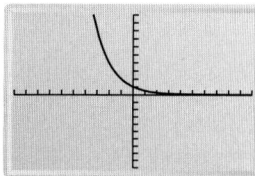

D.
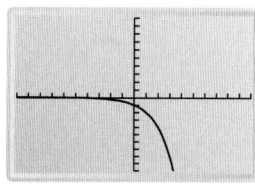

Graph each function. 19–22. See margin.

19. $y = 10 \cdot 2^x$ **20.** $y = 0.1 \cdot 2^x$ **21.** $y = \frac{1}{4} \cdot 2^x$ **22.** $y = 4^x$

24.
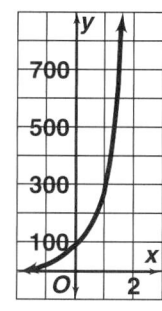

Example 4
(page 432)

23. Photocopying Suppose you are photocopying an image, reducing it to 85% its original size. The function $y = 0.85^x$ models the size of an image after x number of times it is reduced. Graph the function. **See margin.**

24. Science A population of 100 insects triples in size every month. The function $y = 100 \cdot 3^x$ models the population after x months. Graph the function. **See left above.**

 Apply Your Skills

Evaluate each function for the domain $\{-2, -1, 0, 1, 2, 3\}$. As the values of the domain increase, do the values of the range *increase* or *decrease*? 25–32. See left.

25. 0.04, 0.2, 1, 5, 25, 125; increase

26. 0.16, 0.4, 1, 2.5, 6.25, 15.625; increase

27. 100, 10, 1, 0.1, 0.01, 0.001; decrease

28. 0.3125, 1.25, 5, 20, 80, 320; increase

29. 4, 2, 1, 0.5, 0.25, 0.125; decrease

30. $\frac{9}{4}, \frac{3}{2}, 1, \frac{2}{3}, \frac{4}{9}, \frac{8}{27}$; **decrease**

31. 0.04, 0.4, 4, 40, 400, 4000; increase

32. 1111.$\overline{1}$, 333.$\overline{3}$, 100, 30, 9, 2.7; decrease

25. $f(x) = 5^x$ **26.** $y = 2.5^x$ **27.** $h(x) = 0.1^x$ **28.** $f(x) = 5 \cdot 4^x$

29. $y = 0.5^x$ **30.** $y = \left(\frac{2}{3}\right)^x$ **31.** $g(x) = 4 \cdot 10^x$ **32.** $y = 100 \cdot 0.3^x$

33. a. Open-Ended Write an exponential function for which values of y increase as values of x increase. **Answers may vary. Sample: $y = 2(3)^x$**
   b. Write an exponential function for which values of y decrease as values of x increase. **Answers may vary. Sample: $y = 2(0.3)^x$**

🌐 **34. Biology** A certain species of bacteria in a laboratory culture begins with 75 cells and doubles in number every 20 min.
   a. Copy, complete, and extend the table to find when there will be more than 5,000 bacteria cells. **See back of book.**

Time (min)	Number of 20-min Time Periods	Pattern	Number of Bacteria Cells
Initial	0	75	75
20	1	$75 \cdot 2$	$75 \cdot 2^{■} = ■$
40	■	$75 \cdot 2 \cdot 2$	$75 \cdot 2^{■} = ■$
60	■	■	$75 \cdot 2^{■} = ■$
■	■	■	■

   b. Write a function rule to model the situation.
   $y = 75 \cdot 2^x$, where x is the number of 20-min time periods

Lesson 8-7 Exponential Functions   **433**

Exercises 15–18 Suggest students review graphs from the lesson and make generalizations about their shapes before doing these exercises.

Technology Tip
Exercise 34 Suggest that students write an equation for the problem. Let x equal the number of 20-min time periods. Let y equal the number of bacteria cells. Students can check their answer to the exercise by using the **TABLE** function on a graphing calculator.

Error Prevention
Exercise 41 Some students may begin by multiplying 100 by 10 and then squaring the product. Remind them that the order of operations is: parentheses, exponents, multiplication and division, addition and subtraction.

pages 432–435   Exercises

19.
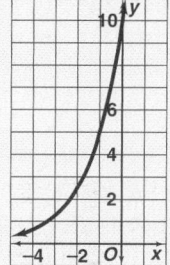

20.
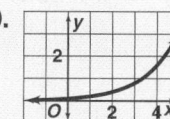

21.
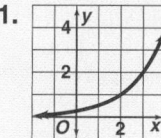

22.
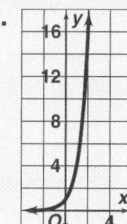

23.
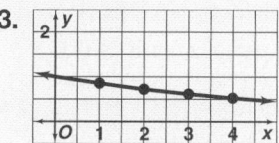

433

1. Evaluate each function rule for the given value.
   a. $y = 0.5^x$ for $x = 3$ **0.125**
   b. $f(x) = 4 \cdot 3^x$ for $x = -2$ $\frac{4}{9}$

2. Suppose an investment of $5000 doubles every 12 years.
   a. How much is the investment worth after 24 years? **$20,000**
   b. After 48 years? **$80,000**

3. Graph $y = 0.5 \cdot 3^x$.

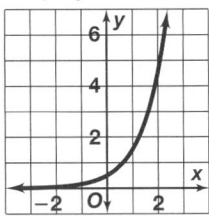

4. Graph $y = -0.5 \cdot 3^x$.

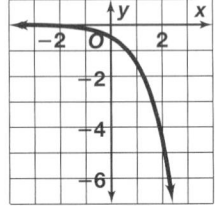

Alternative Assessment

Write $y = 3x$ on a transparency and project it with an overhead projector. Give students three seconds to look at the equation and write on their own paper whether the equation is *exponential* or *not exponential*. Repeat with various functions. Cover each function as you proceed. Include exponential, linear, quadratic, and absolute value functions. At the end of the activity, uncover the whole list of functions. Have students compare their answers with those of classmates and determine which are correct.

Standardized Test Prep

434

35c. No; there is no value of *x* for which $y = 0$.

d. If the base is >1, the graph gets steeper as the base increases. If the base is <1, the graph gets steeper as the base decreases.

37a.

x	y
1	−2
2	4
3	−8
4	16
5	−32

b. Every other value is negative. The absolute value of one term is double the previous term.

---

35. a. Graph $y = 2^x$, $y = 4^x$, and $y = (0.25)^x$. **See margin.**
    b. What point is on each graph? **(0, 1)**
    c. Does the graph of an exponential function intersect the *x*-axis? Explain.
    d. **Critical Thinking** How does the graph of an exponential function change as the base increases or decreases? **c–d. See left.**

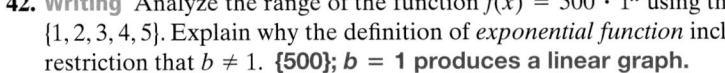

36. **Ecology** In 50 days, a water hyacinth can generate 1000 offspring (the number of plants is multiplied by 1000). **a. 1,000,000,000 plants**
    a. How many hyacinth plants could there be after 150 days?
    b. How many hyacinth plants could there be after 200 days? **1,000,000,000,000 plants**

37. a. Make a table of values for the domain $\{1, 2, 3, 4, 5\}$ of the function $y = (-2)^x$. **See left.**
    b. What pattern do you see in the outputs? **See left.**
    c. **Critical Thinking** Is $y = (-2)^x$ an exponential function? Justify your answer. **No; in $y = a \cdot b^x$, $b > 0$. $-2 < 0$, so it is not exponential.**

Which function is greater at the given value? 38. $y = x^5$ 39. $f(t) = 200 \cdot t^2$

38. $y = 5^x$ or $y = x^5$ at $x = 3$
39. $f(t) = 10 \cdot 2^t$ or $f(t) = 200 \cdot t^2$ at $t = 7$
40. $y = 3^x$ or $y = x^3$ at $x = 4$ $y = 3^x$
41. $f(x) = 2^x$ or $f(x) = 100x^2$ at $x = 10$ $f(x) = 100x^2$

42. **Writing** Analyze the range of the function $f(x) = 500 \cdot 1^x$ using the domain $\{1, 2, 3, 4, 5\}$. Explain why the definition of *exponential function* includes the restriction that $b \neq 1$. **{500}; $b = 1$ produces a linear graph.**

43. a. **Graphing Calculator** Graph the functions $y = x^2$ and $y = 2^x$.
    b. What happens to the graphs between $x = 1$ and $x = 3$? **a–b. See margin.**
    c. **Critical Thinking** How do you think the graph of $y = 6^x$ would compare to the graphs of $y = x^2$ and $y = 2^x$? **The graph of $y = 6^x$ is steeper than $y = x^2$ and $y = 2^x$.**

C Challenge

Solve each equation.

44. $3^x = 9$ **2**
45. $3^x = \frac{1}{27}$ **−3**
46. $2^x = 64$ **6**
47. $3 \cdot 2^x = 24$ **3**
48. $2 \cdot 3^x = 162$ **4**
49. $5 \cdot 2^x - 152 = 8$ **5**

50. Suppose $(0, 4)$ and $(2, 36)$ are on the graph of an exponential function.
    a. Use $(0, 4)$ in the general form of an exponential function $y = a \cdot b^x$ to find the value of the constant a. **4**
    b. Use your answer from part (a) along with $(2, 36)$ to find the value of the constant b. **3**
    c. Write a rule for the function. $y = 4 \cdot 3^x$
    d. Evaluate the function for $x = -2$ and $x = 4$. $\frac{4}{9}$, **324**

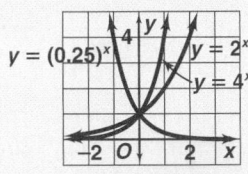

Standardized Test Prep

Multiple Choice

51. For the function $y = -3^x$, what is the value of *y* when $x = -2$? **B**
    A. −9 B. $-\frac{1}{9}$ C. $\frac{1}{9}$ D. 9

52. Which function contains the points $(1, 3)$ and $(3, 6.75)$? **G**
    F. $y = 1.675x + 1.325$ G. $y = 2 \cdot 1.5^x$
    H. $y = 1.5 \cdot 2^x$ I. $y = 1.325x + 1.675$

53. Which function has the same *y*-intercept as $y = 2^x$? **A**
    A. $y = x + 1$ B. $y = 2x$ C. $y = x$ D. $y = 2(x + 1)$

pages 432–435 Exercises

35a.

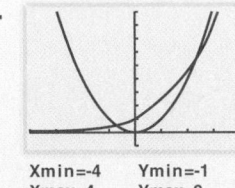

$y = (0.25)^x$ $y = 2^x$ $y = 4^x$

43a.

$Xmin=-4$ $Ymin=-1$
$Xmax=4$ $Ymax=9$

b. Between $x = 1$ and $x = 3$, the graph of $y = x^2$ rises faster than the graph of $y = 2^x$. The graphs intersect at $x = 2$.

Take It to the NET
Online lesson quiz at
www.PHSchool.com
Web Code: aea-0807

Short Response

54. A population of 6000 doubles in size every 10 years. Which equation relates the size of the population y to the number of 10-year periods x? **H**

F. $y = 6000 \cdot 10^x$ **G.** $y = 10 \cdot 2^x$

H. $y = 6000 \cdot 2^x$ **I.** $y = 2 \cdot 100^x$

55. Between what two integer values of x do the graphs of $y = 20(0.5)^x$ and $y = 0.5 \cdot 4^x$ intersect? Show your work. **See margin.**

✓ **Chapter Checkpoint 2**

To check understanding of Lessons 8-5 to 8-7:

Checkpoint Quiz 2 (p. 435)

📁 **Core Resources**
Checkpoint Quiz 2 (also in Prentice Hall Assessment System)

👥 **Reaching All Students**
Reading and Math Literacy 8B

Spanish versions available

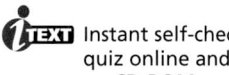 **Mixed Review**

Lesson 8-6

56. 5; 1250, 6250, 31,250

57. −3; 567, −1701, 5103

58. 2; −3.2, −6.4, −12.8

59. $-\frac{1}{3}; \frac{1}{3}, -\frac{1}{9}, \frac{1}{27}$

Lesson 6-5

Find each common ratio. Then find the next three terms in each sequence. 56–59.
See left.

56. $2, 10, 50, 250, \ldots$ **57.** $7, -21, 63, -189, \ldots$

58. $-0.2, -0.4, -0.8, -1.6, \ldots$ **59.** $27, -9, 3, -1, \ldots$

60. $450, 45, 4.5, 0.45, \ldots$ **61.** $7168, 1792, 448, 112, \ldots$
0.1; 0.045, 0.0045, 0.00045   **0.25; 28, 7, 1.75**

Write an equation for the line that passes through the given point and is parallel to the given line.

62. $y = 5x + 1; (0, 0)$ $y = 5x$ **63.** $y = 3x - 2; (0, 1)$ $y = 3x + 1$

64. $y = -2x + 5; (4, 0)$ $y = -2x + 8$ **65.** $y = 0.4x + 5; (2, -3)$ $y = 0.4x - 3.8$

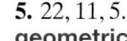 **Checkpoint Quiz 2**   **Lessons 8-5 through 8-7**

iTEXT Instant self-check quiz online and on CD-ROM

Simplify each expression.

1. $\left(\frac{3^2}{3^{-1}}\right)^4$ 3^{12} **2.** $\left(\frac{x^2}{y^3}\right)^{-5} \frac{y^{15}}{x^{10}}$ **3.** $\left(\frac{10m^{-3}}{25n^{-6}}\right)^2 \frac{4n^{12}}{25m^6}$ **4.** $\left(\frac{6^2t^{-3}}{6^2r^0t^2}\right)^2 \frac{1}{t^{10}}$

Determine whether each sequence is *arithmetic* or *geometric*.

5. $22, 11, 5.5, 2.75, \ldots$ **6.** $5, 10, 20, 40, 80, \ldots$ **7.** $5, 10, 15, 20, 25, \ldots$
geometric   **geometric**   **arithmetic**

8. Use the sequence $-100, 20, -4, \ldots$

   a. What is the first term? **−100**

   b. What is the common ratio? $-\frac{1}{5}$ **or −0.2**

   c. Write a rule for the sequence. $A(n) = -100 \cdot (-0.2)^{n-1}$

   d. Use your rule to find the fifth and seventh terms in the sequence.
   −0.16; −0.0064

9. Physics On the first swing, a pendulum swings through an arc of length 40 cm. On each successive swing, the length of the arc is 85% of the length of the previous swing.

   a. Write a rule to model this situation. $A(n) = 40 \cdot (0.85)^{n-1}$

   b. Find the length of the arc on the fifth swing. Round your answer to the nearest millimeter. **209 mm**

10. Commuting Refer to the information at the left.

   a. Write the number of vehicles that crossed the George Washington Bridge in scientific notation. 1.08×10^8

   b. The Port Authority collected about $249 million in tolls from this bridge. Write this number in scientific notation. 2.49×10^8

   c. What was the average toll per vehicle? **about $2.31**

Real-World 🌐 **Connection**

About 108 million vehicles crossed the George Washington Bridge between New York and New Jersey in 2000.

Lesson 8-7 Exponential Functions **435**

55. [2]

x	$y = 20 \cdot 0.5^x$	$y = 0.5 \cdot 4^x$
0	20	0.5
1	10	2
2	5	8

The graphs intersect between $x = 1$ and $x = 2$ (OR equivalent explanation).

[1] answer with no work shown

Fitting Exponential Curves to Data

 **Technology** **Fitting Exponential Curves to Data**

FOR USE WITH LESSON 8-7

Technology

Fitting Exponential Curves to Data

Students use the STAT feature of their graphing calculators to find the best-fitting exponential function for given data. They write and graph the function that best fits the data and make predictions based on the graph of the function.

Resources

Students may use any graphing calculator to explore graphs and functions.

Teaching Notes

Technology Tip

Remind students that before they begin, they will need to clear existing lists in the STAT menu. They do this by pressing 2nd **MEM** 4 ENTER. Then they are ready to begin entering the data in L$_1$ and L$_2$. Students may also need to choose DiagnosticsOn under Catalog to view r-values.

Teaching Tip

Explain to students that what they are trying to do is find out if there is an association between two variables. To do this, they determine the function that best describes the data. It could be a straight curve (a linear function) or an exponential curve (an exponential function). A curve of best fit is drawn or displayed on the calculator. If the data points are close to the curve, this indicates a strong association between the variables thus allowing a more accurate prediction based on the data. If the points are scattered and not very close to the curve, the association is not as strong and predictions based on the function are less reliable.

In Chapter 6 you learned how to find a line of best fit for a set of data. You can model some data better using an exponential function. To graph an exponential function, you may need to adjust your viewing window. Use your data to choose appropriate Xmax and Ymax values.

Take It to the NET
Graphing Calculator procedures online at **www.PHSchool.com**
Web Code: aee-2122

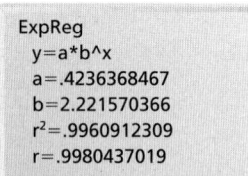 **EXAMPLE**

The table at the right shows the predicted number of customers downloading music files. Use a graphing calculator to find the best-fitting exponential function for the data. Then graph the function.

Digital Download

Year	Customers (millions)
2000	0.4
2001	1.0
2002	2.2
2003	4.4

Step 1 Use your calculator's STAT feature. Enter the data. Let 2000 correspond to $x = 0$.

Step 2 To get the equation of the best-fitting exponential function, press STAT ▶ 0 ENTER.

```
ExpReg
 y=a*b^x
 a=.4236368467
 b=2.221570366
 r²=.9960912309
 r=.9980437019
```

Step 3 To view the graph of the function press Y= CLEAR VARS 5 ▶ ▶ 1 GRAPH.

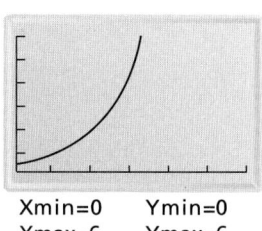

Xmin=0   Ymin=0
Xmax=6   Ymax=6

EXERCISES

Use a graphing calculator to find the exponential function that fits each set of data. Then (a) write a function for the data rounding decimals to the nearest hundredth, (b) sketch a graph of the function, and (c) use your answer from part (a) to predict the value of the function in the year 2010.

1. Shipment of Record Singles Let 1990 correspond to $x = 0$.

Year	1990	1994	1995	1996	1997	1998	1999
Record Singles (millions)	27.6	11.7	10.2	10.1	7.5	5.4	5.3

a. $y = 26.87(0.83)^x$
b. See back of book.
c. 0.65

2. U.S. Energy Consumption Let 1990 correspond to $x = 0$.

Year	1990	1992	1993	1994	1995	1996	1997	1998
Btu (quadrillions)	84.3	85.5	87.3	89.2	90.9	93.9	94.3	94.6

a. $y = 83.59(1.017)^x$
b. See margin.
c. 117.1

3. U.S. Homes Heated by Coal Let 1950 correspond to $x = 0$.

Year	1950	1960	1970	1980	1991	1997
Percent of Homes	34.6	12.2	2.9	0.6	0.3	0.2

a. $y = 31.53(0.89)^x$
b. See margin.
c. 0.03

page 436   Technology   3b.

2b.

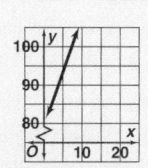

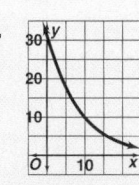

Exponential Growth and Decay

 4.04   Graph and evaluate exponential functions to solve problems.

Lesson Preview

What You'll Learn

OBJECTIVE 1 To model exponential growth

OBJECTIVE 2 To model exponential decay

. . . And Why

To find the balance of a bank account, as in Examples 2 and 3

 North Carolina Objectives

✔ **Check Skills You'll Need**   (For help, go to Lesson 4-3.)

Use the formula $I = prt$ to find the interest for principal p, interest rate r, and time t in years.

1. principal: $1000; interest rate: 5%; time: 2 years   **$100**

2. principal: $360; interest rate: 6%; time: 3 years   **$64.80**

3. principal: $2500; interest rate: 4.5%; time: 2 years   **$225**

4. principal: $1680; interest rate: 5.25%; time: 4 years   **$352.80**

5. principal: $1350; interest rate: 4.8%; time: 5 years   **$324**

New Vocabulary   • exponential growth   • growth factor   • compound interest
• interest period   • exponential decay   • decay factor

Lesson Preview

✔ **Check Skills You'll Need**

Proportions and Percent Equations
Lesson 4-3
Exercise 53
Extra Practice, p. 705

Lesson Resources

📁 **Teaching Resources**
Practice, Reteaching, Enrichment

👥 **Reaching All Students**
Practice Workbook 8-8
Spanish Practice Workbook 8-8
Technology Activities 8
Hands-On Activities 19
Basic Algebra Planning Guide 8-8

⏱ **Presentation Assistant Plus!**
Transparencies
• Check Skills You'll Need 8-8
• Additional Examples 8-8
• Student Edition Answers 8-8
• Lesson Quiz 8-8
PH Presentation Pro CD 8-8

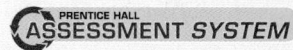 **PRENTICE HALL ASSESSMENT** *SYSTEM*

Computer Test Generator CD

🔬 **Technology**
Resource Pro® CD-ROM
Computer Test Generator CD
Prentice Hall Presentation Pro CD

💻 **www.PHSchool.com**
Student Site
• Teacher Web Code: aek-5500
• Self-grading Lesson Quiz
Teacher Center
• Lesson Planner
• Resources

Plus

OBJECTIVE
 1 Exponential Growth

Real-World 🌐 Connection

In 2000, Florida's population was about 16 million. Roughly 23% of the population was under the age of 18.

 *i*TEXT   Interactive lesson includes instant self-check, tutorials, and activities.

In 1990, Florida's population was about 13 million. Since 1990, the state's population has grown about 1.7% each year. This means that Florida's population is growing exponentially.

To find Florida's population in 1991, multiply the 1990 population by 1.7% and add this to the 1990 population. So the population in 1991 is (1.7% + 100%) of the 1990 population, or 101.7% of the 1990 population. Here is a function that models Florida's population since 1990.

$$\underset{\text{population in millions}}{\downarrow}$$
$$y = 13.0(1.017)^x \longleftarrow \text{number of years since 1990}$$
$$\underset{\uparrow}{101.7\% \text{ as a decimal}}$$

The following is a general rule for modeling exponential growth.

 Key Concepts

Rule   **Exponential Growth**
Exponential growth can be modeled with the function $y = a \cdot b^x$ for $a > 0$ and $b > 1$.
starting amount (when $x = 0$)
$y = a \cdot b^x \longleftarrow$ exponent
The base, which is greater than 1, is the **growth factor**.

Lesson 8-8   Exponential Growth and Decay   **437**

⟳ **Ongoing Assessment and Intervention**

Before the Lesson
Diagnose prerequisite skills using:
• Check Skills You'll Need

During the Lesson
Monitor progress using:
• Check Understanding
• Additional Examples
• Standardized Test Prep

After the Lesson
Assess knowledge using:
• Lesson Quiz
• Computer Test Generator CD

437

2. Teach

Math Background

Exponential functions are widely used to model many types of growth and decay. The graph of an exponential growth function rises from left to right at an ever-increasing rate while that of an exponential decay function falls from left to right at an ever-decreasing rate.

OBJECTIVE

1 Teaching Notes

1 EXAMPLE Teaching Tip

Even though students may understand the word *exponent*, they may not understand what *growing exponentially* means. Have students extend this table.

Multiply by 2	Square
2	2
4	4
8	16
64	256

Continue until the student sees that the geometric sequence formed with the common ratio 2 grows much more slowly than the sequence formed by squaring (using the exponent 2).

2 EXAMPLE Alternative Method

Have students solve the problem using the [TABLE] function on a graphing calculator. First put the equation into [Y=]. Then press 2nd [TABLE]. Use the arrows to scroll to x = 18. The amount in the y-column is 4660. The amounts in the y-column have been rounded to the nearest tenth. Ask students to find how long it took to double the amount deposited. Guide students to look in the y-column for the amount closest to 3000.
a little over 11 years

438

---

1 EXAMPLE Modeling Exponential Growth

Medical Care Since 1985, the daily cost of patient care in community hospitals in the United States has increased about 8.1% per year. In 1985, such hospital costs were an average of $460 per day.

a. Write an equation to model the cost of hospital care.

Relate $y = a \cdot b^x$ Use an exponential function.

Define Let x = the number of years since 1985.
Let y = the cost of community hospital care at various times.
Let a = the initial cost in 1985, $460.
Let b = the growth factor, which is $100\% + 8.1\% = 108.1\% = 1.081$.

Write $y = 460 \cdot 1.081^x$

b. Use your equation to find the approximate cost per day in 2000.

$y = 460 \cdot 1.081^x$

$y = 460 \cdot 1.081^{15}$ **2000 is 15 years after 1985, so substitute 15 for x.**

≈ 1480 **Use a calculator. Round to the nearest dollar.**

The average cost per day in 2000 was about $1480.

✔ **Check Understanding** **1 a.** Suppose your community has 4512 students this year. The student population is growing 2.5% each year. Write an equation to model the student population.
b. What will the student population be in 3 years?
a. $y = 4512 \cdot 1.025^x$ **b. about 4859 students**

When a bank pays interest on both the principal *and* the interest an account has already earned, the bank is paying **compound interest**. An **interest period** is the length of time over which interest is calculated.

2 EXAMPLE Compound Interest

Savings Suppose your parents deposited $1500 in an account paying 6.5% interest compounded annually (once a year) when you were born. Find the account balance after 18 years.

Relate $y = a \cdot b^x$ Use an exponential function.

Define Let x = the number of interest periods.
Let y = the balance.
Let a = the initial deposit, $1500.
Let b = $100\% + 6.5\% = 106.5\% = 1.065$.

Write $y = 1500 \cdot 1.065^x$

$= 1500 \cdot 1.065^{18}$ **Once a year for 18 years is 18 interest periods. Substitute 18 for x.**

≈ 4659.98 **Use a calculator. Round to the nearest cent.**

The balance after 18 years will be $4659.98.

✔ **Check Understanding** **2 a.** Suppose the interest rate on the account in Example 2 was 8%. How much would be in the account after 18 years? **$5994.03**
b. Another formula for compound interest is $B = p(1 + r)^x$, where B is the balance, p is the principal, and r is the interest rate in decimal form. Use this formula to find the balance in the account in part (a). **$5994.03**
c. Critical Thinking Explain why the two formulas for finding compound interest are actually the same. **$(1 + r)$ is the same as $100\% + 100r\%$ written as a decimal.**

👥 Reaching All Students

Below Level Have students draw a tree diagram illustrating the following: one person sends an e-mail to two friends; then each person forwards the e-mail to two friends, and so on.	**Advanced Learners** Ask students to explain whether the consumption per person of whole milk in the United States as modeled in Example 5 will ever reach 0 gal/person.	**English Learners** See note on page 440. **Error Prevention** See note on page 441.

Calculator Hint

To evaluate $460 \cdot 1081^{15}$, press

460 ☒ 1.081 ⟑

15 ⎡ENTER⎤.

BANK 1

Deposit **$1500**

Interest compounded annually **6.5%**

Balance after 18 years **$4659.98**

When interest is compounded quarterly (four times per year), you divide the interest rate by 4, the number of interest periods per year. To find the number of payment periods, you multiply the number of years by the number of interest periods per year.

Annual Interest Rate of 8%

Compounded	Periods per Year	Interest Rate per Period
annually	1	8% every year
semi-annually	2	$\frac{8\%}{2} = 4\%$ every 6 months
quarterly	4	$\frac{8\%}{4} = 2\%$ every 3 months
monthly	12	$\frac{8\%}{12} = 0.\overline{6}\%$ every month

3 EXAMPLE Compound Interest

Savings Suppose the account in Example 2 paid interest compounded quarterly instead of annually. Find the account balance after 18 years.

Relate $y = a \cdot b^x$ Use an exponential function.

Define Let x = the number of interest periods.
Let y = the balance.
Let a = the initial deposit, $1500.

Let $b = 100\% + \frac{6.5\%}{4}$ **There are 4 interest periods in 1 year, so divide the interest into 4 parts.**

$= 1 + 0.01625 = 1.01625$

Write $y = 1500 \cdot 1.01625^x$

$= 1500 \cdot 1.01625^{72}$ **Four interest periods a year for 18 years is 72 interest periods. Substitute 72 for x.**

≈ 4787.75 **Use a calculator. Round to the nearest cent.**

The balance after 18 years will be $4787.75.

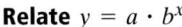

BANK 2

Deposit **$1500**

Interest compounded quarterly **6.5%**

Balance after 18 years **$4787.75**

✓ **Check Understanding** **3 a.** Suppose the account in Example 3 paid interest compounded monthly. How much money would be in the account after 18 years? **$4817.75**

b. You deposit $200 into an account earning 5%, compounded monthly. How much will be in the account after 1 year? After 2 years? After 5 years? **$210.23; $220.99; $256.67**

OBJECTIVE

2 Exponential Decay

The graphs at the right show exponential growth and exponential decay. For exponential growth, as x increases, y increases exponentially. For exponential decay, as x increases, y decreases exponentially.

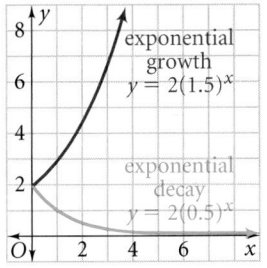

exponential growth $y = 2(1.5)^x$

exponential decay $y = 2(0.5)^x$

Additional Examples

1 In 1998, a certain town had a population of about 13,000 people. Since 1998, the population has increased about 1.4% a year.
a. Write an equation to model the population increase.
$y = 13,000 \cdot 1.014^x$
b. Use your equation to find the approximate population in 2006. about 14,529 people

2 Suppose you deposit $1000 in a college fund that pays 7.2% interest compounded annually. Find the account balance after 5 years. about $1415.71

3 Suppose the account in the above problem paid interest quarterly instead of annually. Find the account balance after 5 years. about $1428.75

Help student understand the term *decay*. Explain that decay is the opposite of growth; it's a breaking down or decrease. Elicit examples such as tooth decay or an orange turning moldy and decaying. Point out that exponential decay is the opposite of exponential growth. The same model can be used by substituting a *decay factor* for the growth factor.

Additional Examples

4 Technetium-99 has a half-life of 6 hours. Suppose a lab has 80 mg of technetium-99. How much technetium-99 is left after 24 hours? **5 mg**

5 Suppose the population of a certain endangered species has decreased 2.4% each year. Suppose there were 60 of these animals in a given area in 1999.
a. Write an equation to model the number of animals in this species that remain alive in that area. $y = 60 \cdot 0.976^x$
b. Use your equation to find the approximate number of animals remaining in 2005. **about 52 animals**

Closure

Ask students to explain the difference between modeling using an exponential growth function and modeling using an exponential decay function.
In an exponential growth function, you add the percent of increased growth to 100% to find the base. In an exponential decay function, you subtract the percent of decreased growth from 100% to find the base.

Reading Math

Marie Curie (1867–1934) received Nobel prizes in physics and chemistry for her pioneering work with radioactive elements. The curie (a unit of radioactivity) is named for Marie Curie.

✔ **Check Understanding**

Real-World 🌐 **Connection**

One cup of milk contains 300 mg of calcium. The body absorbs about 32% of the calcium in milk.

A real-world example of exponential decay is radioactive decay, in which radioactive elements break down by releasing particles and energy.

4 EXAMPLE **Real-World** 🌐 **Problem Solving**

Medicine The half-life of a radioactive substance is the length of time it takes for one half of the substance to decay into another substance. To treat some forms of cancer, doctors use radioactive iodine. The half-life of iodine-131 is 8 days. A patient receives a 12-mCi (millicuries, a measure of radiation) treatment. How much iodine-131 is left in the patient 16 days later?

In 16 days, there are two 8-day half-lives.
After one half-life, there are 6 mCi left in the patient.
After two half-lives, there are 3 mCi left in the patient.

4 **a.** How many half-lives of iodine-131 occur in 32 days? **4 half-lives**
b. Suppose you start with a 50-mCi sample of iodine-131. How much iodine-131 is left after one half-life? After two half-lives? **25 mCi; 12.5 mCi**
c. **Chemistry** Cesium-137 has a half-life of 30 years. Suppose a lab stored a 30-mCi sample in 1973. How much of the sample will be left in 2003? In 2063? **15 mCi; 3.75 mCi**

The function $y = a \cdot b^x$ can model exponential decay as well as exponential growth.

🔑 **Key Concepts**

Rule	Exponential Decay

The function $y = a \cdot b^x$ models exponential decay for $a > 0$ and $0 < b < 1$.

starting amount (when $x = 0$)
$$y = a \cdot b^x \longleftarrow \text{exponent}$$
The base, which is between 0 and 1, is the **decay factor.**

When a number is decreased by 5%, the result is 95% of the original number. So when you find the decay factor, think 100% minus the percent a number is decreasing.

5 EXAMPLE **Modeling Exponential Decay**

Milk Consumption Since 1980, the number of gallons of whole milk each person in the United States drinks each year has decreased 4.1% each year. In 1980, each person drank an average of 16.5 gallons of whole milk per year.
a. Write an equation to model the gallons of whole milk drunk per person.

Relate $y = a \cdot b^x$ Use an exponential function.

Define Let x = the number of years since 1980.
Let y = the consumption of whole milk, in gallons.
Let a = 16.5, the initial number of gallons in 1980.
Let b = the decay factor, which is 100% − 4.1% = 95.9% = 0.959.

Write $y = 16.5 \cdot 0.959^x$

b. Use your equation to find the approximate consumption per person of whole milk in 2000.

$y = 16.5 \cdot 0.959^x$

$y = 16.5 \cdot 0.959^{20}$ **2000 is 20 years after 1980, so substitute 20 for x.**

≈ 7.1 **Use a calculator. Round to the nearest tenth of a gallon.**

The average annual consumption of whole milk in 2000 was about 7 gal/person.

 Check Understanding   **5** **Statistics** In 1990, the population of Washington, D.C., was about 604,000 people. Since then the population has decreased about 1.8% per year.
a. What is the initial number of people? **604,000**
b. What is the decay factor? **0.982**

5c. $y = 604{,}000 \cdot (0.982)^x$
c. Write an equation to model the population of Washington, D.C., since 1990.
d. Suppose the current trend in population change continues. Predict the population of Washington, D.C., in 2010. **about 420,017 people**

EXERCISES

For more practice, see *Extra Practice*.

Practice and Problem Solving

A **Practice by Example**

Example 1
(page 438)

Identify the initial amount *a* and the growth factor *b* in each exponential function.

1. $g(x) = 20 \cdot 2^x$ **2.** $y = 200 \cdot 1.0875^x$ **3.** $y = 10{,}000 \cdot 1.01^x$ **4.** $f(t) = 1.5^t$
20; 2   **200; 1.0875**   **10,000; 1.01**   **1; 1.5**
5. Suppose the population of a city is 50,000 and is growing 3% each year.
   a. The initial amount *a* is ■. **50,000**
   b. The growth factor *b* is 100% + 3%, which is 1 + ■ = ■. **0.03; 1.03**
   c. To find the population after one year, you multiply 50,000 · ■. **1.03**

5d. 50,000; 1.03; *x*
   d. Complete the equation $y = ■ \cdot ■^■$ to find the population after *x* years.
   e. Use your equation to predict the population after 25 years.
     about 104,689 people

Examples 2, 3
(pages 438, 439)

Each percent is an annual interest rate. In the formula $y = a \cdot b^x$, what value would you use for *b*?

6. 4% **1.04**   **7.** 5% **1.05**   **8.** 3.7% **1.037**   **9.** 8.75% **1.0875**   **10.** 0.5% **1.005**

Assume each interest rate below is an annual interest rate. Find the interest rate for an account that is compounded quarterly and monthly. 11–15. See left.

11. 0.75%, 0.25%   **11.** 3%   **12.** 4%   **13.** 4.5%   **14.** 7.6%   **15.** 6.25%

12. 1%; 0.$\overline{3}$%

13. 1.125%; 0.375%

Find the balance in each account.

14. 1.9%; 0.6$\overline{3}$%

16. $4000 principal earning 6% compounded annually, after 5 years **$5352.90**

15. 1.5625%; 0.52083%

17. $12,000 principal earning 4.8% compounded annually, after 7 years **$16,661.35**

18. $500 principal earning 4% compounded quarterly, after 6 years **$634.87**

19. $20,000 deposit earning 3.5% compounded quarterly, after 10 years **$28,338.18**

Example 4
(page 440)

20. Chemistry The half-life of iodine-124 is 4 days. A technician measures a 40-mCi sample of iodine-124.
   a. How many half-lives of iodine-124 occur in 16 days? **4 half-lives**
   b. How much iodine-124 is in the sample 16 days after the technician measures the original sample? **2.5 mCi**

Assignment Guide

▼ **1** **Objective**
   Ⓐ Ⓑ **Core** 1–19, 31–43
   Ⓒ **Extension** 54

▼ **2** **Objective**
   Ⓐ Ⓑ **Core** 20–30, 44–52
   Ⓒ **Extension** 53, 55

Standardized Test Prep 56–59

Mixed Review 60–63

Error Prevention

Exercises 6–10 Remind students that money invested at interest 'grows.' The base is the growth factor, the percent of growth, as a decimal, added to 1.00.

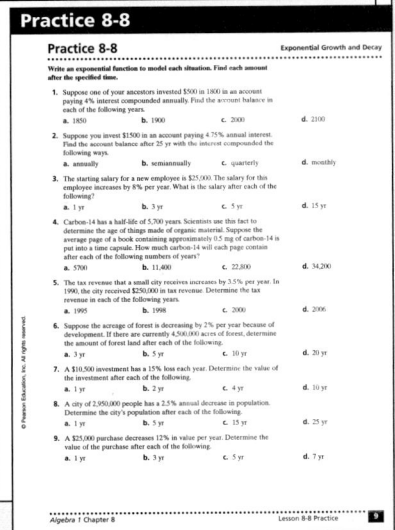

Exercises 26–29 Remind students that a growth factor is greater than 1 and a decay factor is less than 1.

Exercises 36–39 Suggest students review Lessons 5-3 and 8-7.

21. Chemistry The half-life of carbon-11 is 20 min. A sample of carbon-11 has 25 mCi.
 a. How many half-lives of carbon-11 occur in 1 hour? **3 half-lives**
 b. How much carbon-11 is in the sample 1 hour after the original sample is measured? **3.125 mCi**

Example 5
(page 440)

Identify the decay factor in each function.

22. $y = 5 \cdot 0.5^x$ **0.5**   **23.** $f(x) = 10 \cdot 0.1^x$ **0.1**

24. $g(x) = 100 \cdot \left(\frac{2}{3}\right)^x$ **$\frac{2}{3}$**   **25.** $y = 0.1 \cdot 0.9^x$ **0.9**

Identify each function as *exponential growth* or *exponential decay*.

26. $y = 0.68 \cdot 2^x$ **27.** $y = 2 \cdot 0.68^x$ **28.** $y = 68 \cdot 2^x$ **29.** $y = 68 \cdot 0.2^x$
exp. growth   **exp. decay**   **exp. growth**   **exp. decay**

30. Cars The value of a new car decreases exponentially. Suppose your mother buys a new car for $22,000. The value of the car decreases by 20% each year.
 a. What is the initial price of the car? The decay factor? **$22,000; 0.8**

30b. $y = 22,000 \cdot (0.8)^x$

 b. Write an equation to model the value of the car x years after she buys it.
 c. Find the value of the car after 6 years. **$5767.17**

B **Apply Your Skills**

Write an exponential function to model each situation. Find each amount after the specified time. 31. $y = 130,000 \cdot (1.01)^x$; about 142,179 people

32. $y = 3,000,000 \cdot (0.985)^x$; about 2,579,191 people

31. A population of 130,000 grows 1% per year for 9 years.

32. A population of 3,000,000 decreases 1.5% annually for 10 years.

33. $y = 2400 \cdot (1.07)^x$; $4721.16

33. A $2400 principal earns 7% compounded annually for 10 years.

34. A $2400 principal earns 7% compounded monthly for 10 years.
 $y = 2400 \cdot (1.00583333)^x$; $4823.19

35. Education Since 1985, the average annual cost y (in dollars) for tuition and fees at public two-year colleges in the United States has increased about 6.5% per year. In 1985, tuition and fees were an average of $584 per year.
 a. Write an equation to model the cost of two-year colleges. Predict the average annual cost for 2005. $y = 584 \cdot (1.065)^x$; $2057.81
 b. Open-Ended Predict the average annual cost for the year you plan to graduate from high school. **Check students' work.**

Tell whether each graph shows a *linear function*, an *exponential function*, or *neither*. Justify your reasoning. 36–39. See margin.

36. 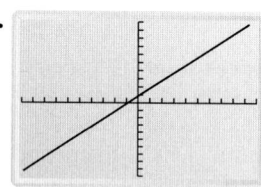   **37.**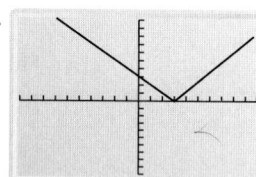

38. 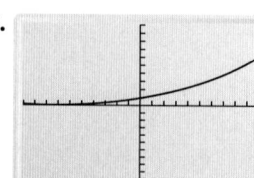   **39.**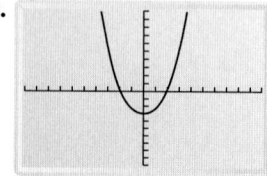

442   Chapter 8 Exponents and Exponential Functions

pages 441–444   Exercises

36. Linear function; it is a straight line.

37. Neither; it is not just one straight line.

38. Exponential function; it is a curve with y-values that increase as x-values increase.

39. Neither; it decreases, then increases, unlike an exponential function.

40. linear function

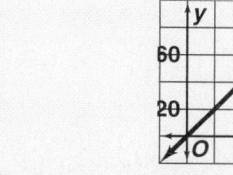

41. exponential function

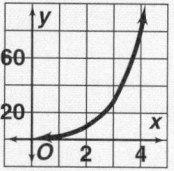

Graph the function represented in each table. Then tell whether the table represents a *linear function* or an *exponential function*. 40–42. See margin p. 442.

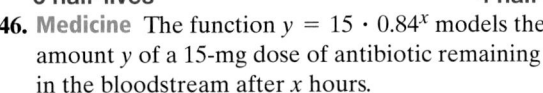

40.	x	y
	1	20
	2	40
	3	60
	4	80

41.	x	y
	1	3
	2	9
	3	27
	4	81

42.	x	y
	1	3
	2	9
	3	15
	4	21

43. **Writing** Would you rather have $500 in an account paying 6% interest compounded quarterly or $600 in an account paying 5% compounded annually? Summarize your reasoning. **See margin.**

Reading Math

For help with Exercise 46 go to page 445.

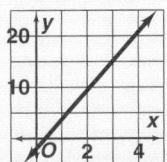

Real-World Connection

Careers A medical researcher may use equipment such as a scanning electron microscope.

How many half-lives occur in each period of time?

44. 2 days (1 half-life = 8 h)
   6 half-lives

45. 300 years (1 half-life = 75 yr)
   4 half-lives

46. **Medicine** The function $y = 15 \cdot 0.84^x$ models the amount y of a 15-mg dose of antibiotic remaining in the bloodstream after x hours.
   a. **Estimation** Use the graphing calculator screen to estimate the half-life of this antibiotic in the bloodstream. **about 4 h**
   b. Use your estimate to predict the fraction of the dose that will remain in the bloodstream after 8 hours. $\frac{1}{4}$
   c. Verify your prediction by using the function to find the amount of antibiotic remaining after 8 hours. **See margin.**

Antibiotic Decay in the Bloodstream

X=4.0106383 Y=7.4542313
Xmin=0 Ymin=0
Xmax=13 Ymax=15

47. **Population Growth** Since 1990, the population of Virginia has grown at an average annual rate of about 1%. In 1990, the population was about 6,284,000.
   a. Write an equation to model the population growth in Virginia since 1990.
   b. Suppose this rate of growth continues. Predict Virginia's population in 2010.
   a. $y = 6,284,000 \cdot (1.01)^x$ b. **7,667,674 people**

By which percent would you multiply a number to decrease it by the given amount?

48. 6% **94%**   49. 12% **88%**   50. 3.5% **96.5%**   51. 53.9% **46.1%**

52. a. **Estimation** Use the graph at the right. Estimate the half-life of cesium-134. **2 years**
   b. Suppose a scientist had 800 mCi of cesium-134 in a sample. After how many years would the sample have 200 mCi of cesium-134? **4 years**

Cesium-134 Decay

(graph: Level (mCi) vs Time (years), 0 to 14)

Challenge

53. **Credit Card Balances** Suppose you charge $250 for a new suit. If you do not pay the whole amount the first month, you are charged 1.8% monthly interest on your account balance. Suppose you can make a $30 payment each month.
   a. What is your balance after your first payment? **$220.00**
   b. How much interest are you charged after your first payment? **$3.96**
   c. What is your balance just before you make your second payment? **$223.96**
   d. What is your balance after your second payment? **$193.96**
   e. How many months will it take for you to pay off the entire bill? **9 months**
   f. How much interest will you have paid in all? **$18.07**

Lesson 8-8 Exponential Growth and Decay **443**

42. **linear function**

(graph)

43. **Answers may vary. Sample: $600; even after 10 years, there is more money in the account with an initial deposit of $600 ($977.34) than there is in the account with an** initial deposit of $500 ($907.01).

46c. about 3.7 mg using the function and 15 mg × $\frac{1}{4}$ = 3.75 mg using the prediction

443

4. **Assess**

Lesson Quiz 8-8

1. Identify the original amount a and the growth factor b in the exponential function $y = 10 \cdot 1.036^x$.
   $a = 10, b = 1.036$

2. A population of 24,500 people has been increasing at a rate of 1.8% a year. What will be the population in 15 years if it continues at that rate?
   about 32,017 people

3. Write an exponential function to represent $2000 principal earning 5.6% interest compounded annually. $y = 2000 \cdot 1.056^x$

4. Find the account balance on $3000 principal earning 6.4% interest compounded quarterly for 7 years. **about $4678.91**

5. The half-life of a certain substance is 4 days. If you have 100 mg of the substance, how much of it will remain after 12 days?
   12.5 mg

6. The value of a $1200 computer decreases 27% annually. What will be the value of the computer after 3 years? **about $466.82**

Alternative Assessment

Group students in pairs. Instruct one student to write a question that can be modeled by an exponential growth function. Have the other student write a question that can be modeled by an exponential decay function. Direct students to exchange problems, write the appropriate function, and solve.

📁 **Resources**
For additional practice with a variety of test item formats:
- Standardized Test Prep, p. 451
- Test-Taking Strategies, p. 446
- Test-Taking Strategies with Transparencies

Exercise 56 Remind students that the *y*-values decrease as *x*-values increase in exponential decay functions, but they increase in exponential growth functions.

pages 441-444   Exercises

60.

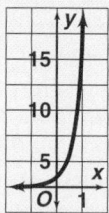

61.

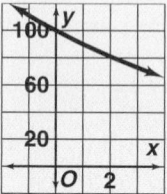

62.

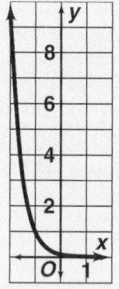

54. Data Collection Complete the table at the right using any ball. The height 0 is the starting height. Record the maximum height after the first, second, and third bounce. **a-b. Check student's work.**
a. Graph your data.
b. Write an exponential decay function that models your data.

Bounce	Height (centimeters)
0	■
1	■
2	■
3	■

55. On January 1, 2000, Chessville had a population of 40,000 people. Its population increases 7% each year. On the same day, Checkersville had a population of 60,000 people. Its population decreases 4% each year. During what year will the population of Chessville exceed that of Checkersville? **2003**

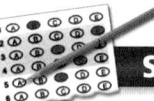

Standardized Test Prep

Multiple Choice

56. For which function will values of *y* decrease as values of *x* increase? **C**
A. $y = 12.5(1.325)^x$ B. $y = 300(1.06)^x$
C. $y = 5000(0.98)^x$ D. $y = 1.02^x$

57. Suppose you deposit $1000 in an account earning 6% interest. You make no further deposits to the account and interest is compounded semi-annually. What is the balance after 5 years? **H**
F. $538.62   G. $1006.00   H. $1343.92   I. $1790.85

Reading Comprehension

58. Read the passage below and answer the following problem.

Manhattan, Then and Now

In 1626, the Dutch landed on the island we now call Manhattan. They bought the island for $24 worth of merchandise. Today Manhattan is one of the most expensive places in the world to live. Rent for a one-bedroom apartment averages $2000 a month.

Suppose $24 had been invested in 1626 in an account paying 4.5% interest compounded annually. Which amount is closest to the balance in 2000? **A**
A. $339 million   B. $89 million   C. $9400   D. $8900

Short Response

💻 **Take It to the NET**
Online lesson quiz at
www.PHSchool.com
⋯⋯⋯ Web Code: aea-0808

59. [2] Using $1000 for deposit, quarterly:
$1000(1 + \frac{0.05}{4})^{20}$
≈ 1282.04; annually:
$1000(1 + 0.055)^5 \approx$
1306.96. The account paying 5.5% will be greater (OR equivalent explanation).
[1] correct approach with minor computational error

59. Which is greater, the amount in an account that pays 5% interest compounded quarterly for 5 years or the amount in an account that pays 5.5% compounded annually for 5 years? Assume the accounts start with the same amount. Show your work. **See left.**

Mixed Review

Lesson 8-7   **Graph each function.   60–62. See margin.**

60. $y = 2 \cdot 10^x$ **61.** $f(x) = 100 \cdot 0.9^x$ **62.** $g(x) = \frac{1}{10} \cdot 0.1^x$

Lesson 8-3   **63. Geography** In 2000, about 1.4×10^4 ships passed through the Panama Canal. About 5.2×10^7 gallons of water flow out of the canal with each ship. About how many gallons of water flowed out of the canal with ships in 2000? Write your answer in scientific notation. **7.28×10^{11} gal**

Reading a Graph

FOR USE WITH PAGE 443, EXERCISE 46

Read the exercise below, and then learn how to use a graphing calculator to solve it. Check your understanding by solving the exercise at the bottom of the page.

Medicine The function $y = 15 \cdot 0.84^x$ models the amount y of a 15-mg dose of antibiotic remaining in the bloodstream after x hours.

a. Estimation Use the graphing calculator screen to estimate the half-life of this antibiotic in the bloodstream.

b. Use your estimate to predict the fraction of the dose that will remain in the bloodstream after 8 hours.

c. Verify your prediction by using the function to find the amount of antibiotic remaining after 8 hours.

Antibiotic Decay in the Bloodstream

A

B   C

X=4.0106383   Y=7.4542313

D Xmin=0   E Ymin=0
   Xmax=13   Ymax=15

To solve this problem, use the graphing calculator screen shown at the left. Parts of this screen are explained below.

A	The point shown on the screen is a point (x, y) on the graph.
B and C	These are the x-coordinates and y-coordinates of the highlighted point. The coordinates of the point are (4.0106383, 7.4542313).
D and E	These give the domain and range for the x- and y-axes. The screen displays the graph for x-values from 0 to 13 and y-values from 0 to 15.

a. *Half-life* is the time required for the body to eliminate half of the initial dose. How do the coordinates (4.0106383, 7.4542313) relate to the half-life of the antibiotic? At time $x = 0$, the amount in the bloodstream is $y = 15$. When $y = \frac{15}{2} = 7.5$, the corresponding value of x represents the half-life. When $y \approx 7.5$, $x \approx 4$, so the half-life is about 4 hours.

b. If 7.5 mg remain after 4 hours, then $\frac{7.5}{2} = 3.75$ mg will remain after 8 hours.

c. $y = 15 \cdot 0.84^x$
  $y = 15 \cdot 0.84^8$ **Substitute 8 for x.**
  $y \approx 3.72$ **Use a calculator.**

The amount of antibiotic remaining after 8 hours will be about 3.72 mg.

EXERCISE

Memory Suppose the function $y = 40 \cdot 0.75^x$ models the number y of foreign-language words recalled from a list of 40 words after x weeks (without additional practice or study).

a. Estimation Use the graphing calculator to estimate the number of vocabulary words recalled after 5 weeks. **about 9 or 10 words**

b. Verify your prediction by using the function to find the number of vocabulary words recalled after 5 weeks. **about 9.49 or 9 words**

Reading Graphs

Students must be able to make a meaningful connection between the graph, the function, and the situation in the problem. They will use the graph and the coordinates of points to answer questions. They will use the graphing calculator to find coordinates of points on the graph. This feature helps students see that a graph is a useful tool to make estimates and answer questions.

Teaching Notes

Remind students to look at the function and try to make sense of it by asking themselves questions. In the example they could ask: *What does this function tell me about the amount of medicine in the bloodstream after x number of hours? Do I expect the amount to decrease or increase over time? Does y decrease as x increases in this example? How do I know? What is the amount of medicine when x = 0? Does that answer make sense?* These questions help students make sense of the function and should also help them read the graph.

Error Prevention

Some students may think that raising a number to a power always gives a number larger than the starting number. If they don't understand how the function in the first example can model an amount that is decreasing, have them try some simple examples such as $\left(\frac{1}{2}\right)^2$ and $\left(\frac{1}{2}\right)^3$. They should see that the values decrease as the exponents increase.

Exercise

Have students work independently on a similar problem. Then have them verify their predictions by substituting into the function, after which they should pair up to share their answers with each other. You can take note of the kinds of discussions students have with each other to assess their understanding.

445

 **Test-Taking Strategies**

Testing Multiple Choices

This feature helps students develop strategies for answering questions on a multiple-choice test by testing the answers in the problem rather than the more straightforward way of solving the problem.

Resources

ASSESSMENT *SYSTEM*

Test-Taking Strategies with Transparencies
- Transparency 8
- Practice sheet p. 8

Teaching Notes

Help students understand that if three answers are not correct, the fourth choice must be the correct answer.

Teaching Tip

Suggest to students that if the problem involves several time-consuming computations they should look at the answers before testing. Suggest that they do a quick mental estimate or look for obviously incorrect answers first. Then they can eliminate those and only test the remaining answers. This will shorten this particular strategy even further.

Test-Taking Strategies with Transparencies

Test-Taking Strategy: Testing Multiple Choices

When you take a multiple-choice test, one of the answer choices is always correct. You can solve a problem by testing the answer choices to find the correct one.

Solve $5^x + 12 = 637$.

   A. 2   B. 3   C. 4   D. 5

Work backward by substituting each answer choice for x.

$5^2 + 12 = ?$
$25 + 12 = 37$ not correct

$5^3 + 12 = ?$
$125 + 12 = 137$ not correct

$5^4 + 12 = ?$
$625 + 12 = 637$ correct

You do not have to continue substituting answer choices once you find the correct choice.

The answer is C, 4.

Solve these problems by working backward.

1. Solve $4^x - 7 = 4089$.

   A. 5   B. 6   C. 7   D. 8

2. Solve $y^4 - 24 = 57$.

   A. 7   B. 5   C. 3   D. 1

Solutions

1. B

2. C

Transparency 8

446

 **Test-Taking Strategies**

Testing Multiple Choices

One advantage of multiple-choice tests is that the correct answer is among the choices. A strategy is to work backward by taking answers and testing them in the original problem.

1 EXAMPLE

Find the value of x if x, $x + 2$, and $4x$ are three consecutive terms of a geometric sequence.

  A. 0   **B.** 1   **C.** 2   **D.** 3

The ratios of consecutive terms of a geometric sequence are the same. So $\frac{x + 2}{x}$ must equal $\frac{4x}{x + 2}$. Find the number for which this is true by substituting each answer choice for x.

Let $x = 0$. The sequence 0, 2, 0 is not a geometric sequence because $\frac{2}{0} \neq \frac{0}{2}$. So A is not correct.

Let $x = 1$. The sequence 1, 3, 4 is not a geometric sequence because $\frac{3}{1} \neq \frac{4}{3}$. So B is not correct.

Let $x = 2$. The sequence 2, 4, 8 is a geometric sequence because $\frac{4}{2} = \frac{8}{4}$. The correct answer is C.

● You do not need to try choice D.

2 EXAMPLE

Find the value of x if $2x^{-3} = \frac{1}{4}$.

  F. 1   **G.** 2   **H.** 3   **I.** 4

Solve by substituting each answer choice into the original equation.

Let $x = 1$. $\longrightarrow$ $2(1)^{-3} = 2(1) = 2$. $\longrightarrow$ $2 \neq \frac{1}{4}$.   F is not the answer.

Let $x = 2$. $\longrightarrow$ $2(2)^{-3} = 2\left(\frac{1}{8}\right) = \frac{2}{8}$ $\longrightarrow$ $\frac{1}{4} = \frac{1}{4}$.   G is the answer.

● You do not have to test answer choices H and I.

EXERCISES

Solve each of the following by working backward.

1. Find the value of x if $x - 2$, x, and $x + 3$ are three consecutive terms of a geometric sequence. **B**

  A. 4   **B.** 6   **C.** 8   **D.** 10

2. Find the value of x if $x^{-1} + x^{-2} = 0$. **G**

  F. -2 **G.** -1 **H.** 1   **I.** 2

3. The area of a square is 1.21×10^{-4}. What is its perimeter? **C**

  A. 0.00044   **B.** 0.0044   **C.** 0.044   **D.** 0.44

4. Find the value of x if x, $3x + 1$, and $6x - 1$ are three consecutive terms of an arithmetic sequence. **I**

  F. -3 **G.** -1 **H.** 1   **I.** 3

Chapter Review

Vocabulary

common ratio (p. 424)
compound interest (p. 438)
decay factor (p. 440)
exponential decay (p. 440)

exponential function (p. 430)
exponential growth (p. 437)
geometric sequence (p. 424)
growth factor (p. 437)

interest period (p. 438)
scientific notation (p. 400)

Reading Math
Understanding
Vocabulary

Take It to the NET
Online vocabulary quiz
at www.PHSchool.com
Web Code: aej-0851

3. Scientific notation

4. exponential decay

5. decay factor

Choose the correct term to complete each sentence.

1. The function $y = a \cdot b^x$ models __?__ for $a > 0$ and $b > 1$. **exponential growth**

2. For the function $y = a \cdot b^x$, where $a > 0$ and $b > 1$, b is the __?__. **growth factor**

3. __?__ is a shorthand way to write very large and very small numbers. **3–5. See left.**

4. The function rule $y = a \cdot b^x$ models __?__ for $a > 0$ and $0 < b < 1$.

5. For the function $y = a \cdot b^x$, where $a > 0$ and $0 < b < 1$, b is the __?__.

6. __?__ is calculated using both the principal and the interest that an account has already earned. **Compound interest**

7. Each term of a geometric sequence is found by multiplying the previous term by a fixed number called the __?__. **common ratio**

8. The length of time over which interest is calculated is the __?__. **interest period**

9. When a sequence has a common ratio, it is a(n) __?__. **geometric sequence**

10. The rule $y = 7^x$ is a(n) __?__. **exponential function**

Skills and Concepts

8-1 Objectives

▼ To simplify expressions with zero and negative exponents (p. 394)

▼ To evaluate exponential expressions (p. 396)

You can use zero and negative numbers as exponents. For every nonzero number a, $a^0 = 1$. For every nonzero number a and any integer n, $a^{-n} = \frac{1}{a^n}$.

Simplify each expression.

11. $b^{-4}c^0d^6$ $\quad \dfrac{d^6}{b^4}$

12. $\dfrac{x^{-2}}{y^{-8}} \quad \dfrac{y^8}{x^2}$

13. $7k^{-8}h^3 \quad \dfrac{7h^3}{k^8}$

14. $\dfrac{1}{p^2q^{-4}r^0} \quad \dfrac{q^4}{p^2}$

15. $\left(\dfrac{2}{5}\right)^{-4} \quad \dfrac{625}{16}$ or $39\frac{1}{16}$

16. $(-2)^{-3} \quad -\frac{1}{8}$

17. $-2^{-3} \quad -\frac{1}{8}$

18. $7^{-2}y^{-4} \quad \dfrac{1}{49y^4}$

19. $\dfrac{9w^{-4}}{x^{-2}y^7} \quad \dfrac{9x^2}{w^4y^7}$

Evaluate each expression for $p = 2$, $q = -3$, and $r = 0$.

20. p^2q^2 **36**

21. $(-p)^2q^{-2} \quad \frac{4}{9}$

22. $p^qq^p \quad \frac{9}{8}$ or $1\frac{1}{8}$

23. p^rq^r **1**

24. $-p^2q^3$ **108**

25. Which expression has the greatest value for $a = 4$, $b = -3$, and $c = 0$? **C**

A. a^b B. b^c C. $\dfrac{1}{b^{-a}}$ D. $\dfrac{a^c}{b^c}$ E. $\dfrac{c}{a^{-b}}$

26. **Critical Thinking** Is $(-3b)^4 = -12b^4$? Explain why or why not.
No; for values other than 0, $(-3b)^4 = 81b^4 \neq -12b^4$.

8-2 Objectives

▼ To write numbers in scientific and standard notation (p. 400)

▼ To use scientific notation (p. 401)

You can use **scientific notation** to express very large or very small numbers. A number is in scientific notation if it is in the form $a \times 10^n$, where $1 \leq a < 10$, and n is an integer.

Is each number written in scientific notation? If not, explain.

27. 950×10^5
No; $950 > 10$.

28. 72.35×10^8
No; $72.35 > 10$.

29. 1.6×10^{-6}
yes

30. 0.84×10^{-5}
No; $0.84 < 1$.

31. The space probe Voyager 2 traveled 2,793,000 miles. Write the number of miles in scientific notation. **2.793×10^6 mi**

32. There are 189 million passenger cars and trucks in use in the United States. Write the number of passenger cars and trucks using scientific notation.
1.89×10^8 cars and trucks

8-3 and 8-4 Objectives

▼ To multiply powers (p. 405)

▼ To work with scientific notation (p. 406)

▼ To raise a power to a power (p. 411)

▼ To raise a product to a power (p. 412)

36. 1.34^2 or 1.7956

37. $\dfrac{243x^2y^{14}}{64}$

38. $-\dfrac{4}{3r^{10}z^8}$

To multiply powers with the same base, add the exponents.

$$a^m \cdot a^n = a^{m+n}$$

To raise a power to a power, multiply the exponents.

$$(a^m)^n = a^{mn}$$

To raise a product to a power, raise each factor in the product to the power.

$$(ab)^n = a^n b^n$$

Simplify each expression.

33. $2d^2d^3$ **$2d^5$**

34. $(q^3r)^4$ **$q^{12}r^4$**

35. $(5c^{-4})(-4m^2c^8)$ **$-20c^4m^2$**

36. $(1.34^2)^5(1.34)^{-8}$

37. $(12x^2y^{-2})^5(4xy^{-3})^{-8}$

38. $(-2r^{-4})^2(-3r^2z^8)^{-1}$

39. Estimation Each square inch of your body has about 6.5×10^2 pores. Suppose the back of your hand has an area of about 0.12×10^2 in.^{2}. About how many pores are on the back of your hand? **about 7.8×10^3 pores**

40. Open-Ended Write and solve a problem that involves multiplying exponents.
Answers may vary. Sample: Simplify $(2a^{-2})^{-2}(-3a)^2$; $\frac{9a^6}{4}$.

8-5 Objectives

▼ To divide powers with the same base (p. 417)

▼ To raise a quotient to a power (p. 418)

50. Answers may vary. Sample: Simplify and use div. prop: $\left(\frac{a^2}{2}\right)^{-3}$; use raising a quot. to a power prop.: $\frac{a^{-6}}{2^{-3}}$; use the def. of neg. exp.: $\frac{2^3}{a^6}$ or $\frac{8}{a^6}$

To divide powers with the same base, subtract the exponents.

$$\frac{a^m}{a^n} = a^{m-n}$$

To raise a quotient to a power, raise the dividend and the divisor to the power.

$$\left(\frac{a}{b}\right)^n = \frac{a^n}{b^n}$$

Simplify each expression.

41. $\dfrac{w^2}{w^5}$ **$\dfrac{1}{w^3}$**

42. $(8^3) \cdot 8^{-5}$ **$\dfrac{1}{64}$**

43. $\left(\dfrac{21x^3}{3x}\right)$ **$7x^2$**

44. $\left(\dfrac{n^5}{v^3}\right)^7$ **$\dfrac{n^{35}}{v^{21}}$**

45. $\dfrac{e^{-6}c^3}{e^5}$ **$\dfrac{c^3}{e^{11}}$**

Simplify each quotient. Give your answer in scientific notation.

46. $\dfrac{4.2 \times 10^8}{2.1 \times 10^{11}}$
2×10^{-3}

47. $\dfrac{3.1 \times 10^4}{12.4 \times 10^2}$
2.5×10^1

48. $\dfrac{4.5 \times 10^3}{9 \times 10^7}$
5×10^{-5}

49. $\dfrac{5.1 \times 10^5}{1.7 \times 10^2}$
3×10^3

50. Writing List the steps that you would use to simplify $\left(\dfrac{5a^8}{10a^6}\right)^{-3}$. **See left.**

8-6 Objectives

▼ To use geometric sequences (p. 424)

▼ To use formulas when describing geometric sequences (p. 425)

You find each term of a **geometric sequence** by multiplying the previous term by a fixed number called the common ratio.

Find the common ratio in each geometric sequence.

51. $750, 75, 7.5, 0.75, \ldots$ **52.** $0.04, 0.12, 0.36, 1.08, \ldots$ **53.** $20, -10, 5, -\frac{5}{2}, \ldots$
0.1   3 $-\frac{1}{2}$

Determine whether each sequence is *arithmetic*, *geometric*, or *neither*. Find the next three terms.

54. $1600, 400, 100, 25, \ldots$ **55.** $-40, -39, -37, -34, \ldots$ **56.** $14, 21, 28, 35, \ldots$
geometric; $\frac{25}{4}, \frac{25}{16}, \frac{25}{64}$ neither; $-30, -25, -19$ arithmetic; $42, 49, 56$

8-7 Objectives

▼ To evaluate exponential functions (p. 430)

▼ To graph exponential functions (p. 431)

You can use exponents to show repeated multiplication. An **exponential function** involves repeated multiplication of an initial amount by the same positive number.

Evaluate each function for the given values.

57. $f(x) = 3 \cdot 2^x$ for the domain $\{1, 2, 3, 4\}$ **6, 12, 24, 48**

58. $y = 10 \cdot (0.75)^x$ for the domain $\{1, 2, 3\}$ **7.5, 5.625, 4.21875**

59. a. One kind of bacteria in a laboratory culture triples in number every 30 minutes. Suppose a culture is started with 30 bacteria cells. How many bacteria will there be after 2 hours?   **2430 bacteria**
     b. After how many minutes will there be more than 20,000 bacteria cells? **about 180 min**

8-8 Objectives

▼ To model exponential growth (p. 437)

▼ To model exponential decay (p. 439)

The general form of an exponential function is $y = a \cdot b^x$.

When $b > 1$, the function increases, and the function shows **exponential growth.** The base of the exponent, b, is called the **growth factor.** An example of exponential growth is **compound interest.**

When $0 < b < 1$, the function decreases, and the function shows **exponential decay.** Then the base of the exponent b is called the **decay factor.** An example of exponential decay is the half-life model.

Identify the initial amount a and the growth or decay factor b in each exponential function.

60. $y = 100 \cdot 1.025^x$ **61.** $y = 32 \cdot 0.75^x$ **62.** $y = 0.4 \cdot 2^x$
$a = 100, b = 1.025$ $a = 32, b = 0.75$ $a = 0.4, b = 2$

Identify each function as *exponential growth* or *exponential decay*. Then identify the growth or decay factor.

63. $y = 5.2 \cdot 3^x$ **64.** $y = 0.15 \cdot \left(\frac{3}{2}\right)^x$ **65.** $y = 7 \cdot 0.32^x$ **66.** $y = 1.3 \cdot \left(\frac{1}{4}\right)^x$
growth; 3   growth; 1.5   decay; 0.32   decay; $\frac{1}{4}$

Graph each function. 67–68. See left.   69–70. See margin.

67. $f(x) = 2.5^x$ **68.** $y = 0.5 \cdot (0.5)^x$ **69.** $f(x) = \left(\frac{1}{2}\right) \cdot 3^x$ **70.** $y = 0.1^x$

71. The function $y = 25 \cdot 0.80^x$ models the amount y of a 25-mg dose of medicine remaining in the bloodstream after x hours. How many milligrams of medicine remain in the bloodstream after 5 hours?   **about 8.2 mg**

67.
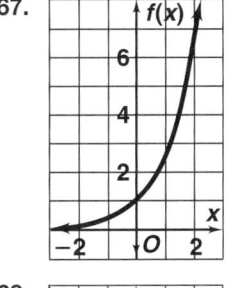

68.
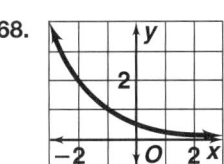

pages 447–449   Chapter Review

69.
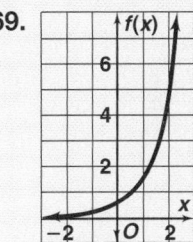

70.
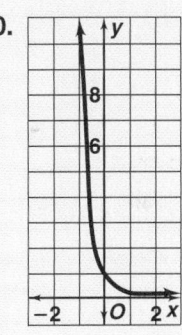

Resources

Teaching Resources
Ch. 8 Test, Forms A & B
Ch. 8 Alternative Assessment,
Form C

Reaching All Students
Spanish Ch. 8 Test, Forms A & B
Spanish Ch. 8 Alternative
Assessment, Form C
Basic Algebra Ch. 8 Test,
Forms D & E

 PRENTICE HALL
ASSESSMENT SYSTEM

Assessment Masters
• Ch. 8 Test, Forms A & B
• Ch. 8 Alternative Assessment,
Form C
Computer Test Generator CD
• Ch. 8 pre-made Test
• Make your own Ch. 8 test

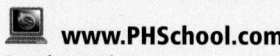 **www.PHSchool.com**
Student Site
• Self-grading Chapter 8 Test
Teacher Center
• Resources

Plus  **iTEXT**

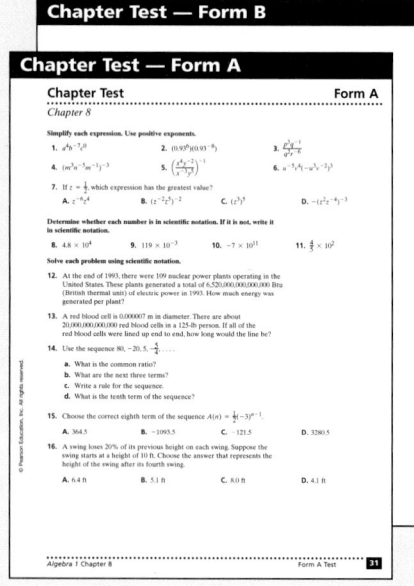

page 450   Chapter Test

18a. about
6.7068 × 10⁸ mi

450

Chapter Test

Take It to the NET
Online chapter test at
www.PHSchool.com
Web Code: aea-0852

Simplify each expression.

1. $\dfrac{r^3 t^{-7}}{t^5} \cdot \dfrac{r\,3}{t^{12}}$

2. $\left(\dfrac{a^3}{m}\right)^{-4} \dfrac{m^4}{a^{12}}$

3. $\dfrac{t^{-8}m^2}{m^{-3}} \cdot \dfrac{m^5}{t^8}$

4. $c^3 v^9 c^{-1} c^0$ $c^2 v^9$

5. $h^2 k^{-5} d^3 k^2 \;\; \dfrac{h^2 d^3}{k^3}$

6. $9y^4 j^2 y^{-9} \;\; \dfrac{9j^2}{y^5}$

7. $(w^2 k^0 p^{-5})^{-7} \;\; \dfrac{p^{35}}{w^{14}}$

8. $2y^{-9} h^2 (2y^0 h^{-4})^{-6} \;\; \dfrac{h^{26}}{32 y^9}$

9. $(1.2)^5 (1.2)^{-2}$ **1.728**

10. $(-3q^{-1})^3 q^2 \;\; \dfrac{-27}{q}$

11. If $n = -3$, which expression has the least value? **C**

A. $n^2 n^0$

B. n^n

C. $n^8 n^{-5}$

D. $-n^n n^{-4}$

Write each number in scientific notation.

12. 4.4909 × 10⁷ votes

12. History There were 44,909,000 votes cast for Bill Clinton in the 1992 presidential election.

13. Pets More than 450,000 households in the United States have reptiles as pets. **4.5 × 10⁵ reptiles**

Is each number written in scientific notation? If not, explain.

14. 76×10^{-9} **No; 76 > 10.** **15.** 7.3×10^5 **yes**

16. $4.05 \times 10 \times 10^{-8}$ **no; two powers of 10**

17. 32.5×10^{13} **No; 32.5 > 10.**

18. a. Astronomy The speed of light in a vacuum is about 186,300 mi/s. Use scientific notation to express how far light travels in one hour. **See margin.**

   b. At its farthest, Saturn is about 1.03×10^9 mi from Earth. About how many hours does it take for light to travel from Earth to Saturn? **about 1.5 h**

19. Use the sequence $-32, 16, -8, 4, \ldots$

   a. What is the common ratio? $-\frac{1}{2}$

   b. What are the next three terms? $-2, 1, -\frac{1}{2}$

   c. Write a rule for the sequence. $A(n) = -32\left(-\frac{1}{2}\right)^{n-1}$

   d. What is the ninth term of the sequence? $-\frac{1}{8}$

20. You drop a ball from a height of 12 ft. Each path has $\frac{3}{5}$ the height of the previous path.

   a. Write a rule for the sequence. The initial height is given by the term $n = 1$. $A(n) = 12 \cdot \left(\frac{3}{5}\right)^{n-1}$

   b. What height will the ball reach at the top of the fourth path ($n = 4$)? **2.592 ft**

---

21. Find the fifth term of the sequence $A(n) = -3(-2)^{n+1}$. **−192**

Evaluate each function for $x = 1, 2,$ and 3.

22. $y = 3 \cdot 5^x$ **15, 75, 375**

23. $f(x) = \frac{1}{2} \cdot 4^x$ **2, 8, 32**

24. $f(x) = 4(0.95)^x$ **3.8, 3.61, 3.4295**

25. $g(x) = 5\left(\frac{3}{4}\right)^x$ **3.75, 2.8125, 2.109375**

Graph each function. 26–27. See margin.

26. $y = \frac{1}{2} \cdot 2^x$

27. $y = 2 \cdot \left(\frac{1}{2}\right)^x$

28. $f(x) = 3^x$ **See back of book.**

29. Open-Ended Write and solve a problem involving exponential decay. **See margin.**

30. Writing Explain when the function $y = a \cdot b^x$ shows exponential growth and when it shows exponential decay. **growth for $b > 1$, decay for $0 < b < 1$**

31. Banking A customer deposits $1000 in a savings account that pays 4% interest compounded quarterly. How much money will the customer have in the account after 2 years? After 5 years? **$1082.86; $1220.19**

32. The function $y = 1.3 \cdot (1.07)^x$ models a city's annual electrical consumption for x years since 1985, where y is kilowatt-hours.

   a. Determine whether the function models exponential growth or decay, and find the growth or decay factor. **growth; 1.07**

   b. According to the model, what will be the annual electrical usage in 2010? **about 7.1 kw-h**

   c. According to the model, what was the annual electrical usage in 1975? **about 0.66 kw-h**

   d. What value of x should you substitute to find the value of y now? Use this value for x to find y. **Check students' work.**

33. Automobiles Suppose a new car is worth $20,000. You can use the function $y = 20{,}000(0.85)^x$ to estimate the car's value after x years. **33a. See margin.**

   a. What is the decay factor? What does it mean?

   b. Estimate the car's value after one year. **$17,000**

   c. Estimate the car's value after four years. **$10,440**

34. The function $y = 10 \cdot 1.08^x$ models the cost of annual tuition (in thousands of dollars) at a local college x years after 1997. **34b. $10,000; $12,597.12**

   a. What is the annual percent increase? **8%**

   b. How much was tuition in 1997? In 2000? **See above.**

   c. How much will the tuition be the year you plan to graduate from high school? **Check students' work.**

26.

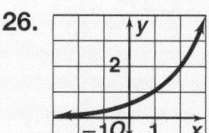

27.

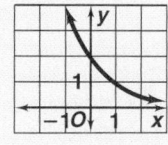

29. Answers may vary. Sample: A computer loses 20% of its value each year. How much will a $3500 computer be worth in 3 years? $1792

33a. 0.85; the car's value depreciates 15% annually.

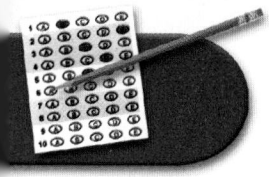

Standardized Test Prep

Standardized Test Prep

Multiple Choice

For Exercises 1–10, choose the correct letter.

1. If a is positive and b is negative, which of the following is negative? **C**
   A. $a + |b|$ B. $a|b|$
   C. $|a|b$ D. $|a| - b$

2. The scores on your first five algebra tests are 88, 78, 81, 83, and 90. What score must you get on your next test to raise the mean to 85? **F**
   F. 90   G. 87   H. 86   I. 85

3. Which value of x is NOT a solution to the inequality $5 - 6x < -x + 2$? **A**
   A. -1 B. 1   C. 3   D. 5

4. You earn a commission of 6% on your first $500 of sales and 10% on all sales above $500. If you earn $130 in commission, what are your total sales? **I**
   F. $800   G. $1000   H. $1300   I. $1500

5. Find the solution of the system of equations. **C**
   $$\tfrac{1}{3}x - y = 4$$
   $$x + 3y = 0$$
   A. $(9, -1)$ B. $(-6, 2)$
   C. $(6, -2)$ D. $(-9, 1)$

6. You flip a coin and roll a number cube. What is the probability of getting a head and a multiple of three? **G**
   F. $\frac{1}{12}$ G. $\frac{1}{6}$ H. $\frac{1}{4}$ I. $\frac{3}{2}$

7. Which number has the least value? **D**
   A. 2.8×10^{-5} B. 5.3×10^{-4}
   C. 8.3×10^{-7} D. 1.6×10^{-8}

8. Potassium-42 has a half-life of 12.5 h. How many half-lives are in 75 h? **F**
   F. 6   G. 8   H. 25   I. 150

9. Simplify $-3a^8 \cdot cb^{-3} \cdot b^{12} \cdot 9c.^5$ **B**
   A. $6a^9b^5c^6$ B. $-27a^8b^9c^6$
   C. $-27a^8b^{15}c^6$ D. $-3abc$

10. Which statement is true for every solution of the following system? **I**
    $$y > x + 4$$
    $$y + x > 4$$
    F. $x \le -3$ G. $y < 5$
    H. $x > 4$ I. $y > 4$

Quantitative Comparison

Compare the boxed quantity in Column A with the boxed quantity in Column B. Choose the best answer.

   A. The quantity in Column A is greater.
   B. The quantity in Column B is greater.
   C. The two quantities are equal.
   D. The relationship cannot be determined from the information given.

Column A	Column B
the growth factor of an exponential function	the decay factor of an exponential function

A 11.

$$\begin{bmatrix} 6 & 1 \\ 0 & x \end{bmatrix} + \begin{bmatrix} 1 & y \\ -5 & 3 \end{bmatrix} = \begin{bmatrix} 7 & 9 \\ -5 & 6 \end{bmatrix}$$

B 12.

x	y

Gridded Response

13. A cafeteria charges $.21/oz for frozen yogurt. How many dollars would a 9-oz serving cost?
    1.89

14. For a spinner numbered from 1 to 6, the outcomes are equally likely. What is the probability of getting an odd number? $\frac{1}{2}$

Short Response

Show all work.

15. On April 1, 2000, the day of the 2000 national census, the population of the United States was 281,421,906 people. This was a 13.2% increase from the 1990 census. What was the 1990 population of the United States? **See margin.**

16. Graph the inequality $|x - 2| \le 9$ on a number line. **See margin.**

Extended Response

17. The slopes of four different lines are $\frac{3}{5}, -\frac{10}{6}, -\frac{5}{3}$, and $\frac{9}{15}$. Do these lines determine a rectangle? Explain why or why not. **See back of book.**

Resources

📁 **Teaching Resources**
Cumulative Review

👥 **Reaching All Students**
Spanish Cumulative Review

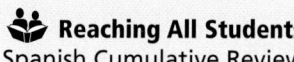

PRENTICE HALL
ASSESSMENT SYSTEM

Standardized Test Prep Workbook
• Ch. 8 Standardized Test Practice
Assessment Masters
• Cumulative Review
Computer Test Generator CD
• Standardized Test Practice

💻 **www.PHSchool.com**
• Standardized Test Practice
• Resources

Plus

Cumulative Review

Cumulative Review
Chapters 1–8

Item	Lesson	Item	Lesson
1	1-3	10	7-5
2	2-7	11	8-8
3	3-4	12	1-4
4	2-5	13	4-1
5	7-3	14	4-6
6	4-6	15	8-7
7	8-2	16	3-6
8	8-8	17	6-5
9	8-3		

page 451   Standardized Test Prep

15. [2] $(1.132)x = 281,421,906$
    $x = 248,605,924$
    248,605,924 people

    [1] no work shown

16. [2] $-9 \le x - 2 \le 9$
    $-7 \le x \le 11$

    −7   0   11

    [1] no work shown

How Fast Can You Run?

In these activities students apply their knowledge of rates, systems of equations, and solving systems by graphing.

Connecting to Prior Knowledge

Have students make conjectures about the difference between the velocity they can run for a short sprint as compared to the velocity they can run for a mile. Discuss whether or not long-distance runners maintain a constant velocity during the entire run.

Teaching Notes

Have a volunteer read the introductory paragraph. Ask: *What assumption does the display of animals make in order to compare the velocities of these animals?* Sample answer: It assumes that the animals are running at their top speed for an entire hour.

Visual Learners

If possible, bring a stopwatch to the classroom and demonstrate how it can be used to measure time with great accuracy.

Inclusion

To make sure that all students read and understand the display, have them make a list of the five fastest animals and the five slowest.

Connection to Science

Explain that the difference between speed and velocity is that velocity is speed in a specified direction. If the animals in the picture are facing east, what is the velocity of the mule deer? **35 mi/h east**

English Learners

Ask students to name some pairs of animals from the display that are predators and some that are prey.

452

 **Real-World Snapshots**

How Fast Can You Run?

Applying Linear Equations Animals run to escape predators and to chase prey. The display below compares animals as if they were able to sprint along at their top velocities or speeds for a whole hour. Linear equations and graphs are good tools for describing and comparing motion at constant velocities.

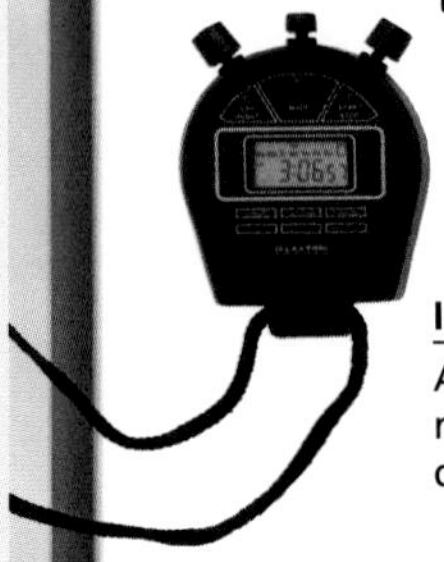

Instant Records

A stopwatch is a watch used to time races. It can be started and stopped quickly for accurate timing.

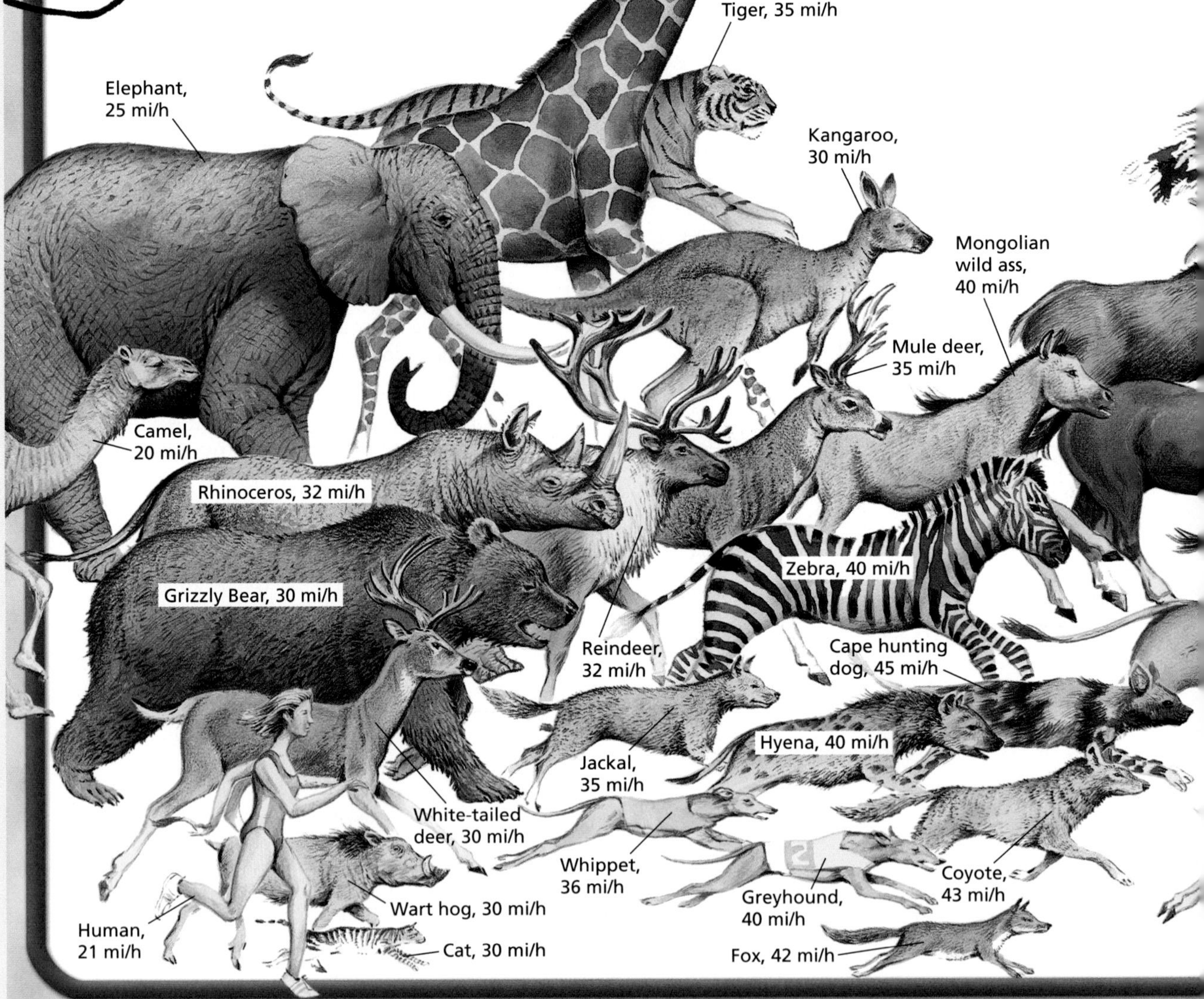

Giraffe, 32 mi/h

Tiger, 35 mi/h

Kangaroo, 30 mi/h

Mongolian wild ass, 40 mi/h

Elephant, 25 mi/h

Mule deer, 35 mi/h

Camel, 20 mi/h

Rhinoceros, 32 mi/h

Zebra, 40 mi/h

Grizzly Bear, 30 mi/h

Reindeer, 32 mi/h

Cape hunting dog, 45 mi/h

Hyena, 40 mi/h

Jackal, 35 mi/h

White-tailed deer, 30 mi/h

Whippet, 36 mi/h

Coyote, 43 mi/h

Greyhound, 40 mi/h

Human, 21 mi/h

Wart hog, 30 mi/h

Cat, 30 mi/h

Fox, 42 mi/h

452 All photographs © Dorling Kindersley Limited unless otherwise credited on acknowledgments page

---

pages 452–453
Real World Snapshots
Answers may vary.
Sample:
Activity 1
  a. Human: ≈10 yd/s
     Giraffe: ≈16 yd/s

b. 20 yd;
  Human:
   $H(t) = 10t + 20$
  Giraffe:
   $G(t) = 16t$

c.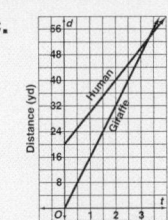

d. ≈3.3 s; ≈54 yd

e. 10 yd;
  Human:
   $H(t) = 10t + 10$
  Giraffe:
   $G(t) = 16t$

Car Racing
Formula 1 cars compete at speeds as high as 200 mi/h. The speed limit on most U.S. highways and interstates is 65 mi/h.

Activity 1

Materials graph paper, pencil

Diversity
Ask students to tell which of the animals in the display they have seen in the wild (and tell where) and which they have seen in zoos. Discuss which animals might be found near where students live now or near where they have lived in the past.

Activity 2

Materials graph paper, pencil

Visual Learners
Have students make a photocopy of the animals chosen for their graph so they can use cut-outs of those animals on a poster board display that shows and explains the graph of the three equations.

Scoring Rubric

This scoring rubric applies to both activities. Share this scoring rubric with students before they begin work.

4 Calculations, equations, and graphs are correct and completely labeled.

3 Calculations, equations, and graphs are mostly correct, with some minor errors or omissions.

2 Calculations, equations, and graphs contain both major and minor errors.

1 Correct answer or graph, but no labels or work is shown.

Ostrich, 45 mi/h

Moose, 45 mi/h

Horse, 43 mi/h

Wildebeest, 50 mi/h

Lion, 50 mi/h

Thomson's gazelle, 50 mi/h

Activity 1

Materials: graph paper, pencil

a. Suppose two animals are in a race. Choose the two animals and calculate the speed of each animal in yards per second.

b. Decide how much of a head start (in yards) the faster animal offers the slower animal. For each animal, write an equation relating distance from the starting line to time.

c. Graph the two equations on the same coordinate plane.

d. How long will it take the faster animal to overtake the slower animal? How many yards from the starting line are the animals when the faster animal overtakes the slower animal?

e. Reduce the head start by half and repeat parts (c) and (d).

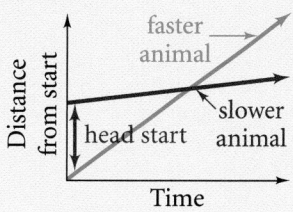

Activity 2

a. Choose a third animal. Calculate its speed in yards per second. Compare its speed with the speed of the two animals you chose in Activity 1.

b. Decide which two animals should get head starts and how much of a head start each should get. Write three equations relating distance from the starting line to time.

c. Graph all three equations on the same coordinate plane.

Cheetah, 70 mi/h

Take It to the NET For more information about speeds, go to **www.PHSchool.com**.
Web Code: aee-0853

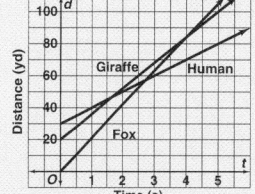

453

Activity 2
a. Fox: ≈21 yd/s; the fox is about twice as fast as the human and about one third faster than the giraffe.

b. 20 yd head start for the giraffe, 30 yd head start for the human;
Human: $H(t) = 10t + 30$
Giraffe: $G(t) = 16t + 20$
Fox: $F(t) = 21t$

c.

Polynomials and Factoring

Chapter at a Glance

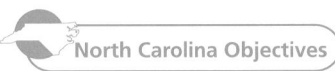
North Carolina Objectives

9-1	Adding and Subtracting Polynomials	1.01b

NCTM
2, 3, 8,
10
▼ Describing Polynomials
▼ Adding and Subtracting Polynomials

9-2	Multiplying and Factoring	1.01b

NCTM
2, 8,
10
▼ Distributing a Monomial
▼ Factoring a Monomial from a Polynomial

9-3	Multiplying Binomials	1.01b

NCTM
2, 3, 8,
10
▼ Multiplying Two Binomials
▼ Multiplying a Trinomial and a Binomial

9-4	Multiplying Special Cases	1.01b

NCTM
2, 7, 8,
9, 10
▼ Finding the Square of a Binomial
▼ Difference of Squares

9-5	Factoring Trinomials of the Type $x^2 + bx + c$	1.01c

NCTM
2, 6, 8,
10
▼ Factoring Trinomials

9-6	Factoring Trinomials of the Type $ax^2 + bx + c$	1.01c

NCTM
2, 6, 8,
10
▼ Factoring $ax^2 + bx + c$

9-7	Factoring Special Cases	1.01c

NCTM
2, 6, 8,
10
▼ Factoring Perfect-Square Trinomials
▼ Factoring the Difference of Squares

9-8	Factoring by Grouping	1.01c

NCTM
2, 3, 6,
8,10
▼ Factoring Polynomials With Four Terms
▼ Factoring Trinomials by Grouping

NCTM STANDARDS 2000

1	Number and Operations	6	Problem Solving
2	Algebra	7	Reasoning and Proof
3	Geometry	8	Communication
4	Measurement	9	Connections
5	Data Analysis and Probability	10	Representation

Pacing Options

This chart suggests pacing only for the lessons and their parts. It is provided as a possible guide. It will help you determine how much time you have in your schedule to cover other components, such as the features, Chapter Review, and Chapter Test.

Day	Traditional 45 min.	Two-Year 45 min.	Block 90 min.
1	9-1 ▼ ▼	9-1 ▼	9-1 ▼ ▼ 9-2 ▼ ▼
2	9-2 ▼ ▼	9-1 ▼	9-3 ▼ ▼ 9-4 ▼
3	9-3 ▼ ▼	9-2 ▼	9-4 ▼
4	9-4 ▼	9-2 ▼	9-5 ▼
5	9-4 ▼	9-3 ▼	9-6 ▼
6	9-5 ▼	9-3 ▼	9-7 ▼ ▼
7	9-5 ▼	9-4 ▼	9-8 ▼ ▼
8	9-6 ▼	9-4 ▼ ▼	
9	9-6 ▼	9-4 ▼	
10	9-7 ▼	9-5 ▼	
11	9-7 ▼	9-5 ▼	
12	9-8 ▼	9-5 ▼	
13	9-8 ▼	9-6 ▼	
14		9-6 ▼	
15		9-6 ▼	
16		9-7 ▼	
17		9-7 ▼ ▼	
18		9-7 ▼	
19		9-8 ▼	
20		9-8 ▼	

NAEP Correlation (National Assessment of Educational Progress 2000 Mathematics Objectives)

9-1	9-2	9-3	9-4	9-5	9-6	9-7	9-8
N3a	N3a, A1f	N3a, M4a	N3a, M4a	N2c, N6c	N2c, N6c	N6c	N2c, N6c

N = Number Sense, Properties, and Operations; **M** = Measurement; **G** = Geometry and Spatial Sense;
D = Data Analysis, Statistics, and Probability; **A** = Algebra and Functions

Math Background

Chapter Overview

This chapter presents a number of skills that are necessary prerequisites to solving equations. These skills involve combining, simplifying, and factoring polynomials. Factoring polynomials is made easier by recognizing patterns that frequently occur in the products. Students will use factoring again in Chapter 10 to solve quadratic equations.

Adding and Subtracting Polynomials   9-1

Polynomials are the basic building blocks of algebraic expressions. Many physical situations result in polynomial models, and skill in their manipulation is essential to future work. One of the most important descriptions of a polynomial includes what it is *not*: a polynomial has *no* variables in the denominator and *no* variables that cannot be expressed with exponents that are whole numbers.

Multiplying and Factoring   9-2

A product can be "un-multiplied," or factored, to find the component factors that were originally multiplied to form the product. Be sure students grasp that the Distributive Property makes it clear that any factoring can be checked by multiplying the factors to see if they do indeed result in the original expression or product.

Multiplying Binomials   9-3, 9-4

Two special cases, the square of a binomial and the difference of squares, are presented as patterns students can easily recognize. These examples and exercises provide ample practice to help students with the factoring that is presented in the rest of the chapter.

Factoring Trinomials   9-5, 9-6

Factoring trinomials can be reduced to a set of procedures that will ultimately result in finding the factors, if they exist. However, the process can involve several steps, especially if the coefficients of the variables have many factors, resulting in a large number of possible combinations to be tested.

With experience, students will learn various common characteristics and gain insights that can shortcut this process significantly. For example, students will learn the characteristics of odd and even numbers. Two factors that are both even, or two factors that are both odd, must have a sum or difference that is also even.

Factoring Special Cases   9–7

In algebra, solving many problems can be greatly facilitated if some patterns are committed to memory. Of course, it is much easier to recall these patterns if the reasons why the patterns work (FOIL, for example) are understood. Later on, when students solve quadratic equations, they will find it extremely useful to be able to recognize a special pattern whenever they see it.

To help students remember patterns accurately, let them experiment with the most common errors. For example, students may think that $x^2 + 16$ can be factored. Encourage them to work in groups to try to find factors that work, before confirming their discovery that this binomial cannot be factored.

Discuss the fact that, in one sense, any expression can be factored. $x^2 + 16$ could be written as the product $x(x + x + \frac{16}{x})$, but this form does not meet the definition of a polynomial, since a variable occurs in the denominator. Therefore, the expression is not factorable within the definitions agreed upon.

Factoring by Grouping   9-8

Some students may find factoring by grouping somewhat frustrating, for a number of reasons. The patterns of expressions that can be factored are not easily recognizable, and how the terms should be grouped is often not obvious. Encourage students to think of these problems as a puzzle, where time must be spent trying several possibilities until one is found that works.

Remind students to always look first for a common factor, which may be a variable or an integer. Ask those students who are able to do this easily to share their thinking and procedural strategies with the class.

 # Ongoing Assessment and Intervention

Tools for Monitoring Student Progress

The Prentice Hall *Algebra 1* program provides you with many options for assessment in the Student Edition, the Teacher's Edition and the teaching resources. From these options you may choose instructional materials and techniques that are appropriate for your students and support your district's curriculum requirements.

Instant Check System™ in Chapter 9

Allows students to check their own learning before, during, and after each lesson.

Diagnosing Readiness before the chapter (p. 454)

Check Skills You'll Need exercises in each lesson (pp. 456, 462, 467, 474, 481, 486, 490, 496)

Check Understanding questions with each Example (pp. 457, 458, 462, 463, 467, 468, 469, 475, 476, 477, 481, 482, 483, 486, 487, 491, 492, 496, 497, 498)

Checkpoint Quiz (pp. 472, 495)

 Test Prep in Chapter 9

Teaches students strategies and gives them practice with all the test item formats they will encounter on state tests and standardized national exams.

Standardized Test Prep exercises in each lesson (pp. 461, 465, 472, 479, 485, 489, 494, 495, 500, 501)

Test-Taking Strategies (p. 502: Eliminating Answers)

Standardized Test Prep (p. 507: Reading Comprehension)

All your assessment needs in one place!

Program Assessment

Assess student progress throughout the *Algebra 1* text with blackline masters and CD-ROM.

Assessment Resources

- Checkpoint Quizzes 1 & 2
- Chapter Test, Forms A & B
- Chapter Alternative Assessment

Spanish versions available. Tests for Basic Algebra also available.

Computer Test Generator

- Unlimited questions of varying difficulty for every lesson objective.
- Create your own practice sheets, quizzes, and tests, or use the pre-made Chapter Tests.
- Diagnose readiness with questions on prerequisite skills.
- Prepare students by making tests based on standardized test objectives.
- Access Algebra 1, Geometry, and Algebra 2 content—all on one CD-ROM.

Test Preparation

A three-step approach to preparing students for high stakes, national, and state exams.

❶ Diagnose & Prescribe

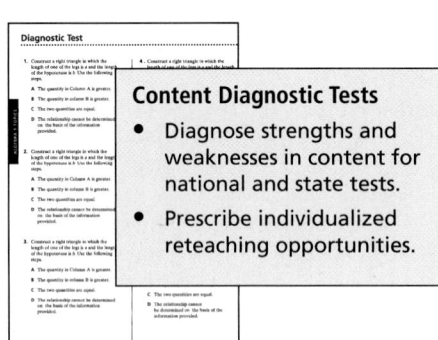

Content Diagnostic Tests

- Diagnose strengths and weaknesses in content for national and state tests.
- Prescribe individualized reteaching opportunities.

❷ Review & Reteach

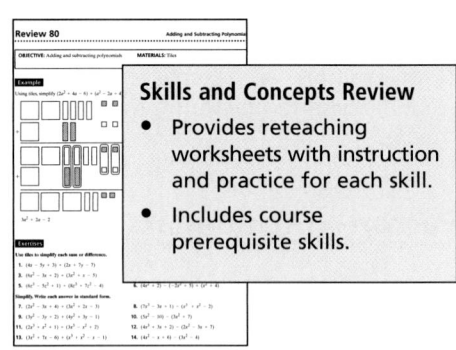

Skills and Concepts Review

- Provides reteaching worksheets with instruction and practice for each skill.
- Includes course prerequisite skills.

❸ Practice & Assess

Test Preparation

- Features practice tests for End-of-Course and SAT/ACT exams.
- Includes standardized test practice by chapter for ongoing review.

Teacher's Guide with answers and correlations.

Test-Taking Strategies with Transparencies

- Support the Test-Taking Strategies pages in the Student Edition.
- Provide a teaching transparency and a practice worksheet for each strategy.

 **Reaching All Students**

Support in the Student Text and Additional Resources

The textbook, the iText, and other technology components provide numerous opportunities to reach students of various ability levels and learning styles. Each Teacher's Edition lesson suggests how you can help *all* your students be successful and understand the mathematics in Chapter 9.

Below Level

Student Edition
- Diagnosing Readiness*: p. 454
- Check Skills You'll Need*: pp. 456, 462, 467, 474, 481, 486, 490, 496

Reteaching
Chapter 9 Support File: pp. 10–17

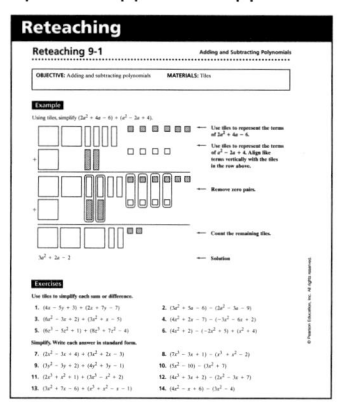

Basic Algebra Planning Guide
Chapter 9 Lesson Plans: pp. 56–63
Chapter 9 Tests: pp. 121–124

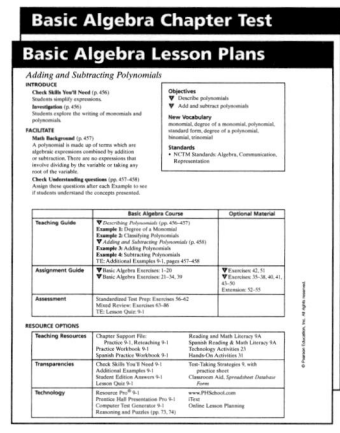

* Can be used with all ability levels to ensure mastery of prerequisite skills.

Advanced Learners

Student Edition
- Challenge exercises: pp. 460, 464, 465, 471, 478, 479, 484, 488, 494, 500

Enrichment
Chapter 9 Support File: pp. 18–25

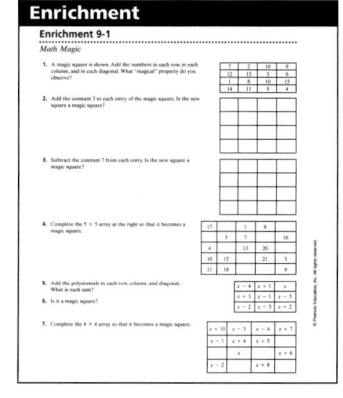

Reading and Math Literacy

Student Edition
- Vocabulary: pp. 455, 503, *plus* in every Lesson Preview
- Reading Math: pp. 473, 503
- Illustrated Glossary: pp. 757–785

Reading and Math Literacy Masters
Chapter 9: pp. 33–36

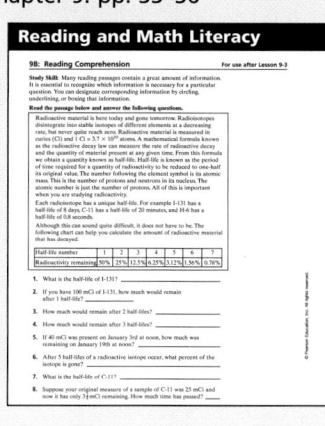

English Learners

Student Edition
- English/Spanish Illustrated Glossary: pp. 757–785

Workbook and Masters
Spanish Practice Workbook: pp. 56–63
Spanish Reading and Math Literacy Masters: pp. 33–36

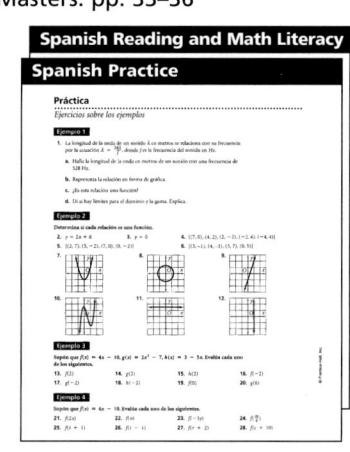

Learning Styles

Student Edition
- Investigation: pp. 456, 466, 474, 480, 490
- Technology: p. 495
- Writing: pp. 460, 464, 470, 478, 484, 488, 493, 500, 506

Activity Masters
Hands-On Activities: 20, 21, 22
Technology Activities: 23

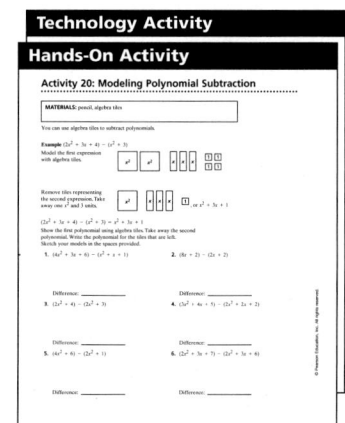

Program Resources

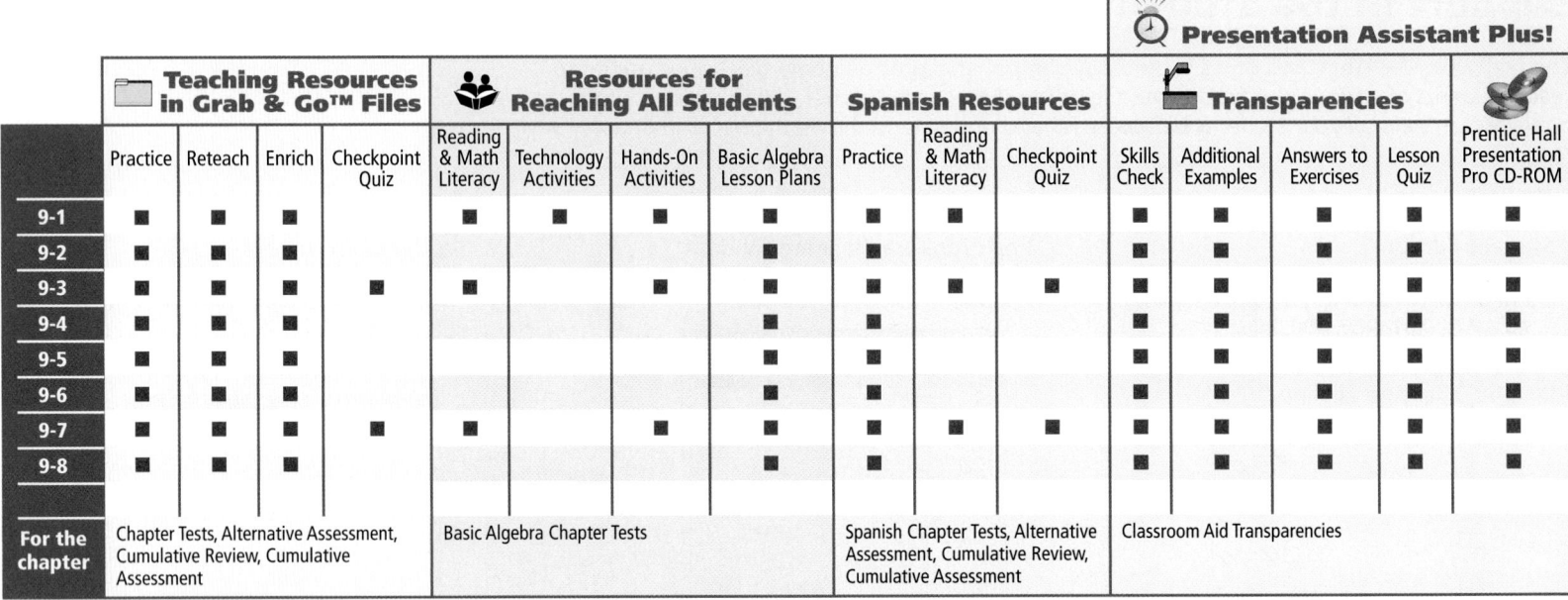

	Teaching Resources in Grab & Go™ Files				Resources for Reaching All Students				Spanish Resources			Transparencies				Prentice Hall Presentation Pro CD-ROM
	Practice	Reteach	Enrich	Checkpoint Quiz	Reading & Math Literacy	Technology Activities	Hands-On Activities	Basic Algebra Lesson Plans	Practice	Reading & Math Literacy	Checkpoint Quiz	Skills Check	Additional Examples	Answers to Exercises	Lesson Quiz	
9-1	■	■	■		■	■	■	■	■	■		■	■	■	■	■
9-2	■	■	■					■	■	■		■	■	■	■	■
9-3	■	■	■	■	■		■	■	■	■	■	■	■	■	■	■
9-4	■	■	■					■	■	■		■	■	■	■	■
9-5	■	■	■					■	■	■		■	■	■	■	■
9-6	■	■	■					■	■	■		■	■	■	■	■
9-7	■	■	■	■	■		■	■	■	■	■	■	■	■	■	■
9-8	■	■	■					■	■	■		■	■	■	■	■
For the chapter	Chapter Tests, Alternative Assessment, Cumulative Review, Cumulative Assessment				Basic Algebra Chapter Tests				Spanish Chapter Tests, Alternative Assessment, Cumulative Review, Cumulative Assessment			Classroom Aid Transparencies				

Also available for use with the chapter:

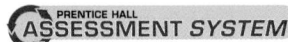 *See page 454C.*

- Practice Workbook
- Solution Key

- For teacher support and access to student Web site materials, use Web Code aek-5500.
- For additional online and technology resources, see below.

 ## Technology

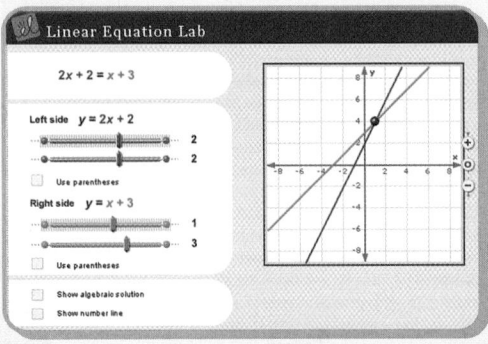

Online and on CD-ROM

Complete Interactive Student Text online and on CD-ROM—with instant feedback assessment, tutorial help, dynamic activities, instructional and real-world videos, audio, and additional practice.

www.PHSchool.com
For Students

Use **Web codes** for easy access to online activities, chapter projects, self-grading lesson quizzes and chapter tests, vocabulary quizzes, updated data sources, graphing calculator procedures, and more.

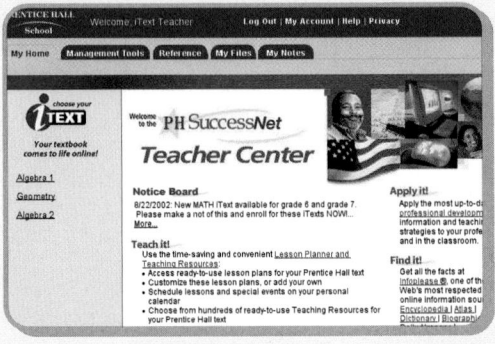

PH SuccessNet
For Teachers

Online lesson planning with built-in state correlations, all the teaching resources, complete reference library, your own calendar and Teacher Web page, professional development, and more.

Presentation Assistant Plus!

The Prentice Hall *Presentation Assistant Plus!* provides you with the material you need to teach a lesson from beginning to end. Two easy-to-use formats—Transparencies and CD-ROM—allow you to present a lesson the way you are most comfortable.

 ## Transparencies

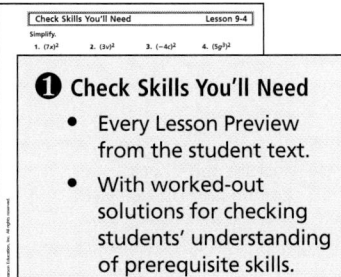
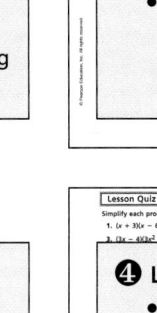
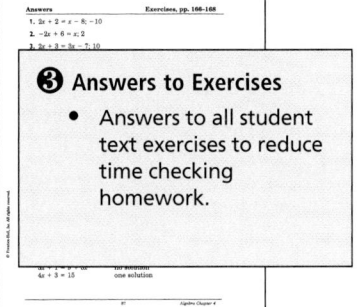
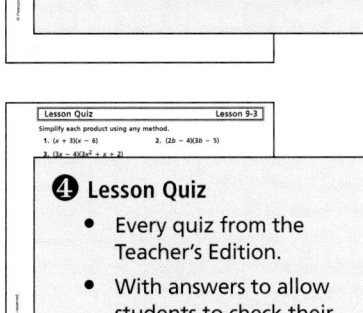

❶ **Check Skills You'll Need**
- Every Lesson Preview from the student text.
- With worked-out solutions for checking students' understanding of prerequisite skills.

❷ **Additional Examples**
- Every example from the Teacher's Edition.
- Fully worked-out, step-by-step solutions for easy demonstration.

❸ **Answers to Exercises**
- Answers to all student text exercises to reduce time checking homework.

❹ **Lesson Quiz**
- Every quiz from the Teacher's Edition.
- With answers to allow students to check their own work.

 Throughout the Teacher's Edition, this symbol indicates material that is available on transparency in the Presentation Assistant Plus!

 ## Prentice Hall Presentation Pro CD-ROM

- Includes all Transparencies.
- Conveniently organized by lesson so you can easily ❶ Introduce, ❷ Teach, ❸ Check Homework, and ❹ Assess each lesson.
- Animated examples allow step-by-step instruction at your own pace.
- Easy to edit so you can create custom presentations.

Teaching Chapter 9 Using Presentation Assistant Plus!

	❶ Introduce	❷ Teach	❸ Check Homework	❹ Assess
	Check Skills You'll Need	Additional Examples	Student Edition Answers	Lesson Quiz
9-1	p. 56	pp. 125–126	✔	p. 125
9-2	p. 57	pp. 126–127	✔	p. 125
9-3	p. 58	pp. 127–129	✔	p. 126
9-4	p. 59	pp. 129–131	✔	p. 126
9-5	p. 60	pp. 132–134	✔	p. 127
9-6	p. 61	pp. 134–135	✔	p. 127
9-7	p. 62	pp. 136–137	✔	p. 128
9-8	p. 63	pp. 137–139	✔	p. 128

 ### Prentice Hall Presentation Pro

CD-ROM with dynamic PowerPoint® presentations for every lesson. Helps you introduce and develop concepts, check homework, and assess progress. Part of Presentation Assistant Plus! *(See above.)*

 ### Computer Test Generator

CD-ROM to create practice sheets and tests for course objectives and standardized tests. Includes Instant Chapter Tests™, online testing, and student reports. Part of the PH Assessment System. *(See page 454C.)*

 ### Resource Pro® with Planning Express®

CD-ROM with a lesson planning tool that allows you to import state and local objectives. Includes electronic versions of all the teaching resources.

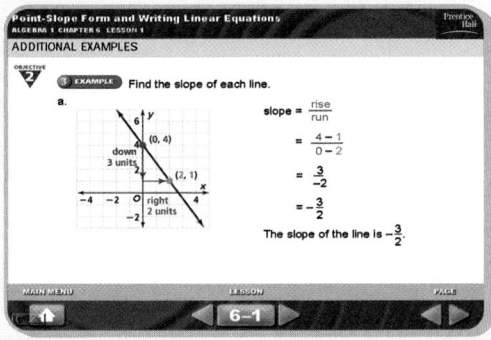
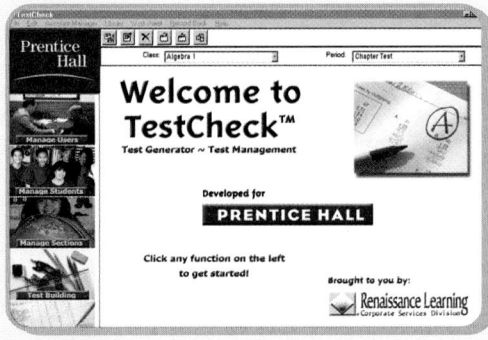

Chapter 9

Polynomials and Factoring

 Diagnosing Readiness

Students will find answers to these exercises in the back of their textbooks.

For intervention, direct students to:

Finding Factors of Composite Numbers
Skills Handbook p. 720, Example 2,
Exercises 19–47

Simplifying Expressions
Lesson 1-7: Examples 3–5
Exercises 15–42
Extra Practice, p. 702

Multiplying Expressions with Exponents
Lesson 8-3: Example 2
Exercises 7–15
Lesson 8-4: Examples 1, 2
Exercises 1–8
Extra Practice, p. 709

Dividing Expressions with Exponents
Lesson 8-5: Example 3
Exercises 21–28
Extra Practice, p. 709

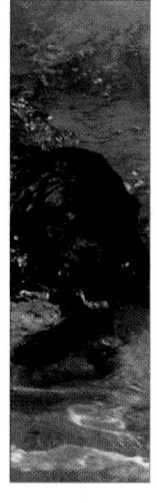

Where You've Been

- In Chapter 1, you learned how to use variables and applied the Distributive Property to variable expressions.

- In Chapter 2, you combined like terms to solve equations.

- In Chapter 8, you simplified variable expressions with exponents by using the multiplication and division properties of exponents.

 Instant self-check online and on CD-ROM

Diagnosing Readiness (For help, go to the Lesson in green.)

Finding Factors of Composite Numbers (Skills Handbook page 720)

List all the factors of each number. **5–8. See margin.**

1. 12 **1, 2, 3, 4, 6, 12**   **2.** 56   **3.** 31 **1, 31**   **4.** 27 **1, 3, 9, 27**
                           1, 2, 4, 7, 8, 14, 28, 56

5. 110   **6.** 65   **7.** 50   **8.** 200

9. 11 **1, 11**   **10.** 42   **11.** 66   **12.** 73 **1, 73**
              1, 2, 3, 6, 7, 14, 21, 42   **1, 2, 3, 6, 11, 22, 33, 66**

Simplifying Expressions (Lesson 1-7)

Simplify each expression.

13. $2x^2 - x + x^2 - 3x$ $\mathbf{3x^2 - 4x}$ **14.** $-b + 2 + 3b + 4$ $\mathbf{2b + 6}$

15. $-5y - y^2 + 4y^2 - 6y$ $\mathbf{3y^2 - 11y}$ **16.** $(3w - 2w^2 + 4w - 2w^2)\frac{1}{6}$ $\mathbf{-\frac{2}{3}w^2 + \frac{7}{6}w}$

17. $-8(z + 2) + 5(3z - 10)$ $\mathbf{7z - 66}$ **18.** $2(x + 4x^2 - 2x - 2x^2)$ $\mathbf{4x^2 - 2x}$

19. $12t - 5t^2 - 2t - t^2$ $\mathbf{-6t^2 + 10t}$ **20.** $p - 3 - (p^2 - 3) - 3p$ $\mathbf{-p^2 - 2p}$

Multiplying Expressions With Exponents (Lessons 8-3 and 8-4)

Simplify each expression.

21. $(7w)^2$ $\mathbf{49w^2}$ **22.** $(-5n^2)(-5n)$ $\mathbf{25n^3}$ **23.** $(3z^2)^2$ $\mathbf{9z^4}$ **24.** $(2t^3)(5t^4)$ $\mathbf{10t^7}$

25. $(4y^3)^2$ $\mathbf{16y^6}$ **26.** $(-9ab)^2$ $\mathbf{81a^2b^2}$ **27.** $4(x^2)^2$ $\mathbf{4x^4}$ **28.** $(-6p^4)^2$ $\mathbf{36p^8}$

Dividing Expressions With Exponents (Lesson 8-5)

Simplify each expression.

29. $\frac{x^5y^8}{x^3y^4}$ $\mathbf{x^2y^4}$ **30.** $\frac{(3c)^2}{(3c)}$ $\mathbf{3c}$ **31.** $\frac{-5t}{(10t^3)(2t)}$ $\mathbf{-\frac{1}{4t^3}}$ **32.** $\frac{(3a)(4a^3)}{6a^2}$ $\mathbf{2a^2}$

page 454   Diagnosing Readiness

5. 1, 2, 5, 10, 11, 22, 55, 110   **7.** 1, 2, 5, 10, 25, 50

6. 1, 5, 13, 65   **8.** 1, 2, 4, 5, 8, 10, 20, 25, 40, 50, 100, 200

Polynomials and Factoring

Where You're Going

- In this chapter, you will categorize polynomials by their degree and number of terms.

- You will learn to add, subtract, and multiply polynomials.

 Real-World Connection Applying what you learn, you will multiply binomials to model combinations of inherited color genes, on page 475.

Chapter 9

LESSONS

9-1 Adding and Subtracting Polynomials

9-2 Multiplying and Factoring

9-3 Multiplying Binomials

9-4 Multiplying Special Cases

9-5 Factoring Trinomials of the Type $x^2 + bx + c$

9-6 Factoring Trinomials of the Type $ax^2 + bx + c$

9-7 Factoring Special Cases

9-8 Factoring by Grouping

Key Vocabulary

- binomial (p. 457)
- degree of a monomial (p. 457)
- degree of a polynomial (p. 457)
- factor by grouping (p. 496)
- monomial (p. 456)
- perfect-square trinomial (p. 490)
- polynomial (p. 457)
- standard form of a polynomial (p. 457)
- trinomial (p. 457)

Chapter 9 Overview

This chapter helps students build knowledge and skills relative to polynomials—the basic building blocks of algebraic expressions. These skills include combining monomials, binomials, and polynomials using the operations of addition, subtraction, and multiplication. Factoring, the inverse process for multiplying polynomials, is used to factor trinomials, including recognizing certain special patterns and factoring by grouping.

Reading Math
Reading a Diagram, p. 473

Vocabulary
A complete list of terms, plus vocabulary exercises, appears in the Chapter Review, p. 503.

Illustrated Glossary
Examples for each vocabulary term, plus definitions in both English and Spanish, appear starting on p. 757.

Test-Taking Strategies
Eliminating Answers, p. 502

Real-World Connections
Some of the applications you will find in this chapter are manufacturing (9-2), genetics (9-4), and geometry (9-7).

www.PHSchool.com
Internet support for this chapter includes:
- Self-grading Vocabulary and Chapter 9 Tests
- Chapter Project
- Chapter Planner
- Chapter 9 Resources

Plus **iTEXT**

1. Plan

✓ Check Skills You'll Need

The Distributive Property
Lesson 1-7: Example 5
Exercises 35–42
Extra Practice, p. 702

Lesson Resources

📁 **Teaching Resources**
Practice, Reteaching, Enrichment

👥 **Reaching All Students**
Practice Workbook 9-1
Spanish Practice Workbook 9-1
Reading and Math Literacy 9A
Spanish Reading & Literacy 9A
Technology Activities 23
Hands-On Activities 20
Basic Algebra Planning Guide 9-1

⏰ **Presentation Assistant Plus!**
Transparencies
• Check Skills You'll Need 9-1
• Additional Examples 9-1
• Student Edition Answers 9-1
• Lesson Quiz 9-1
PH Presentation Pro CD 9-1

PRENTICE HALL ASSESSMENT SYSTEM

Computer Test Generator CD

💿 **Technology**
Resource Pro® CD-ROM
Computer Test Generator CD
Prentice Hall Presentation Pro CD

🖥 **www.PHSchool.com**
Student Site
• Teacher Web Code: aek-5500
• Reasoning & Puzzles pp. 73, 74
• Self-grading Lesson Quiz
Teacher Center
• Lesson Planner
• Resources

Plus

456

Adding and Subtracting Polynomials

1.01 Write equivalent forms of algebraic expressions to solve problems. b) Operate with polynomials.

Lesson Preview

What You'll Learn

OBJECTIVE 1 To describe polynomials

OBJECTIVE 2 To add and subtract polynomials

...And Why

To combine and simplify polynomials, as in Example 4

✓ Check Skills You'll Need

(For help, go to Lesson 1-7.)

Simplify each expression.

1. $6t + 13t$ **19t**
2. $5g + 34g$ **39g**
3. $7k - 15k$ **−8k**
4. $2b - 6 + 9b$ **11b − 6**
5. $4n^2 - 7n^2$ **−3n²**
6. $8x^2 - x^2$ **7x²**

New Vocabulary
• monomial • degree of a monomial • polynomial
• standard form of a polynomial • degree of a polynomial
• binomial • trinomial

---

iTEXT Interactive lesson includes instant self-check, tutorials, and activities.

OBJECTIVE 1 ▼ Describing Polynomials

2. Davis: 24*m*

Brooks: 3.99*s* + 2*c*

Martino:
3.99*s* + 2.29*g* + 1.89*p*

Rocky's Friends Bird Supplies

bird seed (5 lb)	$3.99
cuttlebone (2 ct)	$2.00
spray millet (5 lb)	$24.00
gravel paper (1 pkg)	$2.29
perches (2 ct)	$1.89

Investigation: Using Polynomials

Business Suppose you work at a pet store. The spreadsheet below shows the details of several customers' orders.

	A	B	C	D	E	F
1	Customer	Seed	Cuttlebone	Millet	G. Paper	Perches
2	Davis			✔		
3	Brooks	✔	✔			
4	Casic	✔		✔		
5	Martino	✔			✔	✔

The following variables represent the number of each item ordered.

s = bags of birdseed m = bags of millet
c = packages of cuttlebone g = packages of gravel paper
p = packages of perches

1. Which expression represents the cost of Casic's order? **B**
   A. $27.99(s + m)$ **B.** $3.99s + 24m$ **C.** $27.99sm$

2. Write expressions to represent each of the other customers' orders.
   See left.

3. Martino buys 10 bags of birdseed, 4 packages of gravel paper, and 2 packages of perches. What is the total cost of his order? **$52.84**

A **monomial** is an expression that is a number, a variable, or a product of a number and one or more variables. Each of the following is a monomial.

$$12 \qquad\qquad y \qquad\qquad -5x^2y \qquad\qquad \frac{c}{3}$$

INSTANT CHECK SYSTEM ## Ongoing Assessment and Intervention

Before the Lesson
Diagnose prerequisite skills using:
• Check Skills You'll Need

During the Lesson
Monitor progress using:
• Check Understanding
• Additional Examples
• Standardized Test Prep

After the Lesson
Assess knowledge using:
• Lesson Quiz
• Computer Test Generator CD

Reading Math

The prefix *mono* means "one."

The fraction $\frac{c}{3}$ is a monomial, but the expression $\frac{c}{x}$ is *not* a monomial because there is a variable in the denominator.

The **degree of a monomial** is the sum of the exponents of its variables. For a nonzero constant, the degree is 0. Zero has no degree.

1 EXAMPLE **Degree of a Monomial**

Find the degree of each monomial.

a. $\frac{2}{3}x$ Degree: 1 $\frac{2}{3}x = \frac{2}{3}x^1$. The exponent is 1.
b. $7x^2y^3$ Degree: 5   The exponents are 2 and 3. Their sum is 5.
c. -4 Degree: 0   The degree of a nonzero constant is 0.

✓ **Check Understanding** ① **Critical Thinking** What is the degree of $9x^0$? Explain.
0; the degree of a nonzero constant is 0.

A **polynomial** is a monomial or the sum or difference of two or more monomials.

$$3x^4 + 5x^2 - 7x + 1$$
$$\qquad\uparrow\qquad\uparrow\qquad\uparrow\qquad\uparrow$$
degree → $\qquad$ 4 $\qquad$ 2 $\qquad$ 1 $\qquad$ 0

The polynomial shown above is in standard form. **Standard form of a polynomial** means that the degrees of its monomial terms decrease from left to right. The **degree of a polynomial** in one variable is the same as the degree of the monomial with the greatest exponent. The degree of $3x^4 + 5x^2 - 7x + 1$ is 4.

After you simplify a polynomial by combining like terms, you can name the polynomial based on its degree or the number of monomials it contains.

Polynomial	Degree	Name Using Degree	Number of Terms	Name Using Number of Terms
$7x + 4$	1	linear	2	**binomial**
$3x^2 + 2x + 1$	2	quadratic	3	**trinomial**
$4x^3$	3	cubic	1	monomial
$9x^4 + 11x$	4	fourth degree	2	binomial
5	0	constant	1	monomial

2 EXAMPLE **Classifying Polynomials**

Write each polynomial in standard form. Then name each polynomial based on its degree and the number of its terms.

a. $5 - 2x$

$-2x + 5$ **Place terms in order.**

linear binomial

b. $3x^4 - 4 + 2x^2 + 5x^4$

$3x^4 + 5x^4 + 2x^2 - 4$ **Place terms in order.**

$8x^4 + 2x^2 - 4$ **Combine like terms.**

fourth degree trinomial

✓ **Check Understanding** ② Write each polynomial in standard form. Then name each polynomial based on its degree and the number of its terms. **See left.**
a. $6x^2 + 7 - 9x^4$ **b.** $3y - 4 - y^3$ **c.** $8 + 7v - 11v$

2a. $-9x^4 + 6x^2 + 7$; fourth degree trinomial

b. $-y^3 + 3y - 4$; cubic trinomial

c. $-4v + 8$; linear binomial

Lesson 9-1 Adding and Subtracting Polynomials **457**

👥 **Reaching All Students**

| **Below Level** Show students that $\frac{c}{3}$ is a monomial because it can be rewritten as $c \cdot \frac{1}{3}$. However, since $\frac{c}{x} = c \cdot \frac{1}{x}$, it does not fit the definition of a monomial. | **Advanced Learners** Have students simplify $\left(\frac{1}{2}x^2 + \frac{2}{3}x - 5\right) - \left(\frac{1}{7}x^2 + \frac{1}{2}x - \frac{1}{5}\right)$. $\frac{5}{14}x^2 + \frac{1}{6}x - \frac{21}{5}$ | **Tactile Learners** See note on page 457. **Error Prevention** See note on page 458. |

---

2. Teach

Professional Development

Math Background

A polynomial is made up of terms, which are algebraic expressions combined by addition or subtraction. In a polynomial, there are no expressions that involve dividing by the variable or taking any root of a variable.

OBJECTIVE
1 Teaching Notes

Investigation (Optional)
Diversity
Ask knowledgeable students to describe the purpose of the bird supplies.

1 EXAMPLE **Math Tip**

Explain to students that it is reasonable that the degree of -4 is 0 because -4 can be written as $-4x^0$, for $x \neq 0$.

2 EXAMPLE **Tactile Learners**

Have each student write a polynomial similar to one shown in the table above Example 2. Redistribute the papers. Direct students to move, using instructions such as: *All linear binomials go to the front of the room. All cubic monomials go to the windows.* Use different combinations of polynomial names until all students have moved to an area of the room. Have students check with each other to make sure they are in the correct locations.

📋 **Additional Examples**

1 Find the degree of each monomial.
a. 18 0   **b.** $3xy^3$ 4   **c.** 6c 1

2 Write each polynomial in standard form. Then name each polynomial based on its degree and the number of its terms.
a. $-2 + 7x$ $7x - 2$; linear binomial
b. $3x^5 - 2 - 2x^5 + 7x$ $x^5 + 7x - 2$; fifth degree trinomial

457

3 EXAMPLE Alternative Method

Use tiles to demonstrate adding polynomials. Have students model each polynomial. Group like tiles together. Remove zero pairs. Then write an expression for the remaining tiles. Remind students that red tiles represent negative amounts.

4 EXAMPLE Error Prevention

Remind students to distribute the negative sign to all terms in the second parentheses. You may want to encourage students to mark the terms, such as by circling the whole parentheses, as a reminder.

Additional Examples

3 Simplify
$(6x^2 + 3x + 7) + (2x^2 - 6x - 4)$.
$8x^2 - 3x + 3$

4 Simplify
$(2x^3 + 4x^2 - 6) - (5x^3 + 2x - 2)$.
$-3x^3 + 4x^2 - 2x - 4$

Closure

Say the name of a polynomial using its degree and number of terms. Instruct students to write a polynomial to match the name. Repeat for different types of polynomials. Let students choose two of the polynomials to both add and subtract.

You can add polynomials by adding like terms.

3 EXAMPLE Adding Polynomials

Simplify $(4x^2 + 6x + 7) + (2x^2 - 9x + 1)$.

Method 1 Add vertically.

Line up like terms. Then add the coefficients.

$$\begin{array}{r} 4x^2 + 6x + 7 \\ + 2x^2 - 9x + 1 \\ \hline 6x^2 - 3x + 8 \end{array}$$

Method 2 Add horizontally.

Group like terms. Then add the coefficients.

$$(4x^2 + 6x + 7) + (2x^2 - 9x + 1) = (4x^2 + 2x^2) + (6x - 9x) + (7 + 1)$$
$$= 6x^2 - 3x + 8$$

✔ **Check Understanding** **3** Simplify each sum. **20**m^2 **+ 9**
a. $(12m^2 + 4) + (8m^2 + 5)$ b. $(t^2 - 6) + (3t^2 + 11)$ **4t^2 + 5**
c. $(9w^3 + 8w^2) + (7w^3 + 4)$ d. $(2p^3 + 6p^2 + 10p) + (9p^3 + 11p^2 + 3p)$
16w^3 + 8w^2 + 4   **11p^3 + 17p^2 + 13p**

In Chapter 1, you learned that subtraction means to add the opposite. So when you subtract a polynomial, change each of the terms to its opposite. Then add the coefficients.

4 EXAMPLE Subtracting Polynomials

Simplify $(2x^3 + 5x^2 - 3x) - (x^3 - 8x^2 + 11)$.

Method 1 Subtract vertically.

$$\begin{array}{r} 2x^3 + 5x^2 - 3x \\ - (x^3 - 8x^2 \quad\;\; + 11) \\ \hline \end{array}$$ Line up like terms.

$$\begin{array}{r} 2x^3 + 5x^2 - 3x \\ -x^3 + 8x^2 \quad\;\; - 11 \\ \hline x^3 + 13x^2 - 3x \; - 11 \end{array}$$ Then add the opposite of each term in the polynomial being subtracted.

Method 2 Subtract horizontally.

$(2x^3 + 5x^2 - 3x) - (x^3 - 8x^2 + 11)$
$= 2x^3 + 5x^2 - 3x - x^3 + 8x^2 - 11$ Write the opposite of each term in the polynomial being subtracted.
$= (2x^3 - x^3) + (5x^2 + 8x^2) - 3x - 11$ Group like terms.
$= x^3 + 13x^2 - 3x - 11$ Simplify.

4a. $-8v^3 + 13v^2 - 4v$
b. $28d^3 - 30d^2 - 3d$

✔ **Check Understanding** **4** Simplify each difference. **a–b. See left.**
a. $(v^3 + 6v^2 - v) - (9v^3 - 7v^2 + 3v)$ b. $(30d^3 - 29d^2 - 3d) - (2d^3 + d^2)$
c. $(4x^2 + 5x + 1) - (6x^2 + x + 8)$ **−2x^2 + 4x − 7**

pages 459–461 Exercises

15. $-3x^2 + 4x$;
quadratic binomial

16. $4x + 9$;
linear binomial

17. $c^2 + 4c - 2$;
quadratic trinomial

18. $-2z^2 + 5z - 5$;
quadratic trinomial

19. $15y^8 - 7y^3 + y$;
eighth degree trinomial

EXERCISES

Practice and Problem Solving

For more practice, see *Extra Practice*.

3. Practice

Assignment Guide

1 Objective
Ⓐ Ⓑ **Core** 1–20, 42, 51

2 Objective
Ⓐ Ⓑ **Core** 21–41, 43–50
Ⓒ **Extension** 52–55

Standardized Test Prep 56–62

Mixed Review 63–86

Ⓐ **Practice by Example**

Example 1
(page 457)

Find the degree of each monomial.

1. $4x$ **1**   **2.** $7c^3$ **3**   **3.** -16 **0**   **4.** $6y^2w^8$ **10**

5. $8ab^3$ **4**   **6.** 6 **0**   **7.** $-9x^4$ **4**   **8.** 11 **0**

Example 2
(page 457)

Name each expression based on its degree and number of terms. 9–11. See left.

9. $5x^2 - 2x + 3$ **10.** $\frac{3}{4}z + 5$ **11.** $7a^3 + 4a - 12$

9. quadratic trinomial

10. linear binomial

11. cubic trinomial

12. $\frac{3}{x} + 5$ **13.** -15 **14.** $w^2 + 2$
not a polynomial   constant monomial   quadratic binomial

Write each polynomial in standard form. Then name each polynomial based on its degree and number of terms. 15–20. See margin p. 458.

15. $4x - 3x^2$ **16.** $4x + 9$ **17.** $c^2 - 2 + 4c$

18. $9z^2 - 11z^2 + 5z - 5$ **19.** $y - 7y^3 + 15y^8$ **20.** $-10 + 4q^4 - 8q + 3q^2$

Example 3
(page 458)

Simplify each sum. 25–27. See margin.

21. $\begin{array}{r} 5m^2 + 9 \\ + 3m^2 + 6 \end{array}$ $8m^2 + 15$ **22.** $\begin{array}{r} 3k - 8 \\ + 7k + 12 \end{array}$ $10k + 4$ **23.** $\begin{array}{r} w^2 + w - 4 \\ + 7w^2 - 4w + 8 \\ \hline 8w^2 - 3w + 4 \end{array}$

24. $(8x^2 + 1) + (12x^2 + 6)$ $20x^2 + 7$ **25.** $(g^4 + 4g) + (9g^4 + 7g)$

26. $(a^2 + a + 1) + (5a^2 - 8a + 20)$ **27.** $(7y^3 - 3y^2 + 4y) + (8y^4 + 3y^2)$

Example 4
(page 458)

Simplify each difference. 28–32. See margin.

28. $\begin{array}{r} 6c - 5 \\ - (4c + 9) \end{array}$ **29.** $\begin{array}{r} 2b + 6 \\ -(b + 5) \end{array}$ **30.** $\begin{array}{r} 7h^2 + 4h - 8 \\ - (3h^2 - 2h + 10) \end{array}$

31. $(17n^4 + 2n^3) - (10n^4 + n^3)$ **32.** $(24x^5 + 12x) - (9x^5 + 11x)$

33. $(6w^2 - 3w + 1) - (w^2 + w - 9)$ **34.** $(-5x^4 + x^2) - (x^3 + 8x^2 - x)$
$5w^2 - 4w + 10$ $-5x^4 - x^3 - 7x^2 + x$

Ⓑ **Apply Your Skills**

Simplify. Write each answer in standard form. 35–38. See left.

35. $18y^2 + 5y$

36. $-6x^3 + 3x^2 - 4$

37. $-7z^3 + 6z^2 + 2z - 5$

38. $7a^3 + 11a^2 - 4a - 4$

35. $(7y^2 - 3y + 4y) + (8y^2 + 3y^2 + 4y)$ **36.** $(2x^3 - 5x^2 - 1) - (8x^3 + 3 - 8x^2)$

37. $(-7z^3 + 3z - 1) - (-6z^2 + z + 4)$ **38.** $(7a^3 - a + 3a^2) + (8a^2 - 3a - 4)$

 **Geometry** Find the perimeter of each figure.

39. $28c - 16$ $9c - 10$

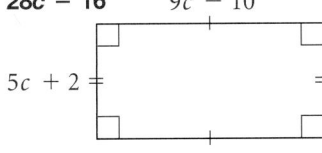

$5c + 2$

40. $39x - 7$ $9x$
$5x + 1$ $8x - 2$
$17x - 6$

?

Need Help?

Recall that the perimeter of a figure is the sum of all the sides of the figure.

41. Error Analysis Kwan's work is shown below. What mistake did he make?

See margin.

$(5x^2 - 3x + 1) - (2x^2 - 4x - 2) = 5x^2 - 3x + 1 - 2x^2 - 4x - 2$
$= 5x^2 - 2x^2 - 3x - 4x + 1 - 2$
$= 3x^2 - 7x - 1$

Lesson 9-1 Adding and Subtracting Polynomials   **459**

Error Prevention

Exercises 15–20 Many students forget that the sign in front of a term must move with the term. Have students circle each term, including the sign in front of the term. Everything that is inside each circle must move together.

Error Prevention

Exercise 23 Some students may use zero for the coefficient of w. Remind them that w means $1w$.

Exercises 49, 50 Tell students these are multi-step problems in which they must add the known sides before subtracting from the perimeter.

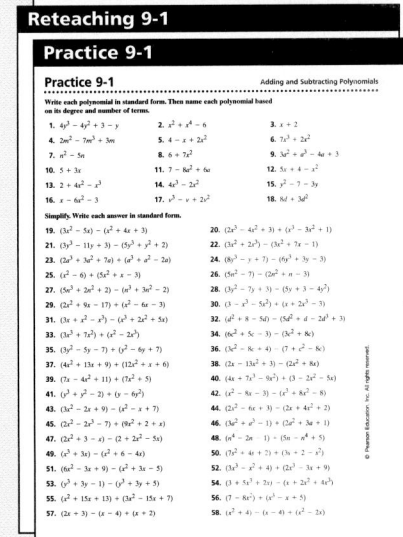

20. $4q^4 + 3q^2 - 8q - 10$;
fourth degree polynomial with 4 terms

25. $10g^4 + 11g$

26. $6a^2 - 7a + 21$

27. $8y^4 + 7y^3 + 4y$

28. $2c - 14$

29. $b + 1$

30. $4h^2 + 6h - 18$

31. $7n^4 + n^3$

32. $15x^5 + x$

41. Kwan did not take the opposite of each term in the polynomial being subtracted.

Lesson Quiz 9-1

Write each expression in standard form. Then name each polynomial by its degree and number of terms.

1. $-4 + 3x - 2x^2$
   $-2x^2 + 3x - 4$;
   quadratic trinomial

2. $2b^2 - 4b^3 + 6$
   $-4b^3 + 2b^2 + 6$;
   cubic trinomial

3. $(2x^4 + 3x - 4) +$
   $(-3x + 4 + x^4)$ $3x^4$; fourth
   degree monomial

4. $(-3r + 4r^2 - 3) -$
   $(4r^2 + 6r - 2)$ $-9r - 1$;
   linear binomial

Alternative Assessment

Direct one student to state the name of a polynomial. Instruct another student to give an example of the named polynomial. Write the polynomial on the board. Let another student name a polynomial. Ask another student to give an example of the polynomial while you write it next to the previous polynomial. On their own pieces of paper, have each student add the two polynomials, write the new polynomial in standard form, and write its name. Repeat for subtraction.

pages 459–461   Exercises

42a. *monogram:* a design composed of one or more letters, typically the initials of a name; used as an identifying mark
   binocular: relating to, used by, or involving both eyes at the same time
   tricuspid: having three cusps, usually said of a molar tooth
   polyglot: a person with a speaking, reading, or writing knowledge of several languages

 42. a. Writing Write the definition of each word. Use a dictionary if necessary.
   monogram   binocular   tricuspid   polyglot **a–b. See margin.**
   b. Open-Ended Find other words that begin with *mono, bi, tri,* or *poly.*
   c. Do these prefixes have meanings similar to those in mathematics? **yes**

Simplify. Write each answer in standard form. 43–48. See margin.

43. $(x^3 + 3x) + (12x - x^4)$ 44. $(6g - 7g^8) - (4g + 2g^3 + 11g^2)$

45. $(2h^4 - 5h^9) - (-8h^5 + h^{10})$ 46. $(-4t^4 - 9t + 6) + (13t + 5t^4)$

47. $(8b - 6b^7 + 3b^8) + (2b^7 - 5b^9)$ 48. $(11 + k^3 - 6k^4) - (k^2 - k^4)$

Geometry Find each missing length.

49. Perimeter = $25x + 8$

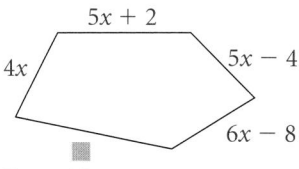

$5x + 2$
$4x$
$5x - 4$
$6x - 8$
$5x + 18$

50. Perimeter = $23a - 7$

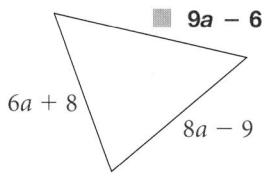

$9a - 6$
$6a + 8$
$8a - 9$

51. **Critical Thinking** Is it possible to write a binomial with degree 0? Explain.
   No; both terms of a binomial cannot be constants.

Challenge

52a. $y = 2x - 1$;
   $y = 0.5x + 3$

c. $\frac{8}{3}$ or $2\frac{2}{3}$

d. The lines intersect at
   $x = 2\frac{2}{3}$.

52. **a.** Write the equations for line P and line Q.
   Use slope-intercept form. **a, c–d. See left.**
   b. Use the expressions on the right side of each equation to write a function for the vertical distance $D(x)$ between points on lines P and Q with the same x-value. **$D(x) = 1.5x - 4$**
   c. For what value of x does $D(x)$ equal zero?
   d. Critical Thinking How does the x-value in part (c) relate to the graph?

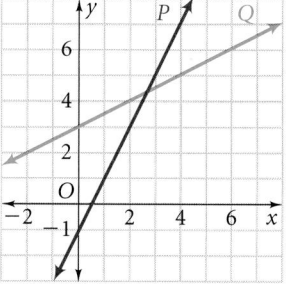

Simplify each expression.

53. $(ab^2 + ba^3) + (4a^3b - ab^2 - 5ab)$ 54. $(9pq^6 - 11p^4q) - (-5pq^6 + p^4q^4)$
   $5a^3b - 5ab$ $-p^4q^4 - 11p^4q + 14pq^6$

55. **Graduation** You can model the number of men and women in the United States who enrolled in college within a year of graduating from high school with the linear equations shown below. Let t equal the year of enrollment, with $t = 0$ corresponding to 1990. Let $m(t)$ equal the number of men in thousands, and let $w(t)$ equal the number of women in thousands.

$$m(t) = 35.4t + 1146.8 \qquad \text{men enrolled in college}$$
$$w(t) = 21.6t + 1185.5 \qquad \text{women enrolled in college}$$

   a. Add the expressions on the right side of each equation to model the total number of recent high school graduates $p(t)$ who enrolled in college between 1990 and 1998. **$p(t) = 57t + 2332.3$**
   b. Use the equation you created in part (a) to find the number of high school graduates who enrolled in college in 1995. **2,617,300**
   c. Critical Thinking If you had subtracted the expressions on the right side of each equation above, what information would the resulting expression model?   **the difference between the number of men and the number of women enrolled in a college**

Real-World Connection

There were about 12 million students enrolled in college in 1980, 13.8 million in 1990, and 15 million in 2000.

b. **Answers may vary.
   Sample: monopoly,
   biathlon, tripod,
   polychrome**

43. $-x^4 + x^3 + 15x$

44. $-7g^8 - 2g^3 - 11g^2 + 2g$

45. $-h^{10} - 5h^9 + 8h^5 + 2h^4$

46. $t^4 + 4t + 6$

47. $-5b^9 + 3b^8 - 4b^7 + 8b$

48. $-5k^4 + k^3 - k^2 + 11$

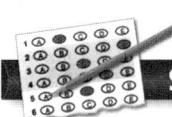
Standardized Test Prep

📁 **Resources**
For additional practice with a variety of test item formats:
- Standardized Test Prep, p. 507
- Test-Taking Strategies, p. 502
- Test-Taking Strategies with Transparencies

Exercise 56 Explain to students that since they are finding the sum of four terms, each containing n, the result must include $4n$. Tell students to always be careful when working with integer problems. If the problem has consecutive odd or consecutive even integers, each term increases by 2, not 1.

Multiple Choice

56. Which expression represents the sum of an odd integer n and the next three odd integers? **D**

    A. $n + 6$ **B.** $n + 12$ **C.** $4n + 6$ **D.** $4n + 12$

57. Simplify $(8x^2 + 3) + (7x^2 + 10)$. **G**

    F. $x^2 - 7$ **G.** $15x^2 + 13$ **H.** $15x^4 + 13$ **I.** $56x^4 + 30$

Quantitative Comparison

Compare the boxed quantity in Column A with the boxed quantity in Column B. Choose the best answer.

    A. The quantity in Column A is greater.
    B. The quantity in Column B is greater.
    C. The two quantities are equal.
    D. The relationship cannot be determined from the information given.

Column A	Column B
58. **A** sum of the coefficients of $3a^4 - 2a^3 + a + 8$	sum of the coefficients of $3a^7 - 6a + 9$
59. **C** sum of the exponents of $11a^5 - 5a^3 - 3$	sum of the exponents of $10a^4 + 4a^3 + 5a + 6$
60. **B** value of $4a^2 - 9a + 7$ for $a = 2$	value of $-a^2 + 12a + 8$ for $a = 2$
61. **C** $(2k - 6) + (3k + 1)$	$(k^2 + 4k) - (k^2 - k + 5)$

💻 **Take It to the NET**
Online lesson quiz at **www.PHSchool.com**
Web Code: aea-0901

Short Response

62. Simplify $(9x^3 - 4x^2 + 1) - (x^2 + 2)$. Show your work. **See margin.**

Mixed Review

Lesson 8-8

67. exponential growth
68. exponential decay
69. exponential growth
70. exponential decay

Identify the growth factor in each function.

63. $y = 6 \cdot 2^x$ **2**   **64.** $y = 0.6 \cdot 1.4^x$ **1.4**   **65.** $y = 2 \cdot 5^x$ **5**   **66.** $y = 0.3 \cdot 5^x$ **5**

Identify each function as *exponential growth* or *exponential decay*. 67–70. See left.

67. $y = 10 \cdot 3^x$ **68.** $y = 1.8 \cdot 0.4^x$ **69.** $y = 0.3 \cdot 7^x$ **70.** $y = 0.3 \cdot 0.5^x$

Lesson 8-3

74. $3a^3b^2$
75. $\dfrac{-30}{t^7}$
76. $(-3)^2$
77. $-12h^{10}$
78. $10q^7$

Simplify each expression. 74–78. See left.

71. $7^8 \cdot 7^{10}$ **7^{18}**   **72.** $2^6 \cdot 2^{-7}$ **$\frac{1}{2}$**   **73.** $(4x^2)(9x^3)$ **$36x^5$**   **74.** $(3ab)(a^2b)$

75. $(-5t^2)(6t^{-9})$ **76.** $(-3)^6 \cdot (-3)^{-4}$ **77.** $(6h^2)(-2h^8)$ **78.** $(2q^5)(5q^2)$

Lesson 6-7

Write an equation for each translation of $y = |x|$. 79–82. See margin.

79. 5 units up   **80.** right 6 units   **81.** 12 units down   **82.** 7 units up

83. left 10 units   **84.** left 0.4 units   **85.** 5.2 units up   **86.** 2.3 units down
      $y = |x + 10|$ $y = |x + 0.4|$ $y = |x| + 5.2$ $y = |x| - 2.3$

Lesson 9-1 Adding and Subtracting Polynomials   **461**

62. **[2]** $(9x^3 - 4x^2 + 1) - (x^2 + 2) =$
     $9x^3 - 4x^2 + 1 - x^2 - 2 =$
     $(9x^3) + (-4x^2 - x^2) + (1 - 2) =$
     $9x^3 - 5x^2 - 1$

[1] one incorrect term OR no work shown

79. $y = |x| + 5$
80. $y = |x - 6|$
81. $y = |x| - 12$
82. $y = |x| + 7$

Lesson Preview

✓ Check Skills You'll Need

The Distributive Property
Lesson 1-7: Examples 1, 3
Exercises 1–8, 15–26
Extra Practice, p. 702

Lesson Resources

📁 **Teaching Resources**
Practice, Reteaching, Enrichment

👥 **Reaching All Students**
Practice Workbook 9-2
Spanish Practice Workbook 9-2
Basic Algebra Planning Guide 9-2

⏰ **Presentation Assistant Plus!**
Transparencies
• Check Skills You'll Need 9-2
• Additional Examples 9-2
• Student Edition Answers 9-2
• Lesson Quiz 9-2
PH Presentation Pro CD 9-2

PRENTICE HALL
ASSESSMENT SYSTEM

Computer Test Generator CD

💿 **Technology**
Resource Pro® CD-ROM
Computer Test Generator CD
Prentice Hall Presentation Pro CD

🖥 **www.PHSchool.com**
Student Site
• Teacher Web Code: aek-5500
• Reasoning & Puzzles p. 75
• Self-grading Lesson Quiz
Teacher Center
• Lesson Planner
• Resources

Plus 📱**TEXT**

462

9-2

Multiplying and Factoring

1.01 Write equivalent forms of algebraic expressions to solve problems. b) Operate with polynomials. c) Factor polynomials.

Lesson Preview

What You'll Learn

OBJECTIVE 1
To multiply a polynomial by a monomial

OBJECTIVE 2
To factor a monomial from a polynomial

...And Why

To factor a monomial out of a polynomial, as in Example 3

✓ Check Skills You'll Need

(For help, go to Lesson 1-7.)

Multiply.

1. $3(302)$ **906**   **2.** $41(7)$ **287**   **3.** $9(504)$ **4536**

Simplify each expression.

4. $4(6 + 5x)$ **24 + 20x**   **5.** $-8(2y + 1)$ **−16y − 8**   **6.** $(5v - 1)5$ **25v − 5**

7. $7(p - 2)$ **7p − 14**   **8.** $(6 - x)9$ **54 − 9x**   **9.** $-2(4q - 1)$
$\qquad\qquad\qquad\qquad\qquad\qquad\qquad\qquad\qquad$ **−8q + 2**

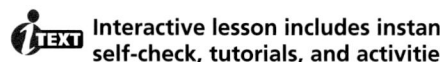

📱**TEXT** Interactive lesson includes instant self-check, tutorials, and activities.

1 ▼ **Distributing a Monomial**

In Chapter 1 you used the Distributive Property to multiply a number by a sum or difference.

$$5(a + 3) = 5a + 15 \quad (x - 2)(3) = 3x - 6 \quad -2(2y + 7) = -4y - 14$$

You can also use the Distributive Property or an area model to multiply polynomials. The diagram shows the product of $2x$ and $(3x + 1)$.

The same product is found below using the Distributive Property.

$$2x(3x + 1) = 2x(3x) + 2x(1)$$
$$= 6x^2 + 2x$$

You can use the Distributive Property for multiplying powers with the same base when multiplying by a monomial.

? ......
Need Help?
Multiplying powers with the same base:
$3^5 \cdot 3^4 = 3^{5 + 4} = 3^9$

1 EXAMPLE **Multiplying a Monomial and a Trinomial**

Simplify $-4y^2(5y^4 - 3y^2 + 2)$.

$-4y^2(5y^4 - 3y^2 + 2)$

$= -4y^2(5y^4) - 4y^2(-3y^2) - 4y^2(2)$ **Use the Distributive Property.**

$= -20y^{2 + 4} + 12y^{2 + 2} - 8y^2$ **Multiply the coefficients and add the exponents of powers with the same base.**

$= -20y^6 + 12y^4 - 8y^2$ **Simplify.**

✓ Check Understanding Simplify each product.

a. $4b(5b^2 + b + 6)$ **b.** $-7h(3h^2 - 8h - 1)$ **c.** $2x(x^2 - 6x + 5)$
    $20b^3 + 4b^2 + 24b$ $-21h^3 + 56h^2 + 7h$ $2x^3 - 12x^2 + 10x$

462 Chapter 9 Polynomials and Factoring

Ongoing Assessment and Intervention

Before the Lesson	**During the Lesson**	**After the Lesson**
Diagnose prerequisite skills using:	Monitor progress using:	Assess knowledge using:
• Check Skills You'll Need	• Check Understanding	• Lesson Quiz
	• Additional Examples	• Computer Test Generator CD
	• Standardized Test Prep	

OBJECTIVE

2 Factoring a Monomial From a Polynomial

Need Help?

The greatest common factor (GCF) is the greatest factor that divides evenly into each term of an expression. See Skills Handbook page 721.

Factoring a polynomial reverses the multiplication process. To factor a monomial from a polynomial, first find the greatest common factor (GCF) of its terms.

2 EXAMPLE Finding the Greatest Common Factor

Find the GCF of the terms of $4x^3 + 12x^2 - 8x$.

List the prime factors of each term. Identify the factors common to all terms.

$4x^3 = 2 \cdot 2 \cdot x \cdot x \cdot x$

$12x^2 = 2 \cdot 2 \cdot 3 \cdot x \cdot x$

$8x = 2 \cdot 2 \cdot 2 \cdot x$

● The GCF is $2 \cdot 2 \cdot x$ or $4x$.

✓ **Check Understanding** ② Find the GCF of the terms of each polynomial.
a. $5v^5 + 10v^3$ **5v³** **b.** $3t^2 - 18$ **3** **c.** $4b^3 - 2b^2 - 6b$ **2b**

To factor a polynomial completely, you must factor until there are no common factors other than 1.

3 EXAMPLE Factoring Out a Monomial

Factor $3x^3 - 12x^2 + 15x$.

Step 1 Find the GCF.

$3x^3 = 3 \cdot x \cdot x \cdot x$

$12x^2 = 2 \cdot 2 \cdot 3 \cdot x \cdot x$

$15x = 3 \cdot 5 \cdot x$

● The GCF is $3 \cdot x$ or $3x$.

Step 2 Factor out the GCF.

$3x^3 - 12x^2 + 15x$

$= 3x(x^2) + 3x(-4x) + 3x(5)$

$= 3x(x^2 - 4x + 5)$

✓ **Check Understanding** ③ Use the GCF to factor each polynomial.
a. $8x^2 - 12x$ **b.** $5d^3 + 10d$ **c.** $6m^3 - 12m^2 - 24m$
  $4x(2x - 3)$ $5d(d^2 + 2)$ $6m(m^2 - 2m - 4)$

EXERCISES

For more practice, see *Extra Practice*.

Practice and Problem Solving

 Practice by Example

Example 1
(page 462)

Simplify each product. 5–12. See back of book.

1. $8m(m + 6)$ **8m² + 48m** **2.** $(x + 10)3x$ **3x² + 30x** **3.** $9k(7k + 4)$ **63k² + 36k**

4. $-5a(a - 1)$ **-5a² + 5a** **5.** $2x^2(9 + x)$ **6.** $-p^2(p - 11)$

7. $2x(6x^3 - x^2 + 5x)$ **8.** $4y^2(9y^3 + 8y^2 - 11)$ **9.** $-5c^3(9c^2 - 8c - 5)$

10. $-7q^2(6q^5 - 2q - 7)$ **11.** $-3g^7(g^4 - 6g^2 + 5)$ **12.** $-4x^6(10x^3 + 3x^2 - 7)$

Example 2
(page 463)

Find the GCF of the terms of each polynomial.

13. $15w + 21$ **3**   **14.** $6a^2 - 8a$ **2a**   **15.** $36v + 24$ **12**

16. $x^3 + 7x^2 - 5x$ **x**   **17.** $5b^3 + 15b - 30$ **5**   **18.** $9x^3 - 6x^2 + 12x$ **3x**

👪 Reaching All Students

| **Below Level** To help students keep track of which terms they have already multiplied, suggest that they arrange their work carefully. | **Advanced Learners** Help students understand that factoring and multiplying polynomials are each applications of the distributive property. | **Alternative Method** See note on page 463. **Error Prevention** See note on page 463. |

---

2. Teach

Professional Development

Math Background

The process of applying the distributive property with polynomials combines the distributive property for real numbers with the rules for multiplying powers. Factoring reverses this process.

OBJECTIVE 1 Teaching Notes

1 EXAMPLE Error Prevention

Remind students that the negative sign is part of the monomial. It is $-4y^2$ that must be distributed.

Additional Example

① Simplify $-2g^2(3g^3 + 6g - 5)$.
$-6g^5 - 12g^3 + 10g^2$

OBJECTIVE 2 Teaching Notes

3 EXAMPLE Alternative Method

Help students learn to factor expressions mentally by scanning. They should first scan the coefficients and find their GCF. Next, they should scan for the least power of the variable.

Additional Examples

② Find the GCF of the terms of $2x^4 + 10x^2 - 6x$. **2x**

③ Factor $4x^3 - 8x^2 + 12x$.
$4x(x^2 - 2x + 3)$

Closure

Ask students how to find the GCF of a polynomial. First, list the prime factors of each coefficient. Then identify the factors common to all coefficients. Finally, write the product of these common factors with the least power of the variable used in any term.

463

Assignment Guide

 **Objective**

Ⓐ Ⓑ **Core** 1–12, 25–32

Ⓒ **Extension** 43

 **Objective**

Ⓐ Ⓑ **Core** 13–24, 33–42

Ⓒ **Extension** 44

Standardized Test Prep 45–50

Mixed Review 51–67

Connection to History

Exercise 33 European castles usually consisted of two concentric square or triangular shaped systems of steep walls and round towers surrounding an inner courtyard. Outside the outer wall, a deep dry ditch or a moat served as defense, garbage dump, and sewer. Moats also contained eels and fish for food.

Math Tip

Exercise 44 Remind students that "in terms of s" means that s is the variable in the formula.

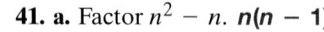

Example 3
(page 463)

Factor each polynomial.

19. $6x - 4$ **2(3x − 2)**   **20.** $v^2 + 4v$ **v(v + 4)**   **21.** $10x^3 - 25x^2 + 20$
$5(2x^3 - 5x^2 + 4)$

22. $2t^2 - 10t^4$ **2t²(1 − 5t²)** **23.** $15n^3 - 3n^2 + 12n$ **24.** $6p^6 + 24p^5 + 18p^3$
3n(5n² − n + 4)   **6p³(p³ + 4p² + 3)**

Ⓑ **Apply Your Skills**

25. Error Analysis Kevin said that $-2x(4x - 3) = -8x^2 - 6x$. Karla said that $-2x(4x - 3) = -8x^2 + 6x$. Who is correct? Explain. **Karla; Kevin multiplied −2x by 3 instead of −3.**

26. Open-Ended Write a polynomial that has a common factor in each term. Factor your polynomial. **See margin.**

Simplify. Write in standard form. 27–29. See margin.

27. $-3a(4a^2 - 5a + 9)$ **28.** $-7p^2(-2p^3 + 5p)$ **29.** $12c(-5c^2 + 3c - 4)$

30. $y(y + 3) - 5y(y - 2)$ **31.** $x^2(x + 1) - x(x^2 - 1)$ **32.** $4t(3t^2 - 4t) - t(7t)$
−4y² + 13y   **x² + x**   **12t³ − 23t²**

🌐 **33. Building Models** Suppose you are building a model of the square castle shown at the left. The moat of the model castle is made of blue paper.
  a. Find the area of the moat using the diagram with the photo. **A = 16πx² − 4x²**
  b. Write your answer in factored form. **A = 4x²(4π − 1)**

Factor each polynomial. 34–39. See margin.

34. $9m^{12} - 36m^7 + 81m^5$ **35.** $24x^3 - 96x^2 + 48x$ **36.** $16n^3 + 48n^2 - 80n$

37. $5x^4 + 4x^3 + 3x^2$ **38.** $13ab^3 + 39a^2b^4$ **39.** $7g^2k^3 - 35g^5k^2$

40. Critical Thinking The GCF of two numbers p and q is 5. What is the GCF of p^2 and q^2? Explain your answer. **25; 5² = 25.**

✎ **41. a.** Factor $n^2 - n$. **n(n − 1)**
  b. Writing Suppose n is an integer. Is $n^2 - n$ *always*, *sometimes*, or *never* even? Justify your answer. **Always; the product of two consecutive integers is always even, since one of the integers is even.**

42. A triangular number is a number you can represent with a triangular arrangement of objects. A triangular number can also be written as a product of two factors, as in the table.
  a. Find the values of $a, b, c,$ and d, and then write an expression in factored form for the nth triangular number. **1; 2; 3; 4; $\frac{n}{2}(n + 1)$**

	1	2	3	4
Triangular Number	1	3	6	10
Factored Form	$\frac{a}{2}(a + 1)$	$\frac{b}{2}(b + 1)$	$\frac{c}{2}(c + 1)$	$\frac{d}{2}(d + 1)$

  b. Use the expression you wrote to find the 100th triangular number. **5050**

Ⓒ **Challenge** ◫ **43. a. Geometry** How many sides does the polygon have? How many of its diagonals come from one vertex? **6; 3**
  b. Suppose a polygon has n sides. How many diagonals will it have from one vertex? **n − 3**
  c. The number of diagonals from all the vertices is $\frac{n}{2}(n - 3)$. Multiply the two factors. **$\frac{1}{2}n^2 - \frac{3}{2}n$**
  d. For a polygon with 8 sides, what is the total number of diagonals that can be drawn from the vertices? **20**

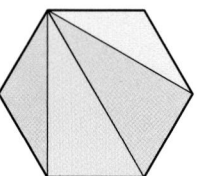

pages 463–465   **Exercises**

26. Answers may vary.
  Sample: $8x^3 + 12x^2 + 24x$; $4x(2x^2 + 3x + 6)$

27. $-12a^3 + 15a^2 - 27a$

28. $14p^5 - 35p^3$

29. $-60c^3 + 36c^2 - 48c$

34. $9m^5(m^7 - 4m^2 + 9)$

35. $24x(x^2 - 4x + 2)$

36. $16n(n^2 + 3n - 5)$

37. $x^2(5x^2 + 4x + 3)$

38. $13ab^3(1 + 3ab)$

39. $7g^2k^2(k - 5g^3)$

Enrichment 9-2

Reteaching 9-2

Practice 9-2

Practice 9-2   Multiplying and Factoring

Simplify each product.

Find the GCF of the terms of each polynomial.

Factor each polynomial.

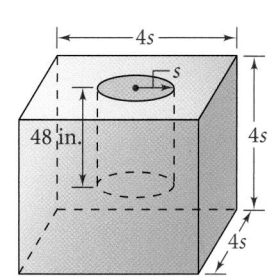

44. Manufacturing The diagram shows a cube of metal with a cylinder cut out of it. The formula for the volume of a cylinder is $V = \pi r^2 h$, where r is the radius and h is the height.
   a. Write a formula for the volume of the cube in terms of s. **$V = 64s^3$**
   b. Write a formula for the volume of the cylinder in terms of s. **$V = 48\pi s^2$**
   c. Write a formula in terms of s for the volume V of the metal left after the cylinder has been removed. **$V = 64s^3 - 48\pi s^2$**
   d. Factor your formula from part (c). **$V = 16s^2(4s - 3\pi)$**
   e. Find V in cubic inches for $s = 15$ in. **about 182,071 in.^{3}**

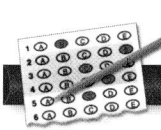

Standardized Test Prep

Multiple Choice

45. $x(6x^2 - 4x - 2)$ equals which of the following expressions? **B**
   A. $6x^3 - 4x - 2$ **B.** $6x^3 - 4x^2 - 2x$
   C. $6x^3 - 4x^2 - 2$ **D.** $7x^3 - 5x^2 - 3x$

46. Simplify $(p^2 - 3) - (5 - p + 2p^2) - (4p + 5 - 2p^2)$. What is the coefficient of p^2? **F**
   F. 1   **G.** 2   **H.** 4   **I.** 5

47. Let $\boxed{n}$ represent the number of different pairs of integers whose product is n. For example, -1×10, -2×5, $1 \times (-10)$, and $2 \times (-5)$ give -10. So $\boxed{-10} = 4$. What does $\boxed{-24}$ equal? **C**
   A. 4   **B.** 6   **C.** 8   **D.** 10

48. Which of the following represents an odd number for any integer n? **G**
   F. $n + 1$ **G.** $2n + 1$ **H.** $3n$ **I.** $3n + 1$

Take It to the NET
Online lesson quiz at
www.PHSchool.com
Web Code: aea-0902

49. Factor $6g^8 - 3g^4 + 9g^2$ completely. **B**
   A. $g^2(6g^4 - 3g^2 + 9)$ **B.** $3g^2(2g^6 - g^2 + 3)$
   C. $g^2(6g^6 - 3g^2 + 9g)$ **D.** $3g^2(2g^6 - g^2 + 3g)$

Short Response

50. How do you know if you've factored out the GCF of a polynomial? Illustrate your explanation by using the GCF to factor $10x^4 + 6x^3 + 2x^2$.
   See margin.

Mixed Review

Lesson 9-1   **Simplify. Write each answer in standard form. 52–54. See margin.**

51. $(x^2 + 3) - (4x^2 - 7)$ **$-3x^2 + 10$**   **52.** $(m^3 + 8m + 6) + (-5m^2 + 4m)$

53. $(g^2 + 6g - 2) + (4g^2 - 7g + 2)$ **54.** $(3r^2 - 8r + 7) - (2r^2 + 8r - 9)$

55. $(t^4 - t^3 + 1) + (t^3 + 5t^2 - 10)$ **56.** $(3b^3 - b^2) - (5b^2 + 12)$
   $t^4 + 5t^2 - 9$ **$3b^3 - 6b^2 - 12$**

Lesson 8-1   **Simplify each expression.**

57. 5^{-1} **$1\frac{1}{5}$**   **58.** 5^{-2} **$\frac{1}{25}$**   **59.** $(-2)^{-3}$ **$-\frac{1}{8}$**   **60.** 8^0 **1**

61. $n^{-3}m^2\frac{m^2}{n^3}$ **62.** $v^3w^{-5}\frac{v^3}{w^5}$ **63.** $\frac{4}{c^{-3}}$ **$4c^3$**   **64.** $\frac{ab^{-8}}{c^5}\frac{a}{b^8c^5}$

Lesson 7-3   **Solve by elimination.**

65. $7x + 6y = 33$ **66.** $8x + 4y = 28$ **67.** $4x + 2y = 16$ **(1, 6)**
     $2x - 6y = -6$ **(3, 2)** $3x - 2y = 21$ **(5, -3)** $11x - 3y = -7$

50. **[2]** $2x^2(5x^2 + 3x + 1)$; the terms $5x^2$, $3x$, and 1 have no common factor other than 1.

[1] incorrect factoring OR incorrect explanation

52. $m^3 - 5m^2 + 12m + 6$
53. $5g^2 - g$
54. $r^2 - 16r + 16$

Lesson Quiz 9-2

1. Simplify
   $-2x^2(-3x^2 + 2x + 8)$.
   $6x^4 - 4x^3 - 16x^2$

2. Find the GCF of
   $16b^4 - 4b^3 + 8b^2$. $4b^2$

3. Factor $3x^3 + 9x^2$.
   $3x^2(x + 3)$

4. Factor $10y^3 + 5y^2 - 15y$.
   $5y(2y^2 + y - 3)$

Alternative Assessment

Organize students into groups of three. Using the examples in this lesson, have each group write a similar polynomial and its factors on cards. For example, students should write $6x^2 - 4x$ on one card, the factor $2x$ on one card, and the factor $(3x - 2)$ on a third card. Collect all the cards from the class and shuffle them. Randomly redistribute the cards to the class. Have students find their matching cards. Tell students not to be alarmed if there is more than one card with the same factor on it. Each factor will have a polynomial to match it.

Standardized Test Prep

Resources
For additional practice with a variety of test item formats:
• Standardized Test Prep, p. 507
• Test-Taking Strategies, p. 502
• Test-Taking Strategies with Transparencies

Exercise 48 Remind students that any odd number is one more than an even number. $2n$ always represents an even number for any integer n.

Investigation

Using Models to Multiply

Students learn the concept of multiplying two binomials by using algebra tiles.

Resources

algebra tiles

Teaching Notes

Error Prevention

An x-tile and 5 unit tiles are very close in length. Make sure students do not think that an x-tile equals 5 unit tiles. Remind students that x can represent any number.

Teaching Tip

Help students see that the product is the area of a rectangle with side lengths of the given binomials.

Using Models to Multiply

FOR USE WITH LESSON 9-3

You can use algebra tiles to multiply two binomials.

1 EXAMPLE Multiplying Binomials

Find the product $(2x + 1)(x + 5)$.

$(x + 5)$

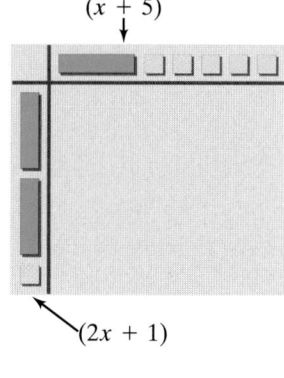 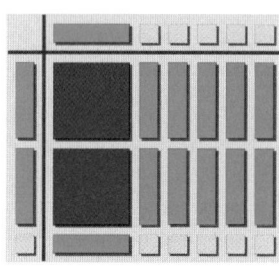

$(2x + 1)$

$2x^2 + 10x + x + 5$
$2x^2 + 11x + 5$ **Add coefficients of like terms.**

● The product is $2x^2 + 11x + 5$.

You can also model products that involve subtraction. Red tiles indicate negative variables and negative numbers.

2 EXAMPLE Multiplying With Negative Tiles

Find the product $(x - 2)(3x + 1)$.

$(3x + 1)$

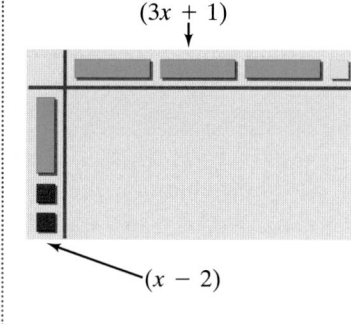 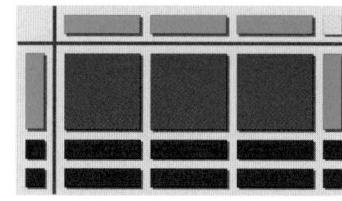

$(x - 2)$

$3x^2 - 6x + x - 2$
$3x^2 - 5x - 2$ **Add coefficients of like terms.**

● The product is $3x^2 - 5x - 2$.

EXERCISES

Use algebra tiles to find each product.

1. $(x + 1)(x + 6)$ $x^2 + 7x + 6$ **2.** $(x + 1)(x - 2)$ $x^2 - x - 2$ **3.** $(x + 1)(4x - 1)$ $4x^2 + 3x - 1$

4. $(x + 4)(2x + 1)$ $2x^2 + 9x + 4$ **5.** $(x - 3)(3x + 5)$ $3x^2 - 4x - 15$ **6.** $(2x + 3)(3x + 5)$ $6x^2 + 19x + 15$

Multiplying Binomials

North Carolina Objectives

1.01 Write equivalent forms of algebraic expressions to solve problems. b) Operate with polynomials.

Lesson Preview

What You'll Learn

 OBJECTIVE 1
To multiply binomials using FOIL

 OBJECTIVE 2
To multiply trinomials by binomials

. . . And Why

To find the area of a geometric figure, as in Example 3

✓ Check Skills You'll Need   (For help, go to Lesson 9-2.)

Find each product.

1. $4r(r - 1)$ $4r^2 - 4r$
2. $6h(h^2 + 8h - 3)$ $6h^3 + 48h^2 - 18h$
3. $y^2(2y^3 - 7)$ $2y^5 - 7y^2$

Simplify. Write each answer in standard form. 4–9. See margin p. 469.

4. $(x^3 + 3x^2 + x) + (5x^2 + x + 1)$
5. $(3t^3 - 6t + 8) + (5t^3 + 7t - 2)$
6. $w(w + 1) + 4w(w - 7)$
7. $6b(b - 2) - b(8b + 3)$
8. $m(4m^2 - 6) + 3m^2(m + 9)$
9. $3d^2(d^3 - 6) - d^3(2d^2 + 4)$

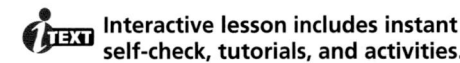 Interactive lesson includes instant self-check, tutorials, and activities.

OBJECTIVE 1

Multiplying Two Binomials

You can use an area model to multiply two binomials. The diagram below shows $(2x + 3)(x + 4)$.

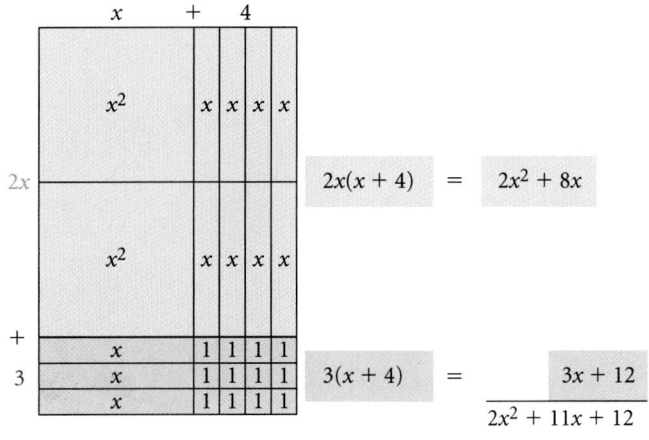

You can also use the Distributive Property to find the product of two binomials.

1 EXAMPLE Using the Distributive Property

Simplify $(2x + 3)(x + 4)$.

$(2x + 3)(x + 4) = 2x(x + 4) + 3(x + 4)$ **Distribute $x + 4$.**
$= 2x^2 + 8x + 3x + 12$ **Now distribute $2x$ and 3.**
$= 2x^2 + 11x + 12$ **Simplify.**

✓ Check Understanding 1 Simplify each product.

a. $(6h - 7)(2h + 3)$
$12h^2 + 4h - 21$

b. $(5m + 2)(8m - 1)$
$40m^2 + 11m - 2$

c. $(9a - 8)(7a + 4)$
$63a^2 - 20a - 32$

Lesson 9-3 Multiplying Binomials   **467**

---

1. Plan

Lesson Preview

✓ **Check Skills You'll Need**

Multiplying and Factoring
Lesson 9-2: Example 1
Exercises 1–12
Extra Practice, p. 710

Lesson Resources

 **Teaching Resources**
Practice, Reteaching, Enrichment
Checkpoint Quiz 1

Reaching All Students
Practice Workbook 9-3
Spanish Practice Workbook 9-3
Reading and Math Literacy 9B
Spanish Reading & Literacy 9B
Spanish Checkpoint Quiz 1
Hands-On Activities 21
Basic Algebra Planning Guide 9-3

Presentation Assistant Plus!
Transparencies
• Check Skills You'll Need 9-3
• Additional Examples 9-3
• Student Edition Answers 9-3
• Lesson Quiz 9-3
PH Presentation Pro CD 9-3

PRENTICE HALL ASSESSMENT SYSTEM

Checkpoint Quiz 1
Computer Test Generator CD

Technology
Resource Pro® CD-ROM
Computer Test Generator CD
Prentice Hall Presentation Pro CD

www.PHSchool.com
Student Site
• Teacher Web Code: aek-5500
• Reasoning & Puzzles pp. 76, 78, 95
• Self-grading Lesson Quiz
Teacher Center
• Lesson Planner
• Resources

Plus

✓ Ongoing Assessment and Intervention

Before the Lesson	During the Lesson	After the Lesson
Diagnose prerequisite skills using:	**Monitor progress using:**	**Assess knowledge using:**
• Check Skills You'll Need	• Check Understanding • Additional Examples • Standardized Test Prep	• Lesson Quiz • Computer Test Generator CD • Chapter Checkpoint 1 (p. 472)

Math Background

Finding the product of two binomials by the FOIL method is a shortcut for distributing the first binomial to each term of the second, and then distributing again to find these individual products. However, no corresponding shortcut exists when one factor is a trinomial.

OBJECTIVE

▼ Teaching Notes

1 EXAMPLE **Tactile Learners**

Encourage students to draw an area model showing multiplication of the two binomials. Students can easily see there are four products when multiplying binomials.

2 EXAMPLE **Auditory Learners**

On the board, write an expression that multiplies two binomials. Call on students to say aloud the different parts of FOIL for the expression. Repeat with new expressions until all students have responded.

3 EXAMPLE **Visual Learners**

Some students may not understand why you subtract the area of the inner rectangle. Cut a rectangle out of a sheet of construction paper to represent the example.

Additional Examples

1 Simplify $(2y - 3)(y + 2)$.
$2y^2 + y - 6$

2 Simplify $(4x + 2)(3x - 6)$.
$12x^2 - 18x - 12$

3 Find the area of the shaded region. Simplify. $5x^2 - 2x - 2$

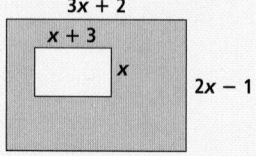

468

One way to organize multiplying two binomials is to use FOIL, which stands for "First, Outer, Inner, Last." The term *FOIL* is a memory device for applying the Distributive Property to the product of two binomials.

2 EXAMPLE **Multiplying Using FOIL**

Simplify $(3x - 5)(2x + 7)$.

	First	Outer	Inner	Last
$(3x - 5)(2x + 7)$ =	$(3x)(2x)$ +	$(3x)(7)$ −	$(5)(2x)$ −	$(5)(7)$
=	$6x^2$ +	$21x$ −	$10x$ −	35
=	$6x^2$ +		$11x$	− 35

● The product is $6x^2 + 11x - 35$.

✓ **Check Understanding** **2** Simplify each product using FOIL.
  a. $(3x + 4)(2x + 5)$ $6x^2 + 23x + 20$ **b.** $(3x - 4)(2x + 5)$ $6x^2 + 7x - 20$
  c. $(3x + 4)(2x - 5)$ $6x^2 - 7x - 20$ **d.** $(3x - 4)(2x - 5)$ $6x^2 - 23x + 20$

You can use FOIL to find the area of some geometric figures.

3 EXAMPLE **Applying Multiplication of Polynomials**

Geometry Find the area of the shaded region. Simplify.

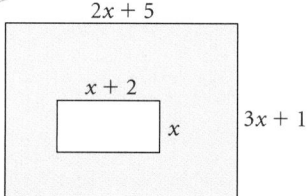

area of outer rectangle = $(3x + 1)(2x + 5)$

area of hole = $x(x + 2)$

area of shaded region

= area of outer rectangle − area of hole

= $(3x + 1)(2x + 5)$ − $x(x + 2)$ **Substitute.**

= $6x^2 + 15x + 2x + 5$ − $x^2 - 2x$ **Use FOIL to simplify $(3x + 1)(2x + 5)$ and the Distributive Property to simplify $-x(x + 2)$.**

= $6x^2 - x^2 + 15x + 2x - 2x + 5$ **Group like terms.**

● = $5x^2 + 15x + 5$ **Simplify.**

✓ **Check Understanding** **3** Find the area of each shaded region. Simplify.

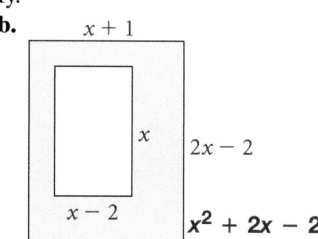

a. $25x^2 + 28x + 16$

b. $x^2 + 2x - 2$

👥 Reaching All Students

Below Level Suggest that students use one method to multiply a trinomial by a binomial, and then use the other method to check their work.	**Advanced Learners** Ask students to explain the statement, "The degree of the product of two nonzero polynomials is the sum of the degrees of the polynomials."	**Visual Learners** See note on page 468. **Tactile Learners** See note on page 468.

FOIL works when you multiply two binomials, but it is not helpful when multiplying a trinomial and a binomial. You can use the vertical method or the horizontal method to distribute each term in such factors.

4 **EXAMPLE** Multiplying a Trinomial and a Binomial

Simplify the product $(4x^2 + x - 6)(2x - 3)$.

Method 1 Multiply using the vertical method.

$$
\begin{array}{r}
4x^2 + x - 6 \\
2x - 3 \\
\hline
-12x^2 - 3x + 18 \\
8x^3 + 2x^2 - 12x \\
\hline
8x^3 - 10x^2 - 15x + 18
\end{array}
$$
Multiply by -3.
Multiply by $2x$.
Add like terms.

Method 2 Multiply using the horizontal method.

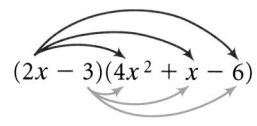

$$(2x - 3)(4x^2 + x - 6)$$

$$= 2x(4x^2) + 2x(x) + 2x(-6) - 3(4x^2) - 3(x) - 3(-6)$$
$$= 8x^3 + 2x^2 - 12x - 12x^2 - 3x + 18$$
$$= 8x^3 - 10x^2 - 15x + 18 \qquad \text{Add like terms.}$$

● The product is $8x^3 - 10x^2 - 15x + 18$.

 **Check Understanding** **4** Simplify $(6n - 8)(2n^2 + n + 7)$ using both methods shown in Example 4.
$12n^3 - 10n^2 + 34n - 56$

Problem Solving Hint

For Check Understanding 4, drawing arrows between terms can help you identify all six products.

EXERCISES

For more practice, see *Extra Practice*.

Practice and Problem Solving

A Practice by Example

Example 1
(page 467)

Copy and fill in each blank.

1. $(5a + 2)(6a - 1) = \blacksquare a^2 + 7a - 2$ 30   **2.** $(3c - 7)(2c - 5) = 6c^2 - 29c + \blacksquare$ 35

3. $(z - 4)(2z + 1) = 2z^2 - \blacksquare z - 4$ 7   **4.** $(2x + 9)(x + 2) = 2x^2 + \blacksquare x + 18$ 13

Simplify each product using the Distributive Property. 5–10. See margin.

5. $(x + 2)(x + 5)$ **6.** $(h + 3)(h + 4)$ **7.** $(k + 7)(k - 6)$

8. $(a - 8)(a - 9)$ **9.** $(2x - 1)(x + 2)$ **10.** $(2y + 5)(y - 3)$

Example 2
(page 468)

Simplify each product using FOIL. 11–16. See margin.

11. $(r + 6)(r - 4)$ **12.** $(y + 4)(5y - 8)$ **13.** $(x + 6)(x - 7)$

14. $(m - 6)(m - 9)$ **15.** $(4b - 2)(b + 3)$ **16.** $(8w + 2)(w + 5)$

17. $(x - 7)(x + 9)$ **18.** $(a + 11)(a + 5)$ **19.** $(p - 1)(p + 10)$
$x^2 + 2x - 63$ $a^2 + 16a + 55$ $p^2 + 9p - 10$

Lesson 9-3 Multiplying Binomials **469**

OBJECTIVE

2 Teaching Notes

4 **EXAMPLE** Teaching Tip

Help students understand the vertical method for multiplying polynomials by relating it to multiplying whole numbers. Write 312×23 in vertical format on the board and ask volunteers to help you solve it. Stress how partial products are lined up according to place value.

Additional Example

4 Simplify the product $(3x^2 - 2x + 3)(2x + 7)$.
$6x^3 + 17x^2 - 8x + 21$

Closure

Ask students what the letters in FOIL represent. F: first terms, O: outer terms, I: inner terms, L: last terms

page 467 Check Skills You'll Need

4. $x^3 + 8x^2 + 2x + 1$

5. $8t^3 + t + 6$

6. $5w^2 - 27w$

7. $-2b^2 - 15b$

8. $7m^3 + 27m^2 - 6m$

9. $d^5 - 4d^3 - 18d^2$

pages 469–472 Exercises

5. $x^2 + 7x + 10$

6. $h^2 + 7h + 12$

7. $k^2 + k - 42$

8. $a^2 - 17a + 72$

9. $2x^2 + 3x - 2$

10. $2y^2 - y - 15$

11. $r^2 + 2r - 24$

12. $5y^2 + 12y - 32$

13. $x^2 - x - 42$

14. $m^2 - 15m + 54$

15. $4b^2 + 10b - 6$

16. $8w^2 + 42w + 10$

Assignment Guide

▼**1** Objective
Ⓐ Ⓑ **Core** 1–21, 30–35, 42–46
Ⓒ **Extension** 47–51

▼**2** Objective
Ⓐ Ⓑ **Core** 22–29, 36–41
Ⓒ **Extension** 52–58

Standardized Test Prep 59–63

Mixed Review 64–89

Exercises 3, 4 Remind students to combine the "Outer" and "Inner" products to determine the middle term of the answer.

Error Prevention

Exercises 22–25 Suggest that students write the binomial on the second line when using the vertical method.

Connection to Geometry

Exercise 43 Remind students that the bases of a trapezoid are the two parallel sides.

Enrichment 9-3
Reteaching 9-3
Practice 9-3

Example 3 (page 468)

Geometry Find the area of each shaded region. Simplify.

20.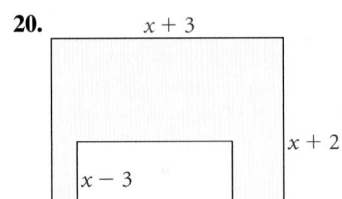
$8x + 6$

21.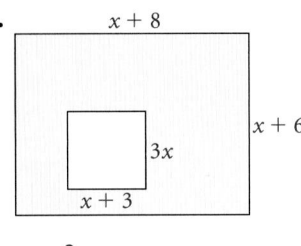
$-2x^2 + 5x + 48$

Example 4 (page 469)

Simplify. Use the vertical method. 22–25. See margin.

22. $(x + 9)(x^2 - 4x + 1)$ 23. $(a - 4)(a^2 - 2a + 1)$
24. $(g - 3)(2g^2 + 3g + 3)$ 25. $(k + 8)(3k^2 - 5k + 7)$

Simplify. Use the horizontal method. 26–29. See margin.

26. $(x^2 + 2x + 1)(9x - 3)$ 27. $(t^2 - 6t + 3)(2t - 5)$
28. $(7p^2 + 5p - 1)(8p + 9)$ 29. $(12w^2 - w - 1)(4w - 2)$

Ⓑ **Apply Your Skills**

Simplify each product. Write in standard form. 30–38. See margin.

30. $(p - 7)(p + 8)$ 31. $(-7 + p)(8 + p)$ 32. $(p^2 - 7)(p + 8)$
33. $(5c - 9)(5c + 1)$ 34. $(n^2 + 3)(n + 11)$ 35. $(3k^2 + 2)(k + 5k^2)$
36. $(6h - 1)(4h^2 + h + 3)$ 37. $(9y^2 + 2)(y^2 - y - 1)$ 38. $(8q - 4)(6q^2 + q + 1)$

 39. **Construction** You are planning a rectangular garden. Its length is twice its width. You want a walkway 2 ft wide around the garden.
a. Write an expression for the area of the garden and walk. $2x^2 + 12x + 16$
b. Write an expression for the area of the walk only. $12x + 16$
c. You have enough gravel to cover 76 ft² and want to use it all on the walk. How big should you make the garden? **10 ft by 5 ft**

40. Answers may vary. Sample: $(x + 2)(x^2 + 3x + 4)$; $x^3 + 5x^2 + 10x + 8$

41. Answers may vary. Sample: vertical method, so you can keep terms aligned

 40. **Open-Ended** Write a binomial and a trinomial. Find their product. **See left.**

 41. **Writing** Which method do you prefer for multiplying a binomial and a trinomial? Explain. **See left.**

Geometry Write an expression for the area of each shaded region. Write your answer in simplest form.

Reading Math

For help with Exercise 42, go to page 473.

44a. $x^2 + 2x + 1$, 121
$x^2 + 3x + 2$, 132
$x^2 + 4x + 3$, 143

b. For $ax^2 + bx + c$, a corresponds to the hundreds place, b to the tens place, and c to the ones place.

42.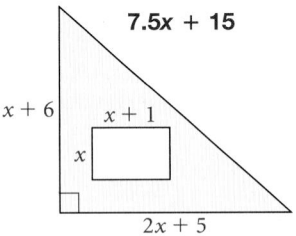

43.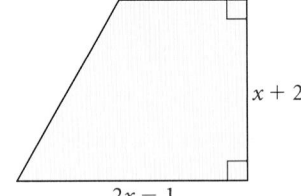

44. a. Simplify each pair of products. **a–b. See left.**
   i. $(x + 1)(x + 1)$ ii. $(x + 1)(x + 2)$ iii. $(x + 1)(x + 3)$
   $11 \cdot 11$ $11 \cdot 12$ $11 \cdot 13$
   b. **Critical Thinking** What are the similarities between the two answers in each pair of products?

pages 469–472 **Exercises**
22. $x^3 + 5x^2 - 35x + 9$
23. $a^3 - 6a^2 + 9a - 4$
24. $2g^3 - 3g^2 - 6g - 9$

25. $3k^3 + 19k^2 - 33k + 56$
26. $9x^3 + 15x^2 + 3x - 3$
27. $2t^3 - 17t^2 + 36t - 15$
28. $56p^3 + 103p^2 + 37p - 9$

29. $48w^3 - 28w^2 - 2w + 2$
30. $p^2 + p - 56$
31. $p^2 + p - 56$
32. $p^3 + 8p^2 - 7p - 56$

45. Geometry Use the formula $V = \ell wh$ to write a polynomial in standard form for the volume of the box. $n^3 + 15n^2 + 56n$

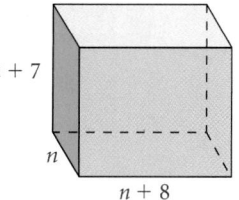
$n + 7$
n
$n + 8$

46. If n represents an even number, write an expression that represents the product of the next two even numbers. Simplify. $n^2 + 6n + 8$

C Challenge

For Exercises 47–49, each expression represents the side length of a cube. Write an expression in standard form for the surface area of each cube.

47. $x + 3$ $6x^2 + 36x + 54$ **48.** $4t + 1$ $96t^2 + 48t + 6$ **49.** $2w^2 + 7$
$24w^4 + 168w^2 + 294$

50. a. Vegetable Consumption Multiply the expressions on the right side of each equation to create a model for the total number of pounds of fresh vegetables $V(t)$ consumed in a year in the United States.
$$V(t) = 7.02t^2 + 1098.6t + 40,920$$
$C(t) = 2.7t + 165$ — the U.S. annual per capita consumption of fresh vegetables, in pounds, from 1990 to 1997

$P(t) = 2.6t + 248$ — the U.S. population, in millions, from 1990 to 1997

  b. Evaluate the equation you found in part (a) with $t = 5$ to find the total vegetable consumption for 1995. ($t = 0$ corresponds to the year 1990.)
  46,588.5 million lb

51. Financial Planning Suppose you deposit $2000 for college in a savings account that has an annual interest rate r. At the end of three years, the value of your account will be $2000(1 + r)^3$ dollars. **a. $2000r^3 + 6000r^2 + 6000r + 2000$**
  a. Rewrite the expression $2000(1 + r)^3$ by finding the product $2000(1 + r)(1 + r)(1 + r)$. Write your answer in standard form.
  b. Find the amount of money in the account if the interest rate is 3%. **$2185.45**

For Exercises 52–54, each expression represents the radius of a circle. Write an expression in standard form for the area of each circle.

52. $g + 2$ $\pi g^2 + 4\pi g + 4\pi$ **53.** $4k + 5$ **54.** $3x + 1$
$16\pi k^2 + 40\pi k + 25\pi$ $9\pi x^2 + 6\pi x + \pi$

For Exercises 55–58, find each product using lattice multiplication, which is explained below.

Lattice multiplication probably originated in India in the twelfth century. It came into use in Italy in the fourteenth century.

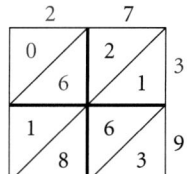

This example shows $27 \cdot 39$. Each number is treated as a binomial. The four products are placed in the small, diagonally split squares. The product of 2 and 3, shown in red, is 6. The first square shows 0/6, which indicates 6. The product of 7 and 3 is 21. The second square shows 2/1.

The products are totaled diagonally. For the diagonal shaded blue, the tens place of the sum $1 + 6 + 8$ is carried into the diagonal above and added into that diagonal: $1 + (2 + 6 + 1)$. The product 1053 appears down the left side of the lattice and across the bottom.

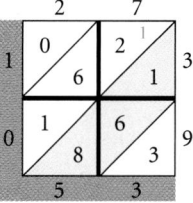

55. $14 \cdot 72$ **1008** **56.** $53 \cdot 87$ **4611**

57. $91 \cdot 64$ **5824** **58.** $38 \cdot 64$ **2432**

Lesson 9-3 Multiplying Binomials **471**

Real-World Connection

In 2000, the U.S. consumption of fresh tomatoes was 17.8 lb per person.

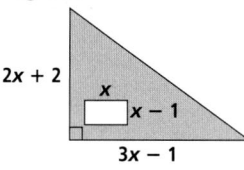
33. $25c^2 - 40c - 9$
34. $n^3 + 11n^2 + 3n + 33$
35. $15k^4 + 3k^3 + 10k^2 + 2k$

36. $24h^3 + 2h^2 + 17h - 3$
37. $9y^4 - 9y^3 - 7y^2 - 2y - 2$
38. $48q^3 - 16q^2 + 4q - 4$

Resources

For additional practice with a variety of test item formats:
• Standardized Test Prep, p. 507
• Test-Taking Strategies, p. 502
• Test-Taking Strategies with Transparencies

Exercise 61 Remind students that only the product of odd numbers is odd. Ask them to consider which product's factors are both odd numbers.

Chapter Checkpoint 1

To check understanding of Lessons 9-1 to 9-3:

Checkpoint Quiz 1 (p. 472)

Teaching Resources

Checkpoint Quiz 1 (also in Prentice Hall Assessment System)

Reaching All Students

Reading and Math Literacy B

Spanish versions available

---

pages 469–472 Exercises

64. $20v^2 - 28v$

65. $3c^2 - 27c$

66. $8t^3 + 48t^2$

67. $3y^2 - 10y$

68. $-5x^3 + 55x^2$

69. $-6t^4 + t^3$

70. $-4r^6 + 12r$

71. $9b^5 + 18b^3$

72. $5(w + 9)$

73. $x(3x - 11)$

74. $4a(a + 3)$

75. $9n^2(1 - n)$

472

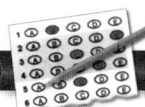

Standardized Test Prep

Multiple Choice

59. $(n - 1)(n - 4)$ is equivalent to which expression? **A**
   A. $n^2 - 5n + 4$ B. $n^2 - 3n + 4$
   C. $n^2 + 3n + 4$ D. $n^2 - 5n - 5$

60. $(8k - 3)(k^2 - k + 1)$ is equivalent to which expression? **H**
   F. $8k^3 + 11k^2 - 11k - 3$ G. $9k^3 - 8k^2 + 8k - 2$
   H. $8k^3 - 11k^2 + 11k - 3$ I. $9k^3 - 3k^2 + 3k - 3$

61. Which of the following products is always odd for integer values of n? **B**
   A. $(n + 1)(n + 1)$ B. $(2n - 1)(2n + 1)$
   C. $(2n - 1)(n + 1)$ D. $(2n + 1)(n - 1)$

Short Response

62. Explain how to find the product of $(4v - 1)(2v^2 + v + 1)$, and simplify. **See back of book.**

Extended Response

63. Find the area of the shaded region. Show your work. **See back of book.**

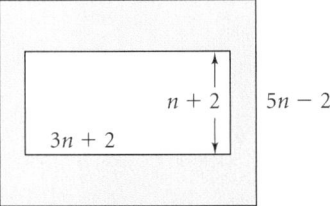

Take It to the NET
Online lesson quiz at **www.PHSchool.com**
Web Code: aea-0903

Mixed Review

Lesson 9-2

Simplify each product. 64–71. See margin.

64. $4v(5v - 7)$ 65. $(c - 9)3c$ 66. $8t^2(t + 6)$ 67. $y(3y - 10)$

68. $5x^2(11 - x)$ 69. $-t^3(6t - 1)$ 70. $4r(3 - r^5)$ 71. $9b^2(b^3 + 2b)$

Factor. 72–75. See margin.

72. $5w + 45$ 73. $3x^2 - 11x$ 74. $4a^2 + 12a$ 75. $9n^2 - n^3$

76. $34t - 51$ 77. $63v^2 + 45v$ 78. $25m - 60m^3$ 79. $11k + 77k^6$
   $17(2t - 3)$ $9v(7v + 5)$ $5m(5 - 12m^2)$ $11k(1 + 7k^5)$

Lesson 8-5

Simplify each expression.

80. $\frac{3^5}{3^2}$ 27   81. $\frac{3^2}{3^5}$ $\frac{1}{27}$ 82. $\frac{y^{12}}{y^8}$ y^4 83. $\frac{2w^{-3}}{6w^2}$ $\frac{1}{3w^5}$ 84. $\frac{x^{-8}}{2x^3}$ $\frac{1}{2x^{11}}$

85. $\left(\frac{5}{3}\right)^{-1}$ $\frac{3}{5}$ 86. $\left(\frac{5}{3}\right)^{-2}$ $\frac{9}{25}$ 87. $\left(\frac{5}{3}\right)^{0}$ 1   88. $\left(\frac{4x}{7}\right)^{-2}$ $\frac{49}{16x^2}$ 89. $\left(\frac{y^{-2}}{8}\right)^{-2}$ $64y^4$

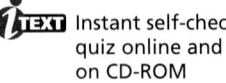
Checkpoint Quiz 1   Lessons 9-1 through 9-3

Instant self-check quiz online and on CD-ROM

Simplify each expression. 1–7. See margin.

1. $(4x^2 + x + 3) + (5x^2 + 9x - 2)$ 2. $(7b^2 - 5b + 3) - (b^2 + 8b - 6)$

3. $3w(12w - 1) - 8w$ 4. $6k(4k + k^2) + 9k(2k - 6k^2)$

5. $(x + 3)(x - 5)$ 6. $(2n^3 - 5)(6n^2 + n)$ 7. $(g^2 + 4)(4g^2 + 8g - 9)$

Factor each polynomial.

8. $12y^2 - 10$ $2(6y^2 - 5)$ 9. $5t^6 + 25t^3 - 10t$ 10. $18v^4 + 27v^3 + 36v^2$
                                   $5t(t^5 + 5t^2 - 2)$ $9v^2(2v^2 + 3v + 4)$

page 472 Checkpoint Quiz 1

1. $9x^2 + 10x + 1$

2. $6b^2 - 13b + 9$

3. $36w^2 - 11w$

4. $-48k^3 + 42k^2$

5. $x^2 - 2x - 15$

6. $12n^5 + 2n^4 - 30n^2 - 5n$

7. $4g^4 + 8g^3 + 7g^2 + 32g - 36$

Reading a Diagram

FOR USE WITH PAGE 470, EXERCISE 42

Read the exercise below and then the explanation of how to interpret the diagram. Check your understanding by solving the problem at the bottom of the page.

Geometry Write an expression for the area of the shaded region. Write your answer in simplest form.

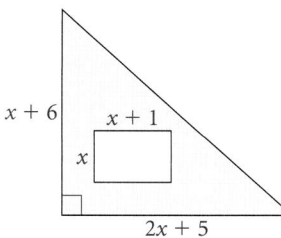

To solve this problem, you must refer to the diagram. It contains the rest of the information you need. To find this information, ask yourself a few questions.

What do I see?

There are two figures—a right triangle and a rectangle inside it. The rectangle is *not* shaded. There are also some variable expressions.

What do the variable expressions tell me?

The expressions represent the dimensions of the figures.

Triangle: The length of the base is $2x + 5$.
The height is $x + 6$.

Rectangle: The length is x.
The width is $x + 1$.

Now you can solve the problem.

area of shaded region $=$ area of triangle $-$ area of the rectangle

$= \frac{1}{2}(\text{base})(\text{height}) - (\text{length})(\text{width})$

$= \frac{1}{2}(2x + 5)(x + 6) - x(x + 1)$ **Use values in the diagram to substitute.**

$= \frac{1}{2}(2x^2 + 5x + 12x + 30) - (x^2 + x)$ **Simplify $(x + 6)(2x + 5)$ and $(x + 1)(x)$.**

$= x^2 + \frac{17}{2}x + 15 - x^2 - x$ **Use the Distributive Property.**

$= 7.5x + 15$ **Simplify.**

EXERCISE

Geometry Write an expression for the area of the colored region. Write your answer in simplest form.

7x + 16

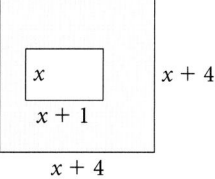

Reading a Diagram

The students must be able to understand the diagram in order to solve the problem. In these examples the only place they can get the needed information is from the diagram. Therefore students should "read" the diagram to extract the information they need in order to solve the problem. This feature helps students translate the information from a diagram and use prior knowledge of formulas to find the solution.

Teaching Notes

Some students might not think of Reading a Diagram as actual reading. Remind them that the broad definition of reading is to be able to interpret and understand the symbols on the page. In this case the symbols on the page are figures in a diagram.

Tactile Learner

Some students will have a better understanding of the problem if they can make a model of the diagram. Let students cut out a rectangle from a right triangle. Then they can conclude that you must subtract the area of the rectangle from the area of the triangle to find the remaining area.

Exercise

Have the students work independently on a similar problem. Then have volunteers come to the board or overhead, draw the diagram, and explain how they solved the problem. Encourage those who thought about it differently and those who disagree with the answer to share their thinking about the problem. In this way, you will be able to assess students' understanding or misunderstanding.

1. Plan

Lesson Preview

✓ **Check Skills You'll Need**

More Multiplication Properties of Exponents
Lesson 8-4: Example 3
Exercises 10–22
Extra Practice, p. 709

Multiplying Binomials
Lesson 9-3: Example 2
Exercises 11–19
Extra Practice, p. 710

Lesson Resources

📁 **Teaching Resources**
Practice, Reteaching, Enrichment

👥 **Reaching All Students**
Practice Workbook 9-4
Spanish Practice Workbook 9-4
Basic Algebra Planning Guide 9-4

⏱ **Presentation Assistant Plus!**
Transparencies
• Check Skills You'll Need 9-4
• Additional Examples 9-4
• Student Edition Answers 9-4
• Lesson Quiz 9-4
PH Presentation Pro CD 9-4

ASSESSMENT SYSTEM

Computer Test Generator CD

💾 **Technology**
Resource Pro® CD-ROM
Computer Test Generator CD
Prentice Hall Presentation Pro CD

🖥 **www.PHSchool.com**
Student Site
• Teacher Web Code: aek-5500
• Reasoning & Puzzles pp. 78, 80, 81
• Self-grading Lesson Quiz
Teacher Center
• Lesson Planner
• Resources

Plus **iTEXT**

474

9-4 Multiplying Special Cases

North Carolina Objectives

1.01 Write equivalent forms of algebraic expressions to solve problems. b) Operate with polynomials.

Lesson Preview

What You'll Learn

OBJECTIVE 1 To find the square of a binomial

OBJECTIVE 2 To find the difference of squares

. . . And Why

To find the probability of a Labrador retriever inheriting dark fur, as in Example 2

✓ Check Skills You'll Need

(For help, go to Lessons 8-4 and 9-3.)

Simplify.

1. $(7x)^2$ **$49x^2$**
2. $(3v)^2$ **$9v^2$**
3. $(-4c)^2$ **$16c^2$**
4. $(5g^3)^2$ **$25g^6$**

Use FOIL to find each product.

5. $(j + 5)(j + 7)$ **$j^2 + 12j + 35$**
6. $(2b - 6)(3b - 8)$ **$6b^2 - 34b + 48$**
7. $(4y + 1)(5y - 2)$ **$20y^2 - 3y - 2$**
8. $(x + 3)(x - 4)$ **$x^2 - x - 12$**
9. $(8c^2 + 2)(c^2 - 10)$ **$8c^4 - 78c^2 - 20$**
10. $(6y^2 - 3)(9y^2 + 1)$ **$54y^4 - 21y^2 - 3$**

iTEXT Interactive lesson includes instant self-check, tutorials, and activities.

OBJECTIVE 1 Finding the Square of a Binomial

Investigation: Exploring Special Products

1. Find each product. **1–3. See back of book.**

Row 1: $(x + 8)(x + 8)$ $(y + 5)(y + 5)$ $(2p + 3)(2p + 3)$

Row 2: $(d - 3)(d - 3)$ $(t - 1)(t - 1)$ $(9r - 2)(9r - 2)$

Row 3: $(x + 4)(x - 4)$ $(k + 9)(k - 9)$ $(3c + 7)(3c - 7)$

2. Describe the pattern or patterns you found in each row.

3. Based on the patterns you found, predict each product.

$(p + 6)(p + 6)$ $(v - 5)(v - 5)$ $(x + 8)(x - 8)$

4. Use FOIL to find each product in Question 2. Were your predictions correct? **yes**

You can write the expression $(a + b)^2$ as $(a + b)(a + b)$. You can find $(a + b)^2$ using the methods you learned in Lesson 9-3.

Area Model

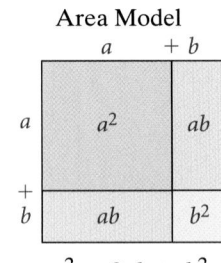

$a^2 + 2ab + b^2$

FOIL

$(a + b)(a + b)$
$= a^2 + ab + ba + b^2$ **Use FOIL.**
$= a^2 + 2ab + b^2$ **Simplify.**

474 Chapter 9 Polynomials and Factoring

✓ **Ongoing Assessment and Intervention**

Before the Lesson	During the Lesson	After the Lesson
Diagnose prerequisite skills using:	**Monitor progress using:**	**Assess knowledge using:**
• Check Skills You'll Need	• Check Understanding • Additional Examples • Standardized Test Prep	• Lesson Quiz • Computer Test Generator CD

The expressions $(a - b)^2$ and $(a + b)^2$ are squares of binomials. To square a binomial, you can use FOIL or the following rule.

 Key Concepts

Rule	The Square of a Binomial

$(a + b)^2 = a^2 + 2ab + b^2$

$(a - b)^2 = a^2 - 2ab + b^2$

The square of a binomial is the square of the first term plus twice the product of the two terms plus the square of the last term.

1 EXAMPLE Squaring a Binomial

a. Find $(x + 7)^2$.

$(x + 7)^2 = x^2 + 2x(7) + 7^2$ Square the binomial.

$= x^2 + 14x + 49$ Simplify.

b. Find $(4k - 3)^2$.

$(4k - 3)^2 = (4k)^2 - 2(4k)(3) + 3^2$ Square the binomial.

$= 16k^2 - 24k + 9$ Simplify.

✓ **Check Understanding** **1** Find each square. **See left.**

a. $(t + 6)^2$ **b.** $(5y + 1)^2$ **c.** $(7m - 2p)^2$ **d.** $(9c - 8)^2$

1a. $t^2 + 12t + 36$

b. $25y^2 + 10y + 1$

c. $49m^2 - 28mp + 4p^2$

d. $81c^2 - 144c + 64$

You can square binomials to find probabilities that apply to real-world situations.

2 EXAMPLE Real-World Problem Solving

Among Labrador retrievers, the dark-fur gene D is dominant, and the yellow-fur gene Y is recessive. This means that a dog with at least one dominant gene (DD or DY) will have dark fur. A dog with two recessive genes (YY) will have yellow fur.

The Punnett square at the right models the possible combinations of color genes that parents who carry both genes can pass on to their offspring. Since YY is $\frac{1}{4}$ of the outcomes, the probability that a puppy has yellow fur is $\frac{1}{4}$.

	D	Y
D	DD	DY
Y	DY	YY

You can model the probabilities found in the Punnett square with the expression $(\frac{1}{2}D + \frac{1}{2}Y)^2$. Show that this product gives the same result as the Punnett square.

$(\frac{1}{2}D + \frac{1}{2}Y)^2 = (\frac{1}{2}D)^2 + 2(\frac{1}{2}D)(\frac{1}{2}Y) + (\frac{1}{2}Y)^2$ Square the binomial.

$= \frac{1}{4}D^2 + \frac{1}{2}DY + \frac{1}{4}Y^2$ Simplify.

The expressions $\frac{1}{4}D^2$ and $\frac{1}{4}Y^2$ indicate that the probability offspring will have either two dominant genes or two recessive genes is $\frac{1}{4}$. The expression $\frac{1}{2}DY$ indicates that there is $\frac{1}{2}$ chance that the offspring will inherit both genes. These are the same probabilities shown in the Punnett square.

Real-World Connection

The color of a Labrador retriever is determined by a pair of genes. The offspring inherits a single gene at random from each of its parents.

Reaching All Students

Below Level Suggest to students that when squaring a binomial, they write out what *a* and *b* equal before substituting in the formula.	**Advanced Learners** Ask students to compute $(a + b)^3$ and $(a - b)^3$.	**English Learners** See note on page 475. **Auditory Learners** See note on page 475.

---

2. Teach

 Professional Development

Math Background

All polynomials can be multiplied using the processes taught in the previous lessons. Some special cases are easy to identify and have a pattern to their products that makes their multiplication quicker and easier.

OBJECTIVE

1 Teaching Notes

Investigation (Optional) Teaching Tip

Ask: *Why do you think the first two rows are referred to as "squares of binomials?"* Each factor is the same. *How is Row 3 different from the other two rows?* The signs of the second terms are not the same. *What happens when the signs of the second terms are different?* There is no middle term in the product.

1 EXAMPLE Error Prevention

Some students may think the product is $x^2 + 7^2$, or $x^2 + 49$. Remind students that the expression $(x + 7)^2$ means to write the group of terms that are inside the parentheses twice, and then multiply them. Writing the product as $x^2 + 7^2$ is squaring each term separately.

2 EXAMPLE English Learners

Some students may not understand the concepts of *dominant gene* and *recessive gene*. Relate the words to their root words of *dominate* and *recede*.

3 EXAMPLE Auditory Learners

Students sometimes forget the factor 2 in the middle term. Have students repeat the following: *For the <u>second</u> term, multiply the product by <u>2</u>.* Encourage students to stress *second* and *2* while they repeat the phrase five more times.

475

1 a. Find $(y + 11)^2$.
$y^2 + 22y + 121$
b. Find $(3w - 6)^2$.
$9w^2 - 36w + 36$

2 Among guinea pigs, the black fur gene (B) is dominant and the white fur gene (W) is recessive. This means that a guinea pig with at least one dominant gene (BB or BW) will have black fur. A guinea pig with two recessive genes (WW) will have white fur. You can model the probabilities with the expression $\left(\frac{1}{2}B + \frac{1}{2}W\right)^2$. Show the result this product gives.
$\frac{1}{4}B^2 + \frac{1}{2}BW + \frac{1}{4}W^2$

3 a. Find 81^2 using mental math. **6561**
b. Find 59^2 using mental math.
3481

4 EXAMPLE Teaching Tip

Have students multiply the binomials using the FOIL method to reassure themselves that the sum of the middle terms is zero.

 Additional Examples

4 Find $(p^4 - 8)(p^4 + 8)$ $p^8 - 64$

5 Find $43 \cdot 37$. **1591**

Closure

Ask students to describe in words how to square a binomial. **The square of a binomial is the square of the first term, plus twice the product of the two terms, plus the square of the last term.**

✔ **Check Understanding**  **Games** When you play a game with two number cubes, you can find probabilities by squaring a binomial. Let A represent rolling 1 or 2 and B represent rolling 3, 4, 5, or 6. The probability of A is $\frac{1}{3}$, and the probability of B is $\frac{2}{3}$.

a. Find $\left(\frac{1}{3}A + \frac{2}{3}B\right)^2$. $\frac{1}{9}A^2 + \frac{4}{9}AB + \frac{4}{9}B^2$

b. What is the probability that both number cubes you roll show 1 or 2? $\frac{1}{9}$

c. What is the probability that one number cube shows a 1 or 2 and the other shows 3, 4, 5, or 6? $\frac{4}{9}$

d. What is the probability that both number cubes show 3, 4, 5, or 6? $\frac{4}{9}$

Using mental math, you can square a binomial to find the square of a number.

3 EXAMPLE Mental Math

a. Find 51^2 using mental math.
$51^2 = (50 + 1)^2$

$= 50^2 + 2(50 \cdot 1) + 1^2$ ← Square the binomial. →

$= 2500 + 100 + 1 = 2601$ ← Simplify. →

b. Find 49^2 using mental math.
$49^2 = (50 - 1)^2$

$= 50^2 - 2(50 \cdot 1) + 1^2$

$= 2500 - 100 + 1 = 2401$

✔ **Check Understanding** 3 Find each square using mental math.
a. 31^2 **961**   b. 29^2 **841**   c. 98^2 **9604**   d. 203^2 **41,209**

The product of the sum and difference of the same two terms also produces a pattern.

$$(a + b)(a - b) = a^2 - ab + ba - b^2$$
$$= a^2 - b^2$$

Notice that the sum $-ab$ and ba is 0, leaving $a^2 - b^2$. This product is called the difference of squares.

🔑 **Key Concepts**

Rule	The Difference of Squares
$(a + b)(a - b) = a^2 - b^2$	

The product of the sum and difference of the same two terms is the difference of their squares.

Need Help?
When you raise a power to a power, multiply the exponents.
$(t^3)^2 = t^6$

4 EXAMPLE Finding the Difference of Squares

Find $(t^3 - 6)(t^3 + 6)$.

$(t^3 - 6)(t^3 + 6) = (t^3)^2 - (6)^2$ Find the difference of squares.

$= t^6 - 36$ Simplify.

✔ **Check Understanding** 4 Find each product.
a. $(d + 11)(d - 11)$ b. $(c^2 + 8)(c^2 - 8)$ c. $(9v^3 + w^4)(9v^3 - w^4)$
$d^2 - 121$ $c^4 - 64$ $81v^6 - w^8$

pages 477–479 Exercises

1. $c^2 + 2c + 1$

2. $x^2 + 8x + 16$

3. $4v^2 + 44v + 121$

You can use the difference of squares to calculate products using mental math.

5 EXAMPLE **Mental Math**

Find $82 \cdot 78$.

$82 \cdot 78 = (80 + 2)(80 - 2)$ **Express each factor using 80 and 2.**

$ = 80^2 - 2^2$ **Find the difference of squares.**

$ = 6400 - 4 = 6396$ **Simplify.**

✓ **Check Understanding** ⑤ Find each product.
a. $18 \cdot 22$ **396** **b.** $19 \cdot 21$ **399** **c.** $59 \cdot 61$ **3599** **d.** $87 \cdot 93$ **8091**

EXERCISES

For more practice, see *Extra Practice.*

Practice and Problem Solving

Ⓐ **Practice by Example**

Examples 1, 2
(page 475)

Find each square. 1–8. See margin p. 476.

1. $(c + 1)^2$ **2.** $(x + 4)^2$ **3.** $(2v + 11)^2$ **4.** $(3m + 7)^2$

5. $(w - 12)^2$ **6.** $(b - 5)^2$ **7.** $(6x - 8)^2$ **8.** $(9j - 2)^2$

9. Games Suppose you play a game with two spinners like the one shown at the right. Let C represent spinning an even number. Let D represent spinning an odd number. The probability of C is $\frac{1}{4}$. The probability of D is $\frac{3}{4}$.
a. Simplify $\left(\frac{1}{4}C + \frac{3}{4}D\right)^2$. $\frac{1}{16}C^2 + \frac{3}{8}CD + \frac{9}{16}D^2$
b. Find $P(C$ and $C)$. $\frac{1}{16}$
c. How does the answer in part (b) relate to the polynomial in part (a)? **It is the coefficient of C^2.**

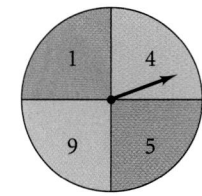

Example 3
(page 476)

Mental Math Find each square.

10. 61^2 **3721** **11.** 99^2 **9801** **12.** 48^2 **2304** **13.** 302^2 **91,204** **14.** 499^2 **249,001**

Example 4
(page 476)

Find each product. 15–20. See margin.

15. $(x + 4)(x - 4)$ **16.** $(a + 8)(a - 8)$ **17.** $(d + 7)(d - 7)$

18. $(h + 15)(h - 15)$ **19.** $(y + 12)(y - 12)$ **20.** $(k + 5)(k - 5)$

Example 5
(page 477)

Mental Math Find each product.

21. $31 \cdot 29$ **899** **22.** $89 \cdot 91$ **8099** **23.** $52 \cdot 48$ **2496** **24.** $197 \cdot 203$ **39,991** **25.** $299 \cdot 301$ **89,999**

Ⓑ **Apply Your Skills** **Geometry** Find the area of each shaded region. Write your answers in standard form.

26.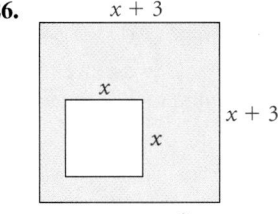

(6x + 9) units^2

27.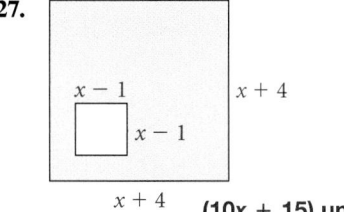

(10x + 15) units^2

Lesson 9-4 Multiplying Special Cases **477**

4. $9m^2 + 42m + 49$ **8.** $81j^2 - 36j + 4$ **18.** $h^2 - 225$

5. $w^2 - 24w + 144$ **15.** $x^2 - 16$ **19.** $y^2 - 144$

6. $b^2 - 10b + 25$ **16.** $a^2 - 64$ **20.** $k^2 - 25$

7. $36x^2 - 96x + 64$ **17.** $d^2 - 49$

Assignment Guide

1 Objective
Ⓐ Ⓑ **Core** 1–14, 26–40, 42–43
Ⓒ **Extension** 53–54

2 Objective
Ⓐ Ⓑ **Core** 15–25, 41, 44–52
Ⓒ **Extension** 55–57

Standardized Test Prep 58–63

Mixed Review 64–80

Error Prevention

Exercises 1–8 Remind students that the square of a binomial has a negative middle term only when the binomial is a difference.

Careers

Exercise 40 A genetic counselor helps families analyze inheritance patterns and risks of recurrence of genetic disorders. Have interested students research inheritance of diseases such as cystic fibrosis that result from having two copies of a mutant gene. They could create different scenarios and tell the probabilities that a child would be born with the disease.

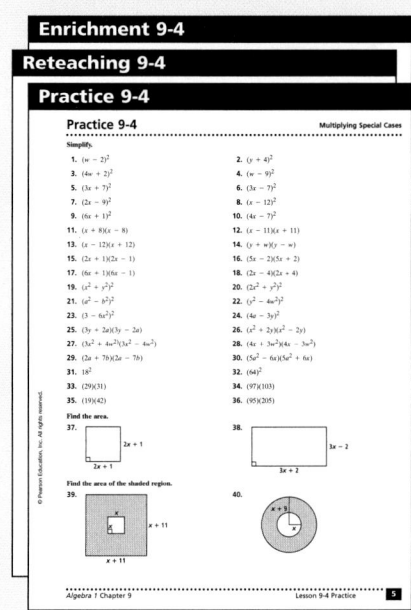

Lesson Quiz 9-4

Find each square.

1. $(y + 9)^2$ $y^2 + 18y + 81$

2. $(2h - 7)^2$ $4h^2 - 28h + 49$

3. 41^2 1681

4. 29^2 841

5. Find $(p^3 - 7)(p^3 + 7)$.
   $p^6 - 49$

6. Find $32 \cdot 28$. 896

Alternative Assessment

Group students in pairs. Give each group three number cubes. Instruct the students to write down any variable. Then have them roll one number cube and write the result as the exponent of the variable. Instruct students to roll another number cube. If the result is even, they are to write a plus sign; if it is odd, they are to write a negative sign. Tell students to roll the last number cube and write the result as the second term of the binomial. Have each student in the group square the binomial and check their results with the others. Repeat. You may also wish to have students just roll two number cubes and let these results represent a and b. Then have students write a plus sign and a minus sign in the binomials and square them.

pages 477–479   Exercises

28. $x^2 + 6xy + 9y^2$

29. $25p^2 - 10pq + q^2$

30. $36m^2 + 12mn + n^2$

31. $x^2 - 14xy + 49y^2$

32. $16k^2 + 56kj + 49j^2$

33. $4y^2 - 36xy + 81x^2$

34. $9w^2 + 60wt + 100t^2$

35. $36a^2 + 132ab + 121b^2$

36. $25p^2 - 60pq + 36q^2$

37. $36h^2 - 96hp + 64p^2$

38. $y^{10} - 18x^4y^5 + 81x^8$

39. $64k^2 + 64kh + 16h^2$

478

Real-World **Connection**

The cow in the photo shows a typical roan coat.

40a. $\left(\frac{1}{2}R + \frac{1}{2}W\right)^2 =$
$\frac{1}{4}R^2 + \frac{1}{2}RW + \frac{1}{4}W^2$

C **Challenge**

Find each square. 28–39. See margin.

28. $(x + 3y)^2$ 29. $(5p - q)^2$ 30. $(6m + n)^2$ 31. $(x - 7y)^2$

32. $(4k + 7j)^2$ 33. $(2y - 9x)^2$ 34. $(3w + 10t)^2$ 35. $(6a + 11b)^2$

36. $(5p - 6q)^2$ 37. $(6h - 8p)^2$ 38. $(y^5 - 9x^4)^2$ 39. $(8k + 4h)^2$

40. **Biology** The coat color of shorthorn cattle is determined by two genes, Red R and White W. RR produces red, WW produces white, and RW produces a third type of coat color called roan.
   a. Model the Punnett square with the square of a binomial. **See below left.**
   b. If both parents have RW, what is the probability the offspring will also be RW? $\frac{1}{2}$
   c. Write an expression to model a situation where one parent is RW while the other is RR. $\left(\frac{1}{2}R + \frac{1}{2}W\right)(R) = \frac{1}{2}R^2 + \frac{1}{2}RW$
   d. What is the probability that the offspring of the parents in step (c) will have a white coat? **0**

	R	W
R	RR	RW
W	RW	WW

41. a. Copy and complete the table. a–c. See margin.
    b. Describe any patterns you see.
    c. **Writing** How does the difference of squares account for the pattern in the table?

$4^2 = 16$	$3 \cdot 5 = 15$
$5^2 = \blacksquare$	$4 \cdot 6 = 24$
$6^2 = \blacksquare$	$5 \cdot 7 = \blacksquare$
$7^2 = \blacksquare$	$6 \cdot 8 = \blacksquare$

42. **Open-Ended** Give a counterexample to show that $(x + y)^2 = x^2 + y^2$ is false. **Answers may vary. Sample:** $(2 + 2)^2 \overset{?}{=} 2^2 + 2^2$, $16 \neq 8$

43. **Critical Thinking** Does $\left(3\frac{1}{2}\right)^2 = 9\frac{1}{4}$? Explain. **See margin.**

Find each product. 44–52. See margin.

44. $(3y + 5w)(3y - 5w)$ 45. $(p + 9q)(p - 9q)$ 46. $(2d + 7g)(2d - 7g)$

47. $(7b - 8c)(7b + 8c)$ 48. $(g + 7h)(g - 7h)$ 49. $(g^3 + 7h^2)(g^3 - 7h^2)$

50. $(2a^2 + b)(2a^2 - b)$ 51. $(11x - y^3)(11x + y^3)$ 52. $(4k - 3h^2)(4k + 3h^2)$

53. Find the general formula for $(a + b + c)^2$. $a^2 + b^2 + c^2 + 2ab + 2bc + 2ac$

54. **Games** Suppose you play a game by tossing 3 coins. You can find the probabilities by simplifying $\left(\frac{1}{2}H + \frac{1}{2}T\right)^3$.
    a. Simplify the expression. $\frac{1}{8}H^3 + \frac{3}{8}H^2T + \frac{3}{8}HT^2 + \frac{1}{8}T^3$
    b. Use the answer you found in part (a) to find the probability of getting a head and two tails $\left(HT^2\right)$. $\frac{3}{8}$

55. **Number Theory** You can use factoring to show that the sum of two multiples of 3 is also a multiple of 3. **a–b. See margin p. 479.**

> If m and n are integers, then $3n$ and $3m$ are multiples of three.
> $3m + 3n = 3(m + n)$
> Since $(m + n)$ is an integer, $3(m + n)$ is a multiple of three.

   a. Show that if a number is one more than a multiple of 3, then its square is also one more than a multiple of 3.
   b. **Reasoning** If a number is two more than a multiple of 3, is its square also two more than a multiple of 3? Explain.

56. The formula $V = \frac{4}{3}\pi r^3$ gives the volume of a sphere. Find the formula for the volume of a sphere that has a radius 3 more than r. Write your answer in standard form. $V = \frac{4}{3}\pi r^3 + 12\pi r^2 + 36\pi r + 36\pi$

478   Chapter 9   Polynomials and Factoring

41a.

$4^2 = 16$	$3 \cdot 5 = 15$
$5^2 = 25$	$4 \cdot 6 = 24$
$6^2 = 36$	$5 \cdot 7 = 35$
$7^2 = 49$	$6 \cdot 8 = 48$

b. n^2 is one more than the product $(n - 1)(n + 1)$.

c. The product $(n - 1)(n + 1)$ is $n^2 - 1$.

43. No; $\left(3\frac{1}{2}\right)^2 = \left(3 + \frac{1}{2}\right)^2 =$
$\left(3 + \frac{1}{2}\right)\left(3 + \frac{1}{2}\right) =$
$3^2 + 2(3)\left(\frac{1}{2}\right) + \left(\frac{1}{2}\right)^2 =$
$9 + 3 + \frac{1}{4} = 12\frac{1}{4} \neq 9\frac{1}{4}$.

57. The area of the shaded region in the diagram is $9^2 - 2^2$.

a. Copy the figure. Make a single cut across the shaded region and reassemble it to show that $9^2 - 2^2 = (9 - 2)(9 + 2)$.

b. Draw your reassembled figure. Include its dimensions.
a–b. See back of book.

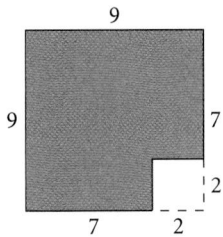

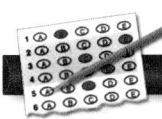

Multiple Choice

58. Which value of a makes $(9x - 1)^2 = ax^2 - 18x + 1$ true? **D**

A. 9   B. 18   C. 64   D. 81

59. Which value of n makes $(b^7 + 2)^2 = b^n + 4b^7 + 4$ true? **F**

F. 14   G. 28   H. 42   I. 49

Quantitative Comparison

Compare the boxed quantity in Column A with the boxed quantity in Column B. Choose the best answer.

A. The quantity in Column A is greater.
B. The quantity in Column B is greater.
C. The two quantities are equal.
D. The relationship cannot be determined from the information given.

63. [2] The middle term is twice the product of the first and last terms; $2(3x)(-4y) = -24xy$.

[1] incorrect explanation

	Column A	Column B
C **60.**	coefficient of a^2 in the product $(3a - 10)(3a + 10)$	coefficient of b^2 in the product $(9b - 10)(b - 10)$
B **61.**	coefficient of a in the product $(4a - 6)(5a + 1)$	coefficient of b in the product $(8b - 7)(3b + 9)$
C **62.**	constant term in the product $(7a + 3)(8a + 2)$	constant term in the product $(12b - 1)(b - 6)$

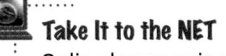

Take It to the NET
Online lesson quiz at www.PHSchool.com
Web Code: aea-0904

Short Response

63. Explain how to compute the xy term of the product $(3x - 4y)^2$.
See above left.

Lesson 9-3

Find each product. 64–72. See margin.

64. $(k + 7)(k - 9)$ **65.** $(2x - 11)(x - 6)$ **66.** $(5p + 4)(3p - 1)$

67. $(3y + 1)(y + 1)$ **68.** $(4h - 2)(6h + 1)$ **69.** $(9b + 7)(8b + 2)$

70. $(2w^2 + 5)(w + 8)$ **71.** $(r - 7)(r^2 + 3r - 9)$ **72.** $(5m^2 - 2)(6m^3 + 4m)$

Lesson 8-2

Write each number in scientific notation.

73. 8713 8.713×10^3 **74.** 0.031 3.1×10^{-2} **75.** 68,952 6.8952×10^4 **76.** 1.2 million 1.2×10^6

77. 11 1.1×10^1 **78.** 523 5.23×10^2 **79.** 6 billion 6×10^9 **80.** 0.72 7.2×10^{-1}

Lesson 9-4   Multiplying Special Cases   **479**

44. $9y^2 - 25w^2$ **47.** $49b^2 - 64c^2$ **50.** $4a^4 - b^2$

45. $p^2 - 81q^2$ **48.** $g^2 - 49h^2$ **51.** $121x^2 - y^6$

46. $4d^2 - 49g^2$ **49.** $g^6 - 49h^4$ **52.** $16k^2 - 9h^4$

Standardized Test Prep

Resources
For additional practice with a variety of test item formats:
• Standardized Test Prep, p. 507
• Test-Taking Strategies, p. 502
• Test-Taking Strategies with Transparencies

Exercise 59 You may wish to review the Multiplication Properties of Exponents in Lessons 8-3 and 8-4.

55a. $(3n + 1)(3n + 1) = 9n^2 + 6n + 1 = 3(3n^2 + 2n) + 1$; since $3n^2 + 2n$ is an integer, then $3(3n^2 + 2n)$ is a multiple of three and $3(3n^2 + 2n) + 1$ is one more than a multiple of three.

b. No; its square is one more than a multiple of three.

64. $k^2 - 2k - 63$

65. $2x^2 - 23x + 66$

66. $15p^2 + 7p - 4$

67. $3y^2 + 4y + 1$

68. $24h^2 - 8h - 2$

69. $72b^2 + 74b + 14$

70. $2w^3 + 16w^2 + 5w + 40$

71. $r^3 - 4r^2 - 30r + 63$

72. $30m^5 + 8m^3 - 8m$

479

Using Models to Factor

Students learn the concept of factoring trinomials by using algebra tiles.

Resources

algebra tiles

Teaching Notes

Teaching Tip

It is sometimes difficult and frustrating when trying to find the correct arrangement of tiles to form a rectangle. Let students work in pairs or small groups so they can discuss where to place tiles.

Error Prevention

Remind students that corresponding lengths are placed side by side. You cannot place a few unit tiles along the long edge of an x-tile as seen in the first and second tries. The length of a unit tile matches the width of an x-tile, therefore, unit tiles are placed along the short side of x-tiles.

Investigation

Using Models to Factor

You can sometimes write a trinomial as the product of two binomial factors. You can use algebra tiles to find the factors by arranging all of the tiles to form a rectangle. The lengths of the sides of the rectangle are the factors of the trinomial.

EXAMPLE

Write $2x^2 + 7x + 6$ as the product of two binomial factors.

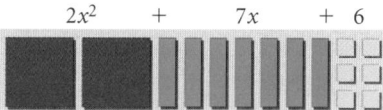

Model of polynomial

Use the tiles to form a rectangle.

First try:

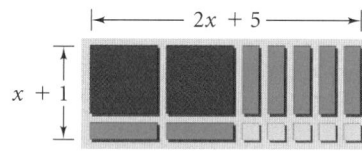

Left over: ▢

Second try:

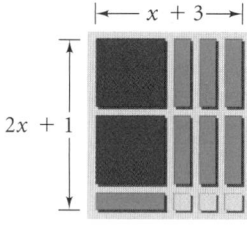

Left over: ▢ ▢ ▢

Third try:

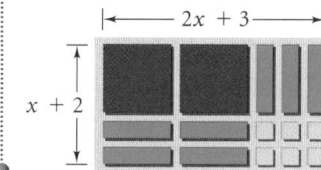

Correct! No tiles are left over.
$2x^2 + 7x + 6 = (2x + 3)(x + 2)$

EXERCISES

Use tiles to find binomial factors of each trinomial.

1. $x^2 + 8x + 15$ **$(x + 5)(x + 3)$**   **2.** $x^2 + 4x + 4$ **$(x + 2)(x + 2)$**   **3.** $x^2 + 8x + 7$ **$(x + 7)(x + 1)$**

4. $2x^2 + 7x + 3$ **$(2x + 1)(x + 3)$**   **5.** $4x^2 + 12x + 5$ **$(2x + 5)(2x + 1)$** **6.** $6x^2 + 7x + 2$ **$(3x + 2)(2x + 1)$**

7. Critical Thinking Explain why the trinomial $x^2 + 3x + 5$ cannot be represented as a rectangle using algebra tiles.   **The trinomial cannot be written as the product of two binomial factors.**

8. Critical Thinking Complete $2x^2 + \blacksquare x + 6$ with three different integers so that each trinomial has two binomial factors. Write each trinomial as the product of binomial factors.

7, $(2x + 3)(x + 2)$;
8, $(2x + 2)(x + 3)$
or $(2x + 6)(x + 1)$;
13, $(2x + 1)(x + 6)$

9-5
Factoring Trinomials of the Type $x^2 + bx + c$

1.01 Write equivalent forms of algebraic expressions to solve problems. c) Factor polynomials.

Lesson Preview

What You'll Learn

OBJECTIVE 1 To factor trinomials

. . . And Why

To factor trinomials like $h^2 - 4hk - 77k^2$, as in Example 4

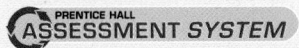 **Check Skills You'll Need**   (For help, go to the Skills Handbook p.720)

List all of the factors of each number. 1–8. See back of book.

1. 24	**2.** 12	**3.** 54	**4.** 15
5. 36	**6.** 56	**7.** 64	**8.** 96

OBJECTIVE

1 **Factoring Trinomials**

iTEXT Interactive lesson includes instant self-check, tutorials, and activities.

In earlier courses, you learned how to find the factors of whole numbers like 15. Since $3 \times 5 = 15$, 3 and 5 are factors of 15. You can also find the factors of some trinomials. Consider the product below.

$$(x + 3)(x + 5) = x^2 + 5x + 3x + 3 \cdot 5$$
$$(5 + 3)x$$
$$= x^2 + 8x + 15$$

Notice that the coefficient of the middle term $8x$ is the sum of 3 and 5. Also the constant term 15 is the product of 3 and 5. To factor a trinomial of the form $x^2 + bx + c$, you must find two numbers that have a sum of b and a product of c.

The next example shows how to use a table to list the factors of the constant term c and how to add the factors until the sum is the middle term b.

1 **EXAMPLE** Factoring $x^2 + bx + c$

Factor $x^2 + 7x + 12$.

Find the factors of 12. Identify the pair that has a sum of 7.

Factors of 12	Sum of Factors
1 and 12	13
2 and 6	8
3 and 4	7 ✓

$x^2 + 7x + 12 = (x + 3)(x + 4)$.

Check $x^2 + 7x + 12 \overset{?}{=} (x + 3)(x + 4)$
$= x^2 + 4x + 3x + 12$
$= x^2 + 7x + 12$ ✓

✓ **Check Understanding** **1** Factor each expression. Check your answer.
a. $g^2 + 7g + 10$ **b.** $v^2 + 21v + 20$ **c.** $a^2 + 13a + 30$
$(g + 5)(g + 2)$ $(v + 20)(v + 1)$ $(a + 10)(a + 3)$

Lesson 9-5 Factoring Trinomials of the Type $x^2 + bx + c$ **481**

---

1. Plan

Lesson Preview

✓ **Check Skills You'll Need**

Skills Handbook: p. 720, Example 2, Exercises 19–47

Lesson Resources

📁 **Teaching Resources**
Practice, Reteaching, Enrichment

👥 **Reaching All Students**
Practice Workbook 9-5
Spanish Practice Workbook 9-5
Basic Algebra Planning Guide 9-5

🕐 **Presentation Assistant Plus!**
Transparencies
• Check Skills You'll Need 9-5
• Additional Examples 9-5
• Student Edition Answers 9-5
• Lesson Quiz 9-5
PH Presentation Pro CD 9-5

PRENTICE HALL
ASSESSMENT SYSTEM
Computer Test Generator CD

💻 **Technology**
Resource Pro® CD-ROM
Computer Test Generator CD
Prentice Hall Presentation Pro CD

🖥 **www.PHSchool.com**
Student Site
• Teacher Web Code: aek-5500
• Reasoning & Puzzles p. 82
• Self-grading Lesson Quiz
Teacher Center
• Lesson Planner
• Resources

Plus **iTEXT**

✓ **Ongoing Assessment and Intervention**

Before the Lesson	During the Lesson	After the Lesson
Diagnose prerequisite skills using:	**Monitor progress using:**	**Assess knowledge using:**
• Check Skills You'll Need	• Check Understanding	• Lesson Quiz
	• Additional Examples	• Computer Test Generator CD
	• Standardized Test Prep	

Math Background

Factoring a trinomial that shows no special pattern involves a process of identifying possible pairs of factors and then verifying which pair will produce the correct sum or difference.

OBJECTIVE
1 Teaching Notes

 **3** EXAMPLE Math Tip

Choosing the correct signs of the factors is very important. To emphasize this, have students multiply $(m + 3)$ and $(m - 9)$.

4 EXAMPLE Error Prevention

It is a common error to forget to write the last variable in the factors. Encourage students to write the parentheses, and place both variables inside the parentheses before factoring. Remind students to leave spaces for the numbers.

Additional Examples

Factor each expression.

1 Factor $x^2 + 8x + 15$.
$(x + 3)(x + 5)$

2 Factor $c^2 - 9c + 20$.
$(c - 5)(c - 4)$

3 a. Factor $x^2 + 13x - 48$.
$(x + 16)(x - 3)$
b. Factor $n^2 - 5n - 24$.
$(n + 3)(n - 8)$

4 Factor $d^2 + 17dg - 60g^2$.
$(d - 3g)(d + 20g)$

Closure

Ask students to explain how to determine what numbers are used in the binomial factors when factoring expressions of the type $x^2 + bx + c$. You must find two numbers that have a product of c and a sum of b.

Some factorable trinomials have a negative middle term and a positive constant term. If the middle term is negative, you need to inspect the negative factors of c to find the factors of the trinomial.

2 EXAMPLE Factoring $x^2 - bx + c$

Factor $d^2 - 17d + 42$.

Since the middle term is negative, find the negative factors of 42. Identify the pair that has a sum of -17.

Factors of 42	Sum of Factors
-1 and -42	-43
-2 and -21	-23
-3 and -14	-17 ✓

$d^2 - 17d + 42 = (d - 3)(d - 14)$

✓ **Check Understanding** **2** Factor each expression.
a. $k^2 - 10k + 25$
$(k - 5)(k - 5)$
b. $x^2 - 11x + 18$
$(x - 2)(x - 9)$
c. $q^2 - 15q + 36$
$(q - 12)(q - 3)$

When you factor trinomials with a negative constant, you will need to inspect pairs of positive and negative factors of c.

3 EXAMPLE Factoring Trinomials With a Negative c

a. Factor $m^2 + 6m - 27$.

Identify the pair of factors of -27 that has a sum of 6.

Factors of -27	Sum of Factors
1 and -27	-26
27 and -1	26
3 and -9	-6
9 and -3	6 ✓

$m^2 + 6m - 27 = (m - 3)(m + 9)$

b. Factor $p^2 - 3p - 18$.

Identify the pair of factors of -18 that has a sum of -3.

Factors of -18	Sum of Factors
1 and -18	-17
18 and -1	17
-6 and 3	-3 ✓

$p^2 - 3p - 18 = (p + 3)(p - 6)$

✓ **Check Understanding** **3** Factor each expression.
a. $m^2 + 8m - 20$
$(m + 10)(m - 2)$
b. $p^2 - 3p - 40$
$(p - 8)(p + 5)$
c. $y^2 - y - 56$
$(y + 7)(y - 8)$

482 Chapter 9 Polynomials and Factoring

Reaching All Students

Below Level Suggest that students always check their factoring by multiplying the factors.	Advanced Learners Challenge students to write a trinomial of the type $x^2 + bx + c$ that cannot be written as $(x + m)(x + n)$, where m and n are integers.	Error Prevention See note on page 482. Error Prevention See note on page 483.

You can also factor some trinomials that have more than one variable. Consider the product $(p + 10q)(p + 4q)$.

$$(p + 10q)(p + 4q) = p^2 + 4pq + 10pq + 10q \cdot 4q$$
$$(4 + 10)pq$$
$$= p^2 + \qquad 14pq + 40q^2$$

You can see that the first term is the square of the first variable, the middle term includes both variables, and the last term includes the square of the second variable.

4 **EXAMPLE** Factoring Trinomials With Two Variables

Factor $h^2 - 4hk - 77k^2$.

Find the factors of -77. Identify the pair that has a sum of -4.

Factors of −77	Sum of Factors
1 and −77	−76
77 and −1	76
7 and −11	−4 ✓

● $h^2 - 4hk - 77k^2 = (h + 7k)(h - 11k)$

✓ **Check Understanding** 4 Factor each expression.
a. $x^2 + 11xy + 24y^2$ **b.** $v^2 + 2vw - 48w^2$ **c.** $m^2 - 17mn - 60n^2$
$(x + 8y)(x + 3y)$ $(v + 8w)(v - 6w)$ $(m - 20n)(m + 3n)$

EXERCISES

For more practice, see *Extra Practice*.

Practice and Problem Solving

A Practice by Example

Examples 1, 2
(pages 481, 482)

Complete.

1. $t^2 + 7t + 10 = (t + 2)(t + \blacksquare)$ **5**   **2.** $y^2 - 13y + 36 = (y - 4)(y - \blacksquare)$ **9**

3. $x^2 - 8x + 7 = (x - 1)(x - \blacksquare)$ **7**   **4.** $x^2 + 9x + 18 = (x + 3)(x + \blacksquare)$ **6**

Factor each expression. Check your answer. 5–13. See margin.

5. $r^2 + 4r + 3$ **6.** $n^2 - 3n + 2$ **7.** $k^2 + 5k + 6$

8. $y^2 + 6y + 8$ **9.** $x^2 - 2x + 1$ **10.** $p^2 + 19p + 18$

11. $k^2 - 16k + 28$ **12.** $w^2 + 6w + 5$ **13.** $m^2 - 9m + 8$

14. $d^2 + 21d + 38$ **15.** $t^2 - 13t + 42$ **16.** $q^2 - 18q + 45$
$(d + 19)(d + 2)$ $(t - 7)(t - 6)$ $(q - 15)(q - 3)$

Example 3
(page 482)

Complete.

17. $m^2 + 3m - 10 = (m - 2)(m + \blacksquare)$ **5**   **18.** $v^2 - 2v - 24 = (v + 4)(v - \blacksquare)$ **6**

19. $k^2 - 8k - 9 = (k + 1)(k - \blacksquare)$ **9**   **20.** $q^2 + 3q - 18 = (q - 3)(q + \blacksquare)$ **6**

Factor each expression. 21–26. See margin.

21. $x^2 + 3x - 4$ **22.** $q^2 - 2q - 8$ **23.** $y^2 + y - 20$

24. $h^2 + 16h - 17$ **25.** $x^2 - 14x - 32$ **26.** $d^2 + 6d - 40$

27. $m^2 - 13m - 30$ **28.** $p^2 + 3p - 54$ **29.** $p^2 - 15p - 54$
$(m + 2)(m - 15)$ $(p - 6)(p + 9)$ $(p + 3)(p - 18)$

Lesson 9-5 Factoring Trinomials of the Type $x^2 + bx + c$ **483**

8. $(y + 4)(y + 2)$ **12.** $(w + 5)(w + 1)$ **23.** $(y + 5)(y - 4)$

5. $(r + 3)(r + 1)$ **9.** $(x - 1)(x - 1)$ **13.** $(m - 1)(m - 8)$ **24.** $(h + 17)(h - 1)$

6. $(n - 2)(n - 1)$ **10.** $(p + 18)(p + 1)$ **21.** $(x + 4)(x - 1)$ **25.** $(x - 16)(x + 2)$

7. $(k + 3)(k + 2)$ **11.** $(k - 14)(k - 2)$ **22.** $(q - 4)(q + 2)$ **26.** $(d + 10)(d - 4)$

483

3. Practice

Assignment Guide

 **Objective**
Ⓐ Ⓑ **Core** 1–58
Ⓒ **Extension** 59–64

Standardized Test Prep 65–71

Mixed Review 72–86

Error Prevention
Exercises 21–29 Suggest students circle the signs in each expression before factoring.

Enrichment 9-5
Reteaching 9-5
Practice 9-5

Practice 9-5   Factoring Trinomials of the Type $x^2 + bx + c$

Alternative Assessment

Have students make posters displaying how the signs in a trinomial affect the binomial factors. Instruct them to write examples using the standard form of a quadratic equation with $a = 1$. Encourage them to use one color for plus signs and another color for minus signs. Here is an example:

$x^2 + bx + c$ $x^2 - bx + c$
$(+)(+)$ $(-)(-)$

$x^2 + bx - c$ $x^2 - bx - c$
$(+)(-)$ $(+)(-)$

pages 483–485 Exercises

39–41. Answers may vary.
         Samples are given.

39. 18; $(x - 6)(x + 3)$
    28; $(x - 7)(x + 4)$
    10; $(x - 5)(x + 2)$

40. 12; $(x + 4)(x - 3)$
    2; $(x + 2)(x - 1)$
    20; $(x + 5)(x - 4)$

41. 7; $(x + 4)(x + 3)$
    8; $(x + 6)(x + 2)$
    13; $(x + 12)(x + 1)$

484

Example 4
(page 483)

Choose the correct factoring for each expression.

30. $p^2 + 10pq + 9q^2$ **A**   **A.** $(p + 9q)(p + q)$ **B.** $(p + 9)(p + q^2)$

31. $m^2 + 4mn + 3n^2$ **B**   **A.** $(m + n)(3m + n)$ **B.** $(m + 3n)(m + n)$

32. $x^2 + 8xy + 15y^2$ **B**   **A.** $(x + 15y^2)(x + 1)$ **B.** $(x + 5y)(x + 3y)$

Factor each expression. 33–38. See left.

33. $(t + 9v)(t - 2v)$
34. $(x + 7y)(x + 5y)$
35. $(p - 8q)(p - 2q)$
36. $(m - 9n)(m + 6n)$
37. $(h + 17j)(h + j)$
38. $(x - 13y)(x + 3y)$

33. $t^2 + 7tv - 18v^2$ 34. $x^2 + 12xy + 35y^2$ 35. $p^2 - 10pq + 16q^2$

36. $m^2 - 3mn - 54n^2$ 37. $h^2 + 18hj + 17j^2$ 38. $x^2 - 10xy - 39y^2$

Open-Ended Find three different values to complete each expression so that it can be factored into the product of two binomials. Show each factorization.

39. $x^2 - 3x - \blacksquare$ 40. $x^2 + x - \blacksquare$ 41. $x^2 + \blacksquare x + 12$

    39–42. See margin.

42. **Writing** Suppose you can factor $x^2 + bx + c$ into the product of two binomials.
    a. Explain what you know about the factors if $c > 0$.
    b. Explain what you know about the factors if $c < 0$.

B **Apply Your Skills**

Factor each expression. 43–51. See margin.

43. $k^2 + 10k + 16$ 44. $m^2 + 10m - 24$ 45. $n^2 + 10n - 56$

46. $g^2 + 20g + 96$ 47. $x^2 + 8x - 65$ 48. $t^2 + 28t + 75$

49. $x^2 - 11x - 42$ 50. $k^2 + 23k + 42$ 51. $m^2 + 14m - 51$

52. $x^2 + 29xy + 100y^2$ 53. $t^2 - 10t - 75$ 54. $d^2 - 19de + 48e^2$
    $(x + 25y)(x + 4y)$ $(t - 15)(t + 5)$ $(d - 16e)(d - 3e)$

Write the standard form for each of the polynomials modeled below. Then factor each expression.

55. $4x^2 + 12x + 5$;
    $(2x + 1)(2x + 5)$

56. $6x^2 + 13x + 6$;
    $(3x + 2)(2x + 3)$

55.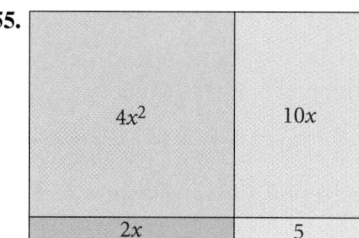

56.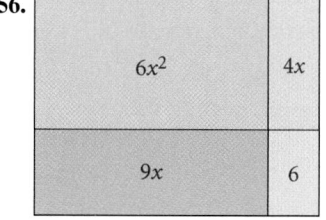

57. **Critical Thinking** Let $x^2 - 12x - 28 = (x + a)(x + b)$. **a–b. See margin p. 485.**
    a. What do you know about the signs of a and b?
    b. Suppose $|a| > |b|$. Which number, a or b, is a negative integer? Explain.

58. **Critical Thinking** Let $x^2 + 12x - 28 = (x + a)(x + b)$. **a–b. See margin p. 485.**
    a. What do you know about the signs of a and b?
    b. Suppose $|a| > |b|$. Which number, a or b, is a negative integer? Explain.

C **Challenge**

Factor each trinomial. 59–61. See margin p. 485.

Sample $n^6 + n^3 - 56 = n^{3 + 3} + n^3 - 56$
$$= (n^3 + 8)(n^3 - 7)$$

59. $x^{12} + 12x^6 + 35$ 60. $t^8 + 5t^4 - 24$ 61. $r^6 - 21r^3 + 80$

62. $m^{10} + 18m^5 + 17$ 63. $x^{12} - 19x^6 - 120$ 64. $p^6 + 14p^3 - 72$
    $(m^5 + 17)(m^5 + 1)$ $(x^6 - 24)(x^6 + 5)$ $(p^3 - 4)(p^3 + 18)$

42a. Factors contain the same operation.

    b. Factors contain opposite operations.

43. $(k + 2)(k + 8)$

44. $(m - 2)(m + 12)$

45. $(n - 4)(n + 14)$

46. $(g + 12)(g + 8)$

47. $(x - 5)(x + 13)$

48. $(t + 3)(t + 25)$

49. $(x - 14)(x + 3)$

50. $(k + 21)(k + 2)$

51. $(m - 3)(m + 17)$

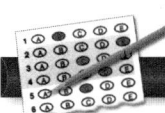

Multiple Choice

65. Which of the following is NOT a factor of 72? **B**
 A. 12 **B.** 16 **C.** 18 **D.** 24

66. Which value of b would make the expression $x^2 + bx - 36$ factorable? **F**
 F. 5 **G.** 4 **H.** 3 **I.** 2

67. Which value of c would NOT make $x^2 + 10x + c$ factorable? **D**
 A. 25 **B.** 24 **C.** 21 **D.** 18

68. Which of the following products is **I** represented by the area model?
 F. $(x + 1)(x + 18)$
 G. $(x + 3)(x + 6)$
 H. $(x - 1)(x - 18)$
 I. $(x + 2)(x + 9)$

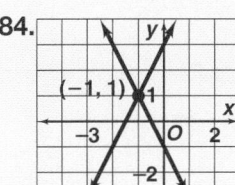

x^2	$9x$
$2x$	18

69. Which of the following shows the factors of $g^2 + 18g + 72$? **A**
 A. $(g + 6)(g + 12)$
 B. $(g + 18)(g + 72)$
 C. $(g - 6)(g - 12)$
 D. $(g - 18)(g - 72)$

Take It to the NET
Online lesson quiz at
www.PHSchool.com
Web Code: aea-0905

70. Which of the following shows the factors of $n^2 - 15g + 50$? **F**
 F. $(n - 5)(n - 10)$
 G. $(n + 5)(n - 10)$
 H. $(n - 15)(n + 50)$
 I. $(n + 15)(n - 50)$

Short Response

71. Explain how to factor the trinomial $x^2 - 18x - 40$ and state the factors.
See margin.

Mixed Review

Lesson 9-4

Simplify each product. 72–77. See margin.

72. $(x + 4)(x + 4)$ **73.** $(w - 6)(w - 6)$ **74.** $(r - 5)(r + 5)$

75. $(2q + 7)(2q + 7)$ **76.** $(8v - 2)(8v + 2)$ **77.** $(3a - 9)(3a - 9)$

78. $(3a - 5)(3a + 5)$ **79.** $(6t + 9)(6t + 9)$ **80.** $(2x + 8y)(2x - 8y)$
 $9a^2 - 25$ $36t^2 + 108t + 81$ $4x^2 - 64y^2$

Lesson 7-4

81. You start with $40 in your bank account and deposit $18 each week. At the same time, your friend starts with $220 but withdraws $12 each week. When will your accounts have the same balance? **6 weeks**

82. The sum of the two numbers is 42. The smaller number is 63 less than twice the larger number. Find both numbers. **7, 35**

83. Sales A department store sells two types of DVD players. Total sales of players for the year were $16,918.71. The total number of players sold was 129. The basic model costs $119.99. The deluxe model costs $149.99.
 a. Find the number sold of each type of player. **81 basic players, 48 deluxe players**
 b. What were the sales for the basic player? **$9719.19**

Lesson 7-1

Solve each system by graphing. 84–86. See margin.

84. $y = -2x - 1$ **85.** $y = x + 4$ **86.** $2x + 4y = 12$
 $y = 2x + 3$ $y = 0.5x + 5$ $x - y = 3$

Lesson 9-5 Factoring Trinomials of the Type $x^2 + bx + c$ **485**

57a. The signs of a and b must be opposite.

 b. Since the middle term is negative, the number with the larger absolute value must be negative. Therefore, a must be a negative integer.

58a. The signs of a and b must be opposite.

 b. Since the middle term is positive, the number with the larger absolute value must be positive. Therefore, b is a negative integer.

📁 **Resources**

For additional practice with a variety of test item formats:
- Standardized Test Prep, p. 507
- Test-Taking Strategies, p. 502
- Test-Taking Strategies with Transparencies

Exercise 69 Tell students they can quickly eliminate some of the incorrect answer choices. Point out that since all signs are positive in the trinomial, all signs are positive in the factors.

59. $(x^6 + 7)(x^6 + 5)$

60. $(t^4 + 8)(t^4 - 3)$

61. $(r^3 - 16)(r^3 - 5)$

71. **[2]** Find a pair of factors of -40 that has a sum of -18: -20 and 2.
 $x^2 - 18x - 40 = (x - 20)(x + 2)$

 [1] correct explanation with incorrect factoring OR incorrect explanation with correct factoring

72. $x^2 + 8x + 16$

73. $w^2 - 12w + 36$

74. $r^2 - 25$

75. $4q^2 + 28q + 49$

76. $64v^2 - 4$

77. $9a^2 - 54a + 81$

84.

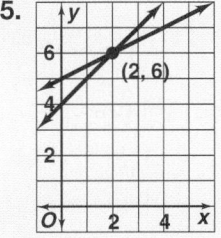

85.

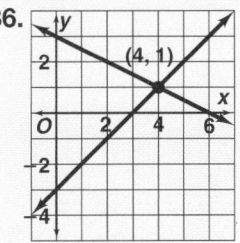

86.

485

9-6

North Carolina Objectives 1.01c

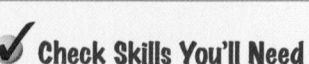

1. Plan

Lesson Preview

✓ **Check Skills You'll Need**

Multiplying and Factoring
Lesson 9-2: Example 2
Exercises 13–18
Extra Practice, p. 710

Factoring Trinomials of the Type $x^2 + bx + c$
Lesson 9-5: Examples 1–3
Exercises 1–26
Extra Practice, p. 710

Lesson Resources

 **Teaching Resources**
Practice, Reteaching, Enrichment

Reaching All Students
Practice Workbook 9-6
Spanish Practice Workbook 9-6
Basic Algebra Planning Guide 9-6

Presentation Assistant Plus!
Transparencies
• Check Skills You'll Need 9-6
• Additional Examples 9-6
• Student Edition Answers 9-6
• Lesson Quiz 9-6
PH Presentation Pro CD 9-6

ASSESSMENT SYSTEM

Computer Test Generator CD

Technology
Resource Pro® CD-ROM
Computer Test Generator CD
Prentice Hall Presentation Pro CD

 **www.PHSchool.com**
Student Site
• Teacher Web Code: aek-5500
• Self-grading Lesson Quiz
Teacher Center
• Lesson Planner
• Resources

Plus **iTEXT**

486

9-6

Factoring Trinomials of the Type $ax^2 + bx + c$

 North Carolina Objectives — 1.01 Write equivalent forms of algebraic expressions to solve problems. c) Factor polynomials.

Lesson Preview

What You'll Learn

OBJECTIVE 1 ▼ To factor trinomials of the type $ax^2 + bx + c$

. . . And Why

To factor trinomials in order to solve equations in Chapter 10

✓ **Check Skills You'll Need**   (For help, go to Lessons 9-2 and 9-5.)

Find the GCF of the terms of each polynomial.

1. $12x^2 + 6x$ **6x**

2. $28m^2 - 35m + 14$ **7**

3. $4v^3 + 36v^2 + 10$ **2**

Factor each expression.

4. $x^2 + 5x + 4$
$(x + 1)(x + 4)$

5. $y^2 - 3y - 28$
$(y - 7)(y + 4)$

6. $t^2 - 11t + 30$
$(t - 5)(t - 6)$

OBJECTIVE 1 ▼ **Factoring $ax^2 + bx + c$**

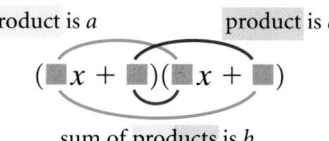 **iTEXT** Interactive lesson includes instant self-check, tutorials, and activities.

To understand how to factor $ax^2 + bx + c$, where a is a positive integer greater than 1, consider the following product simplified using FOIL.

$$\begin{array}{cccc} \text{F} & \text{O} & \text{I} & \text{L} \end{array}$$

$$(2x + 3)(5x + 4) = 10x^2 + 8x + 15x + 12 = 10x^2 + 23x + 12$$

To go from $ax^2 + bx + c$ to its factors, look for binomials that have the following characteristics:

product is a product is c

$$(\blacksquare x + \blacksquare)(\blacksquare x + \blacksquare)$$

sum of products is b

If c is positive and b is positive, the two factors of c are positive. If c is positive and b is negative, the two factors of c are negative.

① EXAMPLE c Is Positive

Factor $6n^2 + 23n + 7$.

$$\begin{array}{cccc} 6n^2 & + & 23n & + & 7 \end{array}$$

	F	O	I		L	
		$1 \cdot 7 + 1 \cdot 6 = 13$			$1 \cdot 7$	
factors of a	$1 \cdot 6$	$1 \cdot 1 + 7 \cdot 6 = 43$			$7 \cdot 1$	factors of c
	$2 \cdot 3$	$2 \cdot 7 + 1 \cdot 3 = 17$			$1 \cdot 7$	
		$2 \cdot 1 + 7 \cdot 3 = 23$ ✓			$7 \cdot 1$	

$$6n^2 + 23n + 7 = (2n + 7)(3n + 1)$$

✓ **Check Understanding** ① Factor each expression.

a. $2y^2 + 5y + 2$
$(2y + 1)(y + 2)$

b. $6n^2 - 23n + 7$
$(3n - 1)(2n - 7)$

c. $2y^2 - 5y + 2$
$(2y - 1)(y - 2)$

INSTANT CHECK SYSTEM ## Ongoing Assessment and Intervention

Before the Lesson	**During the Lesson**	**After the Lesson**
Diagnose prerequisite skills using:	**Monitor progress using:**	**Assess knowledge using:**
• Check Skills You'll Need	• Check Understanding	• Lesson Quiz
	• Additional Examples	• Computer Test Generator CD
	• Standardized Test Prep	

In the next example, c is negative. In this case, you need to consider combinations that equal -8, like $(-8)(1)$. You must also consider $(-1)(8)$.

2 EXAMPLE **c Is Negative**

Factor $7x^2 - 26x - 8$.

$7x^2$	$-26x$	-8
$1 \cdot 7$	$(1)(-8) + (1)(7) = -1$	$(1)(-8)$
	$(1)(1) + (-8)(7) = -55$	$(-8)(1)$
	$(1)(-4) + (2)(7) = 10$	$(2)(-4)$
	$(1)(2) + (-4)(7) = -26$ ✓	$(-4)(2)$

$7x^2 - 26x - 8 = (1x + -4)(7x + 2)$

✓ **Check Understanding** **2** Factor each expression.
a. $5d^2 - 14d - 3$
$(5d + 1)(d - 3)$
b. $2n^2 + n - 3$
$(2n + 3)(n - 1)$
c. $20p^2 - 31p - 9$
$(5p - 9)(4p + 1)$

Some polynomials can be factored repeatedly. Continue the process of factoring until there are no common factors other than 1. If a trinomial has a common monomial factor, factor it out before trying to find binomial factors.

3 EXAMPLE **Factoring Out a Monomial First**

Factor $20x^2 + 80x + 35$ completely.

$20x^2 + 80x + 35 = 5(4x^2 + 16x + 7)$ **Factor out the GCF.**

Factor $4x^2 + 16x + 7$.

$4x^2$	$16x$	7
$1 \cdot 4$	$1 \cdot 7 + 1 \cdot 4 = 11$	$1 \cdot 7$
	$1 \cdot 1 + 7 \cdot 4 = 29$	$7 \cdot 1$
$2 \cdot 2$	$2 \cdot 7 + 1 \cdot 2 = 16$ ✓	$1 \cdot 7$

$4x^2 + 16x + 7 = (2x + 1)(2x + 7)$

$20x^2 + 80x + 35 = 5(2x + 1)(2x + 7)$ **Include the GCF in your final answer.**

✓ **Check Understanding** **3** Factor each expression.
a. $2v^2 - 12v + 10$
$2(v - 1)(v - 5)$
b. $4y^2 + 14y + 6$
$2(2y + 1)(y + 3)$
c. $18k^2 - 12k - 6$
$6(3k + 1)(k - 1)$

Answers to Practice by Example:
1. $(2n + 1)(n + 7)$
2. $(7d + 1)(d + 7)$
3. $(11w - 3)(w - 1)$
4. $(3x - 2)(x - 5)$
5. $(3t + 11)(2t + 1)$
6. $(3d - 5)(d - 4)$
7. $(2m + 1)(8m + 9)$
8. $(p - 1)(15p - 11)$
9. $(2y + 1)(4y + 13)$
10. $(2y + 1)(y + 17)$
11. $(x - 3)(7x - 9)$
12. $(4x + 3)(2x + 3)$

EXERCISES

For more practice, see *Extra Practice*.

Practice and Problem Solving

A **Practice by Example**

Example 1
(page 486)

Factor each expression. **1–12.** See above left.

1. $2n^2 + 15n + 7$
2. $7d^2 + 50d + 7$
3. $11w^2 - 14w + 3$
4. $3x^2 - 17x + 10$
5. $6t^2 + 25t + 11$
6. $3d^2 - 17d + 20$
7. $16m^2 + 26m + 9$
8. $15p^2 - 26p + 11$
9. $8y^2 + 30y + 13$
10. $2y^2 + 35y + 17$
11. $7x^2 - 30x + 27$
12. $8x^2 + 18x + 9$

Lesson 9-6 Factoring Trinomials of the Type $ax^2 + bx + c$ **487**

👥 Reaching All Students

Below Level When students check to make sure the binomial factors they've written are correct, make sure they pay careful attention to the signs when checking the sum of the inner terms.	**Advanced Learners** Challenge students to use what they learned in this lesson to factor $12x^4 + 5x^3 - 2x^2$. $[x^2(3x + 2)(4x - 1)]$	**Error Prevention** See note on page 488. **Alternative Method** See note on page 487.

2. Teach

Professional Development

Math Background

Factoring trinomials in which there is a coefficient for the x^2 term involves an additional level of making careful conjectures and verifying them.

OBJECTIVE

1 **Teaching Notes**

2 EXAMPLE **Alternative Method**

Have students draw a square with four sections and follow these steps:
1. Enter the first and last terms as shown.

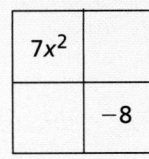

2. Multiply the numbers. Then find factors of the product that have a sum of b.
$7(-8) = -56$; $7 + (-8) \ne -26$
$2(-28) = -56$;
$2 + (-28) = -26$
3. Fill in the other two sections as shown. Find the GCF of each column and row. A GCF is negative if both terms are negative.

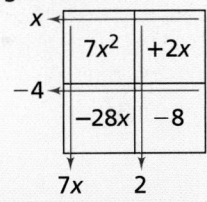

4. The binomial factors are $(x - 4)(7x + 2)$.

🖥 Additional Examples

1 Factor $20x^2 + 17x + 3$. $(4x + 1)(5x + 3)$

2 Factor $3n^2 - 7n - 6$. $(n - 3)(3n + 2)$

3 Factor $18x^2 + 33x - 30$ completely. $3(2x + 5)(3x - 2)$

Closure

Ask students: *What is the first thing you should look for when factoring a trinomial?* You should first look for a monomial factor common to all the terms.

487

Assignment Guide

▼ **Objective**
- Ⓐ Ⓑ **Core** 1–41
- Ⓒ **Extension** 42–47

Standardized Test Prep 48–53

Mixed Review 54–80

Error Prevention

Exercises 1–21 It is easy to find correct factors of *a* and *c* and then place them in the wrong order. Encourage students to check their factoring by multiplying.

Error Prevention

Exercises 22–27 Encourage students to immediately write the factored out monomial in the place it will hold in the final answer.

Example 2
(page 487)

Factor each expression. 13–27. See margin.

13. $2t^2 - t - 3$ **14.** $8y^2 - 10y - 3$ **15.** $2q^2 - 11q - 21$

16. $7x^2 - 20x - 3$ **17.** $13p^2 + 8p - 5$ **18.** $5k^2 - 2k - 7$

19. $10w^2 + 11w - 8$ **20.** $12d^2 - d - 20$ **21.** $14n^2 + 23n - 15$

Example 3
(page 487)

22. $24m^2 - 32m + 8$ **23.** $21v^2 - 70v + 49$ **24.** $6t^2 + 26t + 24$

25. $25x^2 - 10x - 15$ **26.** $11p^2 + 77p + 66$ **27.** $24v^2 + 10v - 6$

Ⓑ **Apply Your Skills**

Open-Ended Find three different values that complete each expression so that the trinomial can be factored into the product of two binomials. Factor your trinomials. 28–30. See back of book.

28. $4g^2 + \blacksquare g + 10$ **29.** $15m^2 + \blacksquare m - 24$ **30.** $35g^2 + \blacksquare g - 16$

31. a. Write each area as a product of two binomials.

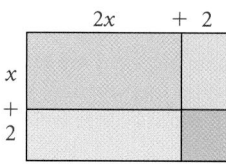
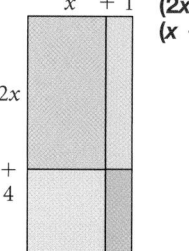

(2x + 2)(x + 2); (x + 1)(2x + 4)

b. Are the products equal? $2x^2 + 6x + 4$; $2x^2 + 6x + 4$; yes

31c. Answers may vary. Sample: Neither factoring is complete. Each one has a common factor, 2.

c. Critical Thinking Explain how the two products you found in part (a) can equal the same trinomial. **See left.**

32. Writing Explain how you would factor the expression $50x^2 - 90x + 16$. See back of book.

Factor each expression. 33–38. See margin p. 489.

33. $54p^2 + 87p + 28$ **34.** $66r^2 + 57r + 12$ **35.** $14x^2 - 53x + 14$

36. $28m^2 + 28m - 56$ **37.** $21h^2 + 72h - 48$ **38.** $55n^2 - 52n + 12$

39. $36y^2 + 114y - 20$ **40.** $63w^2 - 89w + 30$ **41.** $99q^2 - 92q + 9$
2(6y − 1)(3y + 10)   (9w − 5)(7w − 6)   (9q − 1)(11q − 9)

Ⓒ **Challenge**

42. Critical Thinking If *a* and *c* in $ax^2 + bx + c$ are prime numbers, and the trinomial is factorable, how many positive values are possible for *b*? **2**

43. Open-Ended Write three different factorable trinomials that are of the form $\blacksquare x^2 - 12x + \blacksquare$. Factor your trinomials. **See back of book.**

Factor each expression.

44. $56x^3 + 43x^2 + 5x$ **45.** $49p^2 + 63pq - 36q^2$ **46.** $108g^2h - 162gh + 54h$
x(8x + 5)(7x + 1)   (7p − 3q)(7p + 12q)   54h(2g − 1)(g − 1)

47. The graph of the function $y = x^2 + 5x + 6$ is shown at the right.

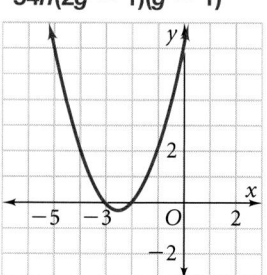

a. What are the *x*-intercepts? **−2 and −3**
b. Factor $x^2 + 5x + 6$. **(x + 2)(x + 3)**
c. Critical Thinking Describe the relationship between the binomial factors you found in part (b) and the *x*-intercepts. **Answers may vary. Sample: Each x-intercept is the opposite of the last term in a binomial factor.**

488 Chapter 9 Polynomials and Factoring

pages 487–489 Exercises

13. (2t − 3)(t + 1)

14. (4y + 1)(2y − 3)

15. (2q + 3)(q − 7)

16. (7x + 1)(x − 3)

17. (13p − 5)(p + 1)

18. (5k − 7)(k + 1)

19. (5w + 8)(2w − 1)

20. (4d + 5)(3d − 4)

21. (7n + 15)(2n − 1)

22. 8(3m − 1)(m − 1)

23. 7(3v − 7)(v − 1)

24. 2(3t + 4)(t + 3)

25. 5(5x + 3)(x − 1)

26. 11(p + 1)(p + 6)

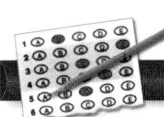

Multiple Choice

48. Which of the following expressions does NOT equal $12n^2 + 32n - 140$? **D**
  A. $4(n + 5)(3n - 7)$ **B.** $(4n + 20)(3n - 7)$
  C. $(2n + 10)(6n - 14)$ **D.** $(n + 5)(12n - 7)$

49. Which value would make the expression $8p^2 + \blacksquare p + 11$ factorable? **G**
  F. 24   **G.** 46   **H.** 48   **I.** 52

50. Which binomial is one of the factors of $13x^2 + 32x - 21$? **D**
  A. $13x + 3$ **B.** $13x + 7$ **C.** $13x + 21$ **D.** $13x - 7$

51. A rectangle has dimensions that are the binomial factors of $3x^2 + 22x + 24$. Which of the following expressions describes the perimeter of the rectangle? **H**
  F. $4x + 10$ **G.** $4x + 25$ **H.** $8x + 20$ **I.** $8x + 50$

52. The table at the right shows the atomic masses, rounded to the nearest whole number, for the first five elements. Which of the following values is the median of the data? **D**
  A. 5.5   **B.** 6
  C. 6.4   **D.** 7

Element	Atomic Mass
Hydrogen	1
Helium	4
Lithium	7
Beryllium	9
Boron	11

Take It to the NET
Online lesson quiz at
www.PHSchool.com
Web Code: aea-0906

Short Response

53. What are the factors of $3x^2 + 40x - 75$? Show your work.
  [2] $3x^2 + 40x - 75 = (3x - 5)(x + 15)$
  [1] one computational error OR no work shown

Mixed Review

Lesson 9-5 **Factor each expression. 54–59. See margin.**

54. $y^2 + 8y + 7$ **55.** $t^2 - 7t + 12$ **56.** $p^2 - p - 20$

57. $m^2 - 15m + 36$ **58.** $k^2 + 16k - 36$ **59.** $g^2 + 17g + 72$

60. $h^2 - 13h - 48$ **61.** $x^2 - 13x - 30$ **62.** $d^2 - 18d + 56$
  $(h - 16)(h + 3)$ $(x - 15)(x + 2)$ $(d - 4)(d - 14)$

Lesson 9-4 **Mental Math Find each square.**

63. 89^2 **7921**   **64.** 401^2 **160,801**   **65.** 903^2 **815,409**   **66.** 197^2 **38,809**

Mental Math Find each product.

67. $39 \cdot 41$ **1599**   **68.** $38 \cdot 42$ **1596**   **69.** $198 \cdot 202$ **39,996**   **70.** $73 \cdot 67$ **4891**

Evaluate each exponential function for the domain $\{-3, 0, 2\}$. 71–76. See margin.

71. $f(x) = 4 \cdot 2^x$ **72.** $h(x) = -3 \cdot 3^x$ **73.** $k(x) = \frac{1}{3} \cdot 3^x$

74. $g(x) = 5 \cdot \left(\frac{1}{10}\right)^x$ **75.** $g(x) = \frac{1}{10} \cdot 5^x$ **76.** $h(x) = 8 \cdot (0.2)^x$

Lesson 8-7 **Graph each function.**

77. $y = 3 \cdot 2^x$ **78.** $y = -3 \cdot 2^x$ **79.** $y = \frac{1}{2} \cdot 2^x$ **80.** $y = \frac{1}{3} \cdot 3^x$
See margin.   **78–80. See back of book.**

Lesson 9-6   Factoring Trinomials of the Type $ax^2 + bx + c$ **489**

27. $2(4v + 3)(3v - 1)$
33. $(9p + 4)(6p + 7)$
34. $3(11r + 4)(2r + 1)$
35. $(7x - 2)(2x - 7)$
36. $28(m - 1)(m + 2)$

37. $3(7h - 4)(h + 4)$
38. $(11n - 6)(5n - 2)$
54. $(y + 7)(y + 1)$
55. $(t - 4)(t - 3)$
56. $(p - 5)(p + 4)$

57. $(m - 3)(m - 12)$
58. $(k + 18)(k - 2)$
59. $(g + 9)(g + 8)$
71. $\frac{1}{2}$, 4, 16
72. $-\frac{1}{9}$, -3, -27

---

4. Assess

Lesson Quiz 9-6

Factor each expression.

1. $3x^2 - 14x + 11$
  $(x - 1)(3x - 11)$

2. $6t^2 + 13t - 63$
  $(2t + 9)(3t - 7)$

3. $9y^2 - 48y - 36$
  $3(3y + 2)(y - 6)$

Alternative Assessment

Instruct each student to write two linear binomials and then multiply them. Give each student an index card. Direct students to write their binomials on one side of the card and the trinomial product on the other side. Have students exchange cards and look only at the side with the trinomial. Instruct students to factor the trinomial on their own paper, and then use the other side of the card to check their work. Repeat.

Standardized Test Prep

Resources
For additional practice with a variety of test item formats:
• Standardized Test Prep, p. 507
• Test-Taking Strategies, p. 502
• Test-Taking Strategies with Transparencies

Exercise 51 Caution students to be sure they add all four sides together and not just two sides.

73. $\frac{1}{81}, \frac{1}{3}, 3$

74. 5000, 5, $\frac{5}{100}$ or $\frac{1}{20}$

75. $\frac{1}{1250}, \frac{1}{10}, 2\frac{1}{2}$

76. 1000, 8, 0.32

77.

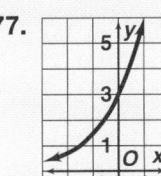

1. Plan

Lesson Preview

 Check Skills You'll Need

**More Multiplication Properties
of Exponents**
Lesson 8-4: Example 3
Exercises 9–16
Extra Practice, p. 709

Multiplying Special Cases
Lesson 9-4: Example 1
Exercises 1–8
Extra Practice, p. 710

Lesson Resources

 Teaching Resources
Practice, Reteaching, Enrichment
Checkpoint Quiz 2

 **Reaching All Students**
Practice Workbook 9-7
Spanish Practice Workbook 9-7
Reading and Math Literacy 9C
Spanish Reading & Literacy 9C
Spanish Checkpoint Quiz 2
Hands-On Activities 22
Basic Algebra Planning Guide 9-7

 Presentation Assistant Plus!
Transparencies
• Check Skills You'll Need 9-7
• Additional Examples 9-7
• Student Edition Answers 9-7
• Lesson Quiz 9-7
PH Presentation Pro CD 9-7

**PRENTICE HALL
ASSESSMENT SYSTEM**

Checkpoint Quiz 2
Computer Test Generator CD

 Technology
Resource Pro® CD-ROM
Computer Test Generator CD
Prentice Hall Presentation Pro CD

 **www.PHSchool.com**
Student Site
• Teacher Web Code: aek-5500
• Self-grading Lesson Quiz
Teacher Center
• Lesson Planner
• Resources

Plus

490

Factoring Special Cases

   **1.01** Write equivalent forms of algebraic expressions to solve problems. c) Factor
polynomials.

Lesson Preview

What You'll Learn

 OBJECTIVE 1
To factor
perfect-square
trinomials

 OBJECTIVE 2
To factor the
difference of squares

. . . And Why
To find the length of a side of
a square, as In Example 2

 Check Skills You'll Need   (For help, go to Lessons 8-4 and 9-4.)

Simplify each expression.

1. $(3x)^2$ **$9x^2$**   **2.** $(5y)^2$ **$25y^2$**   **3.** $(15h^2)^2$ **$225h^4$**   **4.** $(2ab^2)^2$
$4a^2b^4$

Simplify each product.

5. $(c - 6)(c + 6)$ **6.** $(p - 11)(p - 11)$ **7.** $(4d + 7)(4d + 7)$
$c^2 - 36$ **$p^2 - 22p + 121$**   **$16d^2 + 56d + 49$**

New Vocabulary   • perfect-square trinomial

 TEXT Interactive lesson includes instant
self-check, tutorials, and activities.

OBJECTIVE 1   Factoring Perfect-Square Trinomials

Investigation: Perfect-Square Trinomials

1. Factor each trinomial. **1–2. See back of book.**

$x^2 + 6x + 9$ $x^2 + 10x + 9$ $m^2 + 15m + 36$

$m^2 + 12m + 36$ $k^2 + 26k + 25$ $k^2 + 10k + 25$

2. a. Which trinomials have pairs of binomial factors that are identical?
   b. Describe the relationship between the middle and last terms of the
   trinomials that have identical pairs of factors.

In Lesson 9-4 you found the square of a binomial.

$$(a + b)^2 = (a + b)(a + b) = a^2 + 2ab + b^2 \text{ and}$$
$$(a - b)^2 = (a - b)(a - b) = a^2 - 2ab + b^2$$

Any trinomial of the form $a^2 + 2ab + b^2$ or $a^2 - 2ab + b^2$ is a **perfect-square
trinomial.** You can factor a perfect-square trinomial into identical binomial factors.

Key Concepts

Rule	**Perfect-Square Trinomials**

For every real number a and b:

$a^2 + 2ab + b^2 = (a + b)(a + b) = (a + b)^2$
$a^2 - 2ab + b^2 = (a - b)(a - b) = (a - b)^2$

Examples $x^2 + 10x + 25 = (x + 5)(x + 5) = (x + 5)^2$
          $x^2 - 10x + 25 = (x - 5)(x - 5) = (x - 5)^2$

INSTANT CHECK SYSTEM Ongoing Assessment and Intervention

| **Before the Lesson**
Diagnose prerequisite skills using: | **During the Lesson**
Monitor progress using: | **After the Lesson**
Assess knowledge using: |
|---|---|---|
| • Check Skills You'll Need | • Check Understanding
• Additional Examples
• Standardized Test Prep | • Lesson Quiz
• Computer Test Generator CD
• Chapter Checkpoint 2 (p. 495) |

You can factor a perfect-square trinomial using the method shown in the previous lesson. Or you can recognize a perfect-square trinomial and then factor it quickly. Here is how to recognize a perfect-square trinomial.

- The first and the last terms can both be written as the product of two identical factors.

- The middle term is twice the product of one factor from the first term and one factor from the last term.

Consider the following trinomials.

$$4x^2 \quad + \quad 12x \quad + \quad 9$$
$$2x \cdot 2x \qquad\qquad\quad 3 \cdot 3$$
$$2(2x \cdot 3) = 12x$$

$$4x^2 \quad + \quad 20x \quad + \quad 9$$
$$2x \cdot 2x \qquad\qquad\quad 3 \cdot 3$$
$$2(2x \cdot 3) \neq 20x$$

This is a perfect-square trinomial. In factored form the trinomial is $(2x + 3)(2x + 3)$, or $(2x + 3)^2$.

This is not a perfect-square trinomial. Factor by listing factors, as shown in Lesson 9-6.

When you factor a perfect-square trinomial, it may help to write the first and last terms as the products of identical factors.

① EXAMPLE Factoring a Perfect-Square Trinomial With $a = 1$

Factor $x^2 - 8x + 16$.

$$x^2 - 8x + 16 = x \cdot x - 8x + 4 \cdot 4 \qquad \textbf{Rewrite first and last terms.}$$
$$= x \cdot x - 2(x \cdot 4) + 4 \cdot 4 \qquad \textbf{Does the middle term equal } 2ab? \ 8x = 2(x \cdot 4)$$
$$= (x - 4)^2 \qquad \textbf{Write the factors as the square of a binomial.}$$

 ✓ Check Understanding ① Factor each expression.
a. $x^2 + 8x + 16$
$(x + 4)^2$
b. $n^2 + 16n + 64$
$(n + 8)^2$
c. $n^2 - 16n + 64$
$(n - 8)^2$

When you write the identical factors of the first and last terms, you can write them as square terms. Notice in Example 2, $9g^2$ is written as $(3g)^2$ and 4 is written as 2^2.

? Need Help?

For $a \neq 0$, $b \neq 0$, and all integers n,
$a^n b^n = (ab)^n$.
$9g^2 = 3^2 g^2 = (3g)^2$

② EXAMPLE Factoring a Perfect-Square Trinomial with $a \neq 1$

Geometry The area of the square shown at the right is $(9g^2 + 12g + 4)$ cm². Find the length of a side.

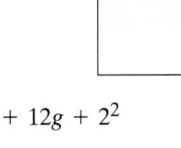

$$9g^2 + 12g + 4 = (3g)^2 + 12g + 2^2 \qquad \textbf{Rewrite } 9g^2 \textbf{ as } (3g)^2 \textbf{ and 4 as } 2^2.$$
$$= (3g)^2 + 2(3g)(2) + 2^2 \qquad \textbf{Does the middle term equal } 2ab? \ 12g = 2(3g)(2) ✓$$
$$= (3g + 2)^2 \qquad \textbf{Write the factors as the square of a binomial.}$$

The side of the square has length of $(3g + 2)$ cm.

✓ Check Understanding ② Factor each expression.
a. $9g^2 - 12g + 4$
$(3g - 2)^2$
b. $4t^2 + 36t + 81$
$(2t + 9)^2$
c. $4t^2 - 36t + 81$
$(2t - 9)^2$

👁 Reaching All Students

Below Level Assure students that the method of lesson 9-6 also can be used, but that they will save time and effort if they first consider the possibility of a perfect square.	Advanced Learners Ask students to explain in their own terms why $x^2 - 64$ can be factored but $x^2 + 64$ cannot be factored.	English Learners See note on page 491. Visual Learners See note on page 492.

Math Background

Recognizing special cases for factoring trinomials significantly shortens the process. These special cases involve a process that is the inverse of the patterns used to multiply in Lesson 9-4.

OBJECTIVE
▼① Teaching Notes

Investigation (Optional)
Math Tip
Pattern recognition is an essential tool in mathematics. Lead students to understand that, in this lesson, they will be learning about patterns that will save time and effort.

① EXAMPLE English Learners

Encourage students to model the expression using tiles. Ask: *What is true about the length of each side of the model?* Each side is $x - 4$. *What shape do the tiles form?* a square Help students make the connection between the square shape of the model and the name "perfect square trinomial."

② EXAMPLE Teaching Tip

Write $9g^2 + 12g + 4$ on the board. Ask a student volunteer to explain and show on the board how to determine that the expression is a perfect square trinomial. The first and last terms, $9g^2$ and 4, can each be written as the product of two identical factors, $3g \cdot 3g$ and $2 \cdot 2$. The middle term, $12g$, is twice the product of one factor from the first term and one factor from the last term, $2 \cdot 3g \cdot 2$.

Additional Examples

① Factor $m^2 - 6m + 9$. $(m - 3)^2$

② The area of a square is $(16h^2 + 40h + 25)$ in.² Find the length of a side. $(4h + 5)$ in.

Recall from Lesson 9-4 that $(a + b)(a - b) = a^2 - b^2$. So you can factor a difference of two squares as $(a + b)(a - b)$.

 Key Concepts

Rule	Difference of Two Squares

For every real number a and b:

$$a^2 - b^2 = (a + b)(a - b)$$

Examples $x^2 - 81 = (x + 9)(x - 9)$

$16x^2 - 49 = (4x + 7)(4x - 7)$

3 EXAMPLE The Difference of Two Squares for $a = 1$

Factor $x^2 - 64$.

$x^2 - 64 = x^2 - 8^2$ **Rewrite 64 as 8^2.**

$= (x + 8)(x - 8)$ **Factor.**

Check Use FOIL to multiply.

$(x + 8)(x - 8)$

$x^2 - 8x + 8x - 64$

$x^2 - 64$ ✓

✔ **Check Understanding** ③ Factor each expression. Check your answer.

a. $x^2 - 36$ **b.** $m^2 - 100$ **c.** $p^2 - 49$
$(x + 6)(x - 6)$ $(m + 10)(m - 10)$ $(p + 7)(p - 7)$

4 EXAMPLE The Difference of Two Squares for $a \neq 1$

Factor $4x^2 - 121$.

$4x^2 - 121 = (2x)^2 - (11)^2$ **Rewrite $4x^2$ as $(2x)^2$ and 121 as 11^2.**

$= (2x + 11)(2x - 11)$ **Factor.**

✔ **Check Understanding** ④ Factor each expression.

a. $9v^2 - 4$ **b.** $25x^2 - 64$ **c.** $4w^2 - 49$
$(3v + 2)(3v - 2)$ $(5x + 8)(5x - 8)$ $(2w + 7)(2w - 7)$

Some binomials that do not appear to be the difference of squares may have the form $n(a^2 - b^2)$ after a GCF is factored out.

5 EXAMPLE Factoring Out a Common Factor

Factor $10x^2 - 40$.

$10x^2 - 40 = 10(x^2 - 4)$ **Factor out the GCF of 10.**

$= 10(x - 2)(x + 2)$ **Factor $(x^2 - 4)$.**

✔ **Check Understanding** ⑤ Factor each expression.

a. $8y^2 - 50$ **b.** $3c^2 - 75$ **c.** $28k^2 - 7$
$2(2y + 5)(2y - 5)$ $3(c + 5)(c - 5)$ $7(2k + 1)(2k - 1)$

Teaching Notes (left column)

3 EXAMPLE Error Prevention

Many students will want to write the factor as $(x - 8)^2$ since the sign in the expression is negative. Write the expression as $x^2 + 0x - 64$. Ask students what types of numbers have a sum of 0. **additive inverses** Stress that the signs in the factors must be different to have 0 as the coefficient of the middle term in the trinomial.

4 EXAMPLE Visual Learners

Encourage students to make a poster listing the special cases and describing how to factor them. Have students provide examples for each special case. Students may wish to color code the variables and/or signs. If students made the posters described in the Alternative Assessment for Lesson 9-5, they may wish to continue with the same color pattern.

5 EXAMPLE Math Tip

There are some cases where students can factor successfully and *then* remove the GCF, but not always. It is always safer to remove the GCF first.

Additional Examples

③ Factor $a^2 - 16$. $(a + 4)(a - 4)$

④ Factor $9b^2 - 225$.
$(3b + 15)(3b - 15)$

⑤ Factor $5x^2 - 80$.
$5(x + 4)(x - 4)$

Closure

Ask students to name and give examples of two types of special cases they learned to factor in this lesson. **perfect square trinomials and difference of two squares; check students' work for examples.**

pages 493–495   Exercises

10. $(5g - 3)^2$

11. $(8r - 9)^2$

12. $(10v - 11)^2$

13. $(x + 2)(x - 2)$

14. $(y + 9)(y - 9)$

15. $(k + 14)(k - 14)$

16. $(r + 12)(r - 12)$

17. $(h + 10)(h - 10)$

18. $(m + 15)(m - 15)$

19. $(w + 16)(w - 16)$

20. $(x + 20)(x - 20)$

21. $(y + 30)(y - 30)$

22. $(5q + 3)(5q - 3)$

23. $(7y + 2)(7y - 2)$

EXERCISES

Practice and Problem Solving

A Practice by Example

Example 1
(page 491)

Factor each expression.

1. $c^2 + 10c + 25$ **$(c + 5)^2$** 2. $x^2 - 2x + 1$ **$(x - 1)^2$** 3. $h^2 + 12h + 36$ **$(h + 6)^2$**

4. $m^2 - 24m + 144$
$(m - 12)^2$

5. $k^2 - 16k + 64$
$(k - 8)^2$

6. $t^2 - 14t + 49$
$(t - 7)^2$

Example 2
(page 491)

Find the side length of each square.

7.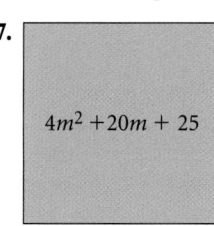
$4m^2 + 20m + 25$

(2m + 5)

8.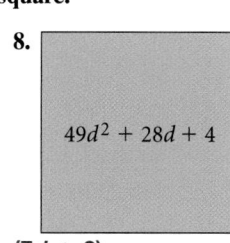
$49d^2 + 28d + 4$

(7d + 2)

9.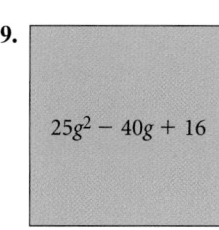
$25g^2 - 40g + 16$

(5g − 4)

Factor each expression. Check your answer. 10–36. See margin p. 492.

10. $25g^2 - 30g + 9$ 11. $64r^2 - 144r + 81$ 12. $100v^2 - 220v + 121$

Example 3
(page 492)

13. $x^2 - 4$ 14. $y^2 - 81$ 15. $k^2 - 196$

16. $r^2 - 144$ 17. $h^2 - 100$ 18. $m^2 - 225$

19. $w^2 - 256$ 20. $x^2 - 400$ 21. $y^2 - 900$

Example 4
(page 492)

22. $25q^2 - 9$ 23. $49y^2 - 4$ 24. $9c^2 - 64$

25. $4m^2 - 81$ 26. $16k^2 - 49$ 27. $144p^2 - 1$

28. $81v^2 - 100$ 29. $400n^2 - 121$ 30. $25w^2 - 196$

Example 5
(page 492)

31. $3m^2 - 12$ 32. $5k^2 - 245$ 33. $3x^2 + 48x + 192$

34. $2t^2 - 36t + 162$ 35. $6r^3 - 150r$ 36. $7h^2 - 56h + 112$

B Apply Your Skills

37. Writing Summarize the procedure for factoring a perfect-square trinomial. Give at least two examples. **See margin.**

38. Error Analysis Suppose a classmate factored the binomial at the right. What error did your classmate make?

$$4x^2 - 121 = (4x - 11)(4x - 11)$$
$$= (4x - 11)^2$$

$4x^2 - 121$ is the difference of two squares. So the answer should be $(2x + 11)(2x - 11)$.

Mental Math **Find a pair of factors for each number by using the difference of two squares.**

Sample $143 = 144 - 1$ Write 143 as the difference of two squares.

$= 12^2 - 1^2$ Rewrite 144 as 12^2 and 1 as 1^2.

$= (12 - 1)(12 + 1)$ Factor.

$= (11)(13)$ Simplify.

44a. Answers may vary.
 Sample:
 $4x^2 + 24x + 36$

b. because $(2x)^2 =$ $4x^2$, $2(2x \cdot 6) = 24x$, and $6^2 = 36$

39. 99 **11, 9**   40. 91 **13, 7**   41. 75 **15, 5**   42. 117 **13, 9**   43. 224 **16, 14**

44. a. Open-Ended Write an expression that is a perfect-square trinomial.
 b. Explain how you know your trinomial is a perfect-square trinomial.
 a–b. See left.

24. $(3c + 8)(3c - 8)$

25. $(2m + 9)(2m - 9)$

26. $(4k + 7)(4k - 7)$

27. $(12p + 1)(12p - 1)$

28. $(9v + 10)(9v - 10)$

29. $(20n + 11)(20n - 11)$

30. $(5w + 14)(5w - 14)$

31. $3(m + 2)(m - 2)$

32. $5(k + 7)(k - 7)$

33. $3(x + 8)^2$

34. $2(t - 9)^2$

35. $6r(r + 5)(r - 5)$

Assignment Guide

1 Objective
 A **B** Core 1–12, 37, 46–54

2 Objective
 A **B** Core 13–36, 38–45, 55–64
 C Extension 65–66

Standardized Test Prep 67–72

Mixed Review 73–91

Error Prevention

Exercise 35 Some students may factor out 6 as the GCF. Point out that a variable can also be a common factor and that here the GCF is $6r$.

36. $7(h - 4)^2$

37. Answers may vary. Sample: Rewrite the first and last terms as a square. Check to see if the middle term is $2ab$. Factor as a square binomial: $4x^2 + 12x + 9 = (2x)^2 + 12x + 3^2 = (2x)^2 + 2(2x)(3) + 3^2 = (2x + 3)^2$; $9x^2 - 30x + 25 = (3x)^2 - 30x + 5^2 = (3x)^2 - 2(3x)(5) + 5^2 = (3x - 5)^2$.

493

Alternative Assessment

Have each student write a short essay explaining the ways to recognize and factor the special cases in this lesson.

Standardized Test Prep

A sheet of blank grids is available with the Test-Taking Strategies booklet. Give this sheet to students for practice with filling in the grids.

Resources

For additional practice with a variety of test item formats:
- Standardized Test Prep, p. 507
- Test-Taking Strategies, p. 502
- Test-Taking Strategies with Transparencies

Exercise 67 Standardized tests are often designed so that the average student will run out of time before completing the test. The ability to recognize special cases can help students overcome this constraint.

Factor each expression. 45–53. See margin.

45. $100v^2 - 25w^2$ **46.** $16p^2 - 48pq + 36q^2$ **47.** $28c^2 + 140cd + 175d^2$

48. $\frac{1}{4}m^2 - \frac{1}{9}$ **49.** $x^2 + x + \frac{1}{4}$ **50.** $64g^2 - 192gh + 144h^2$

51. $\frac{1}{4}p^2 - 2p + 4$ **52.** $\frac{1}{9}n^2 - \frac{1}{25}$ **53.** $\frac{1}{25}k^2 + \frac{6}{5}k + 9$

54a. $3.14n^2 - 3.14m^2 = 3.14(n + m)(n - m)$

 **54. a. Geometry** Write an expression in terms of n and m for the area of the top of the block that was drilled at the right. Use 3.14 for π. Factor your expression.
   b. Find the area of the top of the block if $n = 10$ in. and $m = 3$ in. **285.74 in.^{2}**

55. a. Factor $4x^2 - 100$ by removing the common monomial factor and then factoring the remaining expression as the difference of squares. **$4(x + 5)(x - 5)$**
   b. Factor $4x^2 - 100$ as the difference of squares, and then remove the common monomial factors. **$4(x + 5)(x - 5)$**
   c. Critical Thinking Why can $4x^2 - 100$ be factored in two different ways?
   d. Can you factor $3x^2 - 75$ in the two ways you factored $4x^2 - 100$ in parts (a) and (b)? Explain your answer. **c–d. See margin.**

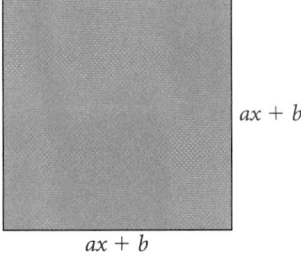
block illustration with labels $3.14n$, n, m

C Challenge

Factor each expression. 56–64. See margin.

56. $64r^6 - 144r^3 + 81$ **57.** $p^6 + 40p^3q + 400q^2$ **58.** $36m^4 + 84m^2 + 49$

59. $81p^{10} + 198p^5 + 121$ **60.** $108m^6 - 147$ **61.** $x^{20} - 4x^{10}y^5 + 4y^{10}$

62. $256g^4 - 100h^6$ **63.** $45x^4 - 60x^2y + 20y^2$ **64.** $37g^8 - 37h^8$

65. a. The expression $(t - 3)^2 - 16$ is a difference of two squares. Identify a and b.
   b. Factor $(t - 3)^2 - 16$ and simplify. **$(t + 1)(t - 7)$**   **a.** $t - 3$; 4

66. The binomial $16 - 81n^4$ can be factored twice as the difference of squares.
   a. Factor $16 - 81n^4$ completely. **$(4 + 9n^2)(2 + 3n)(2 - 3n)$**
   b. Critical Thinking What characteristics do 16 and $81n^4$ share that make this possible? **They are squares of square terms.**
   c. Open-Ended Write a binomial that can be factored twice as the difference of squares. **Answers may vary. Sample: $16x^4 - 1$**

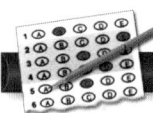

Standardized Test Prep

Gridded Response

67. The area of the square shown at the right is $4x^2 + 28x + 49$. What is the sum of a and b? **9**

68. For what value of p would $(x + p)(x + p)$ be the factored form of $x^2 - 24x + 144$? **−12**

69. For what positive value of k are the factors of $x^2 - kx + 225$ the same? **30**

square labeled $ax + b$ on two sides

---

pages 493–495   Exercises

45. $25(2v + w)(2v - w)$

46. $4(2p - 3q)^2$

47. $7(2c + 5d)^2$

48. $\left(\frac{1}{2}m + \frac{1}{3}\right)\left(\frac{1}{2}m - \frac{1}{3}\right)$

49. $\left(x + \frac{1}{2}\right)^2$

50. $16(2g - 3h)^2$

51. $\left(\frac{1}{2}p - 2\right)^2$

52. $\left(\frac{1}{3}n + \frac{1}{5}\right)\left(\frac{1}{3}n - \frac{1}{5}\right)$

53. $\left(\frac{1}{5}k + 3\right)^2$

55c. The polynomial has a GCF that has two identical factors.

d. $3(x + 5)(x - 5)$; no, because 3 does not have a pair of identical factors.

56. $(8r^3 - 9)^2$

57. $(p^3 + 20q)^2$

58. $(6m^2 + 7)^2$

59. $(9p^5 + 11)^2$

70. The diagram shows two squares. The area of the region shaded green is $4x^2 + 16x + 16$. The area of the region shaded purple is $5x^2 + 14x + 9$. What is the value of b? **5**

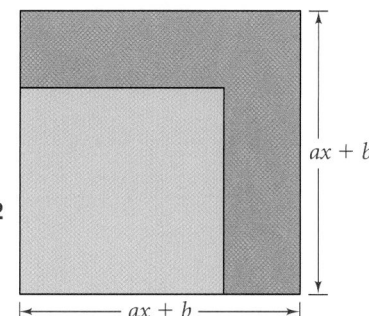

$ax + b$

$|\longleftarrow ax + b \longrightarrow|$

71. For what value of a does $144x^4 - 121 = (ax^2 + 11)(ax^2 - 11)$? **12**

72. The expression $81x^2 - 36$ can factored as $9(ax + b)(ax - b)$. What is the mean of a and b? **2.5**

Take It to the NET
Online lesson quiz at
www.PHSchool.com
Web Code: aea-0907

Mixed Review

Lesson 9-6   **Factor each expression. 73–78. See margin.**

73. $2d^2 + 11d + 5$ **74.** $2x^2 - 11x + 12$ **75.** $4t^2 + 16t + 7$

76. $5w^2 - 44w - 9$ **77.** $6t^2 + 19t + 8$ **78.** $21m^2 - 20m - 9$

79. $14x^2 - 11x - 9$ **80.** $4y^2 + 32y + 55$ **81.** $12k^2 - 5k - 2$
$(7x - 9)(2x + 1)$ $(2y + 11)(2y + 5)$ $(3k - 2)(4k + 1)$

Lesson 8-6   **Find the next three terms of each sequence. Then write a rule for each sequence.**
82–90. See margin.
82. $3, 12, 48, 192, \ldots$ **83.** $-3, 5, 13, 21, \ldots$ **84.** $25, 16, 7, -2, \ldots$

85. $200, 20, 2, 0.2, \ldots$ **86.** $-2, 4, -8, 16, \ldots$ **87.** $0.1, 0.6, 3.6, 21.6, \ldots$

88. $10, 4, \frac{8}{5}, \frac{16}{25}, \ldots$ **89.** $\frac{1}{2}, 2, 3\frac{1}{2}, 5, \ldots$ **90.** $\frac{1}{32}, \frac{1}{8}, \frac{1}{2}, 2, \ldots$

Lesson 6-6   **91.** A teacher is comparing time her students spent studying, in hours, with their grades on a math test.

 a. Graphing Calculator Use a graphing calculator to find the equation of the line of best fit. $y = 11.4x + 64.8$

b. What test score would you predict for a student who studied 2.5 hours? **93**

c. What test score would you predict for a student who studied 1.25 hours? **79**

Student	Time Studying	Grade
1	1	82
2	2	92
3	1.5	80
4	2	88
5	1	70
6	3	97
7	0.5	70

✓ Checkpoint Quiz 2   Lessons 9-4 through 9-7

 Instant self-check quiz online and on CD-ROM

Simplify each expression.

1. $(k - 7)^2$
$k^2 - 14k + 49$

2. $(5t + 9)^2$
$25t^2 + 90t + 81$

3. $(h - 11)(h - 11)$
$h^2 - 22h + 121$

Factor each expression.

4. $v^2 + 20v + 100$ **5.** $p^2 - 6p - 40$ **6.** $k^2 - 17k + 60$

7. $2x^2 + 13x + 11$ **8.** $10m^2 + 19m + 7$ **9.** $3w^2 - 6w - 24$
$(5m + 7)(2m + 1)$ $3(w + 2)(w - 4)$

10. $9t^2 - 25$ $(3t + 5)(3t - 5)$

4. $(v + 10)^2$

5. $(p - 10)(p + 4)$

6. $(k - 12)(k - 5)$

7. $(2x + 11)(x + 1)$

Lesson 9-7   Factoring Special Cases   **495**

Chapter Checkpoint 2

To check understanding of Lessons 9-4 to 9-7:

Checkpoint Quiz 2 (p. 495)

Teaching Resources
Checkpoint Quiz 2 (also in Prentice Hall Assessment System)

Reaching All Students
Reading and Math Literacy C

Spanish versions available

82. 768; 3072; 12,288; $3 \cdot 4^{n-1}$

83. 29; 37; 45; $-11 + 8n$

84. -11; -20; -29; $34 - 9n$

85. 0.02; 0.002; 0.0002; $2000 \cdot \left(\frac{1}{10}\right)^n$

86. -32; 64; -128; $(-2)^n$

87. 129.6; 777.6; 4665.6; $0.1(6)^{n-1}$

88. $\frac{32}{125}$; $\frac{64}{625}$; $\frac{128}{3125}$; $10 \cdot \left(\frac{2}{5}\right)^{n-1}$

89. $6\frac{1}{2}$; 8; $9\frac{1}{2}$; $-1 + \frac{3}{2}n$

90. 8; 32; 128; $\frac{1}{32} \cdot 4^{n-1}$
or $\frac{1}{2} \cdot 4^{n-3}$

---

60. $3(6m^3 - 7)(6m^3 + 7)$

61. $(x^{10} - 2y^5)^2$

62. $4(8g^2 - 5h^3)(8g^2 + 5h^3)$

63. $5(3x^2 - 2y)^2$

64. $37(g^4 + h^4)(g^2 + h^2)$
$(g + h)(g - h)$

73. $(2d + 1)(d + 5)$

74. $(2x - 3)(x - 4)$

75. $(2t + 1)(2t + 7)$

76. $(5w + 1)(w - 9)$

77. $(3t + 8)(2t + 1)$

78. $(7m - 9)(3m + 1)$

1. Plan

Lesson Preview

✓ **Check Skills You'll Need**

Multiplying and Factoring
Lesson 9-2: Example 2
Exercises 13–18
Extra Practice, p. 710

Multiplying Binomials
Lesson 9-3: Examples 1–4
Exercises 1–29
Extra Practice, p. 710

Lesson Resources

📁 **Teaching Resources**
Practice, Reteaching, Enrichment

👥 **Reaching All Students**
Practice Workbook 9-8
Spanish Practice Workbook 9-8
Basic Algebra Planning Guide 9-8

⏰ **Presentation Assistant Plus!**
Transparencies
• Check Skills You'll Need 9-8
• Additional Examples 9-8
• Student Edition Answers 9-8
• Lesson Quiz 9-8
PH Presentation Pro CD 9-8

ASSESSMENT SYSTEM
PRENTICE HALL

Computer Test Generator CD

💿 **Technology**
Resource Pro® CD-ROM
Computer Test Generator CD
Prentice Hall Presentation Pro CD

🖥 **www.PHSchool.com**
Student Site
• Teacher Web Code: aek-5500
• Reasoning & Puzzles p. 83
• Self-grading Lesson Quiz
Teacher Center
• Lesson Planner
• Resources

Plus 📱 **iTEXT**

496

9-8

Factoring by Grouping

North Carolina Objectives

1.01 Write equivalent forms of algebraic expressions to solve problems. c) Factor polynomials.

Lesson Preview

What You'll Learn

OBJECTIVE 1 To factor polynomials with four terms

OBJECTIVE 2 To factor trinomials by grouping

. . . And Why

To find expressions for the dimensions of a rectangular prism, as in Example 4

✓ **Check Skills You'll Need**   (For help, go to Lessons 9-2 and 9-3.)

Find the GCF of the terms of each polynomial.

1. $6y^2 + 12y - 4$ **2**
2. $9r^3 + 15r^2 + 21r$ **3r**
3. $30h^3 - 25h^2 - 40h$ **5h**
4. $16m^3 - 12m^2 - 36m$ **4m**

Find each product.

5. $(v + 3)(v^2 + 5)$ $v^3 + 3v^2 + 5v + 15$
6. $(2q^2 - 4)(q - 5)$
   6. $2q^3 - 10q^2 - 4q + 20$
7. $(2t - 5)(3t + 4)$ $6t^2 - 7t - 20$
8. $(4x - 1)(x^2 + 2x + 3)$
   8. $4x^3 + 7x^2 + 10x - 3$

New Vocabulary • factor by grouping

📱 **iTEXT** Interactive lesson includes instant self-check, tutorials, and activities.

OBJECTIVE
1
Factoring Polynomials With Four Terms

You can use the Distributive Property to **factor by grouping** if two groups of terms have the same factor.

$$y^3 + 3y^2 \quad + \quad 4y + 12$$
$$\underbrace{y^2(y + 3)}_{} \quad + \quad \underbrace{4(y + 3)}_{}$$
$$(y^2 + 4)(y + 3)$$

These factors are the same, so factor again.

To factor by grouping, look for a common binomial factor of two pairs of terms.

1 EXAMPLE **Factoring a Four-Term Polynomial**

Factor $4n^3 + 8n^2 - 5n - 10$.

$4n^3 + 8n^2 - 5n - 10 = 4n^2(n + 2) - 5(n + 2)$ **Factor the GCF from each group of two terms.**

$= (4n^2 - 5)(n + 2)$ **Factor out $(n + 2)$.**

Check $4n^3 + 8n^2 - 5n - 10 \overset{?}{=} (4n^2 - 5)(n + 2)$

$= 4n^3 + 8n^2 - 5n - 10$ ✓   **Use FOIL.**

✓ **Check Understanding** ① Factor each expression. Check your answer.
a. $5t^4 + 20t^3 + 6t + 24$
   $(5t^3 + 6)(t + 4)$
b. $2w^3 + w^2 - 14w - 7$
   $(w^2 - 7)(2w + 1)$

Before you factor by grouping, you may need to factor the GCF of all the terms of a polynomial. Remember, a polynomial is not completely factored until there are no common factors other than 1.

496 Chapter 9 Polynomials and Factoring

Ongoing Assessment and Intervention

Before the Lesson	During the Lesson	After the Lesson
Diagnose prerequisite skills using:	**Monitor progress using:**	**Assess knowledge using:**
• Check Skills You'll Need	• Check Understanding • Additional Examples • Standardized Test Prep	• Lesson Quiz • Computer Test Generator CD

2 EXAMPLE — Factoring Completely

Factor $12p^4 + 10p^3 - 36p^2 - 30p$.

$$12p^4 + 10p^3 - 36p^2 - 30p = 2p(6p^3 + 5p^2 - 18p - 15) \qquad \text{Factor out the GCF, } 2p.$$
$$= 2p[(p^2(6p + 5) - 3(6p + 5)] \qquad \text{Factor by grouping.}$$
$$= 2p(p^2 - 3)(6p + 5) \qquad \text{Factor again.}$$

✓ **Check Understanding** ② Factor $45m^4 - 9m^3 + 30m^2 - 6m$. $3m(3m^2 + 2)(5m - 1)$

OBJECTIVE
2 Factoring Trinomials by Grouping

You can also factor by grouping to find the factors of a trinomial of the form $ax^2 + bx + c$. You may want to use this method when you cannot quickly factor a trinomial using the method you learned in Lesson 9-6.

You can use these steps to factor a trinomial such as $48x^2 + 46x + 5$.

Step 1 Find the product ac.

$$48 \cdot 5 = 240$$

Step 2 Find the two factors of ac that have sum b.

Factors	→	Sum		Factors	→	Sum
$1 \cdot 240$	→	$1 + 240 = 241$		$4 \cdot 60$	→	$4 + 60 = 64$
$2 \cdot 120$	→	$2 + 120 = 122$		$5 \cdot 48$	→	$5 + 48 = 53$
$3 \cdot 80$	→	$3 + 80 = 83$		$6 \cdot 40$	→	$6 + 40 = 46$ ✓

Step 3 Rewrite the trinomial using the sum.

$$48x^2 + 46x + 5 = 48x^2 + (6 + 40)x + 5$$
$$= 48x^2 + 6x + 40x + 5$$

Step 4 Factor by grouping.

$$48x^2 + 6x + 40x + 5$$
$$6x(8x + 1) + 5(8x + 1)$$
$$(6x + 5)(8x + 1)$$

As you look for factors of the product ac that have a sum b, you do not have to list all the possible factors. Use mental math to eliminate those factors that give sums too great or too small to be reasonable choices.

Problem Solving Hint
Use mental math to determine where to start. $-10, 60$ and $-20, 30$ are two pairs of factors of 600 that have sums 50 and 10. Since 25 is between 50 and 10, the negative factor must be between -10 and -20.

3 EXAMPLE — Factoring a Trinomial by Grouping

Factor $24q^2 + 25q - 25$.

Step 1 $24(-25) = -600$ Find the product ac.

Step 2 Factors → Sum
$$(-12)(50) \to -12 + 50 = 38$$
$$(-15)(40) \to -15 + 40 = 25 \ ✓$$
Find two factors of ac that have sum b. Use mental math to determine a good place to start.

Step 3 $24q^2 - 15q + 40q - 25$ Rewrite the trinomial.

Step 4 $3q(8q - 5) + 5(8q - 5)$ Factor by grouping.
$(3q + 5)(8q - 5)$ Factor again.

Lesson 9-8   Factoring by Grouping   **497**

👫 Reaching All Students

Below Level Remind students that they can always check their work by multiplying the factors.	**Advanced Learners** Have students research and explain why this method of factoring a trinomial works.	**Inclusion** See note on page 497. **Error Prevention** See note on page 497.

---

2. Teach

Professional Development

Math Background

Familiarity with the form and patterns of binomial factors makes it easier to see how to group polynomials with four terms in order to factor them.

OBJECTIVE 1 Teaching Notes

1 EXAMPLE — Error Prevention

Some students may want to factor 5, instead of -5, from $-5n - 10$ and get $5(-n - 2)$. Help students see that since the first two terms have a factor of $(n + 2)$ and they want the new factor to be identical, they need to factor out -1 as well.

2 EXAMPLE — Inclusion

This type of problem is very difficult, especially for slower learners. You may want to pair students who need extra help with those who understand the exercise.

🖌 Additional Examples

❶ Factor $6x^3 + 3x^2 - 4x - 2$.
$(2x + 1)(3x^2 - 2)$

❷ Factor $8t^4 + 12t^3 + 16t^2 + 24t$.
$4t(2t + 3)(t^2 + 2)$

OBJECTIVE 2 Teaching Notes

3 EXAMPLE — Teaching Tip

Direct students' attention to the list in Step 2. Lead them to notice that the farther apart the factors, the greater their sum. Help them see how this information is useful in limiting the number of factors to test.

4 EXAMPLE — Connection to Geometry

When you use factoring to find dimensions of a prism, you are finding possible dimensions. Other dimensions giving the same volume are possible, but they are not all polynomials.

Additional Examples

3 Factor $24h^2 + 10h - 6$.
$2(4h + 3)(3h - 1)$

4 A rectangular prism has a volume of $36x^3 + 51x^2 + 18x$. Factor to find the possible expressions for the length, width, and height of the prism.
$3x, (4x + 3), (3x + 2)$

Closure

Ask students: *What is the first thing to do when factoring?* Look to see if there is a GCF to factor out.

✓ **Check Understanding** **3** Factor each trinomial by grouping.

a. $63d^2 + 44d + 5$ **b.** $11k^2 + 49k + 20$ **c.** $4y^2 + 33y - 70$
$(9d + 5)(7d + 1)$ $(11k + 5)(k + 4)$ $(4y - 7)(y + 10)$

Given a polynomial expression for the volume of a rectangular prism, you can sometimes factor to find possible expressions for the length, width, and height.

4 EXAMPLE **Finding the Dimensions of a Rectangular Prism**

Geometry The volume (ℓwh) of the rectangular prism at the right is $80x^3 + 224x^2 + 60x$. Factor to find possible expressions for the length, width, and height of the prism.

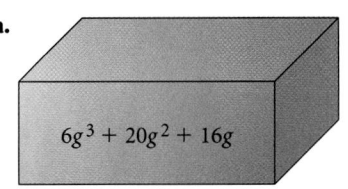

Factor $80x^3 + 224x^2 + 60x$.

Step 1 $4x(20x^2 + 56x + 15)$ Factor out the GCF, 4x.

Step 2 $20 \cdot 15 = 300$ Find the product ac.

Step 3 Factors → Sum
         $5 \cdot 60$ → $5 + 60$ = 65   Find two factors of ac that have
         $10 \cdot 30$ → $10 + 30$ = 40   sum b. Use mental math to
         $15 \cdot 20$ → $15 + 20$ = 35   determine a good place to start.
         $6 \cdot 50$ → $6 + 50$ = 56 ✓

Step 4 $4x(20x^2 + 50x + 6x + 15)$ Rewrite the trinomial.

Step 5 $4x[10x(2x + 5) + 3(2x + 5)]$ Factor by grouping.
         $4x(10x + 3)(2x + 5)$ Factor again.

● The possible dimensions of the prism are $4x, (10x + 3)$, and $(2x + 5)$.

✓ **Check Understanding** **4** Find expressions for the possible dimensions of each rectangular prism.

a.

$6g^3 + 20g^2 + 16g$

Answers may vary.
Sample: 2g, (3g + 4),
and (g + 2)

b.

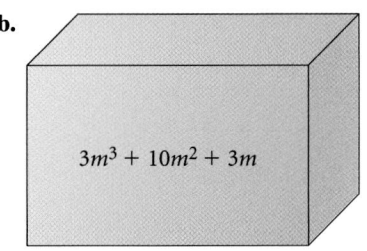

$3m^3 + 10m^2 + 3m$

$m, (3m + 1)$, and $(m + 3)$

Here is a summary of what to remember as you factor polynomials.

🔑 **Key Concepts**

Summary	**Factoring Polynomials**

1. Factor out the greatest common factor (GCF).
2. If the polynomial has two terms or three terms, look for a difference of two squares, a product of two squares, or a pair of binomial factors.
3. If there are four or more terms, group terms and factor to find common binomial factors.
4. As a final check, make sure there are no common factors other than 1.

For more practice, see *Extra Practice*.

Practice and Problem Solving

 A **Practice by Example**

Example 1
(page 496)

Find the GCF of the first two terms and the GCF of the last two terms for each polynomial.

1. $2m^3 + 6m^2 + 3m + 9$ **$2m^2$; 3**
2. $10p^3 - 25p^2 + 4p - 10$ **$5p^2$; 2**
3. $2z^3 + 12z^2 - 5z - 30$ **$2z^2$; −5**
4. $6n^3 + 3n^2 + 2n + 1$ **$3n^2$; 1**

Factor each expression. 5–8. See margin.

5. $6n^3 + 8n^2 + 3n + 4$
6. $14t^3 + 21t^2 + 16t + 24$

7. $27t^3 + 45t^2 - 3t - 5$
8. $13y^3 - 8y^2 + 13y - 8$

9. $45x^3 + 20x^2 + 9x + 4$
  $(5x^2 + 1)(9x + 4)$
10. $10w^3 + 16w^2 - 15w - 24$
  $(2w^2 - 3)(5w + 8)$

Example 2
(page 497)

Factor completely. 11–14. See margin.

11. $12v^3 - 32v^2 + 6v - 16$
12. $7q^4 - 4q^3 + 28q^2 - 16q$

13. $20m^3 - 18m^2 + 40m - 36$
14. $6x^4 + 4x^3 - 6x^2 - 4x$

15. $12y^3 - 20y^2 + 30y - 50$
  $2(2y^2 + 5)(3y - 5)$
16. $9c^3 - 12c^2 + 18c - 24$
  $3(c^2 + 2)(3c - 4)$

Example 3
(page 497)

Factor by grouping. 17–22. See margin.

17. $12p^2 + 16p + 5$
18. $16t^2 + 24t + 9$
19. $18n^2 + 57n - 10$

20. $9w^2 - 27w + 20$
21. $24m^2 + 8m - 2$
22. $36v^2 - 9v - 7$

23. $6x^2 + 11x - 10$
  $(3x - 2)(2x + 5)$
24. $20v^2 - 41v + 9$
  $(4v - 1)(5v - 9)$
25. $63q^2 - 52q - 20$
  $(7q + 2)(9q - 10)$

Example 4
(page 498)

Find expressions for the possible dimensions of each rectangular prism.

26.
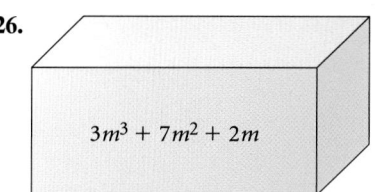
$3m^3 + 7m^2 + 2m$

m, $(3m + 1)$, and $(m + 2)$

27.
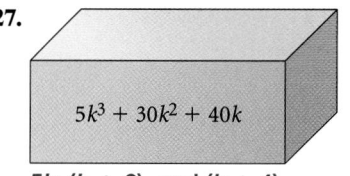
$5k^3 + 30k^2 + 40k$

$5k$, $(k + 2)$, and $(k + 4)$

 B **Apply Your Skills**

30. **$8(d^2 + 3)(d + 2)$**
31. **$4(3x - 7y)(x + 2y)$**

Factor completely.

28. $7h^3 - 35h^2 - 42h$ **$7h(h - 6)(h + 1)$**
29. $60t^3 - 200t^2 - 66t + 220$
  29. $2(10t^2 - 11)(3t - 10)$

30. $8d^3 + 16d^2 + 24d + 48$
31. $12x^2 - 4xy - 56y^2$

32. $54r^3 - 45r^2 + 9r$
  $9r(3r - 1)(2r - 1)$
33. $150k^3 + 350k^2 + 180k + 420$
  $10(5k^2 + 6)(3k + 7)$

34. a. Factor $(28x^3 - 7x^2) + (36x - 9)$. **$(7x^2 + 9)(4x - 1)$**

  b. Factor $(28x^3 + 36x) + (-7x^2 - 9)$. **$(4x - 1)(7x^2 + 9)$**

  c. Critical Thinking Why can you factor the same polynomial using different pairs of terms? **Answers may vary. Sample: The factorings are equivalent, but the factors may appear in a different order.**

Write each expression in standard form and factor.

35. **$(7w^2 - 4)(2w + 7)$**
36. **$(2m^2 - 1)(m - 16)$**

35. $-8w + 49w^2 + 14w^3 - 28$
36. $2m^3 + 16 - m - 32m^2$

37. $-6 + 44t^3 - 4t^2 + 66t$
  $2(2t^2 + 3)(11t - 1)$
38. $2 - 50x - x^2 + 25x^3$
  $(x^2 - 2)(25x - 1)$

Lesson 9-8 Factoring by Grouping **499**

pages 499–501 Exercises

5. $(2n^2 + 1)(3n + 4)$
6. $(7t^2 + 8)(2t + 3)$
7. $(3t + 1)(3t - 1)(3t + 5)$

8. $(y^2 + 1)(13y - 8)$
11. $2(2v^2 + 1)(3v - 8)$
12. $q(q^2 + 4)(7q - 4)$
13. $2(m^2 + 2)(10m - 9)$

14. $2x(x + 1)(x - 1)(3x + 2)$
17. $(6p + 5)(2p + 1)$
18. $(4t + 3)^2$
19. $(6n - 1)(3n + 10)$

20. $(3w - 5)(3w - 4)$
21. $2(6m - 1)(2m + 1)$
22. $(12v - 7)(3v + 1)$

Assignment Guide

1 Objective
  A B Core 1–16, 33–38, 40–41
  C Extension 42–45

2 Objective
  A B Core 17–32, 39
  C Extension 46–49

Standardized Test Prep 50–53

Mixed Review 54–84

Error Prevention

Exercises 12, 14 Remind students that a variable can be a common factor.

Exercises 42, 43 Point out to students that each factor will contain both variables.

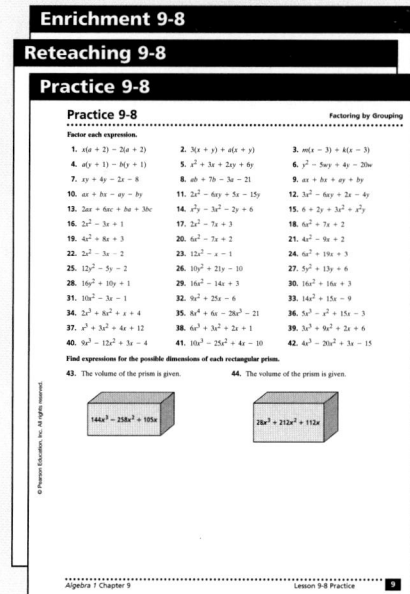

Alternative Assessment

Direct students to write instructions for factoring by grouping for a student who was absent. Tell them they only need to explain one of the two methods.

pages 499–501   Exercises

40. Answers may vary.
    Sample:
    $30x^2 + 36x + 40x + 48$;
    $2(3x + 4)(5x + 6)$

41. Answers may vary.
    Sample: Split the expression into two groups. Remove the GCF from each group, and then factor again.

42. $(6m^3 - 7n^2)(5m^2 + 4n)$

43. $(x^2 + y)(p + q^5)$

44. $(h + 2)(h - 2)(h + 11)$

45. $(w^2 + 3)(w^2 - 3)$
    $(w + 1)(w - 1)$

52. [2] $9a^4 - 54a^3 - 2a + 12 = 9a^3(a - 6) - 2(a - 6) = (9a^3 - 2)(a - 6)$

    [1] appropriate methods with one computational error

 39. **Geometry** The polynomial shown at the right represents the volume of the rectangular prism. Factor the polynomial to find possible expressions for the length, width, and height of the prism.
    2w, (6w + 5), and (7w + 1)

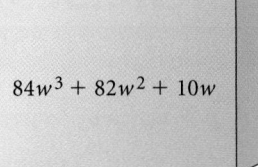
$84w^3 + 82w^2 + 10w$

40. **Open-Ended** Write a four-term polynomial that can be factored by grouping. Factor your polynomial. **See margin.**

 41. **Writing** Describe how to factor the expression $10x^3 - 15x^2 + 2x - 3$ by grouping. **See margin.**

 **Challenge**

Factor by grouping. 42–45. See margin.

42. $30m^5 + 24m^3n - 35m^2n^2 - 28n^3$ 43. $x^2p + x^2q^5 + yp + yq^5$

44. $h^3 + 11h^2 - 4h - 44$ 45. $w^6 - w^4 - 9w^2 + 9$

46. **Geometry** The polynomial $2\pi x^3 - 12\pi x^2 + 18\pi x$ represents the volume of a cylinder. The formula for volume of a cylinder is $V = \pi r^2 h$.
    a. Factor $2\pi x^3 + 12\pi x^2 + 18\pi x$. $2\pi x(x + 3)^2$
    b. Based on your answer to part (a), write an expression for a possible radius of the cylinder. $x + 3$

The number 63 can be written as $2^5 + 2^4 + 2^3 + 2^2 + 2^1 + 2^0$. For exercises 47 and 48, factor each expression by grouping. Then simplify the powers of 2 to write 63 as the product of two numbers.

47. $(2^5 + 2^4 + 2^3) + (2^2 + 2^1 + 2^0)$ $(2^3 + 2^0)(2^2 + 2^1 + 2^0)$; (9)(7)

48. $(2^5 + 2^4) + (2^3 + 2^2) + (2^1 + 2^0)$ $(2^4 + 2^2 + 2^0)(2^1 + 2^0)$; (21)(3)

49. **a. Open-Ended** For the rectangular prism below, let $x = 3$. Write linear expressions for the length, width, and height of the prism.

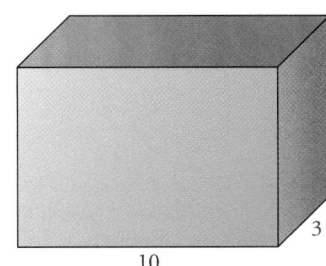

Answers may vary. Samples are given:
a. length = $2x + 4$;
   width = x;
   height = $x + 4$
b. $2x^3 + 12x^2 + 16x$

b. Using your answers from part (a), write a polynomial that represents the volume of the prism.

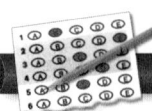

Standardized Test Prep

Multiple Choice

50. Which of the following expressions is a factor of $27x^4 + 15x^3 + 63x + 35$? **C**
    A. $3x + 7$ **B.** $3x^2 + 7$ **C.** $3x^3 + 7$ **D.** $3x^4 + 7$

51. Which of the following expressions equals the sum of the factors of $6q^3 - 5q^2 + 24q - 20$? **H**
    F. $7q^3 - 1$ **G.** $6q^3 - 1$ **H.** $q^2 + 6q - 1$ **I.** $q^2 + 6q + 1$

Short Response

52. Factor $9a^4 - 54a^3 - 2a + 12$ completely. Show your work. **See margin.**

Extended Response

Take It to the NET
Online lesson quiz at
www.PHSchool.com
Web Code: aea-0908

53. The volume of the rectangular prism is $96x^3 + 48x^2 + 6x$. Find an expression that could describe the perimeter of one of the prism's square faces. Show your work. **See margin.**

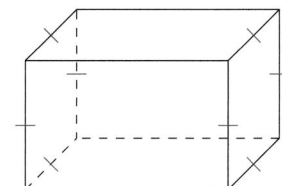

Standardized Test Prep

📁 **Resources**

For additional practice with a variety of test item formats:
- Standardized Test Prep, p. 507
- Test-Taking Strategies, p. 502
- Test-Taking Strategies with Transparencies

Mixed Review

Lesson 9-7

57. $2(t + 3)^2$

58. $(m + 8)(m - 8)$

59. $4(g + 5)^2$

Factor each expression.

54. $k^2 + 14k + 49$ $(k + 7)^2$ **55.** $r^2 + 6r + 9$ $(r + 3)^2$ **56.** $y^2 - 16y + 64$ $(y - 8)^2$

57. $2t^2 + 12t + 18$ **58.** $m^2 - 64$ **59.** $4g^2 + 40g + 100$

60. $4d^2 - 25$ **61.** $5n^2 - 45$ **62.** $25q^2 + 40q + 16$
$(2d + 5)(2d - 5)$ $5(n + 3)(n - 3)$ $(5q + 4)^2$

Lesson 8-4

Simplify each expression.

63. $(b^2)^2$ b^4 **64.** $x^4 \cdot x^{-2}$ x^2 **65.** $(t^3)^5$ t^{15} **66.** $(c^5d)^7$ $c^{35}d^7$

67. $(2y)^3$ $8y^3$ **68.** $(9m)^0$ 1 **69.** $(x^3)(x^7)^{-2}$ $\frac{1}{x^{11}}$ **70.** $(3w^2v^3)^4$ $81w^8v^{12}$

71. 1.6×10^{21}

72. 9×10^{12}

73. 4.9×10^{-11}

74. 3.2×10^{36}

Simplify . Write each answer in scientific notation.

71. $(2 \times 10^5)^4$ **72.** $(3 \times 10^6)^2$ **73.** $(7 \times 10^{-6})^2$ **74.** $(2 \times 10^7)^5$

75. $(5.3 \times 10^2)^2$ **76.** $(8.1 \times 10^{-3})^2$ **77.** $(1.9 \times 10^8)^3$ **78.** $(4 \times 10^{-3})^{-2}$
2.809×10^5 6.561×10^{-5} 6.859×10^{24} 6.25×10^4

Lesson 7-2

Solve each system using substitution.

79. $y = -7x + 12$ **80.** $y = -3x + 4$ **81.** $10x + 2y = 15$
     $y = 3x + 2$ **(1, 5)** $y = -5x + 12$ **(4, −8)** $y = -4x + 7$ **(0.5, 5)**

82. $x + y = -28$ **83.** $8x + 2y = 50$ **84.** $y = x - 5$
     $y = -2x - 26$ **(2, −30)** $y = -4x + 25$ $11x - 6y = 65$ **(7, 2)**
                        infinitely many
                        solutions on the line
                        $y = -4x + 25$

53. **[4]** $96x^3 + 48x^2 + 6x =$
$6x(16x^2 + 8x + 1) =$
$6x(4x + 1)^2$. Side of square equals $4x + 1$.
Perimeter $=$
$4(4x + 1) = 16x + 4$.

[3] appropriate methods, but with one computational error

[2] found factors of polynomial, but did not find perimeter

[1] correct answer, without work shown

A Point in Time

1000   1200   1400   1600   1800   2000

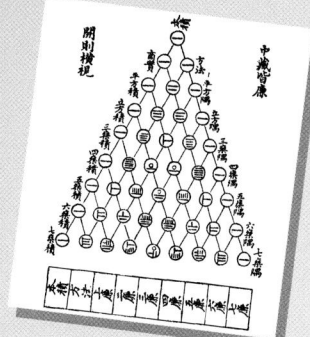

Very little is known about the life of Chu Shih-Chieh, the Chinese mathematician and teacher who had many students during the last two decades of the 1200s. In 1303, Chu wrote *Ssu-yüan-yü-chien*, or *The Precious Mirror of Four Elements*. He described what is now known as Pascal's Triangle and explained how it could be used to solve polynomial equations. He also invented "the method of celestial element" to write and solve polynomial equations and linear systems with up to four variables.

💻 **Take It to the NET** For more information about Pascal's Triangle, go to **www.PHSchool.com**.
Web Code: aee-2032

Eliminating Answers

Students see how eliminating answer choices can save time and help make an "educated" guess.

Resources

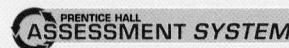

Test-Taking Strategies with Transparencies
- Transparency 9
- Practice sheet p. 9

Teaching Notes

Error Prevention

Students may think they can eliminate all incorrect answers using these "shortcut" methods. Stress that you are just reducing the number of answer choices that are possibly correct so you do not have to work out each possibility.

Teaching Tip

Brainstorm with students to write a list of ways to eliminate answers. Suggest they keep this list and study it before taking multiple choice tests.

Test-Taking Strategies with Transparencies

Test-Taking Strategy: Eliminating Answers

The easiest way to narrow down the answer choices in a multiple-choice item is to eliminate obviously wrong answers.

Solve $\left|\frac{2x + 16}{x - 8}\right| = 10$.

  A. –4   B. 8   C. 10   D. 12

Look at each answer choice to see if it can be eliminated.

–4   If –4 is substituted then the denominator would be negative which would make the quotient negative. The given quotient is positive, so this answer choice can be eliminated.

8   If 8 is substituted, the denominator would be zero and division by zero is undefined. This answer choice can be eliminated.

The answer choice is either C or D. Substitute these choices for x to select the correct one. D is correct.

Solve these problems by eliminating answer choices.

1. Solve $\frac{625}{y} = -125$.

  A. –25   B. –5   C. 5   D. 25

2. Solve $\frac{1295}{b} = 259$.

  A. 5   B. 8   C. 10   D. 12

Solutions

1. B

2. A

Transparency 9

Eliminating Answers

Before you do all the work involved in solving a multiple-choice problem, you usually can eliminate some answer choices. This can save you time in arriving at the answer to the problem, or in making an "educated" guess if you do not actually know how to find the answer.

1 EXAMPLE

One factor of $x^3 + x^2 + x - 3$ is $x - 1$. What is the other factor?

  A. $x^2 + 2x - 3$ **B.** $x^2 + 2x + 3$ **C.** $x^3 + 2x + 3$ **D.** $x^2 - 2x + 3$

Look at the degrees of the polynomials. The original polynomial has degree 3 and the given factor has degree 1. The answer must have degree $3 - 1 = 2$. Since answer choice C has degree 3, you can eliminate choice C.

Look at the constant terms of the polynomials. The constant term of the original polynomial is -3. Since the constant term of the factor is -1, the other constant term must be 3 for the product of the two factors to be -3. The constant term of answer choice A is -3, so you can eliminate choice A.

● The correct answer is either B or D.

2 EXAMPLE

$(3x + 5)(x - 2) = \blacksquare$

  A. $3x^2 - 2x - 10$ **B.** $3x^2 - 5x - 2$ **C.** $3x^2 + 2x - 10$ **D.** $3x^2 - x - 10$

Substitute a number. The original polynomial has $x - 2$ as a factor. If you let x equal 2, then the polynomial will equal 0. The correct answer will have to equal 0 when x is 2.

Choice A: $3(2)^2 - 2(2) - 10 = 3(4) - 4 - 10 = 12 - 4 - 10 = -2$.   You can eliminate A.

Choice B: $3(2)^2 - 5(2) - 2 = 3(4) - 10 - 2 = 12 - 10 - 2 = 0$.   B is a possible answer.

Choice C: $3(2)^2 + 2(2) - 10 = 3(4) + 4 - 10 = 12 + 4 - 10 = 6$.   You can eliminate C.

Choice D: $3(2)^2 - 2 - 10 = 3(4) - 2 - 10 = 12 - 2 - 10 = 0$.   D is a possible answer.

● The correct answer is either B or D.

EXERCISES

1. Multiply $x - 1$ by choices B and D in Example 1 to find the correct answer. **B**

2. Look at the constant terms in choices B and D in Example 2, and explain why you can eliminate choice B. **The constant term must be -10.**

3. Consider the following multiple-choice problem.

   One factor of $3x^3 + 2x^2 + x - 6$ is $x - 1$. What is the other factor?

     F. $3x^2 - 5x - 6$ **G.** $3x^2 + 5x + 6$ **H.** $3x^3 + x^2 - 3$ **I.** $3x^2 - 5x + 6$

   a. Explain why you can eliminate answer choices F and H. **The correct answer must**
   b. What is the correct answer to the problem?   **have a constant term of 6.**
   G

Chapter Review

Vocabulary

binomial (p. 457)
degree of a monomial (p. 457)
degree of a polynomial (p. 457)

factor by grouping (p. 496)
monomial (p. 456)
perfect-square trinomial (p. 490)

polynomial (p. 457)
standard form of a polynomial (p. 457)
trinomial (p. 457)

Reading Math
Understanding
Vocabulary

Match the vocabulary term in the column on the left with the most accurate description in the column on the right.

1. binomial **A**

2. degree of a monomial **D**

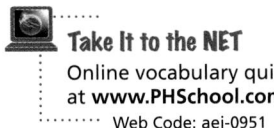

Take It to the NET
Online vocabulary quiz
at www.PHSchool.com
Web Code: aej-0951

3. monomial **E**

4. perfect-square trinomial **C**

5. standard form of a polynomial **B**

A. a polynomial with two terms

B. a polynomial in which the terms decrease in degree from left to right and there are no like terms

C. a polynomial with two identical binomial factors

D. the sum of the exponents of the variables

E. an expression that is a number, a variable, or a product of a number and one or more variables

Skills and Concepts

9-1 Objectives

▼ To describe polynomials (p. 456)

▼ To add and subtract polynomials (p. 458)

The degree of a term with one variable is the exponent of the variable. A **polynomial** is one monomial or the sum or difference of two or more monomials. The **degree of a polynomial** is the same as the degree of the term with the highest degree. A polynomial can be named by its degree or by the number of its terms. You can simplify polynomials by adding the coefficients of like terms.

Write each polynomial in standard form. Then name each polynomial based on its degree and number of terms. 6–11. See margin.

6. $5y + 2 - 6y^2 + 3y$

7. $1 + 9h^2$

8. $k^3 + 3k^5 + k - k^3$

9. $6t^3 + 9 + 8t + 7t^2 - 6t^3$

10. x^2y^2

11. $5 + x^2 + x^3$

12. **Open-Ended** Write a polynomial using the variable z. What is the degree of your polynomial? **Answers may vary. Sample: $3z^4 - 5z^2 + 1$; 4**

Simplify. Write each answer in standard form.

13. $(-4b^5 + 3b^3 - b + 10) + (3b^5 - b^3 + b - 4)$ $-b^5 + 2b^3 + 6$

14. $(3g^4 + 5g^2 + 5) + (5g^4 - 10g^2 + 11g)$ $8g^4 - 5g^2 + 11g + 5$

15. $(3x^3 + 8x^2 + 2x + 9) - (-4x^3 + 5x - 3)$ $7x^3 + 8x^2 - 3x + 12$

16. $(2t^3 - 4t^2 + 9t - 7) - (t^3 + t^2 - 3t + 1)$ $t^3 - 5t^2 + 12t - 8$

17. $(6y^2 + 3y + 5) - (2y^2 + 1)$ $4y^2 + 3y + 4$

18. $(7w^5 - 7w^3 + 3w) - (5w^4 - w^2 + 3)$ $7w^5 - 5w^4 - 7w^3 + w^2 + 3w - 3$

Resources

Student Edition
Extra Practice, Ch. 9, p. 710
English/Spanish Glossary, p. 757
Properties and Formulas, p. 752
Table of Symbols, p. 749

 **Reaching All Students**
Reading and Math Literacy 9D
Spanish Reading and Math Literacy 9D

ASSESSMENT SYSTEM

Standardized Test Prep
• Ch. 9 practice in standardized test formats

 **www.PHSchool.com**
Student Site
• Self-grading Vocabulary Test
Teacher Center
• Resources

Plus **iTEXT**

Spanish Reading and Math Literacy

Reading and Math Literacy

9D: Vocabulary   For use with Chapter Review

Study Skill: When you complete a puzzle such as a word search, remember to read the list of words carefully and completely. As you identify each word in the word search, circle it and then cross off the word from the list. Pay special attention to the spelling of each word.

Complete the word search.

binomial	interest	translation
factor	common ratio	median
monomial	sequence	distributive
standard form	scatter plot	variable
polynomial	outlier	probability
trinomial	reciprocal	degree
systems	elimination	substitution

```
E Y R N P O L Y N O M I A L N
L T E E O L A I M O N I R T O
I I C J S I S F A C T O R S I
M L I L M C T M L Q H M T E T
I I P A R O A U E A P O V Q A
N B R I E M N T T T B B Y U L
A A O M I E D O T I S T H E S
T B C O L D A L M E T Y N N N
I O A N T I R W Q I R S S C A
O R L I U A D W M U A P B E R
N P V B O N F I Z W W L L U T
S Q C O M M O N R A T I O O S
Q V I N T E R E S T E M S T T
E E R G E D M E L B A I R A V
E V I T U B I R T S I D G B W
```

36   Reading and Math Literacy Masters   Algebra 1

---

pages 503–505   Chapter Review

6. $-6y^2 + 8y + 2$; quadratic trinomial

7. $9h^2 + 1$; quadratic binomial

8. $3k^5 + k$; fifth degree binomial

9. $7t^2 + 8t + 9$; quadratic trinomial

10. x^2y^2; fourth degree monomial

11. $x^3 + x^2 + 5$; cubic trinomial

25. $3x$; $3x(3x^3 + 4x^2 + 2)$

26. $4t^2$; $4t^2(t^3 - 3t + 2)$

27. $10n^3$; $10n^3(4n^2 + 7n - 3)$

28. 2; $2(k^4 + 2k^3 - 3k - 4)$

29. $3d$; $3d(d - 2)$

30. $2m^2$; $2m^2(5m^2 - 6m + 2)$

31. 5; $5(2v - 1)$

32. $4w$; $4w(3w^2 + 2w + 5)$

33. $3d^3$; $3d^3(6d^2 + 2d + 3)$

34. 12; if the GCF of x and y is 3, the GCF of $4x$ and $4y$ is $4 \cdot 3$ or 12.

35. Kim; 4, m, and n are factors of both monomials. The GCF is their product.

36. $x^2 + 8x + 15$

37. $15v^2 - 29v - 14$

38. $6b^2 + 11b - 10$

39. $-k^2 + 5k - 4$

40. $p^3 + 3p^2 + 3p + 2$

41. $4a^2 - 21a + 5$

42. $y^3 - 9y^2 + 18y + 8$

43. $3x^2 + 10x + 8$

44. $-2h^3 + 11h^2 - 6h + 5$

45. $q^2 - 8q + 16$

46. $4k^6 + 20k^3 + 25$

47. $64 - 9t^4$

53. $(x + 2)(x + 1)$

54. $(y - 7)(y - 2)$

55. $(x - 5)(x + 3)$

56. $(2w - 3)(w + 1)$

57. $(b - 3)(b - 4)$

58. $(2t - 1)(t + 2)$

59. $(x + 6)(x - 1)$

60. $2(3x + 2)(x + 1)$

61. $(7x + 2)(3x - 4)$

9-2 Objectives

▼ To multiply a polynomial by a monomial (p. 462)

▼ To factor a monomial from a polynomial (p. 463)

19. $-40x^2 + 16x$

20. $35g^3 + 15g^2 - 45g$

21. $-40t^4 + 24t^3 - 32t^2$

You can multiply a monomial and a polynomial using the Distributive Property. You can factor a polynomial by finding the greatest common factor (GCF) of the terms of the polynomial.

Simplify each product. Write in standard form.

19. $8x(2 - 5x)$

20. $5g(3g + 7g^2 - 9)$

21. $8t^2(3t - 4 - 5t^2)$

22. $5m(3m + m^2)$
$5m^3 + 15m^2$

23. $-2w^2(4w - 10 + 3w^2)$
$-6w^4 - 8w^3 + 20w^2$

24. $b(10 + 5b - 3b^2)$
$-3b^3 + 5b^2 + 10b$

Find the GCF of the terms of each polynomial. Then factor the polynomial.

25. $9x^4 + 12x^3 + 6x$

26. $4t^5 - 12t^3 + 8t^2$

27. $40n^5 + 70n^4 - 30n^3$

28. $2k^4 + 4k^3 - 6k - 8$

29. $3d^2 - 6d$

30. $10m^4 - 12m^3 + 4m^2$

31. $10v - 5$

32. $12w^3 + 8w^2 + 20w$

33. $18d^5 + 6d^4 + 9d^3$

25–33. See margin.

34. **Critical Thinking** The GCF of two numbers x and y is 3. Can you predict the GCF of $4x$ and $4y$? Explain your answer. **See margin.**

35. **Critical Thinking** Amanda says the GCF of $8m^2n$ and $4mn$ is 4. Kris says the GCF is $4n$. Kim says the GCF is $4mn$. Which student is correct? Explain your answer. **See margin.**

9-3 and 9-4 Objectives

▼ To multiply binomials using FOIL (p. 467)

▼ To multiply trinomials by binomials (p. 469)

▼ To find the square of a binomial (p. 474)

▼ To find the difference of squares (p. 476)

51. $(2x + 1)(x + 4)$;
$2x^2 + 9x + 4$

You can use tiles or the Distributive Property to multiply polynomials. You can use the FOIL method (First, Outer, Inner, Last) to multiply two binomials.

Simplify each product. Write in standard form. 36–47. See margin.

36. $(x + 3)(x + 5)$

37. $(5v + 2)(3v - 7)$

38. $(2b + 5)(3b - 2)$

39. $(k - 1)(-k + 4)$

40. $(p + 2)(p^2 + p + 1)$

41. $(4a - 1)(a - 5)$

42. $(y - 4)(y^2 - 5y - 2)$

43. $(3x + 4)(x + 2)$

44. $(-2h^2 + h - 1)(h - 5)$

45. $(q - 4)(q - 4)$

46. $(2k^3 + 5)^2$

47. $(8 - 3t^2)(8 + 3t^2)$

48. $(2m^2 + 5)(2m^2 - 5)$
$4m^4 - 25$

49. $(w - 4)(w + 4)$
$w^2 - 16$

50. $(4g^2 - 5h^4)(4g^2 + 5h^4)$
$16g^4 - 25h^8$

51. **Geometry** A rectangle has dimensions $2x + 1$ and $x + 4$. Write an expression for the area of the rectangle as a product and as a polynomial in standard form.

52. **Error Analysis** Suppose a classmate claims that the difference between $(x^2 - y^2)$ and $(x - y)^2$ must be 0. Is your classmate correct? Explain your answer.
No; $(x - y)^2 = x^2 - 2xy + y^2 \neq x^2 - y^2$.

9-5 and 9-6 Objectives

▼ To factor trinomials (p. 481)

▼ To factor trinomials of the type $ax^2 + bx + c$ (p. 486)

Some quadratic trinomials are the product of two binomial factors. You can factor trinomials using tiles or by using FOIL. Factor any common monomial factors first.

Factor each expression. 53–61. See margin.

53. $x^2 + 3x + 2$

54. $y^2 - 9y + 14$

55. $x^2 - 2x - 15$

56. $2w^2 - w - 3$

57. $b^2 - 7b + 12$

58. $2t^2 + 3t - 2$

59. $x^2 + 5x - 6$

60. $6x^2 + 10x + 4$

61. $21x^2 - 22x - 8$

62. $3x^2 + x - 2$
$(3x - 2)(x + 1)$

63. $15y^2 + 16y + 1$
$(15y + 1)(y + 1)$

64. $15y^2 - 16y + 1$
$(15y - 1)(y - 1)$

9-7 Objectives

▼ To factor perfect-square trinomials (p. 490)

▼ To factor the difference of squares (p. 492)

When you factor a **perfect-square trinomial,** the two binomial factors are the same.

$$a^2 + 2ab + b^2 = (a + b)(a + b) = (a + b)^2 \text{ and}$$
$$a^2 - 2ab + b^2 = (a - b)(a - b) = (a - b)^2$$

When you factor the difference of squares of two terms, the two binomial factors are the sum and the difference of the two terms.

$$a^2 - b^2 = (a + b)(a - b)$$

Factor each expression. 66–70. See margin.

65. $q^2 + 2q + 1$ **$(q + 1)^2$** **66.** $b^2 - 16$ **67.** $x^2 - 4x + 4$

68. $4t^2 - 121$ **69.** $4d^2 - 20d + 25$ **70.** $9c^2 + 6c + 1$

71. $9k^2 - 25$ **72.** $x^2 + 6x + 9$ **73.** $24y^2 - 6$
$(3k + 5)(3k - 5)$ **$(x + 3)^2$**   **$6(2y + 1)(2y - 1)$**

74. Geometry Find the length of a side of the square with an area of $\frac{1}{4}d^2 + d + 1$. **$\frac{1}{2}d + 1$**

75. Critical Thinking Suppose you are using tiles to factor a quadratic trinomial. What do you know about the factors of the trinomial if the tiles form a square?
The factors are equal.
76. The area of a rectangle is $25u^2 + 65u + 36$. If the dimensions of the rectangle are factors of $25u^2 + 65u + 36$, could the rectangle be a square? Explain.
No; only the square $(5u + 6)^2$ would have $25u^2$ and 36 as the first and last terms, however $2(5u)(6) \neq 65u$.

9-8 Objectives

▼ To factor polynomials with four terms (p. 496)

▼ To factor trinomials by grouping (p. 497)

To factor a polynomial, first see if you can factor out the GCF. If the polynomial has four or more terms, you can group the terms and look for a common binomial factor. Then you can use the Distributive Property to factor the polynomial. If you do not quickly recognize the binomial factors of a polynomial of the form $ax^2 + bx + c$, grouping the terms may help you factor the polynomial.

Find the GCF of the first two terms and the GCF of the last two terms for each polynomial.

77. $16x^3 + 12x^2 - 8x - 6$ **$4x^2; -2$**   **78.** $9k^3 + 15k^2 - 6k - 10$ **$3k^2; -2$**

79. $72y^3 + 24y^2 - 12y - 4$ **$24y^2; -4$** **80.** $20n^4 - 10n^3 + 14n - 7$ **$10n^3; 7$**

Factor completely.

81. $6x^3 + 3x^2 + 8x + 4$ **$(3x^2 + 4)(2x + 1)$** **82.** $20y^4 - 45y^2$ **$5y^2(2y + 3)(2y - 3)$**

83. $9g^2 + 15g - 6$ **$3(3g - 1)(g + 2)$**   **84.** $6c^2 - 5cd + d^2$ **$(3c - d)(2c - d)$**

85. $11k^2 + 23k + 2$ **$(11k + 1)(k + 2)$** **86.** $3u^2 + 21u + 18$ **$3(u + 6)(u + 1)$**

87. $15p^2 + 14p + 3$ **$(5p + 3)(3p + 1)$** **88.** $3u^2 - 21u + 18$ **$3(u - 6)(u - 1)$**

89. $15h^3 + 11h^2 - 45h - 33$ **90.** $30x^3 + 42x^2 - 5x - 7$

91. $12s^4t + 20s^3t - 8s^2t$ **92.** $2x^3 + 7x^2 + 4x + 14$

93. Geometry The volume of the rectangular prism is $6p^3 + 38p^2 + 40p$. Find expressions for the possible dimensions of the prism.
$2p$, $(p + 5)$, and $(3p + 4)$

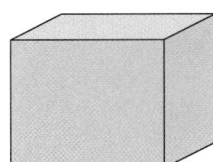

89. $(h^2 - 3)(15h + 11)$
90. $(5x + 7)(6x^2 - 1)$
91. $4s^2t(3s - 1)(s + 2)$
92. $(x^2 + 2)(2x + 7)$

Alternative Assessment, Form C

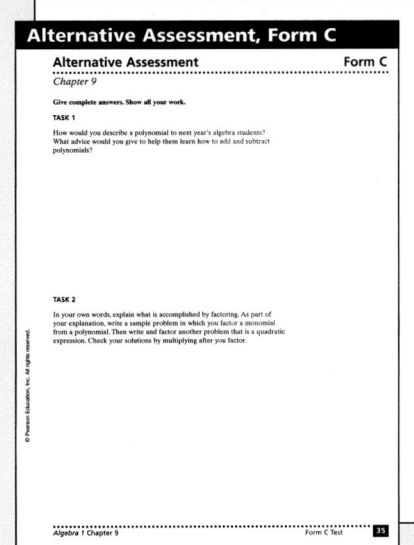

Alternative Assessment   Form C
Chapter 9

Give complete answers. Show all your work.

TASK 1

How would you describe a polynomial to next year's algebra students? What advice would you give to help them learn how to add and subtract polynomials?

TASK 2

In your own words, explain what is accomplished by factoring. As part of your explanation, write a sample problem in which you factor a monomial from a polynomial. Then write and factor another problem that is a quadratic expression. Check your solutions by multiplying after you factor.

Algebra 1 Chapter 9   Form C Test   **35**

66. $(b + 4)(b - 4)$

67. $(x - 2)^2$

68. $(2t + 11)(2t - 11)$

69. $(2d - 5)^2$

70. $(3c + 1)^2$

Resources

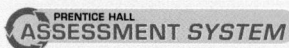

Chapter 9

Chapter Test

 **Take It to the NET**
Online chapter test at
www.PHSchool.com
Web Code: aea-0952

Write each polynomial in standard form. Then name each polynomial based on its degree and number of terms. 1–4. **See margin.**

1. $y^2 + 2y + 5 - 3y^2 - 5y$

2. $4 - 5v - 12v - 6v^2 - 4 - 2v^3$

3. $-4x^4 + x^2 - 10 + 12x^4 - 7x^2$

4. $3k^5 + 4k^2 - 6k^5 - 5k^2$

Simplify. Write each answer in standard form. 5–9. **See margin.**

5. $(4x^2 + 2x + 5) + (7x^2 - 5x + 2)$

6. $(9a^2 - 4 - 5a) - (12a - 6a^2 + 3)$

7. $(-4m^2 + m - 10) + (3m + 12 - 7m^2)$

8. $(3c - 4c^2 + c^3) - (5c^2 + 8c^3 - 6c)$

9. **Open-Ended** Write a trinomial with a degree of 6.

10. Write the standard form for the polynomial modeled at the right. Then factor the expression.
$x^2 + 5x + 6; (x + 3)(x + 2)$

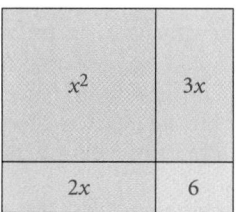

Simplify each product. Write in standard form. 11–18. **See back of book.**

11. $8b(3b + 7 - b^2)$

12. $-t(5t^2 + t)$

13. $3q(4 - q + 3q^3)$

14. $2c(c^5 + 4c^3)$

15. $(x + 6)(x + 1)$

16. $(d + 4)(d - 3)$

17. $(2h - 1)(h - 4)$

18. $(2m + 5)(3m - 7)$

19. $(p + 2)(2p^2 - 5p + 4)$ $2p^3 - p^2 - 6p + 8$

20. $(a - 4)(6a^2 + 10a - 3)$ $6a^3 - 14a^2 - 43a + 12$

21. $(3x + 5)(7x^2 - 2x + 1)$ $21x^3 + 29x^2 - 7x + 5$

Find the GCF of the terms of each polynomial.

22. $21x^4 + 18x^2 + 36x^3$ $3x^2$ 23. $3t^2 - 5t - 2t^4$ t

24. $-3a^{10} + 9a^5 + 6a^{15}$ $3a^5$ 25. $9m^3 - 7m^4 + 8m^2$ m^2

26. **Writing** Explain how to use the Distributive Property to multiply polynomials. Include an example. **See back of book.**

Write an expression for each situation as a product. Then write each expression in standard form.

27. A plot of land has width x meters. The length of the plot of land is 5 meters more than 3 times its width. What is the area of the land?

28. The height of a box is 2 in. less than its width w. The length of the box is 3 in. more than 4 times its width. What is the volume of the box in terms of w? 27–28. **See back of book.**

Geometry Write an expression for the area of each shaded region. Write your answer in simplest form.

29.

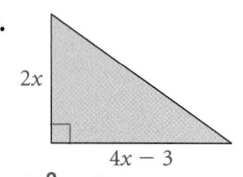
$2x$
$4x - 3$
$4x^2 - 3x$

30.

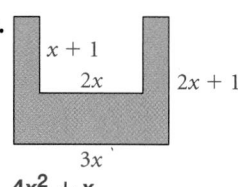
$x + 1$
$2x$
$2x + 1$
$3x$
$4x^2 + x$

Factor each expression. 31–38. **See back of book.**

31. $w^2 - 5w - 14$

32. $g^2 + 10g + 25$

33. $9k^2 + 24k + 16$

34. $n^2 - 100$

35. $y^2 - 4y + 4$

36. $4x^2 - 49$

37. $4p^2 + 164p + 81$

38. $13c^2 - 52$

Write the missing value in each perfect-square trinomial.

39. $x^2 + \blacksquare x + 49$ **14**

40. $\blacksquare t^2 + 12t + 9$ **4**

41. $9x^2 - 30x + \blacksquare$ **25**

42. $4w^2 - \blacksquare w + 81$ **36**

Find the GCF of the first two terms and the GCF of the last two terms for each polynomial.

43. $6x^4 + 9x^3 - 8x + 12$ $3x^3; -4$

44. $16n^3 + 20n^2 - 4n - 5$ $4n^2; -1$

Factor completely. 45–50. **See back of book.**

45. $12n^3 + 15n^2 + 4n + 5$

46. $4x^2 - 10x + 6$

47. $x^3 - 5x^2 + 5x - 25$

48. $6r^3 - 9r^2 - 4r + 6$

49. $12y^3 + 28y^2 - 3y - 7$

50. $3n^3 - 4n^2 - 6n + 8$

51. **Open-Ended** Find three different values to complete the expression $x^2 + \blacksquare x + 30$ so that it can be factored into the product of two binomials. Show each factorization. **Answers may vary. Sample: 13, $(x + 10)(x + 3)$; 11, $(x + 5)(x + 6)$; 31, $(x + 1)(x + 30)$**

page 506   Chapter Test

1. $-2y^2 - 3y + 5$; quadratic trinomial

2. $-2v^3 - 6v^2 - 17v$; cubic trinomial

3. $8x^4 - 6x^2 - 10$; fourth degree trinomial

4. $-3k^5 - k^2$; fifth degree binomial

5. $11x^2 - 3x + 7$

6. $15a^2 - 17a - 7$

7. $-11m^2 + 4m + 2$

8. $-7c^3 - 9c^2 + 9c$

9. Answers may vary.
Sample: $p^6 + p^2 + 1$

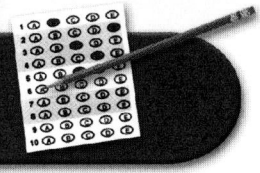

Standardized Test Prep

Reading Comprehension Read the passage below, and then answer the questions on the basis of what is *stated* or *implied* in the passage.

> **Saving for College** For years, college costs have risen steadily. Although general inflation in our economy averages 3.0% to 3.5%, the rate of increase in college costs is about 5% a year. While many prospective students expect to benefit from financial aid, they also must prepare to pay some portion of the costs themselves.
>
> To help with these preparations, Congress has authorized special college-saver plans, called "529 Plans" because they are described in section 529 of the Internal Revenue Code. The plans allow the gains (interest from savings accounts or dividends from stocks) on college savings to grow without incurring federal income tax when the money is withdrawn for college expenses.
>
> If college savings are invested in stocks, you could expect an average increase of about 10.5% each year. This has been the historical rate of growth for stocks in the United States. Of course, it is impossible to predict what the growth will be in any particular year. But if you start saving for college early, with 5 or more years for your money to grow, you can expect good returns.

1. Suppose that total freshman year costs are $20,000. About what will the total costs be for senior year, assuming average increases? **C**
   A. $20,000.00
   B. $23,000.00
   C. $23,152.50
   D. $24,310.13

2. Which expression represents college costs over time? Let t = the time in years and c = the starting cost in dollars. **G**
   F. $c \cdot 0.05^t$
   G. $c \cdot 1.05^t$
   H. $t \cdot 1.05^c$
   I. $c \cdot 2^{5\%}$

3. Which equation represents the average value of stock investments over time? Let t = the time in years, x = the amount of the initial investment in dollars, and V = the value of the investment in dollars. **B**
   A. $V = x \cdot 0.05^t$
   B. $V = x \cdot 1.105^t$
   C. $V = x \cdot 10.5^t$
   D. $V = x \cdot 210.5\%$

4. Suppose you have a scholarship that will pay 75% of your college costs each year. Total freshman year costs are $20,000. To prepare for your senior year costs, you invest $4,870 in bonds paying 4% a year at the beginning of your freshman year.

   Which answer gives the best estimates of the investment value and of your college costs at the beginning of your senior year? **F**
   F. investment $5478, costs $5788
   G. investment $6571, costs $6500
   H. investment $5800, costs $23,000
   I. investment $5454, costs $5788

5. a. Suppose your grandparents put $1000 for your college costs in a savings account earning 6% interest compounded annually. In 10 years, how much money would be in the savings account? **a–b. See margin.**
   b. Suppose your grandparents did not know about the 529 plan. If you had to pay a 23% tax on the interest the account earned, how much would you have to pay?

page 507   Standardized Test Prep

5. [2] a. $1000(1 + 0.06)^{10} \approx 1790.85$

   b. $790.85 \times 0.23 = \$181.90$

[1] minor calculation error OR no answer to part (b)

Students must be able to extract information from reading passages, answer multiple choice questions, and construct responses in order to be successful on current state and national assessments.

To answer the questions, students apply skills and concepts from this chapter and previous chapters.
Multiple Choice: Items 1–4
Extended Response: Item 5

Resources

 Teaching Resources
Cumulative Review
Quarter 3 Test, Forms A & B

Reaching All Students
Spanish Cumulative Review
Spanish Quarter 3 Test,
   Forms A & B

ASSESSMENT SYSTEM

Standardized Test Prep
• Ch. 9 Standardized Test Practice
Assessment Masters
• Cumulative Review
• Quarter 3 Test, Forms A & B
Computer Test Generator CD
• Standardized Test Practice

 **www.PHSchool.com**
• Standardized Test Practice
• Resources

Plus **iTEXT**

Cumulative Review

Cumulative Review
Chapters 1–9

For Questions 1–11, choose the correct letter.

1. What are the next three terms in the sequence 6, 12, 24, 48, . . . ?
   A. 72, 96, 120   B. 96, 162, 240   C. 96, 192, 344   D. 50, 52, 54
2. Solve $8y = -100$.
   A. -800 B. -12.5 C. 800 D. 12.5
3. Find the equation of the line passing through $(-2, -1)$ and parallel to $y = -3x - 1$.
   A. $y = -3x + 5$ B. $y = -\frac{3x}{4} - 1$ C. $y = \frac{x}{3} + 5$ D. $y = 3x + 1$
4. Solve $\begin{smallmatrix} 3x + 7y = -2 \\ 4x - 3y = 22 \end{smallmatrix}$
   A. $(-4, -2)$ B. $(-4, 2)$ C. $(4, 2)$ D. $(4, -2)$
5. Simplify $\frac{10x^3y^2}{2x^2y}$.
   A. $5xy^2$ B. $\frac{5x^2}{y}$ C. $\frac{5x}{y^2}$ D. $\frac{x}{5y^2}$
6. Simplify $(3x - 1)(x + 4)$.
   A. $3x^2 - 4$ B. $3x^2 - 11x - 4$ C. $3x^2 + 11x - 4$ D. $3x^2 + 13x - 4$
7. A scuba diver at a depth of 80 ft begins her ascent to the ocean surface. Her rate of change in depth is 2 ft/s. Which equation represents her depth in feet t seconds after she begins her ascent?
   A. $2t - 80$ B. $80 - 2t$ C. $-80 - 2t$ D. $80 + 2t$
8. Factor $4x^2 - x - 14$.
   A. $(4x + 7)(x - 2)$ B. $(2x - 7)(2x + 2)$ C. $(4x - 7)(x + 2)$ D. $(2x + 7)(2x - 2)$
9. A bowl contains five green olives and eight black ones. Wilma sticks a fork into the bowl and brings out two olives. What is the probability that she gets one green and one black olive?
   A. $\frac{1}{2}$ B. $\frac{40}{169}$ C. $\frac{20}{39}$ D. $\frac{3}{8}$
10. Which number is *not* a solution of the compound inequality $7 - 4x \le 3$ and $-x - 5 > -10$?
   A. 5   B. 4   C. 2   D. 1
11. Which of the following is a cubic binomial?
   A. $x^3 - 6x^2 + 9$ B. $7x^3 + 4x^2$ C. $-y^3 + 3y^2$ D. $x^2 - 2x^3$

Algebra 1 Chapter 9   Cumulative Review   **37**

Quadratic Equations and Functions

Chapter at a Glance

North Carolina Objectives

10-1 Exploring Quadratic Graphs   4.02

NCTM 2, 8, 9, 10
- ▼ Graphing $y = ax^2$
- ▼ Graphing $y = ax^2 + c$

10-2 Quadratic Functions   4.02

NCTM 2, 8, 9, 10
- ▼ Graphing $y = ax^2 + bx + c$
- ▼ Graphing Quadratic Inequalities

10-3 Finding and Estimating Square Roots

NCTM 1, 2, 9, 10
- ▼ Finding Square Roots
- ▼ Estimating and Using Square Roots

10-4 Solving Quadratic Equations   4.02

NCTM 1, 2, 3, 9, 10
- ▼ Solving Quadratic Equations by Graphing
- ▼ Solving Quadratic Equations Using Square Roots

10-5 Factoring to Solve Quadratic Equations   4.02

NCTM 1, 2, 3, 9, 10
- ▼ Solving Quadratic Equations

10-6 Completing the Square   4.02

NCTM 1, 2, 3, 9, 10
- ▼ Solving by Completing the Square

10-7 Using the Quadratic Formula   1.02, 4.02

NCTM 1, 2, 3, 7, 9
- ▼ Using the Quadratic Formula
- ▼ Choosing an Appropriate Method for Solving a Quadratic Equation

10-8 Using the Discriminant   4.02

NCTM 1, 2, 3, 7, 9, 10
- ▼ Number of Real Solutions of a Quadratic Equation

3.03, 4.02, 4.04

10-9 Choosing a Linear, Quadratic, or Exponential Model

NCTM 2, 5, 9, 10
- ▼ Choosing a Linear, Quadratic, or Exponential Model

NCTM STANDARDS 2000

1	Number and Operations	6	Problem Solving
2	Algebra	7	Reasoning and Proof
3	Geometry	8	Communication
4	Measurement	9	Connections
5	Data Analysis and Probability	10	Representation

Pacing Options

This chart suggests pacing only for the lessons and their parts. It is provided as a possible guide. It will help you determine how much time you have in your schedule to cover other components, such as the features, Chapter Review, and Chapter Test.

Day	Traditional 45 min.	Two-Year 45 min.	Block 90 min.
1	10-1 ▼ ▼	10-1 ▼	10-1 ▼ ▼ 10-2 ▼
2	10-2 ▼	10-1 ▼	10-2 ▼
3	10-2 ▼	10-2 ▼	10-3 ▼ ▼ 10-4 ▼ ▼
4	10-3 ▼ ▼	10-2 ▼	10-5 ▼
5	10-4 ▼ ▼	10-3 ▼ ▼	10-6 ▼
6	10-5 ▼	10-4 ▼	10-7 ▼ ▼
7	10-5 ▼	10-4 ▼	10-8 ▼
8	10-6 ▼	10-5 ▼	10-9 ▼
9	10-6 ▼	10-5 ▼	
10	10-7 ▼	10-6 ▼	
11	10-7 ▼	10-6 ▼	
12	10-8 ▼	10-7 ▼	
13	10-8 ▼	10-7 ▼	
14	10-9 ▼	10-8 ▼	
15	10-9 ▼	10-8 ▼	
16		10-9 ▼	
17		10-9 ▼	

NAEP Correlation (National Assessment of Educational Progress 2000 Mathematics Objectives)

10-1	10-2	10-3	10-4	10-5	10-6	10-7	10-8	10-9
A3a, A5a, A12	A3a, A5a	N4b, A5a	A5a, A9	N4f, N6c, A9	N6c, A5b	N6c, A5b	A5b	N4f, D7, A13

N = Number Sense, Properties, and Operations; M = Measurement; G = Geometry and Spatial Sense;
D = Data Analysis, Statistics, and Probability; A = Algebra and Functions

Math Background

Chapter Overview

In this chapter, students see how the skills and ideas they learned to use with linear functions can be expanded for use with quadratic functions. Students examine the graphs of $y = ax^2 + bx + c$, starting with $b = c = 0$. Then they explore what happens when only $b = 0$, and finally look at the general case where a, b, and c are all non-zero. Because a quadratic function has a term that contains x^2, simplifying, graphing, and solving quadratic functions involve estimating, finding, and using square roots. Students learn to solve quadratic equations by graphing, by finding square roots, by factoring, which was introduced in Chapter 9, and by completing the square. Finally, students learn to use the quadratic formula and characterize the roots of any quadratic equation by using the discriminant. Their knowledge of functions is applied to selecting a linear, quadratic, or exponential model to fit specific data.

Graphs of Quadratic Functions   10-1, 10-2

A quadratic function is a function that can be written in the form $y = f(x) = ax^2 + bx + c$. The standard form of a quadratic equation, is $ax^2 + bx + c = 0$. The shape of a quadratic function is called a parabola.

Parabolic curves can be seen in the steel cables of a suspension bridge or in the supporting arches of some highway or railroad bridges, for it is this shape that naturally holds up a uniformly weighted road surface. A baseball in flight and the arc of water at the lip of a waterfall both follow parabolic paths (ignoring air resistance).

A parabola can be defined as the locus of all points in a plane such that each point on the curve is the same (perpendicular) distance from a given point as it is from a given line. The given point is the focus and the given line is the directrix. Some students may know that there are other conic sections. Later they will study ellipses and hyperbolas.

Finding and Estimating Square Roots   10-3

It is vital for proper use of the quadratic formula that students understand the difference between $x^2 = 4$ and $x = \sqrt{4}$. The first equation has two roots ($+2$ and -2) while the second has only one ($+2$). Mathematicians have agreed that $\sqrt{a^2} \geq 0$ for all non-negative real numbers a, so $x = \sqrt{4}$ has only one root. (Students will learn about imaginary numbers in Algebra 2, when dealing with complex numbers and indexes for the radical that are greater than 2.)

When solving an equation like $x^2 = 4$, students should indicate that it has two roots by including the $\pm$ sign before the radical.

This means that the steps should be:

$$x^2 = 4$$
$$x = \pm\sqrt{4}$$
$$x = \pm 2$$

Solving Quadratic Equations   10-4, 10-5, 10-6

In these sections, students learn to solve quadratic equations by graphing, finding square roots, factoring, and completing the square. Learning when it is best to apply each method is just as important as learning to use each method. Graphing can be used to solve quadratic equations when the equations are relatively simple, or when a graphing calculator can be used to find the solutions. Finding square roots works best when there is no x-term in the equation, and the constant term is a perfect square. Solving by factoring, of course, works best with equations that can be factored, as completing the square works best with equations that can be easily transformed into perfect squares. Make sure in these lessons that students practice identifying which method would be best to solve each individual equation.

Using the Quadratic Formula   10-7

Once students learn how to complete the square, they are able to derive the quadratic formula from the general quadratic equation $ax^2 + bx + c = 0$. As students apply the quadratic formula to solve quadratic equations, they need to be aware that the formula produces two solutions, because it involves finding a square root. Students also need to be prepared to check both of the solutions. Depending on the problem, one of the solutions may not make sense.

Using the Discriminant   10-8

A discriminant, in mathematical terms, is a parameter that when calculated helps to classify the solutions to a system. When using the quadratic formula to solve quadratic equations, a quick calculation of the discriminant reveals whether there are any real solutions to the equation. If the answer to this question is no, there is no need to work out the formula.

Choosing a Linear, Quadratic, or Exponential Model   10-9

Now that students are familiar with different types of functions, they are shown how to choose which function type models a given data set. Graphing data points and recognizing patterns in data displayed in a table are two techniques presented. Since real-world data often does not fit a linear model, being able to model data with exponential or quadratic functions is an especially useful skill.

 # Ongoing Assessment and Intervention

Tools for Monitoring Student Progress

The Prentice Hall *Algebra 1* program provides you with many options for assessment in the Student Edition, the Teacher's Edition and the teaching resources. From these options you may choose instructional materials and techniques that are appropriate for your students and support your district's curriculum requirements.

Instant Check System™ in Chapter 10

Allows students to check their own learning before, during, and after each lesson.

Diagnosing Readiness before the chapter (p. 508)

Check Skills You'll Need exercises in each lesson (pp. 510, 517, 524, 529, 536, 541, 547, 554, 559)

Check Understanding questions with each Example (pp. 511, 512, 513, 518, 519, 524, 525, 526, 530, 531, 536, 537, 542, 543, 548, 549, 550, 555, 560, 562, 563)

Checkpoint Quiz (pp. 534, 558)

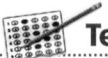 Test Prep in Chapter 10

Teaches students strategies and gives them practice with all the test item formats they will encounter on state tests and standardized national exams.

Standardized Test Prep exercises in each lesson (pp. 516, 523, 528, 533, 534, 539, 540, 546, 552, 557, 558, 566)

Test-Taking Strategies (p. 568: Choosing "Cannot Be Determined")

Standardized Test Prep (p. 573: Cumulative Review)

All your assessment needs in one place!

Program Assessment

Assess student progress throughout the *Algebra 1* text with blackline masters and CD-ROM.

Assessment Resources

- Checkpoint Quizzes 1 & 2
- Chapter Test, Forms A & B
- Chapter Alternative Assessment

Spanish versions available. Tests for Basic Algebra also available.

 ### Computer Test Generator

- Unlimited questions of varying difficulty for every lesson objective.
- Create your own practice sheets, quizzes, and tests, or use the pre-made Chapter Tests.
- Diagnose readiness with questions on prerequisite skills.
- Prepare students by making tests based on standardized test objectives.
- Access Algebra 1, Geometry, and Algebra 2 content—all on one CD-ROM.

Test Preparation

A three-step approach to preparing students for high stakes, national, and state exams.

❶ Diagnose & Prescribe

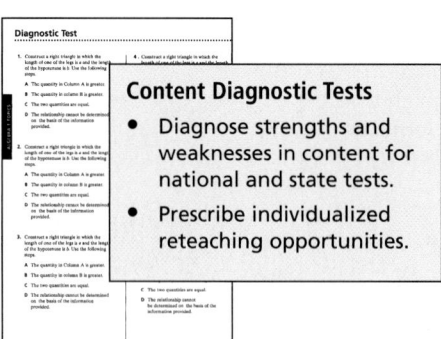

Content Diagnostic Tests
- Diagnose strengths and weaknesses in content for national and state tests.
- Prescribe individualized reteaching opportunities.

❷ Review & Reteach

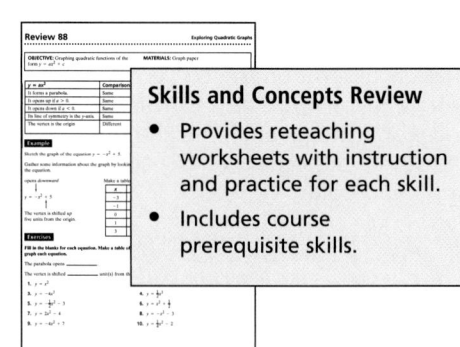

Skills and Concepts Review
- Provides reteaching worksheets with instruction and practice for each skill.
- Includes course prerequisite skills.

❸ Practice & Assess

Test Preparation
- Features practice tests for End-of-Course and SAT/ACT exams.
- Includes standardized test practice by chapter for ongoing review.

Teacher's Guide with answers and correlations.

Test-Taking Strategies with Transparencies
- Support the Test-Taking Strategies pages in the Student Edition.
- Provide a teaching transparency and a practice worksheet for each strategy.

 # Reaching All Students

Support in the Student Text and Additional Resources

The textbook, the iText, and other technology components provide numerous opportunities to reach students of various ability levels and learning styles. Each Teacher's Edition lesson suggests how you can help *all* your students be successful and understand the mathematics in Chapter 10.

Below Level

Student Edition
- Diagnosing Readiness*: p. 508
- Check Skills You'll Need*: pp. 510, 517, 524, 529, 536, 541, 547, 554, 559

Reteaching
Chapter 10 Support File: pp. 10–18

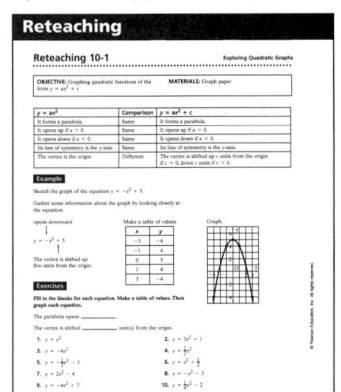

Basic Algebra Planning Guide
Chapter 10 Lesson Plans: pp. 64–72
Chapter 10 Tests: pp. 125–128

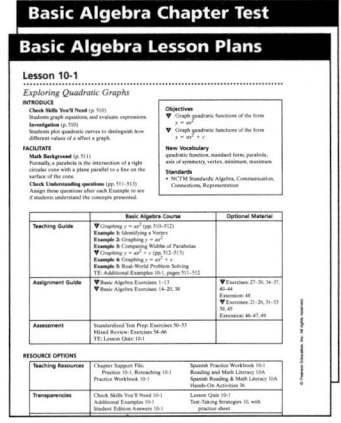

* Can be used with all ability levels to ensure mastery of prerequisite skills.

Advanced Learners

Student Edition
- Challenge exercises: pp. 515, 516, 522, 527, 528, 533, 539, 545, 546, 557, 565
- Extension, p. 567

Enrichment
Chapter 10 Support File: pp. 19–27

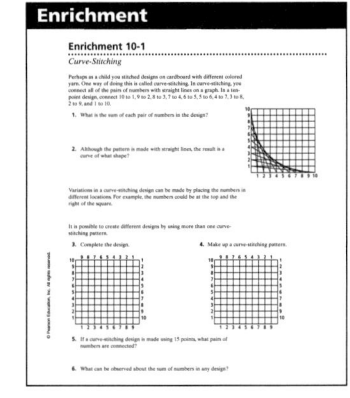

Reading and Math Literacy

Student Edition
- Vocabulary: pp. 509, 569, *plus* in every Lesson Preview
- Reading Math: pp. 524, 548, 553, 569
- Illustrated Glossary: pp. 757–785

Reading and Math Literacy Masters
Chapter 10: pp. 37–40

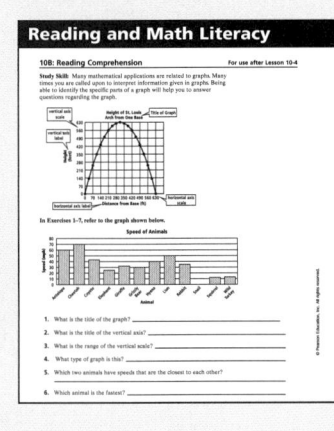

English Learners

Student Edition
- English/Spanish Illustrated Glossary: pp. 757–785

Workbook and Masters
Spanish Practice Workbook: pp. 64–72
Spanish Reading and Math Literacy Masters: pp. 37–40

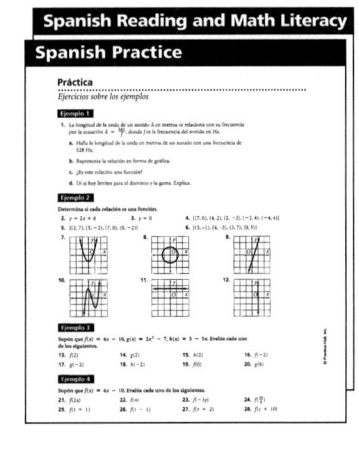

Learning Styles

Student Edition
- Investigation: p. 510, 529
- Technology: pp. 525, 535
- Writing: pp. 514, 522, 527, 533, 538, 545, 551, 557, 564, 571, 572
- DK Activities: pp. 574–575

Activity Masters
Hands-On Activities: 23, 24, 25
Technology Activities: 5, 7, 9, 24

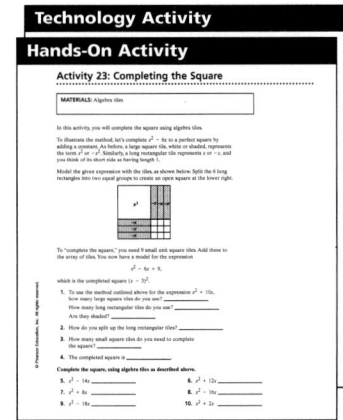

Program Resources

	Teaching Resources in Grab & Go™ Files				Resources for Reaching All Students				Spanish Resources			Transparencies				Presentation Assistant Plus!
	Practice	Reteach	Enrich	Checkpoint Quiz	Reading & Math Literacy	Technology Activities	Hands-On Activities	Basic Algebra Lesson Plans	Practice	Reading & Math Literacy	Checkpoint Quiz	Skills Check	Additional Examples	Answers to Exercises	Lesson Quiz	Prentice Hall Presentation Pro CD-ROM
10-1	■	■	■		■			■	■			■	■	■	■	■
10-2	■	■	■					■	■			■	■	■	■	■
10-3	■	■	■					■	■			■	■	■	■	■
10-4	■	■	■	■	■	■		■	■	■	■	■	■	■	■	■
10-5	■	■	■					■	■			■	■	■	■	■
10-6	■	■	■				■	■	■			■	■	■	■	■
10-7	■	■	■					■	■			■	■	■	■	■
10-8	■	■	■	■	■		■	■	■		■	■	■	■	■	■
10-9	■	■	■				■	■	■			■	■	■	■	■
For the chapter	Chapter Tests, Alternative Assessment, Cumulative Review, Cumulative Assessment				Basic Algebra Chapter Tests				Spanish Chapter Tests, Alternative Assessment, Cumulative Review, Cumulative Assessment			Classroom Aid Transparencies				

Also available for use with the chapter:

 *See page 508C.*

- Practice Workbook
- Solution Key

- For teacher support and access to student Web site materials, use Web Code aek-5500.
- For additional online and technology resources, see below.

 Technology

 iTEXT Online and on CD-ROM

Complete Interactive Student Text online and on CD-ROM—with instant feedback assessment, tutorial help, dynamic activities, instructional and real-world videos, audio, and additional practice.

www.PHSchool.com For Students

Use **Web codes** for easy access to online activities, chapter projects, self-grading lesson quizzes and chapter tests, vocabulary quizzes, updated data sources, graphing calculator procedures, and more.

PH SuccessNet For Teachers

Online lesson planning with built-in state correlations, all the teaching resources, complete reference library, your own calendar and Teacher Web page, professional development, and more.

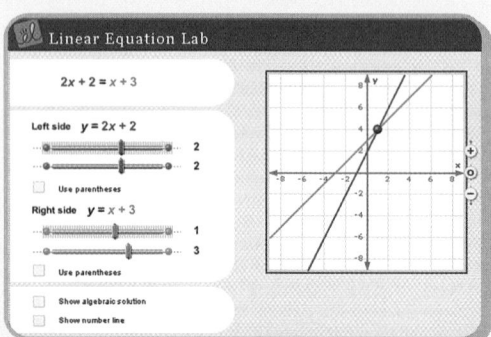

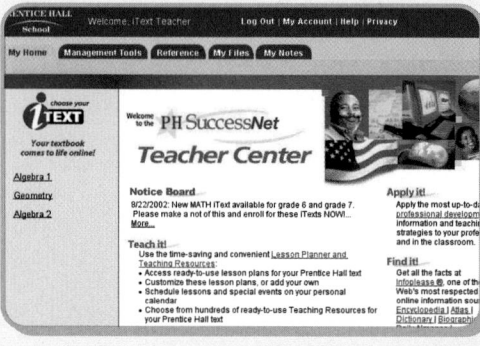

Presentation Assistant Plus!

The Prentice Hall *Presentation Assistant Plus!* provides you with the material you need to teach a lesson from beginning to end. Two easy-to-use formats—Transparencies and CD-ROM—allow you to present a lesson the way you are most comfortable.

 ## Transparencies

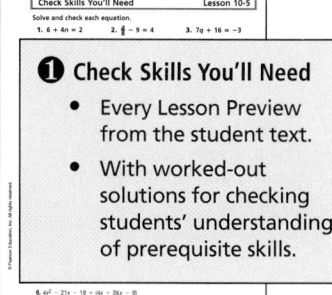

❶ Check Skills You'll Need
- Every Lesson Preview from the student text.
- With worked-out solutions for checking students' understanding of prerequisite skills.

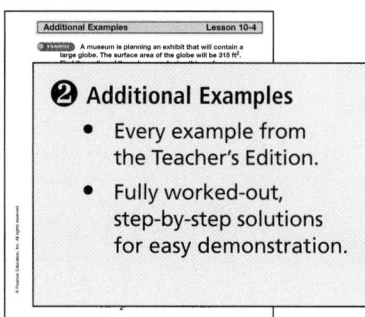

❷ Additional Examples
- Every example from the Teacher's Edition.
- Fully worked-out, step-by-step solutions for easy demonstration.

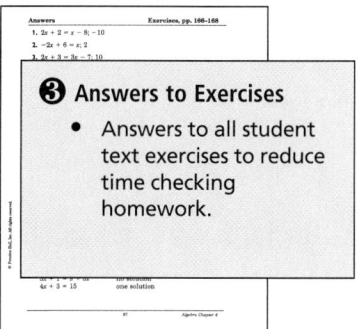

❸ Answers to Exercises
- Answers to all student text exercises to reduce time checking homework.

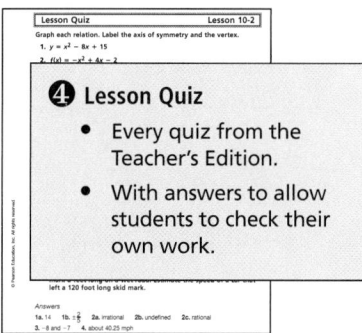

❹ Lesson Quiz
- Every quiz from the Teacher's Edition.
- With answers to allow students to check their own work.

 Throughout the Teacher's Edition, this symbol indicates material that is available on transparency in the Presentation Assistant Plus!

 ## Prentice Hall Presentation Pro CD-ROM

- Includes all Transparencies.
- Conveniently organized by lesson so you can easily ❶ Introduce, ❷ Teach, ❸ Check Homework, and ❹ Assess each lesson.
- Animated examples allow step-by-step instruction at your own pace.
- Easy to edit so you can create custom presentations.

Teaching Chapter 10 Using Presentation Assistant Plus!

	❶ Introduce	❷ Teach	❸ Check Homework	❹ Assess
	Check Skills You'll Need	Additional Examples	Student Edition Answers	Lesson Quiz
10-1	p. 64	pp. 140–142	✔	p. 129
10-2	p. 65	pp. 143–144	✔	p. 130
10-3	p. 66	pp. 145–146	✔	p. 130
10-4	p. 67	pp. 147–148	✔	p. 131
10-5	p. 68	pp. 148–150	✔	p. 131
10-6	p. 69	pp. 151–153	✔	p. 132
10-7	p. 70	pp. 154–156	✔	p. 132
10-8	p. 71	pp. 156–157	✔	p. 133
10-9	p. 72	pp. 157–161	✔	p. 133

 ### Prentice Hall Presentation Pro

CD-ROM with dynamic PowerPoint® presentations for every lesson. Helps you introduce and develop concepts, check homework, and assess progress. Part of Presentation Assistant Plus! *(See above.)*

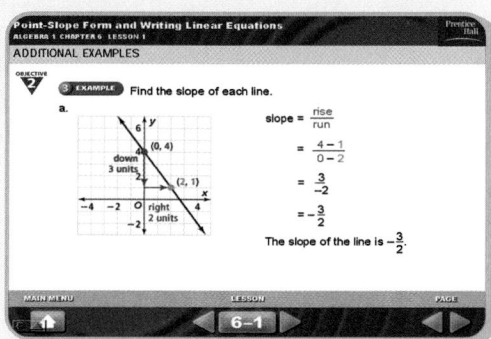

 ### Computer Test Generator

CD-ROM to create practice sheets and tests for course objectives and standardized tests. Includes Instant Chapter Tests™, online testing, and student reports. Part of the PH Assessment System. *(See page 508C.)*

Resource Pro® with Planning Express®

CD-ROM with a lesson planning tool that allows you to import state and local objectives. Includes electronic versions of all the teaching resources.

Quadratic Equations and Functions

 Diagnosing Readiness

Students will find answers to these exercises in the back of their textbooks.

For intervention, direct students to:

Evaluating Expressions
Lesson 1-6: Example 6
Exercises 48–53
Extra Practice, p. 702

Evaluating Function Rules
Lesson 5-2: Example 4
Exercises 17–21
Extra Practice, p. 706

Graphing Functions
Lesson 5-3: Examples 1 and 3
Exercises 11–17
Extra Practice, p. 706

Multiplying Binomials
Lesson 9-3: Example 2
Exercises 11–16
Extra Practice, p. 710

Factoring
Lesson 9-5: Examples 1, 2, and 3
Exercises 11–19
Lesson 9-6: Examples 1 and 2
Exercises 2–11
Extra Practice, p. 710

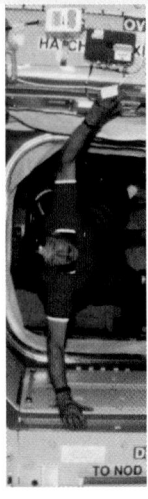

Where You've Been

- In Chapter 5, you learned about functions and their graphs.
- In Chapter 8, you discovered that not all functions are linear as you explored exponential functions and fit data to them.
- In Chapter 9, you learned to factor trinomials of the form $ax^2 + bx + c$.

 Instant self-check online and on CD-ROM

Diagnosing Readiness (For help, go to the Lesson in green.)

Evaluating Expressions (Lesson 1-6)

Evaluate each expression for $a = -1$, $b = 3$, and $c = -2$.

1. $2a - b^2 + c$ **−13**

2. $\frac{c^2 - ab}{2a}$ **−$\frac{7}{2}$**

3. $bc - 3a^2$ **−9**

4. $\frac{b^2 - 4ac}{2a}$ **−$\frac{1}{2}$**

5. $5a + 2b(c - 1)$ **−23**

6. $c^2 + 2ab - 1$ **−3**

Evaluating Function Rules (Lesson 5-2)

Evaluate each function rule for $x = -6$.

7. $f(x) = -3x^2$ **−108**

8. $y = x^2 - 10$ **26**

9. $h(x) = x^2 + 6x$ **0**

10. $y = (x - 1)^2$ **49**

11. $y = 5 - 2x^2$ **−67**

12. $y = (1 + x)^2$ **25**

13. $g(x) = \frac{2}{3}x^2$ **24**

14. $y = (2x)^2$ **144**

Graphing Functions (Lesson 5-3)

Graph each function. **15–17. See margin.**

15. $y = x$

16. $y = -x^2$

17. $y = |x|$

Multiplying Binomials (Lesson 9-3)

Simplify each product using FOIL.

18. $(x + 2)(x - 3)$
$x^2 - x - 6$

19. $(2y + 1)(2y + 3)$
$4y^2 + 8y + 3$

20. $(3x - 7)(x + 4)$
$3x^2 + 5x - 28$

Factoring (Lessons 9-5 and 9-6)

Factor each expression.

21. $4x^2 + 4x + 1$ $(2x + 1)^2$

22. $5x^2 + 32x - 21$
$(5x - 3)(x + 7)$

23. $8x^2 - 10x + 3$
$(4x - 3)(2x - 1)$

24. $m^2 - 7m - 18$
$(m - 9)(m + 2)$

25. $12y^2 + 8y - 15$
$(6y - 5)(2y + 3)$

26. $x^2 - 18x + 81$
$(x - 9)^2$

page 508 Diagnosing Readiness

15.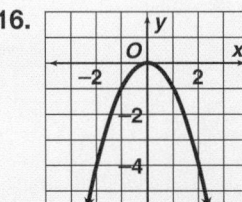

16.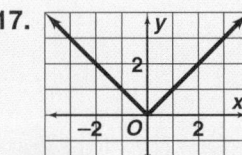

17.

Quadratic Equations and Functions

Chapter 10

Where You're Going

- In this chapter, you will examine quadratic graphs and their equations.

- You will solve quadratic equations by various techniques such as factoring, finding square roots, completing the square, and applying the quadratic formula.

- You will determine an appropriate linear, quadratic, or exponential model for real-world data.

Real-World Snapshots Applying what you learn, you will do activities involving space station design, on pages 574–575.

LESSONS

10-1 Exploring Quadratic Graphs

10-2 Quadratic Functions

10-3 Finding and Estimating Square Roots

10-4 Solving Quadratic Equations

10-5 Factoring to Solve Quadratic Equations

10-6 Completing the Square

10-7 Using the Quadratic Formula

10-8 Using the Discriminant

10-9 Choosing a Linear, Quadratic, or Exponential Model

Key Vocabulary

- axis of symmetry (p. 511)
- completing the square (p. 541)
- discriminant (p. 554)
- maximum (p. 511)
- minimum (p. 511)
- parabola (p. 510)
- quadratic equation (p. 530)
- quadratic formula (p. 547)
- quadratic function (p. 510)
- square root (p. 524)
- vertex (p. 511)
- Zero-Product Property (p. 536)

509

Chapter 10 Overview

In this chapter, students extend their skills in graphing and solving linear equations and inequalities to quadratic equations and inequalities. Students apply the skills of the previous chapter as they factor to solve quadratic equations. To prepare for the derivation of the general quadratic formula, students practice completing the square, and then use the quadratic formula to solve any quadratic equation. The discriminant is used to characterize the roots of a quadratic equation. Finally, students use many skills to choose a model that best fits a set of data.

Reading Math
Reading Using a Formula, p. 553.

Vocabulary
A complete list of terms, plus vocabulary exercises, appears in the Chapter Review, p. 569.

Illustrated Glossary
Examples for each vocabulary term, plus definitions in both English and Spanish, appear starting on p. 757.

Real-World Snapshots
See pages 574–575 for a real-world application applying circles that utilizes Dorling Kindersley's (DK) unique graphic presentation.

Test-Taking Strategies
Choosing "Cannot be Determined," p. 568

Real-World Connections
Some of the applications you will find in this chapter are gravity (10-1), construction (10-3), city planning (10-4), and zoology (10-9).

www.PHSchool.com
Internet support for this chapter includes:
- Self-grading Vocabulary and Chapter 10 Tests
- Chapter Project
- Chapter Planner
- Chapter 10 Resources

Plus

1. Plan

Lesson Preview

✓ **Check Skills You'll Need**

Exponents, Order of Operations
Lesson 1-2: Example 5
Exercises 21–28
Extra Practice, p. 702

Function Rules, Tables, Graphs
Lesson 5-3: Examples 1, 3
Exercises 4–12, 15–29
Extra Practice, p. 706

Lesson Resources

📁 **Teaching Resources**
Practice, Reteaching, Enrichment

👥 **Reaching All Students**
Practice Workbook 10-1
Spanish Practice Workbook 10-1
Reading and Math Literacy 10A
Spanish Reading & Literacy 10A
Basic Algebra Planning Guide 10-1

⏱ **Presentation Assistant Plus!**
Transparencies
• Check Skills You'll Need 10-1
• Additional Examples 10-1
• Student Edition Answers 10-1
• Lesson Quiz 10-1
PH Presentation Pro CD 10-1

ASSESSMENT SYSTEM
Computer Test Generator CD

💿 **Technology**
Resource Pro® CD-ROM
Computer Test Generator CD
Prentice Hall Presentation Pro CD

🖥 **www.PHSchool.com**
Student Site
• Teacher Web Code: aek-5500
• Reasoning & Puzzles p. 88
• Self-grading Lesson Quiz
Teacher Center
• Lesson Planner
• Resources

Plus

510

10-1

Exploring Quadratic Graphs

North Carolina Objectives

4.02 Graph, factor, and evaluate quadratic functions to solve problems.

Lesson Preview

What You'll Learn

OBJECTIVE 1
To graph quadratic functions of the form $y = ax^2$

OBJECTIVE 2
To graph quadratic functions of the form $y = ax^2 + c$

. . . And Why

To model a problem involving gravity, as in Example 5

✓ Check Skills You'll Need

(For help, go to Lessons 1-2 and 5-3.)

Evaluate each expression for $h = 3$, $k = 2$, and $j = -4$.

1. hkj −24   **2.** kh^2 18   **3.** hk^2 12   **4.** $kj^2 + h$ 35

Graph each equation. 5–7. See back of book.

5. $y = 2x - 1$ **6.** $y = |x|$ **7.** $y = x^2 + 2$

New Vocabulary

• quadratic function • standard form of a quadratic function • parabola • axis of symmetry • vertex • minimum • maximum

---

 TEXT Interactive lesson includes instant self-check, tutorials, and activities.

OBJECTIVE

1   Graphing $y = ax^2$

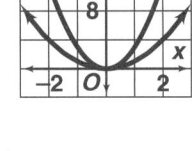

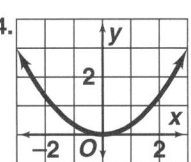

Yes; the graph is wider than $y = x^2$.

Investigation: Plotting Quadratic Curves

1. Graph the equations $y = x^2$ and $y = 3x^2$ on the same coordinate plane. **See left.**

2. a. Describe how the graphs are alike. a–b. See back of book.
   b. Describe how the graphs are different.

3. Predict how the graph of $y = \frac{1}{3}x^2$ will be similar to and different from the graph of $y = x^2$. **See back of book.**

4. Graph $y = \frac{1}{3}x^2$. Were your predictions correct? Explain. **See left.**

The functions shown above are quadratic functions.

🔑 **Key Concepts**

| **Definition** | **Standard Form of a Quadratic Function** |

A **quadratic function** is a function that can be written in the form $y = ax^2 + bx + c$, where $a \neq 0$. This form is called the **standard form of a quadratic function. Examples** $y = 5x^2$ $y = x^2 + 7$ $y = x^2 - x - 3$

The graph of a quadratic function is a U-shaped curve called a **parabola.** The graph of $y = x^2$, shown at the right, is a parabola.

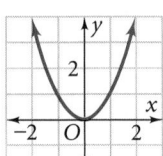

Ongoing Assessment and Intervention

Before the Lesson	**During the Lesson**	**After the Lesson**
Diagnose prerequisite skills using:	Monitor progress using:	Assess knowledge using:
• Check Skills You'll Need	• Check Understanding • Additional Examples • Standardized Test Prep	• Lesson Quiz • Computer Test Generator CD

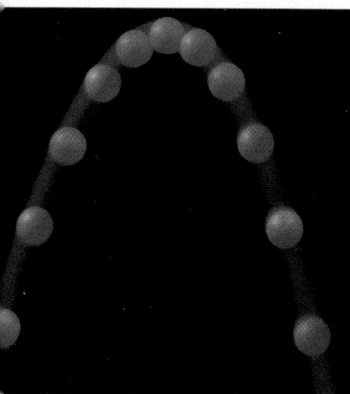

You can fold a parabola so that the two sides match exactly. This property is called *symmetry*. The fold or line that divides the parabola into two matching halves is called the **axis of symmetry.**

The highest or lowest point of a parabola is its **vertex,** which is on the axis of symmetry.

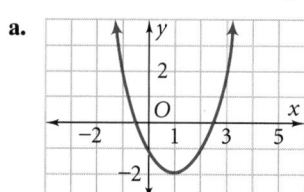   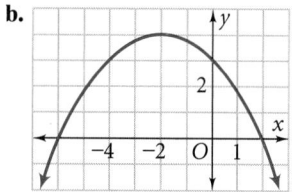

If $a > 0$ in $y = ax^2 + bx + c$
↓
the parabola opens upward.
↓
The vertex is the **minimum** point or lowest point of the parabola.

If $a < 0$ in $y = ax^2 + bx + c$
↓
the parabola opens downward.
↓
The vertex is the **maximum** point or highest point of the parabola.

1 EXAMPLE Identifying a Vertex

Identify the vertex of each graph. Tell whether it is a minimum or maximum.

a. 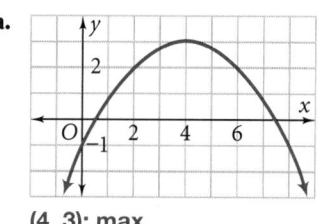   b.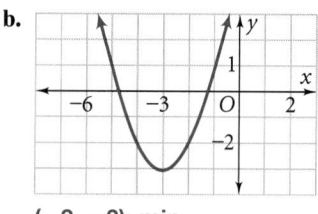

The vertex is $(1, -2)$. It is a minimum.   The vertex is $(-2, 4)$. It is a maximum.

✓ **Check Understanding** 1 Identify the vertex of each graph. Tell whether it is a minimum or maximum.

a.   b.

(4, 3); max.   (−3, −3); min.

You can use the fact that a parabola is symmetric to graph it quickly. First find the coordinates of the vertex and several points on either side of the vertex. Then reflect the points across the axis of symmetry. For functions of the form $y = ax^2$, the vertex is at the origin.

2 EXAMPLE Graphing $y = ax^2$

Make a table of values and graph the quadratic function $y = \frac{1}{2}x^2$.

x	$y = \frac{1}{2}x^2$	(x, y)
0	$\frac{1}{2}(0)^2 = 0$	$(0, 0)$
2	$\frac{1}{2}(2)^2 = 2$	$(2, 2)$
4	$\frac{1}{2}(4)^2 = 8$	$(4, 8)$

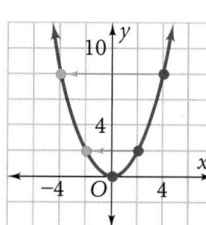

Find the corresponding points on the other side of the axis of symmetry.

✓ **Check Understanding** 2 Make a table of values and graph the quadratic function $f(x) = -2x^2$. See back of book.

Lesson 10-1 Exploring Quadratic Graphs **511**

👥 Reaching All Students

Below Level Help students to see that quadratic functions have curved graphs by comparing tables of values for $y = x$ and $y = x^2$.	**Advanced Learners** Ask students to predict what kind of quadratic function would have a graph whose vertical axis of symmetry is either to the right or to the left of the origin.	**English Learners** See note on page 514. **Tactile Learners** See note on page 512.

Math Background

Formally, a parabola is the intersection of a right circular cone with a plane parallel to a line on the surface of the cone (a generating line).

OBJECTIVE
1 Teaching Notes

Investigation (Optional)
Make sure students understand that quadratic equations are graphed as curves connecting the points, not as segments connecting the points. Demonstrate by graphing $y = x^2$ on the board.

2 EXAMPLE Teaching Tip

Since x^2 is multiplied by $\frac{1}{2}$, encourage students to choose even numbers for x.

📋 Additional Examples

1 Identify the vertex of each graph. Tell whether the vertex is a minimum or a maximum.
a.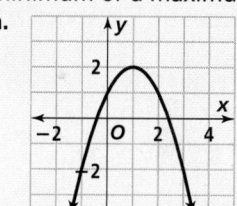

(1, 2); maximum

b.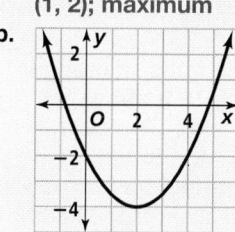

(2, −4); minimum

2 Make a table of values and graph the quadratic function $y = \frac{1}{3}x^2$. **See back of book.**

③ Use the graphs below.
Order the quadratic functions
$f(x) = -x^2$, $f(x) = -3x^2$, and
$f(x) = \frac{1}{2}x^2$ from widest to
narrowest graph.

$f(x) = -x^2$ $f(x) = -3x^2$

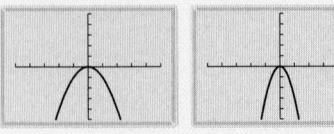

$f(x) = \frac{1}{2}x^2$

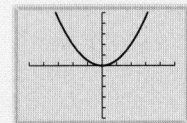

$f(x) = \frac{1}{2}x^2$, $f(x) = -x^2$,
$f(x) = -3x^2$

OBJECTIVE
2 **Teaching Notes**

④ **EXAMPLE** Tactile Learners

After students have graphed
$y = 2x^2$, have them bend a paper
clip into the shape of the graph.
Then instruct them to move the
paper clip around to model
translating the graph.

④ Graph the quadratic functions
$y = 3x^2$ and $y = 3x^2 - 2$.
Compare the graphs. The graph
of $y = 3x^2 - 2$ has the same
shape as the graph of $y = 3x^2$,
but it is shifted down 2 units.
See back of book.

⑤ A monkey drops an orange
from a branch 26 ft above the
ground. The force of gravity
causes the orange to fall
toward the Earth. The function
$h = -16t^2 + 26$ gives the height
of the orange h in feet after
t seconds. Graph this quadratic
function. See back of book.

Closure

Ask: *What is the shape of a
quadratic graph?* U-shaped
*How do a and c affect a quadratic
graph?* The greater the absolute
value of *a*, the narrower the
graph. If *a* is positive, the graph
opens upward. If *a* is negative,

The value of a, the coefficient of the x^2 term in a quadratic function, affects the
width of a parabola as well as the direction in which it opens.

③ **EXAMPLE** Comparing Widths of Parabolas

Use the graphs below. Order the quadratic functions $f(x) = -4x^2$, $f(x) = \frac{1}{4}x^2$, and
$f(x) = x^2$ from widest to narrowest graph.

$y = -4x^2$ 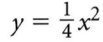 $y = \frac{1}{4}x^2$ $y = x^2$

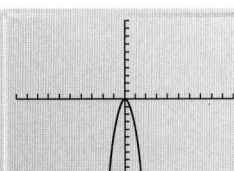 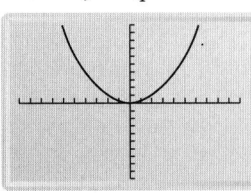 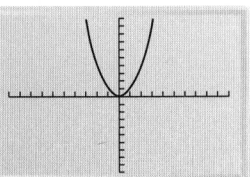

Of the three graphs, $f(x) = \frac{1}{4}x^2$ is the widest and $f(x) = -4x^2$ is the narrowest. So,
the order from widest to narrowest is $f(x) = \frac{1}{4}x^2$, $f(x) = x^2$, and $f(x) = -4x^2$.

✔ **Check Understanding** ③ Order the quadratic functions $y = x^2$, $y = \frac{1}{2}x^2$, and $y = -2x^2$ from widest to
narrowest graph. $y = \frac{1}{2}x^2$, $y = x^2$, $y = -2x^2$

As you can see in Example 3, for $|m| < |n|$, the graph of $y = mx^2$ is wider than
the graph of $y = nx^2$.

OBJECTIVE
2 **Graphing $y = ax^2 + c$**

The value of c, the constant term in a quadratic function, translates the graph up
or down.

The y-axis is the axis of symmetry for functions in the form $y = ax^2 + c$.

④ **EXAMPLE** Graphing $y = ax^2 + c$

Graph the quadratic functions $y = 2x^2$ and $y = 2x^2 + 3$. Compare the graphs.

Problem Solving Hint

You can use symmetry
of the parabola to
check calculated (x, y)
coordinates or points
on the graph.

x	$y = 2x^2$	$y = 2x^2 + 3$
-2	8	11
-1	2	5
0	0	3
-1	2	5
-2	8	11

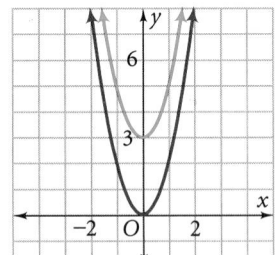

The graph of $y = 2x^2 + 3$ has the same shape as the graph of $y = 2x^2$, but it is
shifted up 3 units.

✔ **Check Understanding** ④ **a.** Graph $y = x^2$ and $y = x^2 - 4$. Compare the graphs. **See back of book.**
b. **Critical Thinking** Describe what positive and negative values of c do to the
position of the vertex. **Positive values of c shift the vertex up.**
Negative values of c shift the vertex down.

the graph opens downward. The
value of c determines the number
of units, and also in which
direction, the graph is shifted
vertically.

page 513 Check Understanding
5a.

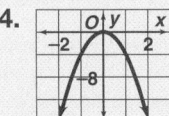
Time (seconds)

pages 513–516 Exercises
4.

You can model the height of an object moving under the influence of gravity using a quadratic function. As an object falls, its speed continues to increase. Ignoring air resistance, you can find the approximate height of a falling object using the function $h = -16t^2 + c$. The height h is in feet, the time t is in seconds, and the initial height of the object c is in feet.

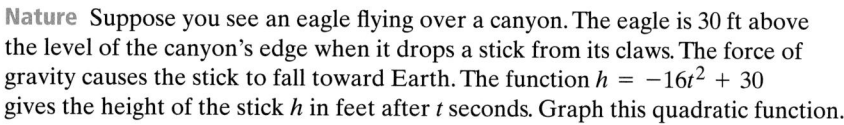

5 EXAMPLE **Real-World** **Problem Solving**

Nature Suppose you see an eagle flying over a canyon. The eagle is 30 ft above the level of the canyon's edge when it drops a stick from its claws. The force of gravity causes the stick to fall toward Earth. The function $h = -16t^2 + 30$ gives the height of the stick h in feet after t seconds. Graph this quadratic function.

t	$h = -16t^2 + 30$
0	30
1	14
2	−34

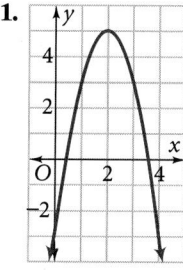

Height h is dependent on time t. Graph t on the x-axis and h on the y-axis. Use nonnegative values for t.

✓ **Check Understanding** **5** **a.** Suppose a squirrel is in a tree 24 ft above the ground. She drops an acorn. The function $h = -16t^2 + 24$ gives the height of the acorn in feet after t seconds. Graph this function. **See margin.**
b. **Critical Thinking** In Example 5, why is the domain nonnegative values of t? **Time must be nonnegative.**

EXERCISES

For more practice, see *Extra Practice*.

Practice and Problem Solving

 **Practice by Example**

Example 1
(page 511)

Identify the vertex of each graph. Tell whether it is a minimum or maximum.

1.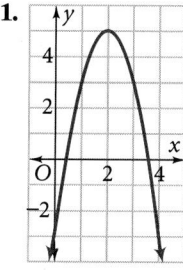

2. 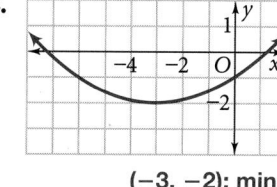 (−3, −2); min.

3. 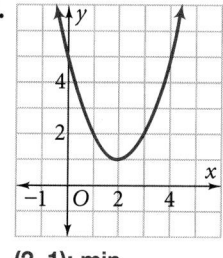 (2, 1); min.

(2, 5); max.

Example 2
(page 511)

Graph each function. 4–9. See margin.

4. $y = -4x^2$ **5.** $f(x) = 1.5x^2$ **6.** $y = \frac{2}{3}x^2$

7. $f(x) = -\frac{1}{2}x^2$ **8.** $y = -\frac{1}{3}x^2$ **9.** $f(x) = 3x^2$

Example 3
(page 512)

Order each group of quadratic functions from widest to narrowest graph.

10–13. See margin.

10. $y = 3x^2, y = \frac{1}{2}x^2, y = 4x^2$ **11.** $f(x) = 5x^2, f(x) = \frac{1}{3}x^2, f(x) = x^2$

12. $y = -\frac{1}{2}x^2, y = 5x^2, y = -\frac{1}{4}x^2$ **13.** $f(x) = -2x^2, f(x) = -\frac{2}{3}x^2, f(x) = -4x^2$

Lesson 10-1 Exploring Quadratic Graphs **513**

5. 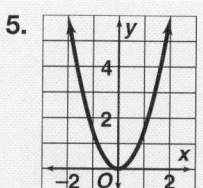   **6.** 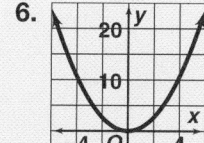   **7.** 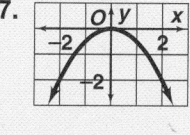   **8.** 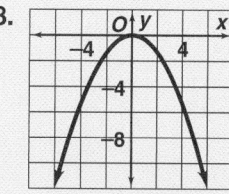   **9.**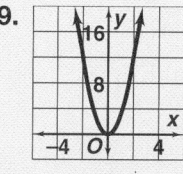

3. Practice

Assignment Guide

▼**1** Objective
Ⓐ Ⓑ **Core** 1–13, 27–30, 34–37, 40–44
Ⓒ **Extension** 48

▼**2** Objective
Ⓐ Ⓑ **Core** 14–26, 31–33, 38–39, 45
Ⓒ **Extension** 46–47, 49

Standardized Test Prep 50–53

Mixed Review 54–66

Error Prevention
Exercises 10–13 Remind students to use the absolute value of a when comparing graphs.

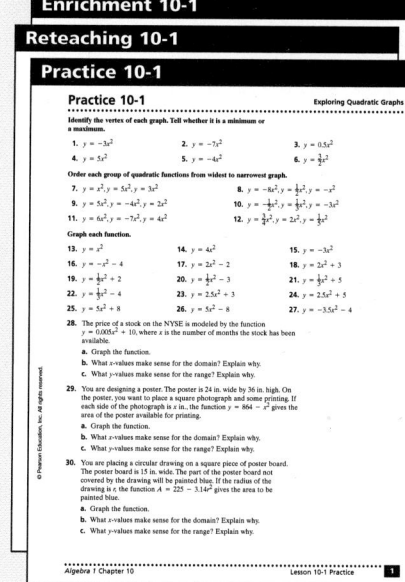

Enrichment 10-1
Reteaching 10-1
Practice 10-1

10. $y = \frac{1}{2}x^2, y = 3x^2,$
$y = 4x^2$

11. $f(x) = \frac{1}{3}x^2, f(x) = x^2,$
$f(x) = 5x^2$

12. $y = -\frac{1}{4}x^2, y = -\frac{1}{2}x^2,$
$y = 5x^2$

13. $f(x) = -\frac{2}{3}x^2, f(x) = -2x^2,$
$f(x) = -4x^2$

513

pages 513–516   Exercises

14.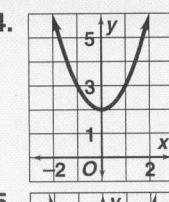

15.

16.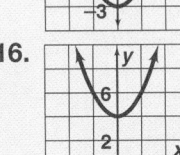

17.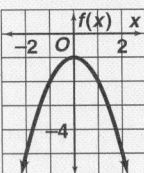

18.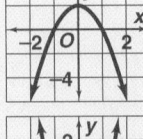

19.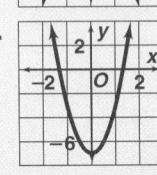

514

Example 4
(page 512)

Graph each function. 14–19. See margin.

14. $f(x) = x^2 + 2$ 15. $y = x^2 - 3$ 16. $y = \frac{1}{2}x^2 + 4$

17. $f(x) = -x^2 - 1$ 18. $y = -2x^2 + 2$ 19. $f(x) = 4x^2 - 7$

Example 5
(page 513)

20. A gull drops a clam shell onto some rocks from a height of 50 ft. The function $h = -16t^2 + 50$ gives the shell's approximate height h in feet after t seconds. Graph the function. **See left.**

B **Apply Your Skills**

20.

Time (seconds)

Match each graph with its function.

A. $f(x) = x^2 - 1$ **B.** $f(x) = x^2 + 4$ **C.** $f(x) = -x^2 + 2$

D. $f(x) = 3x^2 - 5$ **E.** $f(x) = -3x^2 + 8$ **F.** $f(x) = -0.2x^2 + 5$

21. E 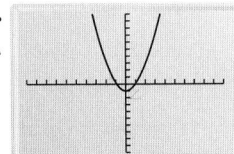   22. A   23. F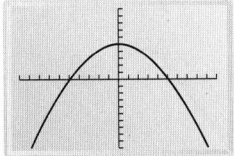

24. B 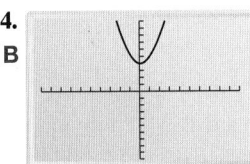   25. C 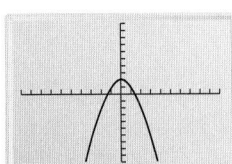   26. D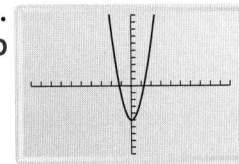

27. The graph of $y = 2x^2$ is narrower.

28. The graph of $y = -x^2$ opens downward.

29. The graph of $y = 1.5x^2$ is narrower.

30. The graph of $y = \frac{1}{2}x^2$ is wider.

31.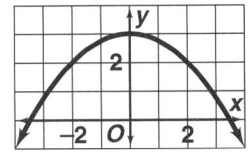

32.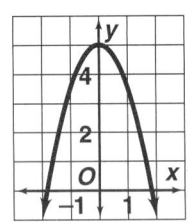

33.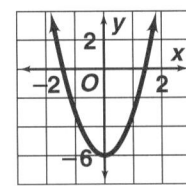

✎ **Writing Without graphing, describe how each graph differs from the graph of $y = x^2$.**

27. $y = 2x^2$ 28. $y = -x^2$ 29. $y = 1.5x^2$ 30. $y = \frac{1}{2}x^2$
27–30. See left.

Graph each function. 31–33. See left.

31. $y = -\frac{1}{4}x^2 + 3$ 32. $f(x) = -1.5x^2 + 5$ 33. $y = 3x^2 - 6$

Trace each parabola on a sheet of paper and draw its axis of symmetry.

34.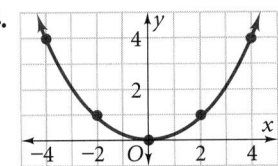

34–37. See margin.

35.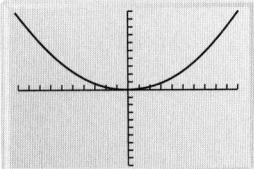

36.

37.

34. 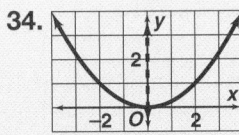   35.   36. 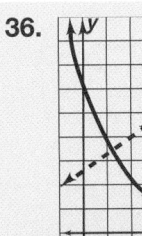   37.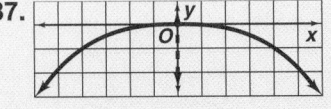

38a.

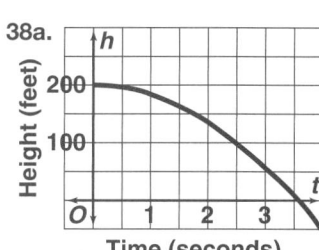

39b. $0 < A < 36\pi \approx 113.1$

38. A bungee jumper dives from a platform. The function $h = -16t^2 + 200$ gives her approximate height h in feet after t seconds.
 a. Graph the function. Graph t on the x-axis and h on the y-axis. **See left.**
 b. What will the jumper's height be after 1 second? **184 ft**
 c. What will the jumper's height be after 3 seconds? **56 ft**

39. Geometry Suppose that a pizza must fit into a box with a base that is 12 in. long and 12 in. wide. You can use the quadratic function $A = \pi r^2$ to find the area of a pizza in terms of its radius.
 a. What values of r make sense for the function? **$0 < r < 6$**
 b. What values of A make sense for the function?
 c. Graph the function. Round values of A to the nearest tenth. **See margin.**

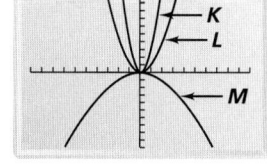

Three graphs are shown below. For Exercises 40–43, identify the graph(s) that fit each description.

40. $a > 0$ **K, L**

41. $a < 0$ **M**

42. $|a|$ has the greatest value. **K**

43. $|a|$ has the least value. **M**

44. Open-Ended Give an example of a quadratic function for each description. **Answers may vary.**
 a. Its graph opens upward and its vertex is at the origin. $y = 5x^2$
 b. Its graph has the same shape as the graph in part (a), but the graph opens downward. $y = -5x^2$
 c. Its graph is wider than the graph of the function in part (a). $y = 3x^2$

45a.

c. No; the apple falls 48 ft from $t = 1$ to $t = 2$, because it is accelerating.

45. Gravity Suppose a person is riding in a hot-air balloon, 144 feet above the ground. He drops an apple. The height of the apple above the ground is given by the formula $h = -16t^2 + 144$, where h is height in feet and t is time in seconds.
 a. Graph the function. **See left.**
 b. How far has the apple fallen from time $t = 0$ to $t = 1$? **16 ft**
 c. Critical Thinking Does the apple fall as far from time $t = 1$ to $t = 2$ as it does from time $t = 0$ to $t = 1$? Explain. **See left.**

C Challenge

46a. $c \neq 0$ and a and c have opp. signs.

 b. $c \neq 0$ and a and c have the same signs.

46. Critical Thinking Complete each statement. Assume $a \neq 0$. **a–b. See left.**
 a. The graph of $y = ax^2 + c$ intersects the x-axis in two places when __?__.
 b. The graph of $y = ax^2 + c$ does not intersect the x-axis when __?__.

47. Landscaping The plan for a 20 ft-by-12 ft patio has a square garden in the middle of it. If each side of the garden is x ft, the function $y = 240 - x^2$ gives the area of the patio in square feet.
 a. Graph the function. **See back of book.**
 b. What values make sense for the domain? Explain. **b–c. See margin.**
 c. What is the range of the function? Explain.
 d. Use the graph to estimate the side length of the garden if the area of the patio is 200 ft². **about 6 ft**

48. Consider the graphs of $y = ax^2$ and $y = (ax)^2$. Assume $a \neq 0$.
 a. For what values of a will both graphs lie in the same quadrants? $a > 0$
 b. For what values of a will the graph of $y = ax^2$ be wider than the graph of $y = (ax)^2$? $|a| > 1$

39c.

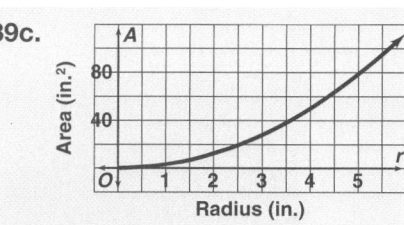

47b. $0 < x < 12$; the side length of the square garden must be less than the width of the patio.

c. $96 < A < 240$; as the side length of the garden increases from 0 to 12, the area of the patio decreases from 240 to 96.

Lesson Quiz 10-1

1. a. Graph $y = -\frac{1}{2}x^2 - 1$.

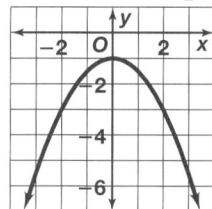

 b. Identify the vertex. Tell whether it is a maximum or a minimum. **(0, −1); maximum**

 c. Compare this graph to the graph of $y = -x^2$. **This graph is wider, opens downward, and is shifted 1 unit down.**

2. a. Graph $y = 4x^2 + 3$.

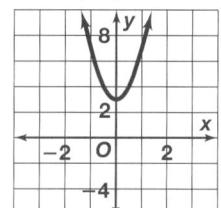

 b. Identify the vertex. Tell whether it is a maximum or a minimum. **(0, 3); minimum**

 c. Compare this graph to the graph of $y = x^2$. **This graph is narrower and shifted 3 units up.**

3. Order the quadratic functions $y = -4x^2$, $y = \frac{1}{4}x^2$, and $y = 2x^2$ from widest to narrowest graph. $y = \frac{1}{4}x^2, y = 2x^2, y = -4x^2$

Alternative Assessment

Direct all students to stand. Instruct them to model the function $y = x^2$ with their arms. Write a quadratic function in the form of $y = ax^2 + c$ on the board. Tell students to move their arms wider or narrower to represent a, and curve their arms downward to model negative a. They can raise their shoulders and stand on their toes, or bend their knees to model the value of c. Repeat with various quadratic functions.

515

Resources

For additional practice with a variety of test item formats:
- Standardized Test Prep, p. 573
- Test-Taking Strategies, p. 568
- Test-Taking Strategies with Transparencies

Exercise 52 Point out to students that they can logically eliminate answer choices B and C because these choices are reflections over the *y*-axis. They are either both on, or both not on, the graph. Only one answer choice is not on the graph. Therefore, they both must be on the graph.

pages 513–516   Exercises

53. [4] a.

t	h
0	200
1	184
2	136
3	56
4	−56

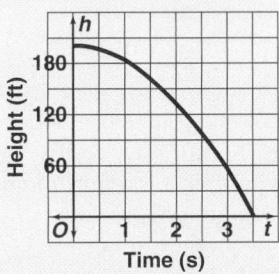

b. 3.5 s

[3] estimate incorrect or missing

[2] error in table or graph

[1] table OR reasonable graph only

49. Architecture An architect wants to design an archway with the following requirements.
- The archway is 6 ft wide and has vertical sides 7 ft high.
- The top of the archway is modeled by the function $y = -\frac{1}{3}x^2 + 10$.

a. Sketch the archway by drawing vertical lines 7 units high at $x = -3$ and $x = 3$ and graphing the portion of the quadratic function that lies between $x = -3$ and $x = 3$. **See back of book.**

b. The plan for the archway is then changed so that the top is modeled by the function $y = -0.5x^2 + 11.5$. Make a revised sketch of the archway. **See back of book.**

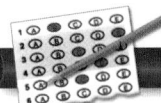

Standardized Test Prep

Multiple Choice

50. Which of the following equations has a graph that is narrower than the graph of $y = 2x^2 + 3$? **B**
- **A.** $y = 2x^2 - 3$
- **B.** $y = -3x^2 + 2$
- **C.** $y = 0.5x^2 + 3$
- **D.** $y = -0.5x^2 - 2$

51. Which of the following equations has a graph that crosses the *y*-axis at a point lower than the graph of $y = -2x^2 - 1$? **G**
- **F.** $y = -3x^2 - 1$
- **G.** $y = 3x^2 - 3$
- **H.** $y = -3x^2 + 1$
- **I.** $y = -3x^2 + 3$

52. The graph of $y = 4x^2 + 3$ does NOT pass through which of the following points? **D**
- **A.** (0, 3)
- **B.** (1, 7)
- **C.** (−1, 7)
- **D.** (3, 27)

Extended Response

Take It to the NET
Online lesson quiz at
www.PHSchool.com
Web Code: aea-1001

53. A construction worker drops a tool from the top of a building that is 200 ft high. The height of the tool above the ground can be modeled by $h = -16t^2 + 200$, where *h* is height in feet and *t* is time in seconds.
- **a.** Make a table and graph this function. **a–b. See margin.**
- **b.** Use your graph to estimate the amount of time it takes for the tool to hit the ground. Round to the nearest tenth of a second.

Mixed Review

Lesson 9-8

57. $(y + 2)(y - 2)(y + 3)$

Factor each expression. $(3a^2 - 2)(5a - 6)$

54. $x^3 - 4x^2 + 2x - 8$ $(x^2 + 2)(x - 4)$ **55.** $15a^3 - 18a^2 - 10a + 12$

56. $7b^3 + 14b^2 + b + 2$ $(7b^2 + 1)(b + 2)$ **57.** $y^3 + 3y^2 - 4y - 12$ **See left.**

58. $2n^3 - 2n^2 - 24n$ $2n(n + 3)(n - 4)$ **59.** $30m^3 + 51m^2 + 9m$
$3m(2m + 3)(5m + 1)$

Lesson 9-2   **Simplify each expression.** $-12t^3 + 22t^2$

60. $5x(3x - 4)$ $15x^2 - 20x$ **61.** $(n - 7)9n$ $9n^2 - 63n$ **62.** $-2t^2(6t - 11)$

63. $4m^2(3m^4 - m^3 + 5)$ **64.** $-5y(3y^5 + 2y^3 - 4)$ **65.** $3c^3(-4c^2 + 7c - 8)$
$12m^6 - 4m^5 + 20m^2$ $-15y^6 - 10y^4 + 20y$ $-12c^5 + 21c^4 - 24c^3$

66. Business The City Council invites your art club to sell helium balloons during a citywide celebration. The rental of the helium tank is $27.00 for the day. Each balloon costs $.20. If the balloons sell for $2.00 each, how many will your art club have to sell to break even? **15 balloons**

10-2

Quadratic Functions

4.02 Graph, factor, and evaluate quadratic functions to solve problems.

 North Carolina Objectives

Lesson Preview

What You'll Learn

OBJECTIVE 1 To graph quadratic functions of the form $y = ax^2 + bx + c$

OBJECTIVE 2 To graph quadratic inequalities

. . . And Why

To model height of fireworks, as in Example 2

✓ **Check Skills You'll Need**

(For help, go to Lessons 1-6 and 10-1.)

Evaluate the expression $\frac{-b}{2a}$ for the following values of a and b.

1. $a = -6, b = 4$ $\frac{1}{3}$

2. $a = 15, b = 20$ $-\frac{2}{3}$

3. $a = -8, b = -56$ $-3\frac{1}{2}$

4. $a = -9, b = 108$ 6

Graph each function. **5–7. See margin p. 519.**

5. $y = x^2$

6. $y = -x^2 + 2$

7. $y = \frac{1}{2}x^2 - 1$

OBJECTIVE

1   Graphing $y = ax^2 + bx + c$

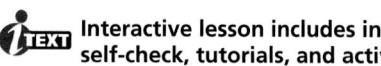 **Interactive lesson** includes instant self-check, tutorials, and activities.

In Lesson 10-1, you investigated the graphs of $y = ax^2$ and $y = ax^2 + c$. In the quadratic function $y = ax^2 + bx + c$, the value of b affects the position of the axis of symmetry.

Consider the graphs of the following functions.

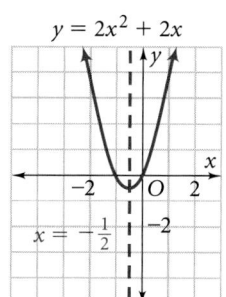
$y = 2x^2 + 2x$

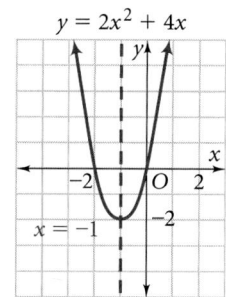
$y = 2x^2 + 4x$

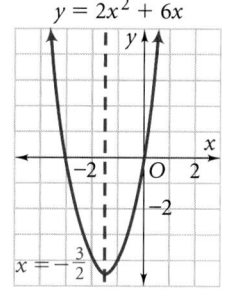
$y = 2x^2 + 6x$

Notice that all three graphs have the same y-intercept. This is because in all three equations $c = 0$. The axis of symmetry changes with each change in the b value. The equation of the axis of symmetry is related to the ratio $\frac{b}{a}$.

equation:	$y = 2x^2 + 2x$	$y = 2x^2 + 4x$	$y = 2x^2 + 6x$
$\frac{b}{a}$:	$\frac{2}{2} = 1$	$\frac{4}{2} = 2$	$\frac{6}{2} = 3$
axis of symmetry:	$x = -\frac{1}{2}$	$x = -1$, or $-\frac{2}{2}$	$x = -\frac{3}{2}$

The equation of the axis of symmetry is $x = -\frac{1}{2}\left(\frac{b}{a}\right)$, or $\frac{-b}{2a}$.

Key Concepts

Property	**Graph of a Quadratic Function**

The graph of $y = ax^2 + bx + c$, where $a \neq 0$, has the line $x = \frac{-b}{2a}$ as its axis of symmetry. The x-coordinate of the vertex is $\frac{-b}{2a}$.

Lesson 10-2   Quadratic Functions   **517**

Ongoing Assessment and Intervention

Before the Lesson
Diagnose prerequisite skills using:
- Check Skills You'll Need

During the Lesson
Monitor progress using:
- Check Understanding
- Additional Examples
- Standardized Test Prep

After the Lesson
Assess knowledge using:
- Lesson Quiz
- Computer Test Generator CD

10-2    North Carolina Objectives 4.02

1. Plan

Lesson Preview

✓ **Check Skills You'll Need**

Multiplying and Dividing
Lesson 1-6: Example 6
Exercises 48–53
Extra Practice, p. 702

Exploring Quadratic Graphs
Lesson 10-1: Examples 2–4
Exercises 4–19
Extra Practice, p. 711

Lesson Resources

📁 **Teaching Resources**
Practice, Reteaching, Enrichment

👥 **Reaching All Students**
Practice Workbook 10-2
Spanish Practice Workbook 10-2
Technology Activities 5
Basic Algebra Planning Guide 10-2

⏱ **Presentation Assistant Plus!**
Transparencies
- Check Skills You'll Need 10-2
- Additional Examples 10-2
- Student Edition Answers 10-2
- Lesson Quiz 10-2
PH Presentation Pro CD 10-2

PRENTICE HALL ASSESSMENT SYSTEM
Computer Test Generator CD

💿 **Technology**
Resource Pro® CD-ROM
Computer Test Generator CD
Prentice Hall Presentation Pro CD

🖥 **www.PHSchool.com**
Student Site
- Teacher Web Code: aek-5500
- Self-grading Lesson Quiz
Teacher Center
- Lesson Planner
- Resources

Plus

517

Math Background

The formula used to find the height of a projectile would be different on another planet that has another value for the force of gravity. For example, the moon has a force of gravity that is about one-sixth that of Earth.

OBJECTIVE
1 Teaching Notes

1 EXAMPLE Math Tip

Encourage students to enter $Y_1 = -3x^2 + 6x + 5$ into their graphing calculators. Have them press 2nd **TABLE** and identify pairs of points which are reflections across the axis of symmetry.

2 EXAMPLE Inclusion

Visually impaired students may not have seen an aerial fireworks display. Ask a volunteer to describe one in detail so that all students can understand the "stars" in the example.

Additional Examples

1 Graph the function $y = 2x^2 + 4x - 3$.

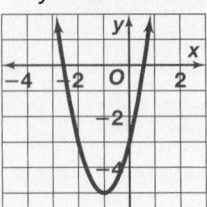

2 Suppose a particular star is projected from an aerial firework at a starting height of 610 ft with an initial upward velocity of 88 ft/s. How long will it take for the star to reach its maximum height? How far above the ground will it be? **2.75 s; 731 ft**

518

When you substitute $x = 0$ into the equation $y = ax^2 + bx + c$, $y = c$. So the y-intercept of a quadratic function is the value of c. You can use the axis of symmetry and the y-intercept to help you graph a quadratic function.

1 EXAMPLE Graphing $y = ax^2 + bx + c$

Graph the function $y = -3x^2 + 6x + 5$.

Step 1 Find the equation of the axis of symmetry and the coordinates of the vertex.

$x = \frac{-b}{2a} = \frac{-6}{2(-3)} = 1$ **Find the equation of the axis of symmetry.**

The axis of symmetry is $x = 1$.

$y = -3x^2 + 6x + 5$

$y = -3(1)^2 + 6(1) + 5$ **To find the y-coordinate of the vertex, substitute 1 for x.**

$\quad = 8$

The vertex is $(1, 8)$.

Step 2 Find two other points on the graph.

Use the y-intercept.

For $x = 0$, $y = 5$, so one point is $(0, 5)$.

Choose a value for x on the same side of the vertex as the y-intercept. Let $x = -1$.

$y = -3(-1)^2 + 6(-1) + 5$ **Find the y-coordinate for $x = -1$.**

$\quad = -4$

For $x = -1$, $y = -4$, so another point is $(-1, -4)$.

Step 3 Reflect $(0, 5)$ and $(-1, -4)$ across the axis of symmetry to get two more points. Then draw the parabola.

1.
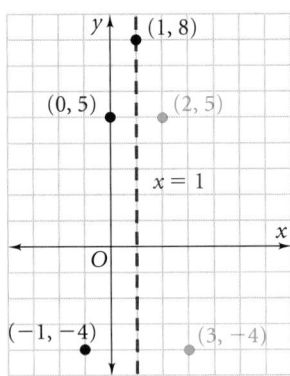 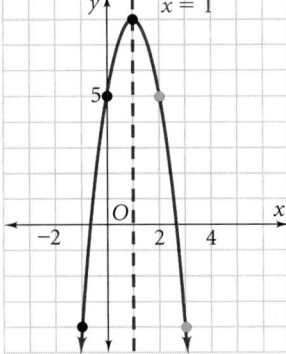

✓ **Check Understanding** **1** Graph $f(x) = x^2 - 6x + 9$. Label the axis of symmetry and the vertex. **See left.**

You saw in the previous lesson that the formula $h = -16t^2 + c$ describes the height above the ground of an object falling from an initial height c, at time t. If an object is given an initial upward velocity v and continues with no additional force of its own, the formula $h = -16t^2 + vt + c$ describes its approximate height above the ground.

👥 Reaching All Students

| **Below Level** Height corresponds with the y-axis, so h is used instead of y; and t is used instead of x. | **Advanced Learners** Have students graph the quadratic function in Example 2. | **Inclusion** See note on page 518. **Auditory Learners** See note on page 519. |

2 EXAMPLE | Real-World Problem Solving

Fireworks In professional fireworks displays, aerial fireworks carry "stars" upward, ignite them, and project them into the air.

Suppose a particular star is projected from an aerial firework at a starting height of 520 ft with an initial upward velocity of 72 ft/s. How long will it take for the star to reach its maximum height? How far above the ground will it be?

The equation $h = -16t^2 + 72t + 520$ gives the star's height h in feet at time t in seconds. Since the coefficient of t^2 is negative, the curve opens downward, and the vertex is the maximum point.

Real-World Connection

Aerial fireworks like those shown above follow a parabolic path.

Step 1 Find the t-coordinate of the vertex.

$$\frac{-b}{2a} = \frac{-(72)}{2(-16)} = 2.25$$

After 2.25 seconds, the star will be at its greatest height.

Step 2 Find the h-coordinate of the vertex.

$h = -16(2.25)^2 + 72(2.25) + 520$ **Substitute 2.25 for t.**

$h = 601$ **Simplify using a calculator.**

The maximum height of the star will be 601 ft.

✓ Check Understanding ② A ball is thrown into the air with an initial upward velocity of 48 ft/s. Its height h in feet after t seconds is given by the function $h = -16t^2 + 48t + 4$.
a. In how many seconds will the ball reach its maximum height? **1.5 s**
b. What is the ball's maximum height? **40 ft**

OBJECTIVE
2 Graphing Quadratic Inequalities

Graphing a quadratic inequality is similar to graphing a linear inequality. The curve is dashed if the inequality involves < or >. The curve is solid if the inequality involves ≤ or ≥.

3 EXAMPLE | Graphing Quadratic Inequalities

Graph the quadratic inequality $y \le x^2 - 3x - 4$.

? Need Help?

If an inequality is written in terms of $y <$ or $y \le$, shade below the boundary. If an inequality is written in terms of $y >$ or $y \ge$, shade above the boundary.

Graph the boundary curve, $y = x^2 - 3x - 4$. Use a solid line because the solution of the inequality $y \le x^2 - 3x - 4$ includes the boundary. Shade below the curve.

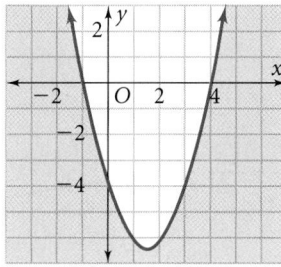

✓ Check Understanding ③ Graph each quadratic inequality. **a–b. See margin.**
a. $y \le x^2 + 2x - 5$
b. $y > x^2 + x + 1$

Lesson 10-2 Quadratic Functions **519**

page 517 Check Skills You'll Need

5.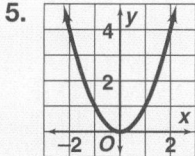

6.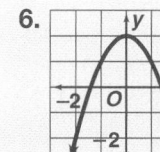

7.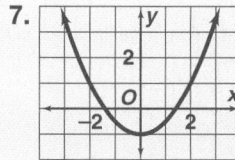

519

OBJECTIVE
2 Teaching Notes

3 EXAMPLE | Auditory Learners

Help students remember where to shade a quadratic inequality by having them say the following: *If y is less than, then shade below.* Stress the *l* in *less than* and in *be<u>l</u>ow.*

Additional Examples

③ Graph the quadratic inequality $y > -x^2 + 6x - 5$.

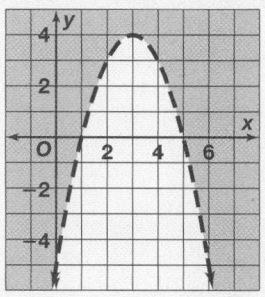

Closure

Ask students to explain how to find the vertex and y-intercept of a quadratic function. To find the vertex, you calculate $\frac{-b}{2a}$ to determine the x-coordinate, then substitute that value into the equation to find its corresponding y-coordinate. The value of c is the y-intercept. Then ask them how to determine where to shade for a quadratic inequality. If the inequality contains y >, you shade above the boundary. If the inequality contains y <, you shade below the boundary.

page 519 Check Understanding

3a.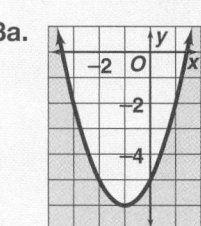

b.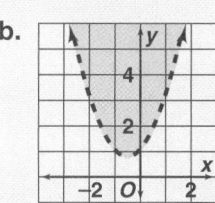

Assignment Guide

1 Objective

Ⓐ Ⓑ **Core** 1–16, 23–35, 40–42

Ⓒ **Extension** 43, 46

2 Objective

Ⓐ Ⓑ **Core** 17–22, 36–39

Ⓒ **Extension** 44–45

Standardized Test Prep 47–50

Mixed Review 51–62

Exercises 5–10 Tell students they can quickly find the correct matches for some of the functions by first checking the sign and value of *a*, then *c*.

Connection to Science

Exercise 16 The vertical motion formula is $h = -\frac{1}{2}gt^2 + vt + c$ where *g* is the acceleration due to gravity. Near the Earth's surface, this is about 32 ft/s², or about 9.8 m/s². So, the customary equation becomes $h = -16t^2 + vt + c$ and the metric equation becomes $h = -4.9t^2 + vt + c$.

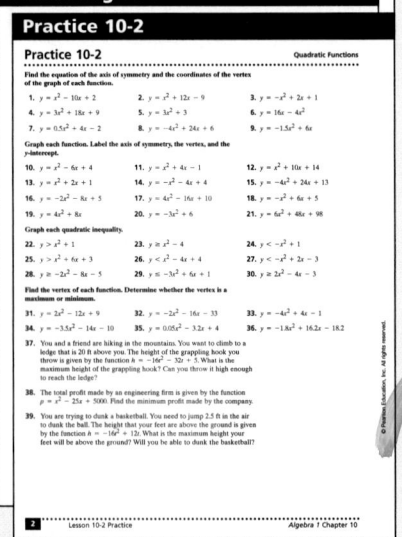

EXERCISES

Practice and Problem Solving

For more practice, see *Extra Practice*.

Ⓐ **Practice by Example**

Example 1 (page 518)

Find the equation of the axis of symmetry and the coordinates of the vertex of the graph of each function.

1. $y = 2x^2 + 4$ $x = 0$, (0, 4)
2. $f(x) = 2x^2 + 4x - 5$ $x = -1$, (−1, −7)
3. $y = x^2 - 8x - 9$ $x = 4$, (4, −25)
4. $y = 3x^2 - 9x + 5$ $x = 1.5$, (1.5, −1.75)

Match each graph with its function.

A. $y = x^2 - 6x$
B. $y = x^2 + 6x$
C. $y = -x^2 - 6x$
D. $y = -x^2 + 6x$
E. $y = -x^2 + 6$
F. $y = x^2 - 6$

11. $x = -2$

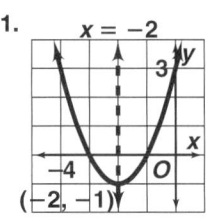

(−2, −1)

5. B
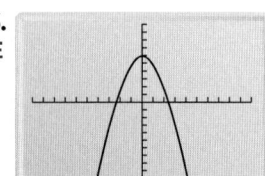

6. E

12. $x = 1.5$

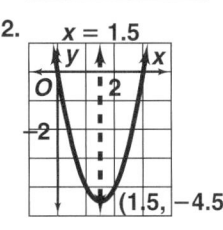

(1.5, −4.5)

7. C
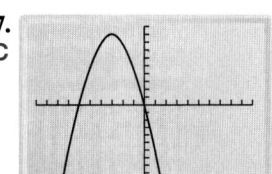

8. F
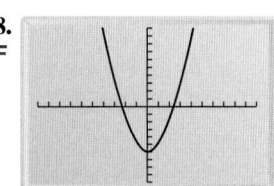

13. $x = 2$

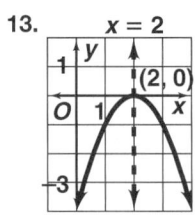

(2, 0)

9. A
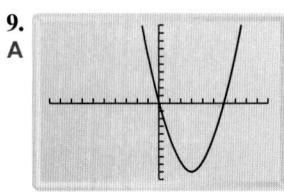

10. D
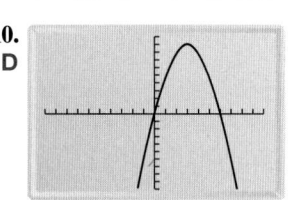

14. $x = -0.75$

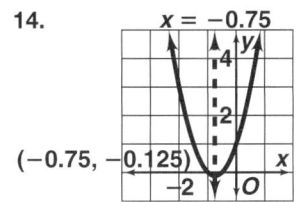

(−0.75, −0.125)

Graph each function. Label the axis of symmetry and the vertex. 11–14. See left.

11. $f(x) = x^2 + 4x + 3$
12. $y = 2x^2 - 6x$
13. $y = -x^2 + 4x - 4$
14. $y = 2x^2 + 3x + 1$

Example 2 (page 519)

15. Gardening Suppose you have 80 ft of fence to enclose a rectangular garden. The function $A = 40x - x^2$ gives you the area of the garden in square feet where *x* is the width in feet.
a. What width gives you the maximum gardening area? **20 ft**
b. What is the maximum area? **400 ft²**

16. A ball is thrown into the air with an upward velocity of 40 ft/s. Its height *h* in feet after *t* seconds is given by the function $h = -16t^2 + 40t + 6$.
a. In how many seconds does the ball reach its maximum height? **1.25 s**
b. What is the ball's maximum height? **31 ft**

Example 3 (page 519)

Graph each quadratic inequality. 17–22. See margin.

17. $y > x^2$
18. $f(x) < -x^2$
19. $y \le x^2 + 3$
20. $y < -x^2 + 4$
21. $y \ge -2x^2 + 6$
22. $f(x) > -x^2 + 4x - 4$

520 Chapter 10 Quadratic Equations and Functions

pages 520–523
Exercises

17.
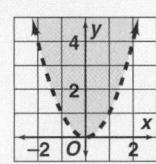

18.
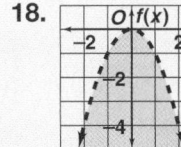

19.
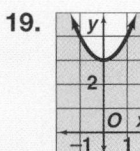

20.
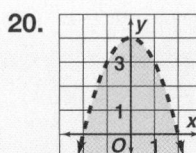

21.
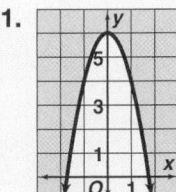

B **Apply Your Skills**

Graph each function. Label the axis of symmetry and the vertex. 23–31. See margin.

23. $y = x^2 - 9x + 3$ **24.** $f(x) = -x^2 - 4x - 6$ **25.** $f(x) = x^2 - 2x + 1$

26. $y = 2x^2 + x - 3$ **27.** $y = x^2 + 3x + 2$ **28.** $y = -x^2 + 8x - 5$

29. $y = \frac{1}{2}x^2 + 2x + 1$ **30.** $y = \frac{1}{4}x^2 + 2x + 1$ **31.** $y = -\frac{1}{4}x^2 + 2x - 3$

Open-Ended **For Exercises 32–34, give an example of a quadratic function for each description.** 32–34. Answers may vary. Samples are given.

32. Its axis of symmetry is to the right of the y-axis. $y = 2x^2 - 8x + 1$

33. Its graph opens downward and has its vertex at $(0, 0)$. $y = -3x^2$

34. Its graph lies entirely above the x-axis. $y = 2x^2 + 4$

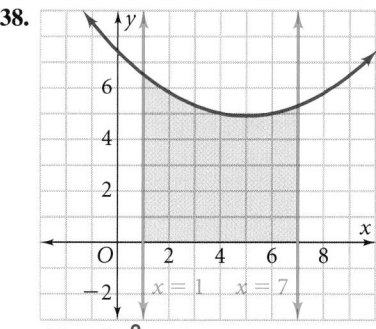

35. Diving An athlete dives from the 3-meter springboard. Her altitude y, at horizontal distance x, can be approximated by the function $y = -2.2x^2 + 5.3x + 4$. Both the altitude and distance are in meters.
   a. How far has she traveled horizontally when she reaches her maximum altitude? Round to the nearest tenth of a meter. **1.2 m**
   b. What is her maximum altitude? Round to the nearest tenth of a meter. **7.2 m**

36. Road Construction An archway over a road is cut out of rock. Its shape is modeled by the quadratic function $y = -0.1x^2 + 12$ for $y \geq 0$.
   a. Write an inequality that describes the opening of the archway. $y \leq -0.1x^2 + 12$
   b. Graph the inequality. **See margin.**
   c. Critical Thinking Can a camper 6 ft wide and 7 ft high fit under the arch without crossing the median line? Explain.
   Yes; when $x = 6$, $y = 8.4$, so the camper will fit.

37. Business A small company markets a new toy. The function $S = -64p^2 + 1600p$ predicts, in dollars, the total sales S as a function of the price p of the toy.
   a. What price will produce the highest total sales? **$12.50**
   b. What is the maximum total sales predicted? **$10,000**

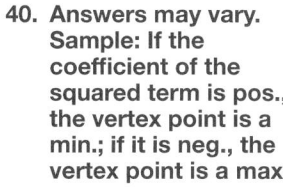

Real-World 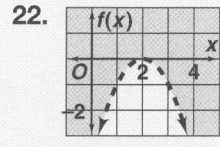 **Connection**

After turning a somersault, the diver followed a parabolic path.

Estimation **For each of the graphs below, estimate the area enclosed by the parabola, the x-axis, and the vertical lines $x = 1$ and $x = 7$. Follow the instructions below.**

• Count the number of whole grid squares in the region.
• If half a square or more is included in the region, count it as one.
• If less than half a square is included in the region, do *not* count it.
• Add the counted squares to estimate the area.

38.

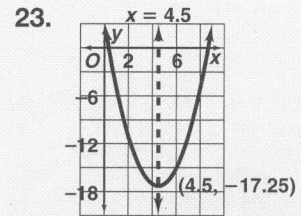

32 units²

39.

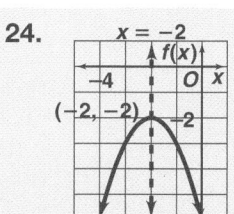

26 units²

40. Answers may vary. Sample: If the coefficient of the squared term is pos., the vertex point is a min.; if it is neg., the vertex point is a max.

40. Critical Thinking Why is it important to consider the coefficient of the squared term when solving a real-world maximum or minimum problem? **See left.**

Lesson 10-2   Quadratic Functions   **521**

22.

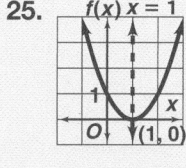

23.

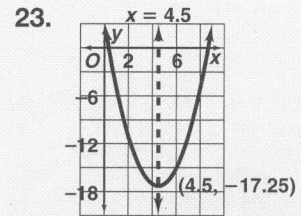 *(see margin graph)*

$x = 4.5$

$(4.5, -17.25)$

24.

$x = -2$

$(-2, -2)$

25.

$f(x)$ $x = 1$

$(1, 0)$

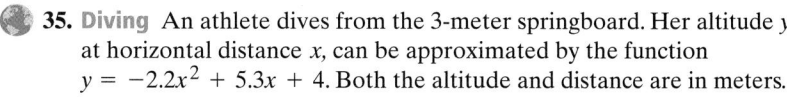
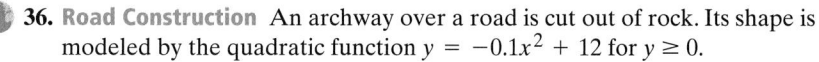
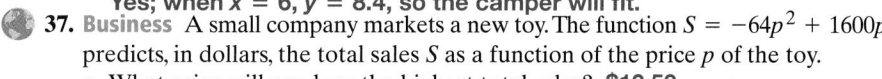

26. $x = -0.25$

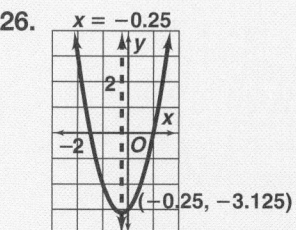

$(-0.25, -3.125)$

27. $x = -1.5$

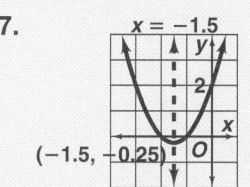

$(-1.5, -0.25)$

28. $x = 4$

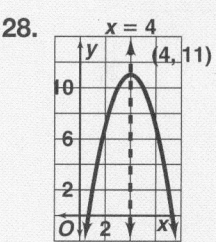

$(4, 11)$

29. $x = -2$

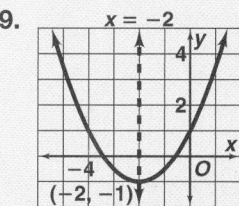

$(-2, -1)$

30. $x = -4$

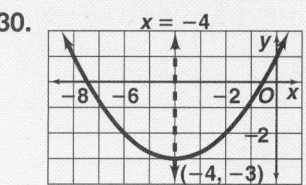

$(-4, -3)$

31. $x = 4$

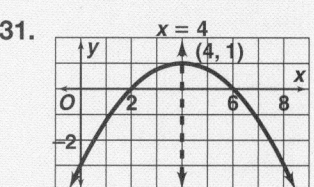

$(4, 1)$

36b.

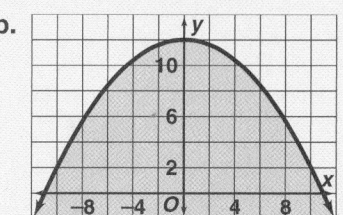

521

4. Assess

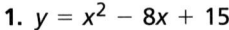

Lesson Quiz 10-2

Graph each relation. Label the axis of symmetry and the vertex.

1. $y = x^2 - 8x + 15$

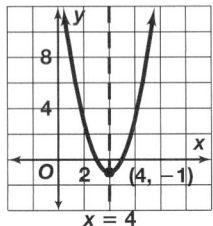

2. $f(x) = -x^2 + 4x - 2$

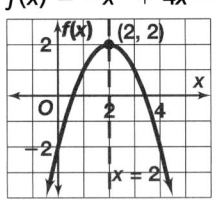

3. $y \leq -\frac{1}{4}x^2 - 2x - 6$

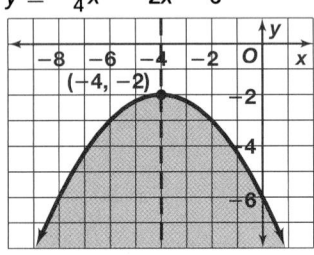

Alternative Assessment

Give students laminated coordinate planes and pipe cleaners. Have each student write his or her own quadratic function, and then model its graph with the pipe cleaner. Direct students to move to another desk and check the work of a classmate. Repeat with a quadratic inequality. Give each student a marker with which to indicate the part of the graph that should be shaded.

41. Answers may vary. Sample: *a* affects whether the parabola opens up or down, *b* affects the axis of symmetry, and *c* affects the *y*-intercept.

41. Writing Explain how changing the values of *a*, *b*, and *c* in a quadratic function affects the graph of the function. **See left.**

 42. Pets Suppose you have 26 ft of fence and want to build a rectangular enclosure for rabbits. You want to make an enclosure with the greatest possible area. **a.** $w = 13 - \ell$ **b.** $A = -1\ell^2 + 13\ell$
a. Write an expression for the width of the rectangle in terms of the length.
b. Write an equation for the area of the rectangle in terms of the length.
c. Find the vertex of the parabola described by the equation in part (b). **(6.5, 42.25)**
d. Which dimensions give the rectangle the greatest area? **6.5 ft by 6.5 ft**

C Challenge **43. Sports** Suppose a volleyball player serves from 1 m behind the back line. If no other player touches the ball, it will land in bounds. The equation $h = -4.9t^2 + 3.82t + 1.7$ gives the ball's height *h* in meters in terms of time *t* in seconds.

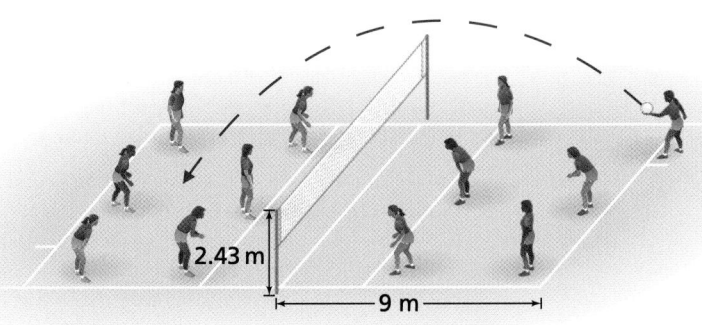

a. When will the ball be at its highest point? Round to the nearest tenth of a second. **0.4 s**

43b. No; after 0.6 s, the ball will have a height of about 2.23 m but the net has a height of 2.43 m.

b. The ball will reach the net at $t = 0.6$ s. Will it clear the net? Explain. **See left.**

44. Architecture An architect designs a monument for a new park. The solution of the following system of inequalities describes the shape of the monument. Make a graph of the monument. **See back of book.**

$$y \geq -x^2 + 6 \qquad y \leq -\frac{1}{2}x^2 + 8 \qquad y \geq 0$$

Real-World Connection

A standard tennis court is 78 ft long and 36 ft wide.

45. Sports Suppose a tennis player hits a ball over the net. The ball leaves his racket 0.5 m above the ground. The equation $h = -4.9t^2 + 3.8t + 0.5$ gives the ball's height *h* in meters at time *t* in seconds.
a. When will the ball be at the highest point in its path? Round to the nearest tenth of a second. **0.4 s**
b. Critical Thinking If you double the answer from part (a), will you find the amount of time the ball is in the air before it hits the court? Explain. **See margin.**

46. The parabola shown at the right is of the form $y = x^2 + bx + c$. **46b.** $x = -2.5$
a. Use the graph to find the *y*-intercept. **(0, 2)**
b. Find the equation of the axis of symmetry.
c. Use the vertex formula $x = \frac{-b}{2a}$ to find *b*. **5**
d. Write the equation of the parabola.
e. Test one point using the equation from part (d). **d–f. See margin.**
f. Critical Thinking Would this method work if the value of *a* were not known? Explain.

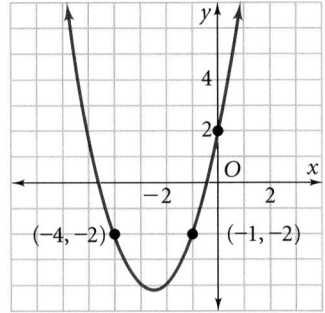

pages 520–523 **Exercises**

45b. No; it takes about 0.8 s to return to $h = 0.5$ m, so it will take more time to reach the ground.

46d. $y = x^2 + 5x + 2$

e. Answers may vary. Sample: Test $(-4, -2)$.
$-2 \overset{?}{=} (-4)^2 + 5(-4) + 2$
$-2 \overset{?}{=} 16 - 20 + 2$
$-2 = -2$ ✓

f. No; you would not be able to determine the *b* value using the vertex formula.

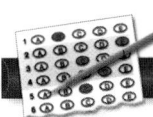

Multiple Choice

47. Which of the following are the coordinates of the vertex of $y = x^2 - 2x - 1$? **A**

A. $(1, -2)$ B. $(0, 3)$ C. $(1, -4)$ D. $(2, -3)$

48. Which of the following parabolas has the greatest b-value? **I**

F. $y = -x^2 - 2x$ G. $y = -x^2 - 3x$

H. $y = -x^2 + 2x$ I. $y = -x^2 + 3x$

49. Which of the following is the graph of $y = 0.5x^2 - 2x + 1$? **B**

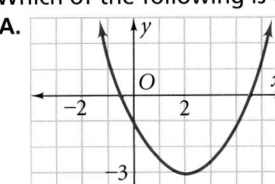
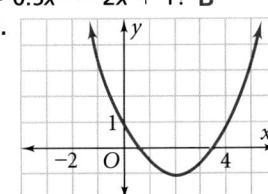

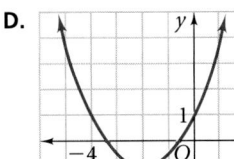

Short Response

50. An arrow is shot into the air. It follows a path given by the equation $y = -0.009x^2 + 0.3x + 4.5$, where x and y are in feet. Find its maximum height. Show your work. **See margin.**

Mixed Review

Lesson 10-1

Match each graph with its function.

A. $y = \frac{1}{8}x^2 + 2$ B. $y = \frac{1}{2}x^2 + 2$ C. $y = -x^2 - 2$

D. $y = x^2 + 2$ E. $y = -x^2 + 2$ F. $y = -\frac{1}{2}x^2 - 2$

51.
C
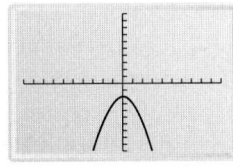

52.
A
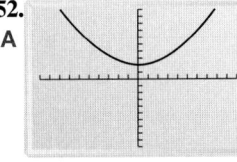

53.
F
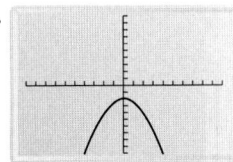

54.
D
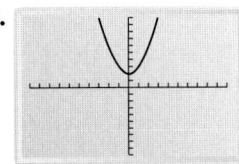

55.
B
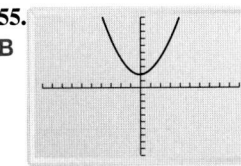

56.
E
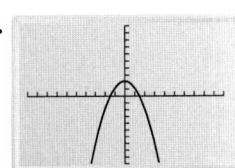

Lesson 9-3

Find each product. 57–62. **See margin.**

57. $(c + 4)(c - 9)$ **58.** $(2x - 5)(x + 6)$ **59.** $(4t + 1)(5t + 3)$

60. $(7n^2 - 2)(3n^2 - 8)$ **61.** $(a + 5)(2a^2 - a + 4)$ **62.** $(3r^2 + 6r - 7)(2r - 1)$

Lesson 10-2   Quadratic Functions   **523**

---

50. [2] axis of symmetry

$x = \frac{-b}{2a} = \frac{-0.3}{2(-0.009)}$

≈ 16.7

maximum height:

$y \approx -0.009(16.7)^2 + 0.3(16.7) + 4.5$ $y \approx 7$ ft

[1] appropriate methods, but with a minor computational error

57. $c^2 - 5c - 36$

58. $2x^2 + 7x - 30$

59. $20t^2 + 17t + 3$

60. $21n^4 - 62n^2 + 16$

61. $2a^3 + 9a^2 - a + 20$

62. $6r^3 + 9r^2 - 20r + 7$

10-3

1. Plan

Lesson Preview

Check Skills You'll Need

Exponents and Order of Operations
Lesson 1-2: Example 1
Exercises 1–6
Extra Practice, p. 702

Division Properties of Exponents
Lesson 8-5: Example 3
Exercises 21–28
Extra Practice, p. 709

Lesson Resources

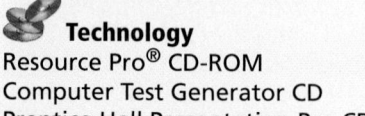
Teaching Resources
Practice, Reteaching, Enrichment

Reaching All Students
Practice Workbook 10-3
Spanish Practice Workbook 10-3
Basic Algebra Planning Guide 10-3

Presentation Assistant Plus!
Transparencies
- Check Skills You'll Need 10-3
- Additional Examples 10-3
- Student Edition Answers 10-3
- Lesson Quiz 10-3
PH Presentation Pro CD 10-3

ASSESSMENT SYSTEM
Computer Test Generator CD

Technology
Resource Pro® CD-ROM
Computer Test Generator CD
Prentice Hall Presentation Pro CD

www.PHSchool.com
Student Site
- Teacher Web Code: aek-5500
- Reasoning & Puzzles p. 90
- Self-grading Lesson Quiz
Teacher Center
- Lesson Planner
- Resources

Plus **iTEXT**

524

10-3 Finding and Estimating Square Roots

Lesson Preview

What You'll Learn

OBJECTIVE 1 To find square roots

OBJECTIVE 2 To estimate and use square roots

...And Why

To apply square roots in a real-world situation involving construction, as in Example 5

Check Skills You'll Need

(For help, go to Lessons 1-2 and 8-5.)

Simplify each expression.

1. 11^2 **121**
2. $(-12)^2$ **144**
3. $-(12)^2$ **−144**
4. 1.5^2 **2.25**
5. 0.6^2 **0.36**
6. $\left(\frac{1}{2}\right)^2$ **$\frac{1}{4}$**
7. $\left(-\frac{2}{3}\right)^2$ **$\frac{4}{9}$**
8. $\left(\frac{4}{5}\right)^2$ **$\frac{16}{25}$**

New Vocabulary
- square root
- principal square root
- negative square root
- radicand
- perfect squares

OBJECTIVE 1

Finding Square Roots

 Interactive lesson includes instant self-check, tutorials, and activities.

The diagram at the right shows the relationship between squares and square roots. Every positive number has *two* square roots.

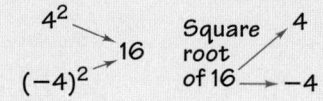

Key Concepts

Definition	**Square Root**

The number a is a **square root** of b if $a^2 = b$.

Example $4^2 = 16$ and $(-4)^2 = 16$, so 4 and −4 are square roots of 16.

Reading Math

Read $\sqrt{16}$ as "the square root of 16."
Read $\pm$ as "plus or minus."

A radical symbol $\sqrt{}$ indicates a square root. The expression $\sqrt{16}$ means the positive, or **principal square root** of 16. The expression $-\sqrt{16}$ means the **negative square root** of 16. The expression under the radical sign is a **radicand**. You can use the symbol $\pm$ to indicate both square roots.

1 EXAMPLE Simplifying Square Root Expressions

Simplify each expression.

a. $\sqrt{64} = 8$ positive square root
b. $-\sqrt{100} = -10$ negative square root
c. $\pm\sqrt{\frac{9}{16}} = \pm\frac{3}{4}$ The square roots are $\frac{3}{4}$ and $-\frac{3}{4}$.
d. $\pm\sqrt{0} = 0$ There is only one square root of 0.
e. $\sqrt{-16}$ is undefined.   For real numbers, the square root of a negative number is undefined.

Check Understanding ① Simplify each expression.
a. $\sqrt{49}$ **7**   b. $\pm\sqrt{36}$ **±6**   c. $-\sqrt{121}$ **−11**   d. $\sqrt{\frac{1}{25}}$ **$\frac{1}{5}$**

524 Chapter 10 Quadratic Equations and Functions

Ongoing Assessment and Intervention

Before the Lesson Diagnose prerequisite skills using:	**During the Lesson** Monitor progress using:	**After the Lesson** Assess knowledge using:
• Check Skills You'll Need	• Check Understanding • Additional Examples • Standardized Test Prep	• Lesson Quiz • Computer Test Generator CD

Need Help?

In decimal form a *rational* number terminates or repeats. In decimal form an *irrational* number continues without repeating.

Some square roots are rational numbers and some are irrational numbers.

Rational: $\sqrt{100} = 10$ $\pm\sqrt{0.36} = \pm 0.6$ $\sqrt{\frac{16}{121}} = \frac{4}{11}$

Irrational: $\sqrt{10} \approx 3.16227766$ $\sqrt{\frac{1}{7}} \approx 0.377964473$

2 EXAMPLE **Rational and Irrational Square Roots**

Tell whether each expression is *rational* or *irrational*.

a. $\pm\sqrt{81} = \pm 9$ rational

b. $-\sqrt{1.44} = -1.2$ rational

c. $-\sqrt{5} \approx -2.23606797$ irrational

d. $\sqrt{\frac{4}{9}} = \frac{2}{3}$ rational

e. $\sqrt{\frac{1}{3}} \approx 0.57735026$ irrational

✓ **Check Understanding** ② Tell whether each expression is *rational* or *irrational*.

a. $\sqrt{8}$ irrational   **b.** $\pm\sqrt{225}$ rational **c.** $-\sqrt{75}$ irrational **d.** $\sqrt{\frac{1}{4}}$ rational

OBJECTIVE

2 Estimating and Using Square Roots

The squares of integers are called **perfect squares.**

consecutive integers:	1	2	3	4	5	6
	↓	↓	↓	↓	↓	↓
consecutive perfect squares:	1	4	9	16	25	36

You can estimate square roots by using perfect squares.

3 EXAMPLE **Estimating Square Roots**

Estimation Between what two consecutive integers is $\sqrt{14.52}$?

$\sqrt{9}$ < $\sqrt{14.52}$ < $\sqrt{16}$ **14.52 is between the two consecutive perfect squares 9 and 16.**

↓   ↓   ↓

3 < $\sqrt{14.52}$ < 4   **The square roots of 9 and 16 are 3 and 4, respectively.**

$\sqrt{14.52}$ is between 3 and 4.

✓ **Check Understanding** ③ Between what two consecutive integers is $-\sqrt{105}$? **−11 and −10**

You can find the approximate value of a square root using a calculator.

Calculator Hint

Use the sequence

$\sqrt{}$ 14.52 [ENTER]

to find $\sqrt{14.52}$.

---

4 EXAMPLE **Approximating Square Roots With a Calculator**

Calculator Find $\sqrt{14.52}$ to the nearest hundredth.

$\sqrt{14.52} \approx 3.810511777$ **Use a calculator.**

≈ 3.81 **Round to the nearest hundredth.**

✓ **Check Understanding** ④ Find $\sqrt{17.81}$ to the nearest hundredth. **4.22**

Lesson 10-3 Finding and Estimating Square Roots   **525**

🌱 **Reaching All Students**

Below Level Take a few minutes to review multiplying fractions before students delve into this lesson.	**Advanced Learners** Have students investigate and explain the connection between the formula in Example 5 and the Pythagorean Theorem.	**Error Prevention** See note on page 526.

---

2. Teach

Professional Development

Math Background

The word "radical" comes from *radix*, the Latin word for *root*.

OBJECTIVE

1 Teaching Notes

Additional Examples

① Simplify each expression.

a. $\sqrt{25}$ 5   **b.** $\pm\sqrt{\frac{9}{25}}$ $\pm\frac{3}{5}$

c. $-\sqrt{64}$ −8 **d.** $\sqrt{-49}$ undefined

e. $\sqrt{\frac{1}{16}}$ $\frac{1}{4}$

② Tell whether each expression is *rational* or *irrational*.

a. $\pm\sqrt{144}$ rational

b. $-\sqrt{\frac{1}{5}}$ irrational

c. $-\sqrt{6.25}$ rational

d. $\sqrt{\frac{1}{9}}$ rational

e. $\sqrt{7}$ irrational

OBJECTIVE

2 Teaching Notes

Additional Examples

③ Between what two consecutive integers is $\sqrt{28.34}$? **5 and 6**

④ Find $\sqrt{28.34}$ to the nearest hundredth. **5.32**

⑤ The formula $d = \sqrt{x^2 + (3x)^2}$ gives the length of the diagonal of a rectangular field that has a length three times its width x. Find the length of the diagonal if $x = 8$ ft. **about 25.3 ft**

Closure

Ask students to explain what $\sqrt{x}$, $-\sqrt{x}$, and $\pm\sqrt{x}$ represent where x is any positive real number. $\sqrt{x}$ represents the principal, or positive, square root of x. $-\sqrt{x}$ represents the negative square root. $\pm\sqrt{x}$ represents the positive and negative square roots.

525

3. Practice

Error Prevention

Exercises 26–34 Remind students that every positive number has *two* square roots.

Teaching Tip

Exercise 54 Encourage students to begin by trying real numbers greater than or equal to 1 and then trying real numbers between 0 and 1. They will discover that the square root of a fraction between 0 and 1 is larger than itself. For example, $\sqrt{\frac{1}{4}} = \frac{1}{2}$. Suggest to students that they reword the statement to make it true.

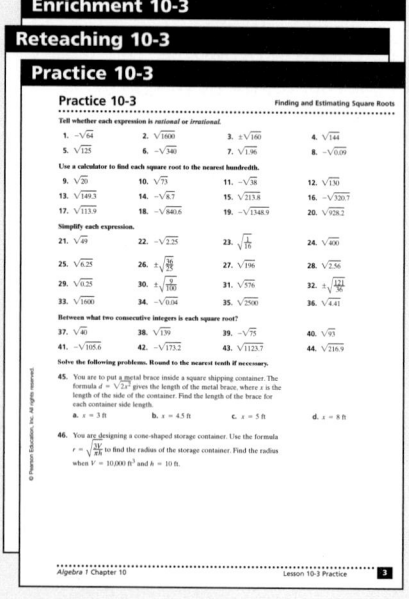

Many real-world formulas involve square roots.

5 EXAMPLE **Real-World 🌐 Problem Solving**

Construction The formula $d = \sqrt{x^2 + (2x)^2}$ gives the length d of each wire for the tower at the left. Find the length of the wire if $x = 12$ ft.

$d = \sqrt{x^2 + (2x)^2}$
$d = \sqrt{12^2 + (2 \cdot 12)^2}$ **Substitute 12 for x.**
$d = \sqrt{144 + 576}$ **Simplify.**
$d = \sqrt{720}$
$d \approx 26.8$ **Use a calculator. Round to the nearest tenth.**

The wire is about 26.8 ft long.

✔ Check Understanding **5** Suppose the tower is 140 ft tall. How long is the supporting wire? Round to the nearest tenth of a foot. **156.5 ft**

EXERCISES

For more practice, see *Extra Practice*.

Practice and Problem Solving

Ⓐ Practice by Example

Example 1
(page 524)

Simplify each expression.

1. $\sqrt{169}$ **13**   **2.** $\sqrt{400}$ **20**   **3.** $\sqrt{\frac{1}{9}}$ $\frac{1}{3}$ **4.** $\sqrt{900}$ **30**

5. $\sqrt{0.25}$ **0.5**   **6.** $\sqrt{\frac{36}{49}}$ $\frac{6}{7}$ **7.** $-\sqrt{1.21}$ **−1.1**   **8.** $\sqrt{1.96}$ **1.4**

9. $\sqrt{0.36}$ **0.6**   **10.** $-\sqrt{144}$ **−12**   **11.** $\sqrt{\frac{25}{16}}$ $\frac{5}{4}$ **12.** $\pm\sqrt{0.01}$ **±0.1**

Example 2
(page 525)

Tell whether each expression is *rational* or *irrational*.

13. $\sqrt{37}$ **irrational**   **14.** $-\sqrt{0.04}$ **rational**   **15.** $\pm\sqrt{\frac{1}{5}}$ **irrational**   **16.** $-\sqrt{\frac{16}{121}}$ **rational**

Example 3
(page 525)

Between what two consecutive integers is each square root?

17. $\sqrt{35}$ **5 and 6**   **18.** $\sqrt{27}$ **5 and 6**   **19.** $-\sqrt{130}$ **−12 and −11**   **20.** $\sqrt{170}$ **13 and 14**

Example 4
(page 525)

Use a calculator to find each square root to the nearest hundredth.

21. $\sqrt{12}$ **3.46**   **22.** $-\sqrt{203}$ **−14.25**   **23.** $\sqrt{11{,}550}$ **107.47**   **24.** $-\sqrt{150}$ **−12.25**

Example 5
(page 526)

25. Sports The elasticity coefficient e of a ball relates the height r of its rebound to the height h from which it is dropped. You can use the function $e = \sqrt{\frac{r}{h}}$ to find the elasticity coefficient. What is the elasticity coefficient of a tennis ball that rebounds 3 ft after it is dropped from a height of 3.5 ft? Round to the nearest hundredth. **0.93**

Ⓑ Apply Your Skills

Find the square root(s) of each number.

26. 400 **±20**   **27.** 0 **0**   **28.** 625 **±25**   **29.** $\frac{9}{49}$ **±$\frac{3}{7}$**

30. 1.69 **±1.3**   **31.** $\frac{1}{81}$ **±$\frac{1}{9}$**   **32.** 729 **±27**   **33.** 2.25 **±1.5**

34. 256 **±16**   **35.** 0.01 **±0.1**   **36.** $\frac{64}{121}$ **±$\frac{8}{11}$**   **37.** 40804 **±202**

38. Critical Thinking What number other than 0 is its own square root? **1**

39. Space The formula
$d = \sqrt{12{,}800h + h^2}$
gives the distance d in
kilometers to the horizon
from a satellite h kilometers
above Earth.

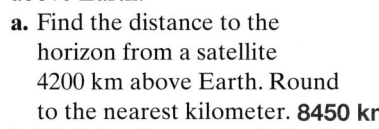
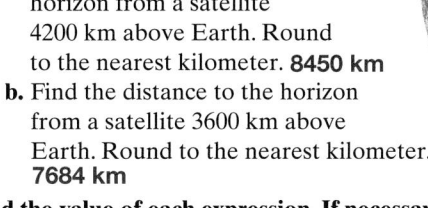
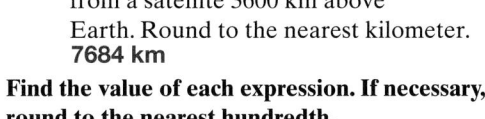

   a. Find the distance to the
horizon from a satellite
4200 km above Earth. Round
to the nearest kilometer. **8450 km**

   b. Find the distance to the horizon
from a satellite 3600 km above
Earth. Round to the nearest kilometer.
7684 km

**Find the value of each expression. If necessary,
round to the nearest hundredth.**

40. $\sqrt{441}$ **21**   **41.** $-\sqrt{\frac{4}{25}}$ $-\frac{2}{5}$ **42.** $\sqrt{2}$ **1.41**

43. $\sqrt{1.6}$ **1.26**   **44.** $-\sqrt{30}$ **−5.48**   **45.** $-\sqrt{1089}$ **−33**

46. $-\sqrt{0.64}$ **−0.8**   **47.** $\sqrt{41}$ **6.40**   **48.** $\sqrt{75}$ **8.66**

**49. Answers may vary.
Sample: The first
expression means
the neg. square root
of 1 and the second
expression means
the pos. square root
of 1.**

 49. Writing Explain the difference between $-\sqrt{1}$ and $\sqrt{1}$. **See left.**

50. Open-Ended Find two integers a and b between 1 and 20 such that $a^2 + b^2$ is a
perfect square. **Answers may vary. Sample: 3 and 4**

51. In the cartoon, to what number is the golfer referring? **4**

C Challenge **52. Physics** If you drop an object, the time t in seconds
that it takes to fall d feet is given by the formula $t = \sqrt{\frac{d}{16}}$.

   a. Find the time it takes an object to fall 400 ft. **5 s**

   b. Find the time it takes an object to fall 1600 ft. **10 s**

   c. Critical Thinking In part (b), the object falls four times as far as in part (a).
Does it take four times as long to fall? Explain.
No; the object takes twice as long to fall.

Critical Thinking For Exercises 53–58, tell whether each statement is *true* or *false*.
If the statement is false, give a counterexample.

53. Every nonnegative number has two square roots. **False; zero has one
square root.**

54. The square root of a positive number is always less than the number.
false; $\sqrt{1} = 1$

55. The square root of an even perfect square is always an even number. **true**

56. If a number is the product of two perfect squares, it has a rational square root.
true

57. $\sqrt{p} + \sqrt{q} = \sqrt{p + q}$ **See margin.**

58. If $\sqrt{p}$ and $\sqrt{q}$ are both irrational, then $\sqrt{pq}$ is always an irrational number.
See margin.

Problem Solving Hint

For Exercise 54, use
positive values less
than 1, equal to 1, and
greater than 1 to help
you solve the problem.

pages 526–528   Exercises

57. False; answers may vary.
Sample: $\sqrt{4} + \sqrt{9} \neq$
$\sqrt{4 + 9}$.

58. False; answers may vary.
Sample: $\sqrt{12}$ and $\sqrt{3}$ are
irrational but $\sqrt{36}$ is
rational.

---

4. Assess

Lesson Quiz 10-3

1. Simplify each expression.

   a. $\sqrt{196}$ **14**

   b. $\pm\sqrt{\frac{4}{25}}$ $\pm\frac{2}{5}$

2. Tell whether each
expression is rational,
irrational, or undefined.

   a. $\pm\sqrt{\frac{3}{5}}$ **irrational**

   b. $\sqrt{-25}$ **undefined**

   c. $-\sqrt{2.25}$ **rational**

3. Between what two
consecutive integers
is $-\sqrt{54}$? **−8 and −7**

4. The formula $s = \sqrt{13.5d}$
estimates the speed s in
miles per hour that a car
was traveling, when it
applied its brakes and left
a skid mark d feet long on
a wet road. Estimate the
speed of a car that left a
120 foot long skid mark.
about 40.25 mph

Alternative Assessment

Have students work in pairs. One
student writes an answer, such as
−12, and the other student must
come up with a square root
expression that yields the answer,
such as $-\sqrt{144}$. Then, the first
student gives the second student
two consecutive integers
(negative or positive) and the
second student comes up with
a square root expression whose
value lies between them. Students
switch roles and repeat.

A sheet of blank grids is available with the Test-Taking Strategies booklet. Give this sheet to students for practice with filling in the grids.

Resources
For additional practice with a variety of test item formats:
- Standardized Test Prep, p. 573
- Test-Taking Strategies, p. 568
- Test-Taking Strategies with Transparencies

Math Tip
Exercise 60 Remind students that 1.69 is equivalent to $\frac{169}{100}$. Encourage students to find the square root using this expression.

pages 526–528 Exercises

66.
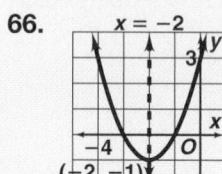

67.
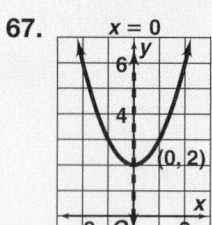

68.
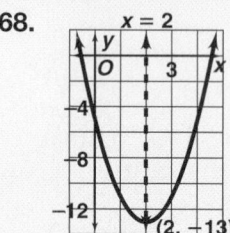

69.
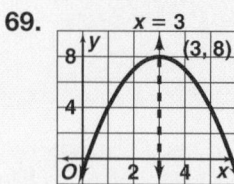

70.
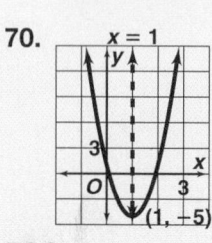

59a. 4 units²

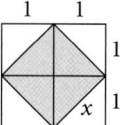

59. a. What is the total area of the large square shown at the right? **4 units²**
   b. What is the area of each shaded triangle? $\frac{1}{2}$ unit²
   c. What is the area of the shaded square? **2 units²**
   d. What is the length of the diagonal of each 1×1 square? $\sqrt{2}$ **units**

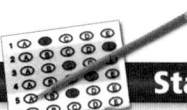
Standardized Test Prep

Gridded Response

60. Find the value of $\sqrt{1.69}$. **1.3**

61. Simplify the following expression. $\sqrt{4^2 + 3^2 + 11}$ **6**

62. Find the value of $\sqrt{\frac{4}{81}}$. $\frac{2}{9}$

63. Round $\sqrt{80}$ to the nearest whole number. **9**

64. The formula $\ell = \sqrt{\frac{A}{6}}$ relates the surface area A of a cube to the length of its edge ℓ. A cube has a surface area of 726 cm². How many centimeters is the length of the edge? **11**

65. Find the area of the shaded region. **128**

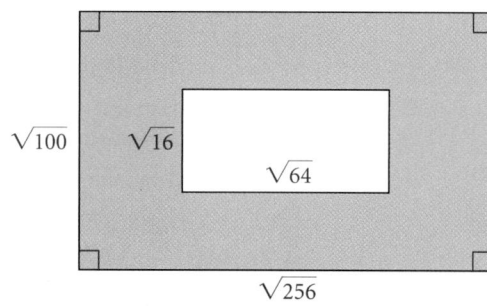

Take It to the NET
Online lesson quiz at
www.PHSchool.com
Web Code: aea-1003

Mixed Review

Lesson 10-2   **Graph each function. Label the axis of symmetry and the vertex. 66–71. See margin.**

66. $y = x^2 + 4x + 3$ **67.** $y = x^2 + 2$

68. $y = 2x^2 - 8x - 5$ **69.** $y = -x^2 + 6x - 1$

70. $y = 6x^2 - 12x + 1$ **71.** $y = -3x^2 + 18x$

Lesson 9-4   **Simplify each expression.**

$9t^2 - 25$

72. $(d + 9)(d - 9)$ $d^2 - 81$ **73.** $(3t - 5)(3t + 5)$ **74.** $85 \cdot 95$ **8075**

75. $x^2 + 26x + 169$ **75.** $(x + 13)^2$ **76.** $(4y - 7)^2$ **77.** 101^2 **10,201**

76. $16y^2 - 56y + 49$ **78.** 902^2 **813,604**   **79.** $(6k - 7)(6k + 7)$ **80.** $(12b - 7)^2$
                                                            $36k^2 - 49$ $144b^2 - 168b + 49$

Lesson 8-1   **Evaluate each expression for $x = 3$, $y = -2$, and $z = 6$.**

81. $x^{-2}y^{-1}z^2$ -2 **82.** $\frac{y^{-2}}{x^{-3}z^2}$ $\frac{3}{16}$ **83.** $\frac{x^0 y^{-3}}{z^{-1}}$ $-\frac{3}{4}$

84. $\frac{x^2 y^{-1}}{z^{-3}}$ -972 **85.** $x^{-1}y^{-2}z^0$ $\frac{1}{12}$ **86.** $x^2 y^{-4}z^2$ $\frac{81}{4}$

---

528   Chapter 10   Quadratic Equations and Functions

71.
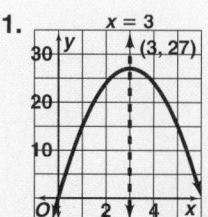

Solving Quadratic Equations

4.02 Graph, factor, and evaluate quadratic functions to solve problems.

Lesson Preview

What You'll Learn

OBJECTIVE 1 To solve quadratic equations by graphing

OBJECTIVE 2 To solve quadratic equations using square roots

. . . And Why

To use square roots in a real-world situation involving city planning, as in Example 3

✓ **Check Skills You'll Need** (For help, go to Lesson 10-3.)

Simplify each expression.

1. $\sqrt{36}$ **6**
2. $-\sqrt{81}$ **−9**
3. $\pm\sqrt{121}$ **±11**
4. $\sqrt{1.44}$ **1.2**
5. $\sqrt{0.25}$ **0.5**
6. $\pm\sqrt{1.21}$ **±1.1**
7. $\sqrt{\frac{1}{4}}$ **$\frac{1}{2}$**
8. $\pm\sqrt{\frac{1}{9}}$ **$\pm\frac{1}{3}$**
9. $\sqrt{\frac{49}{100}}$ **$\frac{7}{10}$**

New Vocabulary • quadratic equation • standard form of a quadratic equation

 Interactive lesson includes instant self-check, tutorials, and activities.

OBJECTIVE 1

Solving Quadratic Equations by Graphing

Investigation: Finding x-intercepts

1. Find the x-intercepts of each graph.

a. $y = 2x - 3$ $1\frac{1}{2}$
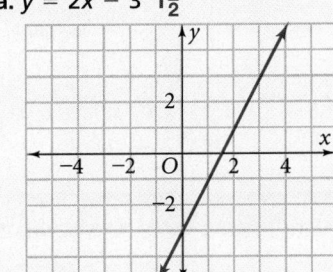

b. $y = x^2 + 3x - 4$ **−4 and 1**
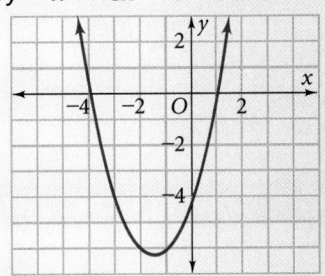

2. a. Solve $2x - 3 = 0$. $1\frac{1}{2}$
   b. Is the solution of $2x - 3 = 0$ the same as the x-intercept of $y = 2x - 3$? **yes**

3. Do the x-intercepts that you found in Question 1b satisfy the equation $x^2 + 3x - 4 = 0$? **yes**

4a.
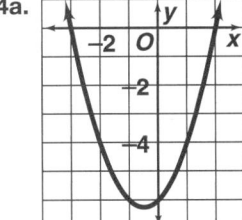

4. a. Graph $y = x^2 + x - 6$. **See left.**
   b. Find the x-intercepts of the graph of $y = x^2 + x - 6$. **−3 and 2**
   c. Do the values you found in part (b) satisfy the equation $x^2 + x - 6 = 0$? **yes**

The equation $x^2 + 3x - 4 = 0$ is called a quadratic equation, and its related quadratic function is $y = x^2 + 3x - 4$. The solutions of a quadratic equation and the x-intercepts of its related quadratic function are the same.

---

1. Plan

Lesson Preview

✓ **Check Skills You'll Need**

Finding and Estimating Square Roots
Lesson 10-3: Example 1
Exercises 1–12
Extra Practice, p. 711

Lesson Resources

📁 **Teaching Resources**
Practice, Reteaching, Enrichment
Checkpoint Quiz 1

👥 **Reaching All Students**
Practice Workbook 10-4
Spanish Practice Workbook 10-4
Reading and Math Literacy 10B
Spanish Reading & Literacy 10B
Spanish Checkpoint Quiz 1
Technology Activities 7, 24
Basic Algebra Planning Guide 10-4

⏱ **Presentation Assistant Plus!**
Transparencies
• Check Skills You'll Need 10-4
• Additional Examples 10-4
• Student Edition Answers 10-4
• Lesson Quiz 10-4
PH Presentation Pro CD 10-4

 **ASSESSMENT SYSTEM**

Checkpoint Quiz 1
Computer Test Generator CD

💿 **Technology**
Resource Pro® CD-ROM
Computer Test Generator CD
Prentice Hall Presentation Pro CD

💻 **www.PHSchool.com**
Student Site
• Teacher Web Code: aek-5500
• Reasoning & Puzzles pp. 96, 97
• Self-grading Lesson Quiz
Teacher Center
• Lesson Planner
• Resources

Plus

Ongoing Assessment and Intervention

Before the Lesson
Diagnose prerequisite skills using:
• Check Skills You'll Need

During the Lesson
Monitor progress using:
• Check Understanding
• Additional Examples
• Standardized Test Prep

After the Lesson
Assess knowledge using:
• Lesson Quiz
• Computer Test Generator CD
• Chapter Checkpoint 1 (p. 534)

2. Teach

Math Background

An equation of the form $y = a(x - h)^2 + k$ represents a translation of the basic parabola h vertical units and k horizonal units.

OBJECTIVE
1 Teaching Notes

Investigation (Optional)
Remind students that the x-intercepts are the x-coordinates of the points where the graph crosses the x-axis. At these points, $y = 0$.

1 EXAMPLE Alternative Method

Have students sketch graphs of quadratic functions whose related quadratic equations have zero, one, or two solution(s).

Additional Examples

1 Solve each equation by graphing the related function.
a. $2x^2 = 0$ **0**
b. $2x^2 + 2 = 0$ **no solution**
c. $2x^2 - 2 = 0$ **±1**

OBJECTIVE
2 Teaching Notes

Additional Examples

2 Solve $3x^2 - 75 = 0$. **±5**

3 A museum is planning an exhibit that will contain a large globe. The surface area of the globe will be 315 ft². Find the radius of the sphere producing this surface area. Use the equation $S = 4\pi r^2$, where S is the surface area and r is the radius. **about 5 ft**

Closure

Ask: *How many solutions does a quadratic equation have?* none, one, or two *How can you determine the number of solutions from the graph?* The number of solutions is the same as the number of x-intercepts.

530

 Key Concepts

Definition	**Standard Form of a Quadratic Equation**

A **quadratic equation** is an equation that can be written in the form $ax^2 + bx + c = 0$, where $a \neq 0$. This form is called the **standard form of a quadratic equation.**

A quadratic equation can have two, one, or no real-number solutions. In a future course you will learn about solutions of quadratic equations that are not real numbers. In this course *solutions* refers to real-number solutions.

You can solve some quadratic equations by graphing their related functions.

1 EXAMPLE Solving by Graphing

Solve each equation by graphing the related function.

a. $x^2 - 4 = 0$
Graph $y = x^2 - 4$.

b. $x^2 = 0$
Graph $y = x^2$.

c. $x^2 + 4 = 0$
Graph $y = x^2 + 4$.

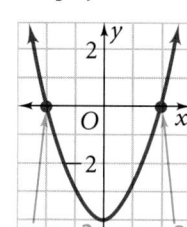
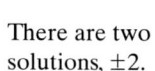

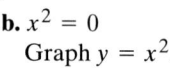
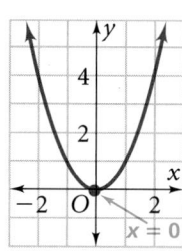

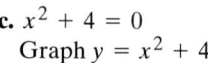
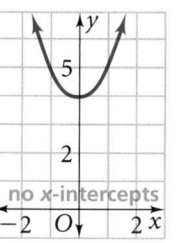

There are two solutions, ±2.

There is one solution, 0.

There is no solution.

✓ Check Understanding **1** Solve each equation by graphing the related function. **a–c. See margin.**
a. $x^2 - 1 = 0$
b. $2x^2 + 4 = 0$
c. $x^2 - 16 = -16$

OBJECTIVE
2 Solving Quadratic Equations Using Square Roots

You can solve equations of the form $x^2 = a$ by finding the square roots of each side. Since $6^2 = 36$ and $(-6)^2 = 36$ are both true statements, 6 and -6 are both solutions to the equation $x^2 = 36$. We write the solution to $x^2 = 36$ as $\pm\sqrt{36}$ or ± 6.

2 EXAMPLE Using Square Roots

Solve $2x^2 - 98 = 0$.

$2x^2 - 98 + 98 = 0 + 98$ **Add 98 to each side.**
$2x^2 = 98$
$x^2 = 49$ **Divide each side by 2.**
$x = \pm\sqrt{49}$ **Find the square roots.**
$x = \pm 7$ **Simplify.**

✓ Check Understanding **2** Solve each equation.
a. $t^2 - 25 = 0$ **±5**
b. $3n^2 + 12 = 12$ **0**
c. $2g^2 + 32 = 0$ **no solution**

530 Chapter 10 Quadratic Equations and Functions

👥 Reaching All Students

Below Level Emphasize that just because a quadratic function can be graphed does not imply that its related equation can be solved.	**Advanced Learners** Have students discuss how to determine if a quadratic equation has any solutions.	**English Learners** See note on page 532. **Alternative Method** See note on page 530.

You can solve real-world problems by finding square roots. In many cases, the negative solution of a quadratic equation will not be a reasonable solution to the original problem.

3 EXAMPLE Real-World  **Problem Solving**

City Planning A city is planning a circular duck pond for a new park. The depth of the pond will be 4 ft. Because of water resources, the maximum volume will be 20,000 ft³. Find the radius of the pond. Use the equation $V = \pi r^2 h$, where V is the volume, r is the radius, and h is the depth.

$$V = \pi r^2 h$$

$20,000 = \pi r^2(4)$ Substitute 20,000 for V and 4 for h.

$\dfrac{20,000}{(\pi \cdot 4)} = r^2$ Put in calculator-ready form.

$\sqrt{\dfrac{20,000}{(\pi \cdot 4)}} = r$ Find the principal square root.

$39.89422804 \approx r$ Use a calculator.

● The pond will have a radius of about 39.9 ft.

Real-World  Connection
Ponds and fountains enhance the quality of life in cities around the world.

 **✓ Check Understanding** ● **3** A city is planning a circular fountain. The depth of the fountain will be 3 ft. The maximum volume will be 1800 ft³. Find the radius of the fountain. **about 14 ft**

EXERCISES

For more practice, see *Extra Practice*.

Practice and Problem Solving

A Practice by Example

Example 1
(page 530)

Solve each equation by graphing the related function. If the equation has no solution, write *no solution*. 1–9. See back of book.

1. $x^2 - 9 = 0$ **2.** $x^2 + 5 = 0$ **3.** $4x^2 = 0$

4. $2x^2 - 8 = 0$ **5.** $x^2 + 16 = 0$ **6.** $\frac{1}{3}x^2 - 3 = 0$

7. $\frac{1}{2}x^2 + 1 = 0$ **8.** $x^2 + 7 = 7$ **9.** $\frac{1}{4}x^2 - 1 = 0$

Example 2
(page 530)

Solve each equation by finding square roots. If the equation has no solution, write *no solution*.

10. $k^2 = 49$ **±7**   **11.** $b^2 = 441$ **±21**   **12.** $m^2 - 225 = 0$ **±15**

13. $c^2 + 25 = 25$ **0**   **14.** $x^2 - 9 = -16$ **no sol.**   **15.** $4r^2 = 25$ **±$\frac{5}{2}$**

16. $64p^2 = 4$ **±$\frac{1}{4}$**   **17.** $6w^2 - 24 = 0$ **±2**   **18.** $27 - y^2 = 0$ **±$\sqrt{27}$**

Example 3
(page 531)

Model each problem with a quadratic equation. Then solve. If necessary, round to the nearest tenth.

19. Find the side of a square with an area of 256 m². $x^2 = 256$; **16 m**

20. Find the side of a square with an area of 90 ft². $x^2 = 90$; **9.5 ft**

21. Find the radius of a circle with an area of 80 cm². $\pi r^2 = 80$; **5.0 cm**

Lesson 10-4 Solving Quadratic Equations **531**

---

pages 530–531 **Check Understanding**

1a. 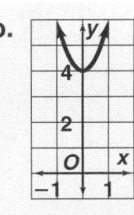 **±1**

b. 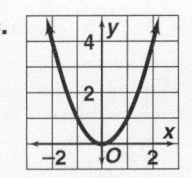 **no solution**

c. [graph] **0**

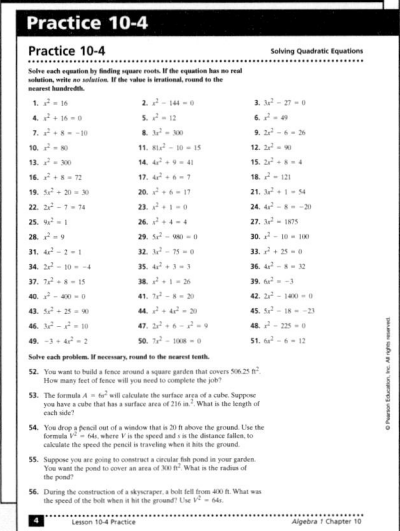

Connection to History
Exercise 34 Galileo used ramps to model the vertical motion formula.

English Learners
Exercise 39 Although they are likely to be aware of logos, some students may not be familiar with the word. Explain that a logo is a symbol, design, or trademark that is used to represent a company or organization. Ask students to give examples of familiar logos.

 **Apply Your Skills** **22. Geometry** Suppose a map company wants to produce a globe with a surface area of 450 in.^{2}. Use the formula $A = 4\pi r^2$, where A is the surface area and r is the radius of the sphere.
    a. What should the radius be? Round to the nearest tenth of an inch. **6.0 in.**
    b. Critical Thinking Why is the principal square root the only root that makes sense in this situation? **The length of a radius cannot be negative.**

Mental Math **Tell the number of solutions each equation has.**

23. $y^2 = -36$ **none**   **24.** $a^2 - 12 = 6$ **two**   **25.** $n^2 - 15 = -15$ **one**

 26. Framing Find dimensions for the square picture at the right that would make the area of the picture equal to 75% of the total area enclosed by the frame. Round to the nearest tenth of an inch. **10.4 in. by 10.4 in.**

x 12 in

27. Suppose you have a can of paint that will cover 400 ft^2.
    a. Find the radius of the largest circle you can paint. Round to the nearest tenth of a foot. (*Hint:* Use the formula $A = \pi r^2$.) **11.3 ft**
    b. Suppose you have two cans of paint, which will cover a total of 800 ft^2. Find the radius of the largest circle you can paint. Round to the nearest tenth of a foot. **16.0 ft**
    c. Critical Thinking Does the radius of the circle double when the amount of paint doubles? Explain. **No; the radius increases by about 1.4 times.**

Solve each equation by finding square roots. If the equation has no solution, write *no solution.* **If the value is irrational, round to the nearest tenth.**

28. $1.2q^2 - 7 = -34$ **no solution**   **29.** $49t^2 - 16 = -7$ $\pm\frac{3}{7}$ **30.** $3d^2 - \frac{1}{12} = 0$ $\pm\frac{1}{6}$
31. $\frac{1}{2}x^2 - 4 = 0$ **±2.8**   **32.** $7h^2 + 0.12 = 1.24$ **±0.4** **33.** $-\frac{1}{4}x^2 + 3 = 0$ **±3.5**

 34. Physics The equation $d = \frac{1}{2}at^2$ gives the distance d an object starting at rest travels given acceleration a and time t.
Suppose a ball rolls down the ramp shown at the right with acceleration $a = 2$ ft/s^2. Find the time it will take to roll from the top of the ramp to the bottom. Round to the nearest tenth of a second. **3.5 s**

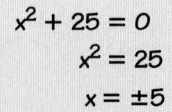

12 ft

35. Find a value for c such that the equation $x^2 - c = 0$ has 11 and -11 as solutions. **121**

36. a. Critical Thinking For what values of n will $x^2 = n$ have two solutions? **$n > 0$**
    b. For what value of n will $x^2 = n$ have exactly one solution? **$n = 0$**
    c. For what values of n will $x^2 = n$ have no solution? **$n < 0$**

37. Answers may vary.
Sample: Michael
subtracted 25 from
the left side of the
equation but added
25 to the right side.

37. Error Analysis Michael's work is shown at the right. Explain the error that he made. **See left.**

$x^2 + 25 = 0$
$x^2 = 25$
$x = \pm5$

38. a. Solve $x^2 - 4 = 0$ and $2x^2 - 8 = 0$ **2, −2; 2, −2** by graphing their related functions.
    b. Critical Thinking Why does it make sense that the graphs have the same x-intercepts? **See margin.**

532   Chapter 10   Quadratic Equations and Functions

pages 531–534   **Exercises**

38a.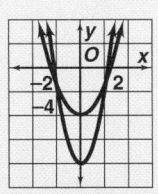

    b. The first equation multiplied by 2 on both sides equals the second equation.

BIKE CLUB

39a. square: $4r^2$, circle: πr^2

 39. Design Suppose your class wants to design a T-shirt logo similar to the one shown at the left. You want the shaded region to have an area of 80 in.^{2}.
a. Write expressions for the area of the square and of the circle. **See left.**
b. Write an equation for the area of the shaded region. $4r^2 - \pi r^2 = 80$
c. Solve the equation to find the radius of the circle and the side of the square. Round to the nearest tenth of an inch. **9.7 in., 19.3 in.**

40. Open-Ended Write and solve equations in the form $ax^2 + c = 0$ for each of the following. **Answers may vary. Sample:**
a. The equation has no solutions. $5x^2 + 10 = 0$, no solution
b. The equation has one solution. $2x^2 + 0 = 0, x = 0$
c. The equation has two solutions. $-20x^2 + 80 = 0, x = \pm 2$

Geometry Find the value of h for each triangle. If necessary, round to the nearest tenth.

41.
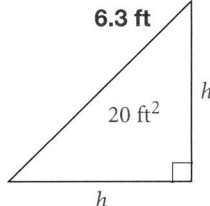
6.3 ft
h
20 ft^2
h

42.
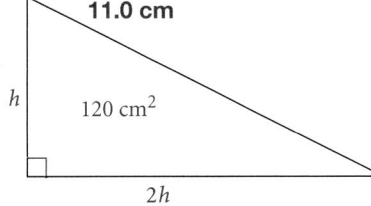
11.0 cm
h
120 cm^2
$2h$

C Challenge

 43. Physics The time t a pendulum takes to make a complete swing back and forth depends on the length of the pendulum. The formula $\ell = \frac{2.45t^2}{\pi^2}$ relates the length of a pendulum ℓ in meters to the time t in seconds.
a. Find the length of the pendulum if $t = 1$ s. Round to the nearest tenth. **0.2 m**
b. Find t if $\ell = 1.6$ m. Round to the nearest tenth. **2.5 s**
c. Find t if $\ell = 2.2$ m. Round to the nearest tenth. **3.0 s**
 d. **Writing** You can adjust a clock that has a pendulum by making the pendulum longer or shorter. If a clock is running slowly, would you lengthen or shorten the pendulum to make the clock run faster? Explain.
Shorten; as ℓ decreases, t decreases.

44. a. Solve the equation $(x + 7)^2 = 0$. **−7**
b. Find the vertex of the related function $y = (x + 7)^2$. **(−7, 0)**
c. **Open-Ended** Choose a value for h and repeat parts (a) and (b) using $(x + h)^2 = 0$ and $y = (x + h)^2$. **Answers may vary. Sample: $h = 5, -5$,**
d. Where would you expect to find the vertex of $y = (x - 4)^2$? Explain. **(−5, 0)**
(4, 0); the vertex is at (−h, 0).

45. Geometry The trapezoid has an area of 1960 cm^2. Use the formula $A = \frac{1}{2}h(b_1 + b_2)$ to find the value of y.
28 cm

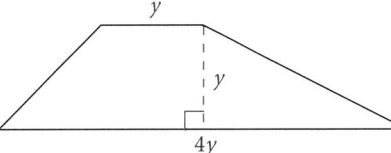
y
y
$4y$

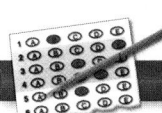

Standardized Test Prep

Multiple Choice

46. Which of the following shows all of the real solutions of $3x^2 - 48 = 0$? **B**
A. 4   B. −4, 4   C. −16, 16   D. no solution

47. For which of the following values of c does $5x^2 + c = 10$ have no real solutions? **I**
F. 1   G. 5   H. 9   I. 12

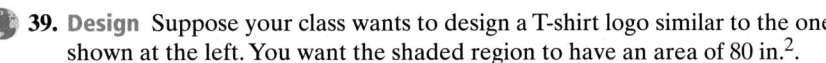

4. Assess

Lesson Quiz 10-4

1. Solve each equation by graphing the related function. If the equation has no solution, write *no solution*.
   a. $2x^2 - 8 = 0$ ±2
   b. $x^2 + 2 = -2$ no solution

2. Solve each equation by finding square roots.
   a. $m^2 - 25 = 0$ ±5
   b. $49q^2 = 9$ $\pm\frac{3}{7}$

3. Find the speed of a 4-kg bowling ball with a kinetic energy of 160 joules. Use the equation $E = \frac{1}{2}ms^2$, where m is the object's mass in kg, E is its kinetic energy, and s is the speed in meters per second. about 8.94 m/s

Alternative Assessment

Divide the class into groups of three. Tell each student to write an equation in the form $ax^2 + 0x + c = 0$ on a sheet of paper. Each student passes the paper to the student to the right. The next student writes the related function, graphs it, and passes the paper to the student on the right. The third student solves the equation using square roots and passes the paper to the originator to check.

533

Resources

For additional practice with a variety of test item formats:
- Standardized Test Prep, p. 573
- Test-Taking Strategies, p. 568
- Test-Taking Strategies with Transparencies

Chapter Checkpoint 1

To check understanding of Lessons 10-1 to 10-4:

Checkpoint Quiz 1 (p. 534)

Teaching Resources
Checkpoint Quiz 1 (also in Prentice Hall Assessment System)

Reaching All Students
Reading and Math Literacy 10B

Spanish versions available

pages 531–534   Exercises

49. [2]

x	y
-2	5
-1	-4
0	-7
1	-4
2	5

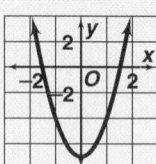

x-intercepts
≈1.5, ≈-1.5

[1] minor error in table OR incorrect graph

50. [4] a. $96 = 6s^2$
$s^2 = 16$
$s = 4$, so side is 4 ft.

b. $6(8)^2 = 6 \cdot 64 = 384$
The surface area is quadrupled.

[3] appropriate methods, but with one computational error

[2] part (a) done correctly

[1] no work shown

534

---

48. The x-intercepts of the graph at the right are solutions to which equation? **B**
A. $-0.25x^2 = 4$
B. $-0.25x^2 + 4 = 0$
C. $-0.5x^2 + 2 = 0$
D. $-4x^2 + 1 = 0$

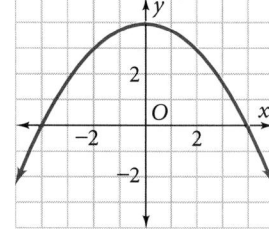

Short Response

49. Make a table for the function $y = 3x^2 - 7$. Graph the function. Estimate the value of the x-intercepts. **See margin.**

Extended Response

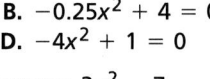
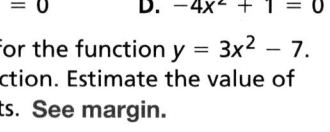
Take It to the NET
Online lesson quiz at
www.PHSchool.com
Web Code: aea-1004

50. The surface area of a cube is 96 ft^2.
a. Find the length of each edge. Show your work. **a–b. See margin.**
b. If you double the length of each edge, what happens to the surface area of the cube? Show your work.

Mixed Review

Lesson 10-3   **Simplify each expression.**

51. $\sqrt{9}$ **3**
52. $-\sqrt{169}$ **-13**
53. $\sqrt{1600}$ **40**
54. $\sqrt{225}$ **15**
55. $\sqrt{0.04}$ **0.2**
56. $-\sqrt{2.56}$ **-1.6**
57. $\sqrt{\frac{25}{64}}$ **$\frac{5}{8}$**
58. $\sqrt{\frac{49}{81}}$ **$\frac{7}{9}$**

Lesson 9-5   **Factor each expression.**

$(y - 13)(y - 2)$ $(a + 5)(a - 2)$
59. (x + 4)(x + 1)
59. $x^2 + 5x + 4$
60. $y^2 - 15y + 26$
61. $a^2 + 3a - 10$
62. $z^2 - 6z - 72$
$(z - 12)(z + 6)$
63. $c^2 - 14cd + 24d^2$
$(c - 12d)(c - 2d)$
64. $t^2 + tu - 2u^2$
$(t + 2u)(t - u)$

Lesson 8-2   **Write each number in scientific notation.**

65. 3,613,500
3.6135 × 10^6
66. 0.0000348
3.48 × 10^{-5}
67. -8.12
-8.12 × 10^0

Write each number in standard notation.

68. 3.1×10^4
31,000
69. 7.01×10^5
701,000
70. 6.2×10^{-4}
0.00062

Checkpoint Quiz 1   **Lessons 10-1 through 10-4**

Instant self-check quiz online and on CD-ROM

Graph each function. Label the axis of symmetry and the vertex. 1–3. See margin.

1. $y = x^2 - 4$
2. $y = 8x^2 - 2x$
3. $f(x) = x^2 + 5x - 6$

4. A ball is thrown up in the air. Its height h in feet after t seconds is given by the function $h = -16t^2 + 24t + 6$.
a. When does the ball reach its maximum height? **0.75 s**
b. What is the ball's maximum height? **15 ft**

Simplify each expression.

5. $\sqrt{100}$ **10**
6. $\pm\sqrt{0.36}$ **±0.6**
7. $-\sqrt{4}$ **-2**

Solve each equation.

8. $t^2 - 64 = 0$ **±8**
9. $6m^2 - 150 = 0$ **±5**

10.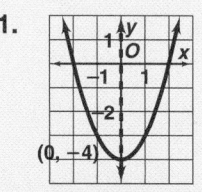
±3

10. Solve $3x^2 - 27 = 0$ by graphing the related function. **See left.**

534   Chapter 10   Quadratic Equations and Functions

---

page 534   Checkpoint Quiz 1

1.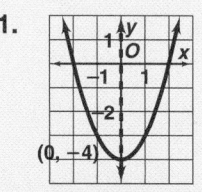
x = 0
(0, -4)

2.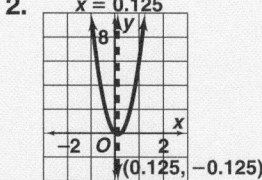
x = 0.125
(0.125, -0.125)

3.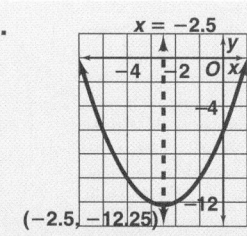
x = -2.5
(-2.5, -12.25)

Finding Roots

FOR USE WITH LESSON 10-5

The solutions of a quadratic equation are the x-intercepts of the related quadratic function. The solutions of a quadratic equation and the related x-intercepts are often called *roots* of the equation or *zeros* of the function.

Take It to the NET
Graphing Calculator procedures online at **www.PHSchool.com**
Web Code: aea-2110

EXAMPLE

Use a graphing calculator to solve $x^2 - 6x + 3 = 0$.

Step 1

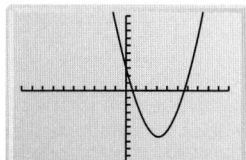

Enter $y = x^2 - 6x + 3$. Use the **CALC** feature. Select 2:**ZERO**. The calculator will plot the graph.

Step 2

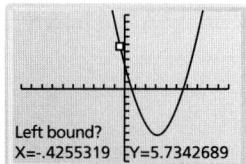

Left bound?
X=-.4255319 Y=5.7342689

Move the cursor to the left of the first x-intercept. Press ENTER to set the left bound.

Step 3

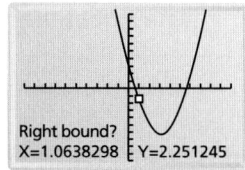

Right bound?
X=1.0638298 Y=2.251245

Move the cursor slightly to the right of the intercept. Press ENTER to set the right bound.

Step 4

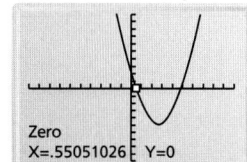

Zero
X=.55051026 Y=0

Press ENTER to display the first root, which is about 0.55.

Repeating the steps near the second intercept, you find that the second root is about 5.45. So the solutions are about 0.55 and 5.45.

Suppose you cannot see both of the x-intercepts on your graph. You can find the values of y that are close to zero by using the **TABLE** feature. You can use the **TBLSET** feature to control how the table behaves. Set ΔTbl to 0.5. Set **Indpnt:** and **Depend:** to **Auto**. The calculator screen at the right shows part of the table for $y = 2x^2 - 48x + 285$.

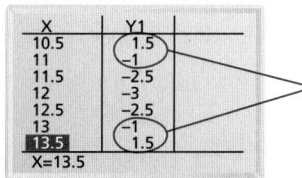

X	Y1
10.5	1.5
11	-1
11.5	-2.5
12	-3
12.5	-2.5
13	-1
13.5	1.5

X=13.5

The graph crosses the x-axis when the values for y change signs. So the range of values of x should include 10.5 and 13.5.

EXERCISES

1. Find the x-intercepts of $y = 2x^2 - 48x + 285$. First use the WINDOW feature. Change Xmin to 10 and Xmax to 14. **10.78, 13.22**

Use a graphing calculator to solve each equation.

2. $x^2 - 6x - 16 = 0$ **−2, 8**   **3.** $2x^2 + x - 6 = 0$ **−2, 1.5**   **4.** $\frac{1}{3}x^2 + 8x - 3 = 0$ **−24.37, 0.37**

5. $x^2 - 18x + 5 = 0$ **0.28, 17.72**   **6.** $0.25x^2 - 8x - 45 = 0$ **7.** $0.5x^2 + 3x - 36 = 0$
−4.88, 36.88   **−12, 6**

8. Geometry A rectangle has a length of x and a width of $2x + 3$. It has an area of 200 cm^2.
  a. Write an equation using the dimensions and the area. **$2x^2 + 3x - 200 = 0$**
  b. Graph the related function using a graphing calculator. **See above.**
  c. Find the dimensions of the rectangle. Round to the nearest hundredth. **9.28 cm by 21.56 cm**

8b.
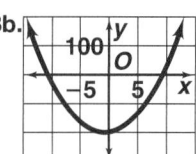

Finding Roots

Students use their graphing calculators to find the roots of quadratic equations, or the zeros of the related quadratic functions. The techniques learned in this feature will help students verify their work in Lesson 10-5.

Resources

Students may use any graphing calculator.

Teaching Notes

Error Prevention

Exercise 8 Remind students that they should first write the equation from part a in the standard form $ax^2 + bx + c = 0$, where $a \neq 0$, to find the related quadratic function for part b.

Lesson Preview

 Check Skills You'll Need

Solving Two-Step Equations
Lesson 2-2: Example 1
Exercises 1–16
Extra Practice, p. 703

Factoring Trinomials of the Type $ax^2 + bx + c$
Lesson 9-6: Examples 1, 2
Exercises 1–18
Extra Practice, p. 710

Lesson Resources

 Teaching Resources
Practice, Reteaching, Enrichment

 Reaching All Students
Practice Workbook 10-5
Spanish Practice Workbook 10-5
Basic Algebra Planning Guide 10-5

 Presentation Assistant Plus!
Transparencies
• Check Skills You'll Need 10-5
• Additional Examples 10-5
• Student Edition Answers 10-5
• Lesson Quiz 10-5
PH Presentation Pro CD 10-5

 ASSESSMENT SYSTEM

Computer Test Generator CD

 Technology
Resource Pro® CD-ROM
Computer Test Generator CD
Prentice Hall Presentation Pro CD

 www.PHSchool.com
Student Site
• Teacher Web Code: aek-5500
• Self-grading Lesson Quiz
Teacher Center
• Lesson Planner
• Resources

Plus

 10-5

Factoring to Solve Quadratic Equations

4.02 Graph, factor, and evaluate quadratic functions to solve problems.

 North Carolina Objectives

Lesson Preview

What You'll Learn

OBJECTIVE 1 To solve quadratic equations by factoring

. . . And Why

To find the dimensions of a box, as in Example 4

✓ **Check Skills You'll Need** (For help, go to Lessons 2-2 and 9-6.)

Solve and check each equation.

1. $6 + 4n = 2$ **−1**   **2.** $\frac{a}{8} - 9 = 4$ **104**   **3.** $7q + 16 = -3$ $-2\frac{5}{7}$

Factor each expression.

4. $2c^2 + 29c + 14$ **5.** $3p^2 + 32p + 20$ **6.** $4x^2 - 21x - 18$
   $(2c + 1)(c + 14)$ $(3p + 2)(p + 10)$ $(4x + 3)(x - 6)$

New Vocabulary • Zero-Product Property

 Interactive lesson includes instant self-check, tutorials, and activities.

In the previous lesson, you solved quadratic equations by finding square roots. This method works if $b = 0$. You can solve some quadratic equations when $b \neq 0$ by using the Zero-Product Property.

 Key Concepts

Property	Zero-Product Property

For every real number a and b, if $ab = 0$, then $a = 0$ or $b = 0$.

Example If $(x + 3)(x + 2) = 0$, then $x + 3 = 0$ or $x + 2 = 0$.

1 EXAMPLE **Using the Zero-Product Property**

Solve $(x + 5)(2x - 6) = 0$.

$(x + 5)(2x - 6) = 0$

$x + 5 = 0$ or $2x - 6 = 0$ **Use the Zero-Product Property.**

$2x = 6$ **Solve for x.**

$x = -5$ or $x = 3$

Check Substitute −5 for x.   Substitute 3 for x.

$(x + 5)(2x - 6) = 0$ $(x + 5)(2x - 6) = 0$

$(-5 + 5)[2(-5) - 6] \stackrel{?}{=} 0$ $(3 + 5)[2(3) - 6] \stackrel{?}{=} 0$

$(0)(-16) = 0 ✓$ $(8)(0) = 0 ✓$

✓ **Check Understanding** ① Solve each equation.

a. $(x + 7)(x - 4) = 0$ **b.** $(3y - 5)(y - 2) = 0$ **c.** $(6k + 9)(4k - 11) = 0$
   −7, 4 $\frac{5}{3}$, **2** $-\frac{3}{2}, \frac{11}{4}$

You can also use the Zero-Product Property to solve equations of the form $ax^2 + bx + c = 0$ if the quadratic expression $ax^2 + bx + c$ can be factored.

 ## Ongoing Assessment and Intervention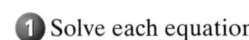

Before the Lesson	During the Lesson	After the Lesson
Diagnose prerequisite skills using:	**Monitor progress using:**	**Assess knowledge using:**
• Check Skills You'll Need	• Check Understanding	• Lesson Quiz
	• Additional Examples	• Computer Test Generator CD
	• Standardized Test Prep	

2 EXAMPLE Solving by Factoring

Solve $x^2 - 8x - 48 = 0$ by factoring.

$x^2 - 8x - 48 = 0$

$(x - 12)(x + 4) = 0$ **Factor $x^2 - 8x - 48$.**

$x - 12 = 0$ or $x + 4 = 0$ **Use the Zero-Product Property.**

$x = 12$ or $x = -4$ **Solve for x.**

✓ Check Understanding   **2** 2. Solve $x^2 + x - 12 = 0$ by factoring. **−4, 3**

Before solving a quadratic equation, you may need to add or subtract terms in order to write the equation in standard form. Then factor the quadratic expression.

3 EXAMPLE Solving by Factoring

Solve $2x^2 - 5x = 88$.

$2x^2 - 5x - 88 = 0$ **Subtract 88 from each side.**

$(2x + 11)(x - 8) = 0$ **Factor $2x^2 - 5x - 88$.**

$2x + 11 = 0$ or $x - 8 = 0$ **Use the Zero-Product Property.**

$2x = -11$ or $x = 8$ **Solve for x.**

$x = -5.5$

✓ Check Understanding   **3** Solve $x^2 - 12x = -36$. **6**

Quadratic equations can model real-world situations.

4 EXAMPLE Real-World 🌐 Problem Solving

Manufacturing The diagram shows a pattern for an open-top box. The total area of the sheet of material used to manufacture the box is 288 in.². The height of the box is 3 in. Therefore, 3-in. × 3-in. squares are cut from each corner. Find the dimensions of the box.

Define   Let x = width of a side of the box.
Then the width of the material = $x + 3 + 3 = x + 6$.
The length of the material = $x + 2 + 3 + 3 = x + 8$.

Relate   length × width = area of the sheet

Write $(x + 8)(x + 6) = 288$

$(x + 8)(x + 6) = 288$

$x^2 + 14x + 48 = 288$ **Find the product $(x + 8)(x + 6)$.**

$x^2 + 14x - 240 = 0$ **Subtract 288 from each side.**

$(x + 24)(x - 10) = 0$ **Factor $x^2 + 14x - 240$.**

$x + 24 = 0$ or $x - 10 = 0$ **Use the Zero-Product Property.**

$x = -24$ or $x = 10$ **Solve for x.**

The only reasonable solution is 10. So the dimensions of the box are 10 in. × 12 in. × 3 in.

waste material

3

3

$x + 2$

x

✓ Check Understanding   **4** Suppose that a box has a base with a width of x, a length of $x + 1$, and a height of 2 in. It is cut from a rectangular sheet of material with an area of 182 in.². Find the dimensions of the box. **9 in. × 10 in. × 2 in.**

2. Teach

Professional Development

Math Background

Another way of stating the Zero-Product Property is to say that zero is the only factor that yields a product of zero. Thus, if a product is zero, at least one of the factors must be zero.

OBJECTIVE
1 Teaching Notes

1 EXAMPLE Teaching Tip

Encourage students to rewrite the quadratic equation in Example 1 in standard form to help them see how Examples 1 and 2 are related.

4 EXAMPLE Visual Learners

Some students may have difficulty visualizing how the diagram is used to form a box. Using a piece of paper, cut out 3 in. squares from each corner and fold the edges to form the open-top box. This will also help students understand the expressions representing the width and length of the box.

📋 Additional Examples

1 Solve $(2x + 3)(x - 4) = 0$.
$-\frac{3}{2}, 4$

2 Solve $x^2 + x - 42 = 0$ by factoring. **−7, 6**

3 Solve $3x^2 - 2x = 21$. $-\frac{7}{3}, 3$

4 Suppose that a box has a base with a width of x, a length of $x + 3$, and a height of 1 in. It is cut from a square sheet of material with an area of 130 in.². Find the dimensions of the box.
8 in. × 11 in. × 1 in.

Closure

Ask students to explain the process of solving a quadratic equation by factoring. Begin by writing the equation in standard form. Then, factor the equation. Finally, apply the Zero-Product Property and solve.

👥 Reaching All Students

Below Level Review factoring polynomial expressions with students. In particular, remind them how the signs of b and c affect the factors of the expression.	**Advanced Learners** Ask: *What is the importance of the term* or *in the statement of the zero product property?* **both *a* and *b* may equal zero.**	**Visual Learners** See note on page 537. **Error Prevention** See note on page 538.

537

Assignment Guide

▼ **Objective**

🅐 🅑 **Core** 1–46

🅒 **Extension** 47–50

Standardized Test Prep 51–56

Mixed Review 57–64

Exercises 7–21 Encourage students to check their answers by either graphing or substituting.

Error Prevention

Exercises 13–21 Remind students to begin by writing the quadratic equations in standard form.

Enrichment 10-5

Reteaching 10-5

Practice 10-5

EXERCISES

For more practice, see *Extra Practice*.

Practice and Problem Solving

🅐 **Practice by Example**

Example 1 (page 536)

Use the Zero-Product Property to solve each equation.

3, 7
1. $(x - 3)(x - 7) = 0$

−4, 4.5
2. $(x + 4)(2x - 9) = 0$

0, −1
3. $t(t + 1) = 0$

4. $-3n(2n - 5) = 0$
0, 2.5

5. $(7x + 2)(5x + 4) = 0$
$-\frac{2}{7}, -\frac{4}{5}$

6. $(4a - 7)(3a + 8) = 0$
$\frac{7}{4}, -\frac{8}{3}$

Example 2 (page 537)

Solve by factoring.

7. $b^2 + 3b - 4 = 0$ **1, −4**   **8.** $m^2 - 5m - 14 = 0$ **−2, 7**   **9.** $w^2 - 8w = 0$ **0, 8**

10. $x^2 - 16x + 55 = 0$ **5, 11**   **11.** $k^2 - 3k - 10 = 0$ **−2, 5**   **12.** $n^2 + n - 12 = 0$ **3, −4**

Example 3 (page 537)

13. $x^2 + 8x = -15$ **−3, −5**   **14.** $t^2 - 3t = 28$ **−4, 7**   **15.** $n^2 = 6n$ **0, 6**

16. $2c^2 - 7c = -5$ **1, 2.5**   **17.** $3q^2 + 16q = -5$ **−5, $-\frac{1}{3}$**   **18.** $4y^2 = 25$ **−2.5, 2.5**

19. $5q^2 + 18q = 8$ **$\frac{2}{5}$, −4**   **20.** $2z^2 - 10z = -12$ **2, 3**   **21.** $12 = 2x^2 + 5x$ **$\frac{3}{2}$, −4**

Example 4 (page 537)

22. Geometry The sides of a square are all increased by 3 cm. The area of the new square is 64 cm². Find the length of a side of the original square. **5 cm**

23. Geometry A rectangular box has volume 280 in.³. Its dimensions are 4 in. × $(n + 2)$ in. × $(n + 5)$ in. Find n. Use the formula $V = \ell wh$. **5**

🌐 **24. Construction** You are building a rectangular wading pool. You want the area of the bottom to be 90 ft². You want the length of the pool to be 3 ft longer than twice its width. What will the dimensions of the pool be? **6 ft × 15 ft**

🌐 **25. Sailing** Suppose the area of the sail shown in the photo at the left is 110 ft². Find the dimensions of the sail. **base: 10 ft height: 22 ft**

26. The product of two consecutive numbers is 14 less than 10 times the smaller number. Find each number. **2 and 3 or 7 and 8**

🅑 **Apply Your Skills**

Write each equation in standard form. Then solve. 27–34. See margin.

27. $2q^2 + 22q = -60$

28. $4 = -5n + 6n^2$

29. $6y^2 + 12y + 13 = 2y^2 + 4$

30. $3a^2 + 4a = 2a^2 - 2a - 9$

31. $3t^2 + 8t = t^2 - 3t - 12$

32. $4x^2 + 20 = 10x + 3x^2 - 4$

33. $2k^2 - 3 + 12k = k + 60$

34. $15y^2 + 45y - 9 = 4y - 5y^2$

🌐 **35. Manufacturing** The length of an open box is 2 in. greater than its width. The box was made from an 80 in.² rectangular sheet of material. The height of the box is 1 in. Therefore 1-in. × 1-in. squares are cut from each corner. What were the dimensions of the original sheet of material? (*Hint:* Draw a diagram.) **8 in. × 10 in.**

🌐 **36. Baseball** Suppose you throw a baseball into the air with an initial upward velocity of 29 ft/s and an initial height of 6 ft. The formula $h = -16t^2 + 29t + 6$ gives the ball's height h in feet at time t in seconds.
  a. The ball's height h is 0 when it is on the ground. Find the number of seconds that pass before the ball lands by solving $0 = -16t^2 + 29t + 6$. **2 s**
  📱 **b. Graphing Calculator** Graph the related function for the equation in part (a). Use your graph to estimate how high the ball is tossed. **about 19 ft**

✏️ **37. Writing** Summarize the procedure for solving a quadratic equation by factoring. Include an example. **See margin.**

538 Chapter 10 Quadratic Equations and Functions

---

pages 538–540 **Exercises**

27. $2q^2 + 22q + 60 = 0$;
  −6, −5

28. $6n^2 - 5n - 4 = 0$; $\frac{4}{3}, -\frac{1}{2}$

29. $4y^2 + 12y + 9 = 0$; $-\frac{3}{2}$

30. $a^2 + 6a + 9 = 0$; −3

31. $2t^2 + 11t + 12 = 0$;
  −1.5, −4

538

32. $x^2 - 10x + 24 = 0$; 4, 6

33. $2k^2 + 11k - 63 = 0$;
  $\frac{7}{2}$, −9

34. $20y^2 + 41y - 9 = 0$;
  $\frac{1}{5}, -\frac{9}{4}$

37. Answers may vary. Sample: To solve a quadratic equation, write the equation in standard form, factor the quadratic expression, use the Zero- Product Property, and solve for the variable.

$x^2 + 8x = -15$
$x^2 + 8x + 15 = 0$
$(x + 3)(x + 5) = 0$
$x + 3 = 0$ or $x + 5 = 0$
$x = -3$ or $x = -5$

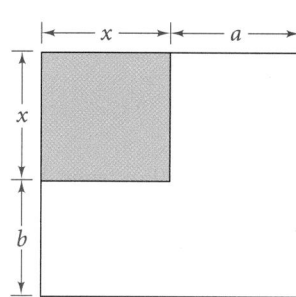

38. **Geometry** In the diagram at the left, x is a positive integer, and a and b are integers. List several possible values for x, a, and b such that the large rectangle has an area of 56 square units. **See margin.**

39. **Open-Ended** Write and solve a quadratic equation using the Zero-Product Property. **Answers may vary. Sample:**
$x^2 - 2x - 8 = 0$
$(x - 4)(x + 2) = 0$
$x - 4 = 0$ or $x + 2 = 0$
$x = 4$ or $x = -2$

40. a. Solve $x^2 = x$ and $x^2 = -x$ by factoring. **0, 1; −1, 0**
b. What number is a solution to both equations? **0**

Solve each cubic equation.

Sample $x^3 + 7x^2 + 12x = 0$

$x(x^2 + 7x + 12) = 0$	Factor out the GCF.
$x(x + 3)(x + 4) = 0$	Factor the quadratic trinomial.
$x = 0$ or $x + 3 = 0$ or $x + 4 = 0$	Use the Zero-Product Property.
$x = 0$ or $x = -3$ or $x = -4$	Solve for x.

41. $x^3 - 10x^2 + 24x = 0$ **0, 4, 6**
42. $x^3 - 5x^2 + 4x = 0$ **0, 1, 4**
43. $3x^3 - 9x^2 = 0$ **0, 3**
44. $x^3 + 3x^2 - 70x = 0$ **0, 7, −10**
45. $3x^3 - 30x^2 + 27x = 0$ **0, 1, 9**
46. $2x^3 = -2x^2 + 40x$ **0, 4, −5**

C Challenge

47. **Construction** You are building a rectangular patio with two rectangular openings for gardens. You have 124 one-foot-square paving stones. Using the diagram below, what value of x would allow you to use all of the stones? **4**

48. Find an equation that has the given numbers as solutions. For example, 4 and −3 are solutions to $x^2 - x - 12 = 0$. **See left.**

a. $-5, 8$ **b.** $3, -2$ **c.** $\frac{1}{2}, -10$ **d.** $\frac{2}{3}, -\frac{5}{7}$

Factor the expression on the left side of each equation by grouping. Then solve.

49. $x^3 + 5x^2 - x - 5 = 0$ **−1, 1, −5**
50. $x^3 + x^2 - 4x - 4 = 0$ **−2, 2, −1**

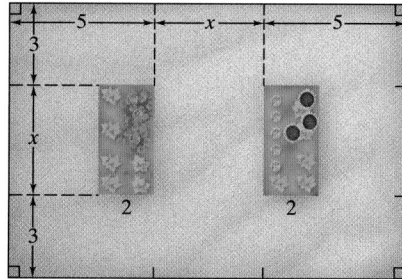

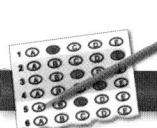

Standardized Test Prep

Multiple Choice

51. What are the solutions of $(x - 7)(2x + 8) = 0$? **D**
A. 7, 8 **B.** 7, 4 **C.** 7, −8 **D.** 7, −4

52. Which of the following is the sum of the solutions of $4x^2 - 35x - 9 = 0$? **H**
F. −8 **G.** 8 **H.** 8.75 **I.** 9.25

53. Which of the following is NOT a solution of $(n)(2n - 5)(10n + 3) = 0$? **A**
A. −3 **B.** −0.3 **C.** 0 **D.** 2.5

48. Answers may vary. Samples:
a. $x^2 - 3x - 40 = 0$
b. $x^2 - x - 6 = 0$
c. $2x^2 + 19x - 10 = 0$
d. $21x^2 + x - 10 = 0$

38. Answers may vary. Sample:
$x = 6, a = 2, b = 1$
$x = 3, a = 1, b = 11$

4. Assess

Lesson Quiz 10-5

1. Solve $(2x - 3)(x + 2) = 0$. $-2, \frac{3}{2}$

Solve by factoring.

2. $6 = a^2 - 5a$ $-1, 6$
3. $12x + 4 = -9x^2$ $-\frac{2}{3}$
4. $4y^2 = 25$ $\pm\frac{5}{2}$

Alternative Assessment

Have students write their own open-top box problem using Example 4 as a guide. Tell them to draw a pattern and label it using a variable. Have them write the expressions and solve to find the dimensions of the box. Then encourage students to create the box from a sheet of paper.

Quantitative Comparison

Take It to the NET
Online lesson quiz at
www.PHSchool.com
Web Code: aea-1005

Short Response

Compare the boxed quantity in Column A with the boxed quantity in Column B. Choose the best answer.

A. The quantity in Column A is greater.
B. The quantity in Column B is greater.
C. The two quantities are equal.
D. The relationship cannot be determined from the information given.

Column A	Column B
54. C — the number of real-number solutions of $3x^2 = 11$	the number of real-number solutions of $5y^2 - 12 = 0$
55. D — twice the square of a number n	the square of twice a number n

56. Find the solutions of the equation $3x^2 + 20x + 1 = 8$. Show your work. See margin.

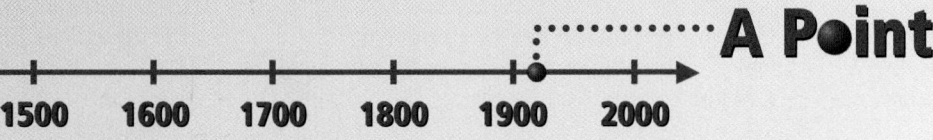

Mixed Review

Lesson 10-4

Geometry Model each situation with a quadratic equation. Then solve. Round answers to the nearest tenth.

57. Find the side of a square with an area of 320 ft². $x^2 = 320$; **17.9 ft**

58. Find the radius of a circle with an area of 38 ft². $38 = \pi r^2$; **3.5 ft**

Lesson 9-6

59. $(2x + 3)(x + 5)$

Factor each expression.

59. $2x^2 + 13x + 15$

60. $3y^2 - 10y + 3$ $(3y - 1)(y - 3)$

61. $4t^2 + 5t - 6$ $(4t - 3)(t + 2)$

62. $6n^2 + 7n - 3$ $(3n - 1)(2n + 3)$

63. $15a^3 - 50a^2 - 40a$ $5a(3a + 2)(a - 4)$

64. $-18b^3 + 42b^2 - 20b$ $-2b(3b - 2)(3b - 5)$

A Point in Time

1500   1600   1700   1800   1900   2000

In 1923, Juan de la Cierva (1895–1936) designed the first successful autogyro, a rotor-based aircraft. The autogyro had rotating blades to give the aircraft lift, a propeller for forward thrust, and short, stubby wings for balance. Autogyros needed only short runways for takeoff and could descend almost vertically.

By hinging the rotor blades at the hub, de la Cierva allowed each blade to respond to aerodynamic forces. This was a significant contribution in the development of the modern helicopter.

De la Cierva's work on problems of lift and gravity, like the work of aeronautical engineers of today, involved quadratic functions.

Take It to the NET For more information about autogyros, go to **www.PHSchool.com**.
Web Code: aee-2032

pages 538–540   Exercises

56. [2] $3x^2 + 20x + 1 = 8$
    $3x^2 + 20x - 7 = 0$
    $(3x - 1)(x + 7) = 0$
    $x = \frac{1}{3}, x = -7$

[1] appropriate methods, but with one computational error

10-6

Completing the Square

4.02 Graph, factor, and evaluate quadratic functions to solve problems.

Lesson Preview

What You'll Learn

OBJECTIVE 1
To solve quadratic equations by completing the square

...And Why

To solve real-world problems involving carpentry, as in Example 4

 **Check Skills You'll Need**   (For help, go to Lessons 9-4 and 9-7.)

Find each square.

1. $(d - 4)^2$ $d^2 - 8d + 16$ **2.** $(x + 11)^2$ **3.** $(k - 8)^2$
                                    $x^2 + 22x + 121$ $k^2 - 16k + 64$
Factor.

4. $b^2 + 10b + 25$ $(b + 5)^2$ **5.** $t^2 + 14t + 49$ $(t + 7)^2$ **6.** $n^2 - 18n + 81$
                                                                         $(n - 9)^2$

New Vocabulary • completing the square

OBJECTIVE

1 **Solving by Completing the Square**

 Interactive lesson includes instant self-check, tutorials, and activities.

In previous lessons, you solved quadratic equations by finding square roots and by factoring. These methods work in some cases. A third method, completing the square, works with every quadratic equation. Completing the square turns every quadratic equation into the form $m^2 = n$. You can model completing the square of a quadratic expression using algebra tiles.

The algebra tiles at the right represent the expression $x^2 + 8x$.

Here is the same expression rearranged to form part of a square. Notice that the x-tiles have been split evenly into two groups of four.

You can complete the square by adding 4^2, or 16, single tiles. The completed square is $x^2 + 8x + 16$ or $(x + 4)^2$.

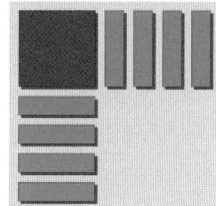

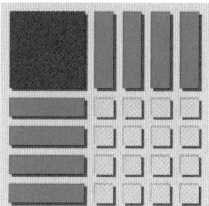

To explore this method algebraically, consider the equation below. In a perfect square trinomial, with $a = 1$, c must be the square of half of b.

$$(x + 4)^2 = x^2 + 2(4)x + 4^2$$
$$= x^2 + 8x + 16$$
$$\frac{8}{2} = 4 \rightarrow 4^2$$

You can change an expression like $x^2 + bx$ into a perfect square trinomial by adding $\left(\frac{b}{2}\right)^2$ to $x^2 + bx$. This process is called **completing the square.** The process is the same whether b is positive or negative.

Lesson 10-6 Completing the Square   **541**

Lesson Preview

 **Check Skills You'll Need**

Multiplying Special Cases
Lesson 9-4: Example 1
Exercises 1–8
Extra Practice, p. 710

Factoring Special Cases
Lesson 9-7: Example 1
Exercises 1–6
Extra Practice, p. 710

Lesson Resources

📁 **Teaching Resources**
Practice, Reteaching, Enrichment

👥 **Reaching All Students**
Practice Workbook 10-6
Spanish Practice Workbook 10-6
Hands-On Activities 23
Basic Algebra Planning Guide 10-6

⏱ **Presentation Assistant Plus!**
Transparencies
• Check Skills You'll Need 10-6
• Additional Examples 10-6
• Student Edition Answers 10-6
• Lesson Quiz 10-6
PH Presentation Pro CD 10-6

ASSESSMENT SYSTEM

Computer Test Generator CD

🖌 **Technology**
Resource Pro® CD-ROM
Computer Test Generator CD
Prentice Hall Presentation Pro CD

💻 **www.PHSchool.com**
Student Site
• Teacher Web Code: aek-5500
• Reasoning & Puzzles pp. 98, 99
• Self-grading Lesson Quiz
Teacher Center
• Lesson Planner
• Resources

Plus

Ongoing Assessment and Intervention

Before the Lesson
Diagnose prerequisite skills using:
• Check Skills You'll Need

During the Lesson
Monitor progress using:
• Check Understanding
• Additional Examples
• Standardized Test Prep

After the Lesson
Assess knowledge using:
• Lesson Quiz
• Computer Test Generator CD

2. Teach

Math Background

The method of completing the square can only be used when the coefficient of the x^2 term is 1. If the x^2 term has a different coefficient, divide every term of the equation by that coefficient to obtain the desired form.

OBJECTIVE

① Teaching Notes

① EXAMPLE **Alternative Method**

Have students use algebra tiles to model the expression $x^2 - 12x$. Then, have them arrange the tiles to form part of a square and complete the square.

② EXAMPLE **Error Prevention**

Some students may forget to add the square to both sides of the equation. Stress the importance of balancing the equation so that the new equation has the same solutions as the original equation.

④ EXAMPLE **Diversity**

Ask students who are knowledgeable in carpentry or woodworking to tell about their experiences. Ask them to give specific examples of projects they have worked on, materials and techniques they have used, and how mathematics was involved.

---

① EXAMPLE **Finding _n_ to Complete the Square**

Find the value of n such that $x^2 - 12x + n$ is a perfect square trinomial.

The value of b in the expression $x^2 - 12x + n$ is -12. The term to add to $x^2 - 12x$ is $\left(-\frac{12}{2}\right)^2$ or 36. So $n = 36$.

✓ **Check Understanding** ① Find the value of n such that $x^2 + 22x + n$ is a perfect square trinomial. **121**

The simplest equations in which to complete the square have the form $x^2 + bx = c$.

② EXAMPLE **Solving $x^2 + bx = c$**

Solve the equation $x^2 + 9x = 136$.

Step 1 Write the left side of $x^2 + 9x = 136$ as a perfect square.

$$x^2 + 9x = 136$$
$$x^2 + 9x + \left(\frac{9}{2}\right)^2 = 136 + \left(\frac{9}{2}\right)^2 \quad \text{Add } \left(\frac{9}{2}\right)^2, \text{ or } \frac{81}{4}, \text{ to each side of the equation.}$$
$$\left(x + \frac{9}{2}\right)^2 = \frac{544}{4} + \frac{81}{4} \quad \begin{array}{l}\text{Write } x^2 + 9x + \left(\frac{9}{2}\right)^2 \text{ as a square.} \\ \text{Rewrite 136 as a fraction with denominator 4.}\end{array}$$
$$\left(x + \frac{9}{2}\right)^2 = \frac{625}{4} \quad \text{Simplify the right side of the equation.}$$

Step 2 Solve the equation.

$$\left(x + \frac{9}{2}\right) = \pm\sqrt{\frac{625}{4}} \quad \text{Find the square root of each side.}$$
$$x + \frac{9}{2} = \pm\frac{25}{2} \quad \text{Simplify.}$$
$$x + \frac{9}{2} = \frac{25}{2} \quad \text{or} \quad x + \frac{9}{2} = -\frac{25}{2} \quad \text{Write as two equations.}$$
$$x = 8 \quad \text{or} \quad x = -17 \quad \begin{array}{l}\text{Solve for } x \text{ by subtracting } \frac{9}{2} \text{ from each} \\ \text{side of the equations and simplifying.}\end{array}$$

✓ **Check Understanding** ② Solve the equation $m^2 - 6m = 247$. **19, −13**

To solve an equation in the form $x^2 + bx + c = 0$, first subtract the constant term c from each side of the equation.

③ EXAMPLE **Solving $x^2 + bx + c = 0$**

Solve $x^2 - 20x + 32 = 0$.

Step 1 Rewrite the equation in the form $x^2 + bx = c$ and complete the square.

$$x^2 - 20x + 32 = 0$$
$$x^2 - 20x = -32 \quad \text{Subtract 32 from each side.}$$
$$x^2 - 20x + 100 = -32 + 100 \quad \begin{array}{l}\text{Add } \left(-\frac{20}{2}\right)^2, \text{ or 100, to each side} \\ \text{of the equation.}\end{array}$$
$$(x - 10)^2 = 68 \quad \text{Write } x^2 - 20x + 100 \text{ as a square.}$$

Step 2 Solve the equation.

$$(x - 10) = \pm\sqrt{68} \quad \text{Find the square root of each side.}$$
$$x - 10 \approx \pm 8.25 \quad \text{Use a calculator to find } \sqrt{68}.$$
$$x - 10 \approx 8.25 \quad \text{or} \quad x - 10 \approx -8.25 \quad \text{Write as two equations.}$$
$$x \approx 8.25 + 10 \quad \text{or} \quad x \approx -8.25 + 10 \quad \text{Add 10 to each side.}$$
$$x \approx 18.25 \quad \text{or} \quad x \approx 1.75 \quad \text{Simplify.}$$

542 Chapter 10 Quadratic Equations and Functions

❧ Reaching All Students

Below Level Remind students that when $a \neq 1$, they must divide all terms on both sides of the equation by a in order to produce an equivalent equation.	**Advanced Learners** Have students discuss why the procedure for solving quadratic equations in this lesson is called 'completing the square.'	**Diversity** See note on page 542. **Error Prevention** See note on page 542.

✓ **Check Understanding** ③ Solve each equation. Round to the nearest hundredth.

a. $x^2 + 5x + 3 = 0$ **−0.70, −4.30** **b.** $x^2 - 14x + 16 = 0$ **12.74, 1.26**

The method of completing the square works when $a = 1$. To solve an equation like $3x^2 + 6x - 9 = 0$, you need to divide each side by 3 before completing the square.

$$3x^2 + 6x - 9 = 0 \rightarrow \frac{3x^2 + 6x - 9}{3} = \frac{0}{3} \rightarrow x^2 + 2x - 3 = 0$$

④ **EXAMPLE** **Real-World 🌐 Problem Solving**

Carpentry Suppose a woodworker wants to build a tabletop like the one shown at the right. If the surface area is 26 ft², what is the value of x?

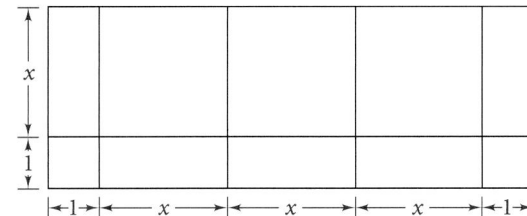

Define width $= x + 1$
length $= x + x + x + 1 + 1 = 3x + 2$

Relate length × width = area

Write $(3x + 2)(x + 1) = 26$
$3x^2 + 5x + 2 = 26$

Step 1 Rewrite the equation in the form $x^2 + bx = c$.

$3x^2 + 5x + 2 = 26$

$\qquad 3x^2 + 5x = 24$ **Subtract 2 from each side.**

$\qquad x^2 + \frac{5}{3}x = 8$ **Divide each side by 3.**

Step 2 Complete the square.

$x^2 + \frac{5}{3}x + \frac{25}{36} = 8 + \frac{25}{36}$ **Add $\left(\frac{5}{6}\right)^2$, or $\frac{25}{36}$, to each side.**

$\left(x + \frac{5}{6}\right)^2 = \frac{288}{36} + \frac{25}{36}$ **Write $x^2 + \frac{5}{3}x + \frac{25}{36}$ as a square. Rewrite 8 as a fraction with denominator 36.**

$\left(x + \frac{5}{6}\right)^2 = \frac{313}{36}$ **Simplify.**

Step 3 Solve the equation.

$\left(x + \frac{5}{6}\right) = \pm\sqrt{\frac{313}{36}}$ **Take the square root of each side.**

$x + \frac{5}{6} \approx \pm 2.95$ **Use a calculator. $\sqrt{\frac{313}{36}} \approx 2.95$**

$x + \frac{5}{6} \approx 2.95$ or $x + \frac{5}{6} \approx -2.95$ **Write as two equations.**

$x \approx 2.95 - \frac{5}{6}$ or $x \approx -2.95 - \frac{5}{6}$ **Subtract $\frac{5}{6}$ from each side.**

$x \approx 2.95 - 0.83$ or $x \approx -2.95 - 0.83$ **$\frac{5}{6} \approx 0.83$, so substitute 0.83 for $\frac{5}{6}$.**

$x \approx 2.12$ or $x \approx -3.78$ **Use the positive answer for this problem.**

● The value of x is about 2.12 ft.

✓ **Check Understanding** ④ Solve each equation. Round to the nearest hundredth.

a. $4a^2 - 8a = 24$ **−1.65, 3.65** **b.** $5n^2 - 3n - 15 = 10$ **2.56, −1.96**

Real-World 🌐 Connection

Careers Woodworkers use mathematical skills to design and create furniture.

📐 **Additional Examples**

① Find the value of c to complete the square for $x^2 - 16x + c$. **64**

② Solve the equation $x^2 + 5x = 50$. **−10, 5**

③ Solve $x^2 + 10x - 16 = 0$. Round to the nearest hundredth. **1.40, −11.40**

④ Suppose you wish to section off a soccer field as shown in the diagram to run a variety of practice drills. If the area of the field is 6000 yd², what is the value of x? **40**

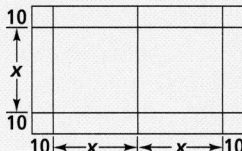

Closure

Ask students to explain the process of solving a quadratic equation by completing the square. **Begin by writing the equation in the form $x^2 + bx = c$. Then, complete the square by writing the equation in the form $\left(x + \frac{b}{2}\right)^2 = c + \left(\frac{b}{2}\right)^2$. Finally, solve for x.**

3. Practice

For more practice, see *Extra Practice*.

EXERCISES
Practice and Problem Solving

Assignment Guide

▼ **Objective**

Ⓐ Ⓑ **Core** 1–41
Ⓒ **Extension** 42–44

Standardized Test Prep 45–49

Mixed Review 50–70

Math Tip

Exercise 35 In rectangle problems without a fixed wall, the two solutions give the same rectangle with the length and width dimensions reversed. The two solutions here describe two different rectangles.

Exercise 44 The vertex is $(p, -q)$. From the x-axis at p, the roots are at a distance $\sqrt{q}$ from $(p, 0)$. The distance from $(p, 0)$ to the vertex is the square of the distance from $(p, 0)$ to either of the roots.

Enrichment 10-6

Reteaching 10-6

Practice 10-6

Ⓐ **Practice by Example**

Example 1
(page 542)

Example 2
(page 542)

Example 3
(page 542)

Example 4
(page 543)

Find the value of n such that each expression is a perfect square trinomial.

1. $k^2 + 14k + n$ **49**   **2.** $m^2 - 8m + n$ **16**   **3.** $y^2 - 40y + n$ **400**

4. $p^2 - 6p + n$ **9**   **5.** $v^2 + 24v + n$ **144**   **6.** $w^2 - 36w + n$ **324**

Solve each equation by completing the square. If necessary, round to the nearest hundredth.

7. $r^2 + 8r = 48$ **4, −12**   **8.** $x^2 - 10x = 40$ **13.06, −3.06**   **9.** $q^2 + 22q = -85$ **−5, −17**

10. $m^2 + 6m = 9$ **1.24, −7.24**   **11.** $r^2 + 20r = 261$ **9, −29**   **12.** $g^2 - 2g = 323$ **19, −17**

13. $r^2 - 2r - 35 = 0$ **7, −5**   **14.** $x^2 + 10x + 17 = 0$ **−2.17, −7.83**   **15.** $p^2 - 12p + 11 = 0$ **11, 1**

16. $w^2 + 3w - 5 = 0$ **1.19, −4.19**   **17.** $m^2 + m - 28 = 0$ **4.82, −5.82**   **18.** $a^2 + 9a - 682 = 0$ **22, −31**

What term do you need to add to each side to complete the square?

19. $2k^2 + 4k = 10$ **1**   **20.** $3x^2 + 12x = 24$ **4**   **21.** $5t^2 + 9t = 15$ $\frac{81}{100}$

Solve each equation by completing the square. If necessary, round to the nearest hundredth.

22. $4y^2 + 8y - 36 = 0$ **2.16, −4.16**   **23.** $3q^2 - 12q = 15$ **5, −1**   **24.** $2x^2 - 10x - 20 = 8$ **7, −2**

25. a. Write an expression for the total area of the model below. **$(2x + 1)(x + 1)$**

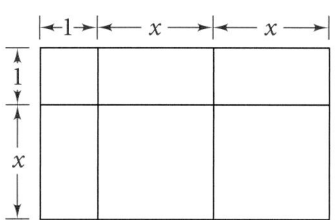

b. The total area is 28 square units. Write an equation to find x.
c. Solve by completing the square. **3** $2x^2 + 3x + 1 = 28$

Ⓑ **Apply Your Skills**

Solve each equation. If necessary, round to the nearest hundredth. If there is no solution, write *no solution*.

26. $b^2 + 4b + 1 = 0$ **−0.27, −3.73**   **27.** $c^2 + 7c = -12$ **−3, −4**   **28.** $h^2 + 6h - 40 = 0$ **4, −10**

29. $y^2 - 8y = -12$ **6, 2**   **30.** $4m^2 - 40m + 56 = 0$ **8.32, 1.68**   **31.** $k^2 + 4k + 11 = -10$ **no solution**

32. $2x^2 - 15x + 6 = 41$ **9.37, −1.87**   **33.** $3d^2 - 24d = 3$ **8.12, −0.12**   **34.** $x^2 + 9x + 20 = 0$ **−4, −5**

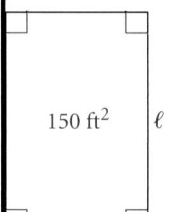

🌐 **35. Gardening** Suppose you want to enclose a rectangular garden plot against a house using fencing on three sides, as shown at the left. Assume you have 50 ft of fencing material and want to create a garden with an area of 150 ft^2.
   a. Let $w =$ the width. Write an expression for the length of the plot. **See below.**
   b. Write and solve an equation for the area of the plot. Round to the nearest tenth of a foot. $w(50 - 2w) = 150;\ 21.5, 3.5$ **35a.** $\ell = 50 - 2w$
   c. What dimensions should the garden have? **7 ft × 21.5 ft or 43 ft × 3.5 ft**
   d. Critical Thinking Find the area of the garden by using the dimensions you found in part (b). Does the area equal 150 ft^2? Explain.
   No; the answers in part (b) were rounded.

544   Chapter 10   Quadratic Equations and Functions

36. The student did not divide each side of the equation by 4.

37. Answers may vary. Sample: Add 1 to each side of the equation, and then complete the square by adding 225 to each side of the equation. Write $x^2 + 30x + 225$ as the square $(x + 15)^2$ and add 1 and 225 to get 226. Then take square roots and solve the resulting equations.

36. Error Analysis A classmate was completing the square to solve $4x^2 + 10x = 0$. For her first step she wrote $4x^2 + 10x + 25 = 25$. What was her error?

 37. Writing Explain to a classmate how to solve $x^2 + 30x - 1 = 0$ by completing the square.

38. Open-Ended Write a quadratic equation and solve it by completing the square. Show your work. **See margin.**

Use each graph to estimate the values of x for which $f(x) = 5$. Write and solve an equation to find the values of x such that $f(x) = 5$. Round to the nearest hundredth.

39. $f(x) = x^2 - 4x - 1$ **5.16, −1.16**

40. $f(x) = -\frac{1}{2}x^2 + 4x + 1$ **6.83, 1.17**

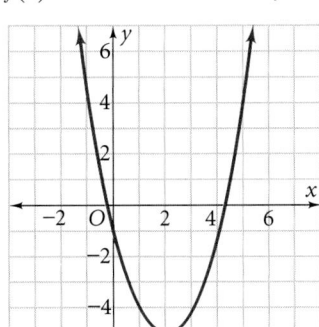 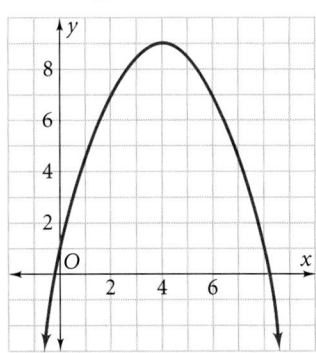

  41. Geometry A rectangle has a length of x. Its width is 3 feet longer than twice the length. Find the dimensions if its area is 80 ft². Round to the nearest tenth of a foot. **5.6 ft by 14.2 ft**

C Challenge **42. Geometry** Suppose the prism shown at the right has the same surface area as an 8-in. cube.
  a. Write an expression for the surface area of the prism shown at the right. **$6x^2 + 28x$**
  b. Write an equation that relates the surface area of the prism to the surface area of the 8-in. cube. **$6x^2 + 28x = 384$**
  c. Solve the equation you wrote in part (b) to find the dimensions of the prism. **13 in. × 6 in. × 6 in.**

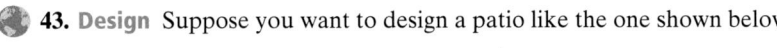

43. Design Suppose you want to design a patio like the one shown below.

  a. Write an expression for the total area. **$A = \frac{7}{2}x^2 + 5x + 1$**
  b. If you want the total area to be 200 ft², what is the value of x? **6.86**
  c. If you rounded the value of x to the nearest integer, what would the total area be? **207.5 ft²**

Lesson Quiz 10-6

Solve each equation by completing the square. If necessary, round to the nearest hundredth.

1. $x^2 + 14x = -43$ **−9.45, −4.55**

2. $3x^2 + 6x - 24 = 0$ **−4, 2**

3. $4x^2 + 16x + 8 = 40$ **−5.46, 1.46**

Alternative Assessment

Have students work in groups. Instruct each group to create a problem of the form $x^2 + bx = c$, where b is an even number, and solve it by completing the square. Tell the group to record the original problem and solution on one side of a piece of paper and the value of c on the other side. Then have the group set up algebra tiles on a desk to represent the expression $x^2 + bx$ and leave the piece of paper with the value of c face up on the desk. Instruct each group to switch desks with another group. Have students write down the expression represented by the algebra tiles and the corresponding quadratic equation using the value of c. Tell students to rearrange the algebra tiles if necessary, complete the square, and solve the problem. Students can flip over the piece of paper on the desk to verify their solutions.

pages 544–546 Exercises

38. Answers may vary. Sample:
$$x^2 + 10x - 50 = 0$$
$$x^2 + 10x = 50$$
$$x^2 + 10x + 25 = 50 + 25$$
$$(x + 5)^2 = 75$$
$$x + 5 = \pm\sqrt{75}$$
$$x + 5 \approx \pm 8.7$$
$$x + 5 \approx 8.7 \text{ or } x + 5 \approx -8.7$$
$$x \approx 3.7 \quad \text{or} \quad x \approx -13.7$$

545

Resources

For additional practice with a variety of test item formats:
- Standardized Test Prep, p. 573
- Test-Taking Strategies, p. 568
- Test-Taking Strategies with Transparencies

Exercise 45 Encourage students to rewrite $x^2 + bx + 100$ as $x^2 + bx + 10^2$. Remind them that the middle term is then $2(1)(10)$ or $-2(1)(10)$. Therefore, the correct answer choice is B.

pages 544–546 Exercises

48. [2] $\frac{1}{2}(x)(x + x + 4) = 200$
$$\frac{1}{2}(x)(2x + 4) = 200$$
$$(x)(x + 2) = 200$$
$$x^2 + 2x = 200$$
$$x^2 + 2x + 1 = 201$$
$$(x + 1)^2 = 201$$
$$x + 1 \approx \pm 14.18$$
$$x = 13.18 \quad x = -15.18$$

The value of x is about 13.18 cm.

[1] appropriate methods, but with one computational error

49. [4] a. $(8 + x)(12 + x)$
$$= 2 \cdot (8 \cdot 12)$$
$$x^2 + 20x - 96 = 0$$

b. $x^2 + 20x = 96$
$$x^2 + 20x + 100 = 196$$
$$(x + 10)^2 = 196$$
$$x + 10 = \pm 14$$
$$x = 4$$

c. 12 ft by 16 ft

[3] appropriate methods, but with one computational error

[2] part (c) not done

[1] no work shown

---

44. a. Solve the equation $x^2 - 6x + 4 = 0$, but leave your answers in the form $p \pm \sqrt{q}$. $\mathbf{3 \pm \sqrt{5}}$

b. Use the vertex formula $x = \frac{-b}{2a}$ to find the coordinates of the vertex of $y = x^2 - 6x + 4$. $\quad\quad\mathbf{(3, -5)}$

c. Critical Thinking Explain the relationship between your answers in part (a) and part (b). **Answers may vary. Sample: p is the x-coordinate of the vertex.**

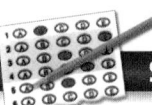

Standardized Test Prep

Multiple Choice

45. Which values of b will make the expression $x^2 + bx + 100$ a perfect square trinomial? **B**
- **A.** $-10, 10$
- **B.** $-20, 20$
- **C.** $-25, 25$
- **D.** $-50, 50$

46. Which of the following expressions is NOT a perfect square trinomial? **I**
- **F.** $t^2 - 14t + 49$
- **G.** $9b^2 + 66b + 121$
- **H.** $4m^2 - 24m + 36$
- **I.** $81k^2 - 120k + 100$

47. Which of the following is closest to a solution of the equation $x^2 + 6x - 11 = 0$? **D**
- **A.** -3
- **B.** -1
- **C.** 0
- **D.** 2

Short Response

48. The area of the figure at the right is 200 cm². Find the value of x. Round to the nearest hundredth. Show your work. **See margin.**

Extended Response

Take It to the NET

Online lesson quiz at **www.PHSchool.com**
Web Code: aea-1006

49. Kevin's office cubicle measures 8 ft by 12 ft.
a. Write an equation to find the amount x that should be added to the current length and width to double the area. **a–c. See margin.**
b. Solve the equation. Show your work.
c. What will the new dimensions be?

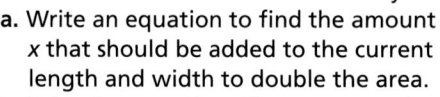

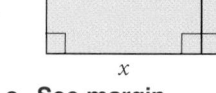

Mixed Review

Lesson 10-5 **Solve each equation.**

50. $x^2 - 4x - 21 = 0$
$-3, 7$

51. $n^2 + 11n + 30 = 0$
$-6, -5$

52. $t^2 - 5t = 0$
$0, 5$

53. $9v^2 - 64 = 0$
$-\frac{8}{3}, \frac{8}{3}$

54. $4c^2 + 12c = -9$
$-\frac{3}{2}$

55. $12w^2 = 28w + 5$
$-\frac{1}{6}, \frac{5}{2}$

Lesson 9-7 **Factor each expression.**

56. $x^2 + 4x + 4$ $(x + 2)^2$

57. $t^2 - 22t + 121$ $(t - 11)^2$

58. $b^2 - 25$ $(b + 5)(b - 5)$

59. $16c^2 + 24c + 9$

60. $49s^2 - 169$

61. $8m^3 - 18m$

62. $25m^2 + 120m + 144$
$(5m + 12)^2$

63. $400k^2 - 9$
$(20k + 3)(20k - 3)$

64. $256g^2 - 121$
$(16g - 11)(16g + 11)$

59. $(4c + 3)^2$

60. $(7s + 13)(7s - 13)$

61. $2m(2m + 3)(2m - 3)$

Lesson 8-4 **Simplify.**

65. $(r^3)^4$ r^{12}

66. $p(p^2)^6$ p^{13}

67. $-y^3(y^{-1})^2$ $-y$

68. $(m^5)^{-8}$ $\frac{1}{m^{40}}$

69. $-w^7(w^8)^{-1}$ $-\frac{1}{w}$

70. $t^8(t^{-7})^{-3}$ t^{29}

Using the Quadratic Formula

 North Carolina Objectives

1.02 Use formulas to model and solve problems.
4.02 Graph, factor, and evaluate quadratic functions to solve problems.

Lesson Preview

What You'll Learn

 OBJECTIVE **1** To use the quadratic formula when solving quadratic equations

 OBJECTIVE **2** To choose an appropriate method for solving a quadratic equation

. . . And Why

To investigate real-world situations involving sports, as in Example 3

 Check Skills You'll Need (For help, go to Lesson 10-6.)

Find the value of c to complete the square for each expression.

1. $x^2 + 6x + c$ **9**   2. $x^2 + 7x + c$ $\frac{49}{4}$ 3. $x^2 - 9x + c$ $\frac{81}{4}$

Solve each equation by completing the square.

4. $x^2 - 10x + 24 = 0$ **6, 4**   5. $x^2 + 16x - 36 = 0$ **2, -18**

6. $3x^2 + 12x - 15 = 0$ **1, -5**   7. $2x^2 - 2x - 112 = 0$ **-7, 8**

New Vocabulary • quadratic formula

OBJECTIVE

1 Using the Quadratic Formula

 Interactive lesson includes instant self-check, tutorials, and activities.

Real-World **Connection**

The path of a golf ball can be modeled with a quadratic function.

In Lesson 10-6, you solved quadratic equations by completing the square. If you complete the square of the general equation $ax^2 + bx + c = 0$, you can derive the **quadratic formula,** which will solve any quadratic equation.

Step 1 Write $ax^2 + bx + c = 0$ so the coefficient of x^2 is 1.

$$ax^2 + bx + c = 0$$
$$x^2 + \frac{b}{a}x + \frac{c}{a} = 0 \qquad \text{Divide each side by } a.$$

Step 2 Complete the square.

$$x^2 + \frac{b}{a}x = -\frac{c}{a} \qquad \text{Subtract } \frac{c}{a} \text{ from each side.}$$

$$x^2 + \frac{b}{a}x + \left(\frac{b}{2a}\right)^2 = -\frac{c}{a} + \left(\frac{b}{2a}\right)^2 \qquad \text{Add } \left(\frac{b}{2a}\right)^2 \text{ to each side.}$$

$$\left(x + \frac{b}{2a}\right)^2 = -\frac{c}{a} + \left(\frac{b}{2a}\right)^2 \qquad \text{Write the trinomial as a perfect square.}$$

$$= -\frac{4ac}{4a^2} + \frac{b^2}{4a^2} \qquad \text{Multiply } -\frac{c}{a} \text{ by } \frac{4a}{4a} \text{ to get like denominators, and simplify } \left(\frac{b}{2a}\right)^2.$$

$$= \frac{b^2 - 4ac}{4a^2} \qquad \text{Simplify the right side.}$$

Step 3 Solve the equation.

$$\sqrt{\left(x + \frac{b}{2a}\right)^2} = \sqrt{\frac{b^2 - 4ac}{4a^2}} \qquad \text{Take the square root of each side.}$$

$$x + \frac{b}{2a} = \pm \frac{\sqrt{b^2 - 4ac}}{2a} \qquad \text{Simplify the right side. } \frac{1}{\sqrt{4a^2}} = \frac{1}{2a}$$

$$x = -\frac{b}{2a} \pm \frac{\sqrt{b^2 - 4ac}}{2a} \qquad \text{Subtract } \frac{b}{2a} \text{ from each side.}$$

$$x = \frac{-b \pm \sqrt{b^2 - 4ac}}{2a} \qquad \text{Simplify.}$$

Lesson 10-7 Using the Quadratic Formula **547**

---

1. Plan

Lesson Preview

 **Check Skills You'll Need**

Completing the Square
Lesson 10-6: Examples 1 and 3
Exercises 1–6, 13–18
Extra Practice, p. 711

Lesson Resources

📁 **Teaching Resources**
Practice, Reteaching, Enrichment

👥 **Reaching All Students**
Practice Workbook 10-7
Spanish Practice Workbook 10-7
Basic Algebra Planning Guide 10-7

⏱ **Presentation Assistant Plus!**
Transparencies
• Check Skills You'll Need 10-7
• Additional Examples 10-7
• Student Edition Answers 10-7
• Lesson Quiz 10-7
PH Presentation Pro CD 10-7

PRENTICE HALL ASSESSMENT SYSTEM

Computer Test Generator CD

💿 **Technology**
Resource Pro® CD-ROM
Computer Test Generator CD
Prentice Hall Presentation Pro CD

🖥 **www.PHSchool.com**
Student Site
• Teacher Web Code: aek-5500
• Reasoning & Puzzles p. 84
• Self-grading Lesson Quiz
Teacher Center
• Lesson Planner
• Resources

Plus

Ongoing Assessment and Intervention

Before the Lesson
Diagnose prerequisite skills using:
• Check Skills You'll Need

During the Lesson
Monitor progress using:
• Check Understanding
• Additional Examples
• Standardized Test Prep

After the Lesson
Assess knowledge using:
• Lesson Quiz
• Computer Test Generator CD

2. Teach

Math Background

The process called *completing the square* is another example of the *working backward* technique so useful in many mathematical situations.

OBJECTIVE

▼ 1 Teaching Notes

1 EXAMPLE Error Prevention

To help students avoid making sign errors when learning how to use the quadratic formula, encourage them to place parentheses around each substituted value.

2 EXAMPLE Math Tip

Have students attempt to solve $2x^2 + 4x - 7 = 0$ by factoring. Then, have students solve the equation by completing the square and by using the quadratic formula. Have them compare the results. Help students see the limitations of factoring. Stress that the quadratic equation is derived from completing the square in the general equation $ax^2 + bx + c = 0$, $a \neq 0$. Remind students that completing the square or using the quadratic formula will always work.

3 EXAMPLE English Learners

Some students may not realize that this example is referring to American football and not soccer or rugby. Have a knowledgeable student explain the difference.

Key Concepts

Rule	Quadratic Formula

If $ax^2 + bx + c = 0$, and $a \neq 0$, then
$$x = \frac{-b \pm \sqrt{b^2 - 4ac}}{2a}$$

Be sure to write a quadratic equation in standard form before using the quadratic formula.

1 EXAMPLE Using the Quadratic Formula

Reading Math
For more help with Example 1, see p. 553.

Solve $x^2 + 6 = 5x$.

$x^2 - 5x + 6 = 0$ — Subtract 5x from each side and write in standard form.

$x = \frac{-b \pm \sqrt{b^2 - 4ac}}{2a}$ — Use the quadratic formula.

$x = \frac{-(-5) \pm \sqrt{(-5)^2 - (4)(1)(6)}}{2(1)}$ — The coefficient of x is 1. Substitute 1 for a, −5 for b, and 6 for c.

$x = \frac{5 \pm \sqrt{1}}{2}$ — Simplify −(−5) and the radicand.

$x = \frac{5+1}{2}$ or $x = \frac{5-1}{2}$ — Write as two equations.

$x = 3$ or $x = 2$ — Simplify.

Check Substitute 3 for x. | Substitute 2 for x.
$(3)^2 + 6 \stackrel{?}{=} 5(3)$ | $(2)^2 + 6 \stackrel{?}{=} 5(2)$
$9 + 6 \stackrel{?}{=} 15$ | $4 + 6 \stackrel{?}{=} 10$
$15 = 15$ ✓ | $10 = 10$ ✓

✓ **Check Understanding** ❶ Use the quadratic formula to solve each equation.
a. $x^2 - 2x - 8 = 0$ **4, −2** **b.** $x^2 - 4x = 117$ **13, −9**

Need Help?
The radicand is the quantity inside the radical symbol. The radicand of $\sqrt{b^2 - 4ac}$ is $b^2 - 4ac$.

When the radicand in the quadratic formula is not a perfect square, you can use a calculator to approximate the solutions of an equation.

2 EXAMPLE Finding Approximate Solutions

Solve $2x^2 + 4x - 7 = 0$. Round the solutions to the nearest hundredth.

$x = \frac{-b \pm \sqrt{b^2 - 4ac}}{2a}$ — Use the quadratic formula.

$x = \frac{-4 \pm \sqrt{4^2 - (4)(2)(-7)}}{2(2)}$ — Substitute 2 for a, 4 for b, and −7 for c.

$x = \frac{-4 \pm \sqrt{72}}{4}$

$x = \frac{-4 + \sqrt{72}}{4}$ or $x = \frac{-4 - \sqrt{72}}{4}$ — Write as two equations.

$x \approx \frac{-4 + 8.49}{4}$ or $x \approx \frac{-4 - 8.49}{4}$ — Use a calculator. $\sqrt{72} \approx 8.49$

$x \approx 1.12$ or $x \approx -3.12$ — Simplify. Round to the nearest hundredth.

✓ **Check Understanding** ❷ Solve each equation. Round to the nearest hundredth.
a. $-3x^2 + 5x - 2 = 0$ **0.67, 1** **b.** $7x^2 - 2x - 8 = 0$ **1.22, −0.94**

548 Chapter 10 Quadratic Equations and Functions

👪 Reaching All Students

Below Level Make sure students understand that, since t is the squared variable, it takes the place of x in the quadratic formula, and h takes the place of y.	**Advanced Learners** Discuss various methods for solving quadratic equations and have students give exact solutions.	**English Learners** See note on page 548. **Visual Learners** See note on page 549.

You can use the quadratic formula to solve real-world problems. You must decide whether a solution makes sense in the real-world situation. For example, a negative value for time would not be a reasonable solution in most situations.

3 EXAMPLE **Real-World** **Problem Solving**

Sports Suppose a football player kicks a ball and gives it an initial upward velocity of 47 ft/s. The starting height of the football is 3 ft. If no one catches the football, how long will it be in the air?

Step 1 Use the vertical motion formula.

$$h = -16t^2 + vt + c$$

The initial upward velocity is v, and the starting height is c.

$$0 = -16t^2 + 47t + 3$$

Substitute 0 for h, 47 for v, and 3 for c.

Step 2 Use the quadratic formula.

$$x = \frac{-b \pm \sqrt{b^2 - 4ac}}{2a}$$

$$t = \frac{-(47) \pm \sqrt{(47)^2 - (4)(-16)(3)}}{2(-16)}$$

Substitute -16 for a, 47 for b, 3 for c, and t for x.

$$t = \frac{-47 \pm \sqrt{2209 + 192}}{-32}$$

Simplify.

$$t = \frac{-47 \pm \sqrt{2401}}{-32}$$

$$t = \frac{-47 + 49}{-32} \quad \text{or} \quad t = \frac{-47 - 49}{-32}$$

Write as two equations.

$$t \approx -0.06 \quad \text{or} \quad t = 3$$

Simplify. Use the positive answer because it is the only reasonable answer in this situation.

The football will be in the air for 3 seconds.

✓ Check Understanding **3** A football player kicks a ball with an initial upward velocity of 38.4 ft/s from a starting height of 3.5 ft. **a.** $0 = -16t^2 + 38.4t + 3.5$
  a. Substitute the values into the vertical motion formula. Let $h = 0$.
  b. Solve. If no one catches the ball, how long will it be in the air? Round to the nearest tenth of a second. $t \approx 2.5$; 2.5 s

OBJECTIVE

2 **Choosing an Appropriate Method**

There are many methods for solving a quadratic equation. You can always use the quadratic formula, but sometimes another method may be easier.

Method	When to Use
Graphing	Use if you have a graphing calculator handy.
Square Roots	Use if the equation has no x term.
Factoring	Use if you can factor the equation easily.
Completing the Square	Use if the x^2 term is 1, but you cannot factor the equation easily.
Quadratic Formula	Use if the equation cannot be factored easily or at all.

Additional Examples

1 Solve $x^2 + 2 = -3x$. −1, −2

2 Solve $3x^2 + 4x - 8 = 0$. Round the solutions to the nearest hundredth. −2.43, 1.10

3 A child throws a ball upward with an initial upward velocity of 15 ft/s from a height of 2 ft. If no one catches the ball, how long will it be in the air? Round to the nearest hundredth of a second. 1.06 seconds

OBJECTIVE
2 **Teaching Notes**

4 EXAMPLE **Visual Learners**

Encourage a group of visual learners to draw a large flow chart as a class poster for students to refer to when trying to decide which method to use.

Additional Examples

4 Which method(s) would you choose to solve each equation? Justify your reasoning.
a. $5x^2 + 8x - 14 = 0$. **Quadratic formula; the equation cannot be factored easily.**
b. $25x^2 - 169 = 0$ **Square roots; there is no x term.**
c. $x^2 - 2x - 3 = 0$. **Factoring; the equation is easily factorable.**
d. $x^2 - 5x + 3 = 0$ **Quadratic formula, completing the square, or graphing; the x^2 term is 1, but the equation is not factorable.**
e. $16x^2 - 96x + 135 = 0$ **Quadratic formula; the equation cannot be factored easily, and the numbers are large.**

Closure

Ask: *What is the quadratic formula?* The quadratic formula finds the solution(s) to $ax^2 + bx + c = 0$, where $a \neq 0$. *Why is it useful?* It can be used to solve any quadratic equation. Then ask: *When is the square root method useful in solving a quadratic equation?* when the equation has no x term

549

3. Practice

Assignment Guide

1 Objective

Ⓐ Ⓑ **Core** 1–17, 33–34, 36–38, 40

Ⓒ **Extension** 41

2 Objective

Ⓐ Ⓑ **Core** 18–32, 35, 39

Ⓒ **Extension** 42

Standardized Test Prep 43–46

Mixed Review 47–55

Error Prevention

Exercises 4, 9 Remind students to write quadratic equations in standard form before using the quadratic formula.

Connection to Calculus

Exercises 16, 17 Remind students that slope measures a rate of change. Ask them to explain why it would be reasonable to think of velocity as the rate of change of position with time, and acceleration as the rate of change of velocity with time. Tell students that one of the topics in calculus, differentiation, has to do with measuring slopes or rates of change. Students of calculus can use these ideas to derive the vertical motion formula.

Enrichment 10-7

Reteaching 10-7

Practice 10-7

---

4 EXAMPLE Choosing an Appropriate Method

Which method(s) would you choose to solve each equation? Justify your reasoning.

a. $2x^2 - 6 = 0$ — Square roots; there is no x term.

b. $6x^2 + 13x - 17 = 0$ — Quadratic formula; the equation cannot be factored easily.

c. $x^2 + 2x - 15 = 0$ — Factoring; the equation is easily factorable.

d. $16x^2 - 96x + 45 = 0$ — Quadratic formula; the equation cannot be factored easily, and the numbers are large.

e. $x^2 - 7x + 4 = 0$ — Quadratic formula, completing the square, or graphing; the coefficient of the x^2 term is 1, but the equation is not factorable.

✓ **Check Understanding** Which method(s) would you choose to solve each equation? Justify your reasoning.

a. $13x^2 - 5x + 21 = 0$
   Quadratic formula; the equation cannot be factored.
b. $x^2 - x - 30 = 0$
   Factoring; the equation is easily factorable.
c. $144x^2 = 25$
   Square roots; there is no x term.

EXERCISES

For more practice, see *Extra Practice*.

Practice and Problem Solving

Ⓐ **Practice by Example**

Example 1
(page 548)

Use the quadratic formula to solve each equation. If necessary, round answers to the nearest hundredth.

1. $2x^2 + 5x + 3 = 0$
   −1, −1.5
2. $5x^2 + 16x - 84 = 0$
   2.8, −6
3. $4x^2 - 12x + 9 = 0$
   1.5
4. $3x^2 + 47x = -30$
   −0.67, −15
5. $12x^2 - 77x - 20 = 0$
   6.67, −0.25
6. $3x^2 + 39x + 108 = 0$
   −4, −9
7. $3x^2 + 40x - 128 = 0$
   2.67, −16
8. $2x^2 - 9x - 221 = 0$
   13, −8.5
9. $5x^2 - 68x = 192$
   16, −2.4

Example 2
(page 548)

10. $5x^2 + 13x - 1 = 0$
    0.07, −2.67
11. $2x^2 - 24x + 33 = 0$
    10.42, 1.58
12. $7x^2 + 100x - 4 = 0$
    0.04, −14.33
13. $8x^2 - 3x - 7 = 0$
    1.14, −0.77
14. $6x^2 + 5x - 40 = 0$
    2.20, −3.03
15. $3x^2 - 11x - 2 = 0$
    3.84, −0.17

Example 3
(page 549)

For Exercises 16 and 17, use the vertical motion formula $h = -16t^2 + vt + c$.

16. A child tosses a ball upward with a starting velocity of 10 ft/s from a height of 3 ft. **a. $0 = -16t^2 + 10t + 3$**
    a. Substitute the values into the vertical motion formula. Let $h = 0$.
    b. Solve. If it is not caught, how long will the ball be in the air? Round to the nearest tenth of a second. **$t \approx 0.8$; 0.8 s**

17. A soccer ball is kicked with a starting upward velocity of 50 ft/s from a starting height of 3.5 ft. **a. $0 = -16t^2 + 50t + 3.5$**
    a. Substitute the values into the vertical motion formula. Let $h = 0$.
    b. Solve. If no one touches the ball, how long will the ball be in the air? Round to the nearest tenth of a second. **$t \approx 3.2$; 3.2 s**

Example 4
(page 550)

Which method(s) would you choose to solve each equation? Justify your reasoning. **18–23. See margin.**

18. $x^2 + 2x - 13 = 0$
19. $4x^2 - 81 = 0$
20. $9x^2 - 31x = 51$
21. $3x^2 - 5x + 9 = 0$
22. $x^2 + 4x - 60 = 0$
23. $-4x^2 + 3x + 2 = 0$

550 Chapter 10 Quadratic Equations and Functions

pages 550–552 Exercises

18. Completing the square or graphing; the x^2 term is 1 but the equation is not factorable.

19. Factoring or square roots; the equation is easily factorable and there is no x term.

20. Quadratic formula; the equation cannot be factored.

21. Quadratic formula; the equation cannot be factored.

22. Factoring; the equation is easily factorable.

B **Apply Your Skills**

Use any method you choose to solve each equation. If necessary, round to the nearest hundredth.

24. $2t^2 = 72$
6, −6

25. $3x^2 + 2x − 4 = 0$
0.87, −1.54

26. $5b^2 − 10 = 0$
1.41, −1.41

27. $3x^2 + 4x = 10$
1.28, −2.61

28. $m^2 − 4m = −4$
2

29. $13n^2 − 117 = 0$
3, −3

30. $3s^2 − 4s = 2$
1.72, −0.39

31. $5b^2 − 2b − 7 = 0$
1.4, −1

32. $15x^2 − 12x − 48 = 0$
2.23, −1.43

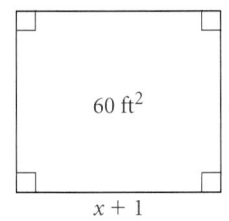

60 ft² x

$x + 1$

 33. Geometry Suppose you want to make a rectangle like the one shown at the left. **a. 7 ft × 8 ft**
  a. Estimate each dimension of the rectangle to the nearest integer.
  b. Write a quadratic equation and use the quadratic formula to find each dimension to the nearest hundredth. $x(x + 1) = 60$, **7.26 ft × 8.26 ft**

 34. Vertical Motion Suppose you throw a ball upward with a starting velocity of 30 ft/s. The ball is 6 ft high when it leaves your hand. After how many seconds will it hit the ground? Use the vertical motion formula $h = −16t^2 + vt + c$. **about 2.1 s**

35. Answers may vary. Sample: You solve the linear equation using transformations and you solve the quadratic equation using the quadratic formula.

 35. Writing Compare the way you solve the linear equation $mx + b = 0$ with the way you solve the quadratic equation $ax^2 + bx + c = 0$. **See left.**

Geometry Find the base and height of each triangle below. If necessary, round to the nearest hundredth.

36. 7.40 ft and 5.40 ft

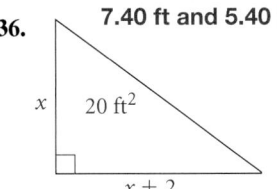

x 20 ft²

$x + 2$

37. 13.44 cm and 7.44 cm

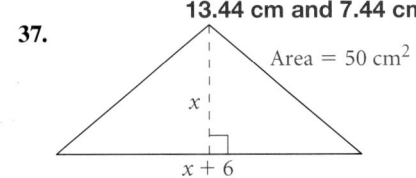

Area = 50 cm²

x

$x + 6$

38. Answers may vary. Sample: A rectangle has length x. Its width is 5 feet longer than three times the length. Find the dimensions if its area is 182 ft².

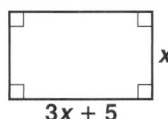

x

$3x + 5$

7 ft. × 26 ft

38. Open-Ended Write a problem in which you find the area of a rectangle that you can solve using a quadratic equation. Draw a diagram and solve. **See left.**

39. Critical Thinking How you can tell from the quadratic formula that a quadratic equation has one solution? Explain. **if the expression $b^2 − 4ac$ equals zero**

C **Challenge**

CLOSE TO HOME by John McPherson

LET'S SEE. 50 FEET UP. ACCELERATION OF GRAVITY IS 32 FEET/SEC²... WHICH MEANS... ..I'LL BE GOING 87.MILES AN HOUR WHEN I HIT THE POOL!!

THERE ARE TIMES WHEN BEING A WHIZ AT PHYSICS CAN BE A DEFINITE DRAWBACK.

40. Vertical Motion Refer to the cartoon. Suppose the man's starting upward velocity v is 5 ft/s. Use $0 = −16t^2 + vt + c$, where c is the starting height. Find the number of seconds t before he hits the water. **about 1.9 s**

Real-World 🌐 **Connection**

Careers Demographers use mathematics to help describe trends in populations.

41. Population The function below models the United States population P in millions since 1900, where t is the number of years after 1900.

$P = 0.0089t^2 + 1.1149t + 78.4491$
  a. Use the function to estimate the United States population the year you graduate from high school. **a. Check students' work.**
  b. Estimate the United States population in 2025. **356.9 million**
  c. Use the function to predict the year in which the population will reach 300 million. **2007**

23. Quadratic formula; the equation cannot be factored.

Resources
For additional practice with a
variety of test item formats:
• Standardized Test Prep, p. 573
• Test-Taking Strategies, p. 568
• Test-Taking Strategies with
  Transparencies

Careers

Exercise 43 Undergraduates
studying to become architects
typically take mathematics,
physics, and design courses
during their freshman and
sophomore years. They must
learn strong problem solving
skills and develop a good sense
of spatial relationships.

42. **Critical Thinking** The two solutions of any quadratic equation are

$$\frac{-b + \sqrt{b^2 - 4ac}}{2a} \text{ and } \frac{-b - \sqrt{b^2 - 4ac}}{2a}.$$

 a. Find a formula for the sum of the solutions. $s = -\frac{b}{a}$
 b. One solution of $2x^2 + 3x - 104 = 0$ is -8. Use the formula you found in part (a) to find the second solution. **6.5**

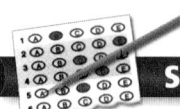

Standardized Test Prep

Reading Comprehension

The Gateway to the West

The Gateway Arch in St. Louis, Missouri, was completed in 1965. The arch spans 630 feet at its base and is 630 feet tall. More than 5100 tons of steel and 38,100 tons of concrete were used in its construction.

43. Use the data in the article above to answer the following questions.
 a. How many pounds of concrete were used in the construction of the Gateway Arch? Write your answer in scientific notation. **7.62×10^7 lb**
 b. How many more tons of concrete than steel were used? Write your answer in scientific notation. **3.3×10^4 tons**
 c. Suppose that a cleaner at the top of the Gateway Arch drops a cleaning brush. Use the vertical motion formula $h = -16t^2 + vt + c$. The starting upward velocity v is 0 and c is the starting height. How many seconds will the brush take to hit the ground? **≈6.27 s**

Take It to the NET
Online lesson quiz at
www.PHSchool.com
Web Code: aea-1007

Multiple Choice

44. The expression $\frac{9 \pm \sqrt{(-9)^2 - 4(5)(-7)}}{2(5)}$ gives the solutions to which of the following equations? **D**
 A. $-9x^2 + 5x = -7$ B. $5x^2 + 7x = 9$
 C. $5x^2 - 9x = -7$ D. $5x^2 - 9x = 7$

45. The graph of $y = 15x^2 - 59x - 112$ crosses the x-axis closest to which of the following x-values? **F**
 F. -1 G. 0   H. 3   I. 6

Short Response

46. Find the solutions to the equation $6x^2 - 40 = 11x$. Round to the nearest tenth. **See margin.**

Mixed Review

Lesson 10-6

Solve each equation by completing the square. If necessary, round to the nearest hundredth.

47. $d^2 - 10d + 13 = 0$ 48. $z^2 + 3z = -2$ 49. $3x^2 + 18x - 1 = 0$
 1.54, 8.46 $-1, -2$ 0.06, -6.06

Lesson 9-8

Factor by grouping.

50. $2c^2 + 11c + 15$ 51. $3z^2 + 10z - 8$ 52. $5n^2 - 33n - 14$
 $(2c + 5)(c + 3)$ $(3z - 2)(z + 4)$ $(5n + 2)(n - 7)$
53. $12v^2 + 32v - 35$ 54. $6x^2 - 13x + 5$ 55. $15t^2 + 19t + 6$
 $(6v - 5)(2v + 7)$ $(2x - 1)(3x - 5)$ $(5t + 3)(3t + 2)$

pages 550–552 Exercises

46. [2] $x = \frac{11 \pm \sqrt{(-11)^2 - 4(6)(-40)}}{2(6)}; -1.8, 3.7$

[1] correct substitution into quadratic formula, with one calculation error

Using a Formula

Read the example below and the explanation about how to use the quadratic formula.

EXAMPLE

Solve $x^2 + 6 = 5x$.

To use the quadratic formula, you must know the following.

$a \rightarrow$ the coefficient of the squared term, which is the term with a power of 2

$b \rightarrow$ the coefficient of the term with a power of 1

$c \rightarrow$ the value of the constant

To determine the values of a, b, and c, write the equation in standard form $ax^2 + bx + c = 0$.

So, for $x^2 + 6 = 5x$, subtract $5x$ from both sides and write in standard form.

$$x^2 \qquad -5x \qquad +6 = 0$$

$$\uparrow \qquad\qquad \uparrow \qquad\qquad \uparrow$$

Coefficient   **Coefficient**   **Constant is 6.**
of x^2 is 1.   **of x is −5.**

Use these values in the quadratic formula. Be careful when substituting negative values that you do not "lose" a negative sign.

$$x = \frac{-b \pm \sqrt{b^2 - 4ac}}{2a}$$

$$x = \frac{-(-5) \pm \sqrt{(-5)^2 - 4 \cdot 1 \cdot 6}}{2(1)}$$ **Substitute 1 for a, −5 for b, and 6 for c.**

$$x = \frac{5 \pm \sqrt{25 - 24}}{2}$$ **Simplify using as many steps as you need to keep the signs of the numbers organized.**

$$x = \frac{5 \pm 1}{2}$$

$$x = \frac{5 + 1}{2} \quad \text{or} \quad x = \frac{5 - 1}{2}$$ **5 ± 1 means 5 + 1 or 5 − 1.**

$$x = \frac{6}{2} \quad \text{or} \quad x = \frac{4}{2}$$

$$x = 3 \quad \text{or} \quad x = 2$$

EXERCISE

Use the equation $4x^2 - 8x = 45$.
a. Write the equation in standard form. $4x^2 - 8x - 45 = 0$
b. Identify a, b, and c. $a = 4$, $b = -8$, $c = -45$
c. Use the quadratic formula to solve the equation. $4.5, -2.5$

Reading Math

Using a Formula

Students use the quadratic formula to solve quadratic equations. The students must be able to write the equation in the correct form and be able to identify the needed coefficients and the constant term.

Teaching Notes

Teaching Tip

Have a student tell the order that he/she would follow to simplify the formula after substituting a, b, and c. The student should relate it to the order of operations. You can explain that the square root sign acts as a grouping symbol like parentheses, that is, the calculations under it are done first. The division line also acts as a grouping symbol so '$-b \pm$ the square root' is actually calculated before the division.

Error Prevention

Students may make fewer errors when substituting in the quadratic formula if they rewrite the quadratic expression so that it shows only addition. For example, if the equation is $4x^2 - 5x - 11 = 0$, have them rewrite it as $4x^2 + (-5)x + (-11) = 0$. This may help prevent errors in identifying a, b, and c and in substituting those values into the formula.

Exercise

Have students work independently to solve a quadratic equation using the formula. Then have them work with partners. The partner will check the answers by substituting them into the original equation. If the answers don't check, have the pair work together to find where the mistake was made. Unresolved errors can be discussed with the whole group.

553

Lesson Preview

 Check Skills You'll Need

Multiplying and Dividing
Lesson 1-6: Examples 2, 4
Exercises 13–24, 32–39
Extra Practice, p. 702

Using the Quadratic Formula
Lesson 10-7: Examples 1, 2
Exercises 1–15
Extra Practice, p. 711

Lesson Resources

 Teaching Resources
Practice, Reteaching, Enrichment
Checkpoint Quiz 2

 Reaching All Students
Practice Workbook 10-8
Spanish Practice Workbook 10-8
Reading and Math Literacy 10C
Spanish Reading & Literacy 10C
Spanish Checkpoint Quiz 2
Hands-On Activities 24
Basic Algebra Planning Guide 10-8

 Presentation Assistant Plus!
Transparencies
• Check Skills You'll Need 10-8
• Additional Examples 10-8
• Student Edition Answers 10-8
• Lesson Quiz 10-8
PH Presentation Pro CD 10-8

 PRENTICE HALL ASSESSMENT SYSTEM

Checkpoint Quiz 2
Computer Test Generator CD

 Technology
Resource Pro® CD-ROM
Computer Test Generator CD
Prentice Hall Presentation Pro CD

 www.PHSchool.com
Student Site
• Teacher Web Code: aek-5500
• Reasoning & Puzzles p. 94
• Self-grading Lesson Quiz
Teacher Center
• Lesson Planner
• Resources

Plus

554

10-8

Using the Discriminant

North Carolina Objectives 4.02 Graph, factor, and evaluate quadratic functions to solve problems.

Lesson Preview

What You'll Learn

OBJECTIVE **1** To find the number of solutions of a quadratic equation

. . . And Why

To solve physics problems, as in Example 2

✓ **Check Skills You'll Need** (For help, go to Lessons 1-6 and 10-7.)

Evaluate $b^2 - 4ac$ for the given values of a, b, and c.

1. $a = 3, b = 4, c = 8$ **2.** $a = -2, b = 0, c = 9$ **3.** $a = 11, b = -5, c = 7$
   -80 72 -283

Solve using the quadratic formula. If necessary, round to the nearest hundredth.

4. $3x^2 - 7x + 1 = 0$ **5.** $4x^2 + x - 1 = 0$ **6.** $x^2 - 12x + 35 = 0$
   2.18, 0.15   0.39, −0.64   7, 5

New Vocabulary • discriminant

 Interactive lesson includes instant self-check, tutorials, and activities.

OBJECTIVE **1** Number of Real Solutions of a Quadratic Equation

Quadratic equations can have two, one, or no solutions. You can determine how many solutions a quadratic equation has, before you solve it, by using the discriminant. The **discriminant** is the expression under the radical in the quadratic formula.

$$x = \frac{-b \pm \sqrt{b^2 - 4ac}}{2a} \leftarrow \text{the discriminant}$$

Consider the graphs of the functions below and the discriminant of each related equation.

$y = x^2 - 6x + 3$ $\qquad$ $y = x^2 - 6x + 9$ $\qquad$ $y = x^2 - 6x + 12$

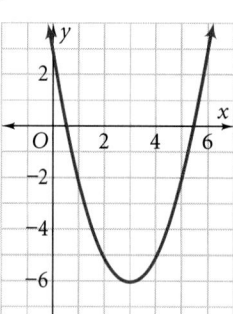 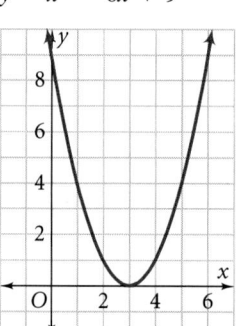 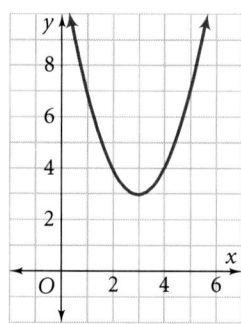

$$x^2 - 6x + 3 = 0 \qquad x^2 - 6x + 9 = 0 \qquad x^2 - 6x + 12 = 0$$

$b^2 - 4ac$: $\quad (-6)^2 - 4(1)(3) \qquad (-6)^2 - 4(1)(9) \qquad (-6)^2 - 4(1)(12)$

$\qquad\qquad = 36 - 12 \qquad\qquad = 36 - 36 \qquad\qquad = 36 - 48$

$\qquad\qquad = 24 \qquad\qquad\qquad = 0 \qquad\qquad\qquad = -12$

The relationship you see between the graphs and discriminants above is true for all cases. If the discriminant is positive, there are two solutions. If the discriminant is zero, there is one solution. If the discriminant is negative, there are no solutions.

Ongoing Assessment and Intervention

Before the Lesson
Diagnose prerequisite skills using:
• Check Skills You'll Need

During the Lesson
Monitor progress using:
• Check Understanding
• Additional Examples
• Standardized Test Prep

After the Lesson
Assess knowledge using:
• Lesson Quiz
• Computer Test Generator CD
• Chapter Checkpoint 2 (p. 558)

This graph shows the three cases together.

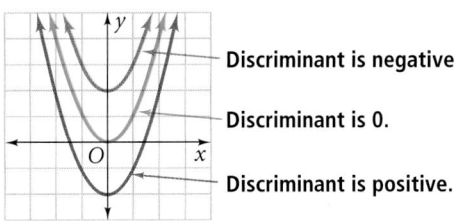

Discriminant is negative.

Discriminant is 0.

Discriminant is positive.

🔑 **Key Concepts**

Property	Property of the Discriminant

For the quadratic equation $ax^2 + bx + c = 0$, where $a \neq 0$, you can use the value of the discriminant to determine the number of solutions.

If $b^2 - 4ac > 0$, there are two solutions.

If $b^2 - 4ac = 0$, there is one solution.

If $b^2 - 4ac < 0$, there are no solutions.

1 EXAMPLE Using the Discriminant

Find the number of solutions of $3x^2 - 5x = 1$.

$3x^2 - 5x - 1 = 0$	**Write in standard form.**
$b^2 - 4ac = (-5)^2 - (4)(3)(-1)$	**Evaluate the discriminant. Substitute for *a*, *b*, and *c*.**
$= 25 - (-12)$	**Use the order of operations.**
$= 37$	**Simplify.**

Since $37 > 0$, the equation has two solutions.

✓ **Check Understanding** ❶ Find the number of solutions for each equation.
   a. $x^2 = 2x - 3$ **0**   **b.** $3x^2 - 4x = 7$ **2**   **c.** $5x^2 + 8 = 2x$ **0**

2 EXAMPLE Real-World 🌐 Problem Solving

Physics A construction worker on the ground tosses an apple to a fellow worker who is 20 ft above the ground. The starting height of the apple is 5 ft. Its initial upward velocity is 30 ft/s. Will the apple reach the second worker?

$h = -16t^2 + vt + c$	**Use the vertical motion formula.**
$20 = -16t^2 + 30t + 5$	**Substitute 20 for *h*, 30 for *v*, and 5 for *c*.**
$0 = -16t^2 + 30t - 15$	**Write in standard form.**
$b^2 - 4ac = (30)^2 - 4(-16)(-15)$	**Evaluate the discriminant.**
$= 900 - 960$	**Use the order of operations.**
$= -60$	**Simplify.**

The discriminant is negative. The apple will not reach the second worker.

✓ **Check Understanding** ❷ Suppose the same construction worker tosses an apple with an initial upward velocity of 32 ft/s. Will the apple reach the second worker? **yes**

Lesson 10-8 Using the Discriminant **555**

👪 **Reaching All Students**

Below Level Use $y = x^2$, $y = 2x^2$ and $y = -x^2$ to remind students that if a quadratic function has its vertex at the origin, $x = 0$ is the solution to the related quadratic equation.	**Advanced Learners** Ask students to solve $y = 9x^2$ and $y = x^2 - 6x + 9$ by factoring. Point out that each has two identical solutions.	**Error Prevention** See note on page 556.

2. Teach

Math Background

When the value of the discriminant is zero, the parabola may open upward or downward, but it is tangent to the *x*-axis. When the value is positive, the parabola intercepts the *x*-axis in two separate points. When the value is negative, the parabola does not intercept the *x*-axis. (This indicates the existence of complex roots.)

OBJECTIVE

1 Teaching Notes

1 EXAMPLE Connection to Language Arts

The word *discriminate* is typically thought of as meaning "to treat unfairly." Point out that the word *discriminate* also means "to make a distinction." By using the discriminant, students can distinguish among quadratic equations with zero, one, or two solution(s).

2 EXAMPLE Math Tip

Challenge students to explain why the apple does not reach a height of 25 ft even though it is thrown with an upward velocity of 30 ft/s.

 Additional Examples

❶ Find the number of solutions of $x^2 = -3x - 7$. **none**

❷ A football is punted from a starting height of 3 ft with an initial upward velocity of 40 ft/s. Will the football ever reach a height of 30 ft? **no**

Closure

Ask: *What is the discriminant and how is it useful?* The discriminant is $b^2 - 4ac$, the radicand in the quadratic formula. It is useful in determining the number of solutions to a quadratic equation without having to actually solve the equation.

555

3. Practice

Assignment Guide

▼ **Objective**

Ⓐ Ⓑ **Core** 1–37

Ⓒ **Extension** 38–42

Standardized Test Prep 43–48

Mixed Review 49–61

Error Prevention

Exercises 19–24 Remind students that the *x*-intercepts are the solutions of each equation. Also, remind students to write each equation in standard form before using the discriminant.

Enrichment 10-8

Reteaching 10-8

Practice 10-8

Practice 10-8   Using the Discriminant

Find the number of real solutions of each equation.

1. $x^2 + 6x + 10 = 0$ 2. $x^2 - 4x - 1 = 0$ 3. $x^2 + 6x + 9 = 0$
4. $x^2 - 8x + 15 = 0$ 5. $x^2 - 5x + 7 = 0$ 6. $x^2 - 4x + 5 = 0$
7. $3x^2 - 18x + 27 = 0$ 8. $4x^2 - 8 = 0$ 9. $-5x^2 - 10x = 0$
10. $-x^2 + 4x + 6$ 11. $4x^2 + 9x - 3$ 12. $8x^2 + 2 + 8x$
13. $5x^2 + 16x + 11 = 0$ 14. $12x^2 - 11x - 2 = 0$ 15. $-9x^2 - 25x + 20 = 0$
16. $16x^2 + 8x = -1$ 17. $-16x^2 + 11x = 11$ 18. $12x^2 - 12x = -3$
19. $0.2x^2 + 4.5x - 2.8 = 0$ 20. $-2.8x^2 + 3.1x = -0.5$ 21. $0.5x^2 + 0.6x = 0$
22. $1.5x^2 - 15x + 2.5 = 0$ 23. $-3x^2 + 27x = -40$ 24. $2.1x^2 + 4.2 = 0$

25. One of the games at a carnival involves trying to ring a bell with a ball by hitting a lever that propels the ball into the air. The height of the ball is modeled by the equation $h = -16t^2 + 39t$. If the bell is 25 ft above the ground, will it be hit by the ball?

26. You are placing a rectangular picture on a square poster board. You can enlarge the picture to any size. The area of the poster board not covered by the picture is modeled by the equation $A = -x^2 - 10x + 300$. Is it possible for the area not covered by the picture to be 100 in.?

27. The equation $h = -16t^2 + 50t + 3$ models the height of a baseball t seconds after it has been hit.
   a. Was the height of the baseball ever 40 ft?
   b. Was the height of the baseball ever 60 ft?

28. A firefighter is on the fifth floor of an office building. She needs to throw a rope into the window above her on the seventh floor. The function $h = -16t^2 + 36t$ models how high above her she is able to throw a rope. If she needs to throw the rope 40 ft above her to reach the seventh-floor window, will the rope get to the window?

Find the number of x-intercepts of each function.

29. $y = x^2 + 10x + 16$ 30. $y = x^2 + 3x + 5$ 31. $y = x^2 - 2x - 7$
32. $y = 3x^2 - 3$ 33. $y = 2x^2 + x$ 34. $y = 3x^2 + 2x + 1$
35. $y = x^2 - 8x - 4$ 36. $y = x^2 - 16x + 64$ 37. $y = -2x^2 - 5x - 6$
38. $y = -4x^2 - 5x - 2$ 39. $y = -x^2 + 12x - 36$ 40. $y = -5x^2 + 11x - 6$

Lesson 10-8 Practice   Algebra 1 Chapter 10

EXERCISES

For more practice, see *Extra Practice*.

Practice and Problem Solving

Ⓐ **Practice by Example**

Example 1
(page 555)

For which discriminant is each graph possible?

1.
A
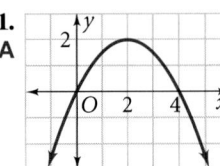

2.
C
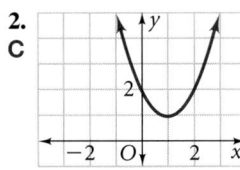

3.
B
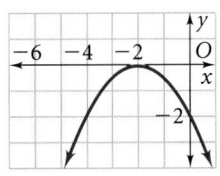

A. $b^2 - 4ac = 4$ **B.** $b^2 - 4ac = 0$ **C.** $b^2 - 4ac = -4$

Mental Math **Find the number of solutions of each equation.**

4. $x^2 - 3x + 4 = 0$ **0**   **5.** $x^2 - 6x + 9 = 0$ **1**   **6.** $x^2 + 4x - 2 = 0$ **2**

7. $x^2 - 1 = 0$ **2**   **8.** $x^2 - 2x - 3 = 0$ **2**   **9.** $x^2 + x = 0$ **2**

10. $2x^2 - 3x + 4 = 0$ **0**   **11.** $0 = x^2 - 6x + 5$ **2**   **12.** $x^2 - 7x + 6 = 0$ **2**

13. $x^2 + 2x + 1 = 0$ **1**   **14.** $0 = 2x^2 + 4x - 3$ **2**   **15.** $0 = x^2 + 2x + 9$ **0**

Example 2
(page 555)

16. Home Improvements The Reeves family's garden is 18 ft long and 15 ft wide. They want to decrease the length by *x* feet and increase the width by the same amount. The equation $A = (18 - x)(15 + x)$ models the new area of the garden. What value of *x*, if any, will give a new area of 280 ft²? **none**

17. Business An apartment rental agency uses the formula $I = 5400 + 300n - 50n^2$ to find its monthly income *I* based on renting *n* apartments. Will the agency's monthly income ever be $7000? Explain. **No; the discriminant is negative.**

18. Physics Suppose the equation $h = -16t^2 + 35t$ models the altitude a football will reach *t* seconds after it is kicked. Is the given altitude possible?
a. $h = 16$ ft **yes**   **b.** $h = 20$ ft **no**   **c.** $h = 30$ ft **no**   **d.** $h = 35$ ft **no**

Ⓑ **Apply Your Skills**

Find the number of *x*-intercepts of the related function of each equation.

19. $2x^2 + 4x = -15$ **0**   **20.** $4x^2 + 5x = -2$ **0**   **21.** $x^2 - 8x = -12$ **2**

22. $\frac{1}{2}x^2 + 4x = 7$ **2**   **23.** $0.25x^2 - 1.2x + 3.2 = 0$ **0**   **24.** $5x^2 = 3.5 + 4.7x$ **2**

 25. Business A software company is producing a new computer application. The equation $S = p(54 - 0.75p)$ relates price *p* in dollars to total sales *S* in thousands of dollars.
   a. Write the equation in standard form. $S = -0.75p^2 + 54p$
   b. Use the discriminant to determine if it is possible for the company to earn $1,000,000 in sales. **no**
   c. According to the model, what price would generate the greatest sales? **$36**
   d. **Critical Thinking** Total sales *S* decrease as *p* increases beyond the value in part (c). Why does this make sense in the given situation? Explain. **If a product is too expensive, fewer people will buy it.**

26. Open-Ended For the equation $x^2 + 4x + k = 0$, find all values of *k* such that the equation has the given number of solutions.
   a. none $k > 4$ **b.** one $k = 4$ **c.** two $k < 4$

556   Chapter 10   Quadratic Equations and Functions

pages 556–558   **Exercises**

37. **Answers may vary. Sample:** Use values for *a*, *b*, and *c* such that the discriminant is positive.

Need Help?

For help with spreadsheets, see Skills Handbook page 747.

27. You can use a spreadsheet like the one at the right to find the discriminant for each value of b shown in column A.

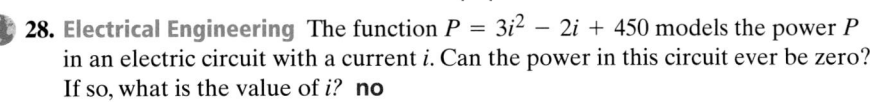

	A	B	C
1	b	x^2 + bx + 1 = 0	x^2 + bx + 2 = 0
2	−3	▪	▪
3	−2	▪	▪
4	−1	▪	▪
5	0	▪	▪
6	1	▪	▪
7	2	▪	▪
8	3	▪	▪

   a. What spreadsheet formula would you use to find the value in cell B2? What value would you use for cell C2? **A2 ^ 2 − 4; A2 ^ 2 − 8**

   b. Describe the integer values of b for which $x^2 + bx + 1 = 0$ has no solutions. **$|b| < 2$**

 28. Electrical Engineering The function $P = 3i^2 - 2i + 450$ models the power P in an electric circuit with a current i. Can the power in this circuit ever be zero? If so, what is the value of i? **no**

29. Error Analysis Kenji claimed that the discriminant of $2x^2 + 5x - 1 = 0$ was 17. What error did he make?
   Answers may vary. Sample: Kenji used $c = 1$ instead of $c = -1$.

30. Find the value of the discriminant and the solutions of each equation. If necessary, round to the nearest hundredth. **b. 81; 4, −5 c. 73; 3.89, −0.39**
   a. $x^2 - 6x + 5 = 0$ **16; 5, 1 b.** $x^2 + x - 20 = 0$ **c.** $2x^2 - 7x - 3 = 0$
   d. Reasoning When the discriminant is a perfect square, are the solutions rational or irrational? Explain. **Rational; the square root of a discriminant that is a perfect square is a pos. integer.**

Does the graph of each function cross the x-axis? If so, find the x-intercepts.

31. $y = x^2 - 2x + 5$ **no**   **32.** $y = 2x^2 - 4x + 3$ **no**   **33.** $y = 4x^2 + x - 5$ **yes; 1, −1.25**

34. $y = -3x^2 - x + 2$ **35.** $y = x^2 - 5x + 7$ **36.** $y = 2x^2 - 3x - 5$
   yes; −1, $\frac{2}{3}$ **no**   **yes; 2.5, −1**

 37. Writing How can you use the discriminant to write an equation that has two solutions? **See margin.**

Real-World 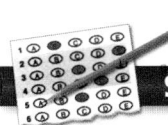 **Connection**

Careers An electrical engineer designs circuits that are used in a wide variety of devices.

C Challenge

Reasoning For each condition given, tell whether $ax^2 + bx + c = 0$ will have two solutions *sometimes*, *always*, or *never*.

38. $b^2 < 4ac$ **never**   **39.** $b^2 = 0$ **sometimes**   **40.** $ac < 0$ **always**

41. **2; since the parabola crosses the x-axis once, it must cross again.**

41. Critical Thinking The graph of a quadratic equation includes the points $(2, -1)$ and $(3, 2)$. How many solutions does the equation have? Explain. **See left.**

42. Critical Thinking The discriminant of $0 = 2x^2 + 6x + 7$ is -20. The discriminant of $0 = 2x^2 + 8x + 10$ is -16. Without graphing, determine which related function has a vertex closer to the x-axis. Explain. **See margin.**

Standardized Test Prep

Multiple Choice

43. Which of the following is equal to $b^2 - 4ac$, if $a = 1$, $b = 7$, and $c = -4$? **C**
   A. −111   **B.** 33   **C.** 65   **D.** 113

44. Which of the following equations has NO real-number solutions? **G**
   F. $3x^2 - 5x + 1 = 0$ **G.** $3x^2 - 5x + 4 = 0$
   H. $-3x^2 - 11x + 4 = 0$ **I.** $-2x^2 - 3x + 1 = 0$

42. $y = 2x^2 + 8x + 10$ has a vertex closer to the x-axis; its discriminant is closer to zero.

4. Assess

 Lesson Quiz 10-8

Find the number of solutions for each equation.

1. $3x^2 - 4x = 7$ **two**

2. $4x^2 = 4x - 1$ **one**

3. $-3x^2 + 2x - 12 = 0$ **none**

4. A ball is thrown from a starting height of 4 ft with an initial upward velocity of 30 ft/s. Is it possible for the ball to reach a height of 18 ft? **yes**

Alternative Assessment

Have students work in pairs. Instruct one student to sketch three graphs—a graph representing a quadratic function that has no solution, a graph representing a quadratic function that has one solution, and a graph representing a quadratic function that has two solutions. Tell the other student to write down three quadratic equations on a piece of paper—one equation for each possible number of solutions. Have students exchange papers and determine the number of solutions for each graph or equation. Encourage them to discuss the results and make the connection between the number of solutions and the number of x-intercepts.

Standardized Test Prep

Resources

For additional practice with a variety of test item formats:
• Standardized Test Prep, p. 573
• Test-Taking Strategies, p. 568
• Test-Taking Strategies with Transparencies

Exercises 45, 46 Point out to students that they don't need to actually solve each expression. They can simply use the discriminant to determine the number of solutions.

To check understanding of Lessons 10-5 to 10-8:

Checkpoint Quiz 2 (p. 558)

📁 **Teaching Resources**
Checkpoint Quiz 2 (also in Prentice Hall Assessment System)

👥 **Reaching All Students**
Reading and Math Literacy 10C

Spanish versions available

Quantitative Comparison

Compare the boxed quantity in Column A with the boxed quantity in Column B. Choose the best answer.
A. The quantity in Column A is greater.
B. The quantity in Column B is greater.
C. The two quantities are equal.
D. The relationship cannot be determined from the information given.

Take It to the NET
Online lesson quiz at
www.PHSchool.com
Web Code: aea-1008

	Column A	Column B
45. **B**	the number of real-number solutions of $35 = 20x^2 - 15x + 47$	the number of real-number solutions of $15x + 7 = 0$
46. **D**	the number of real-number solutions of $ax^2 + 5x - 3 = 0$	the number of real-number solutions of $5x^2 + bx - 3 = 0$
47. **A**	the discriminant of $4x^2 - x = 6$	the discriminant of $4x^2 + 6 = x$

Short Response

48. A rectangle has a perimeter of 50 cm. Is it possible for it to have an area of 136 cm²? If so, what are the dimensions? Show your work. **See margin.**

Mixed Review

Lesson 10-7

Use the quadratic formula to solve each equation. If necessary, round to the nearest hundredth.

49. $4x^2 + 4x - 3 = 0$
0.5, −1.5

50. $x^2 + 2x - 7 = 0$
1.83, −3.83

51. $6x^2 - 2x - 1 = 0$
0.61, −0.27

52. $x^2 + x = 5$
1.79, −2.79

53. $3x^2 - 8x + 1 = 0$
2.54, 0.13

54. $2x^2 - 7x = -6$
2, 1.5

Lesson 8-8

Find the balance in each account.

55. $1000 principal earning 3% compounded quarterly; after 3 years **$1093.81**

56. $200 principal earning 4.5% compounded quarterly; after 10 years **$312.88**

57. $5000 principal earning 5% annual interest compounded monthly; after 4 years **$6104.48**

Lesson 8-6

Determine whether each sequence is *arithmetic* or *geometric*.

58. 5, 9, 13, . . .
arithmetic

59. −11, −16, −21, . . .
arithmetic

60. 10, 20, 40, . . .
geometric

61. 3, 6, 9, . . .
arithmetic

✓ Checkpoint Quiz 2   Lessons 10-5 through 10-8

iTEXT Instant self-check quiz online and on CD-ROM

Solve each equation. If necessary, round to the nearest tenth. If there is no solution, write *no solution*.

1. $(x + 3)(x - 7) = 0$
−3, 7

2. $x^2 + 12x + 27 = 0$
−3, −9

3. $x^2 - 5x = 50$
−5, 10

4. $x^2 + 2x - 1 = 0$
0.4, −2.4

5. $x^2 - 5x - 4 = 0$
5.7, −0.7

6. $x^2 - 8x - 33 = 0$
11, −3

7. $4x^2 - x - 3 = 0$
1, $-\frac{3}{4}$

8. $4x^2 - x + 3 = 0$
no solution

9. $2x^2 - 3x + 1 = 0$
1, 0.5

10. Use the discriminant to determine the number of solutions of the equation $4x^2 - 3x + 5 = 0$. **0**

558   Chapter 10   Quadratic Equations and Functions

---

pages 556–558 Exercises

48. [2]

$$x(25 - x) = 136$$
$$x^2 - 25x + 136 = 0$$
$$x = \frac{-(-25) \pm \sqrt{(-25)^2 - 4(1)(136)}}{2(1)} = \frac{25 \pm 9}{2}$$
$$= 17 \text{ or } 8$$

yes, 17 cm by 8 cm

[1] no work shown OR appropriate methods with one computational error

10-9

Choosing a Linear, Quadratic, or Exponential Model

3.03   Create linear models for sets of data to solve problems.
4.02   Graph and evaluate quadratic functions to solve problems.
4.04   Graph and evaluate exponential functions to solve problems.

Lesson Preview

What You'll Learn

OBJECTIVE 1
To choose a linear, quadratic, or exponential model for data

...And Why

To model changes in an animal population, as in Example 3

✓ **Check Skills You'll Need**   (For help, go to Lessons 6-2, 8-7, and 10-1.)

Graph each function. 1–6. See margin p. 561.

1. $y = 3x - 1$

2. $y = \frac{1}{4}x + 2$

3. $y = 2^x$

4. $y = \left(\frac{1}{3}\right)^x$

5. $y = x^2 + 5$

6. $y = 2x^2 - 1$

 Interactive lesson includes instant self-check, tutorials, and activities.

OBJECTIVE

1 Choosing a Linear, Quadratic, or Exponential Model

You can use the linear, exponential, or quadratic functions you have studied to model some sets of data. Recall the general appearance of each type of function.

🔑 **Key Concepts**

Summary	Linear, Quadratic, and Exponential Functions

Linear	Quadratic	Exponential
$y = mx + b$	$y = ax^2 + bx + c$	$y = a \cdot b^x$

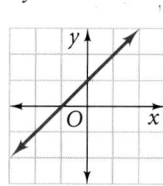   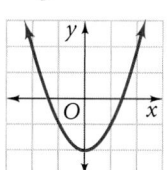   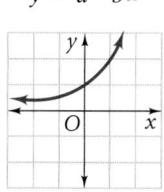

You may be able to use the graph of data points to determine a model for the data.

1 EXAMPLE   Choosing a Model by Graphing

Graph each set of points. Which model is most appropriate for each set?

a. $(-3, 6), (-2, 2), (0, -2),$
$(3, 6), (1, -1), (2, 2)$

b. $(-2, 5), (0, 3),$
$(1, 2.5), (2, 2)$

c. $(-2, 4), (-1, 2),$
$(1, -2), (2, -4)$

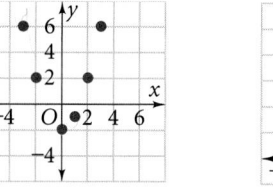

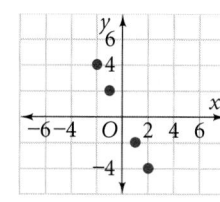

Quadratic model   Exponential model   Linear model

Lesson 10-9   Choosing a Linear, Quadratic, or Exponential Model   **559**

Ongoing Assessment and Intervention

Before the Lesson
Diagnose prerequisite skills using:
• Check Skills You'll Need

During the Lesson
Monitor progress using:
• Check Understanding
• Additional Examples
• Standardized Test Prep

After the Lesson
Assess knowledge using:
• Lesson Quiz
• Computer Test Generator CD

10-9

1. Plan

Lesson Preview

✓ **Check Skills You'll Need**

Slope-Intercept Form
Lesson 6-2: Example 4
Exercises 28–39
Extra Practice, p. 707

Exponential Functions
Lesson 8-7: Example 3
Exercises 12–22
Extra Practice, p. 709

Exploring Quadratic Graphs
Lesson 10-1: Example 4
Exercises 14–19
Extra Practice, p. 711

Lesson Resources

📁 **Teaching Resources**
Practice, Reteaching, Enrichment

👥 **Reaching All Students**
Practice Workbook 10-9
Spanish Practice Workbook 10-9
Technology Activities 9
Hands-On Activities 25
Basic Algebra Planning Guide 10-9

⏱ **Presentation Assistant Plus!**
Transparencies
• Check Skills You'll Need 10-9
• Additional Examples 10-9
• Student Edition Answers 10-9
• Lesson Quiz 10-9
PH Presentation Pro CD 10-9

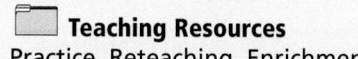 **ASSESSMENT** *SYSTEM*

Computer Test Generator CD

💿 **Technology**
Resource Pro® CD-ROM
Computer Test Generator CD
Prentice Hall Presentation Pro CD

💻 **www.PHSchool.com**
Student Site
• Teacher Web Code: aek-5500
• Updated Data
• Self-grading Lesson Quiz
Teacher Center
• Lesson Planner
• Resources

Plus

Math Background

You can graph points to determine if data are linear, quadratic, or exponential. You can also test ordered data for a common difference or common ratio. A linear model fits data with a common difference and an exponential model fits data with a common ratio. A quadratic model fits data with common second differences. (*Second differences* are differences of the first differences.) One way to remember that you find the second differences to determine quadratic models is to remember that x will be squared. To determine cubic models, you must consider the third differences.

OBJECTIVE

Teaching Notes

1 EXAMPLE Visual Learners

Help students remember the general appearance of each function by drawing the following on the board:

q√adratic
$y = ax^{sq√ared} + bx + c$

e✗ponential
$y = a \cdot b^{✗}$

↕inear
$y = mx + ♭$

2 EXAMPLE Technology Tip

Students can use a graphing calculator to graph the data, determine the type of function that best fits the data, and write an equation to model the data. Press STAT ENTER to enter the data in lists. Press 2nd STAT PLOT ENTER ENTER ZOOM 9 to graph the points. You can see that the model is not linear.

560

✔ **Check Understanding** ① Graph each set of points. Which model is most appropriate for each set?
 a. $(-1.5, -2), (0, 2), (1, 4), (2, 6)$ **b.** $(-1, 1), (0, 0), (1, 1), (2, 4)$
 c. $(-1, 0.5), (0, 1), (1, 2), (2, 4)$ **a–c. See margin.**

You can also analyze data numerically to find the best model.

In Lesson 5-6, you learned that the terms of an arithmetic sequence have a common difference. You can model an arithmetic sequence with a linear function.

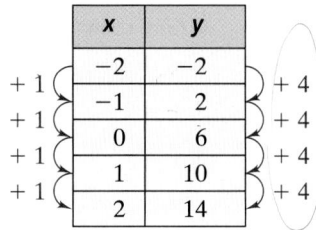

x	y
−2	−2
−1	2
0	6
1	10
2	14

The y-coordinates have a common difference of 4. A linear model fits the data.

In Lesson 8-6, you learned that the terms of a geometric sequence have a common ratio. You can model a geometric sequence with an exponential function.

x	y
−2	$\frac{1}{9}$
−1	$\frac{1}{3}$
0	1
1	3
2	9

The y-coordinates have a common ratio of 3. An exponential model fits the data.

Data from quadratic functions show a different pattern. For linear data, the first differences are the same. For quadratic data, the second differences are the same. If data have a common second difference, then you can model them with a quadratic function.

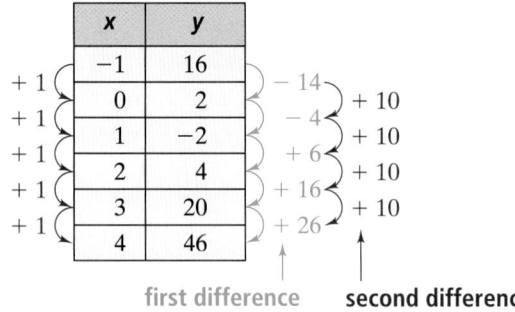

x	y
−1	16
0	2
1	−2
2	4
3	20
4	46

first difference   second difference

The y-coordinates have a common second difference of 10. A quadratic model fits the data.

👥 **Reaching All Students**

| **Below Level** Remind students that in the exponential model, the initial value occurs when $x = 0$. | **Advanced Learners** Have students describe what the graph in Example 3 would look like if the frog population were increasing, rather than decreasing. | **Visual Learners** See note on page 560. **Error Prevention** See note on page 563. |

2 EXAMPLE Modeling Data

x	y
−1	20
0	8
1	3.2
2	1.28
3	0.512

a. Which kind of function best models the data at the left? Write an equation to model the data.

Step 1 Graph the data.

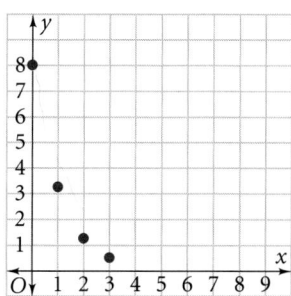

Step 2 The data appear to suggest an exponential model. Test for a common ratio.

x	y	
−1	20	8 ÷ 20 = 0.4
0	8	3.2 ÷ 8 = 0.4
1	3.2	1.28 ÷ 3.2 = 0.4
2	1.28	0.512 ÷ 1.28 = 0.4
3	0.512	

(+1 between each x)

There is a common ratio, 0.4.

Step 3 Write an exponential model.

Relate $y = a \cdot b^x$

Define Let a = the initial value, 8.
Let b = the decay factor, 0.4.

Write $y = 8 \cdot 0.4^x$

Step 4 Test two points other than $(0, 8)$.

$y = 8 \cdot 0.4^1$ $y = 8 \cdot 0.4^3$
$y = 8 \cdot 0.4$ $y = 8 \cdot 0.064$
$y = 3.2$ $y = 0.512$

$(1, 3.2)$ and $(3, 0.512)$ are both data points.

The equation $y = 8 \cdot 0.4^x$ models the data.

x	y
0	0
1	0.3
2	1.2
3	2.7
4	4.8

b. Which kind of function best models the data at the left? Write an equation to model the data.

Step 1 Graph the data.

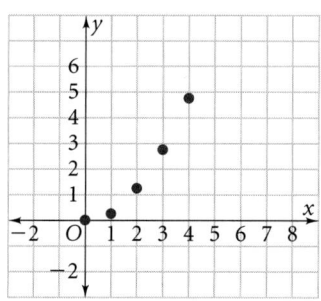

Step 2 The data appear to be quadratic. Test for a common second difference.

x	y		
0	0	+0.3	+0.6
1	0.3	+0.9	+0.6
2	1.2	+1.5	+0.6
3	2.7	+2.1	+0.6
4	4.8		

(+1 between each x)

There is a common second difference, 0.6.

Step 3 Write a quadratic model.

$y = ax^2$
$1.2 = a(2)^2$ Use a point other than (0, 0) to find a.
$1.2 = 4a$ Simplify.
$0.3 = a$ Divide each side by 4.
$y = 0.3x^2$ Write a quadratic function.

Step 4 Test two points other than $(2, 1.2)$ and $(0, 0)$.

$y = 0.3(3)^2$ $y = 0.3(4)^2$
$y = 0.3 \cdot 9$ $y = 0.3 \cdot 16$
$y = 2.7$ $y = 4.8$

$(3, 2.7)$ and $(4, 4.8)$ are both data points.

The equation $y = 0.3x^2$ models the data.

To determine if a quadratic or exponential function best models the data, use the calculator to find each equation that best fits the data. Press STAT ▶ 5 ENTER Y= VARS 5 ▶ ▶ ENTER GRAPH. The quadratic model will appear on the graph. To find the exponential model, follow the same steps except press 0 instead of the first 5, and scroll to Y₂= after you press Y=. Now the exponential model will appear. The exponential model passes through more of the data points. Press Y= and write the exponential equation after Y₂ as $y = 8 \cdot 0.4^x$.

Additional Examples

1 Graph each set of points. Which model is most appropriate for each set?
a. $(−2, 1.45)$, $(0, 3)$, $(1, 4)$ $(2, 6)$ **exponential**
b. $(−2, −2)$, $(0, 2)$, $(1, 4)$, $(2, 6)$ **linear**
c. $(−2, 11)$, $(−1, 5)$, $(0, 3)$, $(1, 5)$, $(2, 11)$ **quadratic**

6.
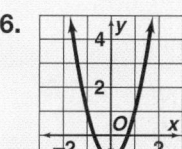

page 560 Check Understanding

1a.
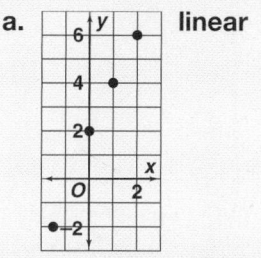   linear

b.
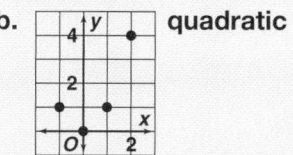   quadratic

c.
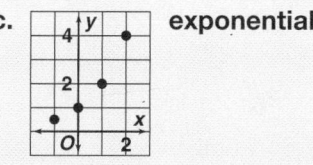   exponential

page 559 Check Skills You'll Need

1.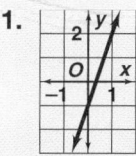
2.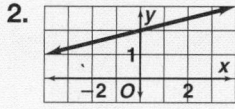
3.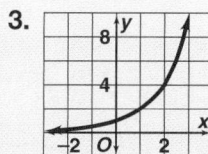
4.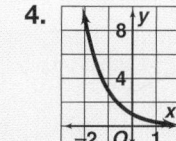
5.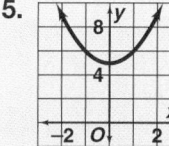

2 Which kind of data best models the data below? Write an equation to model the data.

a.

x	y
0	0
1	1.4
2	5.6
3	12.6
4	22.4

quadratic; $y = 1.4x^2$

b.

x	y
−1	4
0	2
1	1
2	0.5
3	0.25

exponential; $y = 2 \cdot 0.5^x$

3 Suppose you are studying deer that live in an area. The data below were collected by a local conservation organization. It indicates the number of deer estimated to be living in the area over a five-year period. Determine which kind of function best models the data. Write an equation to model the data.

Year	Estimated Population
0	90
1	69
2	52
3	40
4	31

exponential; $y = 90 \cdot 0.77^x$

Closure

Ask students how to choose a linear, quadratic, or exponential model for data. **First graph the data to see if the graph is linear or if it curves. Then look for a best fit model.**

562

✓ **Check Understanding** **2** Which kind of function best models the data in each table? Write an equation to model the data.

a.

x	y
0	4
1	4.4
2	4.84
3	5.324
4	5.8564

exponential; $y = 4 \cdot 1.1^x$

b.

x	y
0	$\frac{1}{2}$
1	1
2	$1\frac{1}{2}$
3	2

linear; $y = \frac{1}{2}x + \frac{1}{2}$

c.

x	y
0	0
1	−0.5
2	−2
3	−4.5
4	−8

quadratic; $y = -\frac{1}{2}x^2$

While real-world data seldom fall exactly into linear, exponential, or quadratic patterns, you can find a best-possible model.

3 EXAMPLE Real-World 🌐 Problem Solving

Zoology Suppose you are studying frogs that live in a nearby wetland area. The data at the right were collected by a local conservation organization. They indicate the number of frogs estimated to be living in the wetland area over a five-year period. Determine which kind of function best models the data. Write an equation to model the data.

Year	Estimated Population
0	120
1	101
2	86
3	72
4	60

Real-World 🌐 Connection

Frog populations around the world have been declining over the past 20 years.

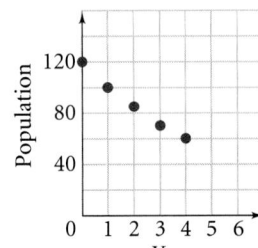

Step 1 Graph the data to decide which model is most appropriate.

The graph curves, and it does not look quadratic. It may be exponential.

Step 2 Test for a common ratio.

	Year	Estimated Population	
+1	0	120	$101 \div 120 = 0.84$
+1	1	101	$86 \div 101 = 0.85$
+1	2	86	$72 \div 86 = 0.84$
+1	3	72	$60 \div 72 = 0.83$
	4	60	

The common ratio is roughly 0.84.

The population of frogs is roughly 0.84 times its value the previous year.

Step 3 Write an exponential model.

Relate $y = a \cdot b^x$

Define Let a = the initial value, 120.
Let b = the decay factor, 0.84.

Write $y = 120 \cdot 0.84^x$

Step 4 Test two points other than $(0, 120)$.

$$y = 120 \cdot 0.84^3 \qquad\qquad y = 120 \cdot 0.84^4$$
$$y \approx 71 \qquad\qquad\qquad y \approx 60$$

The point $(3, 71)$ is close to the data point $(3, 72)$. The predicted value $(4, 60)$ matches the corresponding data point. The equation $y = 120 \cdot 0.84^x$ models the data.

✓ **Check Understanding** ③ The profits of a small company are shown in the table at the right. Let $x = 0$ correspond to the year 2000.
  a. Determine which kind of function best models the data. **quadratic**
  b. Write an equation to model the data. $y = 5000x^2$

Year	Profit (dollars)
0	0
1	5,000
2	20,000
3	44,000
4	79,000

EXERCISES

For more practice, see *Extra Practice*.

Practice and Problem Solving

Ⓐ **Practice by Example**

Example 1 (page 559)

Graph each set of points. Which model is most appropriate for each set? **1–6. See back of book.**

1. $(-2, -3), (-1, 0), (0, 1), (1, 0), (2, -3)$ **2.** $(-2, -8), (0, -4), (3, 2), (5, 6)$

3. $(-3, 6), (-1, 0), (0, -1), (1, -1.5)$ **4.** $(-2, 5), (-1, -1), (0, -3), (1, -1), (2, 5)$

5. $\left(-2, -5\frac{8}{9}\right), \left(-1, -5\frac{2}{3}\right), (0, -5), (2, 3)$ **6.** $(-3, 8), (-1, 6), (0, 5), (2, 3), (3, 2)$

Example 2 (page 561)

Which kind of function best models the data in each table? Write an equation to model the data.

7.

x	y
0	0
1	1.5
2	6
3	13.5
4	24

quadratic; $y = 1.5x^2$

8.

x	y
0	-5
1	-3
2	-1
3	1
4	3

linear; $y = 2x - 5$

9.

x	y
0	0
1	2.8
2	11.2
3	25.2
4	44.8

quadratic; $y = 2.8x^2$

10.

x	y
0	1
1	1.2
2	1.44
3	1.728
4	2.0736

exponential; $y = 1 \cdot 1.2^x$

11.

x	y
0	5
1	2
2	0.8
3	0.32
4	0.128

exponential; $y = 5 \cdot 0.4^x$

12.

x	y
0	2
1	1.5
2	1
3	0.5
4	0

linear; $y = -\frac{1}{2}x + 2$

Example 3 (page 562)

13. The table at the right shows the end-of-the-month balance in a checking account.
  a. Graph the data. Does the graph suggest a linear, exponential, or quadratic model?
  b. Find the differences of consecutive terms. Are they roughly the same? **65, 64, 64; yes**
  c. Estimate a common difference based on your answer to part (b). **64**
  d. Write an equation to model the data. $y = 64x - 5$
  a. See back of book.

Month	Balance (dollars)
1	58
2	123
3	187
4	251

Lesson 10-9 Choosing a Linear, Quadratic, or Exponential Model **563**

Assignment Guide

1 Objective
  Ⓐ Ⓑ **Core** 1–27
  Ⓒ **Extension** 28–29

Standardized Test Prep 30–33

Mixed Review 34–48

Error Prevention

Exercises 1–6 Be sure students do not quickly determine that the best model is exponential as soon as they see that the graph is not linear. They need to graph all points to see if the graph is a quadratic model.

Enrichment 10-9
Reteaching 10-9
Practice 10-9

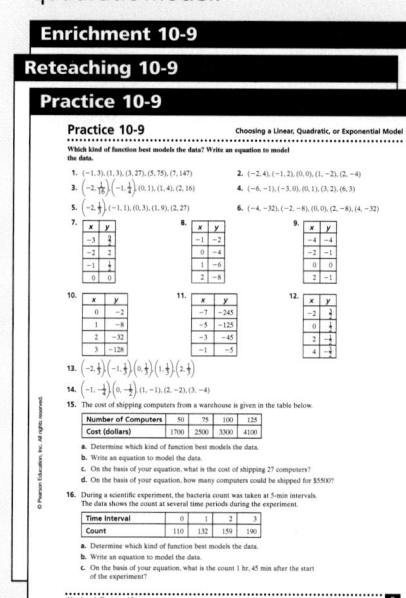

pages 563–566 Exercises

16a.

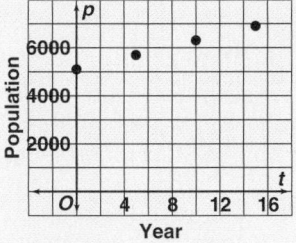

Year

linear

18. Answers may vary. Sample: Linear data have a common first difference, quadratic data have a common second difference, and exponential data have a common ratio.

25a. i.

x	y
1	−2
2	1
3	6
4	13
5	22

) 3) 2
) 5) 2
) 7) 2
) 9

ii.

x	y
1	3
2	12
3	27
4	48
5	75

) 9) 6
) 15) 6
) 21) 6
) 27

iii.

x	y
1	−1
2	6
3	21
4	44
5	75

) 7) 8
) 15) 8
) 23) 8
) 31

29f.

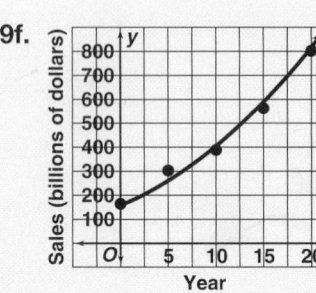

Year

564

Age (years)	Value (dollars)
0	16,500
1	14,500
2	12,750
3	11,200
4	9900

14. Car Value The value of a car over several years is shown in the table at the left.
  a. Determine which model is most appropriate for the data. **exponential**
  b. Write an equation to model the data. $y = 16{,}500 \cdot 0.88^x$

15. Physics Your class collected the data in the table at the right by rolling a ball down a ramp. The ramp had the same angle throughout. **a. 41, 123, 206**
  a. Find the differences of consecutive terms.
  b. Find the second differences. **82, 83**
  c. Write an equation to model the data. Let t be the time in seconds and d be the distance in centimeters. $d = 41t^2$
  d. Based on your equation, how far would the ball have rolled down the ramp in 2.5 seconds? **256.25 cm**

Time (seconds)	Distance (centimeters)
0	0
1	41
2	164
3	370

B Apply Your Skills

16c. 600, 600, 600; 120, 120, 120

16. The table below shows the population of a small town. Let $t = 0$ correspond to the year 2020. **a. See margin.**
  a. Graph the data. Does the graph suggest a linear, exponential, or quadratic model?
  b. What is the difference in years? **5 years**
  c. Find the differences of consecutive terms. Divide by the difference in years to find possible common differences. **See left.**
  d. Write a linear equation to model the data based on your answer to part (c). $p = 120t + 5100$

Year	Population
0	5100
5	5700
10	6300
15	6900

Year	Population (millions)
0	4457
5	4855
10	5284
15	5691
20	6080

SOURCES: U. S. Census Bureau.
Go to **www.PHSchool.com** for a data update.

Web Code: aeg-2041

17. Population The table at the left shows the world population in millions from 1980 to 2000. The year $t = 0$ corresponds to 1980.
  a. What is the difference in years? **5**
  b. Find the differences of consecutive terms. Divide by the difference in years to find possible common differences. **398, 429, 407, 389; 79.6, 85.8, 81.4, 77.8**
  c. Find the average of the common differences you found in part (b). **81.2**
  d. Write a linear equation to model the data based on your answer to part (c).
  e. Use your equation to predict the world population in 2010.
  d. $p = 81.2t + 4457$ **e. 6893 million, or about 6.9 billion**

18. Writing Explain in writing to a classmate how to decide whether a linear, exponential, or quadratic function is the most appropriate equation to model a set of data. **See margin.**

Use LinReg, ExpReg, or QuadReg to find an equation to model the data. The greatest value of r^2 indicates the best model for the data.

19.

x	y
0	1.7
1	1.4
2	4.7
3	7.9

$y = 0.875x^2 - 0.435x + 1.515$

20.

x	y
0	2.0
1	1.5
2	1.2
3	0.9

$y = 1.987 \cdot 0.770^x$

21.

x	y
0	2.8
1	1.4
2	2.7
3	9.8

$y = 2.125x^2 - 4.145x + 2.955$

22.

x	y
−1	4.3
0	5.1
1	4.3
2	2.2
3	1.3

$y = -0.336x^2 - 0.219x + 4.666$

23.

x	y
−1	4.6
0	3.5
1	2.4
2	1.3
3	0.2

$y = -1.1x + 3.5$

24.

x	y
−1	0.04
0	0.10
1	0.26
2	0.68
3	1.76

$y = 0.102 \cdot 2.582^x$

25b. The second common difference is twice the coefficient of x^2.

25c. When second differences are the same, the data are quadratic. You can determine the coefficient of x^2 by dividing the second difference by 2.

26. Answers may vary.
Sample:

x	y
0	5
2	13
4	29
6	53

 Challenge

28e. Answers may vary.
Sample: Check (2, 26).
$26 \overset{?}{=} 2(2^2) + 7(2) + 4$
$26 \overset{?}{=} 8 + 14 + 4$
$26 = 26$ ✓

29c. 54, 89, 66

d. 1.85; the ratio is much larger than the other ratios.

e. 85; the difference is much smaller than the other differences.

25. a. Make a table of five points using consecutive x-values for each function. Find the common second difference. **See margin.**
   i. $f(x) = x^2 - 3$　　　**ii.** $f(x) = 3x^2$　　　**iii.** $f(x) = 4x^2 - 5x$
   b. What is the relationship between the common second difference and the coefficient of x^2? **See left.**
   c. **Critical Thinking** Explain how you could use this relationship to help you model data if the function were not given. **See left.**

26. Open-Ended Write a set of data you could model with a quadratic function. **See left.**

27. Physics A group of students dropped ping-pong balls and found the distance the balls traveled, given a certain amount of time. The diagram below shows their results.
   a. Determine which model is most appropriate for the data. **quadratic**
   b. Write an equation to model the data. If necessary, round to the nearest tenth. $d = 13.6t^2$
   c. Use your equation to predict the distance a ping-pong ball would fall in 2 s. **54.5 ft**

0.2 s	0.4 s	0.6 s	0.8 s	1.0 s
0.5 ft	2.2 ft	4.9 ft	8.7 ft	13.6 ft

28. Data Collection Complete the chart at the right for your town. **a–c. Check students' work.**
   a. Use ExpReg or QuadReg to find an equation to model the data.
   b. Use the equation you found in part (a) to predict the current population of your town.
   c. Use the equation you found in part(a) to predict the population of your town in 2010.

Year	Population (thousands)
1970	■
1980	■
1990	■
2000	■

29. Data Analysis There are times when data show trends but not consistent ratios or differences. The data in the table below show the total U.S. retail auto sales for the years 1980 through 2000. The value $t = 0$ corresponds to the year 1980. **1.85, 1.28, 1.45, 1.43**
   a. Find the ratios of consecutive entries in the sales column. Round to the nearest hundredth.
   b. Find the differences of consecutive entries in the sales column. **139, 85, 174, 240**
   c. Find the second differences of consecutive entries in the sales column.
   d. **Critical Thinking** Which value creates the most inconsistency in the ratios? Explain.
   e. Which value appears to make the differences *not* roughly the same? Explain. **c–e. See left.**
   f. Graph the data. Draw a curve to show the trend. **See margin.**

United States Retail Auto Sales

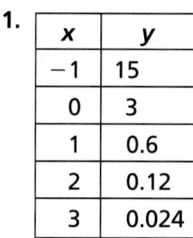

1 car = $1 billion in sales

$164, $303, $388, $562, $802

Year: 0, 5, 10, 15, 20

Lesson Quiz 10-9

Which kind of function best models the data in each table? Write an equation to model the data.

1.

x	y
−1	15
0	3
1	0.6
2	0.12
3	0.024

exponential; $y = 3 \cdot 0.2^x$

2.

x	y
−1	−5
0	−3
1	−1
2	1
3	3

linear; $y = 2x - 3$

3.

x	y
−1	2.2
0	0
1	2.2
2	8.8
3	19.8

quadratic; $y = 2.2x^2$

Alternative Assessment

Have each student graph either a linear, quadratic, or exponential function, and then write four points that are on the graph. Instruct students to exchange the set of points with a classmate. The classmate finds the function that best models the set of points, and then writes an equation to model the data. Direct students to exchange the set of points with another classmate and repeat. Students can compare their results.

📁 **Resources**

For additional practice with a variety of test item formats:
- Standardized Test Prep, p. 573
- Test-Taking Strategies, p. 568
- Test-Taking Strategies with Transparencies

Exercise 31 Remind students that the y-coordinates of an exponential model have a common ratio. After determining that the x-coordinates are written in sequential order with a common difference, students just need to check the first three y-coordinates of each set of data to find the set with a common ratio.

pages 563–566 Exercises

33. [4] a. linear

   b. $d = -2.5n + 43.5$

   c. 18

   [3] appropriate methods, but with one computational error

   [2] part (c) not answered

   [1] no work shown

37.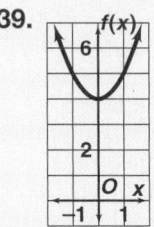

38.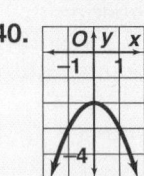

39.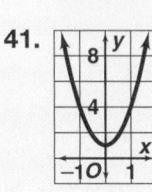

40.

41.

Standardized Test Prep

Multiple Choice

30. Which equation best models the data in the table at the right? **B**

   A. $y = 4x$
   B. $y = 2x + 2$
   C. $y = 2^x$
   D. $y = 2x^2$

x	y
0	2
1	4
2	6
3	8
4	10

31. Which of the following sets of data is best described by an exponential model? **H**

   F. $(-1, 16)$, $\left(-\frac{1}{2}, 4\right)$, $(0, 2)$, $\left(\frac{1}{2}, -2\right)$, $(1, 4)$
   G. $(1, -7)$, $(2, -4)$, $(3, -1)$, $(4, 2)$, $(5, 5)$
   H. $(1, 1)$, $(3, 3)$, $(0, 0.5)$, $(5, 8)$, $(7, 14)$
   I. $(-2, -4)$, $(-1, 3)$, $(0, 8)$, $(1, 14)$, $(2, 12)$

32. [2] $p = 33,500(1.014)^n$, $33,500(1.014)^{10} \approx 38,497$
   [1] correct formula, inaccurate evaluation

Short Response

32. The population of a town was 33,500 in 2000. The population is increasing by about 1.4% each year. Write an equation that will predict the population n years after 2000. Let 2000 correspond to $n = 0$. Predict the town's population in 2010. **See above.**

Extended Response

33. Suppose you put marbles into a cup hanging from an elastic band (spring). You measure the distance d from the floor in centimeters as the number n of marbles is increased.

n	0	1	2	3	4	5
d	43.5	41	38.5	36	33.5	31

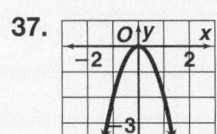 **Take It to the NET**
Online lesson quiz at **www.PHSchool.com**
········· Web Code: aea-1009

   a. Which type of model best fits this data set? **a–c. See margin.**
   b. Write an equation for the data.
   c. Suppose the pattern shown above continues. Find the least number of marbles you need to make the cup rest on the floor.

Mixed Review

Lesson 10-8 Find the number of x-intercepts of each function.

34. $y = -x^2$ **1**
35. $y = x^2 + 3x + 4$ **0**
36. $y = 4x^2 - 10x + 3$ **2**

Lesson 10-1 Graph each function. **37–42. See margin.**

37. $y = -2x^2$
38. $f(x) = \frac{1}{4}x^2$
39. $f(x) = x^2 + 4$
40. $y = -x^2 - 2$
41. $y = 3x^2 + 1$
42. $y = -\frac{1}{2}x^2 + 1$

Lesson 8-7 Evaluate each function rule for the given value.

43. $y = 2^x$ for $x = -3$ **0.125**
44. $f(x) = -2^x$ for $x = 5$ **−32**
45. $g(t) = 2 \cdot 3^t$ for $t = -3$ **$\frac{2}{27}$**
46. $f(t) = 10 \cdot 5^t$ for $t = 2$ **250**
47. $y = \left(\frac{1}{2}\right)^t$ for $t = -4$ **16**
48. $y = 9 \cdot \left(\frac{3}{2}\right)^x$ for $x = 3$ **30.375**

42.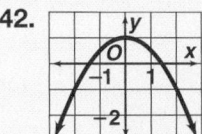

Cubic Functions

FOR USE WITH LESSON 10-9

In this chapter you learned about quadratic functions. You can also construct and explore functions in which the highest power is greater than two. Functions of the form $y = ax^3 + bx^2 + cx + d$, where $a \neq 0$, are called cubic functions.

EXAMPLE

Make a table of values and graph $y = x^3$ and $y = \frac{1}{3}x^3$.

x	$y = x^3$	$y = \frac{1}{3}x^3$
-2	-8	$-2\frac{2}{3}$
-1	-1	$-\frac{1}{3}$
0	0	0
1	1	$\frac{1}{3}$
2	8	$2\frac{2}{3}$

$y = x^3$

$y = \frac{1}{3}x^3$

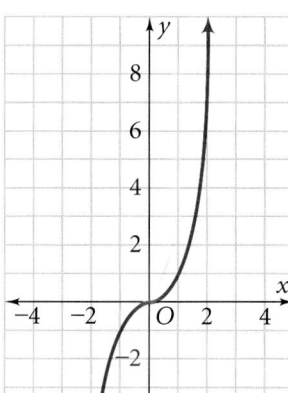
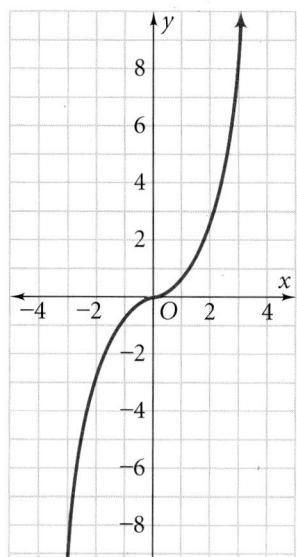

1. Both graphs have the same shape, go through the origin, and lie in Quadrants I and III. The graph of $y = x^3$ is narrower than the graph of $y = \frac{1}{3}x^3$.

EXERCISES

1. **Critical Thinking** Describe the similarities and differences in the graphs in the Example. **See above.**

2. **a.** Graph each of the following functions. **a–b. See margin.**
   i. $y = -x^3$ **ii.** $y = 2x^3$ **iii.** $y = -\frac{1}{4}x^3$
   b. Describe the similarities and differences in the graphs in part (a).

3. **Critical Thinking** Does a play the same role in cubic functions of the form $y = ax^3$ as it does in quadratic functions? Explain. **See margin.**

4. **a.** Do cubic graphs of the form $y = ax^3$ have an axis of symmetry? **no**
   b. **Critical Thinking** Do cubic graphs have any form of symmetry? Explain.
   Yes; half of the graph is reflected over the y-axis and then over the x-axis.

5. The volume V of a sphere with radius r is given by the function $V = \frac{4}{3}\pi r^3$.
   a. Graph $V = \frac{4}{3}\pi r^3$ from $r = 0$ to $r = 2$. **See right.**
   b. Use the graph to estimate the radius of a sphere with a volume of 10 ft³.
   about 1.3 ft

5a.

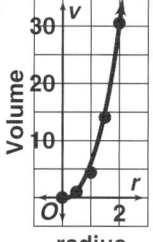

Students explore functions of degree three.

Resources

Technology
Computer Test Generator CD-ROM, Chapter 10, Extension Topics

Teaching Notes

Technology Tip
Suggest that students use graphing calculators to graph the functions. Remind them to put parentheses around the fractions.

Math Tip
Cubic functions have point symmetry. The 'left side' is a rotation of the 'right side,' and vice versa. Some students may forget that this is a type of symmetry.

---

page 567   Extension

2a. **I.** 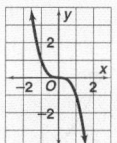   **II.** 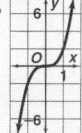   **III.**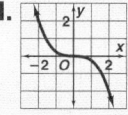

b. The graphs with neg. coefficients of x^3 are in Quadrants II and IV, and the graph with a pos. coefficient of x^3 is in Quadrants I and III. All of the graphs go through the origin.

3. Yes; the sign of a changes which quadrants the graphs are in, and the larger $|a|$, the narrower the graph.

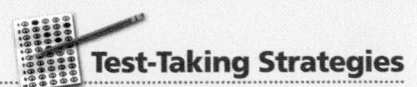

Choosing "Cannot be Determined"

"Cannot be determined" is the correct answer choice if there is not enough information in a question to find the answer. Sometimes it is given as an answer choice just as a distraction from the correct answer.

Resources

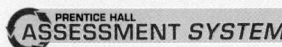

Test-Taking Strategies with Transparencies
• Transparency 10
• Practice sheet p. 10

Teaching Notes

Teaching Tip

Remind students that they have to think of all situations surrounding a problem, such as negative numbers, positive numbers, and 0.

English Learners

Explain that "Cannot be determined" implies that a correct answer may be given, but you cannot be certain that it is correct because you need more information.

Test-Taking Strategies with Transparencies

Test-Taking Strategy: Choosing "Cannot Be Determined"

When you are not given enough information, you may not be able to determine the answer.

Example The area of a rectangle is 12. What is its perimeter?
A. 14   B. 16   C. 26   D. cannot be determined

12 factors into 3 × 4, 2 × 6, and 1 × 12.
The rectangle could have perimeter
3 + 4 + 3 + 4 = 14,
2 + 6 + 2 + 6 = 16, or
1 + 12 + 1 + 12 = 26.
There is not enough information to decide the correct answer.
The answer choice must be D, cannot be determined.

Choose the correct answer. If your choice is "cannot be determined," explain.
1. In isosceles △ABC, AB = 5. How does BC compare to 5?
   A. BC > 5   B. BC = 5
   C. BC < 5   D. cannot be determined
2. In right △DEF, DE = 3 and EF = 4. What is DF?
   F. √7   G. 5   H. 7   I. cannot be determined
3. What is the solution of the inequality $ay + 3 > x$?
   A. $y > \frac{x-3}{a}$ B. $y > \frac{x}{a} - 3$
   C. $y < \frac{x-3}{a}$ D. cannot be determined

Solutions
1. D; the congruent sides are not known.
2. D; the sides that are the legs are not known.
3. D; it is not known whether a is positive or negative.

Transparency 10

Some multiple-choice questions do not contain enough information. One of the answer choices will then be "Cannot be determined." In such cases, you will not be able to find a specific answer. However, just because the answer choice "Cannot be determined" appears, do not assume that you cannot answer the question; the choice may have been put there as a distraction.

1 EXAMPLE

How many real solutions does the equation $x^2 + bx + 4 = 0$ have if $b > 0$?

    A. None   **B.** One   **C.** Two   **D.** Cannot be determined

Calculate the discriminant and see if it is negative, zero, or positive when $b > 0$.

The discriminant is $b^2 - 4ac = b^2 - 4(1)(4) = b^2 - 16$. This expression is negative when $b < 4$, zero when $b = 4$, and positive when $b > 4$. Since the value of the discriminant depends on the value of b, you cannot determine how many real solutions the equation has. The correct answer is D.

2 EXAMPLE

A parabola passes through the points $(2, 8)$, $(6, 2)$, and $(8, 8)$. What is the x-coordinate of its vertex?

    A. 4   **B.** 5   **C.** 7   **D.** Cannot be determined

The x-coordinate of the vertex of $y = ax^2 + bx + c$ is $-\frac{b}{2a}$. However, you don't have an equation for the parabola, so you can't use the formula. You might think that the answer is D.

Graph the points and you will notice that $(2, 8)$ and $(8, 8)$ have the same y value, so they are symmetrically placed about the axis of symmetry. The axis of symmetry will be $x = \frac{2+8}{2} = 5$. Since the x-coordinate of the vertex is on the axis of symmetry, the correct answer is B. Choice D is a distraction; it was put there in case you thought that the problem could not be done.

EXERCISES

1. Use the question below to answer parts a–c.
   How many real solutions does the equation $x^2 + 4x - n^2 = 0$ have?

       A. None   **B.** One   **C.** Two   **D.** Cannot be determined

   a. What is the discriminant of the equation? **$16 + 4n^2$**
   b. Explain why the discriminant is always positive for all values of n. **The smallest value of n^2 is 0, 16 + 0 > 0.**
   c. What is the correct answer to the question? **C**

2. If $x \neq 0$ and $y \neq 0$, and $x^2 + 2xy + y^2 = 0$, which of the following could be the ratio of x to y? **C**
       A. $1 : 1$ **B.** $2 : 1$ **C.** $-1 : 1$ **D.** Cannot be determined

Chapter Review

Vocabulary

axis of symmetry (p. 511)
completing the square (p. 541)
discriminant (p. 554)
maximum (p. 511)
minimum (p. 511)
negative square root (p. 524)
parabola (p. 510)

perfect squares (p. 525)
principal square root (p. 524)
quadratic equation (p. 530)
quadratic formula (p. 547)
quadratic function (p. 510)
radicand (p. 524)
square root (p. 524)

standard form of a quadratic function (p. 510)
standard form of a quadratic equation (p. 530)
vertex (p. 511)
Zero-Product Property (p. 536)

Reading Math
Understanding Vocabulary

Take It to the NET
Online vocabulary quiz at www.PHSchool.com
Web Code: aej-1051

Choose the term that correctly completes each sentence. 1. parabola

1. The U-shaped graph of a quadratic function is a *(parabola, perfect square)*.

2. If the quadratic expression $ax^2 + bx + c$ *cannot* be factored, one good way to solve the equation $ax^2 + bx + c = 0$ is to use *(completing the square, the Zero-Product Property)*. **completing the square**

3. If $a^2 = b$ and $a > 0$, then a is the *(negative square root, principal square root)* of b. **principal square root**

4. The *(radicand, vertex)* of a parabola is the point at which the parabola intersects the axis of symmetry. **vertex**

5. The *(discriminant, axis of symmetry)* can be used to determine the number of solutions of a quadratic equation. **discriminant**

Skills and Concepts

10-1 and 10-2 Objectives

▼ To graph quadratic functions of the form $y = ax^2$ (p. 510)

▼ To graph quadratic functions of the form $y = ax^2 + c$ (p. 512)

▼ To graph quadratic functions of the form $y = ax^2 + bx + c$ (p. 517)

▼ To graph quadratic inequalities (p. 519)

A function of the form $y = ax^2 + bx + c$, where $a \neq 0$, is a **quadratic function.** The shape of its graph is a **parabola.** The **axis of symmetry** of a parabola divides it into two congruent halves. The **vertex** of a parabola is the point at which the parabola intersects the axis of symmetry. The axis of symmetry is the line with the equation $x = \frac{-b}{2a}$. The x-coordinate of the vertex of the parabola is $\frac{-b}{2a}$.

The value of a in a quadratic function $y = ax^2 + bx + c$ determines the width of the parabola and whether it opens upward or downward. The value of c is the y-intercept of the graph. Changing the value of c shifts the parabola up or down.

When the parabola opens downward, the y-coordinate of the vertex is a **maximum** point of the function. When the parabola opens upward, the y-coordinate of the vertex is a **minimum** point of the function.

6–9. Answers may vary. Samples are given.

Open-Ended Give an example of a quadratic function for each description.

6. Its graph opens downward. $y = -2x^2$ 7. Its vertex is at the origin. $y = 2x^2$

8. Its graph opens upward. $y = x^2$ 9. Its graph is wider than $y = x^2$. $y = \frac{1}{2}x^2$

Graph each function. 10–13. See back of book.

10. $y = \frac{2}{3}x^2$

11. $y = -x^2 + 1$

12. $y = x^2 - 4$

13. $y = 5x^2 + 8$

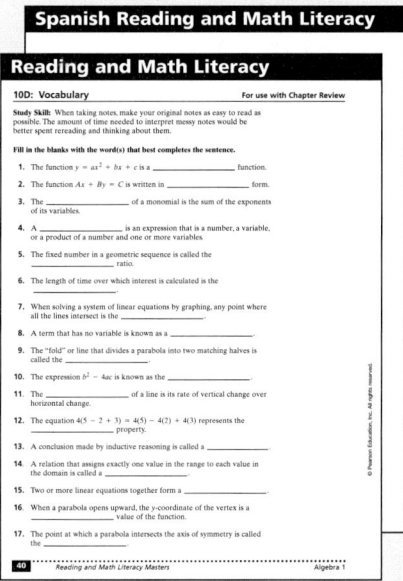

18.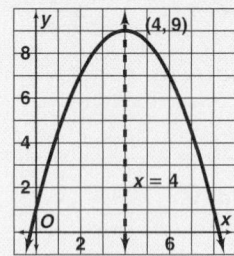

19.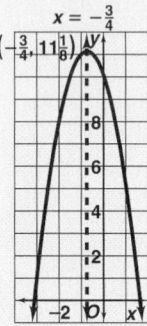

20.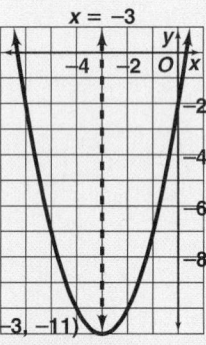

21.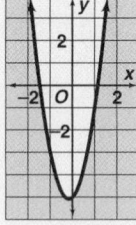

22.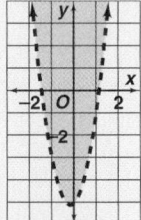

23.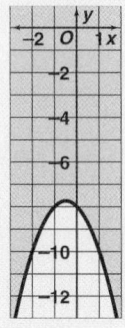

570

State whether each function has a *maximum* or *minimum* point.

14. $y = 4x^2 + 1$
min.

15. $y = -3x^2 - 7$
max.

16. $y = \frac{1}{2}x^2 + 9$
min.

17. $y = -x^2 + 6$
max.

Graph each function. Label the axis of symmetry and the vertex. 18–20. See margin.

18. $y = -\frac{1}{2}x^2 + 4x + 1$ **19.** $y = -2x^2 - 3x + 10$ **20.** $y = x^2 + 6x - 2$

Graph each quadratic inequality. 21–23. See margin.

21. $y \le 3x^2 + x - 5$ **22.** $y > 3x^2 + x - 5$ **23.** $y \ge -x^2 - x - 8$

10-3 Objectives

▼ To find square roots
(p. 524)

▼ To estimate and use
square roots (p. 525)

24. irrat.; 9.27
25. rat.; −11
26. irrat.; ±0.71
27. irrat.; 1.60

If $a^2 = b$, then a is the **square root** of b. The positive or **principal square root** of b is indicated by $\sqrt{b}$. The **negative square root** is indicated by $-\sqrt{b}$. The squares of integers are called **perfect squares**.

Tell whether each expression is *rational* or *irrational*. Then find the value of each expression. If necessary, round to the nearest hundredth. 24–27. See left.

24. $\sqrt{86}$ **25.** $-\sqrt{121}$ **26.** $\pm\sqrt{\frac{1}{2}}$ **27.** $\sqrt{2.55}$ **28.** $-\sqrt{\frac{4}{25}}$ rat.; $-\frac{2}{5}$

29. $-\sqrt{47}$ **30.** $\sqrt{0.36}$ **31.** $\sqrt{140}$ **32.** $-\sqrt{1}$ **33.** $\sqrt{196}$
 irrat.; −6.86   rat.; 0.6   irrat.; 11.83   rat.; −1   rat.; 14

10-4, 10-5, and 10-6 Objectives

▼ To solve quadratic
equations by graphing
(p. 529)

▼ To solve quadratic
equations using square
roots (p. 530)

▼ To solve quadratic
equations by factoring
(p. 536)

▼ To solve quadratic
equations by completing
the square (p. 541)

The **standard form of a quadratic equation** is $ax^2 + bx + c = 0$, where $a \ne 0$. Quadratic equations can have two, one, or no solutions. You can solve some quadratic equations by graphing the related function and finding the x-intercepts. If the quadratic expression $ax^2 + bx + c$ can be factored, you can use the **Zero-Product Property** to find the solutions of the equation $ax^2 + bx + c = 0$. This property states that for all real numbers a and b, if $ab = 0$, then $a = 0$ or $b = 0$.

You can solve any quadratic equation by writing it in the form $x^2 + bx = -c$, **completing the square,** and finding the square roots of each side of the equation.

Solve each equation. If the equation has no solution, write *no solution*.

34. $6(x^2 - 2) = 12$ **2, −2**   **35.** $-5m^2 = -125$ **5, −5**

36. $9(w^2 + 1) = 9$ **0**   **37.** $3r^2 + 27 = 0$ **no solution**

Write each equation in standard form. Then solve by factoring.

38. $x^2 + 7x + 12 = 0$ **−4, −3**   **39.** $5x^2 - 10x = 0$ **0, 2**   **40.** $2x^2 - 9x = x^2 - 20$ **4, 5**

41. $2x^2 + 5x = 3$ **−3, $\frac{1}{2}$**   **42.** $3x^2 - 5x = -3x^2 + 6$ **$-\frac{2}{3}, 1\frac{1}{2}$**   **43.** $x^2 - 5x + 4 = 0$ **1, 4**

Solve each equation by completing the square. If necessary, round to the nearest hundredth.

44. $x^2 + 6x - 5 = 0$
 −6.74, 0.74

45. $x^2 = 3x - 1$
 0.38, 2.62

46. $2x^2 + 7x = -6$
 −2, $-1\frac{1}{2}$

47. Geometry The area of a circle is given by the formula $A = \pi r^2$. Find the radius of a circle with area 16 in.². Round to the nearest tenth of an inch. **2.3 in.**

48. Gardening Alice is planning a rectangular garden. Its length is 3 ft less than twice its width. Its area is 170 ft². Find the dimensions of the garden.
10 ft × 17 ft

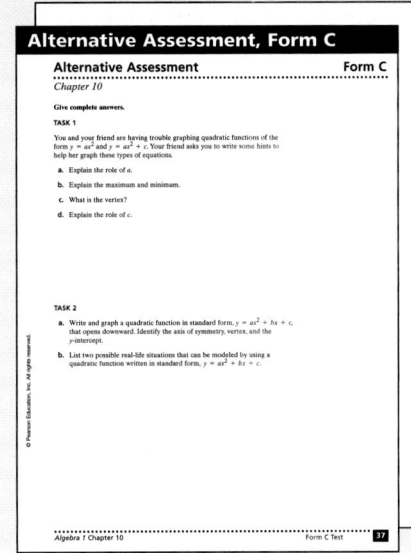
10-7 and 10-8 Objectives

▼ To use the quadratic formula when solving quadratic equations (p. 547)

▼ To choose an appropriate method for solving a quadratic equation (p. 549)

▼ To find the number of solutions of a quadratic equation (p. 554)

57. −5, 5; use factoring, because the equation is easily factorable.

58. −4.12, 0.78; use the quadratic formula, because the trinomial does not factor easily.

59. 4, 5; use factoring, because the equation is easily factorable.

60. 3; use factoring, because the equation is easily factorable.

61. −15, 15; use square roots, because the equation has no x term.

62. −8.47, 0.47; complete the square, because the equation is in the form $x^2 + bx = c$.

You can solve the quadratic equation $ax^2 + bx + c = 0$ when $a \neq 0$ by using the **quadratic formula** $x = \dfrac{-b \pm \sqrt{b^2 - 4ac}}{2a}$. When a quadratic equation is in the form $ax^2 + bx + c = 0$ ($a \neq 0$), the **discriminant** is $b^2 - 4ac$.

If $b^2 - 4ac > 0$, there are two solutions.
If $b^2 - 4ac = 0$, there is one solution.
If $b^2 - 4ac < 0$, there is no solution.

Find the number of solutions of each equation.

49. $x^2 - 10 = 3$ **2**

50. $3x^2 = 27$ **2**

51. $x^2 + 3 = 2x$ **0**

52. $x^2 + 10x = -25$ **1**

Solve each equation using the quadratic formula. Round to the nearest hundredth.

53. $4x^2 + 3x - 8 = 0$ **−1.84, 1.09**

54. $2x^2 - 7x = -3$ **0.5, 3**

55. $-x^2 + 8x + 4 = 5$ **0.13, 7.87**

56. $9x^2 - 270 = 0$ **−5.48, 5.48**

Writing Solve each equation. Explain why you chose the method you used.

57. $5x^2 - 10 = x^2 + 90$

58. $9x^2 + 30x - 29 = 0$

57–62. See left.

59. $2x^2 - 9x = x^2 - 20$

60. $x^2 - 6x + 9 = 0$

61. $x^2 + 3x - 225 = 3x$

62. $x^2 + 8x = 4$

63. Geometry A square pool has side length p. The border of the pool is 1 ft wide. The combined area of the border and the pool is 400 ft². Find the length and the area of the pool. **18 ft; 324 ft²**

64. Vertical Motion Suppose you throw a ball in the air. The ball is 6 ft high when it leaves your hand. Use the equation $0 = -16t^2 + 20t + 6$ to find the number of seconds t that the ball is in the air. **1.5 s**

10-9 Objectives

▼ To choose a linear, quadratic, or exponential model for data (p. 559)

Graphing data points or analyzing data numerically can help you find the best model. Linear data have a common difference. Exponential data have a common ratio. Quadratic data have a common second difference.

65–68. See margin.

Graph each set of points. Which model is most appropriate for each set?

65. $(-3, 0), (1, 4), (-1, 6), (2, 0)$

66. $(0, 5), (1, 3), (3, -1), (-1, 7)$

67. $(0, 6), (5, 2), (1, 4), (8, 1.5), (2, 3)$

68. $(1, 4), (4, 2), (2, 3), (5, 3.5), (6, 5)$

Write an equation to model the data.

69.

x	y
−1	2.5
0	5
1	10
2	20
3	40

$y = 5(2)^x$

70.

x	y
−1	−5
0	−2
1	1
2	4
3	7

$y = 3x - 2$

71.

x	y
−3	4
−2	1
−1	0
0	1
1	4

$y = (x + 1)^2$

72.

x	y
0	0.5
1	5
2	50
3	500
4	5000

$y = \frac{1}{2}(10^x)$

65.
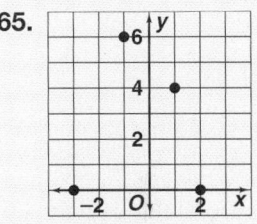
quadratic

66.
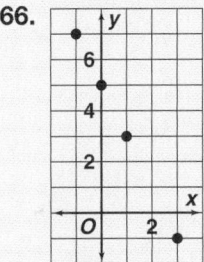
linear

67.
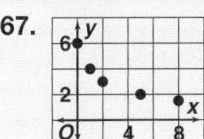
exponential

68.
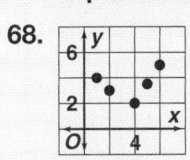
quadratic

Chapter 10 Chapter Review **571**

Chapter 10

Chapter Test

Take It to the NET
Online chapter test at
www.PHSchool.com
Web Code: aea-1052

Resources

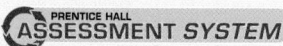

Teaching Resources
Ch. 10 Test, Forms A & B
Ch. 10 Alternative Assessment,
   Form C

Reaching All Students
Spanish Ch. 10 Test, Forms A & B
Spanish Ch. 10 Alternative
   Assessment, Form C
Basic Algebra Ch. 10 Test,
   Forms D & E

PRENTICE HALL
ASSESSMENT SYSTEM

Assessment Masters
- Ch. 10 Test, Forms A & B
- Ch. 10 Alternative Assessment,
  Form C
Computer Test Generator CD
- Ch. 10 pre-made Test
- Make your own Ch. 10 test

www.PHSchool.com
Student Site
- Self-grading Chapter 10 Test
Teacher Center
- Resources

Plus **iTEXT**

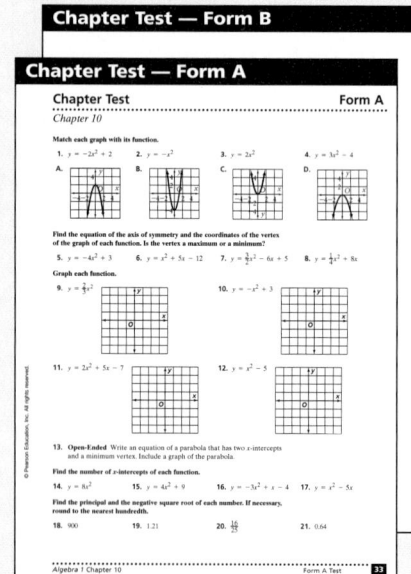

Chapter Test — Form B

Chapter Test — Form A

Match each graph with its function.

A. $y = 3x^2$ **B.** $y = -3x^2 + 1$
C. $y = -2x^2$ **D.** $y = x^2 - 3$

1.
D
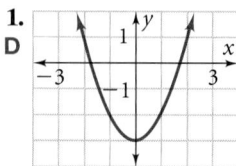

2.
C
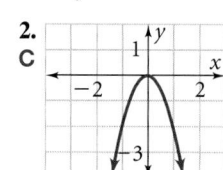

3.
A
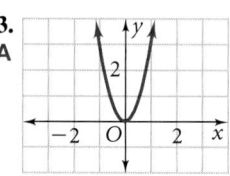

4.
B
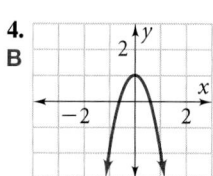

Find the equation of the axis of symmetry and the coordinates of the vertex of the graph of each function. Is the vertex a maximum or a minimum? 5–8. See margin.

5. $y = 3x^2 - 7$ **6.** $y = x^2 - 3x + 2$

7. $y = -2x^2 + 10x - 1$ **8.** $y = \frac{1}{2}x^2 + 6x$

Graph each function. 9–14. See back of book.

9. $y = x^2 - 4$ **10.** $y = -x^2 + 1$

11. $y = 5x^2$ **12.** $y = \frac{1}{2}x^2 + 3x$

13. $y = x^2 - 3x + 5$ **14.** $y = 2x^2 - 5$

15. Writing Explain what you can determine about the shape of a parabola from its equation alone.
See margin.

Find the number of x-intercepts of each function.

16. $y = 5x^2$ **1**   **17.** $y = 3x^2 + 10$ **0**

18. $y = -2x^2 + x + 7$ **2**   **19.** $y = x^2 - 4x$ **2**

Graph each inequality. 20–21. See back of book.

20. $y \le 2x^2 - 1$ **21.** $y > \frac{1}{2}x^2$

Find the principal square root of each number.

22. 1.44 **1.2** **23.** 1600 **40** **24.** $\frac{4}{9}$ **$\frac{2}{3}$** **25.** 0.04 **0.2**

Between what two consecutive integers is each square root?

26. $\sqrt{28}$ **27.** $\sqrt{136}$ **28.** $\sqrt{332}$ **29.** $-\sqrt{8.99}$
5, 6   11, 12   18, 19   -3, -2

572   Chapter 10   Chapter Test

Find the number of solutions of each equation.

30. $x^2 + 4x = -4$ **1**   **31.** $x^2 + 8 = 0$
                                       no solution
32. $2x^2 + x = 0$ **2**   **33.** $3x^2 - 9x = -5$ **2**

34. The equation $kx^2 - 10x + 25 = 0$ has one
solution. Find the value of k. **1**

Solve each equation. If necessary, round to the nearest hundredth.
                                                      3.33, −1
35. $2x^2 = 50$ **5, −5**   **36.** $-3x^2 + 7x = -10$

37. $x^2 + 6x + 9 = 25$ **2, −8** **38.** $-x^2 - x + 2 = 0$
                                                      1, −2
39. $x^2 + 4x = 1$ **0.24, −4.24** **40.** $12x^2 + 16x - 28 = 0$
                                                      1, −2.33
41. Open-Ended Write an equation of a parabola that
has two x-intercepts and a maximum value. Include
a graph of your parabola. **See back of book.**

Model each problem with a quadratic equation. Then solve.

42. Geometry The volume V of a cylinder is given by
the formula $V = \pi r^2 h$, where r is the radius of the
cylinder and h is the height. A cylinder with height
10 ft has volume 140 ft^3. To the nearest tenth of a
foot, what is the radius of the cylinder? **$140 = 10\pi r^2$,
2.1 ft**

43. Landscaping The area of a rectangular patio is
800 ft^2. The patio's length is twice its width. Find
the dimensions of the patio.
$800 = 2w^2$, w = 20 ft, ℓ = 40 ft

Identify each graph as *linear*, *quadratic*, or *exponential*. Write an equation that models the data shown in each graph.

exponential; $y = \frac{1}{2}(2^x)$

44.
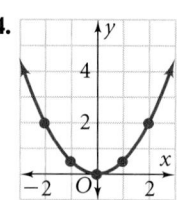
quadratic; $y = \frac{1}{2}x^2$

45.
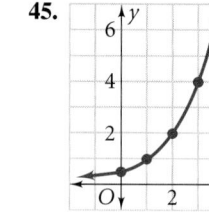

46.
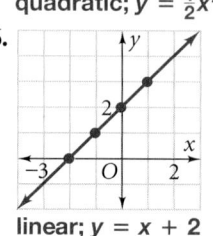
linear; $y = x + 2$

47.
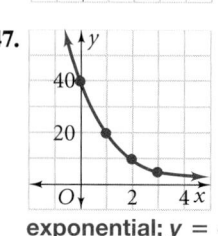
exponential; $y = 40(0.5^x)$

---

page 572   Chapter Test

5. $x = 0$, (0, −7); min.

6. $x = 1.5$, (1.5, −0.25); min.

7. $x = 2.5$, (2.5, 11.5); max.

8. $x = -6$, (−6, −18); min.

15. Answers may vary.
Sample: You can tell how
wide it is and whether it
opens upward or
downward.

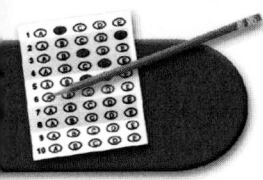

Standardized Test Prep

Standardized Test Prep

Multiple Choice

For Exercises 1–9, choose the correct letter.

1. Choose the best approximation of the solutions of $3x^2 - 5x + 1 = 0$. **D**
   A. 2 and −3   B. 1.5 and 1.75
   C. −3 and 2   D. 1.5 and 0.25

2. Which is the equation of the axis of symmetry of the graph of $y = 5x^2 - 2x + 3$? **F**
   F. $x = \frac{1}{5}$ G. $x = -\frac{1}{5}$
   H. $y = \frac{1}{5}$ I. $y = -\frac{1}{5}$

3. Between which two consecutive integers is $\sqrt{52}$? **C**
   A. 5 and 6   B. 6 and 7
   C. 7 and 8   D. 8 and 9

4. A line perpendicular to $y = 3x - 2$ passes through the point (0, 6). Which other point lies on the line? **F**
   F. (9, 3)   G. (−9, 3)
   H. (−9, −3)   I. (9, −3)

5. What is the probability of *not* rolling a 1 or 2 on a number cube? **D**
   A. $\frac{1}{6}$ B. $\frac{1}{3}$ C. $\frac{1}{2}$ D. $\frac{2}{3}$

6. What is the value of the discriminant of $0 = 3x^2 - 4x - 3$? **I**
   F. −20   G. 4   H. 25   I. 52

7. What is the standard form of the product $(3x - 1)(5x + 3)$? **D**
   A. $15x^2 + 2x - 3$
   B. $15x^2 + 2x + 3$
   C. $15x^2 - 4x - 3$
   D. $15x^2 + 4x - 3$

8. If $x^2 + 4x + 4 = 49$, then which statement is true? **I**
   I. $x = 5$ II. $x = -9$
   III. $x = \sqrt{47}$ IV. $x = -\sqrt{47}$
   F. I only   G. III only
   H. III and IV   I. I and II

9. How many solutions are there for the following system? **B**
   $$y = x - 3$$
   $$6y - x = 24$$
   A. 0   B. 1   C. 2   D. 3

Quantitative Comparison

Compare the boxed quantity in Column A with the boxed quantity in Column B. Choose the best answer.

A. The quantity in Column A is greater.
B. The quantity in Column B is greater.
C. The two quantities are equal.
D. The relationship cannot be determined from the information given.

Column A	Column B

10. **C** For the system of equations
    $$x + y = 5$$
    $$2y - x = 4$$

2	x

11. **A** $x^2 + x - 20 = 0$

the value of the discriminant of the equation	the sum of the solutions of the equation

Gridded Response

12. Find the slope of the line that passes through (−1, 3) and (4, 6). **$\frac{3}{5}$ or 0.6**

13. A new company employed 12 people. Two years later, it employed a total of 20 people. What was the percent of increase rounded to the nearest percent? **67**

Short Response

14. **Geometry** The length of a rectangle is 6 m less than twice its width. The area of the rectangle is 140 m². Find the dimensions of the rectangle. Show your work. **See back of book.**

15. Describe the shape of the graph for each type of function: linear, quadratic, and absolute value. **See back of book.**

16. Simplify $9a + 3b - 3 - 4a + 7 - 8b$. Show your work. **See back of book.**

Extended Response

17. Graph $y = 4x^2 - 3x$. Show the vertex, axis of symmetry, and x-intercepts of the equation. **See back of book.**

Resources

📁 **Teaching Resources**
Cumulative Review

Reaching All Students
Spanish Cumulative Review

PRENTICE HALL
ASSESSMENT SYSTEM

Standardized Test Prep
• Ch. 10 Standardized Test Practice
Assessment Masters
• Cumulative Review
Computer Test Generator CD
• Standardized Test Practice

💻 **www.PHSchool.com**
• Standardized Test Practice
• Resources

Plus **iTEXT**

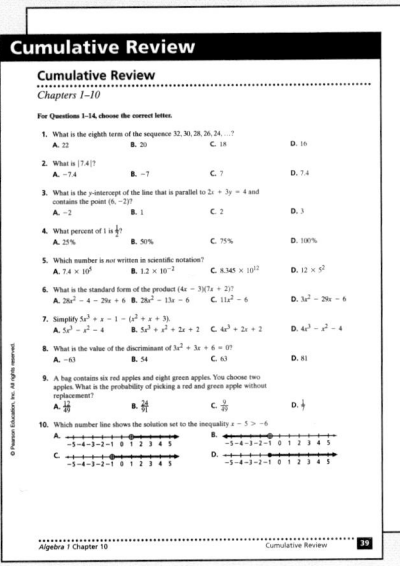

Item	1	2	3	4	5	6	7	8	9	10	11	12	13	14	15	16	17
Lesson	10-4	10-1	10-3	6-5	4-6	10-8	9-3	10-4	7-1	7-2	10-8	6-1	4-4	7-4	10-1	1-1	10-1

573

Weight No More

In these activities students apply their knowledge of circles and the use of formulas.

Connecting to Prior Knowledge

Have students recall their experiences in going around sharp curves or circles in a car or on an amusement park ride. Elicit the fact that they may have experienced a force that makes them lean in one direction. Discuss how perception may fool people into thinking that they are moving when they are still and a boat or plane is moving beside them. Relate this to the paragraph *Which Way is Up?*

Teaching Notes

Have volunteers research why astronauts in the International Space Station feel weightless. Have students share their findings with the class.

Teaching Tip

Contrast centripetal force, which is directed inward toward the center of rotation, with centrifugal force, which moves an object outward from the center of rotation. For example, when a rock is whirled at the end of a string, the rock exerts centrifugal force on the string, and the string exerts centripetal force on the rock.

Connection to Physics

Remind students that mass is the measurement of the amount of material in an object, as measured on a balance. Weight is a measurement similar to mass, but it is affected by the amount of gravitational force acting on the object.

English Learners

Ask a volunteer to explain what is meant by the words *claustrophobic* and *curvature*.

574

Real-World Snapshots

Weight No More

Applying Circles If you traveled in space, you could stay in a weightless environment like the astronauts who inhabit the International Space Station, or you could stay on the circumference of a rotating space station that simulates the feeling of weight you have on Earth. You can calculate the gravitational pull necessary to keep you grounded in space.

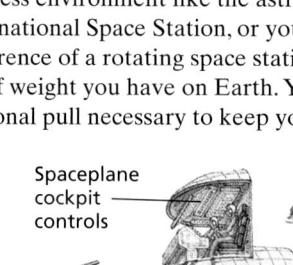

Satellite Capture
One of the main uses of the space station is the repair of damaged satellites.

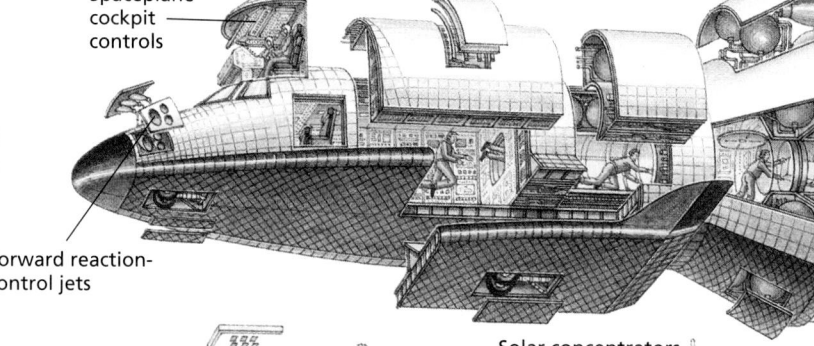

Spaceplane cockpit controls

Forward reaction-control jets

Solar array

Solar concentrators

Docking port

Modular Construction

An important feature of the space station is its modular construction. Each pressurized section is built of similar units, so that if one fails, a similar one can take its place.

How It Works

As the space station rotates, your body wants to move in a straight line. The outside rim of the space station pushes on the bottoms of your feet to keep you moving in a circular path. If the size and rotational speed of the space station are chosen carefully, this push, called the centripetal force, can make you feel the same "weight" that you experience on Earth.

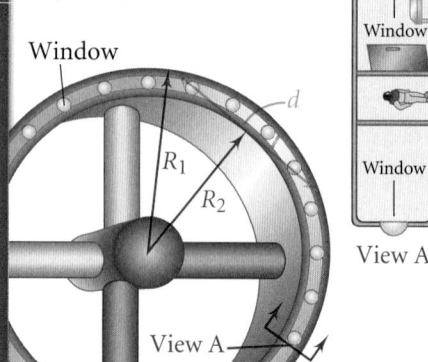

Window

R_1

R_2

d

h

Window

Window

View A

View A

Activity 1

The figures at the left show a diagram of a circular space station and a cross section of the space station.

a. Select R_1 and R_2 so that the height h of the living space, the difference between the two, is a value that makes sense for humans.

b. The station's curvature limits how far inhabitants can see as they walk. In the diagram, d is a measure of the viewing distance. Use the formula $d = 2\sqrt{(R_2)^2 - (R_1)^2}$. Calculate d for your values of R_1 and R_2.

c. If the viewing distance is too short, inhabitants may feel claustrophobic. Keep the height of the living space the same, but adjust your values of R_1 and R_2 so that d is at least 80 ft. Limit the diameter of the space station to 300 ft or less.

574

pages 574–575 **Real-World Snapshots**

Activity 1

Answers may vary. Sample:

  a. Let $R_1 = 31$ ft, $R_2 = 38$ ft.

  b. $d \approx 44$ ft

  c. Let $R_1 = 112$ ft, $R_2 = 119$ ft, $d \approx 80$ ft.

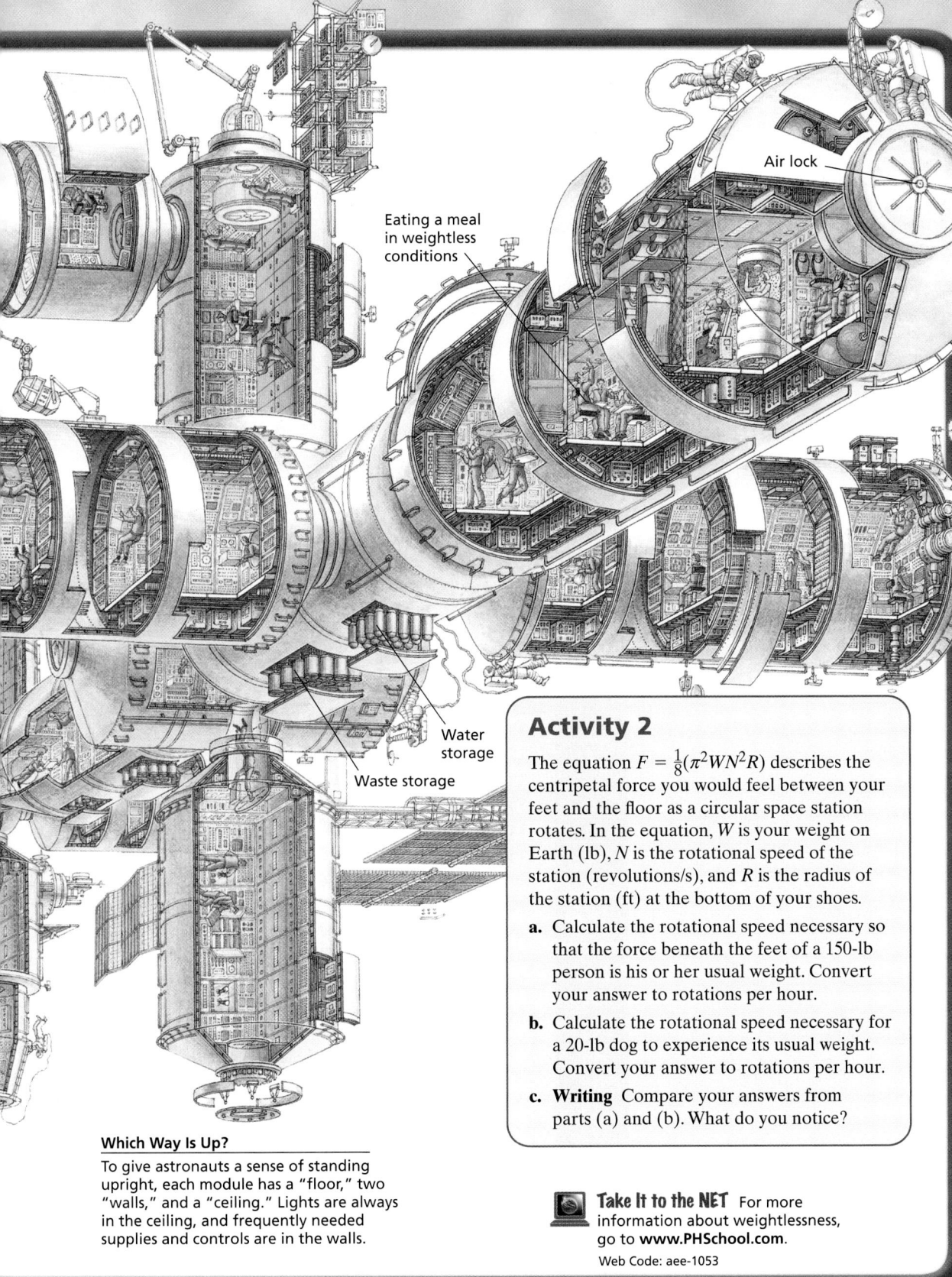

Eating a meal in weightless conditions

Air lock

Water storage

Waste storage

Which Way Is Up?
To give astronauts a sense of standing upright, each module has a "floor," two "walls," and a "ceiling." Lights are always in the ceiling, and frequently needed supplies and controls are in the walls.

Activity 2

The equation $F = \frac{1}{8}(\pi^2 W N^2 R)$ describes the centripetal force you would feel between your feet and the floor as a circular space station rotates. In the equation, W is your weight on Earth (lb), N is the rotational speed of the station (revolutions/s), and R is the radius of the station (ft) at the bottom of your shoes.

a. Calculate the rotational speed necessary so that the force beneath the feet of a 150-lb person is his or her usual weight. Convert your answer to rotations per hour.

b. Calculate the rotational speed necessary for a 20-lb dog to experience its usual weight. Convert your answer to rotations per hour.

c. Writing Compare your answers from parts (a) and (b). What do you notice?

Take It to the NET For more information about weightlessness, go to www.PHSchool.com.
Web Code: aee-1053

575

Teaching Tip

Have each team read through both activities before beginning to work. Ask students to find various parts (such as the solar array, docking port, and water storage) and to describe their possible functions. Have students work in pairs or in small groups to complete the activities.

Activity 1

Materials paper and pencil

Inclusion
Review the circle formulas, and make sure students are clear about the difference between the radius and the diameter.

Activity 2

Materials paper and pencil

Teaching Tip
Connection to Physics The key is that gravitational force and weight are equal. In other words, $F = W$.

Diversity
Suggest that students use the Internet to research biographies of the people who have become astronauts.

Scoring Rubric

This scoring rubric applies to both activities. Share this scoring rubric with students before they begin work.

4 Equations and calculations are correct. Steps are neat, accurate, and clearly show the mathematics. Responses are clearly indicated and give the appropriate units.

3 Equations and calculations are mostly correct, with some minor errors. Steps are neat and mostly accurate. Units are not completely accurate.

2 Calculations contain both major and minor errors.

1 Correct answer, but no work is shown.

Activity 2
a–b. Answers may vary. Sample:

a. Let R = 118 ft; $N \approx 0.083$ revolutions/s, or 298.8 revolutions/h

b. $N \approx 0.083$ revolutions/s, or 298.8 revolutions/h

c. They are the same.

Radical Expressions and Equations

Chapter at a Glance

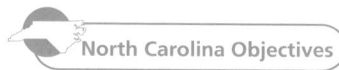

North Carolina Objectives

11-1	Simplifying Radicals	1.01a

NCTM 2, 8, 10
- ▼ Simplifying Radical Expressions Involving Products
- ▽ Simplifying Radical Expressions Involving Quotients

11-2	The Pythagorean Theorem	1.02, 2.02

NCTM 2, 3, 4, 10
- ▼ Solving Problems Using the Pythagorean Theorem
- ▽ Identifying Right Triangles

11-3	The Distance and Midpoint Formulas	1.02, 2.01

NCTM 2, 3, 4, 10
- ▼ Finding the Distance Between Two Points
- ▽ Finding the Midpoint of a Line Segment

11-4	Operations With Radical Expressions	1.01c, 1.02

NCTM 1, 2, 10
- ▼ Simplifying Sums and Differences
- ▽ Simplifying Products and Quotations

11-5	Solving Radical Equations	1.01a

NCTM 1, 2, 10
- ▼ Solving Radical Equations
- ▽ Solving Equations with Extraneous Solutions

11-6	Graphing Square Root Functions

NCTM 2, 8, 10
- ▼ Graphing Square Root Functions
- ▽ Translating Graphs of Square Root Functions

11-7	Trigonometric Ratios	2.01

NCTM 2, 3, 4, 8, 10
- ▼ Finding Trigonometric Ratios
- ▽ Solving Problems Using Trigonometric Ratios

NCTM STANDARDS 2000

1	Number and Operations	6	Problem Solving
2	Algebra	7	Reasoning and Proof
3	Geometry	8	Communication
4	Measurement	9	Connections
5	Data Analysis and Probability	10	Representation

Pacing Options

This chart suggests pacing only for the lessons and their parts. It is provided as a possible guide. It will help you determine how much time you have in your schedule to cover other components, such as the features, Chapter Review, and Chapter Test.

Day	Traditional 45 min.	Two-Year 45 min.	Block 90 min.
1	11-1 ▼	11-1 ▼	11-1 ▼ ▽
2	11-1 ▽	11-1 ▽	11-2 ▼ ▽
3	11-2 ▼ ▽	11-2 ▼	11-3 ▼ ▽
4	11-3 ▼	11-2 ▼ ▽	11-4 ▼ ▽
5	11-3 ▽	11-2 ▽	11-5 ▼ ▽
6	11-4 ▼	11-3 ▼	11-6 ▼ ▽
7	11-4 ▽	11-3 ▼ ▽	11-7 ▼ ▽
8	11-5 ▼	11-3 ▽	
9	11-5 ▽	11-4 ▼	
10	11-6 ▼ ▽	11-4 ▼	
11	11-7 ▼	11-4 ▽	
12	11-7 ▽	11-4 ▽	
13		11-5 ▼	
14		11-5 ▼ ▽	
15		11-5 ▽	
16		11-6 ▼	
17		11-6 ▼ ▽	
18		11-6 ▽	
19		11-7 ▼	
20		11-7 ▽	

NAEP Correlation (National Assessment of Educational Progress 2000 Mathematics Objectives)

11-1	11-2	11-3	11-4	11-5	11-6	11-7
N3a, A5a	G6b, A5a, b	G6b, G9a	A5a, b	A5a, c	D1a, A3a	G6e, G8, A14

N = Number Sense, Properties, and Operations; **M** = Measurement; **G** = Geometry and Spatial Sense; **D** = Data Analysis, Statistics, and Probability; **A** = Algebra and Functions

Math Background

Chapter Overview

For this chapter, skill in manipulating radicals provides the background for formulas and concepts that will often recur. As students learned in Chapter 10, with the application of the quadratic formula, simplifying radicals is a skill that is necessary to solve many types of equations in Algebra. The chapter begins with ways to simplify and combine radicals and then goes on to the familiar use of radicals in the Pythagorean Theorem. Right triangles are used again in the last lesson of the chapter on trigonometric ratios. The distance and midpoint formulas provide students with more practice in using radicals to solve problems. Additional ways to simplify radical expressions, such as rationalizing the denominator by using the conjugate are presented. All of these procedures are applied to the final goal of solving radical equations and graphing square root functions.

Simplifying Radicals   11-1

The Multiplication Property of Square Roots contains some very important constraints: both a and b must not be negative.

Consider the product $\sqrt{-3} \cdot \sqrt{-4}$. This product is not the same as $\sqrt{(-3)(-4)} = \sqrt{12}$, because $\sqrt{-3}$ is an imaginary number and the Multiplication Property of Square Roots does not apply.

When students later work with complex numbers they learn that the product is actually $\sqrt{3} \cdot \sqrt{-1} \cdot \sqrt{4} \cdot \sqrt{-1}$ or $i^2 \sqrt{12}$, where $i = \sqrt{-1}$. Since i^2 by definition is equal to -1, the product $\sqrt{-3} \cdot \sqrt{-4}$ simplifies to $-\sqrt{12}$ or $-2\sqrt{3}$.

As indicated in the Student Edition on page 578, students are to assume that all variables of all radicands represent nonnegative numbers. Without this restriction, the value of x could be negative, so that the value of $\sqrt{x^2}$ must be indicated as $|x|$.

The Pythagorean Theorem   11-2

In any triangle, the side opposite the largest angle is the longest side. Since no triangle can have more than one angle that is greater than or equal to 90°, it follows that the side opposite the right angle, or hypotenuse, will always be the longest side. Sets of integers that satisfy the Pythagorean relationship are called Pythagorean triples, for example, (3, 4, 5), (5, 12, 13), (12, 16, 20), (8, 15, 17).

Since the equation $a^2 + b^2 = c^2$ is quadratic, students must use methods for solving quadratic equations that they have already learned in the previous chapters to use the Pythagorean Theorem.

The Distance and Midpoint Formulas   11-3

The distance formula is a very useful application of the Pythagorean Theorem. It is most interesting that finding the length of a line segment, which does not outwardly appear to involve a right triangle, can be determined by using a right triangle in the coordinate plane. Additionally, using the distance formula requires being able to solve radical expressions, the skill that was introduced in the first lesson of this chapter.

Operations with Radical Expressions   11-4

Which is easier to calculate with paper and pencil, $\frac{2}{\sqrt{3}}$ or $\frac{2\sqrt{3}}{3}$, using $\sqrt{3} \approx 1.732051$? Clearly it is easier to multiply this decimal by 2 and then divide the product by 3 than it is to divide 2 by the decimal. This is why rationalizing the denominator so that irrational roots appear only in the numerator makes sense. However, if you are using a calculator, there is no difference in difficulty.

The word *conjugate*, in mathematics, means inversely or oppositely related to some property. When speaking of a real-number binomial involving radicals, such as $2 + \sqrt{3}$, the conjugate is $2 - \sqrt{3}$. Since $(2 + \sqrt{3})(2 - \sqrt{3}) = 1$ it is not always clear to students that this is a use of the *factoring the difference of squares* formula.

For complex numbers of the form $a + bi$ the conjugate is $a - bi$. The product of two complex number conjugates yields a real number.

Solving Radical Equations and Graphing Square Root Functions   11-5, 11-6

Since x must be non-negative for $\sqrt{x^2} = x$ to be a true equation, solving a radical equation by squaring both sides can lead to extraneous answers that do not check in the original equation. The graph of such an equation may help clarify which solutions are correct.

Trigonometric Ratios   11-7

Some students may be familiar with similar triangles. Others may need to verify that the sine of an angle remains the same regardless of the overall size of the triangle that contains that angle. The many practical applications of Trigonometry in surveying, construction, aeronautics, and so on, will interest many students.

Ongoing Assessment and Intervention

Tools for Monitoring Student Progress

The Prentice Hall *Algebra 1* program provides you with many options for assessment in the Student Edition, the Teacher's Edition and the teaching resources. From these options you may choose instructional materials and techniques that are appropriate for your students and support your district's curriculum requirements.

Instant Check System™ in Chapter 11

Allows students to check their own learning before, during, and after each lesson.

Diagnosing Readiness before the chapter (p. 576)

Check Skills You'll Need exercises in each lesson (pp. 578, 584, 591, 600, 607, 614, 621)

Check Understanding questions with each Example (pp. 578, 579, 580, 581, 585, 586, 587, 592, 593, 600, 601, 602, 607, 608, 609, 614, 615, 622, 623, 624)

Checkpoint Quiz (pp. 597, 619)

 Test Prep in Chapter 11

Teaches students strategies and gives them practice with all the test item formats they will encounter on state tests and standardized national exams.

Standardized Test Prep exercises in each lesson (pp. 583, 590, 596, 605, 606, 612, 618, 619, 627)

Test-Taking Strategies (p. 628: Using Estimation)

Standardized Test Prep (p. 633: Reading Comprehension)

All your assessment needs in one place!

Program Assessment

Assess student progress throughout the *Algebra 1* text with blackline masters and CD-ROM.

Assessment Resources

- Checkpoint Quizzes 1 & 2
- Chapter Test, Forms A & B
- Chapter Alternative Assessment

Spanish versions available. Tests for Basic Algebra also available.

Computer Test Generator

- Unlimited questions of varying difficulty for every lesson objective.
- Create your own practice sheets, quizzes, and tests, or use the pre-made Chapter Tests.
- Diagnose readiness with questions on prerequisite skills.
- Prepare students by making tests based on standardized test objectives.
- Access Algebra 1, Geometry, and Algebra 2 content—all on one CD-ROM.

Test Preparation

A three-step approach to preparing students for high stakes, national, and state exams.

❶ **Diagnose & Prescribe**

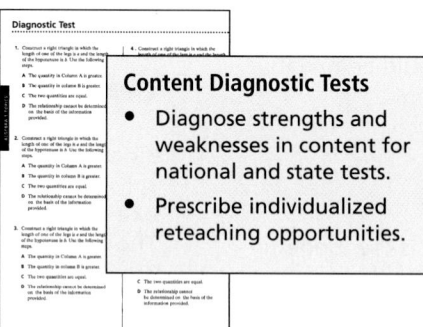

Content Diagnostic Tests
- Diagnose strengths and weaknesses in content for national and state tests.
- Prescribe individualized reteaching opportunities.

❷ **Review & Reteach**

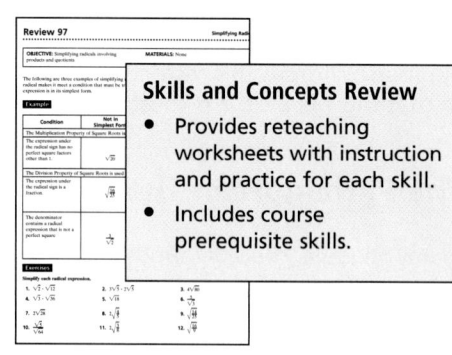

Skills and Concepts Review
- Provides reteaching worksheets with instruction and practice for each skill.
- Includes course prerequisite skills.

❸ **Practice & Assess**

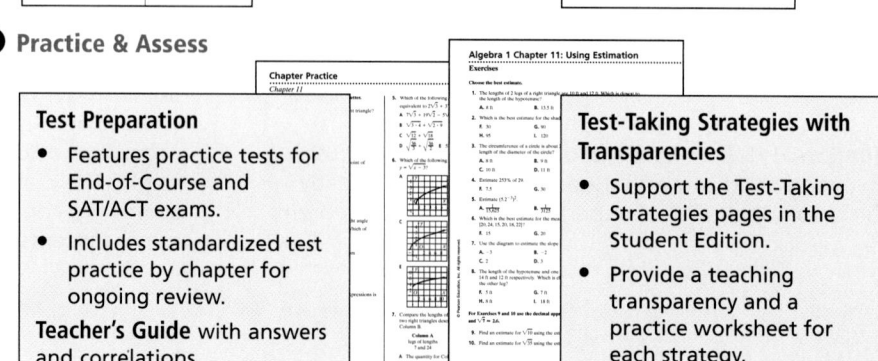

Test Preparation
- Features practice tests for End-of-Course and SAT/ACT exams.
- Includes standardized test practice by chapter for ongoing review.

Teacher's Guide with answers and correlations.

Test-Taking Strategies with Transparencies
- Support the Test-Taking Strategies pages in the Student Edition.
- Provide a teaching transparency and a practice worksheet for each strategy.

 # Reaching All Students

Support in the Student Text and Additional Resources

The textbook, the iText, and other technology components provide numerous opportunities to reach students of various ability levels and learning styles. Each Teacher's Edition lesson suggests how you can help *all* your students be successful and understand the mathematics in Chapter 11.

Below Level

Student Edition
- Diagnosing Readiness*: p. 576
- Check Skills You'll Need*: pp. 578, 584, 591, 600, 607, 614, 621

Reteaching
Chapter 11 Support File: pp. 8–14

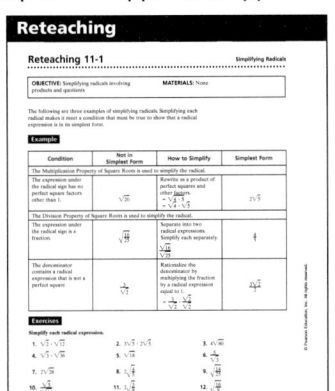

Basic Algebra Planning Guide

Chapter 11 Lesson Plans: pp. 73–79
Chapter 11 Tests: pp. 129–132

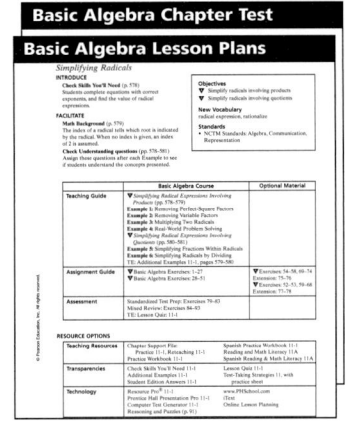

* Can be used with all ability levels to ensure mastery of prerequisite skills.

Advanced Learners

Student Edition
- Challenge exercises: pp. 583, 589, 596, 605, 611, 618, 627
- Extension, pp. 598, 620

Enrichment
Chapter 11 Support File: pp. 15–21

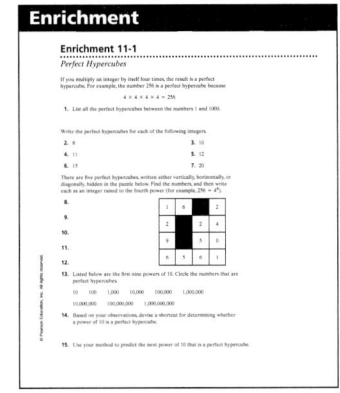

Reading and Math Literacy

Student Edition
- Vocabulary: pp. 577, 629, *plus* in every Lesson Preview
- Reading Math: pp. 580, 584, 611, 613, 629
- Illustrated Glossary: pp. 757–785

Reading and Math Literacy Masters
Chapter 11: pp. 41–44

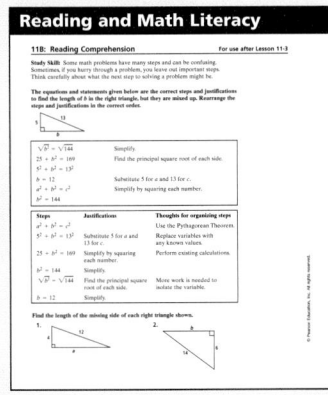

English Learners

Student Edition
- English/Spanish Illustrated Glossary: pp. 757–785

Workbook and Masters
Spanish Practice Workbook: pp. 73–79
Spanish Reading and Math Literacy Masters: pp. 41–44

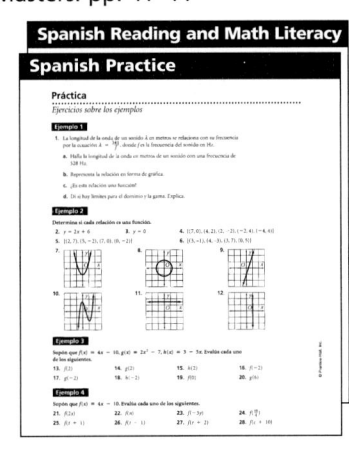

Learning Styles

Student Edition
- Investigation: pp. 584, 621
- Technology: pp. 592, 622
- Writing: pp. 582, 588, 595, 605, 610, 611, 616, 617, 619, 632

Activity Masters
Hands-On Activities: 26, 27, 28
Technology Activities: 25

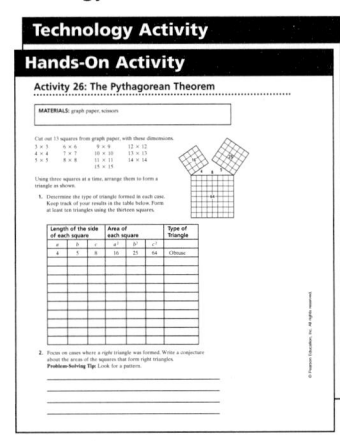

Program Resources

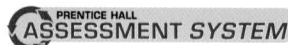

	Practice	Reteach	Enrich	Checkpoint Quiz	Reading & Math Literacy	Technology Activities	Hands-On Activities	Basic Algebra Lesson Plans	Practice	Reading & Math Literacy	Checkpoint Quiz	Skills Check	Additional Examples	Answers to Exercises	Lesson Quiz	Prentice Hall Presentation Pro CD-ROM
	Teaching Resources in Grab & Go™ Files				**Resources for Reaching All Students**				**Spanish Resources**			**Transparencies**				**Presentation Assistant Plus!**
11-1	■	■	■		■			■	■	■		■	■	■	■	■
11-2	■	■	■					■	■	■		■	■	■	■	■
11-3	■	■	■	■	■		■	■	■		■	■	■	■	■	■
11-4	■	■	■					■	■	■		■	■	■	■	■
11-5	■	■	■			■		■	■			■	■	■	■	■
11-6	■	■	■	■	■			■	■		■	■	■	■	■	■
11-7	■	■	■		■			■	■			■	■	■	■	■
For the chapter	Chapter Tests, Alternative Assessment, Cumulative Review, Cumulative Assessment				Basic Algebra Chapter Tests				Spanish Chapter Tests, Alternative Assessment, Cumulative Review, Cumulative Assessment			Classroom Aid Transparencies				

Also available for use with the chapter:

 **PRENTICE HALL ASSESSMENT SYSTEM** *See page 576C.*

- Practice Workbook
- Solution Key

- For teacher support and access to student Web site materials, use Web Code aek-5500.
- For additional online and technology resources, see below.

Technology

 iTEXT **Online and on CD-ROM**

Complete Interactive Student Text online and on CD-ROM—with instant feedback assessment, tutorial help, dynamic activities, instructional and real-world videos, audio, and additional practice.

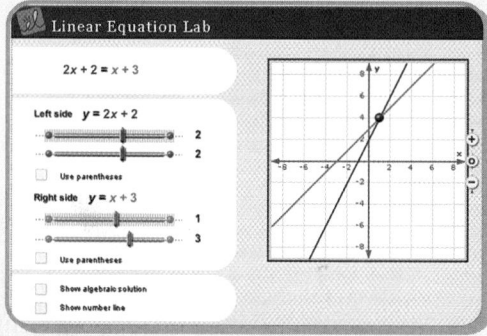

www.PHSchool.com **For Students**

Use **Web codes** for easy access to online activities, chapter projects, self-grading lesson quizzes and chapter tests, vocabulary quizzes, updated data sources, graphing calculator procedures, and more.

PH SuccessNet **For Teachers**

Online lesson planning with built-in state correlations, all the teaching resources, complete reference library, your own calendar and Teacher Web page, professional development, and more.

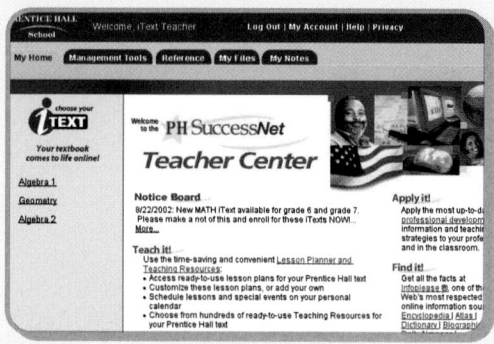

Presentation Assistant Plus!

The Prentice Hall *Presentation Assistant Plus!* provides you with the material you need to teach a lesson from beginning to end. Two easy-to-use formats—Transparencies and CD-ROM—allow you to present a lesson the way you are most comfortable.

Transparencies

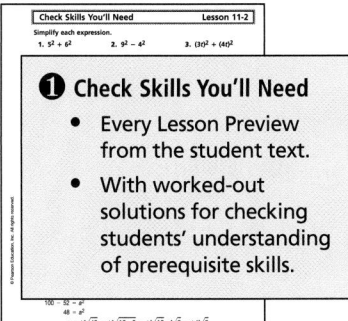

❶ Check Skills You'll Need
- Every Lesson Preview from the student text.
- With worked-out solutions for checking students' understanding of prerequisite skills.

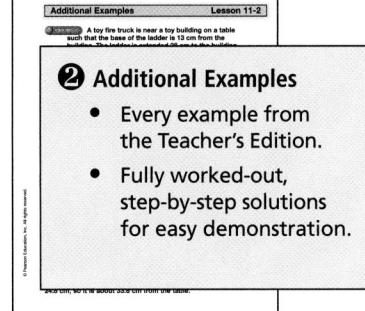

❷ Additional Examples
- Every example from the Teacher's Edition.
- Fully worked-out, step-by-step solutions for easy demonstration.

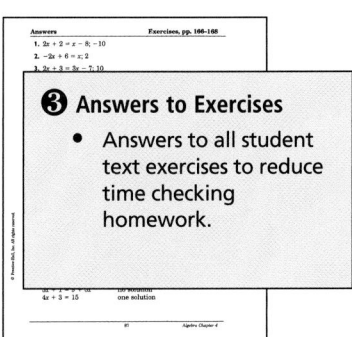

❸ Answers to Exercises
- Answers to all student text exercises to reduce time checking homework.

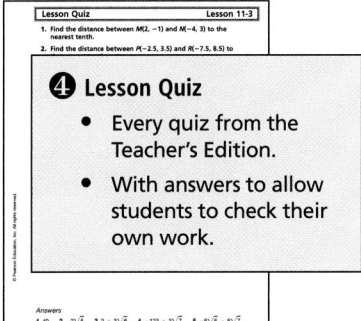

❹ Lesson Quiz
- Every quiz from the Teacher's Edition.
- With answers to allow students to check their own work.

Throughout the Teacher's Edition, this symbol indicates material that is available on transparency in the Presentation Assistant Plus!

Prentice Hall Presentation Pro CD-ROM

- Includes all Transparencies.
- Conveniently organized by lesson so you can easily ❶ Introduce, ❷ Teach, ❸ Check Homework, and ❹ Assess each lesson.
- Animated examples allow step-by-step instruction at your own pace.
- Easy to edit so you can create custom presentations.

Teaching Chapter 11 Using Presentation Assistant Plus!

	❶ Introduce	❷ Teach	❸ Check Homework	❹ Assess
	Check Skills You'll Need	Additional Examples	Student Edition Answers	Lesson Quiz
11-1	p. 73	pp. 162–165	✔	p. 134
11-2	p. 74	pp. 166–169	✔	p. 134
11-3	p. 75	pp. 170–173	✔	p. 135
11-4	p. 76	pp. 173–176	✔	p. 135
11-5	p. 77	pp. 177–179	✔	p. 136
11-6	p. 78	pp. 180–181	✔	p. 136
11-7	p. 79	pp. 181–184	✔	p. 137

 Prentice Hall Presentation Pro

CD-ROM with dynamic PowerPoint® presentations for every lesson. Helps you introduce and develop concepts, check homework, and assess progress. Part of Presentation Assistant Plus! *(See above.)*

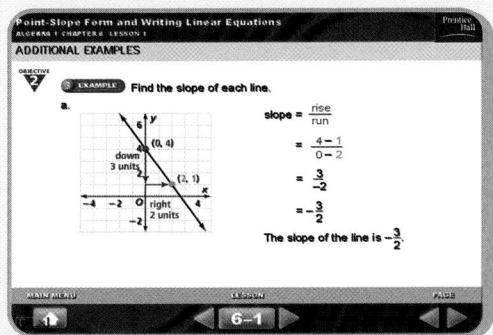

 Computer Test Generator

CD-ROM to create practice sheets and tests for course objectives and standardized tests. Includes Instant Chapter Tests™, online testing, and student reports. Part of the PH Assessment System. *(See page 576C.)*

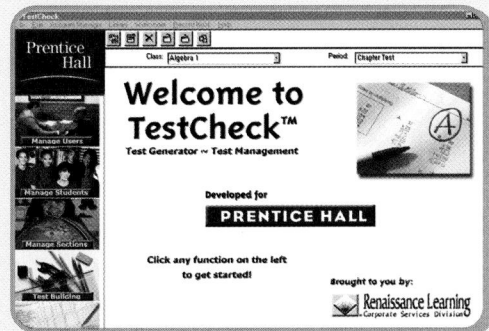

Resource Pro® with Planning Express®

CD-ROM with a lesson planning tool that allows you to import state and local objectives. Includes electronic versions of all the teaching resources.

Radical Expressions and Equations

 Diagnosing Readiness

Students will find answers to these exercises in the back of their textbooks.

For intervention, direct students to:

Calculating the Mean
Lesson 2-7: Example 1
Exercises 1–4
Extra Practice, p. 703

Solving Proportions
Lesson 4-1: Examples 3, 4, and 6
Exercises 14–29, 32–37
Extra Practice, p. 705

Finding Square Roots
Lesson 10-3: Examples 1 and 4
Exercises 1–11
Extra Practice, p. 711

Using the Discriminant
Lesson 10-8: Example 1
Exercises 4–8
Extra Practice, p. 711

Where You've Been

- In Chapter 4, you learned about ratios and how to solve a proportion for a given variable.

- In Chapter 8, you learned to simplify expressions containing exponents.

- In Chapter 10, you learned about square roots and evaluated the discriminants of quadratic equations to determine the number of solutions.

 **Diagnosing Readiness**   *(For help, go to the Lesson in green.)*

Instant self-check
online and on CD-ROM

Calculating the Mean (Lesson 2-7)

Find the mean of each set of data.

1. $1, 4, 2, 5, 3, 2$ **2.8$\overline{3}$ or $2\frac{5}{6}$**   **2.** $40, 55, 60, 52$ **51.75**   **3.** $1.6, 2.1, 1.8, 1.8$ **1.825**

4. $-4, 2, 0, -1$ **-0.75**   **5.** $214, 198, 202$ **204.$\overline{6}$**   **6.** $3, 2, 2, 3, 4, 4$ **3**

Solving Proportions (Lesson 4-1)

Solve each proportion.

7. $\frac{8}{x} = \frac{24}{9}$ **3**   **8.** $\frac{k-4}{27} = \frac{1}{3}$ **13**   **9.** $\frac{5}{6} = \frac{25}{c}$ **30**

10. $\frac{42}{x+8} = \frac{7}{2}$ **4**   **11.** $\frac{9}{13} = \frac{y}{65}$ **45**   **12.** $\frac{6}{x-5} = \frac{1}{2}$ **17**

13. $\frac{3n-1}{14} = \frac{4}{7}$ **3**   **14.** $\frac{4}{33} = \frac{8}{w}$ **66**   **15.** $\frac{y-1}{5} = \frac{y+3}{7}$ **11**

Finding Square Roots (Lesson 10-3)

Simplify each expression.

16. $\sqrt{4}$ **2**   **17.** $\sqrt{225}$ **15**   **18.** $\sqrt{\frac{9}{25}}$ **$\frac{3}{5}$**   **19.** $-\sqrt{0.0036}$ **-0.06**

Simplify each expression. Round to the nearest hundredth.

20. $\sqrt{40}$ **6.32**   **21.** $\sqrt{84}$ **9.17**   **22.** $\sqrt{104}$ **10.20**   **23.** $\sqrt{3.2}$ **1.79**

Using the Discriminant (Lesson 10-8)

Find the number of real solutions of each equation.

24. $x^2 + 6x + 1 = 0$ **2**   **25.** $x^2 - 5x - 6 = 0$ **2**   **26.** $x^2 - 2x + 9 = 0$ **0**

27. $4x^2 - 4x = -1$ **1**   **28.** $6x^2 + 5x - 2 = -3$ **2**   **29.** $(2x - 5)^2 = 121$ **2**

Radical Expressions and Equations

WORLD SOLAR CHALLENGE

8.00.18

Where You're Going

- In this chapter, you will simplify expressions containing radicals.

- You will use the Pythagorean Theorem to find the lengths of sides of right triangles.

- You will solve radical equations.

Real-World Connection Trigonometry is used in real-world situations to find distances that cannot be measured directly.

LESSONS

11-1 Simplifying Radicals

11-2 The Pythagorean Theorem

11-3 The Distance and Midpoint Formulas

11-4 Operations With Radical Expressions

11-5 Solving Radical Equations

11-6 Graphing Square Root Functions

11-7 Trigonometric Ratios

Key Vocabulary

- angle of depression (p. 624)
- angle of elevation (p. 623)
- conjugates (p. 601)
- converse (p. 586)
- cosine (p. 621)
- distance formula (p. 591)
- extraneous solution (p. 609)
- hypotenuse (p. 584)
- hypothesis (p. 586)
- leg (p. 584)
- midpoint formula (p. 593)
- Pythagorean Theorem (p. 584)
- radical equation (p. 607)
- radical expression (p. 578)
- rationalize (p. 581)
- sine (p. 621)
- square root function (p. 614)
- tangent (p. 621)
- trigonometric ratios (p. 621)

577

Chapter 11 Overview

This chapter focuses on the various algebraic and geometric applications that involve using, simplifying, and combining radical expressions. The chapter begins with the various properties that are used to simplify radical expressions. These are then applied to problems using the Pythagorean Theorem, as well as the Distance and Midpoint Formulas, and solving special triangles. Then students solve radical equations, and graph square root functions such as $y = \sqrt{x}$, including translating the graphs. Then the solving of right triangles is generalized into the definitions of three trigonometric functions, and applying them to solve triangles, including problems with angles of elevation and depression.

📖 Reading Math
Reading For Problem Solving, p. 613

📖 Vocabulary
A complete list of terms, plus vocabulary exercises, appears in the Chapter Review, p. 629.

📖 Illustrated Glossary
Examples for each vocabulary term, plus definitions in both English and Spanish, appear starting on p. 757.

✏️ Test-Taking Strategies
Estimating the Answer, p. 628

🌐 Real-World Connections
Some of the applications you will find in this chapter are tourism (11-1), fire rescue (11-2), archeology (11-3), investments (11-4), packaging (11-5), and navigation (11-7).

💻 www.PHSchool.com
Internet support for this chapter includes:
- Self-grading Vocabulary and Chapter 11 Tests
- Chapter Project
- Chapter Planner
- Chapter 11 Resources

Plus

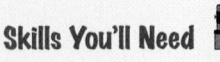

Lesson Preview

 Check Skills You'll Need

Multiplication with Exponents
Lesson 8-3: Example 2
Exercises 7–15
Extra Practice, p. 709

Finding Square Roots
Lesson 10-3: Example 1
Exercises 1–12
Extra Practice, p. 711

Lesson Resources

 Teaching Resources
Practice, Reteaching, Enrichment

Reaching All Students
Practice Workbook 11-1
Spanish Practice Workbook 11-1
Reading and Math Literacy 11A
Spanish Reading & Literacy 11A
Basic Algebra Planning Guide 11-1

Presentation Assistant Plus!
Transparencies
• Check Skills You'll Need 11-1
• Additional Examples 11-1
• Student Edition Answers 11-1
• Lesson Quiz 11-1
PH Presentation Pro CD 11-1

Computer Test Generator CD

 Technology
Resource Pro® CD-ROM
Computer Test Generator CD
Prentice Hall Presentation Pro CD

 www.PHSchool.com
Student Site
• Teacher Web Code: aek-5500
• Reasoning & Puzzles p. 91
• Self-grading Lesson Quiz
Teacher Center
• Lesson Planner
• Resources

Plus

Simplifying Radicals

 North Carolina Objectives

1.01 Write equivalent forms of algebraic expressions to solve problems. a) Apply the laws of exponents.

Lesson Preview

What You'll Learn

OBJECTIVE **1** To simplify radicals involving products

OBJECTIVE **2** To simplify radicals involving quotients

...And Why

To find the distance to the horizon, as in Example 4

 Check Skills You'll Need (For help, go to Lessons 8-3 and 10-3.)

Complete each equation.

1. $a^3 = a^2 \cdot a^{\blacksquare}$ **1**   2. $b^7 = b^6 \cdot b^{\blacksquare}$ **1**   3. $c^6 = c^3 \cdot c^{\blacksquare}$ **3**   4. $d^8 = d^4 \cdot d^{\blacksquare}$ **4**

Find the value of each expression.

5. $\sqrt{4}$ **2**   6. $\sqrt{169}$ **13**   7. $\sqrt{25}$ **5**   8. $\sqrt{49}$ **7**

New Vocabulary • radical expression • rationalize

 Interactive lesson includes instant self-check, tutorials, and activities.

OBJECTIVE **1** **Simplifying Radical Expressions Involving Products**

Radical expressions like $2\sqrt{3}$ and $\sqrt{x+3}$ contain a radical. You read $\sqrt{x+3}$ as "the square root of the quantity x plus three." You can simplify a radical expression by removing perfect-square factors from the radicand. Recall that a radicand is the quantity or expression under the radical sign.

 Key Concepts

Property	**Multiplication Property of Square Roots**
For every number $a \geq 0$ and $b \geq 0$, $\sqrt{ab} = \sqrt{a} \cdot \sqrt{b}$.	
Example $\sqrt{54} = \sqrt{9} \cdot \sqrt{6} = 3 \cdot \sqrt{6} = 3\sqrt{6}$	

You can use the Multiplication Property of Square Roots to simplify radical expressions by rewriting the radicand as a product of the perfect-square factors times the remaining factors.

1 EXAMPLE **Removing Perfect-Square Factors**

Simplify $\sqrt{192}$.

$\sqrt{192} = \sqrt{64 \cdot 3}$ **64 is a perfect square and a factor of 192.**

$\quad\quad = \sqrt{64} \cdot \sqrt{3}$ **Use the Multiplication Property of Square Roots.**

$\quad\quad = 8\sqrt{3}$ **Simplify $\sqrt{64}$.**

✓ **Check Understanding** **1** Simplify each radical expression.

a. $\sqrt{50}$ $5\sqrt{2}$ b. $-5\sqrt{300}$ $-50\sqrt{3}$ c. $\sqrt{18}$ $3\sqrt{2}$

You can simplify radical expressions that contain variables. A variable with a nonzero, even exponent is a perfect square. Variables with odd exponents (other than 1 and −1) are the product of a perfect square and the variable. For example, $n^3 = n^2 \cdot n$, so $\sqrt{n^3} = \sqrt{n^2 \cdot n}$. Assume that all variables of all radicands represent nonnegative numbers..

578 Chapter 11 Radical Expressions and Equations

Ongoing Assessment and Intervention

Before the Lesson Diagnose prerequisite skills using:	**During the Lesson** Monitor progress using:	**After the Lesson** Assess knowledge using:
• Check Skills You'll Need	• Check Understanding • Additional Examples • Standardized Test Prep	• Lesson Quiz • Computer Test Generator CD

2 EXAMPLE Removing Variable Factors

Simplify $\sqrt{45a^5}$.

$\sqrt{45a^5} = \sqrt{9a^4 \cdot 5a}$ $9a^4$ is a perfect square and a factor of $45a^5$.

$\quad\quad\quad = \sqrt{9a^4} \cdot \sqrt{5a}$ Use the Multiplication Property of Square Roots.

$\quad\quad\quad = 3a^2\sqrt{5a}$ Simplify $\sqrt{9a^4}$.

✓ **Check Understanding** ❷ Simplify each radical expression.

a. $\sqrt{27n^2}$ **b.** $-a\sqrt{60a^7}$ **c.** $\sqrt{x^2y^5}$

You can use the Multiplication Property of Square Roots to write $\sqrt{a} \cdot \sqrt{b} = \sqrt{ab}$. Sometimes the product of two radicals has a perfect-square factor.

3 EXAMPLE Multiplying Two Radicals

Simplify each radical expression.

Problem Solving Hint

Another method of simplifying is using prime factors.
$\sqrt{8} \cdot \sqrt{12}$
$= \sqrt{2 \cdot 2 \cdot 2 \cdot 2 \cdot 2 \cdot 3}$
$= \sqrt{2^2 \cdot 2^2 \cdot 2 \cdot 3}$
$= 2 \cdot 2\sqrt{6}$
$= 4\sqrt{6}$

a. $\sqrt{8} \cdot \sqrt{12} = \sqrt{8 \cdot 12}$ Use the Multiplication Property of Square Roots.

$\quad\quad\quad\quad\quad = \sqrt{96}$ Simplify under the radical.

$\quad\quad\quad\quad\quad = \sqrt{16 \cdot 6}$ 16 is a perfect square and a factor of 96.

$\quad\quad\quad\quad\quad = \sqrt{16} \cdot \sqrt{6}$ Use the Multiplication Property of Square Roots.

$\quad\quad\quad\quad\quad = 4\sqrt{6}$ Simplify $\sqrt{16}$.

b. $3\sqrt{2b} \cdot 4\sqrt{10b} = 12\sqrt{20b^2}$ Multiply the whole numbers and use the Multiplication Property of Square Roots.

$\quad\quad\quad\quad\quad\quad = 12\sqrt{4b^2 \cdot 5}$ $4b^2$ is a perfect square and a factor of $20b^2$.

$\quad\quad\quad\quad\quad\quad = 12\sqrt{4b^2} \cdot \sqrt{5}$ Use the Multiplication Property of Square Roots.

$\quad\quad\quad\quad\quad\quad = 12 \cdot 2b\sqrt{5}$ Simplify $\sqrt{4b^2}$.

$\quad\quad\quad\quad\quad\quad = 24b\sqrt{5}$ Simplify.

✓ **Check Understanding** ❸ Simplify each radical expression.

a. $\sqrt{13} \cdot \sqrt{52}$ **b.** $5\sqrt{3c} \cdot \sqrt{6c}$ **c.** $2\sqrt{5a^2} \cdot 6\sqrt{10a^3}$

When you use radical expressions to solve real-world problems, you may need to use a calculator to find an approximate value of the radical expression.

4 EXAMPLE Real-World 🌐 Problem Solving

500 ft

Sightseeing You can use the formula $d = \sqrt{1.5h}$ to estimate the distance d in miles to a horizon when h is the height of the viewer's eyes above the ground in feet. Estimate the distance a visitor at the Washington Monument can see to the horizon from the observation windows. Round your answer to the nearest mile.

$d = \sqrt{1.5h}$

$\quad = \sqrt{1.5 \cdot 500}$ Substitute 500 for h.

$\quad = \sqrt{750}$ Multiply.

$\quad \approx 27$ Use a calculator.

The distance a visitor can see is about 27 miles.

✓ **Check Understanding** ❹ Suppose you are looking out a second floor window 25 ft above the ground. Find the distance you can see to the horizon. Round your answer to the nearest mile.

Lesson 11-1 Simplifying Radicals   **579**

👥 Reaching All Students

| **Below Level** In Example 2, some students may not think the term $3a^2$ is simplified. Remind them that simplifying radicals does not mean getting rid of all exponents. | **Advanced Learners** Have students find $(x - \sqrt{2})(x + \sqrt{2})$. $x^2 - 2$ Then ask them to 'factor' $(x^2 - 5)$. $(x + \sqrt{5})(x - \sqrt{5})$ | **Visual Learners** See note on page 579. **Auditory Learners** See note on page 580. |

---

2. Teach

Professional Development

Math Background

The index of a radical tells which root is indicated by the radical sign. When no index is given, an index of 2, for the square root, is assumed.

OBJECTIVE
❶ Teaching Notes

❶ EXAMPLE **Alternative Method**

On the board, show the prime factors of 192:
$192 = 2 \cdot 2 \cdot 2 \cdot 2 \cdot 2 \cdot 2 \cdot 3$.
Group each pair of 2s. Each pair is a perfect square. The 3 is not paired with another 3, so it is not a perfect square. On the board, write
$\sqrt{192} = \sqrt{(2 \cdot 2) \cdot (2 \cdot 2) \cdot (2 \cdot 2) \cdot 3}$
$\quad\quad = 2 \cdot 2 \cdot 2\sqrt{3}$
$\quad\quad = 8\sqrt{3}$

❷ EXAMPLE **Visual Learners**

Have students make a poster showing all the perfect squares from 0 to 200. Making the poster will help students recognize and memorize perfect squares.

❸ EXAMPLE **Math Tip**

Note that the value of the variable b is assumed to be nonnegative. Without this restriction, you would simplify $\sqrt{4b^2}$ as $2|b|$.

🔖 Additional Examples

❶ Simplify $\sqrt{243}$. $9\sqrt{3}$

❷ Simplify $\sqrt{28x^7}$. $2x^3\sqrt{7x}$

❸ Simplify each radical expression.
a. $\sqrt{12} \cdot \sqrt{32}$ $8\sqrt{6}$
b. $7\sqrt{5x} \cdot 3\sqrt{8x}$ $42x\sqrt{10}$

❹ Suppose you are looking out a fourth floor window 52 ft above the ground. Use the formula $d = \sqrt{1.5h}$ to estimate the distance you can see to the horizon. Round your answer to the nearest mile.   **9 miles**

579

OBJECTIVE 2 — Teaching Notes

5 EXAMPLE Auditory Learners

Encourage students to create and tell each other numerical facts expressed as radicals, for example my brother is $\sqrt{\frac{100}{4}}$ years old.

7 EXAMPLE Teaching Tip

Students may think that $\frac{2}{\sqrt{5}}$ is in a simpler form than $\frac{2\sqrt{5}}{5}$. Have students reread the definition of rationalization and encourage them to pay attention to the denominator when they are deciding whether the expression is in its simplest form.

Additional Examples

5 Simplify each radical expression.
a. $\sqrt{\frac{13}{64}}$ $\frac{\sqrt{13}}{8}$
b. $\sqrt{\frac{49}{x^4}}$ $\frac{7}{x^2}$

6 Simplify each radical expression.
a. $\sqrt{\frac{120}{10}}$ $2\sqrt{3}$
b. $\sqrt{\frac{75x^5}{48x}}$ $\frac{5x^2}{4}$

7 Simplify by rationalizing the denominator.
a. $\frac{3}{\sqrt{7}}$ $\frac{3\sqrt{7}}{7}$
b. $\frac{\sqrt{11}}{\sqrt{12x^3}}$ $\frac{\sqrt{33x}}{6x^2}$

Closure

Ask students to summarize how to simplify a radical. You remove perfect squares that are factors of the radicand, and write their square roots outside the radical sign. You remove any fractions from the radicand by dividing, or by using the Division Property of Square Roots. Then you rationalize any fractions that have radicals in the denominator.

OBJECTIVE 2 — Simplifying Radical Expressions Involving Quotients

You can use the Division Property of Square Roots to simplify expressions.

 Key Concepts

Property	Division Property of Square Roots

For every number $a \geq 0$ and $b > 0$, $\sqrt{\frac{a}{b}} = \frac{\sqrt{a}}{\sqrt{b}}$.

Example $\sqrt{\frac{16}{25}} = \frac{\sqrt{16}}{\sqrt{25}} = \frac{4}{5}$

When the denominator of the radicand is a perfect square, it is easier to simplify the numerator and denominator separately.

Reading Math

Read $\frac{\sqrt{2}}{3}$ as "the square root of 2 over 3," and $\sqrt{\frac{2}{3}}$ as "the square root of two thirds."

5 EXAMPLE Simplifying Fractions Within Radicals

Simplify each radical expression.

a. $\sqrt{\frac{11}{49}} = \frac{\sqrt{11}}{\sqrt{49}}$ Use the Division Property of Square Roots.

$= \frac{\sqrt{11}}{7}$ Simplify $\sqrt{49}$.

b. $\sqrt{\frac{25}{b^4}} = \frac{\sqrt{25}}{\sqrt{b^4}}$ Use the Division Property of Square Roots.

$= \frac{5}{b^2}$ Simplify $\sqrt{25}$ and $\sqrt{b^4}$.

✓ Check Understanding **5** Simplify each radical expression.

a. $\sqrt{\frac{144}{9}}$ 4   b. $\sqrt{\frac{25p^3}{q^2}}$ $\frac{5p\sqrt{p}}{q}$ c. $\sqrt{\frac{75}{16t^2}}$ $\frac{5\sqrt{3}}{4t}$

When the denominator of the radicand is not a perfect square, it may be easier to divide first and then simplify the radical expression.

6 EXAMPLE Simplifying Radicals by Dividing

Simplify each radical expression.

a. $\sqrt{\frac{88}{11}} = \sqrt{8}$ Divide.

$= \sqrt{4 \cdot 2}$ 4 is a perfect square and a factor of 8.

$= \sqrt{4} \cdot \sqrt{2}$ Use the Multiplication Property of Square Roots.

$= 2\sqrt{2}$ Simplify $\sqrt{4}$.

b. $\sqrt{\frac{12a^3}{27a}} = \sqrt{\frac{4a^2}{9}}$ Divide the numerator and denominator by 3a.

$= \frac{\sqrt{4a^2}}{\sqrt{9}}$ Use the Division Property of Square Roots.

$= \frac{\sqrt{4} \cdot \sqrt{a^2}}{\sqrt{9}}$ Use the Multiplication Property of Square Roots.

$= \frac{2a}{3}$ Simplify $\sqrt{4}$, $\sqrt{a^2}$ and $\sqrt{9}$.

✓ Check Understanding **6** Simplify each radical expression.

a. $\sqrt{\frac{90}{5}}$ $3\sqrt{2}$ b. $\sqrt{\frac{48}{75}}$ $\frac{4}{5}$ c. $\sqrt{\frac{27x^3}{3x}}$ $3x$

580 Chapter 11 Radical Expressions and Equations

pages 581–583   Exercises

5. $-6\sqrt{30}$

6. $40\sqrt{5}$

7. $2n\sqrt{7}$

8. $6b^2\sqrt{3}$

A radicand in the denominator of a radical expression may not be a perfect square. To simplify, you may need to **rationalize** the denominator. To do this, you multiply the numerator and the denominator by the same radical expression. You choose a radical expression that will make the denominator a perfect square.

Need Help?

Multiplying by $\frac{\sqrt{5}}{\sqrt{5}}$ is the same as multiplying by 1.

Multiplying by $\frac{\sqrt{5}}{\sqrt{5}}$ changes the appearance of a radical expression but not its value.

7 EXAMPLE Rationalizing a Denominator

Simplify by rationalizing the denominator.

a. $\frac{2}{\sqrt{5}} = \frac{2}{\sqrt{5}} \cdot \frac{\sqrt{5}}{\sqrt{5}}$ **Multiply by $\frac{\sqrt{5}}{\sqrt{5}}$ to make the denominator a perfect square.**

$= \frac{2\sqrt{5}}{\sqrt{25}}$ **Use the Multiplication Property of Square Roots.**

$= \frac{2\sqrt{5}}{5}$ **Simplify $\sqrt{25}$.**

b. $\frac{\sqrt{7}}{\sqrt{8n}} = \frac{\sqrt{7}}{\sqrt{8n}} \cdot \frac{\sqrt{2n}}{\sqrt{2n}}$ **Multiply by $\frac{\sqrt{2n}}{\sqrt{2n}}$ to make the denominator a perfect square.**

$= \frac{\sqrt{14n}}{\sqrt{16n^2}}$ **Use the Multiplication Property of Square Roots.**

$= \frac{\sqrt{14n}}{4n}$ **Simplify $\sqrt{16n^2}$.**

 ✓ Check Understanding **7** Simplify by rationalizing the denominator.

a. $\frac{3}{\sqrt{3}}$ $\sqrt{3}$ **b.** $\frac{\sqrt{5}}{\sqrt{18t}}$ $\frac{\sqrt{10t}}{6t}$ **c.** $\sqrt{\frac{7m}{10}}$ $\frac{\sqrt{70m}}{10}$

The summary below can help you determine whether a radical expression is in simplest radical form.

 Key Concepts

Summary	Simplest Radical Form

A radical expression is in simplest radical form when all three statements are true.
- The radicand has no perfect-square factors other than 1.
- The radicand has no fractions.
- The denominator of a fraction has no radical.

EXERCISES

For more practice, see *Extra Practice*.

Practice and Problem Solving

A Practice by Example

Simplify each radical expression. 5–20. See margin p. 580.

Examples 1, 2
(pages 578, 579)

1. $\sqrt{200}$ $10\sqrt{2}$ **2.** $\sqrt{98}$ $7\sqrt{2}$ **3.** $\sqrt{75}$ $5\sqrt{3}$ **4.** $-\sqrt{80}$ $-4\sqrt{5}$

5. $-3\sqrt{120}$ **6.** $5\sqrt{320}$ **7.** $\sqrt{28n^2}$ **8.** $\sqrt{108b^4}$

9. $3\sqrt{12x^2}$ **10.** $\sqrt{4n^3}$ **11.** $\sqrt{20a^5}$ **12.** $-\sqrt{48b^4}$

Example 3
(page 579)

13. $\sqrt{10} \cdot \sqrt{40}$ **14.** $3\sqrt{6} \cdot \sqrt{6}$ **15.** $\sqrt{22} \cdot \sqrt{11}$ **16.** $2\sqrt{18} \cdot 7\sqrt{6}$

17. $\sqrt{7} \cdot \sqrt{21}$ **18.** $-3\sqrt{20} \cdot \sqrt{15}$ **19.** $\sqrt{3n} \cdot \sqrt{24n}$ **20.** $2\sqrt{7t} \cdot \sqrt{14t}$

21. $\sqrt{3x} \cdot \sqrt{51x^3}$ **22.** $5\sqrt{8t} \cdot \sqrt{32t^5}$ **23.** $\sqrt{2a^2} \cdot \sqrt{9a^4}$ **24.** $-2\sqrt{6a^3} \cdot \sqrt{3a}$
    $3x^2\sqrt{17}$ $80t^3$ $3a^3\sqrt{2}$ $-6a^2\sqrt{2}$

9. $6x\sqrt{3}$ **13.** 20   **17.** $7\sqrt{3}$

10. $2n\sqrt{n}$ **14.** 18   **18.** $-30\sqrt{3}$

11. $2a^2\sqrt{5a}$ **15.** $11\sqrt{2}$ **19.** $6n\sqrt{2}$

12. $-4b^2\sqrt{3}$ **16.** $84\sqrt{3}$ **20.** $14t\sqrt{2}$

---

3. Practice

Assignment Guide

1 Objective
   A B Core 1–27, 54–58, 69–74
   C Extension 75–76

2 Objective
   A B Core 28–53, 59–68
   C Extension 77–78

Standardized Test Prep 79–83

Mixed Review 84–93

Error Prevention

Exercises 1–12 Students may forget to move a square root outside the radical sign as they simplify. For example, they may write $\sqrt{49} = \sqrt{7}$ instead of 7. Remind them to work carefully, and to check their work.

Error Prevention

Exercises 44–51 When rationalizing the denominator, some students may square both the numerator and denominator. For example, they may write $\frac{3}{\sqrt{2}} \cdot \frac{3}{\sqrt{2}}$ for $\frac{3}{\sqrt{2}}$. Suggest to students that they draw a circle around the factor they are rationalizing and remember that they must multiply by an expression equivalent to 1.

Enrichment 11-1

Reteaching 11-1

Practice 11-1

4. Assess

Lesson Quiz 11-1

Simplify each radical expression.

1. $\sqrt{16} \cdot \sqrt{8}$ $8\sqrt{2}$

2. $4\sqrt{144}$ 48

3. $\sqrt{\dfrac{12}{36}}$ $\dfrac{\sqrt{3}}{3}$

4. $\dfrac{2}{\sqrt{a^5}}$ $\dfrac{2\sqrt{a}}{a^3}$

5. $\dfrac{\sqrt{3x}}{\sqrt{15x^3}}$ $\dfrac{\sqrt{5}}{5x}$

Alternative Assessment

Assign half the class to write one problem like Example 3 and one like Example 5, and half the class to write one problem like Example 6 and one like Example 7. Each student should write the two problems on one side of a piece of paper and the solutions on the other side. Then have students exchange papers with the opposite half of the class and solve the problems and check their answers.

pages 581–583   Exercises

52. not simplest form; radical in the denominator of a fraction

53. not simplest form; radical in the denominator of a fraction

54. Simplest form; radicand has no perfect-square factors other than 1.

55. Simplest form; radicand has no perfect-square factors other than 1.

Example 4
(page 579)

For Exercises 25–27, use the formula $d = \sqrt{1.5h}$ to approximate distance d in miles to a horizon when h is the height in feet of the viewer's eyes above the ground. Round your answer to the nearest mile.

25. Find the distance you can see to the horizon from a height of 6 feet. **3 mi**

26. Find the distance you can see to the horizon from a height of 100 feet. **12 mi**

27. Find the distance you can see to the horizon from a height of 200 feet. **17 mi**

Example 5
(page 580)

Simplify each radical expression.

28. $\sqrt{\dfrac{21}{49}}$ $\dfrac{\sqrt{21}}{7}$
29. $3\sqrt{\dfrac{3}{4}}$ $\dfrac{3\sqrt{3}}{2}$
30. $\sqrt{\dfrac{625}{100}}$ $\dfrac{5}{2}$
31. $\sqrt{\dfrac{120}{121}}$ $\dfrac{2\sqrt{30}}{11}$

32. $\sqrt{\dfrac{5}{9a^2}}$ $\dfrac{\sqrt{5}}{3a}$
33. $\sqrt{\dfrac{7}{16c^2}}$ $\dfrac{\sqrt{7}}{4c}$
34. $\sqrt{\dfrac{75a}{49}}$ $\dfrac{5\sqrt{3a}}{7}$
35. $\sqrt{\dfrac{8n^3}{81}}$ $\dfrac{2n\sqrt{2n}}{9}$

Example 6
(page 580)

36. $\sqrt{\dfrac{15}{5}}$ $\sqrt{3}$
37. $\sqrt{\dfrac{54}{24}}$ $\dfrac{3}{2}$
38. $\sqrt{\dfrac{60}{5}}$ $2\sqrt{3}$
39. $-\sqrt{\dfrac{160}{8}}$ $-2\sqrt{5}$

40. $\sqrt{\dfrac{140x^3}{5x}}$ $2x\sqrt{7}$
41. $\sqrt{\dfrac{3s^3}{27s}}$ $\dfrac{s}{3}$
42. $\sqrt{\dfrac{30a^5}{40a}}$ $\dfrac{a^2\sqrt{3}}{2}$
43. $\sqrt{\dfrac{63y}{7y^3}}$ $\dfrac{3}{y}$

Example 7
(page 581)

Simplify each radical expression by rationalizing the denominator.

44. $\dfrac{3}{\sqrt{2}}$ $\dfrac{3\sqrt{2}}{2}$
45. $\dfrac{5}{\sqrt{5}}$ $\sqrt{5}$
46. $\dfrac{\sqrt{3}}{\sqrt{7x}}$ $\dfrac{\sqrt{21x}}{7x}$
47. $\dfrac{2\sqrt{2}}{\sqrt{5n}}$ $\dfrac{2\sqrt{10n}}{5n}$

48. $\dfrac{9}{\sqrt{8}}$ $\dfrac{9\sqrt{2}}{4}$
49. $\dfrac{12}{\sqrt{12}}$ $2\sqrt{3}$
50. $\dfrac{3\sqrt{2}}{\sqrt{9b}}$ $\dfrac{\sqrt{2b}}{b}$
51. $\dfrac{5\sqrt{11}}{\sqrt{20y}}$ $\dfrac{\sqrt{55y}}{2y}$

B **Apply Your Skills**

Writing Explain why each radical expression is or is not in simplest radical form.

52. $\dfrac{13}{\sqrt{4}}$
53. $\dfrac{3}{\sqrt{3}}$
54. $4\sqrt{3}$
55. $5\sqrt{30}$

52–55. See margin.

56a. $\sqrt{18 \cdot 10} = \sqrt{180} = \sqrt{36} \cdot \sqrt{5} = 6\sqrt{5}$

b. Answers may vary. Sample: $a = 36, b = 5$; $a = 9, b = 20$

56. Suppose a and b are positive integers.
   a. Verify that if $a = 18$ and $b = 10$, then $\sqrt{a} \cdot \sqrt{b} = 6\sqrt{5}$. **a–b. See left.**
   b. **Open-Ended** Find two other pairs of positive integers a and b such that $\sqrt{a} \cdot \sqrt{b} = 6\sqrt{5}$.

Simplify each radical expression.

57. $\sqrt{12} \cdot \sqrt{75}$ 30
58. $\sqrt{26 \cdot 2}$ $2\sqrt{13}$
59. $\dfrac{\sqrt{72}}{\sqrt{64}}$ $\dfrac{3\sqrt{2}}{4}$
60. $\dfrac{-2}{\sqrt{a^3}}$ $\dfrac{-2\sqrt{a}}{a^2}$

61. $\dfrac{\sqrt{180}}{\sqrt{3}}$ $2\sqrt{15}$
62. $\dfrac{\sqrt{x^2}}{\sqrt{y^3}}$ $\dfrac{x\sqrt{y}}{y^2}$
63. $\dfrac{-3\sqrt{2}}{\sqrt{6}}$ $-\sqrt{3}$
64. $\sqrt{8} \cdot \sqrt{10}$ $4\sqrt{5}$

65. $\sqrt{20a^2b^3}$ $2ab\sqrt{5b}$
66. $\sqrt{a^3b^5c^3}$ $ab^2c\sqrt{abc}$
67. $\sqrt{\dfrac{3m}{16m^2}}$ $\dfrac{\sqrt{3m}}{4m}$
68. $\dfrac{16a}{\sqrt{6a^3}}$ $\dfrac{8\sqrt{6a}}{3a}$

Solve each equation. Leave your answer in simplest radical form.

69. $x^2 + 6x - 9 = 0$
   $-3 \pm 3\sqrt{2}$
70. $n^2 - 2n + 1 = 5$
   $1 \pm \sqrt{5}$
71. $3y^2 - 4y - 2 = 0$
   $\dfrac{2 \pm \sqrt{10}}{3}$

72a. $\sqrt{50} = \sqrt{25 \cdot 2} = \sqrt{25} \cdot \sqrt{2} = 5\sqrt{2}$

b. The radicand has no perfect-square factors other than 1.

72. a. Show work to verify that $\sqrt{50}$ equals $5\sqrt{2}$.
   b. **Writing** Explain why $5\sqrt{2}$ is in simplest radical form.

73. **Open-Ended** What are three numbers whose square roots can be written in the form $a\sqrt{3}$ for some value of a? **Answers may vary. Sample: 12, 27, 48.**

74. **Newspaper Layout** A square picture on the front page of a newspaper occupies an area of 24 in.^{2}.
   a. Find the length of each side in simplest radical form. **$2\sqrt{6}$ in.**
   b. Calculate the length of each side to the nearest hundredth of an inch. **4.90 in.**

582   Chapter 11   Radical Expressions and Equations

 Challenge

Simplify each radical expression.

75. $\sqrt{24} \cdot \sqrt{2x} \cdot \sqrt{3x}$ **12x** **76.** $2b(\sqrt{5b})^2$ **10b²** **77.** $\sqrt{45a^7} \cdot \sqrt{20a}$ **30a⁴**

 78. Physics The time that a pendulum of a grandfather clock takes to swing back and forth one cycle is the period of the pendulum. The formula for finding the period T in seconds is $T = 2\pi\sqrt{\frac{L}{32}}$, where L is the length of the pendulum in feet. Find the period of a pendulum that is 8 feet long. Write your answer in terms of π.

π seconds

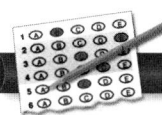

Standardized Test Prep

Multiple Choice

79. Simplify $\sqrt{80}$. **C**
  A. $10\sqrt{8}$ **B.** $8\sqrt{10}$ **C.** $4\sqrt{5}$ **D.** 40

80. Simplify $5\sqrt{3x^2} \cdot \sqrt{6x}$. **F**
  F. $15x\sqrt{2x}$ **G.** $5x\sqrt{18x}$ **H.** $3x\sqrt{10x}$ **I.** $6x\sqrt{5x}$

81. Which of the following equals $\frac{2}{3}$? **B**
  A. $\sqrt{\frac{9}{25}}$ **B.** $\sqrt{\frac{20}{45}}$ **C.** $2\sqrt{\frac{4}{27}}$ **D.** $\sqrt{\frac{6}{9}}$

Take It to the NET
Online lesson quiz at
www.PHSchool.com
Web Code: aea-1101

82. Which of the following equals $1.5\sqrt{0.038}$? **I**
  F. $150\sqrt{3.8}$ **G.** $15\sqrt{3.8}$ **H.** $15\sqrt{0.38}$ **I.** $15\sqrt{0.00038}$

Short Response

83. A square window occupies an area of 96 ft². What is the length of each side of the window in simplest radical form? Show your work. **See margin.**

Mixed Review

Lesson 10-9

Which kind of function best models the data in each table? Write an equation to model the data. **See left.**

84. quadratic; $y = 0.2x^2$
85. exponential; $y = 4(2.5)^x$
86. linear; $y = -4.2x + 7$

84.

x	y
−1	0.2
0	0
1	0.2
2	0.8
3	1.8
4	3.2

85.

x	y
−1	1.6
0	4
1	10
2	25
3	62.5
4	156.25

86.

x	y
−1	11.2
0	7
1	2.8
2	−1.4
3	−5.6
4	−9.8

Lesson 10-2

Graph each function. Label the axis of symmetry and the vertex. 87–89. See margin.

87. $f(x) = x^2 + 8x - 4$ **88.** $y = x^2 - 10x + 7$ **89.** $y = 3x^2 + 12x - 5$

Lesson 9-1

Simplify. Write each answer in standard form. 90–91. See left.

90. $3n^2 + 5n + 5$
91. $3v^2 - v - 9$

90. $(n^2 + 5n - 1) + (2n^2 + 6)$ **91.** $(4v^2 + 8v - 2) - (v^2 + 9v + 7)$

92. $(5t^3 - 14t) + (8t^2 - 11)$ **93.** $(2b^2 - 12b - 8) - (5b^2 + 11b + 13)$
  $5t^3 + 8t^2 - 14t - 11$ $-3b^2 - 23b - 21$

Lesson 11-1 Simplifying Radicals **583**

Standardized Test Prep

 **Resources**

For additional practice with a variety of test item formats:
- Standardized Test Prep, p. 633
- Test-Taking Strategies, p. 628
- Test-Taking Strategies with Transparencies

Exercise 83 Encourage students to sketch a picture and label it to help them visualize the question.

83. [2] $A = 96$ ft²
  $s = \sqrt{96} =$
  $\sqrt{16} \cdot \sqrt{6} = 4\sqrt{6}$ ft

  [1] correct answer, without work shown

87.

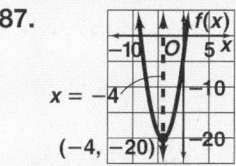

$x = -4$ $(-4, -20)$

88.

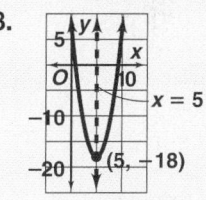

$x = 5$ $(5, -18)$

89.

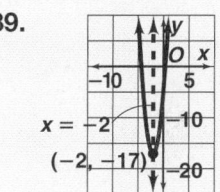

$x = -2$ $(-2, -17)$

583

1. Plan

Lesson Preview

 **Check Skills You'll Need**

Solving Quadratic Equations
Lesson 10-4: Example 2
Exercises 10–18
Extra Practice, p. 711

Lesson Resources

Teaching Resources
Practice, Reteaching, Enrichment

Reaching All Students
Practice Workbook 11-2
Spanish Practice Workbook 11-2
Hands-on Activities 26
Basic Algebra Planning Guide 11-2

Presentation Assistant Plus!
Transparencies
• Check Skills You'll Need 11-2
• Additional Examples 11-2
• Student Edition Answers 11-2
• Lesson Quiz 11-2
PH Presentation Pro CD 11-2

ASSESSMENT SYSTEM
Computer Test Generator CD

Technology
Resource Pro® CD-ROM
Computer Test Generator CD
Prentice Hall Presentation Pro CD

www.PHSchool.com
Student Site
• Teacher Web Code: aek-5500
• Reasoning & Puzzles p. 94
• Graphing Calculator,
  Procedure 19
• Self-grading Lesson Quiz
Teacher Center
• Lesson Planner
• Resources

Plus

584

11-2

The Pythagorean Theorem

 North Carolina Objectives

1.02 Use formulas and algebraic expressions to solve problems.
2.02 Use the parallelism or perpendicularity of lines and segments to solve problems.

Lesson Preview

What You'll Learn

 OBJECTIVE 1 To solve problems using the Pythagorean Theorem

OBJECTIVE 2 To identify right triangles

. . . And Why

To calculate heights indirectly, as in Example 2

✓ Check Skills You'll Need

(For help, go to Lesson 10-4.)

Simplify each expression.

1. $5^2 + 6^2$ **61**
2. $9^2 - 4^2$ **65**
3. $(3t)^2 + (4t)^2$ **25t^2**

Solve each equation.

4. $c^2 = 36$ **−6, 6**
5. $24 + b^2 = 49$ **−5, 5**
6. $a^2 + 16 = 65$ **−7, 7**
7. $12 + b^2 = 32$ **−2√5, 2√5**
8. $80 = c^2$ **−4√5, 4√5**
9. $100 = a^2 + 52$ **−4√3, 4√3**

New Vocabulary • hypotenuse • leg • Pythagorean Theorem
• conditional • hypothesis • conclusion • converse

OBJECTIVE 1

Solving Problems Using the Pythagorean Theorem

iTEXT Interactive lesson includes instant self-check, tutorials, and activities.

1. 9, 16, 25, 25;
25, 144, 169, 169;
$\frac{9}{25}, \frac{16}{25}$, 1, 1;
0.81, 1.44, 2.25, 2.25

2. The sum $a^2 + b^2$ is equal to c^2.

3. equals

Investigation: The Pythagorean Theorem

1. The values in the chart represent the sides of a right triangle. Copy and complete the chart. **1-3. See left.**

a	b	c	a^2	b^2	$a^2 + b^2$	c^2
3	4	5	▪	▪	▪	▪
5	12	13	▪	▪	▪	▪
$\frac{3}{5}$	$\frac{4}{5}$	1	▪	▪	▪	▪
0.9	1.2	1.5	▪	▪	▪	▪

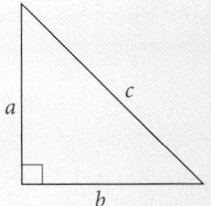

2. Compare the value of $a^2 + b^2$ for each row in the table to the value of c^2.

3. Complete the following statement: For a right triangle, the square of the longest side ? the sum of the squares of the other two sides.

Reading Math

The Pythagorean Theorem is named after Pythagoras, a Greek philosopher and mathematician who taught about 530 B.C.

In a right triangle, the side opposite the right angle is the **hypotenuse.** It is the longest side. Each of the sides forming the right angle is a **leg.**

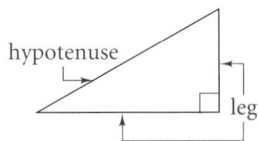

The **Pythagorean Theorem** describes the relationship of the lengths of the sides of a right triangle.

584 Chapter 11 Radical Expressions and Equations

Ongoing Assessment and Intervention

Before the Lesson
Diagnose prerequisite skills using:
• Check Skills You'll Need

During the Lesson
Monitor progress using:
• Check Understanding
• Additional Examples
• Standardized Test Prep

After the Lesson
Assess knowledge using:
• Lesson Quiz
• Computer Test Generator CD

Key Concepts

Theorem	The Pythagorean Theorem

In any right triangle, the sum of the squares of the lengths of the legs is equal to the square of the length of the hypotenuse.

$$a^2 + b^2 = c^2$$

1 EXAMPLE Using the Pythagorean Theorem

What is the length of the hypotenuse of the triangle at the right?

$a^2 + b^2 = c^2$	**Use the Pythagorean Theorem.**
$9^2 + 12^2 = c^2$	**Substitute 9 for a and 12 for b.**
$81 + 144 = c^2$	**Simplify.**
$\sqrt{225} = \sqrt{c^2}$	**Find the principal square root of each side.**
$15 = c$	**Simplify.**

● The length of the hypotenuse is 15 cm.

 **Check Understanding** ❶ What is the length of the hypotenuse of a right triangle with legs of lengths 7 cm and 24 cm? **25 cm**

You can also use the Pythagorean Theorem to find the length of a leg of a right triangle when you know the lengths of the hypotenuse and the other leg.

2 EXAMPLE Real-World  Problem Solving

Fire Rescue A fire truck parks beside a building such that the base of the ladder is 16 ft from the building. The fire truck extends its ladder 30 ft as shown at the left. How high is the top of the ladder above the ground?

Define Let b = height (in feet) of the ladder from a point 10 ft above the ground.

Relate The triangle formed is a right triangle. Use the Pythagorean Theorem.

Write

$a^2 + b^2 = c^2$	
$16^2 + b^2 = 30^2$	**Substitute.**
$256 + b^2 = 900$	**Simplify.**
$b^2 = 644$	**Subtract 256 from each side.**
$\sqrt{b^2} = \sqrt{644}$	**Find the principal square root of each side.**
$b \approx 25.4$	**Use a calculator and round to the nearest tenth.**

● The height to the top of the ladder is 10 feet higher than 25.4 ft, so it is about 35.4 ft from the ground.

 **Check Understanding** ❷ Use the figure at the right. About how many miles is it from downtown to the harbor? Round to the nearest tenth of a mile. **6.9 mi**

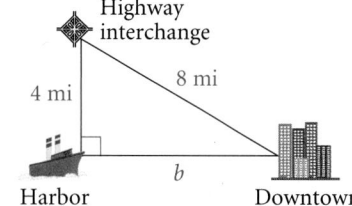

 2. Teach

Math Background

The two acute angles of any right triangle are complementary angles. The side opposite the larger angle will have the greater length.

OBJECTIVE
❶ Teaching Notes

Investigation (Optional)
Connection to History
Pythagoras was a Greek philosopher and religious leader. We now know that the Pythagorean Theorem was known even earlier in other countries.

❶ **EXAMPLE** **Teaching Tip**

Students may think that the hypotenuse is always the side on top. Draw several right triangles oriented different ways and have students label the hypotenuse and legs of each triangle. Ask: *Is one side of a right triangle always the longest side?* **yes** *Which one?* **the hypotenuse**

Additional Examples

❶ What is the length of the hypotenuse of this triangle? **17 m**

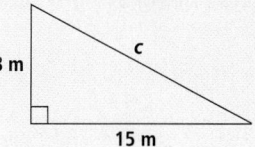

❷ A toy fire truck is positioned so that the base of the ladder is 13 cm from the wall. The ladder is extended 28 cm to the wall. How high above the table is the top of the ladder? **about 33.8 cm**

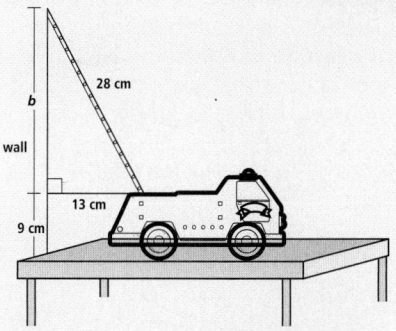

👫 Reaching All Students

Below Level Remind students that they cannot accurately identify a right triangle by visual inspection. They must use the Pythagorean Theorem to unmistakably identify a right triangle.

Advanced Learners Have students research some ways in which the Pythagorean Theorem was used in ancient Egyptian architecture, and share their findings with the class.

English Learners See note on page 587.
Tactile Learners See note on page 586.

585

OBJECTIVE
2 Teaching Notes

3 EXAMPLE Error Prevention

Students may not substitute the values in the correct places in the equation. Suggest to them that they first find the greatest number and substitute this value for the hypotenuse c. Then they can substitute the two smaller numbers for a and b. Point out that it does not matter which of the two smaller values replaces a or b because addition is commutative.

4 EXAMPLE Tactile Learners

The term *resultant force* may be difficult for students to understand. Tie two ropes to a student desk. Have a volunteer pull on one rope. Then ask another volunteer to help pull the desk, but at a right angle. Instruct the first volunteer to describe how the pulling force was changed.

Additional Examples

3 Determine whether the given lengths can be sides of a right triangle.
a. 5 in., 5 in., and 7 in. no
b. 10 cm, 24 cm, and 26 cm yes

4 For a 50-lb force and a 120-lb force, the resultant force is 130 lb. Are the forces pulling at right angles to each other? yes

Closure

Ask students how they can determine which side of a right triangle is the hypotenuse, and for what the Pythagorean Theorem is used. The hypotenuse is always the longest side in a right triangle and it is opposite the right angle. The Pythagorean Theorem is used to determine the length of a missing side in a right triangle when the lengths of any two sides are given.

586

An *if-then* statement like "If an animal is a horse, then it has four legs" is called a **conditional.** Every conditional has two parts. The part following *if* is the **hypothesis,** and the part following *then* is the **conclusion.**

The **converse** of a conditional switches the hypothesis and the conclusion. Somtimes converses of conditionals are not true. For example, "If an animal has four legs, then the animal is a horse" is not a true statement.

You can rewrite the Pythagorean Theorem as an *if-then* statement, "If a triangle is a right triangle with legs of lengths a and b and hypotenuse of length c, then $a^2 + b^2 = c^2$." The Pythagorean Theorem has a converse that is always true.

Key Concepts

Property	The Converse of the Pythagorean Theorem

If a triangle has sides of lengths a, b, and c, and $a^2 + b^2 = c^2$, then the triangle is a right triangle with hypotenuse of length c.

You can use the converse of the Pythagorean Theorem to determine whether a triangle is a right triangle. Since the Pythagorean Theorem and its converse are always true, you can also determine whether a triangle is *not* a right triangle.

3 EXAMPLE Using the Converse of the Pythagorean Theorem

Determine whether the given lengths can be sides of a right triangle.

a. 5 in., 12 in., and 13 in.
$$5^2 + 12^2 \stackrel{?}{=} 13^2$$
$$25 + 144 \stackrel{?}{=} 169$$
$$169 = 169 \checkmark$$
The triangle is a right triangle.

Determine whether $a^2 + b^2 = c^2$, where c is the longest side.

b. 7 m, 9 m, and 12 m
$$7^2 + 9^2 \stackrel{?}{=} 12^2$$
$$49 + 81 \stackrel{?}{=} 144$$
$$130 \neq 144$$
The triangle is not a right triangle.

✓ Check Understanding **3** A triangle has sides of lengths 10 m, 24 m, and 26 m. Is the triangle a right triangle? yes

You can use the converse of the Pythagorean Theorem to solve a physics problem involving force.

4 EXAMPLE Real-World ⊕ Problem Solving

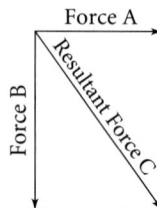

Force A
Resultant Force C
Force B

Physics If two forces pull at right angles to each other, the resultant force is represented as the diagonal of a rectangle, as shown at the left. The diagonal forms a right triangle with two of the perpendicular sides of the rectangle. For a 30-lb force and a 40-lb force, the resultant force is 50 lb. Are the forces pulling at right angles to each other?

$$30^2 + 40^2 \stackrel{?}{=} 50^2$$ Determine whether $a^2 + b^2 = c^2$, where c is the greatest force.
$$900 + 1600 \stackrel{?}{=} 2500$$
$$2500 = 2500 \checkmark$$

Yes, the 30-lb and 40-lb forces are pulling at right angles to each other.

For a 70-lb force and a 60-lb force, the resultant force is 100 lb. Are the forces pulling at right angles to each other? **no**

EXERCISES

For more practice, see *Extra Practice*.

Practice and Problem Solving

A **Practice by Example**

Example 1
(page 585)

Use the triangle at the right. Find the length of the missing side. If necessary, round to the nearest tenth.

1. $a = 6, b = 8$ **10**   2. $a = 15, b = 20$ **25**

3. $a = 8, b = 15$ **17**   4. $a = 10, b = 24$ **26**

5. $a = 1.5, b = 2$ **2.5**   6. $a = \frac{3}{5}, b = \frac{4}{5}$ **1**

Example 2
(page 585)

7. $a = 3, c = 5$ **4**   8. $b = 12, c = 13$ **5**

9. $a = 9, c = 15$ **12**   10. $b = 7, c = 10$ **7.1**

11. $a = 5, c = 9$ **7.5**   12. $a = 0.8, c = 1$ **0.6**

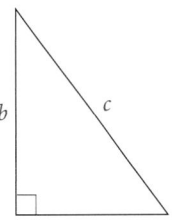

13. **Packaging** Use the diagram at the right. Find the width w that the box needs to be for the fishing rod to fit flat inside of it. **1.2 m**

14. A 16-ft ladder is placed 4 ft from the base of a building. How high on the building will the ladder reach? **about 15.5 ft**

15. A pigeon leaves its nest in New York City and flies 5 km due east. The pigeon then flies 3 km due north. How far is the pigeon from its nest? **about 5.8 km**

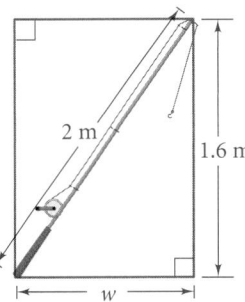

Example 3
(page 586)

Determine whether the given lengths can be sides of a right triangle.

16. 9 ft, 12 ft, 15 ft **yes**   17. 1 in., 2 in., 3 in. **no**   18. 2 m, 4 m, 5 m **no**

19. 16 cm, 30 cm, 34 cm **yes**   20. 4 m, 4 m, 8 m **no**   21. 10 in., 24 in., 26 in. **yes**

Example 4
(page 586)

Physics Determine whether the forces in each pair are pulling at right angles to each other.

22. 45 lb, 24 lb, resultant force 51 lb **yes**   23. 3.5 lb, 6.2 lb, resultant force 9.1 lb **no**

24. 20 lb, 10 lb, resultant force 30 lb **no**   25. 1.25 lb, 3 lb, resultant force 3.25 lb **yes**

B **Apply Your Skills**

For the values given, a and b are legs of a right triangle, and c is the hypotenuse. Find the length of the missing side of each right triangle. If necessary, round to the nearest tenth.

26. $a = 1.2, b = 0.9$ **1.5**   27. $a = \frac{1}{5}, c = \frac{1}{3}$ **$\frac{4}{15}$ or 0.3**   28. $a = \sqrt{5}, c = \sqrt{14}$ **3**

29. $a = \sqrt{7}, b = \sqrt{29}$ **6**   30. $a = 2.4, b = 1.0$ **2.6**   31. $a = 2\frac{1}{2}, b = 6\frac{1}{2}$ **7.0**

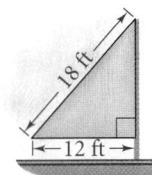

32. **Sailing** The diagram at the left shows a sailboat.
   a. Use the Pythagorean Theorem to find the height of the sail in simplest radical form. **$6\sqrt{5}$ ft**
   b. Use the result of part (a) and the formula for the area of a triangle to find the area of the sail. Round to the nearest tenth. **80.5 ft^2**

Lesson 11-2 The Pythagorean Theorem   **587**

3. Practice

Assignment Guide

1 Objective

Ⓐ Ⓑ Core 1–15, 26–32, 39–47, 52–53

Ⓒ Extension 54–56

2 Objective

Ⓐ Ⓑ Core 16–25, 33–38, 48–51

Ⓒ Extension 57–59

Standardized Test Prep 60–65

Mixed Review 66–85

Error Prevention

Exercise 14, 15 Encourage students to make sketches to help them understand the problem.

English Learners

Exercise 15 Explain that *due* east and *due* north mean *exactly* east and *exactly* north. The convention is that on a horizontal line east is to the right. Due north is associated with the top of a vertical line.

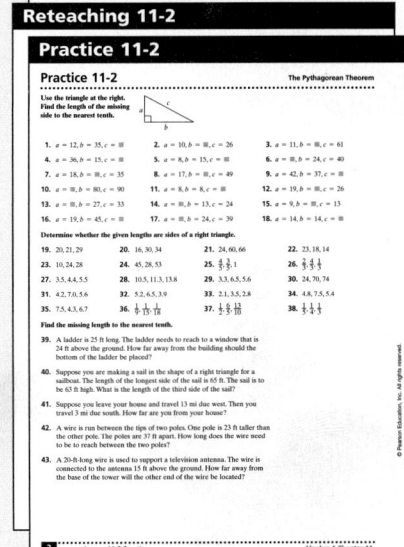

Math Tip

Exercises 33–36 Remind students that the longest side in a right triangle is the hypotenuse.

Error Prevention

Exercises 39–41 When applying the Pythagorean Theorem, students may incorrectly add the squares of the two given lengths, without checking to see if one of the lengths is the hypotenuse. Have students begin by writing the theorem's equation and determining if the value of the hypotenuse is known.

Determine whether the given lengths can be sides of a right triangle.

33. $1, \sqrt{3}, 2$ yes   **34.** $\sqrt{2}, \sqrt{2}, 4$ no   **35.** $\sqrt{6.2}, \sqrt{2.8}, 3$ **36.** $\frac{3}{4}, 1, 1\frac{1}{4}$ yes
                                                                                                yes

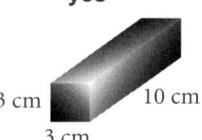 **37. Manufacturing** What is the diameter of the smallest circular opening through which the rectangular rod shown at the right will fit? Round to the nearest tenth. **4.2 cm**

3 cm   10 cm   3 cm

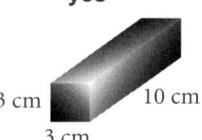 **38. Physics** Two utility vehicles at a 90° angle to each other try to pull a third vehicle out of the snow. If one utility vehicle exerts a force of 600 lb, and the other exerts a force of 800 lb, what is the resulting force on the vehicle stuck in the snow? **1000 lb**

Find the missing length to the nearest tenth.

39. 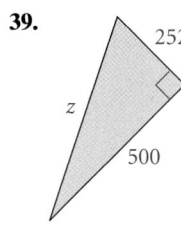   **40.** 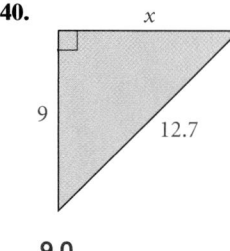   **41.**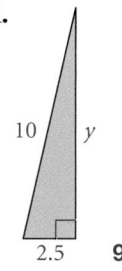

252, z, 500 x, 9, 12.7   10, y, 2.5

559.9   **9.0**   **9.7**

42a. These lengths could be 2 legs or one leg and the hypotenuse.

b. about 12.8 in. or 6 in.

43a. $6^2 + 8^2 = 36 + 64 = 100 = 10^2$

b. 5; 12; 7; 41

c. Answers may vary. Sample: 10, 24, 26

42. You know that two sides of a right triangle measure 10 in. and 8 in.
  a. Writing Explain why this is not enough information to be sure of finding the length of the third side. **See left.**
  b. Give two possible values for the length of the third side.

43. Any set of three positive integers that satisfies the relationship $a^2 + b^2 = c^2$ is called a *Pythagorean triple*. **See left.**
  a. Verify that the numbers 6, 8, and 10 form a Pythagorean triple.
  b. Copy the table at the right. Complete the table so that the values in each row form a Pythagorean triple.
  c. Open-Ended Find a Pythagorean triple that does not appear in the table.

a	b	c
3	4	■
5	■	13
■	24	25
9	40	■

44. Solar Power Solar cars use panels built out of photovoltaic cells, which convert sunlight into electricity. Consider a car like the one shown. Not counting the driver's "bubble," the panels form a rectangle.
  a. The length of the rectangle is 13 ft and the diagonal is 14.7 ft. Find the width. Round to the nearest tenth of a foot. **6.9 ft**
  b. Find the area of the rectangle. **89.2 ft²**
  c. The panels produce a maximum power of about 11 watts/ft². Find the maximum power produced by the panels on the car. Round to the nearest watt. **981 watts**

Real-World Connection

This solar-powered car only weighs 110 lb. It can reach a top speed of 80 mi/h.

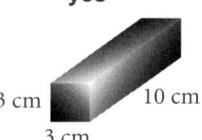 **45. Construction** A carpenter braces an 8 ft × 10 ft wall by nailing a board diagonally across the wall. How long is the bracing board? **12.8 ft**

46. a. Open-Ended Find a right triangle that has legs with irrational length and a hypotenuse with a rational length.
  b. Use a calculator to find the area of your triangle. Round to the nearest tenth.
  Answers may vary. Samples: a. $\sqrt{5}, \sqrt{20}, 5$ **b. 5 units²**

pages 587–590   Exercises

48. An integer has 2 as a factor; the integer is even; if an integer is even, then it has 2 as a factor; true.

49. A figure is a square; the figure is a rectangle; if a figure is a rectangle then the figure is a square; false.

50. You are in Brazil; you are south of the equator; if you are south of the equator you are in Brazil; false.

51. An angle is a right angle; its measure is 90°; if the measure of an angle is 90°, then it is a right angle; true.

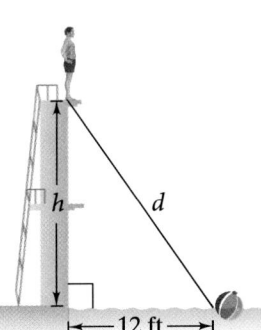

47. Diving Suppose you are standing at the top of a diving platform h feet tall. Looking down, you see a ball on the water 12 feet from the bottom of the diving platform as in the diagram at the left.
  a. Find the distance d to the ball if $h = 6$ feet. **10 ft**
  b. Find the distance d to the ball if $h = 12$ feet. **≈14.4 ft**
  c. Suppose you know the distance d to the ball is 16 feet. About how tall is the diving platform? **≈13.9 ft**
  d. **Critical Thinking** Could the distance d to the ball be 7 feet? Explain. **No; the hypotenuse d must be longer than each leg.**

State the hypothesis and the conclusion of each conditional. Then write the converse. Tell whether the converse is true or false. 48–51. See margin p. 588.

48. If an integer has 2 as a factor, then the integer is even.

49. If a figure is a square, then the figure is a rectangle.

50. If you are in Brazil, then you are south of the equator.

51. If an angle is a right angle, then its measure is 90°.

52. Geometry The yellow, green, and blue figures at the right are squares. Use the Pythagorean Theorem to find the area of the blue square. **52 units²**

53. Geometry The diagonal of a square measures $6\sqrt{2}$ in. Find the length of the side of the square. **6 in.**

C **Challenge**

Use the Pythagorean Theorem to find s. Express s as a radical expression in simplest form.

54. 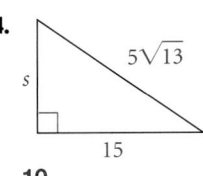 **55.** 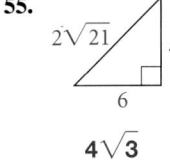 **56.** **5**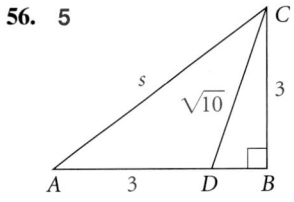

57. Geometry The lengths of the sides of a right triangle are three consecutive integers. Write and solve an equation to find the three integers. $n^2 + (n + 1)^2 = (n + 2)^2$; **3, 4, 5**

58. a. Critical Thinking The vertex of the right angle of a right triangle is at the origin of coordinate axes. The length of the horizontal side is 5 units. The length of the vertical side is 7 units. The triangle is located in Quadrant II. Sketch the graph. **See left.**
  b. Find the length of the hypotenuse in simplified radical form. $\sqrt{74}$

58a.
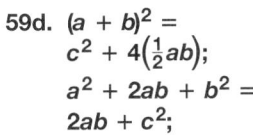

59. On graph paper, draw a right triangle like the one at the right. Then draw the square by drawing four right triangles as shown.
  a. Find the area of the larger square. Write your answer as a trinomial. $a^2 + 2ab + b^2$
  b. Find the area for the smaller square. Write your answer as a monomial. c^2
  c. Find the area of each triangle in terms of a and b. $\frac{ab}{2}$
  d. The area of the larger square equals the sum of the area of the smaller square and the areas of the four triangles. Write this equation and simplify.
  e. What do you notice about the equation you wrote for part (d)?

59d. $(a + b)^2 =$ $c^2 + 4\left(\frac{1}{2}ab\right)$; $a^2 + 2ab + b^2 =$ $2ab + c^2$; $a^2 + b^2 = c^2$
  e. This equation is the same as the Pythagorean Thm.

Lesson Quiz 11-2

1. Find the missing length to the nearest tenth. **16.6**

2. Find the missing length to the nearest tenth. **5.7**
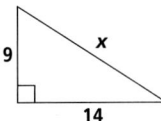

3. A triangle has sides of lengths 12 in., 14 in., and 16 in. Is the triangle a right triangle? **no**

4. A triangular flag is attached to a post. The bottom of the flag is 48 in. above the ground. How far from the ground is the top of the flag? **57 in.**
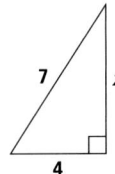

Alternative Assessment

Group students in pairs. Instruct each student to sketch a right triangle and write the lengths of any two sides on the triangle. Have each student determine the third side of his or her partner's triangle.

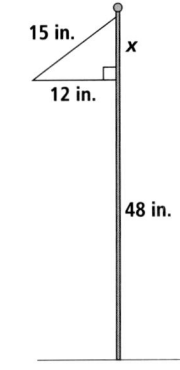

589

Exercises 62–64 Tell students they don't necessarily have to find the missing lengths if they use rules they've learned in this lesson. Remind them that c is always the longest side, and that a and b are interchangeable names of legs because of the commutative property.

pages 587–590   Exercises

65. [2] It is a right triangle. Substitute 17, the longest side, for c and substitute the other lengths for a and b in the Pythagorean Thm.

$$8^2 + 15^2 \stackrel{?}{=} 17^2$$
$$64 + 225 \stackrel{?}{=} 289$$
$$289 = 289 \checkmark$$

[1] incorrect equation OR incorrect explanation

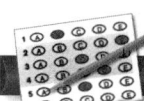

Standardized Test Prep

Multiple Choice

60. Find the approximate length of the hypotenuse of a right triangle with leg lengths 8.4 cm and 7.6 cm. **D**
   A. 4.00 cm   B. 5.66 cm   C. 7.99 cm   D. 11.33 cm

61. Find the length of the leg of a right triangle with one leg length $2\sqrt{3}$ and hypotenuse length $3\sqrt{3}$. **H**
   F. $\sqrt{3}$ G. $\sqrt{14}$ H. $\sqrt{15}$ I. $\sqrt{39}$

Quantitative Comparison

Compare the boxed quantity in Column A with the boxed quantity in Column B. Choose the best answer.
   A. The quantity in Column A is greater.
   B. The quantity in Column B is greater.
   C. The two quantities are equal.
   D. The relationship cannot be determined from the information given.

For Exercises 62–64, a and b represent the lengths of the legs and c represents the length of the hypotenuse of a right triangle.

Column A	Column B
62. b if $a = 9$ and $c = 10$ **B**	c if $a = 9$ and $b = 10$
63. c if $a = 15$ and $b = 11$ **C**	c if $a = 11$ and $b = 15$
64. a if $b = 10$ and $c = 22$ **A**	a if $b = 12$ and $c = 20$

Take It to the NET
Online lesson quiz at
www.PHSchool.com
Web Code: aea-1102

Short Response

65. The sides of a triangular garden are 8 ft, 17 ft, and 15 ft. Is the garden in the shape of a right triangle? Justify your answer. **See margin.**

Mixed Review

Lesson 11-1

Simplify each radical expression.

66. $\sqrt{8} \cdot \sqrt{6}$ $4\sqrt{3}$ 67. $\dfrac{\sqrt{12}}{\sqrt{18}}$ $\dfrac{\sqrt{6}}{3}$ 68. $\sqrt{5} \cdot \sqrt{10}$ $5\sqrt{2}$

69. $\sqrt{40b^5}$ $2b^2\sqrt{10b}$ 70. $\dfrac{\sqrt{2x^2}}{\sqrt{4x^6}}$ $\dfrac{\sqrt{2}}{2x^2}$ 71. $\sqrt{\dfrac{24v}{v^8}}$ $\dfrac{2\sqrt{6v}}{v^4}$

Lesson 10-3

Between which two consecutive integers is each square root?

72. $\sqrt{11}$ 3 and 4   73. $\sqrt{80}$ 8 and 9   74. $-\sqrt{51}$ -8 and -7 75. $\sqrt{125}$ 11 and 12

Tell whether each expression is rational or irrational.

76. $-\sqrt{1.44}$ rational   77. $\sqrt{130}$ irrational   78. $\sqrt{\dfrac{2}{3}}$ irrational   79. $\sqrt{\dfrac{1}{36}}$ rational

Lesson 9-2

Simplify each product.

80. $x(8x - 4)$ $8x^2 - 4x$ 81. $(4a + 5)3a$ $12a^2 + 15a$ 82. $6t^2(3t - 1)$ $18t^3 - 6t^2$

83. $2p^3(13 - 5p)$ $-10p^4 + 26p^3$ 84. $5b(3b^2 + b - 9)$ $15b^3 + 5b^2 - 45b$ 85. $-7v(v^3 - 6v + 1)$ $-7v^4 + 42v^2 - 7v$

590   Chapter 11   Radical Expressions and Equations

11-3

The Distance and Midpoint Formulas

 North Carolina Objectives

1.02 Use formulas and algebraic expressions, including iterative and recursive forms, to model and solve problems.
2.01 Find the lengths and midpoints of segments to solve problems.

Lesson Preview

What You'll Learn

 OBJECTIVE 1
To find the distance between two points on a coordinate plane

 OBJECTIVE 2
To find the coordinates of the midpoint of a line segment

...And Why

To solve problems involving geometric figures, as in Examples 2 and 4

✓ Check Skills You'll Need

(For help, go to Lessons 11-2 and 2-7.)

Find the length of the hypotenuse with the given leg lengths. If necessary, round to the nearest tenth.

1. $a = 3, b = 4$ **5**
2. $a = 2, b = 5$ **5.4**
3. $a = 3, b = 8$ **8.5**
4. $a = 7, b = 5$ **8.6**

For each set of values, find the mean.

5. $x_1 = 6, x_2 = 14$ **10**
6. $y_1 = -4, y_2 = 8$ **2**
7. $x_1 = -5, x_2 = -7$ **−6**
8. $y_1 = -10, y_2 = -3$ **−6.5**

New Vocabulary

• distance formula • midpoint • midpoint formula

 Interactive lesson includes instant self-check, tutorials, and activities.

OBJECTIVE

1 Finding the Distance Between Two Points

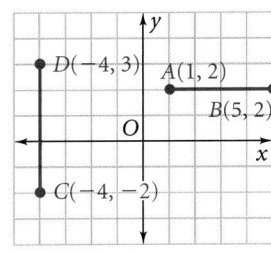

In the diagram at the left, $\overline{AB}$ is a horizontal line segment. You can find its length by subtracting the x-coordinate of A from the x-coordinate of B. The length of $\overline{AB}$ is $5 - 1 = 4$.

Similarly, you can find the length of $\overline{CD}$ by subtracting the y-coordinate of C from the y-coordinate of D. The length of $\overline{CD}$ is $3 - (-2) = 5$.

For any two points $P(x_1, y_1)$ and $Q(x_2, y_2)$ not on a horizontal or vertical line, you can graph the points and form a right triangle as shown at the right. You can then use the Pythagorean Theorem to find the distance between the points.

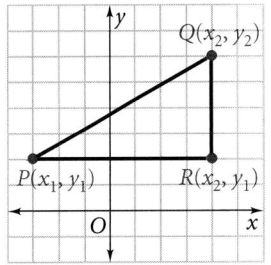

 Need Help?

PQ is the distance between points P and Q and the length of $\overline{PQ}$.

$(PQ)^2 = (PR)^2 + (RQ)^2$ **Use the Pythagorean Theorem.**

$(PQ)^2 = (x_2 - x_1)^2 + (y_2 - y_1)^2$ **Substitute.**

$\sqrt{(PQ)^2} = \sqrt{(x_2 - x_1)^2 + (y_2 - y_1)^2}$ **Find the principal square root of each side.**

$PQ = \sqrt{(x_2 - x_1)^2 + (y_2 - y_1)^2}$

The equation above is known as the distance formula.

 Key Concepts

Theorem	**The Distance Formula**

The distance d between any two points (x_1, y_1) and (x_2, y_2) is

$$d = \sqrt{(x_2 - x_1)^2 + (y_2 - y_1)^2}.$$

 ## Ongoing Assessment and Intervention

Before the Lesson
Diagnose prerequisite skills using:
• Check Skills You'll Need

During the Lesson
Monitor progress using:
• Check Understanding
• Additional Examples
• Standardized Test Prep

After the Lesson
Assess knowledge using:
• Lesson Quiz
• Computer Test Generator CD
• Chapter Checkpoint 1 (p. 597)

11-3

 North Carolina Objectives 1.02, 2.01

1. Plan

Lesson Preview

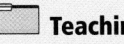 **Check Skills You'll Need**

The Pythagorean Theorem
Lesson 11-2: Example 1
Exercises 1–6
Extra Practice, p. 712

Measures of Central Tendency
Lesson 2-7: Example 1
Exercises 1–4
Extra Practice, p. 703

Lesson Resources

Teaching Resources
Practice, Reteaching, Enrichment
Checkpoint Quiz 1

Reaching All Students
Practice Workbook 11-3
Spanish Practice Workbook 11-3
Reading and Math Literacy 11B
Spanish Reading & Literacy 11B
Spanish Checkpoint Quiz 1
Hands-On Activities 27
Basic Algebra Planning Guide 11-3

Presentation Assistant Plus!
Transparencies
• Check Skills You'll Need 11-3
• Additional Examples 11-3
• Student Edition Answers 11-3
• Lesson Quiz 11-3
PH Presentation Pro CD 11-3

 PRENTICE HALL ASSESSMENT SYSTEM

Checkpoint Quiz 1
Computer Test Generator CD

 Technology
Resource Pro® CD-ROM
Computer Test Generator CD
Prentice Hall Presentation Pro CD

 **www.PHSchool.com**
Student Site
• Teacher Web Code: aek-5500
• Self-grading Lesson Quiz
Teacher Center
• Lesson Planner
• Resources

Plus **iTEXT**

2. Teach

Professional Development

Math Background

The Midpoint Formula says that the coordinates of the midpoint of a line segment are the mean of the x-coordinates of the endpoints and the mean of the y-coordinates of the endpoints of the line segment.

OBJECTIVE
1 Teaching Notes

1 **EXAMPLE** Math Tip

Students may be concerned about which of the two points to call (x_1, y_1). Have students calculate the distance twice, using each point as (x_1, y_1). Since the distances are squared, the order in which students choose the points does not matter.

Additional Examples

1 Find the distance between $F(6, -9)$ and $G(9, -4)$.
about 5.8 units

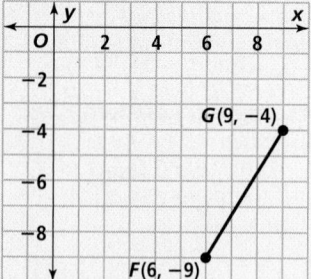

2 Find the exact lengths of each side of quadrilateral $EFGH$. Then find the perimeter to the nearest tenth. $EF = \sqrt{29}$, $FG = \sqrt{26}$, $GH = 5$, $EH = \sqrt{50}$; 22.6 units

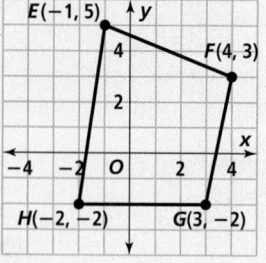

You find an *exact* distance by substituting values in the formula and simplifying the radical expressions. You find an *approximate* distance by using a calculator to estimate when a radical expression is not a perfect square.

1 **EXAMPLE** Using the Distance Formula

Find the distance between $T(1, -5)$ and $V(3, -2)$.

$d = \sqrt{(x_2 - x_1)^2 + (y_2 - y_1)^2}$ Use the distance formula.

$d = \sqrt{(3 - 1)^2 + [-2 - (-5)]^2}$ Substitute (3, −2) for (x_2, y_2) and (1, −5) for (x_1, y_1).

$d = \sqrt{(2)^2 + (3)^2}$ Simplify within parentheses.

$d = \sqrt{13}$ Simplify to find the exact distance.

$d \approx 3.6$ Use a calculator. Round to the nearest tenth.

The distance between T and V is about 3.6 units.

✓ **Check Understanding** **1** Find the distance between $M(-2, 1)$ and $N(-5, 4)$. Round to the nearest tenth.
≈4.2 units

You can use the distance formula to find the lengths of the sides of a geometric figure drawn on a coordinate plane. When adding values that are square roots, use a calculator to add before you round the answer.

2 **EXAMPLE** Finding Lengths of Sides

Find the exact lengths of each side of quadrilateral $ABCD$. Then find the perimeter to the nearest tenth.

$AB = \sqrt{[3 - (-2)]^2 + (4 - 2)^2}$ $BC = 4 - (-3) = 7$

$= \sqrt{5^2 + 2^2}$

$= \sqrt{25 + 4}$

$= \sqrt{29}$

$CD = \sqrt{(-3 - 3)^2 + [-2 - (-3)]^2}$ $AD = \sqrt{[-3 - (-2)]^2 + (-2 - 2)^2}$

$= \sqrt{(-6)^2 + 1^2}$ $= \sqrt{(-1)^2 + (-4)^2}$

$= \sqrt{36 + 1}$ $= \sqrt{1 + 16}$

$= \sqrt{37}$ $= \sqrt{17}$

The perimeter $= \sqrt{29} + 7 + \sqrt{37} + \sqrt{17} \approx 22.6$ units.

Calculator Hint

You find the perimeter by pressing $\sqrt{}$ 29 + 7 + $\sqrt{}$ 37 + $\sqrt{}$ 17 **ENTER**.

✓ **Check Understanding** **2** **a.** Find the perimeter of triangle RST below. **≈27.2 units**

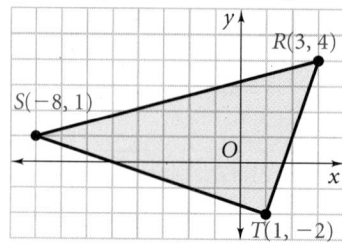

b. $(RS)^2 = (RT)^2 + (ST)^2$
or $(\sqrt{130})^2 = (\sqrt{40})^2 + (\sqrt{90})^2$

b. Critical Thinking Verify that this triangle is a right triangle.

592   Chapter 11   Radical Expressions and Equations

🧑‍🤝‍🧑 Reaching All Students

| **Below Level** In Example 3, show students that the coordinates of the midpoint are the averages of the endpoint coordinates. | **Advanced Learners** Have students use the distance formula to verify the coordinates found with the midpoint formula in Example 3. | **English Learners** See note on page 595. **Error Prevention** See note on page 594. |

592

Finding the Midpoint of a Line Segment

The **midpoint** of $\overline{AB}$ is the point M that divides the segment into two equal segments, such that $AM = MB$.

 Key Concepts

Rule	The Midpoint Formula

The midpoint M of a line segment with endpoints $A(x_1, y_1)$ and $B(x_2, y_2)$ is
$$\left(\frac{x_1 + x_2}{2}, \frac{y_1 + y_2}{2}\right).$$

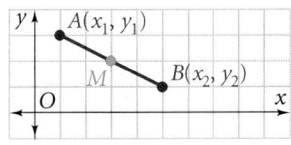

3 EXAMPLE Using the Midpoint Formula

Geometry Find the midpoint of $\overline{CD}$.

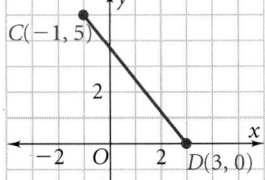

$\left(\dfrac{x_1 + x_2}{2}, \dfrac{y_1 + y_2}{2}\right) = \left(\dfrac{(-1) + 3}{2}, \dfrac{5 + 0}{2}\right)$ Substitute $(-1, 5)$ for (x_1, y_1) and $(3, 0)$ for (x_2, y_2).

$= \left(\dfrac{2}{2}, \dfrac{5}{2}\right)$ Simplify each numerator.

$= \left(1, 2\frac{1}{2}\right)$ Simplify $\frac{2}{2}$ and write $\frac{5}{2}$ as a mixed number.

The midpoint of $\overline{CD}$ is $\left(1, 2\frac{1}{2}\right)$.

✔ **Check Understanding** **3** Find the midpoint of $\overline{PQ}$.

$\left(1, \frac{1}{2}\right)$

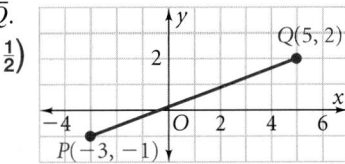

If you know the coordinates of the endpoints of a diameter of a circle, you can use the midpoint formula to find the coordinates of the center of the circle.

4 EXAMPLE Finding the Center of a Circle

Geometry A circle is drawn on a coordinate plane as shown at the left. The endpoints of a diameter are $(-1, 5)$ and $(4, -3)$. What is the center of the circle?

The center of the circle is the midpoint of a diameter.

$\left(\dfrac{x_1 + x_2}{2}, \dfrac{y_1 + y_2}{2}\right) = \left(\dfrac{-1 + 4}{2}, \dfrac{5 + (-3)}{2}\right)$ Substitute $(-1, 5)$ for (x_1, y_1) and $(4, -3)$ for (x_2, y_2).

$= \left(\dfrac{3}{2}, \dfrac{2}{2}\right) = \left(1\frac{1}{2}, 1\right)$

The coordinates of the center of the circle are $\left(1\frac{1}{2}, 1\right)$.

✔ **Check Understanding** **4** $\overline{AB}$ is a diameter of a circle. The coordinates of A are $(-4, 7)$ and the coordinates of B are $(-8, -2)$. Find the center of the circle. $\left(-6, 2\frac{1}{2}\right)$

---

3 EXAMPLE Teaching Tip

Show students that the formula averages the x-coordinates and the y-coordinates of the endpoints to find the midpoint of a line segment.

Additional Examples

3 Find the midpoint of $\overline{CD}$.
$M\left(1, 4\frac{1}{2}\right)$

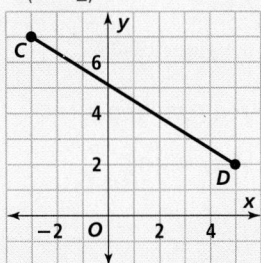

4 A circle is drawn on a coordinate plane. The endpoints of a diameter are $(4, -3)$ and $(-3, 5)$. What is the center of the circle? $\left(\frac{1}{2}, 1\right)$

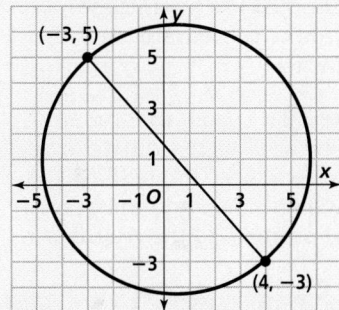

Closure

Ask: *What is the distance formula and why is it useful? What is the midpoint formula and why is it useful?* The distance formula is $\sqrt{(x_2 - x_1)^2 + (y_2 - y_1)^2}$. It is used to find the distance between any two points on a coordinate plane. The midpoint formula is $\left(\dfrac{x_1 + x_2}{2}, \dfrac{y_1 + y_2}{2}\right)$. It is used to find the point that is halfway between two given points on a coordinate plane.

3. Practice

Assignment Guide

 **Objective**

Ⓐ Ⓑ **Core** 1–8, 17–25, 30–31

Ⓒ **Extension** 38

 **Objective**

Ⓐ Ⓑ **Core** 9–16, 26–29, 32–37

Ⓒ **Extension** 39–40

Standardized Test Prep 41–47

Mixed Review 48–65

Error Prevention

Exercises 1–6 Point out to students that when they enter points with negative coordinates into the distance formula, they may easily overlook a negative or a subtraction sign. Encourage them to first use parentheses around the coordinates as they substitute.

Exercise 31 Encourage students to draw a set of coordinate axes. Have them place the political rally at (0, 0) and then add the details of the problem to the coordinate grid.

Enrichment 11-3

Reteaching 11-3

Practice 11-3

Practice 11-3 — The Distance and Midpoint Formulas

EXERCISES

For more practice, see *Extra Practice*.

Practice and Problem Solving

Ⓐ **Practice by Example**

Example 1
(page 592)

Find the distance between each pair of points. If necessary, round to the nearest tenth.

1. $(7, -3), (-8, -3)$ **15**   **2.** $(-2, 7), (-2, -7)$ **14**   **3.** $(0, 0), (6, -8)$ **10**

4. $(-4, -4), (4, 4)$ **11.3**   **5.** $(9, 10), (11, 12)$ **2.8**   **6.** $(3, -2), (-1, 5)$ **8.1**

Example 2
(page 592)

Geometry **Find the perimeter of each figure. Round to the nearest tenth.**

7. **16**

8. **21.6**

Example 3
(page 593)

Find the midpoint of each segment with the given endpoints.

9. $A(2, 5)$ and $B(0, 7)$ **(1, 6)**

10. $X(-3, 14)$ and $Y(1, 10)$ **(−1, 12)**

11. $M(4, 1)$ and $N(-4, -1)$ **(0, 0)**

12. $R(5, 3)$ and $S(-9, 3)$ **(−2, 3)**

13. $C(12, -2)$ and $D(-2, -9)$ $\left(5, -5\frac{1}{2}\right)$

14. $P(0, 6)$ and $Q(-5, -8)$ $\left(-2\frac{1}{2}, -1\right)$

Example 4
(page 593)

15. $\overline{PQ}$ is a diameter of a circle. The coordinates of P are $(-1, 8)$ and the coordinates of Q are $(-7, 0)$. Find the center of the circle. **(−4, 4)**

16. $\overline{RS}$ is a diameter of a circle. The coordinates of R are $(5, -11)$ and the coordinates of S are $(12, -7)$. Find the center of the circle. $\left(8\frac{1}{2}, -9\right)$

Ⓑ **Apply Your Skills**

Find AB. Round to the nearest tenth.

17. **10.6**

18. **9.4**

Find the lengths of the sides of a triangle with the given vertices. If necessary, round to the nearest tenth. 19–24. See margin.

19. $A(2, 2), B(6, 3), C(5, 6)$

20. $D(-1, -7), E(-2, -1), F(-5, -3)$

21. $R(-2, 2), S(1, 1), T(-3, -3)$

22. $M(-1, -5), N(4, -4), P(2, -1)$

23. $J(3, 5), K(3, 9), L(5, 8)$

24. $T(-1, 4), U(6, 7), V(2, -9)$

25. Geometry A quadrilateral is a parallelogram if a pair of its opposite sides are congruent and parallel.

a. For the figure at the left, find the lengths of $\overline{OR}$ and $\overline{ST}$.

b. Find the slope of $\overline{OR}$ and $\overline{ST}$. $\frac{5}{2}; \frac{5}{2}$ $OR = \sqrt{29}, ST = \sqrt{29}$

c. Is $ORST$ a parallelogram? **yes**

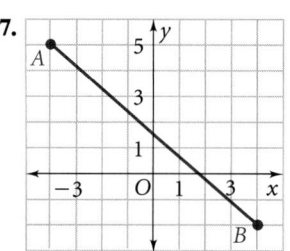

594 Chapter 11 Radical Expressions and Equations

---

pages 594–597 **Exercises**

19. $AB \approx 4.1$; $BC \approx 3.2$; $AC = 5$

20. $DE \approx 6.1$; $EF \approx 3.6$; $DF \approx 5.7$

21. $RS \approx 3.2$; $ST \approx 5.7$; $RT \approx 5.1$

22. $MN \approx 5.1$; $NP \approx 3.6$; $MP = 5$

23. $JK = 4$; $KL \approx 2.2$; $LJ \approx 3.6$

24. $TU \approx 7.6$; $UV \approx 6.5$; $VT \approx 13.3$

 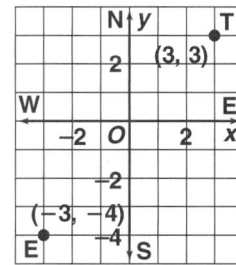
26. Archaeology In an archaeological excavation, a grid resembling the grid at the right is used to identify the location of artifacts. On the grid, 80R30 means 80 ft north and 30 ft east. In a coordinate plane, this location corresponds to the ordered pair (30, 80). **a–c. See margin.**
 a. Rewrite 80R20 and 30L40 as ordered pairs.
 b. Find the distance between the two locations.
 c. Find the midpoint between the two locations.

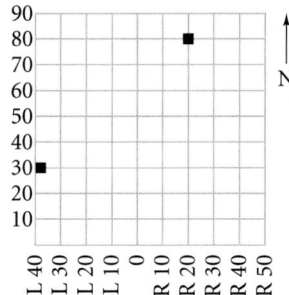

27. Writing Summarize the distance formula and the midpoint formula. Use examples to show the use of each formula. **See margin.**

28. a. Open-Ended Suppose the distance between two points on a coordinate plane is between 10 and 13 units. Find two points A and B not directly above or across from each other that meet this requirement.
 b. Plot your points on graph paper. **a–c. Check students' work.**
 c. Verify that your points satisfy the requirement by finding AB.

29. a. Graph Mr. Tanaka's and Ms. Elisa's locations on a coordinate grid with the substation as the origin. **See left.**

29a.
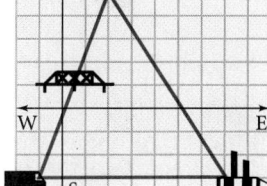

 Ms. Elisa   Mr. Tanaka

 b. What are the coordinates of the point where they will meet? $\left(0, -\frac{1}{2}\right)$
 c. Describe their meeting place in miles north or south and east or west of the substation. **one half mile south of the substation**

30. Hiking The Gato and Wilson families are staying at a campground. The Gatos leave camp and hike 2 km west and 5 km south. The Wilsons leave camp and hike 1 km east and 4 km north. How far apart are the families? **about 9.5 km apart**

31. a. Flight Two news helicopters are flying at the same altitude on their way to a political rally. Helicopter A is 20 mi due west of the rally. Helicopter B is 15 mi south and 15 mi east of the rally. How far apart are they? **38.1 mi**
 b. How far from the rally is each helicopter? **20 mi, 21.2 mi**
 c. Both helicopters are flying at an average of 80 mi/h. How many minutes will it take each of them to arrive at the scene? **15 min, 16 min**

32. Geometry A quadrilateral is a rhombus if all four sides are congruent. Quadrilateral $PQRS$ has vertices $P(6, 5)$, $Q(2, 2)$, $R(6, -1)$, and $S(10, 2)$. Is $PQRS$ a rhombus? **Yes; all sides are congruent.**

33. a. Find the midpoint of the line segment with endpoints $P(-24, -7)$ and $Q(-30, -3)$. Identify the midpoint as R. **R(−27, −5)**
 b. Reasoning Verify that $PR = RQ$. **$PR = \sqrt{13} \approx 3.6$ $RQ = \sqrt{13} \approx 3.6$**

34. a. Transportation On the grid at the left, each unit represents one mile. A van breaks down on its way to a factory. The driver calls a garage for a tow truck. There is a bridge halfway between the garage and the van. How far is the bridge from the van? **about 4.3 mi**
 b. The van is towed to the factory and then to the garage. How many miles did the truck tow the van? **about 17.4 mi**

English Learners
Exercise 29 Ask a student to explain the meaning of "Copy that," spoken by Mr. Tanaka. Explain that Ms. Elisa and Mr. Tanaka are speaking over two-way radios. If students are unsure of the meaning, explain that "copy that" is radio shorthand for "I understand what you are saying."

26a. **(20, 80), (−40, 30)**
 b. **78.1 ft**
 c. **(−10, 55) or 55L10**

27. **Answers may vary. Sample: Suppose you have (1, 1) and (4, −3). To find the distance, square the difference between the x-coordinates. Square the difference between the y-coordinates. Find the sum and take the square root, so $\sqrt{9 + 16} = 5$. To find the midpoint, add x-coordinates together and divide by 2. Repeat for y-coordinates. So, $\left(\frac{1 + 4}{2}, \frac{1 - 3}{2}\right) = \left(\frac{5}{2}, -1\right)$.**

Lesson Quiz 11-3

1. Find the distance between $M(2, -1)$ and $N(-4, 3)$ to the nearest tenth. **7.2**

2. Find the distance between $P(-2.5, 3.5)$ and $R(-7.5, 8.5)$ to the nearest tenth. **7.1**

3. Find the midpoint of $\overline{AB}$ for $A(3, 6)$ and $B(0, 2)$. $(1\frac{1}{2}, 4)$

4. Find the midpoint of $\overline{CD}$ for $C(6, -4)$ and $D(12, -2)$. $(9, -3)$

5. Find the perimeter of triangle RST to the nearest tenth of a unit. **9.5 units**

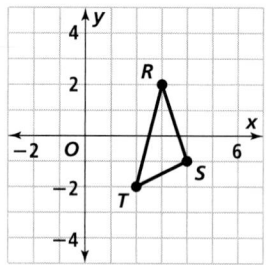

Alternative Assessment

Instruct each student to write the coordinates for two points on a piece of paper. Then find the distance between the points, and also the midpoint of that line segment. Have students exchange papers with classmates to check their work.

35a. $M(-0.5, 3)$; $N(5.5, 3)$

b. They are equal.

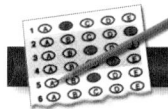 **Challenge**

38b. Answers may vary. Sample: $(5, 0)$, $(0, 5)$, $(-5, 0)$, $(0, -5)$, $(3, -4)$, $(-3, 4)$, $(-3, -4)$

39a. $y = -\frac{4}{3}x + 1$

b. $\left(\frac{9}{5}, -\frac{7}{5}\right)$

35. a. Geometry Quadrilateral $ABCD$ is a trapezoid. Find the midpoints of $\overline{AB}$ and $\overline{CD}$. Label the midpoints M and N.
b. Compare the average of the lengths of $\overline{BC}$ and $\overline{AD}$ to the length of $\overline{MN}$. **See left.**

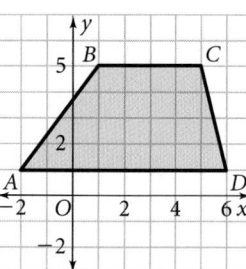

36. $\overline{EF}$ is a diameter of a circle. The coordinates of E are $(x - 3, y + 2)$ and the coordinates of F are $(x + 3, y - 2)$. Find the center of the circle. (x, y)

37. Critical Thinking If the midpoint of a line segment is at the origin, what must be true about the coordinates of the endpoints of the segment? **They are opposites.**

38. a. What is the distance of the point $(3, 4)$ from the origin? **5 units**
b. Find seven other points that are the same distance from the origin. **See left.**
c. Graph $(3, 4)$ and the seven points you named in part (b). What figure do these points suggest? **circle**

39. Use the steps that follow to find the distance between the parallel lines ℓ and m as graphed at the right. **a–b. See left.**
a. An equation for line ℓ is $y = \frac{3}{4}x + 1$.
An equation for line m is $y = \frac{3}{4}x - \frac{11}{4}$.
Write an equation for line n, which is perpendicular to line ℓ at point B.
b. Use the equations of lines m and n to find their point of intersection.
c. Find the distance between points B and C. **3**

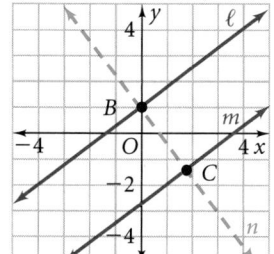

40. Is the point $(-2, 3)$ the center of a circle that passes through $(-6, 0), (1, -1)$, and $(-5, 7)$? Verify your answer.
Yes; the distance from each point to the center is 5.

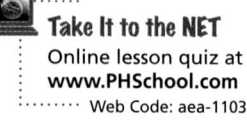

Standardized Test Prep

Gridded Response

41. Find the distance between $(-5, 10)$ and $(8, -4)$. Round to the nearest tenth. **19.1**

42. Find the x-coordinate of the midpoint of the segment with endpoints at $(12, 0)$ and $(-2, -6)$. **5**

43. Find the perimeter of the triangle with vertices at $(4.5, 0.5), (-1.5, -2.5)$, and $(-4.5, 3.5)$. Round to the nearest tenth. **22.9**

44. $\overline{AB}$ is the diameter of a circle. The coordinates of A are $(17, -1)$ and the coordinates of B are $(10, -9)$. What is the y-coordinate of the center of the circle? **−5**

45. The distance between two points with coordinates $(3, -1)$ and $(x, 4)$ is 5. What is the value of x? **3**

46. The midpoint of the segment with endpoints at $(-1, y)$ and $(7, 16)$ is $(3, 4)$. What is the value of y? **−8**

47. One hiker is 4 mi west and 3 mi north of the campground. Another is 6 mi east and 3 mi south of the campground. How many miles apart are the hikers? Round to the nearest tenth. **11.7**

Take It to the NET
Online lesson quiz at
www.PHSchool.com
Web Code: aea-1103

Lesson 11-2

For the values given, a and b are legs of a right triangle, and c is the hypotenuse. Find the length of the missing side of each right triangle. If necessary, round to the nearest tenth.

48. $a = 2, b = 11$ **11.2**

49. $a = 8, c = 13$ **10.2**

50. $a = 10, b = 24$ **26**

51. $a = \sqrt{15}, c = \sqrt{27}$ **3.5**

52. $a = 5, c = \sqrt{89}$ **8**

53. $a = 0.9, b = 4$ **4.1**

Lesson 10-4

Solve each equation by finding square roots. If the equation has no solution, write *no solution*.

54. $t^2 - 196 = 0$ **−14, 14**

55. $3k^2 = 300$ **−10, 10**

56. $5y^2 + 1 = 0$ **no solution**

57. $8m^2 - 9 = 191$ **−5, 5**

58. $16q^2 + 9 = 4$ **no solution**

59. $9b^2 + 1 = 5$ $-\frac{2}{3}, \frac{2}{3}$

Lesson 9-3

Find each product.

60. $(k + 3)(k + 8)$ $k^2 + 11k + 24$

61. $(v - 5)(v + 7)$ $v^2 + 2v - 35$

62. $(2p + 1)(p - 9)$ $2p^2 - 17p - 9$

63. $(8w^2 + 11)(w^2 + 1)$ $8w^4 + 19w^2 + 11$

64. $(7t - 2)(t^2 + t + 1)$ $7t^3 + 5t^2 + 5t - 2$

65. $(6c + 3)(c^2 - 5c + 8)$ $6c^3 - 27c^2 + 33c + 24$

Checkpoint Quiz 1 — Lessons 11-1 through 11-3

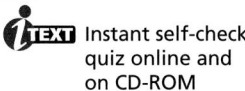 Instant self-check quiz online and on CD-ROM

Simplify each radical expression.

1. $\sqrt{8} \cdot \sqrt{20}$ $4\sqrt{10}$

2. $\sqrt{45} \cdot \sqrt{3}$ $3\sqrt{15}$

3. $\sqrt{\frac{12}{27}}$ $\frac{2}{3}$

4. $\frac{5}{\sqrt{2x^3}}$ $\frac{5\sqrt{2x}}{2x^2}$

Find each missing length. If necessary, round to the nearest tenth.

5.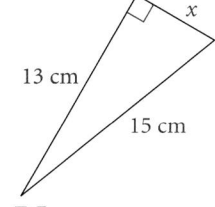
13 cm, 15 cm, 7.5 cm, x

6.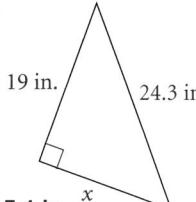
19 in., 24.3 in., 15.1 in., x

7.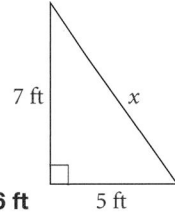
7 ft, x, 8.6 ft, 5 ft

Determine whether the given lengths can be sides of a right triangle.

8. 9 in., 12 in., 15 in. **yes**

9. 2 m, 4 m, 5 m **no**

10. a. Find the midpoint of the segment shown at the right. $\left(0, \frac{1}{2}\right)$

b. Then find the length of the segment to the nearest tenth. **9.4**

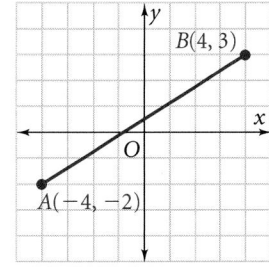
$B(4, 3)$, $A(-4, -2)$

Standardized Test Prep

A sheet of blank grids is available in the Test-Taking Strategies with Transparencies booklet. Give this sheet to students for practice with filling in the grids.

Resources

For additional practice with a variety of test item formats:
- Standardized Test Prep, 633
- Test-Taking Strategies, p. 628
- Test-Taking Strategies with Transparencies

Exercises 45, 46 Tell students to write the appropriate formula, substitute the given values, and solve for the missing information.

Chapter Checkpoint 1

To check understanding of Lessons 11-1 to 11-3:

Checkpoint Quiz 1 (p. 597)

Teaching Resources

Checkpoint Quiz 1 (also in Prentice Hall Assessment System)

Reaching All Students

Reading and Math Literacy 11B

Spanish versions available

Special Right Triangles

Students use the Pythagorean Theorem, and what they know about the comparative lengths of the sides of an isosceles right triangle, to develop a formula for the length of the hypotenuse in a 45°-45°-90° triangle. They also develop a formula for the length of the longer leg of a 30°-60°-90° triangle using the Pythagorean Theorem, and use the fact that the shorter leg is half the length of the hypotenuse. Students must also be able to simplify radical expressions and find square roots.

Resources

 **Technology**
Computer Test Generator CD-ROM, Chapter 11, Extension Topics

Teaching Notes

If the length of the leg of an isosceles right triangle is given as an irrational number, then students may need to be reminded that multiplying $\sqrt{2}$ times the length of the leg will be the square root of the product. Example: If the length of the leg of an isosceles right triangle is $\sqrt{3}$ then the length of the hypotenuse is $\sqrt{2} \times \sqrt{3} = \sqrt{6}$. The same reasoning applies to the length of the longer leg of a 30°-60°-90° triangle if the measure of the shorter leg is irrational.

Extension

Special Right Triangles

Some right triangles have special properties. Consider the isosceles right triangle at the right. It is called a 45°-45°-90° triangle.

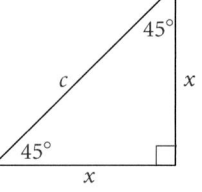

$c^2 = a^2 + b^2$	Use the Pythagorean Theorem.
$c^2 = x^2 + x^2$	Substitute x for b and for a.
$c^2 = 2x^2$	Simplify.
$\sqrt{c^2} = \sqrt{2x^2}$	Find the principal square root of each side.
$c = \sqrt{2} \cdot \sqrt{x^2}$	Use the Multiplication Property of Square Roots.
$c = \sqrt{2} \cdot x$, or $x\sqrt{2}$	Simplify.

> **Theorem** **45°-45°-90° Triangle Theorem**
>
> In a 45°-45°-90° triangle, the length of the hypotenuse is the length of the leg times $\sqrt{2}$.
>
> $$\text{hypotenuse} = \text{leg} \cdot \sqrt{2}$$

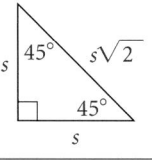

1 EXAMPLE Finding Lengths in a 45°-45°-90° Triangle

Find the length of the hypotenuse in the triangle at the right.

$$\text{hypotenuse} = \text{leg} \cdot \sqrt{2}$$

$x = 8 \cdot \sqrt{2}$ **The length of either leg is 8 in.**

≈ 11.3 **Round to the nearest tenth.**

The length of the hypotenuse is about 11.3 in.

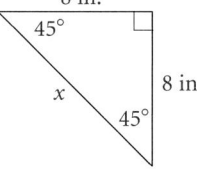

EXERCISES

Find the hypotenuse of each 45°-45°-90° triangle. Round to the nearest tenth.

1.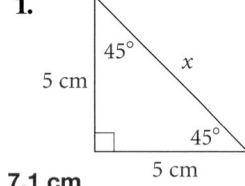

7.1 cm

2.

17.0 in.

3.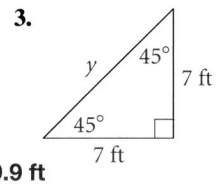

9.9 ft

4. A baseball diamond is a square. The distance from any base to the next base is 90 ft. How far is it from home plate to second base? (*Hint:* Draw a diagram.) **127.3 ft**

5. The hypotenuse of a 45°-45°-90° triangle is 40.2 ft long. How long is each leg? Round to the nearest tenth. **28.4 ft**

6. **Open-Ended** Draw and label a 45°-45°-90° triangle in which the leg length is irrational and the hypotenuse length is rational. **Answers may vary. Sample:**

legs of length $\sqrt{2}$ and hypotenuse of length 2

Another special right triangle is the 30°-60°-90° triangle. You can form two congruent 30°-60°-90° triangles by bisecting an angle of an equilateral triangle. As the diagram at the right shows, the length of the hypotenuse is twice the length of the shorter leg. You can use the Pythagorean Theorem to find the length of the longer leg b shown in the diagram at the right below.

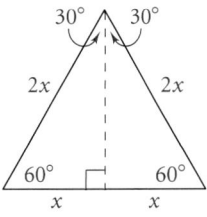

$$(2x)^2 = x^2 + b^2 \quad \text{Use the Pythagorean Theorem.}$$
$$4x^2 = x^2 + b^2 \quad \text{Simplify.}$$
$$3x^2 = b^2 \quad \text{Subtract } x^2 \text{ from each side.}$$
$$\sqrt{3x^2} = \sqrt{b^2} \quad \text{Find the principal square root of each side.}$$
$$\sqrt{3} \cdot \sqrt{x^2} = b \quad \text{Use the Multiplication Property of Square Roots.}$$
$$b = \sqrt{3} \cdot x \quad \text{Simplify.}$$

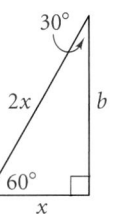

The length of the longer leg is $\sqrt{3} \cdot x$, or $x\sqrt{3}$.

Theorem	30°-60°-90° Triangle Theorem

In a 30°-60°-90° triangle, the length of the hypotenuse is twice the length of the shorter leg. The length of the longer leg is $\sqrt{3}$ times the length of the shorter leg.

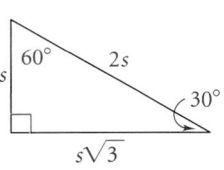

$$\text{hypotenuse} = 2 \cdot \text{shorter leg}$$
$$\text{longer leg} = \sqrt{3} \cdot \text{shorter leg}$$

2 EXAMPLE Finding Lengths in a 30°-60°-90° Triangle

Find the missing lengths in the triangle at the right.

$$\text{hypotenuse} = 2 \cdot \text{shorter leg}$$
$$x = 2 \cdot 9 \quad \text{The length of the shorter leg is 9.}$$
$$x = 18 \quad \text{Simplify.}$$
$$\text{longer leg} = \sqrt{3} \cdot \text{shorter leg}$$
$$y = 9 \cdot \sqrt{3} \quad \text{The length of the shorter leg is 9.}$$
$$y \approx 15.6 \quad \text{Simplify. Round to the nearest tenth.}$$

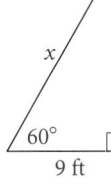

The length of the hypotenuse is 18 ft, and the length of the longer leg is about 15.6 ft.

EXERCISES

Find the missing lengths in each triangle. Round to the nearest tenth. 7–9. See margin.

7.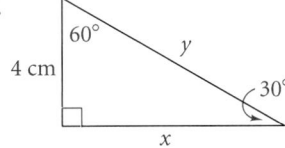

8.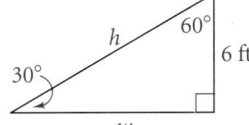

9.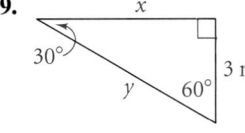

Extension   Special Right Triangles   **599**

pages 598–599   Extension

7. $x \approx 6.9$ cm; $y = 8$ cm

8. $h = 12$ ft; $w \approx 10.4$ ft

9. $x \approx 5.2$ m; $y = 6$ m

599

Math Tip
Students will usually use a calculator when finding lengths of sides with these two formulas. However, you might suggest that students learn the approximate values for the square roots of 2 and 3. This will enable students to quickly estimate the lengths of the unknown sides. Knowing that the square root of 2 is close to 1.4 and that the square root of 3 is close to 1.7 can also be very helpful when a calculator is not available. Knowing these two approximations will also help students when they are trying to determine if an answer is reasonable.

1. Plan

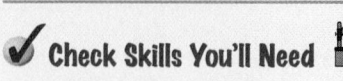

Lesson Preview

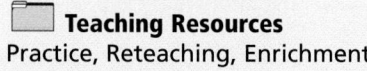 **Check Skills You'll Need**

Operations With Radical Expressions
Lesson 11-1: Examples 1, 2, 7
Exercises 1–12, 44–51
Extra Practice, p. 712

Lesson Resources

📁 **Teaching Resources**
Practice, Reteaching, Enrichment

👥 **Reaching All Students**
Practice Workbook 11-4
Spanish Practice Workbook 11-4
Basic Algebra Planning Guide 11-4

⏰ **Presentation Assistant Plus!**
Transparencies
• Check Skills You'll Need 11-4
• Additional Examples 11-4
• Student Edition Answers 11-4
• Lesson Quiz 11-4
PH Presentation Pro CD 11-4

PRENTICE HALL
 **ASSESSMENT SYSTEM**

Computer Test Generator CD

💿 **Technology**
Resource Pro® CD-ROM
Computer Test Generator CD
Prentice Hall Presentation Pro CD

🖥 **www.PHSchool.com**
Student Site
• Teacher Web Code: aek-5500
• Self-grading Lesson Quiz
Teacher Center
• Lesson Planner
• Resources

 Plus 🔲 **TEXT**

11-4 Operations With Radical Expressions

 North Carolina Objectives

1.01 Write equivalent forms of algebraic expressions to solve problems.

Lesson Preview

What You'll Learn

OBJECTIVE 1 To simplify sums and differences

OBJECTIVE 2 To simplify products and quotients

. . . And Why
To find the width of a painting, as in Example 6

✓ **Check Skills You'll Need** (For help, go to Lesson 11-1.)

Simplify each radical expression.

1. $\sqrt{52}$ $2\sqrt{13}$
2. $\sqrt{200}$ $10\sqrt{2}$
3. $4\sqrt{54}$ $12\sqrt{6}$
4. $\sqrt{125x^2}$ $5x\sqrt{5}$

Rationalize each denominator.

5. $\dfrac{\sqrt{3}}{\sqrt{11}}$ $\dfrac{\sqrt{33}}{11}$
6. $\dfrac{\sqrt{5}}{\sqrt{8}}$ $\dfrac{\sqrt{10}}{4}$
7. $\dfrac{\sqrt{15}}{\sqrt{2x}}$ $\dfrac{\sqrt{30x}}{2x}$

New Vocabulary • like radicals • unlike radicals • conjugates

---

📱 Interactive lesson includes instant self-check, tutorials, and activities.

OBJECTIVE 1

Simplifying Sums and Differences

For radical expressions, **like radicals** have the same radicand. **Unlike radicals** do not have the same radicand. For example, $4\sqrt{7}$ and $-12\sqrt{7}$ are like radicals, but $3\sqrt{11}$ and $2\sqrt{5}$ are unlike radicals. To simplify sums and differences, you use the Distributive Property to combine like radicals.

1 EXAMPLE Combining Like Radicals

Simplify $\sqrt{2} + 3\sqrt{2}$.

$\sqrt{2} + 3\sqrt{2} = 1\sqrt{2} + 3\sqrt{2}$ **Both terms contain $\sqrt{2}$.**

$\qquad\qquad\quad = (1 + 3)\sqrt{2}$ **Use the Distributive Property to combine like radicals.**

$\qquad\qquad\quad = 4\sqrt{2}$ **Simplify.**

✓ **Check Understanding** ❶ Simplify each expression.
a. $-3\sqrt{5} - 4\sqrt{5}$ $-7\sqrt{5}$
b. $\sqrt{10} - 5\sqrt{10}$ $-4\sqrt{10}$

You may need to simplify a radical expression to determine if you have like radicals.

Need Help?
Multiplication Property of Square Roots:
$\sqrt{ab} = \sqrt{a} \cdot \sqrt{b}$ and $\sqrt{a} \cdot \sqrt{b} = \sqrt{ab}$

2 EXAMPLE Simplifying to Combine Like Radicals

Simplify $7\sqrt{3} - \sqrt{12}$.

$7\sqrt{3} - \sqrt{12} = 7\sqrt{3} - \sqrt{4 \cdot 3}$ **4 is a perfect square and a factor of 12.**

$\qquad\qquad\quad = 7\sqrt{3} - \sqrt{4} \cdot \sqrt{3}$ **Use the Multiplication Property of Square Roots.**

$\qquad\qquad\quad = 7\sqrt{3} - 2\sqrt{3}$ **Simplify $\sqrt{4}$.**

$\qquad\qquad\quad = (7 - 2)\sqrt{3}$ **Use the Distributive Property to combine like radicals.**

$\qquad\qquad\quad = 5\sqrt{3}$ **Simplify.**

✓ **Check Understanding** ❷ Simplify each expression.
a. $3\sqrt{20} + 2\sqrt{5}$ $8\sqrt{5}$
b. $3\sqrt{3} - 2\sqrt{27}$ $-3\sqrt{3}$

⏱ **Ongoing Assessment and Intervention**

Before the Lesson
Diagnose prerequisite skills using:
• Check Skills You'll Need

During the Lesson
Monitor progress using:
• Check Understanding
• Additional Examples
• Standardized Test Prep

After the Lesson
Assess knowledge using:
• Lesson Quiz
• Computer Test Generator CD

When simplifying a radical expression like $\sqrt{3}(\sqrt{6} + 7)$, use the Distributive Property to multiply $\sqrt{3}$ times $(\sqrt{6} + 7)$.

3 EXAMPLE Using the Distributive Property

Simplify $\sqrt{3}(\sqrt{6} + 7)$.

$\sqrt{3}(\sqrt{6} + 7) = \sqrt{18} + 7\sqrt{3}$ **Use the Distributive Property.**

$= \sqrt{9} \cdot \sqrt{2} + 7\sqrt{3}$ **Use the Multiplication Property of Square Roots.**

$= 3\sqrt{2} + 7\sqrt{3}$ **Simplify.**

✓ **Check Understanding** **3** Simplify each radical expression.

a. $\sqrt{5}(2 + \sqrt{10})$
$2\sqrt{5} + 5\sqrt{2}$

b. $\sqrt{2x}(\sqrt{6x} - 11)$
$2x\sqrt{3} - 11\sqrt{2x}$

c. $\sqrt{5a}(\sqrt{5a} + 3)$
$5a + 3\sqrt{5a}$

If both radical expressions have two terms, you can multiply the same way you find the product of two binomials, by using FOIL.

4 EXAMPLE Simplifying Using FOIL

Simplify $(\sqrt{5} - 2\sqrt{15})(\sqrt{5} + \sqrt{15})$.

$(\sqrt{5} - 2\sqrt{15})(\sqrt{5} + \sqrt{15})$

$= \sqrt{25} + \sqrt{75} - 2\sqrt{75} - 2\sqrt{225}$ **Use FOIL.**

$= 5 - \sqrt{75} - 2(15)$ **Combine like radicals and simplify $\sqrt{25}$ and $\sqrt{225}$.**

$= 5 - \sqrt{25 \cdot 3} - 30$ **25 is a perfect square factor of 75.**

$= 5 - \sqrt{25} \cdot \sqrt{3} - 30$ **Use the Multiplication Property of Square Roots.**

$= 5 - 5\sqrt{3} - 30$ **Simplify $\sqrt{25}$.**

$= -25 - 5\sqrt{3}$ **Simplify.**

✓ **Check Understanding** **4** Simplify each radical expression.

a. $(2\sqrt{6} + 3\sqrt{3})(\sqrt{6} - 5\sqrt{3})$
$-33 - 21\sqrt{2}$

b. $(\sqrt{7} + 4)^2$
$23 + 8\sqrt{7}$

Conjugates are the sum and the difference of the same two terms. The radical expressions $\sqrt{5} + \sqrt{2}$ and $\sqrt{5} - \sqrt{2}$ are conjugates. The product of two conjugates results in a difference of two squares.

Need Help?

Remember that the difference of two squares can be factored as $(a + b)(a - b)$.

$(\sqrt{5} + \sqrt{2})(\sqrt{5} - \sqrt{2}) = (\sqrt{5})^2 - (\sqrt{2})^2$

$= 5 - 2$

$= 3$

Notice that the product of these conjugates has no radical.

You recall that a simplified radical expression has no radical in the denominator. When a denominator contains a sum or a difference including radical expressions, you can rationalize the denominator by multiplying the numerator and the denominator by the conjugate of the denominator. For example, to simplify a radical expression like $\frac{6}{\sqrt{5} - \sqrt{2}}$, you multiply by $\frac{\sqrt{5} + \sqrt{2}}{\sqrt{5} + \sqrt{2}}$.

Lesson 11-4 Operations With Radical Expressions **601**

---

2. Teach

Professional Development

Math Background

Unlike radicals, such as $\sqrt{2}$ and $\sqrt{3}$, are analogous to different variables, such as x and y. They cannot be combined by adding or subtracting.

OBJECTIVE
1 Teaching Notes

1 EXAMPLE Technology Tip

Suggest that students use a calculator to verify that the combining of like terms is correct. Find the value of the original equation and compare it to the value of the answer.

Additional Examples

1 Simplify $4\sqrt{3} + \sqrt{3}$. $5\sqrt{3}$

2 Simplify $8\sqrt{5} - \sqrt{45}$. $5\sqrt{5}$

OBJECTIVE
2 Teaching Notes

4 EXAMPLE Inclusion

Students with some kinds of vision problems will have difficulty distinguishing between the terms, especially when using FOIL, due to the distraction of so many radical signs. Suggest that they add extra space between the expressions and around each operation sign, and use arcs to connect each pair of terms to be multiplied.

Additional Examples

3 Simplify $\sqrt{5}(\sqrt{8} + 9)$.
$2\sqrt{10} + 9\sqrt{5}$

4 Simplify
$(\sqrt{6} - 3\sqrt{21})(\sqrt{6} + \sqrt{21})$.
$-57 - 6\sqrt{14}$

👥 Reaching All Students

| **Below Level** To emphasize to students that only like radicals can be combined show them $\sqrt{9} + \sqrt{16} \neq \sqrt{25}$. Rather $\sqrt{9} + \sqrt{16} = 3 + 4 = 7$. | **Advanced Learners** Have students simplify $\frac{-4}{\sqrt{x} + \sqrt{5y}}$. | **English Learners** See note on page 602. **Inclusion** See note on page 601. |

⑤ Simplify $\frac{8}{\sqrt{7} - \sqrt{3}}$. $2\sqrt{7} + 2\sqrt{3}$

⑥ The ratio length : width of a painting is approximately equal to the golden ratio $(1 + \sqrt{5})$: 2. The length of the painting is 51 in. Find the exact width of the painting in simplest radical form. Then find the approximate width to the nearest inch. $\frac{-51(1-\sqrt{5})}{2}$ in.; 32 in.

⑤ **EXAMPLE** **English Learners**

The letters *j* and *g* are pronounced differently in different languages. Help students pronounce the word *conjugate*. Explain that conjugate means to join together in pairs.

⑥ **EXAMPLE** **Connection to Art**

Encourage students to research how the golden ratio was used in Renaissance architecture. Invite interested students to make a presentation for the class describing the golden ratio and showing pictures of buildings incorporating the golden ratio proportions.

Closure

Ask students to summarize how to add and subtract radicals. You remove perfect squares that are factors of the radicands, and write their square roots outside the radical signs and combine like terms.

602

5a. $2\sqrt{7} - 2\sqrt{5}$

b. $-2\sqrt{10} + 4\sqrt{2}$

c. $-\frac{5}{8}\sqrt{11} - \frac{5}{8}\sqrt{3}$

Real-World Connection

Mondrian painted straight lines at right angles because he felt this to be the angle of complete equilibrium.

---

⑤ **EXAMPLE** **Rationalizing a Denominator Using Conjugates**

Simplify $\frac{6}{\sqrt{5} - \sqrt{2}}$.

$\frac{6}{\sqrt{5} - \sqrt{2}} = \frac{6}{\sqrt{5} - \sqrt{2}} \cdot \frac{\sqrt{5} + \sqrt{2}}{\sqrt{5} + \sqrt{2}}$ Multiply the numerator and the denominator by the conjugate of the denominator.

$= \frac{6(\sqrt{5} + \sqrt{2})}{5 - 2}$ Multiply in the denominator.

$= \frac{6(\sqrt{5} + \sqrt{2})}{3}$ Simplify the denominator.

$= 2(\sqrt{5} + \sqrt{2})$ Divide 6 and 3 by the common factor 3.

$= 2\sqrt{5} + 2\sqrt{2}$ Simplify the expression.

✔ **Check Understanding** **⑤** Simplify each expression. **See left.**

a. $\frac{4}{\sqrt{7} + \sqrt{5}}$ b. $\frac{-4}{\sqrt{10} + \sqrt{8}}$ c. $\frac{-5}{\sqrt{11} - \sqrt{3}}$

You can solve a ratio involving radical expressions.

⑥ **EXAMPLE** **Real-World 🌐 Problem Solving**

Art The ratio length : width of this painting by Mondrian is approximately equal to the *golden ratio* $(1 + \sqrt{5})$: 2. The length of the painting is 81 inches. Find the width of the painting in simplest radical form. Then find the approximate width to the nearest inch.

Define 81 = length of painting
        x = width of painting

Relate $(1 + \sqrt{5})$: 2 = length : width

Write $\frac{1 + \sqrt{5}}{2} = \frac{81}{x}$

$x(1 + \sqrt{5}) = 162$ Cross multiply.

$\frac{x(1 + \sqrt{5})}{(1 + \sqrt{5})} = \frac{162}{(1 + \sqrt{5})}$ Divide both sides by $(1 + \sqrt{5})$.

$x = \frac{162}{(1 + \sqrt{5})} \cdot \frac{(1 - \sqrt{5})}{(1 - \sqrt{5})}$ Multiply the numerator and the denominator by the conjugate of the denominator.

$x = \frac{162(1 - \sqrt{5})}{1 - 5}$ Multiply in the denominator.

$x = \frac{162(1 - \sqrt{5})}{-4}$ Simplify the denominator.

$x = \frac{-81(1 - \sqrt{5})}{2}$ Divide 162 and -4 by the common factor -2.

$x = 50.06075309$ Use a calculator.

$x \approx 50$

The exact width of the painting is $\frac{-81(1 - \sqrt{5})}{2}$ inches. The approximate width of the painting is 50 inches.

✔ **Check Understanding** **⑥** Another painting has a length : width ratio approximately equal to the golden ratio $(1 + \sqrt{5})$: 2. Find the length of a painting if the width is 34 inches. **55 in.**

602 Chapter 11   Radical Expressions and Equations

 pages 603–606   **Exercises**

22. $-9 - 14\sqrt{6}$

23. $58 - 10\sqrt{30}$

24. $11 - 4\sqrt{7}$

25. $43 + 4\sqrt{30}$

26. $32 + 9\sqrt{11}$

27. $23 - 5\sqrt{13}$

EXERCISES

For more practice, see *Extra Practice*.

Practice and Problem Solving

A Practice by Example

Example 1
(page 600)

Simplify each expression.

1. $-3\sqrt{6} + 8\sqrt{6}$ $5\sqrt{6}$ **2.** $16\sqrt{10} + 2\sqrt{10}$ $18\sqrt{10}$ **3.** $\sqrt{5} - 3\sqrt{5}$ $-2\sqrt{5}$

4. $6\sqrt{7} - 4\sqrt{7}$ $2\sqrt{7}$ **5.** $15\sqrt{2} - \sqrt{2}$ $14\sqrt{2}$ **6.** $-5\sqrt{3} - 3\sqrt{3}$ $-8\sqrt{3}$

Example 2
(page 600)

Tell whether each pair of expressions can be simplified to like radicals.

7. $\sqrt{2}, \sqrt{32}$ yes **8.** $\sqrt{3}, \sqrt{75}$ yes **9.** $\sqrt{5}, \sqrt{50}$ no

Simplify each expression.

10. $\sqrt{18} + \sqrt{2}$ $4\sqrt{2}$ **11.** $2\sqrt{12} - 7\sqrt{3}$ $-3\sqrt{3}$

12. $\sqrt{8} + 2\sqrt{2}$ $4\sqrt{2}$ **13.** $4\sqrt{5} - 2\sqrt{45}$ $-2\sqrt{5}$

14. $3\sqrt{7} - \sqrt{28}$ $\sqrt{7}$ **15.** $-4\sqrt{10} + 6\sqrt{40}$ $8\sqrt{10}$

Example 3
(page 601)

16. $\sqrt{2}(\sqrt{8} - 4)$ $4 - 4\sqrt{2}$ **17.** $\sqrt{3}(\sqrt{27} + 1)$ $9 + \sqrt{3}$

18. $2\sqrt{3}(\sqrt{3} - 1)$ $6 - 2\sqrt{3}$ **19.** $\sqrt{3}(\sqrt{15} + 2)$ $3\sqrt{5} + 2\sqrt{3}$

20. $\sqrt{2}(3 + 3\sqrt{2})$ $3\sqrt{2} + 6$ **21.** $\sqrt{6}(\sqrt{6} - 5)$ $6 - 5\sqrt{6}$

Example 4
(page 601)

22. $(3\sqrt{2} + \sqrt{3})(\sqrt{2} - 5\sqrt{3})$ **23.** $(2\sqrt{5} - \sqrt{6})(4\sqrt{5} - 3\sqrt{6})$

24. $(\sqrt{7} - 2)^2$ **22–27. See margin p. 602.** **25.** $(2\sqrt{10} + \sqrt{3})^2$

26. $(2\sqrt{11} + 5)(\sqrt{11} + 2)$ **27.** $(4 - \sqrt{13})(9 + \sqrt{13})$

Example 5
(page 602)

28. $\dfrac{8}{\sqrt{7} - \sqrt{3}}$ $2\sqrt{7} + 2\sqrt{3}$ **29.** $\dfrac{-12}{\sqrt{8} - \sqrt{2}}$ $-6\sqrt{2}$

30. $\dfrac{48}{\sqrt{6} - \sqrt{18}}$ $-4\sqrt{6} - 12\sqrt{2}$ **31.** $\dfrac{3}{\sqrt{10} - \sqrt{5}}$ $\dfrac{3\sqrt{10} + 3\sqrt{5}}{5}$

32. $\dfrac{-40}{\sqrt{11} - \sqrt{3}}$ $-5\sqrt{11} - 5\sqrt{3}$ **33.** $\dfrac{9}{\sqrt{12} - \sqrt{11}}$ $18\sqrt{3} + 9\sqrt{11}$

Example 6
(page 602)

Find an exact solution for each equation. Find the approximate solution to the nearest tenth. 34–36. See margin.

34. $\dfrac{5\sqrt{2}}{\sqrt{2} - 1} = \dfrac{x}{\sqrt{2}}$ **35.** $\dfrac{3}{1 + \sqrt{5}} = \dfrac{1 - \sqrt{5}}{x}$ **36.** $\dfrac{\sqrt{2} - 1}{\sqrt{2} + 1} = \dfrac{x}{2}$

37. The ratio of the length to the width of a painting is $(1 + \sqrt{5}) : 2$. The length is 12 ft. What is the width? **7.4 ft**

B Apply Your Skills

Simplify each expression. 39–46. See margin.

38. $\sqrt{40} + \sqrt{90}$ $5\sqrt{10}$ **39.** $3\sqrt{2}(2 + \sqrt{6})$ **40.** $\sqrt{12} + 4\sqrt{75} - \sqrt{36}$

41. $(\sqrt{3} + \sqrt{5})^2$ **42.** $\dfrac{\sqrt{13} + \sqrt{10}}{\sqrt{13} - \sqrt{5}}$ **43.** $(\sqrt{7} + \sqrt{8})(\sqrt{7} + \sqrt{8})$

44. $2\sqrt{2}(-2\sqrt{32} + \sqrt{8})$ **45.** $4\sqrt{50} - 7\sqrt{18}$ **46.** $\dfrac{2\sqrt{12} + 3\sqrt{6}}{\sqrt{9} - \sqrt{6}}$

47. Chemistry The ratio of the rates of diffusion of two gases is given by the formula $\dfrac{r_1}{r_2} = \dfrac{\sqrt{m_1}}{\sqrt{m_2}}$, where m_1 and m_2 are the masses of the molecules of the gases. Find $\dfrac{r_1}{r_2}$ if $m_1 = 12$ units and $m_2 = 30$ units. $\dfrac{\sqrt{10}}{5}$

Lesson 11-4 Operations With Radical Expressions **603**

Assignment Guide

1 Objective
A **B** Core 1–15, 48–54, 62–63

2 Objective
A **B** Core 16–47, 55–61
C Extension 64–71

Standardized Test Prep 72–75

Mixed Review 76–92

Error Prevention

Exercises 10–15 Students may think a radical cannot be simplified because they choose factors that do not contain a perfect square. For example, for $\sqrt{18}$ students might choose 6 and 3 instead of 9 and 2. Suggest to them that they factor the radicand completely and look for pairs of factors.

Alternative Method

Exercises 20–27 Help students see that when multiplying the square roots of identical radicands, the product is just the radicand. This method is quicker than multiplying the radicands, and then finding the square root of the product.

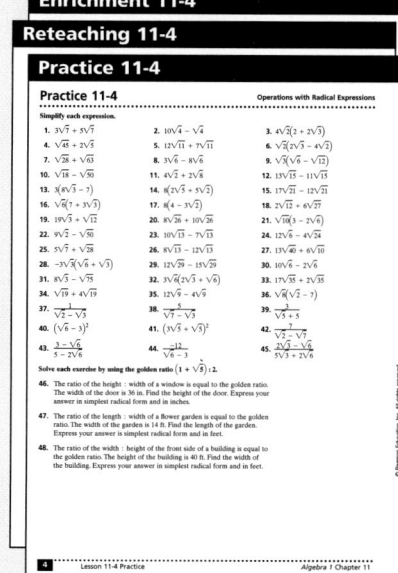

---

34. $10(\sqrt{2} + 1)$; 24.1

35. $-\dfrac{4}{3}$; -1.3

36. $6 - 4\sqrt{2}$; 0.3

39. $6\sqrt{2} + 6\sqrt{3}$

40. $22\sqrt{3} - 6$

41. $8 + 2\sqrt{15}$

42. $\dfrac{13 + \sqrt{65} + \sqrt{130} + 5\sqrt{2}}{8}$

43. $15 + 4\sqrt{14}$

44. -24

45. $-\sqrt{2}$

46. $4\sqrt{3} + 4\sqrt{2} + 3\sqrt{6} + 6$

504

Connection to History

Exercise 54 The greatest number of kites flown on a single line is 11,284. Sadao Harada and a team of assistants achieved this feat in Kagoshima, Japan, in October 1990.

Math Tip

Exercises 55–56 Remind students that for some kinds of problems percents must be rounded up, disregarding the usual rounding rules. Show them that if they round down they will not reach the target amount.

48. $8\sqrt{2}$ units

49. $(10 + 10\sqrt{2})$ units

50. $6\sqrt{10}$ units

51. $(4x + x\sqrt{10})$ units

53a. The student simplified $\sqrt{48}$ as $2\sqrt{24}$ instead of $2\sqrt{12}$ or $4\sqrt{3}$.

b. $2\sqrt{6} + 4\sqrt{3}$

54a. $2\sqrt{2}$ or 2.8 ft

Geometry Find the exact perimeter of each figure below. 48–51. See left.

48.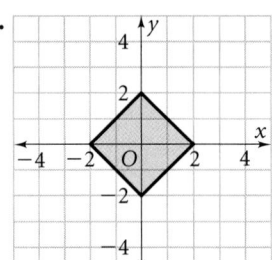

49.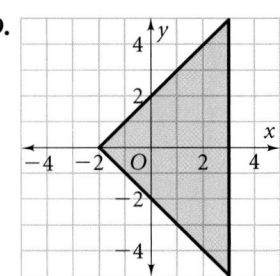

50.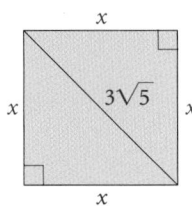

51.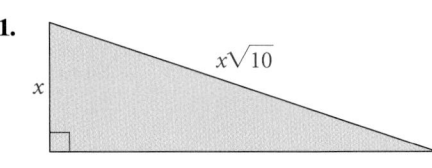

52. **Open-Ended** Make up three sums that are less than or equal to 50. Use the square roots of 2, 3, 5, or 7, and the whole numbers less than 10. For example, $8\sqrt{5} + 9\sqrt{7} \le 50$. **See margin.**

53. **Error Analysis** When simplifying $\sqrt{24} + \sqrt{48}$, a student wrote $3\sqrt{24} = 6\sqrt{6}$.
   a. What error did the student make? **See left.**
   b. Simplify $\sqrt{24} + \sqrt{48}$ correctly.

54. You can make a box kite like the one at the right in the shape of a rectangular solid. The opening at each end of the kite is a square.
   a. Suppose the sides of the square are 2 ft long. How long are the diagonal struts used for bracing? **See left.**
   b. Suppose each side of the square has length s. Find the length of the diagonal struts in terms of s. Write your answer in simplest form. **$s\sqrt{2}$**

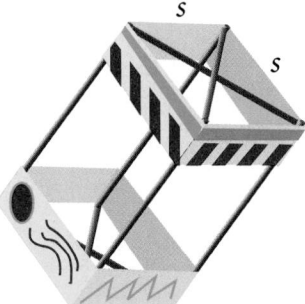

Investments For Exercises 55–57, the formula $r = \sqrt{\frac{A}{P}} - 1$ gives the interest rate r that will allow principal P to grow into amount A in two years, if the interest is compounded annually. Use the formula to find the interest rate you would need to meet each goal.

55. Suppose you have $500 to deposit into an account. Your goal is to have $595 in that account at the end of the second year. **9.1%**

56. Suppose you have $550 to deposit into an account. Your goal is to have $700 in that account at the end of two years. **12.8%**

57. Suppose you have $600 to deposit into an account. Your goal is to have $800 in that account at the end of two years. **15.5%**

58. a. Suppose n is an even number. Simplify $\sqrt{x^n}$. $x^{\frac{n}{2}}$
   b. Suppose n is an odd number greater than 1. Simplify $\sqrt{x^n}$. $x^{\frac{n-1}{2}}\sqrt{x}$

59. **Critical Thinking** Simplify $\frac{a\sqrt{b}}{b\sqrt{a}}$. $\frac{\sqrt{ab}}{b}$

pages 603–606 Exercises

52. **Answers may vary.**
   Sample: $8\sqrt{2} + 4\sqrt{3}$, $2\sqrt{7} + 9\sqrt{3}, 6\sqrt{5} + 3\sqrt{7}$

60. Find the value of the numerical expression for Professor Hinkle's age in the cartoon. **about 251 years**

 61. Writing Explain why $\sqrt{3} + \sqrt{6}$ cannot be simplified. **They are unlike radicands.**

62. a. Copy and complete the table.

a	b	$\sqrt{a}$	$\sqrt{b}$	$\sqrt{a} + \sqrt{b}$	$\sqrt{a+b}$
1	0	■1	■0	■1	■1
16	1	■4	■1	■5	■$\sqrt{17}$
25	9	■5	■3	■8	■$\sqrt{34}$
64	36	■8	■6	■14	■10
100	81	■10	■9	■19	■$\sqrt{181}$

b. No; the only values it worked for were 0 and 1.

b. Does $\sqrt{a} + \sqrt{b}$ always equal $\sqrt{a+b}$? Explain. **See left.**

63. Error Analysis Explain the error in the work below.

$$\sqrt{41} = \sqrt{16 + 25} = \sqrt{16} + \sqrt{25} = 4 + 5 = 9 \quad \sqrt{a+b} \neq \sqrt{a} + \sqrt{b}$$

 **Challenge**

Simplify each expression.

64. $\sqrt{18} + \dfrac{3}{\sqrt{2}}$ **$\dfrac{9\sqrt{2}}{2}$**

65. $\dfrac{\sqrt{28}}{3} + \dfrac{3}{\sqrt{7}}$ **$\dfrac{23\sqrt{7}}{21}$**

66. $\sqrt{\dfrac{3}{5}} + \sqrt{\dfrac{5}{3}}$ **$\dfrac{8\sqrt{15}}{15}$**

67. $\dfrac{\sqrt{27} + \sqrt{48} - \sqrt{75}}{\sqrt{3}}$ **2**

68. $\sqrt{288} + \sqrt{50} - \sqrt{98}$ **$10\sqrt{2}$**

70. $2\sqrt{2} - \sqrt{6} - \sqrt{3} + 3$

69. $(\sqrt{2} + \sqrt{32})(\sqrt{2} + \sqrt{8} + \sqrt{32})$ **70**

70. $\dfrac{\sqrt{5} + \sqrt{10} - \sqrt{15}}{\sqrt{10} - \sqrt{5}}$

71. Find the length of each hypotenuse. Write your answers in simplified radical form.

a.

$\sqrt{10} - \sqrt{2}$
$\sqrt{10} + \sqrt{2}$
$2\sqrt{6}$

b.
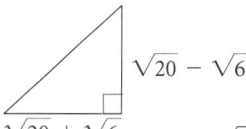
$\sqrt{20} - \sqrt{6}$
$\sqrt{20} + \sqrt{6}$
$2\sqrt{13}$

c. If the length of the legs of a right triangle are $\sqrt{p} + \sqrt{q}$ and $\sqrt{p} - \sqrt{q}$, write an expression for the length of the hypotenuse. **$\sqrt{2(p+q)}$**

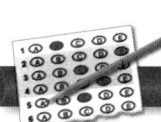

Standardized Test Prep

Multiple Choice

72. Simplify $4\sqrt{75} + \sqrt{27}$. **B**

    A. $12\sqrt{3}$ **B.** $23\sqrt{3}$ **C.** $4\sqrt{102}$ **D.** $5\sqrt{102}$

Lesson Quiz 11-4

Simplify each expression.

1. $12\sqrt{16} - 2\sqrt{16}$ **40**

2. $\sqrt{20} - 4\sqrt{5}$ **$-2\sqrt{5}$**

3. $\sqrt{2}(\sqrt{2} + 3\sqrt{3})$ **$2 + 3\sqrt{6}$**

4. $(\sqrt{3} - 2\sqrt{21})(\sqrt{3} + 3\sqrt{21})$ **$-123 + 3\sqrt{7}$**

5. $\dfrac{16}{\sqrt{5} - \sqrt{7}}$ **$-8\sqrt{5} - 8\sqrt{7}$**

Alternative Assessment

Divide the class into small groups. Tell students they will be team teachers who will teach a class what they should learn in this lesson. Have the group design a problem for each of Examples 2–5 and present to the class the problems and how to solve them. Allow groups to use the board.

Standardized Test Prep

Resources
For additional practice with a variety of test item formats:
- Standardized Test Prep, p. 633
- Test-Taking Strategies, p. 628
- Test-Taking Strategies with Transparencies

Exercise 74 Remind students to use FOIL. Encourage them to draw curved arrows from each term in the first binomial to each term in the second binomial to help in multiplying the terms together.

Take It to the NET
Online lesson quiz at
www.PHSchool.com
Web Code: aea-1104

Short Response

Extended Response

73. Which radical expression is NOT equal to $5\sqrt{2}$? **I**
  F. $\sqrt{8} + \sqrt{18}$ **G.** $\sqrt{98} - \sqrt{8}$
  H. $-\sqrt{32} + \sqrt{162}$ **I.** $\sqrt{48} + \sqrt{2}$

74. Simplify $(3\sqrt{5} - \sqrt{2})(\sqrt{5} + 5\sqrt{2})$. Show your work. **See back of book.**

75. Explain the steps needed to simplify $\frac{5}{\sqrt{7} + \sqrt{21}}$. **See back of book.**

Mixed Review

Lesson 11-3

Find the distance between the points in each pair. If necessary, round to the nearest tenth.

76. $(2, 6), (8, 13)$ **9.2 units**   **77.** $(-1, 7), (5, 10)$ **6.7 units** **78.** $(-6, 2), (20, -1)$
26.2 units

Find the midpoint of each segment with the given endpoints.

79. $A(4, -1)$ and $B(2, 11)$ **(3, 5)**   **80.** $H(-5, 6)$ and $K(1, 7)$ **(−2, 6.5)**

Lesson 10-5

Solve each equation by factoring.

81. $5t^2 - 35t = 0$ **0, 7**   **82.** $p^2 - 7p - 18 = 0$ **−2, 9** **83.** $k^2 + 12k + 27 = 0$ **−9, −3**

84. $y^2 - 2y = 24$ **−4, 6**   **85.** $m^2 + 30 = -17m$ **86.** $2a^2 = -7a - 3$
−15, −2   **−3, −$\frac{1}{2}$**

Lesson 9-4

Find each product. **87–89. See margin.**

87. $(b + 11)(b + 11)$ **88.** $(2p + 7)(2p + 7)$ **89.** $(5g - 7)(5g + 7)$

90. $(3x + 1)(3x - 1)$ **91.** $\left(\frac{1}{3}k - 9\right)\left(\frac{1}{3}k + 9\right)$ **92.** $(d - 1.1)(d - 1.1)$

  $9x^2 - 1$ $\frac{1}{9}k^2 - 81$ $d^2 - 2.2d + 1.21$

Algebra at Work
·········· Auto Mechanic

Auto mechanics work to see that car engines get the most out of every gallon of gasoline. Formulas used by mechanics often involve radicals. For example, a car gets its power when gas and air in each cylinder are compressed and ignited by a spark plug. An engine's efficiency e is given by the formula $e = \frac{c - \sqrt{c}}{c}$, where c is the compression ratio.

Because of the complexity of such formulas and of modern high-performance engines, today's auto mechanic must be a highly trained and educated professional who understands algebra, graph reading, and the operation of computerized equipment.

Take It to the NET For more information about a career as an auto mechanic, go to **www.PHSchool.com**.
Web Code: aeb-2031

pages 603–606   Exercises

87. $b^2 + 22b + 121$

88. $4p^2 + 28p + 49$

89. $25g^2 - 49$

Solving Radical Equations

North Carolina Objectives 1.01 Write equivalent forms of algebraic expressions to solve problems. a) Apply the laws of exponents.

Lesson Preview

What You'll Learn

 OBJECTIVE 1 To solve equations containing radicals

 OBJECTIVE 2 To identify extraneous solutions

. . . And Why

To design an amusement park ride, as in Example 2

✓ **Check Skills You'll Need**   (For help, go to Lesson 10-3.)

Evaluate each expression for the given value.

1. $\sqrt{x} - 3$ for $x = 16$ **1**   2. $\sqrt{x + 7}$ for $x = 9$ **4**   3. $2\sqrt{x + 3}$ for $x = 1$ **4**

Simplify each expression.

4. $(\sqrt{3})^2$ **3**   5. $(\sqrt{x + 1})^2$ **x + 1**   6. $(\sqrt{2x - 5})^2$ **2x − 5**

New Vocabulary • radical equation • extraneous solution

OBJECTIVE 1   Solving Radical Equations

 Interactive lesson includes instant self-check, tutorials, and activities.

Need Help?

For every real number a and b, if $a = b$, then $a^2 = b^2$.

A **radical equation** is an equation that has a variable in a radicand. You can often solve a radical equation by getting the radical by itself on one side of the equation. Then you square both sides. Remember that the expression under a radical must be nonnegative.

When $x \geq 0, (\sqrt{x})^2 = x$.

1 EXAMPLE   Solving by Isolating the Radical

Solve each equation. Check your solution.

a. $\sqrt{x} - 3 = 4$

$\quad \sqrt{x} = 7$ Get the radical on the left side of the equation.

$\quad (\sqrt{x})^2 = 7^2$ Square both sides.

$\quad x = 49$

Check $\sqrt{x} - 3 = 4$

$\qquad \sqrt{49} - 3 \overset{?}{=} 4$ Substitute 49 for x.

$\qquad 7 - 3 = 4 ✓$

b. $\sqrt{x - 3} = 4$

$\quad (\sqrt{x - 3})^2 = 4^2$ Square both sides.

$\quad x - 3 = 16$ Solve for x.

$\quad x = 19$

Check $\sqrt{x - 3} = 4$

$\qquad \sqrt{19 - 3} \overset{?}{=} 4$ Substitute 19 for x.

$\qquad \sqrt{16} = 4 ✓$

✓ **Check Understanding** **1** Solve each equation. Check your solution.

a. $\sqrt{x} + 7 = 12$ **25**   b. $\sqrt{a} - 4 = 5$ **81**   c. $\sqrt{c - 2} = 6$ **38**

Lesson 11-5 Solving Radical Equations **607**

 11-5 North Carolina Objectives 1.01a

1. Plan

Lesson Preview

✓ **Check Skills You'll Need**

Finding and Estimating Square Roots
Lesson 10-3: Examples 1 and 5
Exercises 1–12 and 25
Extra Practice, p. 711

Lesson Resources

Teaching Resources
Practice, Reteaching, Enrichment

 Reaching All Students
Practice Workbook 11-5
Spanish Practice Workbook 11-5
Technology Activities 25
Basic Algebra Planning Guide 11-5

 Presentation Assistant Plus!
Transparencies
• Check Skills You'll Need 11-5
• Additional Examples 11-5
• Student Edition Answers 11-5
• Lesson Quiz 11-5
PH Presentation Pro CD 11-5

PRENTICE HALL ASSESSMENT SYSTEM

Computer Test Generator CD

 Technology
Resource Pro® CD-ROM
Computer Test Generator CD
Prentice Hall Presentation Pro CD

 **www.PHSchool.com**
Student Site
• Teacher Web Code: aek-5500
• Self-grading Lesson Quiz
Teacher Center
• Lesson Planner
• Resources

Plus **iTEXT**

Ongoing Assessment and Intervention

Before the Lesson	During the Lesson	After the Lesson
Diagnose prerequisite skills using:	**Monitor progress using:**	**Assess knowledge using:**
• Check Skills You'll Need	• Check Understanding	• Lesson Quiz
	• Additional Examples	• Computer Test Generator CD
	• Standardized Test Prep	

Math Background

Note that the converse of the statement "For every real number a and b, if $a = b$, then $a^2 = b^2$" is not true. For example, for the real numbers 3 and −3, $(3)^2 = (-3)^2$, but $3 \neq -3$.

OBJECTIVE
1 Teaching Notes

1 EXAMPLE Math Tip

In part b, students may square $(x - 3)$ instead of $\sqrt{x - 3}$. Because the exponent is outside the parentheses, they may be expecting to see an x^2 term. On the board, write $(\sqrt{x})^2 = x$ and $(\sqrt{3})^2 = 3$. Help students understand that when they square a square root, they will get the radicand.

2 EXAMPLE Diversity

Some students may not have ridden a roller coaster or know what one looks like. Bring in pictures of or information about roller coasters. Invite students to speculate about how roller coasters work and why the height of the first drop is important. Tell students that roller coasters rely on the acceleration due to gravity to provide most of their speed.

Additional Examples

1 Solve each equation. Check your answers.
a. $\sqrt{x} - 5 = 4$ **81**
b. $\sqrt{x - 5} = 4$ **21**

2 The loop on a roller coaster ride has a radius of 18 ft. Your car has a velocity of 120 ft/s at the top of the loop. How high is the hill you have just come down before going into the loop? **261 ft**

3 Solve $\sqrt{3x - 4} = \sqrt{2x + 3}$. **7**

For an equation like $2\sqrt{x} = 8$, you could square both sides first, or you could divide by 2 to get $\sqrt{x}$ alone on one side of the equation.

Real-World Connection

When the roller coaster cars are upside down, the riders and the cars fall at the same rate and stay together.

2 EXAMPLE Real-World Problem Solving

Designing a Ride On a roller coaster ride, your speed in a loop depends on the height of the hill you have just come down and the radius of the loop in feet. The equation $v = 8\sqrt{h - 2r}$ gives the velocity v in feet per second of a car at the top of the loop.

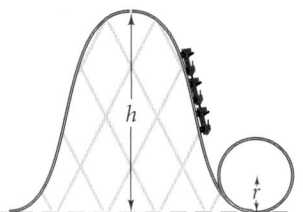

Suppose the loop has a radius of 18 ft. You want the car to have a velocity of 30 ft/s at the top of the loop. How high should the hill be?

Solve $v = 8\sqrt{h - 2r}$ for h when $v = 30$ and $r = 18$.

$30 = 8\sqrt{h - 2(18)}$ **Substitute 30 for v and 18 for r.**

$\dfrac{30}{8} = \dfrac{8\sqrt{h - 2(18)}}{8}$ **Divide each side by 8 to isolate the radical.**

$3.75 = \sqrt{h - 36}$ **Simplify.**

$(3.75)^2 = (\sqrt{h - 36})^2$ **Square both sides.**

$14.0625 = h - 36$

$50.0625 = h$

● The hill should be about 50 ft high.

✔ **Check Understanding** **2 a.** Find the height of the hill when the velocity at the top of the loop is 35 ft/s, and the radius of the loop is 24 ft. **about 67 ft**

b. Critical Thinking Would you expect the velocity of the car to increase as the radius of the loop increases? Explain. **No; $h - 2r$ decreases as r increases.**

You can square both sides of an equation to solve an equation involving radical expressions.

3 EXAMPLE Solving With Radical Expressions on Both Sides

Solve $\sqrt{3n - 2} = \sqrt{n + 6}$.

$(\sqrt{3n - 2})^2 = (\sqrt{n + 6})^2$ **Square both sides.**

$3n - 2 = n + 6$ **Simplify.**

$3n = n + 8$ **Add 2 to each side.**

$2n = 8$ **Subtract n from each side.**

$n = 4$ **Divide each side by 2.**

Check $\sqrt{3n - 2} = \sqrt{n + 6}$

$\sqrt{3(4) - 2} \stackrel{?}{=} \sqrt{4 + 6}$ **Substitute 4 for n.**

$\sqrt{10} = \sqrt{10}$ ✓

● The solution is 4.

✔ **Check Understanding** **3** Solve $\sqrt{3t + 4} = \sqrt{5t - 6}$. Check your answer. **5**

Reaching All Students

| Below Level Make sure students understand that $(\sqrt{x - 3})^2$ is not the same as $(\sqrt{x} - \sqrt{3})^2$. | Advanced Learners Have students predict what the graph of the equation in Example 5 would look like and verify their predictions with a graphing calculator. | Tactile Learners See note on page 610. Error Prevention See note on page 609. |

Solving Equations With Extraneous Solutions

When you solve an equation by squaring each side, you create a new equation. This new equation may have solutions that do not solve the original equation.

Original equation	Square of each side	New equation	Solutions of new equation
$x = 2$	$(x)^2 = (2)^2$	$x^2 = 4$	$2, -2$

In the example above, -2 does not satisfy the original equation. It is an extraneous solution. An **extraneous solution** is a solution that does not satisfy the original equation. Be sure to check all solutions in the original equation to determine whether a solution is extraneous.

4 EXAMPLE Identifying Extraneous Solutions

Solve $x = \sqrt{x + 6}$.

$$(x)^2 = (\sqrt{x + 6})^2 \quad \text{Square both sides.}$$
$$x^2 = x + 6 \quad \text{Simplify.}$$
$$x^2 - x - 6 = 0 \quad \text{Subtract } x \text{ and 6 from both sides.}$$
$$(x - 3)(x + 2) = 0 \quad \text{Solve the quadratic equation by factoring.}$$
$$(x - 3) = 0 \quad \text{or} \quad (x + 2) = 0 \quad \text{Use the Zero-Product Property.}$$
$$x = 3 \quad \text{or} \quad x = -2 \quad \text{Solve for } x.$$

Check $\quad x = \sqrt{x + 6}$

$3 \overset{?}{=} \sqrt{3 + 6} \qquad -2 \overset{?}{=} \sqrt{-2 + 6} \quad$ **Substitute 3 and 2 for x.**

$3 = 3 \checkmark \qquad\qquad -2 \neq 2$

> The solution to the original equation is 3. The value -2 is an extraneous solution.

Problem Solving Hint

For Check Understanding 4b, you can use any method to solve a quadratic equation: graphing, factoring, or the quadratic formula.

✓ **Check Understanding** **4 a. Critical Thinking** How could you determine that -2 was not a solution of $x = \sqrt{x + 6}$ without going through all the steps of the check? **See left.**

4a. A principal square root must be a nonnegative number.

b. Solve $y = \sqrt{y + 2}$. Check your solutions. **2**

It is possible that the only solution you get after squaring both sides of an equation is extraneous. In that case, the original equation has no solution.

5 EXAMPLE No Solution

Solve $\sqrt{2x} + 6 = 4$.

$$\sqrt{2x} = -2$$
$$(\sqrt{2x})^2 = (-2)^2 \quad \text{Square both sides.}$$
$$2x = 4$$
$$x = 2$$

Check $\quad \sqrt{2x} + 6 = 4$

$\sqrt{2(2)} + 6 \overset{?}{=} 4 \quad$ **Substitute 2 for x.**

$\sqrt{4} + 6 \overset{?}{=} 4$

$2 + 6 \neq 4 \quad$ **$x = 2$ does not solve the original equation.**

> $\sqrt{2x} + 6 = 4$ has no solution.

✓ **Check Understanding** **5** Solve $8 - \sqrt{2n} = 20$. Check your solution. **no solution**

Lesson 11-5 Solving Radical Equations **609**

Stress that the possible solutions must be substituted into the *original* equation, not an equation that is part of the solution process.

Additional Examples

4 Solve $x = \sqrt{x + 12}$. **4**

5 Solve $\sqrt{3x} + 8 = 2$.
no solution

Closure

Ask: *What is a radical equation? How do you solve a radical equation?* A radical equation is an equation that has a variable in a radicand. Answers may vary. Sample: First solve for the radical, isolating it on one side of the equation. Then solve the radical equation by squaring both sides. *What is an extraneous solution? How do you find one?* An extraneous solution is a solution of the new equation that does not satisfy the original equation. You find an extraneous solution by checking all solutions using the original equation.

Assignment Guide

1 Objective

Ⓐ Ⓑ **Core** 1–14, 29–30, 44–46

Ⓒ **Extension** 53–54

2 Objective

Ⓐ Ⓑ **Core** 15–28, 31–43, 47

Ⓒ **Extension** 48–52

Standardized Test Prep 55–61

Mixed Review 62–79

Connection to Geometry

Exercise 30 Encourage students to measure the height and radius of cans at home. Have students bring their data to class. Students may wish to display cans of different sizes in the classroom and to label each can with its dimensions and volume.

Tactile Learners

Exercise 46 Some students may have trouble visualizing the box and distinguishing its dimensions. Let them cut out a pattern and assemble the box.

EXERCISES

For more practice, see *Extra Practice*.

Practice and Problem Solving

Ⓐ **Practice by Example**

Example 1
(page 607)

Solve each radical equation. Check your solution.

1. $\sqrt{x} + 3 = 5$ **4**
2. $\sqrt{t} + 2 = 9$ **49**
3. $\sqrt{s} - 1 = 5$ **36**
4. $\sqrt{n + 7} = 12$ **137**
5. $\sqrt{a - 6} = 3$ **15**
6. $\sqrt{z} - 7 = -3$ **16**

Example 2
(page 608)

7. Distance The time t in seconds it takes an object to fall d feet is given by $t = \sqrt{\frac{d}{16}}$. Find the distance an object falls after 6 seconds. **576 ft**

8. Power The current of an electrical circuit I in amps is related to the power P in watts and the resistance R in ohms by the formula $I = \sqrt{\frac{P}{R}}$. Find the power (to the nearest watt) when the current is 8 amps and the resistance is 9.4 ohms. **602 watts**

Example 3
(page 608)

Solve each radical equation. Check your solution.

9. $\sqrt{3x + 1} = \sqrt{5x - 8}$ **4.5**
10. $\sqrt{2y} = \sqrt{9 - y}$ **3**
11. $\sqrt{7v - 4} = \sqrt{5v + 10}$ **7**
12. $\sqrt{s + 10} = \sqrt{6 - s}$ **−2**
13. $\sqrt{n + 5} = \sqrt{5n - 11}$ **4**
14. $\sqrt{3m + 1} = \sqrt{7m - 9}$ **2.5**

Examples 4, 5
(page 609)

Tell which solutions, if any, are extraneous for each equation.

15. $-z = \sqrt{-z + 6}; z = -3, z = 2$ **2**
16. $\sqrt{12 - n} = n; n = -4, n = 3$ **−4**
17. $y = \sqrt{2y}; y = 0, y = 2$ **none**
18. $2a = \sqrt{4a + 3}; a = \frac{3}{2}, a = -\frac{1}{2}$ **−$\frac{1}{2}$**
19. $x = \sqrt{28 - 3x}; x = 4, x = -7$ **−7**
20. $-t = \sqrt{-6t - 5}; t = -5, t = -1$ **none**

Solve each radical equation. Check your solution. If there is no solution, write *no solution*.

21. $x = \sqrt{2x + 3}$ **3**
22. $n = \sqrt{4n + 5}$ **5**
23. $\sqrt{3b} = -3$ **no solution**
24. $2y = \sqrt{5y + 6}$ **2**
25. $-2\sqrt{2r + 5} = 6$ **no solution**
26. $\sqrt{d + 12} = d$ **4**
27. $\sqrt{z + 5} = 2z$ **1.25 or $\frac{5}{4}$**
28. $2t = \sqrt{5t - 1}$ **$\frac{1}{4}$, 1**

Ⓑ **Apply Your Skills** **29. Geometry** In the right triangle $\triangle ABC$, the altitude $\overline{CD}$ is at a right angle to the hypotenuse. You can use $CD = \sqrt{(AD)(DB)}$ to find missing lengths.
   a. Find AD if $CD = 10$ and $DB = 4$. **25**
   b. Find DB if $AD = 20$ and $CD = 15$. **11.25**

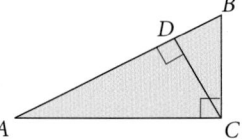

 30. Packaging The volume V in cubic units for a cylindrical can is given by the formula $V = \pi r^2 h$, where r is the radius of the can and h is the height. The volume of the can is 98 in.³, and the height of the can is 5 in. Find the radius of the can. **about 2.5 in.**

 31. Writing Explain what is meant by an extraneous solution. **See margin.**

32. Answers may vary. Sample: $x - 2 = \sqrt{7 - 2x}$, $\sqrt{3x} = 3$

32. Open-Ended Write two radical equations that have 3 for a solution.

33. The formula $t = \sqrt{\frac{n}{16}}$ gives the time t in seconds for an object that is initially at rest to fall n feet. Find the distance an object falls in the first 10 seconds. **1600 ft**

pages 610–612 Exercises

31. An extraneous solution is a solution of a new equation that does not satisfy the original equation.

Solve each radical equation. Check your solution. If there is no solution, write *no solution*.

34. $\sqrt{5x + 10} = 5$ **3**

35. $-6 - \sqrt{3y} = -3$ **no solution**

36. $\sqrt{7p + 5} = \sqrt{p - 3}$ **no solution**

37. $a = \sqrt{7a - 6}$ **1, 6**

38. $\sqrt{y + 12} = 3\sqrt{y}$ **1.5**

39. $\sqrt{x - 10} = 1$ **11**

40. $\frac{x}{2} = \sqrt{3x}$ **0, 12**

41. $\frac{c}{3} = \sqrt{c - 2}$ **3, 6**

42. $7 = \sqrt{x + 5}$ **44**

43. $3 - \sqrt{4a + 1} = 12$ **no solution**

44. a. The equation $v = 8\sqrt{h - 2r}$ gives the velocity v in feet per second of a car at the top of the loop of a roller coaster. Find the radius of the loop when the hill is 150 ft high and the velocity of the car is 30 ft/s. **68 ft**

44b. 20.5 mi/h

c. As radius increases, velocity decreases. As height decreases, velocity decreases.

d. Velocity depends upon the difference of the height and the radius.

b. Find the approximate speed in mi/h for 30 ft/s. (*Hint:* 1 mi = 5280 ft)

c. Critical Thinking Would you expect the velocity of the car to increase or decrease as the radius of the loop increases? As the height of the hill decreases? **b–d. See left.**

d. Explain your reasoning in your answer for part (c).

 45. a. Graphing Calculator Graph the equations $y = \sqrt{2x + 1}$ and $y = \sqrt{3x - 5}$.

b. What is the solution to the system of equations? **a–c. See margin.**

c. Solve $\sqrt{2x + 1} = \sqrt{3x - 5}$. Compare this solution with your answer to part (b).

Reading Math

For help reading and solving exercise 46, go to page 613.

46. Packaging The diagram at the right shows a piece of cardboard that makes a box when sections of it are folded and taped. The ends of the box are x inches by x inches and the body of the box is 10 inches long. **a. $V = 10x^2$**

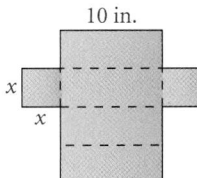

10 in.

x

x

a. Write an equation for the volume V of the box.

b. Solve the equation in part (a) for x. **$x = \sqrt{\frac{V}{10}}$**

c. Find the integer values of x that would give the box a volume between 40 in.^{3} and 490 in.^{3}, inclusive. **2, 3, 4, 5, 6, 7**

52. Subtract $\sqrt{2x}$ from each side. Square both sides. Solve for x. Check the solution if there is one.

47. a. Solve $x^2 - 3 = 4$. **$-\sqrt{7}, \sqrt{7}$**

b. Solve $\sqrt{x} - 3 = 4$. **49**

c. How are solving part (a) and solving part (b) alike? How are they different? **See margin.**

Challenge

Solve each radical equation. Check your solution. If there is no solution, write *no solution*.

48. $\sqrt{x^2 - 6x} = 4$ **$-2, 8$**

49. $\sqrt{2x^2 + 8x} = x$ **0**

50. $\sqrt{x^2 + 4x + 5} = x$ **no solution**

51. $x + 3 = \sqrt{x^2 - 4x - 1}$ **-1**

52. Writing Explain how you would solve the equation $\sqrt{2x} + \sqrt{x + 2} = 0$. **See left.**

53. Critical Thinking Explain the difference between squaring $\sqrt{x - 1}$ and squaring $\sqrt{x} - 1$. **See margin.**

Real-World Connection

In the yo-yo trick called "Around the World," the yo-yo is a satellite circling a person's hand.

54. Physics The equation $T = \sqrt{\frac{2\pi^2 r}{F}}$ gives the time T in seconds it takes a satellite with mass 0.5 kilograms to complete one orbit of radius r meters. The force F in newtons pulls the body toward the center of the orbit.

a. It takes 2 seconds for an object to make one revolution with a force of 10 newtons. Find the radius of the orbit. **about 2.0 m**

b. Find the radius of the orbit if the force is 160 newtons and $T = 2$. **about 32.4 m**

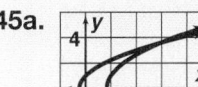 **Lesson Quiz 11-5**

Solve each radical equation.

1. $\sqrt{7x - 3} = 4$ **$2\frac{5}{7}$**

2. $\sqrt{3x - 2} = \sqrt{x + 2}$ **2**

3. $\sqrt{2x + 7} = \sqrt{5x - 8}$ **5**

4. $x = \sqrt{2x + 8}$ **4**

5. $\sqrt{3x + 4} + 5 = 3$ **no solution**

Alternative Assessment

Instruct each student to write two radical equations, one with a solution and one with either an extraneous solution or with no solution. Collect the papers and redistribute them randomly. Have students solve the problems and return the papers to the original writers for checking.

45a.

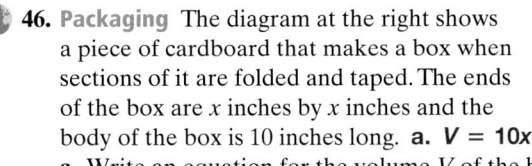

b. approximately (6, 3.6)

c. 6; it is the x-coordinate of the point of intersection.

47c. In both cases 3 is added to each side. To solve the first equation you find the square roots of each side, and in the second equation you find the square of each side.

53. The square of $\sqrt{x - 1}$ will have only 2 terms while $\sqrt{x} - 1$ squared will have 3 terms.

Standardized Test Prep

Multiple Choice

55. What is the solution of $k = \sqrt{5k + 6}$? **C**

   A. 6, −1   **B.** −6, 1   **C.** 6   **D.** −1

56. What is the solution of $\sqrt{2x + 1} = \sqrt{3x - 5}$? **G**

   F. −1   **G.** 6   **H.** $\frac{4}{5}$, 6   **I.** no solution

57. Which radical equation has no solution? **B**

   A. $-\sqrt{x} = -25x$ **B.** $\sqrt{3x + 1} = -10$

   C. $-3\sqrt{3x} = -5$ **D.** $\frac{x}{2} = \sqrt{x - 1}$

Quantitative Comparison

Compare the boxed quantity in Column A with the boxed quantity in Column B. Choose the best answer.

   A. The quantity in Column A is greater.
   B. The quantity in Column B is greater.
   C. The two quantities are equal.
   D. The relationship cannot be determined from the information given.

	Column A	Column B
58. A	the solution of $\sqrt{2n - 4} = 6$	the solution of $\sqrt{9 - 2m} = 7$
59. B	0	the solution of $8 - 3\sqrt{y} = 2$
60. C	the solution of $\frac{2\sqrt{3x - 9}}{3} = 4$	the solution of $\frac{16}{\sqrt{a + 1}} = 4$

Short Response

61. Solve $\sqrt{15 - 5x} = \sqrt{4x - 3}$. Show your work. **See back of book.**

Mixed Review

Lesson 11-4

Simplify each expression.

62. $\sqrt{20} + \sqrt{45}$ **5**$\sqrt{5}$ **63.** $\sqrt{3}(\sqrt{6} + 4)$ **3**$\sqrt{2} + 4\sqrt{3}$

64. $\sqrt{72} - \sqrt{50}$ $\sqrt{2}$ **65.** $\sqrt{2}(2\sqrt{8} + 4\sqrt{18})$ **32**

66. $\frac{8}{\sqrt{5} + \sqrt{3}}$ **4**$(\sqrt{5} - \sqrt{3})$ **67.** $\sqrt{12}(7\sqrt{6} + \sqrt{24})$ **54**$\sqrt{2}$

Lesson 10-6

Solve by completing the square. If necessary, round to the nearest tenth.

68. $w^2 + 2w - 11 = 0$ **2.5, −4.5**   **69.** $k^2 - 8k = 3$ **8.4, −0.4**

70. $d^2 + 5d + 1 = 0$ **−0.2, −4.8**   **71.** $2a^2 + 20a = 16$ **−10.7, 0.7**

72. $\frac{1}{5}x^2 + 2x = 4$ **−11.7, 1.7**   **73.** $6g^2 - 9g - 30 = 0$ **−1.6, 3.1**

Lesson 9-5

Factor each expression.

74. $x^2 + 10x - 24$ **(x + 12)(x − 2)**   **75.** $m^2 - 14m + 13$ **(m − 13)(m − 1)**

76. $b^2 + 16b - 36$ **(b + 18)(b − 2)**   **77.** $2p^2 + 15p + 7$ **(2p + 1)(p + 7)**

78. $3d^2 + 12d - 15$ **3(d − 1)(d + 5)**   **79.** $4v^2 - 25v + 25$ **(4v − 5)(v − 5)**

Reading for Problem Solving

Read the problem below, and then follow along with what Lily thinks as she solves the problem. Check your understanding by solving the exercise at the bottom of the page.

Packaging The diagram at the right shows a piece of cardboard that makes a box when sections of it are folded and taped. The ends of the box are x inches by x inches and the box is 10 inches long.

a. Write an equation for the volume V of the box.

b. Solve the equation in part (a) for x.

c. Find the integer values of x that give the box a volume between 40 in.^{3} and 490 in.^{3}, inclusive.

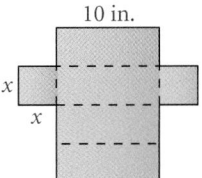
10 in.

What Lily Thinks

What Lily Writes

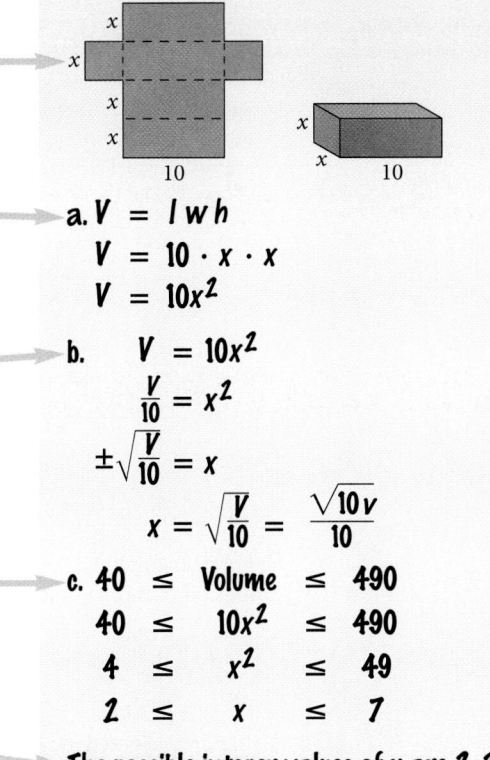

What will this box look like? I'll draw a sketch.

Okay, I can see now that the box has length 10 in., width x in., and height x in. I can substitute these into the formula for the volume of a rectangular prism.

a. $V = lwh$
$V = 10 \cdot x \cdot x$
$V = 10x^2$

Part (b) asks me to solve the equation for x. Since x is a dimension of the box, it can't be negative. So the solution is the positive square root only.

b. $V = 10x^2$
$\dfrac{V}{10} = x^2$
$\pm\sqrt{\dfrac{V}{10}} = x$
$x = \sqrt{\dfrac{V}{10}} = \dfrac{\sqrt{10v}}{10}$

Part (c) asks me to write a sentence showing that the volume is between 40 in.^{3} and 490 in.^{3}. Oh, I can write an inequality! Then I can solve for x.

c. $40 \le \text{Volume} \le 490$
$40 \le 10x^2 \le 490$
$4 \le x^2 \le 49$
$2 \le x \le 7$

Wait! The problem asks for *integer values* only.

The possible integer values of x are 2, 3, 4, 5, 6, and 7.

EXERCISE

Geometry Each edge of a cube has length e.

a. Write an equation for the surface area, S, of the cube in terms of e. $S = 6e^2$

b. Find the integer values of e that will give the cube a surface area between 726 cm^2 and 1176 cm^2, inclusive. **11, 12, 13, 14**

Reading for Problem Solving

Students will read and analyze another student's thoughts about a solution of a multi-step problem before solving a similar type problem. Modeling thinking helps students who have difficulty knowing where and how to get started on a problem.

Teaching Notes

Students will become better problem solvers if they can explain their own thinking about how they solved a problem. Suggest that students pair up after they have solved a problem and explain their thinking to each other. This will help solidify their own strategies as well as give them an appreciation for another student's thoughts about the same problem. Also, students are more likely to find their own errors while they are explaining their solutions to each other.

Visual Learners

Visual learners may benefit from drawing all six of the boxes represented by the answers in the example, and then calculating each volume to see that they are in fact between 40 in^3 and 490 in^3.

Exercise

Give each pair of students a transparency and a marker. Ask them to write their solution to the example under Check Understanding. They should divide the transparency into two columns: write what they think on the left and their solution on the right (similar to Lily's sample). Ask student pairs to volunteer to show their solutions on the overhead projector. Allow for class discussion of the various solutions.

11-6

1. Plan

Lesson Preview

 Check Skills You'll Need

Exploring Quadratic Graphs
Lesson 10-1: Example 4
Exercises 14–19
Extra Practice, p. 711

Square Roots
Lesson 10-3: Example 1
Exercises 1–12
Extra Practice, p. 711

Lesson Resources

📁 **Teaching Resources**
Practice, Reteaching, Enrichment
Checkpoint Quiz 2

👥 **Reaching All Students**
Practice Workbook 11-6
Spanish Practice Workbook 11-6
Reading and Math Literacy 11C
Spanish Reading & Literacy 11C
Spanish Checkpoint Quiz 2
Basic Algebra Planning Guide 11-6

🕐 **Presentation Assistant Plus!**
Transparencies
• Check Skills You'll Need 11-6
• Additional Examples 11-6
• Student Edition Answers 11-6
• Lesson Quiz 11-6
PH Presentation Pro CD 11-6

PRENTICE HALL ASSESSMENT SYSTEM

Checkpoint Quiz 2
Computer Test Generator CD

💿 **Technology**
Resource Pro® CD-ROM
Computer Test Generator CD
Prentice Hall Presentation Pro CD

🖥 **www.PHSchool.com**
Student Site
• Teacher Web Code: aek-5500
• Self-grading Lesson Quiz
Teacher Center
• Lesson Planner
• Resources

Plus

614

 11-6

Graphing Square Root Functions

Lesson Preview

What You'll Learn

OBJECTIVE 1
To graph square root functions

OBJECTIVE 2
To translate graphs of square root functions

. . . And Why

To solve problems involving police work, as in Example 2

✓ **Check Skills You'll Need** (For help, go to Lessons 10-1 and 10-3.)

Graph each pair of quadratic functions on the same graph. 1–2. See back of book.

1. $y = x^2, y = x^2 + 3$ **2.** $y = x^2, y = x^2 - 4$

Evaluate each expression for the given value of x.

3. $\sqrt{x}$ for $x = 4$ **2**   **4.** $\sqrt{x + 7} - 3$ for $x = 2$ **0**   **5.** $3\sqrt{x} + 2$ for $x = 9$ **11**

New Vocabulary   • square root function

OBJECTIVE 1

Graphing Square Root Functions

📱 **TEXT** Interactive lesson includes instant self-check, tutorials, and activities.

Need Help?

For the function $y = \sqrt{x}$, the domain is all nonnegative values of x. The range is all the corresponding values of y.

A **square root function** is a function that contains the independent variable in the radicand. The function $y = \sqrt{x}$ is the simplest square root function. For x-values that are not perfect squares, you can approximate the y-values to the nearest tenth.

You can graph a square root function by plotting points. Plot the least value in the domain and several other points. Then join the points using a curve.

x	y
0	0
1	1
2	1.4
4	2
6	2.4
9	3

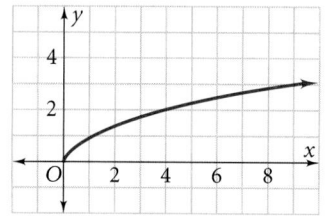

For real numbers, the value of the radicand cannot be negative. So the domain is limited to those values of x that make the radicand greater than or equal to 0.

1 EXAMPLE **Finding the Domain of a Square Root Function**

Find the domain of each function.

a. $y = \sqrt{x + 3}$

$x + 3 \geq 0$ ←Make the radicand ≥ 0.→

$x \geq -3$

The domain is the set of all numbers greater than or equal to -3.

b. $y = 3\sqrt{2x - 8}$

$2x - 8 \geq 0$

$2x \geq 8$

$x \geq 4$

The domain is the set of all numbers greater than or equal to 4.

✓ **Check Understanding** ① Find the domain of $y = \sqrt{x - 7}$. $x \geq 7$

614 Chapter 11 Radical Expressions and Equations

 Ongoing Assessment and Intervention

Before the Lesson
Diagnose prerequisite skills using:
• Check Skills You'll Need

During the Lesson
Monitor progress using:
• Check Understanding
• Additional Examples
• Standardized Test Prep

After the Lesson
Assess knowledge using:
• Lesson Quiz
• Computer Test Generator CD
• Chapter Checkpoint 2 (p. 619)

Real-World Connection

Careers Police officers use mathematics and logical reasoning to analyze accidents.

2 EXAMPLE Real-World  Problem Solving

Measurement For good weather conditions, police can use the formula $r = 2\sqrt{5L}$ to find the approximate speed r of a car that leaves a skid mark of length L in feet. Graph the function.

Length of Skid Mark (ft)	Speed (mi/h)
0	0
10	14.1
20	20
30	24.5
40	28.3

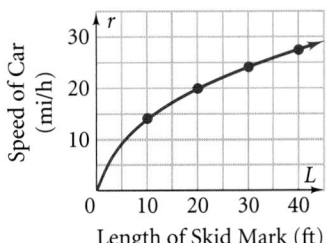

Length of Skid Mark (ft)

See back of book.

✓ **Check Understanding** 2 **a.** Copy and extend the graph in Example 2 for skid mark lengths from 60 ft to 100 ft.
b. Critical Thinking How long is the skid mark when a car's speed before putting on the brakes is 85 mi/h? **361.25 ft**

OBJECTIVE

2 **Translating Graphs of Square Root Functions**

For any positive number k, $y = \sqrt{x} + k$ translates the graph of $y = \sqrt{x}$ up k units, while $y = \sqrt{x} - k$ translates the graph of $y = \sqrt{x}$ down k units.

3 EXAMPLE Graphing a Vertical Translation

Graph $y = \sqrt{x} + 3$ by translating the graph of $y = \sqrt{x}$.

3.
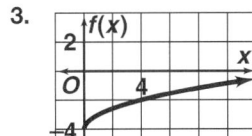

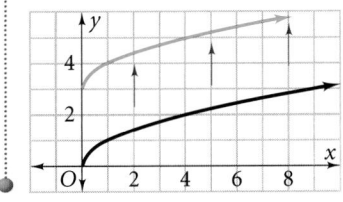

For the graph of $y = \sqrt{x} + 3$, the graph of $y = \sqrt{x}$ is shifted 3 units up.

✓ **Check Understanding** 3 Graph $f(x) = \sqrt{x} - 4$ by translating the graph of $f(x) = \sqrt{x}$. **See left.**

For any positive number h, $y = \sqrt{x + h}$ translates the graph of $y = \sqrt{x}$ to the left h units, while $y = \sqrt{x - h}$ translates the graph of $y = \sqrt{x}$ to the right h units.

4 EXAMPLE Graphing a Horizontal Translation

Graph $f(x) = \sqrt{x + 4}$ by translating the graph of $f(x) = \sqrt{x}$.

4.
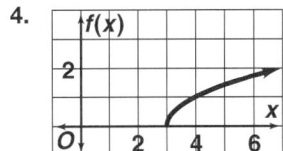

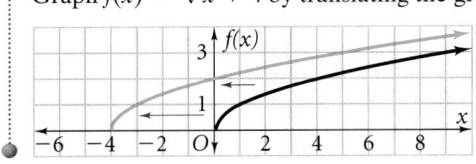

For the graph of $f(x) = \sqrt{x + 4}$, the graph of $f(x) = \sqrt{x}$ is shifted 4 units to the left.

✓ **Check Understanding** 4 Graph $f(x) = \sqrt{x - 3}$ by translating the graph of $f(x) = \sqrt{x}$. **See left.**

Lesson 11-6 Graphing Square Root Functions **615**

Reaching All Students

Below Level When finding the domain of a square root function, students may square the radicand. Emphasize that they are looking for values of x that will make y a real number.	**Advanced Learners** Ask students to describe the effect of a on the graph of $y = \sqrt{x}$ in graphing $y = a\sqrt{x}$.	**Error Prevention** See note on page 616.

Math Background

Since the radicand must be nonnegative, the graph of $y = a\sqrt{bx + c}$ will have no points below the x-axis unless $a < 0$. Note that the radicand is the expression inside the radical sign and does not include the radical sign itself.

OBJECTIVE
1 Teaching Notes

1 EXAMPLE Teaching Tip

The domain of a function containing a square root can have negative values. Encourage students to substitute -3, -2, and -1 for x in the equation $y = \sqrt{x + 3}$ to explore this.

Additional Examples

1 Find the domain of each function.
a. $y = \sqrt{x + 5}$ $x \geq -5$
b. $y = 6\sqrt{4x - 12}$ $x \geq 3$

2 The size of a television screen is the length of the screen's diagonal d in inches. The equation $d = \sqrt{2A}$ estimates the length of a diagonal of a television with screen area A. Graph the function. See back of book.

OBJECTIVE
2 Teaching Notes

Additional Examples

3 Graph $y = \sqrt{x} + 4$ by translating the graph of $y = \sqrt{x}$. See back of book.

4 Graph $f(x) = \sqrt{x + 3}$ by translating the graph of $y = \sqrt{x}$. See back of book.

Closure

Explain how to graph a square root function. **First, determine the domain of the function. Then, graph the function by plotting points. The function may also be graphed by identifying it as a translation of a parent function.**

615

3. Practice

Assignment Guide

1 Objective
 Ⓐ Ⓑ **Core** 1–16, 30–33, 51–58
 Ⓒ **Extension** 59, 62

2 Objective
 Ⓐ Ⓑ **Core** 17–29, 34–50
 Ⓒ **Extension** 60–61

Standardized Test Prep 63–69

Mixed Review 70–87

Error Prevention

Exercises 5, 6, 9 Make sure students understand that adding or subtracting 1 to or from the radical affects the range but not the domain.

Exercises 33 Tell students to use the same value of *n* for each of the three functions.

Enrichment 11-6
Reteaching 11-6
Practice 11-6

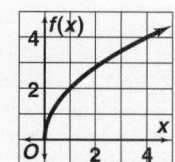

pages 616–619 **Exercises**

2. $x \geq \frac{3}{4}$

3. $x \geq 0$

4. $x \geq -7$

5. $x \geq -3$

6. $x \geq 5$

Ⓐ **Practice by Example**

Example 1
(page 614)

Find the domain of each function. 2–6. See margin.

1. $y = \sqrt{x - 2}$ $x \geq 2$
2. $f(x) = \sqrt{4x - 3}$
3. $y = \sqrt{1.5x}$
4. $f(x) = \sqrt{7 + x}$
5. $y = \sqrt{x + 3} - 1$
6. $f(x) = \sqrt{x - 5} + 1$
7. $f(x) = \sqrt{3x + 5}$ $x \geq -\frac{5}{3}$
8. $f(x) = \sqrt{2 + x}$ $x \geq -2$
9. $f(x) = \sqrt{6x - 8} + 1$ $x \geq \frac{4}{3}$

Example 2
(page 615)

Make a table of values and graph each function. 10–15. See margin.

10. $y = \sqrt{2x}$
11. $f(x) = 2\sqrt{x}$
12. $y = \sqrt{4x - 8}$
13. $y = \sqrt{3x}$
14. $f(x) = 3\sqrt{x}$
15. $y = -3\sqrt{x}$

16. **Physics** You can use the function $v = \sqrt{64h}$ to find the velocity v of an object, ignoring air resistance, after it has fallen h feet. Make a table of values and graph the function. **See margin p. 617.**

Examples 3, 4
(page 615)

Match each graph with its function.

17. $y = \sqrt{x} + 4$ **D**
18. $y = \sqrt{x - 2}$ **A**
19. $y = \sqrt{x} + 4$ **C**
20. $y = \sqrt{x} - 2$ **B**

A.

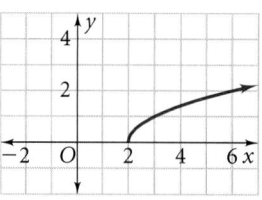

B.

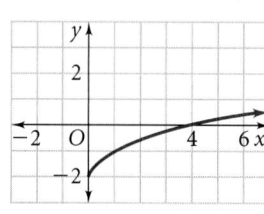

C.

D.

Graph each function by translating the graph of $y = \sqrt{x}$. 21–29. See back of book.

21. $y = \sqrt{x} + 5$
22. $y = \sqrt{x} - 5$
23. $y = \sqrt{x} - 3$
24. $y = \sqrt{x} + 2$
25. $f(x) = \sqrt{x - 2}$
26. $f(x) = \sqrt{x - 4}$
27. $y = \sqrt{x} + 1$
28. $y = \sqrt{x + 1}$
29. $y = \sqrt{x - 1}$

Ⓑ **Apply Your Skills**

30. $x \geq 4; y \geq 0$

31. $x \leq 4; y \geq 0$

30. What are the domain and the range of the function $y = \sqrt{2x - 8}$? **See left.**

31. What are the domain and the range of the function $y = \sqrt{8 - 2x}$? **See left.**

32. **Writing** Explain how to find the domain of a square root function. Include an example. **See margin p. 617.**

33. **Open-Ended** Give an example of a square root function in each form. Choose $n \neq 0$. **a–c. See margin p. 617.**
   a. $y = \sqrt{x} + n$
   b. $y = \sqrt{x + n}$
   c. $y = n\sqrt{x}$
   d. Graph each function in parts (a)–(c). **Check students' work.**

616 Chapter 11 Radical Expressions and Equations

10.

x	y
0	0
2	2
4.5	3

11.

x	f(x)
0	0
1	2
4	4

Writing Describe how to translate the graph of $y = \sqrt{x}$ to obtain the graph of each function. **34–37. See left.**

34. Translate the graph of $y = \sqrt{x}$ 8 units to the left.

35. Translate the graph of $y = \sqrt{x}$ 10 units down.

36. Translate the graph of $y = \sqrt{x}$ 12 units up.

37. Translate the graph of $y = \sqrt{x}$ 9 units right.

34. $y = \sqrt{x + 8}$

35. $f(x) = \sqrt{x} - 10$

36. $f(x) = \sqrt{x} + 12$

37. $y = \sqrt{x - 9}$

Make a table of values and graph each function. 38–46. See back of book.

38. $y = \sqrt{x} - 2.5$ **39.** $f(x) = 4\sqrt{x}$ **40.** $y = \sqrt{x + 6}$

41. $y = \sqrt{0.5x}$ **42.** $y = \sqrt{x - 2} + 3$ **43.** $f(x) = \sqrt{x + 2} - 4$

44. $y = \sqrt{2x} + 3$ **45.** $y = \sqrt{2x + 6} + 1$ **46.** $y = \sqrt{3x - 3} - 2$

Match each graph with its function.

47. $y = \sqrt{x + 1} - 3$ **B**

48. $y = \sqrt{x - 1} + 3$ **D**

49. $y = \sqrt{x - 3} - 1$ **A**

50. $y = \sqrt{x + 3} + 1$ **C**

A.
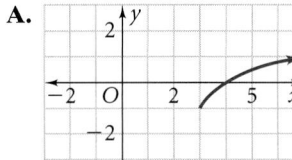

B.
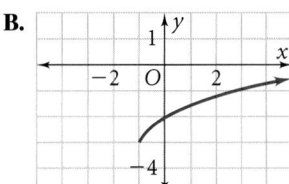

C.
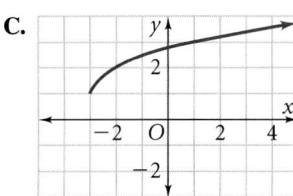

D.
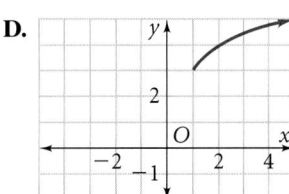

51. Firefighting When firefighters are trying to put out a fire, the rate at which they can spray water on the fire depends on the nozzle pressure. You can find the flow rate f in gallons per minute (gal/min) using the function $f = 120\sqrt{p}$, where p is the nozzle pressure in pounds per square inch (lb/in.²).
a. What is the domain of the function? $p \geq 0$
b. Graph the function. **See margin.**
c. Use the graph to estimate the pressure when the flow rate is 800 gal/min.
  about 45 lb/in.²

52. The graph of $x = y^2$ is shown at the right.
a. Is this the graph of a function? **no**
b. How does $x = y^2$ relate to the square root function $y = \sqrt{x}$? **See margin.**
c. **Critical Thinking** What is a function for the part of the graph that is shown in Quadrant IV?
  $y = -\sqrt{x}$

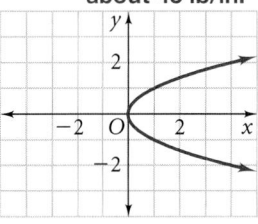

53. Without graphing, determine which graph rises more steeply, $y = \sqrt{3x}$ or $y = 3\sqrt{x}$. Explain your answer. **See margin.**

Determine whether each statement is true or false. If it is false, explain why.

54. If $\sqrt{x} = 9$, then $x = 3$. **False; x must equal 81.**

55. The expression $3 + 4\sqrt{x}$ is equivalent to $7\sqrt{x}$. **False; only combine like terms.**

56. For $\sqrt{x + 5} = 12, x = 139$. **true**

57. $\sqrt{x + 5} = 2$ has no solution. **False; x = −1.**

Real-World Connection

Lesson 11-6 Graphing Square Root Functions **617**

12.
x	y
2	0
3	2
6	4
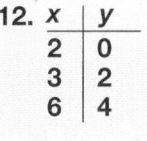

13.
x	y
0	0
3	3
5.3	4
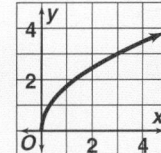

14.
x	f(x)
0	0
1	3
4	6
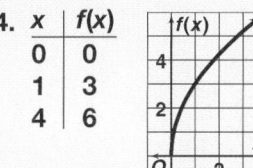

15.
x	y
0	0
1	−3
4	−6
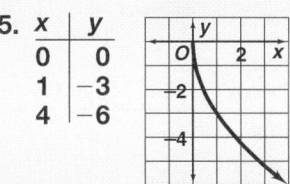

16.
h	v
0	0
1	8
4	16
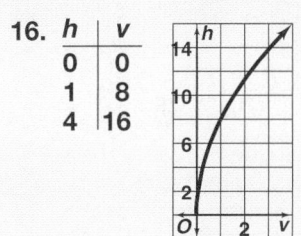

32. **Form an inequality setting the radicand ≥ 0. Solve for x. Answers may vary. Sample:**
$y = \sqrt{x - 2}$
Domain: $x - 2 \geq 0$
$x \geq 2$

33a–c. **Answers may vary. Samples:**
a. $y = \sqrt{x} + 2$
b. $y = \sqrt{x + 2}$
c. $y = 2\sqrt{x}$

51b.
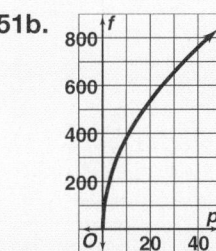

52b. **Answers may vary. Sample: The graph of $y = \sqrt{x}$ is the first quadrant of the graph of $x = y^2$.**

53. $y = 3\sqrt{x}$ **rises more steeply because** $3\sqrt{x} > \sqrt{3x}$ **for all positive values of x.**

617

Lesson Quiz 11-6

1. Find the domain of the function $f(x) = \sqrt{2x - 4}$.
   $x \geq 2$

2. Graph $y = 3\sqrt{x}$.

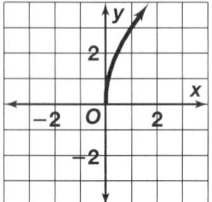

3. Graph $y = \sqrt{x - 3}$.

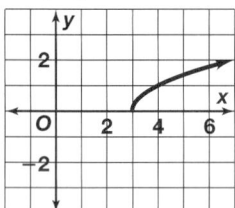

4. Describe how to translate the graph of $y = \sqrt{x}$ to obtain the graph of the function $y = \sqrt{x - 15}$.
   Shift the graph to the right 15 units.

Alternative Assessment

Display several graphs of square root functions and have students determine the equations of the graphs.

Standardized Test Prep

Resources

For additional practice with a variety of test item formats:
• Standardized Test Prep, p. 633
• Test-Taking Strategies, p. 628
• Test-Taking Strategies with Transparencies

Exercise 63 Remind students that the principal square root of an expression can never have a negative value. Since y is always nonnegative, answer choices C and D can be eliminated since they contain points in quadrants III and IV.

618

Real-World **Connection**

Single-use cameras were introduced in 1986. By 1992, manufacturers had redesigned the cameras so that their parts could be reused or recycled.

C Challenge

60. Translate the graph of $y = \sqrt{x}$ right 2 units and up 3 units.

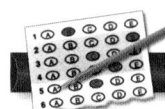

58. **Business** Last year a store had an advertising campaign. The graph shows the sales for single-use cameras. The function $n = 27\sqrt{5t} + 53$ models the sales volume n for the cameras as a function of time t, the number of months after the start of the advertising campaign.
    a. Evaluate the function to find how many disposable cameras the store sold in the seventh month.
    b. Solve an equation to find the month in which the number of single-use cameras sold was about 175.
    a. about 213 cameras   **b. month 4**

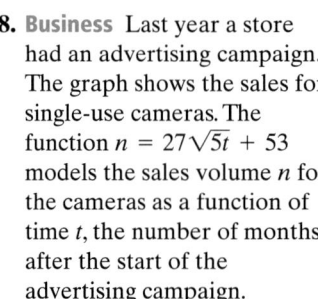

Single-Use Camera Sales

59. a. Graph $y = \sqrt{x^2} + 5$. **a–b. See margin.**
    b. Write a function for the graph you drew that does not require a radical.

60. Explain how you can translate $y = \sqrt{x}$ to graph $y = \sqrt{x - 2} + 3$.

61. a. Graph each function. **a–b. See margin.**
    i. $y = \sqrt{4x}$ ii. $y = \sqrt{5x}$ iii. $y = \sqrt{6x}$ iv. $y = \sqrt{-6x}$
    b. **Critical Thinking** Describe how the graph of $y = \sqrt{nx}$ changes as the value of n varies.

62. **Data Collection** Roll a ball down a ramp which is at least 6 ft long. Record the time the ball takes to roll several different distances down the ramp, up to its full length.
    a. Graph your data with time as a function of distance (d, t).
    b. Describe your graph. Explain why it is *not* linear.
    a–b. Check students' work.

Standardized Test Prep

Multiple Choice

63. Which of the following is the graph of $y = \sqrt{1 - x}$? **B**

    A.
    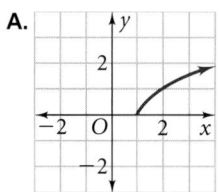

    B.
    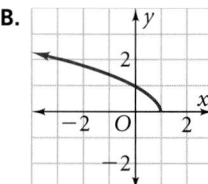

    C.
    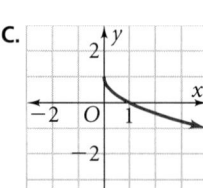

    D.
    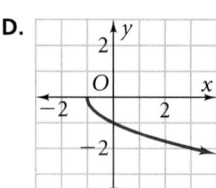

64. What is the least possible value for x for the graph of $y = \sqrt{2x - 44} + 3$? **H**
    F. 3   **G.** 19   **H.** 22   **I.** 25

618   Chapter 11   Radical Expressions and Equations

pages 616–619   Exercises

59a. 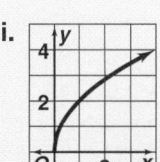   b. $y = |x| + 5$ 61a. i. 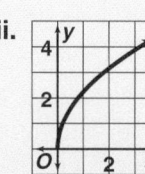   ii. 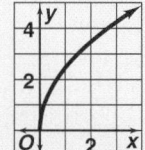   iii. 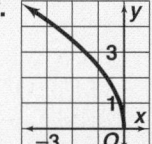   iv.

65. What is the greatest possible value of y for the graph of $y = -\sqrt{5x - 10}$?C

A. -10 B. -2 C. 0 D. 2

66. If $x = -2$, which function has the least value? H

F. $y = \sqrt{7 - x}$ G. $y = \sqrt{7 + x}$

H. $y = \sqrt{-x} - 7$ I. $y = \sqrt{-x} + 7$

67. If $a = \sqrt{24}$, and $\frac{a}{b} = \frac{\sqrt{6}}{c}$, then what does $\frac{c}{b}$ equal? B

A. $\frac{1}{4}$ B. $\frac{1}{2}$ C. 2 D. 4

68. In which quadrant(s) is the graph of $y = \sqrt{x} + 7$? H

F. I, II, and III   G. I and IV   H. I   I. I and II

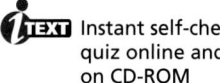
Take It to the NET
Online lesson quiz at
www.PHSchool.com
Web Code: aea-1106

Short Response   **69.** Graph $y = \sqrt{x - 6}$. See margin.

Mixed Review

Lesson 11-5   Solve each equation. Check your solutions.

70. $\sqrt{x} + 7 = 11$ 16   **71.** $\sqrt{c + 1} = \sqrt{2c - 6}$ 7

72. $\sqrt{x} - 4 = 9$ 169   **73.** $13 = 5\sqrt{m - 8}$ 14.76

74. $\sqrt{k + 3} + 12 = 6$ no solution   **75.** $\sqrt{5h - 2} = \sqrt{2h}$ $\frac{2}{3}$

Lesson 10-7   Use the quadratic formula to solve each equation. 76–81. See margin.

76. $2x^2 + 4x - 7 = 0$ **77.** $x^2 - 8x - 23 = 0$

78. $5x^2 - x + 11 = 0$ **79.** $9x^2 + 6x - 10 = 0$

80. $1.2x^2 + x + 6 = 0$ **81.** $9x^2 + 13x - 7 = 0$

Lesson 9-6   Factor completely.

82. $2x^2 - 7x - 4$ $(2x + 1)(x - 4)$ **83.** $3x^2 + x - 10$ $(3x - 5)(x + 2)$

84. $4x^2 + 20x + 9$ $(2x + 1)(2x + 9)$ **85.** $2x^2 - 10x - 48$ $2(x - 8)(x + 3)$

86. $4x^2 - 4x - 60$ $4(x^2 - x - 15)$ **87.** $x^3 - 12x^2 - 13x$ $x(x - 13)(x + 1)$

✓ Checkpoint Quiz 2   Lessons 11-4 through 11-6

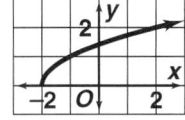
iTEXT Instant self-check quiz online and on CD-ROM

Simplify each expression.

1. $-10\sqrt{7} + 2\sqrt{7}$ $-8\sqrt{7}$ **2.** $\sqrt{16} - 5\sqrt{2}$ $4 - 5\sqrt{2}$

3. $2\sqrt{5} + 3\sqrt{25}$ $2\sqrt{5} + 15$ **4.** $\sqrt{6}(\sqrt{12} - \sqrt{3})$ $3\sqrt{2}$

5. $(\sqrt{3} + \sqrt{2})^2$ $5 + 2\sqrt{6}$ **6.** $\frac{\sqrt{8} - \sqrt{27}}{\sqrt{6} - \sqrt{5}}$

$4\sqrt{3} + 2\sqrt{10} - 9\sqrt{2} - 3\sqrt{15}$

10. It is translated 2 units left.

Solve each equation.

7. $4 - \sqrt{m} = -12$ 256   **8.** $\sqrt{t + 5} = \sqrt{2t - 3}$ 8   **9.** $r = \sqrt{4r + 5}$ 5

10. Writing Describe how to translate the graph of $y = \sqrt{x}$ in order to graph $y = \sqrt{x + 2}$. Then graph the function. **See left.**

b. The greater the absolute value of n, the steeper the graph. If $n < 0$, then the graph lies in Quadrant II. If $n > 0$, the graph lies in Quadrant I.

69. [2]

x	y
6	0
7	1
8	1.4
9	1.7
10	2

[1] incorrect coordinates on graph

76. $-1 - \frac{3}{2}\sqrt{2}, -1 + \frac{3}{2}\sqrt{2}$

77. $4 - \sqrt{39}, 4 + \sqrt{39}$

78. no solution

79. $\frac{-1 - \sqrt{11}}{3}, \frac{-1 + \sqrt{11}}{3}$

80. no solution

81. $\frac{-13 - \sqrt{421}}{18}, \frac{-13 + \sqrt{421}}{18}$

✓ Chapter Checkpoint 2

To check understanding of Lessons 11-4 to 11-6:

Checkpoint Quiz 2 (p. 619)

Teaching Resources
Checkpoint Quiz 2 (also in Prentice Hall Assessment System)

Reaching All Students
Reading and Math Literacy 11C

Spanish versions available

Extension

Rational Exponents

Rational Exponents

Students make connections between finding other roots with finding square roots. They also learn that you can express roots using fractions as exponents.

Resources

Technology
Computer Test Generator CD-ROM, Chapter 11, Extension Topics

Teaching Notes

Teaching Tip
Square roots, cube roots, and all other roots get their names because they are roots of equations. For instance, the square roots $\sqrt{3}$ is a root of the equation $x^2 - 3 = 0$. Students may wish to revisit the Technology Extension for Lesson 10–4 and find this root with a graphing calculator.

Visual Learners
The radical sign $(\sqrt{})$ is a distorted letter r. The words *radical* and *radicand* are both derived from the Latin word for *root*.

You can have roots other than square roots. The third root of a number x is written as $\sqrt[3]{x}$. For example, $\sqrt[3]{8} = 2$ because $2^3 = 8$. You can also express roots using exponents. The expression $a^{\frac{1}{n}}$ is defined as $\sqrt[n]{a}$. An example is $9^{\frac{1}{2}} = \sqrt[2]{9} = 3$.

Rational exponents follow the same rules as integer exponents, so $9^{\frac{1}{2}} \cdot 9^{\frac{1}{2}} = 9^{\left(\frac{1}{2} + \frac{1}{2}\right)} = 9^1 = 9$, just as $\sqrt{9} \cdot \sqrt{9} = 9$.

1 EXAMPLE

Simplify $16^{\frac{1}{4}}$.

$16^{\frac{1}{4}} = 2$ $16 = 2 \cdot 2 \cdot 2 \cdot 2$, so $\sqrt[4]{16} = 2$

An exponent can be any rational number. You can simplify rational exponents using the property of raising a power to a power, $a^{mn} = \left(a^m\right)^n$.

2 EXAMPLE

Simplify $8^{\frac{2}{3}}$.

a. $\quad 8^{\frac{2}{3}} = 8^{\frac{1}{3} \cdot 2}$ ←——— Write $\frac{2}{3}$ as a product of 2 and $\frac{1}{3}$. ———→ b. $8^{\frac{2}{3}} = 8^{2 \cdot \frac{1}{3}}$

$\quad = \left(8^{\frac{1}{3}}\right)^2$ ←—— Use the property of raising a power to a power. ——→ $= \left(8^2\right)^{\frac{1}{3}}$

$\quad = (2)^2$ ←——— Simplify within the parentheses. ———→ $= (64)^{\frac{1}{3}}$

$\quad = 4$ ←——————— Simplify. ———————→ $= 4$

3 EXAMPLE

Simplify $\left(x^{\frac{3}{4}}\right)^5\left(y^{\frac{1}{2}}\right)y^{\frac{2}{5}}$.

$\left(x^{\frac{3}{4}}\right)^5\left(y^{\frac{1}{2}}\right)y^{\frac{2}{5}} = \left(x^{\frac{15}{4}}\right)\left(y^{\frac{1}{2}} \cdot y^{\frac{2}{5}}\right)$ Multiply exponents in $\left(x^{\frac{3}{4}}\right)^5$.

$\qquad = x^{\frac{15}{4}}\left(y^{\frac{1}{2} + \frac{2}{5}}\right)$ Add exponents of powers with the same base.

$\qquad = x^{\frac{15}{4}} y^{\frac{9}{10}}$ Simplify fractions. $\frac{1}{2} + \frac{2}{5} = \frac{9}{10}$. Leave $\frac{15}{4}$ as an improper fraction.

EXERCISES

Simplify each expression.

1. $100^{\frac{1}{2}}$ **10**

2. $25^{\frac{1}{2}}$ **5**

3. $8^{\frac{1}{3}}$ **2**

4. $\left(49^{\frac{1}{2}}\right)^3$ **343**

5. $\left(8^{\frac{1}{3}}\right)^2$ **4**

6. $8^{\frac{4}{3}}$ **16**

7. $25^{\frac{3}{2}}$ **125**

8. $64^{\frac{4}{3}}$ **256**

9. $\left(x^{\frac{1}{3}}\right)^6$ x^2

10. $\left(b^{\frac{1}{4}}\right)^4$ b

11. $\left(m^{\frac{2}{5}}\right)^{\frac{5}{3}}$ $m^{\frac{2}{3}}$

12. $\left(m^{\frac{2}{5}}\right)\left(m^{\frac{3}{5}}\right)$ m

page 621   Investigation

1. **Check students' work.**

   a–c. 3, 4, 5, $\frac{3}{4}, \frac{3}{5}, \frac{4}{5}$ 6, 8, 10, $\frac{3}{4}, \frac{3}{5}, \frac{4}{5}$

2. **Answers may vary. Sample:**

3. **For both triangles, corresponding ratios are equal.**

Trigonometric Ratios

2.01 Find the lengths and midpoints of segments to solve problems.

Lesson Preview

What You'll Learn

OBJECTIVE 1
To find trigonometric ratios

OBJECTIVE 2
To solve problems using trigonometric ratios

. . . And Why

To solve problems involving navigation and aviation, as in Examples 4 and 5

✓ Check Skills You'll Need

(For help, go to Lessons 1-6 and 4-2.)

Let $c = \frac{A}{H}$, $s = \frac{O}{H}$, $t = \frac{O}{A}$. Calculate c, s, and t for the given values.

1. $A = 3, O = 4, H = 5$ $\frac{3}{5}; \frac{4}{5}; \frac{4}{3}$

2. $A = 5, O = 12, H = 13$ $\frac{5}{13}; \frac{12}{13}; \frac{12}{5}$

Solve each equation.

3. $\frac{15}{x} = \frac{0.75}{1}$ 20

4. $\frac{x}{20} = \frac{0.34}{1}$ 6.8

5. $\frac{0.84}{1} = \frac{21}{x}$ 25

6. $\frac{x}{0.52} = \frac{14}{1}$ 7.28

New Vocabulary • trigonometric ratios • sine • cosine • tangent • angle of elevation • angle of depression

OBJECTIVE 1

Finding Trigonometric Ratios

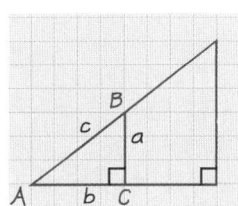

iTEXT Interactive lesson includes instant self-check, tutorials, and activities.

Investigation: Trigonometric Ratios

1. On graph paper, draw a right triangle like the one at the left. Extend sides $\overline{AB}$ and $\overline{AC}$ to form a second triangle similar to the first.

2. a. Copy the table at the right. Measure and record the lengths of the legs of each triangle.

   b. Calculate c, the length of each hypotenuse.

   c. Calculate and record the ratios $\frac{a}{b}$, $\frac{a}{c}$, and $\frac{b}{c}$ for each triangle.

3. How do corresponding ratios in the two triangles compare?

Triangle	a	b	c	$\frac{a}{b}$	$\frac{a}{c}$	$\frac{b}{c}$
First	■	■	■	■	■	■
Second	■	■	■	■	■	■

1–3. See margin.

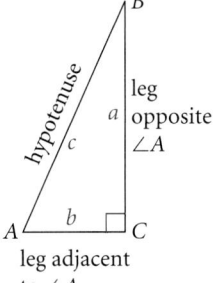

Ratios of corresponding sides of similar right triangles are called **trigonometric ratios.** In $\triangle ABC$, at the left, you see the relationships between an angle and the legs of a triangle. The same letter indicates the lengths of the sides of the triangle and the angle opposite that side.

You can use these relationships to express trigonometric ratios.

sine of $\angle A = \dfrac{\text{length of leg opposite } \angle A}{\text{length of hypotenuse}}$ or $\sin A = \dfrac{a}{c} = \dfrac{\text{opposite leg}}{\text{hypotenuse}}$

cosine of $\angle A = \dfrac{\text{length of leg adjacent to } \angle A}{\text{length of hypotenuse}}$ or $\cos A = \dfrac{b}{c} = \dfrac{\text{adjacent leg}}{\text{hypotenuse}}$

tangent of $\angle A = \dfrac{\text{length of leg opposite } \angle A}{\text{length of leg adjacent to } \angle A}$ or $\tan A = \dfrac{a}{b} = \dfrac{\text{opposite leg}}{\text{adjacent leg}}$

Ongoing Assessment and Intervention

Before the Lesson
Diagnose prerequisite skills using:
• Check Skills You'll Need

During the Lesson
Monitor progress using:
• Check Understanding
• Additional Examples
• Standardized Test Prep

After the Lesson
Assess knowledge using:
• Lesson Quiz
• Computer Test Generator CD

1. Plan

Lesson Preview

✓ Check Skills You'll Need

Multiplying and Dividing Real Numbers
Lesson 1-6: Examples 6 and 7
Exercises 48–57
Extra Practice, p. 702

Proportions and Similar Figures
Lesson 4-2: Examples 1–3
Exercises 1–14
Extra Practice, p. 705

Lesson Resources

📁 **Teaching Resources**
Practice, Reteaching, Enrichment

👥 **Reaching All Students**
Practice Workbook 11-7
Spanish Practice Workbook 11-7
Hands-On Activities 28
Basic Algebra Planning Guide 11-7

⏰ **Presentation Assistant Plus!**
Transparencies
• Check Skills You'll Need 11-7
• Additional Examples 11-7
• Student Edition Answers 11-7
• Lesson Quiz 11-7
PH Presentation Pro CD 11-7

PRENTICE HALL ASSESSMENT SYSTEM

Computer Test Generator CD

💿 **Technology**
Resource Pro® CD-ROM
Computer Test Generator CD
Prentice Hall Presentation Pro CD

🖥 **www.PHSchool.com**
Student Site
• Teacher Web Code: aek-5500
• Graphing Calculator, Procedure 10
• Self-grading Lesson Quiz
Teacher Center
• Lesson Planner
• Resources

Plus

Math Background

Similar geometric figures have the same shape, but may not be the same size. The corresponding sides of similar figures are proportional. Two right triangles will be similar if they have one acute angle with the same measure.

OBJECTIVE

1 Teaching Notes

Investigation (Optional)

Connection to Language Arts

Tell students that a *polygon* is a many-sided figure. A *trigon* is a three-sided figure. The suffix—*metry* means "measure." *Trigonometry* means the study of finding the measures of three-sided figures, which are triangles.

1 EXAMPLE Teaching Tip

To help students remember the trigonometric ratios, encourage them to create their own mnemonic devices. They might use the classic SOH-CAH-TOA, or create their own phrases.

2 EXAMPLE Error Prevention

Students may become confused when finding the opposite and adjacent sides if the angles are switched or the triangle is rotated to other positions. Show students triangles in a variety of positions and have them name the sides that are opposite and adjacent to various angles.

1 EXAMPLE Finding Trigonometric Ratios

Use the triangle below. Find sin A, cos A, and tan A.

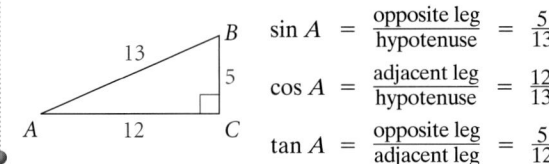

$$\sin A = \frac{\text{opposite leg}}{\text{hypotenuse}} = \frac{5}{13}$$

$$\cos A = \frac{\text{adjacent leg}}{\text{hypotenuse}} = \frac{12}{13}$$

$$\tan A = \frac{\text{opposite leg}}{\text{adjacent leg}} = \frac{5}{12}$$

✓ **Check Understanding** **1** a. Use the triangle in Example 1. Find sin B, cos B, and tan B. $\frac{12}{13}$; $\frac{5}{13}$; $\frac{12}{5}$

b. Critical Thinking What is the relationship between sin A and cos B?
They are equal.

You can use a calculator to find the values of the trigonometric ratios when you know the measure of an angle.

2 EXAMPLE Finding a Trigonometric Ratio With a Calculator

Find sin 50°.

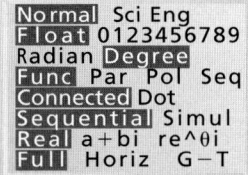

Use degree mode when finding trigonometric ratios.

To find sin 50°, press SIN 50 ENTER.

● Rounded to the nearest ten-thousandth, sin 50° is 0.7660.

✓ **Check Understanding** **2** Find the value of each expression. Round to the nearest ten-thousandth.
a. sin 70° **0.9397**   **b.** cos 70° **0.3420**   **c.** tan 70° **2.7475**

You can use trigonometry to find missing lengths in a triangle when you know the length of one side and the measure of one of the angles.

3 EXAMPLE Finding Missing Side Lengths

Find the value of x in the triangle at the right.

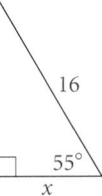

Step 1 Decide which trigonometric ratio to use.

You know the angle and the length of the hypotenuse. You are trying to find the adjacent side. Use the cosine.

Step 2 Write an equation and solve.

$$\cos 55° = \frac{\text{adjacent leg}}{\text{hypotenuse}}$$

$$\cos 55° = \frac{x}{16}$$ **Substitute x for adjacent leg and 16 for hypotenuse.**

$$x = 16(\cos 55°)$$ **Solve for x.**

16 ✗ COS 55 = 9.177222982   **Use a calculator.**

$$x \approx 9.2$$ **Round to the nearest tenth.**

● The value of x is about 9.2.

👥 Reaching All Students

| **Below Level** Remind students that one leg of an angle of elevation or depression is always horizontal. | **Advanced Learners** Challenge students to explain how they would find an angle of elevation given the lengths of the opposite leg and the adjacent leg of a right triangle. | **English Learners** See note on page 625. **Visual Learners** See note on page 623. |

✓ **Check Understanding** ③ Find the value of x in each triangle. Round to the nearest tenth.

a.
x 6.9

$35°$ 12

b.   5.6

$42°$

x

5

OBJECTIVE

2 Solving Problems Using Trigonometric Ratios

You can use trigonometric ratios to measure distances indirectly when you know an angle of elevation. An **angle of elevation** is an angle from the horizontal up to a line of sight.

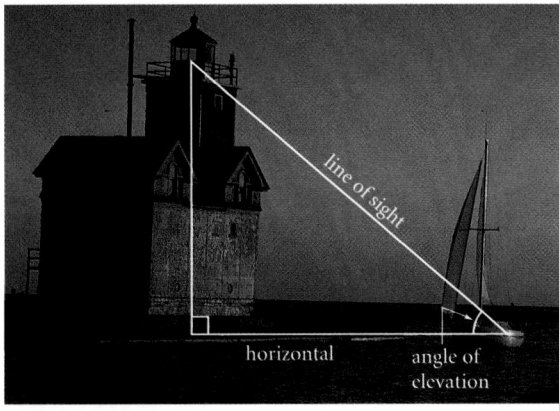

line of sight

horizontal   angle of elevation

4 **EXAMPLE**   Using Angle of Elevation

Navigation Suppose the angle of elevation from a rowboat to the light of a lighthouse is 35°. You know that the lighthouse is 96 ft tall. How far from the lighthouse is the rowboat? Round your answer to the nearest foot.

Draw a diagram.

Define Let x = the distance from the boat to the lighthouse.

Relate You know the angle of elevation and the opposite leg. You are trying to find the adjacent leg. Use the tangent.

96 ft

35°

x

Write $\tan A = \dfrac{\text{opposite leg}}{\text{adjacent leg}}$

$\tan 35° = \dfrac{96}{x}$ **Substitute for the angle and the legs.**

$x(\tan 35°) = 96$ **Multiply each side by x.**

$x = \dfrac{96}{\tan 35}$ **Divide each side by tan 35°.**

$x \approx 137.1022086$ **Use a calculator.**

$x \approx 137$ **Round to the nearest unit.**

● The rowboat is about 137 ft from the lighthouse.

Lesson 11-7   Trigonometric Ratios   **623**

📖 **Additional Examples**

① Use the triangle. Find sin A, cos A, and tan A.
$\dfrac{3}{5}, \dfrac{4}{5}, \dfrac{3}{4}$

A

8 10

C 6 B

② Find sin 40° by using a calculator. Round to the nearest ten-thousandth. **0.6428**

③ Find the value of x in the triangle. Round to the nearest tenth. **13.0**

C

15

$30°$

B x A

OBJECTIVE

2 Teaching Notes

④ **EXAMPLE** Teaching Tip

Discuss whether it would be possible to try to solve this problem by directly measuring the distance. Ask students how they could measure a distance of 137 ft. Develop the conclusion that indirect measurement also can save enormous amounts of time, money, and labor.

⑤ **EXAMPLE** Visual Learners

Encourage students to use color to keep track of which length (side) is in the numerator and which length (side) is in the denominator.

📖 **Additional Example**

④ Suppose the angle of elevation from a rowboat to the top of a lighthouse is 70°. You know that the lighthouse is 70 ft tall. How far from the lighthouse is the rowboat? Round your answer to the nearest foot. **about 25 ft**

623

Closure

Ask students to give the definition of trigonometric ratios in their own words without using terms such as adjacent, opposite, or hypotenuse. **Answers may vary. Sample: Sine is the side directly across from the angle divided by the longest side. Cosine is the side next to the angle that is not the longest side, divided by the longest side. Tangent is the side directly across from the angle, divided by the side next to the angle that is not the longest side.**

✓ **Check Understanding** ④ The angle of elevation from a point on the ground 300 ft from a tower is 42°. How tall is the tower? **about 270 ft**

An **angle of depression** is an angle measured below the horizontal line of sight. In the picture below, a ranger is looking down from the tower to the distant fire.

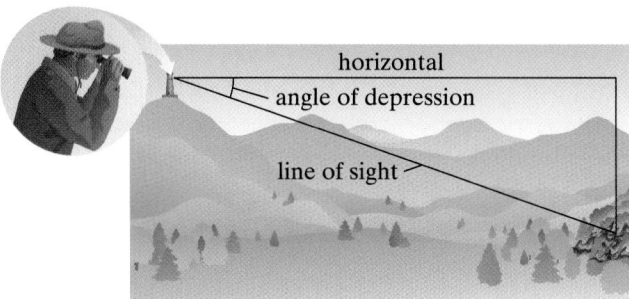

horizontal
angle of depression
line of sight

When you solve real-world problems involving trigonometry, you frequently have to round your answers. Round your answers to the measurements used in the problem. If the problem has measurements to the nearest foot, round your answer to the nearest foot. If the problem has measurements to the nearest 10,000 feet, round your answer to the nearest 10,000 feet.

5 EXAMPLE Using Angle of Depression

Aviation A pilot is flying a plane 20,000 ft above the ground. The pilot begins a 2° descent to an airport runway. How far is the airplane from the start of the runway (in ground distance)?

Draw a diagram.

2°   x
                    20,000 ft
Ground   x   Start of Runway

Define Let x = the ground distance from the start of the runway.

Relate You know the angle of depression and the opposite leg. You are trying to find the adjacent leg. Use the tangent.

Write $\tan B = \dfrac{\text{opposite leg}}{\text{adjacent leg}}$

$\tan 2° = \dfrac{20{,}000}{x}$ **Substitute for the angle and the legs.**

$x(\tan 2°) = 20{,}000$ **Multiply each side by x.**

$x = \dfrac{20{,}000}{\tan 2}$ **Divide each side by tan 2.**

$x \approx 572{,}725.0657$ **Use a calculator.**

$x \approx 570{,}000$ **Round to the nearest 10,000 feet.**

The airplane is about 570,000 feet (or about 110 miles) from the start of the runway.

✓ **Check Understanding** ⑤ Suppose the pilot in Example 5 is flying at an altitude of 26,000 ft when the airplane begins a 2° descent. How far is the airplane from the start of the runway? **745,000 ft**

EXERCISES

For more practice, see *Extra Practice*.

Practice and Problem Solving

 Practice by Example

Example 1
(page 622)

Use △ RST at the right. Find the value of each expression.

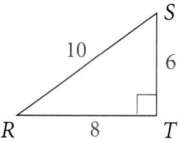

1. sin R $\frac{3}{5}$ **2.** cos R $\frac{4}{5}$ **3.** tan R $\frac{3}{4}$

4. sin S $\frac{4}{5}$ **5.** cos S $\frac{3}{5}$ **6.** tan S $\frac{4}{3}$

Example 2
(page 622)

Find the value of each expression. Round to the nearest ten-thousandth.

7. sin 32°   **8.** cos 55°   **9.** tan 52°   **10.** sin 85°   **11.** cos 15°
  0.5299   0.5736   1.2799   0.9962   0.9659

Example 3
(page 622)

Find the value of x to the nearest tenth.

12. 5.5 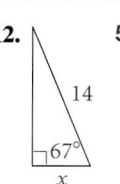   **13.** 10.4 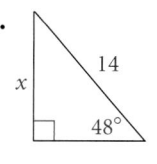   **14.** 19.2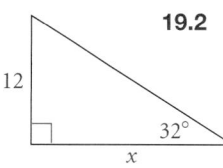

15. 38.1    **16.** 66.0 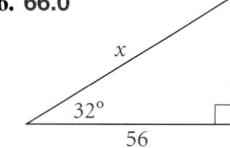   **17.** 21.1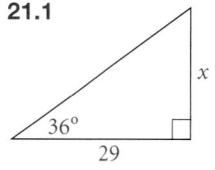

Example 4
(page 623)

18. Aviation Suppose you live about 5.1 miles from a tower. From your home, you see a plane directly above the tower. Your angle of elevation to the plane is 21°. What is the plane's altitude? **about 2.0 mi**

19. Nature At a point 80 ft from a tree a forest ranger measures the angle of elevation to the top of the tree as 65°. How tall is the tree? **about 172 ft**

Example 5
(page 624)

20. Nature Suppose you look down from the top of a vertical cliff to a cabin on the floor of a canyon. The angle of depression is 58°. The cabin is 510 ft from the base of the canyon wall. How high is the canyon wall? **about 816 ft**

21. Navigation A submarine travels 2.6 miles diving at an angle of 8°. How deep is the submarine beneath the surface of the water? **about 0.4 mi**

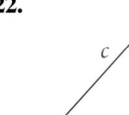 **Apply Your Skills**

For each triangle, find the value of the variable. Then find sin A, cos A, and tan A.

22. 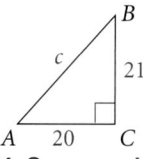   **23.** 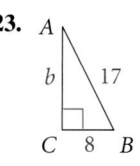   **24.**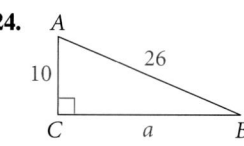

22–24. See margin.

Suppose △ ABC has right angle C. Find the measures of the other sides to the nearest whole number.

25. $m\angle A = 40°, BC = 5$ $AC \approx 6; AB \approx 8$ **26.** $m\angle A = 32°, AB = 42$ $AC \approx 36; BC \approx 22$

27. $m\angle B = 71°, AC = 17$ $BC \approx 6; AB \approx 18$ **28.** $m\angle B = 5°, BC = 50$ $AC \approx 4; AB \approx 50$

Lesson 11-7   Trigonometric Ratios   **625**

Assignment Guide

Objective

   A B Core 1–17, 22–28, 34–37

   C Extension 45

**Objective**

   A B Core 18–21, 29–33, 38–42

   C Extension 43–44, 46

Standardized Test Prep 47–50

Mixed Review 51–62

English Learners

Exercise 20 Unfamiliar vocabulary or the use of certain words in different contexts may make this problem difficult for students to visualize. On the board, sketch and label the *cabin*, the *canyon*, the *floor of the canyon*, the *vertical cliff*, and the *canyon wall* to illustrate their physical relationship.

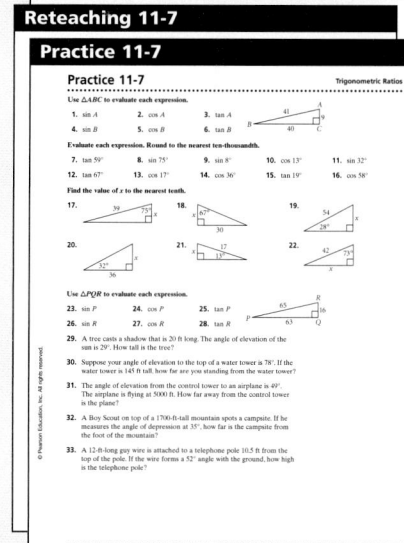

---

pages 625–627   **Exercises**

22. sin A = $\frac{21}{29}$; cos A = $\frac{20}{29}$;

   tan A = $\frac{21}{20}$

23. sin A = $\frac{8}{17}$; cos A = $\frac{15}{17}$;

   tan A = $\frac{8}{15}$

24. sin A = $\frac{12}{13}$; cos A = $\frac{5}{13}$;

   tan A = $\frac{12}{5}$

4. Assess

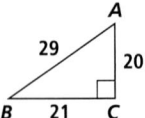

Lesson Quiz 11-7

1. Use the figure to find sin A, cos A, and tan A. $\frac{21}{29}, \frac{20}{29}, \frac{21}{20}$

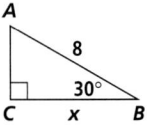

2. Find the value of x to the nearest tenth. **6.9**

3. A group of skateboarders wants to build a ramp with an angle of incline of 14°. What should the rise be for every 10 meters of run? **about 2.5 m**

4. A park ranger on a 220 ft tower spots a fire at an angle of depression of 4°. How far is the fire from the base of the tower? **about 3146 ft**

5. A wheelchair ramp is to have an angle of 3.5° with the ground. The deck at the top of the ramp is 18 in. above the ground. How long should the ramp be? **about 294.3 in.**

Alternative Assessment

Group students in pairs. Have each student create a situation and draw a diagram of it similar in character to those in Examples 4 and 5 and Practice Exercises 18–21. Then have the students exchange papers and solve the problems.

29. **Hobbies** Suppose you are flying a kite. The kite string is 60 m long, and the angle of elevation of the string is 65° from your hand. Your hand is 1 m above the ground. How high above the ground is the kite? **about 55 m**

30. **Engineering** To support a pole, a cable is drawn tightly between the pole and the ground. The cable is 4.1 m from the base of the pole, and the angle of elevation from the bottom of the cable to the top of the pole is 47°. How tall is the pole? **about 4.4 m**

31. a. **Aviation** A pilot is flying a plane at an altitude of 30,000 ft. The pilot begins a 1° descent to an airport runway. How far is the airplane from the start of the runway (in ground distance)? **1,720,000 ft**
    b. What is your answer to part (a) in miles? **326 mi**

32. **Nature** The length of a tree's shadow is 15 m. The angle of elevation of the sun is 38°. What is the height of the tree? **12 m**

33. A 7-meter ladder rests against the side of a house. The angle of elevation of the ladder is 75°. How high is the top of the ladder? **about 6.8 m**

Find the value of the variable in each figure to the nearest tenth.

34. 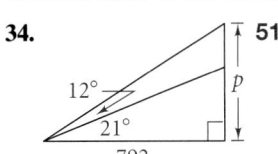 **514.3**

35. 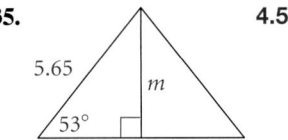 **4.5**

36. 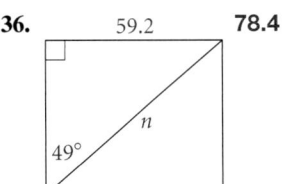 **78.4**

37. 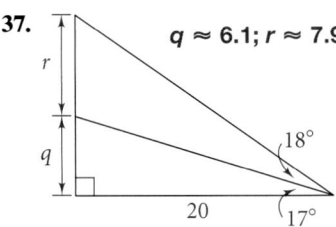 $q \approx 6.1; r \approx 7.9$

38. **Recreation** Use the Ferris wheel photo at the left.
    a. Find the height at the top of the Ferris wheel. **about 177 ft**
    b. If the hub or center of the wheel is about 91 feet off the ground, what is the radius of the wheel? **about 86 ft**

39. **Nature** Suppose you are lying on the ground looking up at a California redwood tree. Your angle of elevation to the top of the tree is 42°. You are 280 ft from the base of the tree.
    a. How tall is the tree? **about 252 ft**
    b. How far would a bird have to fly to get from the top of the tree to your location? **about 377 ft**

40. **Open-Ended** Draw a right triangle. Measure one acute angle and one leg. Use a trigonometric ratio to find the length of the other leg. **See margin p. 627.**

41. A person is in a lighthouse 225 ft above sea level. She sees a ship in the harbor. The angle of depression from her position to the ship is 48°. How far is the ship from shore? **about 203 ft**

42. An air-traffic controller is in a 78-meter-high tower and sees a plane, which is 7500 meters away (in ground distance), at an angle of elevation of 38°. What is the altitude of the plane? **about 5938 m**

 **Challenge**

43. An architect is designing an access ramp. The angle of the ramp with the ground will be 5°. The top of the ramp will be 5 ft above the ground. How long will the ramp be? **about 57 ft**

44. At a certain point in a large, level park, the angle of elevation to the top of an office building is 30°. If you move 400 ft closer to the building, the angle of elevation is 45°. To the nearest 10 feet, how tall is the building? **550 ft**

45. A line passes through the origin and forms an angle of 14° with the x-axis. Find the slope of the line. Round to the nearest hundreth. **0.25**

46. An airplane flies at an altitude of 12 km.
   a. If the pilot wants the angle of descent to be 3°, how far from the airport must he start descending? **about 229 km**
   b. Assume the pilot begins his descent at the distance you found in part (a). If he uses an angle of descent of 2°, what will his altitude be as the plane passes over the airport? **about 4 km**

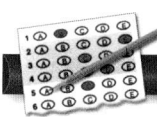

Standardized Test Prep

Multiple Choice

47. Find the value of x to the nearest tenth. **C**
   A. 7.2   **B.** 9.1
   C. 10.9   **D.** 11.9
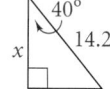

48. $\triangle KLM$ is a right triangle with a right angle at M. Which of the given statements is false? **G**
   F. $\sin K = \frac{LM}{KL}$ **G.** $\cos K = \frac{KL}{KM}$ **H.** $\tan K = \frac{LM}{KM}$ **I.** $\cos L = \frac{LM}{KL}$

Short Response

49. Using the triangle at the right, find $\sin A$, $\cos A$, and $\tan A$. **See margin.**

Extended Response

Take It to the NET
Online lesson quiz at
www.PHSchool.com
Web Code: aea-1107

50. A fox is at the edge of a cliff 850 ft above the base of the cliff. He sees a mouse in a canyon. The angle of depression from his position to the mouse is 56°. Draw and label a diagram for the situation. Then write and solve a trigonometric equation that will determine how far the mouse is from the base of the cliff. Round to the nearest foot. **See margin.**

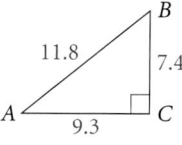

Mixed Review

Lesson 11-6

Graph each function. **51–53. See margin.**
   51. $y = \sqrt{5x}$ **52.** $y = \sqrt{x + 3}$ **53.** $y = \sqrt{x - 7}$

Lesson 10-8

Find the number of real solutions of each equation.
   54. $2x^2 - x - 4 = 0$ **2**   **55.** $7x^2 + x + 20 = 0$ **0**   **56.** $9x^2 + 6x + 1 = 0$ **1**

Lesson 9-7

Factor each expression.
57. $(n - 20)(n + 20)$ **57.** $n^2 - 400$ **58.** $x^2 - 30x + 225$ $(x - 15)^2$ **59.** $100p^2 - 49$ $(10p - 7)(10p + 7)$
60. $\frac{1}{16}d^2 - \frac{9}{4}$ **61.** $98w^2 - 128$ $2(7w - 8)(7w + 8)$ **62.** $x^2 + 26x + 169$ $(x + 13)^2$
$\left(\frac{1}{4}d - \frac{3}{2}\right)\left(\frac{1}{4}d + \frac{3}{2}\right)$

Lesson 11-7 Trigonometric Ratios **627**

Standardized Test Prep

 **Resources**
For additional practice with a variety of test item formats:
• Standardized Test Prep, p. 633
• Test-Taking Strategies, p. 628
• Test-Taking Strategies with Transparencies

pages 625–627 Exercises

40. Answers may vary. Sample:

about 8.2 cm

49. [2] $\sin A = \frac{7.4}{11.8}$,

$\cos A = \frac{9.3}{11.8}$,

$\tan A = \frac{7.4}{9.3}$

[1] at least one correct equation

50. [4]

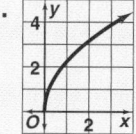

$\tan 56° = \frac{850}{x}$

$x \approx 573.3$

573 ft

[3] correct equation, but minor computational error

[2] incorrect equation used

[1] no work shown

51.

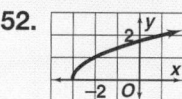

52.

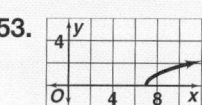

53.

627

Test-Taking Strategies

Using Estimation

This feature helps students develop skills in estimating answers that involve square roots.

Resources

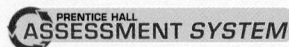

Test-Taking Strategies with Transparencies
- Transparency 11
- Practice sheet p. 11

Teaching Notes

Help students understand that being able to estimate answers with speed and accuracy will allow them to complete more problems while doing fewer paper and pencil calculations.

Math Tip

Suggest that students memorize the perfect squares from 1^2 to 25^2. Then, for example, they will know that the square root of 250 is between 15 and 16 and closer to 16. When looking at the suggested answers in a multiple-choice test, students will be able to eliminate all answers that fall outside the parameters of their estimate.

Test-Taking Strategies with Transparencies

Test-Taking Strategy: Using Estimation

Sometimes you can estimate to find the answer.

Example Shannon used a calculator to find 7.95 × 13. Which is a reasonable number to see in the calculator display?

A. 1.0335   B. 10.335   C. 103.35   D. 1033.5

Estimate: Round to the nearest whole number.

7.95 × 13

8 × 13 = 104

Only C is near 104.

The answer is 103.35, or choice C.

Estimate to find the answer.

1. A pair of shoes is on sale for 33% off the original price of $47.99. About how much will the shoes cost on sale?

   A. $64   B. $48   C. $32   D. $16

2. The circumference of a circle with radius 5 in. is about

   F. 29 in.   G. 31 in.   H. 33 in.   I. 35 in.

3. Estimate the value of $2x^2 + 5$ when $x = 4.1$.

   A. 69   B. 37   C. 23   D. 21

Solutions

1. C
2. G
3. B

Transparency 11

Test-Taking Strategies

Using Estimation

Using estimation may help you find answers, check an answer, or eliminate one or more answer choices.

EXAMPLE

The length of the hypotenuse of a right triangle is 9 cm and the length of one leg is 4 cm. Which is closest to the length of the other leg?

A. 7.7 cm   **B.** 7.8 cm   **C.** 8.1 cm   **D.** 9.8 cm

First, use the Pythagorean Theorem to find the length of the other leg in radical form. Then use estimation to see which answer choice is closest to it.

$a^2 + b^2 = c^2$ **Use the Pythagorean Theorem.**

$4^2 + b^2 = 9^2$ **Substitute 4 for a and 9 for c.**

$16 + b^2 = 81$ **Simplify.**

$b^2 = 65$ **Subtract 16 from each side.**

$b = \sqrt{65}$ **Take the square root of each side.**

A good estimate for $\sqrt{65}$ is 8, since $\sqrt{65}$ is close to $\sqrt{64}$. You can now eliminate answer choices A, B, and D, which are not as close to 8 as C. C is the correct answer.

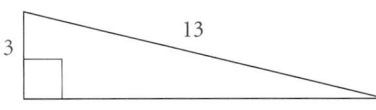

EXERCISES

1. The lengths of the two legs of a right triangle are 8 ft and 9 ft. Which is closest to the length of the hypotenuse? **D**

   A. 4.1 ft   **B.** 8.5 ft   **C.** 9.3 ft   **D.** 12.0 ft

2. Which is the best estimate of the area of the figure below? **G**

   ```
        ┌──────────────
        │ ⌐         13
      3 │  ───────
        │        ───────
   ```

   F. 12.7   **G.** 19.0   **H.** 19.5   **I.** 22

3. The area of a circle is about 118 in.^{2}. Which is closest to the length of the radius of the circle? **B**

   A. 5 in.   **B.** 6 in.   **C.** 7 in.   **D.** 8 in.

For Exercises 4–6, use the decimal approximations $\sqrt{2} \approx 1.4$ and $\sqrt{3} \approx 1.7$.

4. **Error Analysis** Bill multiplied $(\sqrt{3} + 3)(\sqrt{3} - 1)$ and got the answer $3 - 3 = 0$. Use estimation to show that his answer is wrong. **See above.**

5. Find an estimate for $\sqrt{8}$ using the estimate for $\sqrt{2}$. $\sqrt{8} = 2\sqrt{2} \approx 2(1.4) \approx 2.8$

6. Find an estimate for $\sqrt{12}$ using the estimate for $\sqrt{3}$. $\sqrt{12} = 2\sqrt{3} \approx 2(1.7) \approx 3.4$

628 Test-Taking Strategies   Using Estimation

Chapter 11 Chapter Review

Vocabulary

angle of depression (p. 624)	extraneous solution (p. 609)	radical equation (p. 607)
angle of elevation (p. 623)	hypotenuse (p. 584)	radical expression (p. 578)
conclusion (p. 586)	hypothesis (p. 586)	rationalize (p. 581)
conditional (p. 586)	leg (p. 584)	sine (p. 621)
conjugates (p. 601)	like radicals (p. 600)	square root function (p. 614)
converse (p. 586)	midpoint (p. 593)	tangent (p. 621)
cosine (p. 621)	midpoint formula (p. 593)	trigonometric ratios (p. 621)
distance formula (p. 591)	Pythagorean Theorem (p. 584)	unlike radicals (p. 600)

Reading Math
Understanding
Vocabulary

Choose the vocabulary term that correctly completes each sentence.

1. Two radical expressions that are the sum and the difference of the same two terms are ? . **conjugates**

2. The two sides of a right triangle that form the right angle are the ? . **legs**

3. One method of simplifying a radical expression is to ? the denominator. **rationalize**

4. A(n) ? is a value that satisfies the new equation but not the original equation. **extraneous solution**

5. Radicals with the same radicand are ? . **like radicals**

6. The ? states that in a right triangle with sides a, b, and c, in which the longest side is c, $a^2 + b^2 = c^2$. **Pythagorean Theorem**

7. In a right triangle, the ? is the trigonometric ratio of the length of the leg opposite an angle to the length of the hypotenuse of the triangle. **sine**

8. **angle of elevation**

Take It to the NET
Online vocabulary quiz
at **www.PHSchool.com**
Web Code: aej-1151

8. A horizontal and the line of sight to an object above the horizontal form a(n) ? .

9. The expression $\sqrt{(x_2 - x_1)^2 + (y_2 - y_1)^2}$ is part of the ? , which determines the length of the line from point (x_1, y_1) to point (x_2, y_2). **distance formula**

10. The coordinates $\left(\dfrac{x_1 + x_2}{2}, \dfrac{y_1 + y_2}{2}\right)$ identify the ? between points (x_1, y_1) and (x_2, y_2). **midpoint**

Skills and Concepts

11-1 Objectives

▼ To simplify radicals involving products (p. 578)

▼ To simplify radicals involving quotients (p. 580)

You can simplify some radical expressions by using products or quotients. The Multiplication Property of Square Roots states that for $a \geq 0$ and $b \geq 0$, $\sqrt{ab} = \sqrt{a} \cdot \sqrt{b}$. The Division Property of Square Roots states that for $a \geq 0$ and $b > 0$, $\sqrt{\dfrac{a}{b}} = \dfrac{\sqrt{a}}{\sqrt{b}}$.

Simplify each radical expression.

11. $\sqrt{32} \cdot \sqrt{144}$ **48$\sqrt{2}$**
12. $\sqrt{\dfrac{84}{121}}$ **$\dfrac{2\sqrt{21}}{11}$**
13. $\sqrt{96c^3} \cdot \sqrt{25c}$  **$20c^2\sqrt{6}$**
14. $\dfrac{10}{\sqrt{13}}$ **$\dfrac{10\sqrt{13}}{13}$**

15. A rectangle is 7 times as long as it is wide. Its area is 1400 cm^2. Find the dimensions of the rectangle in simplest radical form. **10$\sqrt{2}$ cm by 70$\sqrt{2}$ cm**

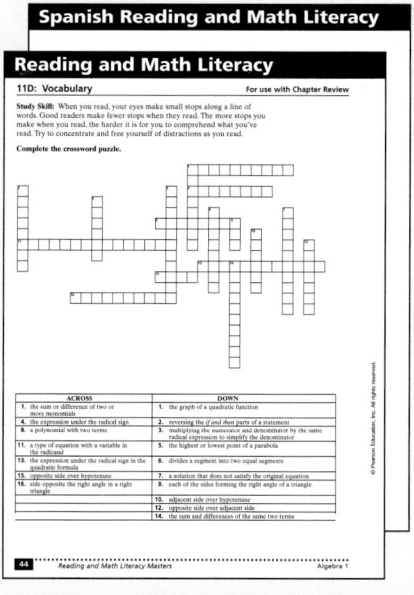

26. Answers may vary.
Sample:

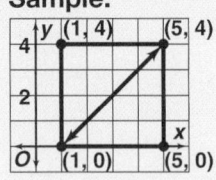

$\sqrt{32}$ (or about 5.7) units

29. $2\sqrt{7}$

30. $30\sqrt{5}$

31. $\sqrt{6}$

32. $2\sqrt{5}$

33. $10 - 10\sqrt{2}$

34. $-1 + 2\sqrt{14}$

11-2 Objectives

▼ To solve problems using the Pythagorean Theorem (p. 584)

▼ To identify right triangles (p. 586)

For a right triangle with **legs** a and b and **hypotenuse** c, the **Pythagorean Theorem** states that $a^2 + b^2 = c^2$. The converse of the Pythagorean Theorem states that if a triangle has sides of lengths a, b, and c, and if $a^2 + b^2 = c^2$, then it is a right triangle with hypotenuse of length c.

Find the length of the hypotenuse with the given leg lengths. If necessary, round to the nearest tenth.

16. $a = 3, b = 5$ **17.** $a = 11, b = 14$ **18.** $a = 7, b = 13$ **19.** $a = 4, b = 9$
      5.8   17.8   14.8   9.8

Determine whether the given lengths can be sides of a right triangle.

20. $XY = 16, YZ = 34, XZ = 30$ **yes**   **21.** $XY = 2.5, YZ = 2.4, XZ = 0.7$ **yes**

22. Baseball The bases on a playground baseball diamond form a square, 60 ft on a side. How far would a catcher standing on home plate need to throw the ball to get a runner out at second base? **about 85 ft**

11-3 Objectives

▼ To find the distance between two points on a coordinate plane (p. 591)

▼ To find the coordinates of the midpoint of a line segment (p. 593)

The **distance formula** $d = \sqrt{(x_2 - x_1)^2 + (y_2 - y_1)^2}$ gives the distance between two points (x_1, x_2) and (y_1, y_2). The **midpoint formula** $M = \left(\frac{x_1 + x_2}{2}, \frac{y_1 + y_2}{2}\right)$ gives the coordinates of their midpoint.

Find the distance between the points in each pair. If necessary, round to the nearest tenth.

23. $A(4, 0), B(1, 4)$ **24.** $C(-2, -3), D(-4, 5)$ **25.** $P(-3, 2), Q(6, -4)$
      5 units   8.2 units   10.8 units

26. Open-Ended Draw a square on a coordinate plane. Find the length of the diagonal of the square you drew. **See margin.**

Find the midpoint of the segment with the given endpoints.

27. $A(3, 7), B(-2, 4)$ **(0.5, 5.5)**   **28.** $A\left(4\frac{3}{4}, -2\right), B\left(6\frac{1}{4}, 10\frac{1}{2}\right)$ $\left(5\frac{1}{2}, 4\frac{1}{4}\right)$

11-4 and 11-5 Objectives

▼ To simplify sums and differences (p. 600)

▼ To simplify products and quotients (p. 601)

▼ To solve equations containing radicals (p. 607)

▼ To identify extraneous solutions (p. 609)

You can use the Distributive Property to simplify expressions with sums and differences of radicals. First, simplify the radicals and check for **like radicals.** When a denominator contains a sum or a difference including radical expressions, you can **rationalize** the denominator by multiplying the numerator and the denominator by the **conjugate** of the denominator.

A **radical equation** has a variable in the radicand. Sometimes you can solve such an equation by squaring both sides. You may also square both sides of the equation when each side is a square root. Squaring both sides of a radical equation may produce an **extraneous solution.** It is not a solution of the original equation.

Simplify each radical expression. 29–34. See margin.

29. $6\sqrt{7} - 2\sqrt{28}$ **30.** $5\left(\sqrt{20} + \sqrt{80}\right)$ **31.** $\sqrt{54} - 2\sqrt{6}$

32. $\sqrt{125} - 3\sqrt{5}$ **33.** $\sqrt{10}\left(\sqrt{10} - \sqrt{20}\right)$ **34.** $\left(\sqrt{2} + \sqrt{7}\right)\left(3\sqrt{2} - \sqrt{7}\right)$

35. $\left(\sqrt{5} + 4\sqrt{3}\right)^2$ **36.** $\sqrt{28} + 5\sqrt{63}$ **37.** $\frac{3}{\sqrt{6} - \sqrt{3}}$

      $53 + 8\sqrt{15}$ $17\sqrt{7}$ $\sqrt{6} + \sqrt{3}$

Solve each radical equation.

38. $\sqrt{x+7} = 3$ **2**

39. $\sqrt{x} + 3\sqrt{x} = 16$ **16**

40. $\sqrt{x+7} = \sqrt{2x-1}$ **8**

41. $\sqrt{x} - 5 = 4$ **81**

Tell which of the given solutions is extraneous for each equation.

42. $\sqrt{4x} = x - 3$; $x = 1, x = 9$ **9**

43. $\sqrt{d-3} = 5 - d$; $d = 4, d = 7$ **4**

44. A rectangle has a width of $2\sqrt{5}$ cm and an area of 50 cm^2. Find the length of the rectangle. **$5\sqrt{5}$ cm**

45. The volume V of a cylinder is given by $V = \pi r^2 h$, where r is the radius of a cylinder and h is its height. If the volume of the cylinder is 54 in.^{3}, and its height is 2 in., what is its radius to the nearest 0.01 in.? **2.93 in.**

11-6 Objectives

▼ To graph square root functions (p. 614)

▼ To translate graphs of square root functions (p. 615)

The simplest square root function is $y = \sqrt{x}$. The graphs of $y = \sqrt{x} + k$ and $y = \sqrt{x} - k$ are vertical translations of $y = \sqrt{x}$. The graphs of $y = \sqrt{x-h}$ and $y = \sqrt{x+h}$ are horizontal translations of $y = \sqrt{x}$.

Make a table of values and graph each function. 46–49. See margin.

46. $y = \sqrt{\dfrac{x}{2}}$

47. $y = \dfrac{\sqrt{x}}{2}$

48. $y = \sqrt{2x}$

49. $y = 1 + \sqrt{x}$

Find the domain of each function. Then graph each function by translating the graph of $y = \sqrt{x}$. 50–53. See margin.

50. $y = \sqrt{x} + 5$

51. $y = \sqrt{x} - 2$

52. $y = \sqrt{x+1}$

53. $f(x) = 2\sqrt{x}$

11-7 Objectives

▼ To find trigonometric ratios (p. 621)

▼ To solve problems using trigonometric ratios (p. 623)

Trigonometric ratios are triangle measurement ratios. For a right triangle of a given shape, the ratios do not change no matter how large or small the triangle is. Three trigonometric ratios—**sine** (sin), **cosine** (cos), and **tangent** (tan)—are shown below.

sine of $\angle A = \dfrac{\text{length of leg opposite } \angle A}{\text{length of hypotenuse}}$

cosine of $\angle A = \dfrac{\text{length of leg adjacent to } \angle A}{\text{length of hypotenuse}}$

tangent of $\angle A = \dfrac{\text{length of leg opposite } \angle A}{\text{length of leg adjacent to } \angle A}$

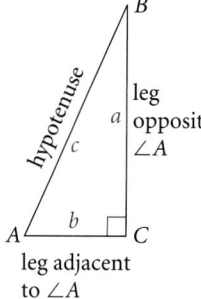

You can use trigonometric ratios to measure distances indirectly. You can use an angle of elevation or angle of depression to measure heights indirectly.

Suppose $\triangle ABC$ has right angle C. Find the measures of the other sides to the nearest whole number. 54–57. See left.

54. $AC \approx 10; BC \approx 7$

55. $AB \approx 29; AC \approx 28$

56. $AB \approx 10; BC \approx 6$

57. $AC \approx 22; BC \approx 13$

54. $AB = 12, m\angle A = 34°$

55. $BC = 9, m\angle B = 72°$

56. $AC = 8, m\angle B = 52°$

57. $AB = 25, m\angle A = 12°$

58. During a violent thunderstorm, a tree near John's house was broken by the wind. The top part of the tree was bent so that it touched the ground 21 ft from the base of the tree. If the broken top part of the tree made a 48° angle with the ground, how tall was the tree before the storm? **about 55 ft**

Chapter 11 Chapter Review **631**

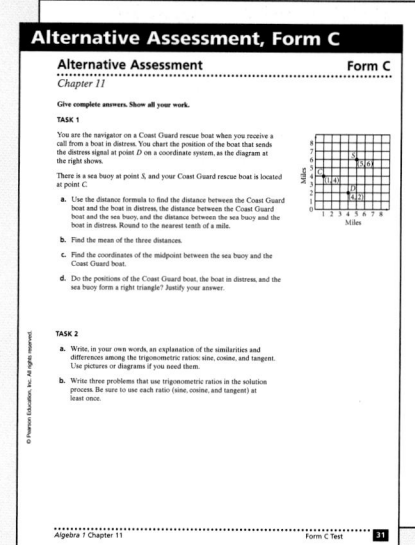
48.

x	y
0	0
$\frac{1}{2}$	1
2	2
8	4

49.

x	y
0	1
1	2
4	3
9	4

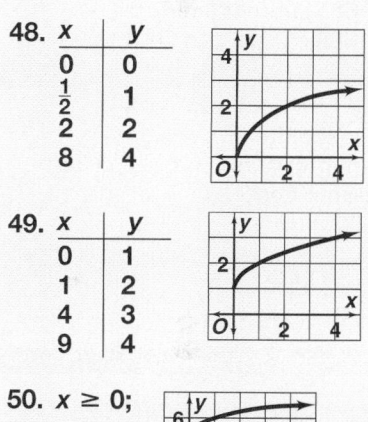

50. $x \geq 0$;

51. $x \geq 2$;

52. $x \geq -1$;

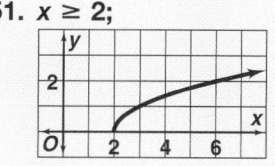

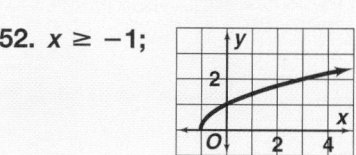

53. $x \geq 0$;

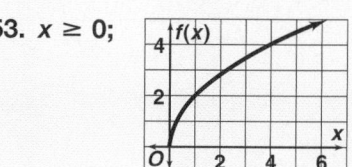

46.

x	y
2	0
0.5	0.5
2	1
4	1.4
8	2

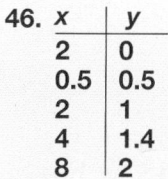

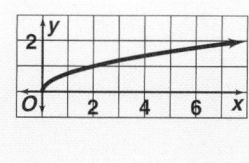

47.

x	y
0	0
1	$\frac{1}{2}$
4	1
9	$1\frac{1}{2}$

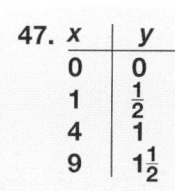

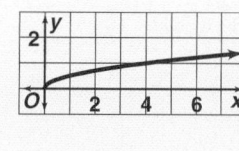

631

Chapter Test

Chapter Test

Take It to the NET
Online chapter test at
www.PHSchool.com
Web Code: aea-1152

Resources

 Teaching Resources
Ch. 11 Test, Forms A & B
Ch. 11 Alternative Assessment,
Form C

 **Reaching All Students**
Spanish Ch. 11 Test, Forms A & B
Spanish Ch. 11 Alternative
Assessment, Form C
Basic Algebra Ch. 11 Test,
Forms D & E

ASSESSMENT SYSTEM

Assessment Masters
• Ch. 11 Test, Forms A & B
• Ch. 11 Alternative Assessment,
Form C
Computer Test Generator CD
• Ch. 11 pre-made Test
• Make your own Ch. 11 test

www.PHSchool.com
Student Site
• Self-grading Chapter 11 Test
Teacher Center
• Resources

Plus **iTEXT**

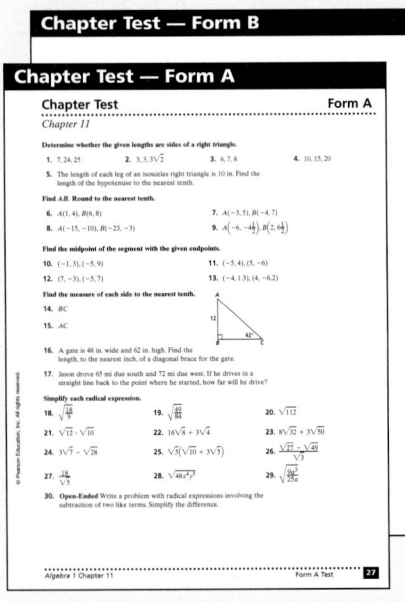

page 632 Chapter Test

6. 9.8 units

7. 4.1 units

632

Determine whether the given lengths can be sides of a right triangle.

1. 6, 8, 10 **yes**
2. 6, 7, 9 **no**
3. 4, 5, 11 **no**
4. 10, 24, 26 **yes**

5. The length of each leg of an isosceles right triangle is 40.9 cm. Find the length of the hypotenuse to the nearest tenth. **57.8 cm**

Find AB. Round to the nearest tenth. 6–7. See margin.

6. $A(1, -2), B(5, 7)$
7. $A(3.1, 5), B(7.2, 4.6)$
8. $A(4, 7), B(-11, -6)$ **19.8 units**
9. $A(0, -5), B(3, 2)$ **7.6 units**

Find the midpoint of the segment with the given endpoints. 10–13. See margin.

10. $A(4, 9), B(1, -5)$
11. $P(-2, -7), Q(3, 0)$
12. $D(3, -10), E(-4, 6)$
13. $K\left(0, 8\frac{1}{2}\right), L\left(-1, 1\frac{1}{2}\right)$

Find the measure of each side to the nearest tenth.

14. AB **29.5**
15. AC **27.0**

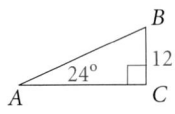

16. A wire is stretched from the top of a 3-ft pole to the top of an 8-ft fence. If the pole and fence are 12 ft apart, how long is the wire? **13 ft**

17. One house is 12 mi east of a school. Another house is 9 mi north of the school. How far apart are the houses? **15 mi**

Simplify each radical expression. 22–28. See margin.

18. $\sqrt{\frac{128}{64}}$ **$\sqrt{2}$**
19. $\sqrt{\frac{27}{75}}$ **$\frac{3}{5}$**
20. $\sqrt{48}$ **$4\sqrt{3}$**
21. $\sqrt{12} \cdot \sqrt{8}$ **$4\sqrt{6}$**
22. $3\sqrt{32} + 5\sqrt{2}$
23. $2\sqrt{27} + 5\sqrt{3}$
24. $7\sqrt{125} - 3\sqrt{175}$
25. $\sqrt{128} - \sqrt{192}$
26. $\frac{15}{\sqrt{3}}$
27. $\frac{8}{\sqrt{10} + \sqrt{6}}$

28. **Open-Ended** Write an expression involving addition of two like radicals. Simplify the sum.

10. $\left(2\frac{1}{2}, 2\right)$
11. $\left(\frac{1}{2}, -3\frac{1}{2}\right)$
12. $\left(-\frac{1}{2}, -2\right)$
13. $\left(-\frac{1}{2}, 5\right)$
22. $17\sqrt{2}$

---

29. Which expression shows $\sqrt{24x^2y^3}$ written in simplest radical form? **B**
    A. $2xy\sqrt{12xy^2}$ B. $2xy\sqrt{6y}$
    C. $xy\sqrt{24y}$ D. $4xy\sqrt{3y}$

Solve each radical equation.

30. $3\sqrt{x} + 2\sqrt{x} = 10$ **4**
31. $8 = \sqrt{5x - 1}$ **13**
32. $5\sqrt{x} = \sqrt{15x + 60}$ **6**
33. $\sqrt{x} = \sqrt{2x - 7}$ **7**
34. $3\sqrt{x + 3} = 2\sqrt{x + 9}$ **$\frac{9}{5}$**
35. $\sqrt{3x} = x - 5$ **≈10.65**

36. A rectangle is 5 times as long as it is wide. The area of the rectangle is 100 ft². How wide is the rectangle? Express your answer in simplest radical form. **$2\sqrt{5}$ ft**

37–40. See back of book.
Find the domain of each function. Graph the function.

37. $y = 3\sqrt{x}$
38. $y = \sqrt{x} + 4$
39. $y = \sqrt{x - 4}$
40. $y = \sqrt{x + 9}$

41. The hypotenuse of a right triangle is 26 cm. The length of one leg is 10 cm. Find the length of the other leg. **24 cm**

42. **Writing** Explain how to graph $y = \sqrt{x} - 3$ by translating the graph of $y = \sqrt{x}$. **See margin.**

43. **Geometry** The formula for the volume V of a cylinder with height h and radius r is $V = \pi r^2 h$. Solve for r in terms of V and h. **$r = \sqrt{\frac{V}{\pi h}}$**

44. From ground level you can see a satellite dish on the roof of a building 60 ft high. The angle of elevation is 62°. How far away from you is the building? **about 32 ft**

45–48. See margin.
Find the values for △RST.

45. RT
46. ST
47. $\tan T$
48. $\sin T$

49. **Geometry** In △ABC, ∠C is a right angle, $\overline{AB} = 7$, and $m\angle B = 28°$. What are the lengths of $\overline{BC}$ and $\overline{AC}$ to the nearest tenth? **See margin p. 633.**

50. Ken has a 20-ft ladder to use for washing windows. When leaned against a building, the ladder forms an angle of 75° with the ground. How far from the side of the building is the base of the ladder? **about 5 ft**

23. $11\sqrt{3}$
24. $35\sqrt{5} - 15\sqrt{7}$
25. $8\sqrt{2} - 8\sqrt{3}$
26. $5\sqrt{3}$
27. $2(\sqrt{10} - \sqrt{6})$

28. **Answers may vary. Sample:** $2\sqrt{5} + 4\sqrt{5} = 6\sqrt{5}$

42. The graph of $y = \sqrt{x}$ is shifted 3 units down.

45. about 8.1

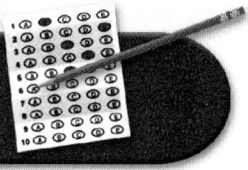

Standardized Test Prep

Standardized Test Prep

Reading Comprehension Read the passage below and then answer the questions on the basis of what is *stated* or *implied* in the passage.

> **Pricing Products** Carlos and Anna have created a new electronic game that they think will be a big hit. But they can't decide how much to sell it for. They have manufactured 2500 to start out, at a cost to them of $18 for each game, but they doubt they can sell all of them right away.
>
> They have completed a market study. By interviewing potential buyers, they have learned that if they set a price of $40, they should be able to sell 1000 games during the first six months. They have also discovered that for every $5 they increase the price they will lose 50 sales.
>
> Carlos and Anna realize that the data are important. They need help in determining the price that will maximize their sales revenue, which is the amount of total sales.

1. What is the total cost to Carlos and Anna for manufacturing 2500 electronic games? **B**
   A. $36,000   B. $45,000
   C. $50,000   D. $60,000

2. At a selling price of $40 each, how much revenue does the market research indicate they could expect in the first six months? **H**
   F. $100,000   G. $55,000
   H. $40,000   I. $22,000

3. Suppose Carlos and Anna raise the price to $45. From their market analysis, how many sales and how much revenue can they expect? **D**
   A. 1050, $57,750
   B. 1050, $47,250
   C. 1000, $45,000
   D. 950, $42,750

4. Their accountant tells them that they can use the function $r = 40{,}000 + 3000n - 250n^2$ to find the price for the game that will produce the greatest revenue r. The variable n is the number of times they increase the price $5. What type of function is this? **G**
   F. linear
   G. quadratic
   H. exponential
   I. absolute value

5. The accountant found the function in Exercise 4 by writing functions for the price p and the number of sales s, given the number of times n the price is increased. Which functions did he use? **D**
   A. $s = 1000 - 5n$, $p = 40 - 5n$
   B. $s = 1000 + 50n$, $p = 40 - 5n$
   C. $s = 1000 - 50n$, $p = 40n$
   D. $s = 1000 - 50n$, $p = 40 + 5n$

6. Carlos and Anna want to find the maximum of the function $r = 40{,}000 + 3000n - 250n^2$, where r is the revenue and n is the number of times the price is increased.
   a. How many times can they increase the price to obtain the maximum?
   b. What is the maximum revenue possible using this model?
   c. What would be the number of sales?
   d. Based on this information, what price should Carlos and Anna set for the electronic game?
   a–d. See back of book.

7. Suppose the market analysis also indicated that with each $5 decrease in price, Carlos and Anna could expect an increase of 50 sales. Would you suggest they decrease the price to increase the sales? Explain. **See back of book.**

Students must be able to extract information from reading passages, answer multiple choice questions, and construct responses in order to be successful on current state and national assessments.

To answer the questions, students apply skills and concepts from this chapter and previous chapters.
Multiple Choice: Items 1–5
Extended Response: Items 6, 7

Resources

Teaching Resources
Cumulative Review

Reaching All Students
Spanish Cumulative Review

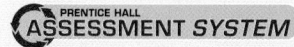
PRENTICE HALL
ASSESSMENT *SYSTEM*

Standardized Test Prep
• Ch. 11 Standardized Test Practice
Assessment Masters
• Cumulative Review
Computer Test Generator CD
• Standardized Test Practice

www.PHSchool.com
• Standardized Test Practice
• Resources

Plus

Cumulative Review
Cumulative Review
Chapters 1–11

46. about 12.1
47. about 1.1
48. about 0.74
49. $BC \approx 6.2$, $AC \approx 3.3$

Chapter 12

Rational Expressions and Functions

Chapter at a Glance

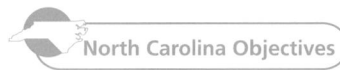 North Carolina Objectives

12-1 Inverse Variation — 1.03

NCTM 2, 6, 8, 9
- ▼ Solving Inverse Variations
- ▽ Comparing Direct and Inverse Variation

12-2 Graphing Rational Functions

NCTM 2, 8, 9, 10
- ▼ Graphing Rational Functions
- ▽ Types of Functions

12-3 Simplifying Rational Expressions — 1.01b

NCTM 2, 8, 9, 10
- ▼ Simplifying Rational Expressions

12-4 Multiplying and Dividing Rational Expressions — 1.01b

NCTM 2, 6, 8, 10
- ▼ Multiplying Rational Expressions
- ▽ Dividing Rational Expressions

12-5 Dividing Polynomials — 1.01b

NCTM 1, 2, 9
- ▼ Dividing Polynomials

12-6 Adding and Subtracting Rational Expressions — 1.01b

NCTM 1, 2, 6, 8, 9
- ▼ Adding and Subtracting Rational Expressions With Like Denominators
- ▽ Adding and Subtracting Rational Expressions With Unlike Denominators

12-7 Solving Rational Equations — 1.01b

NCTM 1, 2, 8, 9
- ▼ Solving Rational Equations
- ▽ Solving Proportions

12-8 Counting Methods and Permutations

NCTM 1, 2, 6, 8, 10
- ▼ Using the Multiplication Counting Principle
- ▽ Finding Permutations

12-9 Combinations

NCTM 1, 2, 8, 9, 10
- ▼ Combinations
- ▽ Probability With Counting Techniques

NCTM STANDARDS 2000

1	Number and Operations	6	Problem Solving
2	Algebra	7	Reasoning and Proof
3	Geometry	8	Communication
4	Measurement	9	Connections
5	Data Analysis and Probability	10	Representation

Pacing Options

This chart suggests pacing only for the lessons and their parts. It is provided as a possible guide. It will help you determine how much time you have in your schedule to cover other components, such as the features, Chapter Review, and Chapter Test.

Day	Traditional 45 min.	Two-Year 45 min.	Block 90 min.
1	12-1 ▼▽	12-1 ▼	12-1 ▼▽
2	12-2 ▼	12-1 ▽	12-2 ▼▽
3	12-2 ▽	12-2 ▼	12-3 ▼
4	12-3 ▼	12-2 ▽	12-4 ▼▽
5	12-3 ▽	12-3 ▼	12-5 ▼
6	12-4 ▼	12-3 ▼	12-6 ▼▽
7	12-4 ▽	12-4 ▼	12-7 ▼▽
8	12-5 ▼	12-4 ▽	12-8 ▼▽
9	12-5 ▽	12-5 ▼	
10	12-6 ▼	12-5 ▽	
11	12-6 ▽	12-6 ▼	
12	12-7 ▼	12-6 ▼	
13	12-7 ▽	12-6 ▽	
14	12-8 ▼▽	12-6 ▽	
15	12-9 ▼	12-7 ▼	
16	12-9 ▽	12-7 ▼▽	
17		12-7 ▽	
18		12-8 ▼▽	
19		12-9 ▼	
20		12-9 ▽	

NAEP Correlation (National Assessment of Educational Progress 2000 Mathematics Objectives)

12-1	12-2	12-3	12-4	12-5	12-6	12-7	12-8	12-9
A11	A3a, A12, A13	A5b	N3a	A5a, b	A5a, b	N4f, A5a	N3c, D9	N3c, D9

N = Number Sense, Properties, and Operations; **M** = Measurement; **G** = Geometry and Spatial Sense; **D** = Data Analysis, Statistics, and Probability; **A** = Algebra and Functions

Math Background

Chapter Overview

This chapter examines a number of different forms and uses of rational expressions, beginning with a discussion of inverse variation. Then students use their earlier skills to translate the basic graph of a rational function both vertically and horizontally. The various ways of combining and simplifying rational expressions are examined, and used in problem situations. These procedures are then used to solve rational equations. A further discussion of solving probability problems, this time using permutations and combinations, is also included.

Inverse Variation 12-1

Variation is a statement of how one quantity changes relative to the way another quantity changes. A variation may be expressed as an equation that states a constant relationship between the values of two variables. Students should recognize how the graphs of variations reflect this. In a direct variation, as the value of one variable increases or decreases, the value of the other variable increases or decreases proportionately. In this case, the ratio, or quotient, of the two variables remains constant. In an inverse variation, as the value of one variable increases, the value of the other variable decreases so that the product of the two variables remains constant.

Graphing Rational Functions 12-2

Students can see that the graph of the equation for an inverse variation, $xy = k$, is in the shape of a hyperbola, a two-branched curve, that has the x- and y-axis as asymptotes. For many real-world problems, only one branch is used.

Vertical asymptotes occur in the graphs of rational functions for values of x that make the denominator (and not the numerator) equal to zero. Horizontal asymptotes occur in the graphs of rational functions when the degrees of the numerator and denominator are the same. A third kind of asymptote, a slant asymptote, occurs if the degree of the numerator exceeds the degree of the denominator by one.

Simplifying, Multiplying, Dividing, Adding, and Subtracting, Rational Expressions 12-3, 12-4, 12-6

Any rational expression is defined only for values of the variable that do not make the denominator equal to zero. However, this is assumed most of the time. Specific values need to be noted as excluded only if not doing so might lead to incorrect results or misinterpretation.

Here students need much of their earlier work in manipulating polynomials.

Dividing Polynomials 12-5

Some students may be familiar with using synthetic division to divide a polynomial by a binomial. The coefficients of the polynomial, written in descending powers of the variable (supplying 0 as needed for any missing powers) are written in a row. The binomial is set equal to zero, and solved for the value of the variable. This value is used as the synthetic divisor. Synthetic division makes it possible to find the coefficients of the quotient by a process of multiplying and adding that parallels the multiplying and subtracting steps of long division. For example, here is the work for

$$(x^2 + 3x - 1) \div (x + 2) = x + 1 + \frac{-3}{x + 2}.$$

$$
\begin{array}{r|rrr}
 & 1 & 3 & -1 \\
-2 & & -2 & -2 \\
\hline
 & 1 & 1 & -3
\end{array}
$$

Solving Rational Equations 12-7

Solving a rational equation is much like solving other algebraic equations. The goal is to isolate the variable on one side of the equation. This may involve some of the equality properties, or even some of the skills used to solve quadratic equations if the rational equation is also quadratic.

When working with rational expressions, it is usually assumed that the variable does not take on any values that would make the expression undefined without explicitly stating the excluded values of the variable.

Counting Methods, Permutations, and Combinations 12-8, 12-9

It will soon become apparent to students that finding the number of permutations or combinations by making an organized list or a tree diagram works very well for a small set of objects, but becomes quite tedious for a larger set. Once students understand the methods of arranging and selecting objects, they can use the various formulas to solve problems much more efficiently.

To help students understand the underlying process when using the special notation of permutations, have them always read $_nP_r$ as "the number of permutations of n objects arranged r at a time" rather than a shortcut. Similarly, have them read $_nC_r$ as "the number of combinations of n objects chosen r at a time."

 # Ongoing Assessment and Intervention

Tools for Monitoring Student Progress

The Prentice Hall *Algebra 1* program provides you with many options for assessment in the Student Edition, the Teacher's Edition and the teaching resources. From these options you may choose instructional materials and techniques that are appropriate for your students and support your district's curriculum requirements.

Instant Check System™ in Chapter 12

Allows students to check their own learning before, during, and after each lesson.

Diagnosing Readiness before the chapter (p. 634)

Check Skills You'll Need exercises in each lesson (pp. 636, 644, 652, 657, 662, 667, 672, 679, 686)

Check Understanding questions with each Example (pp. 637, 638, 639, 644, 645, 646, 648, 652, 653, 654, 657, 658, 659, 662, 663, 664, 667, 668, 669, 672, 673, 674, 680, 681, 682, 687, 688, 689)

Checkpoint Quiz (pp. 656, 685)

 Test Prep in Chapter 12

Teaches students strategies and gives them practice with all the test item formats they will encounter on state tests and standardized national exams.

Standardized Test Prep exercises in each lesson (pp. 642, 650, 655, 656, 661, 666, 671, 677, 684, 685, 691)

Test-Taking Strategies (p. 692: Answering the Question Asked)

Standardized Test Prep (pp. 697–699: Cumulative Review)

 PRENTICE HALL ASSESSMENT *SYSTEM*

All your assessment needs in one place!

Program Assessment

Assess student progress throughout the *Algebra 1* text with blackline masters and CD-ROM.

Assessment Resources

- Checkpoint Quizzes 1 & 2
- Chapter Test, Forms A & B
- Chapter Alternative Assessment

Spanish versions available. Tests for Basic Algebra also available.

 Computer Test Generator

- Unlimited questions of varying difficulty for every lesson objective.
- Create your own practice sheets, quizzes, and tests, or use the pre-made Chapter Tests.
- Diagnose readiness with questions on prerequisite skills.
- Prepare students by making tests based on standardized test objectives.
- Access Algebra 1, Geometry, and Algebra 2 content—all on one CD-ROM.

Test Preparation

A three-step approach to preparing students for high stakes, national, and state exams.

❶ **Diagnose & Prescribe**

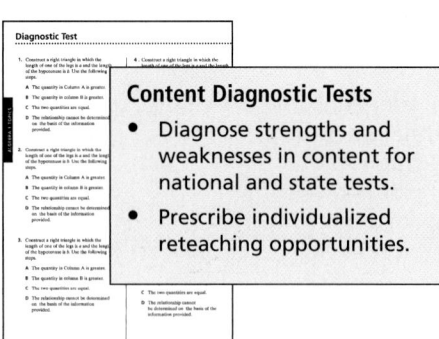

Content Diagnostic Tests

- Diagnose strengths and weaknesses in content for national and state tests.
- Prescribe individualized reteaching opportunities.

❷ **Review & Reteach**

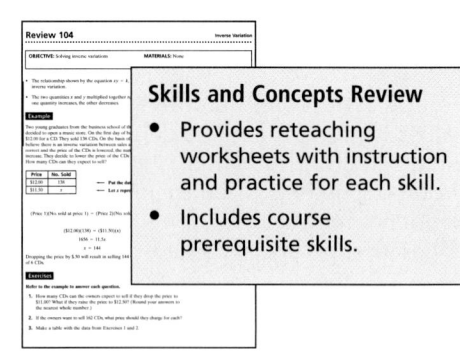

Skills and Concepts Review

- Provides reteaching worksheets with instruction and practice for each skill.
- Includes course prerequisite skills.

❸ **Practice & Assess**

Test Preparation

- Features practice tests for End-of-Course and SAT/ACT exams.
- Includes standardized test practice by chapter for ongoing review.

Teacher's Guide with answers and correlations.

Test-Taking Strategies with Transparencies

- Support the Test-Taking Strategies pages in the Student Edition.
- Provide a teaching transparency and a practice worksheet for each strategy.

 # Reaching All Students

Support in the Student Text and Additional Resources

The textbook, the iText, and other technology components provide numerous opportunities to reach students of various ability levels and learning styles. Each Teacher's Edition lesson suggests how you can help *all* your students be successful and understand the mathematics in Chapter 12.

Below Level

Student Edition
- Diagnosing Readiness*: p. 634
- Check Skills You'll Need*: pp. 636, 644, 652, 657, 662, 667, 672, 679, 686

Reteaching
Chapter 12 Support File: pp. 10–18

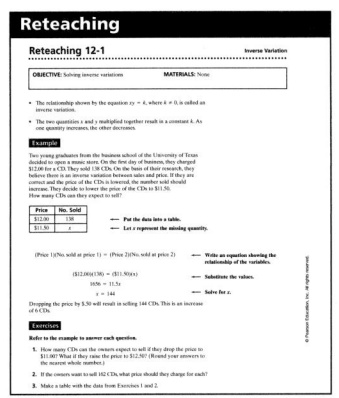

Basic Algebra Planning Guide
Chapter 12 Lesson Plans: pp. 80–88
Chapter 12 Tests: pp. 133–136

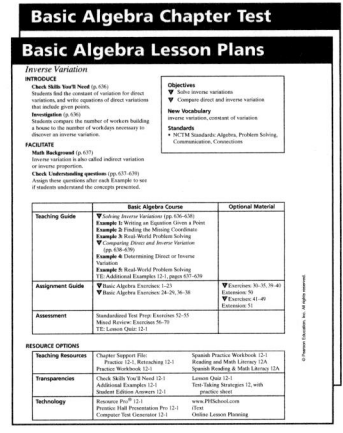

* Can be used with all ability levels to ensure mastery of prerequisite skills.

Advanced Learners

Student Edition
- Challenge exercises: pp. 642, 649, 650, 655, 661, 665, 666, 670, 676, 677, 684, 690, 691
- Extension, p. 651

Enrichment
Chapter 12 Support File: pp. 19–27

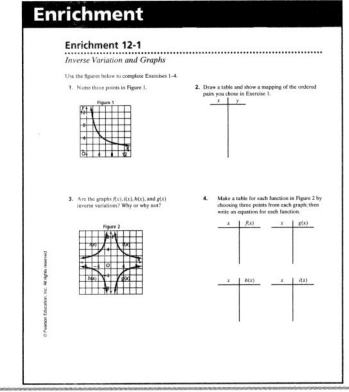

Reading and Math Literacy

Student Edition
- Vocabulary: pp. 635, 693, *plus* in every Lesson Preview
- Reading Math: pp. 637, 673, 678, 681, 693
- Illustrated Glossary: pp. 757–785

Reading and Math Literacy Masters
Chapter 12: pp. 45–48

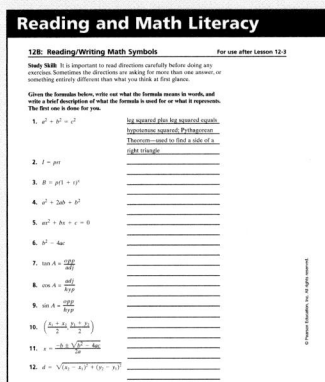

English Learners

Student Edition
- English/Spanish Illustrated Glossary: pp. 757–785

Workbook and Masters
Spanish Practice Workbook: pp. 80–88
Spanish Reading and Math Literacy Masters: pp. 45–48

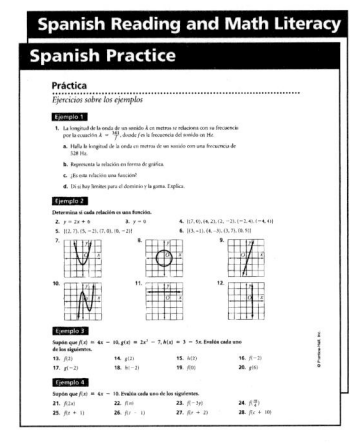

Learning Styles

Student Edition
- Investigation: pp. 636, 679
- Technology: pp. 643, 649, 675, 681, 687
- Writing: pp. 641, 649, 655, 660, 665, 670, 675, 683, 690, 694, 696, 699
- DK Activities: pp. 700–701

Activity Masters
Hands-On Activities: 29, 30
Technology Activities: 26

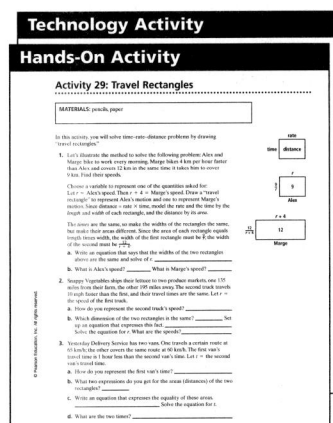

Program Resources

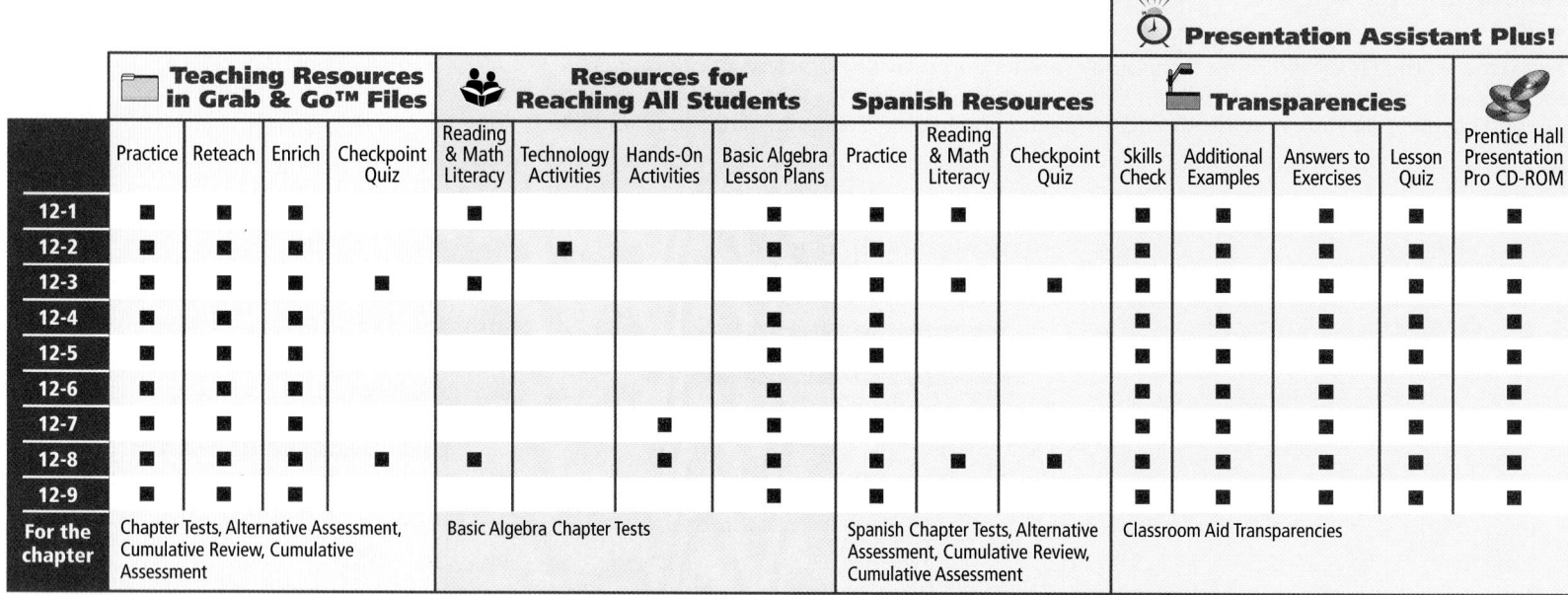

	Teaching Resources in Grab & Go™ Files				Resources for Reaching All Students				Spanish Resources			Transparencies				Presentation Assistant Plus!
	Practice	Reteach	Enrich	Checkpoint Quiz	Reading & Math Literacy	Technology Activities	Hands-On Activities	Basic Algebra Lesson Plans	Practice	Reading & Math Literacy	Checkpoint Quiz	Skills Check	Additional Examples	Answers to Exercises	Lesson Quiz	Prentice Hall Presentation Pro CD-ROM
12-1	■	■	■		■			■	■	■		■	■	■	■	■
12-2	■	■	■			■		■	■			■	■	■	■	■
12-3	■	■	■	■	■			■	■		■	■	■	■	■	■
12-4	■	■	■					■	■			■	■	■	■	■
12-5	■	■	■					■	■			■	■	■	■	■
12-6	■	■	■					■	■			■	■	■	■	■
12-7	■	■	■				■	■	■			■	■	■	■	■
12-8	■	■	■	■	■		■	■	■	■	■	■	■	■	■	■
12-9	■	■	■					■	■			■	■	■	■	■
For the chapter	Chapter Tests, Alternative Assessment, Cumulative Review, Cumulative Assessment				Basic Algebra Chapter Tests				Spanish Chapter Tests, Alternative Assessment, Cumulative Review, Cumulative Assessment			Classroom Aid Transparencies				

Also available for use with the chapter:

 PRENTICE HALL **ASSESSMENT SYSTEM** *See page 634C.*

- Practice Workbook
- Solution Key

- For teacher support and access to student Web site materials, use Web Code aek-5500.
- For additional online and technology resources, see below.

 ## Technology

iTEXT Online and on CD-ROM

Complete Interactive Student Text online and on CD-ROM—with instant feedback assessment, tutorial help, dynamic activities, instructional and real-world videos, audio, and additional practice.

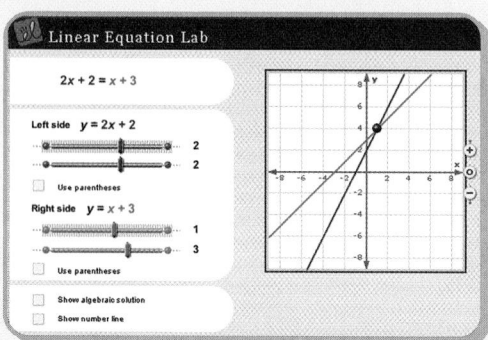

www.PHSchool.com For Students

Use **Web codes** for easy access to online activities, chapter projects, self-grading lesson quizzes and chapter tests, vocabulary quizzes, updated data sources, graphing calculator procedures, and more.

PH SuccessNet For Teachers

Online lesson planning with built-in state correlations, all the teaching resources, complete reference library, your own calendar and Teacher Web page, professional development, and more.

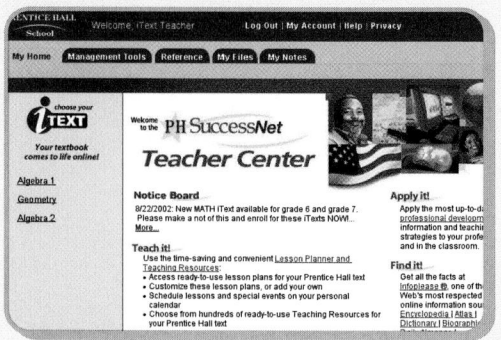

Presentation Assistant Plus!

The Prentice Hall *Presentation Assistant Plus!* provides you with the material you need to teach a lesson from beginning to end. Two easy-to-use formats—Transparencies and CD-ROM—allow you to present a lesson the way you are most comfortable.

Transparencies

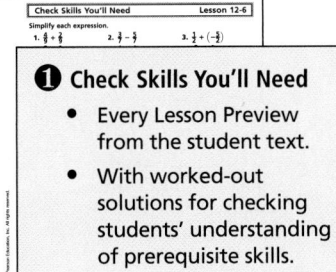

❶ Check Skills You'll Need
- Every Lesson Preview from the student text.
- With worked-out solutions for checking students' understanding of prerequisite skills.

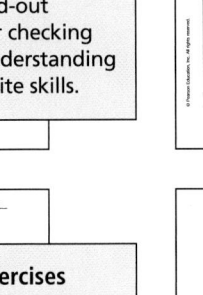

❷ Additional Examples
- Every example from the Teacher's Edition.
- Fully worked-out, step-by-step solutions for easy demonstration.

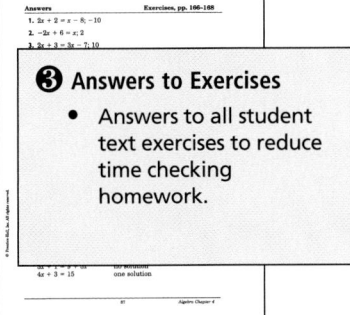

❸ Answers to Exercises
- Answers to all student text exercises to reduce time checking homework.

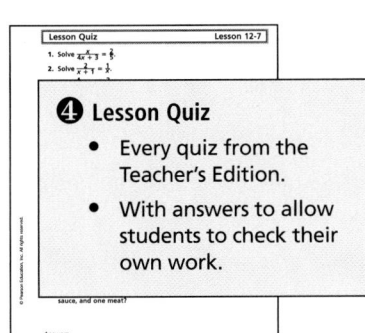

❹ Lesson Quiz
- Every quiz from the Teacher's Edition.
- With answers to allow students to check their own work.

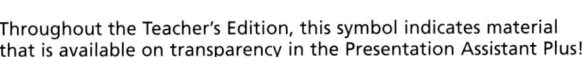

Throughout the Teacher's Edition, this symbol indicates material that is available on transparency in the Presentation Assistant Plus!

Prentice Hall Presentation Pro CD-ROM

- Includes all Transparencies.
- Conveniently organized by lesson so you can easily ❶ Introduce, ❷ Teach, ❸ Check Homework, and ❹ Assess each lesson.
- Animated examples allow step-by-step instruction at your own pace.
- Easy to edit so you can create custom presentations.

Teaching Chapter 12 Using Presentation Assistant Plus!

	❶ Introduce	❷ Teach	❸ Check Homework	❹ Assess
	Check Skills You'll Need	Additional Examples	Student Edition Answers	Lesson Quiz
12-1	p. 80	pp. 185–188	✔	p. 138
12-2	p. 81	pp. 188–191	✔	p. 139
12-3	p. 82	pp. 192–193	✔	p. 140
12-4	p. 83	pp. 193–195	✔	p. 140
12-5	p. 84	pp. 196–197	✔	p. 141
12-6	p. 85	pp. 198–200	✔	p. 141
12-7	p. 86	pp. 201–205	✔	p. 142
12-8	p. 87	pp. 206–207	✔	p. 142
12-9	p. 88	pp. 208–209	✔	p. 143

Prentice Hall Presentation Pro

CD-ROM with dynamic PowerPoint® presentations for every lesson. Helps you introduce and develop concepts, check homework, and assess progress. Part of Presentation Assistant Plus! *(See above.)*

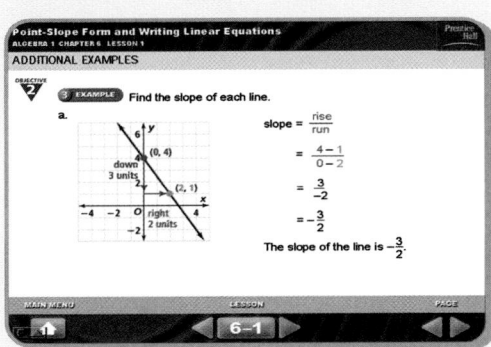

Computer Test Generator

CD-ROM to create practice sheets and tests for course objectives and standardized tests. Includes Instant Chapter Tests™, online testing, and student reports. Part of the PH Assessment System. *(See page 634C.)*

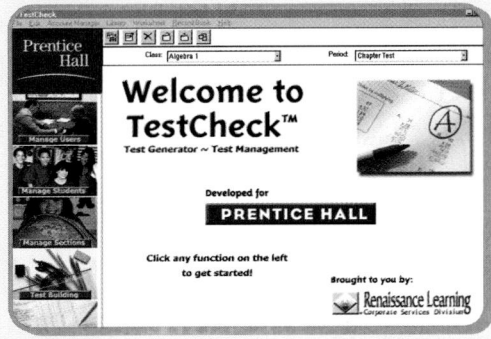

Resource Pro® with Planning Express®

CD-ROM with a lesson planning tool that allows you to import state and local objectives. Includes electronic versions of all the teaching resources.

Chapter 12

Rational Expressions and Functions

 Diagnosing Readiness

Students will find answers to these exercises in the back of their textbooks.

For intervention, direct students to:

Adding and Subtracting Fractions
Skills Handbook, p. 726
Example 2
Exercises 5–15, 21–30

Finding Probabilities
Lesson 4-6: Example 1
Exercises 1–4
Extra Practice, p. 705

Simplifying Expressions
Lesson 8-5: Example 1
Exercises 7–10
Extra Practice, p. 709

Solving Radical Equations
Lesson 11-5: Examples 1, 5
Exercises 1–3
Extra Practice, p. 712

Finding the Domain
Lesson 11-6: Example 1
Exercises 1–5
Extra Practice, p. 712

Where You've Been

- In Chapter 4, you used ratios to express probability.

- In Chapter 5, you learned to model some situations with a direct variation.

- In Chapter 8, you used the properties of exponents to simplify expressions containing exponents that are zero or negative.

- In Chapters 10 and 11, you solved quadratic and radical equations and checked for extraneous solutions.

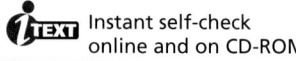 Instant self-check online and on CD-ROM

 **Diagnosing Readiness**   (For help, go to the Lesson in green.)

Adding and Subtracting Fractions (Skills Handbook page 726)

Add or subtract. Write each answer in simplest form.

1. $\frac{2}{3} + \frac{1}{2}$ $1\frac{1}{6}$ **2.** $\frac{3}{13} + \frac{6}{13}$ $\frac{9}{13}$ **3.** $\frac{16}{25} + \frac{3}{10}$ $\frac{47}{50}$ **4.** $\frac{5}{9} - \frac{5}{36}$ $\frac{5}{12}$

Finding Probabilities (Lesson 4-6)

You have three $1 bills and two $5 bills in your pocket. You choose two bills without looking. Find each probability.

5. P(two $1 bills) $\frac{3}{10}$ **6.** P(two $5 bills) $\frac{1}{10}$

7. P(two bills of the same kind) $\frac{2}{5}$ **8.** P(two different kinds of bills) $\frac{3}{5}$

Simplifying Expressions (Lesson 8-5)

Simplify each expression.

9. $\frac{6w^3x^2}{2wx}$ $3w^2x$ **10.** $\frac{81r^{10}s^6}{(3r^2s)^4}$ r^2s^2 **11.** $\frac{(5k^5)(2k^3)}{(2k^2)^2}$ $\frac{5}{2}k^4$

Solving Radical Equations (Lesson 11-5)

Solve each radical equation. If there is no solution, write *no solution*.

12. $\sqrt{x} - 4 = 6$ **100**   **13.** $\sqrt{3x} + 5 = 2$ **no solution**   **14.** $2x = \sqrt{3x + 1}$ **1**

Finding the Domain (Lesson 11-6)

Find the domain of each function.

15. $f(x) = 5 - \sqrt{x}$ **$x \geq 0$**   **16.** $y = -2 + \sqrt{3x}$ **$x \geq 0$**   **17.** $y = \sqrt{10 - 3x}$ **$x \leq \frac{10}{3}$**

Rational Expressions and Functions

Where You're Going

- In this chapter, you will study inverse variation and learn to distinguish between direct and inverse variation.

- You will graph and solve equations involving rational expressions, utilizing your knowledge of polynomials and domains.

- You will use permutations and combinations to find the number of outcomes of real-world situations.

 **Real-World Snapshots** Applying what you learn, you will solve inverse variation equations for vibrating strings in order to construct a guitar "neck," on pages 700–701.

LESSONS

12-1 Inverse Variation

12-2 Graphing Rational Functions

12-3 Simplifying Rational Expressions

12-4 Multiplying and Dividing Rational Expressions

12-5 Dividing Polynomials

12-6 Adding and Subtracting Rational Expressions

12-7 Solving Rational Equations

12-8 Counting Methods and Permutations

12-9 Combinations

Key Vocabulary

- asymptote (p. 644)
- combination (p. 686)
- constant of variation (p. 637)
- inverse variation (p. 637)
- multiplication counting principle (p. 680)
- permutation (p. 681)
- rational equation (p. 672)
- rational expression (p. 652)
- rational function (p. 644)

635

Chapter 12 Overview

This chapter examines various aspects of working with rational expressions, or the ratio of two integers. First, inverse variation is discussed, where $\frac{y}{x}$ equals a constant. Then graphing, simplifying, and combining rational expressions are examined and applied to solving problems. This leads to dividing polynomials and then to solving rational equations. Finally, counting methods and permutations and combinations are applied to various kinds of problems.

Reading Math
Reading an Example, p. 678

Vocabulary
A complete list of terms, plus vocabulary exercises, appears in the Chapter Review, p. 693.

Illustrated Glossary
Examples for each vocabulary term, plus definitions in both English and Spanish, appear starting on p. 757.

Real-World Snapshots
See pages 700–701 for a real-world application of measuring force that utilizes Dorling Kindersley's (DK) unique graphic presentation.

Test-Taking Strategies
Answering the Question Asked, p. 692

Real-World Connections
Some of the applications you will find in this chapter are surveying (12-1), photography (12-2), baking (12-3), mortgages (12-4), encryption (12-8), and jury selection (12-9).

www.PHSchool.com
Internet support for this chapter includes:
- Self-grading Vocabulary and Chapter 12 Tests
- Chapter Project
- Chapter Planner
- Chapter 12 Resources

Plus

1. Plan

North Carolina Objectives

Inverse Variation

1.03   Model and solve problems using direct variation.

Lesson Preview

Lesson Preview

✓ Check Skills You'll Need

Direct Variation
Lesson 5-5: Examples 1, 2
Exercises 1–21
Extra Practice, p. 706

Lesson Resources

📁 Teaching Resources
Practice, Reteaching, Enrichment

👥 Reaching All Students
Practice Workbook 12-1
Spanish Practice Workbook 12-1
Reading and Math Literacy 12A
Spanish Reading & Literacy 12A
Basic Algebra Planning Guide 12-1

⏰ Presentation Assistant Plus!
Transparencies
• Check Skills You'll Need 12-1
• Additional Examples 12-1
• Student Edition Answers 12-1
• Lesson Quiz 12-1
PH Presentation Pro CD 12-1

PRENTICE HALL ASSESSMENT SYSTEM

Computer Test Generator CD

💿 Technology
Resource Pro® CD-ROM
Computer Test Generator CD
Prentice Hall Presentation Pro CD

🖥 www.PHSchool.com
Student Site
• Teacher Web Code: aek-5500
• Self-grading Lesson Quiz
Teacher Center
• Lesson Planner
• Resources

Plus ✏️**TEXT**

What You'll Learn

OBJECTIVE 1
To solve inverse variations

OBJECTIVE 2
To compare direct and inverse variation

...And Why

To balance weights on a fulcrum, as in Example 3

✓ Check Skills You'll Need

(For help, go to Lesson 5-5.)

Suppose y varies directly with x. Find each constant of variation.

1. $y = 5x$ **5**   **2.** $y = -7x$ **−7**   **3.** $3y = x$ $\frac{1}{3}$ **4.** $0.25y = x$ **4**

Write an equation of the direct variation that includes the given point.

5. $(2, 4)$ $y = 2x$ **6.** $(3, 1.5)$ $y = 0.5x$ **7.** $(-4, 1)$ $y = -0.25x$ **8.** $(-5, -2)$ $y = 0.4x$

New Vocabulary   • inverse variation   • constant of variation

 Interactive lesson includes instant self-check, tutorials, and activities.

OBJECTIVE 1
Solving Inverse Variations

Real-World 🌐 Connection

With volunteer labor, Habitat for Humanity helped build over 115,000 homes for families around the world in its first 25 years.

Source: *Habitat for Humanity*

Investigation: Inverse Variation

Suppose you are part of a volunteer crew constructing affordable housing. Building a house requires a total of 160 workdays. For example, a crew of 20 people can complete a house in 8 days.

1. How long should it take a crew of 40 people?

2. Copy and complete the table.

Crew size (x)	Construction Days (y)	Total Workdays
2	80	160
5	**32**	160
8	**20**	**160**
10	16	**160**
20	8	160
40	**4**	**160**

3. Graph the (x, y) data in the table above.   **See margin p. 638.**

4. Describe what happens to construction time as the crew size increases.   **Construction time decreases.**

In the table, the total number of workdays remains the same. The number of construction days decreases as the number of people on the crew increases. The relationship of construction days and crew size is an inverse variation.

636   Chapter 12   Rational Expressions and Functions

Ongoing Assessment and Intervention

Before the Lesson
Diagnose prerequisite skills using:
• Check Skills You'll Need

During the Lesson
Monitor progress using:
• Check Understanding
• Additional Examples
• Standardized Test Prep

After the Lesson
Assess knowledge using:
• Lesson Quiz
• Computer Test Generator CD

Key Concepts

Definition	Inverse Variation

An equation in the form $xy = k$ or $y = \frac{k}{x}$, where $k \neq 0$, is an **inverse variation**.

The **constant of variation** is k.

Inverse variations have graphs with the same general shape. You can see from the graph at the right how the constant of variation k affects the graph of $xy = k$.

If you know the values of x and y for one point on the graph of an inverse variation, you can use the point to find the constant of variation k and the equation of the inverse variation.

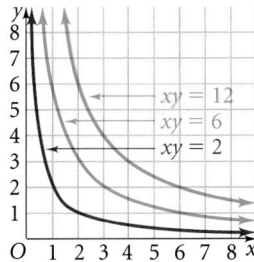

$$xy = 12$$
$$xy = 6$$
$$xy = 2$$

Reading Math

There are several ways to describe an inverse variation:

• y varies inversely with x.
• y varies inversely as x.
• y is inversely proportional to x.

1 EXAMPLE **Writing an Equation Given a Point**

Suppose y varies inversely with x and $y = 7$ when $x = 5$. Write an equation for the inverse variation.

$xy = k$	**Use the general form of an inverse variation.**
$5(7) = k$	**Substitute 5 for x and 7 for y.**
$35 = k$	**Multiply to solve for k.**
$xy = 35$	**Write an equation. Substitute 35 for k in $xy = k$.**

● The equation of the inverse variation is $xy = 35$, or $y = \frac{35}{x}$.

✔ **Check Understanding** **1** Suppose y varies inversely with x and $y = 9$ when $x = 2$. Write an equation for the inverse variation. **$xy = 18$**

Suppose (x_1, y_1) and (x_2, y_2) are two ordered pairs of an inverse variation. Each ordered pair of an inverse variation has the same product k, that is $x_1 \cdot y_1 = k$ and $x_2 \cdot y_2 = k$. So $x_1 \cdot y_1 = x_2 \cdot y_2$.

2 EXAMPLE **Finding the Missing Coordinate**

The points $(3, 8)$ and $(2, y)$ are two points on the graph of an inverse variation. Find the missing value.

$x_1 \cdot y_1 = x_2 \cdot y_2$	**Use the equation $x_1 \cdot y_1 = x_2 \cdot y_2$ since you know coordinates but not the constant of variation.**
$3(8) = 2(y_2)$	**Substitute 3 for x_1, 8 for y_1, and 2 for x_2.**
$24 = 2(y_2)$	**Simplify.**
$12 = y_2$	**Solve for y_2.**

The missing value is 12. The point $(2, 12)$ is on the graph of the inverse variation ● that includes the point $(3, 8)$.

✔ **Check Understanding** **2** Each pair of points is on the graph of an inverse variation. Find the missing value.
a. $(3, y)$ and $(5, 9)$ **15**   **b.** $(75, 0.2)$ and $(x, 3)$ **5**

Professional Development

Math Background

Inverse variation is also called indirect variation or inverse proportion.

OBJECTIVE
1 Teaching Notes

Investigation (Optional)
Ask students to compare the time 2 people would take to build a house versus the time 160 people would take. Ask students if they think either situation is realistic. Help students understand the necessity of considering real-world circumstances when trying to model a situation using math.

1 EXAMPLE **Teaching Tip**

For students not familiar with the word *inverse*, have them look up the word in a dictionary or thesaurus. Two synonyms for *inverse* are *opposite* and *reverse*. Lead students to understand that when x changes, y changes in the opposite way.

2 EXAMPLE **Alternative Method**

Some students may find it helpful to use the point $(3, 8)$ and the technique from Example 1 to write an equation for the inverse variation. Then, students should find the y-value when $x = 2$.

Additional Examples

1 Suppose y varies inversely with x, and a point on the graph of the equation is $(8, 9)$. Write an equation for the inverse variation. **$xy = 72$, or $y = \frac{72}{x}$**

2 The points $(5, 6)$ and $(3, y)$ are two points on the graph of an inverse variation. Find the missing value. **10**

 **Reaching All Students**

Below Level Make sure students understand that the equations $y = \frac{k}{x}$ and $xy = k$ are equivalent.	**Advanced Learners** Ask students to research joint variation and combined variations and provide an example of each.	**English Learners** See note on page 639. **Tactile Learners** See note on page 638.

637

3 EXAMPLE Tactile Learners

Encourage students to model the lever by placing a ruler across a pencil and then balancing tiles on each end of the ruler.

page 636 Investigation

3.

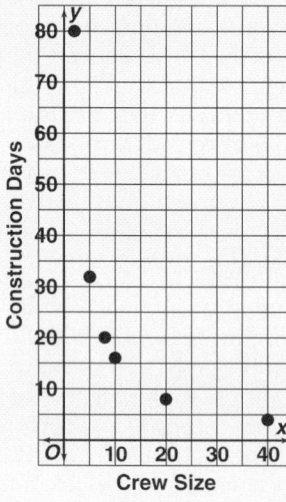

3 EXAMPLE Real-World Problem Solving

Physics The weight needed to balance a lever varies inversely with the distance from the fulcrum to the weight. Where should Julio, who weighs 150 lb, sit to balance the lever?

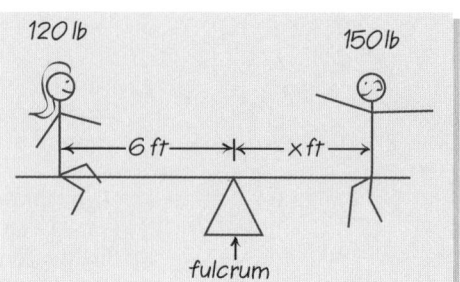

Relate A weight of 120 lb is 6 ft from the fulcrum. A weight of 150 lb is x ft from the fulcrum.
Weight and distance vary inversely.

Define Let weight$_1$ = 120 lb.
Let weight$_2$ = 150 lb.
Let distance$_1$ = 6 ft.
Let distance$_2$ = x ft.

Write weight$_1$ · distance$_1$ = weight$_2$ · distance$_2$

$$120 \cdot 6 = 150 \cdot x \quad \text{Substitute.}$$
$$720 = 150x \quad \text{Simplify.}$$
$$\frac{720}{150} = x \quad \text{Solve for } x.$$
$$4.8 = x \quad \text{Simplify.}$$

● Julio should sit 4.8 feet from the fulcrum to balance the lever.

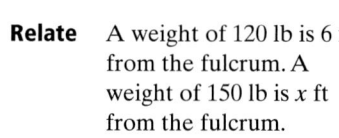 **Real-World Connection**

A fulcrum is the point at which a lever pivots. Students can use levers in science labs to investigate physical properties.

✓ **Check Understanding** **3 a. Physics** A 100-lb weight is placed 4 ft from a fulcrum. How far from the fulcrum should a 75-lb weight be placed to balance the lever? **5.3 ft**

b. An 80-lb weight is placed 9 ft from a fulcrum. What weight should you put 6 ft from the fulcrum to balance the lever? **120 lb**

OBJECTIVE

2 Comparing Direct and Inverse Variation

Recall that a direct variation is an equation in the form $y = kx$. This summary will help you recognize and use direct and inverse variations.

🔧 **Key Concepts**

Summary	Direct and Inverse Variation
Direct Variation	**Inverse Variation**

Direct Variation	Inverse Variation
y varies directly with x.	y varies inversely with x.
y is directly proportional to x.	y is inversely proportional to x.
The ratio $\frac{y}{x}$ is constant.	The product xy is constant.

4 EXAMPLE Determining Direct or Inverse Variation

Do the data in each table represent a *direct variation* or an *inverse variation*? For each table, write an equation to model the data.

a.

x	y
2	5
4	10
10	25

The values of y seem to vary directly with the values of x. Check each ratio $\frac{y}{x}$.

$$\frac{y}{x} \to \frac{5}{2} = 2.5 \qquad \frac{10}{4} = 2.5 \qquad \frac{25}{10} = 2.5$$

The ratio $\frac{y}{x}$ is the same for all pairs of data. So this is a direct variation, and $k = 2.5$.

The equation is $y = 2.5x$.

b.

x	y
5	20
10	10
25	4

The values of y seem to vary inversely with the values of x. Check each product xy.

xy: $5(20) = 100$ $10(10) = 100$ $25(4) = 100$

The product xy is the same for all pairs of data. So this is an inverse variation, and $k = 100$.

The equation is $xy = 100$.

✓ **Check Understanding** **4** Determine whether the data in each table represent a direct variation or an inverse variation. Write an equation to model the data in each table.

a.

x	y
3	12
6	6
9	4

inverse variation; $xy = 36$

b.

x	y
3	12
5	20
8	32

direct variation; $y = 4x$

Many real-world situations involve variation. You can look for a constant ratio or a constant product to determine whether the relationship is a direct variation or an inverse variation.

5 EXAMPLE Real-World 🌐 Problem Solving

Explain whether each situation represents a direct variation or an inverse variation.

a. Carpooling The cost of $20 worth of gasoline is split among several people.

The cost per person times the number of people equals the total cost of the gasoline. Since the total cost is a constant product of $20, this is an inverse variation.

b. School Supplies You buy several markers for 70¢ each.

The cost per marker times the number of markers equals the total cost of the markers. Since the ratio $\frac{\text{cost}}{\text{marker}}$ is constant at 70¢ each, this is a direct variation.

✓ **Check Understanding** **5** Explain whether each situation represents a direct variation or an inverse variation. **a. See left.**
  a. You are in a discount store. All sweaters are on sale for $15 each.
  b. You walk 5 miles each day. Your speed and time vary from day to day.
    Inverse variation, since the total number of miles walked each day is a constant product of 5.

5a. Direct variation, since the ratio $\frac{\text{cost}}{\text{sweater}}$ is constant at $15 each.

OBJECTIVE
2 Teaching Notes

4 EXAMPLE Teaching Tip

Students may not understand why they need to check each of the values in the table. Draw the following table on the board:

x	2	4	6
y	4	16	36

Ask: *Is this an inverse variation or a direct variation.* **neither**

5 EXAMPLE English Learners

Some students may think *carpooling* has something to do with a car and a swimming pool. Explain that *pooling* can also mean sharing something through an arrangement with other people.

🖐 **Additional Examples**

4 Decide if each data set represents a *direct variation* or an *inverse variation*. Then write an equation to model the data.

a.

x	y
3	10
5	6
10	3

b.

x	y
2	3
4	6
8	12

inverse variation; $xy = 30$

direct variation; $y = 1.5x$

5 Explain whether each situation represents a direct variation or an inverse variation.
a. You buy several souvenirs for $10 each. **direct variation**
b. The cost of a $25 birthday present is split among several friends. **inverse variation**

Closure

Ask students to describe how a direct variation and an inverse variation are different. A direct variation has an equation of the form $y = kx$, where $k \neq 0$. So, the ratio $\frac{y}{x}$ is a constant. It is a linear function whose graph passes through (0, 0). An inverse variation has an equation of the form $y = \frac{k}{x}$, where $k \neq 0$. So, the product xy is a constant. Its graph is a curve.

EXERCISES
For more practice, see *Extra Practice*.

Practice and Problem Solving

Assignment Guide

▼ **1** Objective
- Ⓐ Ⓑ **Core** 1–23, 30–35, 39–40
- Ⓒ **Extension** 50

▼ **2** Objective
- Ⓐ Ⓑ **Core** 24–29, 36–38, 41–49
- Ⓒ **Extension** 51

Standardized Test Prep 52–55

Mixed Review 56–70

Error Prevention
Exercises 10–21 Remind students that the product xy is constant for each pair of points (x, y) of an inverse variation. The ratio $\frac{y}{x}$ is constant for each pair of points (x, y) of a direct variation.

Auditory Learners
Exercises 27–29 Encourage students to read each statement to a partner. Then have them ask their partner: *What could variables represent here? How would those variables be related to each other?*

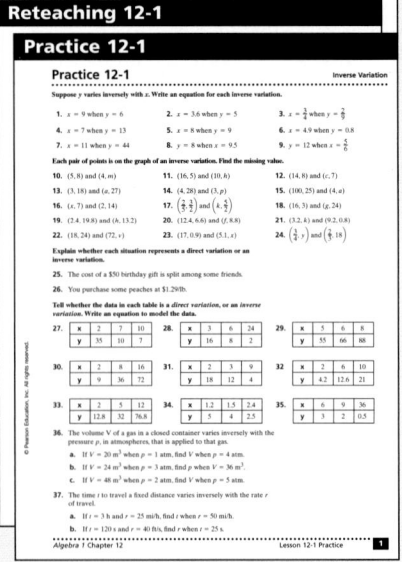

Ⓐ **Practice by Example**

Example 1
(page 637)

Example 2
(page 637)

Example 3
(page 638)

Example 4
(page 639)

Example 5
(page 639)

1–9. See margin.
Suppose y varies inversely with x. Write an equation for the inverse variation.

1. $y = 6$ when $x = 3$ **2.** $y = 1$ when $x = 2$ **3.** $y = 7$ when $x = 8$

4. $y = 3$ when $x = 0.5$ **5.** $y = 10$ when $x = 2.4$ **6.** $y = 3.5$ when $x = 2.2$

7. $y = 6$ when $x = \frac{1}{3}$ **8.** $y = \frac{1}{16}$ when $x = 8$ **9.** $y = \frac{1}{10}$ when $x = \frac{3}{5}$

Each pair of points is on the graph of an inverse variation. Find the missing value.

10. $(6, 12)$ and $(9, y)$ **8**   **11.** $(3, 5)$ and $(1, n)$ **15**   **12.** $(x, 11)$ and $(1, 66)$ **6**

13. $(x, 55)$ and $(5, 77)$ **7**   **14.** $(9.4, b)$ and $(6, 4.7)$ **3**   **15.** $(50, 13)$ and $(t, 5)$ **130**

16. $(4, 3.6)$ and $(1.2, g)$ **12**   **17.** $(24, 1.6)$ and $(c, 0.4)$ **96**   **18.** $(500, 25)$ and $(4, n)$ **3125**

19. $\left(\frac{1}{2}, 24\right)$ and $(6, y)$ **2**   **20.** $\left(x, \frac{1}{2}\right)$ and $\left(\frac{1}{3}, \frac{1}{4}\right)$ $\frac{1}{6}$ **21.** $\left(\frac{1}{2}, 5\right)$ and $\left(b, \frac{1}{8}\right)$ **20**

22. Travel Suppose you take $2\frac{1}{2}$ h to drive from your house to the lake at 48 mi/h. How long will your return trip take at 40 mi/h? **3 h**

23. Bicycling Suppose a camper took 2 h to ride around a reservoir at 10 mi/h at the beginning of the summer. By the end of the summer, she can ride around the reservoir in $1\frac{1}{2}$ h. What is her rate at the end of the summer? **13.3̄ mi/h**

Do the data in each table represent a direct variation or an inverse variation? Write an equation to model the data in each table.

26. inverse variation; $xy = 72$

24.

x	y
2	1
5	2.5
8	4

direct variation; $y = 0.5x$

25.

x	y
4	15
6	10
10	6

inverse variation; $xy = 60$

26.

x	y
3	24
9	8
12	6

Explain whether each situation represents a direct variation or an inverse variation. **27–29. See margin.**

27. You buy some chicken for $1.79/lb.

28. An 8-slice pizza is shared equally by a group of friends.

29. You find the length and width of several rectangles. Each has an area of 24 square units.

Ⓑ **Apply Your Skills**

Find the constant of variation k for each inverse variation. Then write an equation for the inverse variation.

30. 32; $xy = 32$ 31. 1.1; $rt = 1.1$ 32. 2.5; $xy = 2.5$

30. $y = 8$ when $x = 4$ **31.** $r = 3.3$ when $t = \frac{1}{3}$ **32.** $x = \frac{1}{2}$ when $y = 5$

33. $a = 25$ when $b = 0.04$ **34.** $p = 10.4$ when $q = 1.5$ **35.** $x = 5$ when $y = 75$
33. 1; $ab = 1$ 34. 15.6; $pq = 15.6$ 35. 375; $xy = 375$

🔲 **Geometry** Does each formula represent a direct or an inverse variation? Explain.

36. the perimeter of an equilateral triangle: $P = 3s$ **36–38. See margin.**

37. the time t to travel 150 mi at r mi/h: $t = \frac{150}{r}$

38. the circumference of a circle with radius r: $C = 2\pi r$

pages 640–642 **Exercises**

1. $xy = 18$
2. $xy = 2$
3. $xy = 56$
4. $xy = 1.5$

5. $xy = 24$
6. $xy = 7.7$
7. $xy = 2$
8. $xy = 0.5$
9. $xy = 0.06$

27. Direct variation; the ratio $\frac{cost}{pound}$ is constant at $1.79.

28. Inverse variation; the total number of slices is constant at 8.

Real-World **Connection**

Careers Surveyors determine boundaries and elevations of geographical features.

44a. greater

  b. greater

  c. less

45a.16 h; 10 h; 8 h; 4 h

  b. hr worked, rate of pay

  c. $rt = 80$

🌐 **39. Surveying** Each of two rectangular building lots is one quarter acre in size. One lot measures 99 ft by 110 ft. The other lot is 90 ft wide. What is the second lot's length? **121 ft**

🌐 **40. Construction** Suppose 4 people can paint a house if they work 3 days each. How long would it take a crew of 5 people to paint the house? **2.4 days**

Do the data in each table represent a direct or an inverse variation? Write an equation to model the data. Then complete the table.

41.

x	y
10	4
20	■
8	3.2

direct variation;
$y = 0.4x$; **8**

42.

x	y
0.4	28
1.2	84
■	63

direct variation;
$y = 70x$; **0.9**

43.

x	y
1.6	30
4.8	10
■	96

inverse variation; $xy = 48$; **0.5**

🌐 **44. Math in the Media** According to the First Law of Air Travel, for each situation below, will the distance to your gate be *greater* or *less* for this trip than for your last trip? **See left.**
  a. You have more luggage.
  b. You have less time to make your flight.
  c. You have less luggage.

🌐 **45. a. Earnings** Suppose you want to earn $80. How long will it take you if you are paid $5/h; $8/h; $10/h; $20/h? **See left.**
  b. What are the two variable quantities in part (a)?
  c. Write an equation to represent this situation.

46. Open-Ended Write and graph a direct variation and an inverse variation that have the same constant of variation. **Check students' work.**

47. Physics Boyle's Law states that volume V varies inversely with pressure P for any gas at a constant temperature in an enclosed space. Suppose a gas at constant temperature occupies 15.3 liters at a pressure of 40 millimeters of mercury. What is the volume of the gas when the pressure is 60 millimeters of mercury? **10.2 L**

48. Critical Thinking The graphs of p and q represent a direct variation and an inverse variation. Write an equation for each graph. $p: y = 0.5x$; $q: xy = 8$

49. Writing Explain how the variable y changes in each situation.
  a. y varies directly with x. The value of x is doubled. **y is doubled**
  b. y varies inversely with x. The value of x is doubled. **y is halved**

CLOSE TO HOME by John McPherson

GATE 31-Y
3.4 MILES

The First Law of Air Travel
The distance to your connecting gate is directly proportional to the amount of luggage you are carrying and inversely proportional to the amount of time you have.

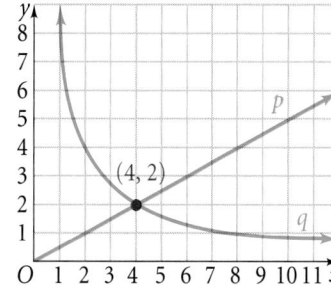

Graph showing lines p and q intersecting at point (4, 2), with y-axis labeled 1–8 and x-axis labeled O 1 2 3 4 5 6 7 8 9 10 11 x

Lesson 12-1 Inverse Variation   **641**

29. Inverse variation; the product of the length and width remains constant with an area of 24 square units.

36. Direct variation; the ratio of the perimeter to the side length is constant at 3.

37. Inverse variation; the product of the rate and the time is always 150.

38. Direct variation; the ratio of the circumference to the radius is constant at 2π.

Standardized Test Prep

Resources
For additional practice with a variety of test item formats:
- Standardized Test Prep, pp. 697–699
- Test-Taking Strategies, p. 692
- Test-Taking Strategies with Transparencies

Exercise 54 Remind students to check every value in the table.

 Challenge

50. 4; $s\left(\frac{1}{2}d\right)^2 = \frac{1}{4}sd^2 = k$,

so $s = \frac{4k}{d^2}$.

50. Physics The intensity of a sound s varies inversely with the square of the distance d from the sound. This can be modeled by the equation $sd^2 = k$. If you move half the distance closer to the source of a sound, by what factor will the intensity of the sound increase? Explain your reasoning. **See left.**

51. Write an equation to model each situation.
  a. y varies inversely with the fourth power of x. $x^4y = k$
  b. y varies inversely with the fourth power of x and directly with z. $\frac{x^4y}{z} = k$

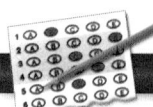

Standardized Test Prep

Multiple Choice

52. Suppose y varies inversely with x and $x = 12$ when $y = 3$. What is the equation of the inverse variation? **C**

  A. $\frac{y}{x} = 36$ **B.** $y = \frac{12}{3}$ **C.** $y = \frac{36}{x}$ **D.** $12 = \frac{3}{y}$

53. The volume V of a gas varies inversely with the pressure P. When the volume is 75 in.^{2}, the pressure is 30 lb/in.^{3}. Which equation models this relationship? **F**

  F. $VP = 2250$ **G.** $V = \frac{P}{75}$ **H.** $V = \frac{75}{P}$ **I.** $V = \frac{P}{2250}$

Short Response

54. Use the table at the right. Find a value such that the y-values vary directly with the x-values. Then find a value such that the y-values vary inversely with the x-values. Show your work. **See margin.**

x	y
5	10
8	■

Extended Response

55. You are traveling to visit your best friend who moved 100 miles away.
  a. Copy and complete the table below to find the time the trip takes at different speeds.
  b. Describe the relationship of the variables.
  c. How long would the round trip take if you could travel at 80 mi/h?
  a–c. See margin.

Distance (d)	100	100	100	100
Speed (r)	30	40	50	60
Time (t)	■	■	■	■

Take It to the NET
Online lesson quiz at
www.PHSchool.com
Web Code: aea-1201

Mixed Review

Lesson 11-7   Use $\triangle FGH$ to evaluate each expression.

56. $\sin F$ $\frac{8}{17}$ **57.** $\sin G$ $\frac{15}{17}$ **58.** $\cos F$ $\frac{15}{17}$

59. $\cos G$ $\frac{8}{17}$ **60.** $\tan F$ $\frac{8}{15}$ **61.** $\tan G$ $\frac{15}{8}$

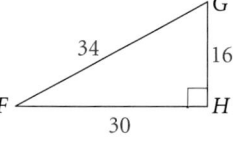

Lesson 11-3   Find the distance between the points in each pair. Round to the nearest tenth.

62. $(5, 2)$ and $(4, 7)$ **5.1**   **63.** $(-2, 9)$ and $(6, 0)$ **12.0**   **64.** $(4, 8)$ and $(-4, -1)$ **12.0**

65. $(8, 10)$ and $(1, 2)$ **10.6**   **66.** $(-3, -5)$ and $(-2, -7)$ **2.2**   **67.** $(1.5, 1)$ and $(2, 3.5)$ **2.5**

Lesson 9-6   Factor each expression.

68. $3a^2 + 11a - 4$
   $(3a - 1)(a + 4)$

69. $15x^2 + 41x + 14$
   $(5x + 2)(3x + 7)$

70. $2y^2 + 13y - 24$
   $(2y - 3)(y + 8)$

pages 640–642   Exercises

54. [2] Direct variation:
$y = kx$, $10 = 5k$,
$k = 2$. So when
$x = 8$, $y = 2 \cdot 8 = 16$.
Inverse variation:
$xy = k$, $5 \cdot 10 = 50$, So
when $x = 8$,
$y = \frac{50}{8}$, or 6.25.

[1] no work shown OR one computational error

55. [4] a.

Distance (d)	100	100	100	100
Speed (r)	30	40	50	60
Time (t)	$3\frac{1}{3}$	$2\frac{1}{2}$	2	$1\frac{2}{3}$

b. The variables speed and time are inversely related.

c. $2\frac{1}{2}$ h

[3] one computational error

[2] one part missing

[1] two parts missing

Graphing Rational Functions

Functions like $y = \frac{1}{x}$, $y = \frac{1}{x+2}$, and $y = \frac{1}{x} - 4$ are rational functions. When you use a graphing calculator to graph a rational function, sometimes false connections appear on the screen. When this happens, you need to make adjustments to see the true shape of the graph.

Graph the function $y = \frac{1}{x+2} - 4$. You can enter this as $y = 1 \div (x + 2) - 4$. The graph of the function may look like the graph at the right on your screen. The highest point and lowest point on the graph that appear on the screen are not supposed to connect. If you use the trace feature on the calculator, no point on the graph lies on this connecting line. So this is a false connection.

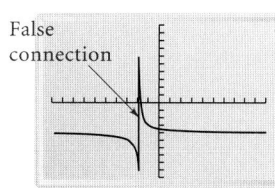

False connection

Here's how you can graph a rational function and avoid false connections.

Step 1 Press the MODE key. Then scroll down and right to highlight the word **Dot**. Then press ENTER.

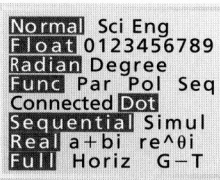

Step 2 Graph again. Now the false connection is gone!

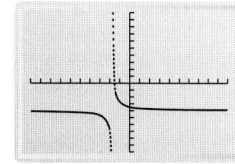

Step 3 Use the TRACE key or TABLE key to find points on the graph. Sketch the graph.

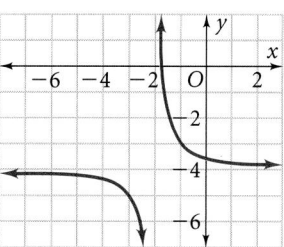

EXERCISES

Use a graphing calculator to graph each function. Then sketch the graph. 1–9. See back of book.

1. $y = \frac{4}{x}$

2. $y = \frac{-2}{x}$

3. $y = \frac{1}{x+3}$

4. $y = \frac{1}{x-4}$

5. $y = \frac{1}{x} + 3$

6. $y = \frac{1}{x} - 4$

7. $y = \frac{1}{x-2} - 3$

8. $y = \frac{4}{x+1} - 3$

9. $y = \frac{-4}{x+1} - 3$

10. **a.** Graph $y = \frac{1}{x}$, $y = \frac{1}{x-3}$, and $y = \frac{1}{x+4}$. **a–b. See back of book.**

    b. Make a Conjecture How does adding or subtracting a number in the denominator translate the graph?

11. **a.** Graph $y = \frac{1}{x}$, $y = \frac{1}{x} - 3$, and $y = \frac{1}{x} + 4$. **See back of book.**

    b. Make a Conjecture How does adding or subtracting a number to the expression translate the graph? **See right.**

11b. The graphs are the same shape as $y = \frac{1}{x}$. $y = \frac{1}{x} - 3$ shifts the graph down 3 units; $y = \frac{1}{x} + 4$ shifts the graph up 4 units.

Graphing Rational Functions

Students learn that the graphs of some rational functions show connections on the screen but should not in fact be connected. In this feature students learn the steps to take to avoid these false connections.

Resources

Students may use any graphing calculator to explore graphs and functions.

Teaching Notes

Students may not recognize or connect certain kinds of equations with what the graph will look like. They have now encountered many different shapes of graphs. If students are not sure what happens as the constant changes in $xy = k$ or what happens when a number is added to the denominator, it would probably be helpful if they made a prediction first before using their calculator to graph it or before using paper and pencil to graph it. By doing this, they will become more proficient at looking at an equation and having an idea of what the graph will look like.

Teaching Tip

Have students make conjectures as in Exercises 10 and 11. Allow students to discuss each other's conjectures. Encourage them to use mathematical language in their discussions. A student may say that he or she has a *counter-example* to a conjecture. A student may *justify* a conjecture or *withdraw* the conjecture. This type of mathematical language encourages precise clear communication and gives a way for students to disagree with each other without hurting feelings.

Lesson Preview

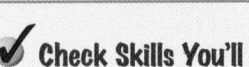 **Check Skills You'll Need**

Function Rules, Tables, and Graphs
Lesson 5-3: Examples 1–3
Exercises 1–20
Extra Practice, p. 706

Exponential Functions
Lesson 8-7: Examples 1, 3
Exercises 1–8, 12–22
Extra Practice, p. 709

Exploring Quadratic Graphs
Lesson 10-1: Examples 2, 4
Exercises 4–9, 14–19
Extra Practice, p. 711

Lesson Resources

 **Teaching Resources**
Practice, Reteaching, Enrichment

 **Reaching All Students**
Practice Workbook 12-2
Spanish Practice Workbook 12-2
Technology Activities 26
Basic Algebra Planning Guide 12-2

Presentation Assistant Plus!
Transparencies
• Check Skills You'll Need 12-2
• Additional Examples 12-2
• Student Edition Answers 12-2
• Lesson Quiz 12-2
PH Presentation Pro CD 12-2

ASSESSMENT SYSTEM

Computer Test Generator CD

Technology
Resource Pro® CD-ROM
Computer Test Generator CD
Prentice Hall Presentation Pro CD

 www.PHSchool.com
Student Site
• Teacher Web Code: aek-5500
• Self-grading Lesson Quiz
Teacher Center
• Lesson Planner
• Resources

Plus **iTEXT**

644

Graphing Rational Functions

Lesson Preview

 What You'll Learn

OBJECTIVE 1 To graph rational functions

OBJECTIVE 2 To identify types of functions

. . . And Why

To solve problems involving travel, as in Example 1

✓ **Check Skills You'll Need** (For help, go to Lessons 5-3, 8-7, and 10-1.)

Evaluate each function for $x = -2, 0, 3$.

1. $f(x) = x - 8$ **2.** $g(x) = x^2 + 4$ **8, 4, 13** **3.** $y = 3^x$ **$\frac{1}{9}$, 1, 27**
   $-10; -8; -5$

Graph each function. **4–6. See margin p. 646.**

4. $f(x) = 2x + 1$ **5.** $g(x) = -x^2$ **6.** $y = 2^x$

New Vocabulary • rational function • asymptote

---

iTEXT Interactive lesson includes instant self-check, tutorials, and activities.

You can write the inverse variation $xy = 3$ as $y = \frac{3}{x}$. This is a rational function. In simplest form, a **rational function** has a polynomial of at least degree 1 in the denominator.

1 EXAMPLE Graphing a Rational Function

Travel On any trip, the time you travel in a car varies inversely with your average speed. The function $t = \frac{60}{r}$ models the time it will take you to travel 60 miles at different rates of speed. Graph this function.

Step 1 Make a table of values.

r	t
10	6
15	4
20	3
30	2
40	1.5
60	1

Step 2 Plot the points.

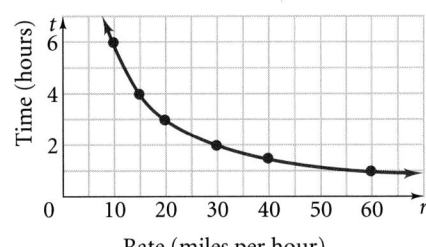

Rate (miles per hour)

✓ **Check Understanding** **1 a.** The function $t = \frac{40}{r}$ models the time it will take you to travel 40 miles at different rates of speed. Graph this function. **See margin p. 646.**

b. Critical Thinking Why is it reasonable in this situation to graph the function in Quadrant I only? **Speed and time are both positive values, so graphing it in the first quadrant only makes sense.**

As you can see in the graph in Example 1, the graph approaches both axes but does not cross either axis. A line is an **asymptote** of a graph if the graph of the function gets closer to the line as x or y gets larger in absolute value. In the graph in Example 1, the horizontal and vertical axes are asymptotes.

644 Chapter 12 Rational Expressions and Functions

Ongoing Assessment and Intervention

Before the Lesson
Diagnose prerequisite skills using:
• Check Skills You'll Need

During the Lesson
Monitor progress using:
• Check Understanding
• Additional Examples
• Standardized Test Prep

After the Lesson
Assess knowledge using:
• Lesson Quiz
• Computer Test Generator CD

The graphs of many rational functions are related to each other. Look at the graphs of the functions below.

$$y = \frac{1}{x}$$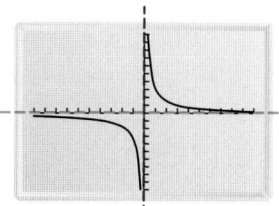

$$y = \frac{1}{x-2}$$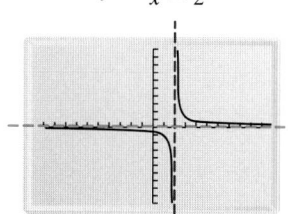

vertical asymptote at $x = 0$ vertical asymptote at $x = 2$
horizontal asymptote at $y = 0$ horizontal asymptote at $y = 0$

The graphs are identical in shape, but the second graph is translated two units to the right.

When the numerator and denominator of a rational function have no common factors other than 1, there is a vertical asymptote at the x-value that makes the denominator equal zero. This is because division by zero is undefined. The domain of a function does not include that x-value where there is a vertical asymptote.

2 EXAMPLE   **Using a Vertical Asymptote**

Identify the vertical asymptote of $y = \frac{4}{x+3}$. Then graph the function.

Step 1 Find the vertical asymptote.

$x + 3 = 0$ **The numerator and denominator have no common factors. Find any value(s) where the denominator equals zero.**

$x = -3$ **This is the equation of the vertical asymptote.**

Step 2 Make a table of values. Use values of x near -3, the asymptote.

Step 3 Graph the function.

Use a dashed line for the asymptote $x = -3$.

x	y
-6	$-\frac{4}{3}$
-5	-2
-4	-4
-2	4
-1	2
0	$\frac{4}{3}$
3	$\frac{2}{3}$

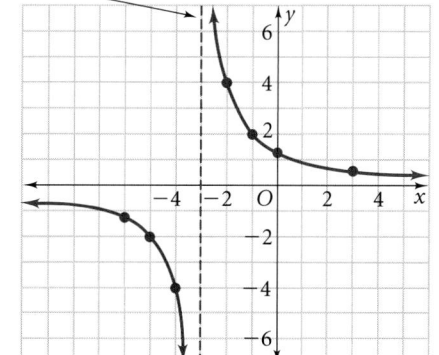

2a. asymptote $x = -2$;

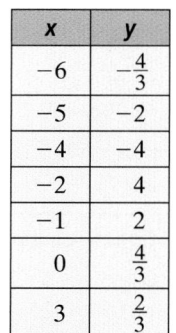

b. asymptote $x = 3$;

✔ **Check Understanding**   **2** Identify the vertical asymptote of each function. Then graph the function.
  a. $f(x) = \frac{1}{x+2}$ **a–b. See left.**   **b.** $h(x) = \frac{2}{x-3}$

👥 **Reaching All Students**

| **Below Level** Ask students to write an example function for each of the six families of functions. Have them graph their functions and verify that each one models the correct family. | **Advanced Learners** Have a student graph a rational function. Have a partner write a function of the same type as the graph. Switch roles and repeat the activity. | **Error Prevention** See note on page 645. |

Math Background

The vertical line $x = h$ is a vertical asymptote if, as x approaches h from the right or from the left, the value of y approaches either positive or negative infinity. A rational function in lowest terms will have a vertical asymptote whenever the denominator is zero.

OBJECTIVE
1 Teaching Notes

1 EXAMPLE   **Connection to Advanced Algebra**
This particular type of graph is known as a hyperbola. Students will study hyperbolas as well as other conic sections in Algebra 2.

2 EXAMPLE   **Error Prevention**

Students may think that the asymptote moves four places in some direction because of the 4 in the numerator. Point out that they need only look at the denominator when finding the asymptotes. Have them graph $y = \frac{1}{x+3}$ and compare it to the graph of $y = \frac{4}{x+3}$ shown in the book to see that the 4 has no effect on the asymptotes.

Additional Examples

1 The function $t = \frac{70}{r}$ models the time it will take you to travel 70 miles at different rates of speed. Graph this function.

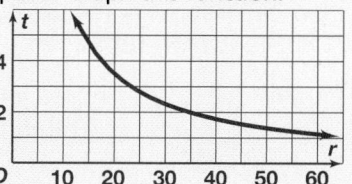

2 Identify the vertical asymptote of $y = \frac{4}{x-3}$. Then graph the function. $x = 3$

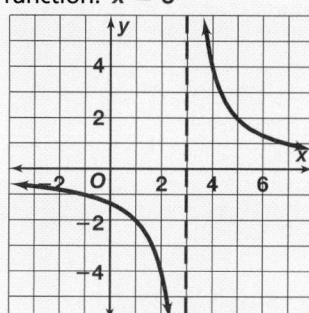

❸ Identify the asymptotes of $y = \frac{4}{x+4} + 3$. Then graph the function. $x = -4, y = 3$

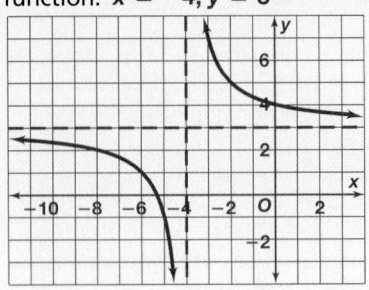

page 644   Check Skills You'll Need

4.

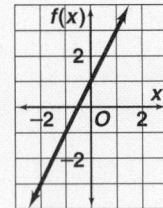

5.

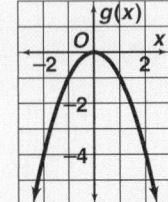

6.

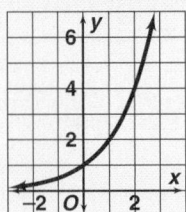

page 644   Check Understanding

1a.

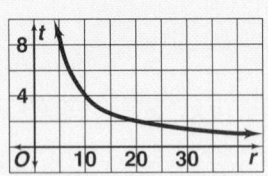

3a. $x = -2, y = -3;$

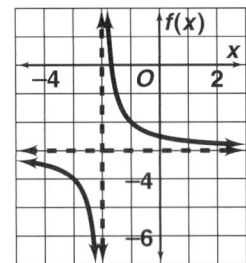

b. $x = 4, y = 1;$

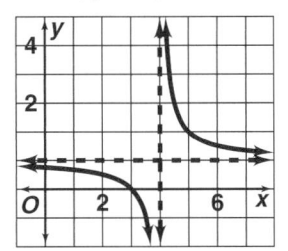

You can also see how to shift the graph of a rational function vertically.

$$y = \frac{1}{x}$$

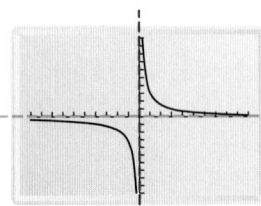

$$y = \frac{1}{x} - 2$$

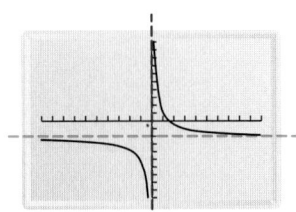

vertical asymptote at $x = 0$ vertical asymptote at $x = 0$
horizontal asymptote at $y = 0$ horizontal asymptote at $y = -2$

The graphs are identical in shape, but the second graph is translated two units down.

❸ EXAMPLE   Using Vertical and Horizontal Asymptotes

Identify the asymptotes of $y = \frac{4}{x+3} + 2$. Then graph the function.

Step 1 From the form of the function, you can see that there is a vertical asymptote at $x = -3$ and a horizontal asymptote at $y = 2$. Sketch the asymptotes.

Step 2 Make a table of values using values of x near -3.

Step 3 Graph the function.

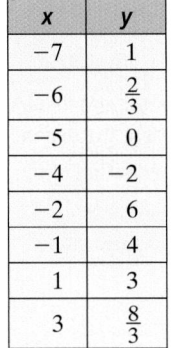

x	y
-7	1
-6	$\frac{2}{3}$
-5	0
-4	-2
-2	6
-1	4
1	3
3	$\frac{8}{3}$

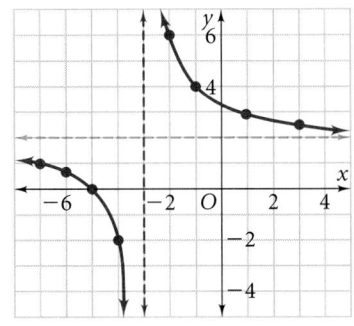

✔ **Check Understanding** ❸ Identify the asymptotes of each function. Then graph the function.

a. $f(x) = \frac{1}{x+2} - 3$ **a–b. See left.**   **b.** $y = \frac{1}{x-4} + 1$

🔑 **Key Concepts**

Summary	Graphs of Rational Functions

The graph of a rational function in the form $y = \frac{a}{x-b} + c$ has a vertical asymptote at $x = b$ and a horizontal asymptote at $y = c$. The graph is a translation of $y = \frac{a}{x}$, b units right or left (for b positive or negative) and c units up or down (for c positive or negative).

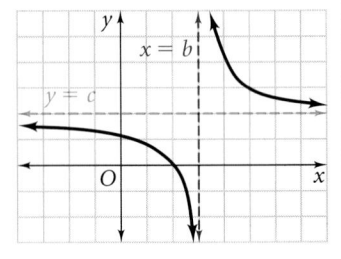

You can think of graphs of functions with similar features as families of functions. You have studied six families of functions this year. Their properties and graphs are shown in this summary.

 Key Concepts

Summary	Families of Functions

Linear function
$y = mx + b$

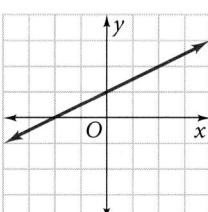

slope $= m$
y-intercept $= b$
The greatest exponent is 1.

Absolute value function
$y = |x - a| + b$

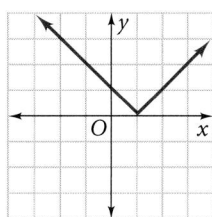

shift $y = |x|$ horizontally a units
shift $y = |x|$ vertically b units
vertex at (a, b)
The greatest exponent is 1.

Quadratic function
$y = ax^2 + bx + c$

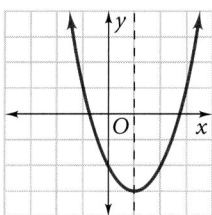

parabola with axis of
symmetry at $x = -\frac{b}{2a}$
The greatest exponent is 2.

Exponential function
$y = ab^x$

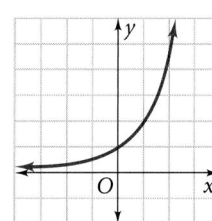

growth for $b > 1$
decay for $0 < b < 1$
The variable is the exponent.

Radical function
$y = \sqrt{x - b} + c$

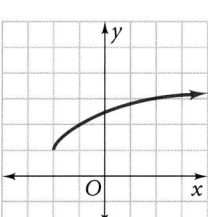

shift $y = \sqrt{x}$ horizontally b units
shift $y = \sqrt{x}$ vertically c units
The variable is under the radical.

Rational function
$y = \frac{a}{x - b} + c$

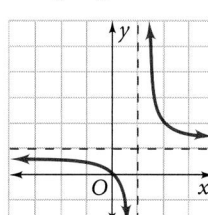

vertical asymptote at $x = b$
horizontal asymptote at $y = c$
The variable is in the denominator.

Additional Examples

④ Describe the graph of each function.
a. $y = \frac{x}{6}$ line with slope $\frac{1}{6}$ and y-intercept 0
b. $y = 6^x$ exponential growth
c. $y = 6x^2$ parabola with axis of symmetry at $x = 0$
d. $y = |x - 6|$ absolute value function with a vertex at (6, 0)
e. $y = \frac{6}{x}$ rational function with vertical asymptote at $x = 0$ and horizontal asymptote at $y = 0$
f. $y = \sqrt{x - 6}$ radical function $y = \sqrt{x}$ shifted right 6 units
g. $y = 6x$ line with slope 6 and y-intercept 0

Closure

Ask students to explain the difference between the graphs of a rational function and a linear function. A rational function usually has a curved graph while the graph of a linear function is a line. Ask students to explain the steps in graphing a rational function. First find the horizontal and vertical asymptotes. Next make a table of values using values of x near the value of the vertical asymptote. Then, sketch the asymptotes, plot the points from the table, and draw the curve.

Assignment Guide

▼1 **Objective**
Ⓐ Ⓑ **Core** 1–25, 35–52
Ⓒ **Extension** 57–59

▼2 **Objective**
Ⓐ Ⓑ **Core** 26–34, 53–56
Ⓒ **Extension** 60–62

Standardized Test Prep 63–67

Mixed Review 68–77

Enrichment 12-2
Reteaching 12-2
Practice 12-2

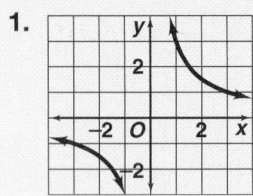

4 EXAMPLE Identifying Functions

Describe the graph of each function.

a. $y = 5^x$ — The graph is of exponential growth.

b. $y = 5x$ — The graph is a line with slope 5 and y-intercept 0.

c. $y = \frac{x}{5}$ — The graph is a line with slope $\frac{1}{5}$ and y-intercept 0.

d. $y = \frac{5}{x}$ — The graph is a rational function with vertical asymptote at $x = 0$ and horizontal asymptote at $y = 0$.

e. $y = 5x^2$ — The graph is a parabola with an axis of symmetry at $x = 0$.

f. $y = \sqrt{x - 5}$ — The graph is the radical function $y = \sqrt{x}$ shifted right 5 units.

● **g.** $y = |x - 5|$ — The graph is an absolute value function with a vertex at $(5, 0)$.

✔ **Check Understanding** ④ Describe the graph of each function.

a. $g(x) = |x + 4|$
an absolute value function with vertex $(-4, 0)$

b. $f(x) = 8 \cdot 2^x$
a graph of exponential growth

c. $h(x) = \frac{2}{x + 1}$
a rational function with asymptotes $x = -1$ and $y = 0$

EXERCISES

For more practice, see *Extra Practice*.

Practice and Problem Solving

Ⓐ **Practice by Example**

Example 1
(page 644)

Graph each function. 1–4. See margin.

1. $y = \frac{3}{x}$ **2.** $y = \frac{4}{x}$ **3.** $f(x) = \frac{5}{x}$ **4.** $h(x) = \frac{6}{x}$

5. The function $t = \frac{24}{r}$ models the time it will take you to travel 24 miles at different rates of speed. Graph this function. **See margin.**

Example 2
(page 645)

What value of x makes the denominator of each function equal zero?

6. $f(x) = \frac{3}{x}$ **0**   **7.** $y = \frac{1}{x - 2}$ **2**   **8.** $y = \frac{x}{x + 2}$ **−2**   **9.** $h(x) = \frac{3}{2x - 4}$ **2**

Identify the asymptotes of each graph.

10. 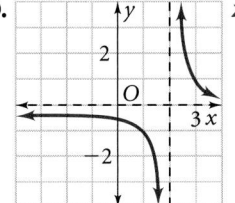 $x = 2, y = 0$

11. 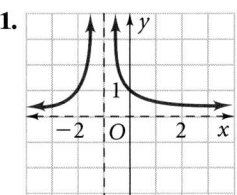 $x = -1, y = 0$

12. 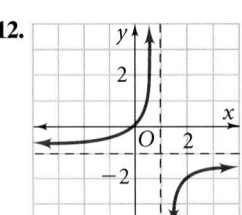 $x = 1, y = -1$ **13.** 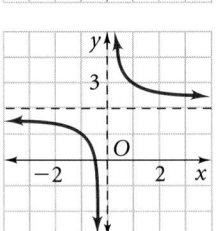 $x = 0, y = 2$

Identify the vertical asymptote of each function. Then graph the function. 14–19. See back of book.

14. $g(x) = \frac{10}{x}$ **15.** $f(x) = \frac{12}{x}$ **16.** $y = \frac{1}{x + 1}$

17. $f(x) = \frac{1}{x - 5}$ **18.** $g(x) = \frac{4}{x + 4}$ **19.** $y = \frac{2}{x + 4}$

pages 648–650 Exercises

1.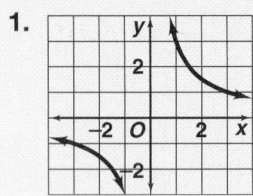

2.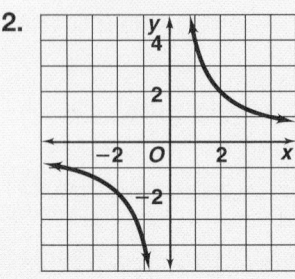

3.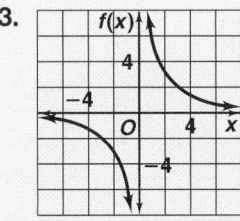

4.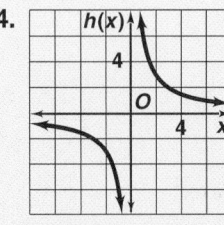

5.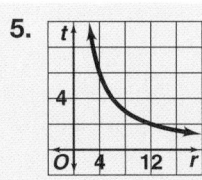

26. line with slope 4, y-int. 1

27. absolute value function with vertex $(4, 0)$

28. exponential decay

29. line with slope $\frac{1}{4}$, y-int. 0

648

20–25. See back of book.

Example 3
(page 646)

Identify the asymptotes of each function. Then graph the function.

20. $y = \frac{1}{x} - 5$

21. $y = \frac{1}{x} + 5$

22. $y = \frac{1}{x} - 6$

23. $h(x) = \frac{2}{x+1} + 4$

24. $f(x) = \frac{1}{x-3} - 5$

25. $h(x) = \frac{1}{x-1} - 2$

Example 4
(page 648)

Describe the graph of each function. 26–34. See margin.

26. $y = 4x + 1$

27. $h(x) = |x - 4|$

28. $y = 0.4^x$

29. $f(x) = \frac{x}{4}$

30. $y = \frac{4}{x} + 1$

31. $h(x) = \sqrt{x-4} + 1$

32. $g(x) = x^2 - 4$

33. $f(x) = \frac{4}{x+4} - 1$

34. $g(x) = 4x^2 + 2x + 1$

35–42. See margin.

B Apply Your Skills

Describe how the graphs of each function are translations of the graph of $f(x) = \frac{7}{x}$.

35. $g(x) = \frac{7}{x+1}$

36. $y = \frac{7}{x-3}$

37. $y = \frac{7}{x} - 15$

38. $f(x) = \frac{7}{x+12}$

39. $g(x) = \frac{7}{x} + 12$

40. $h(x) = \frac{7}{x+3}$

41. $g(x) = \frac{7}{x} - 2$

42. $y = \frac{7}{x+3} - 2$

Identify the asymptotes of each function. Then graph the function. 43–51. See back of book.

43. $f(x) = \frac{-1}{x}$

44. $y = \frac{-4}{x}$

45. $g(x) = \frac{-2}{x+4}$

46. $y = \frac{-1}{x} + 1$

47. $y = \frac{1}{x+1} + 4$

48. $g(x) = \frac{1}{x+1} - 3$

49. $f(x) = \frac{1}{x-1} + 3$

50. $g(x) = \frac{2}{x+5} + 1$

51. $h(x) = \frac{-4}{x-3} - 2$

52. Answers may vary.
Sample: $f(x) = \frac{1}{x} + 3$,
$g(x) = \frac{1}{x}$

52. Open-Ended Write two rational functions whose graphs are identical except that one has been shifted vertically 3 units. **See left.**

53. Light In the formula $I = \frac{445}{x^2}$, I is the intensity of light in lumens at a distance x feet from a light bulb with 445 watts. What is the intensity of light 5 ft from the light bulb? 15 ft from the light bulb? **17.8 lumens; 1.97 lumens**

54. a. Graph $y = \frac{1}{x}$ and $y = \frac{1}{x^2}$. **See margin p. 650.**
b. What are the vertical and horizontal asymptotes of the graph of each function? $x = 0, y = 0; x = 0, y = 0$
c. What is the range of $y = \frac{1}{x}$? Of $y = \frac{1}{x^2}$? **y is any real number except 0; $y > 0$.**

55. Physics As radio signals move away from a transmitter, they become weaker. The function $s = \frac{1600}{d^2}$ relates the strength s of a signal at a distance d miles from a transmitter. **a. See margin p. 650.**
a. Graphing Calculator Graph the function. For what distances is $s \leq 1$?
b. Find the signal strength at 10 mi, 1 mi, and 0.1 mi. **16; 1600; 160,000**
c. Critical Thinking Suppose you drive by the transmitter for one radio station while your car radio is tuned to a second station. The signal from the transmitter can interfere and come through your radio. Use your results from part (b) to explain why. **See margin p. 650.**

Real-World 🌐 **Connection**

Careers Photographers use high-intensity lights to get dramatic photos.

56. Writing Describe the similarities and differences between the graphs of $y = \frac{3}{x}$ and $y = \frac{-3}{x}$. **See back of book.**

C Challenge

Graph each function. Include a dashed line for each asymptote. 57–60. See back of book.

57. $g(x) = \frac{x}{x-1}$

58. $y = \frac{1}{(x-1)^2}$

59. $y = \frac{2}{(x-2)(x+2)}$

60. $y = \frac{1}{x^2 - 2x}$

30. rational function, with asymptotes $x = 0, y = 1$

31. radical function; $y = \sqrt{x}$ shifted right 4, up 1

32. parabola with axis of symmetry $x = 0$

33. rational function with asymptotes $x = -4$, $y = -1$

34. parabola with axis of symmetry $x = -\frac{1}{4}$

35. moves graph 1 unit to the left

36. moves graph 3 units to the right

37. lowers graph 15 units

38. moves graph 12 units left

39. moves the graph up 12 units

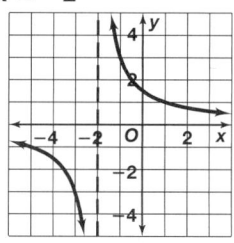
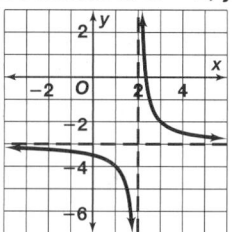
40. moves the graph left 3 units

41. moves the graph down 2 units

42. moves the graph 3 units left and 2 units down

Resources

For additional practice with a variety of test item formats:
- Standardized Test Prep, pp. 697–699
- Test-Taking Strategies, p. 692
- Test-Taking Strategies with Transparencies

Exercise 65 Remind students that a vertical asymptote occurs where the denominator of the function is undefined.

pages 648–650 Exercises

54a.

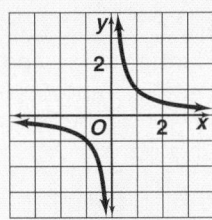

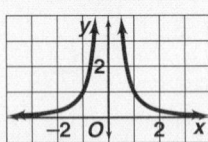

55a.

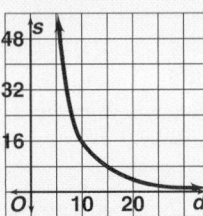

$d \geq 40$

c. The signal is extremely strong when you are in the immediate vicinity of a transmitter and it will interfere with the other station.

62.

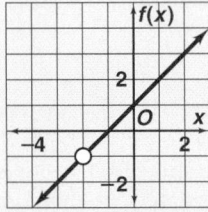

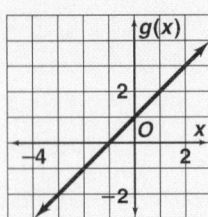

No; $f(x) = \dfrac{(x + 2)(x + 1)}{x + 2}$ is equivalent to $g(x) = x + 1$ for all values except $x = -2$.

650

61a. $x = -3, y = -2$

b. $y = \dfrac{1}{x + 3} - 2$

61. Use the graph at the right. It is a translation of the graph of $y = \frac{1}{x}$.
  a. What are the asymptotes of the graph?
  b. Reasoning Write a function rule for the graph.

62. Graph $f(x) = \dfrac{(x + 2)(x + 1)}{x + 2}$ and $g(x) = x + 1$. Are the graphs the same? Explain. **See margin.**

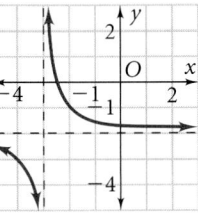

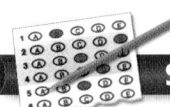

Standardized Test Prep

Multiple Choice

63. Which describes the graph of the function $y = \frac{3}{x} + 2$? **C**
  A. a line with slope 3 and y-intercept 2
  B. a line with slope $\frac{1}{3}$ and y-intercept 2
  C. a rational function with asymptotes at $x = 0$ and $y = 2$
  D. a rational function with asymptotes at $x = -3$ and $y = -2$

64. The graph of $y = \frac{2}{x}$ is translated down 3 units. What is the equation of the new graph? **I**
  F. $y = \dfrac{2}{x + 3}$ **G.** $y = \dfrac{2}{x - 3}$ **H.** $y = \dfrac{2}{x} + 3$ **I.** $y = \dfrac{2}{x} - 3$

Quantitative Comparison

Compare the quantity in Column A with the quantity in Column B. Choose the best answer.
  A. The quantity in Column A is greater.
  B. The quantity in Column B is greater.
  C. The two quantities are equal.
  D. The relationship cannot be determined from the information given.

	Column A	Column B
65. **A**	the value of x for which $y = \dfrac{3}{x - 2} + 1$ is undefined	the value of x for which $y = \dfrac{3}{x + 2} + 1$ is undefined
66. **A**	the value of x for which $y = \dfrac{1}{x - 1} + 2$ is undefined	the value of x for which $y = \dfrac{1}{x + 1} + 2$ is undefined

Take It to the NET
Online lesson quiz at
www.PHSchool.com
Web Code: aea-1202

Short Response

67. a. Describe how the graph of $g(x) = \dfrac{4}{x - 1} + 5$ is a translation of $f(x) = \dfrac{4}{x}$.
  b. What are the asymptotes of $g(x) = \dfrac{4}{x - 1} + 5$? **a–b. See margin.**

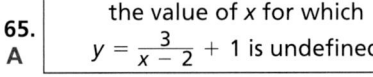

Mixed Review

Lesson 12-1 Write the equation of an inverse variation that includes the given point.

68. $(3, 7)$ $xy = 21$ **69.** $(8, 2)$ $xy = 16$ **70.** $(4, 5.5)$ $xy = 22$ **71.** $(6.2, 3.4)$ $xy = 21.08$

Lesson 10-8 Find the number of real solutions of each equation.

72. $x^2 + x + 1 = 0$ **0**   **73.** $x^2 + 2x + 1 = 0$ **1**   **74.** $x^2 - 8x = 7$ **2**

Lesson 9-8 Factor completely.

75. $3d^2 - 108$ **76.** $2m^2 - 14m - 120$ **77.** $t^3 - t^2 + 3t - 3$
    $3(d - 6)(d + 6)$ $2(m - 12)(m + 5)$ $(t^2 + 3)(t - 1)$

67. [2] a. The graph of $g(x) = \dfrac{4}{x - 1} + 5$ is a translation of $f(x) = \frac{4}{x}$ 5 units up and 1 unit right.
  b. $x = 1$ and $y = 5$

[1] one part answered correctly

page 651 Extension

10. See back of book for graph.
  a. The limit of $y = 0.4^x$ and $y = 0.5^x$ as x increases is 0.

The limit of $y = 0.5^x - 4$ as x increases is -4.
  b. Answers may vary. Sample: Exponential decay functions have a limit as x gets larger, but not as x gets smaller.

Determining Limits

Use the graph at the right to answer Questions 1–3.

1. In Quadrant I, as x increases, y gets closer and closer to __?__. **−1**

2. In Quadrant III, as x decreases, y gets closer and closer to __?__.

3. What happens to y as x gets very close to 1 from the right? From the left? **gets very small; gets very large**

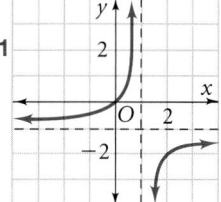

You can think of an asymptote as showing the *limit* of a rational function as $|x|$ or $|y|$ increases. In the graph above, the limit of y as $|x|$ increases is $−1$, and the limit of x as $|y|$ increases is 1.

4. Use the graph at the right.
    a. What is the limit as x increases? **3**
    b. What is the limit as y increases? **1**
    c. What is the limit as x decreases? **3**
    d. What is the limit as y decreases? **1**

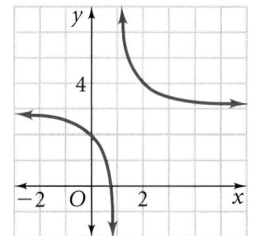

8a.
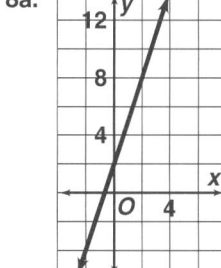

Find the limits as $|x|$ increases for each graph.

5. **0**
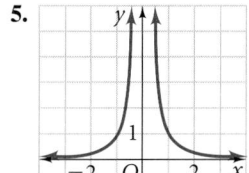

6. **−1**
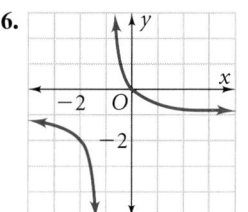

7. **2**
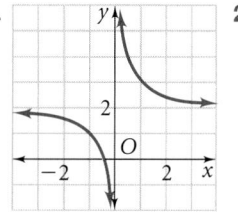

8. a. Graph the linear function $y = 3x + 2$. **See above.**
    b. Does this function have a limit as $|x|$ increases? Explain. **No; there is no asymptote.**

9. a. Copy and extend the table at the right for the first 7 terms of the sequence. **a–b. See back of book.**
    b. Use each term number as an x-value and the term value as its y-value. Graph the points.
    c. What is the limit of the sequence? **3**

 10. a. Graph the exponential functions $y = 0.4^x$, $y = 0.5^x$, and $y = 0.5^x − 4$. Describe any limits as x increases.
    b. **Make a Conjecture** Describe the limits of exponential decay functions. **a–b. See back of book.**

11. a. Graph the functions $y = \dfrac{1}{x^2}$ and $y = \dfrac{1}{x^2 + 1}$. **See margin.**
    b. Describe the limits of each function. **See right.**

Term Number	Term
1	4
2	$3\frac{1}{2}$
3	$3\frac{1}{4}$

11b. For $y = \dfrac{1}{x^2}$, the limit of y as $|x|$ gets larger is 0, and the limit of x as y gets larger is 0. For $y = \dfrac{1}{x^2 + 1}$, the limit as $|x|$ gets larger is 0.

11a. $y = \dfrac{1}{x^2}$
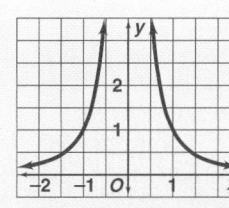

$y = \dfrac{1}{x^2 + 1}$
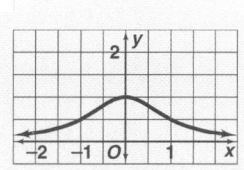

Determining Limits

Students explore rational functions whose graphs are hyperbolas. In this feature students are introduced to the concept of limits. Asymptotes illustrate the limit of the function. That is, as the absolute value of x in the function increases, the y value reaches closer and closer to a number referred to as the limit. As the absolute value of y increases, the x value also reaches a limit.

Resources

 Technology
Computer Test Generator CD-ROM, Chapter 12, Extension Topics

Teaching Notes

Remind students that as the denominators of fractions become larger, the fraction becomes smaller. For equations in the form of $y = \frac{k}{x}$, as $|x|$ increases, the y value decreases. The values get closer and closer to zero. The limit is said to be zero and the y-axis is the asymptote.

Math Tip

Discuss with students why we say *the absolute value of x* when talking about the limit. If you look at the graph in Example 4, as x increases and is greater than 1, y approaches 3 and as x decreases and is less than 1, the y value also approaches 3. It is easier and shorter to say "As the absolute value of x increases, the y value approaches 3."

English Learners

The words *hyperbola* and *parabola* may be difficult to remember and differentiate for some students. Students may benefit from making posters of these curves and labeling them with the correct names. They can keep them in their notebooks or you may choose to hang them in the room for students to refer to.

1. Plan

Lesson Preview

✓ **Check Skills You'll Need**

Factoring $x^2 + bx + c$
Lesson 9-5: Examples 1–3
Exercises 1–26
Extra Practice, p. 710

Lesson Resources

📁 **Teaching Resources**
Practice, Reteaching, Enrichment
Checkpoint Quiz 1

👥 **Reaching All Students**
Practice Workbook 12-3
Spanish Practice Workbook 12-3
Reading and Math Literacy 12B
Spanish Reading & Literacy 12B
Spanish Checkpoint Quiz 1
Basic Algebra Planning Guide 12-3

⏰ **Presentation Assistant Plus!**
Transparencies
• Check Skills You'll Need 12-3
• Additional Examples 12-3
• Student Edition Answers 12-3
• Lesson Quiz 12-3
PH Presentation Pro CD 12-3

PRENTICE HALL ASSESSMENT SYSTEM

Checkpoint Quiz 1
Computer Test Generator CD

💾 **Technology**
Resource Pro® CD-ROM
Computer Test Generator CD
Prentice Hall Presentation Pro CD

💻 **www.PHSchool.com**
Student Site
• Teacher Web Code: aek-5500
• Reasoning & Puzzles pp. 32, 33
• Self-grading Lesson Quiz
Teacher Center
• Lesson Planner
• Resources

Plus

12-3

Simplifying Rational Expressions

North Carolina Objectives
1.01 Write equivalent forms of algebraic expressions to solve problems. b) Operate with polynomials.

Lesson Preview

What You'll Learn

OBJECTIVE 1
To simplify rational expressions

. . . And Why

To find the baking time for bread, as in Example 4
4. $(x + 4)(x - 3)$

✓ **Check Skills You'll Need** (For help, go to Skills Handbook page 724 and Lesson 9-5)

Write each fraction in simplest form.

1. $\frac{8}{2}$ 4   **2.** $-\frac{15}{24}$ $-\frac{5}{8}$ **3.** $\frac{25}{35}$ $\frac{5}{7}$

Factor each quadratic expression.

4. $x^2 + x - 12$ See left.   **5.** $x^2 + 6x + 8$ $(x + 4)(x + 2)$ **6.** $x^2 - 2x - 15$ $(x - 5)(x + 3)$

7. $x^2 + 8x + 16$ $(x + 4)^2$ **8.** $x^2 - x - 12$ $(x + 3)(x - 4)$ **9.** $x^2 - 7x + 12$ $(x - 3)(x - 4)$

New Vocabulary • rational expression

OBJECTIVE 1
Simplifying Rational Expressions

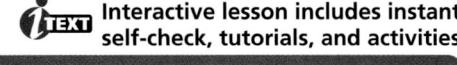
iTEXT Interactive lesson includes instant self-check, tutorials, and activities.

Fractions like $\frac{5}{9}$, $\frac{7}{12}$, and $\frac{1}{2}$ are rational numbers. An expression with a variable in the denominator is a **rational expression.** Here are some examples of rational expressions.

$$\frac{1}{x} \qquad \frac{x + 2}{x - 3} \qquad \frac{x^2 - 5}{x^2 - 10x + 25}$$

Of course, the value of the expression in the denominator cannot be zero, since division by zero is undefined. For the rest of this chapter, assume that the values of the variables that make the denominator zero are excluded from the domain.

Like rational numbers, a rational expression is in simplest form if the numerator and denominator have no common factors except 1. For example, $\frac{z + 5}{10z}$ is in simplest form since neither 10 nor z is a factor of $z + 5$.

1 EXAMPLE **Simplifying a Rational Expression**

Simplify $\frac{6x + 12}{x + 2}$.

$$\frac{6x + 12}{x + 2} = \frac{6(x + 2)}{x + 2}$$ **Factor the numerator. The denominator cannot be factored.**

$$= \frac{6(x + 2)^1}{\underset{1}{x + 2}}$$ **Divide out the common factor $x + 2$.**

$$= 6$$ **Simplify.**

✓ **Check Understanding** ① Simplify each expression.

a. $\frac{15b}{25b^2}$ $\frac{3}{5b}$ **b.** $\frac{12c^2}{3c + 6}$ $\frac{4c^2}{c + 2}$ **c.** $\frac{4m - 2}{2m - 1}$ 2   **d.** $\frac{20 + 4t}{t + 5}$ 4

Recall that you learned to factor quadratic expressions in Lessons 9-5 and 9-6. You may need to factor a quadratic expression to simplify a rational expression.

INSTANT CHECK SYSTEM
Ongoing Assessment and Intervention

Before the Lesson **Diagnose prerequisite skills using:**	**During the Lesson** **Monitor progress using:**	**After the Lesson** **Assess knowledge using:**
• Check Skills You'll Need	• Check Understanding • Additional Examples • Standardized Test Prep	• Lesson Quiz • Computer Test Generator CD • Chapter Checkpoint 1 (p. 656)

2 EXAMPLE Simplifying a Rational Expression

Simplify $\dfrac{2x - 12}{x^2 - 7x + 6}$.

$\dfrac{2x - 12}{x^2 - 7x + 6} = \dfrac{2(x - 6)}{(x - 6)(x - 1)}$ **Factor the numerator and the denominator.**

$= \dfrac{2(x - 6)^1}{1(x - 6)(x - 1)}$ **Divide out the common factor $x - 6$.**

$= \dfrac{2}{x - 1}$ **Simplify.**

✔ **Check Understanding** ❷ Simplify each expression.

a. $\dfrac{3x + 12}{x^2 - x - 20}$ **b.** $\dfrac{2z - 2}{z^2 - 4z + 3}$ **c.** $\dfrac{8a + 16}{2a^2 + 5a + 2}$ **d.** $\dfrac{c^2 - c - 6}{c^2 + 5c + 6}$

$\dfrac{3}{x - 5}$ $\dfrac{2}{z - 3}$ $\dfrac{8}{2a + 1}$ $\dfrac{c - 3}{c + 3}$

The numerator and denominator of $\dfrac{x - 3}{3 - x}$ are opposites. To simplify the expression, you can factor -1 from $3 - x$ to get $-1(-3 + x)$, which you can rewrite as $-1(x - 3)$. Then simplify $\dfrac{x - 3}{-1(x - 3)}$.

3 EXAMPLE Recognizing Opposite Factors

Simplify $\dfrac{5x - 15}{9 - x^2}$.   *5(x − 3)*

$\dfrac{5x - 15}{9 - x^2} = \dfrac{5(x - 3)}{(3 - x)(3 + x)}$ **Factor the numerator and the denominator.**

$= \dfrac{5(x - 3)}{-1(x - 3)(3 + x)}$ **Factor -1 from $3 - x$.**

$= \dfrac{5(x - 3)^1}{-1_1(x - 3)(x + 3)}$ **Divide out the common factor $x - 3$.**

$= -\dfrac{5}{x + 3}$ **Simplify.**

✔ **Check Understanding** ❸ Simplify each expression.

a. $\dfrac{x - 4}{4 - x}$ -1 **b.** $\dfrac{8 - m}{m^2 - 64}$ $-\dfrac{1}{m + 8}$ **c.** $\dfrac{8 - 4r}{r^2 + 2r - 8}$ **d.** $\dfrac{2c^2 - 2}{3 - 3c^2}$ $-\dfrac{2}{3}$

                                                          $-\dfrac{4}{r + 4}$

You can use a rational expression to model some real-world situations.

4 EXAMPLE Evaluating a Rational Expression

Baking The baking time for bread depends, in part, on its size and shape. A good approximation for the baking time, in minutes, of a cylindrical loaf is $\dfrac{60 \cdot \text{volume}}{\text{surface area}}$, or $\dfrac{30rh}{r + h}$, where the radius r and the length h of the baked loaf are in inches. Find the baking time for a loaf that is 5 inches long and has a radius of 4 inches. Round your answer to the nearest minute.

$\dfrac{30rh}{r + h} = \dfrac{30(4)(5)}{4 + 5}$ **Substitute 4 for r and 5 for h.**

$= \dfrac{600}{9}$ **Simplify.**

≈ 67 **Round to the nearest whole number.**

The baking time is approximately 67 minutes.

Real-World Connection

For a given volume of dough, the greater the surface area is, the shorter the baking time.

Lesson 12-3   Simplifying Rational Expressions   **653**

Math Background

When the numerator and denominator of a rational expression have a common factor, such as in Example 2, the graph will have a hole, or discontinuity. In this example there is no y value when $x = 6$. This hole may not be visible with some graphing programs in some windows.

OBJECTIVE

1 Teaching Notes

2 EXAMPLE Math Tip

Remind students that they must factor the numerator and the denominator in order to find the GCF. Stress that factors, not terms, must be divided out.

4 EXAMPLE Teaching Tip

Students may be confused by using h for length. Tell them to look at the length as the height of the cylinder.

Additional Examples

❶ Simplify $\dfrac{3x + 9}{x + 3}$.   3

❷ Simplify $\dfrac{4x - 20}{x^2 - 9x + 20}$. $\dfrac{4}{x - 4}$

❸ Simplify $\dfrac{3x - 27}{81 - x^2}$. $-\dfrac{3}{x + 9}$

❹ Find the baking time for a loaf of bread that is 8 inches long and has a radius of 3 inches. Round your answer to the nearest minute.   65 minutes

Closure

Ask students to explain how to simplify a rational expression. If possible, factor the numerator and denominator. Remove common factors and then simplify.

🔖 Reaching All Students

Below Level Students may be confused by opposite factors. Suggest that they use the Distributive Property to show $(3 - x) = -1(x - 3)$.	**Advanced Learners** Ask students to justify the technique of dividing out a common factor. A factor divided by itself equals 1, and 1 does not need to be written as a factor.	**Error Prevention** See note on page 654.

653

Assignment Guide

▼ **1** Objective
  Ⓐ Ⓑ **Core** 1–41
  Ⓒ **Extension** 42–47

Standardized Test Prep 48–53

Mixed Review 54–64

Error Prevention

Exercises 1–21 When only one factor is left in the denominator, some students bring that factor into the numerator. Have students put a 1 above and below factors that were divided into the numerator and denominator to help them to see the answer is 1 over the remaining factor.

Connection To History

Exercises 22–24 In March 1988, in Johannesburg, South Africa, a team baked the world's largest pan loaf. The loaf weighed 3163 lb 10 oz and had dimensions of 9 ft 10 in. by 4 ft 1 in. by 3 ft 7 in. Sketch the rectangular loaf and label it with the dimensions.

 Check Understanding ④ **a.** Find the baking time for a loaf that is 4 inches long and has a radius of 3 inches. Round your answer to the nearest minute. **51 min**

b. Critical Thinking The ratio $\frac{60 \cdot \text{volume}}{\text{surface area}}$ for a cylinder is $\frac{60\pi r^2 h}{2\pi r^2 + 2\pi rh}$. Simplify this expression to show that it is the same as the expression evaluated in Example 4. $\frac{30rh}{r + h}$

EXERCISES

For more practice, see *Extra Practice*.

Practice and Problem Solving

Ⓐ **Practice by Example**

Simplify each expression.

Example 1
(page 652)

1. $\frac{6a + 9}{12}$ $\frac{2a + 3}{4}$

2. $\frac{4x^3}{28x^4}$ $\frac{1}{7x}$

3. $\frac{2m - 5}{6m - 15}$ $\frac{1}{3}$

4. $\frac{2p - 24}{4p - 48}$ $\frac{1}{2}$

5. $\frac{3x^2 - 9x}{x - 3}$ $3x$

6. $\frac{3x + 6}{3x^2}$ $\frac{x + 2}{x^2}$

Example 2
(page 653)

7. $\frac{2x^2 + 2x}{3x^2 + 3x}$ $\frac{2}{3}$

8. $\frac{2b - 8}{b^2 - 16}$ $\frac{2}{b + 4}$

9. $\frac{m + 6}{m^2 - m - 42}$ $\frac{1}{m - 7}$

10. $\frac{w^2 + 7w}{w^2 - 49}$ $\frac{w}{w - 7}$

11. $\frac{a^2 + 2a + 1}{5a + 5}$ $\frac{a + 1}{5}$

12. $\frac{m^2 + 7m + 12}{m^2 + 6m + 8}$ $\frac{m + 3}{m + 2}$

13. $\frac{c^2 - 6c + 8}{c^2 + c - 6}$ $\frac{c - 4}{c + 3}$

14. $\frac{b^2 + 8b + 15}{b + 5}$ $b + 3$

15. $\frac{m + 4}{m^2 + 2m - 8}$ $\frac{1}{m - 2}$

Example 3
(page 653)

16. $\frac{5 - 4n}{4n - 5}$ -1

17. $\frac{12 - 4t}{t^2 - 2t - 3}$ $-\frac{4}{t - 1}$

18. $\frac{4m - 8}{4 - 2m}$ -2

19. $\frac{m - 2}{4 - 2m}$ $-\frac{1}{2}$

20. $\frac{v - 5}{25 - v^2}$ $-\frac{1}{v + 5}$

21. $\frac{4 - w}{w^2 - 8w + 16}$ $-\frac{1}{w - 4}$

Example 4
(page 653)

Baking Use the expression $\frac{30rh}{r + h}$ to estimate the baking time in minutes for each type of bread. Round your answer to the nearest minute.

22. baguette: $r = 1.25$ in., $h = 26$ in. **36 min**

23. pita: $r = 3.5$ in., $h = 0.5$ in. **13 min**

24. biscuit: $r = 1$ in., $h = 0.75$ in. **13 min**

Ⓑ **Apply Your Skills**

Simplify each expression.

25. $\frac{2r^2 + 9r - 5}{r^2 + 10r + 25}$ $\frac{2r - 1}{r + 5}$

26. $\frac{7z^2 + 23z + 6}{z^2 + 2z - 3}$ $\frac{7z + 2}{z - 1}$

27. $\frac{5t^2 + 6t - 8}{3t^2 + 5t - 2}$ $\frac{5t - 4}{3t - 1}$

28. $\frac{32a^3}{16a^2 - 8a}$ $\frac{4a^2}{2a - 1}$

29. $\frac{3z^2 + 12z}{z^4}$ $\frac{3(z + 4)}{z^3}$

30. $\frac{2s^2 + s}{s^3}$ $\frac{2s + 1}{s^2}$

31. $\frac{4a^2 - 8a - 5}{15 - a - 2a^2}$ $-\frac{2a + 1}{a + 3}$

32. $\frac{16 + 16m + 3m^2}{m^2 - 3m - 28}$ $\frac{4 + 3m}{m - 7}$

33. $\frac{10c + c^2 - 3c^3}{5c^2 - 6c - 8}$ $\frac{-c(3c + 5)}{5c + 4}$

34. **Open-Ended** Write an expression that has 2 and -3 excluded from the domain. **Answers may vary. Sample:** $\frac{3}{(x - 2)(x + 3)}$

654 Chapter 12 Rational Expressions and Functions

Real-World **Connection**

A cylinder with a height of 500 ft and a volume of 1×10^6 ft^3 has about 89% of the surface area of a square prism with the same height and volume.

35. a. Construction To keep heating costs down for a structure, architects want the ratio of surface area to volume as small as possible. Find an expression for the ratio of the surface area to volume for each shape.

i. square prism $\frac{2b + 4h}{bh}$ **ii.** cylinder $\frac{2h + 2r}{rh}$

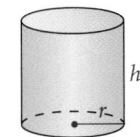

b. Find the ratio for each figure when $b = 12$ ft, $h = 18$ ft, and $r = 6$ ft. $\frac{4}{9}; \frac{4}{9}$

36. Error Analysis Explain what error the student made in simplifying the rational expression at the right. **See left.**

$$\frac{x^2 + 2x}{2x} = \frac{x^2 + \cancel{2x}}{\cancel{2x}} = x^2$$

36. The student canceled terms instead of factors.

37. Writing Explain why $\frac{x^2 - 9}{x + 3}$ is not the same as $x - 3$.
-3 is not in the domain of $\frac{x^2 - 9}{x + 3}$.

Probability If a point is selected at random from a figure and is equally likely to be any point in the figure, then the probability that the point is in a shaded part of the figure is $\frac{\text{area of shaded part}}{\text{area of whole figure}}$. Find the probability that a point will be in the shaded part of each figure.

38. 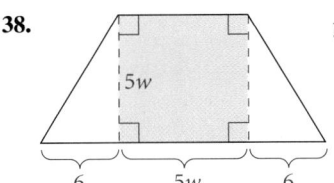 $\frac{5w}{5w + 6}$ **39.** 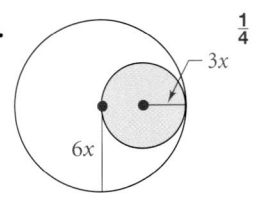 $\frac{1}{4}$

40. 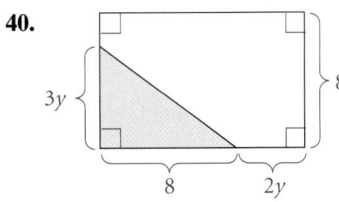 $\frac{3y}{4(y + 4)}$ **41.** 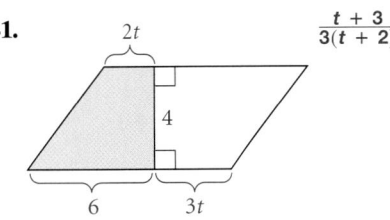 $\frac{t + 3}{3(t + 2)}$

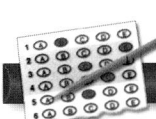

C Challenge

42. $\frac{m - n}{m + 10n}$

43. $\frac{a - 3b}{a + 4b}$

44. $\frac{6v - 7w}{3v - 2w}$

Simplify each expression. 42–44. See left.

42. $\frac{m^2 - n^2}{m^2 + 11mn + 10n^2}$ **43.** $\frac{a^2 - 5ab + 6b^2}{a^2 + 2ab - 8b^2}$ **44.** $\frac{36v^2 - 49w^2}{18v^2 + 9vw - 14w^2}$

Reasoning Determine whether each statement is *sometimes*, *always*, or *never* true for real numbers a and b.

45. $\frac{2b}{b} = 2$ **sometimes**   **46.** $\frac{ab^3}{b^4} = ab$ **sometimes**   **47.** $\frac{a^2 + 6a - 5}{2a + 2} = \frac{a + 5}{2}$ **never**

Standardized Test Prep

Multiple Choice

48. Which expression simplifies to -1? **C**

     A. $\frac{x + 1}{x - 1}$ **B.** $\frac{r + 3}{3 - r}$ **C.** $\frac{n - 2}{2 - n}$ **D.** $\frac{4 - p}{4 + p}$

 Lesson Quiz 12-3

Simplify each expression.

1. $\frac{6 - 2x}{x - 3}$ -2

2. $\frac{x^2 + 8x}{x^2 - 64}$ $\frac{x}{x - 8}$

3. $\frac{x - 6}{36 - x^2}$ $\frac{-1}{x + 6}$

4. $\frac{6x^2 - x - 12}{8x^2 - 10x - 3}$ $\frac{3x + 4}{4x + 1}$

5. $\frac{4x^2 + x}{x^3}$ $\frac{4x + 1}{x^2}$

Alternative Assessment

Write rational expressions on individual index cards. Make enough for half of the class. Write the simplifications of the rational expressions on other index cards for the other half of the class. Have students find "matching" cards. Shuffle the cards and repeat.

Standardized Test Prep

Resources

For additional practice with a variety of test item formats:
- Standardized Test Prep, pp. 697–699
- Test-Taking Strategies, p. 692
- Test-Taking Strategies with Transparencies

Exercises 51, 52 Encourage students to simplify the expressions as much as possible before comparing them.

To check understanding of Lessons 12-1 to 12-3:

Checkpoint Quiz 1 (p. 656)

📁 **Teaching Resources**
Checkpoint Quiz 1 (also in Prentice Hall Assessment System)

Reaching All Students
Reading and Math Literacy 12B

Spanish versions available

---

pages 654–656   Exercises

53. **[2]** The student put the 4 in the numerator rather than in the denominator.
$\frac{x-5}{4x-20} = \frac{x-5}{4(x-5)} = \frac{1}{4}$

[1] no explanation OR no correctly simplified expression

54. vertical asymptote: $x = 0$
horizontal asymptote: $y = 2$;
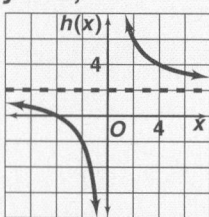

55. vertical asymptote: $x = 4$
horizontal asymptote: $y = 0$;
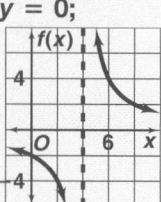

56. vertical asymptote: $x = 0$
horizontal asymptote: $y = -4$;
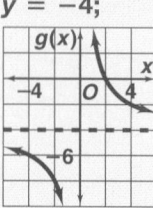

---

49. Simplify $\frac{y^2 + 8y - 9}{y^2 - 81}$.   **I**

   F. $\frac{8y}{9}$ G. $\frac{y+9}{y+81}$ H. $\frac{1}{9}$ I. $\frac{y-1}{y-9}$

50. Which expression is in simplest form?   **B**

   A. $\frac{t+1}{t^2-1}$ B. $\frac{2n-1}{n^2+4}$ C. $\frac{c-7}{7-c}$ D. $\frac{2r-4}{8+6r}$

Quantitative Comparison   Compare the quantity in Column A with the quantity in Column B. Choose the best answer.
   A. The quantity in Column A is greater.
   B. The quantity in Column B is greater.
   C. The two quantities are equal.
   D. The relationship cannot be determined from the information given.

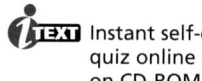
Take It to the NET
Online lesson quiz at
www.PHSchool.com
Web Code: aea-1203

Column A	Column B
D 51. $\frac{-5(x+5)}{x+1}$	$-10x \cdot \frac{2x}{4x^2}$
C 52. $\frac{4}{8-2b}, b \neq 4$	$\frac{2}{4-b}, b \neq 4$

Short Response   53. A student simplified $\frac{x-5}{4x-20}$ to 4. What error did the student make? Show how to simplify the expression correctly.   **See margin.**

Mixed Review

54–56. See margin.

Lesson 12-2   Identify the asymptotes of each function. Then graph the function.
   54. $h(x) = \frac{8}{x} + 2$ 55. $f(x) = \frac{8}{x-4}$ 56. $g(x) = \frac{8}{x} - 4$

Lesson 11-1   Simplify each radical expression.
   57. $\sqrt{20} \cdot \sqrt{10}$ 58. $\sqrt{a^4 b^7 c^8}$ 59. $\frac{\sqrt{80}}{\sqrt{10}}$ $2\sqrt{2}$ 60. $\sqrt{\frac{2m}{25m^5}}$ $\frac{\sqrt{2}}{5m^2}$
   $10\sqrt{2}$ $a^2 b^3 c^4 \sqrt{b}$

Lesson 10-1   Order each group of quadratic functions from widest to narrowest graph.

61. $y = x^2, y = -2x^2,$ 61. $y = x^2, y = 3x^2, y = -2x^2$ 62. $y = \frac{1}{3}x^2, y = \frac{1}{4}x^2, y = \frac{2}{5}x^2$
   $y = 3x^2$
63. $y = 2x^2, y = 0.5x^2, y = -4x^2$ 64. $y = -x^2, y = 2.3x^2, y = -3.8x^2$
62. $y = \frac{1}{4}x^2, y = \frac{1}{3}x^2,$ $y = 0.5x^2, y = 2x^2, y = -4x^2$ $y = -x^2, y = 2.3x^2, y = -3.8x^2$
   $y = \frac{2}{5}x^2$

✓ Checkpoint Quiz 1

Lessons 12-1 through 12-3

📱 **iTEXT** Instant self-check quiz online and on CD-ROM

Each pair of points is on the graph of an inverse variation. Find the missing value.
   1. $(9, 2)$ and $(x, 6)$ **3**   2. $(8.2, -3)$ and $(12.3, y)$ **−2**   3. $(0.5, 7.2)$ and $(0.9, y)$ **4**

Identify the asymptotes of each function. Then graph the function. 4–6. See margin.
   4. $y = \frac{5}{x}$ 5. $f(x) = \frac{8}{x-4}$ 6. $y = \frac{1}{x} + 4$

Simplify each expression.
   7. $\frac{6x^2 - 24}{x+2}$ $6(x-2)$ 8. $\frac{3c+9}{3c-9}$ $\frac{c+3}{c-3}$ 9. $\frac{k-2}{k^2 + 2k - 8}$ $\frac{1}{k+4}$

10. **Open-Ended** Write an expression that is not defined when the variable equals 3.
   Answers may vary. Sample: $\frac{15}{x-3}$

---

page 656   Checkpoint Quiz 1

4. $x = 0, y = 0$;
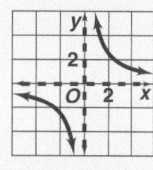

5. $x = 4, y = 0$;
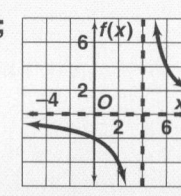

6. $x = 0, y = 4$;
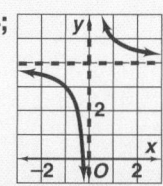

12-4 Multiplying and Dividing Rational Expressions

 North Carolina Objectives
1.01 Write equivalent forms of algebraic expressions to solve problems. b) Operate with polynomials.

Lesson Preview

What You'll Learn

 OBJECTIVE 1 To multiply rational expressions

 OBJECTIVE 2 To divide rational expressions

. . . And Why

To find loan payments, as in Exercises 38–40

 **Check Skills You'll Need** (For help, go to Lessons 8-3 and 9-6.)

Simplify each expression.

1. $r^2 \cdot r^8$ r^{10}
2. $b^3 \cdot b^4$ b^7
3. $c^7 \div c^2$ c^5
4. $3x^4 \cdot 2x^5$ $6x^9$
5. $5n^2 \cdot n^2$ $5n^4$
6. $15a^3(-3a^2)$ $-45a^5$

Factor each polynomial.

7. $2c^2 + 15c + 7$ $(2c + 1)(c + 7)$
8. $15t^2 - 26t + 11$ $(15t - 11)(t - 1)$
9. $2q^2 + 11q + 5$ $(2q + 1)(q + 5)$

 iTEXT Interactive lesson includes instant self-check, tutorials, and activities.

Lesson Preview

 Check Skills You'll Need

Multiplication Properties of Exponents
Lesson 8-3: Example 2
Exercises 7–9
Extra Practice, p. 709

Factoring Trinomials of the Type $ax^2 + bx + c$
Lesson 9-6: Example 1
Exercises 1–9
Extra Practice, p. 710

Lesson Resources

Teaching Resources
Practice, Reteaching, Enrichment

Reaching All Students
Practice Workbook 12-4
Spanish Practice Workbook 12-4
Basic Algebra Planning Guide 12-4

Presentation Assistant Plus!
Transparencies
• Check Skills You'll Need 12-4
• Additional Examples 12-4
• Student Edition Answers 12-4
• Lesson Quiz 12-4
PH Presentation Pro CD 12-4

PRENTICE HALL ASSESSMENT SYSTEM

Computer Test Generator CD

Technology
Resource Pro® CD-ROM
Computer Test Generator CD
Prentice Hall Presentation Pro CD

www.PHSchool.com
Student Site
• Teacher Web Code: aek-5500
• Self-grading Lesson Quiz
Teacher Center
• Lesson Planner
• Resources

Plus  **iTEXT**

 OBJECTIVE 1  **Multiplying Rational Expressions**

Multiplying rational expressions is similar to multiplying rational numbers. If $a, b, c,$ and d represent polynomials (with $b \neq 0$ and $d \neq 0$), then $\frac{a}{b} \cdot \frac{c}{d} = \frac{ac}{bd}$.

Need Help?
Remember that the value of the expression in the denominator cannot be zero.

1 EXAMPLE Multiplying Rational Expressions

Multiply.

a. $\frac{3}{x} \cdot \frac{4}{x^2}$

$\frac{3}{x} \cdot \frac{4}{x^2} = \frac{12}{x^3}$

Multiply the numerators and multiply the denominators.

b. $\frac{x}{x + 4} \cdot \frac{x - 3}{x - 2}$

$\frac{x}{x + 4} \cdot \frac{x - 3}{x - 2} = \frac{x(x - 3)}{(x + 4)(x - 2)}$

Multiply the numerators and multiply the denominators. Leave the answer in factored form.

 **Check Understanding** **1** Multiply.

a. $\frac{6}{a^2} \cdot \frac{-2}{a^3}$ $\frac{-12}{a^5}$

b. $\frac{x - 5}{x + 3} \cdot \frac{x - 7}{x}$ $\frac{(x - 5)(x - 7)}{x(x + 3)}$

As with rational numbers, the product $\frac{ac}{bd}$ may not be in simplest form. Look for factors common to the numerator and the denominator to divide out.

2 EXAMPLE Using Factoring

Multiply $\frac{2x + 1}{3}$ and $\frac{6x}{4x^2 - 1}$.

$\frac{2x + 1}{3} \cdot \frac{6x}{4x^2 - 1} = \frac{2x + 1}{3} \cdot \frac{6x}{(2x + 1)(2x - 1)}$

Factor the denominator.

$= \frac{2x + 1}{1^3} \cdot \frac{6^2 x}{1(2x + 1)(2x - 1)}$

Divide out the common factors 3 and $(2x + 1)$.

$= \frac{2x}{2x - 1}$

Simplify.

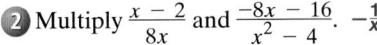 **Check Understanding** **2** Multiply $\frac{x - 2}{8x}$ and $\frac{-8x - 16}{x^2 - 4}$. $-\frac{1}{x}$

 **Ongoing Assessment and Intervention**

Before the Lesson	During the Lesson	After the Lesson
Diagnose prerequisite skills using:	**Monitor progress using:**	**Assess knowledge using:**
• Check Skills You'll Need	• Check Understanding	• Lesson Quiz
	• Additional Examples	• Computer Test Generator CD
	• Standardized Test Prep	

2. Teach

Math Background

In addition to excluding values of the variable that make the function undefined, eliminating values that do not apply is particularly important in application problems.

OBJECTIVE

1 Teaching Notes

Additional Examples

1 Multiply.

a. $\frac{7}{y} \cdot \frac{8}{y^2}$ $\frac{56}{y^3}$

b. $\frac{x}{x + 5} \cdot \frac{x - 2}{x - 6}$ $\frac{x(x - 2)}{(x + 5)(x - 6)}$

2 Multiply $\frac{3x + 1}{4}$ and $\frac{8x}{9x^2 - 1}$.

$\frac{2x}{3x - 1}$

3 Multiply $\frac{5x + 1}{3x + 12}$ and

$x^2 + 7x + 12$. $\frac{(5x + 1)(x + 3)}{3}$

OBJECTIVE

2 Teaching Notes

Additional Examples

4 Divide $\frac{x^2 + 13x + 40}{x - 7}$ by $\frac{x + 8}{x^2 - 49}$.
$(x + 5)(x + 7)$

5 Divide $\frac{x^2 + 9x + 14}{11x}$ by

$(8x^2 + 16x)$. $\frac{x + 7}{88x^2}$

Closure

Ask students to explain how to multiply and divide rational expressions. To multiply rational expressions, factor each numerator and denominator, divide the numerators and denominators by any common factors, then multiply the remaining factors of the numerators and denominators. To divide rational expressions, multiply the dividend by the reciprocal of the divisor and proceed as above.

658

You can also multiply a rational expression by a polynomial. Leave the product in factored form.

3 EXAMPLE Multiplying a Rational Expression by a Polynomial

Multiply $\frac{3s + 2}{2s + 4}$ and $s^2 + 5s + 6$.

$\frac{3s + 2}{2s + 4} \cdot (s^2 + 5s + 6) = \frac{3s + 2}{2(s + 2)} \cdot \frac{(s + 2)(s + 3)}{1}$ Factor.

$= \frac{3s + 2}{2_1(s + 2)} \cdot \frac{(s + 2)^1(s + 3)}{1}$ Divide out the common factor $s + 2$.

$= \frac{(3s + 2)(s + 3)}{2}$ Leave in factored form.

✓ **Check Understanding** **3** Multiply.

a. $\frac{3}{c} \cdot (c^3 - c)$ **b.** $\frac{2v}{v + 3} \cdot (v^2 - 2v - 15)$ **c.** $(m - 1) \cdot \frac{4m + 8}{m^2 - 1}$

 $3(c - 1)(c + 1)$ $2v(v - 5)$ $\frac{4(m + 2)}{m + 1}$

OBJECTIVE

2 Dividing Rational Expressions

Recall that $\frac{a}{b} \div \frac{c}{d} = \frac{a}{b} \cdot \frac{d}{c}$, where $b \neq 0$, $c \neq 0$, and $d \neq 0$.

When you divide rational expressions that can be factored, first rewrite the expression using the reciprocal before dividing out common factors.

Reading Math

The vinculum or fraction bar is a grouping symbol.

4 EXAMPLE Dividing Rational Expressions

Divide $\frac{a^2 + 7a + 10}{a - 6}$ by $\frac{a + 5}{a^2 - 36}$.

$\frac{a^2 + 7a + 10}{a - 6} \div \frac{a + 5}{a^2 - 36} = \frac{a^2 + 7a + 10}{a - 6} \cdot \frac{a^2 - 36}{a + 5}$ Multiply by $\frac{a^2 - 36}{a + 5}$, the reciprocal of $\frac{a + 5}{a^2 - 36}$.

$= \frac{(a + 2)(a + 5)}{(a - 6)} \cdot \frac{(a - 6)(a + 6)}{a + 5}$ Factor.

$= \frac{(a + 2)(a + 5)^1}{_1(a - 6)} \cdot \frac{(a - 6)^1(a + 6)}{_1 a + 5}$ Divide out the common factors $a + 5$ and $a - 6$.

$= (a + 2)(a + 6)$ Leave in factored form.

✓ **Check Understanding** **4** Divide.

a. $\frac{a - 2}{ab} \div \frac{a - 2}{a}$ **b.** $\frac{5m + 10}{2m - 20} \div \frac{7m + 14}{14m - 20}$ **c.** $\frac{6n^2 - 5n - 6}{2n^2 - n - 3} \div \frac{2n - 3}{n + 1}$

 $\frac{1}{b}$ $\frac{5(7m - 10)}{7(m - 10)}$ $\frac{3n + 2}{2n - 3}$

The reciprocal of a polynomial such as $5x^2 + 5x$ is $\frac{1}{5x^2 + 5x}$.

5 EXAMPLE Dividing a Rational Expression by a Polynomial

Divide $\frac{x^2 + 3x + 2}{4x}$ by $(5x^2 + 5x)$.

$\frac{x^2 + 3x + 2}{4x} \div \frac{5x^2 + 5x}{1} = \frac{x^2 + 3x + 2}{4x} \cdot \frac{1}{5x^2 + 5x}$ Multiply by the reciprocal of $5x^2 + 5x$.

$= \frac{(x + 1)(x + 2)}{4x} \cdot \frac{1}{5x(x + 1)}$ Factor.

$= \frac{(x + 1)^1(x + 2)}{4x} \cdot \frac{1}{5x_1(x + 1)}$ Divide out the common factor $x + 1$.

$= \frac{x + 2}{20x^2}$ Simplify.

Chapter 12 Rational Expressions and Functions

Reaching All Students

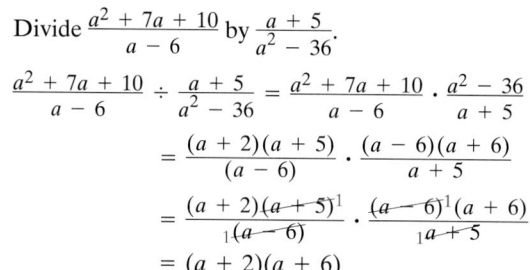

| **Below Level** Caution students that only common factors of the entire numerator and denominator can be divided out. For example, $\frac{x^2 - y^2}{x - y} \neq x - y$. | **Advanced Learners** Have students simplify $\left(\frac{x + 4}{x + 1} \cdot \frac{x - 3}{x - 2}\right) \div \frac{x + 4}{x^3 - x^2 - 2x}$. $x^2 - 3x$ | **Error Prevention** See note on page 659. |

✓ **Check Understanding** ⑤ Divide.

a. $\dfrac{3x^3}{2} \div (-15x^5)$

$-\dfrac{1}{10x^2}$

b. $\dfrac{y+3}{y+2} \div (y+2)$

$\dfrac{y+3}{(y+2)^2}$

c. $\dfrac{z^2 + 2z - 15}{z^2 + 9z + 20} \div (z-3)$

$\dfrac{1}{z+4}$

EXERCISES

For more practice, see *Extra Practice*.

Practice and Problem Solving

Ⓐ **Practice by Example**

Multiply.

Example 1
(page 657)

1. $\dfrac{7}{3} \cdot \dfrac{5x}{12}$ $\dfrac{35x}{36}$

2. $\dfrac{3}{t} \cdot \dfrac{4}{t}$ $\dfrac{12}{t^2}$

3. $\dfrac{5}{3a^2} \cdot \dfrac{8}{a^3}$ $\dfrac{40}{3a^5}$

4. $\dfrac{m-2}{m+2} \cdot \dfrac{m}{m-1}$ $\dfrac{m(m-2)}{(m+2)(m-1)}$

5. $\dfrac{2x}{x+1} \cdot \dfrac{x-1}{3}$ $\dfrac{2x(x-1)}{3(x+1)}$

6. $\dfrac{6x^2}{5} \cdot \dfrac{2}{x+1}$ $\dfrac{12x^2}{5(x+1)}$

Example 2
(page 657)

7. $\dfrac{4c}{2c+2} \cdot \dfrac{c+1}{c-1}$ $\dfrac{2c}{c-1}$

8. $\dfrac{5x^3}{x^2} \cdot \dfrac{3x^4}{6x}$ $\dfrac{5x^4}{2}$

9. $\dfrac{3t}{t-2} \cdot \dfrac{3t-6}{t^2}$ $\dfrac{9}{t}$

10. $\dfrac{m-2}{3m+9} \cdot \dfrac{2m+6}{2m-4}$ $\dfrac{1}{3}$

11. $\dfrac{x-5}{4x+6} \cdot \dfrac{6x+9}{3x-15}$ $\dfrac{1}{2}$

12. $\dfrac{4x+1}{5x+10} \cdot \dfrac{30x+60}{2x-2}$ $\dfrac{3(4x+1)}{x-1}$

Example 3
(page 658)

13. $\dfrac{4t+4}{t-3} \cdot (t^2 - t - 6)$ $4(t+1)(t+2)$

14. $\dfrac{2m+1}{3m-6} \cdot (9m^2 - 36)$ $3(2m+1)(m+2)$

15. $(x^2 - 1) \cdot \dfrac{x-2}{3x+3}$ $\dfrac{(x-1)(x-2)}{3}$

Example 4
(page 658)

Find the reciprocal of each expression.

16. $\dfrac{2}{x+1}$ $\dfrac{x+1}{2}$

17. $\dfrac{-6d^2}{2d-5}$ $-\dfrac{2d-5}{6d^2}$

18. $c^2 - 1$ $\dfrac{1}{c^2 - 1}$

19. $s+4$ $\dfrac{1}{s+4}$

Divide. 20–28. See margin.

20. $\dfrac{x-1}{x+4} \div \dfrac{x+3}{x+4}$

21. $\dfrac{3t+12}{5t} \div \dfrac{t+4}{10t}$

22. $\dfrac{y-4}{10} \div \dfrac{4-y}{5}$

23. $\dfrac{x-3}{6} \div \dfrac{3-x}{2}$

24. $\dfrac{x^2 + 6x + 8}{x^2 + x - 2} \div \dfrac{x+4}{2x+4}$

25. $\dfrac{2n^2 - 5n - 3}{4n^2 - 12n - 7} \div \dfrac{4n+5}{2n-7}$

Example 5
(page 658)

26. $\dfrac{3x+9}{x} \div (x+3)$

27. $\dfrac{11k+121}{7k-15} \div (k+11)$

28. $\dfrac{x^2 + 10x - 11}{x^2 + 12x + 11} \div (x-1)$

Ⓑ **Apply Your Skills**

Multiply or divide.

29. $\dfrac{t^2 + 5t + 6}{t-3} \cdot \dfrac{t^2 - 2t - 3}{t^2 + 3t + 2}$ $t+3$

30. $\dfrac{c^2 + 3c + 2}{c^2 - 4c + 3} \div \dfrac{c+2}{c-3}$ $\dfrac{c+1}{c-1}$

32. $\dfrac{5(2x-5)}{x-5}$

31. $\dfrac{7t^2 - 28t}{2t^2 - 5t - 12} \cdot \dfrac{6t^2 - t - 15}{49t^3}$ $\dfrac{3t-5}{7t^2}$

32. $\dfrac{5x^2 + 10x - 15}{5 - 6x + x^2} \div \dfrac{2x^2 + 7x + 3}{4x^2 - 8x - 5}$ **See left.**

33. $\dfrac{x^2 + x - 6}{x^2 - x - 6} \div \dfrac{x^2 + 5x + 6}{x^2 + 4x + 4}$ $\dfrac{x-2}{x-3}$

34. $\left(\dfrac{x^2 - 25}{x^2 - 4x}\right)\left(\dfrac{x^2 + x - 20}{x^2 + 10x + 25}\right)$ $\dfrac{x-5}{x}$

35. The student forgot to rewrite the expression using the reciprocal before canceling.

36. Check students' work.

35. **Error Analysis** In the work shown at the right, what error did the student make in dividing the rational expressions?

36. **Open-Ended** Write two rational expressions. Find the product.

37. **Critical Thinking** For what values of x is the expression

$\dfrac{2x^2 - 5x - 12}{6x} \div \dfrac{-3x - 12}{x^2 - 16}$ undefined? **0, 4, −4**

$$\dfrac{3a}{a+2} \div \dfrac{(a+2)^2}{a-4} = \dfrac{3a}{\cancel{a+2}} \div \dfrac{\cancel{(a+2)^2}}{a-4}$$

$$= 3a \div \dfrac{a+2}{a-4}$$

$$= 3a \cdot \dfrac{a-4}{a+2}$$

$$= \dfrac{3a(a-4)}{a+2}$$

Lesson 12-4 Multiplying and Dividing Rational Expressions **659**

Assignment Guide

▼ ❶ Objective

Ⓐ Ⓑ Core 1–15, 29, 36, 41–45

Ⓒ Extension 47–48

▼ ❷ Objective

Ⓐ Ⓑ Core 16–28, 30–35, 37–40, 46

Ⓒ Extension 49–53

Standardized Test Prep 54–58

Mixed Review 59–76

Error Prevention

Exercises 7–28 When all factors of the numerator and denominator are eliminated, students may indicate a value of 0 instead of 1. Remind students that $\dfrac{x}{x} = 1$.

Careers

Exercises 38–40 A loan officer guides clients through the process of applying for a commercial, consumer, or mortgage loan. Loan officers must keep abreast of new types of loans and other financial products and services, so they can meet their customers' needs.

Enrichment 12-4
Reteaching 12-4
Practice 12-4

pages 659–661 **Exercises**

20. $\dfrac{x-1}{x+3}$

21. 6

22. $-\dfrac{1}{2}$

23. $-\dfrac{1}{3}$

24. $\dfrac{2(x+2)}{x-1}$

25. $\dfrac{n-3}{4n+5}$

26. $\dfrac{3}{x}$

27. $\dfrac{11}{7k-15}$

28. $\dfrac{1}{x+1}$

659

Loan Payments The formula below gives the monthly payment m on a loan when you know the amount borrowed A, the annual rate of interest r, and the number of months of the loan n. Use this formula and a calculator for Exercises 38–40.

$$m = \frac{A\left(\frac{r}{12}\right)\left(1 + \frac{r}{12}\right)^n}{\left(1 + \frac{r}{12}\right)^n - 1}$$

38. What is the monthly payment on a loan of $1500 at 8% annual interest for 18 months? **$88.71**

39. What is the monthly payment on a loan of $3000 at 6% annual interest for 24 months? **$132.96**

40. Suppose your parents want to buy the house shown at the left. They have $15,000 for a down payment. Their mortgage will have an annual interest rate of 6%. The loan is to be repaid over a 30-year period.
  a. How much will your parents have to borrow? **$100,000**
  b. How many monthly payments will there be? **360 payments**
  c. What will the monthly payment be? **$599.55**
  d. How much will it cost your parents to repay this mortgage over the 30-year period? **$215,838**

Geometry Find the volume of each rectangular solid.

41.
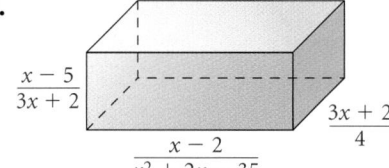

42.
$$\frac{2m^2(m + 2)}{(m - 1)(m + 4)}$$
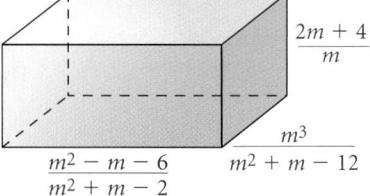

43.
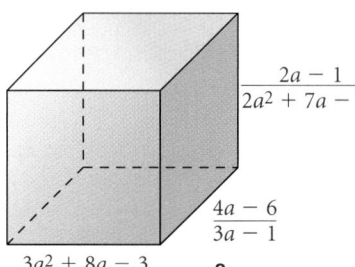

44.
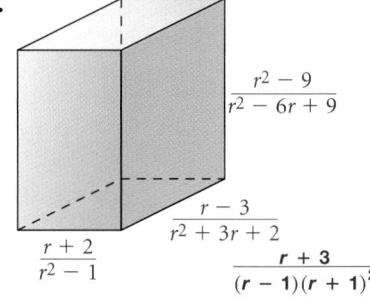

45. **Writing** Robin's first step in finding the product $\frac{2}{w} \cdot w^5$ was to rewrite the expression as $\frac{2}{w} \cdot \frac{w^5}{1}$. Why do you think Robin did this? **See left.**

46. **Probability** If a point is selected at random from a figure and is equally likely to be any point in the figure, then the probability that the point is in a shaded part of the figure is $\frac{\text{area of shaded part}}{\text{area of whole figure}}$. Suppose two points are chosen.
  a. What is the probability that both points will be in the shaded part? $\frac{x^2}{4(2x + 1)^2}$
  b. What is the probability that one point will be in the shaded part and the other point will *not* be in the shaded part? $\frac{x(3x + 2)}{4(2x + 1)^2}$

Lesson Quiz 12-4

Multiply or divide.

1. $\frac{7x^2}{5} \cdot \frac{15}{14x}$ $\frac{3x}{2}$

2. $\frac{6x + 3}{x + 6} \cdot \frac{x^2 + 9x + 18}{2x + 1}$
$3(x + 3)$

3. $\frac{x + 3}{x + 1} \div (x^2 + 5x + 6)$
$\frac{1}{(x + 1)(x + 2)}$

4. $\frac{4x + 8}{3x} \cdot \frac{9x^2}{x + 2}$ $12x$

5. $\frac{2x + 4}{x^2 + 11x + 18} \div \frac{x + 1}{x^2 + 14x + 45}$
$\frac{2(x + 5)}{x + 1}$

6. $(x^2 + 12x + 11) \cdot$
$\frac{x + 9}{x^2 + 20x + 99}$ $x + 1$

Alternative Assessment

Number five sets of index cards each from 1 to 5 (25 cards total). Randomly distribute the cards to the class. Ask students to write their own rational expressions modeling the example whose number is on their card. Students should write their expressions directly on their cards. Collect the cards and redistribute. Have each student solve the expression on the card.

45. She wrote w^5 as a fraction so she could easily see what she could cancel.

? Need Help?

If two events A and B are independent, then $P(A \text{ and } B) = P(A) \cdot P(B)$.

Multiply or divide. (*Hint:* Remember that $\frac{\frac{a}{b}}{\frac{c}{d}} = \frac{a}{b} \div \frac{c}{d}$.)

47. $\frac{9m^2(m+1)}{2}$

50. $\frac{-(2a+3b)(a+2b)}{(5a+b)(2a-3b)}$

53. $\frac{1}{(w+2)(w+3)}$

47. $\frac{3m^3 - 3m}{4m^2 + 4m - 8} \cdot (6m^2 + 12m)$

48. $\frac{t^2 - r^2}{t^2 + tr - 2r^2} \cdot \frac{t^2 + 3tr + 2r^2}{t^2 + 2tr + r^2}$ **1**

49. $\frac{5x^2}{y^2 - 25} \div \frac{5xy - 25x}{y^2 - 10y + 25}$ $\frac{x}{y+5}$

50. $\frac{2a^2 - ab - 6b^2}{2b^2 + 9ab - 5a^2} \div \frac{2a^2 - 7ab + 6b^2}{a^2 - 4b^2}$

51. $\frac{\frac{3m}{m-1}}{\frac{6m^2}{m-2}}$ $\frac{m-2}{2m(m-1)}$

52. $\frac{\frac{3x}{x^2-1}}{\frac{6}{x^2-x-2}}$ $\frac{x(x-2)}{2(x-1)}$

53. $\frac{\frac{w-3}{w^2-4}}{\frac{w^2-9}{w-2}}$

Multiple Choice

54. Simplify $(2x - 5) \cdot \frac{2x}{2x^2 - 9x + 10}$. **B**

   A. 1   B. $\frac{2x}{x-2}$ C. $\frac{x-5}{-4x+5}$ D. $\frac{2x-5}{-8x-10}$

58. [2] $\frac{x^2-1}{x} \cdot \frac{3x}{x-1} =$

$\frac{(x+1)(x-1)(3x)}{x(x-1)} =$

$3(x+1)$

[1] one computational error OR answer with no work shown

55. Simplify $\frac{a^2-9}{a^2} \div \frac{a+3}{a}$. **G**

   F. -3 G. $\frac{a-3}{a}$ H. $\frac{a(a-3)}{a^2}$ I. $\frac{a(a^2-9)}{a^2(a+3)}$

56. Which expression is equivalent to $\frac{r^2-1}{r} \div (2r^2 - 2)$? **D**

   A. $\frac{r^2-1}{r} \cdot \frac{1}{2}(r^2-1)$ B. $\frac{r^2-1}{r} \cdot \frac{2}{r^2-1}$

   C. $\frac{r^2-1}{r} \cdot \left(\frac{1}{2r^2} - 2\right)$ D. $\frac{r^2-1}{r} \cdot \frac{1}{2r^2-2}$

57. Which CANNOT be the first step in multiplying $\frac{x^2-2x-3}{x+3}$ by $\frac{2x+6}{2x+2}$? **G**

   F. Multiply the numerators.   G. Find the reciprocal of $\frac{2x+6}{2x+2}$.

   H. Factor each polynomial.   I. Multiply the denominators.

Short Response

58. Simplify $\frac{x^2-1}{x} \cdot \frac{3x}{x-1}$. Write the product in factored form. Show your work.
   See left.

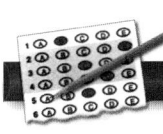

Take It to the NET
Online lesson quiz at
www.PHSchool.com
Web Code: aea-1204

Mixed Review

Lesson 12-3

Simplify each expression.

59. $\frac{5b-25}{10}$ $\frac{b-5}{2}$

60. $\frac{36k^3}{48k^4}$ $\frac{3}{4k}$

61. $\frac{7m-14}{3m-6}$ $\frac{7}{3}$

62. $\frac{7q^5}{28q}$ $\frac{q^4}{4}$

63. $\frac{15t^2-27}{24}$ $\frac{5t^2-9}{8}$

64. $\frac{6m^3}{12m-18m^2}$ $\frac{m^2}{2-3m}$

65. $\frac{5a^2}{10a^4-15a^2}$ $\frac{1}{2a^2-3}$

66. $\frac{2z^2-11z-21}{z^2-6z-7}$ $\frac{2z+3}{z+1}$

67. $\frac{4c^2-36c+81}{4c^2-2c-72}$ $\frac{2c-9}{2c+8}$

Lesson 11-2

Assume a and b are legs of a right triangle, and c is the hypotenuse. Find the length of the missing side of each right triangle. If necessary, round to the nearest tenth.

68. $a = 2, b = 8$ **8.2**   69. $a = 3.1, b = 4.3$ **5.3**   70. $a = \sqrt{7}, c = \sqrt{32}$ **5**

71. $a = \sqrt{10}, b = \sqrt{111}$ **11**   72. $a = \frac{1}{5}, b = \frac{1}{12}$ **0.2**   73. $a = 2\frac{1}{3}, b = 6\frac{2}{3}$ **7.1**

Lesson 10-2

Graph each function. Label the axis of symmetry and the vertex. 74–76. See margin.

74. $y = x^2 + 10x - 2$ 75. $y = x^2 - 10x - 2$ 76. $y = 2x^2 + x + 5$

Lesson 12-4 Multiplying and Dividing Rational Expressions   **661**

Standardized Test Prep

 **Resources**
For additional practice with a variety of test item formats:
• Standardized Test Prep, pp. 697–699
• Test-Taking Strategies, p. 692
• Test-Taking Strategies with Transparencies

Exercise 56 Remind students to multiply by the reciprocal of $2r^2 - 2$.

pages 659–661   Exercises

74.
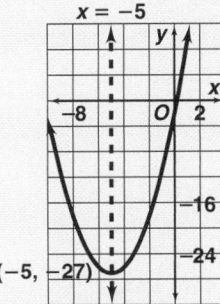
$x = -5$
$(-5, -27)$

75.
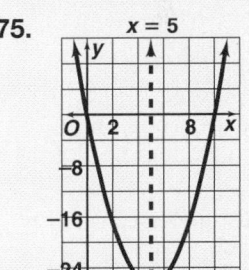
$x = 5$
$(5, -27)$

76.
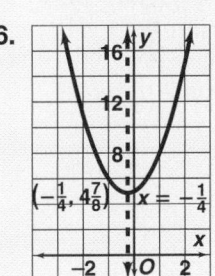
$\left(-\frac{1}{4}, 4\frac{7}{8}\right)$ $x = -\frac{1}{4}$

12-5

1. Plan

Lesson Preview

✓ Check Skills You'll Need

Adding and Subtracting Polynomials
Lesson 9-1: Example 2
Exercises 10–15
Extra Practice, p. 710

Multiplying Binomials
Lesson 9-3: Examples 1, 2
Exercises 1–19
Extra Practice, p. 710

Lesson Resources

📁 **Teaching Resources**
Practice, Reteaching, Enrichment

👥 **Reaching All Students**
Practice Workbook 12-5
Spanish Practice Workbook 12-5
Basic Algebra Planning Guide 12-5

⏰ **Presentation Assistant Plus!**
Transparencies
• Check Skills You'll Need 12-5
• Additional Examples 12-5
• Student Edition Answers 12-5
• Lesson Quiz 12-5
PH Presentation Pro CD 12-5

ASSESSMENT SYSTEM
Computer Test Generator CD

🔧 **Technology**
Resource Pro® CD-ROM
Computer Test Generator CD
Prentice Hall Presentation Pro CD

💻 **www.PHSchool.com**
Student Site
• Teacher Web Code: aek-5500
• Self-grading Lesson Quiz
Teacher Center
• Lesson Planner
• Resources

Plus

12-5

Dividing Polynomials

1.01 Write equivalent forms of algebraic expressions to solve problems. b) Operate with polynomials.

Lesson Preview

What You'll Learn

🎯 **OBJECTIVE**
1 To divide polynomials

. . . And Why

To find the length of a rectangle, as in Example 3

✓ Check Skills You'll Need (For help, go to Lessons 9-1 and 9-3.)

Write each polynomial in standard form.
1. $-4a^2 + 9a + 1$
2. $-x^3 + 3x^2 + 5x - 6$

1. $9a - 4a^2 + 1$ **2.** $3x^2 - 6 + 5x - x^3$ **3.** $-2 + 8t$ $8t - 2$

Find each product.   4–6. See back of book.
4. $(2x + 4)(x + 3)$ **5.** $(-3n - 4)(n - 5)$ **6.** $(3a^2 + 1)(2a - 7)$

OBJECTIVE

1 **Dividing Polynomials**

🔲 **TEXT** **Interactive lesson includes instant self-check, tutorials, and activities.**

To divide a polynomial by a monomial, divide each term of the polynomial by the monomial divisor.

1 EXAMPLE **Dividing a Polynomial by a Monomial**

Divide $8x^3 + 4x^2 - 12x$ by $2x^2$.

$8x^3 + 4x^2 - 12x \div 2x^2 = (8x^3 + 4x^2 - 12x)\frac{1}{2x^2}$ **Multiply by the reciprocal of $2x^2$.**

$= \frac{8x^3}{2x^2} + \frac{4x^2}{2x^2} - \frac{12x}{2x^2}$ **Use the Distributive Property.**

$= 4x^1 + 2x^0 - \frac{6}{x}$ **Use the division rules for exponents.**

$= 4x + 2 - \frac{6}{x}$ **Simplify.**

✓ Check Understanding ❶ Divide.

a. $(3m^3 - 6m^2 + m) \div 3m^2$ **b.** $(8t^5 + 16t^3 - 4t^2 + 2t) \div 4t^2$

$m - 2 + \frac{1}{3m}$ $2t^3 + 4t - 1 + \frac{1}{2t}$

Need Help?

$\underset{\text{divisor}}{\underbrace{}}\overline{)\underset{\text{dividend}}{\underbrace{}}}$
quotient

The process of dividing a polynomial by a binomial is similar to long division. For example, consider dividing 737 by 21.

$$\begin{array}{r} 35 \\ 21\overline{)737} \\ \underline{63} \\ 107 \\ \underline{105} \\ 2 \end{array}$$

1. Divide: 21 can go into 73 about 3 times.
2. Multiply 3×21, then subtract from 73.
3. Bring down the 7. Divide: $107 \div 21 \approx 5$.
4. Multiply 5×21, and then subtract from 107.
5. The remainder is 2.

$737 \div 21 = 35\frac{2}{21}$

You can summarize the process for long division as

"Divide, multiply, subtract, bring down, and repeat as necessary."

In the division above, the answer is written as a mixed number: $35\frac{2}{21}$ means $35 + \frac{2}{21}$. In dividing polynomials, write the answer as quotient $+ \frac{\text{remainder}}{\text{divisor}}$.

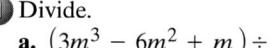**Ongoing Assessment and Intervention**

Before the Lesson
Diagnose prerequisite skills using:
• Check Skills You'll Need

During the Lesson
Monitor progress using:
• Check Understanding
• Additional Examples
• Standardized Test Prep

After the Lesson
Assess knowledge using:
• Lesson Quiz
• Computer Test Generator CD

When the divisor and dividend are in standard form, divide the first term of the dividend by the first term of the divisor to find the first term of the quotient.

2 EXAMPLE Dividing a Polynomial by a Binomial

Divide $2y^2 + 3y - 40$ by $y + 5$.

Step 1 Begin the long division process.

$\downarrow$

Align terms by their degrees.
So put 2y above 3y of the dividend.

$$
\begin{array}{r}
2y \\
y + 5 \overline{)2y^2 + 3y - 40} \\
\underline{2y^2 + 10y} \\
-7y - 40
\end{array}
$$

Divide: Think $2y^2 \div y = 2y$.
Multiply: $2y(y + 5) = 2y^2 + 10y$. Then subtract.
Bring down -40.

?

Need Help?

When subtracting the polynomial $-7y - 35$ from $-7y - 40$, think

$$
\begin{array}{r}
-7y - 40 \\
-(-7y - 35) \\
\end{array}
$$

is

$$
\begin{array}{r}
-7y - 40 \\
\underline{+(7y + 35)}. \\
-5
\end{array}
$$

Step 2 Repeat the process: divide, multiply, subtract, and bring down.

$$
\begin{array}{r}
2y - 7 \\
y + 5 \overline{)2y^2 + 3y - 40} \\
\underline{2y^2 + 10y} \\
-7y - 40 \\
\underline{-7y - 35} \\
-5
\end{array}
$$

Divide: $-7y \div y = -7$.
Multiply: $-7(y + 5) = -7y - 35$. Then subtract.
The remainder is -5.

The answer is $2y - 7 + \frac{-5}{y + 5}$, or $2y - 7 - \frac{5}{y + 5}$.

✓ **Check Understanding** 2 Divide.

a. $(2b^2 - b - 3) \div (b + 1)$

$2b - 3$

b. $(6m^2 - 5m - 7) \div (2m + 1)$

$3m - 4 - \frac{3}{2m + 1}$

When the dividend is in standard form and a power is missing, add a term of that power with 0 as its coefficient. For example, rewrite $4b^3 + 5b - 3$, as $4b^3 + 0b^2 + 5b - 3$.

3 EXAMPLE Dividing Polynomials With a Zero Coefficient

Geometry The width and area of a rectangle are shown in the figure. What is the length?

$W = (2b - 1)$ in.

Since $A = \ell w$, divide the area by the width to find the length.

$$
\begin{array}{r}
2b^2 + b + 3 \\
2b - 1 \overline{)4b^3 + 0b^2 + 5b - 3} \\
\underline{4b^3 - 2b^2} \\
2b^2 + 5b \\
\underline{2b^2 - b} \\
6b - 3 \\
\underline{6b - 3} \\
0
\end{array}
$$

Rewrite the dividend with $0b^2$.

$A = (4b^3 + 5b - 3)$ in.^{2}

The length of the rectangle is $(2b^2 + b + 3)$ in.

✓ **Check Understanding** 3 Divide.

a. $(t^4 + t^2 + t - 3) \div (t - 1)$

$t^3 + t^2 + 2t + 3$

b. $(c^3 - 4c + 12) \div (c + 3)$

$c^2 - 3c + 5 - \frac{3}{c + 3}$

👫 Reaching All Students

Below Level Help students understand division of polynomials by connecting the process of long division with the process of dividing polynomials.	**Advanced Learners** Challenge students to predict the degree of the quotient when a polynomial of degree 5 is divided by a polynomial of degree 2. **3**	**Error Prevention** See note on page 663.

---

2. Teach

Professional Development

Math Background

The process of dividing a polynomial by a binomial reviews the procedure of subtracting a term by adding its opposite.

OBJECTIVE

1 Teaching Notes

2 EXAMPLE Teaching Tip

Point out to students that lining the terms up in vertical columns makes the division much easier to read.

3 EXAMPLE Error Prevention

Students sometimes make errors when subtracting the binomials by subtracting only the first term. Suggest to students that they put parentheses around the whole binomial to be subtracted.

Additional Examples

1 Divide $18x^3 + 9x^2 - 15x$ by $3x^2$. $6x + 3 - \frac{5}{x}$

2 Divide $5x^2 + 2x - 3$ by $x + 2$. $5x - 8 + \frac{13}{x + 2}$

3 The width and area of a rectangle are shown in the figure below. What is the length? $(3x^2 + 2x + 3)$ in.^{2}

$(6x^3 - 5x^2 - 9)$ in.^{2} $(2x - 3)$ in.

4 Divide $-8x - 2 + 6x^2$ by $-1 + x$. $6x - 2 - \frac{4}{x - 1}$

Closure

Ask students to explain how division of polynomials is similar to long division. The division of polynomials is similar to long division in that both processes involve dividing, multiplying, and subtracting, then 'bringing down,' and repeating as needed.

663

3. Practice

Assignment Guide

1 Objective

Ⓐ Ⓑ Core 1–47

Ⓒ Extension 48–52

Standardized Test Prep 53–57

Mixed Review 58–72

Enrichment 12-5

Reteaching 12-5

Practice 12-5

Practice 12-5 — Dividing Polynomials

Divide.

1. $\frac{10x - 25}{5}$
2. $\frac{4x^2 - 3x}{x}$
3. $(3x^2 - 6x) \div 3x$
4. $(10x^2 - 6x) \div 2x$
5. $(-8x^2 + 16x^4 - 24x^3 + 32x^2) \div 8x^2$
6. $(15x^2 - 30x) \div 5x$
7. $(x^2 - 14x + 49) \div (x - 7)$
8. $(2x^2 - 13x + 21) \div (x - 3)$
9. $(4x^2 - 16) \div (2x + 4)$
10. $(x^2 + 4x - 12) \div (x - 2)$
11. $(x^2 + 10x + 16) \div (x + 2)$
12. $(12x^2 - 5x - 2) \div (3x - 2)$
13. $(x^2 + 5x + 10) \div (x + 2)$
14. $(x^2 - 8x - 9) \div (x - 3)$
15. $(3x^2 - 2x - 13) \div (x - 2)$
16. $(x^3 + 3x^2 + 5x + 3) \div (x + 1)$
17. $(5 - 23x + 12x^2) \div (4x - 1)$
18. $(24 + 6x^2 + 25x) \div (3x - 1)$
19. $(2x^2 + 11x - 5) \div (x + 6)$
20. $(x^2 + 5x - 10) \div (x + 2)$
21. $(8x + 3 + 4x^2) \div (2x - 1)$
22. $(3x^2 + 11x - 4) \div (3x - 1)$
23. $(x^3 + x - x^2 - 1) \div (x - 1)$
24. $(10 + 21x + 10x^2) \div (2x + 3)$
25. $(6x^2 - 35x + 36) \div (3x - 4)$
26. $(-2x^2 - 33x + x^3 - 7) \div (x - 7)$

27. The volume of a rectangular prism is $15x^3 + 38x^2 - 23x - 6$. The height of the prism is $5x + 1$, and the width of the prism is $x + 3$. Find the length of the prism.

28. The width of a rectangle is $x + 1$, and the area is $x^3 + 2x^2 - 5x - 6$ cm. What is the length of the rectangle?

© Pearson Education, Inc. All rights reserved.

Algebra 1 Chapter 12 — Lesson 12-5 Practice — 5

To review standard form, see Lesson 9-1.

 Need Help?

To use the process for long division, write any divisor or dividend in standard form before you begin to divide.

4 EXAMPLE Reordering Terms and Dividing Polynomials

Divide $-3x + 4 + 9x^2$ by $1 + 3x$.

Rewrite $-3x + 4 + 9x^2$ as $9x^2 - 3x + 4$ and $1 + 3x$ as $3x + 1$. Then divide.

$$
\begin{array}{r}
3x - 2 \\
3x + 1{\overline{\smash{\big)}\,9x^2 - 3x + 4}} \\
\underline{9x^2 + 3x} \\
-6x + 4 \\
\underline{-6x - 2} \\
6
\end{array}
$$

● The answer is $3x - 2 + \frac{6}{3x + 1}$.

✓ Check Understanding 4 Divide.

a. $(10x - 1 + 8x^2) \div (1 + 2x)$

$4x + 3 - \frac{4}{2x + 1}$

b. $(9 - 6a^2 - 11a) \div (3a - 2)$

$-2a - 5 - \frac{1}{3a - 2}$

 Key Concepts

Summary — Dividing a Polynomial by a Polynomial

Step 1 Arrange the terms of the dividend and divisor in standard form.

Step 2 Divide the first term of the dividend by the first term of the divisor. This is the first term of the quotient.

Step 3 Multiply the first term of the quotient by the divisor and place the product under the dividend.

Step 4 Subtract this product from the dividend.

Step 5 Bring down the next term.

Repeat Steps 2–5 as necessary until the degree of the remainder is less than the degree of the divisor.

EXERCISES

For more practice, see *Extra Practice*.

Practice and Problem Solving

Ⓐ **Practice by Example**

Divide. 1–18. See margin.

Example 1 (page 662)

1. $(x^6 - x^5 + x^4) \div x^2$
2. $(12x^8 - 8x^3) \div 4x^4$
3. $(9c^4 + 6c^3 - c^2) \div 3c^2$
4. $(n^5 - 18n^4 + 3n^3) \div n^3$
5. $(8q^2 - 32q) \div 2q^2$
6. $(-7t^5 + 14t^4 - 28t^3 + 35t^2) \div 7t^2$

Example 2 (page 663)

7. $(x^2 - 5x + 6) \div (x - 2)$
8. $(2t^2 + 3t - 11) \div (t - 3)$
9. $(n^2 - 5n + 4) \div (n - 4)$
10. $(y^2 - y + 2) \div (y + 2)$
11. $(3x^2 - 10x + 3) \div (x - 3)$
12. $(-4q^2 - 22q + 12) \div (2q + 1)$

Example 3 (page 663)

13. $(5t^2 - 500) \div (t + 10)$
14. $(2w^3 + 3w - 15) \div (w - 1)$
15. $(3b^3 - 10b^2 + 4) \div (3b - 1)$
16. $(c^3 - c^2 - 1) \div (c - 1)$
17. $(t^3 - 6t - 4) \div (t + 2)$
18. $(n^3 - 25n - 50) \div (n + 2)$

664 Chapter 12 Rational Expressions and Functions

pages 664–666 Exercises

1. $x^4 - x^3 + x^2$
2. $3x^4 - \frac{2}{x}$
3. $3c^2 + 2c - \frac{1}{3}$

664

4. $n^2 - 18n + 3$
5. $4 - \frac{16}{q}$
6. $-t^3 + 2t^2 - 4t + 5$
7. $x - 3$
8. $2t + 9 + \frac{16}{t - 3}$

9. $n - 1$
10. $y - 3 + \frac{8}{y + 2}$
11. $3x - 1$
12. $-2q - 10 + \frac{22}{2q + 1}$
13. $5t - 50$

14. $2w^2 + 2w + 5 - \frac{10}{w - 1}$
15. $b^2 - 3b - 1 + \frac{3}{3b - 1}$
16. $c^2 - \frac{1}{c - 1}$
17. $t^2 - 2t - 2$
18. $n^2 - 2n - 21 - \frac{8}{n + 2}$

19. Geometry The width of a rectangle is $(r - 5)$ cm and the area is $(r^3 - 24r - 5)$ cm^2. What is the length? **$(r^2 + 5r + 1)$ cm**

20. Geometry The base of a triangle is $(c + 2)$ ft and the area is $(2c^3 + 16)$ ft^2. What is the height? $\left(\textit{Hint:} \text{ The formula for the area of a triangle is } A = \frac{1}{2}bh.\right)$
$(4c^2 - 8c + 16)$ ft

Example 4
(page 664)

Divide. 21–40. See margin.

21. $\left(49 + 16b + b^2\right) \div (b + 4)$

22. $\left(a^2 - 6 + 3a\right) \div (4 + a)$

23. $\left(39w + 14 + 10w^2\right) \div (72 + w)$

24. $\left(4t + t^2 - 9\right) \div (4 + t)$

25. $\left(-13x + 2x^3 - 6 - x^2\right) \div (x - 3)$

26. $\left(6 - q + 3q^3 - 4q^2\right) \div (q - 2)$

B Apply Your Skills

27. $\left(6x^4 + 4x^3 - x^2\right) \div 2x^3$

28. $\left(c^3 + 11c^2 - 15c + 8\right) \div c$

29. $\left(8b + 2b^3\right) \div (b - 1)$

30. $\left(4y + y^3 - 7\right) \div (y - 5)$

31. $\left(56a^2 + 4a - 12\right) \div (2a + 1)$

32. $\left(5t^4 - 10t^2 + 6\right) \div (t + 5)$

33. $\left(3k^3 - 0.9k^2 - 1.2k\right) \div 3k$

34. $\left(-7s + 6s^2 + 5\right) \div (2s + 3)$

35. $\left(-2z^3 - z + z^2 + 1\right) \div (z + 1)$

36. $\left(6m^3 + 3m + 70\right) \div (m + 4)$

41a. Answers may vary.
Sample: $(c^3 + 3c^2 - 2c - 4)$; $(c + 1)$

37. $\left(64c^3 - 125\right) \div (5 - 4c)$

38. $\left(21 - 5r^4 - 10r^2 + 2r^6\right) \div (r^2 - 3)$

39. $\left(2t^4 - 2t^3 + 3t - 1\right) \div (2t^3 + 1)$

40. $\left(z^4 + z^2 - 2\right) \div (z + 3)$

b. $(c^3 + 3c^2 - 2c - 4) \div (c + 1) = c^2 + 2c - 4$

41. a. Open-Ended Write a binomial and a trinomial using the same variable.
  b. Divide the trinomial by the binomial. **a–b. See left.**

42c. vertical asymptote:
$x = -3$
horizontal asymptote:
$y = 2$

42. Use the function rule $y = \frac{2x + 5}{x + 3}$.
  a. Rewrite the function rule as a quotient plus a remainder. $y = 2 - \frac{1}{x + 3}$
  b. Make a table of values and graph the function. **See margin.**
  c. What are the vertical and horizontal asymptotes? **See left.**

43. Writing Suppose you divide a polynomial by a binomial. Explain how you know if the binomial is a factor of the polynomial. **See margin.**

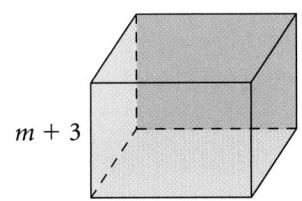

$m + 3$

44. Geometry The volume of the rectangular prism shown at the left is $m^3 + 8m^2 + 19m + 12$. Find the area of the base of the prism. **$m^2 + 5m + 4$**

45. a. Find $\left(d^2 - d + 1\right) \div (d + 1)$. $d - 2 + \frac{3}{d + 1}$
  b. Find $\left(d^3 - d^2 + d - 1\right) \div (d + 1)$. $d^2 - 2d + 3 - \frac{4}{d + 1}$
  c. Find $\left(d^4 - d^3 + d^2 - d + 1\right) \div (d + 1)$. $d^3 - 2d^2 + 3d - 4 + \frac{5}{d + 1}$
  d. Patterns Predict the result of dividing $d^5 - d^4 + d^3 - d^2 + d - 1$ by $d + 1$.
  e. Verify your prediction by dividing the polynomials. **d–e. See left.**

45d. Answers may vary.
Sample: $d^4 - 2d^3 + 3d^2 - 4d + 5 - \frac{6}{d + 1}$

e. $d^4 - 2d^3 + 3d^2 - 4d + 5 - \frac{6}{d + 1}$

46. Critical Thinking Find the value of k if $x + 3$ is a factor of $x^2 - x - k$. **12**

47. a. Solve $d = rt$ for t. $t = \frac{d}{r}$
  b. Use your answer from part (a) to find an expression for the time it takes to travel a distance of $t^3 - 6t^2 + 5t + 12$ miles at a rate of $t + 1$ miles per hour.
  $t^2 - 7t + 12$

C Challenge

Divide.

48. $\left(4a^3b^4 - 6a^2b^5 + 10a^2b^4\right) \div 2ab^2$ $2a^2b^2 - 3ab^3 + 5ab^2$

49. $\left(15x^2 + 7xy - 2y^2\right) \div (5x - y)$ $3x + 2y$

50. $\left(90r^6 + 28r^5 + 45r^3 + 2r^4 + 5r^2\right) \div (9r + 1)$ $10r^5 + 2r^4 + 5r^2$

51. $\left(2b^6 + 2b^5 - 4b^4 + b^3 + 8b^2 - 3\right) \div \left(b^3 + 2b^2 - 1\right)$ $2b^3 - 2b^2 + 3$

Lesson 12-5 Dividing Polynomials **665**

21. $b + 12 + \frac{1}{b + 4}$

22. $a - 1 - \frac{2}{a + 4}$

23. $10w - 681 + \frac{49,046}{w + 72}$

24. $t - \frac{9}{t + 4}$

25. $2x^2 + 5x + 2$

26. $3q^2 + 2q + 3 + \frac{12}{q - 2}$

27. $3x + 2 - \frac{1}{2x}$

28. $c^2 + 11c - 15 + \frac{8}{c}$

29. $2b^2 + 2b + 10 + \frac{10}{b - 1}$

30. $y^2 + 5y + 29 + \frac{138}{y - 5}$

31. $28a - 12$

32. $5t^3 - 25t^2 + 115t - 575 + \frac{2881}{t + 5}$

33. $k^2 - 0.3k - 0.4$

34. $3s - 8 + \frac{29}{2s + 3}$

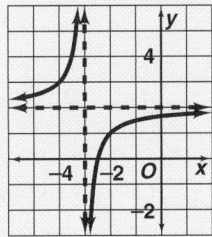

Exercise 54 Remind students that the remainder is a polynomial whose degree is less than the divisor. Thus, answer choices H and I can be eliminated.

pages 664–666 Exercises

57. [4] a.

$$x + 4 \overline{)3x + 10}$$
$$\underline{3x + 12}$$
$$3$$
$$-2$$

$$y = 3 - \frac{2}{x + 4}$$

b. Tables may vary. Sample:

x	y
0	$2\frac{1}{2}$
2	$2\frac{2}{3}$
-2	2
-6	4
-5	5
-3	1
-8	$3\frac{1}{2}$

vertical asymptote:
$x = -4$
horizontal
asymptote: $y = 3$;

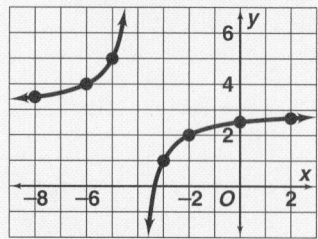

[3] appropriate methods, but with one computational error

[2] no asymptotes OR no graph

[1] one part only

---

52. In Lesson 12-2, you saw horizontal and vertical asymptotes of rational functions. Some rational functions have asymptotes that are neither horizontal nor vertical. Consider the function $f(x) = \frac{x^2 + 2x - 5}{x + 5}$.

52d.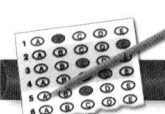

a. Divide $x^2 + 2x - 5$ by $x + 5$. $x - 3 + \frac{10}{x + 5}$

b. Rewrite the function using the quotient. $f(x) = x - 3 + \frac{10}{x + 5}$

c. As $|x|$ increases, the remainder will become smaller, approaching zero, though never reaching it. So an asymptote is defined by the quotient without the remainder. Write an equation of that asymptote. $y = x - 3$

d. Graph the original equation and the asymptote. **See left.**

Standardized Test Prep

Multiple Choice

53. Which of the following expressions equals $(3x^3 - 4x - 1) \div (x + 1)$? **C**

A. $3x^2 - 3x - 7 + \frac{6}{x + 1}$ B. $3x^2 - 3x - 7 - \frac{8}{x + 1}$

C. $3x^2 - 3x - 1$ D. $3x^2 - 7x + 8$

54. What is the remainder when $x^2 - 4$ is divided by $x - 3$? **G**

F. -13 G. 5 H. $\frac{-13}{x - 3}$ I. $\frac{5}{x + 3}$

55. Which of the following must be true for $(x^2 + 2x + 1) \div (x + 3)$? **B**

I. The remainder is negative.
II. The dividend is in standard form.
III. The quotient is larger than the divisor for positive values of x.

A. I only   B. II only   C. I and II   D. II and III

Short Response

56. The volume of a rectangular prism is $2x^3 + 5x^2 + x - 2$. The height of the prism is $2x - 1$, and the length of the prism is $x + 2$. Find the width of the prism. Show your work. **See back of book.**

Extended Response

57. a. Write the function $y = \frac{3x + 10}{x + 4}$ as a quotient plus a remainder.

b. Make a table and find the vertical and horizontal asymptotes. Graph the function. **a–b. See margin.**

Mixed Review

Lesson 12-4   **Multiply or divide.**

58. $\frac{n^2 + 7n - 8}{n - 1} \cdot \frac{n^2 - 4}{n^2 + 6n - 16}$ $n + 2$

59. $\frac{6t^2 - 30t}{2t^2 - 53t - 55} \cdot \frac{6t^2 + 35t + 11}{18t^2}$ $\frac{(t - 5)(3t + 1)(2t + 11)}{(2t - 55)(t + 1)(3t)}$

61. $\frac{(x + 5)(x + 4)^2}{(x + 7)(x + 8)^2}$

60. $\frac{3c^2 - 4c - 32}{2c^2 + 17c + 35} \div \frac{c - 4}{c + 5}$ $\frac{3c + 8}{2c + 7}$

61. $\frac{x^2 + 9x + 20}{x^2 + 5x - 24} \div \frac{x^2 + 15x + 56}{x^2 + x - 12}$ **See left.**

Lesson 11-3   **Find the distance between each pair of points. If necessary, round to the nearest tenth.**

62. $(1, 2), (4, 6)$ **5**   **63.** $(-1, 2), (4, -6)$ **9.4**   **64.** $(7, 5), (-8, 5)$ **15**

65. $(7, 5), (-9, -3)$ **17.9**   **66.** $(-1, 5), (-2, -7)$ **12.0**   **67.** $(0, -5), (-6, 10)$ **16.2**

Lesson 10-3   **Find the value of each expression. If the value is irrational, round to the nearest hundredth.**

68. $\sqrt{28.9}$ **5.38**   **69.** $\sqrt{289}$ **17**   **70.** $-\sqrt{161.29}$ **-12.7**   **71.** $\sqrt{4000}$ **63.25**   **72.** $\sqrt{40}$ **6.32**

Adding and Subtracting Rational Expressions

 North Carolina Objectives 1.01 Write equivalent forms of algebraic expressions to solve problems. b) Operate with polynomials.

Lesson Preview

What You'll Learn

OBJECTIVE 1 To add and subtract rational expressions with like denominators

OBJECTIVE 2 To add and subtract rational expressions with unlike denominators

. . . And Why

To find the time of a round-trip flight, as in Example 5

 Check Skills You'll Need   (For help, go to Lessons 1-5 and 9-5.)

Simplify each expression.

1. $\frac{4}{9} + \frac{2}{9}$ $\frac{2}{3}$

2. $\frac{3}{7} - \frac{5}{7}$ $-\frac{2}{7}$

3. $\frac{1}{2} + \left(-\frac{5}{2}\right)$ -2

4. $\frac{5}{6} + \frac{2}{9}$ $1\frac{1}{18}$

5. $\frac{1}{4} - \frac{1}{3}$ $-\frac{1}{12}$

6. $\frac{5}{12} - \frac{3}{4}$ $-\frac{1}{3}$

7. $\frac{4x}{9} + \frac{2x}{9}$ $\frac{2x}{3}$

8. $\frac{7x}{12} - \frac{x}{12}$ $\frac{x}{2}$

9. $\frac{7}{12y} - \frac{1}{12y}$ $\frac{1}{2y}$

Factor each quadratic expression.

10. $x^2 + 3x + 2$
$(x + 2)(x + 1)$

11. $y^2 + 7y + 12$
$(y + 3)(y + 4)$

12. $t^2 - 4t + 4$
$(t - 2)^2$

OBJECTIVE

1 Adding and Subtracting Rational Expressions With Like Denominators

Adding rational expressions with like denominators is like adding rational numbers with like denominators. If a, b, and c represent polynomials (with $c \neq 0$), then $\frac{a}{c} + \frac{b}{c} = \frac{a + b}{c}$.

1 EXAMPLE Adding Expressions With Like Denominators

Add $\frac{2}{x + 3}$ and $\frac{5}{x + 3}$.

$\frac{2}{x + 3} + \frac{5}{x + 3} = \frac{2 + 5}{x + 3}$ **Add the numerators.**

$= \frac{7}{x + 3}$ **Simplify the numerator.**

Check Understanding ① Add.

a. $\frac{3}{x + 2} + \frac{2}{x + 2}$ $\frac{5}{x + 2}$

b. $\frac{y}{y - 5} + \frac{3y}{y - 5}$ $\frac{4y}{y - 5}$

c. $\frac{5n}{n + 1} + \frac{2n}{n + 1}$ $\frac{7n}{n + 1}$

Similarly, you can subtract rational expressions with like denominators.

2 EXAMPLE Subtracting Expressions With Like Denominators

Subtract $\frac{2n + 1}{2n^2 + 5n - 3}$ from $\frac{3n + 4}{2n^2 + 5n - 3}$.

$\frac{3n + 4}{2n^2 + 5n - 3} - \frac{2n + 1}{2n^2 + 5n - 3} = \frac{3n + 4 - (2n + 1)}{2n^2 + 5n - 3}$ **Subtract the numerators.**

$= \frac{3n + 4 - 2n - 1}{2n^2 + 5n - 3}$ **Use the Distributive Property.**

$= \frac{n + 3}{2n^2 + 5n - 3}$ **Simplify the numerator.**

$= \frac{n + 3^1}{(2n - 1)_1(n + 3)}$ **Factor the denominator. Divide out the common factor $n + 3$.**

$= \frac{1}{2n - 1}$ **Simplify.**

---

1. Plan

Lesson Preview

 **Check Skills You'll Need**

Subtracting Real Numbers
Lesson 1-5: Example 3
Exercises 17–20
Extra Practice, p. 702

Lesson Resources

 **Teaching Resources**
Practice, Reteaching, Enrichment

Reaching All Students
Practice Workbook 12-6
Spanish Practice Workbook 12-6
Basic Algebra Planning Guide 12-6

Presentation Assistant Plus!
Transparencies
• Check Skills You'll Need 12-6
• Additional Examples 12-6
• Student Edition Answers 12-6
• Lesson Quiz 12-6
PH Presentation Pro CD 12-6

ASSESSMENT SYSTEM
Computer Test Generator CD

Technology
Resource Pro® CD-ROM
Computer Test Generator CD
Prentice Hall Presentation Pro CD

 www.PHSchool.com
Student Site
• Teacher Web Code: aek-5500
• Reasoning & Puzzles p. 36
• Self-grading Lesson Quiz
Teacher Center
• Lesson Planner
• Resources

Plus  **iTEXT**

Ongoing Assessment and Intervention

Before the Lesson
Diagnose prerequisite skills using:
• Check Skills You'll Need

During the Lesson
Monitor progress using:
• Check Understanding
• Additional Examples
• Standardized Test Prep

After the Lesson
Assess knowledge using:
• Lesson Quiz
• Computer Test Generator CD

Math Background *Professional Development*

Rewriting rational expressions with a common denominator uses the fact that 1 is the multiplicative identity and also the fact that $\frac{a}{a} = 1$ for $a \neq 0$.

OBJECTIVE

1 **Teaching Notes**

 Additional Examples

1 Add $\frac{4}{x+3}$ and $\frac{2}{x+3}$. $\frac{6}{x+3}$

2 Subtract $\frac{3x+5}{3x^2+2x-8}$ from $\frac{4x+7}{3x^2+2x-8}$. $\frac{1}{3x-4}$

OBJECTIVE

2 **Teaching Notes**

5 EXAMPLE **English Learners**

Relate a *round trip* to a circle; if you start in one place and continue around the circle, you return to where you started.

Additional Examples

3 Add $\frac{3}{4x} + \frac{1}{8}$. $\frac{6+x}{8x}$

4 Add $\frac{7}{x+4}$ and $\frac{3}{x-5}$. $\frac{10x-23}{(x+4)(x-5)}$

5 The distance between Seattle, Washington, and Miami, Florida, is about 5415 miles. The ground speed for jet traffic from Seattle to Miami can be about 14% faster than the ground speed from Miami to Seattle. Use r for the jet's ground speed. Write and simplify an expression for the round-trip air time. $\frac{5415}{r} + \frac{5415}{1.14r}$; $\frac{10,165}{r}$

Closure

Ask: *How do you add and subtract rational expressions?* If the expressions have like denominators, add or subtract numerators as indicated and place over the denominator. If they have unlike denominators, factor if needed, find the LCD, rewrite the expressions with the common denominator, add or subtract as indicated, and simplify.

668

✓ **Check Understanding** **2** Subtract.
  a. $\frac{4}{t-2} - \frac{5}{t-2}$ $-\frac{1}{t-2}$
  b. $\frac{7b-2}{3b+6} - \frac{b+7}{3b+6}$ $\frac{2b-3}{b+2}$
  c. $\frac{2c+1}{5m+2} - \frac{3c-4}{5m+2}$ $\frac{-c+5}{5m+2}$

OBJECTIVE

2 **Adding and Subtracting Rational Expressions With Unlike Denominators**

To add or subtract rational expressions with different denominators, you can write the expressions with the least common denominator (LCD), which is the least common multiple (LCM) of the denominators.

LCM of Whole Numbers	LCM of Variable Expressions
$4 = 2 \cdot 2$	$4x = 2 \cdot 2 \cdot x$
$6 = 2 \cdot 3$	$6x^2 = 2 \cdot 3 \cdot x \cdot x$
$LCM = 2 \cdot 2 \cdot 3 = 12$	$LCM = 2 \cdot 2 \cdot 3 \cdot x \cdot x = 12x^2$

3 EXAMPLE **Adding Expressions With Monomial Denominators**

Add $\frac{2}{3x} + \frac{1}{6}$.

Step 1 Find the LCD of $\frac{2}{3x}$ and $\frac{1}{6}$.

$3x = 3 \cdot x$ **Factor each denominator.**
$6 = 2 \cdot 3$
$LCD = 2 \cdot 3 \cdot x = 6x$.

Step 2 Rewrite using the LCD and add.

$\frac{2}{3x} + \frac{1}{6} = \frac{2 \cdot 2}{2 \cdot 3x} + \frac{1 \cdot x}{6 \cdot x}$ **Rewrite each fraction using the LCD.**

$= \frac{4}{6x} + \frac{x}{6x}$ **Simplify numerators and denominators.**

$= \frac{4+x}{6x}$ **Add the numerators.**

✓ **Check Understanding** **3** Add or subtract.
  a. $\frac{3}{7y^4} + \frac{2}{3y^2}$ $\frac{9+14y^2}{21y^4}$
  b. $\frac{4}{25x} - \frac{49}{100}$ $\frac{16-49x}{100x}$
  c. $\frac{5}{12b} + \frac{15}{36b^2}$ $\frac{5b+5}{12b^2}$

You can also find the LCD of rational expressions that have polynomials with two or more terms in the denominator.

4 EXAMPLE **Adding Expressions With Polynomial Denominators**

Add $\frac{5}{c+2}$ and $\frac{6}{c-3}$.

Step 1 Find the LCD of $c + 2$ and $c - 3$.
Since there are no common factors, the LCD is $(c+2)(c-3)$.

Step 2 Rewrite using the LCD and add.

$\frac{5}{c+2} + \frac{6}{c-3} = \frac{5(c-3)}{(c+2)(c-3)} + \frac{6(c+2)}{(c+2)(c-3)}$ **Rewrite the fractions using the LCD.**

$= \frac{5c-15}{(c+2)(c-3)} + \frac{6c+12}{(c+2)(c-3)}$ **Simplify each numerator.**

$= \frac{5c-15+6c+12}{(c+2)(c-3)}$ **Add the numerators.**

$= \frac{11c-3}{(c+2)(c-3)}$ **Simplify the numerator.**

668   Chapter 12   Rational Expressions and Functions

👥 **Reaching All Students**

| **Below Level** Have students explain the steps they use to add and subtract fractions in Check Skills You'll Need. | **Advanced Learners** Challenge students to simplify $3 + \frac{a}{\frac{a}{2}-1}$. $\frac{5a-6}{a-2}$ | **English Learners** See note on page 668. **Error Prevention** See note on page 669. |

✓ **Check Understanding** ④ Add.

a. $\dfrac{5}{t+4} + \dfrac{3}{t-1}$
$\dfrac{8t+7}{(t+4)(t-1)}$

b. $\dfrac{m}{2m+1} + \dfrac{3}{m-1}$
$\dfrac{m^2+5m+3}{(2m+1)(m-1)}$

c. $\dfrac{-2}{a+2} + \dfrac{3a}{2a-1}$
$\dfrac{3a^2+2a+2}{(a+2)(2a-1)}$

You can combine rational expressions to investigate real-world situations.

5 EXAMPLE Real-World 🌐 Problem Solving

2500 miles
New York
Los Angeles

Air Travel The ground speed for jet traffic from Los Angeles to New York City can be about 15% faster than the ground speed from New York City to Los Angeles. This difference is due to a strong westerly wind at high altitudes. If r is a jet's ground speed from New York City to Los Angeles, write and simplify an expression for the round-trip air time. The two cities are about 2500 miles apart.

NYC to LA time: $\dfrac{2500}{r}$ time = $\dfrac{\text{distance}}{\text{rate}}$

LA to NYC time: $\dfrac{2500}{1.15r}$ time = $\dfrac{\text{distance}}{\text{rate}}$ 15% more than a number is 115% of the number.

An expression for the total time is $\dfrac{2500}{r} + \dfrac{2500}{1.15r}$.

$\dfrac{2500}{r} + \dfrac{2500}{1.15r} = \dfrac{2875}{1.15r} + \dfrac{2500}{1.15r}$ **Rewrite using the LCD, 1.15r.**

$= \dfrac{5375}{1.15r}$ **Add the numerators.**

$\approx \dfrac{4674}{r}$ **Simplify.**

✓ **Check Understanding** ⑤ **Air Travel** The distance between Atlanta, Georgia, and Albuquerque, New Mexico, is about 1270 miles. The ground speed for jet traffic from Atlanta to Albuquerque can be about 12% faster than the ground speed from Albuquerque to Atlanta. Use r for a jet's ground speed. Write and simplify an expression for the round-trip air time.
$\dfrac{1270}{r} + \dfrac{1270}{1.12r} \approx \dfrac{2404}{r}$

EXERCISES

Practice and Problem Solving

For more practice, see *Extra Practice*.

Ⓐ Practice by Example

Add or subtract.

Example 1
(page 667)

1. $\dfrac{5}{2m} + \dfrac{4}{2m}$ $\dfrac{9}{2m}$

2. $\dfrac{4}{6t-1} + \dfrac{3}{6t-1}$ $\dfrac{7}{6t-1}$

3. $\dfrac{n}{n+3} + \dfrac{2}{n+3}$ $\dfrac{n+2}{n+3}$

4. $\dfrac{5}{c-5} + \dfrac{9}{c-5}$ $\dfrac{14}{c-5}$

5. $\dfrac{s^2+3}{4s^2+2} + \dfrac{s^2-2}{4s^2+2}$ $\dfrac{2s^2+1}{4s^2+2}$

6. $\dfrac{5c}{2c+7} + \dfrac{c-28}{2c+7}$ $\dfrac{6c-28}{2c+7}$

Example 2
(page 667)

7. $\dfrac{1}{2-b} - \dfrac{4}{2-b}$ $\dfrac{-3}{2-b}$

8. $\dfrac{5}{t^2+1} - \dfrac{6}{t^2+1}$ $\dfrac{1}{t^2+1}$

9. $\dfrac{3t}{2t-3} - \dfrac{5t}{2t-3}$ $\dfrac{-2t}{2t-3}$

10. $\dfrac{2y+1}{y-1} - \dfrac{y+2}{y-1}$ 1

11. $\dfrac{3n+2}{n+4} - \dfrac{n-6}{n+4}$ 2

12. $\dfrac{3}{b-3} - \dfrac{b}{b-3}$ -1

Example 3
(page 668)

Find the LCD of each pair of expressions.

13. $\dfrac{1}{2}; \dfrac{4}{x^2}$ $2x^2$

14. $\dfrac{b}{6}; \dfrac{2b}{9}$ 18

15. $\dfrac{1}{z}; \dfrac{3}{7z}$ $7z$

16. $\dfrac{8}{5b}; \dfrac{12}{7b^3c}$ $35b^3c$

Add or subtract.

17. $\dfrac{7}{3a} + \dfrac{2}{5}$ $\dfrac{35+6a}{15a}$

18. $\dfrac{4}{x} - \dfrac{2}{3}$ $\dfrac{12-2x}{3x}$

19. $\dfrac{6}{5x^8} + \dfrac{4}{3x^6}$ $\dfrac{18+20x^2}{15x^8}$

20. $\dfrac{3}{8m^3} + \dfrac{1}{12m^2}$ $\dfrac{9+2m}{24m^3}$

21. $\dfrac{27}{n^3} - \dfrac{9}{7n^2}$ $\dfrac{189-9n}{7n^3}$

22. $\dfrac{9}{4x^2} + \dfrac{9}{5}$ $\dfrac{45+36x^2}{20x^2}$

Lesson 12-6 Adding and Subtracting Rational Expressions   **669**

Assignment Guide

1 Objective
Ⓐ Ⓑ Core 1–12, 30–33

2 Objective
Ⓐ Ⓑ Core 13–29, 34–50
Ⓒ Extension 51–54

Standardized Test Prep 55–58

Mixed Review 59–66

Diversity

Exercise 29 Use this problem for a discussion about stereotypes of older people. Ask students to describe the stereotype and then name people they know who do not fit the stereotype. The *Guiness Book of Records* describes a 98-year-old man and an 82-year-old woman who each completed marathons.

Error Prevention

Exercises 30–40 When subtracting, students sometimes forget to distribute the negative sign to all terms in the numerator. Suggest to them that they put parentheses around the numerator.

Enrichment 12-6
Reteaching 12-6
Practice 12-6

Practice 12-6   Adding and Subtracting Rational Expressions

Simplify.

1. $\dfrac{3z}{4} - \dfrac{z}{4}$ 2. $\dfrac{2}{5} + \dfrac{7}{5}$ 3. $\dfrac{5x}{6} - \dfrac{3x}{6}$

4. $\dfrac{4}{9} + \dfrac{2}{9}$ 5. $\dfrac{5m}{2d} + \dfrac{6m}{2d}$ 6. $\dfrac{8x}{14} - \dfrac{3x}{14}$

7. $\dfrac{6}{7t} - \dfrac{3}{7t}$ 8. $\dfrac{4}{9} + \dfrac{5d}{9}$ 9. $\dfrac{7}{3t} - \dfrac{1}{5t}$

10. $\dfrac{1}{5x^2} + \dfrac{4x}{5x}$ 11. $\dfrac{8}{n+1} + \dfrac{5}{n+1}$ 12. $\dfrac{3}{z} - \dfrac{1}{z}$

13. $\dfrac{7x}{9} + \dfrac{4}{9}$ 14. $\dfrac{4}{x+3} + \dfrac{5}{x+3}$ 15. $\dfrac{3}{4z^2} + \dfrac{1}{4z^2}$

16. $\dfrac{6}{x-1} - \dfrac{4}{x-1}$ 17. $\dfrac{5}{z-1} - \dfrac{3}{z-1}$ 18. $\dfrac{3y}{8} + \dfrac{9y}{8}$

19. $\dfrac{3x}{5c} - \dfrac{1}{5c}$ 20. $\dfrac{2}{x+4} + \dfrac{3}{x+4}$ 21. $\dfrac{7}{x+5} + \dfrac{6}{x+5}$

22. $\dfrac{5}{3x} - \dfrac{8}{6x}$ 23. $\dfrac{1}{3x+6} + \dfrac{x}{6x+12}$ 24. $\dfrac{5}{6x} - \dfrac{1}{4x}$

25. $\dfrac{5}{x^2-4} + \dfrac{7}{x-2}$ 26. $\dfrac{2}{x^2-1} - \dfrac{3}{x-1}$ 27. $\dfrac{2x}{7} - \dfrac{5}{7}$

28. $\dfrac{3}{6x+6} + \dfrac{x}{2x+2}$ 29. $\dfrac{3}{x^2-6x+9} + \dfrac{x}{x-3}$ 30. $\dfrac{5}{2x-4} + \dfrac{x}{x-2}$

31. Brian rode his bike 2 mi to his friend's home. Brian's bike had a flat tire, so he had to walk home. His walking rate is 25% of his biking rate.
   a. Write an expression for the amounts of time Brian spent walking and riding his bike.
   b. If Brian's biking rate is 12 mi/h, how much time did he spend walking and riding his bike?

32. Trudi and Sean are on a river canoeing. Because of the current of the river, their downstream rate is 250% of their upstream rate. They canoe 3 mi upstream and then return to their starting point.
   a. Write an expression for the amount of time Trudi and Sean spend canoeing.
   b. If their upstream rate is 2 mi/h, how much time do Trudi and Sean spend canoeing?
   c. If their upstream rate is 3 mi/h, how much time do Trudi and Sean spend canoeing?

Lesson 12-6 Practice   Algebra 1 Chapter 12

Alternative Assessment

Group students in pairs. Have each student write detailed step-by-step solutions to problems that his or her partner creates that are analogous to the examples in the lesson.

Example 4
(page 668)

Add. $\frac{17m - 47}{(m + 2)(m - 7)}$

23. $\frac{9}{m + 2} + \frac{8}{m - 7}$

24. $\frac{a}{a + 3} + \frac{4}{a + 5}$ $\frac{a^2 + 9a + 12}{(a + 3)(a + 5)}$

25. $\frac{a}{a + 3} + \frac{a + 5}{4}$ $\frac{a^2 + 12a + 15}{4(a + 3)}$

26. $\frac{c}{c + 5} + \frac{4}{c + 3}$

27. $\frac{5}{t^2} + \frac{4}{t + 1}$

28. $\frac{3}{2a + 1} + \frac{6}{2a - 1}$

26–28. See left.

Example 5
(page 669)

26. $\frac{c^2 + 7c + 20}{(c + 5)(c + 3)}$

27. $\frac{4t^2 + 5t + 5}{t^2(t + 1)}$

28. $\frac{18a + 3}{(2a + 1)(2a - 1)}$

B Apply Your Skills

42c. Yes; they both represent the time it takes to make a round trip.

43. Answers may vary. Sample: Not always; the numerator may contain a factor of the LCD.

29. **Exercise** Jane walks one mile from her house to her grandparents' house. Then she returns home, walking with her grandfather. Her return rate is 70% of her normal walking rate. Let r represent her normal walking rate.
   a. Write an expression for the amount of time Jane spends walking. $\frac{1}{r} + \frac{1}{0.7r}$
   b. Simplify your expression. $\frac{17}{7r}$
   c. Suppose Jane's normal walking rate is 3 mi/h. About how much time does she spend walking? **about 0.8 h**

Add or subtract.   30–40. See margin.

30. $\frac{y^2 + 2y - 1}{3y + 1} - \frac{2y^2 - 3}{3y + 1}$

31. $\frac{h^2 + 1}{2t^2 - 7} + \frac{h}{2t^2 - 7}$

32. $\frac{r - 5}{9 + p^3} - \frac{2k + 1}{9 + p^3}$

33. $\frac{2 - x}{xy^2z} - \frac{5 + z}{xy^2z}$

34. $\frac{k}{2m^2} + \frac{3k}{2m}$

35. $\frac{12}{ab} - \frac{15}{bc}$

36. $\frac{c^2}{ab} - \frac{a^2}{bc}$

37. $9 + \frac{x - 3}{x + 2}$

38. $\frac{t}{2t - 3} - 11$

39. $\frac{x}{x^2 - 9} - \frac{x}{x^2 + 6x + 9}$

40. $\frac{k - 24}{k^2 - 3k - 18} - \frac{3}{k + 3} + \frac{k + 1}{k - 6}$

41. **Error Analysis** A student wrote that $\frac{2}{x + 3} + \frac{3}{x + 1} = \frac{5}{2x + 4}$. What error did the student make? **The student added the terms in the denominators.**

🌐 42. **Rowing** A rowing team practices rowing 2 mi upstream and 2 mi downstream. The team can row downstream 25% faster than they can row upstream.
   a. Let r represent their rate upstream. Write and simplify an expression for the amount of time they spend rowing. $\frac{2}{r} + \frac{2}{1.25r}$; $\frac{18}{5r}$
   b. Let d represent their rate downstream. Write and simplify an expression for the amount of time they spend rowing. $\frac{2}{d} + \frac{2}{0.8d}$; $\frac{9}{2d}$
   c. **Critical Thinking** Do the expressions you wrote in parts (a) and (b) represent the same time? Explain. **See left.**

✏️ 43. **Writing** When adding or subtracting rational expressions, will the answer be in simplest form if you use the LCD? Explain. **See left.**

44. **Open-Ended** Write two rational expressions with different denominators. Find the LCD and add the two expressions. **See margin.**

For $f(x) = 8x, g(x) = \frac{1}{x}$, and $h(x) = \frac{4}{x - 5}$, perform the indicated operation.

Samples $f(x) + g(x) = 8x + \frac{1}{x}$ $f(x) \div g(x) = 8x \div \frac{1}{x}$

$= \frac{8x}{1}\left(\frac{x}{x}\right) + \frac{1}{x}$ $= 8x\left(\frac{x}{1}\right)$

$= \frac{8x^2}{x} + \frac{1}{x}$ $= 8x^2$

$= \frac{8x^2 + 1}{x}$

Real-World 🌐 Connection

Rowing competitions include races for 1-, 2-, 4- and 8-person boats. There is a coxswain to direct 4- and 8-person boats.

45. $f(x) - g(x)$ $\frac{8x^2 - 1}{x}$

46. $f(x) \cdot g(x)$ 8

47. $g(x) - h(x)$ $\frac{-3x - 5}{x(x - 5)}$

48. $f(x) \cdot h(x)$ $\frac{32x}{x - 5}$

49. $g(x) \div h(x)$ $\frac{x - 5}{4x}$

50. $h(x) \div f(x)$ $\frac{1}{2x(x - 5)}$

C Challenge

Simplify each expression.

51. $\frac{7d - 2}{d^2 + 2d - 8} - \frac{4}{d + 4} - \frac{d}{d - 2}$ $\frac{-d + 3}{d + 4}$

52. $\frac{7x - 10}{x^3 + x^2 - 10x} - \frac{1}{x + 5}$ $\frac{-x^3 + 6x^2 + 35x - 50}{x(x + 5)(x^2 + x - 10)}$

53. $\frac{x^2}{x^2 + x - 12} - \frac{x}{x + 4} \cdot \frac{3}{x - 3} \cdot \frac{x}{x + 4}$

54. $\frac{2}{a - 5} \cdot \frac{a - 1}{a + 2} - \frac{a - 2}{2 + a} \cdot \frac{3}{5 - a}$ $\frac{5a - 8}{(a + 2)(a - 5)}$

670   Chapter 12   Rational Expressions and Functions

---

pages 669–671 **Exercises**

30. $\frac{-y^2 + 2y + 2}{3y + 1}$

31. $\frac{h^2 + h + 1}{2t^2 - 7}$

32. $\frac{r - 2k - 6}{9 + p^3}$

33. $\frac{-3 - x - z}{xy^2z}$

34. $\frac{k + 3km}{2m^2}$

35. $\frac{12c - 15a}{abc}$

36. $\frac{c^3 - a^3}{abc}$

37. $\frac{10x + 15}{x + 2}$

38. $\frac{-21t + 33}{2t - 3}$

39. $\frac{6x}{(x - 3)(x + 3)^2}$

40. $\frac{k - 1}{k - 6}$

44. **Answers may vary.**

Sample: $\frac{2w}{w + 3}, \frac{3w^2}{w - 3}$;

$\frac{3w^3 + 11w^2 - 6w}{(w + 3)(w - 3)}$

Multiple Choice

55. Subtract $\frac{2x}{3x - 2}$ from $\frac{5x}{3x - 2}$. **D**

    A. -2 **B.** $\frac{-3x}{3x - 2}$ **C.** $\frac{7x}{3x - 2}$ **D.** $\frac{3x}{3x - 2}$

56. What is the least common denominator of $\frac{x}{x^2 - 1}$ and $\frac{-2}{x - 1}$? **H**

    F. $x + 1$ **G.** $x - 1$ **H.** $x^2 - 1$ **I.** $(x^2 - 1)(x - 1)$

57. A band director found that he could line up the musicians in the brass section in rows of 4, 5, or 8. What is the least number of brass players in the band? **D**

    A. 16 players   **B.** 24 players   **C.** 32 players   **D.** 40 players

Short Response

58. The members of a bicycle club rode a 20-mile round-trip route. On the way back, they had a tail wind and averaged 3 mi/h faster than on the first 10 miles of the trip. **a–b. See margin.**

    a. Use r for the rate. Write an expression for the total ride time. Simplify the expression.

    b. Suppose the bicyclists averaged a rate of 12 mi/h for the first half of the ride. How long did the round trip take? Show your work.

Take It to the NET
Online lesson quiz at
www.PHSchool.com
Web Code: aea-1206

Mixed Review

Lesson 12-5

Divide.

$\frac{x^2}{2} + 2x - 1$

59. $(2x^4 + 8x^3 - 4x^2) \div 4x^2$

$5b^2 - 10b + 30 - \frac{60}{b + 2}$

60. $(10b + 5b^3) \div (b + 2)$

Lesson 11-5

Solve each radical equation. Check your answers. If there is no solution, write *no solution*.

61. $x = \sqrt{5x + 6}$ **6**   **62.** $n = \sqrt{24 - 5n}$ **3**   **63.** $\sqrt{16y} = -8$

    no solution

Lesson 10-4

Solve each equation by finding square roots. Round to the nearest tenth. If the equation has no solution, write *no solution*.

64. $a^2 - 48 = 0$ **±6.9**   **65.** $2n^2 = 30$ **±3.9**   **66.** $3p^2 + 60 = 0$

    no solution

Standardized Test Prep

📁 **Resources**
For additional practice with a variety of test item formats:
• Standardized Test Prep, pp. 697–699
• Test-Taking Strategies, p. 692
• Test-Taking Strategies with Transparencies.

58. [2] a. $\frac{10}{r} + \frac{10}{r + 3} =$ total time;

$$\frac{10(r + 3) + 10r}{r(r + 3)} =$$

$$\frac{10r + 30 + 10r}{r(r + 3)} =$$

$$\frac{20r + 30}{r(r + 3)} =$$

$$\frac{10(2r + 3)}{r(r + 3)}$$

b. $\frac{10(2(12) + 3)}{12(12 + 3)} =$

$$\frac{10(24 + 3)}{12(15)} =$$

$$\frac{10(27)}{180} = \frac{270}{180} = \frac{3}{2}$$

The ride took $1\frac{1}{2}$ hours.

[1] one computational error OR no work shown

Algebra at Work

·········· Electrician

More than half a million men and women work as electricians. All are highly skilled technicians licensed by the states in which they work. Electricians use formulas containing rational expressions. For example, when a circuit connected in parallel contains two resistors with resistances R_1 and R_2 ohms, the total resistance R_T (in ohms) of the circuit can be found using the formula $\frac{1}{R_T} = \frac{1}{R_1} + \frac{1}{R_2}$.

Take It to the NET For more information about a career as an electrician, go to **www.PHSchool.com**.
Web Code: aeb-2031

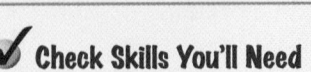

1. Plan

Lesson Preview

 **Check Skills You'll Need**

Ratios and Proportions
Lesson 4-1: Examples 3, 4
Exercises 14–29
Extra Practice, p. 705

Adding and Subtracting Rational Expressions
Lesson 12-6: Example 3
Exercises 13–16
Extra Practice, p. 713

Lesson Resources

📁 **Teaching Resources**
Practice, Reteaching, Enrichment

👥 **Reaching All Students**
Practice Workbook 12-7
Spanish Practice Workbook 12-7
Hands-On Activities 29
Basic Algebra Planning Guide 12-7

⏰ **Presentation Assistant Plus!**
Transparencies
• Check Skills You'll Need 12-7
• Additional Examples 12-7
• Student Edition Answers 12-7
• Lesson Quiz 12-7
PH Presentation Pro CD 12-7

ASSESSMENT SYSTEM (PRENTICE HALL)

Computer Test Generator CD

💿 **Technology**
Resource Pro® CD-ROM
Computer Test Generator CD
Prentice Hall Presentation Pro CD

🖥 **www.PHSchool.com**
Student Site
• Teacher Web Code: aek-5500
• Self-grading Lesson Quiz
Teacher Center
• Lesson Planner
• Resources

 Plus **iTEXT**

12-7

Solving Rational Equations

North Carolina Objectives

1.01 Write equivalent forms of algebraic expressions to solve problems. **b)** Operate with polynomials. **c)** Factor polynomials.

Lesson Preview

What You'll Learn

OBJECTIVE **1** To solve rational equations

OBJECTIVE **2** To solve proportions

. . . And Why

To find the time it will take two people to do a job, as in Example 3

✔ **Check Skills You'll Need** (For help, go to Lessons 4-1 and 12-6.)

Solve each proportion.

1. $\frac{1}{x} = \frac{3}{5}$ $1\frac{2}{3}$

2. $\frac{3}{t} = \frac{5}{2}$ $1\frac{1}{5}$

3. $\frac{m}{3} = \frac{27}{m}$ $-9, 9$

Find the LCD of each group of expressions.

4. $\frac{3}{4n}; \frac{1}{2}; \frac{2}{n}$ $4n$

5. $\frac{1}{3x}; \frac{2}{5}; \frac{4}{3x}$ $15x$

6. $\frac{1}{8y}; \frac{1}{y^2}; \frac{5}{6}$ $24y^2$

New Vocabulary • rational equation

OBJECTIVE
1 **Solving Rational Equations**

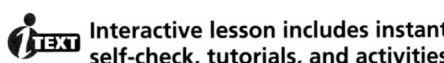 **Interactive lesson includes instant self-check, tutorials, and activities.**

A **rational equation** contains one or more rational expressions. One method for solving rational equations is similar to the method you learned in Chapter 2 for solving equations with rational numbers.

$$\frac{1}{2}x + \frac{3}{10} = \frac{1}{5}$$ The denominators are 2, 10, and 5. The LCD is 10.

$$10\left(\frac{1}{2}x + \frac{3}{10}\right) = 10\left(\frac{1}{5}\right)$$ Multiply each side by 10.

$$^5 10\left(\frac{1}{2_1}x\right) + {}^1 10\left(\frac{3}{10_1}\right) = {}^2 10\left(\frac{1}{5_1}\right)$$ Use the Distributive Property.

$$5x + 3 = 2$$ No fractions! This equation is easier to solve.

1 EXAMPLE **Solving Equations With Rational Expressions**

Solve $\frac{1}{2x} + \frac{3}{10} = \frac{1}{5x}$. Check the solution.

$$\frac{1}{2x} + \frac{3}{10} = \frac{1}{5x}$$ The denominators are 2x, 10, and 5x. The LCD is 10x.

$$10x\left(\frac{1}{2x} + \frac{3}{10}\right) = 10x\left(\frac{1}{5x}\right)$$ Multiply each side by 10x.

$$^5 10x\left(\frac{1}{2x_1}\right) + {}^1 10x\left(\frac{3}{10_1}\right) = {}^2 10x\left(\frac{1}{5x_1}\right)$$ Use the Distributive Property.

$$5 + 3x = 2$$ No rational expressions! Now you can solve.

$$3x = -3$$ Subtract 5 from each side.

$$x = -1$$ Divide each side by 3, and then simplify.

Check See if -1 makes $\frac{1}{2x} + \frac{3}{10} = \frac{1}{5x}$ true.

$$\frac{1}{2(-1)} + \frac{3}{10} \stackrel{?}{=} \frac{1}{5(-1)}$$

$$-\frac{5}{10} + \frac{3}{10} = -\frac{1}{5} ✔$$

✔ **Check Understanding** **1** Solve each equation. Check your solution.

a. $\frac{1}{3} + \frac{1}{3x} = \frac{1}{6}$ -2

b. $\frac{4}{c} = \frac{3}{2c} - \frac{1}{5}$ $-\frac{25}{2}$

🔄 **Ongoing Assessment and Intervention**

Before the Lesson
Diagnose prerequisite skills using:
• Check Skills You'll Need

During the Lesson
Monitor progress using:
• Check Understanding
• Additional Examples
• Standardized Test Prep

After the Lesson
Assess knowledge using:
• Lesson Quiz
• Computer Test Generator CD

To solve some rational equations, you need to factor a quadratic expression.

2 EXAMPLE Solving by Factoring

Solve $\frac{5}{x^2} = \frac{6}{x} - 1$. Check the solution.

$$x^2\left(\frac{5}{x^2}\right) = x^2\left(\frac{6}{x} - 1\right)$$ **Multiply each side by the LCD, x^2.**

$$1 x^2\left(\frac{5}{1 x^2}\right) = {}^x x^2\left(\frac{6}{x_1}\right) - x^2(1)$$ **Use the Distributive Property.**

$$5 = 6x - x^2$$ **Simplify.**

$$x^2 - 6x + 5 = 0$$ **Collect terms on one side.**

$$(x - 5)(x - 1) = 0$$ **Factor the quadratic expression.**

$$(x - 5) = 0 \quad \text{or} \quad (x - 1) = 0$$ **Use the Zero-Product Property.**

$$x = 5 \quad \text{or} \quad x = 1$$ **Solve.**

Check $\frac{5}{5^2} \stackrel{?}{=} \frac{6}{5} - 1 \qquad \frac{5}{1^2} \stackrel{?}{=} \frac{6}{1} - 1$

$\qquad\qquad \frac{1}{5} = \frac{1}{5}\ \checkmark \qquad\qquad 5 = 5\ \checkmark$

✔ **Check Understanding** **2** Solve each equation. Check your solution.

a. $\frac{5}{m} = \frac{2}{m^2} + 2\ \frac{1}{2}, 2$

b. $t - 2 = \frac{8 - 2t}{t - 1}\ -2, 3$

You can solve a work problem by finding the part of the job each person does in one unit of time (hour or minute). Find the part of the job each person does, and then write an equation.

3 EXAMPLE Work-Rate Problem

Volunteerism Max can wash and wax a car in 60 min. His older sister Kayla can do the same job in 45 min. How long will the car take them if they work together?

Define Let n = the time to complete the job if they work together (in minutes).

Relate fraction of job   fraction of job   fraction of
Max can do   + Kayla can do = job completed
in 1 minute   in 1 minute   in 1 minute

Write $\qquad \frac{1}{60} \qquad + \qquad \frac{1}{45} \qquad = \qquad \frac{1}{n}$

$180n\left(\frac{1}{60} + \frac{1}{45}\right) = 180n\left(\frac{1}{n}\right)$ **Multiply each side by the LCD, $180n$.**

$\qquad 3n + 4n = 180$ **Use the Distributive Property.**

$\qquad\qquad 7n = 180$ **Simplify.**

$\qquad\qquad n = \frac{180}{7}, \text{ or } 25\frac{5}{7}$ **Simplify.**

It will take the two of them about 26 minutes to wash the car working together.

Check Max will do $\frac{180}{7} \cdot \frac{1}{60} = \frac{3}{7}$ of the job, and Kayla will do $\frac{180}{7} \cdot \frac{1}{45} = \frac{4}{7}$ of the job.

Together, they will do $\frac{3}{7} + \frac{4}{7} = 1$, or the whole job.

✔ **Check Understanding** **3** Peggy can pick a bushel of apples in 45 min. Peter can pick a bushel of apples in 75 min. How long will it take them to pick a bushel if they work together? $28\frac{1}{8}$ min

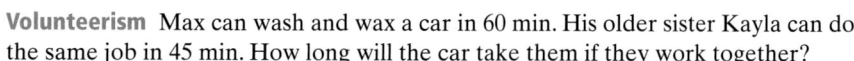

Real-World Connection

Many student groups hold car washes to raise money.

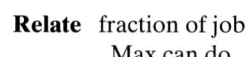
Reading Math

For help with Example 3, see page 678.

Lesson 12-7 Solving Rational Equations **673**

2. Teach

Professional Development

Math Background

Some rational functions may have extraneous solutions. For example, solutions may make a denominator equal 0 when substituted into the expression.

OBJECTIVE
1 Teaching Notes

1 EXAMPLE Alternative Method

Suggest to students that they graph $Y_1 = \frac{1}{2x} + \frac{3}{10} - \frac{1}{5x}$ on their graphing calculators and find any x-intercepts.

2 EXAMPLE Teaching Tip

Remind students that once they have found a solution, they should substitute the value back into the *original* equation to check their work. Remind them to check for values that are excluded from the domain.

3 EXAMPLE Visual Learners

Some students will benefit from organizing information into a table, since it is a good way to help sort out information in a visual manner.

Additional Examples

1 Solve $\frac{3}{8} + \frac{4}{x} = \frac{14}{2x}$. Check the solution. **8**

2 Solve $\frac{6}{x^2} = \frac{5}{x} - 1$. Check the solution. **2, 3**

3 Renee can mow the lawn in 20 minutes. Joanne can do the same job in 30 minutes. How long will it take them if they work together? **12 min**

👥 Reaching All Students

| **Below Level** Emphasize to students that, if a person can complete a job in x days, then the rate of that person = $\frac{1}{x}$ job per day. The work done = rate × time. | **Advanced Learners** Challenge students to solve $\frac{x}{2x - 1} \leq 1$. x real, $x \neq \frac{1}{2}$ | **Visual Learners** See note on page 673. **Error Prevention** See note on page 675. |

673

Some students may think there is an error if an equation produces no solution. On the board write $x + 1 = x + 2$. Ask students to study the equation and suggest values for x that solve the equation. Once students recognize that no such values exist, use this to help them remember that equations with no solutions are possible.

Additional Examples

4 Solve $\frac{4}{x^2} = \frac{1}{x + 8}$. Check the solution. $-4, 8$

5 Solve $\frac{x + 3}{x - 1} = \frac{4}{x - 1}$. no solution

Closure

Ask students to describe how to solve an equation containing a rational expression. Eliminate the fractions by multiplying each side of the equation by the LCD, or, if it is a proportion, by writing cross products. Collect like terms on one side and solve the equation. If necessary, factor and use the Zero-Product Property. Finally, check the solutions to rule out any extraneous solutions.

OBJECTIVE
2 **Solving Proportions**

Some rational equations are proportions. You can solve them by using cross products.

4 EXAMPLE Solving a Rational Proportion

Solve $\frac{2}{x} = \frac{1}{x + 4}$. Check the solution.

$$\frac{2}{x} = \frac{1}{x + 4}$$

$2(x + 4) = x(1)$ Write cross products.

$2x + 8 = x$ Use the Distributive Property.

$x = -8$ Solve for *x*.

Check $\frac{2}{x} = \frac{1}{x + 4}$

$\frac{2}{-8} \stackrel{?}{=} \frac{1}{-8 + 4}$

$-\frac{1}{4} = -\frac{1}{4}$ ✓

Need Help?

If $\frac{a}{b} = \frac{c}{d}$, then $ad = bc$.

✓ **Check Understanding** **4** Solve each equation. Check your solution.

a. $\frac{3}{a} = \frac{5}{a - 2}$ -3 **b.** $\frac{n}{5} = \frac{4}{n + 1}$ $-5, 4$

The process of cross multiplying or multiplying by the LCD may give an extraneous solution to an equation, or a solution that makes a denominator in the original equation equal zero. An extraneous solution solves a new equation but not the original one. So you must check your solutions.

5 EXAMPLE Checking to Find an Extraneous Solution

Solve $\frac{-2}{x - 2} = \frac{x - 4}{x^2 - 4}$.

$$\frac{-2}{x - 2} = \frac{x - 4}{x^2 - 4}$$

$-2(x^2 - 4) = (x - 2)(x - 4)$ Write cross products.

$-2x^2 + 8 = x^2 - 6x + 8$ Simplify each side of the equation.

$0 = 3x^2 - 6x$ Collect terms on one side.

$0 = 3x(x - 2)$ Factor.

$0 = 3x$ or $0 = x - 2$ Use the Zero-Product Property.

$x = 0$ $x = 2$ Solve.

Check $\frac{-2}{x - 2} = \frac{x - 4}{x^2 - 4}$

$\frac{-2}{0 - 2} \stackrel{?}{=} \frac{0 - 4}{0^2 - 4}$ $\frac{-2}{2 - 2} \stackrel{?}{=} \frac{2 - 4}{2^2 - 4}$

$\frac{-2}{-2} \stackrel{?}{=} \frac{-4}{-4}$ $\frac{-2}{0} = \frac{-2}{0}$ Undefined!

$1 = 1$ ✓

The equation has one solution, 0.

✓ **Check Understanding** **5** Solve each equation. Check your solutions.

a. $\frac{2}{c^2} = \frac{2}{c^2 + 1}$ no solution   **b.** $\frac{w^2}{w - 1} = \frac{1}{w - 1}$ -1

EXERCISES

Practice and Problem Solving

For more practice, see *Extra Practice*.

A **Practice by Example**

Examples 1, 2
(pages 672, 673)

Solve each equation. Check your solutions.

1. $\frac{1}{2} + \frac{2}{x} = \frac{1}{x}$ **−2**

2. $5 + \frac{2}{p} = \frac{17}{p}$ **3**

3. $\frac{3}{a} - \frac{5}{a} = 2$ **−1**

4. $y - \frac{6}{y} = 5$ **6, −1**

5. $\frac{5}{2s} + \frac{3}{4} = \frac{9}{4s}$ **$-\frac{1}{3}$**

6. $\frac{1}{t-2} = \frac{t}{8}$ **−2, 4**

7. $\frac{2}{c-2} = 2 - \frac{4}{c}$ **1, 4**

8. $\frac{5}{3p} + \frac{2}{3} = \frac{5+p}{2p}$ **5**

9. $\frac{8}{x+3} = \frac{1}{x} + 1$ **1, 3**

10. $\frac{\_+2}{\_} + \frac{4}{3} = 11$ **$\frac{1}{3}$**

11. $\frac{4}{3(c+4)} + 1 = \frac{2c}{c+4}$ **$\frac{16}{3}$**

12. $\frac{a}{a+4} = 3 - \frac{4}{a+4}$ **−4**

13. $\frac{z}{z+2} = 3 - \frac{2}{z+2}$ **−2**

14. $\frac{a}{a+3} = \frac{2a}{a-3} - 1$ **−1**

15. $\frac{z}{z+2} - \frac{1}{z} = 1$ **$-\frac{2}{3}$**

Example 3
(page 673)

16. **Gardening** Marian can weed a garden in 3 hours. Robin can weed the same garden in 4 hours. How long will the weeding take them if they work together? **$1\frac{5}{7}$ h**

17. David can unload a delivery truck in 20 min. Allie can unload a delivery truck in 35 min. How long will the unloading take them if they work together? **≈12.7 min**

Examples 4, 5
(page 674)

Solve each equation. Check your solutions. If there is no solution, write *no solution*.

18. $\frac{5}{x+1} = \frac{x+2}{x+1}$ **3**

19. $\frac{4}{c+4} = \frac{c}{c+25}$ **10, −10**

20. $\frac{3}{m-1} = \frac{2m}{m+4}$ **$-\frac{3}{2}$, 4**

21. $\frac{2x+4}{x-3} = \frac{3x}{x-3}$ **4**

22. $\frac{30}{x+3} = \frac{30}{x-3}$ **no solution**

23. $\frac{x+2}{x+4} = \frac{x-2}{x-1}$ **6**

B **Apply Your Skills**

Solve each equation. Check your solutions.

24. $\frac{2r}{r-4} - 2 = \frac{4}{r+5}$ **−14**

25. $6 - \frac{2}{b} = \frac{-5}{b-3}$ **$\frac{1}{2}$, 2**

26. $\frac{r+1}{r-1} = \frac{r}{3} + \frac{2}{r-1}$ **3**

27. $\frac{3}{s-1} + 1 = \frac{12}{s^2-1}$ **−5, 2**

28. $\frac{d}{d+2} - \frac{2}{2-d} = \frac{d+6}{d^2-4}$ **−1**

29. $\frac{u+1}{u} + \frac{1}{2u} = 4$ **$\frac{1}{2}$**

30. $\frac{s}{3s+2} + \frac{s+3}{2s-4} = \frac{-2s}{3s^2-4s-4}$ **$-\frac{6}{5}$, −1**

31. $\frac{u+1}{u+2} = \frac{-1}{u-3} + \frac{u-1}{u^2-u-6}$ **0, 2**

32. Two pipes fill a storage tank in 9 hours. The larger pipe fills the tank three times as fast as the smaller one. How long would it take the larger pipe to fill the tank alone? **12 h**

33. A teacher assigned the equation $\frac{40}{x} = \frac{15}{x-20}$. Carlos studied the equation and said, "I'll start by finding the LCD." Ingrid studied the equation and said, "I'll start by cross multiplying."

  a. Solve the equation using Carlos's method and then Ingrid's method. **32**

  b. **Writing** Which method do you prefer? Explain why. **b–c. See margin.**

  c. **Critical Thinking** Will Ingrid's method work for all rational equations? Explain.

34. Find the value of each variable. $\begin{bmatrix} \frac{5a}{3} & \frac{7}{3b} \\ 2c-15 & \frac{5}{2d} + \frac{3}{4} \\ \frac{}{35c} & \end{bmatrix} = \begin{bmatrix} 2 + \frac{7a}{6} & 9 \\ \frac{1}{5c} & \frac{9}{4d} \end{bmatrix}$ **$a = 4, b = \frac{7}{27}, c = 11, d = -\frac{1}{3}$**

35. **a.** Write two functions using the expressions on the two sides of the equation $\frac{6}{x^2} + 1 = \frac{(x+7)^2}{6}$. Graph the functions. **a–b. See margin.**

  b. Find the coordinates of the points of intersection.

  c. Are the *x*-values of the points of intersection solutions to the equation? Explain. **Yes; the x-values are solutions to the original equation since both sides are equal.**

Problem Solving Hint

For Exercise 32, making a table may help you organize the information in the question.

Assignment Guide

1 **Objective**

A **B** **Core** 1–17, 24–32, 35–39

C **Extension** 42–45

2 **Objective**

A **B** **Core** 18–23, 33–34, 40–41

C **Extension** 46–48

Standardized Test Prep 49–52

Mixed Review 53–67

Error Prevention

Exercises 24–31 Students may try to eliminate the denominator when simplifying. Remind students to be sure to apply the correct properties of equations.

Exercise 33 Ask students which equations from Exercises 1–15 can be solved using Ingrid's method and why. **Exercise 6; it is a rational proportion.**

Enrichment 12-7

Reteaching 12-7

Practice 12-7

---

pages 675–677   Exercises

33b. **Answers may vary. Sample: Cross-multiplying; I think it's quicker.**

c. **No; it only works for rational equations that**   are proportions.

35a.

Xmin=-12   Ymin=-4
Xmax=4   Ymax=12
Xsci=1   Yscal=1

$y_1 = \frac{6}{x^2} + 1,$

$y_2 = \frac{(x+7)^2}{6}$

b. **(−9.53, 1.07), (−4.16, 1.35), (−1.12, 5.76), (0.81, 10.16)**

675

Alternative Assessment

Divide the class into small groups. Tell the groups to write a quiz for the lesson that consists of three problems—one problem modeling each of Examples 1, 2, and 4. Then have each group exchange quizzes with another group and solve the problems, including checking the solutions.

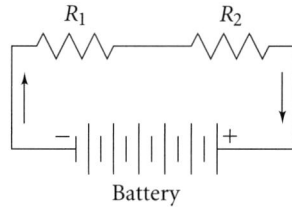

Circuit connected in series.

Circuit connected in parallel.

Real-World Connection

The resistance of a conductor is the opposition it gives to the flow of electrical current through it.

Electricity Lamps can be connected to a battery in a circuit in series or in parallel. You can calculate the total resistance R_T in a circuit if you know the resistance in each lamp. Resistance is measured in ohms (Ω).

Circuit Connected in Series

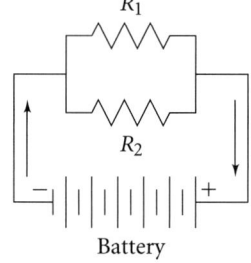

Battery

$$R_T = R_1 + R_2$$

Circuit Connected in Parallel

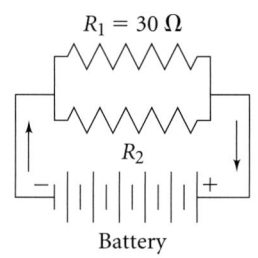

Battery

$$\frac{1}{R_T} = \frac{1}{R_1} + \frac{1}{R_2}$$

36. Find R_T. **$66.\overline{6}\ \Omega$**

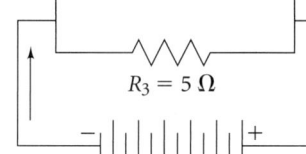

Battery

37. $R_T = 12\ \Omega$; find R_2. **$20\ \Omega$**

38. Find R_T. (*Hint:* The lamps in this circuit are connected in series *and* in parallel.) **$3.75\ \Omega$**

39. $R_T = 10\ \Omega$; find R_2. **$20\ \Omega$**

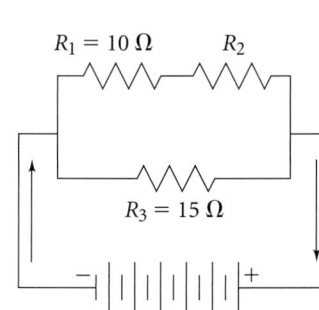

Battery

Battery

40. Answers may vary.
Sample: $\frac{2b}{b + 2} = \frac{6b}{4b + 3}$

40. Open-Ended Write a rational equation that has 3 as a solution. **See left.**

41. Travel A plane flies 450 mi/h. It can travel 980 miles with a wind in the same amount of time as it travels 820 mi against the wind. Solve the equation $\frac{980}{450 + s} = \frac{820}{450 - s}$ to find the speed s of the wind. **40 mi/h**

C Challenge

Solve each equation. Be sure to check your answers.

42. $\frac{x - 6}{x + 3} + \frac{2x}{x - 3} = \frac{4x + 3}{x + 3}$ **9**

43. $\frac{n}{n - 2} + \frac{n}{n + 2} = \frac{n}{n^2 - 4}$ **$0, \frac{1}{2}$**

44. $\frac{2}{r} + \frac{1}{r^2} + \frac{r^2 + r}{r^3} = \frac{1}{r}$ **−1**

45. $\frac{3}{t} - \frac{t^2 - 2t}{t^3} = \frac{4}{t^2}$ **1**

46. It takes Jon 75 min to paint a room. It takes Jeff 60 min and Jackie 80 min each to paint the same room. How long will the painting take if all three work together? **≈ 23.5 min**

Real-World 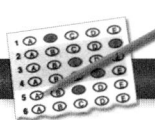 Connection

Many chemistry classes include a lab on testing acidity.

47. **Chemistry** A chemist has one solution that is 80% acid and a second solution that is 30% acid. The chemist needs to mix some of both solutions to make 50 liters of a solution that is 62% acid. Let s = the number of liters of the 80% solution used in the mixture. **0.80s**

   a. Write an expression for the amount of acid in s liters of the 80% solution.
   b. Write an expression for the number of liters of the 30% acid used in the mixture. **50 − s**

   c. Write an expression for the amount of acid in a 30% acid solution. **0.30(50 − s)**

   d. Write an equation that combines the amount of acid in each solution to make the total amount of acid in 50 liters of 62% acid solution. **0.8s + 0.3 (50 − s) = (0.62)(50)**

   e. Solve the equation you wrote in part (d). **32**

   f. How many liters of each solution will the chemist need to make 50 liters of 62% acid solution? **32 L of 80% solution and 18 L of 30% solution**

48. Sumi can wash the windows of an office building in $\frac{3}{4}$ the time it takes her apprentice. One day they worked on a building together for 2 h 16 min, and then Sumi continued alone. It took 4 h 32 min more to complete the job. How long would it take her apprentice to wash all the windows alone? **$11\frac{1}{3}$ h**

Standardized Test Prep

Multiple Choice

49. Which is a solution of $\frac{2}{n} + \frac{1}{2} = \frac{1}{n}$? **B**
   A. −4   B. −2   C. 2   D. 4

50. Which inequality contains both solutions of $x = \frac{1}{2} + \frac{3}{x}$? **G**
   F. $-1 < x < 3$ G. $-2 < x \le 2$ H. $-2 \le x < 0$ I. $-3 \le x \le -1$

51. What is the least common denominator of $\frac{1}{x}$, $\frac{x}{3}$, and $\frac{3}{2x}$? **C**
   A. $2x$ B. $3x$ C. $6x$ D. $6x^2$

Short Response

52. You are trying to find the number you would add to both the numerator and denominator of $\frac{3}{16}$ to make a fraction equal to $\frac{1}{2}$. Write a rational equation that can be used to find this number. Then solve the equation to find the number and check your solution. **See margin.**

Mixed Review

Lesson 12-6   **Add or subtract.**

54. $\frac{3h^2 + 2ht + 4h}{2(t-2)(t+2)}$

55. $\frac{-4k - 61}{(k-4)(k+10)}$

53. $\frac{5}{x^2 y^2 z} - \frac{8}{x^2 y^2 z} - \frac{3}{x^2 y^2 z}$ 54. $\frac{3h^2}{2t^2 - 8} + \frac{h}{t-2}$ 55. $\frac{k-11}{k^2 + 6k - 40} - \frac{5}{k-4}$

Lesson 11-6   **Graph each function either by translating the graph of $y = \sqrt{x}$ or by making a table of values.** 56–61. See margin.

56. $f(x) = -2\sqrt{x}$ 57. $y = \sqrt{x+7}$ 58. $f(x) = \sqrt{x-2} - 8$

59. $y = \sqrt{0.25x}$ 60. $y = \sqrt{2x} + 3$ 61. $y = \sqrt{4x-2} - 2$

62. −18, −5
63. 8, 11
64. −23, 1
65. −8, 6
66. −13, −4
67. −91, −1

Lesson 10-5   **Solve each equation by factoring.** 62–67. See left.

62. $x^2 + 23x + 90 = 0$ 63. $x^2 - 19x + 880 = 0$ 64. $x^2 + 22x - 230 = 0$

65. $x^2 + 2x - 48 = 0$ 66. $x^2 + 52 = -17x$ 67. $x^2 + 92x - 9 = -100$

pages 675–677 Exercises

52. [2] $\frac{3+x}{16+x} = \frac{1}{2};$

   $\frac{3+10}{16+10} \stackrel{?}{=} \frac{1}{2}$

   $\frac{13}{26} = \frac{1}{2}$ ✓

   $2(3 + x) = 16 + x$
   $6 + 2x = 16 + x$
   $x = 10$

   [1] appropriate method, but with one computational error

📁 **Resources**

For additional practice with a variety of test item formats:
• Standardized Test Prep, pp. 697–699
• Test-Taking Strategies, p. 692
• Test-Taking Strategies with Transparencies

Error Prevention

Exercise 49 Remind students to multiply each term by the LCD. Some students forget to multiply a constant by the LCD.

56.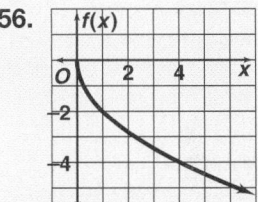

57.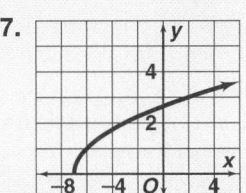

58.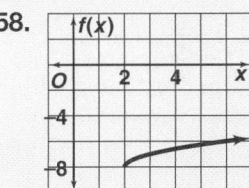

59.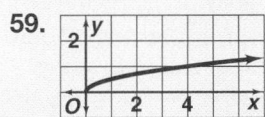

60.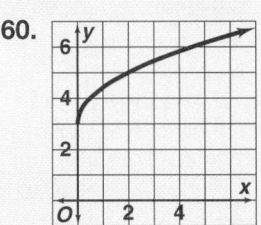

61.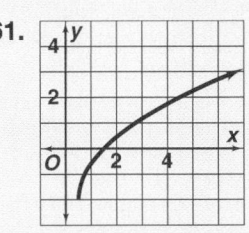

Reading an Example

This feature shows students that there is more than one way to read and think about a problem.

Teaching Notes

Students will become better problem solvers if they realize that there is not just one way to solve a problem. If students believe there is only one correct strategy for solving a problem and they forget that one way, they may feel that there is no point in trying to solve the problem. Students who are used to trying different strategies and who realize that there is more than one way are more likely to persevere.

Visual Learners

Visual learners may benefit from a third solution strategy for this problem. They could represent the car as a rectangle. Max will clean and polish $\frac{1}{60}$ of the car in a minute. This can be represented by a small rectangle within the larger one and labeled $\frac{1}{60}$. During the first minute his sister washed and waxed $\frac{1}{45}$ of the area. This too can be represented by a somewhat larger rectangle within the larger one. Together they washed $\frac{1}{60} + \frac{1}{45}$ or $\frac{7}{180}$ of the area in the first minute. To wash the full $\frac{180}{180}$ they may think: How many $\frac{7}{180}$ are there in $\frac{180}{180}$, or the whole car? This would lead to dividing $\frac{180}{180}$ by $\frac{7}{180}$, giving the same answer of $25\frac{5}{7}$ minutes as was obtained using the other two methods.

Exercises

After students have solved the problems, have them find partners who solved the problems in a different way. Have them explain to each other how they each solved the problem. Encourage them to question each other if they are not clear about something. Hearing another student's explanation may help them understand the solution method that they felt less comfortable using.

Example 3 shows one method for solving a work problem. Here is another way to solve the same problem.

Max can wash and wax a car in 60 min. His older sister Kayla can do the same job in 45 min. How long will the car take them if they work together?

You can use a formula, $rt = 1$, to solve this problem. In this formula,
t = the time (in minutes) it takes to complete a job and
r = the rate for doing the job (in job per minute).

Max can do the job in 60 min, so his rate is $\frac{1}{60}$ job per minute (job/min).

Kayla can do the job in 45 min, so her rate is $\frac{1}{45}$ job/min.

Their combined rate is $r = \left(\frac{1}{60} + \frac{1}{45}\right)$ job/min.

The following table contains all the information.

	Rate	Time	Work
Max	$\frac{1}{60}$	60	$\left(\frac{1}{60}\right)(60) = 1$
Kayla	$\frac{1}{45}$	45	$\left(\frac{1}{45}\right)(45) = 1$
Max and Kayla	$\frac{1}{60} + \frac{1}{45}$	t	$\left(\frac{1}{60} + \frac{1}{45}\right)t = 1$

Now you can solve the equation to find the time t the job will take Max and Kayla working together.

$$\left(\frac{1}{60} + \frac{1}{45}\right)t = 1 \qquad \text{Substitute.}$$

$$180\left(\frac{1}{60} + \frac{1}{45}\right)t = 180 \cdot 1 \qquad \text{Multiply each side by the LCD of 60 and 45, which is 180.}$$

$$(3 + 4)t = 180 \qquad \text{Use the Distributive Property.}$$

$$7t = 180 \qquad \text{Simplify within the parentheses.}$$

$$t = \frac{180}{7} \text{ or } 25\frac{5}{7} \qquad \text{Divide each side by 7.}$$

It will take Max and Kayla together about 26 minutes to wash and wax the car.

EXERCISES

Test your understanding by solving the problems below using either the method shown here or the one shown on page 673.

1. Dawn can clean the garage in 15 minutes. Phil can clean the garage in 10 minutes.
   a. Find the rate in terms of job/min for Dawn and for Phil. $\frac{1}{15}$; $\frac{1}{10}$
   b. What is their rate if they are working together? $\left(\frac{1}{15} + \frac{1}{10}\right)$
   c. How long will the job take them if they work together? **6 min**

2. Working together, Maureen and Nan can prepare and paint a room in 6 hours. Working alone, Maureen can prepare and paint the room in 10 hours. How long will it take Nan to prepare and paint the room when she works alone? **15 h**

12-8 Counting Methods and Permutations

Lesson Preview

What You'll Learn

 OBJECTIVE 1 To use the multiplication counting principle

 OBJECTIVE 2 To find permutations

. . . And Why

To find the number of possible six-letter passwords, as in Example 5

 Check Skills You'll Need (For help, go to Lessons 4-5 and 4-6.)

You roll a number cube. Find each probability.

1. P(even number) $\frac{1}{2}$
2. P(prime number) $\frac{1}{2}$
3. P(a number greater than 5) $\frac{1}{6}$
4. P(a negative number) 0

You roll a blue number cube and a yellow number cube. Find each probability.

5. P(blue 1 and yellow 2) $\frac{1}{36}$
6. P(blue even and yellow odd) $\frac{1}{4}$

New Vocabulary • Multiplication Counting Principle • permutation

---

Lesson Preview

 **Check Skills You'll Need**

Applying Ratios to Probability
Lesson 4-5: Example 1
Exercises 1–9
Extra Practice, p. 705

Probability of Compound Events
Lesson 4-6: Examples 1–3
Exercises 1–8, 15–20
Extra Practice, p. 705

Lesson Resources

Teaching Resources
Practice, Reteaching, Enrichment
Checkpoint Quiz 2

Reaching All Students
Practice Workbook 12-8
Spanish Practice Workbook 12-8
Reading and Math Literacy 12C
Spanish Reading & Literacy 12C
Spanish Checkpoint Quiz 2
Hands-On Activities 30
Basic Algebra Planning Guide 12-8

Presentation Assistant Plus!
Transparencies
• Check Skills You'll Need 12-8
• Additional Examples 12-8
• Student Edition Answers 12-8
• Lesson Quiz 12-8
PH Presentation Pro CD 12-8

ASSESSMENT SYSTEM

Checkpoint Quiz 2
Computer Test Generator CD

Technology
Resource Pro® CD-ROM
Computer Test Generator CD
Prentice Hall Presentation Pro CD

 www.PHSchool.com
Student Site
• Teacher Web Code: aek-5500
• Graphing Calculator, Procedure 16
• Self-grading Lesson Quiz
Teacher Center
• Lesson Planner
• Resources

Plus

OBJECTIVE 1 Using the Multiplication Counting Principle

Interactive lesson includes instant self-check, tutorials, and activities.

Investigation: Determining Order

Suppose you have to read the following works over the summer for English class next year.

1. In how many different orders can you read the books? **6**

2. Describe how you determined the number of different ways you could order the books. **See left.**

3. Suppose you choose one of the orders at random. What is the probability that you will read the books in alphabetical order by title? By author? $\frac{1}{6}$; $\frac{1}{6}$

2. Answers may vary. Sample: You can make a list of all the possibilities.

You can find the possible orders of objects by making an organized list. Another way is to make a tree diagram. Both methods help you see if you have thought of all of the possibilities.

Lesson 12-8 Counting Methods and Permutations **679**

Ongoing Assessment and Intervention

Before the Lesson
Diagnose prerequisite skills using:
• Check Skills You'll Need

During the Lesson
Monitor progress using:
• Check Understanding
• Additional Examples
• Standardized Test Prep

After the Lesson
Assess knowledge using:
• Lesson Quiz
• Computer Test Generator CD
• Chapter Checkpoint 2 (p. 685)

2. Teach

Math Background

A permutation is any possible arrangement, or ordering, of the distinct items in a set. The Multiplication Counting Principle is also called the fundamental principle of counting.

OBJECTIVE

1 Teaching Notes

Investigation (Optional)
Connection to Language Arts
Point out to students that books in alphabetical order by title do not include first words such as *the* and *a;* books in alphabetical order by author are arranged by the author's last name.

1 EXAMPLE Alternative Method
Another way to represent the possible outfits is to use a table to organize the information.

	Shirt 1	Shirt 2	Shirt 3
Pants 1	s1, p1	s2, p1	s3, p1
Pants 2	s1, p2	s2, p2	s3, p2

Additional Examples

1 Suppose you have three shirts and three ties that coordinate well. Make a tree diagram to find the number of shirt/tie choices you have. **9**

```
Shirts        Ties         Outfits
                 Tie 1 → Shirt 1, Tie 1
Shirt 1          Tie 2 → Shirt 1, Tie 2
                 Tie 3 → Shirt 1, Tie 3
                 Tie 1 → Shirt 2, Tie 1
Shirt 2          Tie 2 → Shirt 2, Tie 2
                 Tie 3 → Shirt 2, Tie 3
                 Tie 1 → Shirt 3, Tie 1
Shirt 3          Tie 2 → Shirt 3, Tie 2
                 Tie 3 → Shirt 3, Tie 3
```

2 Suppose there are two routes you can drive to get from Austin, Texas to Dallas, Texas, and four routes from Dallas, Texas to Tulsa, Oklahoma. How many possible routes are there from Austin to Tulsa through Dallas? **8 routes**

680

---

1 EXAMPLE Using a Tree Diagram

Suppose you have three shirts and two pair of pants that coordinate well. Make a tree diagram to find the number of possible outfits you have.

Shirts	Pants	Outfits
Shirt 1	Pants 1	Shirt 1, Pants 1
	Pants 2	Shirt 1, Pants 2
Shirt 2	Pants 1	Shirt 2, Pants 1
	Pants 2	Shirt 2, Pants 2
Shirt 3	Pants 1	Shirt 3, Pants 1
	Pants 2	Shirt 3, Pants 2

● There are six possible outfits.

a. See margin.

✓ **Check Understanding** **1 a.** Suppose you have two T-shirts and four pairs of shorts you could bring for gym class. Make a tree diagram to find the number of possible outfits for gym.

b. Critical Thinking Would you want to use a tree diagram to find the number of outfits for five T-shirts and eight pairs of shorts? Explain.
Answers may vary. Sample: No, because it would take a lot of room to make such a diagram.

Recall that when one event does not affect the result of a second event, the events are *independent*. When events are independent, you can find the number of outcomes using the Multiplication Counting Principle.

Key Concepts

Rule	Multiplication Counting Principle

If there are *m* ways to make a first selection and *n* ways to make a second selection, there are $m \times n$ ways to make the two selections.

Example For five shirts and eight pairs of shorts, the number of possible outfits is $5 \cdot 8 = 40$.

2 EXAMPLE Using the Multiplication Counting Principle

Travel On the map there are two tunnels for cars going from New Jersey to Manhattan, New York, and three bridges from Manhattan to Brooklyn, New York. How many routes using a tunnel and then a bridge are there from New Jersey to Brooklyn through Manhattan?

$2 \cdot 3 = 6$ ← **routes from New Jersey to Brooklyn through Manhattan**

routes by tunnel, from New Jersey to Manhattan   **routes by bridge, from Manhattan to Brooklyn**

● There are six possible routes from New Jersey to Brooklyn.

✓ **Check Understanding** **2 Pizza** At the neighborhood pizza shop, there are five vegetable toppings and three meat toppings for a pizza. How many different pizzas can you order with one meat and one vegetable topping? **15 pizzas**

Reaching All Students

Below Level Have students reread Examples 2 and 5. Point out words or phrases that signal whether to use the Multiplication Counting Principle or permutations.	**Advanced Learners** Have students calculate the number of possible ways the top 3 runners can finish in a race with 8 competitors. **336**	**English Learners** See note on page 681. **Inclusion** See note on page 681.

One kind of counting problem is to find the number of possible arrangements of the objects in a set. Here are the possible arrangements for the letters A, B, and C without repeating any letters.

ABC   BAC   CAB   ACB   BCA   CBA

Each of the arrangements is a permutation. A **permutation** is an arrangement of objects in a specific order.

Reading Math

A short way to write the product in Example 3 is 9!, read "nine factorial." For positive integers, factorial means the product of integers from the given number to 1.

3 EXAMPLE **Counting Permutations**

Baseball How many different batting orders can you have with 9 baseball players?

There are 9 choices for the first batter, 8 for the second, 7 for the third, and so on.

$9 \cdot 8 \cdot 7 \cdot 6 \cdot 5 \cdot 4 \cdot 3 \cdot 2 \cdot 1 = 362,880$ **Use a calculator.**

There are 362,880 possible batting orders.

✓ **Check Understanding** **3 Swimming** A swimming pool has eight lanes. In how many ways can eight swimmers be assigned lanes for a race? **40,320 ways**

In how many ways can you select a right, center, and left fielder from eight players on a baseball team? To answer this question, you need to find the number of permutations of 8 objects (players) arranged 3 at a time.

Key Concepts

Definition	Permutation Notation

The expression $_nP_r$ represents the number of permutations of n objects arranged r at a time.

n will be the first factor.

$$_nP_r = n(n-1)(n-2) \ldots$$

Stop when you have *r* factors.

Example $_8P_3$ represents 8 objects (players) chosen 3 at a time, or $8 \cdot 7 \cdot 6 = 336$.

4 EXAMPLE **Using Permutation Notation**

Simplify $_7P_4$.

Method 1 Use pencil and paper.

$_7P_4 = 7 \cdot 6 \cdot 5 \cdot 4$ **The first factor is 7, and there are 4 factors.**
$= 840$ **Simplify.**

Method 2 Use a graphing calculator. Use MATH to select nPr in the PRB screen.

$_7P_4 = 840$

7 nPr 4	
	840

Take It to the NET
Graphing Calculator procedures online at **www.PHSchool.com**
Web Code: aee-2116

✓ **Check Understanding** **4** Simplify each expression.

a. $_9P_3$
504

b. $_7P_3$
210

c. $_5P_2$
20

page 680 Check Understanding

1a. Shirt 1 → Shorts 1 → Shirt 1, Shorts 1
→ Shorts 2 → Shirt 1, Shorts 2
→ Shorts 3 → Shirt 1, Shorts 3
→ Shorts 4 → Shirt 1, Shorts 4

Shirt 2 → Shorts 1 → Shirt 2, Shorts 1
→ Shorts 2 → Shirt 2, Shorts 2
→ Shorts 3 → Shirt 2, Shorts 3
→ Shorts 4 → Shirt 2, Shorts 4

There are eight possible outfits.

3 EXAMPLE Inclusion

This problem provides an opportunity for students with short attention spans to participate in class. Have 9 students come to the front of the class and model the problem. Ask: *How many choices are there for the first position?* 9 Have one student sit down. Now ask: *How many choices are there for the second position?* 8 Continue through the remaining seven students.

5 EXAMPLE English Learners

Make sure students are counting the letters in the English alphabet. Give them a copy of the alphabet if they do not remember it.

Additional Examples

3 In how many orders can 11 students enter a classroom one at a time? **39,916,800 orders**

4 Simplify $_8P_5$. **6720**

5 Suppose you use five different letters from the 26 letters of the alphabet to make a password. Find the number of possible five-letter passwords if letters cannot repeat. **7,893,600 passwords**

Closure

Ask: *How can you use the Multiplication Counting Principle to find the number of possible outcomes? How do you use a tree diagram?*
The Multiplication Counting Principle is used to find the number of outcomes by multiplying the choices. The counting principle gives the number of outcomes but does not list what the specific outcomes are. A tree diagram is a way to make an organized list to show all possible outcomes. It would not be useful for a large number of branches.

Assignment Guide

1 Objective
- **A** **B** Core 1–4, 27
- **C** Extension 32

2 Objective
- **A** **B** Core 5–26, 28–31
- **C** Extension 33–35

Standardized Test Prep 36–39

Mixed Review 40–55

Error Prevention

Exercises 3–6 Students may add rather than multiply when applying the counting principle. Suggest to them that they use a tree diagram or table to help them see all of the choices.

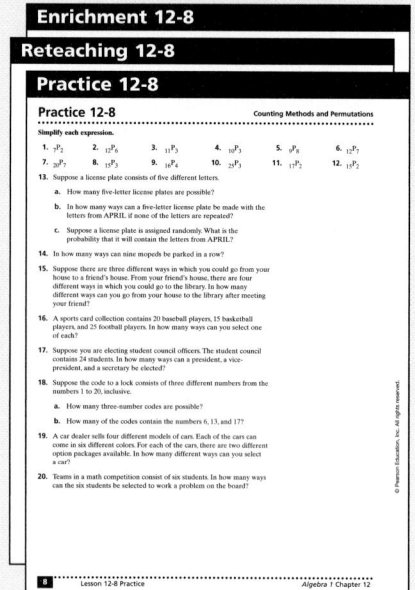

In some situations, order matters, but repetition is allowed. In that case, use the Multiplication Counting Principle. However, when repetition is not allowed, use permutations to find the number of arrangements.

5 EXAMPLE Real-World Problem Solving

Computers Suppose you use six different letters to make a computer password. Find the number of possible six-letter passwords.

There are 26 letters in the alphabet. You are finding the number of permutations of 26 letters arranged 6 at a time.

$$_{26}P_6 = 26 \cdot 25 \cdot 24 \cdot 23 \cdot 22 \cdot 21 \qquad \textbf{Use a calculator.}$$
$$= 165{,}765{,}600$$

● There are 165,765,600 six-letter passwords in which letters do not repeat.

Real-World  **Connection**

Using 100,000 encryption operations per second, a 6-letter password can be cracked in about 50 min.

✔ **Check Understanding**

5 a. Suppose your cousin needs to choose a four-digit number to use with a new debit card. Find the number of possible four-digit numbers without repeating a digit. **5040**

b. Critical Thinking Is a six-letter password or a six-digit number harder for someone to guess? Explain.
A six-letter password; there are more possible passwords, since 26 > 10.

EXERCISES

For more practice, see *Extra Practice*.

Practice and Problem Solving

A **Practice by Example**

Example 1
(page 680)

1. **Job Interview** James must wear a shirt and tie for a job interview. He has two dress shirts and five ties. Use a tree diagram to find the number of shirt-tie choices he has. **See margin.**

2. **Catering** Suppose your grandparents are planning an anniversary party. The caterer offers the following choices for a menu. Guests can have either spinach salad or chef's salad, and either vegetable soup or chicken soup. The main course is chicken, beef, or salmon. Use a tree diagram to find the number of possible menus. **See margin.**

Example 2
(page 680)

3. **Telephones** A seven-digit telephone number can begin with any digit except 0 or 1.
   a. How many possible choices are there for the first digit? The second digit? The third digit? The seventh digit? **8, 10, 10, 10**
   b. How many different seven-digit telephone numbers are possible?
   8,000,000 telephone numbers

4. Use the diagram and the Multiplication Counting Principle to find each of the following:
   a. the number of routes from A to C **6**
   b. the number of routes from A to D **12**

   A ⇄ B → C ⇄ D

Example 3
(page 681)

5. **Sports** In ice-skating competitions, the order in which competitors skate is determined by a drawing. Suppose there are ten skaters in the finals. How many different orders are possible for the final program? **3,628,800 orders**

6. Suppose you are lining up with four cousins for a photo. How many different arrangements are possible? **120 arrangements**

Example 4
(page 681)

Simplify each expression.

7. $_8P_4$ **1680**   8. $_9P_4$ **3024**   9. $_6P_4$ **360**   10. $_5P_4$ **120**

11. $_7P_7$ **5040**   12. $_7P_6$ **5040**   13. $_7P_5$ **2520**   14. $_7P_2$ **42**

Example 5
(page 682)

15. On a bookshelf there are ten books: five novels, two volumes of short stories, and three biographies. In how many ways can you select four books to read in order? **5040**

16. A student council has 24 members. A 3-person committee must arrange a car wash. Each person on the committee will have a task: one person will find a location, another person will organize publicity, and the third person will schedule workers. In how many different ways can three students be chosen and given a job? **12,144**

B Apply Your Skills

Which is greater?

17. $_8P_6$ or $_6P_2$ $_8\mathbf{P_6}$ 18. $_9P_7$ or $_9P_2$ $_9\mathbf{P_7}$ 19. $_{10}P_3$ or $_8P_4$ $_8\mathbf{P_4}$

Use the tiles at the left for Exercises 20 and 21.

20. a. How many vowels are there? How many consonants are there? **2; 2**
   b. In how many ways can you choose at random a vowel and then a consonant? **4**
   c. **Critical Thinking** Would your answer to part (b) be different if you chose a consonant first and then a vowel? Explain. **See margin.**

21. a. What is the number of possible arrangements in which you can select three letters? **24**
   b. Find the probability that you select C, A, and then R. $\frac{1}{24}$

22b. $\frac{1}{14,950}$

c. **Answers may vary. Sample: No; if someone tries to guess your password, they'll probably try your name or initials first.**

22. a. Lena wants a password that uses the four letters of her name. How many permutations are possible using each letter only once? **24**
   b. A four-letter password with no repeated letters is assigned randomly from the alphabet. What is the probability that it uses the letters L, E, N, and A?
   c. **Writing** Is creating a password based on your name a good idea? Explain your reasoning. **b–c. See left.**

Simplify each expression.

23. $\frac{_5P_3}{_5P_2}$ **3**   24. $\frac{_4P_3}{_4P_2}$ **2**   25. $\frac{_7P_3}{_7P_2}$ **5**

26b. **Without repetition; there are more permutations when repetition is allowed.**

26. a. Suppose your cousin needs to choose a four-digit number to use with a new debit card, and repetition is allowed. Find the number of possible four-digit numbers with repetition. **10,000**
   b. **Critical Thinking** Is it easier to guess a password with or without repetition? Explain. **See left.**

27. **License Plates** In Indiana, a regular license plate has two numbers that are fixed by county, then one letter, and then four numbers. **260,000 license plates**
   a. How many different license plates are possible in each county?
   b. There are 92 counties in Indiana. How many license plates are possible in the entire state? **23,920,000 license plates**

28. a. **Open-Ended** Use the letters of your last name. If any letters are repeated, use only one of them. For example, for the last name Bell, use the letters B, E, and L. In how many ways can the resulting letters be arranged?
   b. In how many ways can two different letters be selected and arranged from your last name? **a–b. Check students' work.**

Exercise 22 Point out that the letters can be arranged in any order.

Exercise 28b Make sure students understand the number of letters selected is the value of r in permutation notation.

pages 682–685   Exercises

1. **10 choices**
   Shirt 1 → Tie 1 → S1, T1
       → Tie 2 → S1, T2
       → Tie 3 → S1, T3
       → Tie 4 → S1, T4
       → Tie 5 → S1, T5
   Shirt 2 → Tie 1 → S2, T1
       → Tie 2 → S2, T2
       → Tie 3 → S2, T3
       → Tie 4 → S2, T4
       → Tie 5 → S2, T5

2. **12 menus**

Salad	Soup	Main Course	Menu
		C →	SVC
	V →	B →	SVB
S →		S →	SVS
		C →	SCC
	C →	B →	SCB
		S →	SCS
		C →	CVC
	V →	B →	CVB
C →		S →	CVS
		C →	CCC
	C →	B →	CCB
		S →	CCS

20c. **No; number of consonants · number of vowels = number of vowels · number of consonants.**

Lesson Quiz 12-8

Lesson Quiz 12-8

1. Jeff has five shirts, three pairs of pants, and two ties. How many possible outfits can he make? **30 outfits**

2. 3 of 18 students are to be selected for the student government positions of president, vice-president, and treasurer. In how many different ways can the three positions be filled? **4896 ways**

3. Calculate $_6P_3$. **120**

4. An Italian restaurant offers four different choices of pasta, three choices of sauce, and two choices of meat. How many different dishes can you order that each consist of one pasta choice, one sauce, and one meat? **24**

Alternative Assessment

Group students in pairs. Have one student make up a problem that can best be solved by using the counting principle and one student make up a problem that can best be solved by using a tree diagram. Have students exchange problems and solve.

Standardized Test Prep

A sheet of blank grids is available with the Test-Taking Strategies booklet. Give this sheet to students for practice with filling in the grids.

 **Resources**

For additional practice with a variety of test item formats:
- Standardized Test Prep, pp. 697–699
- Test-Taking Strategies, p. 692
- Test-Taking Strategies with Transparencies.

Exercise 36 Have students make an organized list if they are having trouble determining the number of different lunches.

---

 29. Travel The International Airline Transportation Association (IATA) assigns three-letter codes to each airport. For example, LAX is the code for the Los Angeles International Airport. Letters can be repeated within a code.
   a. How many possible codes are there? **17,576 codes**
   b. Of the possible codes, the IATA has kept 50 codes for internal purposes. How many codes are available for airports? **17,526 codes**

 30. Radio Stations The call letters of radio and television stations in the United States generally begin with the letter W east of the Mississippi River and the letter K west of the Mississippi. Repetition of letters is allowed.
   a. How many different call letters are possible if each station uses a W or K followed by three letters? **35,152 call letters**
   b. How many different call letters are possible if each station uses a W or K followed by four letters? **913,952 call letters**

Real-World  Connection

NASDAQ (NAZ dak) started as an acronym for National Association of Securities Dealers Automated Quotations. Today its volume of trade is larger than the New York Stock Exchange.

31. Stock Exchange The companies listed on the New York Stock Exchange have a one- to three-letter ticker symbol. The companies listed on the NASDAQ exchange have a four- or five-letter symbol. Letters can be repeated in a ticker symbol. **a.18,278 companies   b.12,338,352 companies**
   a. How many companies can be listed on the New York Stock Exchange?
   b. How many companies can be listed on the NASDAQ Exchange?
   c. Which stock exchange can list more companies, and how many more?
      NASDAQ; 12,320,074 more companies

C **Challenge**

32. You know there are 3!, or 6, arrangements of 3 objects. Consider the number of clockwise arrangements of objects placed in a loop, without a beginning or end.

   A   ABC, BCA, and CAB are all part of the same clockwise
   C ← B loop arrangement.

   a. Find the number of clockwise loop arrangements of the ABC. **2**
   b. Use the diagram at the right to help find the number of loop arrangements of ABCD. **6**
   c. Write an expression for the number of clockwise loop arrangements for n objects. **$(n-1)!$**

   A → B
   D ← C

33. Reasoning Suppose $_nP_r = 210$ and $r = 3$. What is the value of n? **7**

34. A three-digit number is formed by randomly selecting from the digits $1, 2, 3, 4,$ and 5 without replacement.
   a. How many different three-digit numbers can be formed? **60 numbers**
   b. How many different numbers with three odd digits can be formed? **6 numbers**
   c. Find the probability that the number formed has three odd digits. $\frac{1}{10}$
   d. Find the probability that the number formed has at least one even digit. $\frac{9}{10}$

35. Critical Thinking Assume a and b are positive integers. Is the statement $(a - b)! = a! - b!$ true or false? If it is true, explain why. If it is false, give a counterexample.
   False; if $a = 3$ and $b = 2$, then $(a - b)! = 1! = 1$, but $a! - b! = 3! - 2! = 4$.

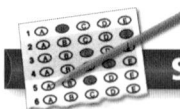

Standardized Test Prep

Gridded Response

36. The school cafeteria has lunches of one entrée, one vegetable, one salad, and one dessert. The menu has choices of two entrées, 3 vegetables, 3 salads, and 4 desserts. How many different lunches are there? **72**

37. You are planning your schedule for next year. You already know your classes for the last three periods. There are four choices for period 1, two choices for period 2, and 2 choices for period 3. How many combinations are there for the first three periods? **16**

38. Southside High School T-shirts come in two styles, three colors, and four sizes. A student wants to buy a large or extra large black T-shirt. How many choices does the student have? **4**

39. Simplify $_4P_3$. **24**

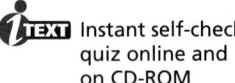
Take It to the NET
Online lesson quiz at **www.PHSchool.com**
Web Code: aea-1208

Chapter Checkpoint 2

To check understanding of Lessons 12-4 to 12-8:

Checkpoint Quiz 2 (p. 685)

Teaching Resources
Checkpoint Quiz 2 (also in Prentice Hall Assessment System)

Reaching All Students
Reading and Math Literacy 12C

Spanish versions available

Mixed Review

Lesson 12-7   **Solve each equation. Check your solution.**

40. $\frac{1}{x} + \frac{1}{2x} = 5 \quad \frac{3}{10}$

41. $\frac{2}{n} + \frac{1}{n+1} = \frac{11}{n^2+n}$ **3**

42. $\frac{m}{2} = \frac{24-m}{m}$ **−8, 6**

43. $\frac{10}{3v+6} = \frac{3v}{v+2} + \frac{v^2}{3v+6}$ **−10, 1**

44. $\frac{3w}{w-1} - \frac{2w}{w+3} = \frac{8w+40}{w^2+2w-3}$ **−8, 5**   **45.** $\frac{h-5}{h+4} + \frac{h+1}{h+3} = \frac{-6h-6}{h^2+7h+12}$ **$\frac{1}{2}$, −5**

Lesson 11-7   **Suppose △ABC has right angle C. Find the lengths of the other sides to the nearest whole number.**

46. $m\angle A = 45°, BC = 5$ **AB ≈ 7, AC = 5**

47. $m\angle A = 32°, AB = 64$ **BC ≈ 34, AC ≈ 54**

48. $m\angle B = 75°, AC = 20$
AB ≈ 21, BC ≈ 5

49. $m\angle B = 8°, BC = 48$
AB ≈ 48, AC ≈ 7

Lesson 10-6   **Solve by completing the square. If there is no real solution, write *no solution*.**

50. $x^2 + 12x + 1 = 0$ **$-6 \pm \sqrt{35}$**

51. $x^2 + 6x + 20 = 0$ **no solution**

52. $x^2 + 8x = 11$ **$-4 \pm 3\sqrt{3}$**

53. $x^2 + 7x + 1 = 13$ **$-\frac{7}{2} \pm \frac{\sqrt{97}}{2}$**

54. $2x^2 + 8x + 7 = 9$ **$-2 \pm \sqrt{5}$**

55. $x^2 - 18x + 65 = 0$ **5, 13**

Checkpoint Quiz 2   Lessons 12-4 through 12-8

Instant self-check quiz online and on CD-ROM

Find each product or quotient.

1. $\frac{x^2-4}{x+3} \cdot \frac{x^2+7x+12}{x-2}$
$(x+2)(x+4)$

2. $\frac{z+5}{z} \div \frac{3z+15}{4z}$ **$\frac{4}{3}$**

3. $\frac{a^3+2a^2-1}{a-3}$
$a^2 + 5a + 15 + \frac{44}{a-3}$

Find each sum or difference.

4. $\frac{9}{x-3} - \frac{4}{x-3}$ **$\frac{5}{x-3}$**

5. $\frac{8}{m+2} - \frac{6}{3-m}$
$\frac{14m-12}{(m+2)(m-3)}$

6. $\frac{6}{t} + \frac{3}{t^2}$ **$\frac{6t+3}{t^2}$**

Solve each equation.

7. $\frac{9}{t} + \frac{3}{2} = 12$ **$\frac{6}{7}$**

8. $\frac{10}{z+4} = \frac{30}{2z+3}$ **−9**

9. $c - \frac{8}{c} = -7$ **−8, 1**

10. Hiking Suppose there are four different trails up a mountain.
  a. In how many ways can someone climb up and down the mountain? **16**
  b. In how many ways can someone climb up and down the mountain if that person does not want to take the same trail in both directions? **12**

Lesson Preview

✓ **Check Skills You'll Need**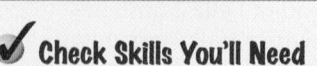

Counting Methods and Permutations
Lesson 12-8: Example 4
Exercises 7–14
Extra Practice, p. 713

Probability of Compound Events
Lesson 4-6: Examples 1, 2
Exercises 1–14
Extra Practice, p. 705

Lesson Resources

📁 **Teaching Resources**
Practice, Reteaching, Enrichment

👥 **Reaching All Students**
Practice Workbook 12-9
Spanish Practice Workbook 12-9
Basic Algebra Planning Guide 12-9

⏱ **Presentation Assistant Plus!**
Transparencies
• Check Skills You'll Need 12-9
• Additional Examples 12-9
• Student Edition Answers 12-9
• Lesson Quiz 12-9
PH Presentation Pro CD 12-9

ASSESSMENT SYSTEM

Computer Test Generator CD

💿 **Technology**
Resource Pro® CD-ROM
Computer Test Generator CD
Prentice Hall Presentation Pro CD

💻 **www.PHSchool.com**
Student Site
• Teacher Web Code: aek-5500
• Self-grading Lesson Quiz
Teacher Center
• Lesson Planner
• Resources

Plus

Combinations

Lesson Preview

What You'll Learn

 OBJECTIVE 1
To find combinations

 OBJECTIVE 2
To find probability with counting techniques

. . . And Why

To find the number of different possible 12-person juries, as in Example 2

✓ **Check Skills You'll Need** (For help, go to Lessons 12-8 and 4-6.)

Evaluate each expression.

1. $_5P_3$ **60**   **2.** $_6P_3$ **120**   **3.** $_7P_3$ **210**   **4.** $_7P_4$ **840**

***A* and *B* are independent events. Find *P*(*A* and *B*) for the given probabilities.**

5. $P(A) = \frac{1}{3}, P(B) = \frac{3}{4}$ $\frac{1}{4}$ **6.** $P(A) = \frac{1}{8}, P(B) = \frac{5}{9}$ $\frac{5}{72}$

7. $P(A) = \frac{9}{10}, P(B) = \frac{5}{6}$ $\frac{3}{4}$ **8.** $P(A) = 0.35, P(B) = 0.2$ **0.07**

New Vocabulary   • combination

OBJECTIVE

▼ 1 Combinations

 **Interactive lesson includes instant self-check, tutorials, and activities.**

Suppose you are making a sandwich with three of these ingredients: turkey, cheese, tomato, and lettuce. Below are the permutations of the four ingredients chosen three at a time.

turkey cheese **tomato**
turkey **tomato** cheese
cheese **tomato** turkey
cheese turkey **tomato**
tomato turkey cheese
tomato cheese turkey

turkey cheese **lettuce**
turkey **lettuce** cheese
cheese **lettuce** turkey
cheese turkey **lettuce**
lettuce turkey cheese
lettuce cheese turkey

turkey **tomato** lettuce
turkey lettuce **tomato**
tomato lettuce turkey
tomato turkey lettuce
lettuce turkey **tomato**
lettuce **tomato** turkey

cheese **tomato** lettuce
cheese lettuce **tomato**
tomato lettuce cheese
tomato cheese lettuce
lettuce cheese **tomato**
lettuce **tomato** cheese

For most people, the *order* of the ingredients within the sandwich does not matter. Ignoring order, there are only four different sandwiches. Each sandwich type is a **combination,** a collection of objects without regard to order.

Every combination of three ingredients has $_3P_3$ or 6 permutations, which are considered the same. Dividing the total number of permutations, $_4P_3$ or 24, by 6 gives the number of different sandwiches without regard to order.

number of different sandwiches =

$$= \frac{\text{number of permutations of ingredients } (_4P_3)}{\text{number of permutations of ingredients in one sandwich } (_3P_3)}$$

$$= \frac{4 \cdot 3 \cdot 2}{3 \cdot 2 \cdot 1}$$

$$= 4$$

 Ongoing Assessment and Intervention

Before the Lesson
Diagnose prerequisite skills using:
• Check Skills You'll Need

During the Lesson
Monitor progress using:
• Check Understanding
• Additional Examples
• Standardized Test Prep

After the Lesson
Assess knowledge using:
• Lesson Quiz
• Computer Test Generator CD

Key Concepts

Definition	Combination Notation

The expression $_nC_r$ represents the number of combinations of n objects arranged r at a time.

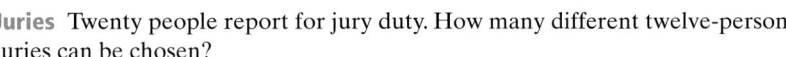

$$_nC_r = \frac{_nP_r}{_rP_r} = \frac{n(n-1)(n-2)\ldots}{r(r-1)(r-2)\ldots} \quad \begin{array}{l} \leftarrow r \text{ factors, starting with } n \\ \leftarrow r \text{ factors, starting with } r \end{array}$$

Example $_4C_3 = \frac{_4P_3}{_3P_3} = \frac{4 \cdot 3 \cdot 2}{3 \cdot 2 \cdot 1} = 4$

1 EXAMPLE **Counting Combinations**

Simplify $_8C_5$.

$_8C_5 = \frac{_8P_5}{_5P_5}$ **Write using permutation notation.**

$= \frac{8 \cdot 7 \cdot 6 \cdot 5 \cdot 4}{5 \cdot 4 \cdot 3 \cdot 2 \cdot 1}$ **Write the product represented by the notation.**

$= 56$ **Simplify.**

✓ **Check Understanding** **1** Simplify each expression.

   a. $_4C_2$ **6**   **b.** $_7C_3$ **35**   **c.** $_{10}C_4$ **210**

You can use combinations to model real-world situations.

2 EXAMPLE **Real-World 🌐 Problem Solving**

Juries Twenty people report for jury duty. How many different twelve-person juries can be chosen?

The order in which jury members are listed once the jury members are chosen does not distinguish one jury from another. You need the number of combinations of 20 potential jurors chosen 12 at a time. Evaluate $_{20}C_{12}$.

Method 1 Use pencil and paper.

$_{20}C_{12} = \frac{_{20}P_{12}}{_{12}P_{12}}$

$= \frac{20 \cdot 19 \cdot 18 \cdot 17 \cdot 16 \cdot 15 \cdot 14 \cdot 13 \cdot 12 \cdot 11 \cdot 10 \cdot 9}{12 \cdot 11 \cdot 10 \cdot 9 \cdot 8 \cdot 7 \cdot 6 \cdot 5 \cdot 4 \cdot 3 \cdot 2 \cdot 1}$

$= 125{,}970$ **Use a calculator.**

Method 2 Use a graphing calculator.
Use MATH to select nCr in the PRB screen.
$_{20}C_{12} = 125{,}970$

20 nCr 12
125970

Real-World 🌐 Connection

Most civil and criminal cases in the United States are tried by a judge with a jury of 12 people.

There are 125,970 different twelve-person juries that can be chosen from a group of 20 people.

✓ **Check Understanding** **2 a.** For your history report, you can choose to write about two of a list of five presidents of the United States. Use $_nC_r$ notation to write the number of combinations possible for your report. $_5C_2$

    b. Calculate the number of combinations of presidents on whom you could report. **10**

    c. Critical Thinking Explain why you should model this situation with combinations, not permutations. **Order does not matter.**

👥 Reaching All Students

Below Level In Example 4, remind students that $\frac{_6C_3}{_{10}C_3} = \frac{\frac{_6P_3}{_3P_3}}{\frac{_{10}P_3}{_3P_3}}$. $\frac{_6C_3}{_{10}C_3} = \frac{_6P_3}{_{10}P_3}$.	Advanced Learners Discuss with students how the permutation notation might change if all the objects considered were identical.	Tactile Learners See note on page 687. **Error Prevention** See note on page 689.

2. Teach

Professional Development

Math Background

The branch of mathematics devoted to the study of permutations and combinations is called combinatory analysis.

OBJECTIVE
1 **Teaching Notes**

2 EXAMPLE **Tactile Learners**

Help students grasp the magnitude of the answer to this problem by acting out a simpler problem. Present the problem as a group of two students being selected from six students. Have six students come to the front of the class. Ask them to form as many pairs as they can. Have a volunteer keep track of the pairs by writing the students' names on the board. When students have completed this part of the task, ask them to explain how this number is different from the number of permutations they could have formed.

Additional Examples

1 Simplify $_9C_6$. **84**

2 Eighteen people enter a talent contest. In how many ways can the top ten finalists be chosen? **43,758 ways**

687

OBJECTIVE 2 · Teaching Notes

3 EXAMPLE Math Tip

Make sure students understand that the number of possibilities when choosing the second CD is 5, not 6.

Additional Examples

3 Suppose you have eight new CDs (three rock, two jazz, and three country). If you choose the CDs at random, what is the probability that the first one is country and the second one is jazz? $\frac{3}{28}$

4 Suppose you have eight red pens and four black pens in a box. You choose five pens without looking. What is the probability that all the pens you choose are red? $\frac{7}{99}$, or about 7%

Closure

Ask: *How can you find the number of combinations? How do you solve problems that require distinguishing between permutations and combinations?* Use the formula to determine the number of combinations where *n* is the number of items being chosen from and *r* is the number of items being chosen. To distinguish between permutations and combinations, keep in mind that the order does not matter for combinations.

688

OBJECTIVE 2 · Probability With Counting Techniques

Some probability problems can be solved using permutations.

3 EXAMPLE Using Permutations in Probability

Music Suppose you have six new CDs (two rock, two rhythm and blues, and two jazz) to put on a rack. If you choose the CDs at random, what is the probability that the first one is jazz and the second one is rhythm and blues?

number of ways to select jazz then rhythm and blues = $2 \cdot 2$ **Use the Multiplication Counting Principle.**

number of ways to order 6 CDs arranged 2 at a time = $_6P_2$

$P(\text{jazz, then rhythm and blues}) = \dfrac{\text{number of ways to select jazz, then rhythm and blues}}{\text{number of ways to order all 6 CDs}}$

$\qquad = \dfrac{2 \cdot 2}{_6P_2}$ **Substitute.**

$\qquad = \dfrac{4}{30}$ **Simplify the numerator, Find $_6P_2$.**

$\qquad = \dfrac{2}{15}$ **Simplify.**

● The probability that you choose jazz, and then rhythm and blues, is $\frac{2}{15}$.

✔ **Check Understanding** **3** Suppose you have three novels and two history books to read over the summer. If you choose books at random, what is the probability that you first choose a novel, and then a history book? $\frac{3}{10}$

You can rewrite the probability formula using combination notation, where *f* is the number of favorable items, *t* is the total number of items, and *r* is the number of items being chosen.

$$P(\text{event}) = \frac{\text{number of favorable outcomes}}{\text{total number of outcomes}} = \frac{_fC_r}{_tC_r}$$

Real-World 🌐 Connection

The United States Mint began issuing quarters for each state in 1999.

4 EXAMPLE Using Combinations in Probability

Money Suppose you have six Virginia quarters and four Connecticut quarters in a change purse. You choose three quarters without looking. What is the probability that all the quarters you choose have a boat on them?

There are 10 quarters in all. The six Virginia quarters have boats on them.

number of favorable outcomes $= _6C_3$ **number of ways to choose 3 quarters from the 6 quarters with boats on them**

number of possible outcomes $= _{10}C_3$ **number of ways to choose 3 quarters from 10 possible quarters**

$P(\text{3 quarters with boats})$

$\qquad = \dfrac{\text{number of favorable outcomes}}{\text{total number of outcomes}}$ **Use the definition of probability.**

$\qquad = \dfrac{_6C_3}{_{10}C_3}$ **Substitute.**

$\qquad = \dfrac{20}{120} = \dfrac{1}{6}$ **Simplify each expression. Simplify fraction.**

● The probability that you choose three quarters with boats is $\frac{1}{6}$, or about 17%.

Check Understanding **4** **a.** Suppose you have the quarters in Example 4. You choose four quarters at random. How many combinations are possible? **210**
   b. How many combination have only trees? **1**
   c. What is the probability that all of the quarters have trees? $\frac{1}{210}$

EXERCISES

For more practice, see *Extra Practice*.

Practice and Problem Solving

A **Practice by Example**

Example 1
(page 687)

Simplify each expression.

1. $_6C_6$ **1** **2.** $_6C_5$ **6** **3.** $_6C_4$ **15** **4.** $_6C_3$ **20** **5.** $_6C_2$ **15**

6. $_6C_1$ **6** **7.** $_8C_6$ **28** **8.** $_8C_2$ **28** **9.** $_7C_5$ **21** **10.** $_7C_2$ **21**

Example 2
(page 687)

11. Law For some civil cases, at least nine of twelve jurors must agree on a verdict. How many combinations of nine jurors are possible on a twelve-person jury? **220**

12. For your birthday you received a gift certificate from a music store for three CDs. There are eight you would like to have. If you select the CDs at random, how many different groups of three CDs could you select? **56**

Example 3
(page 688)

13. The colors red, orange, yellow, green, blue, indigo, and violet are written on slips of paper and placed in a hat. What is the probability that the slips will be chosen in the order of the colors of a rainbow (the order listed above)? $\frac{1}{5040}$

Example 4
(page 688)

14. The letters A, B, C, D, E, F, G, H, I, and J are written on slips of paper and placed in a hat. Two letters are then drawn from the hat.
   a. What is the number of possible combinations of two letters? **45**
   b. How many combinations consist only of the vowels A, E, or I? **3**
   c. What is the probability that the letters chosen would consist only of vowels? $\frac{1}{15}$
   d. What is the probability that the letters chosen would be only B, C, D, or F? $\frac{2}{15}$

15. a. The class president plans to randomly select a committee of three people from three boys and five girls. How many committees are possible? **56**
   b. How many possible committees have all boys? **1**
   c. What is the probability that the committee will have all boys? $\frac{1}{56}$
   d. Critical Thinking What is the probability that the committee will have no boys? $\frac{5}{28}$

B **Apply Your Skills**

 Find the number of combinations of letters taken three at a time that can be formed from each set of cards.

16. **10** **17.** **1**

18. 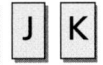 **35** **19.**  **4**

Classify each situation as a permutation or a combination problem. Explain.

20. A locker contains eight books. You select three books at random. How many different sets of books could you select? **combination, since order is *not* important**

21. You take four books out of the library to read during spring vacation. In how many different orders can you read the four books? **permutation, since order *is* important**

Lesson 12-9 Combinations **689**

Assignment Guide

1 **Objective**
   A **B** **Core** 1–12, 16–23, 25–27
   C **Extension** 31–33

2 **Objective**
   A **B** **Core** 13–15, 24, 28–30
   C **Extension** 34–36

Standardized Test Prep 37–40

Mixed Review 41–58

Exercise 22a Point out that lines should connect all the points to each other, including diagonal lines.

Error Prevention

Exercise 23b If students have difficulty visualizing the problem, have them draw ten dots in a large circle on a piece of paper. Then, tell them to connect the pairs of dots and count how many line segments they draw. Suggest to students that they draw five segments in one color and then change colors so that the number of segments is easier to count.

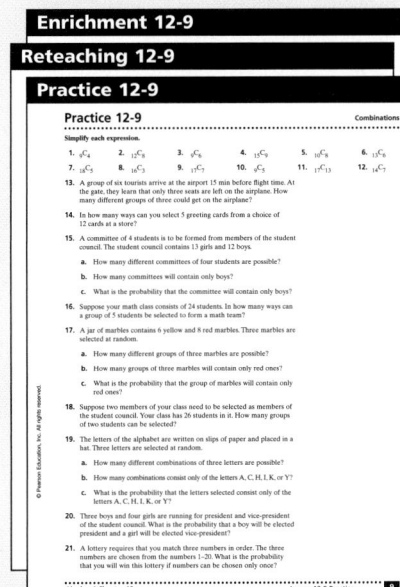

Enrichment 12-9

Reteaching 12-9

Practice 12-9

1. Simplify $_{30}C_4$. **27,405**

2. You have just received a box of chocolates. There are three turtles, four caramels, and three chocolate covered cherries. If you choose two chocolates at random, what is the probability that the first one is caramel and the second is a turtle? $\frac{2}{15}$

3. There are twelve congressmen who want to be on the same committee. Eight are Republicans and four are Democrats. If three people are chosen for the committee, what is the probability that three Republicans are chosen? $\frac{14}{55}$

4. A friend has loaned you five books and you plan to read all of them. In how many ways could you read the five books? **120 ways**

Alternative Assessment

Divide the class into small groups. Have each group make up three games with rules for winning. The games should use the work in Examples 2, 3, and 4 as models. Then have groups exchange games and calculate the probability of winning each game.

22a.
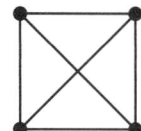

24d. **Answers may vary. Sample: It is unlikely someone will guess the right sequence with more than 59,000 possibilities.**

25. **Answers may vary. Sample: Both permutations and combinations are arrangements of some or all of a group of objects. However, permutations take into account order, and combinations do not.**

22. **a. Geometry** Draw four points on your paper like those in Figure 1. Draw line segments so that every point is joined to every other point.
   b. How many segments did you draw? **6**
   c. Find the number of segments using combinations. You are joining four points, two at a time. **6**
   d. How many segments would you need to join each point to all the others in Figure 2? **45**

Figure 1   Figure 2

23. A famous problem known as the handshake problem asks, "If ten people in a room shake hands with everyone else in the room, how many different handshakes occur?" **a. See margin.**
   a. Is this a combination or a permutation problem? Justify your answer.
   b. Solve the problem. **45**
   c. **Critical Thinking** Is the handshake problem similar to the problem in Exercise 24 part (d)? Explain. **See margin.**

24. **Locks** A lock like the one at the left is called a combination lock. However, mathematically speaking, it should be called a permutation lock! This is because the order of the numbers *is* important. Suppose a three-number sequence opens the lock, and no numbers are repeated.
   a. How many different sequences are possible? **59,280 sequences**
   b. How many sequences use 32 as the first number? **1482 sequences**
   c. What is the probability that the sequence of numbers that opens this lock uses 32 as the first number? $\frac{1}{40}$
   d. Explain why the lock is unlikely to be opened by someone who does not know the correct sequence. **See left.**

25. **Writing** Explain the difference between a permutation and a combination. **See left.**

Simplify each expression.

26. $_2C_2 + _2C_1 + _2C_0$ **4**

27. $_3C_3 + _3C_2 + _3C_1 + _3C_0$ **8**

28. a. How many different 3-digit numbers are possible using 2, 3, 5, and 7 if you do not repeat any digits? **24**
   b. What is the probability that a number selected at random is even? $\frac{1}{4}$

29. **Open-Ended** Write and solve two problems: one that can be solved using permutations and one that can be solved using combinations. **Check students' work.**

30. Twelve computer monitors are stored in a warehouse. The warehouse manager knows that three monitors are defective, but the report telling him which ones are defective is missing. He selects five monitors at random to begin testing.
   a. How many different choices of five monitors does the manager have? **792**
   b. In how many ways could he happen to select five monitors that include the defective ones? **36**
   c. What is the probability that he will find the three defective monitors when he tests the first five monitors? $\frac{1}{22}$

Challenge

Determine whether each statements is *sometimes*, *always*, or *never* true.

31. $_nC_1 = n$ **always**   32. $_3C_x > x$ **sometimes**   33. $_nC_{(n-1)} = n$ **always**

34. The numerals 3, 4, 5, 6, 7, 10, 12, and 13 are written on slips of paper and placed in a hat. Three slips of paper are then drawn from the hat. What is the probability that the numbers will form a Pythagorean triple? $\frac{1}{28}$

pages 689–691   Exercises

23a. **Answers may vary. Sample: It is a combination problem because order is not important.**

c. **Yes; Each line segment joins two points and each handshake connects two people.**

36b. **It is a quadratic function; it represents the number of combination groups of 2.**

35. On a particular test, you must answer seven out of ten questions. You also must answer at least four of the first six questions.
  a. In how many ways can you choose four of the first six questions? **15**
  b. How many questions are left after you have answered four of the first six questions? How many must you still answer? **6; 3**
  c. In how many ways can you choose questions to finish the test? **20**
  d. How many different ways are there of completing the test (meeting all its requirements)? **300**

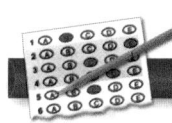

36a.

36. a. Graph the function $f(x) = {}_xC_2$ using the replacement set $\{2, 3, 4, 5\}$. **See left.**
  b. Critical Thinking What is $f(x)$? Explain. **b–c. See margin.**
  c. Critical Thinking Explain why you should not connect the points you graphed in part (a).

Standardized Test Prep

Multiple Choice

37. A florist has twelve different flowers to choose from to make a bouquet. In how many different ways can the florist choose three of these flowers? **B**
  A. 36   **B.** 220   **C.** 1320   **D.** 1728

38. What is ${}_5C_3 - {}_8C_2$? **F**
  F. -18 **G.** -2 **H.** -1 **I.** 4

Take It to the NET
Online lesson quiz at
www.PHSchool.com
Web Code: aea-1209

39. Suppose a teacher gives a four-question true-or-false quiz. The correct answers are F, T, T, and F. If a student guesses the answers, how many of the outcomes have exactly 2 correct answers? **C**
  A. 1   **B.** 4   **C.** 6   **D.** 16

Short Response

40. The Pizza Palace offers five different toppings, but you have just enough money for a two-topping pizza. How many different two-topping pizzas can you choose? Is this a combination or a permutation? Explain.
  See margin.

Mixed Review

Lesson 12-8

Simplify each expression.

41. ${}_4P_2$ **12**   **42.** ${}_7P_6$ **5040**   **43.** ${}_7P_4$ **840**   **44.** ${}_9P_1$ **9**   **45.** ${}_{23}P_1$ **23**

46. License Plates In North Carolina, a regular license plate for cars and light trucks has seven characters: three letters followed by four digits. The letters G, I, O, Q, and U are not used. How many different license plates are possible?
  92,610,000 license plates

Lessons 12-7 and 11-5

Solve each equation. Check your solution. If there is no real solution, write *no solution.*

53. $-6.81, 0.81$
54. $0.30, 6.70$
55. $-5.46, 1.46$

no solution
47. $\dfrac{4}{x} + \dfrac{x}{x-4} = 1$ **2**   **48.** $\sqrt{r-7} = \sqrt{2r+4}$ **49.** $\dfrac{2}{z} - \dfrac{3}{2z} = 5$ **$\frac{1}{10}$**
50. $\sqrt{3v + 10} = v$ **5**   **51.** $\dfrac{1}{a+2} + \dfrac{1}{a-2} = \dfrac{10}{a-2}$ **52.** $\sqrt{16m} = \sqrt{m^2}$ **0, 16**
  $-2\frac{1}{2}$

Lesson 10-7

Use the Quadratic Formula to solve each equation. If necessary, round answers to the nearest hundredth. **53–58. See left.**

56. $-1.24, 1.35$
57. $-6, 3$
58. $-0.05, 13.38$

53. $2x^2 + 12x - 11 = 0$ **54.** $x^2 - 7x + 2 = 0$ **55.** $x^2 + 4x - 8 = 0$
56. $-9x^2 + x + 15 = 0$ **57.** $-x^2 - 3x + 18 = 0$ **58.** $1.5x^2 - 20x - 1 = 0$

36c. Groups can only be made from sets of objects, which means they must be integers.

40. **[2]** There are 10 possible pizzas; combination; order does not matter;
$${}_5C_2 = \frac{{}_5P_2}{{}_2P_2} = \frac{5 \cdot 4}{2 \cdot 1} = 10$$

[1] incorrect explanation OR minor error

Standardized Test Prep

Resources
For additional practice with a variety of test item formats:
• Standardized Test Prep, pp. 697–699
• Test-Taking Strategies, p. 692
• Test-Taking Strategies with Transparencies

Exercise 39 Many students will quickly respond that the correct answer choice is A because they will think there is only one way to get two correct and two incorrect answers. Help students see that two correct answers can occur when questions 1 and 2, 1 and 3, 1 and 4, and so on are correct.

Test-Taking Strategies

Answering the Question Asked

This feature helps students develop the habit of checking to make sure that their answer choice is in fact the answer to the question that is asked in the problem.

Resources

Test-Taking Strategies with Transparencies
- Transparency 12
- Practice sheet p. 12

Teaching Notes

Students may need to be reminded that, just because their answer matches one of the answer choices, their answer is not necessarily the correct one. They should be encouraged to take a few more seconds to go back and make sure that they are answering the question being asked before selecting a response.

Students will discover that answer choices often include answers to questions about the problem other than the one being asked.

Test-Taking Strategies with Transparencies

Test-Taking Strategy: Answering the Question Asked

Incorrect choices may answer related questions.

Example A savings account earns interest compounded annually at a rate of 7%. If $1000 is deposited, what is the account balance after 1 year?

A. $1000   B. $70   C. $1070   D. $7000

Calculate the interest earned: 0.07 × 1000 = $70

Choice B is $70, but this is the interest earned, not the account balance.

Calculate the account balance: 1000 + 70 = $1070

The answer is $1070, or choice C.

Answer the question asked. Explain your reasoning.

1. Seven friends went bowling. Here are their scores.

    78 110 99 81 104 84 81

   Find the mean of the scores.

   A. 81   B. 84   C. 78   D. 91

2. If 3x − 7 = 8, what is the value of 4x? Write in your response on the grid.

3. Write in standard form the equation of the line perpendicular to y = x − 6 through (−2, 3).

   A. x − y = −5   B. x + y = 1
   C. −x + y = −6   D. x + y = −1

Solutions

1. D
2. 20
3. B

Transparency 12

Answering the Question Asked

When answering a question, be sure to answer the question that is asked. Read the question carefully and identify the quantity that you are asked to find.

1 EXAMPLE

What is the y-intercept of the graph of $y = \frac{6}{x + 2} - 4$?

A. -4 　　　　　B. -2 　　　　　C. -1 　　　　　D. -0.5

The question is asking for the y-intercept. To find the y-intercept, let $x = 0$.
Therefore $y = \frac{6}{0 + 2} - 4 = \frac{6}{2} - 4 = 3 - 4 = -1$. The correct answer is C.

In Example 1, notice that the answer for A is the horizontal asymptote, the answer for B is the vertical asymptote, and the answer for D is the x-intercept. Usually answer choices only have meaning for a given question, so you must be careful to answer the question asked.

2 EXAMPLE

If $5x^2 - x + 4$ is divided by $x + 1$, what is the remainder?

F. $5x - 6$ 　　　　　G. $5x + 1$ 　　　　　H. 10 　　　　　I. 0

Use long division.

$$
\begin{array}{r}
5x - 6 \\
x + 1 \overline{)5x^2 - x + 4} \\
\underline{5x^2 + 5x} \\
-6x + 4 \\
\underline{-6x - 6} \\
10
\end{array}
$$

Choice F is the quotient, and you might be tempted to choose it. The question, however, is asking for the remainder. Choice H is the remainder. That is the correct answer to the question.

EXERCISES

1. What is the remainder when $3x^3 - 2x^2 - 4$ is divided by $x^2 - 2$? **A**

   A. $6x - 8$ 　　　B. $6x + 8$ 　　　C. $3x + 2$ 　　　D. $3x - 2$

2. What is the horizontal asymptote of $y = \frac{3}{x + 2} + 2$? **G**

   F. $y = -2$ 　　　G. $y = 2$ 　　　H. $y = 0.5$ 　　　I. $y = 1.5$

3. If $\frac{4x}{3} + \frac{4x}{5} = 1$, what is the value of $4x$? **B**

   A. $\frac{15}{32}$ 　　　B. $\frac{15}{8}$ 　　　C. 4 　　　D. 8

Chapter Review

Vocabulary

asymptote (p. 644)
combination (p. 686)
constant of variation (p. 637)
inverse variation (p. 637)

multiplication counting principle (p. 680)
permutation (p. 681)
rational equation (p. 672)

rational expression (p. 652)
rational function (p. 644)

 Reading Math
Understanding Vocabulary

Take It to the NET
Online vocabulary quiz at www.PHSchool.com
Web Code: aej-1251

Choose the correct vocabulary term to complete each sentence.

1. A(n) _?_ is in simplest form if the numerator and the denominator have no common factors other than 1. **rational expression**

2. The y-axis is a vertical _?_ of the function $y = \frac{1}{x}$. **asymptote**

3. A(n) _?_ is an arrangement of some or all of a set of objects in a specific order. **permutation**

4. The first step in solving a(n) _?_ is to find the least common denominator. **rational equation**

5. An equation of the form $y = \frac{k}{x}$, where k is a constant, is called a(n) _?_. **inverse variation**

Skills and Concepts

12-1 Objectives
▼ To solve inverse variations (p. 636)
▼ To compare direct and inverse variation (p. 638)

When two quantities are related so that their product is constant, they form an **inverse variation.** An inverse variation can be written $xy = k$, where k is the **constant of variation.**

Suppose y varies inversely with x. Write an equation for each inverse variation.

6. $x = 6$ when $y = 1$
$xy = 6$

7. $x = 90$ when $y = 0.1$
$xy = 9$

8. $x = 88$ when $y = 0.05$
$xy = 4.4$

Each pair of points is on the graph of an inverse variation. Find the missing value.

9. $(9, x)$ and $(3, 12)$ **4**

10. $(4, 2.65)$ and $(y, 4.24)$ **2.5**

11. $(r, 100)$ and $(75, 25)$ **18.75**

Do the data in each table represent a direct variation or an inverse variation? Write an equation to model the data in each table.

12.

x	y
2	35
5	14
10	7

inverse; $xy = 70$

13.

x	y
3	24.6
5	41
10	82

direct; $y = 8.2x$

14.

x	y
1	3
4	$\frac{3}{4}$
9	$\frac{1}{3}$

inverse; $xy = 3$

12-2 Objectives
▼ To graph rational functions (p. 644)
▼ To identify types of functions (p. 647)

A **rational function** has a polynomial of at least degree 1 in the denominator. The graph of a rational function may have asymptotes. A line is an **asymptote** of a graph if the graph of the function gets closer to the line as x or y gets larger in absolute value.

15–18. See back of book.

Identify the asymptotes of each function. Then graph the function.

15. $y = \frac{8}{x}$

16. $xy = 20$

17. $y = \frac{6}{x - 5}$

18. $y = \frac{3}{x} + 2$

Resources

Student Edition
Extra Practice, Ch. 12, p. 713
English/Spanish Glossary, p. 757
Properties and Formulas, p. 752
Table of Symbols, p. 749

Reaching All Students
Reading and Math Literacy 12D
Spanish Reading and Math Literacy 12D

PRENTICE HALL ASSESSMENT SYSTEM

Standardized Test Prep
• Ch. 12 practice in standardized test formats

www.PHSchool.com
Student Site
• Self-grading Vocabulary Test
Teacher Center
• Resources

Plus **iTEXT**

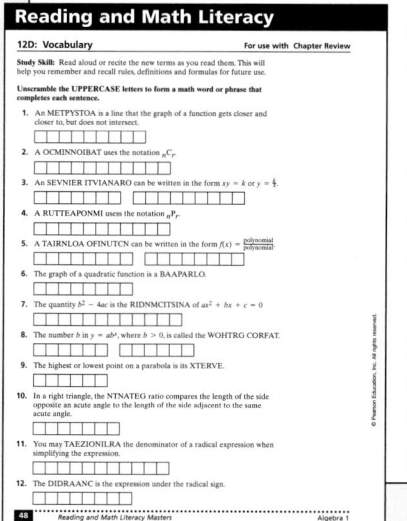

20. The graph of $f(x) = \frac{5}{x+3}$ gets closer and closer to the lines $x = -3$ and $y = 0$.

19. Open-Ended Write the equation of a rational function with a graph that is in three quadrants only. **Answers may vary. Sample:** $y = \frac{1}{x+1}$

20. Writing Explain why the function $f(x) = \frac{5}{x+3}$ has asymptotes. **See margin.**

12-3 and 12-4 Objectives

▼ To simplify rational expressions (p. 652)

▼ To multiply rational expressions (p. 657)

▼ To divide rational expressions (p. 658)

A **rational expression** is an expression with a variable in the denominator. The **domain** of a variable is all real numbers excluding the values for which the denominator is zero. A rational expression is in simplest form when the numerator and denominator have no common factors other than 1.

You can multiply and divide rational expressions.

$\frac{a}{b} \cdot \frac{c}{d} = \frac{ac}{bd}$ where b and d are nonzero.

$\frac{a}{b} \div \frac{c}{d} = \frac{a}{b} \cdot \frac{d}{c}$ where $b, c,$ and d are nonzero.

Simplify each expression.

21. $\frac{x^2 - 4}{x + 2}$ $x - 2$

22. $\frac{5x}{20x + 15}$ $\frac{x}{4x + 3}$

23. $\frac{6x - 18}{x - 3}$ 6

24. $\frac{-3t}{t^3 - t^2}$ $\frac{-3}{t(t-1)}$

25. $\frac{z + 2}{2z^2 + z - 6}$ $\frac{1}{2z - 3}$

26. $\frac{x^2 - 3x - 10}{x^2 - x - 20}$ $\frac{x + 2}{x + 4}$

Multiply or divide.

27. $\frac{8}{m - 3} \cdot \frac{3m}{m + 1}$ $\frac{24m}{(m - 3)(m + 1)}$

28. $\frac{4t - 12}{t^2 - 9} \cdot (3t + 9)$ 12

29. $\frac{4n + 8}{3n} \div \frac{4}{9n}$ $3(n + 2)$

30. $\frac{2e + 1}{8e - 4} \div \frac{4e^2 + 4e + 1}{4e - 2}$ $\frac{1}{2(2e + 1)}$

12-5 Objectives

▼ To divide polynomials (p. 662)

To divide a polynomial by a monomial, divide each term by the monomial divisor. To divide a polynomial by another polynomial, use long division. When dividing polynomials, write the answer as quotient $+ \frac{\text{remainder}}{\text{divisor}}$.

Divide. 32–34. See left.

32. $3x^4 + 4x^3 - 1$

33. $50x^2 - 7x + \frac{1}{x}$

34. $x + 7 - \frac{5}{x + 1}$

31. $(14x^2 - 28x) \div 7x$ $2x - 4$

32. $(24x^6 + 32x^5 - 8x^2) \div 8x^2$

33. $(50x^5 - 7x^4 + x^2) \div x^3$

34. $(x^2 + 8x + 2) \div (x + 1)$

35. $(x^2 + 8x - 16) \div (x + 4)$
$x + 4 - \frac{32}{x + 4}$

36. $(8x^3 - 22x^2 - 5x + 12) \div (4x + 3)$
$2x^2 - 7x + 4$

12-6 Objectives

▼ To add and subtract rational expressions with like denominators (p. 667)

▼ To add and subtract rational expressions with unlike denominators (p. 668)

You can add and subtract rational expressions. Restate each expression with the LCD as the denominator, and then add or subtract the numerators.

If $a, b,$ and c represent polynomials (with $c \neq 0$),

then $\frac{a}{c} + \frac{b}{c} = \frac{a + b}{c}$.

Add or subtract.

37. $\frac{8x}{x - 7} - \frac{4}{x - 7}$ $\frac{8x - 4}{x - 7}$

38. $\frac{6}{7x} + \frac{1}{4}$ $\frac{7x + 24}{28x}$

39. $\frac{9}{3x - 1} + \frac{5x}{2x + 3}$ $\frac{15x^2 + 13x + 27}{(3x - 1)(2x + 3)}$

40. $\frac{7m}{m^2 - 1} - \frac{10}{m + 1}$ $\frac{-3m + 10}{(m + 1)(m - 1)}$

41. What is the LCD of $\frac{1}{4}, \frac{2}{x}, \frac{5x}{3x - 2},$ and $\frac{3}{8x}$? **C**

  A. $96x^3 - 64x^2$ **B.** $12x + 2$ **C.** $24x^2 - 16x$ **D.** $27x^2 - 6x - 8$

12-7 Objectives

▼ To solve rational equations (p. 672)

▼ To solve rational proportions (p. 674)

You can use the least common denominator (LCD) to solve **rational equations.** Check possible solutions to make sure each answer satisfies the original equation.

Solve each equation. Check your solution.

42. $\frac{1}{2} + \frac{3}{t} = \frac{5}{8}$ **24**

43. $9 + \frac{1}{t} = \frac{1}{4} - \frac{4}{35}$

44. $\frac{3}{m-4} + \frac{1}{3(m-4)} = \frac{6}{m}$ **9**

45. $\frac{2c}{c-4} - 2 = \frac{4}{c+5}$ **−14**

46. $\frac{5}{2x-3} = \frac{7}{3x}$ **−21**

47. $\frac{2}{x} = \frac{2}{x^2} + \frac{1}{2}$ **2**

48. **Business** A new photocopier can make 72 copies in 2 min. When an older photocopier is working, the two photocopiers can make 72 copies in 1.5 min. How long will it take the older photocopier working alone to make 70 copies?   **≈ 6 min**

12-8 Objectives

▼ To use the multiplication counting principle (p. 679)

▼ To find permutations (p. 681)

You can find the number of different outcomes using the **multiplication counting principle.** If there are m ways to make a first selection and n ways to make a second selection, there are $m \times n$ ways to make the two selections.

A **permutation** is an arrangement of objects in a definite order. To calculate $_nP_r$, the number of permutations of n objects taken r at a time, use the following formula.

$$_nP_r = n(n-1)(n-2)\ldots \leftarrow r \text{ factors starting with } n$$

Simplify each expression.

49. $_5P_3$ **60**   50. $_8P_4$ **1680**   51. $_6P_4$ **360**   52. $_5P_2$ **20**   53. $_9P_4$ **3024**

54a. 160 possible area codes

54. **a. Telephones** Before 1995, three-digit area codes could begin with any number except 0 or 1. The middle number was either 0 or 1, and the last number could be any digit. How many possible area codes were there?

  b. Beginning in 1995, area codes were not limited to having 0 or 1 as the middle number. How many new area codes became available?   **640 new area codes**

12-9 Objectives

▼ To find combinations (p. 686)

▼ To find probability with counting techniques (p. 688)

A **combination** is an arrangement of objects without regard to order.

To find $_nC_r$, the combinations of n objects taken r at a time, use the following formula:

$$_nC_r = \frac{_nP_r}{_rP_r} = \frac{n(n-1)(n-2)\ldots}{r(r-1)(r-2)\ldots} \quad \begin{array}{l} \leftarrow r \text{ factors starting with } n \\ \leftarrow r \text{ factors starting with } r \end{array}$$

Simplify each expression.

55. $_6C_5$ **6**   56. $_{10}C_4$ **210**   57. $_9C_2$ **36**   58. $_{11}C_3$ **165**   59. $_5C_4$ **5**

60. **Nutrition** You want to have three servings of dairy products without having the same food more than once. Milk, yogurt, cottage cheese, and cheddar cheese are in the refrigerator. How many different combinations can you have?   **4 combinations**

61. A group of 15 friends wants to go to an amusement park. Unfortunately, there are only 10 seats available on the bus they would take. How many combinations of 10 friends could take the bus to the amusement park?   **3003 combinations**

Chapter 12   Chapter Review   **695**

Resources

Chapter 12 — Chapter Test

🖥 **Take It to the NET**
Online chapter test at
www.PHSchool.com
Web Code: aea-1252

Find the constant of variation k for each inverse variation.

1. $y = 5$ when $x = 6$ **30**

2. $y = 78$ when $x = 0.1$ **7.8**

3. $y = 2.4$ when $x = -10$ **−24**

4. $y = 5.3$ when $x = 9.1$ **48.23**

5. Which point is *not* on the same graph of an inverse variation as the others? **D**
   A. $(3, 12)$
   B. $(-9, -4)$
   C. $(6, 6)$
   D. $(-18, 2)$

6. It took you 1.5 hours to drive to a concert at 40 miles per hour. How long will it take you to drive back at 50 miles per hour? **1.2 h**

Identify the asymptotes of each function. Then graph the function. 7–10. See back of book.

7. $y = \dfrac{6}{x}$

8. $xy = 20$

9. $y = \dfrac{1}{x} + 3$

10. $y = \dfrac{4}{x} + 3$

11. **Writing** Explain how direct variations and inverse variations are similar and different. Include an example of each. **See back of book.**

Multiply or divide.

12. $\dfrac{3}{x-2} \cdot \dfrac{x^2 - 4}{12}$ $\dfrac{x+2}{4}$

13. $\dfrac{5x}{x^2 + 2x} \div \dfrac{30x^2}{x+2}$ $\dfrac{1}{6x^2}$

14. $\dfrac{4w}{3w-5} \cdot \dfrac{7}{2w}$ $\dfrac{14}{3w-5}$

15. $\dfrac{6c-2}{c+5} \div \dfrac{3c-9}{c}$
See margin.

16. **Open-Ended** Write a rational expression for which 6 and 3 are restricted from the domain.
Answers may vary. Sample: $\dfrac{x+2}{(x-6)(x-3)}$

Divide.

17. $(12x^4 + 9x^3 - 10x^2) \div 3x^3$ $4x + 3 - \dfrac{10}{3x}$

18. $(x^4 - 16) \div (x + 2)$ $x^3 - 2x^2 + 4x - 8$

19. $(4x^4 - 6x^3 + x + 7) \div (2x - 1)$ $2x^3 - 2x^2 - x + \dfrac{7}{2x-1}$

20. $(6x^3 - 11x^2 - 16x + 13) \div (3x + 2)$ $2x^2 - 5x - 2 + \dfrac{17}{3x+2}$

21. If three people working together can clean an office suite in two hours, how long will it take a crew of four people to clean the office? **$1\frac{1}{2}$ h**

Solve each equation. Check your solution.

22. $\dfrac{v}{3} + \dfrac{v}{v+5} = \dfrac{-4}{v+5}$ **−6, −2**

23. $\dfrac{16}{x+10} = \dfrac{8}{2x-1}$ **4**

24. $\dfrac{2}{3} + \dfrac{t+6}{t-3} = \dfrac{18}{2(t-3)}$ **no solution**

Add or subtract.

25. $\dfrac{5}{t} + \dfrac{t}{t+1}$ $\dfrac{t^2 + 5t + 5}{t(t+1)}$

26. $\dfrac{9}{n} - \dfrac{8}{n+1}$ $\dfrac{n+9}{n(n+1)}$

27. $\dfrac{2y}{y^2 - 9} - \dfrac{1}{y-3}$ $\dfrac{1}{y+3}$

28. $\dfrac{4b-2}{3b} + \dfrac{b}{b+2}$ $\dfrac{7b^2 + 6b - 4}{3b(b+2)}$

Classify each situation as a permutation or a combination problem. Explain your choice. Then solve the problem. 29–31. See margin.

29. The 30-member debate club needs a president and treasurer. How many different pairs are possible?

30. How many different ways can you choose two books from the six books on your shelf?

31. You have enough money for two extra pizza toppings. If there are six possible toppings, how many different pairs of toppings can you choose?

Find the number of combinations of letters taken four at a time that can be formed from each set of letters.

32. A E I O U Y **15**

33. E Q U A T I O N **70**

34. L E A R N **5**

35. A B C D E F G **35**

Simplify each expression.

36. $_4C_3$ **4**

37. $_8P_6$ **20,160**

38. $_{10}P_7$ **604,800**

39. $_5C_2$ **10**

40. You have 5 kinds of wrapping paper and 4 different bows. How many different combinations of paper and a bow can you have? **20 different combinations**

41. **Probability** There are 15 books on your summer reading list. Three of them are plays, one is poetry, and the rest are novels. What is the probability that you will choose two novels and a play if you choose the books at random? $\dfrac{33}{91}$

page 696   Chapter Test

15. $\dfrac{2c(3c-1)}{3(c+5)(c-3)}$

29. Permutation; order is important; 870 different pairs.

30. Combination; order is not important; 15 different ways.

31. Combination; order is not important; 15 different pairs of toppings.

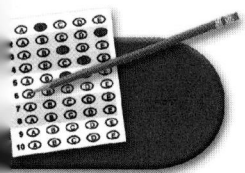

Standardized Test Prep

Take It to the NET
Online end-of-course test
at **www.PHSchool.com**
Web Code: aea-1254

Multiple Choice

For Exercises 1–42, choose the correct letter.

1. If $\frac{2x}{3} = 5$, $\frac{2y - 2}{4} = 3$, and $\frac{z}{2} + \frac{z}{3} = 5$, which of the following is true? **A**
A. $x > y$ B. $y < z$
C. $x = z$ D. $z > x$

2. **Business** A manufacturing company spends $1200 each day on plant costs plus $7 per item for labor and materials. The items sell for $23 each. How many items must the company sell in one day to equal its daily costs? **G**
F. 52   G. 75   H. 150   I. 200

3. A rectangle has a perimeter of 72 in. The length is 3 in. more than twice the width. What is the length of the rectangle in inches? **C**
A. 11   B. 22   C. 25   D. 36

4. The test scores of one student are 79, 82, 83, 87, and 94. Find the mean of these scores. **H**
F. 15   G. 83   H. 85   I. 94

5. **Consumer** Russell wants to purchase a computer that costs $1575. With a better disk drive, the cost of the computer will go up 8%. How much will an upgraded computer cost? **A**
A. $1701   B. $1449
C. $1458.33   D. $1712

6. A and B are independent events. If $P(A) = \frac{5}{6}$ and $P(A \text{ and } B) = \frac{1}{8}$, what is $P(B)$? **G**
F. $\frac{1}{10}$ G. $\frac{3}{20}$ H. $\frac{1}{5}$ I. $\frac{1}{4}$

7. Which relations are functions? **C**

I.
x	1	−1	2	1
y	3	4	5	7

II.
x	1	2	3	4
y	1	1	3	5

III.
x	0	1	2	3
y	0	1	3	2

A. I   B. II
C. II and III   D. I, II, and III

8. What is the value of $f(x) = \frac{-3}{x - 1}$ for $f(-1)$? **G**
F. 2   G. $\frac{3}{2}$ H. undefined   I. $-\frac{3}{2}$

9. Which function is modeled by the table? **B**

x	−1	1	3	5
y	−5	−1	3	7

A. $y = 2x$ B. $y = 2x - 3$
C. $y = \frac{1}{2}x$ D. $y = \frac{1}{2}x + 3$

10. Find the sixth term of the sequence 14, 9, 4, . . . **G**
F. −13   G. −11   H. −1   I. 1

11. A parachutist opens her parachute at 800 ft. Her rate of change in altitude is −30 ft/s. Which equation represents her altitude a in feet t seconds after she opens her parachute? **B**
A. $a = 30t$ B. $a = 800 - 30t$
C. $a = 800 + 30t$ D. $a = -30t$

12. What is the slope of a line perpendicular to $3x + 2y = 7$? **H**
F. $-\frac{3}{2}$ G. $-\frac{2}{3}$ H. $\frac{2}{3}$ I. $\frac{3}{2}$

13. What is true of the graphs of the two lines $3y - 8 = -5x$ and $3x = 2y - 18$? **C**
A. no intersection   B. intersect at $(2, -6)$
C. intersect at $(-2, 6)$ D. identical

14. What is the solution of the system $-2x - 3y = -15$ and $3x + 2y = 0$? **F**
F. $(-6, 9)$ G. $(-6, -9)$ H. $(6, -9)$ I. $(6, 9)$

15. Which of the following points are solutions of $4y - 3x \le 8$? **D**
I. $(0, 2)$ II. $\left(-3, \frac{1}{4}\right)$
III. $(5, -17.6)$ IV. $\left(-4, \frac{2}{5}\right)$

A. I only   B. IV only
C. II and IV   D. I and III

16. Which statement is true for every solution of the following system? **I**
$$2y > x + 4$$
$$3y + 3x > 13$$
F. $x \le -3$ G. $y < 5$
H. $x > 4$ I. $y > 1$

17. Simplify $(2.5 \times 10^4)(3.0 \times 10^{-15})$. **D**
A. 7.5×10^{19} B. 7.5×10^{-19}
C. 7.5×10^{11} D. 7.5×10^{-11}

Resources

Teaching Resources
Cumulative Review
Quarter 4 Test, Forms A & B
Final Test, Forms A & B

Reaching All Students
Spanish Cumulative Review
Spanish Quarter 4 Test, Forms A & B
Spanish Final Test, Forms A & B
Basic Algebra Final Tests

PRENTICE HALL
ASSESSMENT SYSTEM

Standardized Test Prep
• Ch. 12 Standardized Test Practice
Assessment Masters
• Cumulative Review
• Quarter 4 Test, Forms A & B
• Final Test, Forms A & B
Computer Test Generator CD
• Standardized Test Practice

www.PHSchool.com
• Standardized Test Practice
• Resources

Plus **iTEXT**

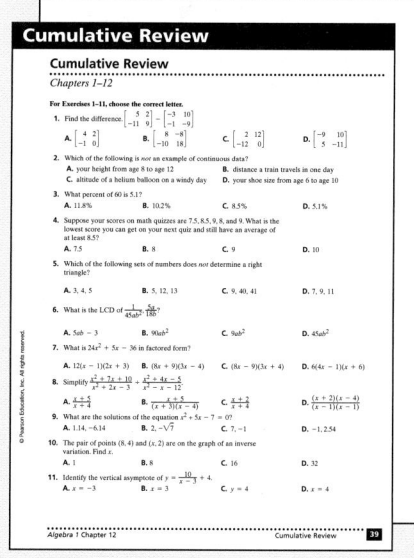

Item	1	2	3	4	5	6	7	8	9	10	11	12	13	14	15	16	17
Lesson	12-6	2-3	2-3	2-7	4-3	4-6	5-2	5-2	5-3	8-6	6-1	6-5	7-1	7-2/3	7-5	7-6	8-2

50. [2] $_{10}P_3$
$= 10 \cdot 9 \cdot 8 = 720$

[1] appropriate methods,
but with one
computational error

51. [2] $\dfrac{4x + 10}{2x^2 + 7x + 5}$
$= \dfrac{2(2x + 5)}{(2x + 5)(x + 1)}$
$= \dfrac{2}{x + 1}$

[1] appropriate methods,
but with one
computational error

52. [2] $4x^2 - 12x + 9 =$
$(2x - 3)(2x - 3)$

[1] appropriate methods,
incorrect factorization

53. [2] $6^2 + 10^2 = c^2$
$136 = c^2$
$c = \sqrt{136} \approx 11.66$
about 11.66 cm

[1] appropriate methods,
but with one
computational error

54. [2] Extraneous solutions
are false solutions;
they can occur when
solving rational and
radical equations.

[1] definition without
equation types

55. [2] a. $\dfrac{7}{12} \cdot \dfrac{5}{11} = \dfrac{35}{132}$

b. $\dfrac{7}{12} \cdot \dfrac{6}{11} = \dfrac{7}{22}$

[1] one part correct

---

18. Evaluate $a^2b^3c^{-1}$ for $a = 2$, $b = -1$, and $c = -2$.
G F. -2 G. 2   H. 4   I. 8

19. Simplify $\dfrac{20x^2y^4}{30x^5y^2}$. **B**

A. $\dfrac{4x^7y^6}{6}$ B. $\dfrac{2y^2}{3x^3}$

C. $\dfrac{3y^6}{2x^7}$ D. $\dfrac{2}{3}x^{10}y^8$

20. Interest Suppose you deposit \$1000 in an
account paying 5.5% interest, compounded
annually. Which expression represents the value
of the investment after 10 years? **G**
F. $1000 \cdot 1.55^{10}$ G. $1000 \cdot 1.055^{10}$
H. $1000 \cdot 0.055^{10}$ I. $1000 \cdot 10^{1.055}$

21. Simplify $(3x^2 - 7x - 2) - (8x - 3)$. **D**
A. $3x^2 + x - 5$ B. $-5x^3 + 1$
C. $3x^2 - 5x - 5$ D. $3x^2 - 15x + 1$

22. Find the greatest common factor (GCF) of the
polynomial $12x^5 + 4x^3 - 16x^2$. **H**
F. $4x^3$ G. x^3 H. $4x^2$ I. $-2x$

23. What is the standard form of the product
$(3x - 1)(5x + 3)$? **D**
A. $15x^2 + 2x - 3$ B. $15x^2 + 2x + 3$
C. $15x^2 + 4x + 3$ D. $15x^2 + 4x - 3$

24. Simplify $(2x - 3)(5x + 4)$. **G**
F. $10x^2 - 12$ G. $10x^2 - 7x - 12$
H. $10x^2 + 23x - 12$ I. $10x^2 - 7x + 12$

25. Factor $x^2 + 3x - 10$. **A**
A. $(x - 2)(x + 5)$ B. $(x + 2)(x - 5)$
C. $(x - 2)(x - 5)$ D. $-(x + 2)(x - 5)$

26. What is the maximum value of y in
$y = -3x^2 - 6x - 1$? **I**
F. -2 G. -1 H. 1   I. 2

27. Find the solutions of $2x^2 + 5x + 3 = 0$. **D**
A. $-3, -1$ B. $-3, -2$
C. $\frac{3}{2}, 1$ D. $-\frac{3}{2}, -1$

28. Which are the solutions of $x^2 + 4x - 5 = 0$? **H**
F. $x = 1$ and $x = 5$
G. $x = -1$ and $x = 5$
H. $x = 1$ and $x = -5$
I. $x = -1$ and $x = -5$

29. How many solutions are there to the quadratic
equation $2x^2 + 5x + 1 = 0$? **C**
A. 0   B. 1   C. 2   D. many

30. What are the solutions of the equation
$x^2 - 6x - 11 = 0$? **I**
F. -8 and 3   G. $3 \pm 4\sqrt{5}$
H. 8 and -3 I. $3 \pm 2\sqrt{5}$

---

31. A support wire from the top of a tower is 100 ft
long. It is anchored at a spot 60 ft from the base
of the tower. Find the height of the tower. **B**
A. 160 ft   B. 80 ft
C. 40 ft   D. $4\sqrt{10}$ ft

32. Each leg of a right isosceles triangle is 8 cm long.
What is the length of the hypotenuse to the
nearest tenth? **I**
F. 27.7 cm   G. 16 cm
H. 13.9 cm   I. 11.3 cm

33. Solve the equation $4 + \sqrt{y - 3} = 11$. **A**
A. 52   B. 46   C. 14   D. 10

34. Triangle DEF is a right triangle with a right angle
at F. Which of the following is false? **G**
F. $\sin D = \dfrac{EF}{DE}$ G. $\cos D = \dfrac{DE}{DF}$

H. $\sin E = \dfrac{DF}{DE}$ I. $\cos E = \dfrac{EF}{DE}$

35. The pair of points, (2, 5) and $(x, 10)$ are on the
graph of an inverse variation. Find x. **B**
A. 0   B. 1   C. 4   D. 5

36. Travel In the equation $d = rt$, the time t varies
inversely with the rate r for a given distance d. If
a trip takes 3 hours at 50 mi/h, find the time for
the same trip when the rate is 60 mi/h. **H**
F. 3.6 hours   G. 3.3 hours
H. 2.5 hours   I. 2.3 hours

37. Bakery A baker can shape 2 loaves of bread in
5 minutes. How many loaves can the baker
shape in an hour? **D**
A. 120   B. 12   C. 60   D. 24

38. Which expression is equal to $\dfrac{3x - 9}{x^2 - 6x + 9}$? **G**
F. $\frac{1}{3}x - \frac{1}{3}$ G. $\dfrac{3}{x - 3}$

H. $\dfrac{1}{x + 3}$ I. $x^2 + \frac{1}{3}x - \frac{1}{3}$

39. Identify the vertical asymptote of $y = \dfrac{8}{x - 10}$. **D**
A. $x = 7$ B. $x = 8$ C. $x = 9$ D. $x = 10$

40. Divide $\dfrac{x - 4}{x^2 + 2x} \div \dfrac{x^2 - 16}{x^2 - x}$. **F**

F. $\dfrac{x - 1}{x^2 + 6x + 8}$ G. $\dfrac{1}{x^2 + x - 4}$

H. $\dfrac{x^2 - 6x + 4}{x^2 + x - 4}$ I. 1

41. Divide $\dfrac{5}{m^3}$ by $\dfrac{10}{m^2}$. **D**

A. $\dfrac{m}{2}$ B. $\dfrac{2}{m}$ C. $\dfrac{50}{m^5}$ D. $\dfrac{1}{2m}$

42. Multiply $\dfrac{x - 1}{x + 3} \cdot \dfrac{x - 3}{x^2 - 1}$. **G**

F. $\dfrac{x - 1}{x^2 - 1}$ G. $\dfrac{x - 3}{x^2 + 4x + 3}$

H. $\dfrac{x - 3}{x + 3}$ I. $\dfrac{x - 3}{x^2 + 2x - 3}$

Item	18	19	20	21	22	23	24	25	26	27	28	29	30	31	32	33	34	35	36	37	38	39	40	41	42
Lesson	8-4/5	8-5	8-8	9-1	9-2	9-3	9-3	9-5	10-1	10-5	10-5/7	10-8	10-7	11-2	11-2	11-5	11-7	12-1	12-1	4-1	12-3	12-2	12-4	12-4	12-4

Quantitative Comparison

Compare the boxed quantity in Column A with the boxed quantity in Column B. Choose the best answer.

A. The quantity in Column A is greater.
B. The quantity in Column B is greater.
C. The two quantities are equal.
D. The relationship cannot be determined from the information given.

Column A	Column B

D 43. | $a^2 - b^2$ | $a^2 + b^2$ |

D 44. Use $2x - y = 3$ and $0.5(4x - 2y) = 3$.

| x | y |

C 45. | the degree of $4x^3 - 8x^2 - 7x$ | the GCF of $6x^3$, $-9x^2$, and 12 |

B 46. | $f(4)$ when $f(x) = 2x^2 - 23$ | $f(3)$ when $f(x) = x^2 + 5$ |

B 47. | the slope of $2x - 3y = 5$ | the slope of $4y - 2 = 7x$ |

C 48. Use $-3, -2, -2, -1, 0, 1, 1, 1, 1, 2, 4, 7$.

| median of data | mode of data |

A 49. Use the function $f(x) = x^3 - x$.

| $f(0)$ | $f(-2)$ |

Short Response 50–55. See margin.

50. Find the value of $_{10}P_3$.

51. Simplify $\dfrac{4x + 10}{2x^2 + 7x + 5}$.

52. Factor $4x^2 - 12x + 9$.

53. Geometry What is the length of the diagonal of a rectangle with sides 6 cm and 10 cm?

54. Writing What are extraneous solutions? In what type of equations do they occur?

55. Probability A bag contains 5 green cubes and 7 yellow cubes. You pick two cubes without replacing the first one.
a. What is the probability of choosing a yellow cube and then a green cube?
b. What is the probability of choosing two yellow cubes?

56. Evaluate the expression $a(bc)^4$ for $a = -2$, $b = -1$, and $c = 4$. 56–60. See margin.

57. Solve $\dfrac{x}{6} + \dfrac{1}{2} = \dfrac{3}{x}$.

58. The product of two positive integers is 45. The first is 4 less than the second. Find the integers.

59. The solution of the system $ax - 3y = 13$ and $x - by = 8$ is $(2, -3)$. Find a and b.

60. Transportation In 1996, the City Council of New York City voted to increase the number of taxis in the city from 11,787 to 12,187. What was the percent of increase? **61–67. See back of book.**

61. Find the asymptotes, the x-intercept, and the y-intercept of the graph of $y = \dfrac{5}{x - 2} + 1$.

62. Serena bought a sweatshirt on sale for \$32. The regular price was \$42. What was the percent of decrease, to the nearest tenth of a percent?

63. Do the equations $x - 2 = 5$ and $\dfrac{x}{x - 7} - \dfrac{2}{x - 7} = \dfrac{5}{x - 7}$ have the same solution(s)?

64. Suppose $x - 472 = 1634$. Find the value of $x + 472$.

Extended Response

65. There is a linear relationship between the total length ℓ of a certain species of snake and the tail length (t) of this snake. Here are the measurements for two snakes of this species. Snake 1: $\ell = 150$ mm and $t = 19$ mm; Snake 2: $\ell = 300$ mm and $t = 40$ mm. Use the ordered pairs (ℓ, t).
a. Find a linear equation for these data points.
b. Use this linear equation to estimate the tail length of a snake with a total length of 200 mm.
c. Use this linear equation to estimate the total length of a snake with a tail length of 61 mm.

66. Geometry In $\triangle ABC$, $\angle C$ is a right angle, $AB = 7$, and $m\angle B = 28°$. What are the lengths of $\overline{BC}$ and $\overline{AC}$ to the nearest hundredth?

67. The table shows the closing prices of a stock over a period of 5 days. Graph this relation and determine whether it is a linear function. Explain why or why not.

Day	1	2	3	4	5
Price	12	$12\frac{1}{2}$	$12\frac{1}{4}$	13	$13\frac{1}{4}$

56. [2] $(-2)(-1 \cdot 4)^4 =$ $-2(256) = -512$

[1] appropriate methods, but with one computational error

57. [2] $6x\left(\dfrac{x}{6} + \dfrac{1}{2}\right) = 6x\left(\dfrac{3}{x}\right)$
$x^2 + 3x = 18$
$x^2 + 3x - 18 = 0$
$(x + 6)(x - 3) = 0$
$x + 6 = 0$ or
$x - 3 = 0$
$x = -6$ or $x = 3$

[1] appropriate methods, but with one computational error

58. [2] $x(x - 4) = 45$
$x^2 - 4x - 45 = 0$
$(x - 9)(x + 5) = 0$
9 and -5
-5 is an extraneous solution; the solution 9 gives the numbers 9 and 5.

[1] both numbers not given

59. [2] $2a - 3(-3) = 13$
$2a = 4$
$a = 2$
$2 + 3b = 8$
$3b = 6$
$b = 2$

[1] appropriate methods, but with one computational error

60. [2] a. $\dfrac{12{,}187 - 11{,}787}{11{,}787}$
≈ 0.034
about 3.4%

[1] appropriate methods, but with one computational error

Item	43	44	45	46	47	48	49	50	51	52	53	54	55	56	57	58	59	60	61	62	63	64	65
Lesson	9-7	7-2/3	9-1	5-2	6-4	2-7	5-3	12-8	12-3	9-6	11-2	12-7	4-6	1-2	2-5	7-2/3	7-2	4-4	12-2	4-4	12-2	2-1	10-9

Good Vibrations

In these activities students apply their knowledge of functions, ratios, the use of formulas, and graphs.

Connecting to Prior Knowledge

Discuss any experiences the students have had with playing stringed instruments, or with experimenting with the sounds made by stretched rubber bands. Elicit the fact that the length of the string is the main factor on whether the sound that is played is lower or higher.

Teaching Notes

Tactile Learners

If possible, have one or more stringed instruments in the classroom. Or have students make a box guitar with a small wooden box and stretched rubber bands. Let students examine various guitar strings and compare them, predicting how their sounds might differ.

Careers

Have students brainstorm about what a guitar maker needs to know, including woodworking, physics, music, and so forth.

English Learners

Make sure that students understand the difference between an acoustic guitar and an electric guitar. Have a volunteer explain the meaning of frequency for a note, and how it relates to the vibrations of the string.

Diversity

Students who are not familiar with stringed instruments may think that the first fret can be at either end of the "neck." Have them look at the labeling on the guitar.

700

Real-World Snapshots

Good Vibrations

Applying Functions When you pluck a guitar string, it vibrates at a frequency corresponding to the note being played. In an acoustic guitar the hollow chamber and vibration of the wood shell amplify the sound produced by the strings. Electric guitars rely on electromagnetic pickups to detect the string's vibration and relay a signal to an amplifier. You can use the frequencies of musical notes to calculate the length of a guitar string.

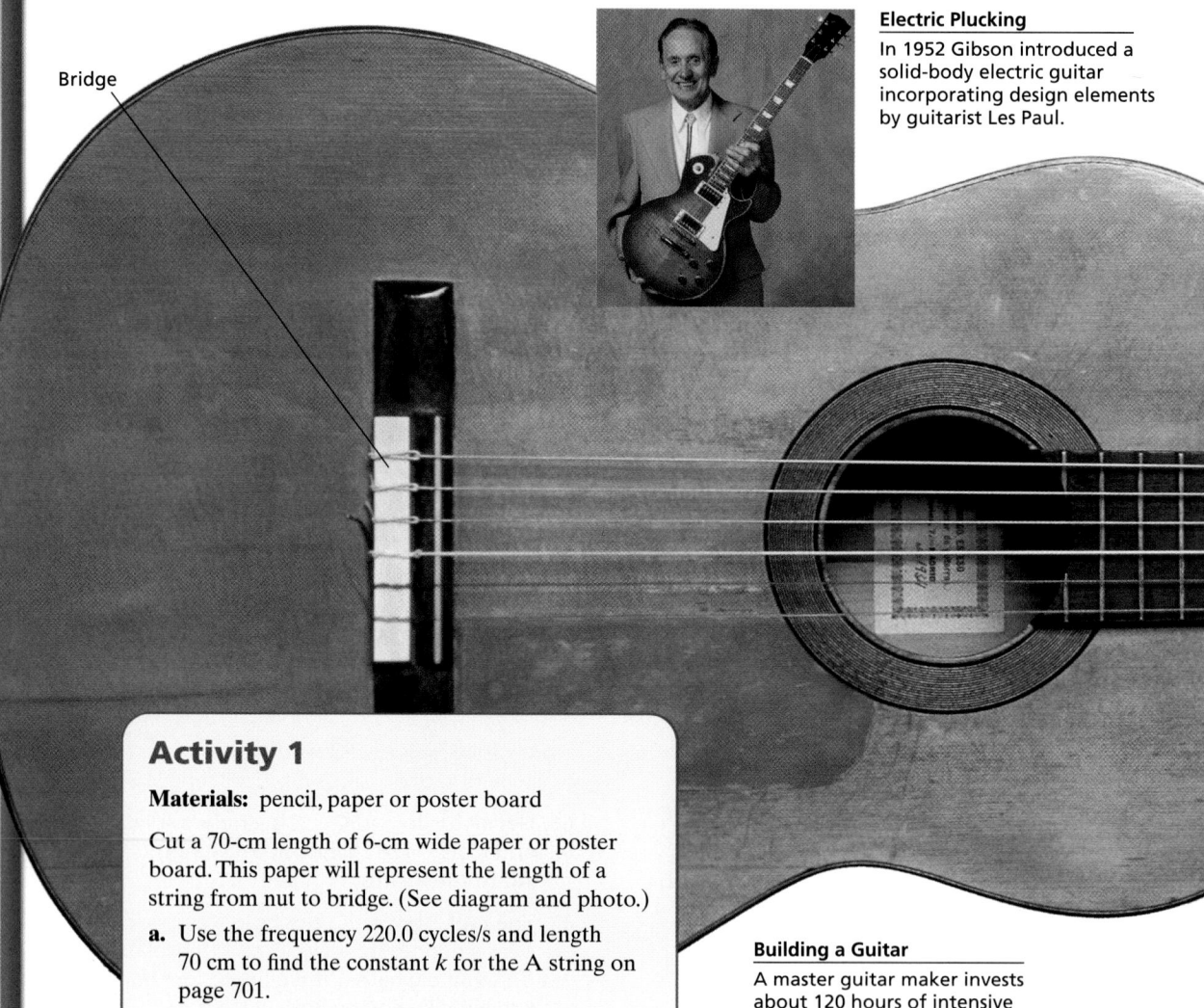

Electric Plucking

In 1952 Gibson introduced a solid-body electric guitar incorporating design elements by guitarist Les Paul.

Bridge

Activity 1

Materials: pencil, paper or poster board

Cut a 70-cm length of 6-cm wide paper or poster board. This paper will represent the length of a string from nut to bridge. (See diagram and photo.)

a. Use the frequency 220.0 cycles/s and length 70 cm to find the constant k for the A string on page 701.

b. Use the value of k and the frequencies in the diagram to calculate the positions of each of the frets shown. Draw the frets on your model.

Building a Guitar

A master guitar maker invests about 120 hours of intensive work to build a guitar. The tonal properties of the wood used for the soundboard are crucial to the sound the guitar produces.

700 All photographs © Dorling Kindersley Limited unless otherwise credited on acknowledgments page

---

pages 700–701 **Real-World Snapshots**
Activity 1
  a. $k = 15,400$
  b. See back of book

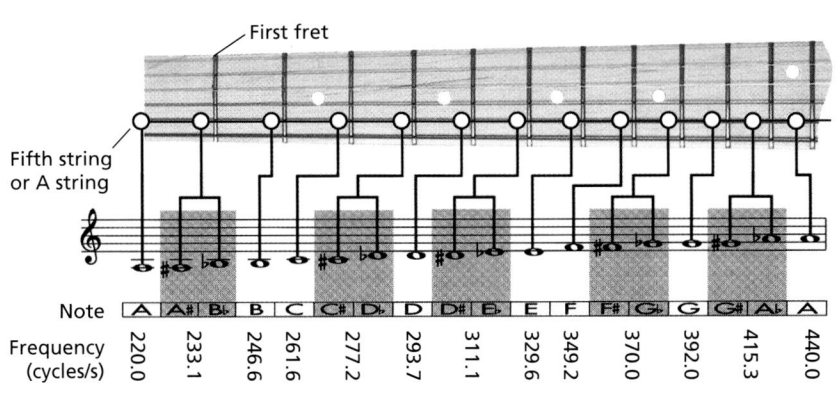

First fret

Fifth string or A string

Note	A	A♯ B♭	B	C	C♯ D♭	D	D♯ E♭	E	F	F♯ G♭	G	G♯ A♭	A
Frequency (cycles/s)	220.0	233.1	246.6	261.6	277.2	293.7	311.1	329.6	349.2	370.0	392.0	415.3	440.0

Musical Interlude

When you pluck the A string, it vibrates according to the equation below. Pressing a string against a fret changes its length and consequently its frequency.

$f = \dfrac{k}{L}$, where

f = frequency of string vibration (cycles/s)

k = constant

L = length of string (cm)

Activity 2

a. The distance from C to G is 7 frets, which corresponds to 7 half-steps or 3.5 full steps. The C and G notes form a musical interval called a perfect fifth. Calculate the ratio of the frequency of G to the frequency of C.

b. Locate other perfect fifths and calculate each frequency ratio. What do you notice?

c. Calculate the frequency ratio of an octave (6 steps) and of a major third (2 steps).

d. Make a Conjecture Predict the ratio of a perfect fourth (2.5 steps). Check your prediction by calculating the ratio.

Activity 3

Materials: graphing calculator or graphing utility

Use your model from Activity 1.

a. Plot the points (Frequency, String Length).

b. Plot the points (Fret Number, Frequency).

c. Reasoning Which of the sets of points plotted above lie on the graph of an inverse function? Explain.

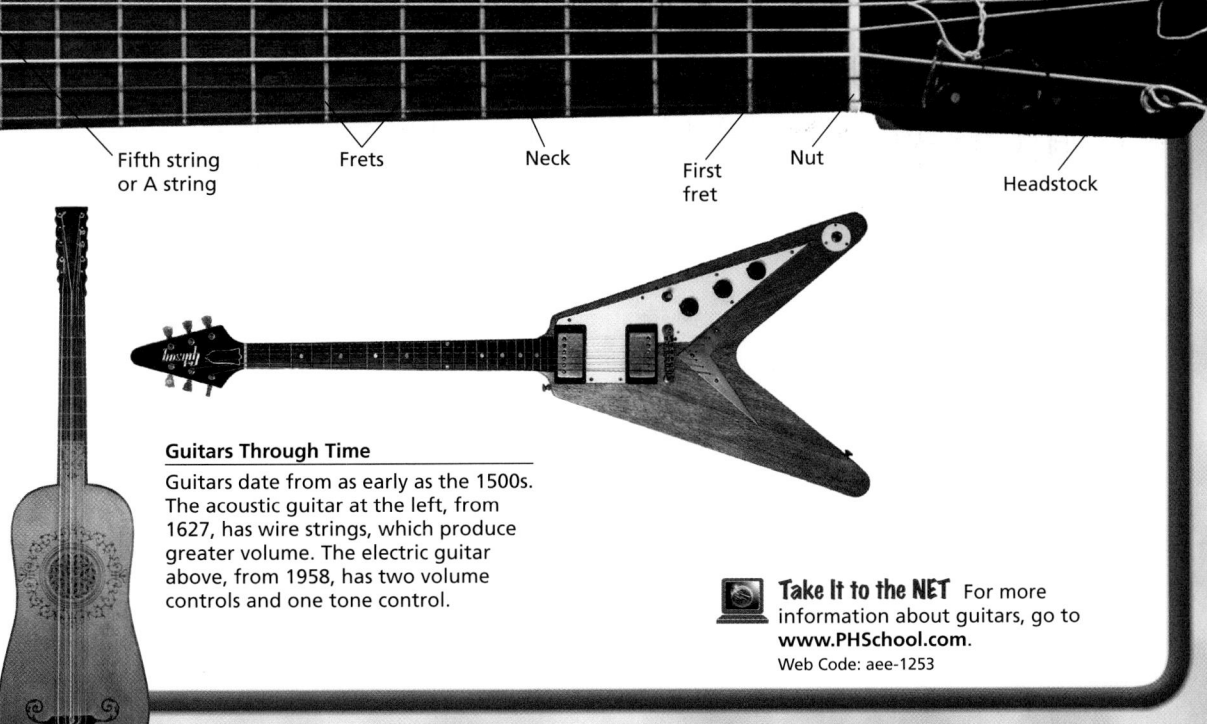

Fifth string or A string

Frets

Neck

First fret

Nut

Headstock

Guitars Through Time

Guitars date from as early as the 1500s. The acoustic guitar at the left, from 1627, has wire strings, which produce greater volume. The electric guitar above, from 1958, has two volume controls and one tone control.

Take It to the NET For more information about guitars, go to **www.PHSchool.com.**
Web Code: aee-1253

701

Teaching Tip

Have students work in pairs or in small groups to complete the activities. Have each team read through all three activities before beginning to work. Consider playing a recording of guitar or sitar music softly in the background as students work on these activities. If time is limited, have half of the teams complete Activity 1 while the other half goes directly to Activity 2.

Activity 1

Materials pencil, paper or poster board, tape

Teaching Tip

Have students begin by locating the bridge, the nut, and the frets on the guitar in the picture.

Activity 2

Materials paper and pencil

Teaching Tip

Bring a small electronic keyboard to class and have volunteers play the notes that are discussed in this activity.

Activity 3

Materials graphing calculator or graphing utility

Scoring Rubric

This scoring rubric applies to all three activities. Share this scoring rubric with students before they begin work.

4 Equations and calculations are correct. Models and steps are neat, accurate, and clearly show the mathematics.

3 Equations and calculations are mostly correct, with some minor errors. Models and steps are neat and mostly accurate.

2 Models, equations, and calculations contain both major and minor errors.

1 Correct answer, but no work is shown.

Activity 2

a. ≈1.5

b. They are all close to 1.5.

c. 2, ≈1.26

d. Answers may vary. Sample: about 1.3, ≈1.33

Activity 3

a–b. See back of book

c. Answers may vary. Sample: The graph of frequency vs. string length is the graph of an inverse function. The graph of fret number vs. frequency appears to be the graph of an exponential function.

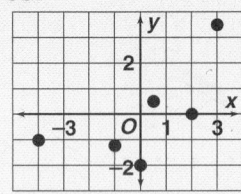

66.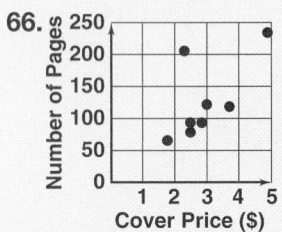

positive correlation

● **Lesson 1-1**   Define variables and write an equation to model each situation.

1. The total length of the edges of a cube is 12 times the length of an edge.   **s = side length; $\ell = 12s$**

2. The total cost of lunch is \$5.50 times the number of people at the table.   **n = number of people; $c = 5.50n$**

3. The area of a rectangle is 12 cm times the length of the rectangle.   **e = length of rectangle; $a = 12e$**

4. The cost of a telephone call is 75 cents plus 25 cents times the number of minutes.   **t = time in minutes; $c = 75 + 25t$**

● **Lesson 1-2**   Simplify each expression.

5. $4 + 3 \cdot 8$ **28**

6. $2 \cdot 3^2 - 7$ **11**

7. $6 \cdot (5 - 2) - 9$ **9**

8. $2 - 12 \div 3$ **−2**

9. $4^2 + 8 \div 2$ **20**

10. $\frac{1}{2} \div \frac{4}{3}$ **$\frac{3}{8}$**

11. $-6 \cdot 4.2 - 5 \div 2$ **−27.7**

12. $9 - (3 + 1)^2$ **−7**

13. $2 + 6 \cdot 8 \div 4$ **14**

14. $6 + 8 \div 2 - 3$ **7**

15. $10 \div 5 \cdot 2 + 6$ **10**

16. $5 + 4 \cdot (8 - 6)^2$ **21**

● **Lesson 1-3**   Use <, =, or > to compare.

17. $0.45 \blacksquare 0.54$ **<**

18. $-1.08 \blacksquare -1.008$ **<**

19. $\frac{3}{7} \blacksquare \frac{11}{25}$ **<**

20. $1.4 \blacksquare \frac{18}{11}$ **<**

21. $0.444\ldots \blacksquare \frac{4}{9}$ **=**

22. $\frac{4}{13} \blacksquare \frac{4}{15}$ **>**

23. $0.101101110\ldots \blacksquare \frac{1}{9}$ **<**

24. $\pi \blacksquare \frac{22}{7}$ **<**

● **Lessons 1-4 to 1-8**   Simplify each expression.

25. $22 + (-33)$ **−11**

26. $45 + (-54)$ **−9**

27. $-\frac{4}{3} - \frac{4}{5}$ **$-\frac{32}{15}$**

28. $\frac{4}{13} - \frac{4}{13}$ **0**

29. $|12 - 21|$ **9**

30. $|12| - |-21|$ **−9**

31. $-(-(11 - 22))$ **−11**

32. $\left|\frac{2}{3} + \frac{4}{5}\right|$ **$\frac{22}{15}$**

33. $(-2)(44)$ **−88**

34. $(-3)^2$ **9**

35. -3^2 **−9**

36. $\left(\frac{3}{2}\right)\left(-\frac{22}{33}\right)$ **−1**

37. $\frac{3^2}{2^3}$ **$\frac{9}{8}$**

38. $\frac{-5^2}{(-5)^2}$ **−1**

39. $81 \div (-9)$ **−9**

40. $\frac{4^2}{5^2}$ **$\frac{16}{25}$**

41. $\frac{2 \cdot 3 + 4}{2(3 + 4)}$ **$\frac{5}{7}$**

42. $1 + \dfrac{1}{2 + \frac{1}{3}}$ **$\frac{10}{7}$**

43. $\left(\frac{5}{7}\right)^2$ **$\frac{25}{49}$**

44. $\frac{2}{3} \div \frac{4}{9}$ **$\frac{3}{2}$**

45. $\begin{bmatrix} -3 & 0 \\ 11 & -5 \end{bmatrix} + \begin{bmatrix} -4 & 6 \\ -8 & 13 \end{bmatrix}$ $\begin{bmatrix} -7 & 6 \\ 3 & 8 \end{bmatrix}$

46. $\begin{bmatrix} 6 & 12 \\ -9 & 7 \end{bmatrix} - \begin{bmatrix} 8 & -6 \\ 15 & 0 \end{bmatrix}$ $\begin{bmatrix} -2 & 18 \\ -24 & 7 \end{bmatrix}$

47. $\begin{bmatrix} 4.2 & 0.6 \\ 1.7 & 9.5 \end{bmatrix} + \begin{bmatrix} 5.8 & -3.5 \\ 0.2 & 4.9 \end{bmatrix}$ $\begin{bmatrix} 10 & -2.9 \\ 1.9 & 14.4 \end{bmatrix}$

Simplify each expression.

48. $-4(a + 3)$ **$-4a - 12$**

49. $-12\left(\frac{4}{3}x - 1\right)$ **$-16x + 12$**

50. $5 + 6(m + 1)$ **$6m + 11$**

51. $\frac{4}{9}(18 - 9t)$ **$8 - 4t$**

52. $1 + 3 + 5 + 7$ **16**

53. $1 - 3 + 5 - 7$ **−4**

54. $-3(7w) + 7(3w)$ **0**

55. $2(1 - d) - (2d + 1)$ **$1 - 4d$**

56. $6c + 2(4c - 3)$ **$14c - 6$**

57. $5(2 - j) + (2j - 3)$ **$7 - 3j$**

58. $\frac{1}{3}(12 - 6r)$ **$4 - 2r$**

59. $6\left(\frac{1}{2} - \frac{2}{3}y\right)$ **$3 - 4y$**

● **Lesson 1-9**   Graph the points on the same coordinate plane.   60–65. See margin.

60. $(2, 0)$

61. $(-4, -1)$

62. $(0, -2)$

63. $\left(-1, -1\frac{1}{4}\right)$

64. $\left(\frac{1}{2}, \frac{1}{2}\right)$

65. $(3, 3.5)$

66. Make a scatter plot of the data. Describe the trend of the data.   **See margin.**

Cover Price and Number of Pages of Some Magazines

Cover Price	\$2.25	\$2.50	\$3.75	\$3.00	\$4.95	\$1.95	\$2.95	\$2.50
Number of Pages	208	68	122	124	234	72	90	90

Extra Practice

47. mean = 39.375
    median = 38
    mode = 35

48. mean = 0.943
    median = 0.9
    mode = none

49. mean = 6.3
    median = 6
    modes = 5, 8

Lessons 2-1 to 2-3 Solve each equation.

1. $h - 4 = 10$ **14**

2. $8p - 3 = 13$ **2**

3. $8j - 5 + j = 67$ **8**

4. $6t = -42$ **−7**

5. $-n + 8.5 = 14.2$ **−5.7**

6. $6(t + 5) = -36$ **−11**

7. $m - 9 = 11$ **20**

8. $\frac{1}{2}(s + 5) = 7.5$ **10**

9. $\frac{s}{3} = 8$ **24**

10. $7h + 2h - 3 = 15$ **2**

11. $\frac{7}{12}x = \frac{3}{14}$ **$\frac{18}{49}$**

12. $3r - 8 = -32$ **−8**

13. $8g - 10g = 4$ **−2**

14. $-3(5 - t) = 18$ **11**

15. $3(c - 4) = -9$ **1**

16. $\frac{3}{8}z = 9$ **24**

17. $0.1(h + 20) = 3$ **10**

18. $\frac{3m}{5} = 6$ **10**

19. $4 - y = 10$ **−6**

20. $8q + 2q = -7.4$ **−0.74**

Define a variable and write an equation for each situation. Then solve.

21. Your test scores for the semester are 87, 84, and 85. Can you raise your test average to 90 with your next test? t = test score; $\frac{87 + 84 + 85 + t}{4} = 90$; no

22. You spend $\frac{1}{2}$ of your allowance each week on school lunches. Each lunch costs $1.25. How much is your weekly allowance? a = allowance; $\frac{1}{2}a = 5(1.25)$; $12.50

Lesson 2-4 Solve each equation. If the equation is an identity, write *identity*. If it has no solution, write *no solution*.

23. $6t = 6$ **1**

24. $5m + 3 = 9m - 1$ **1**

25. $8d = 4d - 8$ **−2**

26. $4h + 5 = 9h$ **1**

27. $2(3x - 6) = 3(2x - 4)$ **identity**

28. $7t = 80 + 9t$ **−40**

29. $w - 9 = 4w$ **−3**

30. $m + 3m = 4$ **1**

31. $-b + 4b = 8b - b$ **0**

32. $-p = p - 4$ **2**

33. $-(h + 7) = -8h$ **1**

34. $6p + 1 = 3(2p + 1)$ **no solution**

35. $10z - 5 + 3z = 8 - z$ **$\frac{13}{14}$**

36. $3(g - 1) + 7 = 3g + 4$ **identity**

37. $17 - 20q = (-13 - 5q)4$ **no solution**

Lesson 2-5

38. Transportation A bus traveling 40 mi/h and a car traveling 50 mi/h cover the same distance. The bus travels 1 h more than the car. How many hours did each travel? **bus: 5 h; car: 4 h**

Lesson 2-6 Solve each equation for the given variable.

39. $A = \ell w; w$ **$\frac{A}{\ell}$**

40. $C = \frac{W + t}{V}; t$ **$CV - W$**

41. $h = \frac{r}{t}(p - m); r$ **$\frac{ht}{p - m}$**

42. $P = 2\ell + 2w; \ell$ **$\frac{P - 2w}{2}$**

43. $V = \pi r^2 h; h$ **$\frac{V}{\pi r^2}$**

44. $m = \frac{t}{b - a}; t$ **$m(b - a)$**

45. $y = bt - c; b$ **$\frac{y + c}{t}$**

46. $g = 1.9\frac{m}{r^2}; m$ **$\frac{gr^2}{1.9}$**

Lesson 2-7 Find the mean, median, and mode for each set of data. 47–49. See margin.

47. 36, 42, 35, 40, 35, 51, 41, 35

48. 1.2, 0.9, 0.7, 1.1, 0.8, 1.3, 0.6

49. 5, 8, 6, 8, 3, 5, 8, 6, 5, 9

50. A student surveyed the members of the drama club. She included a question about age. Her results are below.

Ages of Drama Club Members
14 18 16 15 17 14 15 18 15
13 14 15 18 14 17 16 14 16

a.
```
1 | 8 8 8
1 | 7 7
1 | 6 6 6
1 | 5 5 5 5
1 | 4 4 4 4 4
1 | 3
1 | 4 → means 14
```

a. Make a stem-and-leaf plot for the data.

b. What is the median age of the drama club members? **15**

1.
-4 -3 -2 -1 0 1

2.
-8 -4 0 4 8 12

3.
-4 -3 -2 -1 0 1

4.
-4 -2 0 2 4

5.
-8 -4 0 4

6.
-12 -8 -4 0 4 8

7.
$-\frac{1}{2}$ 0 $\frac{1}{2}$ 1

8.
-12 -6 0 6 12 18

9.
-10 -5 0 5

10.
-4 -3 -2 -1 0 1

11.
0 2 4 6

12.
0 2 4 6

13.
0 6 12 18

14.
0 6 12 18

15.
-3 -2 -1 0 1

16.
-12 -8 -4 0 4 8

17.
0 1 2 3 4

18.
-4 -2 0 2

19.
0 4 8 12

20.
-4 -2 0 2

21.
-6 -4 -2 0

22.
-4 -2 0 2

23.
-2 -1 0 1

24.
0 2 4 6

42.
-8 -4 0 4 8

● **Lessons 3-1 to 3-4 Solve each inequality. Graph and check your solution. 1–24. See margin for graphs.**

1. $-8w < 24$ **w > -3**

2. $9 + p \le 17$ **p ≤ 8**

3. $\frac{r}{4} > -1$ **r > -4**

4. $7y + 2 \le -8$ **y ≤ -$\frac{10}{7}$**

5. $t - 5 \ge -13$ **t ≥ -8**

6. $9h > -108$ **h > -12**

7. $8w + 7 > 5$ **w > -$\frac{1}{4}$**

8. $\frac{s}{6} \le 3$ **s ≤ 18**

9. $\frac{6c}{5} \ge -12$ **c ≥ -10**

10. $-8\ell + 3.7 \le 31.7$ **ℓ ≥ -3.5**

11. $9 - t \le 4$ **t ≥ 5**

12. $m + 4 \ge 8$ **m ≥ 4**

13. $y + 3 < 16$ **y < 13**

14. $n - 6 \le 8.5$ **n ≤ 14.5**

15. $12b - 5 > -29$ **b > -2**

16. $4 - a > 15$ **a < -11,**

17. $4 - x \le 3$ **x ≥ 1**

18. $1 - 4d \ge 4 - d$ **d ≤ -1**

19. $n + 7 \le 3n - 1$ **n ≥ 4**

20. $\frac{s}{2} + 1 < s + 2$ **s > -2**

21. $3 - \frac{2x}{3} > 5$ **x < -3**

22. $8r - \frac{r}{6} > \frac{1}{6} - 8$ **r > -1**

23. $1.4 + 2.4x < 0.6$ **x < -$\frac{1}{3}$**

24. $x - 2 < 3x - 4$ **x > 1**

25. The booster club raised $102 in their car wash. They want to buy $18 soccer balls for the soccer team. Write and solve an inequality to find how many soccer balls they can buy. **18x ≤ 102, 5 balls**

26. You earn $7.50 per hour and need to earn $35. Write and solve an inequality to find how many hours you must work. **7.5h ≥ 35, 4$\frac{2}{3}$ h**

● **Lesson 3-5 Solve each compound inequality.**

27. $8 < w + 3 < 10$ **5 < w < 7**

28. $-6 < t - 1 < 6$ **-5 < t < 7**

29. $6m - 15 \le 9$ or $10m > 84$ **m ≤ 4 or m > 8.4**

30. $9j - 5j \ge 20$ and $8j > -36$ **j ≥ 5**

31. $37 < 3c + 7 < 43$ **10 < c < 12**

32. $3 < 5 + 6h < 10$ **-$\frac{1}{3}$ < h < $\frac{5}{6}$**

33. $1 + t < 4 < 2 + t$ **2 < t < 3**

34. $2 + 3w < -1 < 3w + 5$ **-2 < w < -1**

35. $2x - 3 \le x$ and $2x + 1 \ge x + 3$ **2 ≤ x ≤ 3**

36. $3n - 7 > n + 1$ or $4n - 5 < 3n - 3$ **n < 2 or n > 4**

● **Lesson 3-6 Choose a variable and write an absolute value inequality that represents each set of numbers.**

37. all real numbers less than 2 units from 0 **|x| < 2**

38. all real numbers more than 0.5 units from 4.5 **|x − 4.5| > 0.5**

39. all real numbers less than 1 unit from −4 **|x + 4| < 1**

40. all real numbers 3 or more units from −1 **|x + 1| ≥ 3**

41. all real numbers less than or equal to 5 units from 3 **|x − 3| ≤ 5**

Solve each inequality. Graph and check your solution. 42–50. See margin for graphs.

42. $|x| < 5$ **-5 < x < 5**

43. $|t| > 1$ **t < -1 or t > 1**

44. $|t| - 5 \le 3$ **-8 ≤ t ≤ 8**

45. $|-6m + 2| > 20$

46. $|3c| - 1 \ge 11$ **c ≤ -4 or c ≥ 4**

47. $|8 - w| \le 8$ **0 ≤ w ≤ 16**

48. $|2b + 3| < 7$ **-5 < b < 2**

49. $|c - 5| \le 6$ **-1 ≤ c ≤ 11**

50. $|n| + 4 \le 5$ **-1 ≤ n ≤ 1**

45. **m < -3 or m > $\frac{11}{3}$**

51. Write an absolute value inequality that has numbers between 2 and 3 as the solutions. **|x − 2.5| < 0.5**

52. Holes with radius 3 cm must be drilled in sheets of metal. The radius must have an error no more than 0.01 cm. Write an absolute value inequality whose solutions are acceptable radii. **|x − 3| ≤ 0.01**

43.
-4 -2 0 2 4

44.
-16 -8 0 8 16

45.
-8 -4 0 4 8

46.
-8 -4 0 4 8

47.
-8 0 8 16 24

48.
-8 -4 0 4

49.
-5 0 5 10 15

50.
-4 -2 0 2 4

● **Lessons 4-1 and 4-2** Solve each proportion.

1. $\frac{3}{4} = \frac{-6}{m}$ **-8**

2. $\frac{t}{7} = \frac{3}{21}$ **1**

3. $\frac{9}{j} = \frac{3}{16}$ **48**

4. $\frac{2}{5} = \frac{w}{65}$ **26**

5. $\frac{s}{15} = \frac{4}{45}$ $\frac{4}{3}$

6. $\frac{9}{4} = \frac{x}{10}$ $\frac{45}{2}$

7. $\frac{10}{q} = \frac{8}{62}$ $\frac{155}{2}$

8. $\frac{3}{2} = \frac{18}{y}$ **12**

9. $\frac{5}{9} = \frac{t}{3}$ $\frac{5}{3}$

10. $\frac{6}{m} = \frac{3}{5}$ **10**

11. $\frac{c}{8} = \frac{13.5}{36}$ **3**

12. $\frac{7}{9} = \frac{35}{x}$ **45**

13. Architecture A blueprint scale is 1 in. : 4 ft. On the plan, the garage is 2 in. by 3 in. What are the actual dimensions of the garage? **8 ft by 12 ft**

14. The ratio of the weights of two pieces of pottery is 3 : 5. The weight of the lighter piece is 4.3 lb. Find the weight of the heavier. **about 7.2 lb**

15. The scale on a map is 1 in. : 15 mi. The distance between two cities is 25 mi. Find the distance in inches between the cities on the map. **about 1.7 in.**

● **Lesson 4-3** Write an equation to model each question and solve. **16–24. See margin.**

16. What is 10% of 94?

17. What percent of 10 is 4?

18. 147 is 14% of what?

19. What percent of 1.2 is 6?

20. 13.2 is 55% of what?

21. What is 0.4% of 800?

22. What is 75% of 68?

23. 5 is 200% of what?

24. What percent of 54 is 28?

25. 114 is 95% of what?
114 = 0.95x, 120

26. What percent of 20 is 31?
20x = 31, 155%

27. What is 35% of 15?
x = 0.35 · 15, 5.25

● **Lesson 4-4** Find each percent of change. Describe each as a percent of increase or decrease. Round to the nearest percent.

28. $4.50 to $5.00 **11% increase**

29. 56 in. to 65 in. **16% increase**

30. 18 oz to 12 oz **33% decrease**

31. 1 s to 3 s **200% increase**

32. 8 lb to 5 lb **38% decrease**

33. 6 km to 6.5 km **8% increase**

34. 39 h to 40 h **3% increase**

35. 7 ft to 2 ft **71% decrease**

36. 0.2 mL to 0.45 mL **125% increase**

37. $\frac{1}{2}$ tsp to $\frac{1}{8}$ tsp **75% decrease**

38. 18 kg to 20 kg **11% increase**

39. 55 min to 50 min **9% decrease**

Find the percent error of each measurement. Round to the nearest tenth of a percent.

40. 18 mm **2.8%**

41. 1.8 cm **2.8%**

42. 18.0 cm **0.3%**

43. 3 mm **16.7%**

● **Lesson 4-5** The results of rolling a number cube 54 times are at the right. Use the results to find each probability.

```
6 3 4 5 1 1 5 5 3 6 3 2 1 3 3 3 2 1
2 3 6 3 3 4 5 1 2 2 6 3 3 6 5 4 5 3
2 5 1 4 5 2 6 2 5 2 1 2 5 3 2 4 6 3
```

44. $P(3)$ $\frac{14}{54}$ **45.** $P(4)$ $\frac{5}{54}$

46. $P(\text{not } 5)$ $\frac{44}{54}$

47. $P(7)$ **0** **48.** $P(\text{even number})$ $\frac{23}{54}$

49. $P(\text{not } 1)$ $\frac{47}{54}$

● **Lesson 4-6** You roll a blue number cube and a red number cube. Find each probability.

50. $P(\text{blue 3 and red 2})$ $\frac{1}{36}$

51. $P(\text{blue odd and red 6})$ $\frac{1}{12}$

52. $P(\text{blue 5 and red less than 4})$ $\frac{1}{12}$

You have 3 green marbles, 5 red marbles, and 1 yellow marble in a bag. You pick two marbles from the bag. You pick the second one without replacing the first one. Find each probability.

53. $P(\text{red then green})$ $\frac{5}{24}$

54. $P(\text{yellow then red})$ $\frac{5}{72}$

55. $P(\text{two greens})$ $\frac{1}{12}$

Extra Practice

CHAPTER 4

page 705   Extra Practice

16. x = 0.1 · 94, 9.4

17. 10x = 4, 40%

18. 147 = 0.14x, 1050

19. 1.2x = 6, 500%

20. 13.2 = 0.55x, 24

21. x = 0.004 · 800, 3.2

22. x = 0.75 · 68, 51

23. 5 = 2x, $\frac{5}{2}$

24. 54x = 28, 51.9%

1.

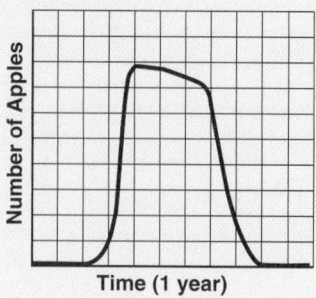

2.

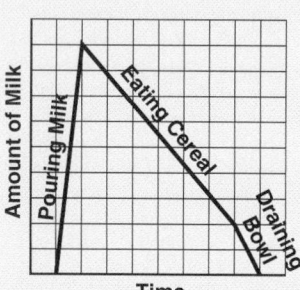

3.

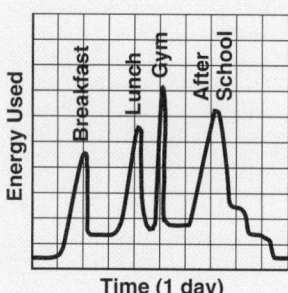

4.

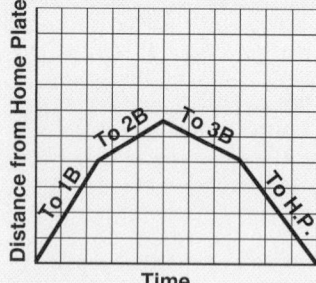

18.

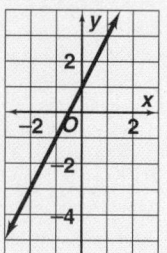

19.

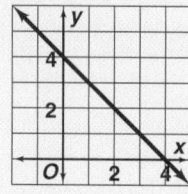

● **Lesson 5-1** **Sketch a graph to describe each situation. Label each section of the graph. 1–4. See margin.**

 1. the number of apples on a tree over one year

 2. the amount of milk in your bowl as you eat cereal

 3. the energy you use in a 24-h period

 4. your distance from home plate after your home run

● **Lesson 5-2** **Find the range of each function when the domain is {−4, −1, 0, 3}.**

 5. $y = 6x - 5$ **{−29, −11, −5, 13}** **6.** $y = |x| - 2$ **{2, −1, −2, 1}** **7.** $y = x^2 + 3x + 1$ **{5, −1, 1, 19}**

 8. $y = \frac{1}{2}x + 8$ **{6, 7.5, 8, 9.5}** **9.** $y = -x^2 - x$ **{−12, 0}** **10.** $y = \frac{2}{3}x$ $\left\{-\frac{8}{3}, -\frac{2}{3}, 0, 2\right\}$

 11. $y = |x - 2|$ **{6, 3, 2, 1}** **12.** $y = 2x^2 - 5$ **{27, −3, −5, 13}** **13.** $y = |4 - x|$ **{8, 5, 4, 1}**

 Use a mapping diagram to determine whether each relation is a function.

 14. $\{(1, 2), (2, 3), (3, 4), (4, 5), (5, 6)\}$ **yes**

 15. $\{(5, 2), (1, 3), (4, 7), (5, 6), (0, 4)\}$ **no**

 16. $\{(3.4, 2), (5.6, 2), (0.1, 2), (2.8, 2)\}$ **yes**

 17. $\{(6, 7), (5, 2), (7, 7), (4, 3), (0, 0)\}$ **yes**

● **Lesson 5-3** **Graph each function. 18–20. See margin.**

 18. $y = 2x + 1$ **19.** $y = 4 - x$ **20.** $y = |x| - 3$

● **Lessons 5-3 and 5-4** **Write a function rule for each table.**

21.

x	$f(x)$
−3	−1
−1	1
1	3
3	5

$f(x) = x + 2$

22.

x	$f(x)$
0	0
3	6
6	12
9	18

$f(x) = 2x$

23.

x	$f(x)$
21	14
25	18
29	22
33	26

$f(x) = x - 7$

24.

x	$f(x)$
−8	−4
−6	−3
−4	−2
−2	−1

$f(x) = \frac{1}{2}x$

25. a. Write a sentence and an equation to describe the relationship between the number of notebooks and the price. **a–b. See margin.**

 b. If you have $5, can you buy a notebook for each of your classes? Explain.

Notebooks	Price
1	$0.99
2	$1.98
3	$2.97

● **Lesson 5-5** **Graph the direct variation that includes the given point. Write the equation of the line. 26–31. See back of book.**

 26. $(5, 4)$ **27.** $(7, 7)$ **28.** $(-3, -10)$

 29. $(4, -8)$ **30.** $(-2, 9)$ **31.** $(11, 1)$

 32. The stretch s of a spring is directly proportional to the force F. A force of 2 newtons produces a stretch of 3 cm. Find the force that produces a stretch of 4.5 cm. **3 newtons**

● **Lesson 5-6** **Find the second and fifth terms of each sequence.**

 33. $A(n) = 22 + (n - 1)11$ **33, 66** **34.** $A(n) = -2 + (n - 1)(-2)$ **−4, −10**

 35. $A(n) = -2 + (n - 1)$ **−1, 2** **36.** $A(n) = 1 + 4(n - 1)$ **5, 17**

20.

25a. Price is the product of $.99 and the number of notebooks. $p = n \cdot 0.99$

 b. yes, if you have fewer than six classes

Chapter 6 Extra Practice

● Lesson 6-1 **Find the rate of change for each situation.**

1. growing from 1.4 m to 1.6 m in one year **0.2 m/yr**

2. bicycling 3 mi in 15 min and 7 mi in 55 min **0.1 mi/min**

3. growing 22.4 mm in 14 s **1.6 mm/s**

4. reading 8 pages in 9 min and 22 pages in 30 min **$\frac{2}{3}$ pages per minute**

Lessons 6-2 to 6-4 Find the slope and y-intercept. 5–8. See margin.

5. $y = 6x + 8$
6. $3x + 4y = -24$
7. $2y = 8$
8. $y = \frac{-3}{4}x - 8$

Find the x- and y-intercepts for each equation. 9–12. See margin.

9. $6x + y = 12$
10. $y = -7x$
11. $y = \frac{1}{2}x + 3$
12. $-2y = 5x - 12$

Write the equation in point-slope form for the line through the given point with the given slope. 13–16. See margin.

13. $(4, 6); m = -5$
14. $(3, -1); m = 1$
15. $(8, 5); m = \frac{1}{2}$
16. $(0, -6); m = \frac{4}{3}$

17. $(-2, 7); m = 2$
    $y - 7 = 2(x + 2)$
18. $(-5, -9); m = -3.5$
    $y + 9 = -3.5(x + 5)$
19. $(4, 0); m = 7$
    $y = 7(x - 4)$
20. $(6, -4); m = -\frac{1}{5}$
    $y + 4 = -\frac{1}{5}(x - 6)$

Graph each equation. 21–28. See margin.

21. $y = 2x - 3$
22. $x + 4y = 8$
23. $y - 5 = -2(x + 1)$
24. $x + 3 = 0$

25. $4x - 3y = 12$
26. $y = -1$
27. $y = \frac{2}{3}x - 4$
28. $y + 1 = -\frac{1}{2}(x + 2)$

A line passes through the given points. Write an equation for the line in slope-intercept form. 29–32. See margin.

29. $(2, 5)$ and $(4, 8)$
30. $(1, 6)$ and $(7, 3)$
31. $(-2, 4)$ and $(3, 9)$
32. $(1, 6)$ and $(9, -4)$

33. $(0, -7)$ and $(-1, 0)$
    $y = -7x - 7$
34. $(7, 0)$ and $(3, -4)$
    $y = x - 7$
35. $(0, 0)$ and $(-7, 1)$
    $y = -\frac{1}{7}x$
36. $(10, 0)$ and $(0, 7)$
    $y = -\frac{7}{10}x + 7$

● Lesson 6-5 **Write an equation in standard form that satisfies the given conditions. 37–44. See back of book.**

37. parallel to $y = 4x + 1$, through $(-3, 5)$
38. perpendicular to $y = -x - 3$, through $(0, 0)$

39. perpendicular to $3x + 4y = 12$, through $(7, 1)$
40. parallel to $2x - y = 6$, through $(-6, -9)$

41. perpendicular to $y = -2x + 5$, through $(4, -10)$
42. parallel to $2y = 5x + 12$, through $(2, -1)$

43. parallel to the x-axis and through $(4, -1)$
44. through $(4, 44)$ and parallel to the y-axis

● Lesson 6-6

45. a. Graph the (ages, grades) data of some students in a school at the right. **a–c. See margin.**
    b. Draw a trend line.
    c. Find the equation of the line of best fit.

    $(10, 6), (16, 10), (15, 10), (18, 12), (17, 11),$
    $(17, 12), (19, 12), (16, 11), (11, 7), (15, 9), (13, 8)$

● Lesson 6-7 **Graph each equation by translating $y = |x|$ or $y = -|x|$. 46–53. See back of book.**

46. $y = |x| + 1$
47. $y = |x + 2|$
48. $y = |x - 2|$
49. $y = -|x - 1|$

50. $y = -|x + 1|$
51. $y = -|x| + 1$
52. $y = |x + 0.5|$
53. $y = |x| - 4$

21.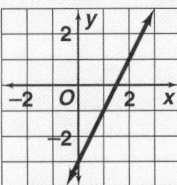
22.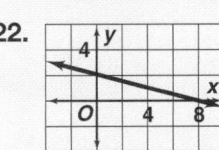
23.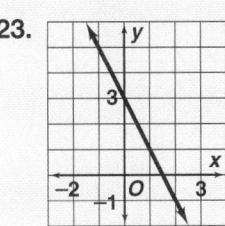
24.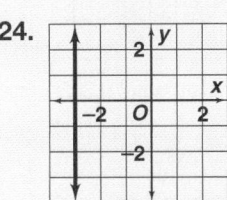
25.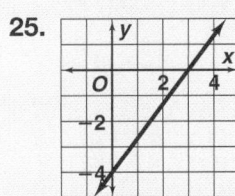
26.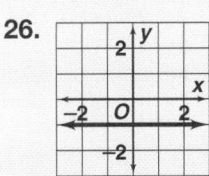
27.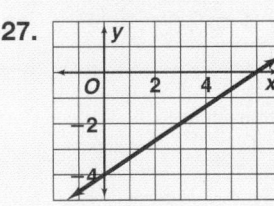
28.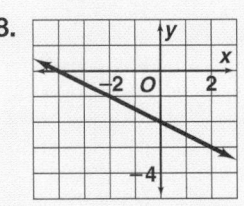

CHAPTER 6

page 707   Extra Practice

5. slope = 6,
   y-intercept = 8

6. slope = $-\frac{3}{4}$,
   y-intercept = -6

7. slope = 0,
   y-intercept = 4

8. slope = $-\frac{3}{4}$,
   y-intercept = -8

9. x-intercept = 2,
   y-intercept = 12

10. x-intercept = 0,
    y-intercept = 0

11. x-intercept = -6,
    y-intercept = 3

12. x-intercept = $\frac{12}{5}$,
    y-intercept = 6

13. $y - 6 = -5(x - 4)$

14. $y + 1 = x - 3$

15. $y - 5 = \frac{1}{2}(x - 8)$

16. $y + 6 = \frac{4}{3}x$

29. $y = \frac{3}{2}x + 2$

30. $y = -\frac{1}{2}x + 6\frac{1}{2}$

31. $y = x + 6$

32. $y = -\frac{5}{4}x + 7\frac{1}{4}$

707

page 708   Extra Practice

1. (4, −3);

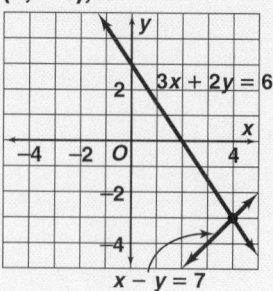

2. (−2, −1);

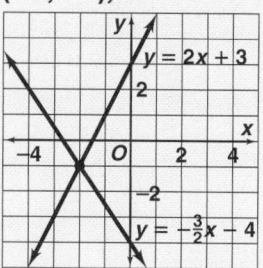

3. (0, 6);

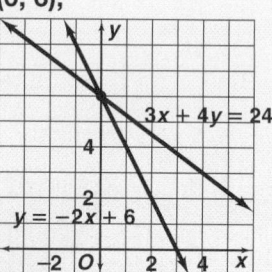

19.

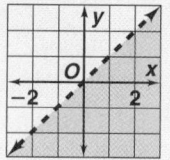

20.

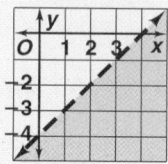

21.

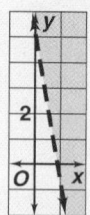

22.

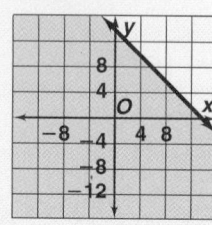

708

● Lesson 7-1 **Solve each system by graphing. 1–3. See margin.**

1. $x - y = 7$
   $3x + 2y = 6$

2. $y = 2x + 3$
   $y = -\frac{3}{2}x - 4$

3. $y = -2x + 6$
   $3x + 4y = 24$

● Lesson 7-2 **Solve each system by using substitution.**

4. $x - y = 13$ **infinite number**
   $y - x = -13$ **of solutions**

5. $3x - y = 4$ **x = 1, y = −1**
   $x + 5y = -4$

6. $x + y = 4$ **x = 0, y = 4**
   $y = 7x + 4$

● Lesson 7-3 **Solve each system by elimination.**

7. $x + y = 19$ **x = 6, y = 13**
   $x - y = -7$

8. $-3x + 4y = 29$ **x = −7, y = 2**
   $3x + 2y = -17$

9. $3x + y = 3$ **x = 4, y = −9**
   $-3x + 2y = -30$

10. $6x + y = 13$ **x = 3, y = −5**
    $y - x = -8$

11. $4x - 9y = 61$ **x = 4, y = −5**
    $10x + 3y = 25$

12. $4x - y = 105$ **x = 25, y = −5**
    $x + 7y = -10$

● Lesson 7-4 **Write a system of equations to model each problem and solve.**

13. Suppose you have 12 coins that total 32 cents. Some of the coins are nickels and the rest are pennies. How many of each coin do you have? **x + y = 12, 5x + y = 32; 5 nickels, 7 pennies**

14. Claire bought three bars of soap and five sponges for $2.31. Steve bought five bars of soap and three sponges for $3.05. Find the cost of each item. **3x + 5y = 2.31, 5x + 3y = 3.05; soap: $.52, sponges: $.15**

15. The perimeter of a rectangular lot is 74 feet. The cost of fencing along the two lengths is $1 per foot, and the cost of fencing along the two widths is $3.50 per foot. Find the dimensions of the lot if the total cost of the fencing is $159. **2x + 2y = 74, 7x + 2y = 159; length: 20 ft, width: 17 ft**

16. A chemist wants to make a 10% solution of fertilizer. How much water and how much of a 30% solution should the chemist mix to get 30 L of a 10% solution? **x + y = 30, x + 0.7y = 0.9(30); water: 20 L, 30% solution: 10 L**

17. Fruit drink A consists of 6% pure fruit juice and drink B consists of 15% pure fruit juice. How much of each kind of drink should you mix together to get 4 L of a 10% concentration of fruit juice? **x + y = 4, 0.06x + 0.15y = 0.1(4); A: $2\frac{2}{9}$ L, B: $1\frac{7}{9}$ L**

18. A motor boat traveled 12 miles with the current, turned around, and returned 12 miles against the current to its starting point. The trip with the current took 2 hours and the trip against the current took 3 hours. Find the speed of the boat and the speed of the current. **(x + y)2 = 12, (x − y)3 = 12; boat: 5 mph, current: 1 mph**

● Lesson 7-5 **Graph each linear inequality. 19–24. See margin.**

19. $y < x$

20. $y < x - 4$

21. $y > -6x + 5$

22. $y \leq 14 - x$

23. $y \geq \frac{1}{4}x - 3$

24. $2x + 3y \leq 6$

● Lesson 7-6 **Solve each system by graphing. 25–30. See margin.**

25. $y \leq 5x + 1$
    $y > x - 3$

26. $y > 4x + 3$
    $y \geq -2x - 1$

27. $y > -x + 2$
    $y > x - 4$

28. $y < -2x + 1$
    $y > -2x - 3$

29. $y \leq 5$
    $y \geq -x + 1$

30. $y \leq 5x - 2$
    $y > 3$

23.

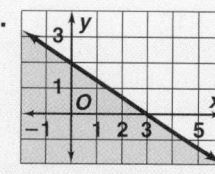

24.

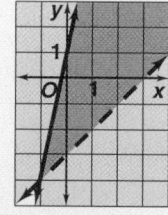

25.

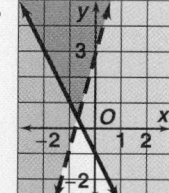

26.

Chapter 8 Extra Practice

 **Lessons 8-1 to 8-5** Simplify each expression. Use only positive exponents.

1. $(2t)^{-6}$ $\frac{1}{64t^6}$

2. $5m^5m^{-8}$ $\frac{5}{m^3}$

3. $(4.5)^4(4.5)^{-2}(4.5)^2$

4. $(m^7t^{-5})^2$ $\frac{m^{14}}{t^{10}}$

5. $(x^2n^4)(n^{-8})$ $\frac{x^2}{n^4}$

6. $(w^{-2}j^{-4})^{-3}(j^7j^3)$ w^6j^{22}

7. $(t^6)^3(m)^2$ $t^{18}m^2$

8. $(3n^4)^2$ $9n^8$

9. $\frac{r^5}{g^{-3}}$ r^5g^3

10. $\frac{1}{a^{-4}}$ a^4

11. $\frac{w^7}{w^{-6}}$ w^{13}

12. $\frac{6}{t^{-4}}$ $6t^4$

13. $\frac{a^2b^{-7}c^4}{a^5b^3c^{-2}}$ $\frac{c^6}{a^3b^{10}}$

14. $\frac{(2t^5)^3}{4t^8t^{-1}}$ $2t^8$

15. $\left(\frac{a^6}{a^7}\right)^{-3}$ a^3

16. $\left(\frac{c^5c^{-3}}{c^{-4}}\right)^{-2}$ $\frac{1}{c^{12}}$

Evaluate each expression for $m = 2, t = -3, w = 4,$ and $z = 0.$

17. t^m 9

18. t^{-m} $\frac{1}{9}$

19. $(w \cdot t)^m$ 144

20. $w^m \cdot t^m$ 144

21. $(w^z)^m$ 1

22. w^mw^z 16

23. $z^{-t}(m^t)^z$ 0

24. $w^{-t}t^t$ $-\frac{64}{27}$

Write each number in scientific notation.

25. 34,000,000 3.4×10^7

26. 0.00063 6.3×10^{-4}

27. 1500 1.5×10^3

28. 0.0002 2×10^{-4}

29. 360,000 3.6×10^5

30. 6,200,000,000 6.2×10^9

31. 0.05 5×10^{-2}

32. 0.000000000891 8.91×10^{-10}

Write each number in standard notation.

33. 8.05×10^6 8,050,000

34. 3.2×10^{-7} 0.00000032

35. 9.0×10^8 900,000,000

36. 4.25×10^{-4} 0.000425

37. 2.35×10^2 235

38. 6.3×10^4 63,000

39. 2.001×10^{-5} 0.00002001

40. 5.2956×10^3 5295.6

 **Lesson 8-6** Find the common ratio of each sequence. Then find the next two terms. 41–48. See margin.

41. $12, 18, 27, \ldots$

42. $2, 1, 0.5, \ldots$

43. $-1, -0.2, -0.04, \ldots$

44. $-2, -4, -8, \ldots$

45. $2, 6, 18, \ldots$

46. $1.2, -0.6, 0.3, \ldots$

47. $30, 10, \frac{10}{3}, \ldots$

48. $-2.25, -9, -36, \ldots$

 **Lesson 8-7** Evaluate each function for the domain $\{-1, 0, 1, 2\}$. As the values of the domain increase, do the values of the function *increase* or *decrease*? 49–60. See margin.

49. $y = 3^x$

50. $y = \left(\frac{3}{4}\right)^x$

51. $y = 1.5^x$

52. $y = \frac{1}{2} \cdot 3^x$

53. $y = -3 \cdot 7^x$

54. $y = -(4)^x$

55. $y = 3 \cdot \left(\frac{1}{5}\right)^x$

56. $y = 2^x$

57. $y = 2 \cdot 3^x$

58. $y = (0.8)^x$

59. $y = 2.5^x$

60. $y = -4 \cdot (0.2)^x$

 **Lesson 8-8** Identify each function as *exponential growth* or *exponential decay*. Then identify the growth factor or decay factor. 61–68. See margin.

61. $y = 8^x$

62. $y = \frac{3}{4} \cdot 2^x$

63. $y = 9 \cdot \left(\frac{1}{2}\right)^x$

64. $y = 4 \cdot 9^x$

65. $y = 0.65^x$

66. $y = 3 \cdot 1.5^x$

67. $y = \frac{2}{5} \cdot \left(\frac{1}{4}\right)^x$

68. $y = 0.1 \cdot 0.9^x$

Write an exponential function to model each situation. Find each amount after the specified time.

69. $200 principal, 4% compounded annually for 5 years $y = 200(1.04)^x$; \$243.33

70. $1000 principal, 3.6% compounded monthly for 10 years $y = 1000(1.003)^x$; \$1432.56

71. $3000 investment, 8% loss each year for 3 years $y = 3000(0.92)^x$; \$2336.06

41. 1.5; 40.5, 60.75

42. 0.5; 0.25, 0.125

43. 0.2; −0.008, −0.0016

44. 2; −16, −32

45. 3; 54, 162

46. −0.5; −0.15, 0.075

47. $\frac{1}{3}$; $\frac{10}{9}$, $\frac{10}{27}$

48. 4; −144, −576

49. $\left\{\frac{1}{3}, 1, 3, 9\right\}$; increase

50. $\left\{\frac{4}{3}, 1, \frac{3}{4}, \frac{9}{16}\right\}$; decrease

51. $\left\{\frac{2}{3}, 1, \frac{3}{2}, \frac{9}{4}\right\}$; increase

52. $\left\{\frac{1}{6}, \frac{1}{2}, \frac{3}{2}, \frac{9}{2}\right\}$; increase

53. $\left\{-\frac{3}{7}, -3, -21, -147\right\}$; decrease

54. $\left\{-\frac{1}{4}, -1, -4, -16\right\}$; decrease

55. $\left\{15, 3, \frac{3}{5}, \frac{3}{25}\right\}$; decrease

56. $\left\{\frac{1}{2}, 1, 2, 4\right\}$; increase

57. $\left\{\frac{2}{3}, 2, 6, 18\right\}$; increase

58. $\left\{\frac{5}{4}, 1, \frac{4}{5}, \frac{16}{25}\right\}$; decrease

59. $\left\{\frac{2}{5}, 1, \frac{5}{2}, \frac{25}{4}\right\}$; increase

60. $\left\{-20, -4, -\frac{4}{5}, -\frac{4}{25}\right\}$; increase

61. exponential growth; growth factor = 8

62. exponential growth; growth factor = 2

63. exponential decay; decay factor = $\frac{1}{2}$

64. exponential growth; growth factor = 9

65. exponential decay; decay factor = 0.65

66. exponential growth; growth factor = 1.5

67. exponential decay; decay factor = $\frac{1}{4}$

68. exponential decay; decay factor = 0.9

27.

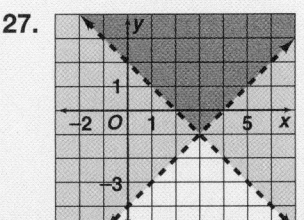

28.

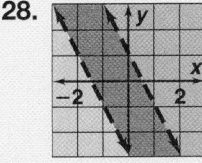

29.

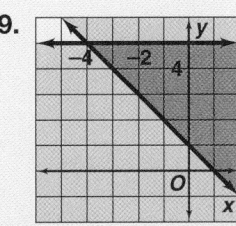

30.

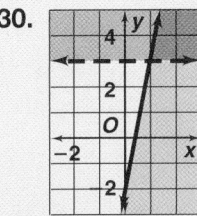

page 710 Extra Practice

1. $2x^3 + 4x^2 - 11x + 11$

2. $5x^2 - 2x$

3. $6m^3 + m + 4$

4. $-t^2 + 10t + 11$

5. $-10c^3 - c^2 - 9c - 7$

6. $-19v^3 - v^2 + 13v$

7. $-4s^4 - 2s^3 + 2s^2 + 4s$

8. $4w^2 + 14w + 17$

19. $t^2(t^4 - t^3 + t^2 + 1)$

20. $3(m^2 + 3m - 2)$

21. $4c^2(3c^3 - c + 4)$

22. $-2v^5(5v^4 - 4v - 1)$

23. $n^2(2n^2 - 3n + 6)$

24. $5r(4r^2 + 3r + 1)$

25. $x^5(4x^2 + 9x + 5)$

26. $-d^4(2d^6 - 4d^4 - 7)$

27. $-5c^2 + 7c + 6$

28. $6t^2 + t - 1$

29. $w^3 + 4w^2 + 3w - 2$

30. $3t^2 + 8t + 5$

31. $4n^2 + 2n - 12$

32. $b^2 + 10b + 21$

33. $9x^2 + 6x + 1$

34. $25t^2 + 40t + 16$

35. $w^3 - 1$

36. $a^2 - 16$

37. $9y^2 - 4$

38. $w^4 - 4$

41. $(x - 3)(x - 1)$

42. $(3x - 1)(x - 1)$

43. $(v - 1)(v + 2)$

44. $(t - 2)(5t + 9)$

45. $(m - 2)(m + 11)$

46. $(x - 5)(x + 3)$

47. $(n - 1)(2n + 3)$

48. $(h - 3)(2h + 1)$

49. $(m - 5)(m + 5)$

50. $(3y + 1)(3y - 1)$

51. $(3y + 1)^2$

52. $(p + 1)^2$

53. $(x + 3)^2$

710

● **Lesson 9-1 Simplify. Write each answer in standard form. 1–8. See margin.**

1. $(5x^3 + 3x^2 - 7x + 10) - (3x^3 - x^2 + 4x - 1)$ 2. $(x^2 + 3x - 2) + (4x^2 - 5x + 2)$

3. $(4m^3 + 7m - 4) + (2m^3 - 6m + 8)$ 4. $(8t^2 + t + 10) - (9t^2 - 9t - 1)$

5. $(-7c^3 + c^2 - 8c - 11) - (3c^3 + 2c^2 + c - 4)$ 6. $(6v + 3v^2 - 9v^3) + (7v - 4v^2 - 10v^3)$

7. $(s^4 - s^3 - 5s^2 + 3s) - (5s^4 + s^3 - 7s^2 - s)$ 8. $(9w - 4w^2 + 10) + (8w^2 + 7 + 5w)$

9. The sides of a rectangle are $4t - 1$ and $5t + 9$. Write an expression for the perimeter of the rectangle. **$18t + 16$**

10. Three consecutive integers are $n - 1$, n, and $n + 1$. Write an expression for the sum of the three integers. **$3n$**

● **Lesson 9-2 Simplify each product.**

11. $4b(b^2 + 3)$ $4b^3 + 12b$ 12. $9c(c^2 - 3c + 5)$ $9c^3 - 27c^2 + 45c$ 13. $8m(4m - 5)$ $32m^2 - 40m$ 14. $5k(k^2 + 8k)$ $5k^3 + 40k^2$

15. $5r^2(r^2 + 4r - 2)$ $5r^4 + 20r^3 - 10r^2$ 16. $2m^2(m^3 + m - 2)$ $2m^5 + 2m^3 - 4m^2$ 17. $-3x(x^2 + 3x - 1)$ $-3x^3 - 9x^2 + 3x$ 18. $-x(1 + x + x^2)$ $-x^3 - x^2 - x$

Find the GCF of the terms of each polynomial. Factor. 19–26. See margin.

19. $t^6 + t^4 - t^5 + t^2$ 20. $3m^2 - 6 + 9m$ 21. $16c^2 - 4c^3 + 12c^5$ 22. $8v^6 + 2v^5 - 10v^9$

23. $6n^2 - 3n^3 + 2n^4$ 24. $5r + 20r^3 + 15r^2$ 25. $9x^6 + 5x^5 + 4x^7$ 26. $4d^8 - 2d^{10} + 7d^4$

● **Lessons 9-3 and 9-4 Simplify each product. Write in standard form. 27–38. See margin.**

27. $(5c + 3)(-c + 2)$ 28. $(3t - 1)(2t + 1)$ 29. $(w + 2)(w^2 + 2w - 1)$ 30. $(3t + 5)(t + 1)$

31. $(2n - 3)(2n + 4)$ 32. $(b + 3)(b + 7)$ 33. $(3x + 1)^2$ 34. $(5t + 4)^2$

35. $(w - 1)(w^2 + w + 1)$ 36. $(a + 4)(a - 4)$ 37. $(3y - 2)(3y + 2)$ 38. $(w^2 + 2)(w^2 - 2)$

39. **Geometry** A rectangle has dimensions $3x - 1$ and $2x + 5$. Write an expression for the area of the rectangle as a product and in standard form. **$(3x - 1)(2x + 5), 6x^2 + 13x - 5$**

40. Write an expression for the product of the two consecutive odd integers $n - 1$ and $n + 1$. **$(n - 1)(n + 1) = n^2 - 1$**

● **Lessons 9-5 to 9-7 Factor each expression. 41–60. See margin.**

41. $x^2 - 4x + 3$ 42. $3x^2 - 4x + 1$ 43. $v^2 + v - 2$ 44. $5t^2 - t - 18$

45. $m^2 + 9m - 22$ 46. $x^2 - 2x - 15$ 47. $2n^2 + n - 3$ 48. $2h^2 - 5h - 3$

49. $m^2 - 25$ 50. $9y^2 - 1$ 51. $9y^2 + 6y + 1$ 52. $p^2 + 2p + 1$

53. $x^2 + 6x + 9$ 54. $25x^2 - 9$ 55. $4t^2 + t - 3$ 56. $9c^2 - 169$

57. $4m^2 - 121$ 58. $3v^2 + 10v - 8$ 59. $4g^2 + 4g + 1$ 60. $-w^2 + 5w - 4$

61. $9t^2 + 12t + 4$ $(3t + 2)^2$ 62. $12m^2 - 5m - 2$ $(3m - 2)(4m + 1)$ 63. $36s^2 - 1$ $(6s + 1)(6s - 1)$ 64. $c^2 - 10c + 25$ $(c - 5)^2$

● **Lesson 9-8 Factor each expression. 65–72. See margin.**

65. $3y^3 + 9y^2 - y - 3$ 66. $3u^3 + u^2 - 6u - 2$ 67. $w^3 - 3w^2 + 3w - 9$ 68. $4z^3 + 2z^2 - 2z - 1$

69. $3x^3 + 8x^2 - 3x$ 70. $y^5 - 9y$ 71. $2p^3 - 4p^2 + 2p - 4$ 72. $3y^3 - 3y^2 - 6y$

---

54. $(5x + 3)(5x - 3)$

55. $(t + 1)(4t - 3)$

56. $(3c - 13)(3c + 13)$

57. $(2m + 11)(2m - 11)$

58. $(v + 4)(3v - 2)$

59. $(2g + 1)^2$

60. $-(w - 4)(w - 1)$

65. $(y + 3)(3y^2 - 1)$

66. $(3u + 1)(u^2 - 2)$

67. $(w - 3)(w^2 + 3)$

68. $(2z + 1)(2z^2 - 1)$

69. $x(x + 3)(3x - 1)$

70. $y(y^2 - 3)(y^2 + 3)$

71. $2(p - 2)(p^2 + 1)$

72. $3y(y - 2)(y + 1)$

Extra Practice

Lessons 10-1 and 10-2 Without graphing, describe how each graph differs from the graph of $y = x^2$. 1–8. **See margin.**

1. $y = 3x^2$ **2.** $y = -4x^2$ **3.** $y = -0.5x^2$ **4.** $y = 0.2x^2$

5. $y = x^2 - 4$ **6.** $y = x^2 + 1$ **7.** $y = 2x^2 + 5$ **8.** $y = -0.3x^2 - 7$

Identify the axis of symmetry and the vertex of each function.

9. $y = 3x^2$ **x = 0, (0, 0)**   **10.** $y = -2x^2 + 1$ **x = 0, (0, 1)**   **11.** $y = 0.5x^2 - 3$ **x = 0, (0, -3)**

12. $y = -x^2 + 2x + 1$ **x = 1, (1, 2)**   **13.** $y = 3x^2 + 6x$ **x = -1, (-1, -3)**   **14.** $y = \frac{3}{4}x^2$ **x = 0, (0, 0)**

15. $y = 2x^2 - 9$ **x = 0, (0, -9)**   **16.** $y = -5x^2 + x + 4$ **17.** $y = x^2 - 8x$ **x = 4, (4, -16)**
$x = \frac{1}{10}, \left(\frac{1}{10}, \frac{81}{20}\right)$

Graph each quadratic inequality. 18–20. **See margin.**

18. $y > x^2 - 4$ **19.** $y < 2x^2 + x$ **20.** $y \le x^2 + x - 2$

Lesson 10-3 Find the square roots of each number.

21. 25 **±5**   **22.** $\frac{4}{9}$ **$\pm\frac{2}{3}$**   **23.** 64 **±8**   **24.** $\frac{25}{36}$ **$\pm\frac{5}{6}$**   **25.** 0.81 **±0.9**   **26.** 900 **±30**

27. 144 **±12**   **28.** 324 **±18**   **29.** $\frac{16}{225}$ **$\pm\frac{4}{15}$**   **30.** 0.0001 **±0.01**   **31.** 3600 **±60**   **32.** $\frac{1}{9}$ **$\pm\frac{1}{3}$**

Lessons 10-4 to 10-7 Solve each equation. If the equation has no solution, write *no solution*.

33. $x^2 = 36$ **6, −6**   **34.** $x^2 + x - 2 = 0$ **1, −2**   **35.** $c^2 - 100 = 0$ **10, −10**

36. $9d^2 = 25$ **$\frac{5}{3}, -\frac{5}{3}$**   **37.** $(x - 4)^2 = 100$ **14, −6**   **38.** $3x^2 = 27$ **3, −3**

39. $2x^2 - 54 = 284$ **13, −13**   **40.** $7n^2 = 63$ **3, −3**   **41.** $h^2 + 4 = 0$ **no solution**

42. $x^2 + 6x - 2 = 0$ **$-3 \pm \sqrt{11}$**   **43.** $x^2 - 5x = 7$ **$\frac{5 \pm \sqrt{53}}{2}$**   **44.** $x^2 - 10x + 3 = 0$ **$5 \pm \sqrt{22}$**

45. $2x^2 - 4x + 1 = 0$ **$\frac{2 \pm \sqrt{2}}{2}$**   **46.** $3x^2 + x + 5 = 0$ **no solution**   **47.** $\frac{1}{2}x^2 - 3x - 8 = 0$ **8, −2**

48. $x^2 + 8x + 4 = 0$ **$-4 \pm 2\sqrt{3}$**   **49.** $x^2 - 2x - 6 = 0$ **$1 \pm \sqrt{7}$**   **50.** $-3x^2 + x - 7 = 0$ **no solution**

51. $x^2 + 5x + 6 = 0$ **−2, −3**   **52.** $d^2 - 144 = 0$ **12, −12**   **53.** $c^2 + 6 = 2 - 4c$ **−2**

54. $x^2 + 4x = 2x^2 - x + 6$ **3, 2**   **55.** $3x^2 + 2x - 12 = x^2$ **2, −3**   **56.** $r^2 + 4r + 1 = r$ **$\frac{-3 \pm \sqrt{5}}{2}$**

57. $d^2 + 2d + 10 = 2d + 100$ **$\pm 3\sqrt{10}$**   **58.** $3c^2 + c - 10 = c^2 - 5$ **$\frac{-1 \pm \sqrt{41}}{4}$**   **59.** $t^2 - 3t - 10 = 0$ **5, −2**

60. **Agriculture** You are planting a rectangular garden. It is 5 feet longer than 3 times its width. The area of the garden is 250 ft². Find the dimensions of the garden. **$\frac{25}{3}$ ft by 30 ft**

Lesson 10-8 Find the number of solutions of each equation.

61. $3x^2 + 4x - 7 = 0$ **2**   **62.** $5x^2 - 4x = -6$ **0**   **63.** $x^2 - 20x + 101 = 1$ **1**

64. $2x^2 - 8x + 9 = 4$ **2**   **65.** $4x^2 - 5x + 6 = 0$ **0**   **66.** $x^2 - 2x + 7 = 0$ **0**

Lesson 10-9 Graph each set of data. Which model is most appropriate for each set? 67–69. **See margin.**

67. $(2, 4), (4, 4), (1, 2), (5, 1.5)$ **68.** $(3, 8), (4, 6), (5, 5), (6, 4), (7, 3)$ **69.** $(0, 7), (1, 3), (3, 0.5), (2, 1)$

18.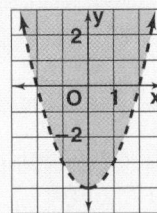

19.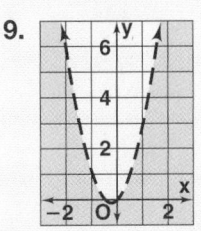

20.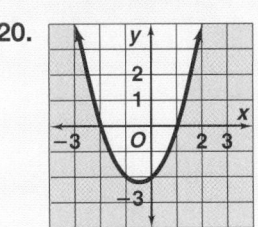

67. quadratic
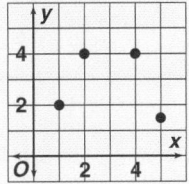

68. linear
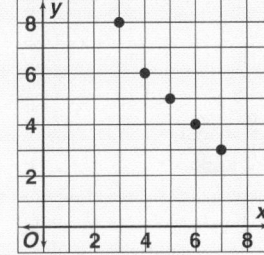

69. exponential
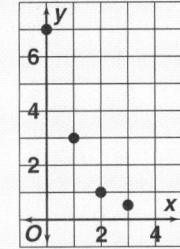

CHAPTER 10

page 711 Extra Practice

1. narrower

2. narrower and reflected over the *x*-axis

3. wider and reflected over the *x*-axis

4. wider

5. translated down 4 units

6. translated up 1 unit

7. narrower and translated up 5 units

8. wider, reflected over the *x*-axis, and translated down 7 units

CHAPTER 11

20. $\sqrt{6} + \sqrt{2} - \sqrt{3} - 1$

21. no; $16 + 25 \neq 49$

22. yes; $6^2 + 8^2 = 10^2$

23. no; $6^2 + 9^2 \neq 13^2$

24. no; $10^2 + 13^2 \neq 17^2$

33. 5.1; $\left(\frac{3}{2}, \frac{11}{2}\right)$

34. 15.3; $\left(-\frac{1}{2}, -6\right)$

35. 1.4; $\left(\frac{9}{2}, -\frac{1}{2}\right)$

36. 8.1; $\left(-\frac{1}{2}, 3\right)$

37. 25.5; $(2, -2)$

38. 5; $\left(\frac{5}{2}, -4\right)$

39. 17.0; $\left(-\frac{3}{2}, \frac{3}{2}\right)$

40. 3.6; $\left(-1, \frac{15}{2}\right)$

41. 11.2; $\left(\frac{5}{2}, 5\right)$

● **Lessons 11-1 and 11-4** Simplify each radical expression.

1. $\frac{\sqrt{27}}{\sqrt{81}}$ $\frac{\sqrt{3}}{3}$

2. $\sqrt{\frac{25}{4}}$ $\frac{5}{2}$

3. $\sqrt{\frac{50}{9}}$ $\frac{5\sqrt{2}}{3}$

4. $\frac{\sqrt{72}}{\sqrt{50}}$ $\frac{6}{5}$

5. $\sqrt{75} - 4\sqrt{75}$ $-15\sqrt{3}$

6. $\sqrt{5}(\sqrt{20} - \sqrt{80})$ -10

7. $\sqrt{25} \cdot \sqrt{4}$ 10

8. $\sqrt{6}(\sqrt{6} - 3)$ $6 - 3\sqrt{6}$

9. $3\sqrt{300} + 2\sqrt{27}$ $36\sqrt{3}$

10. $5\sqrt{2} \cdot 3\sqrt{50}$ 150

11. $\sqrt{8} - 4\sqrt{2}$ $-2\sqrt{2}$

12. $\sqrt{27} \cdot \sqrt{3}$ 9

13. $\frac{\sqrt{3c^2}}{\sqrt{27}}$ $\frac{c}{3}$

14. $\frac{\sqrt{z^3}}{\sqrt{5z}}$ $\frac{z\sqrt{5}}{5}$

15. $\sqrt{\frac{44x^4}{11}}$ $2x^2$

16. $(\sqrt{5} + 1)(\sqrt{5} - 1)$ 4

17. $(\sqrt{3} + \sqrt{2})^2$ $5 + 2\sqrt{6}$

18. $\frac{1}{\sqrt{2} + 1}$ $\sqrt{2} - 1$

19. $\frac{2}{\sqrt{2} - 2}$ $-\left(\sqrt{2} + 2\right)$

20. $\frac{\sqrt{3} + 1}{\sqrt{2} + 1}$

● **Lesson 11-2** Determine whether the given lengths are sides of a right triangle. 20–24. See margin.

21. $4, 5, 7$

22. $6, 8, 10$

23. $6, 9, 13$

24. $10, 13, 17$

25. $15, 36, 39$
yes; $15^2 + 36^2 = 39^2$

26. $3, 7, 10$
no; $3^2 + 7^2 \neq 10^2$

27. $8, 15, 17$
yes; $8^2 + 15^2 = 17^2$

28. $\sqrt{3}, \sqrt{4}, \sqrt{5}$
no; $3 + 4 \neq 5$

For the values given, a and b are legs of a right triangle. Find the length of the hypotenuse. If necessary, round to the nearest tenth.

29. $a = 6, b = 8$ 10

30. $a = 5, b = 9$ 10.3

31. $a = 4, b = 10$ 10.8

32. $a = 9, b = 1$ 9.1

● **Lesson 11-3** Find the distance between each pair of points. If necessary, round your answer to the nearest tenth. Then find the midpoint of each segment. 33–41. See margin.

33. $A(1, 3), B(2, 8)$

34. $R(6, -2), S(-7, -10)$

35. $G(4, 0), H(5, -1)$

36. $A(-4, 1), B(3, 5)$

37. $G(11, 7), H(-7, -11)$

38. $R(1, -6), S(4, -2)$

39. $R(-8, -4), S(5, 7)$

40. $A(0, 6), B(-2, 9)$

41. $G(5, 10), H(0, 0)$

● **Lesson 11-5** Solve each radical equation. Check your solution.

42. $\sqrt{3x + 4} = 1$ -1

43. $6 = \sqrt{8x - 4}$ 5

44. $2x = \sqrt{14x - 6}$ $\frac{1}{2}, 3$

45. $\sqrt{2x + 5} = \sqrt{3x + 1}$ 4

46. $2x = \sqrt{6x + 4}$ 2

47. $\sqrt{5x + 11} = \sqrt{7x - 1}$ 6

48. $\sqrt{3x - 2} = x$ $1, 2$

49. $\sqrt{x + 7} = x + 1$ 2

50. $\sqrt{x + 3} = \frac{x + 9}{5}$ $1, 6$

● **Lesson 11-6** Find the domain of each function. Then graph the function. 51–56. See back of book.

51. $y = \sqrt{x + 5}$

52. $y = \sqrt{x - 2}$

53. $y = \sqrt{x + 1}$

54. $y = \sqrt{x} - 4$

55. $y = \sqrt{x} - 3$

56. $y = \sqrt{x} + 6$

● **Lesson 11-7** Use $\triangle ABC$ to find the value of each expression.

57. $\sin A$ $\frac{9}{41}$

58. $\cos A$ $\frac{40}{41}$

59. $\tan A$ $\frac{9}{40}$

60. $\sin B$ $\frac{40}{41}$

61. $\cos B$ $\frac{9}{41}$

62. $\tan B$ $\frac{40}{9}$

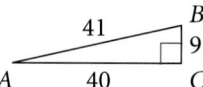

Find the value of each expression. Round to the nearest ten-thousandth.

63. $\sin 72°$ 0.9511

64. $\cos 29°$ 0.8746

65. $\tan 48°$ 1.1106

66. $\tan 52°$ 1.2799

67. A forester is 50 m from the base of a tree and measures the angle between the ground and the top of the tree. If the angle is 76°, find the height of the tree. Round your answer to the nearest meter. **201 m**

Lesson 12-1 Find the constant of variation k for each inverse variation.

1. $y = 10$ when $x = 7$ **70**

2. $y = -8$ when $x = 12$ **−96**

3. $y = 0.2$ when $x = 4$ **0.8**

4. $y = 4$ when $x = -5$ **−20**

5. $y = 0.1$ when $x = 6$ **0.6**

6. $y = -3$ when $x = -7$ **21**

Each pair of points is on the graph of an inverse variation. Find the missing value.

7. $(5.4, 3)$ and $(2, y)$ **8.1**

8. $(x, 4)$ and $(5, 6)$ **7.5**

9. $(3, 6)$ and $(9, y)$ **2**

10. $(100, 2)$ and $(x, 25)$ **8**

11. $(6, 1)$ and $(x, -2)$ **−3**

12. $(8, y)$ and $(-2, 4)$ **−1**

Lesson 12-2 Identify the asymptotes of each function. Then graph the function. 13–20. **See margin.**

13. $y = \frac{6}{x}$

14. $y = \frac{8}{x + 2}$

15. $y = \frac{4}{x} - 3$

16. $y = \frac{5}{x + 1} + 3$

17. $y = \frac{5}{x} - 1$

18. $y = \frac{2}{x - 1}$

19. $y = \frac{3}{x} + 4$

20. $y = \frac{2}{x + 1} - 1$

Lessons 12-3 to 12-6 Simplify each expression.

21. $\frac{4t^2}{16t}$ **$\frac{t}{4}$**

22. $\frac{c - 5}{c^2 - 25}$ **$\frac{1}{c + 5}$**

23. $\frac{4m - 12}{m - 3}$ **4**

24. $\frac{a^2 + 2a - 3}{a + 3}$ **$a - 1$**

25. $\frac{4}{x} - \frac{3}{x}$ **$\frac{1}{x}$**

26. $\frac{6t}{5} + \frac{4t}{5}$ **$2t$**

27. $\frac{6}{c} + \frac{4}{c^2}$ **$\frac{6c + 4}{c^2}$**

28. $\frac{6}{3d} - \frac{4}{3d}$ **$\frac{2}{3d}$**

29. $\frac{5s^4}{10s^3}$ **$\frac{s}{2}$**

30. $\frac{4n^2}{7} \cdot \frac{14}{2n^3}$ **$\frac{4}{n}$**

31. $\frac{8b^2 - 4b}{3b^2} \div \frac{2b - 1}{9b}$ **12**

32. $\frac{v^5}{v^3} \cdot \frac{4v^{-1}}{v^2}$ **$\frac{4}{v}$**

33. $\frac{5}{t + 4} + \frac{3}{t - 4}$ **$\frac{8(t - 1)}{t^2 - 16}$**

34. $\frac{8}{m^2 + 6m + 5} + \frac{4}{m + 1}$ **$\frac{4(m + 7)}{(m + 1)(m + 5)}$**

35. $\frac{3y}{4y - 8} \div \frac{9y}{2y^2 - 4y}$ **$\frac{y}{6}$**

36. $\frac{4}{d^2} - \frac{3}{d^3}$ **$\frac{4d - 3}{d^3}$**

Divide.

37. $(2x^3 - x^2 - 13x - 6) \div (x - 3)$ **$2x^2 + 5x + 2$**

38. $(3x^3 - 3) \div (x + 1)$ **$3x^2 - 3x + 3 - \frac{6}{x + 1}$**

39. $(3x^3 + 5x^2 - 22x + 24) \div (x + 4)$ **$3x^2 - 7x + 6$**

40. $(3x^3 - 3) \div (x - 1)$ **$3(x^2 + x + 1)$**

Lesson 12-7 Solve each equation. Check your answer.

41. $\frac{1}{4} + \frac{1}{x} = \frac{3}{8}$ **8**

42. $\frac{4}{m} - 3 = \frac{2}{m}$ **$\frac{2}{3}$**

43. $\frac{1}{b - 3} = \frac{1}{4b}$ **−1**

44. $\frac{4}{x - 1} = \frac{3}{x}$ **−3**

45. $\frac{4}{n} + \frac{5}{9} = 1$ **9**

46. $\frac{x}{x + 2} = \frac{x - 3}{x + 1}$ **−3**

47. $t - \frac{8}{t} = \frac{17}{t}$ **5, −5**

48. $\frac{x + 2}{x + 5} = \frac{x - 4}{x + 4}$ **$-\frac{28}{5}$**

49. $\frac{4}{c + 1} - \frac{2}{c - 1} = \frac{3c + 6}{c^2 - 1}$ **−12**

50. $\frac{4}{m + 3} = \frac{6}{m - 3}$ **−15**

51. $\frac{4}{t + 5} + 1 = \frac{15}{t^2 - 25}$ **6, −10**

Lessons 12-8 and 12-9 Simplify each expression.

52. ${}_6C_4$ **15**

53. ${}_7P_2$ **42**

54. ${}_{10}C_5$ **252**

55. ${}_8C_7$ **8**

56. ${}_{12}P_6$ **665,280**

57. ${}_9C_7$ **36**

58. How many four-letter groups can be made with the letters A, B, C, and D if no letter can be repeated? **24**

59. Two people are running for president, three are running for vice-president, and two are running for speaker. How many election results are possible? **12**

60. **a.** Suppose your bank assigns a four-digit personal identification number for your bank card. The first digit cannot be zero. How many different numbers are possible? **9000**

   b. What is the probability that the number you are given is 4861? **$\frac{1}{9000}$**

15. $x = 0, y = -3$;

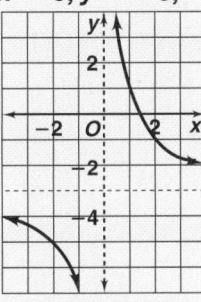

16. $x = -1, y = 3$;

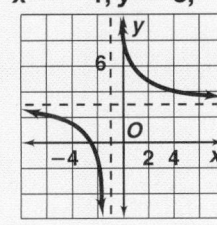

17. $x = 0, y = -1$;

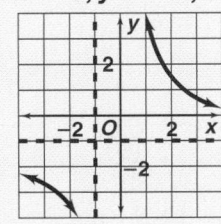

18. $x = 1, y = 0$;

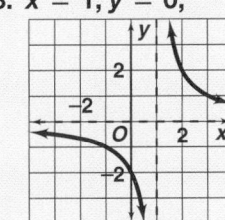

19. $x = 0, y = 4$;

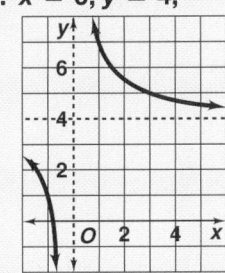

20. $x = -1, y = -1$;

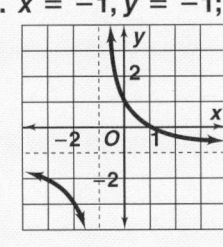

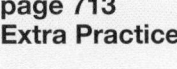

CHAPTER 12

page 713
Extra Practice

13. $x = 0, y = 0$;

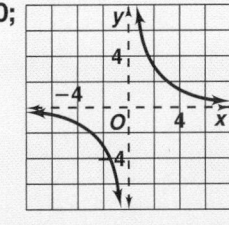

14. $x = -2, y = 0$;

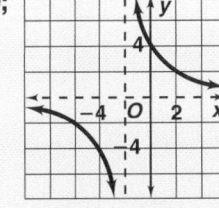

713

Skills Handbook

Problem Solving Strategies

You may find one or more of these strategies helpful in solving a word problem.

STRATEGY	WHEN TO USE IT
Draw a Diagram	The problem describes a picture or diagram.
Try, Check, Revise	Solving the problem directly is too complicated.
Look for a Pattern	The problem describes a relationship.
Make a Table	The problem has data that need to be organized.
Solve a Simpler Problem	The problem is complex or has numbers that are too cumbersome to use at first.
Use Logical Reasoning	You need to reach a conclusion using given information.
Work Backward	You need to find the number that led to the result in the problem.

Problem Solving: Draw a Diagram

> **EXAMPLE**
>
> Two cars started from the same point. One traveled east at 45 mi/h and the other west at 50 mi/h. How far apart were the cars after 5 hours?
>
> Draw a diagram.
>
>
>
> West $\longleftarrow$ 50 mi/h · 5 —— Start —— 45 mi/h · 5 $\longrightarrow$ East
>
> The first car traveled 45 · 5 or 225 mi. The second car traveled 50 · 5 or 250 mi.
>
> The diagram shows that the two distances should be added: $225 + 250 = 475$ mi.
>
> ● After 5 hours, the cars were 475 mi apart.

EXERCISES

1. Jason, Lee, Melda, Aaron, and Bonnie want to play one another in tennis. How many games will be played? **10 games**

2. A playground, a zoo, a picnic area, and a flower garden will be in four corners of a new park. Straight paths will connect each of these areas to all the other areas. How many pathways will be built? **6 paths**

3. Pedro wants to tack 4 posters on a bulletin board. He will tack the four corners of each poster, overlapping the sides of each poster a little bit. What is the least number of tacks that Pedro can use? **9 tacks**

Problem Solving: Try, Check, Revise

When you are not sure how to start, guess an answer and then test it. In the process of testing a guess, you may see a way of revising your guess to get closer to the answer or to get the exact answer.

EXAMPLE

Maria bought books and CDs as gifts. Altogether she bought 12 gifts and spent $84. The books cost $6 each and the CDs cost $9 each. How many of each gift did she buy?

Trial 6 books   **Test** $6 \cdot \$6 = $ $36
         6 CDs $6 \cdot \$9 = $ $+\$54$
                                                $90

Revise your guess. You need fewer CDs to bring the total cost down.

Trial 7 books   **Test** $7 \cdot \$6 = $ $42
         5 CDs $5 \cdot \$9 = $ $+\$45$
                                                $87

The cost is still too high.

Trial 8 books   **Test** $8 \cdot \$6 = $ $48
         4 CDs $4 \cdot \$9 = $ $+\$36$
                                                $84

Maria bought 8 books and 4 CDs.

EXERCISES

1. Find two consecutive odd integers whose product is 323. **17 and 19, or −19 and −17**

2. Find three consecutive integers whose sum is 81. **26, 27, and 28**

3. Find four consecutive integers whose sum is 138. **33, 34, 35, and 36**

4. Mika bought 9 rolls of film to take 180 pictures on a field trip. Some rolls had 36 exposures and the rest had 12 exposures. How many of each type did Mika buy? **3 36-exp. rolls and 6 12-exp. rolls**

5. Tanya is 18 years old. Her brother Shawn is 16 years younger. How old will Tanya be when she is 3 times as old as Shawn? **24 years old**

6. Steven has 100 ft of fencing and wants to build a fence in the shape of a rectangle to enclose the largest possible area. What should be the dimensions of the rectangle? **25 ft wide by 25 ft long**

7. The combined ages of a mother, her son, and her daughter are 61 years. The mother is 22 years older than her son and 31 years older than her daughter. How old is each person? **mother: 38 yr; son: 16 yr; daughter: 7 yr**

8. Kenji traveled 210 mi in a two-day bicycle race. He biked 20 mi farther on the first day than he did on the second day. How many miles did Kenji travel each day? **first day: 115 mi; second day: 95 mi**

9. Darren is selling tickets for the school play. Regular tickets are $4 each, and student tickets are $3 each. Darren sells a total of 190 tickets and collects $650. How many of each kind of ticket did he sell? **regular tickets: 80; student tickets: 110**

Problem Solving: Look for a Pattern and Make a Table

Some problems describe relationships that involve regular sequences of numbers or other things. To solve the problem you need to be able to recognize and describe the pattern that gives the relationship for the numbers or things. One way to organize the information given is to make a table.

EXAMPLE

A tree farm is planted as shown at the right. The dots represent trees. The lot will be enlarged by adding larger squares. How many trees will be in the fifth square?

Make a table to help find a pattern.

Square position	1st	2nd	3rd	4th	5th
Number of trees	4	12	20	▪	▪

Pattern: 8 more trees are planted in each larger square.

The fourth square will have 28 trees. The fifth square will have 36 trees.

EXERCISES

1. Kareem made a display of books at a book fair. One book was in the first row, and each of the other rows had two more books than the row before it. How many books does Kareem have if he has nine rows? **81 books**

2. Chris is using green and white tiles to cover her floor. If she uses tiles in the pattern G, W, G, G, W, G, G, W, G, G, what will be the color of the twentieth tile? **white**

3. Jay read one story the first week of summer vacation, 3 stories the second week, 6 stories the third week, and 10 stories the fourth week. He kept to this pattern for eight weeks. How many stories did he read the eighth week? **36 stories**

4. Jan has 6 coins, none of which is a half dollar. The coins have a value of $.85. What coins does she have? **2 quarters, 3 dimes, 1 nickel**

5. Sam is covering a wall with rows of red, white, and blue siding. The red siding is cut in 1.8-m strips, the white in 2.4-m strips, and the blue in 1.2-m strips. What is the shortest length that Sam can cover with uncut strips to form equal rows of each color? **7.2 m**

6. A train leaves a station at 8:00 A.M. and averages 40 mi/h. Another train leaves the same station one hour later and averages 50 mi/h traveling in the same direction on a parallel track. At what time will the second train catch up with the first train? How many miles would each train have traveled by that time? **1 P.M.; 200 mi**

7. The soccer team held a car wash and earned $200. They charged $7 per truck and $5 per car. In how many different ways could the team have earned the $200? **6 ways**

8. Students are going to march in a parade. There will be one first-grader, two second-graders, three third-graders, and so on through the twelfth grade. How many students will march in the parade? **78 students**

Problem Solving: Solve a Simpler Problem

By solving one or more simpler problems you can often find a pattern that will help solve a more complicated problem.

EXAMPLE

How many different rectangles are in a strip with 10 squares?

Begin with one square, and then add one square at a time. Determine whether there is a pattern.

Squares in the strip:	1	2	3	4	5
Number of rectangles:	1	3	6	10	15
Pattern:		$1 + 2 = 3$	$3 + 3 = 6$	$6 + 4 = 10$	$10 + 5 = 15$

Now continue the pattern.

Squares in the strip:	6	7	8	9	10
Number of rectangles:	21	28	36	45	55

Pattern: $15 + 6 = 21$ $21 + 7 = 28$ $28 + 8 = 36$ $36 + 9 = 45$ $45 + 10 = 55$

• There are 55 rectangles in a strip with 10 squares.

EXERCISES

1. Lockers in the east wing of Hastings High School are numbered 1–120. How many contain the digit 8? **21 lockers**

2. What is the sum of all the numbers from 1 to 100? (*Hint:* What is $1 + 100$? What is $2 + 99$?) **5050**

3. Suppose your heart beats 70 times per minute. At this rate, how many times had it beaten by the time you were 10? **about 370,000,000 times**

4. For a community project you have to create the numbers 1 through 148 using large cardboard digits covered with glitter, which you make by hand. How many cardboard digits will you make? **336 digits**

5. There are 64 teams competing in the state soccer championship. If a team loses a game it is eliminated. How many games have to be played in order to get a single champion team? **63 games**

6. You work in a supermarket. Your boss asks you to arrange oranges in a pyramid for a display. The pyramid's base should be a square with 25 oranges. How many layers of oranges will be in your pyramid? How many oranges will you need? **5 layers; 55 oranges**

7. Kesi has her math book open. The product of the two page numbers on the facing pages is 1056. What are the two page numbers? **32 and 33**

8. There are 12 girls and 11 boys at a school party. A photographer wants to take a picture of each boy with each girl. How many photographs must the photographer set up? **132 shots**

Problem Solving: Use Logical Reasoning

Some problems can be solved without the use of numbers. They can be solved by the use of logical reasoning, given some information.

EXAMPLE

Joe, Melissa, Liz and Greg play different sports. Their sports are running, basketball, baseball, and tennis. Liz's sport does not use a ball. Joe hit a home run in his sport. Melissa is the sister of the tennis player. Which sport does each play?

Make a table to organize what you know.

	Running	Basketball	Baseball	Tennis
Joe	✗	✗	✓	✗
Melissa				✗
Liz	✓	✗	✗	✗
Greg				

← A home run means Joe plays baseball.
← Melissa cannot be the tennis player.
← Liz must run, since running does not involve a ball.

Use logical reasoning to complete the table.

	Running	Basketball	Baseball	Tennis
Joe	✗	✗	✓	✗
Melissa	✗	✓	✗	✗
Liz	✓	✗	✗	✗
Greg	✗	✗	✗	✓

← The only option for Greg is tennis.

● Greg plays tennis, Melissa plays basketball, Liz runs, and Joe plays baseball.

EXERCISES

1. Juan has a dog, a horse, a bird, and a cat. Their names are Bo, Cricket, K.C., and Tuffy. Tuffy and K.C. cannot fly or be ridden. The bird talks to Bo. Tuffy runs from the dog. What is each pet's name? **dog: K. C.; horse: Bo; bird: Cricket; cat: Tuffy**

2. A math class has 25 students. There are 13 students who are only in the band, 4 students who are only on the swimming team, and 5 students who are in both groups. How many students are not in either group? **3 students**

3. Annette is taller than Heather but shorter than Garo. Tanya's height is between Garo's and Annette's. Karin would be the shortest if it weren't for Alexa. List the names in order from shortest to tallest. **Alexa, Karin, Heather, Annette, Tanya, Garo**

4. The Robins, Wrens, and Sparrows teams played one another twice in basketball. The Robins won 3 of their games. The Sparrows won 2 of their games. How many games did each team win and lose? **Robins: 3 W, 1 L; Sparrows: 2 W, 2 L; Wrens: 1 W, 3 L**

5. The girls' basketball league uses a telephone tree when it needs to cancel its games. The leader takes 1 min to call 2 players. These 2 players take 1 min to call 2 more players, and so on. How many players will be called in 6 min? **126 players**

6. Miss White, Miss Gray, and Miss Black are wearing single-colored dresses that are white, gray, and black. Miss Gray remarks to the woman wearing a black dress that no woman's dress color matches her last name. What color dress is each woman wearing? **Miss Gray: white; Miss White: black; Miss Black: gray**

Problem Solving: Work Backward

To solve some problems, you need to start with the end result and work backward to the beginning.

EXAMPLE

On Monday, Rita withdrew $150 from her savings account. On Wednesday, she deposited $400 into her account. She now has $1000. How much was in her account on Monday before she withdrew the money?

money in account now	$1000
Undo the deposit.	$\dfrac{-\$400}{\$600}$
Undo the withdrawal.	$\dfrac{+\$150}{\$750}$

● Rita had $750 in her account on Monday before withdrawing money.

EXERCISES

1. Ned gave Connie the following puzzle: I am thinking of a number. I doubled it, then tripled the result. The final result was 36. What is my number? **6**

2. Fernando gave Maria the following puzzle: I am thinking of a number. I divide it by 3. Then I divide the result by 5. The final result is 8. What is my number? **120**

3. A teacher lends pencils to students. She gave out 7 pencils in the morning, collected 5 before lunch, and gave out 3 after lunch. At the end of the day she had 16 pencils. How many pencils did the teacher have at the start of the day? **21 pencils**

4. This week Sandy withdrew $350 from her savings account. She made a deposit of $125, wrote a check for $ 275, and made a deposit of $150. She now has $225 in her account. How much did she have in her account at the beginning of the week? **$575**

5. Jeff paid $12.50, including a $1.60 tip, for a taxi ride from his home to the airport. City Cab charges $1.90 for the first mile plus $.15 for each additional $\frac{1}{6}$ mile. How many miles is Jeff's home from the airport? **11 mi**

6. Ben sold $\frac{1}{4}$ as many tickets to the fund-raiser as Charles. Charles sold 3 times as many as Susan. Susan sold 4 fewer than Tom. Tom sold 12 tickets. How many did Ben sell? **6 tickets**

7. Two cars start traveling towards each other. One car averages 30 mi/h and the other 40 mi/h. After 4 h the cars are 10 mi apart. How far apart were the cars when they started? **290 mi**

8. Nina has a dentist appointment at 8:45 A.M. She wants to arrive 10 min early. Nina needs to allow 25 min to travel to the appointment and 45 min to dress and have breakfast. What is the latest time Nina should get up? **7:25 A.M.**

9. Jordan spent the day exploring her neighborhood and ended up at the park 2 mi east and 1 mi north of the center of town. She started from her house and walked $\frac{1}{2}$ mi north. Next she walked 3 mi west and then $1\frac{1}{2}$ mi south. Finally, she walked $\frac{1}{4}$ mi east to the park. Where is Jordan's house in relation to the center of town? **$4\frac{3}{4}$ mi east, 2 mi north**

19. 9. 1, 2, 23, 46

20. 1, 2, 4, 8, 16, 32

21. 1, 11

22. 1, 5, 13, 65

23. 1, 3, 9, 27

24. 1, 29

25. 1, 5, 41, 205

26. 1, 3, 41, 123

27. 1, 2, 3, 4, 6, 8, 12, 24

28. 1, 2, 3, 6, 9, 18, 27, 54, 81,
    162

29. 1, 2, 4, 8, 11, 22, 44, 88

30. 1, 2, 3, 4, 6, 12, 17, 34, 51,
    68, 102, 204

Prime Numbers and Composite Numbers

A prime number is a whole number greater than 1 that has exactly two factors, the number 1 and itself.

Prime number	2	5	17	29
Factors	1, 2	1, 5	1, 17	1, 29

A composite number is a number that has more than two factors. The number 1 is neither prime nor composite.

Composite number	6	15	48
Factors	1, 2, 3, 6	1, 3, 5, 15	1, 2, 3, 4, 6, 8, 12, 16, 24, 48

1 EXAMPLE

Is 51 prime or composite?

$51 = 3 \cdot 17$ **Try to find factors other than 1 and 51.**

● 51 is a composite number.

You can use a factor tree to find the prime factors of a number. When all the factors are prime numbers, it is called the prime factorization of the number.

2 EXAMPLE

Use a factor tree to write the prime factorization of 28.

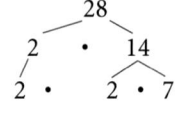   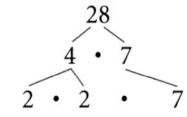

The order of listing the factors may be different, but the end result is the same.

● The prime factorization of 28 is $2 \cdot 2 \cdot 7$.

EXERCISES

Is each number prime or composite?

1. 9 composite   2. 16 composite   3. 34 composite   4. 61 prime   5. 7 prime   6. 13 prime

7. 12 composite   8. 40 composite   9. 57 composite   10. 64 composite   11. 120 composite   12. 700 composite

13. 39 composite   14. 23 prime   15. 63 composite   16. 19 prime   17. 522 composite   18. 101 prime

List all the factors of each number. 19–30. See margin.

19. 46	20. 32	21. 11	22. 65	23. 27	24. 29
25. 205	26. 123	27. 24	28. 162	29. 88	30. 204

31. 183
    1, 3, 61, 183   32. 6 1, 2, 3, 6   33. 98
    1, 2, 7, 14, 49, 98   34. 92
    1, 2, 4, 23, 46, 92   35. 59 1, 59   36. 47 1, 47

Use a factor tree to write the prime factorization of each number.

37. 18 $2 \cdot 3 \cdot 3$ 38. 20 $2 \cdot 2 \cdot 5$ 39. 27 $3 \cdot 3 \cdot 3$ 40. 54 $2 \cdot 3 \cdot 3 \cdot 3$ 41. 64 $2 \cdot 2 \cdot 2 \cdot 2 \cdot 2 \cdot 2$ 42. 96 $2 \cdot 2 \cdot 2 \cdot 2 \cdot 2 \cdot 3$

43. 100 $2 \cdot 2 \cdot 5 \cdot 5$ 44. 125 $5 \cdot 5 \cdot 5$ 45. 84 $2 \cdot 2 \cdot 3 \cdot 7$ 46. 150 $2 \cdot 3 \cdot 5 \cdot 5$ 47. 121 $11 \cdot 11$ 48. 226 $2 \cdot 113$

Factors and Multiples

A common factor is a number that is a factor of two or more numbers. The greatest common factor (GCF) is the greatest number that is a common factor of two or more numbers.

1 EXAMPLE

Find the GCF of 24 and 64.

Method 1 List all the factors of each number.

Factors of 24   1, 2, 3, 4, 6, 8, 12, 24   **Find the common factors: 1, 2, 4, 8.**

Factors of 64   1, 2, 4, 8, 16, 32, 64   **The greatest common factor is 8.**

GCF (24, 64) = 8

Method 2 Use the prime factorization of each number.

$24 = 2 \cdot 2 \cdot 2 \cdot 3$ **Find the prime factorization of each number.**

$64 = 2 \cdot 2 \cdot 2 \cdot 2 \cdot 2 \cdot 2$

$GCF = 2 \cdot 2 \cdot 2 = 8$ **Use each factor the number of times it appears as a common factor.**

A common multiple is a number that is a multiple of two or more numbers. The least common multiple (LCM) is the least number that is a common multiple of two or more numbers.

2 EXAMPLE

Find the LCM of 12 and 18.

Method 1 List the multiples of each number.

Multiples of 12   12, 24, 36, . . .   **List a number of multiples until you find**

Multiples of 18   18, 36, . . .   **the first common multiple.**

LCM (12, 18) = 36

Method 2 Use the prime factorization of each number.

$12 = 2 \cdot 2 \cdot 3$

$18 = 2 \cdot 3 \cdot 3$

$LCM = 2 \cdot 2 \cdot 3 \cdot 3 = 36$ **Use each prime factor the greatest number of times it appears in either number.**

EXERCISES

Find the GCF of each set of numbers.

1. 12 and 22 **2**

2. 7 and 21 **7**

3. 24 and 48 **24**

4. 17 and 51 **17**

5. 9 and 12 **3**

6. 10 and 25 **5**

7. 21 and 49 **7**

8. 27 and 36 **9**

9. 10, 30, and 25 **5**

10. 56, 84, and 140 **28**

11. 42, 63, and 105 **21**

12. 20, 28, and 40 **4**

Find the LCM of each set of numbers.

13. 16 and 20 **80**

14. 14 and 21 **42**

15. 11 and 33 **33**

16. 8 and 9 **72**

17. 5 and 12 **60**

18. 54 and 84 **756**

19. 48 and 80 **240**

20. 25 and 36 **900**

21. 10, 15, and 25 **150**

22. 6, 7, and 12 **84**

23. 5, 8, and 20 **40**

24. 18, 21, and 36 **252**

Divisibility

An integer is divisible by another integer if the remainder is zero. You can use the following tests to determine whether a number is divisible by the numbers below.

Number	Divisibility Test
2	The ones' digit is 0, 2, 4, 6, or 8.
3	The sum of the digits is divisible by 3.
4	The number formed by the last two digits is divisible by 4.
5	The ones' digit is 0 or 5.
6	The number is divisible by 2 and by 3.
8	The number formed by the last three digits is divisible by 8.
9	The sum of the digits is divisible by 9.
10	The ones' digit is 0.

EXAMPLE

Use the divisibility tests to determine the numbers by which 2116 is divisible.

2: Yes; the ones' digit is 6.

3: No; the sum of the digits is $2 + 1 + 1 + 6 = 10$, which is not divisible by 3.

4: Yes; the number formed by the last two digits is 16, which is divisible by 4.

5: No; the ones' digit is 6, *not* 0 or 5.

6: No; 2116 is not divisible by 3.

8: No; the number formed by the last three digits is 116, which is *not* divisible by 8.

9: No; the sum of the digits is $2 + 1 + 1 + 6 = 10$, which is not divisible by 9.

10: No; the ones' digit is 6, *not* 0.

● 2116 is divisible by 2 and 4.

EXERCISES

Determine whether each number is divisible by 2, 3, 4, 5, 6, 8, 9, or 10.

1. 236 2, 4
2. 72 2, 3, 4, 6, 9
3. 105 3, 5
4. 108 2, 3, 4, 6, 9
5. 225 3, 5, 9
6. 364 2, 4

7. 1234 2
8. 4321 none
9. 7848 2, 3, 4, 6, 8, 9
10. 3366 2, 3, 6, 9
11. 1421 none
12. 1071 3, 9

13. 78,765 3, 5
14. 30,303 3, 9
15. 4104 2, 3, 4, 6, 8, 9
16. 700 2, 4, 5, 10
17. 868 2, 4
18. 1155 3, 5

19. Reasoning Since 435 is divisible by both 3 and 5, it is also divisible by what number? **15**

20. Find a number greater than 1000 that is divisible by 4, 5, and 9. **Answers may vary. Sample: 2700, 3240**

21. Critical Thinking If *a* is divisible by 2, what can you conclude about $a + 1$? Justify your answer. **Answers may vary. Sample: $a + 1$ is not divisible by 2. Dividing by 2 will leave a remainder of 1.**

Using Estimation

To make sure the answer to a problem is reasonable, you can estimate before you calculate. If the answer is close to your estimate, the answer is probably correct.

1 EXAMPLE

Estimate to find whether each answer is reasonable.

a. Calculation   **Estimate**

$$
\begin{array}{lll}
\$126.91 & \approx & \$130 \\
\$14.05 & \approx & \$10 \\
+\$25.14 & \approx & +\$30 \\
\hline
\$266.10 & & \$170
\end{array}
$$

The answer is not close to the estimate. It is *not* reasonable. The calculation is *incorrect*.

b. Calculation   **Estimate**

$$
\begin{array}{lll}
372.85 & \approx & 370 \\
-227.31 & \approx & -230 \\
\hline
145.54 & & 140
\end{array}
$$

The answer is close to the estimate. It *is* reasonable. The calculation is *correct*.

For some situations, like estimating a grocery bill, you may not need an exact answer. A *front-end estimate* will give you a good estimate that is usually closer to the exact answer than an estimate you would get by rounding. Add the front-end digits, estimate the sum of the remaining digits by rounding, and then combine sums.

2 EXAMPLE

Tomatoes cost $3.54, squash costs $2.75, and lemons cost $1.20. Estimate the total cost of the produce.

$$
\begin{array}{llcl}
\text{Add the} & 3.54 & \rightarrow & 0.50 \qquad \text{Estimate by rounding.} \\
\text{front-end digits.} & 2.75 & \rightarrow & 0.80 \\
& +1.20 & \rightarrow & +\ 0.20 \\
\cline{2-2}\cline{4-4}
& 6 & + & 1.50 = 7.50
\end{array}
$$

The total cost is about $7.50.

EXERCISES

Estimate by rounding.

1. the sum of $15.70, $49.62, and $278.01 **$350**

2. 563 − 125 **430**

3. the sum of $163.90, $107.21, and $33.56 **$300**

4. 824 − 467 **350**

Use front-end estimation.

5. $1.65 + $5.42 + $9.89 **$17.00**

6. 1.369 + 7.421 + 2.700 **11.50**

7. 9.563 − 2.480 **7.10**

8. 1.17 + 3.92 + 2.26 **7.40**

9. 8.611 − 1.584 **7.00**

10. $2.52 + $3.04 + $5.25 **$10.80**

Estimate using a method of your choice.

11. Ticket prices at an amusement park cost $11.25 for adults and $6.50 for children under 12. Estimate the cost for three children and one adult. **$30.80**

12. Esmeralda has a new checking account. So far, she has deposited $177, $250, and $193. She has also written a check for $26.89. Estimate her current balance. **$590**

Simplifying Fractions

A fraction can name a part of a group or region. The region below is divided into 10 equal parts and 6 of the equal parts are shaded.

$\frac{6}{10}$ ← Numerator
← Denominator   **Read: six tenths**

A fraction can have many names. Different names for the same fraction are called equivalent fractions. You can find an equivalent fraction for any given fraction by multiplying the numerator and denominator of the given fraction by the same number.

1 EXAMPLE

Write five equivalent fractions for $\frac{3}{5}$.

$\frac{3}{5} = \frac{3 \cdot 2}{5 \cdot 2} = \frac{6}{10}$ $\frac{3}{5} = \frac{3 \cdot 3}{5 \cdot 3} = \frac{9}{15}$ $\frac{3}{5} = \frac{3 \cdot 4}{5 \cdot 4} = \frac{12}{20}$ $\frac{3}{5} = \frac{3 \cdot 5}{5 \cdot 5} = \frac{15}{25}$ $\frac{3}{5} = \frac{3 \cdot 6}{5 \cdot 6} = \frac{18}{30}$

The fraction $\frac{3}{5}$ is in simplest form because its numerator and denominator are relatively prime, that is, their only common factor is the number 1. To write a fraction in simplest form, divide its numerator and denominator by their greatest common factor (GCF).

2 EXAMPLE

Write $\frac{6}{24}$ in simplest form.

Step 1 Find the GCF of 6 and 24.

$6 = 2 \cdot 3$ **Multiply the common prime factors.**

$24 = 2 \cdot 2 \cdot 2 \cdot 3$ **GCF = $2 \cdot 3 = 6$.**

Step 2 Divide the numerator and denominator of $\frac{6}{24}$ by the GCF, 6.

$\frac{6}{24} = \frac{6 \div 6}{24 \div 6} = \frac{1}{4}$ **simplest form**

1. $\frac{8}{14}, \frac{12}{21}, \frac{16}{28}, \frac{20}{35}, \frac{24}{42}$

2. $\frac{18}{32}, \frac{27}{48}, \frac{36}{64}, \frac{45}{80}, \frac{54}{96}$

3. $\frac{6}{16}, \frac{9}{24}, \frac{12}{32}, \frac{15}{40}, \frac{18}{48}$

4. $\frac{16}{34}, \frac{24}{51}, \frac{32}{68}, \frac{40}{85}, \frac{48}{102}$

5. $\frac{10}{12}, \frac{15}{18}, \frac{20}{24}, \frac{25}{30}, \frac{30}{36}$

6. $\frac{14}{20}, \frac{21}{30}, \frac{28}{40}, \frac{35}{50}, \frac{42}{60}$

EXERCISES

Write five equivalent fractions for each fraction. 1–6. See above.

1. $\frac{4}{7}$ 2. $\frac{9}{16}$ 3. $\frac{3}{8}$ 4. $\frac{8}{17}$ 5. $\frac{5}{6}$ 6. $\frac{7}{10}$

Complete each statement.

7. $\frac{3}{7} = \frac{\blacksquare}{21}$ 9   8. $\frac{5}{8} = \frac{20}{\blacksquare}$ 32   9. $\frac{11}{12} = \frac{44}{\blacksquare}$ 48   10. $\frac{12}{16} = \frac{\blacksquare}{4}$ 3   11. $\frac{50}{100} = \frac{1}{\blacksquare}$ 2

12. $\frac{5}{9} = \frac{\blacksquare}{27}$ 15   13. $\frac{3}{8} = \frac{\blacksquare}{24}$ 9   14. $\frac{5}{6} = \frac{20}{\blacksquare}$ 24   15. $\frac{12}{20} = \frac{\blacksquare}{5}$ 3   16. $\frac{75}{150} = \frac{1}{\blacksquare}$ 2

Which fractions are in simplest form?

17. $\frac{4}{12}$ no   18. $\frac{3}{16}$ yes   19. $\frac{5}{30}$ no   20. $\frac{9}{72}$ no   21. $\frac{11}{22}$ no   22. $\frac{24}{25}$ yes

Write in simplest form.

23. $\frac{8}{16}$ $\frac{1}{2}$ 24. $\frac{7}{14}$ $\frac{1}{2}$ 25. $\frac{6}{9}$ $\frac{2}{3}$ 26. $\frac{20}{30}$ $\frac{2}{3}$ 27. $\frac{8}{20}$ $\frac{2}{5}$ 28. $\frac{12}{40}$ $\frac{3}{10}$

29. $\frac{15}{45}$ $\frac{1}{3}$ 30. $\frac{14}{56}$ $\frac{1}{4}$ 31. $\frac{10}{25}$ $\frac{2}{5}$ 32. $\frac{9}{27}$ $\frac{1}{3}$ 33. $\frac{45}{60}$ $\frac{3}{4}$ 34. $\frac{20}{35}$ $\frac{4}{7}$

Fractions and Decimals

You can write a fraction as a decimal.

1 EXAMPLE

Write $\frac{3}{5}$ as a decimal.

$$5)\overline{3.0}$$
$$0.6$$
$$-3.0 \quad \textbf{Divide the numerator by the denominator.}$$

The decimal for $\frac{3}{5}$ is 0.6.

You can write a decimal as a fraction.

2 EXAMPLE

Write 0.38 as a fraction.

$0.38 = 38$ hundredths $= \frac{38}{100} = \frac{19}{50}$

Some fractions have decimal forms that do not end, but do repeat.

3 EXAMPLE

Write $\frac{3}{11}$ as a decimal.

Divide the numerator by the denominator. The remainders 8 and 3 keep repeating. Therefore 2 and 7 will keep repeating in the quotient.

$\frac{3}{11} = 0.2727\ldots = 0.\overline{27}$

$$\frac{3}{11} = 11)\overline{3.0000\ldots}$$
$$\phantom{\frac{3}{11} = 11)}0.2727$$
$$\underline{22}$$
$$80$$
$$\underline{77}$$
$$30$$
$$\underline{22}$$
$$80$$
$$\underline{77}$$
$$3$$

You can write a repeating decimal as a fraction.

4 EXAMPLE

Write $0.363636\ldots$ as a fraction.

Let $\qquad x = 0.363636\ldots$

Then $\qquad 100x = 36.36363636\ldots \qquad$ **When 2 digits repeat, multiply by 100.**

$\qquad\qquad 99x = 36 \qquad\qquad\qquad$ **Subtract the first equation from the second.**

$\qquad\qquad x = \frac{36}{99}$ or $\frac{4}{11} \qquad\qquad$ **Divide each side by 99.**

EXERCISES

Write as a decimal.

1. $\frac{3}{10}$ 0.3
2. $\frac{13}{12}$ 1.08$\overline{3}$
3. $\frac{4}{20}$ 0.2
4. $\frac{25}{75}$ 0.$\overline{3}$
5. $\frac{5}{7}$ 0.$\overline{714285}$
6. $4\frac{3}{25}$ 4.12

7. $\frac{5}{9}$ 0.$\overline{5}$
8. $5\frac{7}{8}$ 5.875
9. $\frac{2}{7}$ 0.$\overline{285714}$
10. $\frac{3}{15}$ 0.2
11. $\frac{16}{100}$ 0.16
12. $2\frac{2}{5}$ 2.4

Write as a fraction in simplest form.

13. 0.07 $\frac{7}{100}$
14. 0.25 $\frac{1}{4}$
15. 0.875 $\frac{7}{8}$
16. 0.4545$\ldots$ $\frac{5}{11}$
17. 6.333$\ldots$ $6\frac{1}{3}$
18. 7.2626$\ldots$ $7\frac{26}{99}$

19. 0.77$\ldots$ $\frac{7}{9}$
20. 3.1313$\ldots$ $3\frac{13}{99}$
21. 0.375 $\frac{3}{8}$
22. 0.8333$\ldots$ $\frac{5}{6}$
23. 6.48 $6\frac{12}{25}$
24. 0.8 $\frac{4}{5}$

Adding and Subtracting Fractions

You can add and subtract fractions when they have the same denominator. Fractions with the same denominator are called like fractions.

1 EXAMPLE

a. Add $\frac{4}{5} + \frac{3}{5}$.

$\frac{4}{5} + \frac{3}{5} = \frac{4+3}{5} = \frac{7}{5} = 1\frac{2}{5}$ ← **Add or subtract the numerators and keep the same denominator.**

b. Subtract $\frac{5}{9} - \frac{2}{9}$.

→ $\frac{5}{9} - \frac{2}{9} = \frac{5-2}{9} = \frac{3}{9} = \frac{1}{3}$

Fractions with unlike denominators are called unlike fractions. To add or subtract fractions with unlike denominators, find the least common denominator (LCD) and write equivalent fractions with the same denominator. Then add or subtract the like fractions.

2 EXAMPLE

Add $\frac{3}{4} + \frac{5}{6}$.

$\frac{3}{4} + \frac{5}{6} = \frac{9}{12} + \frac{10}{12}$ **Find the LCD. The LCD is the same as the least common multiple (LCM). The LCD of 4 and 6 is 12.**

$= \frac{9+10}{12} = \frac{19}{12}$ or $1\frac{7}{12}$ **Write equivalent fractions with the same denominator.**

To add or subtract mixed numbers, add or subtract the fractions. Then add or subtract the whole numbers. Sometimes when subtracting mixed numbers you may have to regroup.

3 EXAMPLE

Subtract $5\frac{1}{4} - 3\frac{2}{3}$.

$5\frac{1}{4} - 3\frac{2}{3} = 5\frac{3}{12} - 3\frac{8}{12}$ **Write equivalent fractions with the same denominator.**

$= 4\frac{15}{12} - 3\frac{8}{12}$ **Write $5\frac{3}{12}$ as $4\frac{15}{12}$ so you can subtract the fractions.**

$= 1\frac{7}{12}$ **Subtract the fractions. Then subtract the whole numbers.**

EXERCISES

Add. Write each answer in simplest form.

1. $\frac{2}{7} + \frac{3}{7}$ $\frac{5}{7}$ **2.** $\frac{3}{8} + \frac{7}{8}$ $1\frac{1}{4}$ **3.** $\frac{6}{5} + \frac{9}{5}$ 3 **4.** $\frac{4}{9} + \frac{8}{9}$ $1\frac{1}{3}$ **5.** $6\frac{2}{3} + 3\frac{4}{5}$ $10\frac{7}{15}$

6. $1\frac{4}{7} + 2\frac{3}{14}$ $3\frac{11}{14}$ **7.** $4\frac{5}{6} + 1\frac{7}{18}$ $6\frac{2}{9}$ **8.** $2\frac{4}{5} + 3\frac{6}{7}$ $6\frac{23}{35}$ **9.** $4\frac{2}{3} + 1\frac{6}{11}$ $6\frac{7}{33}$ **10.** $3\frac{7}{9} + 5\frac{4}{11}$ $9\frac{14}{99}$

11. $8 + 1\frac{2}{3}$ $9\frac{2}{3}$ **12.** $8\frac{1}{5} + 3\frac{3}{4}$ $11\frac{19}{20}$ **13.** $11\frac{3}{8} + 2\frac{1}{16}$ $13\frac{7}{16}$ **14.** $9\frac{1}{12} + 8\frac{3}{4}$ $17\frac{5}{6}$ **15.** $33\frac{1}{3} + 23\frac{2}{5}$ $56\frac{11}{15}$

Subtract. Write each answer in simplest form.

16. $\frac{7}{8} - \frac{3}{8}$ $\frac{1}{2}$ **17.** $\frac{9}{10} - \frac{3}{10}$ $\frac{3}{5}$ **18.** $\frac{17}{5} - \frac{2}{5}$ 3 **19.** $\frac{11}{7} - \frac{2}{7}$ $1\frac{2}{7}$ **20.** $\frac{5}{11} - \frac{4}{11}$ $\frac{1}{11}$

21. $8\frac{5}{8} - 6\frac{1}{4}$ $2\frac{3}{8}$ **22.** $3\frac{2}{3} - 1\frac{8}{9}$ $1\frac{7}{9}$ **23.** $8\frac{5}{6} - 5\frac{1}{2}$ $3\frac{1}{3}$ **24.** $12\frac{3}{4} - 4\frac{5}{6}$ $7\frac{11}{12}$ **25.** $17\frac{2}{7} - 8\frac{2}{9}$ $9\frac{4}{63}$

26. $7\frac{3}{4} - 3\frac{3}{8}$ $4\frac{3}{8}$ **27.** $4\frac{1}{12} - 1\frac{11}{12}$ $2\frac{1}{6}$ **28.** $5\frac{5}{8} - 2\frac{7}{16}$ $3\frac{3}{16}$ **29.** $11\frac{2}{3} - 3\frac{5}{6}$ $7\frac{5}{6}$ **30.** $25\frac{5}{8} - 17\frac{15}{16}$ $7\frac{11}{16}$

Multiplying and Dividing Fractions

To multiply two or more fractions, multiply the numerators, multiply the denominators, and simplify the product, if necessary.

1 EXAMPLE

Multiply $\frac{3}{7} \cdot \frac{5}{6}$.

$$\frac{3}{7} \cdot \frac{5}{6} = \frac{3 \cdot 5}{7 \cdot 6} = \frac{15}{42} = \frac{15 \div 3}{42 \div 3} = \frac{5}{14}$$

Sometimes you can simplify before multiplying.

$$\frac{3^1}{7} \cdot \frac{5}{6_2} = \frac{5}{14}$$ **Divide a numerator and a denominator by a common factor.**

To multiply mixed numbers, change the mixed numbers to improper fractions and multiply the fractions. Write the product as a mixed number.

2 EXAMPLE

Multiply $2\frac{4}{5} \cdot 1\frac{2}{3}$.

$$2\frac{4}{5} \cdot 1\frac{2}{3} = \frac{14}{{}_1 5} \cdot \frac{5^1}{3} = \frac{14}{3} = 4\frac{2}{3}$$

To divide fractions, change the division problem to a multiplication problem. Remember that $8 \div \frac{1}{4}$ is the same as $8 \cdot 4$.

To divide mixed numbers, change the mixed numbers to improper fractions and divide the fractions.

3 EXAMPLE

a. Divide $\frac{4}{5} \div \frac{3}{7}$.

$$\frac{4}{5} \div \frac{3}{7} = \frac{4}{5} \cdot \frac{7}{3}$$ ⟵ **Multiply by the reciprocal of the divisor.** ⟶

$$= \frac{28}{15}$$ ⟵ **Simplify the answer.** ⟶

$$= 1\frac{13}{15}$$ ⟵ **Write as a mixed number.**

b. Divide $4\frac{2}{3} \div 7\frac{3}{5}$.

$$4\frac{2}{3} \div 7\frac{3}{5} = \frac{14}{3} \div \frac{38}{5}$$

$$= \frac{14^7}{3} \cdot \frac{5}{38_{19}}$$

$$= \frac{35}{57}$$

EXERCISES

Multiply. Write your answers in simplest form.

1. $\frac{2}{5} \cdot \frac{3}{4}$ $\frac{3}{10}$

2. $\frac{3}{7} \cdot \frac{4}{3}$ $\frac{4}{7}$

3. $1\frac{1}{2} \cdot 5\frac{3}{4}$ $8\frac{5}{8}$

4. $3\frac{4}{5} \cdot 10$ 38

5. $5\frac{1}{4} \cdot \frac{2}{3}$ $3\frac{1}{2}$

6. $4\frac{1}{2} \cdot 7\frac{1}{2}$ $33\frac{3}{4}$

7. $3\frac{2}{3} \cdot 6\frac{9}{10}$ $25\frac{3}{10}$

8. $6\frac{1}{2} \cdot 7\frac{2}{3}$ $49\frac{5}{6}$

9. $2\frac{2}{5} \cdot 1\frac{1}{6}$ $2\frac{4}{5}$

10. $4\frac{1}{9} \cdot 3\frac{3}{8}$ $13\frac{7}{8}$

11. $3\frac{1}{5} \cdot 1\frac{7}{8}$ 6

12. $7\frac{5}{6} \cdot 4\frac{1}{2}$ $35\frac{1}{4}$

13. $1\frac{2}{3} \cdot 5\frac{9}{10}$ $9\frac{5}{6}$

14. $3\frac{3}{4} \cdot 5\frac{1}{3}$ 20

15. $1\frac{2}{3} \cdot 3\frac{9}{16}$ $5\frac{15}{16}$

Divide. Write your answers in simplest form.

16. $\frac{3}{5} \div \frac{1}{2}$ $1\frac{1}{5}$

17. $\frac{4}{5} \div \frac{9}{10}$ $\frac{8}{9}$

18. $2\frac{1}{2} \div 3\frac{1}{2}$ $\frac{5}{7}$

19. $1\frac{4}{5} \div 2\frac{1}{2}$ $\frac{18}{25}$

20. $3\frac{1}{6} \div 1\frac{3}{4}$ $1\frac{17}{21}$

21. $5 \div \frac{3}{8}$ $13\frac{1}{3}$

22. $\frac{4}{9} \div \frac{3}{5}$ $\frac{20}{27}$

23. $\frac{5}{8} \div \frac{3}{4}$ $\frac{5}{6}$

24. $2\frac{1}{5} \div 2\frac{1}{2}$ $\frac{22}{25}$

25. $6\frac{1}{2} \div \frac{1}{4}$ 26

26. $1\frac{3}{4} \div 4\frac{3}{8}$ $\frac{2}{5}$

27. $\frac{8}{9} \div \frac{2}{3}$ $1\frac{1}{3}$

28. $\frac{1}{5} \div \frac{1}{3}$ $\frac{3}{5}$

29. $2\frac{2}{5} \div 7\frac{1}{5}$ $\frac{1}{3}$

30. $7\frac{2}{3} \div \frac{2}{9}$ $34\frac{1}{2}$

Fractions, Decimals, and Percents

Percent means per hundred. 50% means 50 per hundred. $50\% = \frac{50}{100} = 0.50$

You can write fractions as percents by writing the fractions as decimals first. Then move the decimal point two places to the right and write a percent sign.

1 EXAMPLE

Write each number as a percent.

a. $\frac{3}{5}$

$\frac{3}{5} = 0.6$

b. $\frac{7}{20}$

$\frac{7}{20} = 0.35$

c. $\frac{2}{3}$

$\frac{2}{3} = 0.66\overline{6}$

Move the decimal point two places to the right and write a percent sign.

$0.6 = 60\%$

$0.35 = 35\%$

$0.66\overline{6} = 66.\overline{6}\% \approx 66.7\%$

You can write percents as decimals by moving the decimal point two places to the left and removing the percent sign.

You can write a percent as a fraction with the denominator of 100. You then simplify it, if possible.

2 EXAMPLE

Write each number as a decimal and as a fraction or mixed number.

a. 25%

$25\% = 0.25$

$25\% = \frac{25}{100} = \frac{1}{4}$

b. $\frac{1}{2}\%$

$\frac{1}{2}\% = 0.5\% = 0.005$

$\frac{1}{2}\% = \frac{\frac{1}{2}}{100} = \frac{1}{2} \div 100$

$= \frac{1}{2} \cdot \frac{1}{100} = \frac{1}{200}$

c. 360%

$360\% = 3.6$

$360\% = \frac{360}{100} = \frac{18}{5} = 3\frac{3}{5}$

EXERCISES

Write each number as a percent. If necessary, round to the nearest tenth.

1. 0.56 **56%**

2. 0.09 **9%**

3. 6.02 **602%**

4. 5.245 **524.5%**

5. 8.2 **820%**

6. 0.14 **14%**

7. $\frac{1}{7}$ **14.3%**

8. $\frac{9}{20}$ **45%**

9. $\frac{1}{9}$ **11.1%**

10. $\frac{5}{6}$ **83.3%**

11. $\frac{3}{4}$ **75%**

12. $\frac{7}{8}$ **87.5%**

Write each number as a decimal.

13. 7% **0.07**

14. 8.5% **0.085**

15. 0.9% **0.009**

16. 250% **2.5**

17. 83% **0.83**

18. 110% **1.1**

19. 15% **0.15**

20. 72% **0.72**

21. 0.03% **0.0003**

22. 36.2% **0.362**

23. 365% **3.65**

24. 101% **1.01**

Write each number as a fraction or mixed number in simplest form.

25. 19% $\frac{19}{100}$

26. $\frac{3}{4}\%$ $\frac{3}{400}$

27. 450% $4\frac{1}{2}$

28. $\frac{4}{5}\%$ $\frac{1}{125}$

29. 64% $\frac{16}{25}$

30. $\frac{2}{3}\%$ $\frac{1}{150}$

31. 24% $\frac{6}{25}$

32. 845% $8\frac{9}{20}$

33. $\frac{3}{8}\%$ $\frac{3}{800}$

34. 480% $4\frac{4}{5}$

35. 60% $\frac{3}{5}$

36. 350% $3\frac{1}{2}$

37. 2% $\frac{1}{50}$

38. 16% $\frac{4}{25}$

39. 66% $\frac{33}{50}$

40. $\frac{4}{7}\%$ $\frac{1}{175}$

41. 125% $1\frac{1}{4}$

42. 84% $\frac{21}{25}$

Exponents

You can express $2 \cdot 2 \cdot 2 \cdot 2 \cdot 2$ as 2^5. The raised number 5 shows the number of times 2 is used as a factor. The number 2 is the base. The number 5 is the exponent.

$2^5 \leftarrow$ **exponent**
$\uparrow$ **base**

Factored Form	Exponential Form	Standard Form
$2 \cdot 2 \cdot 2 \cdot 2 \cdot 2$	2^5	32

A number with an exponent of 1 is the number itself: $8^1 = 8$.
Any number, except 0, with an exponent of 0 is 1: $5^0 = 1$.

1 EXAMPLE

Write using exponents.

a. $8 \cdot 8 \cdot 8 \cdot 8 \cdot 8$ **b.** $2 \cdot 9 \cdot 9 \cdot 9 \cdot 9 \cdot 9 \cdot 9$ **c.** $6 \cdot 6 \cdot 10 \cdot 10 \cdot 10 \cdot 6 \cdot 6$

Count the number of times the number is used as a factor.

$= 8^5$ $= 2 \cdot 9^6$ $= 6^4 \cdot 10^3$

2 EXAMPLE

Write in standard form.

a. 2^3 **b.** $8^2 \cdot 3^4$ **c.** $10^3 \cdot 15^2$

Write in factored form and multiply.

$2 \cdot 2 \cdot 2 = 8$ $8 \cdot 8 \cdot 3 \cdot 3 \cdot 3 \cdot 3 = 5184$ $10 \cdot 10 \cdot 10 \cdot 15 \cdot 15 = 225{,}000$

In powers of 10, an exponent tells how many zeros are in the equivalent standard form.

$10^1 = 10$

$10^2 = 10 \cdot 10 = 100$

$10^3 = 10 \cdot 10 \cdot 10 = 1000$

$10^4 = 10 \cdot 10 \cdot 10 \cdot 10 = 10{,}000$

$10^5 = 10 \cdot 10 \cdot 10 \cdot 10 \cdot 10 = 100{,}000$

$10^6 = 10 \cdot 10 \cdot 10 \cdot 10 \cdot 10 \cdot 10 = 1{,}000{,}000$

You can use exponents to write numbers in expanded form.

12. $(6 \cdot 10^2) + (5 \cdot 10^1) + (8 \cdot 10^0)$
13. $(1 \cdot 10^3) + (2 \cdot 10^2) + (5 \cdot 10^1) + (4 \cdot 10^0)$
14. $(7 \cdot 10^3) + (1 \cdot 10^2) + (2 \cdot 10^1) + (5 \cdot 10^0)$
15. $(8 \cdot 10^4) + (3 \cdot 10^3) + (4 \cdot 10^2) + (1 \cdot 10^0)$
16. $(2 \cdot 10^5) + (9 \cdot 10^4) + (4 \cdot 10^3) + (8 \cdot 10^2) +$
$(6 \cdot 10^1) + (3 \cdot 10^0)$

3 EXAMPLE

Write 739 in expanded form using exponents.

$739 = 700 + 30 + 9 = (7 \cdot 100) + (3 \cdot 10) + (9 \cdot 1) = (7 \cdot 10^2) + (3 \cdot 10^1) + (9 \cdot 10^0)$

EXERCISES

Write using exponents.

1. $6 \cdot 6 \cdot 6 \cdot 6$ 6^4 **2.** $7 \cdot 7 \cdot 7 \cdot 7 \cdot 7$ 7^5 **3.** $5 \cdot 2 \cdot 2 \cdot 2 \cdot 2$ $5 \cdot 2^4$

4. $3 \cdot 3 \cdot 3 \cdot 3 \cdot 3 \cdot 14 \cdot 14$ $3^5 \cdot 14^2$ **5.** $4 \cdot 4 \cdot 3 \cdot 3 \cdot 2$ $4^2 \cdot 3^2 \cdot 2$ **6.** $3 \cdot 5 \cdot 5 \cdot 7 \cdot 7 \cdot 7$ $3 \cdot 5^2 \cdot 7^3$

Write in standard form.

7. 4^3 **64**   **8.** 9^4 **6561**   **9.** 12^2 **144**   **10.** $6^2 \cdot 7^1$ **252**   **11.** $11^2 \cdot 3^3$ **3267**

Write in expanded form using exponents.   **12–16. See above.**

12. 658   **13.** 1254   **14.** 7125   **15.** 83,401   **16.** 294,863

Measuring and Classifying Angles

An angle is a geometric figure formed by two rays with a common endpoint. The rays are sides of the angle and the endpoint is the vertex of the angle. An angle is measured in degrees. The symbol for an angle is ∠.

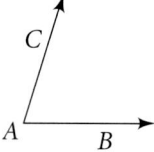

The angle picture at the right can be named in three different ways: ∠A, ∠BAC, or ∠CAB.

Angles can be classified by their measures.

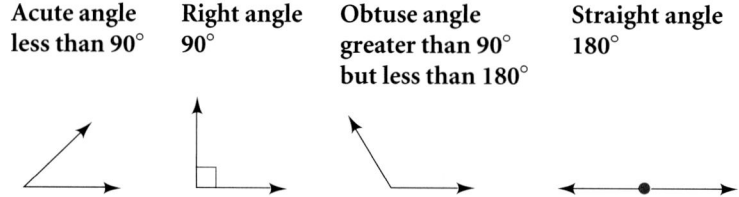

| Acute angle less than 90° | Right angle 90° | Obtuse angle greater than 90° but less than 180° | Straight angle 180° |

EXAMPLE

Measure the angle. Is it *acute*, *right*, *obtuse* or *straight*?

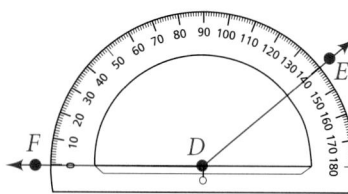

Line up side *DF* through 0° with the vertex at the center of the protractor. Read the scale number through which side *DE* passes.

● The measure of the angle is 140°. The angle is obtuse.

EXERCISES

Measure each angle. Is the angle *acute*, *right*, *obtuse*, or *straight*?

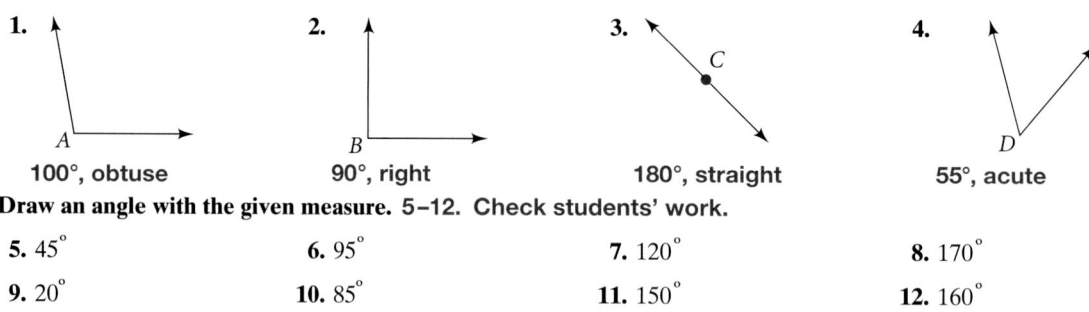

1.
2.
3.
4.

100°, obtuse   90°, right   180°, straight   55°, acute

Draw an angle with the given measure. 5–12. Check students' work.

5. 45°   **6.** 95°   **7.** 120°   **8.** 170°

9. 20°   **10.** 85°   **11.** 150°   **12.** 160°

13. Open-Ended Draw a triangle. Use a protractor to find the measure of each angle of your triangle. **Check students' work.**

Perimeter, Area, and Volume

The perimeter of a figure is the distance around the figure. The area of a figure is the number of square units contained in the figure. The volume of a space figure is the number of cubic units contained in the space figure.

1 EXAMPLE

Find the perimeter of each figure.

a.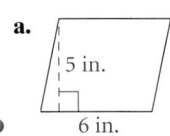
Add the measures of the sides.
$3 + 4 + 5 = 12$
The perimeter is 12 in.

b.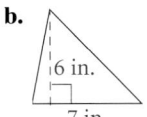
Use the formula $P = 2\ell + 2w$.
$P = 2(3) + 2(4)$
$= 6 + 8 = 14$
The perimeter is 14 cm.

2 EXAMPLE

Find the area of each figure.

a.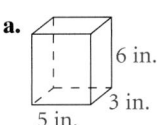
Use the formula $A = bh$.
$A = 6 \cdot 5 = 30$
The area is 30 in.^{2}.

b.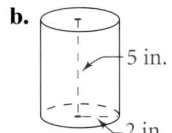
Use the formula $A = \frac{1}{2}(bh)$.
$A = \frac{1}{2}(7 \cdot 6) = 21$
The area is 21 in.^{2}.

3 EXAMPLE

Find the volume of each figure.

a.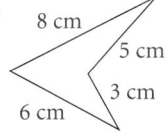
Use the formula $V = Bh$.
(B = area of the base
$= 3 \cdot 5 = 15$).
$V = 15 \cdot 6 = 90$ in.^{3}
The volume is 90 in.^{3}.

b.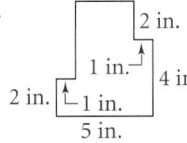
Use the formula $V = \pi r^2 h$.
$V = 3.14 \cdot 2^2 \cdot 5$
$= 3.14 \cdot 4 \cdot 5 = 62.8$ in.^{3}
The volume is 62.8 in.^{3}.

EXERCISES

For Exercises 1–2, find the perimeter of each figure. For Exercises 3–4, find the area of each figure.

1.
8 cm, 5 cm, 3 cm, 6 cm
22 cm

2.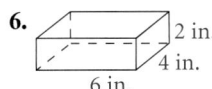
2 in., 1 in., 4 in, 2 in., 1 in., 5 in.
22 in.

3.
10 cm, 6 cm, 8 cm
24 cm^2

4.
8 in., 7 in.
56 in.^{2}

Find the volume of each figure.

5.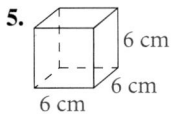
6 cm, 6 cm, 6 cm
216 cm^3

6.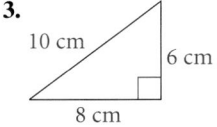
2 in., 4 in., 6 in.
48 in.^{3}

7.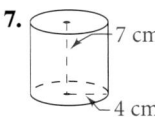
7 cm, 4 cm
351.68 cm^3

1.

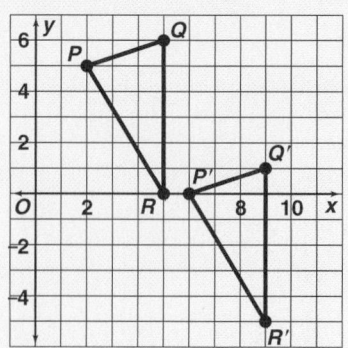

2.

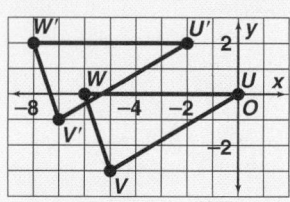

3. $(x, y) \rightarrow (x - 2, y - 1)$

4. $(x, y) \rightarrow (x + 2, y - 18)$

5. $(x, y) \rightarrow (x + 4, y + \frac{1}{2})$

6. $(x, y) \rightarrow (x - 5, y + 1)$

7. $(x, y) \rightarrow (x + 2, y + 5)$

8. $(x, y) \rightarrow (x - 4, y + 6)$

Translations

A translation is a transformation that moves a figure so that every point in the figure moves the same direction and the same distance. Each translated figure is an image of the original figure. If point A is on the original figure, the corresponding point on the image is A'.

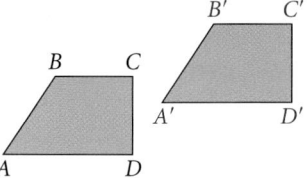

1 EXAMPLE

Graph the image of $\triangle ABC$ after a translation of 4 units right and 2 units down.

To get from $A(-6, 1)$ to $A'(-2, -1)$ by a translation, move
4 units to the right: add 4 to the x-value, $-6 + 4 = -2$,
and 2 units down: add -2 to the y-value, $-1 + (-2) = -1$.

● Similarly, the coordinates of B' are $(3, 3)$ and of C' are $(2, 0)$.

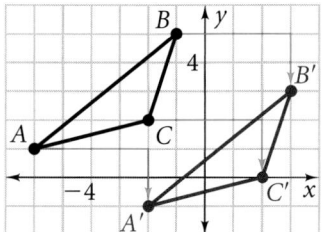

You can describe a translation using arrow $(\rightarrow)$ notation. The translation from A to A' in Example 1 can be written $A(-6, 1) \rightarrow A'(-2, -1)$.

2 EXAMPLE

Write a rule to describe the translation of $\triangle PQR$ to $\triangle P'Q'R'$.

Use any point on the figure and its image to find the horizontal and vertical translations. Try $P(3, 2)$ and its image $P'(-2, 5)$.

horizontal translation: $-2 - 3 = -5$ 5 units left
vertical translation: $5 - 2 = 3$ 3 units up

● The rule for the translation is $(x, y) \rightarrow (x - 5, y + 3)$.

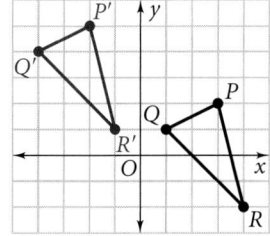

EXERCISES

The vertices of a triangle are given. Graph the triangle and its image after a translation of the specified number of units in each direction. 1–2. See margin.

1. $P(2, 5), Q(5, 6), R(5, 0)$; 4 units right, 5 units down

2. $U(0, 0), V(-5, -3), W(-6, 0)$; 2 units left, 2 units up

Write a rule to describe each translation. 3–8. See margin.

3. $A(4, -4) \rightarrow A'(2, -5)$

4. $G(-1, 9) \rightarrow G'(1, -9)$

5. $M(-2, 0) \rightarrow M'\left(2, \frac{1}{2}\right)$

6. $D(2, 4) \rightarrow D'(-3, 5)$

7. $Q(7, -3) \rightarrow Q'(9, 2)$

8. $W(6, -4) \rightarrow W'(2, 2)$

9.

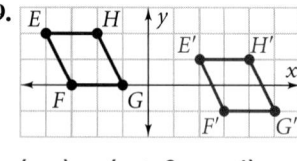

$(x, y) \rightarrow (x + 6, y - 1)$

10.

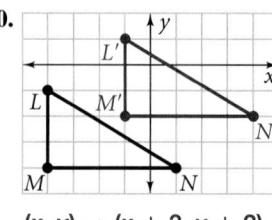

$(x, y) \rightarrow (x + 3, y + 2)$

11.

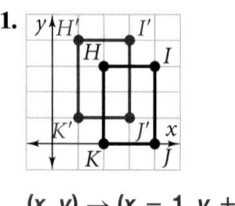

$(x, y) \rightarrow (x - 1, y + 1)$

Reflections

A reflection is a transformation that flips a figure over a line, called a line of reflection. The picture at the right shows $\triangle DEF$ and its reflection over the line of reflection ℓ. The image is $\triangle D'E'F'$.

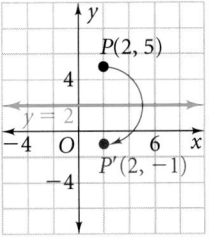

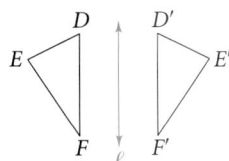 **EXAMPLE**

Reflect the point $P(2,5)$ over the line $y = 2$. What are the coordinates of its image P'?

● The coordinates of P' are $(2, -1)$.

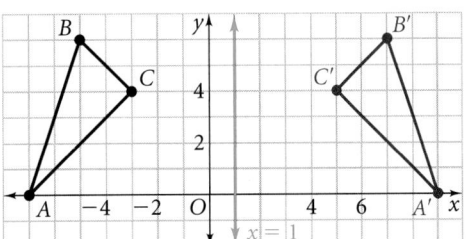

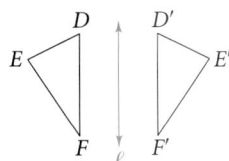 **EXAMPLE**

The vertices of $\triangle ABC$ are $A(-7,0)$, $B(-5,6)$, and $C(-3,4)$. Graph the image of the triangle after a reflection over the line $x = 1$.

To get from $A(-7,0)$ to $A'(9,0)$, point A is reflected the same distance on the other side of the line $x = 1$. The coordinates of the other two vertices in the reflected image are $B'(7,6)$ and $C'(5,4)$.

EXERCISES

Graph each point and its image after a reflection over the specified line. 1–3. See margin.

1. $K(2,3); x = 1$
2. $D(-3,1); y = -2$
3. $Z(2,5); x$-axis

The vertices of various figures are given. Graph both the figure and its image after a reflection over the specified line. 4–7. See margin.

4. $R(2,4), S(-1,3), T(2,0); y = -2$

5. $C(1,4), D(1,7), E(-2,7); x = 3$

6. $H(-5,5),\ I(6,0),\ J(0,0); y$-axis

7. $K(-2,-3), L(-7,-3), M(-7,-5), N(-2,-5); x$-axis

The reflected image of each figure is shown in red. Identify the line of reflection.

8.

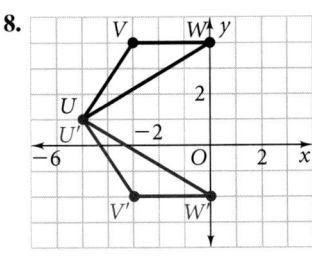

$y = 1$

9.

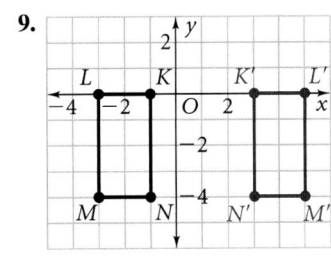

$x = 1$

page 733   **Reflections**

1.

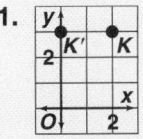

2.

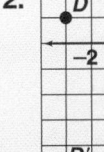

3.

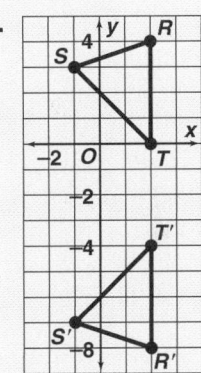

4.

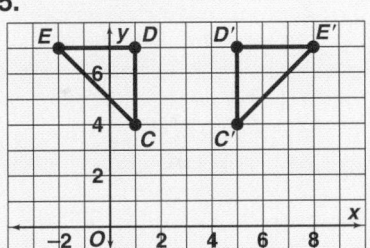

5.

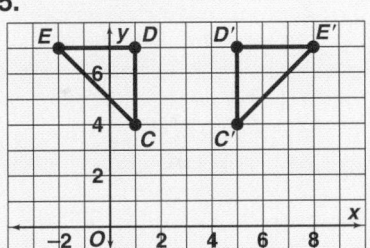

6.

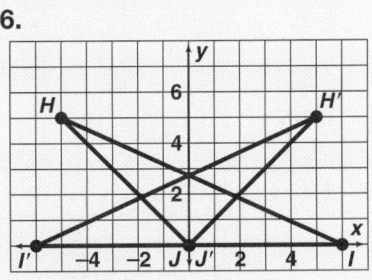

7.

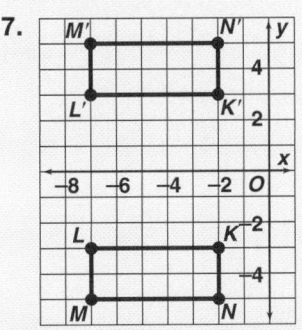

1.
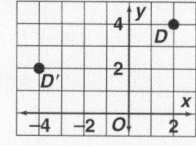

2.
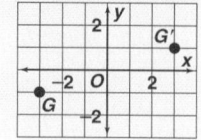

3.

4.
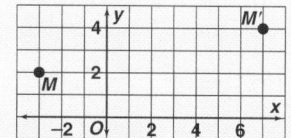

5a.
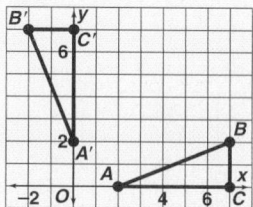

b.
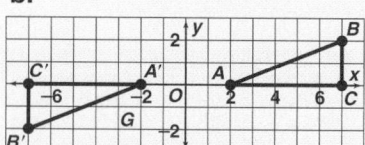

6a.
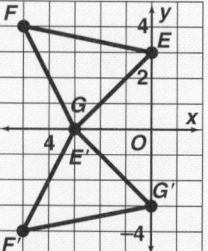

b.
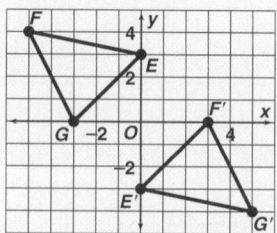

Rotations

A rotation is a transformation that turns a figure about a fixed point, called the *center of rotation*. You can rotate a figure up to 360°. All rotations shown on this page are counterclockwise.

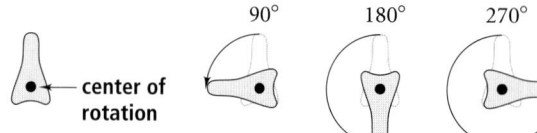

1 EXAMPLE

Find the image of $P(1, 2)$ after a rotation of 90° about the origin.

● The coordinates of P' are $(-2, 1)$.

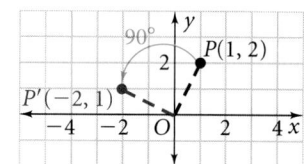

2 EXAMPLE

The vertices of $\triangle ABC$ are $A(0, 2)$, $B(-2, 0)$, and $C(2, 2)$. Find the coordinates of the image of $\triangle ABC$ after a rotation of 180° about the origin.

● The vertices of the image are $A'(0, -2)$, $B'(2, 0)$, and $C'(-2, -2)$.

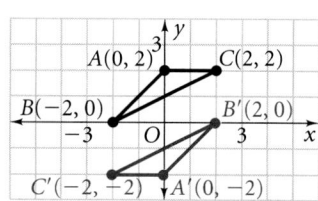

EXERCISES

Graph each point. Then rotate it the given number of degrees counterclockwise about the given center of rotation and graph the new point. 1–4. See margin.

1. $D(2, 4)$; 90° about the origin

2. $G(-3, -1)$; 180° about $(0, 0)$

3. $Z(4, -2)$; 90° about $(2, 0)$

4. $M(-3, 2)$; 180° about $(2, 3)$

The vertices of a triangle are given. On separate coordinate planes, graph each triangle and its image after a rotation of (a) 90° and (b) 180° about the origin. 5–8. See margin.

5. $A(2, 0)$, $B(7, 2)$, $C(7, 0)$

6. $E(0, 3)$, $F(-5, 4)$, $G(-3, 0)$

7. $L(-2, -1)$, $M(-5, -1)$, $N(-2, -5)$

8. $Q(0, -2)$, $R(0, 0)$, $S(2, 0)$

The triangles in the exercises below were formed by rotating the triangle at the left counterclockwise about the origin. What is each angle of rotation?

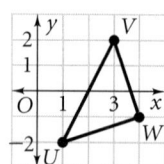

9.
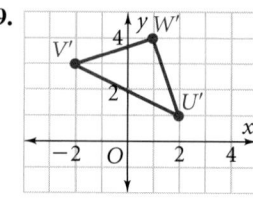

90°

10.
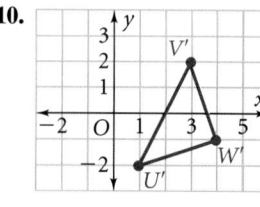

360°

Line Plots

A line plot is created by placing a mark above a number line corresponding to the location of each data item. Line plots have two main advantages:

- You can see the frequency of data items.
- You can see how the data items compare.

EXAMPLE

The table at the right gives the heights (in inches) of a group of twenty-five adults. Display the data in a line plot. Describe the data shown in the line plot.

Height of Adults (inches)

59	60	63	63	64
64	64	65	65	65
67	67	67	67	68
68	68	69	70	70
71	72	73	73	77

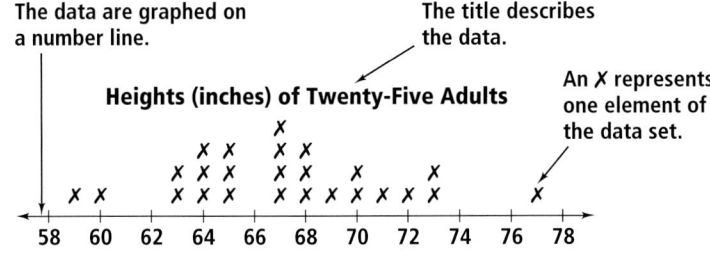

The data are graphed on a number line.

The title describes the data.

An *X* represents one element of the data set.

Heights (inches) of Twenty-Five Adults

The line plot shows that most of the heights are concentrated around 67 inches, the maximum value is 77, and the minimum value is 59.

EXERCISES

Display each set of data in a line plot.

1. 3, 6, 4, 3, 6, 0, 4, 5, 0, 4, 6, 1, 5, 1, 0, 5, 5, 6, 5, 3

2. 19, 18, 18, 18, 19, 20, 19, 18, 18, 17, 18, 20, 19, 17

Draw a line plot for each frequency table. 3–4. See margin.

3.

Number	1	2	3	4	5	6
Frequency	4	1	0	5	7	2

4.

Number	12	13	15	16	18	19
Frequency	2	5	1	3	6	3

5. Olympics Here are the numbers of gold medals won by different countries during the 1998 Winter Olympics (Bulgaria had the least with 1 gold medal and Germany had the most with 12 gold medals).
1, 1, 2, 2, 2, 2, 3, 3, 5, 5, 6, 6, 9, 10, 12
Display the data in a line plot. Describe the data shown in the line plot. **See margin.**

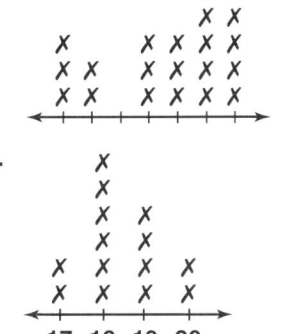

1.

2.

17 18 19 20

Skills Handbook **735**

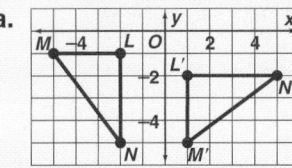

7a.

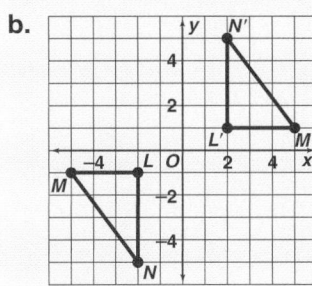

b.

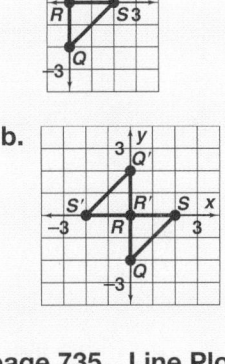

8a.

b.

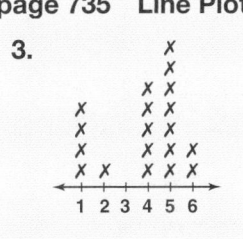

page 735 Line Plots

3.

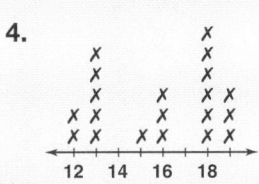

1 2 3 4 5 6

4.

12 14 16 18

5.

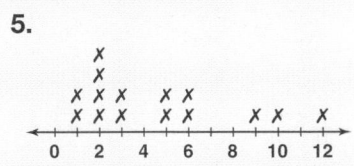

0 2 4 6 8 10 12

The line plot shows that most of the numbers are concentrated around 2, the maximum is 12, and the minimum is 1.

Bar Graphs

Bar graphs are used to compare amounts. The horizontal axis shows the categories and the vertical axis shows the amounts. A multiple bar graph includes a key.

 EXAMPLE

Draw a bar graph for the data in the table below.

Median Household Income

State	1995	1997	1999
Calif.	$40,457	$41,203	$43,744
Conn.	$43,993	$45,657	$50,798
Ind.	$36,496	$40,367	$40,929
Tex.	$35,024	$36,408	$38,978
Utah	$39,879	$44,401	$46,094

SOURCE: U.S. Census Bureau

The categories (in the first column) are placed on the horizontal scale. The amounts (in the second, third, and fourth columns) are placed on the vertical scale.

Graph the data for each state. Use the values in the top row to create the key.

—The highest projected income is $50,798. So a reasonable range for the vertical scale is 0 to $55,000.

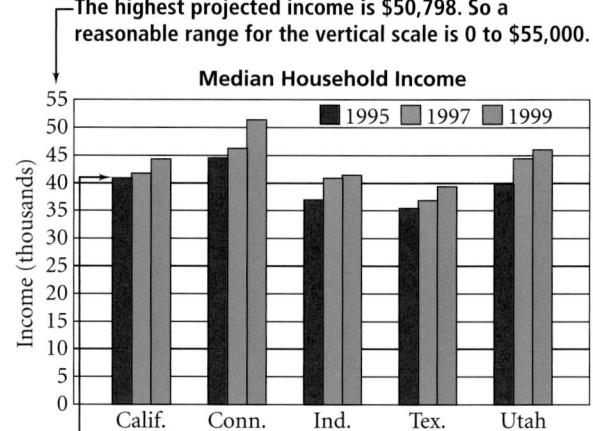

To draw a bar on the graph, estimate its placement based on the vertical scale.

EXERCISES

1. Draw a bar graph for the data in the table below.

Highest Temperatures

City	March	June	August
Juneau, AK	61	86	83
Denver, CO	84	104	101
Atlanta, GA	89	101	102
Honolulu, HI	88	92	93
Detroit, MI	81	104	100
Buffalo, NY	81	96	99
Houston, TX	91	103	107

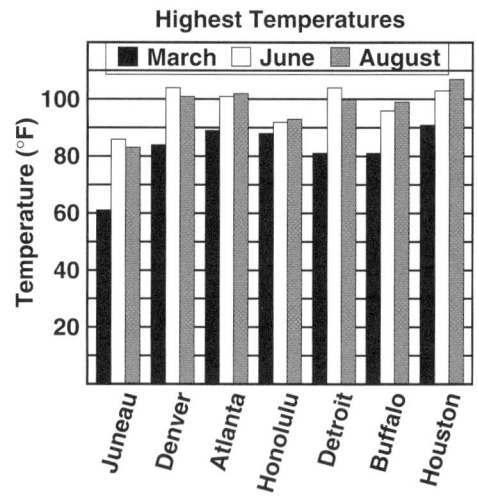

2. a. Critical Thinking If one more column of data were added to the table in the example, how would the bar graph be different? **Each state would have one more bar.**

b. If one more row of data were added to the table in the example, how would the bar graph be different? **There would be another group of three bars added.**

Histograms

A histogram is a bar graph that shows the frequency, or number of times, a data item occurs. Histograms often combine data into intervals of equal size. The intervals do not overlap.

EXAMPLE

The data at the right show the number of hours of battery life for different brands of batteries used in portable CD players. Use the data to make a histogram.

Hours of Battery Life

12 9 10 14 10 11
10 18 21 10 14 22

Step 1 Decide on an interval size.

The data start at 9 hours and go to 22 hours. Use equal-sized intervals of 4 hours, beginning with 8 hours. So the first interval will be 8–11.

Step 2 Make a frequency table.

Battery Life

Hours	Tally	Frequency
8–11	ⅢⅡ Ⅰ	6
12–15	Ⅲ	3
16–19	Ⅰ	1
20–23	Ⅱ	2

Step 3 Make a histogram.

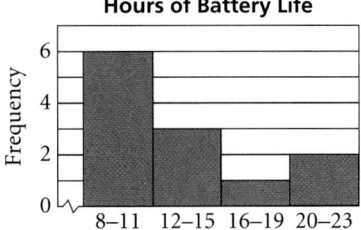

Hours of Battery Life

EXERCISES

1. Students answered a survey question about how long it takes to get ready in the morning. The histogram at the right shows the survey results.

Time to Get Ready

a. Which interval indicates the answers most students gave? **30–39**

b. How many students answered the survey question? **15 students**

c. Why might no students have given an answer in the interval 50–59?

d. Critical Thinking With the information you have, could you redraw the histogram with intervals half their current size? Explain why or why not.

1c. Answers may vary. Sample: If it actually took 50–59 minutes, the student might estimate by saying 1 hour.

d. No; you don't know where inside each interval the answers are.

2. a. An internet company surveyed their users. The first 25 people who responded gave the ages shown at the right. What intervals would you use to make a histogram? **a–c. See margin.**

b. Make a frequency table for the data.

c. Make a histogram.

Age of Internet Users

25, 43, 65, 12, 8, 30, 44, 68, 18, 21, 25, 33, 37, 54, 61, 29, 31, 38, 22, 48, 19, 34, 55, 14, 21

3. a. Data Collection Survey your class to find out what day of the month they were born. For example, 12 if a student's birthday is August 12th.

b. What intervals would you use to make a histogram?

c. Make a frequency table for the data.

d. Make a histogram. **a–d. Check students' work.**

2. Answers may vary. Samples are given.

a. intervals of 10 years, starting with age 5

b.

Age of Internet Users

Age	Tally	Frequency
5–14	Ⅲ	3
15–24	ⅢⅡ	5
25–34	ⅢⅡ Ⅱ	7
35–44	Ⅲ Ⅰ	4
45–54	Ⅱ	2
55–64	Ⅱ	2
65–74	Ⅱ	2

c.

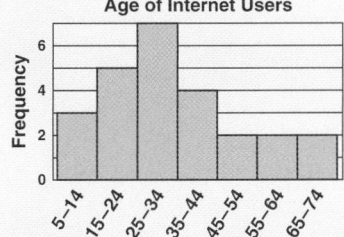

Age of Internet Users

Skills Handbook

Skills Handbook

1.

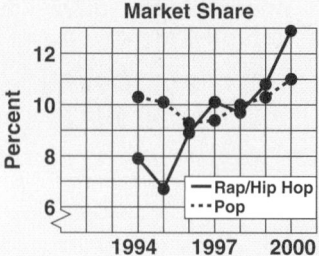

Market Share

Line Graphs

Line graphs are used to display the change in a set of data over a period of time. A multiple-line graph shows change in more than one category of data over time. You can use a line graph to look for trends and make predictions.

 EXAMPLE

Graph the data in the table below.

Households with VCR and Cable TV (millions)

Year	1985	1990	1995	1996	1997	1998
VCR	18	63	77	79	82	83
Cable TV	36	52	60	63	64	66

SOURCE: Television Bureau of Advertising, Inc., *Trends in Television*

Since the data show changes over time for two sets of data, use a double line graph. The horizontal scale displays years. The vertical scale displays the number of households for each category, VCR and cable TV.

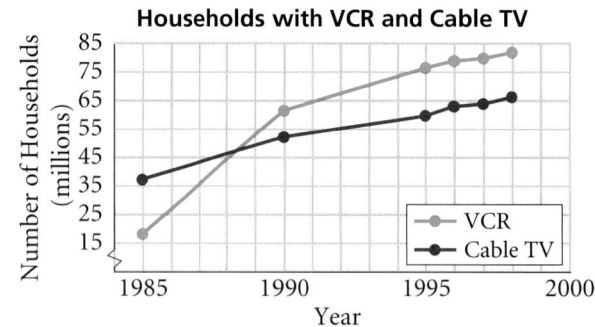

Households with VCR and Cable TV

Notice that there is a *break* in the vertical scale, which goes from 0 to 85. A zigzag line is used to indicate a break from 0 to 15 since there is no data to graph in this part of the *y*-axis.

EXERCISES

Graph the following data. 1. See margin.

1.

Market Shares (percent)

Year	1994	1995	1996	1997	1998	1999	2000
Rap/Hip Hop	7.9	6.7	8.9	10.1	9.7	10.8	12.9
Pop	10.3	10.1	9.3	9.4	10.0	10.3	11.0

SOURCE: The Recording Industry of America

2.

Percents of Schools with Internet Access

Year	1995	1996	1997	1998	1999
Elementary	46	61	75	88	94
Secondary	65	77	89	94	98

SOURCE: U.S. National Center for Education Statistics

Schools with Internet Access

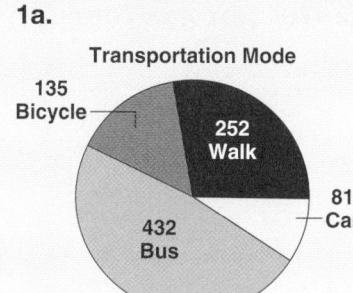

Transportation Mode

Circle Graphs

A circle graph is an efficient way to present certain types of data. The graphs show data as percents or fractions of a whole. The total must be 100% or 1. Circle graphs are used to show the parts of the whole. The angles at the center are central angles, and each angle is proportional to the percent or fraction of the total.

What Do You Think Is the Number One Problem in the World Today?

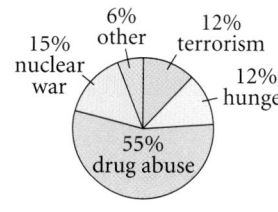

Source: *The Second Kids' World Almanac*

EXAMPLE

The table below shows the number of people in the United States who have at least one grandchild under the age of 18. Draw a circle graph for the data.

Ages of U.S. Grandparents

Age	People (millions)
44 and under	3.6
45–54	10.3
55–64	15.0
65 and over	18.2

Step 1 Add to find the total number.

$$3.6 + 10.3 + 15.0 + 18.2 = 47.1 \text{ (million)}$$

Step 2 For each central angle, set up a proportion to find the measure. Use a calculator to solve each proportion.

$$\frac{3.6}{47.1} = \frac{a}{360°} \qquad \frac{10.3}{47.1} = \frac{b}{360°} \qquad \frac{15.0}{47.1} = \frac{c}{360°} \qquad \frac{18.2}{47.1} = \frac{d}{360°}$$
$$a \approx 27.5° \qquad b \approx 78.7° \qquad c \approx 114.6° \qquad d \approx 139.1°$$

Step 3 Use a compass to draw a circle. Draw the approximate central angles with a protractor.

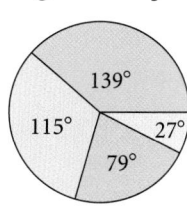

Step 4 Label each sector. Add any necessary information.

Ages of U.S. Grandparents

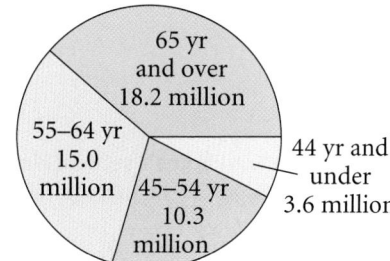

EXERCISES

1. **a.** Use the data in the table to draw a circle graph. **1a. See margin.**
   b. Approximately what percent of students ride the bus? **50%**
   c. Approximately how many times more students walk than ride in a car? **3 times**

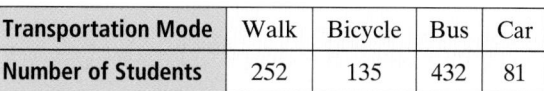

Transportation Mode	Walk	Bicycle	Bus	Car
Number of Students	252	135	432	81

2. **Data Collection** Survey your class to find out how they get to school. Use the data to draw a circle graph. **Check students' work.**

Skills Handbook **739**

1.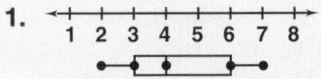

2.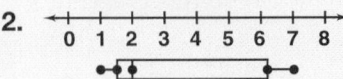

3.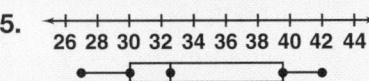

4.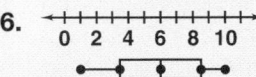

5.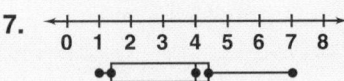

6.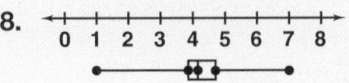

7.

8.

Box-and-Whisker Plots

To show how data items are spread out, you can arrange a set of data in order from least to greatest. The maximum, minimum, and median give you some information about the data. You can better describe the data by dividing it into fourths.

The lower quartile is the median of the lower half of the data. The upper quartile is the median of the upper half of the data. If the data set has an odd number of items, the median is not included in either the upper half or the lower half.

The data below describes the highway gas mileage (mi/gal) for several cars.

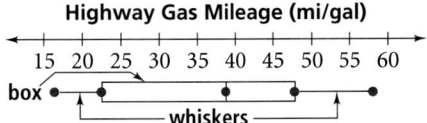

A box-and-whisker plot is a visual representation of data. The box-and-whisker plot below displays the gas mileage information.

Highway Gas Mileage (mi/gal)

The box represents the data from the lower quartile to the upper quartile. The vertical line segment represents the median. Horizontal line segments called whiskers show the spread of the data to the minimum and to the maximum.

EXERCISES

Create a box-and-whisker plot for each data set. 1–8. See margin.

1. $\{3, 2, 3, 4, 6, 6, 7\}$

2. $\{1, 1.5, 1.7, 2, 6.1, 6.2, 7\}$

3. $\{1, 2, 5, 6, 9, 12, 7, 10\}$

4. $\{65, 66, 59, 61, 67, 70, 67, 66, 69, 70, 63\}$

5. $\{29, 32, 40, 31, 33, 39, 27, 42\}$

6. $\{3, 3, 5, 7, 1, 10, 10, 4, 4, 7, 9, 8, 6\}$

7. $\{1, 1.2, 1.3, 4, 4.1, 4.2, 7\}$

8. $\{1, 3.8, 3.9, 4, 4.3, 4.4, 7, 5\}$

9. Jobs Below are the number of hours a student worked each week at her summer job. When she applied for the job, she was told that the typical work week was 29 hours.

29, 25, 21, 20, 17, 16, 15, 33, 33, 30, 15

a. Make a box-and-whisker plot for the data.

b. How many weeks are above the upper quartile? What are the numbers of hours worked? **2; 33, 33**

c. What is the median number of hours she worked? What is the mean? Compare them to the typical work week. **21 h; 23 h; both are much less than the 29-h typical week.**

10. Writing In what ways are histograms and box-and-whisker plots alike, and in what ways are they different? **Each diagram shows how the data are distributed. A histogram shows how many data points are in each part of the range. A box-and-whisker plot gives information about the maximum, the minimum, and the median.**

Choosing an Appropriate Graph

The type of data you want to display can suggest an appropriate graph. You can have data by categories (qualitative data), such as states (page 736), years (page 739), or mode of transportation (page 739). You may also have measurement data (quantitative data), such as height (page 735), time to get ready in the morning (page 737), or gas mileage (page 740).

The table below lists some common types of graphs and how they are frequently used.

Graph	Use
Bar Graph	To display frequency of categories
Circle Graph	To show categories as part of a whole
Line Graph	To show trends over time
Line Plot, Histogram, Stem-and-Leaf Plot	To display frequency distribution of measurement data
Box-and-Whisker Plot	To summarize the distribution of measurement data
Scatter Plot	To display possible relationships in data pairs

1 EXAMPLE

Would you use a line graph or a circle graph to display the percent of fiction books published each year for the last ten years?

A circle graph shows percents, but it would not allow you to show the change over time. A line graph would be more appropriate.

EXERCISES

Choose the appropriate graph to display each set of data. Explain your choice.   1–4. See margin.

1. circle graph or bar graph
   how much the average family spends on rent, food, transportation, utilities, and entertainment in October

2. bar graph or line graph
   the number of runners in the Olympic marathon for each of the last five Olympic games

3. scatter plot or double bar graph
   the ages of twelve cars and their levels of emissions

4. double box-and-whisker plot or scatter plot
   the heights of men and women playing professional basketball in 2004

Open-Ended For each type of graph, describe a set of data that would be appropriate. 5–7. Answers may vary. Samples are given.

5. stem-and-leaf plot **the scores of ten volleyball games**

6. double line graph **the average salaries of working men and women since 2000**

7. circle graph **the distribution of kinds of nuts in a jar of mixed nuts**

Skills Handbook

Skills Handbook

page 741 Choosing an Appropriate Graph

1. Circle graph; the categories seem to cover how an average family spends all of its money in October. A circle graph also shows the percentage of a category more easily that a bar graph.

2. Line graph; the number of runners can change (and show a trend) over time. A bar graph is better for multiple categories.

3. Scatter plot; the levels of emissions most likely increase as the age of a car increases. A double bar graph would only be used if the data had an additional subject.

4. Double box-and-whisker plot; there are two categories for height (men and women), and the height data can be summarized for each category.

1a. The graph implies that the runner's time on the 10-mile run was more than cut in half in six weeks, while actually the runner's time decreased by a bit more than 10%.

b. Add a break on the vertical axis, or redraw the graph with the vertical axis starting at zero.

2a. The graph implies that four times as many towels were sold on Tuesday as on Monday, while actually twice as many towels were sold.

b. Redraw the bars to have the same width.

Misleading Graphs

There are many ways to graph data that show the data accurately. There are also ways to graph data that are misleading. One way that is misleading is graphing data that has less than the whole vertical axis, but doesn't point this out with the use of a break symbol on the axis.

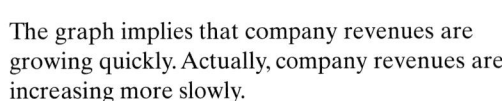 **EXAMPLE**

What impression does the graph at the right give? What is actually true about the data?

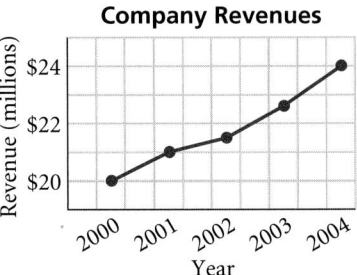

The graph implies that company revenues are growing quickly. Actually, company revenues are increasing more slowly.

Another way a graph can mislead is by using shapes that increase in both height and width, which implies a much bigger increase has happened, since the area increases much more than the height alone.

2 **EXAMPLE**

What makes the graph at the right misleading? Explain.

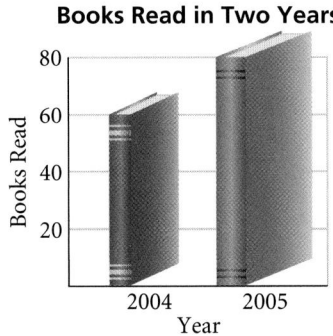

Looking at the vertical axis, you can see that the number of books read increased by one third. However, the bar on the right increased not only in height, but width. The area of the second bar is more than two times the area of the first bar. This gives the impression that the increase was much greater than it really was.

EXERCISES

For each graph below, **(a)** explain how the graph is misleading, and **(b)** explain how to redraw the graph so it is not misleading.   1–2. See margin.

1.

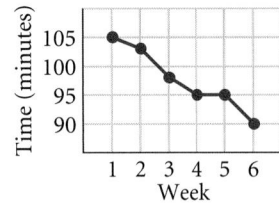

2.

3. Choose one of the graphs on this page. Redraw the graph to display the data accurately. **Check students' work.**

Probability Distributions

A probability distribution is a function that gives the probability of each event in a sample space. You can use a table or a graph to show a probability distribution.

1 EXAMPLE

Experimental Probability   Use the data in the table below to make a graph of the probability distribution.

What Is Your Favorite Color?

Color	Percent
Red	27
Blue	35
Green	17
Black	21

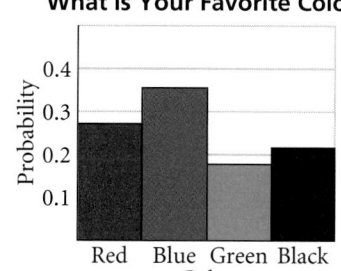

What Is Your Favorite Color?

EXERCISES

Use the data in each table to make a graph of each probability distribution.   1–2. See margin.

1. How Many Siblings Do You Have?

Number	Percent
0	38
1	41
2	17
3 or more	4

2. Where Do People Live in the U.S.?

Region	Percent
Northeast	19.0
Midwest	22.9
South	35.6
West	22.5

3. Theoretical Probability   Suppose you roll two number cubes to find the sum of the numbers.
   a. Show the probability distribution in a table and a graph.   **See margin.**
   b. Find the mean and the range of the distribution.   **7; 10**
   c. What is the probability that the sum is 10? $\frac{1}{12}$
   d. What is the probability that the sum is 7? $\frac{1}{6}$
   e. What is the probability that the sum is less than 9? $\frac{13}{18}$

4. Theoretical Probability   Use the spinner at the right.
   a. Show the probability distribution in a table for getting each color.   **a–b. See margin.**
   b. Show the probability distribution in a graph.
   c. What is the probability that you will spin green?   **20%**
   d. What is the probability that you will spin blue or red?   **70%**

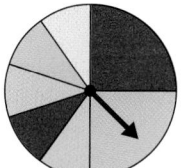

5. Critical Thinking   What is the sum of the probabilities in a probability distribution? Explain.   **100%; Answers may vary. Sample: The probability of all possible outcomes together is 1, or 100%.**

1.

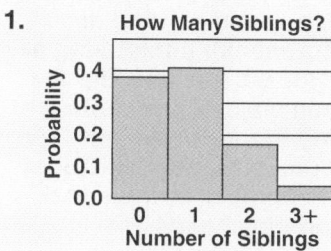

How Many Siblings?

2.

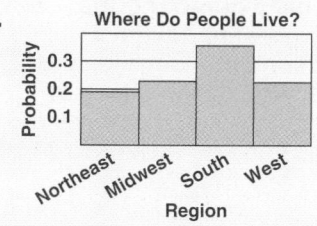

Where Do People Live?

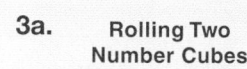

3a.   Rolling Two Number Cubes

Sum	Probability
2	$\frac{1}{36}$
3	$\frac{2}{36}$
4	$\frac{3}{36}$
5	$\frac{4}{36}$
6	$\frac{5}{36}$
7	$\frac{6}{36}$
8	$\frac{5}{36}$
9	$\frac{4}{36}$
10	$\frac{3}{36}$
11	$\frac{2}{36}$
12	$\frac{1}{36}$

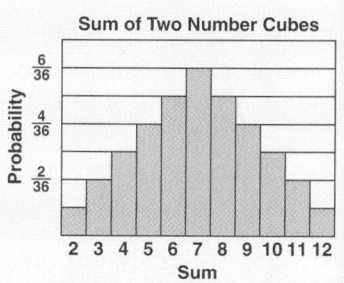

Sum of Two Number Cubes

4a.

Color	Probability
Red	35%
Blue	35%
Green	20%
Yellow	10%

b.

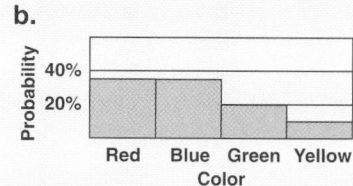

1. Use a coin. Let heads represent a book being a trade paperback. Flip the coin six times to represent one trial. Six rolls represent one trial. Count the number of trials that had only heads.

2. Use a number cube. Let 1 represent having a bachelor's degree, and 2, 3, and 4 represent not having one. If you roll a 5 or 6, do not count this roll in any trial. Ten rolls represent one trial. Count the number of trials that have exactly four 1s.

3. Use a spinner. Shade a region with a 137° central angle. This approximates 38% of the area of the circle. Let this area represent pumpkins from Illinois. Three spins represent one trial. Count the number of trials that had all spins land in the shaded area.

4. Use a number cube. Let 1, 2, 3, and 4 represent students with computer access from home, and 5 and 6 represent students that do not. Six rolls represent one trial. Count the number of trials with only rolls of 1, 2, 3, or 4.

5. Use a spinner. Shade a region with a 295° central angle. This approximates 82% of the area of the circle. Let this area represent making a free throw. Five spins represent one trial. Count the number of trials that had all spins land in the shaded area.

6. Check students' work.

Simulations

On page 218, you learned how to simulate a problem using random numbers generated by a graphing calculator or computer program. You can also simulate some probability problems using a coin, spinner, or number cube.

1 EXAMPLE

Describe a simulation you could use to model each situation.

a. About 10% of the members of Congress in the House of Representatives represent California. What is the probability that three representatives chosen at random are all from California?

There are not two equally likely outcomes, so using a coin is not a good choice.

A spinner lets you represent outcomes that are not equally likely. Here, there are two outcomes: either a representative is from California (10%) or not (90%). So a spinner that models this situation would have a region with the central angle of 36°, showing 10% of the area of the circle.

Each three spins of the spinner would be one trial.

b. One fifth of the students in a school choose blue as a favorite color. What is the probability that four students all prefer blue?

One way to simulate this problem is using a number cube. Choose one number to represent the one fifth of students who prefer blue, and four numbers to represent the four fifths of the students who don't. Ignore the extra number when it is rolled, and do not count that roll in any trial. One choice is to have 1 represent liking blue, 2–5 represent not liking blue, and ignore any 6s that are rolled. Each four rolls of the number cube would be one trial.

EXERCISES

Describe a simulation could you use to represent each situation.   1–6. See margin.

1. Half of the books sold in one bookstore are trade paperbacks. What is the probability that the next six books sold will be trade paperbacks?

2. For a woman aged 25 or more, there is a 25% chance that she has at least a bachelor's degree from college. What is the probability that four out of 10 women over age 25 all have at least a bachelor's degree?

3. By weight, about 38% of the pumpkins grown in the United States come from Illinois. What is the probability that three pumpkins selected at random all come from Illinois?

4. About two thirds of school-aged students have access to a computer at home. What is the probability that six students do not have access to a computer at home?

5. A basketball player has made 82 of her last 100 free throws. What is the probability that she will make her next five free throws?

6. Open-Ended Write a probability problem you could solve using a simulation.

Conducting a Survey

Statisticians collect information about specific groups. Any group of objects or people is a population. When a population is too large to survey, they study a sample, or part, of the population to find out characteristics of the population.

Three kinds of samples, random, systematic, and stratified, are explained in the table below.

Name	Sampling Method	Example
Random	Survey a population at random.	Survey people whose names are drawn out of a hat.
Systematic	Select a number n at random. Then survey every nth person.	Select the number 5 at random. Survey every fifth person.
Stratified	Separate a population into smaller groups, each with a certain characteristic. Then survey at random within each group.	Separate a high school into four groups by grade level. Survey a random sample of students from each grade.

When statisticians survey a sample of a population, they try to write questions that are as unbiased as possible. Biased questions can make assumptions that may or may not be true. They can also make one answer seem better than another.

1 EXAMPLE

Determine whether each question is biased or not. Explain.

a. What kind of pet do you own?

This question is biased. It assumes you own a pet.

b. Do you prefer exciting action movies or sedate foreign films?

This question is biased. It makes action movies seem more appealing than foreign films.

c. What is your favorite food?

This question is unbiased. It does not try to persuade your answer.

EXERCISES

Tell whether each survey plan describes a good sample and, if so, which method of sampling is used.

1. A candidate calls every 50th name in the phone book to find out how the person likes the candidate.   **Good sample; it uses the systematic method.**

2. A factory tests the quality of the last 25 out of 1000 shirts made.   **See above.**

3. A bindery selects 10 of the 450 packages of inserts at random to see if all the inserts were printed properly.   **Good sample; it is a random sample.**

Determine whether each question is biased or not. Explain.

4. What toppings do you like on pizza?   **Biased; it assumes you like pizza.**

5. Where would you most like to go for a vacation?   **Not biased; the question makes no assumptions and does not attempt to persuade you.**

2. Not a good sample; choosing the last 25 shirts out of 1000 is not a random sample. The quality of the shirts toward the end of the run could drop, due to tired workers or failing machinery.

Interpreting Statistical Results

One-variable Data Suppose you survey 50 people and 30% of them like the color blue best. The size of your sample affects the confidence you should have in the result. You can use the margin of error formula to interpret the result.

1 EXAMPLE

Find the margin of error for your survey of 50 people.

$$\text{margin of error} = \pm \frac{1}{\sqrt{n}}$$ **Use the margin of error formula.**

$$= \pm \frac{1}{\sqrt{50}}$$ **Substitute 50 for n, the size of the sample.**

$$\approx \pm 0.1414$$ **Use a calculator.**

The margin of error is about $\pm 14\%$, so about 16% to 44% of the population you sampled is likely to prefer blue.

Two-variable Data Suppose you compare people's height and shoe size. You can use a line of best fit (or trend line) to predict shoe size for various heights.

Predictions within the range of data values (called interpolating) are more reliable than predictions beyond the range of data values (called extrapolating).

2 EXAMPLE

Use the scatter plot at the right. What size shoe would you predict a woman 6 ft 3 in. tall would wear? A woman 7 ft tall?

A woman 6 ft 3 in. tall is 75 inches tall. Use the line of best fit; the shoe size would likely be $y = 0.15(75) - 2.11 \approx 9$.

A woman 7 ft tall is 84 in. The shoe size would likely be $y = 0.15(84) - 2.11 \approx 10.5$. This is an extrapolation, so it is a less reliable result.

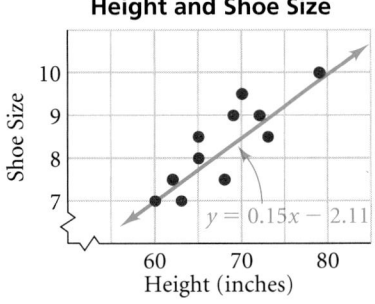

Height and Shoe Size

$y = 0.15x - 2.11$

EXERCISES

Find the margin of error for each sample size.
Round to the nearest percent.

1. 100 people   **±10%**

2. 500 people   **±4%**

3. 1000 people   **±3%**

4. 10,000 people   **±1%**

5. Critical Thinking What sample size will produce a margin of error of ±5%?   **400**

6. Use the scatter plot in Example 2. What would be the shoe size of a woman 5 ft 7 in. tall?   **size 8**

7. Critical Thinking What height would you predict a woman wearing size 9.5 shoes would be?   **about 6 ft 5 in. tall**

8. a. Data Collection Find data that you could display in a scatter plot.
   b. Use your scatter plot to make a prediction about a value not included in one data set.   **a–b. Check students work.**

Spreadsheets

You can use a spreadsheet to evaluate formulas. Spreadsheets use the symbols + for addition and − for subtraction, but different symbols for other operations.

Multiplication: $* \rightarrow$ $\qquad 10 * 2 = 10 \cdot 2 = 20$

Division: $/ \rightarrow$ $\qquad 10 / 2 = 10 \div 2 = 5$

Exponent: $\wedge \rightarrow$ $\qquad 10 \wedge 2 = 10^2 = 100$

EXAMPLE

Evaluate the formula $P = 2\ell + 2w$ for $\ell = 3$ and for whole-number values of w from 8 to 11.

Enter the values of ℓ and w into the first two columns. Cell A2 has the value of ℓ. Cell B2 has the first value of w. In cell C2, enter the expression $= 2*A2 + 2*B2$ to find the perimeter of a figure with length 3 and width 8.

Column names

Row numbers

	A	B	C
1	L	W	2L + 2W
2		3	8	= 2*A2 + 2* B2
3		3	9
4		3	10
5		3	11

Cell B5

The spreadsheet evaluates the expression automatically.

Copy the expression in cell C2 into cells C3, C4, and C5. The spreadsheet automatically updates for the values of ℓ and w in rows 3, 4, and 5.

✗	✓	= 2*A2 + 2* B2

	A	B	C
1	L	W	2L + 2W
2		3	8	22
3		3	9	24
4		3	10	26
5		3	11	28

EXERCISES

Suppose the values of a, b, and c are in cells A2, B2, and C2 of a spreadsheet. Write the expression you would use to enter each formula in the spreadsheet. 1–4. See below.

1. $P = a + b + c$

2. $T = \dfrac{3a + 5b}{8}$

3. $R = \frac{1}{2}bc$

4. $A = c^2$

5. You deposit $200 in an account that earns 6% compounded annually for three years. The spreadsheet below shows the balance at the end of each year.

	A	B	C	D	E
1	Year	Start of Year	Rate	Interest	End of Year
2	1st	$200.00	0.06	$12.00	$212.00
3	2nd	$212.00	0.06	$12.72	$224.72
4	3rd	$224.72	0.06	$13.48	$238.20

1. = A2 + B2 + C2

2. = (3 * A2 + 5 * B2)/8

3. = 1/2 * B2 * C2

4. = C2 ^ 2

a. In which cell of the spreadsheet would you find the formula = B3 * C3? **D3**

b. In which cell of the spreadsheet would you find the formula = B4 + D4? **E4**

Tables

Table 1 Measures

United States Customary	Metric
Length	
12 inches (in.) = 1 foot (ft)	10 millimeters (mm) = 1 centimeter (cm)
36 in. = 1 yard (yd)	100 cm = 1 meter (m)
3 ft = 1 yard	1000 mm = 1 meter
5280 ft = 1 mile (mi)	1000 m = 1 kilometer (km)
1760 yd = 1 mile	
Area	
144 square inches (in.²) = 1 square foot (ft²)	100 square millimeters (mm²) = 1 square centimeter (cm²)
9 ft² = 1 square yard (yd²)	10,000 cm² = 1 square meter (m²)
43,560 ft² = 1 acre (a)	10,000 m² = 1 hectare (ha)
4840 yd² = 1 acre	
Volume	
1728 cubic inches (in.³) = 1 cubic foot (ft³)	1000 cubic millimeters (mm³) = 1 cubic centimeter (cm³)
27 ft³ = 1 cubic yard (yd³)	1,000,000 cm³ = 1 cubic meter (m³)
Liquid Capacity	
8 fluid ounces (fl oz) = 1 cup (c)	1000 milliliters (mL) = 1 liter (L)
2 c = 1 pint (pt)	1000 L = 1 kiloliter (kL)
2 pt = 1 quart (qt)	
4 qt = 1 gallon (gal)	
Weight or Mass	
16 ounces (oz) = 1 pound (lb)	1000 milligrams (mg) = 1 gram (g)
2000 pounds = 1 ton (t)	1000 g = 1 kilogram (kg)
	1000 kg = 1 metric ton
Temperature	
32°F = freezing point of water	0°C = freezing point of water
98.6°F = normal body temperature	37°C = normal body temperature
212°F = boiling point of water	100°C = boiling point of water

Time	
60 seconds (s) = 1 minute (min)	365 days = 1 year (yr)
60 minutes = 1 hour (h)	52 weeks (approx.) = 1 year
24 hours = 1 day (d)	12 months = 1 year
7 days = 1 week (wk)	10 years = 1 decade
4 weeks (approx.) = 1 month (mo)	100 years = 1 century

Table 2 Reading Math Symbols

Symbol	Meaning	Page
·	multiplication sign, times ($\times$)	p. 4
=	equals	p. 5
( )	parentheses for grouping	p. 9
a^n	nth power of a	p. 9
%	percent	p. 11
[ ]	brackets for grouping	p. 12
…	and so on	p. 17
$-a$	opposite of a	p. 17
π	pi, an irrational number, approximately equal to 3.14	p. 18
<	is less than	p. 19
>	is greater than	p. 19
$\lvert a \rvert$	absolute value of a	p. 20
°	degree(s)	p. 26
$\begin{bmatrix} 1 & 2 \\ 3 & 4 \end{bmatrix}$	matrix	p. 27
$\frac{1}{a}, a \neq 0$	reciprocal of a	p. 40
(x, y)	ordered pair	p. 59
$\stackrel{?}{} $	Is the statement true?	p. 75
$\triangle ABC$	triangle ABC	p. 100
$\approx$	is approximately equal to	p. 119
$\leq$	is less than or equal to	p. 134
$\geq$	is greater than or equal to	p. 134
{ }	set braces	p. 160
$a:b$	ratio of a to b	p. 182
$\neq$	is not equal to	p. 182
AB	length of $\overline{AB}$; distance between points A and B	p. 189
$\overline{AB}$	segment with endpoints A and B	p. 189
$\cong$	is congruent to	p. 190

Symbol	Meaning	Page
$\angle A$	angle A	p. 190
$P(\text{event})$	probability of the event	p. 211
$f(x)$	f of x; the function value at x	p. 243
x_1, x_2, etc.	specific values of the variable x	p. 264
y_1, y_2, etc.	specific values of the variable y	p. 264
$\overleftrightarrow{AB}$	line through points A and B	p. 284
m	slope of a linear function	p. 290
b	y-intercept of a linear function	p. 291
a^{-n}	$\frac{1}{a^n}, a \neq 0$	p. 394
$\sqrt{x}$	nonnegative square root of x	p. 524
$\pm$	plus or minus	p. 524
$\sin A$	sine of $\angle A$	p. 621
$\cos A$	cosine of $\angle A$	p. 621
$\tan A$	tangent of $\angle A$	p. 621
$\bar{x}$	mean of data values of x	p. 620
$m\angle A$	measure of angle A	p. 625
$_nP_r$	permutations of n things taken r at a time	p. 681
$_nC_r$	combinations of n things taken r at a time	p. 687
^	raised to a power (in a spreadsheet formula)	p. 741
*	multiply (in a spreadsheet formula)	p. 741
/	divide (in a spreadsheet formula)	p. 741

Table 3 Squares and Square Roots

Number n	Square n^2	Positive Square Root $\sqrt{n}$	Number n	Square n^2	Positive Square Root $\sqrt{n}$	Number n	Square n^2	Positive Square Root $\sqrt{n}$
1	1	1.000	51	2601	7.141	101	10,201	10.050
2	4	1.414	52	2704	7.211	102	10,404	10.100
3	9	1.732	53	2809	7.280	103	10,609	10.149
4	16	2.000	54	2916	7.348	104	10,816	10.198
5	25	2.236	55	3025	7.416	105	11,025	10.247
6	36	2.449	56	3136	7.483	106	11,236	10.296
7	49	2.646	57	3249	7.550	107	11,449	10.344
8	64	2.828	58	3364	7.616	108	11,664	10.392
9	81	3.000	59	3481	7.681	109	11,881	10.440
10	100	3.162	60	3600	7.746	110	12,100	10.488
11	121	3.317	61	3721	7.810	111	12,321	10.536
12	144	3.464	62	3844	7.874	112	12,544	10.583
13	169	3.606	63	3969	7.937	113	12,769	10.630
14	196	3.742	64	4096	8.000	114	12,996	10.677
15	225	3.873	65	4225	8.062	115	13,225	10.724
16	256	4.000	66	4356	8.124	116	13,456	10.770
17	289	4.123	67	4489	8.185	117	13,689	10.817
18	324	4.243	68	4624	8.246	118	13,924	10.863
19	361	4.359	69	4761	8.307	119	14,161	10.909
20	400	4.472	70	4900	8.367	120	14,400	10.954
21	441	4.583	71	5041	8.426	121	14,641	11.000
22	484	4.690	72	5184	8.485	122	14,884	11.045
23	529	4.796	73	5329	8.544	123	15,129	11.091
24	576	4.899	74	5476	8.602	124	15,376	11.136
25	625	5.000	75	5625	8.660	125	15,625	11.180
26	676	5.099	76	5776	8.718	126	15,876	11.225
27	729	5.196	77	5929	8.775	127	16,129	11.269
28	784	5.292	78	6084	8.832	128	16,384	11.314
29	841	5.385	79	6241	8.888	129	16,641	11.358
30	900	5.477	80	6400	8.944	130	16,900	11.402
31	961	5.568	81	6561	9.000	131	17,161	11.446
32	1024	5.657	82	6724	9.055	132	17,424	11.489
33	1089	5.745	83	6889	9.110	133	17,689	11.533
34	1156	5.831	84	7056	9.165	134	17,956	11.576
35	1225	5.916	85	7225	9.220	135	18,225	11.619
36	1296	6.000	86	7396	9.274	136	18,496	11.662
37	1369	6.083	87	7569	9.327	137	18,769	11.705
38	1444	6.164	88	7744	9.381	138	19,044	11.747
39	1521	6.245	89	7921	9.434	139	19,321	11.790
40	1600	6.325	90	8100	9.487	140	19,600	11.832
41	1681	6.403	91	8281	9.539	141	19,881	11.874
42	1764	6.481	92	8464	9.592	142	20,164	11.916
43	1849	6.557	93	8649	9.644	143	20,449	11.958
44	1936	6.633	94	8836	9.695	144	20,736	12.000
45	2025	6.708	95	9025	9.747	145	21,025	12.042
46	2116	6.782	96	9216	9.798	146	21,316	12.083
47	2209	6.856	97	9409	9.849	147	21,609	12.124
48	2304	6.928	98	9604	9.899	148	21,904	12.166
49	2401	7.000	99	9801	9.950	149	22,201	12.207
50	2500	7.071	100	10,000	10.000	150	22,500	12.247

Table 4 Trigonometric Ratios

Angle	Sine	Cosine	Tangent	Angle	Sine	Cosine	Tangent
1°	0.0175	0.9998	0.0175	46°	0.7193	0.6947	1.0355
2°	0.0349	0.9994	0.0349	47°	0.7314	0.6820	1.0724
3°	0.0523	0.9986	0.0524	48°	0.7431	0.6691	1.1106
4°	0.0698	0.9976	0.0699	49°	0.7547	0.6561	1.1504
5°	0.0872	0.9962	0.0875	50°	0.7660	0.6428	1.1918
6°	0.1045	0.9945	0.1051	51°	0.7771	0.6293	1.2349
7°	0.1219	0.9925	0.1228	52°	0.7880	0.6157	1.2799
8°	0.1392	0.9903	0.1405	53°	0.7986	0.6018	1.3270
9°	0.1564	0.9877	0.1584	54°	0.8090	0.5878	1.3764
10°	0.1736	0.9848	0.1763	55°	0.8192	0.5736	1.4281
11°	0.1908	0.9816	0.1944	56°	0.8290	0.5592	1.4826
12°	0.2079	0.9781	0.2126	57°	0.8387	0.5446	1.5399
13°	0.2250	0.9744	0.2309	58°	0.8480	0.5299	1.6003
14°	0.2419	0.9703	0.2493	59°	0.8572	0.5150	1.6643
15°	0.2588	0.9659	0.2679	60°	0.8660	0.5000	1.7321
16°	0.2756	0.9613	0.2867	61°	0.8746	0.4848	1.8040
17°	0.2924	0.9563	0.3057	62°	0.8829	0.4695	1.8807
18°	0.3090	0.9511	0.3249	63°	0.8910	0.4540	1.9626
19°	0.3256	0.9455	0.3443	64°	0.8988	0.4384	2.0503
20°	0.3420	0.9397	0.3640	65°	0.9063	0.4226	2.1445
21°	0.3584	0.9336	0.3839	66°	0.9135	0.4067	2.2460
22°	0.3746	0.9272	0.4040	67°	0.9205	0.3907	2.3559
23°	0.3907	0.9205	0.4245	68°	0.9272	0.3746	2.4751
24°	0.4067	0.9135	0.4452	69°	0.9336	0.3584	2.6051
25°	0.4226	0.9063	0.4663	70°	0.9397	0.3420	2.7475
26°	0.4384	0.8988	0.4877	71°	0.9455	0.3256	2.9042
27°	0.4540	0.8910	0.5095	72°	0.9511	0.3090	3.0777
28°	0.4695	0.8829	0.5317	73°	0.9563	0.2924	3.2709
29°	0.4848	0.8746	0.5543	74°	0.9613	0.2756	3.4874
30°	0.5000	0.8660	0.5774	75°	0.9659	0.2588	3.7321
31°	0.5150	0.8572	0.6009	76°	0.9703	0.2419	4.0108
32°	0.5299	0.8480	0.6249	77°	0.9744	0.2250	4.3315
33°	0.5446	0.8387	0.6494	78°	0.9781	0.2079	4.7046
34°	0.5592	0.8290	0.6745	79°	0.9816	0.1908	5.1446
35°	0.5736	0.8192	0.7002	80°	0.9848	0.1736	5.6713
36°	0.5878	0.8090	0.7265	81°	0.9877	0.1564	6.3138
37°	0.6018	0.7986	0.7536	82°	0.9903	0.1392	7.1154
38°	0.6157	0.7880	0.7813	83°	0.9925	0.1219	8.1443
39°	0.6293	0.7771	0.8098	84°	0.9945	0.1045	9.5144
40°	0.6428	0.7660	0.8391	85°	0.9962	0.0872	11.4301
41°	0.6561	0.7547	0.8693	86°	0.9976	0.0698	14.3007
42°	0.6691	0.7431	0.9004	87°	0.9986	0.0523	19.0811
43°	0.6820	0.7314	0.9325	88°	0.9994	0.0349	28.6363
44°	0.6947	0.7193	0.9657	89°	0.9998	0.0175	57.2900
45°	0.7071	0.7071	1.0000	90°	1.0000	0.0000	

Properties and Formulas

Chapter 1

Order of Operations
1. Perform any operation(s) inside grouping symbols.
2. Simplify powers.
3. Multiply and divide in order from left to right.
4. Add and subtract in order from left to right.

Identity Property of Addition
For every real number n, $n + 0 = n$.

Inverse Property of Addition
For every real number n, there is an additive inverse $-n$ such that $n + (-n) = 0$.

Identity Property of Multiplication
For every real number n, $1 \cdot n = n$.

Multiplication Property of Zero
For every real number n, $n \cdot 0 = 0$.

Multiplication Property of -1
For every real number n, $-1 \cdot n = -n$.

Inverse Property of Multiplication
For every nonzero real number a, there is a multiplicative inverse $\frac{1}{a}$ such that $a\left(\frac{1}{a}\right) = 1$.

Distributive Property
For every real number a, b, and c:
$a(b + c) = ab + ac$
$(b + c)a = ba + ca$
$a(b - c) = ab - ac$
$(b - c)a = ba - ca$

Commutative Property of Addition
For every real number a and b, $a + b = b + a$.

Commutative Property of Multiplication
For every real number a and b, $a \cdot b = b \cdot a$.

Associative Property of Addition
For every real number a, b, and c, $(a + b) + c = a + (b + c)$.

Associative Property of Multiplication
For every real number a, b, and c, $(a \cdot b) \cdot c = a \cdot (b \cdot c)$.

Chapter 2

Addition Property of Equality
For every real number a, b, and c, if $a = b$, then $a + c = b + c$.

Subtraction Property of Equality
For every real number a, b, and c, if $a = b$, then $a - c = b - c$.

Multiplication Property of Equality
For every real number a, b, and c, if $a = b$, then $a \cdot c = b \cdot c$.

Division Property of Equality
For every real number a, b, and c, with $c \neq 0$, if $a = b$, then $\frac{a}{c} = \frac{b}{c}$.

Chapter 3
The following properties of inequality are also true for $\geq$ and $\leq$.

Addition Property of Inequality
For every real number a, b, and c,
if $a > b$, then $a + c > b + c$;
if $a < b$, then $a + c < b + c$.

Subtraction Property of Inequality
For every real number a, b, and c,
if $a > b$, then $a - c > b - c$;
if $a < b$, then $a - c < b - c$.

Multiplication Property of Inequality
For every real number a and b, and for $c > 0$,
if $a > b$, then $ac > bc$;
if $a < b$, then $ac < bc$.
For every real number a and b, and for $c < 0$,
if $a > b$, then $ac < bc$;
if $a < b$, then $ac > bc$.

Division Property of Inequality
For every real number a and b, and for $c > 0$,
if $a > b$, then $\frac{a}{c} > \frac{b}{c}$;
if $a < b$, then $\frac{a}{c} < \frac{b}{c}$.
For every real number a and b, and for $c < 0$,
if $a > b$, then $\frac{a}{c} < \frac{b}{c}$;
if $a < b$, then $\frac{a}{c} > \frac{b}{c}$.

Reflexive Property of Equality
For every real number a, $a = a$.

Symmetric Property of Equality
For every real number a and b,
if $a = b$, then $b = a$.

Transitive Property of Equality
For every real number a, b, and c,
if $a = b$ and $b = c$, then $a = c$.

Transitive Property of Inequality
For every real number a, b, and c,
if $a < b$ and $b < c$, then $a < c$.

Chapter 4

Cross Products of a Proportion
If $\frac{a}{b} = \frac{c}{d}$, then $ad = bc$.

Percent Error Formula
$$\text{percent error} = \frac{\text{greatest possible error}}{\text{measurement}}$$

Probability Formula
$$P(\text{event}) = \frac{\text{number of favorable outcomes}}{\text{number of possible outcomes}}$$

Probability of Complement Formula
$P(\text{event}) + P(\text{not event}) = 1$;
$P(\text{not event}) = 1 - P(\text{event})$

Probability of Two Independent Events
If A and B are independent events,
$P(A \text{ and } B) = P(A) \cdot P(B)$.

Probability of Two Dependent Events
If A and B are dependent events,
$P(A \text{ then } B) = P(A) \cdot P(B \text{ after } A)$.

Chapter 5

Arithmetic Sequence
The form for the rule of an arithmetic sequence is $A(n) = a + (n - 1)d$, where $A(n)$ is the nth term, a is the first term, $n - 1$ is the term number, and d is the common difference.

Chapter 6

Slope
$$\text{slope} = \frac{\text{vertical change}}{\text{horizontal change}} = \frac{\text{rise}}{\text{run}}$$

Slope-Intercept Form of a Linear Equation
The slope-intercept form of a linear equation is $y = mx + b$, where m is the slope and b is the y-intercept.

Standard Form of a Linear Equation
The standard form of a linear equation is $Ax + By = C$, where A, B, C are real numbers and A and B are not both zero.

Point-Slope Form of a Linear Equation
The point-slope form of the equation of a nonvertical line that passes through the point (x_1, y_1) with slope m is $y - y_1 = m(x - x_1)$.

Slopes of Parallel Lines
Nonvertical lines are parallel if they have the same slope and different y-intercepts. Any two vertical lines are parallel.

Slopes of Perpendicular Lines
Two lines are perpendicular if the product of their slopes is -1. A vertical and a horizontal line are perpendicular.

Chapter 7

Solutions of Systems of Linear Equations
A system of linear equations can have one solution, no solution, or infinitely many solutions:
- If the lines have different slopes, the lines intersect, so there is one solution.
- If the lines have the same slopes and different y-intercepts, the lines are parallel, so there are no solutions.
- If the lines have the same slopes and the same y-intercepts, the lines are the same, so there are infinitely many solutions.

Chapter 8

Zero as an Exponent
For every nonzero number a, $a^0 = 1$.

Negative Exponent
For every nonzero number a and integer n, $a^{-n} = \frac{1}{a^n}$.

Scientific Notation
A number in scientific notation is written as the product of two factors in the form $a \times 10^n$, where n is an integer and $1 \leq a < 10$.

Multiplying Powers with the Same Base
For every nonzero number a and integers m and n,
$a^m \cdot a^n = a^{m+n}$.

Dividing Powers with the Same Base
For every nonzero number a and integers m and n,
$\frac{a^m}{a^n} = a^{m-n}$.

Raising a Power to a Power
For every nonzero number a and integers m and n,
$(a^m)^n = a^{mn}$.

Raising a Product to a Power
For every nonzero number a and b and integer n,
$(ab)^n = a^n b^n$.

Raising a Quotient to a Power
For every nonzero number a and b and integer n,
$\left(\frac{a}{b}\right)^n = \frac{a^n}{b^n}$.

Geometric Sequence
The form for the rule of a geometric sequence is $A(n) = a \cdot r^{n-1}$, where $A(n)$ is the nth term, a is the first term, $n - 1$ is the term number, and r is the common ratio.

Exponential Growth and Decay
An exponential function has the form $y = a \cdot b^x$, where a is a nonzero constant, b is greater than 0 and not equal to 1, and x is a real number.
- The function $y = a \cdot b^x$ models exponential growth for $a > 0$ and $b > 1$. b is the growth factor.
- The function $y = a \cdot b^x$ models exponential decay for $a > 0$ and $0 < b < 1$. b is the decay factor.

Chapter 9

Factoring Special Cases
For every nonzero number a and b:
$a^2 - b^2 = (a + b)(a - b)$
$a^2 + 2ab + b^2 = (a + b)(a + b) = (a + b)^2$
$a^2 - 2ab + b^2 = (a - b)(a - b) = (a - b)^2$

Chapter 10

Graph of a Quadratic Function
The graph of $y = ax^2 + bx + c$, where $a \neq 0$, has the line $x = \frac{-b}{2a}$ as its axis of symmetry. The x-coordinate of the vertex is $\frac{-b}{2a}$.

Zero-Product Property
For every real number a and b, if $ab = 0$, then $a = 0$ or $b = 0$.

Quadratic Formula
If $ax^2 + bx + c = 0$ and $a \neq 0$,
then $x = \frac{-b \pm \sqrt{b^2 - 4ac}}{2a}$.

Property of the Discriminant
For the quadratic equation $ax^2 + bx + c = 0$, where $a \neq 0$, the value of the discriminant $b^2 - 4ac$ tells you the number of solutions.
- If $b^2 - 4ac > 0$, there are two real solutions.
- If $b^2 - 4ac = 0$, there is one real solution.
- If $b^2 - 4ac < 0$, there are no real solutions.

Chapter 11

Multiplication Property of Square Roots
For every number $a \geq 0$ and $b \geq 0$, $\sqrt{ab} = \sqrt{a} \cdot \sqrt{b}$.

Division Property of Square Roots
For every number $a \geq 0$ and $b > 0$, $\sqrt{\frac{a}{b}} = \frac{\sqrt{a}}{\sqrt{b}}$.

The Pythagorean Theorem
In a right triangle, the sum of the squares of the lengths of the legs is equal to the square of the length of the hypotenuse. $a^2 + b^2 = c^2$

The Converse of the Pythagorean Theorem
If a triangle has sides of lengths a, b, and c, and $a^2 + b^2 = c^2$, then the triangle is a right triangle with hypotenuse of length c.

The Distance Formula
The distance d between any two points (x_1, y_1) and (x_2, y_2) is $d = \sqrt{(x_2 - x_1)^2 + (y_2 - y_1)^2}$.

The Midpoint Formula
The midpoint M of a line segment with endpoints $A(x_1, y_1)$ and $B(x_2, y_2)$ is $\left(\frac{x_1 + x_2}{2}, \frac{y_1 + y_2}{2}\right)$.

Trigonometric Ratios
$$\text{sine of } \angle A = \frac{\text{length of leg opposite } \angle A}{\text{length of hypotenuse}}$$
$$\text{cosine of } \angle A = \frac{\text{length of leg adjacent to } \angle A}{\text{length of hypotenuse}}$$
$$\text{tangent of } \angle A = \frac{\text{length of leg opposite } \angle A}{\text{length of leg adjacent to } \angle A}$$

Chapter 12

Multiplication Counting Principle
If there are m ways to make a first selection and n ways to make a second selection, there are $m \times n$ ways to make the two selections.

Permutation Notation
The expression $_nP_r$ stands for the number of permutations of n objects chosen r at a time.
$_nP_r = n(n - 1)(n - 2) \ldots] r$ factors

Combination Notation
The expression $_nC_r$ stands for the number of combinations of n objects chosen r at a time.
$$_nC_r = \frac{_nP_r}{_rP_r} = \frac{n(n - 1)(n - 2)\ldots}{r(r - 1)(r - 2)\ldots}$$

Formulas of Geometry

You will use a number of geometric formulas as you work through your algebra book. Here are some perimeter, area, and volume formulas.

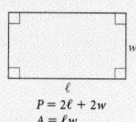

$P = 2\ell + 2w$
$A = \ell w$
Rectangle

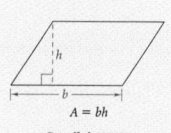

$P = 4s$
$A = s^2$
Square

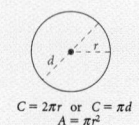

$C = 2\pi r$ or $C = \pi d$
$A = \pi r^2$
Circle

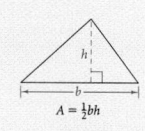

$A = \frac{1}{2}bh$
Triangle

$A = bh$
Parallelogram

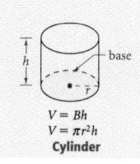

$A = \frac{1}{2}(b_1 + b_2)h$
Trapezoid

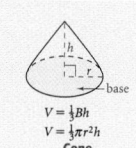

$V = Bh$
$V = \ell wh$
Rectangular Prism

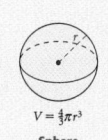

$V = \frac{1}{3}Bh$
Pyramid

$V = Bh$
$V = \pi r^2 h$
Cylinder

$V = \frac{1}{3}Bh$
$V = \frac{1}{3}\pi r^2 h$
Cone

$V = \frac{4}{3}\pi r^3$
Sphere

English/Spanish Illustrated Glossary

A

EXAMPLES

Absolute value (p. 20) The distance that a number is from zero on a number line.

Valor absoluto (p. 20) La distancia a la que un número está del cero en una recta numérica.

-7 is 7 units from 0, so $|-7| = 7$.

Absolute value equation (p. 325) Equation whose graph forms a V that opens up or down.

Ecuación de valor absoluto (p. 325) La ecuación cuya gráfica forma una V que se abre hacia arriba o hacia abajo.

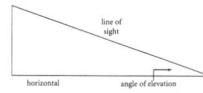

$y = |3 - x|$

Additive inverse (p. 24) The opposite of a number. Additive inverses sum to 0.

Inversos aditivos (p. 24) Un número y su opuesto. La suma de inversos aditivos es igual a 0.

-5 and 5 are additive inverses because $-5 + 5 = 0$.

Algebraic expression (p. 4) A mathematical phrase that can include numbers, variables, and operation symbols.

Expresión algebraica (p. 4) Proposición matemática que incluye números, variables y símbolos de operaciones.

$7 + x$ is an algebraic expression.

Angle of depression (p. 624) An angle below the horizontal line of sight. It is used to measure heights indirectly.

Ángulo de depresión (p. 624) Ángulo con que se miden indirectamente las alturas. También, ángulo formado por debajo de la línea horizontal de visión.

Angle of elevation (p. 623) An angle above the horizontal line of sight. It is used to measure heights indirectly.

Ángulo de elevación (p. 623) Ángulo con que se miden las alturas indirectamente. También, ángulo formado por encima de la línea horizontal de visión.

Arithmetic sequence (p. 269) A number sequence formed by adding a fixed number to each previous term.

Progresión aritmética (p. 269) Sucesión numérica que se obtiene al sumar un número constante a cada término consecutivo.

$4, 7, 10, 13, \ldots$ is an arithmetic sequence.

EXAMPLES

Asymptote (p. 644) A line the graph of a function gets closer to as x or y gets larger in absolute value.

Asíntota (p. 644) Línea recta a la que la gráfica de una función se acerca indefinidamente, mientras el valor absoluto de x o y se aumenta.

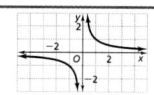

The y-axis is a vertical asymptote for $y = \frac{1}{x}$. The x-axis is a horizontal asymptote for $y = \frac{1}{x}$.

Axis of symmetry (p. 511) The line that divides a parabola into two matching halves.

Eje de simetría (p. 511) Línea recta que divide una parábola en dos mitades exactamente iguales.

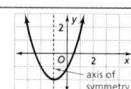

B

Base (p. 9) A number that is multiplied repeatedly.

Base (p. 9) El número que se multiplica repetidas veces.

$4^5 = 4 \cdot 4 \cdot 4 \cdot 4 \cdot 4$. The base 4 is used as a factor 5 times.

Binomial (p. 457) A polynomial of two terms.

Binomio (p. 457) Polinomio compuesto de dos términos.

$3x + 7$ is a binomial.

C

Coefficient (p. 49) The numerical factor when a term has a variable.

Coeficiente (p. 49) Factor numérico de un término que contiene una variable.

In the expression $2x + 3y + 16$, 2 and 3 are coefficients.

Combination (pp. 686–687) An arrangement of some or all of a set of objects without regard to order. The number of combinations

$= \frac{\text{total number of permutations}}{\text{number of times the objects in each group are repeated}}$. You can use the notation $_nC_r$ to write the number of combinations of n objects chosen r at a time.

Combinación (pp. 686–687) Grupo que contiene algunos o todos los objetos de un conjunto, cualquiera que sea su orden. El número de combinaciones

$= \frac{\text{número total de permutaciones}}{\text{número de veces que se repiten los objetos de cada grupo}}$. La notación $_nC_r$ expresa el número de combinaciones de n objetos escogidos r en un momento dado.

The number of combinations 10 things can be taken 4 at a time:

$_{10}C_4 = \frac{_{10}P_4}{_4P_4} = \frac{10 \cdot 9 \cdot 8 \cdot 7}{4 \cdot 3 \cdot 2 \cdot 1} = 210$

EXAMPLES

Common difference (p. 269) The fixed number added to each term of an arithmetic sequence.

Diferencia común (p. 269) Número constante que se suma a cada término para formar una progresión aritmética.

The common difference is 3 in the arithmetic sequence $4, 7, 10, 13, \ldots$

Common ratio (p. 424) The fixed number used to find terms in a geometric sequence.

Razón común (p. 424) Número constante que resulta se usa para hallar los términos en una progresión geométrica.

The common ratio is $\frac{1}{3}$ in the geometric sequence $9, 3, 1, \frac{1}{3}, \ldots$

Complement of an event (p. 212) All possible outcomes that are not in the event.

$P(\text{complement of event}) = 1 - P(\text{event})$

Complemento de un suceso (p. 212) Todos los resultados posibles que no se dan en el suceso.

$P(\text{complemento de suceso}) = 1 - P(\text{suceso})$

The complement of rolling a 1 or a 2 on a number cube is rolling a 3, 4, 5, or 6.

Completing the square (p. 541) A method of solving quadratic equations. Completing the square turns every quadratic equation into the form $x^2 = c$.

Completación del cuadrado (p. 541) Método para solucionar ecuaciones cuadráticas. Cuando se completa el cuadrado se transforma la ecuación cuadrática a la fórmula $x^2 = c$.

$x^2 + 6x - 7 = 11$ is rewritten as $(x + 3)^2 = 25$ by completing the square.

Compound inequalities (p. 161) Two inequalities that are joined by *and* or *or*.

Desigualdades compuestas (p. 161) Dos desigualdades que están enlazadas por medio de una *y* o una *o*.

$5 < x$ and $x < 10$
$14 < x$ or $x \geq -3$

Compound interest (p. 438) Interest paid on both the principal and the interest that has already been paid.

Interés compuesto (p. 438) Interés calculado tanto sobre el capital como sobre los intereses ya pagados.

For an initial deposit of $1000 at a 6% interest rate with interest compounded quarterly, the function $y = 1000\left(\frac{0.06}{4}\right)^{4x}$ gives the account balance y after x years.

Conclusion (p. 586) In a conditional, the part following *then*. See **conditional**.

Conclusión (p. 586) En un enunciado condicional, la parte que sigue a *entonces*. Ver **conditional**.

In the conditional "If an animal has four legs, then it is a horse," the conclusion is "it is a horse."

Conditional (p. 586) An "if-then" statement.

Condicional (p. 586) Un enunciado de la forma "si-entonces."

If an animal has four legs, then it is a horse.

T750

Conjecture (p. 268) Conclusion reached by inductive reasoning.

Conjetura (p. 268) Conclusión a la que se llega mediante razonamiento inductivo.

Conjugates (p. 601) The sum and the difference of the same two terms.

Valores conjugados (p. 601) La suma y resta de los mismos dos términos.

$(\sqrt{3} + 2)$ and $(\sqrt{3} - 2)$ are conjugates.

Consecutive integers (p. 104) Integers that differ by one.

Números enteros consecutivos (p. 104) Número enteros cuya diferencia es 1.

$-5, -4$, and -3 are three consecutive integers.

Constant (p. 49) A term that has no variable factor.

Constante (p. 49) Término que tiene un valor fijo.

In the expression $4x + 13y + 17$, 17 is a constant term.

Constant of variation for direct variation (p. 262) The nonzero constant k in the function $y = kx$.

Constante de variación en variaciones directas (p. 262) La constante k cuyo valor no es cero en la función $y = kx$.

For the function $y = 24x$, 24 is the constant of variation.

Constant of variation for inverse variation (p. 637) The nonzero constant k in the function $y = \frac{k}{x}$.

Constante de variación en variaciones inversas (p. 637) La constante k cuyo valor no es cero en la función $y = \frac{k}{x}$.

For the equation $y = \frac{8}{x}$, 8 is the constant of variation.

Converse (p. 586) The statement obtained by reversing the *if* and *then* parts of an if-then statement.

Expresión recíproca (p. 586) La que se obtiene al invertir los componentes *si* y *entonces* de un enunciado condicional.

The converse of "If I was born in Houston, then I am a Texan," would be "If I am a Texan, then I was born in Houston."

Coordinate plane (p. 59) A plane formed by two number lines that intersect at right angles.

Plano de coordenadas (p. 59) Se forma cuando dos rectas numéricas se cortan formando ángulos rectos.

Coordinates (p. 59) The numbers that make an ordered pair and identify the location of a point.

Coordenadas (p. 59) Números ordenados por pares que determinan la posición de un punto sobre un plano.

The coordinates of R are $(-4, 1)$.

Correlation coefficient (p. 319) A number that tells how closely the equation of best fit models the data. The value of the correlation coefficient is in the range $-1 \le r \le 1$.

Coeficiente de correlación (p. 319) Valor que indica qué tan bien la ecuación más adecuada modela los datos. El valor r del coeficiente de correlación está dentro del rango $-1 \le r \le 1$.

```
LinReg
y=ax+b
a=.0134039132
b=-.3622031627
r²=.886327776
r=.9414498267
```

The correlation coefficient for the data points $(68, 0.5)$, $(85, 0.9)$, $(100, 0.9)$, and $(108, 1.1)$ is approximately 0.94.

Cosine (p. 621) In a right triangle, such as $\triangle ABC$ with right $\angle C$, cosine of $\angle A = \frac{\text{length of side adjacent to } \angle A}{\text{length of hypotenuse}}$ or $\cos A = \frac{b}{c}$.

Coseno (p. 621) En $\triangle ABC$ con $\angle C$ recto, el coseno de $\angle A = \frac{\text{longitud del lado adyacente a } \angle A}{\text{longitud de la hipotenusa}}$, o $\cos A = \frac{b}{c}$.

$\cos A = \frac{4}{5}$

Counterexample (p. 18) Any example that proves a statement false.

Contraejemplo (p. 18) Todo ejemplo que pruebe la falsedad de un enunciado.

Statement: All apples are red.
Counterexample: A Granny Smith apple is green.

Cross products (p. 183) In a proportion, $\frac{a}{b} = \frac{c}{d}$, the products of ad and bc. These products are equal.

Productos en equis (p. 183) En una proporción, $\frac{a}{b} = \frac{c}{d}$, los productos de ad y bc. Estos productos son iguales.

$\frac{3}{4} = \frac{6}{8}$

The cross products are $3 \cdot 8$ and $4 \cdot 6$.
$3 \cdot 8 = 24$ and $4 \cdot 6 = 24$

D

Decay factor (p. 440) The base b in the exponential function $y = ab^x$, where $0 < b < 1$.

Factor decremental (p. 440) La base b en la función exponencial $y = ab^x$ donde $0 < b < 1$.

The decay factor of the function $y = 5(0.3)^x$ is 0.3.

Deductive reasoning (p. 56) A process of reasoning logically from given facts to a conclusion.

Razonamiento deductivo (p. 56) Proceso de razonar lógicamente para llegar a una conclusión a partir de datos dados.

Degree of a monomial (p. 457) The sum of the exponents of the variables of a monomial.

Grado de un monomio (p. 457) La suma de los exponentes de sus variables.

$-4x^3y^2$ is a monomial of degree 5.

Degree of a polynomial (p. 457) The degree of the term with the greatest exponent for a polynomial in one variable.

Grado de un polinomio (p. 457) El valor mayor del exponente de cualquiera de sus variables.

The degree of $3x^2 + x - 9$ is 2.

Dependent events (p. 221) Two events in which the occurrence of one event affects the probability of the second event.

Sucesos dependientes (p. 221) Cuando el resultado de un suceso influye en la probabilidad de que ocurra el segundo suceso, los sucesos son dependientes.

If you pick a marble from a bag and pick another without replacing the first, the events are dependent events.

Dependent variable (p. 248) A variable that provides the output values of a function.

Variable dependiente (p. 248) Variable de la que dependen los valores de salid a una función.

In the equation $y = 3x$ the value of y depends upon the value of x.

Direct variation (p. 262) A linear function that can be expressed in the form $y = kx$, where $k \ne 0$.

Variación directa (p. 262) Función lineal que puede expresarse como $y = kx$, donde $k \ne 0$.

$y = 18x$ is a direct variation.

Discriminant (p. 554) The quantity $b^2 - 4ac$ is the discriminant of $ax^2 + bx + c = 0$.

Discriminante (p. 554) La cantidad $b^2 - 4ac$ es el discriminante de $ax^2 + bx + c = 0$.

The discriminant of $2x^2 + 9x - 2 = 0$ is 65.

Distance Formula (p. 591) The distance d between any two points (x_1, y_1) and (x_2, y_2) is $d = \sqrt{(x_2 - x_1)^2 + (y_2 - y_1)^2}$.

Fórmula de distancia (p. 591) La distancia d entre dos puntos cualesquiera (x_1, y_1) y (x_2, y_2) es $d = \sqrt{(x_2 - x_1)^2 + (y_2 - y_1)^2}$.

The distance between $(-2, 4)$ and $(4, 5)$ is
$$d = \sqrt{(4 - (-2))^2 + (5 - 4)^2}$$
$$= \sqrt{(6)^2 + (1)^2}$$
$$= \sqrt{37}$$

Distributive property (p. 47) For every real number a, b, and c:
$a(b + c) = ab + ac$ $(b + c)a = ba + ca$
$a(b - c) = ab - ac$ $(b - c)a = ba - ca$

Propiedad distributiva (p. 47) Para cada número real a, b, y c:
$a(b + c) = ab + ac$ $(b + c)a = ba + ca$
$a(b - c) = ab - ac$ $(b - c)a = ba - ca$

$3(19 + 4) = 3(19) + 3(4)$
$(19 + 4)3 = 19(3) + 4(3)$
$7(11 - 2) = 7(11) - 7(2)$
$(11 - 2)7 = 11(7) - 2(7)$

Domain (p. 241) The set of all first coordinates in the ordered pairs of a relation.

Dominio (p. 241) Conjunto que comprende todas las primeras coordenadas de los pares ordenados de una relación.

In the function $f(x) = x + 22$, the domain is all real numbers.

E

Element (p. 27) An item in a matrix.

Elemento (p. 27) Componente de una matriz.

$\begin{bmatrix} 5 & -2 \\ 7 & 3 \end{bmatrix}$ $5, 7, -2$, and 3 are the four elements of the matrix.

Elimination method (p. 353) A method for solving a system of linear equations. You add or subtract the equations to eliminate a variable.

Eliminación (p. 353) Método para resolver un sistema de ecuaciones lineales. Se suman o se restan las ecuaciones para eliminar una variable.

$3x + y = 19$
$\underline{2x - y = 1}$
$x + 0 = 18$ $x = 18$
$2(18) - y = 1 \rightarrow$ Substitute 18 for x
$36 - y = 1$ in the second equation.
$y = 35 \rightarrow$ Solve for y.

Equation (p. 5) A mathematical sentence that uses an equal sign.

Ecuación (p. 5) Enunuado matemático que tiene el signo de igual.

$x + 5 = 3x - 7$

Equivalent equations (p. 75) Equations that have the same solution.

Ecuaciones equivalentes (p. 75) Ecuaciones que tienen la misma solución.

$\frac{9}{3} = 3$ and $\frac{9}{3} + a = 3 + a$ are equivalent equations.

Equivalent inequalities (p. 161) Equivalent inequalities have the same set of solutions.

Desigualdades equivalentes (p. 161) Las desigualdades equivalentes tienen el mismo conjunto de soluciones.

$x + 4 < 7$ and $x < 3$ are equivalent inequalities.

Evaluate (p. 10) Substitute a given number for each variable, and then simplify.

Evaluar (p. 10) Método de sustituir cada variable por un número dado para luego simplificar la expresión.

To evaluate $3x + 4$ for $x = 2$, substitute 2 for x and simplify.
$3(2) + 4$
$6 + 4$
10

Event (p. 211) Any group of outcomes in a situation involving probability.

Suceso (p. 211) En la probabilidad, cualquier grupo de resultados.

When rolling a number cube, there are six possible outcomes. Rolling an even number is an event with three possible outcomes, 2, 4, and 6.

T751

EXAMPLES

Experimental probability (p. 212) The ratio of the number of times an event actually happens to the number of times the experiment is done.

$$P(\text{event}) = \frac{\text{number of times an event happens}}{\text{number of times the experiment is done}}$$

Probabilidad experimental (p. 212) La relación entre el número de veces que un suceso sucede en la realidad y el número de veces que se hace el experimento.

$$P(\text{suceso}) = \frac{\text{número de veces que sucede un suceso}}{\text{número de veces que se hace el experimento}}$$

A baseball player's batting average shows how likely it is that a player will get a hit, based on previous times at bat.

Exponent (p. 9) A number that shows repeated multiplication.

Exponente (p. 9) Denota el número de veces que debe multiplicarse.

$3^4 = 3 \cdot 3 \cdot 3 \cdot 3$

The exponent 4 indicates that 3 is used as a factor four times.

Exponential decay (p. 440) A situation modeled with a function of the form $y = ab^x$, where $a > 0$ and $0 < b < 1$.

Decremento exponencial (p. 440) Para $a > 0$ y $0 < b < 1$, la función $y = ab^x$ representa el decremento exponencial.

$y = 5(0.1)^x$

Exponential function (p. 430) A function that repeatedly multiplies an initial amount by the same positive number. You can model all exponential functions using $y = ab^x$, where a is a nonzero constant, $b > 0, b \neq 1$.

Función exponencial (p. 430) Función que multiplica repetidas veces una cantidad inicial por el mismo número positivo. Todas las funciones exponenciales se pueden representar mediante $y = ab^x$, donde a es una constante con valor distinto de cero, $b > 0$ y $b \neq 1$.

$y = 4.8(1.1)^x$

Exponential growth (p. 437) A situation modeled with a function of the form $y = ab^x$, where $a > 0$ and $b > 1$.

Incremento exponencial (p. 437) Para $a > 0$ y $b > 1$, la función $y = ab^x$ representa el incremento exponencial.

$y = 100(2)^x$

Extraneous solution (p. 609) An apparent solution of the equation that does not satisfy the original equation.

Solución extraña (p. 609) Solución aparente de una ecuación que no satisface la ecuación original.

$\frac{b}{b+4} = 3 - \frac{4}{b+4}$

Multiply by $(b+4)$.

$b = 3(b + 4) - 4$
$b = 3b + 12 - 4$
$-2b = 8$
$b = -4$

Replace b with -4 in the original equation. The denominator is 0, and so -4 is an extraneous solution.

EXAMPLES

Extremes of a proportion (p. 183) In the proportion, $\frac{a}{b} = \frac{c}{d}$, a and d are the extremes.

Valores extremos de una proporción (p. 183) En la proporción $\frac{a}{b} = \frac{c}{d}$, a y d son los valores extremos.

The product of the extremes of $\frac{x}{4} = \frac{x+3}{2}$ is $2x$.

F

Factor by grouping (p. 496) A method of factoring that uses the distributive property to remove a common binomial factor of two pairs of terms.

Factor común por agrupación de términos (p. 496) Método de factorización que aplica la propiedad distributiva para sacar un factor común de dos pares de términos en un binomio.

The expression $7x(x - 1) + 4(x - 1)$ can be factored as $(7x + 4)(x - 1)$.

Function (p. 242) A relation that assigns exactly one value in the range to each value of the domain.

Función (p. 242) La relación que asigna exactamente un valor del recorrido a cada valor del dominio.

Earned income is a function of the number of hours worked. If you earn $4.50/h, then your income is expressed by the function $f(h) = 4.5h$.

Function notation (p. 243) To write a rule in function notation, you use the symbol $f(x)$ in place of y.

Notación de una función (p. 243) Para expresar una regla en notación de función se usa el símbolo $f(x)$ en lugar de y.

$f(x) = 3x - 8$ is in function notation.

Function rule (p. 243) An equation that describes a function.

Regla de una función (p. 243) Ecuación que describe una función.

$y = 4x + 1$ is a function rule.

G

Geometric sequence (p. 424) A number sequence formed by multiplying a term in a sequence by a fixed number to find the next term.

Progresión geométrica (p. 424) Tipo de sucesión numérica formada al multiplicar un término por un número constante, para hallar el siguiente término.

$9, 3, 1, \frac{1}{3}, \ldots$ is an example of a geometric sequence.

Greatest possible error (p. 205) One half of the measuring unit, for any measurement.

Máximo error posible (p. 205) Para una medición dada, la mitad de la unidad de medida.

The mass of a rock is measured as 3.8 g. The greatest possible error is one half 0.1 g, or 0.05 g.

EXAMPLES

Growth factor (p. 437) The number b in an exponential growth function of the form $y = ab^x$, where $b > 1$.

Factor incremental (p. 437) Para la función exponencial incremental $y = ab^x$, donde $b > 1$, b es el factor incremental.

The growth factor of $y = 7(1.3)^x$ is 1.3.

H

Hypotenuse (p. 584) The side opposite the right angle in a right triangle. It is the longest side in the triangle.

Hipotenusa (p. 584) En un triángulo rectángulo, el lado opuesto al ángulo recto. Es el lado más largo del triángulo.

c is the hypotenuse.

Hypothesis (p. 586) The part following *if* in a conditional. *See* **conditional**.

Hipótesis (p. 586) En un enunciado condicional, la parte que sigue a siguiente *si*. *Ver* **conditional**.

In the conditional "If an animal has four legs, then it is a horse," the hypothesis is "an animal has four legs."

I

Identity (p. 98) An equation that is true for every value.

Identidad (p. 98) Una ecuación que es verdadera para todos los valores.

$5 - 14x = 5\left(1 - \frac{14}{5}x\right)$ is an identity because it is true for any value of x.

Independent events (p. 220) Two events for which the outcome of one does not affect the other.

Sucesos independientes (p. 220) Dos sucesos son independientes si el resultado de uno de ellos no influye en el resultado del otro.

Picking a colored marble from a bag, and then replacing it and picking another marble, are two independent events.

Independent variable (p. 248) A variable that provides the input values of a function.

Variable independiente (p. 248) Variable de la que dependen los valores de entrada de una función.

In the equation $y = 3x$, x is the independent variable.

Inductive reasoning (p. 268) Making conclusions based on observed patterns.

Razonamiento inductivo (p. 268) Sacar conclusiones a partir de patrones observados.

EXAMPLES

Inequality (p. 19) A mathematical sentence that compares the values of two expressions using an inequality symbol.

Desigualdad (p. 19) Expresión matemática que compara el valor de dos expresiones con el símbolo de desigualdad.

$3 < 7$

Infinitely many solutions (p. 342) The number of solutions of a system of equations in which the graphs of the equations are the same line.

Infinitamente muchas soluciones (p. 342) Cuando las gráficas de las ecuaciones de un sistema son la misma recta.

The system $2x + 4y = 8$ and $y = -\frac{1}{2}x + 2$ has infinitely many solutions.

Integers (p. 16) Whole numbers and their opposites.

Números enteros (p. 16) Números que constan exclusivamente de una o más unidades, y sus opuestos.

$\ldots -3, -2, -1, 0, 1, 2, 3, \ldots$

Interest period (p. 438) The length of time over which interest is calculated.

Período de interés (p. 438) Plazo para el cual se calcula el interés a pagar.

Inverse operations (p. 75) Operations that undo one another.

Operaciones inversas (p. 75) Las operaciones que se cancelan una a la otra.

Addition and subtraction are inverse operations. Multiplication and division are inverse operations.

Inverse variation (p. 637) A function that can be written in the form $xy = k$ or $y = \frac{k}{x}$. The product of the quantities remains constant, so as one quantity increases, the other decreases.

Variación inversa (p. 637) Función que puede expresarse como $xy = k$ ó $y = \frac{k}{x}$. El producto de las cantidades permanece constante, de modo que al aumentar una cantidad, disminuye la otra.

The length x and the width y of a rectangle with a fixed area vary inversely. If the area is 40, $xy = 40$.

Irrational number (p. 18) A number that cannot be written as a ratio of two integers. Irrational numbers in decimal form are nonterminating and nonrepeating.

Número irracional (p. 18) Número que no puede expresarse como cociente de números enteros. Los números irracionales en forma decimal no tienen término y no se repiten.

$\sqrt{11}$ and π are irrational numbers.

English/Spanish Glossary

T752

EXAMPLES

Leg (p. 584) Each of the sides that form the right angle of a right triangle.

Cateto (p. 584) Cada uno de los dos lados que forman el ángulo recto en un triángulo rectángulo.

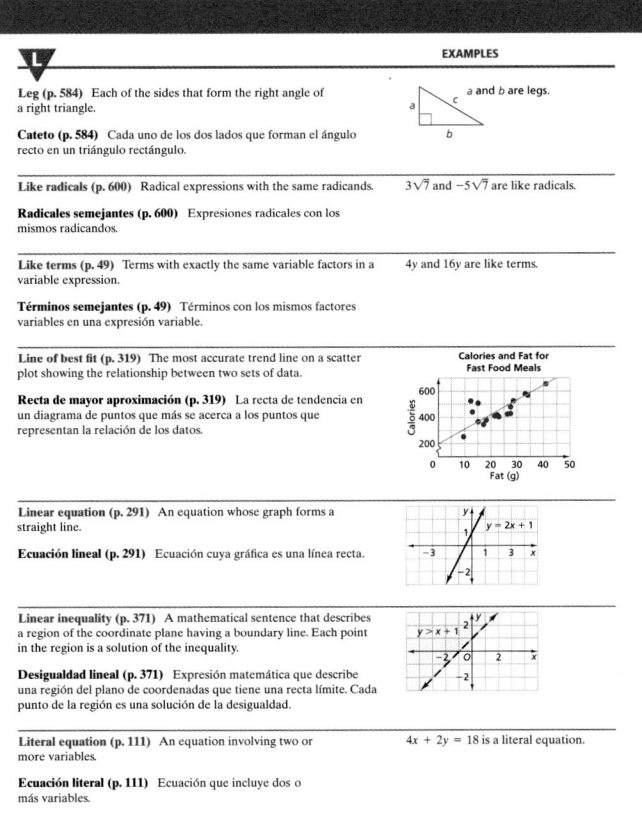

a and b are legs.

Like radicals (p. 600) Radical expressions with the same radicands.

Radicales semejantes (p. 600) Expresiones radicales con los mismos radicandos.

$3\sqrt{7}$ and $-5\sqrt{7}$ are like radicals.

Like terms (p. 49) Terms with exactly the same variable factors in a variable expression.

Términos semejantes (p. 49) Términos con los mismos factores variables en una expresión variable.

$4y$ and $16y$ are like terms.

Line of best fit (p. 319) The most accurate trend line on a scatter plot showing the relationship between two sets of data.

Recta de mayor aproximación (p. 319) La recta de tendencia en un diagrama de puntos que más se acerca a los puntos que representan la relación de los datos.

Calories and Fat for Fast Food Meals

Linear equation (p. 291) An equation whose graph forms a straight line.

Ecuación lineal (p. 291) Ecuación cuya gráfica es una línea recta.

$y = 2x + 1$

Linear inequality (p. 371) A mathematical sentence that describes a region of the coordinate plane having a boundary line. Each point in the region is a solution of the inequality.

Desigualdad lineal (p. 371) Expresión matemática que describe una región del plano de coordenadas que tiene una recta límite. Cada punto de la región es una solución de la desigualdad.

$y > x + 1$

Literal equation (p. 111) An equation involving two or more variables.

Ecuación literal (p. 111) Ecuación que incluye dos o más variables.

$4x + 2y = 18$ is a literal equation.

EXAMPLES

Matrix (p. 27) A rectangular arrangement of numbers. The number of rows and columns of a matrix determines its size. Each item in a matrix is an element.

Matriz (p. 27) Conjunto de números dispuestos en forma de rectángulo. La cantidad de líneas horizontales y verticales de una matriz determina su tamaño. Cada cifra de la matriz es un elemento.

$$\begin{bmatrix} 2 & 5 & 6.3 \\ -8 & 0 & -1 \end{bmatrix}$$ is a 2×3 matrix.

Maximum (p. 511) The y-coordinate of the vertex of a parabola that opens downward.

Valor máximo (p. 511) La coordenada y del vértice en una parábola que se abre hacia abajo.

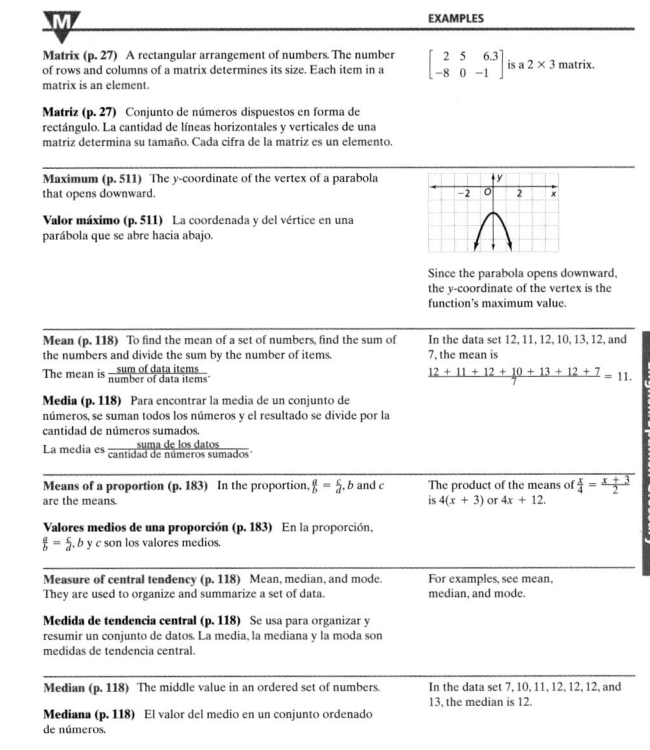

Since the parabola opens downward, the y-coordinate of the vertex is the function's maximum value.

Mean (p. 118) To find the mean of a set of numbers, find the sum of the numbers and divide the sum by the number of items. The mean is $\frac{\text{sum of data items}}{\text{number of data items}}$.

Media (p. 118) Para encontrar la media de un conjunto de números, se suman todos los números y el resultado se divide por la cantidad de números sumados. La media es $\frac{\text{suma de los datos}}{\text{cantidad de números sumados}}$.

In the data set 12, 11, 12, 10, 13, 12, and 7, the mean is $\frac{12 + 11 + 12 + 10 + 13 + 12 + 7}{7} = 11$.

Means of a proportion (p. 183) In the proportion, $\frac{a}{b} = \frac{c}{d}$, b and c are the means.

Valores medios de una proporción (p. 183) En la proporción, $\frac{a}{b} = \frac{c}{d}$, b y c son los valores medios.

The product of the means of $\frac{4}{4} = \frac{x+3}{2}$ is $4(x + 3)$ or $4x + 12$.

Measure of central tendency (p. 118) Mean, median, and mode. They are used to organize and summarize a set of data.

Medida de tendencia central (p. 118) Se usa para organizar y resumir un conjunto de datos. La media, la mediana y la moda son medidas de tendencia central.

For examples, see mean, median, and mode.

Median (p. 118) The middle value in an ordered set of numbers.

Mediana (p. 118) El valor del medio en un conjunto ordenado de números.

In the data set 7, 10, 11, 12, 12, 12, and 13, the median is 12.

EXAMPLES

Midpoint (p. 593) The point M that divides a segment $\overline{AB}$ into two equal segments, $\overline{AM}$ and $\overline{MB}$.

Punto medio (p. 593) El punto M que divide un segmento $\overline{AB}$ en dos segmentos iguales, $\overline{AM}$ y $\overline{MB}$.

M is the midpoint of $\overline{XY}$.

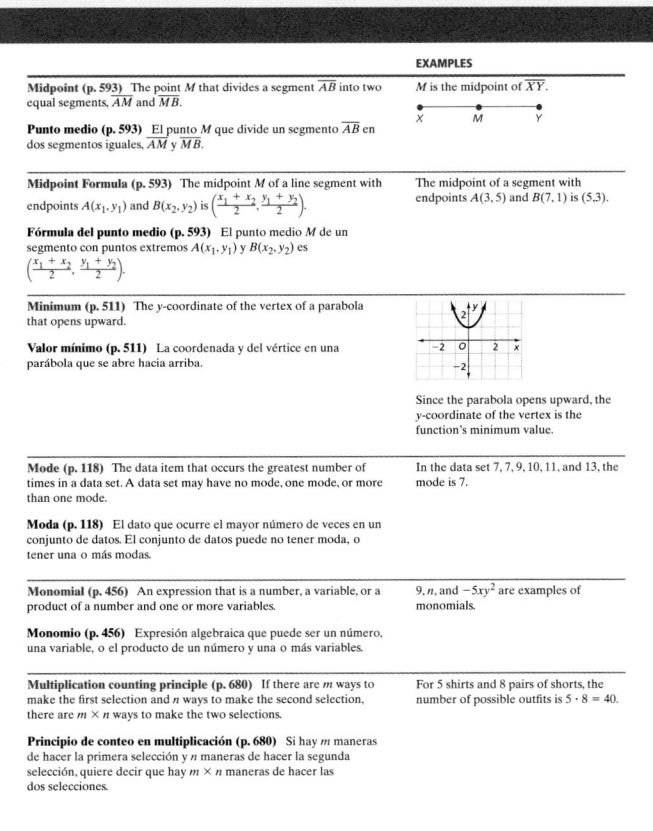

Midpoint Formula (p. 593) The midpoint M of a line segment with endpoints $A(x_1, y_1)$ and $B(x_2, y_2)$ is $\left(\frac{x_1 + x_2}{2}, \frac{y_1 + y_2}{2}\right)$.

Fórmula del punto medio (p. 593) El punto medio M de un segmento con puntos extremos $A(x_1, y_1)$ y $B(x_2, y_2)$ es $\left(\frac{x_1 + x_2}{2}, \frac{y_1 + y_2}{2}\right)$.

The midpoint of a segment with endpoints $A(3, 5)$ and $B(7, 1)$ is $(5,3)$.

Minimum (p. 511) The y-coordinate of the vertex of a parabola that opens upward.

Valor mínimo (p. 511) La coordenada y del vértice en una parábola que se abre hacia arriba.

Since the parabola opens upward, the y-coordinate of the vertex is the function's minimum value.

Mode (p. 118) The data item that occurs the greatest number of times in a data set. A data set may have no mode, one mode, or more than one mode.

Moda (p. 118) El dato que ocurre el mayor número de veces en un conjunto de datos. El conjunto de datos puede no tener moda, o tener una o más modas.

In the data set 7, 7, 9, 10, 11, and 13, the mode is 7.

Monomial (p. 456) An expression that is a number, a variable, or a product of a number and one or more variables.

Monomio (p. 456) Expresión algebraica que puede ser un número, una variable, o el producto de un número y una o más variables.

9, n, and $-5xy^2$ are examples of monomials.

Multiplication counting principle (p. 680) If there are m ways to make the first selection and n ways to make the second selection, there are $m \times n$ ways to make the two selections.

Principio de conteo en multiplicación (p. 680) Si hay m maneras de hacer la primera selección y n maneras de hacer la segunda selección, quiere decir que hay $m \times n$ maneras de hacer las dos selecciones.

For 5 shirts and 8 pairs of shorts, the number of possible outfits is $5 \cdot 8 = 40$.

EXAMPLES

Multiplicative inverse (p. 41) Given a nonzero rational number $\frac{a}{b}$, the multiplicative inverse, or reciprocal, is $\frac{b}{a}$. The product of a nonzero number and its multiplicative inverse is 1.

Inverso multiplicativo (p. 41) Dado un número racional $\frac{a}{b}$ distinto de cero, el inverso multiplicativo, o recíproco, es $\frac{b}{a}$. El producto de un número distinto de cero y su inverso multiplicativo es 1.

$\frac{4}{3}$ is a multiplicative inverse of $\frac{3}{4}$ because $\frac{3}{4} \times \frac{4}{3} = 1$.

Natural numbers (p. 16) The counting numbers.

Números naturales (p. 16) Los números que se emplean para contar.

$1, 2, 3, \ldots$

Negative correlation (p. 61) The relationship between two sets of data, in which one set of data decreases as the other set of data increases.

Correlación negativa (p. 61) Relación entre dos conjuntos de datos en la que uno de los conjuntos decrece a medida que el otro se incrementa.

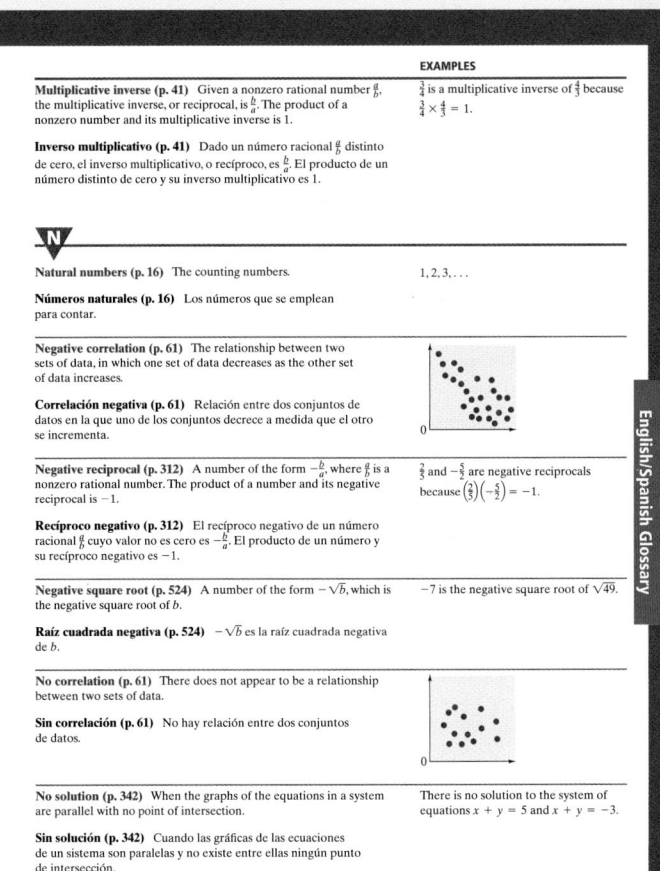

Negative reciprocal (p. 312) A number of the form $-\frac{b}{a}$, where $\frac{a}{b}$ is a nonzero rational number. The product of a number and its negative reciprocal is -1.

Recíproco negativo (p. 312) El recíproco negativo de un número racional $\frac{a}{b}$ cuyo valor no es cero es $-\frac{b}{a}$. El producto de un número y su recíproco negativo es -1.

$\frac{2}{5}$ and $-\frac{5}{2}$ are negative reciprocals because $\left(\frac{2}{5}\right)\left(-\frac{5}{2}\right) = -1$.

Negative square root (p. 524) A number of the form $-\sqrt{b}$, which is the negative square root of b.

Raíz cuadrada negativa (p. 524) $-\sqrt{b}$ es la raíz cuadrada negativa de b.

-7 is the negative square root of $\sqrt{49}$.

No correlation (p. 61) There does not appear to be a relationship between two sets of data.

Sin correlación (p. 61) No hay relación entre dos conjuntos de datos.

No solution (p. 342) When the graphs of the equations in a system are parallel with no point of intersection.

Sin solución (p. 342) Cuando las gráficas de las ecuaciones de un sistema son paralelas y no existe entre ellas ningún punto de intersección.

There is no solution to the system of equations $x + y = 5$ and $x + y = -3$.

O

Open sentence (p. 5) An equation that contains one or more variables.

$5 + x = 12$ is an open sentence.

Ecuación abierta (p. 5) Ecuación que contiene una o más variables.

Opposite (p. 20) A number that is the same distance from zero on the number line as a given number, but lies in the opposite direction.

-3 and 3 are opposites.

Opuestos (p. 20) Dos números son opuestos si están a la misma distancia del cero en la recta numérica, en sentidos opuestos.

Order of operations (p. 10)
1. Perform any operation(s) inside grouping symbols.
2. Simplify powers.
3. Multiply and divide in order from left to right.
4. Add and subtract in order from left to right.

$$6 - \left(4^2 - [2 \cdot 5]\right) \div 3$$
$$= 6 - (16 - 10) \div 3$$
$$= 6 - 6 \div 3$$
$$= 6 - 2$$
$$= 4$$

Orden de las operaciones (p. 10)
1. Se hacer las operaciones que están dentro de símbolos de agrupación.
2. Se simplifican todos los términos que tengan exponentes.
3. Se hacen las multiplicaciones y divisiones en orden de izquierda a derecha.
4. Se hacen las sumas y restas en orden de izquierda a derecha.

Ordered pair (p. 59) Two numbers that identify the location of a point.

The ordered pair $(4, -1)$ identifies the point 4 units to the right on the x-axis and 1 unit down on the y-axis.

Par ordenado (p. 59) Un par ordenado de números denota la localización de un punto en un plano de coordenadas.

Origin (p. 59) The point at which the axes of the coordinate plane intersect.

Origen (p. 59) Punto de intersección de los ejes del plano de coordenadas.

Outcome (p. 211) The result of a single trial in a probability experiment.

The outcomes of rolling a number cube are 1, 2, 3, 4, 5, and 6.

Resultado (p. 211) Lo que se obtiene al hacer una sola prueba en un experimento de probabilidad.

Outlier (p. 118) A data value that is much higher or lower than the other data values in the set.

For the set of values 2, 5, 3, 7, 12, the data value 12 is an outlier.

Valor extralimitado (p. 118) Valor que es mucho mayor o mucho menor que los demás valores de un conjunto.

P

Parabola (p. 510) The graph of a quadratic function.

Parábola (p. 510) La gráfica de una función cuadrática.

Parallel lines (p. 311) Two lines in the same plane that never intersect. Parallel lines have the same slope.

Rectas paralelas (p. 311) Dos rectas situadas en el mismo plano que nunca se cruzan. Las rectas paralelas tienen la misma pendiente.

Lines ℓ and m are parallel.

Percent error (p. 206) The ratio of the greatest possible error to the measurement.

The diameter of a CD is measured as 12.1 cm. The greatest possible error is 0.05 cm. The percent error is $\frac{0.05}{12.1} \approx 0.4\%$.

Error porcentual (p. 206) El valor del máximo error posible dividido por el valor de la medida obtenida.

Percent of change (p. 204) The ratio of the amount of change to the original amount expressed as a percent.

The price of a sweater was $20. The price increases $2. The percent of change is $\frac{2}{20} = 10\%$.

Porcentaje de cambio (p. 204) La cantidad de cambio dividida por la cantidad original y expresada como un porcentaje.

Percent of decrease (p. 204) The percent of change found when the original amount decreases.

The price of a sweater was $22. The price decreases $2. The percent of change is $\frac{2}{22} \approx 9\%$.

Porcentaje de disminución (p. 204) El porcentaje de cambio que resulta cuando la cantidad original disminuye.

Percent of increase (p. 204) The percent of change found when the original amount increases.

See example for percent of change.

Porcentaje de aumento (p. 204) El porcentaje de cambio que resulta cuando la cantidad original aumenta.

Perfect square trinomial (p. 490) Any trinomial of the form $a^2 + 2ab + b^2$ or $a^2 - 2ab + b^2$.

$(x + 3)^2 = x^2 + 6x + 9$

Trinomio cuadrado perfecto (p. 490) Todo trinomio de la forma $a^2 + 2ab + b^2$ ó $a^2 - 2ab + b^2$.

Perfect squares (p. 525) Numbers whose square roots are integers or quotients of integers.

The numbers 1, 4, 9, 16, 25, 36, . . . are perfect squares because they are the squares of integers.

Cuadrado perfecto (p. 525) Número cuya raíz cuadrada es un número entero o el cociente de un número entero.

Permutation (p. 681) An arrangement of some or all of a set of objects in a specific order. You can use the notation $_nP_r$ to express the number of permutations, where n equals the number of objects available and r equals the number of selections to make.

How many ways can 5 children be arranged three at a time?

$_5P_3 = 5 \cdot 4 \cdot 3 = 60$ arrangements

Permutación (p. 681) Disposición de algunos o de todos los objetos de un conjunto en un orden determinado. El número de permutaciones se puede expresar con la notación $_nP_r$, donde n es igual al número total de objetos y r es igual al número de selecciones que han de hacerse.

Perpendicular lines (p. 312) Lines that intersect to form right angles. Two lines are perpendicular if the product of their slopes is -1.

Rectas perpendiculares (p. 312) Rectas que forman ángulos rectos en su intersección . Dos rectas son perpendiculares si el producto de sus pendientes es -1.

Lines ℓ and m are perpendicular.

Point-slope form (p. 304) A linear equation of a nonvertical line written as $y - y_1 = m(x - x_1)$. The line passes through the point (x_1, y_1) with slope m.

An equation with a slope of $-\frac{1}{2}$ passing through $(2, -1)$ would be written $y + 1 = -\frac{1}{2}(x - 2)$ in point-slope form.

Forma punto-pendiente (p. 304) La ecuación lineal de una recta no vertical que pasa por el punto (x_1, y_1) con pendiente m está dada por $y - y_1 = m(x - x_1)$.

Polynomial (p. 457) The sum or difference of two or more monomials. A quotient with a variable in the denominator is not a polynomial.

$2x^2, 3x + 7, 28$, and $-7x^3 - 2x^2 + 9$ are all polynomials.

Polinomio (p. 457) La suma o diferencia de dos o más monomios. Un cociente con una variable en el denominador no es un polinomio.

Positive correlation (p. 61) The relationship between two sets of data in which both sets of data increase together.

Correlación positiva (p. 61) La relación entre dos conjuntos de datos en la que ambos conjuntos se incrementan a la vez.

Power (p. 9) The base and the exponent of an expression of the form a^n.

5^4

Potencia (p. 9) La base y el exponente de una expresión de la forma a^n.

Principal square root (p. 524) A number of the form $\sqrt{b}$. The expression $\sqrt{b}$ is called the principal (or positive) square root of b.

5 is the principal square root of $\sqrt{25}$.

Raíz cuadrada principal (p. 524) La expresión $\sqrt{b}$ se llama raíz cuadrada principal de b.

Probability (p. 211) How likely it is that an event will occur (written formally as P (event)).

You have 4 red marbles and 3 white marbles. The probability that you select one red marble, and then, without replacing it, randomly select another red marble is $P(\text{red}) = \frac{4}{7} \cdot \frac{3}{6} = \frac{2}{7}$.

Probabilidad (p. 211) La probabilidad de un suceso, o P(suceso), expresa que posibilidad hay de que el suceso ocurra.

Properties of equality (pp. 74 and 76) For all real numbers a, b, and c:
Addition: If $a = b$, then $a + c = b + c$.
Subtraction: If $a = b$, then $a - c = b - c$.
Multiplication: If $a = b$, then $a \cdot c = b \cdot c$.
Division: If $a = b$, and $c \neq 0$, then $\frac{a}{c} = \frac{b}{c}$.

Since $\frac{2}{4} = \frac{1}{2}, \frac{2}{4} + 5 = \frac{1}{2} + 5$.

Since $\frac{9}{3} = 3, \frac{9}{3} - 6 = 3 - 6$.

Propiedades de una igualdad (pp. 74 y 76) Para todos los números reales a, b y c:
Suma: Si $a = b$, entonces $a + c = b + c$.
Resta: Si $a = b$, entonces $a - c = b - c$.
Multiplicación: Si $a = b$, entonces $a \cdot c = b \cdot c$.
División: Si $a = b$, y $c \neq 0$, entonces $\frac{a}{c} = \frac{b}{c}$.

Proportion (p. 183) An equation that states that two ratios are equal.
$\frac{a}{b} = \frac{c}{d}$ where $b \neq 0$ and $d \neq 0$

$\frac{7.5}{9} = \frac{5}{6}$

Proporción (p. 183) Es una ecuación que establece que dos relaciones son iguales.
$\frac{a}{b} = \frac{c}{d}$ por $b \neq 0$ y $d \neq 0$

Pythagorean Theorem (p. 585) In any right triangle, the sum of the squares of the lengths of the legs is equal to the square of the length of the hypotenuse: $a^2 + b^2 = c^2$.

$3^2 + 4^2 = 5^2$

Teorema de Pitágoras (p. 585) En un triángulo rectángulo, la suma de los cuadrados de los catetos es igual al cuadrado de la hipotenusa: $a^2 + b^2 = c^2$.

Q

Quadrants (p. 59) The four parts into which the coordinate plane is divided by its axes.

Cuadrantes (p. 59) El plano de coordenadas está dividido por sus ejes en cuatro regiones llamadas cuadrantes.

EXAMPLES

Quadratic equation (p. 530) An equation you can write in the standard form $ax^2 + bx + c = 0$, where $a \neq 0$.

Ecuación cuadrática (p. 530) Ecuación que puede expresarse de la forma $ax^2 + bx + c = 0$, en la que a, b, y c son números reales y $a \neq 0$.

$4x^2 + 9x - 5 = 0$

Quadratic formula (p. 547) If $ax^2 + bx + c = 0$ and $a \neq 0$, then $x = \frac{-b \pm \sqrt{b^2 - 4ac}}{2a}$.

Fórmula cuadrática (p. 547) Si $ax^2 + bx + c = 0$ y $a \neq 0$, entonces $x = \frac{-b \pm \sqrt{b^2 - 4ac}}{2a}$.

$2x^2 + 10x + 12 = 0$

$x = \frac{-b \pm \sqrt{b^2 - 4ac}}{2a}$

$x = \frac{-10 \pm \sqrt{10^2 - 4(2)(12)}}{2(2)}$

$x = \frac{-10 \pm \sqrt{4}}{4}$

$x = \frac{-10 + 2}{4}$ or $\frac{-10 - 2}{4}$

$x = -2$ or -3

Quadratic function (p. 510) A function of the form $y = ax^2 + bx + c$, where $a \neq 0$. The graph of a quadratic function is a parabola, a U-shaped curve that opens up or down.

Función cuadrática (p. 510) La función $y = ax^2 + bx + c$, en la que $a \neq 0$. La gráfica de una función cuadrática es una parábola, o curva en forma de U que se abre hacia arriba o hacia abajo.

$y = 5x^2 - 2x + 1$ is a quadratic function.

R

Radical equation (p. 607) An equation that has a variable in a radicand.

Ecuación radical (p. 607) Ecuación que tiene una variable en un radicando.

$\sqrt{x} - 2 = 12$
$\sqrt{x} = 14$

Radical expression (p. 578) Expression that contains a radical.

Expresión radical (p. 578) Expresiones que contienen radicals.

$\sqrt{3}$, $\sqrt{5x}$, and $\sqrt{x - 10}$ are examples of radical expressions.

Radicand (p. 524) The expression under the radical sign.

Radicando (p. 524) La expresión que aparece debajo del signo radical.

The radicand of the radical expression $\sqrt{x + 2}$ is $x + 2$.

Range (p. 120) The difference between the greatest and the least data values for a set of data.

Rango (p. 120) Diferencia entre el valor mayor y el menor en un conjunto de datos.

For the set 2, 5, 8, 12, the range is $12 - 2 = 10$.

776 Glossary

EXAMPLES

Range (p. 241) The set of all the second coordinates of a function.

Recorrido (p. 241) El conjunto de todos los valores de salida de una función.

In the function $f(x) = |x|$, the range is the set of all nonnegative numbers.

Rate (p. 182) A ratio of a to b where a and b represent quantities measured in different units.

Razón (p. 182) La relación que existe entre a y b cuando a y b son cantidades medidas con distintas unidades.

Traveling 125 miles in 2 hours results in the rate $\frac{125 \text{ miles}}{2 \text{ hours}}$ or 62.5 mi/h.

Rate of change (p. 282) The relationship between two quantities that are changing. The rate of change is also called slope.

rate of change $= \frac{\text{change in the dependent variable}}{\text{change in the independent variable}}$

Tasa de cambio (p. 282) Permite ver la relación entre dos cantidades que cambian. La tasa de cambio se llama también pendiente.

tasa de cambio $= \frac{\text{cambio en la variable dependiente}}{\text{cambio en la variable independiente}}$

Video rental for 1 day is $1.99. Video rental for 2 days is $2.99.

rate of change $= \frac{2.99 - 1.99}{2 - 1}$

$= \frac{1.00}{1}$

$= 1$

Ratio (p. 182) A comparison of two numbers by division.

Razón (p. 182) Comparación de dos números por división.

$\frac{5}{7}$ and $7:3$ are ratios.

Rational equation (p. 672) An equation containing rational expressions.

Ecuación racional (p. 672) Ecuación que contiene expresiones racionales.

$\frac{1}{x} = \frac{3}{2x - 1}$ is a rational equation.

Rational expression (p. 652) An expression with a variable in the denominator. The value of the variable cannot make the denominator equal to 0.

Expresión racional (p. 652) Expresión que contiene variable en el denominador. El valor de la variable no puede hacer el denominador igual a 0.

$\frac{3}{x^3 + x}$ when $x \neq 0$

Rational function (p. 520) A function that can be written in the form $f(x) = \frac{\text{polynomial}}{\text{polynomial}}$. The value of the variable cannot make the denominator equal to 0.

Función racional (p. 520) Función que puede expresarse de forma $f(x) = \frac{\text{polinomio}}{\text{polinomio}}$. El valor de la variable no puede hacer el denominador igual a 0.

$y = \frac{x}{x^2 + 2}$

Glossary 777

EXAMPLES

Rational number (p. 17) A real number that can be written as a ratio of two integers. Rational numbers in decimal form are terminating or repeating.

Número racional (p. 17) Número real que puede expresarse como el cociente de dos números enteros. Los números racionales en forma decimal son exactos o periódicos.

$\frac{2}{3}$, 1.548, and 2.292929 . . . are all rational numbers.

Rationalize (p. 581) Rewrite as a rational number. Rationalizing the denominator of a radical expression may be necessary to obtain the simplest radical form.

Racionalizar (p. 581) Escribir una expresión matemática en forma de número racional. A veces es necesario racionalizar el denominador de una expresión radical a fin de obtener la forma radical más simple.

$\frac{2}{\sqrt{3}} = \frac{2}{\sqrt{3}} \cdot \frac{\sqrt{3}}{\sqrt{3}} = \frac{2\sqrt{3}}{\sqrt{25}} = \frac{2\sqrt{3}}{3}$

Real number (p. 18) A number that is either rational or irrational.

Número real (p. 18) El conjunto de números racionales e irracionales.

5, -3, $\sqrt{11}$, $0.666\ldots$, $5\frac{4}{11}$, 0, and π are all real numbers.

Reciprocal (p. 41) Given a nonzero rational number $\frac{a}{b}$, the reciprocal, or multiplicative inverse, is $\frac{b}{a}$. The product of a nonzero number and its reciprocal is 1.

Recíproco (p. 41) El recíproco, o inverso multiplicativo, de un número racional $\frac{a}{b}$ cuyo valor no es cero es $\frac{b}{a}$. El producto de un número y su valor recíproco es 1.

$\frac{2}{5}$ and $\frac{5}{2}$ are reciprocals because $\frac{2}{5} \times \frac{5}{2} = 1$.

Relation (p. 241) Any set of ordered pairs.

Relación (p. 241) Cualquier grupo de pares ordenados.

$\{(0, 0), (2, 3), (2, -7)\}$ is a relation.

S

Sample space (p. 211) All possible outcomes of an event.

Espacio de muestra (p. 211) El conjunto de todos los resultados posibles de un suceso.

When tossing two coins one at a time, the sample space is (H, H), (T, T), (H, T), (T, H).

Scale (p. 191) The ratio of a distance in a drawing to the actual distance.

Escala (p. 191) Proporción entre las distancias expresadas en un dibujo y las distancias reales.

For a drawing in which a 2-in. length represents an actual length of 18 ft, the scale is 1 in. : 9 ft.

778 Glossary

EXAMPLES

Scale drawing (p. 191) An enlarged or reduced drawing similar to an actual object or place.

Dibujo a escala (p. 191) Dibujo que muestra de mayor o menor tamaño un objeto o lugar dado.

Scatter plot (p. 61) A graph that relates data of two different sets. The two sets of data are displayed as ordered pairs.

Diagrama de puntos (p. 61) Gráfica que muestra la relación entre dos conjuntos. Los datos de ambos conjuntos se presentan como pares ordenados.

The scatter plot displays the amount spent on advertising (in thousands of dollars) versus product sales (in millions of dollars).

Scientific notation (p. 400) A number expressed in the form $a \times 10^n$, where n is an integer and $1 < a < 10$.

Notación científica (p. 400) Un número expresado en forma de $a \times 10^n$, donde n es un número entero y $1 < a < 10$.

3.4×10^6

Sequence (p. 269) A number pattern.

Progresión (p. 269) Sucesión de números.

$-4, 5, 14, 23$ is a sequence.

Similar figures (p. 191) Figures that have the same shape, but not necessarily the same size.

Figuras semejantes (p. 191) Figuras que tienen la misma forma pero no necesariamente el mismo tamaño.

$\triangle DEF$ and $\triangle GHI$ are similar.

Simple interest (p. 201) Interest paid only on the principal.

Interés simple (p. 201) Interés basado en el capital solamente.

The interest on $1000 at 6% for 5 years is $1000(0.06)5 = $300.

Simplify (p. 9) Replace an expression with its simplest name or form.

Simplificar (p. 9) Reemplazar una expresión por su versión o forma más simple.

$\frac{3 + 5}{8}$

Glossary 779

English/Spanish Glossary

T755

Sine (p. 425) In a right triangle, such as $\triangle ABC$, with right $\angle C$,
sine of $\angle A = \dfrac{\text{length of side opposite } \angle A}{\text{length of hypotenuse}}$ or $\sin A = \dfrac{a}{c}$.

Seno (p. 425) En $\triangle ABC$ con $\angle C$ recto,
el seno de $\angle A = \dfrac{\text{longitud del lado opuesto a } \angle A}{\text{longitud de la hipotenusa}}$, o sen $A = \dfrac{a}{c}$.

$\sin A = \dfrac{4}{5}$

Slope (p. 284) The ratio of the vertical change to the horizontal change.
slope $= \dfrac{\text{vertical change}}{\text{horizontal change}} = \dfrac{y_2 - y_1}{x_2 - x_1}$, where $x_2 - x_1 \neq 0$

Pendiente (p. 284) La razón del cambio vertical al cambio horizontal.
pendiente $= \dfrac{\text{cambio vertical}}{\text{cambio horizontal}} = \dfrac{y_2 - y_1}{x_2 - x_1}$, donde $x_2 - x_1 \neq 0$

The slope of the line below is $\dfrac{2}{4} = \dfrac{1}{2}$.

Slope-intercept form (p. 292) A linear equation of a nonvertical line written as $y = mx + b$, where m is the slope and b is the y-intercept.

Forma pendiente-ordenada (p. 292) La ecuación lineal de una recta no vertical expresada como $y = mx + b$, donde m es la pendiente y b es el punto donde la recta corta el eje y.

$y = 8x + 2$

Solution of a system of linear equations (p. 340) Any ordered pair in a system that makes all the equations of that system true.

Solución de un sistema (p. 340) Todo par ordenado de un sistema que hace verdaderas todas las ecuaciones de ese sistema.

$(2, 1)$ is a solution of the system
$y = 2x - 3$
$y = x - 1$
because the ordered pair makes each equation true.

Solution of a system of linear inequalities (p. 377) Any ordered pair that makes all of the inequalities in the system true.

Solución de un sistema de desigualdades lineales (p. 377) Todo par ordenado que hace verdaderas todas las desigualdades del sistema.

The shaded purple area shows the solution of the system
$y > 2x - 5$
$3x + 4y < 12$.

Solution of an equation (p. 75) Any value or values that make an equation true.

Solución de una ecuación (p. 75) Cualquier valor o valores que hagan verdadera una ecuación.

In the equation $y + 22 = 11$, -11 is the solution.

Solution of an inequality (one variable) (p. 134) Any value or values of a variable in the inequality that makes an inequality true.

Solución de una desigualdad (una variable) (p. 134) Cualquier valor o valores de una variable de la desigualdad que hagan verdadera la desigualdad.

The solution of the inequality $x < 9$ is all numbers less than 9.

Solution of an inequality (two variables) (p. 371) Any ordered pair that makes the inequality true.

Solución de una desigualdad (dos variables) (p. 371) Cualquier par ordenado que haga verdadera la desigualdad.

Each ordered pair in the pink area and on the solid pink line is a solution of $3x - 5y \leq 10$.

Square root (p. 524) A number b such that $a^2 = b$. $\sqrt{b}$ is the principal square root. $-\sqrt{b}$ is the negative square root.

Raíz cuadrada (p. 524) Si $a^2 = b$, entonces a es la raíz cuadrada de b. $\sqrt{b}$ es la raíz cuadrada principal. $-\sqrt{b}$ es la raíz cuadrada negativa.

-3 and 3 are square roots of 9.

Square root function (p. 614) A function that contains the independent variable in the radicand.

Función de raíz cuadrada (p. 614) Una función que contiene la variable independiente en el radicando.

$y = \sqrt{2x}$ is a square root function.

Standard form of a linear equation (p. 298) The form of a linear equation $Ax + By = C$, where A, B, and C are real numbers and A and B are not both zero.

Forma normal de una ecuación lineal (p. 298) La forma normal de una ecuación lineal es $Ax + By = C$, donde A, B y C son números reales, y donde A y B no son ambos iguales a cero.

$6x - y = 12$

Standard form of a polynomial (p. 457) The form of a polynomial in which the degree of the terms decreases from left to right (also *descending order*).

Forma normal de un polinomio (p. 457) Cuando el grado de los términos de un polinomio disminuye de izquierda a derecha, está en forma normal, o en orden descendente.

$15x^3 + x^2 + 3x - 9$

Standard form of a quadratic equation (p. 530) The form of a quadratic equation written $ax^2 + bx + c = 0$.

Forma normal de una ecuación cuadrática (p. 530) Cuando una ecuación cuadrática se expresa de forma $ax^2 + bx + c = 0$.

$-x^2 + 2x + 9 = 0$

Standard form of a quadratic function (p. 510) The form of a quadratic function written $y = ax^2 + bx + c$, where $a \neq 0$.

Forma normal de una función cuadrática (p. 510) Cuando una ecuación cuadrática se expresa como $y = ax^2 + bx + c$, donde $a \neq 0$.

$y = 2x^2 - 5x + 2$

Stem-and-leaf plot (p. 120) A display of data made by using the digits of the values.

Diagrama de tallo y hojas (p. 120) Un arreglo de los datos que use los dígitos de los valores.

Substitution method (p. 347) A method of solving a system of equations by replacing one variable with an equivalent expression containing the other variable.

Método de sustitución (p. 347) Método para resolver un sistema de ecuaciones en el que se reemplaza una variable por una expresión equivalente que contenga la otra variable.

$y = 2x + 5$
$x + 3y = 7$
$x + 3(2x + 5) = 7$

System of linear equations (p. 340) Two or more linear equations using the same variables.

Sistema de ecuaciones lineales (p. 340) Dos o más ecuaciones lineales que usen las mismas variables.

$y = 5x + 7, y = \frac{1}{2}x - 3$

System of linear inequalities (p. 375) Two or more linear inequalities using the same variables.

Sistema de desigualdades lineales (p. 375) Dos o más desigualdades lineales que usen las mismas variables.

$y \leq x + 11, y < 5x$

T

Tangent (p. 621) In a right triangle, such as $\triangle ABC$ with right $\angle C$,
tangent of $\angle A = \dfrac{\text{length of side opposite } \angle A}{\text{length of side adjacent to } \angle A}$, or $\tan A = \dfrac{a}{b}$.

Tangente (p. 621) En $\triangle ABC$, con $\angle C$ recto,
tangente de $\angle A = \dfrac{\text{longitud del lado opuesto a } \angle A}{\text{longitud del lado adyacente a } \angle A}$, o la $\tan A = \dfrac{a}{b}$.

$\tan A = \dfrac{4}{3}$

Term (p. 49) A number, variable, or the product or quotient of a number and one or more variables.

Término (p. 49) Un número, una variable o el producto o cociente de un número y una o más variables.

The expression $5x + \frac{y}{2} - 8$ has three terms: $5x$, $\frac{y}{2}$, and -8.

Term of a sequence (p. 269) Any number in a sequence.

Término de una progresión (p. 269) Todos los números de una progresión.

-4 is the first term of the sequence $-4, 5, 14, 23$.

Theoretical probability (p. 211) The ratio of the number of favorable outcomes to the number of possible outcomes if all outcomes have the same chance of happening.
$P(\text{event}) = \dfrac{\text{number of favorable outcomes}}{\text{number of possible outcomes}}$

Probabilidad teórica (p. 211) Si cada resultado tiene la misma probabilidad de darse, la probabilidad teórica de un suceso se calcula como el cociente del número de resultados favorables y el número de resultados posibles.
$P(\text{suceso}) = \dfrac{\text{número de resultados favorables}}{\text{número de resultados posibles}}$

In tossing a coin, the probabilities of getting a head or tail are equally likely. The likelihood of getting a head is $P(\text{head}) = \frac{1}{2}$.

Translation (p. 325) A transformation that shifts a graph horizontally, vertically, or both.

Traslación (p. 325) Proceso de rotar una gráfica horizontalmente, verticalmente o en ambos sentidos.

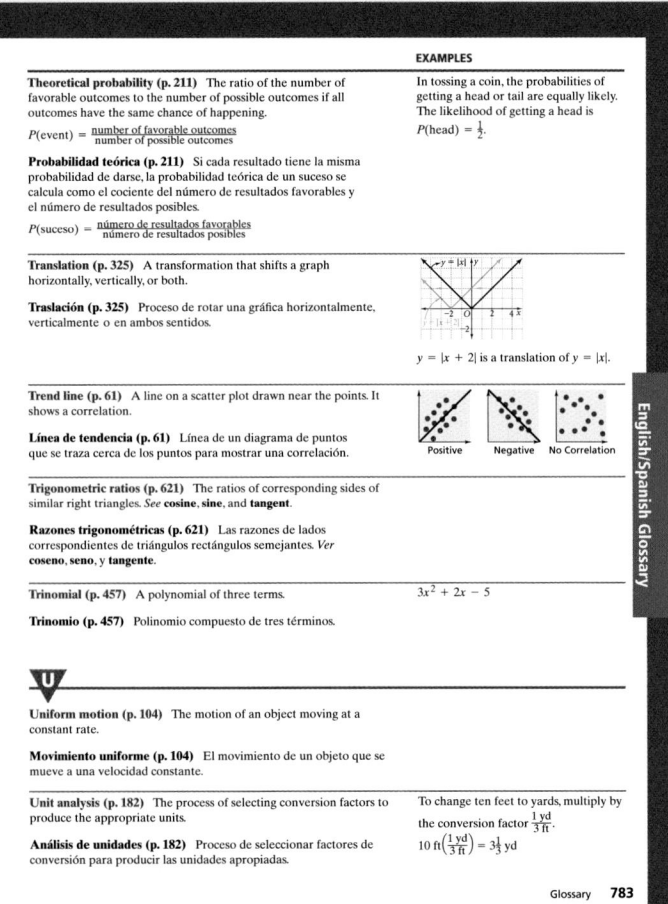

$y = |x + 2|$ is a translation of $y = |x|$.

Trend line (p. 61) A line on a scatter plot drawn near the points. It shows a correlation.

Línea de tendencia (p. 61) Línea de un diagrama de puntos que se traza cerca de los puntos para mostrar una correlación.

Positive   Negative   No Correlation

Trigonometric ratios (p. 621) The ratios of corresponding sides of similar right triangles. See *cosine*, *sine*, and *tangent*.

Razones trigonométricas (p. 621) Las razones de lados correspondientes de triángulos rectángulos semejantes. Ver **coseno**, **seno**, y **tangente**.

Trinomial (p. 457) A polynomial of three terms.

Trinomio (p. 457) Polinomio compuesto de tres términos.

$3x^2 + 2x - 5$

U

Uniform motion (p. 104) The motion of an object moving at a constant rate.

Movimiento uniforme (p. 104) El movimiento de un objeto que se mueve a una velocidad constante.

Unit analysis (p. 182) The process of selecting conversion factors to produce the appropriate units.

Análisis de unidades (p. 182) Proceso de seleccionar factores de conversión para producir las unidades apropiadas.

To change ten feet to yards, multiply by the conversion factor $\frac{1 \text{ yd}}{3 \text{ ft}}$.
$10 \text{ ft} \left(\frac{1 \text{ yd}}{3 \text{ ft}} \right) = 3\frac{1}{3} \text{ yd}$

Unit rate (p. 182) A rate with a denominator of 1.

Razón en unidades (p. 182) Razón cuyo denominador es 1.

The unit rate for 120 miles driven in 2 hours is 60 mi/h.

Unlike radicals (p. 600) Radical expressions that do not have the same radicands.

Radicales desemejantes (p. 600) Expresiones radicales que no tienen radicandos semejantes.

$\sqrt{2}$ and $\sqrt{3}$ are unlike radicals.

V

Variable (p. 4) A symbol, usually a letter, that represents one or more numbers.

Variable (p. 4) Símbolo, generalmente una letra, que representa uno o más valores.

x is a variable in the equation $9 - x = 3$.

Vertex (p. 511) The highest or lowest point on a parabola. The axis of symmetry intersects the parabola at the vertex.

Vértice (p. 511) El punto más alto o más bajo de una parábola. El punto de intersección del eje de simetría y la parábola.

Vertical-line test (p. 242) A method used to determine if a relation is a function or not. If a vertical line passes through a graph more than once, the graph is not the graph of a function.

Prueba de la línea vertical (p. 242) Método que permite determinar si una relación es o no es una función. Si una línea vertical pasa por la gráfica más de una vez, la gráfica no es de función.

A line would pass through $(3, 0)$ and $(3, 2)$, so the relation is not a function.

W

Whole numbers (p. 17) The nonnegative integers.

Números enteros positivos (p. 17) Todos los números enteros que no son negativos.

$0, 1, 2, 3, \dots$

X

x-axis (p. 59) The horizontal axis of the coordinate plane.

Eje x (p. 59) El eje horizontal del plano de coordenadas.

---

x-coordinate (p. 59) The location on the x-axis of a point in the coordinate plane.

Coordenada x (p. 59) La coordenada x de un punto muestra la localización del punto sobre el eje x en el plano de coordenadas.

In the ordered pair $(4, -1)$, 4 is the x-coordinate.

x-intercept (p. 298) The x-coordinate of the point where a line crosses the x-axis.

Abscisa al origen (p. 298) La coordenada horizontal del punto donde una recta cruza el eje x.

The x-intercept of $3x + 4y = 12$ is 3.

Y

y-axis (p. 59) The vertical axis of the coordinate plane.

Eje y (p. 59) El eje vertical del plano de coordenadas.

y-coordinate (p. 59) The location on the y-axis of a point in the coordinate plane.

Coordenada y (p. 59) La coordenada y de un punto muestra la localización del punto sobre el eje y en el plano de coordenadas.

In the ordered pair $(4, -1)$, -1 is the y-coordinate.

y-intercept (p. 290) The y-coordinate of the point where a line crosses the y-axis.

Ordenada al origen (p. 290) La coordenada vertical del punto donde una recta cruza el eje y.

The y-intercept of $y = 5x + 2$ is 2.

Z

Zero-product property (p. 536) For all real numbers a and b, if $ab = 0$, then $a = 0$ or $b = 0$.

Propiedad del producto cero (p. 536) Para todos los números reales a y b, si $ab = 0$, entonces $a = 0$ ó $b = 0$.

$x(x + 3) = 0$
$x = 0$ or $x + 3 = 0$
$x = 0$ or $x = -3$

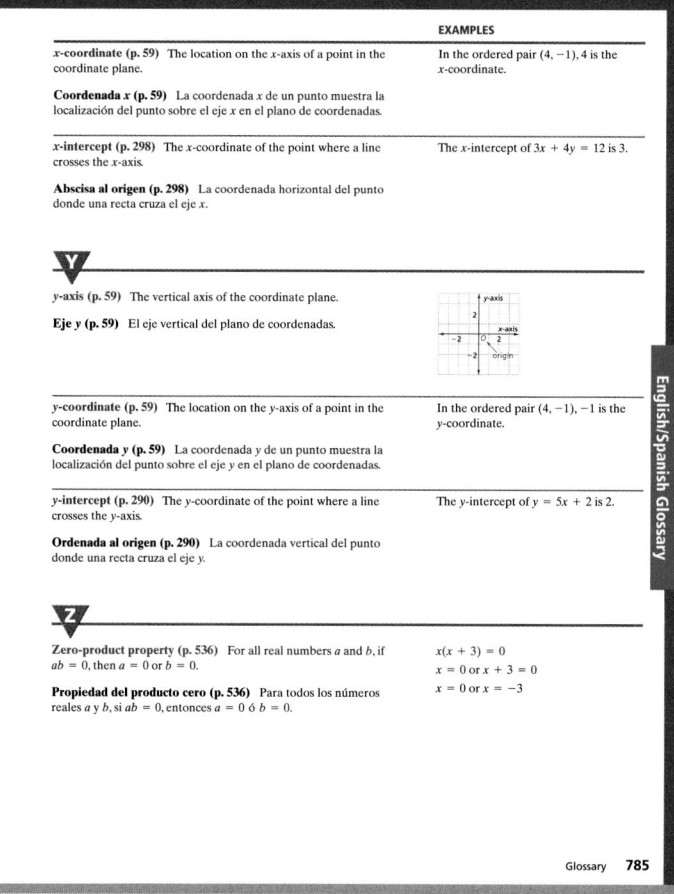

Answers to Instant Check System™

Chapter 1

Diagnosing Readiness p. 2

1. $\frac{4}{5}$ **2.** $\frac{5}{7}$ **3.** $\frac{3}{7}$ **4.** $\frac{1}{7}$ **5.** $\frac{12}{13}$ **6.** $\frac{7}{24}$ **7.** $\frac{6}{11}$ **8.** $1\frac{9}{20}$ **9.** $\frac{23}{39}$ **10.** $12\frac{23}{40}$ **11.** $4\frac{7}{12}$ **12.** $1\frac{5}{6}$ **13.** $13\frac{13}{28}$ **14.** 9^5 **15.** $8 \cdot 7^6$ **16.** $2^2 \cdot 3^6$ **17.** ≈2,650,000 **18.** Texas; ≈1,000,000

Lesson 1-1 pp. 2–6

Check Skills You'll Need **1.** ÷ **2.** − **3.** + **4.** × **5.** − **6.** + **7.** × **8.** ÷ **9.** 21 **10.** 5 **11.** 4 **12.** 50

Check Understanding **1a.** $\frac{4.2}{c}$ **b.** $t - 15$ **2.** Let n be the number. **a.** $n - 9$ **b.** $2n + 31$ **c.** $\frac{1}{2}n$ $\left(\frac{1}{3}n\right)$ **3a.** $c = 15n$ **b.** Each CD costs $10.99. **4.** Answers may vary. Sample: e = money earned, s = money saved, $s = \frac{1}{2}e$

Lesson 1-2 pp. 9–12

Check Skills You'll Need **1.** 16 **2.** 49 **3.** 25 **4.** 81 **5.** 8 **6.** 3 **7.** 11 **8.** 1 **9.** 32 **10.** 10

Check Understanding **1a.** 4 **b.** 10 **c.** 29 **d.** 134 **2a.** 3 **b.** 8 **c.** 6 **d.** 45 **3.** $26.20 **4a.** 26 **b.** 10.5 **5a.** 1764 **b.** 1134 **c.** 15,876 **6a.** 95 **b.** 21 **c.** 29 **7.** 63,000 ft^2

Lesson 1-3 pp. 17–20

Check Skills You'll Need **1.** $\frac{1}{2}$ **2.** $\frac{1}{20}$ **3.** $\frac{13}{4}$ **4.** $\frac{13}{40}$ **5.** 0.4 **6.** 0.375 **7.** $0.\overline{6}$ **8.** $3.\overline{5}$

Check Understanding **1a.** integers, rational numbers **b.** rational numbers **c.** rational numbers **d.** natural numbers, whole numbers, integers, rational numbers **2.** rational numbers **3a.** true **b.** False; answers may vary. Sample: $\frac{3}{1} = 3$ is a whole number. **4.** $-\frac{2}{3}, -\frac{5}{8}, \frac{1}{12}$ **5a.** 5 **b.** 4 **c.** 3.7 **d.** $\frac{5}{7}$

Lesson 1-4 pp. 24–27, 31

Check Skills You'll Need **1.** 6 **2.** 17 **3.** 14 **4.** 59 **5.** 1.3 **6.** 5.2 **7.** 10.9 **8.** 17.1 **9.** $\frac{4}{5}$ **10.** $1\frac{2}{9}$ **11.** $1\frac{1}{4}$ **12.** $\frac{5}{8}$

Check Understanding **1a.** −2 **b.** −2 **c.** −11 **d.** 6 **2a.** −11 **b.** −17.4 **c.** $-1\frac{1}{4}$ **d.** $\frac{1}{18}$ **3.** −15 + 18 = 3, rise of 3° **4a.** −11.4 **b.** −9.1 **c.** 15.6 **d.** 14.59 **5.** Choices of variable may vary. Sample: c = change in temp., $-14 + c$; −25°F

6a. $\begin{bmatrix} -4 \\ 1.5 \\ -16 \end{bmatrix}$ **b.** $\begin{bmatrix} -9 & \frac{1}{8} \\ 1\frac{1}{4} & -1 \end{bmatrix}$

Checkpoint Quiz 1 **1.** $b + 4$; 2 **2.** $\frac{c}{2}$; 1.25 **3.** $4.3a$; 12.9 **4.** $b + c + 2a$; 6.5 **5.** $b + 17$; 15 **6.** $3c$; 7.5 **7.** $24 - a$; 21 **8.** $b + 2a$; 4 **9.** No; the statement is not true for nonpositive numbers. **10.** whole numbers

Lesson 1-5 pp. 32–34

Check Skills You'll Need **1.** −6 **2.** 7 **3.** −3.79 **4.** $\frac{7}{19}$ **5.** 1 **6.** 6 **7.** 5 **8.** $\frac{1}{2}$

Check Understanding **1a.** −4 **b.** −5 **c.** −11 **d.** 5 **2a.** −1 **b.** 14 **c.** 4 **d.** 3 **3a.** −8 **b.** 12 **c.** 8.0 **d.** $-\frac{1}{18}$ **4a.** 1 **b.** 1 **c.** 6 **d.** 6 **5a.** −5 **b.** 5 **c.** 9 **d.** 5 **6.** ABC: $32.47; PQR: $15.46

Lesson 1-6 pp. 37–41

Check Skills You'll Need **1.** −8 **2.** −25 **3.** −24 **4.** −72 **5.** 8, 10, 12 **6.** 0, −2, −4 **7.** 3, 0, −3 **8.** 0, 6, 12

Check Understanding **1a.** −24 **b.** 50 **c.** 39.2 **d.** $-\frac{1}{2}$ **2a.** −56 **b.** 336 **c.** −56 **3a.** −24.75°F **b.** 15.25°F **4a.** −64 **b.** 16 **c.** 0.09 **d.** $-\frac{9}{16}$ **5a.** −6 **b.** 4 **c.** −1 **d.** 13 **6a.** $-4\frac{1}{2}$ **b.** $-\frac{1}{5}$ **c.** $29\frac{1}{2}$ **7.** −10

Lesson 1-7 pp. 47–49

Check Skills You'll Need **1.** 33 **2.** −22 **3.** 1 **4.** −1 **5.** $3t$ **6.** $-4m$

Check Understanding **1a.** 1339 **b.** 2121 **c.** 2352 **d.** 1485 **2.** $17.70 **3a.** $6m + 30$ **b.** $6 - 14t$ **c.** $1.2 + 3.3c$ **4a.** $-2x - 1$ **b.** $-7 + 5b$ **c.** $-3 + 8a$ **5a.** $13y$ **b.** $2t$ **c.** $-12w^3$ **d.** $9d$ **6a.** $-2(t + 7)$ **b.** $14(8 + w)$

Lesson 1-8 pp. 54–56, 58

Check Skills You'll Need **1.** 19 **2.** −30 **3.** 26 **4.** 140 **5.** −1 **6.** 3 **7.** $1 + x$ **8.** $5t - 8$ **9.** $-7m$

Check Understanding **1a.** Ident. Prop. of Mult.; m is mult. by the mult. identity, 1. **b.** Assoc. Prop. of Add.; the grouping of the terms changes. **c.** Assoc. Prop. of Mult.; the grouping of the factors changes. **d.** Ident. Prop. of Add.; the ident. for add., 0, is added. **e.** Comm. Prop. of Mult.; the order of the factors changes.

f. Comm. Prop. of Add.; the order of the terms changes. **2.** $8.80

3a. $5a + 6 + a$

$= 5a + a + 6$	Comm. Prop. of Add.
$= (5a + a) + 6$	Assoc. Prop. of Add.
$= (5a + 1a) + 6$	Ident. Prop. of Mult.
$= (5 + 1)a + 6$	Dist. Prop.
$= 6a + 6$	addition

b. $2(3t - 1) + 2$

$= 6t - 2 + 2$	Dist. Prop.
$= 6t + (-2) + 2$	def. of subtr.
$= 6t + [(-2) + 2]$	Assoc. Prop. of Add.
$= 6t + 0$	Inv. Prop. of Add.
$= 6t$	Ident. Prop. of Add.

Checkpoint Quiz 2 **1.** $13 + 5t$ **2.** 160 **3.** 42 **4.** −49 **5.** $-12 - 9w$ **6.** $5 + 4m$ **7.** 1.5 **8.** −2.5 **9.** $-5x + 5y$

10a. $9t + 3(t + 4)$

$= 9t + 3t + 12$	Dist. Prop.
$= (9t + 3t) + 12$	Assoc. Prop. of Add.
$= (9 + 3)t + 12$	Dist. Prop.
$= 12t + 12$	Add.

b. −24

Lesson 1-9 pp. 59–62

Check Skills You'll Need **1.** 4 6 8 **2.** −8 −6 −4 −2 **3.** 1 2 3 4 **4.** −2 0 2 **5.** 1 **6.** −2.5 **7.** 3.5 **8.** −4

Check Understanding **1a.** (3, −3) **b.** (−1, 1) **c.** (4, 1) **d.** (0, 2) **2.** a–d.

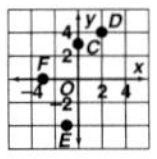

y
x
D
C
F
O
E
4
2
-4
2
4
-2

3a. x-axis **b.** IV **c.** III **d.** I

4.

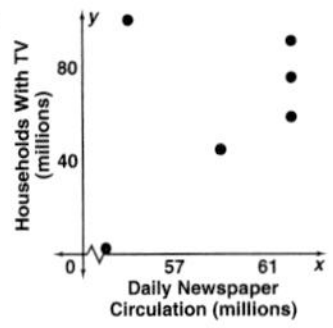

y
Households With TV (millions)
80
40
0
57
61
x
Daily Newspaper Circulation (millions)

5a. 4-year-old car with an asking price of $14,900 **b.** $5000

Chapter 2

Diagnosing Readiness p. 72

1. $0.45n = 3.60$ **2.** $3s = 124$ **3.** 34 **4.** 10 **5.** 5 **6.** 30 **7.** 3 **8.** −10 **9.** 8 **10.** −8 **11.** 7.14 **12.** 16.4 **13.** $-\frac{9}{20}$ **14.** $-\frac{7}{15}$ **15.** 17 **16.** −3 **17.** 576 **18.** −2.75 **19.** $16k^2$ **20.** $13xy$ **21.** $2t + 2$ **22.** $12x - 4$

Lesson 2-1 pp. 74–77

Check Skills You'll Need **1.** x **2.** n **3.** c **4.** m **5.** $-2, \frac{1}{2}$ **6.** $2, -\frac{1}{2}$ **7.** $-\frac{3}{5}, \frac{5}{3}$ **8.** $\frac{3}{5}, -\frac{5}{3}$

Check Understanding **1a.** 12 **b.** 11.6 **c.** −4 **2a.** 1 **b.** $-\frac{5}{12}$ **c.** −24 **3.** $268.19 **4a.** 30 **b.** −54 **c.** 100 **5a.** −32 **b.** −40 **c.** $1\frac{1}{3}$ **6a.** 4 **b.** −10 **c.** $-1\frac{3}{5}$

Lesson 2-2 pp. 81–83

Check Skills You'll Need **1.** 19; Add. Prop. of Eq. **2.** 5.2; Subtr. Prop. of Eq. **3.** 14; Add. Prop. of Eq. **4.** 33; Add. Prop. of Eq. **5.** 32; Mult. Prop. of Eq. **6.** 3; Div. Prop. of Eq. **7.** $\frac{1}{5}$; **8.** −9; **9.** $3\frac{3}{4}$

Check Understanding **1a.** 5 **b.** $-1\frac{2}{3}$ **c.** 243 **2.** 18 bulbs **3a.** −5 **b.** 3 **c.** 7

4.

$\frac{3}{5}w + 9 - 9 = -1 - 9$	Subtr. Prop. of Eq.
$\frac{3}{5}w = -10$	Simplify.
$\frac{3}{5}w \cdot \frac{5}{3} = -10 \cdot \frac{5}{3}$	Mult. Prop. of Eq.
$w = -16\frac{2}{3}$	Simplify.

5.

$-9 - 4m + 9 = 3 + 9$	Add. Prop. of Eq.
$-4m = 12$	Simplify.
$\frac{-4m}{-4} = \frac{12}{-4}$	Div. Prop. of Eq.
$m = -3$	Simplify.

Lesson 2-3 pp. 88–91, 94

Check Skills You'll Need **1.** $-n$ **2.** $8b - 2$ **3.** $9w - 45$ **4.** $-10b + 120$ **5.** $-3x + 12$ **6.** $30 - 5w$ **7.** 43 **8.** 26 **9.** −45 **10.** −35

Check Understanding **1a.** 8 **b.** 3 **c.** 3 **d.** 4 **2.** 135 ft **3a.** −1 **b.** −1 **4a.** $\frac{5}{6}$ **b.** 624 **5a.** 28 **b.** 4

Checkpoint Quiz 1 **1.** 1 **2.** 33 **3.** 20 **4.** $2\frac{1}{2}$ **5.** 120 **6.** −2 **7.** $-19\frac{1}{5}$ **8.** −16 **9.** $\frac{3}{5}$ **10.** $154.00

Lesson 2-4 pp. 96–98

Check Skills You'll Need **1.** $4x$ **2.** $-4x$ **3.** 0 **4.** 0 **5.** −2 **6.** −5 **7.** −7 **8.** $\frac{1}{3}$

Check Understanding **1a.** $-\frac{4}{7}$ **b.** −2 **c.** $-\frac{5}{2}$ **d.** 10 **2.** at least 15 bottles **3a.** no solution **b.** identity

Lesson 2-5 pp. 103–105

Check Skills You'll Need **1.** $25q$ **2.** 2ℓ **3.** $34h$ **4.** $5x$ **5.** $3.99n$

Check Understanding **1.** 5 cm **2a.** Let x = the first integer. **b.** $x + 1$ is the second integer and $x + 2$ is the third integer. **c.** $3x + 3 = 48$, 15, 16, 17 **3a.** $3\frac{2}{3}$ h **b.** $1\frac{2}{3}$ h **4.** 1 h **5.** John: 38 mi/h; Sarah: 50 mi/h

Lesson 2-6 pp. 111–113, 115

Check Skills You'll Need **1.** 180 mi **2.** 32 cm **3.** 28 m^2

Check Understanding **1.** $w = \frac{P}{2} - \ell$ **2.** $x = \frac{y + 4}{3}$ **3.** $p = \frac{m - d}{h}$; $h \neq 0$ **4.** $n = 4F - 148$; 92 chirps/min

Checkpoint Quiz 2 **1.** $-\frac{3}{4}$ **2.** $-14\frac{2}{7}$ **3.** $-2\frac{13}{21}$ **4.** 5 **5.** −13 **6.** 4 **7.** $y = \frac{35 - 2x}{7}$ **8.** $y = \frac{5x - 15}{2}$ **9.** $y = 12 - \frac{8}{9}x$ **10.** first car: 5 h, second car: 4 h

Lesson 2-7 pp. 118–121

Check Skills You'll Need **1.** 1.9, 2.4, 3.6, 7.5, 9.8 **2.** 58, 72, 98, 144, 195, 235 **3.** −12, −8, −3, 0, 7, 14 **4.** $-4\frac{3}{8}, -3\frac{2}{3}, -2\frac{5}{8}, 2\frac{1}{2}, 4\frac{1}{2}, 6\frac{1}{4}$ **5.** 5 **6.** 7

Check Understanding **1a.** about $6.53/h; about $6.38/h; $6.25/h **b.** Median; the mean is still larger than 8 of 10 wages. **2.** No; you would need at least a 104 to have a 92 average. **3.** Maine: mean = 0.4°F, range = 13°F; Michigan: mean = 4.4°F, range = 34°F. On average, Maine was colder. The temperatures for Michigan were more spread out.

4.

0	2 8 8
1	4
2	6
3	5
4	3 3 5
6	0

4 | 3 means 4.3

5a. city: 28 mi/gal; highway: 32 mi/gal **b.** city: 23 mi/gal; 31 mi/gal; highway: 32 mi/gal; 38 mi/gal **c.** city: 15 mi/gal; highway: 14 mi/gal

Chapter 3

Diagnosing Readiness p. 132

1. > **2.** = **3.** > **4.** < **5.** 7 **6.** −4 **7.** 1 **8.** 2 **9.** 3 **10.** −12 **11.** 32.4 **12.** 23 **13.** 29.5 **14.** −28 **15.** −12 **16.** 48 **17.** 5 **18.** −24 **19.** −10 **20.** 1.85 **21.** −24 **22.** −2 **23.** 3 **24.** −4 **25.** 3 **26.** $\frac{1}{2}$ **27.** $\frac{5}{2}$ **28.** 4.1 **29.** 48

Lesson 3-1 pp. 134–136

Check Skills You'll Need **1–5.** −4 −3 −2 −1 0 1 2 3 4 **6.** > **7.** < **8.** = **9.** = **10.** > **11.** <

Check Understanding **1a.** no **b.** yes **c.** yes **d.** yes **2a.** no **b.** no **c.** yes **d.** yes **3a.** −2 −1 0 1 2 **b.** −5 −4 −3 −2 −1 0 1 **c.** −1 0 1 2 3 4 5 **4a–b.** Choice of variable may vary. **a.** $x \geq 2$ **b.** $x < 0$ **5a.** No; speeds cannot be negative, so you can't use all real numbers. **b.** No; answers may vary. Sample: Hourly wages are not likely to be in hundreds of dollars.

Lesson 3-2 pp. 140–142

Check Skills You'll Need **1.** > **2.** < **3.** > **4.** 9 **5.** −2 **6.** −9 **7.** $\frac{1}{6}$

Check Understanding **1.** $m > 2$; 0 1 2 3 4 5 **2.** $n \leq 5$; 3 4 5 6 7 8 **3.** $t \geq 5$; −1 0 1 2 3 4 5 6 **4.** at least 53 blankets

Lesson 3-3 pp. 146–149, 151

Check Skills You'll Need **1.** 16 **2.** $-\frac{2}{3}$ **3.** −6 **4.** 6.4 **5.** −18 **6.** 18 **7.** $x \leq -1$ **8.** $x > 3$

Check Understanding **1a.** $b > 2$; −1 0 1 2 3 **b.** $d \geq 2\frac{1}{2}$; −1 0 1 2 3 4 **c.** $y \leq -1.5$; −3 −2 −1 0 1 **2a.** $k < 4$; −1 0 1 2 3 4 5 **b.** $t > -\frac{1}{2}$; −3 −2 −1 0 1 2 **c.** $w \leq -10$; −20 −10 0 5 **3a.** $t > 4$; −2 0 2 4 6 8 **b.** $w \leq -4$; −7 −6 −5 −4 −3 −2 **c.** $n > -3$; −4 −3 −2 −1 0 1 **4.** $0.4c > 327$; 818 calendars

Checkpoint Quiz 1 **1.** $c > 5$; −5 0 5 10 15 **2.** $x < -6$; −10 −8 −6 −4 −2 0 2

3. $p \leq -6$; −10 −8 −6 −4 −2 0 2 **4.** $y \geq 2$; −1 0 1 2 3 4 **5.** $g < -8$; −12 −10 −8 −6 −4 −2 0 2 **6.** $b \leq -5$; −8 −6 −4 −2 0 2

7a. yes **b.** no **c.** yes **d.** no **8a.** no **b.** no **c.** no **d.** yes **9a.** $m + 38 + 50 \geq 180$ **b.** $m \geq 92$ **10a.** $1.50p \leq 20$ **b.** 13 plants

Lesson 3-4 pp. 153–155

Check Skills You'll Need **1.** −2 **2.** no solution **3.** $-3\frac{1}{3}$ **4.** identity **5.** $1\frac{2}{9}$ **6.** −11 **7.** 40 cm **8.** 13 in.

Check Understanding **1a.** $x \geq -6$ **b.** $t < 1$ **c.** $n > 3$ **d.** $k \leq -2$ **2.** $2(12) + 2w \leq 40$, so the banner's width must be 8 feet or less. **3a.** $p < -1$ **b.** $m \leq -3$ **c.** $b > 3$ **4.** $b > 3$ **5.** $x \leq 2\frac{1}{4}$

Lesson 3-5 pp. 161–163, 166

Check Skills You'll Need **1.** 6 7 8 9 10 11 12 **2.** −6 −5 −4 −3 −2 −1 **3.** 5 6 7 8 9 10 11 12 13 14 **4.** 6 **5.** −3 **6.** 14 **7.** 3

Check Understanding **1a.** $n > -2$ and $n < 9$ or $-2 < n < 9$; −4 −2 0 2 4 6 8 10 **b.** $3.50 \leq b \leq 6$; 0 1 2 3 4 5 6 7 **2a.** $-2 \leq x < 5$; −4 −2 0 2 4 6 **b.** $-1 < x < 4$; −2 −1 0 1 2 3 4 5 **c.** $-4 \leq n < -2$; −5 −4 −3 −2 −1 0 1 **3a.** $6.7 \leq p \leq 8.5$ **b.** $5.2 \leq p \leq 7$. No; readings in this range are unlikely if the first readings are high. **4.** $n \leq -5$ or $n \geq 3$; −6 −4 −2 0 2 4 6 **5.** $x < 2$ or $x \geq 3$; −1 0 1 2 3 4

Checkpoint Quiz 2
1. $d < -3$ −5 −4 −3 −2 −1 0 1 **2.** $n \geq -2$ −4 −3 −2 −1 0 1 2 3 4 **3.** $-2 \leq m \leq 1$ −3 −2 −1 0 1 2 **4.** $s < 2$ −1 0 1 2 3

5. $p > 4$ −2 0 2 4 6 8 **6.** $x \leq -4$ or $x > 4$ −6 −4 −2 0 2 4 6 **7.** $c < 8$ **8.** $65 \leq t \leq 75$ **9.** $2(15) + 2(w) \leq 48$, $w \leq 9$ **10.** $x \geq -19$

Lesson 3-6 pp. 167–169

Check Skills You'll Need **1.** 15 **2.** 3 **3.** 6 **4.** −7 **5.** 24 **6.** 2 **7.** = **8.** > **9.** < **10.** > **11.** > **12.** =

Check Understanding **1a.** −1, 1 **b.** −5, 5 **c.** −2, 2 **d.** No; an absolute value cannot be negative. **2a.** −4, 8 **b.** no solution **c.** −2, 2 **3a.** $w < -7$ or $w > 3$, −8 −6 −4 −2 0 2 4 6 **b.** all real numbers **4.** 33.81 oz to 33.91 oz, inclusive

Chapter 4

Diagnosing Readiness p. 180

1. $\frac{2}{5}$ **2.** $\frac{9}{16}$ **3.** $3\frac{1}{5}$ **4.** 3 **5.** 75% **6.** 62.5% **7.** 1250% **8.** 0.2% **9.** 70% **10.** $n - 22$ **11.** $p + 40$ **12.** $20m$ **13.** $z + 17$ **14.** $6 - 3n$ **15.** $0.4t + 2$ **16.** $-8x + 8$ **17.** $25a + 200$ **18.** $-10 + 2.5c$ **19.** $-b - 12$ **20.** 24 **21.** −10 **22.** $1\frac{1}{5}$ **23.** $9\frac{3}{4}$ **24.** $-1\frac{1}{4}$ **25.** $-\frac{1}{10}$ **26.** $\frac{2}{3}$ **27.** $1\frac{4}{11}$

Lesson 4-1 pp. 182–185

Check Skills You'll Need **1.** $\frac{7}{12}$ **2.** $\frac{4}{7}$ **3.** $\frac{3}{4}$ **4.** 4 **5.** $\frac{3}{4}$ **6.** $\frac{1}{2}$

Check Understanding **1a.** 3.75¢/oz, 2.5¢/oz **b.** 64-oz **2.** 13.2 ft/min **3a.** $6\frac{2}{3}$ **b.** $6\frac{6}{7}$ **c.** 5.4 **4a.** $8\frac{1}{3}$ **b.** 33.6 **c.** 48 **5a.** $\frac{2}{35} = \frac{x}{60}$ **b.** ≈3.4 **6a.** 5 **b.** −8.75 **c.** −21 **d.** −5

Lesson 4-2 pp. 189–191, 195

Check Skills You'll Need **1.** $\frac{6}{7}$ **2.** $\frac{3}{4}$ **3.** $\frac{1}{2}$ **4.** $2\frac{4}{5}$ **5.** $2\frac{2}{15}$ **6.** $6\frac{2}{3}$ **7.** $1\frac{1}{9}$ **8.** 10 **9.** $\frac{3}{5}$

Check Understanding **1.** 15 cm **2a.** 9.75 ft **b.** 42 ft **3a.** about 21 mi **b.** 3.5 in.

Checkpoint Quiz 1 **1.** 2880 **2.** $6.00/h **3.** 10.5 **4.** −20 **5.** 4.4 **6.** 33.6 min **7.** 3.125 cm **8.** 4.5 ft **9.** 35 ft **10.** $36\frac{2}{3}$ mi

Lesson 4-3 pp. 197–200

Check Skills You'll Need **1.** 5.4 **2.** 25.84 **3.** $\frac{1}{6}$ **4.** $\frac{1}{54}$ **5.** 0.7, 70% **6.** 0.23, 23% **7.** 0.4, 40% **8.** 0.65, 65% **9.** 0.875, 87.5% **10.** 0.4375, 43.75% **11.** 0.16, 16%

12. 0.85, 85%

Check Understanding **1.** 75% **2.** 12 **3.** 36 h **4a.** $\frac{85}{100} = \frac{x}{320}$, 272 **b.** $\frac{60}{100} = \frac{393}{x}$, 655 **5a.** 84 **b.** 0.5% **c.** 2000% **d.** 3,000,000 **6a.** 140 **b.** 222 **c.** 33 **d.** 52 **7a.** $19 **b.** $37

Lesson 4-4 pp. 204–206

Check Skills You'll Need **1.** $\frac{x}{20} = \frac{20}{100}$, 4 **2.** $\frac{8}{20} = \frac{x}{100}$, 40% **3.** $\frac{18}{x} = \frac{90}{100}$, 20 **4.** $\frac{27}{x} = \frac{90}{100}$, 30 **5.** 16 **6.** 32

Check Understanding **1a.** 8% **b.** 7% **2.** 1899% **3.** 0.5 cm **4.** 86.25 ft^2, 106.25 ft^2 **5a.** about 0.3% **b.** about 0.03% **6.** about 66%

Lesson 4-5 pp. 211–213, 217

Check Skills You'll Need **1.** 32% **2.** 9% **3.** 22.5% **4.** 18%

Check Understanding **1.** $\frac{2}{7}$ **2.** increases **3.** 98% **4.** about 35,260 light bulbs

Checkpoint Quiz 2 **1.** 120 **2.** 80% **3.** 24 **4.** 70 **5.** 25% **6.** 50% **7.** 11.25 ft^2, 19.25 ft^2 **8.** 10% **9.** $\frac{2}{7}$ **10.** 2352 bicycles

Lesson 4-6 pp. 219–221

Check Skills You'll Need **1.** $\frac{1}{3}$ **2.** $\frac{1}{3}$ **3.** $\frac{1}{6}$ **4.** 0 **5.** $\frac{1}{6}$ **6.** $\frac{1}{4}$ **7.** $1\frac{3}{5}$

Check Understanding **1.** $\frac{1}{18}$ **2.** $\frac{4}{225}$ **3.** $\frac{4}{105}$ **4a.** $\frac{2}{39}$ **b.** $\frac{2}{39}$ **c.** No; according to the Comm. Prop. of Mult., the order of the terms does not change the result.

Chapter 5

Diagnosing Readiness p. 234

1. Let n = number of pens and t = total price; $t = 0.59n$. **2.** Let h = height of house and t = height of tower; $t = h + 200$. **3.** Let s = length of a side and p = perimeter; $p = 3s$. **4.** −7 **5.** −18 **6.** 2 **7.** −1

8–11.

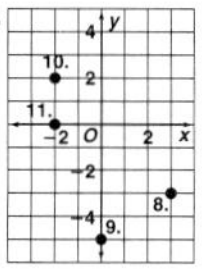

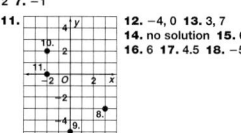

12. −4, 0 **13.** 3, 7 **14.** no solution **15.** $6\frac{2}{5}$ **16.** 6 **17.** 4.5 **18.** −58

Lesson 5-1 pp. 236–237

Check Skills You'll Need **1.** *C* **2.** *D* **3.** *E* **4.** *A* **5.** (0, 0) **6.** (−4, −2) **7.** (−3, 3)

Check Understanding **1–2.** Labels may vary. Samples are given.

1.

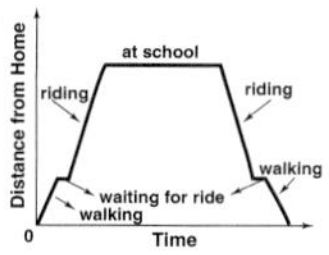

Distance from Home
at school
riding
riding
walking
waiting for ride
walking
0
Time

2.

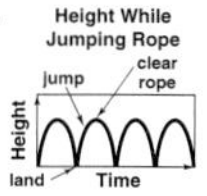

Height While Jumping Rope
jump
clear rope
Height
land
Time

3a. III **b.** I **c.** II The height of the water in A will increase at a steady rate. The rate that the water rises in B will decrease steadily because it gets wider from the bottom to the top. The rate that the water rises in C will decrease as it gets wider and then increase as it gets narrower towards the top.

Lesson 5-2 pp. 241–243, 246

Check Skills You'll Need

1.

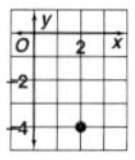

5. −17 **6.** −1 **7.** 108

Check Understanding **1.** {−2, −1, 4}, {−2, 1, 3} **2a.** function **b.** not a function **3a.** not a function **b.** function **4a.** 5.2 **b.** 0.41 **c.** −0.1 **5a.** {−8, −6, −1} **b.** {−20, 0, 8} **c.** {1, 5, 26}

Checkpoint Quiz 1 **1–3.** Graphs may vary. Samples are given. **1.**

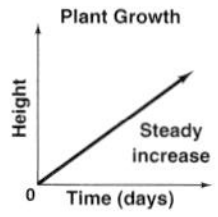

Plant Growth
Height
Steady increase
0
Time (days)

Instant Check System™ Answers

2.

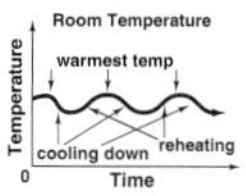

Room Temperature
warmest temp
Temperature
cooling down
reheating
0
Time

3.

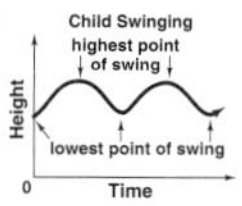

Child Swinging
highest point of swing
Height
lowest point of swing
0
Time

4. Yes; it passes the vertical line test. **5.** −2.4 **6.** 2.13 **7.** 1.7 **8.** 1.08 **9.** 33.4 **10.** −1.8

Lesson 5-3 pp. 247–249

Check Skills You'll Need

1.

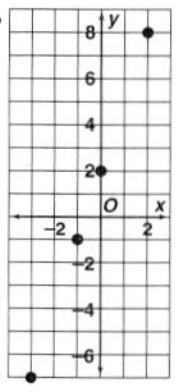

2.

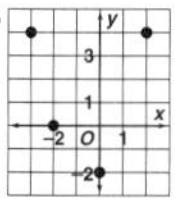

3.

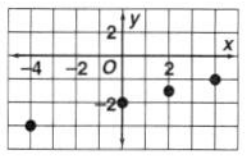

Check Understanding

1. Tables may vary. Sample:

x	$f(x)$
0	4
1	7
−1	1
−2	−2

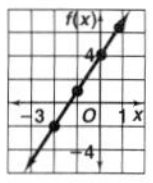

2a. Tables may vary. Sample:

c	$P(c)$
0	300
100	550
200	800
300	1050
500	1550

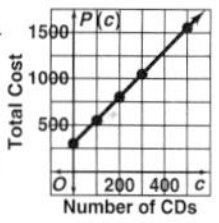

Total Cost
Number of CDs

b. as many as 99 CDs

3a. Tables may vary. Sample:

x	y
−2	1
−1	0
0	−1
1	0
2	1

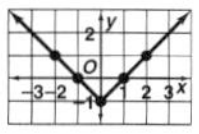

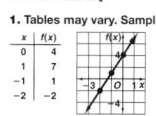

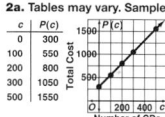

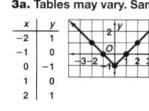

b. Tables may vary. Sample:

x	$f(x)$
−2	3
−1	0
0	−1
1	0
2	3

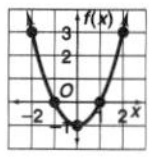

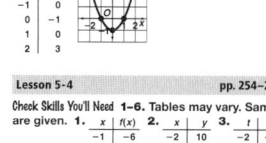

Lesson 5-4 pp. 254–255

Check Skills You'll Need **1–6.** Tables may vary. Samples are given.

1.

x	$f(x)$
−1	−6
0	−1
1	4
2	9
3	14

2.

x	y
−2	10
−1	7
0	4
1	1
2	−2

3.

t	$g(t)$
−2	−7.4
−1	−7.2
0	−7
1	−6.8
2	−6.6

4.

x	y
−2	−7
−1	−3
0	1
1	5
2	9

5.

x	$f(x)$
−2	8
−1	7
0	6
1	5
2	4

6.

d	$c(d)$
−2	−1.1
−1	−0.1
0	0.9
1	1.9
2	2.9

7. 3 **8.** −2 **9.** 4

Check Understanding **1a.** $f(x) = x - 2$ **b.** $y = 2x$ **c.** $y = x + 2$ **2a.** $C(x) = 1.19x$ **b.** $14.28 **3.** $p(n) = 15n - 199$

Lesson 5-5 pp. 261–264, 267

Check Skills You'll Need **1.** $q = \frac{m}{n}$ **2.** $r = \frac{d}{t}$ **3.** $y = -\frac{ax}{b}$ **4.** 7.5 **5.** 20 **6.** 5 **7.** 10 **8.** 14.4 **9.** 81

Check Understanding **1a.** yes; $\frac{2}{7}$ **b.** no **c.** yes; 7.5 **2.** $y = 2x$ **3.** $y = 12x$ **4a.** no **b.** yes; $y = 1.5x$ **5.** 2.5 lb

Checkpoint Quiz 2

1.

x	y
−1	−3
0	1
1	5

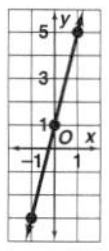

2.

x	y
−2	−1
0	0
2	1

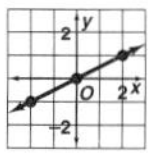

$\frac{1}{2}$

3.

x	$f(x)$
−1	3
0	0
1	−3

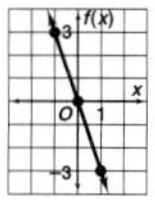

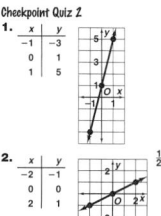

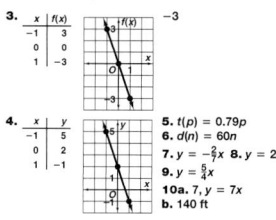

−3

4.

x	y
−1	5
0	2
1	−1

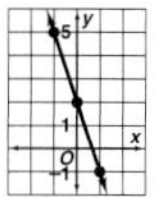

5. $t(p) = 0.79p$ **6.** $d(n) = 60n$ **7.** $y = -\frac{2}{7}x$ **8.** $y = 2x$ **9.** $y = \frac{5}{4}x$ **10a.** 7, $y = 7x$ **b.** 140 ft

Lesson 5-6 pp. 268–270

Check Skills You'll Need **1.** 12, 15, 18 **2.** 15, 22, 29 **3.** −2.6, −5.6, −8.6 **4.** 14 **5.** −17 **6.** −1.9

Check Understanding **1a.** "Multiply the previous term by 3"; 243, 729. **b.** "Add 6 to the previous term"; 33, 39. **c.** "Multiply the previous term by −2"; 32, −64. **2a.** 12 **b.** −5 **3a.** −5, 10, 28 **b.** 6.3, 31.3, 61.3

Chapter 6

Diagnosing Readiness p. 280

1. 2 **2.** 5 **3.** $\frac{1}{12}$ **4.** 7 **5.** 7

6.

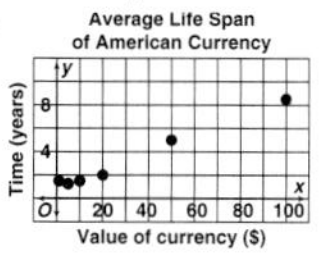

Average Life Span of American Currency
Time (years)
Value of currency ($)

7. 1 **8.** 3 **9.** 3 **10.** $y = \frac{1}{2}x + 2$ **11.** $y = 3x - 2$ **12.** $y = -x - 2$

13.

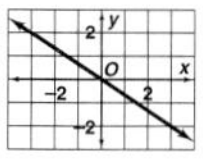

14.

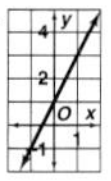

15.

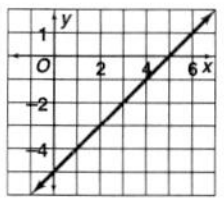

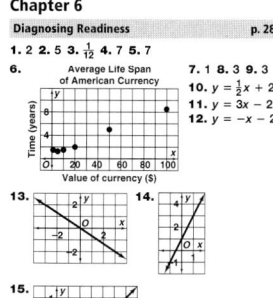

Lesson 6-1 pp. 282–285

Check Skills You'll Need **1.** −12 **2.** 12 **3.** −5 **4.** 5 **5.** 2 **6.** $-\frac{1}{3}$ **7.** −3 **8.** $\frac{3}{5}$ **9.** $\frac{1}{4}$ **10.** −1

Check Understanding **1a.** 15 **b.** No; the rate of change for each consecutive pair of days does not have to be the same. **2.** 50 mi/h **3a.** $\frac{3}{5}$ **b.** $-\frac{1}{6}$ **4a.** 1 **b.** $-\frac{3}{2}$ **c.** $\frac{d-b}{c-a}$ **5a.** 0 **b.** undefined

Lesson 6-2 pp. 291–293

Check Skills You'll Need **1.** 15 **2.** −11 **3.** 6 **4.** 5 **5.** $y = 4x + 5$ **6.** $y = -2x + 7$ **7.** $y = -4x - 3$

Check Understanding **1a.** $m = -2; b = 1$ **b.** $m = \frac{7}{6}; b = -\frac{3}{4}$ **c.** $m = -\frac{4}{5}; b = 0$ **2.** $y = -3x + 4$ **3.** $y = \frac{1}{2}x + 1$

4.

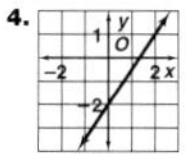

5.

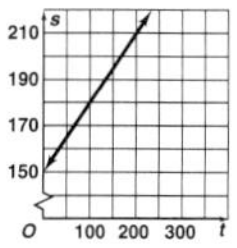

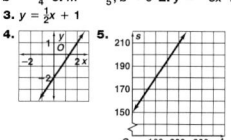

Lesson 6-3 pp. 298–300, 303

Check Skills You'll Need **1.** $y = -3x + 5$ **2.** $y = 2x + 10$ **3.** $y = x - 6$ **4.** $y = -5x + 2$ **5.** $y = -\frac{1}{3}x + \frac{1}{9}$ **6.** $y = \frac{2}{5}x + \frac{4}{5}$ **7.** $625x + 850 = 775$ **8.** $4 = 2x - 50$ **9.** $900 - 222x = 1000$

Check Understanding **1.** −3; $\frac{4}{3}$

2.

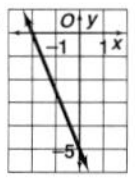

3a.

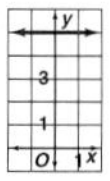

b.

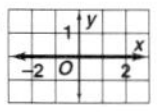

c.

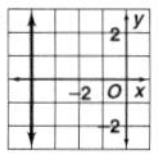

d.

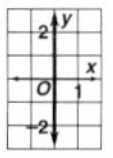

4. $2x + 5y = 5$ **5.** $4x + 5y = 250$

Checkpoint Quiz 1 **1.** $-\frac{5}{7}$ **2.** $\frac{3}{4}$ **3.** −4 **4.** −1 **5.** $121.75 billion

Instant Check System™ Answers

6.

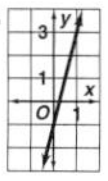

7.

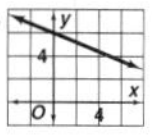

8.

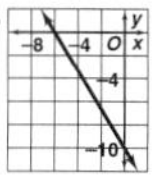

9.

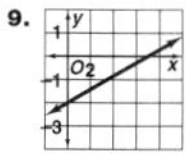

10. same y-intercepts; different slopes

Lesson 6-4 pp. 304–307

Check Skills You'll Need **1.** −2 **2.** $\frac{1}{2}$ **3.** 2 **4.** $-3x + 15$ **5.** $5x + 10$ **6.** $-\frac{4}{9}x + \frac{8}{3}$

Check Understanding

1.

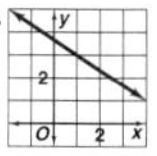

2. $y + 8 = \frac{2}{5}(x - 10)$ **3a.** $y + 5 = \frac{8}{3}(x + 1)$ **b.** $y = \frac{8}{3}x - 2\frac{1}{3}$ **c.** They are the same.

4. Yes; answers may vary. Sample: $y - 5 = \frac{2}{5}(x - 19)$ **5.** Yes; answers may vary. Sample: $y - 3030 = -\frac{50}{3}(x - 68)$

Lesson 6-5 pp. 311–313

Check Skills You'll Need **1.** $\frac{2}{1}$ **2.** $\frac{3}{4}$ **3.** $-\frac{5}{2}$ **4.** $-\frac{5}{7}$ **5.** $\frac{5}{3}$; 4 **6.** $\frac{5}{3}$; −8 **7.** 6; 0 **8.** 6; 2

Check Understanding **1.** Yes; same slope, different y-intercept **2.** $y = 3x - 12$ **3.** $y = -\frac{4}{3}x + 9\frac{1}{3}$ **4.** $y = 2x + 4$

Lesson 6-6 pp. 318–320, 324

Check Skills You'll Need

1.

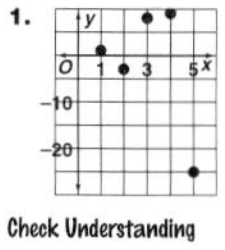

2.

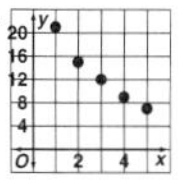

Check Understanding

1.

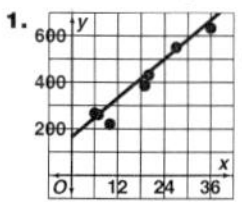

Answers may vary. Sample: $y = 14x + 166$; 362 calories

2. $y = 0.33x - 25.35$; 0.9751360069

Checkpoint Quiz 2 **1.** $y - 4 = -\frac{1}{4}(x - 3)$ **2.** $y + 3 = 18x$ **3.** $y = -5$ **4.** $y + 6 = -\frac{2}{3}(x - 2)$ **5.** $y - 4 = -(x - 5)$ **6.** $y - 6 = -\frac{3}{2}(x + 2)$ **7.** $y - 2 = \frac{1}{4}x$ **8.** $y - 2 = -\frac{3}{2}(x + 6)$ **9.** Answers may vary. Sample: $y = 5.33x + 1.34$ **10.** $y = -6.07x + 62.71$

Lesson 6-7 pp. 325–327

Check Skills You'll Need **1.** 5 **2.** 5 **3.** 18 **4.** 12

5.

x	y
0	6
1	5
2	4
3	3

6.

x	y
0	1
1	2
2	3
3	4

7.

x	y
0	1
1	2
−1	0
−2	1

Check Understanding **1a.** Answers may vary. Sample: same shape, different y-intercepts 0 and 3 **b.** Answers may vary. Sample: same shape, different y-intercepts 0 and −3

2a. **b.**

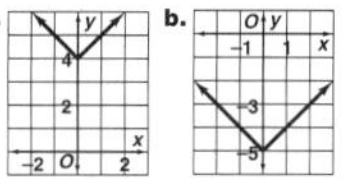

3a. $y = |x| + 2$ **b.** $y = |x| - 5$

4a. **b.**

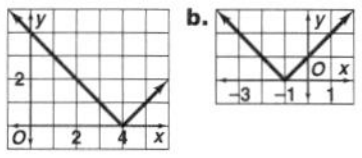

5a. $y = |x - 5|$ **b.** $y = |x + 7|$

Chapter 7

Diagnosing Readiness p. 338

1. identity **2.** 1 **3.** no solution **4.** 3 **5.** $\frac{3}{2}$ **6.** no solution **7.** $y = \frac{3}{2}x + 1$ **8.** $y = -\frac{1}{5}x + 2$ **9.** $y = -x - 4$

10. $-10 < x < 3$; **11.** $x < 12$ or $x > 60$

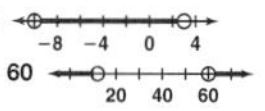

12a. $C(t) = 39.50t$ **b.** $118.50 **c.** 6

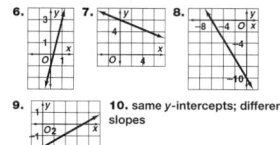

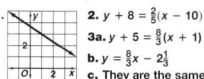

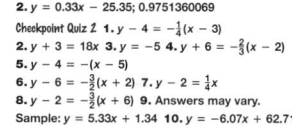

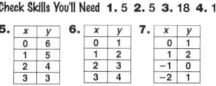

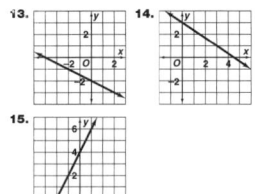

13. 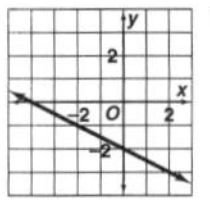
14. 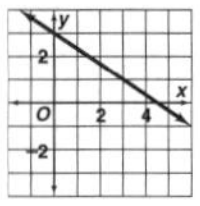
15. 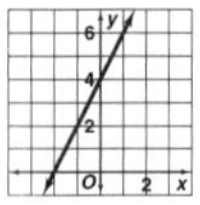

Lesson 7-1 pp. 340–342

Check Skills You'll Need **1.** $1\frac{2}{3}$ **2.** $3\frac{1}{2}$ **3.** 7
5. 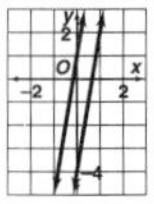

Check Understanding
1a. (−1, 4); 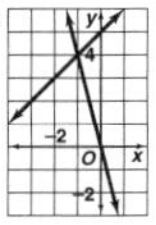 **b.** (−2, 3); 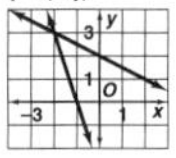

2. after 6 days; 17 cm
3. If the slopes are the same, but the y-intercepts are different, the system will have no solution.
4. all the ordered pairs (x, y) such that $y = \frac{1}{5}x + 9$

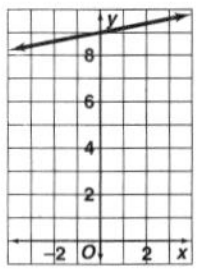

Lesson 7-2 pp. 347–349, 352

Check Skills You'll Need **1.** $-4\frac{2}{3}$ **2.** $1\frac{1}{2}$ **3.** 15 **4.** no **5.** no

Check Understanding **1.** (3, 6) **2.** (2.3, 1.6) **3.** 3 cm by 12 cm

Checkpoint Quiz 1
1. (1, −1); 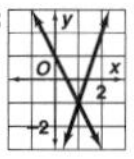 **2.** (3, 2); 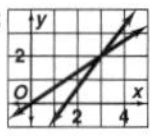
3. (−4, −2); 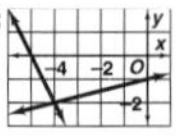 **4.** (2, −8) **5.** (1, 7) **6.** (−15, −22) **7.** $\left(\frac{28}{5}, -\frac{6}{5}\right)$ **8.** (6, 0) **9.** $2L + 2W = 44$, $3W = L$; 5.5 cm by 16.5 cm **10.** $p + c = 420$, $c = p + 250$; 85 acres pumpkins, 335 acres corn

Lesson 7-3 pp. 353–356

Check Skills You'll Need **1.** (8, 29) **2.** (2, −6) **3.** (3, −4)

Check Understanding **1.** (2, 3) **2.** 30 adult; 34 student **3.** (1, −2) **4.** 85 cards, 135 gift wrap **5.** (1, −2)

Lesson 7-4 pp. 362–365

Check Skills You'll Need **1.** 3.25 h **2.** 275 mi

Check Understanding **1.** 32 kg 50% alloy; 8 kg 25% alloy **2.** 3850 copies **3.** 440 mi/h; 40 mi/h

Lesson 7-5 pp. 370–372, 376

Check Skills You'll Need **1.** never **2.** always **3.** sometimes **4.** $y = \frac{2}{3}x - 3$ **5.** $y = -3x + 6$ **6.** $y = \frac{3}{4}x + \frac{1}{4}$

Check Understanding
1. 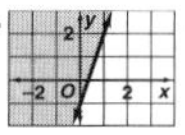 **2.** 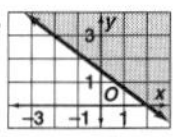

3. Answers may vary. Sample: 6 lb hamburger and 2 lb chicken, 3 lb hamburger and 6 lb chicken, 5 lb hamburger and 3 lb chicken

Checkpoint Quiz 2 **1.** (11, −4) **2.** (−9, 1) **3.** (3.5, 10) **4.** no solution **5.** $\left(15, -\frac{1}{2}\right)$ **6.** $n + d = 21$, $0.05n + 0.10d = 1.70$; 8 nickels, 13 dimes **7.** $y = 200 + 0.35x$, $y = 1.20x$; about 236 ice cream cones **8.** $x + y = 4$, $x - y = 3$; 0.5 mi/h, 3.5 mi/h
9. 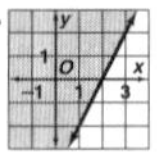 **10.** 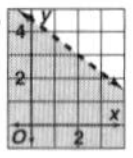

Lesson 7-6 pp. 377–380

Check Skills You'll Need **1.** (2, 0); 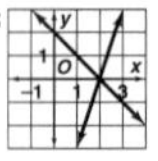
2. no solution; 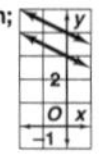 **3.** (4, 0); 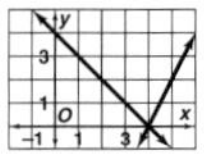
4. 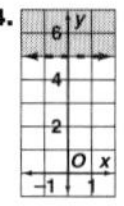 **5.** 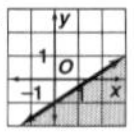 **6.** 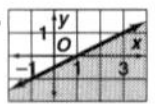

Check Understanding
1. 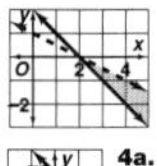 **2a.** $y \geq \frac{1}{2}x - 1$ and $y < 2$ **b.** $y \leq -\frac{2}{3}x$ and $x > -3$
3. 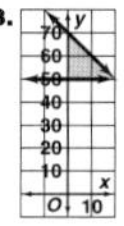 **4a.** Answers may vary. Sample: 2 20¢ stamps and 6 34¢ stamps; 3 20¢ stamps and 5 34¢ stamps **b.** no **c.** You cannot have a negative or fractional number of stamps.

Chapter 8

Diagnosing Readiness p. 392

1. 0.7 **2.** 6.4 **3.** 0.008 **4.** 3.5 **5.** $0.\overline{27}$ **6.** 49 **7.** 5.027 **8.** 0.75 **9.** 4 **10.** 100 **11.** 49 **12.** 17 **13.** −31 **14.** \$120 **15.** \$800 **16.** {−24.5, −8, 0} **17.** {−32.875, 10, 18} **18.** {−11, −1, 16.5} **19.** 9, 11 **20.** 14, 20 **21.** 31, 37

Lesson 8-1 pp. 394–396

Check Skills You'll Need **1.** 8 **2.** $\frac{1}{16}$ **3.** 4 **4.** −27 **5.** −27 **6.** 3 **7.** $\frac{1}{2}$ **8.** −1 **9.** 4

Check Understanding **1a.** $\frac{1}{81}$ **b.** 1 **c.** $-\frac{1}{64}$ **d.** $\frac{1}{7}$ **e.** $-\frac{1}{9}$ **2a.** $\frac{11}{m^5}$ **b.** $\frac{7t^2}{s^4}$ **c.** $2a^3$ **d.** $\frac{1}{n^5v^2}$ **3a.** $-\frac{1}{8}$ **b.** $-\frac{1}{50}$ **c.** $\frac{1}{16}$ **d.** $-12\frac{1}{2}$ **4.** 600; 5400; for $x = -2$, the population is 600, 2 months before the population is 5400. For $x = 0$, it is the population when time is 0.

Lesson 8-2 pp. 400–402

Check Skills You'll Need **1.** 60,000 **2.** 0.07 **3.** 820,000 **4.** 0.003 **5.** 34 **6.** 524 **7.** 367.8

Check Understanding **1a.** yes **b.** No; 52 > 10. **c.** No; 0.04 < 1. **2a.** 2.67×10^5 **b.** 4.6205×10^7 **c.** 3.25×10^{-5} **d.** 9.0×10^{-9} **e.** 436 is 436 times greater than 1, and $436 = 4.36 \times 10^2$. Then $(4.36 \times 10^2) \cdot 10^9 = 4.36 \times 10^{11}$. **3a.** 3,200,000,000,000 **b.** 50,700 **c.** 0.00056 **d.** 0.083 **4.** electron, proton, neutron **5.** 60.2×10^{-5}, 61×10^{-2}, 0.067×10^3, 63×10^4 **6a.** 1.5×10^4 **b.** 8×10^{-10}

Lesson 8-3 pp. 405–407

Check Skills You'll Need **1.** t^7 **2.** $(6 - m)^3$ **3.** $(r + 5)^5$ **4.** 5^3s^3 **5.** −625 **6.** 625 **7.** 1 **8.** $\frac{1}{625}$

Check Understanding **1a.** 5^9 **b.** 2^1 **c.** 7^5 **2a.** a^6 **b.** $7n^6$ **c.** $36y$ **3a.** a^6b **b.** $28x^2y^7$ **c.** $\frac{7m^3}{n^2}$ **4a.** 1.5×10^{12} **b.** 4.5×10^2 **c.** 6.3×10^{-14} **5.** about 2.56×10^{13} red blood cells

Lesson 8-4 pp. 411–413, 416

Check Skills You'll Need **1.** 3^6 **2.** 2^{12} **3.** 5^{28} **4.** 7^3 **5.** x^6 **6.** a^6 **7.** $\frac{1}{y^6}$ **8.** $\frac{1}{n^6}$

Check Understanding **1.** a^{28}; $\frac{1}{a^{28}}$ **2a.** n^{17} **b.** $\frac{1}{t^{12}}$ **c.** a^{18} **3a.** $16z^4$ **b.** $\frac{1}{16g^{10}}$ **c.** 81 **4a.** $81c^{26}$ **b.** $864a^{18}b^6$ **c.** $\frac{5400n^3}{m^3}$ **5a.** 5.22×10^5 joules **b.** about 1.7×10^8 h

Checkpoint Quiz 1 p. 416 **1.** $\frac{1}{45}$ **2.** r^{20} **3.** $6x^{17}$ **4.** $\frac{mq^2}{n^4}$ **5.** $\frac{1}{a}$ **6.** $\frac{64m^6}{9}$ **7.** $6m^9$ **8.** $\frac{27t^6}{8}$ **9.** 500; 2000; 16,000 **10a.** 6.8×10^3 km **b.** about 5.81×10^8 km² **c.** 145,000,000 km²

Lesson 8-5 pp. 417–419

Check Skills You'll Need **1.** $\frac{1}{4}$ **2.** 5 **3.** $\frac{3}{5}$ **4.** 31 **5.** $\frac{2}{5}$ **6.** $\frac{4}{15}$ **7.** $\frac{2}{7}$ **8.** $\frac{2}{7}$ **9.** $\frac{y}{3}$ **10.** $\frac{2y^2}{x}$ **11.** $\frac{c}{4}$ **12.** $\frac{4}{n^2}$

Check Understanding **1a.** $\frac{1}{b^5}$ **b.** z^5 **c.** $\frac{1}{a^2b^2}$ **d.** $\frac{n}{m^4}$ **e.** $\frac{xz^7}{y^5}$ **2a.** 2.5×10^{-6} **b.** 3.0×10^{16} **c.** $3.\overline{3} \times 10^2$ **d.** about 1.18×10^{-2} tons **3a.** $\frac{9}{x^4}$ **b.** $\frac{x^3}{y^6}$ **c.** $\frac{t^{14}}{64}$ **4a.** $\frac{64}{27}$ **b.** −32 **c.** $\frac{s}{2r}$ **d.** $\frac{m^2}{49a^2}$

Lesson 8-6 pp. 424–427

Check Skills You'll Need **1.** 2 **2.** −2 **3.** −1.2 **4.** 3.5 **5.** 32, 64 **6.** 108, 324 **7.** 3.2, 6.4 **8.** 12.5, 6.25

Check Understanding **1a.** $\frac{1}{5}$ **b.** 2 **c.** $\frac{3}{2}$ **2a.** 81, 243, 729 **b.** 7.5, −3.75, 1.875 **c.** 17.6, 35.2, 70.4 **3a.** arithmetic **b.** geometric **c.** arithmetic **4a.** 4; 972; 708,588 **b.** −2; −6250; −97,656,250 **5.** $A(n) = 200 \cdot 0.56^{n-1}$; 35.1 cm

Lesson 8-7 pp. 430–432, 435

Check Skills You'll Need
1. 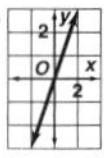 **2.** 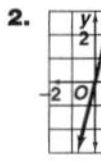 **3.** 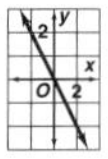
4. 9 **5.** $\frac{1}{125}$ **6.** 162 **7.** $\frac{2}{9}$ **8.** $\frac{3}{2}$ **9.** 90

Check Understanding **1a.** $\frac{1}{16}$, 1, 64 **b.** $\frac{2}{5}$, 10, 1250 **c.** $-\frac{2}{9}$, −2, −54 **2.** 40,960 animals
3a. 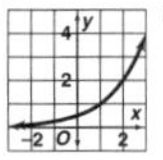 **b.** 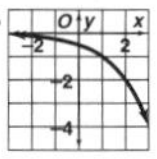
c. 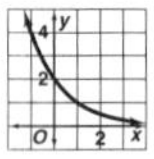 **4a.** 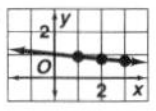
b. $f(0) = 1$, so copies are made at the same size of the original, or at 100%.

Checkpoint Quiz 2 **1.** 3^{12} **2.** $\frac{y^{15}}{x^{10}}$ **3.** $\frac{4n^{12}}{25m^6}$ **4.** $\frac{1}{t^{10}}$ **5.** geometric **6.** geometric **7.** arithmetic **8a.** −100 **b.** $-\frac{1}{5}$ or −0.2 **c.** $A(n) = -100 \cdot (-0.2)^{n-1}$ **d.** −0.16; −0.0064 **9a.** $A(n) = 40 \cdot (0.85)^{n-1}$ **b.** 209 mm **10a.** 1.08×10^8 **b.** 2.49×10^8 **c.** about \$2.31

Lesson 8-8 pp. 437–441

Check Skills You'll Need **1.** \$100 **2.** \$64.80 **3.** \$225 **4.** \$352.80 **5.** \$324

Check Understanding **1a.** $y = 4512 \cdot 1.025^x$ **b.** about 4859 students **2a.** \$5994.03 **b.** \$5994.03 **c.** $(1 + r)$ is the same as 100% + 100r% written as a decimal. **3a.** \$4817.75 **b.** \$210.23; \$220.99; \$256.67 **4a.** 4 half-lives **b.** 25 mCi; 12.5 mCi **c.** 15 mCi; 3.75 mCi **5a.** 604,000 **b.** 0.982 **c.** $y = 604{,}000 \cdot (0.982)^x$ **d.** about 420,017 people

Chapter 9

Diagnosing Readiness p. 454

1. 1, 2, 3, 4, 6, 12 **2.** 1, 2, 4, 7, 8, 14, 28, 56 **3.** 1, 31 **4.** 1, 3, 9, 27 **5.** 1, 2, 5, 10, 11, 22, 55, 110 **6.** 1, 5, 13, 65 **7.** 1, 2, 5, 10, 25, 50 **8.** 1, 2, 4, 5, 8, 10, 20, 25, 40, 50, 100, 200 **9.** 1, 11 **10.** 1, 2, 3, 6, 7, 14, 21, 42 **11.** 1, 2, 3, 6, 11, 22, 33, 66 **12.** 1, 73 **13.** $3x^2 - 4x$ **14.** $2b + 6$ **15.** $3y^2 - 11y$ **16.** $-\frac{2}{3}w^2 + \frac{7}{6}w$ **17.** $7z - 66$ **18.** $4x^2 - 2x$ **19.** $-6t^2 + 10t$ **20.** $-p^2 - 2p$ **21.** $49w^2$ **22.** $25n^3$ **23.** $9z^4$ **24.** $10t^7$ **25.** $16y^6$ **26.** $81a^2b^2$ **27.** $4x^4$ **28.** $36p^8$ **29.** x^2y^4 **30.** $3c$ **31.** $-\frac{1}{4t^3}$ **32.** $2a^2$

Lesson 9-1 pp. 456–458

Check Skills You'll Need **1.** $19t$ **2.** $39g$ **3.** $-8k$ **4.** $11b - 6$ **5.** $-3n^2$ **6.** $7x^2$

Check Understanding **1.** 0; the degree of a nonzero constant is 0. **2a.** $-9x^4 + 6x^2 + 7$; fourth degree trinomial **b.** $-y^3 + 3y - 4$; cubic trinomial **c.** $-4v + 8$; linear binomial **3a.** $20m^2 + 9$ **b.** $4t^2 + 5$ **c.** $16w^3 + 8w^2 + 4$ **d.** $11p^3 + 17p^2 + 13p$ **4a.** $-8v^3 + 13v^2 - 4v$ **b.** $28d^3 - 30d^2 - 3d$ **c.** $-2x^2 + 4x - 7$

Lesson 9-2 pp. 462–463

Check Skills You'll Need **1.** 906 **2.** 287 **3.** 4536 **4.** $24 + 20x$ **5.** $-16y - 8$ **6.** $25v - 5$ **7.** $7p - 14$ **8.** $54 - 9x$ **9.** $-8q + 2$

Check Understanding **1a.** $20b^3 + 4b^2 + 24b$ **b.** $-21h^3 + 56h^2 + 7h$ **c.** $2x^3 - 12x^2 + 10x$ **2a.** $5v^3$ **b.** 3 **c.** $2b$ **3a.** $4x(2x - 3)$ **b.** $5d(d^2 + 2)$ **c.** $6m(m^2 - 2m - 4)$

Lesson 9-3 pp. 467–469, 472

Check Skills You'll Need **1.** $4r^2 - 4r$ **2.** $6h^3 + 48h^2 - 18h$ **3.** $2y^5 - 7y^2$ **4.** $x^3 + 8x^2 + 2x + 1$ **5.** $8t^3 + t + 6$ **6.** $5w^2 - 27w$ **7.** $-2b^2 - 15b$ **8.** $7m^3 + 27m^2 - 6m$ **9.** $d^5 - 4d^3 - 18d^2$

Check Understanding **1a.** $12h^2 + 4h - 21$ **b.** $40m^2 + 11m - 2$ **c.** $63a^2 - 20a - 32$ **2a.** $6x^2 + 23x + 20$ **b.** $6x^2 + 7x - 20$ **c.** $6x^2 - 7x - 20$ **d.** $6x^2 - 23x + 20$ **3a.** $25x^2 + 28x + 16$ **b.** $x^2 + 2x - 2$ **4.** $12n^3 - 10n^2 + 34n - 56$

Checkpoint Quiz 1 **1.** $9x^2 + 10x + 1$ **2.** $6b^2 - 13b + 9$ **3.** $4g^4 + 8g^3 + 7g^2 + 32g - 36$ **4.** $-48k^3 + 42k^2$ **5.** $x^2 - 2x - 15$ **6.** $12n^5 + 2n^4 - 30n^2 - 5n$ **7.** $36w^2 - 11w$ **8.** $2(6y^2 - 5)$ **9.** $5t(t^5 + 5t^2 - 2)$ **10.** $9v^2(2v^2 + 3v + 4)$

Lesson 9-4 pp. 474–477

Check Skills You'll Need **1.** $49x^2$ **2.** $9v^2$ **3.** $16c^2$ **4.** $25g^6$ **5.** $j^2 + 12j + 35$ **6.** $6b^2 - 34b + 48$ **7.** $20y^2 - 3y - 2$ **8.** $x^2 - x - 12$ **9.** $8c^4 - 78c^2 - 20$ **10.** $54y^4 - 21y^2 - 3$

Check Understanding **1a.** $t^2 + 12t + 36$ **b.** $25y^2 + 10y + 1$ **c.** $49m^2 - 28mp + 4p^2$ **d.** $81c^2 - 144c + 64$ **2a.** $\frac{1}{9}A^2 + \frac{4}{9}AB + \frac{4}{9}B^2$ **b.** $\frac{1}{9}$ **c.** $\frac{4}{9}$ **d.** $\frac{4}{9}$ **3a.** 961 **b.** 841 **c.** 9604 **d.** 41,209 **4a.** $d^2 - 121$ **b.** $c^4 - 64$ **c.** $81v^6 - w^8$ **5a.** 396 **b.** 399 **c.** 3599 **d.** 8091

Lesson 9-5 pp. 481–483

Check Skills You'll Need **1.** 1, 2, 3, 4, 6, 8, 12, 24 **2.** 1, 2, 3, 4, 6, 12 **3.** 1, 2, 3, 6, 9, 18, 27, 54 **4.** 1, 3, 5, 15 **5.** 1, 2, 3, 4, 6, 9, 12, 18, 36 **6.** 1, 2, 4, 7, 8, 14, 28, 56 **7.** 1, 2, 4, 8, 16, 32, 64 **8.** 1, 2, 3, 4, 6, 8, 12, 16, 24, 32, 48, 96

Check Understanding **1a.** $(g + 5)(g + 2)$ **b.** $(v + 20) \cdot (v + 1)$ **c.** $(a + 10)(a + 3)$ **2a.** $(k - 5)(k - 5)$ **b.** $(x - 2)(x - 9)$ **c.** $(q - 12)(q - 3)$ **3a.** $(m + 10) \cdot (m - 2)$ **b.** $(p - 8)(p + 5)$ **c.** $(y + 7)(y - 8)$ **4a.** $(x + 8y)(x + 3y)$ **b.** $(v + 8w)(v - 6w)$ **c.** $(m - 20n)(m + 3n)$

Lesson 9-6 pp. 486–487

Check Skills You'll Need **1.** $6x$ **2.** 7 **3.** 2 **4.** $(x + 1)(x + 4)$ **5.** $(y - 7)(y + 4)$ **6.** $(t - 5)(t - 6)$

Check Understanding **1a.** $(2y + 1)(y + 2)$ **b.** $(3n - 1)(2n - 7)$ **c.** $(2y - 1)(y - 2)$ **2a.** $(5d + 1)(d - 3)$ **b.** $(2n + 3)(n - 1)$ **c.** $(5p - 9)(4p + 1)$ **3a.** $2(v - 1)(v - 5)$ **b.** $2(2y + 1)(y + 3)$ **c.** $6(3k + 1)(k - 1)$

Lesson 9-7 pp. 490–492, 495

Check Skills You'll Need **1.** $9x^2$ **2.** $25y^2$ **3.** $225h^4$ **4.** $4a^2b^4$ **5.** $c^2 - 36$ **6.** $p^2 - 22p + 121$ **7.** $16d^2 + 56d + 49$

Check Understanding **1a.** $(x + 4)^2$ **b.** $(n + 8)^2$ **c.** $(n - 8)^2$ **2a.** $(3g - 2)^2$ **b.** $(2t + 9)^2$ **c.** $(2t - 9)^2$ **3a.** $(x + 6)(x - 6)$ **b.** $(m + 10)(m - 10)$ **c.** $(p + 7)(p - 7)$ **4a.** $(3v + 2)(3v - 2)$ **b.** $(5x + 8)(5x - 8)$ **c.** $(2w + 7)(2w - 7)$ **5a.** $2(2y + 5)(2y - 5)$ **b.** $3(c + 5)(c - 5)$ **c.** $7(2k + 1)(2k - 1)$

Checkpoint Quiz 2 **1.** $k^2 - 14k + 49$ **2.** $25t^2 + 90t + 81$ **3.** $h^2 - 22h + 121$ **4.** $(v + 10)^2$ **5.** $(p - 10)(p + 4)$ **6.** $(k - 12)(k - 5)$

7. $(2x + 11)(x + 1)$ **8.** $(5m + 7)(2m + 1)$ **9.** $3(w + 2)(w - 4)$ **10.** $(3t + 5)(3t - 5)$

Lesson 9-8 pp. 496–498

Check Skills You'll Need **1.** 2 **2.** $3r$ **3.** $5h$ **4.** $4m$ **5.** $v^3 + 3v^2 + 5v + 15$ **6.** $2q^3 - 10q^2 - 4q + 20$ **7.** $6t^2 - 7t - 20$ **8.** $4x^3 + 7x^2 + 10x - 3$

Check Understanding **1a.** $(5t^3 + 6)(t + 4)$ **b.** $(w^2 - 7)(2w + 1)$ **2.** $3m(3m^2 + 2)(5m - 1)$ **3a.** $(9d + 5)(7d + 1)$ **b.** $(11k + 5)(k + 4)$ **c.** $(4y - 7)(y + 10)$ **4a.** Answers may vary. Sample: $2g$, $(3g + 4)$, and $(g + 2)$ **b.** m, $(3m + 1)$, and $(m + 3)$

Chapter 10

Diagnosing Readiness p. 508

1. −13 **2.** $-\frac{7}{2}$ **3.** −9 **4.** $-\frac{1}{2}$ **5.** −23 **6.** −3 **7.** −108 **8.** 26 **9.** 0 **10.** 49 **11.** −67 **12.** 25 **13.** 24 **14.** 144
15. 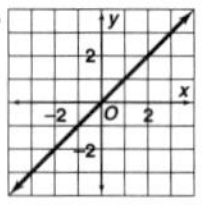 **16.** 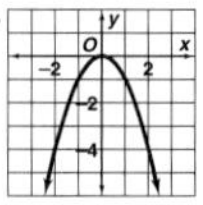
17. 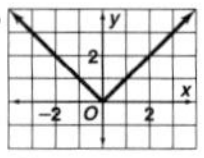
18. $x^2 - x - 6$ **19.** $4y^2 + 8y + 3$ **20.** $3x^2 + 5x - 28$ **21.** $(2x + 1)^2$ **22.** $(5x - 3)(x + 7)$ **23.** $(4x - 3)(2x - 1)$ **24.** $(m - 9)(m + 2)$ **25.** $(6y - 5)(2y + 3)$ **26.** $(x - 9)^2$

Lesson 10-1 pp. 510–513

Check Skills You'll Need **1.** −24 **2.** 18 **3.** 12 **4.** 35
5. 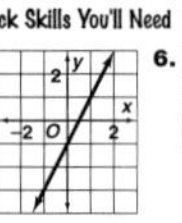 **6.** 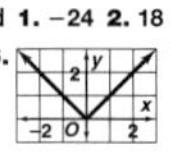 **7.** 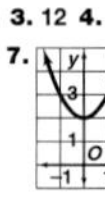

Check Understanding **1a.** (4, 3); max. **b.** (−3, −3); min.

Page 799 (top-left)

2.

x	$f(x) = -2x^2$	(x, y)
0	$-2(0)^2 = 0$	$(0, 0)$
1	$-2(1)^2 = -2$	$(1, -2)$
2	$-2(2)^2 = -8$	$(2, -8)$

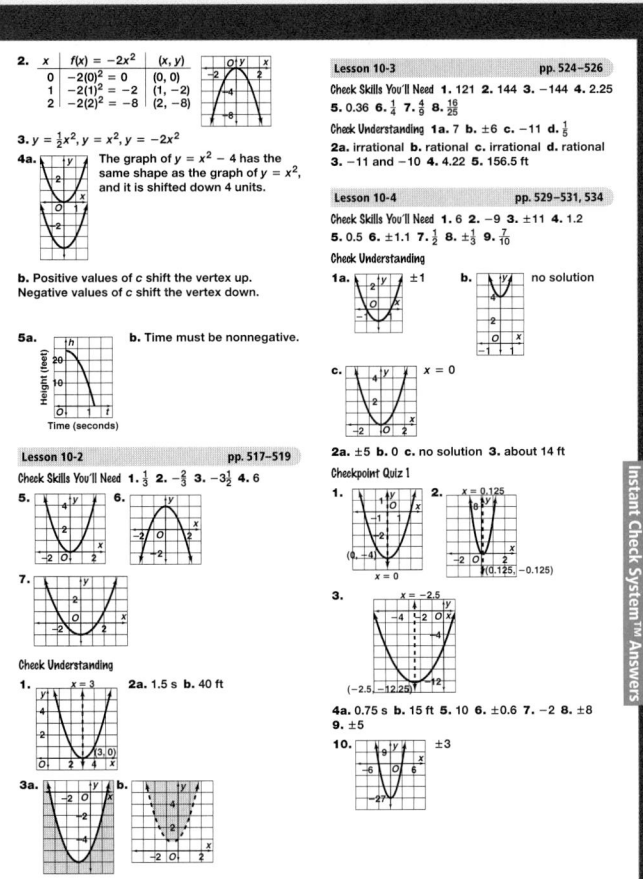

3. $y = \frac{1}{2}x^2$, $y = x^2$, $y = -2x^2$

4a. The graph of $y = x^2 - 4$ has the same shape as the graph of $y = x^2$, and it is shifted down 4 units.

b. Positive values of c shift the vertex up. Negative values of c shift the vertex down.

5a.
b. Time must be nonnegative.

Lesson 10-2 pp. 517–519

Check Skills You'll Need 1. $\frac{1}{3}$ **2.** $-\frac{2}{3}$ **3.** $-3\frac{1}{2}$ **4.** 6

5. **6.** **7.**

Check Understanding
1. **2a.** 1.5 s **b.** 40 ft

3a. **b.**

Lesson 10-3 pp. 524–526

Check Skills You'll Need 1. 121 **2.** 144 **3.** −144 **4.** 2.25
5. 0.36 **6.** $\frac{1}{4}$ **7.** $\frac{4}{5}$ **8.** $\frac{16}{25}$

Check Understanding 1a. 7 **b.** ±6 **c.** −11 **d.** $\frac{1}{5}$
2a. irrational **b.** rational **c.** irrational **d.** rational
3. −11 and −10 **4.** 22 **5.** 156.5 ft

Lesson 10-4 pp. 529–531, 534

Check Skills You'll Need 1. 6 **2.** −9 **3.** ±11 **4.** 1.2
5. 0.5 **6.** ±1.1 **7.** $\frac{1}{2}$ **8.** $\frac{1}{3}$ **9.** $\frac{7}{10}$

Check Understanding
1a. ±1 **b.** no solution

c. $x = 0$

2a. ±5 **b.** 0 **c.** no solution **3.** about 14 ft

Checkpoint Quiz 1
1. **2.** $x = 0.125$

$(0, -4)$ $(0.125, -0.125)$

3. $x = -2.5$

$(-2.5, -12.25)$

4a. 0.75 s **b.** 15 ft **5.** 10 **6.** ±0.6 **7.** −2 **8.** ±8
9. ±5
10. ±3

Page 800 (top-right)

Lesson 10-5 pp. 536–537

Check Skills You'll Need 1. −1 **2.** 104 **3.** $-2\frac{5}{7}$
4. $(2c + 1)(c + 14)$ **5.** $(3p + 2)(p + 10)$
6. $(4x + 3)(x - 6)$

Check Understanding 1a. −7, 4 **b.** $\frac{5}{3}$, 2 **c.** $-\frac{3}{2}$, $\frac{11}{4}$
2. −4, 3 **3.** 6 **4.** 9 in. × 10 in. × 2 in.

Lesson 10-6 pp. 541–543

Check Skills You'll Need 1. $d^2 - 8d + 16$
2. $x^2 + 22x + 121$ **3.** $k^2 - 16k + 64$ **4.** $(b + 5)^2$
5. $(t + 7)^2$ **6.** $(n - 9)^2$

Check Understanding 1. 121 **2.** 19, −13
3a. −0.70, −4.30 **b.** 12.74, 1.26 **4a.** −1.65, 3.65
b. 2.56, −1.96

Lesson 10-7 pp. 547–550

Check Skills You'll Need 1. 9 **2.** $\frac{49}{4}$ **3.** $\frac{81}{4}$ **4.** 6, 4
5. 2, −16 **6.** 1, −5 **7.** −7, 8

Check Understanding 1a. 4, −2 **b.** 13, −9 **2a.** 0.67, 1
b. 1.22, −0.94 **3a.** 0 **b.** $-16t^2 + 38.4t + 3.5$
b. $t \approx 2.5$; 2.5 s **4a.** Quadratic formula; the equation cannot be factored easily. **b.** Factoring; the equation is easily factorable. **c.** Square roots; there is no x term.

Lesson 10-8 pp. 554–555, 558

Check Skills You'll Need 1. −80 **2.** 72 **3.** −283 **4.** 2.18, 0.15 **5.** 0.39, −0.64 **6.** 7, 5

Check Understanding 1a. 0 **b.** 2 **c.** 0 **2.** yes

Checkpoint Quiz 1 1. −3, 7 **2.** −3, −9 **3.** −5, 10
4. 0.4, −2.4 **5.** 5.7, −0.7 **6.** 11, −3 **7.** 1, $-\frac{3}{4}$
8. no solution **9.** 1, 0.5 **10.** 0

Lesson 10-9 pp. 559–563

Check Skills You'll Need
1. **2.**
3. **4.**

5. **6.**

Check Understanding
1a. **b.**
quadratic
linear

c.
exponential

2a. exponential; $y = 4 \cdot 1.1^x$ **b.** linear; $y = \frac{1}{2}x + \frac{1}{2}$
c. quadratic; $y = -\frac{1}{2}x^2$ **3a.** quadratic
b. $y = 5000x^2$

Chapter 11

Diagnosing Readiness p. 576

1. 2.83 or $2\frac{5}{6}$ **2.** 51.75 **3.** 1.825 **4.** −0.75 **5.** 204.6
6. 3 **7.** 3 **8.** 13 **9.** 30 **10.** 4 **11.** 45 **12.** 17 **13.** 3
14. 66 **15.** 11 **16.** 2 **17.** 15 **18.** $\frac{2}{5}$ **19.** −0.06
20. 6.32 **21.** 9.17 **22.** 10.20 **23.** 1.79 **24.** 2 **25.** 2
26. 0 **27.** 1 **28.** 2 **29.** 2

Lesson 11-1 pp. 578–581

Check Skills You'll Need 1. 1 **2.** 1 **3.** 3 **4.** 4 **5.** 2 **6.** 13
7. 5 **8.** 7

Check Understanding 1a. $5\sqrt{2}$ **b.** $-50\sqrt{3}$ **c.** $3\sqrt{2}$
2a. $3n\sqrt{3}$ **b.** $-2a^4\sqrt{15a}$ **c.** $xy^2\sqrt{y}$ **3a.** 26
b. $15c\sqrt{2}$ **c.** $60a^2\sqrt{2a}$ **4.** 6 mi **5a.** $\frac{5p\sqrt{p}}{q}$
c. $\frac{5\sqrt{3}}{4t}$ **6a.** $3\sqrt{2}$ **b.** $\frac{4}{5}$ **c.** $3x$ **7a.** $\sqrt{3}$ **b.** $\frac{\sqrt{10t}}{6t}$
c. $\frac{\sqrt{70m}}{10}$

Lesson 11-2 pp. 584–587

Check Skills You'll Need 1. 61 **2.** 65 **3.** $25t^2$ **4.** −6, 6
5. −5, 5 **6.** −7, 7 **7.** $-2\sqrt{5}$, $2\sqrt{5}$ **8.** $-4\sqrt{5}$, $4\sqrt{5}$
9. $-4\sqrt{3}$, $4\sqrt{3}$

Check Understanding 1. 25 cm **2.** 6.9 mi **3.** yes **4.** no

Page 801 (bottom-left)

Lesson 11-3 pp. 591–593, 597

Check Skills You'll Need 1. 5 **2.** 5.4 **3.** 8.5 **4.** 8.6 **5.** 10
6. 2 **7.** −6 **8.** −6.5

Check Understanding 1. ≈4.5 units **2a.** ≈27.2 units
b. $(RS)^2 = (RT)^2 + (ST)^2$ or
$(\sqrt{130})^2 = (\sqrt{40})^2 + (\sqrt{90})^2$ **3.** $(1, \frac{1}{2})$ **4.** $(-6, 2\frac{1}{2})$

Checkpoint Quiz 1 1. $4\sqrt{10}$ **3.** $\frac{2}{3}$ **5.** 7.5 cm **7.** 8.6 ft
9. no

Lesson 11-4 pp. 600–602

Check Skills You'll Need 1. $2\sqrt{13}$ **2.** $10\sqrt{2}$ **3.** $12\sqrt{6}$
4. $5x\sqrt{5}$ **5.** $\frac{\sqrt{33}}{11}$ **6.** $\frac{\sqrt{10}}{4}$ **7.** $\frac{\sqrt{30x}}{2x}$

Check Understanding 1a. $-7\sqrt{5}$ **b.** $-4\sqrt{10}$ **2a.** $8\sqrt{5}$
b. $-3\sqrt{3}$ **3a.** $2\sqrt{5} + 5\sqrt{2}$ **b.** $2x\sqrt{3} - 11\sqrt{2x}$
c. $5a + 3\sqrt{5a}$ **4a.** $-33 - 21\sqrt{2}$ **b.** $23 + 8\sqrt{7}$
5a. $2(\sqrt{7} - \sqrt{5})$ **b.** $-2(\sqrt{10} - 2\sqrt{2})$
c. $\frac{-\sqrt{5}(\sqrt{17} + \sqrt{3})}{8}$ **6.** 55 in.

Lesson 11-5 pp. 607–609

Check Skills You'll Need 1. 1 **2.** 4 **3.** 4 **4.** 3 **5.** $x + 1$
6. $2x - 5$

Check Understanding 1a. 25 **b.** 81 **c.** 38 **2a.** about
67 ft **b.** No; $h - 2r$ decreases as r increases.
3. 5 **4a.** A principal square root must be a nonnegative number. **b.** 2 **5.** no solution

Lesson 11-6 pp. 614–615, 619

Check Skills You'll Need
1. **2.**

3. 2 **4.** 0 **5.** 11

Check Understanding 1. $x \geq 7$

2a.
b. 361.25 ft

3. **4.**

Checkpoint Quiz 1 1. $-8\sqrt{2}$ **2.** $4 - 5\sqrt{2}$
3. $2\sqrt{5} + 15$ **4.** $3\sqrt{3}$ **5.** $5 + 2\sqrt{6}$
6. $4\sqrt{3} + 2\sqrt{10} - 9\sqrt{2} - 3\sqrt{15}$ **7.** 256
8. 9 **9.** 5 **10.** It is translated 2 units left.

Lesson 11-7 pp. 621–624

Check Skills You'll Need 1. $\frac{9}{4}$; $\frac{3}{4}$ **2.** $\frac{12}{13}$; $\frac{13}{12}$ **3.** 20
4. 6.8 **5.** 25 **6.** 7.28

Check Understanding 1a. $\frac{12}{13}$; $\frac{5}{13}$; $\frac{12}{5}$ **b.** They are equal.
2a. 0.9397 **b.** 0.3420 **c.** 2.7475 **3a.** 6.9 **b.** 5.6
4. about 270 ft **5.** 745,000 ft

Chapter 12

Diagnosing Readiness p. 634

1. $\frac{1}{2}$ **2.** $\frac{3}{13}$ **3.** $\frac{5}{4}$ **4.** $\frac{5}{10}$ **5.** $\frac{1}{10}$ **6.** $\frac{1}{2}$ **7.** $\frac{2}{3}$ **8.** $\frac{3}{4}$
9. $3w^2x$ **10.** r^2s^2 **11.** $\frac{9x}{8}k^4$ **12.** 100 **13.** no
solution **14.** 1 **15.** $x \geq 0$ **16.** $x \geq 0$ **17.** $x \leq \frac{10}{3}$

Lesson 12-1 pp. 636–639

Check Skills You'll Need 1. 5 **2.** −7 **3.** $\frac{1}{3}$ **4.** 4 **5.** $y = 2x$
6. $y = 0.5x$ **7.** $y = -0.25x$ **8.** $y = 0.4x$

Check Understanding 1. $xy = 18$ **2a.** 15 **b.** 5 **3a.** $5.\overline{3}$ ft
b. 120 lb **4a.** inverse variation; $xy = 36$ **b.** direct
variation; $y = 4x$ **5a.** Direct variation, since the
ratio $\frac{cost}{sweater}$ is constant at $15 each. **b.** Inverse
variation, since the total number of miles walked
each day is a constant product of 5.

Lesson 12-2 pp. 644–648

Check Skills You'll Need 1. −10; −8; −5 **2.** 8, 4, 13
3. $\frac{1}{9}$, 1, 27

Page 802 (bottom-right)

4. $f(x)$ **5.** $g(x)$

6.

Check Understanding
1a.
b. Speed and time are both positive values, so graphing it in the first quadrant only makes sense.
2a. asymptote $x = -2$; **b.** asymptote $x = 3$;

3a. $x = -2$, $y = -3$; **b.** $x = 4$, $y = 1$;

4a. an absolute value function with vertex $(-4, 0)$
b. a graph of exponential growth **c.** a rational function with asymptotes $x = -1$ and $y = 0$

Lesson 12-3 pp. 652–654, 656

Check Skills You'll Need 1. 4 **2.** $-\frac{5}{6}$ **3.** $\frac{5}{7}$
4. $(x + 4)(x - 3)$ **5.** $(x + 4)(x + 2)$
6. $(x - 5)(x - 1)$ **7.** $(x + 4)^2$ **8.** $(x + 3)(x - 4)$
9. $(x - 3)(x - 4)$

Check Understanding 1a. $\frac{5b}{2}$ **b.** $\frac{4c^2}{c + 2}$ **c.** 2 **d.** 4
2a. $\frac{5}{x - 5}$ **b.** $\frac{2}{z - 3}$ **c.** $\frac{8}{2a + 1}$ **d.** $\frac{c - 3}{c + 5}$ **3a.** −1

b. $-\frac{1}{m + 8}$ **c.** $-\frac{4}{r + 4}$ **d.** $-\frac{2}{3}$ **4a.** 51 min **b.** $\frac{30rh}{r + h}$

Checkpoint Quiz 1 1. 3 **2.** −2 **3.** 4
4. $x = 0$, $y = 0$; **5.** $x = 4$, $y = 0$;

6. $x = 0$, $y = 4$; **7.** $6(x - 2)$ **8.** $\frac{c + 3}{c - 3}$ **9.** $\frac{1}{k + 4}$
10. Answers may vary.
Sample: $\frac{15}{x - 3}$

Lesson 12-4 pp. 657–659

Check Skills You'll Need 1. r^{10} **2.** b^7 **3.** c^5 **4.** $6x^9$
5. $5n^4$ **6.** $-45a^5$ **7.** $(2c + 1)(c + 7)$
8. $(15t - 11)(t - 1)$ **9.** $(2q + 1)(q + 5)$

Check Understanding 1a. $\frac{-12}{x}$ **b.** $\frac{(x - 5)(x - 7)}{x(x + 3)}$ **2.** $-\frac{1}{x}$
3a. $3(c - 1)(c + 1)$ **b.** $2v(v - 5)$ **c.** $\frac{4(m + 2)}{m + 1}$ **4a.** $\frac{1}{b}$
b. $\frac{5(7m - 10)}{7(m - 10)}$ **c.** $\frac{3n + 2}{2n - 3}$ **5a.** $\frac{1}{10x^2}$ **b.** $\frac{y + 3}{(y + 2)^2}$
c. $\frac{1}{z + 4}$

Lesson 12-5 pp. 662–664

Check Skills You'll Need 1. $-4a^2 + 9a + 1$ **2.** $-x^3 + 3x^2 + 5x - 6$ **3.** $8t - 24x$ **4.** $2x^2 + 10x + 12$
5. $-3n^2 + 11n + 20$ **6.** $6a^3 - 21a^2 + 2a - 7$

Check Understanding 1a. $m - 2 + \frac{1}{3m}$ **b.** $2t^3 + 4t - 1 + \frac{1}{2t}$ **2a.** $2b - 3$ **b.** $3m - 4 - \frac{2}{3m + 1}$
3a. $t^3 + t^2 + 2t + 3$ **b.** $c^2 - 3c + 5 - \frac{3}{c - 2}$
4a. $4x + 3 - \frac{4}{2x + 1}$ **b.** $-2a - 5 - \frac{3}{3a - 2}$

Lesson 12-6 pp. 667–669

Check Skills You'll Need 1. $\frac{3}{50}$ **2.** $-\frac{2}{9}$ **3.** $-2\frac{4}{1}$ **4.** $1\frac{1}{18}$
5. $-\frac{5}{12}$ **6.** $-\frac{1}{3}$ **7.** $\frac{2x}{5}$ **8.** $\frac{x}{5}$ **9.** $\frac{1}{2}$ **10.** $(x + 2)(x + 1)$
11. $(y + 3)(y + 4)$ **12.** $(t - 7)^2$

Check Understanding 1a. $\frac{5}{x + 2}$ **b.** $\frac{4y}{y - 5}$ **c.** $\frac{7n}{n + 1}$
2a. $\frac{1}{t - 2}$ **b.** $\frac{2b - 3}{b + 2}$ **c.** $\frac{-c + 5}{5m + 2}$ **3a.** $\frac{9 + 14y^2}{21y^4}$
b. $\frac{16 - 49x}{100x}$ **c.** $\frac{5b + 5}{12b^2}$ **4a.** $\frac{8t + 7}{(t + 4)(t - 1)}$
b. $\frac{m^2 + 5m + 3}{(2m + 1)(m - 1)}$ **c.** $\frac{3a^2 + 2a + 2}{(a + 2)(2a - 1)}$

T761

5. $\frac{1270}{r} + \frac{1270}{1.12r} \approx \frac{2404}{r}$

Lesson 12-7 pp. 672–685

Check Skills You'll Need **1.** $1\frac{2}{3}$ **2.** $1\frac{1}{5}$ **3.** −9, 9 **4.** $4n$ **5.** $15x$ **6.** $24y^2$

Check Understanding **1a.** −2 **b.** $-\frac{25}{2}$ **2a.** $\frac{1}{2}$, 2 **b.** −2, 3 **3.** $28\frac{1}{8}$ min **4a.** −3 **b.** −5, 4 **5a.** no solution **b.** −1

Lesson 12-8 pp. 679–682, 685

Check Skills You'll Need **1.** $\frac{1}{2}$ **2.** $\frac{1}{2}$ **3.** $\frac{1}{6}$ **4.** 0 **5.** $\frac{1}{36}$ **6.** $\frac{1}{4}$

Check Understanding
1a. Shirt 1 → Shorts 1 → Shirt 1, Shorts 1
→ Shorts 2 → Shirt 1, Shorts 2
→ Shorts 3 → Shirt 1, Shorts 3
→ Shorts 4 → Shirt 1, Shorts 4
Shirt 2 → Shorts 1 → Shirt 2, Shorts 1
→ Shorts 2 → Shirt 2, Shorts 2
→ Shorts 3 → Shirt 2, Shorts 3
→ Shorts 4 → Shirt 2, Shorts 4
There are eight possible outfits.
b. Answers may vary. Sample: No, because it would take a lot of room to make such a diagram. **2.** 15 pizzas **3.** 40,320 ways **4a.** 504 **b.** 210 **c.** 20 **5a.** 5040 **b.** A six-letter password; there are more possible passwords, since 26 > 10.

Checkpoint Quiz 2 **1.** $(x + 2)(x + 4)$ **2.** $\frac{4}{3}$ **3.** $a^2 + 5a + 15 + \frac{44}{a-3}$ **4.** $\frac{5}{x-3}$ **5.** $\frac{14m - 12}{(m+2)(m-3)}$ **6.** $\frac{6t+3}{t^2}$ **7.** $\frac{6}{7}$ **8.** −9 **9.** −8, 1 **10a.** 16 **b.** 12

Lesson 12-9 pp. 686–689

Check Skills You'll Need **1.** 60 **2.** 120 **3.** 210 **4.** 840 **5.** $\frac{1}{4}$ **6.** $\frac{5}{72}$ **7.** $\frac{3}{4}$ **8.** 0.07

Check Understanding **1a.** 6 **b.** 35 **c.** 210 **2a.** ${}_5C_2$ **b.** 10 **c.** Order does not matter. **3.** $\frac{3}{10}$ **4a.** 210 **b.** 1 **c.** $\frac{1}{210}$

Selected Answers

Chapter 1

Lesson 1-1 pp. 6–8

EXERCISES **1.** $p + 4$ **3.** $12 - m$ **9–11.** Choice of variable for the number may vary. **9.** $2n + 2$ **11.** $9 - n$ **17.** c = total cost, n = number of cans, $c = 0.70n$ **19.** ℓ = total length in feet, n = number of tents, $\ell = 60n$ **21–23.** Choices of variables may vary. Samples are given. **21.** w = number of workers, r = number of radios, $r = 13w$ **23.** n = number of sales, t = total earnings, $t = 0.4n$ **25.** $9 + k - 17$ **27.** $37t - 9.85$ **35–37.** Answers may vary. Samples are given. **35.** the difference of 3 and t **37.** the quotient of y and 5 **39.** Choices of variables may vary. Sample is given. n = number of days, c = change in height (m), $c = 0.165n$ **55.** 1.04 **57.** 1.46

Lesson 1-2 pp. 12–15

EXERCISES **1.** 59 **3.** 7 **7.** 21 **9.** 124 **13.** \$37.09 **15.** 22 **17.** 44 **21.** 704 **23.** 185 **29.** 18 **31.** 0 **35.** 8 cm^3 **37.** 21 ft^3 **41.** 15 **43.** 111 **57.** 9 **59.** 135 **65.** \$.16 **67a.** 523.60 cm^3 **b.** 381.70 cm^3 **c.** about 73% **69.** 127 **71.** 10 **73a.** 23.89 $in.^3$ **b.** 2.0 $in.^3$ **c.** 47.38 $in.^2$ **89.** $c + 2$ **91.** $t - 21$ **93.** 50% **95.** 95% **99.** 18.9 **101.** 60.3 **103–105.** Answers may vary. Samples are given. **103.** 55, 100, 250 **105.** 60, 150, 240

Lesson 1-3 pp. 20–23

EXERCISES **1.** integers, rational numbers **3.** rational numbers **11.** Answers may vary. Sample: −17 **13.** Answers may vary. Sample: 0.3 **15.** whole numbers **17.** whole numbers **19.** true **21.** False; answers may vary. Sample: 6 **25.** < **27.** = **29.** $-9\frac{3}{4}, -9\frac{2}{3}, -9\frac{7}{12}$ **31.** −1.01, −1.001, −1.0009 **35.** 9 **37.** 0.5 **43.** Answers may vary. Sample: $\frac{5}{1}$ **45.** Answers may vary. Sample: $\frac{1034}{1000}$ **47.** natural numbers, whole numbers, integers, rational numbers **49.** rational numbers **51.** = **53.** < **57.** 6 **59.** a **69.** sometimes **71.** always **86.** 33 **87.** 48 **88.** 315 **89.** 7 **90.** 0 **91.** $7\frac{1}{2}$ **92.** 25 **93.** 4 **94.** 195 **95–98.** Choices of variables may vary. **95.** n = number of tickets, $6.25n$ **96.** i = cost of item, $i + 3.98$ **97.** n = number of hours, d = distance traveled, $d = 7n$ **98.** c = total cost, n = number of books, $c = 3.5n$

Lesson 1-4 pp. 27–31

EXERCISES **1.** $6 + (-3)$; 3 **3.** $-5 + 7$; 2 **5.** 15 **7.** −19 **25.** $-47 + 12 = -35$, 35 ft **27.** $-6 + 13 = 7$, 7°F **29.** −1.7 **31.** −8.7 **37.** Choices of variable may vary. c = change in amount of money, $74 + c$ **a.** \$92 **b.** \$45 **c.** \$27 **39.** $\begin{bmatrix} -18.2 \\ 11.6 \\ 19.1 \end{bmatrix}$ **41.** $\begin{bmatrix} 1.8 & 22 \\ -\frac{1}{2} & 7 \end{bmatrix}$ **43.** −13 **45.** $11\frac{19}{24}$ **57.** 6.3 million people **59a.** $\frac{100}{442} = \frac{50}{221}$ **b.** 0.23 **c.** about 23% **61.** −2 **63.** −5 **71.** −13.7 **73.** 8.7 **81.** \$7 **105.** < **107.** < **111.** 9 **113.** 18

Lesson 1-5 pp. 34–36

EXERCISES **1.** −1 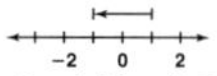

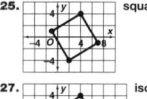

3. −6 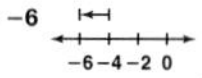

9. −4 **11.** −10 **21.** 3 **23.** 6 **29.** −10 **31.** 1 **37.** \$50.64 **39.** −1.5 **41.** 5.5 **53.** false; $2 - (-1) = 3$, $3 \not< 2$ or −1 **57.** $\begin{bmatrix} -\frac{1}{4} & 0 & -3 \end{bmatrix}$ **73.** −9 **75.** −4.1 **77.** $\begin{bmatrix} 1.2 \\ -2.5 \\ 5.2 \end{bmatrix}$ **79–81.** Choices of variables may vary. **79.** t = total cost, p = pounds of pears, $t = 1.19p$ **81.** c = check (\$), s = your share, $s = \frac{c}{6}$

Lesson 1-6 pp. 41–44

EXERCISES **1.** −15 **3.** 15 **13.** −12 **15.** −15 **25.** −64 **27.** 4 **33.** 8 **35.** 81 **41.** −4 **43.** 6 **49.** −7 **51.** 0 **55.** −15 **57.** $-\frac{6}{25}$ **59.** 18 **61.** $-\frac{8}{15}$ **73.** $-\frac{5}{6}$ **75.** $-\frac{1}{5}$ **77.** $-4\frac{1}{2}$ **79.** $\frac{1}{5}$ **85.** 31¢ **91.** $\begin{bmatrix} -15 & 21 \\ \frac{2}{3} & -9 \end{bmatrix}$ **93.** $\begin{bmatrix} -12 & -2\frac{2}{3} \end{bmatrix}$ **97a.** $a = 5000 - 25t$ **b.** 312.5 ft **c.** 4687.5 ft **115.** −20 **117.** 9.8 **121.** 56 **123.** $\frac{3}{4}$ **125.** 121 **127.** \$34.93

Technology p. 45

1. $\begin{bmatrix} -1 & 10 \\ 8 & 9 \end{bmatrix}$ **3.** $\begin{bmatrix} -1 & 17 \\ 1 & -16 \end{bmatrix}$ **11.** $\begin{bmatrix} -3 & -7 & 3 \\ -6 & -8 & 9 \\ 12 & 16 & 19 \end{bmatrix}$

13. $\begin{bmatrix} -6 & -28 & -12 \\ -32 & -23 & 26 \\ 48 & 10 & 53 \end{bmatrix}$

Lesson 1-7 pp. 50–53

EXERCISES **1.** 2412 **3.** 5489 **9.** \$3.96 **11.** \$29.55 **15.** $7t - 28$ **17.** $3m + 12$ **27.** $-x - 3$ **29.** $-3 - x$ **35.** $-3t$ **37.** $7x$ **43.** $3(m - 7)$ **45.** $2(b + 9)$ **49.** 44,982 **51.** 14.021 **65.** $2\frac{1}{4}\left(5\frac{1}{2} - k\right)$ **67.** $\frac{11}{20}\left(b - \frac{13}{30}\right)$ **68.** $\frac{17}{z - 34}$ **75.** $-76p^2 - 20p - 9$ **77.** $1.5m - 12.5v$ **105.** −68 **107.** 4 **115.** 12.127 **117.** 45.7 **123a.** $4 + \frac{m}{3}$ **b.** 7; 5; 8

Lesson 1-8 pp. 56–58

EXERCISES **1.** Ident. Prop. of Add.; 0, the identity for addition, is added. **3.** Ident. Prop. of Mult.; 1, the identity for multiplication, is multiplied. **11.** 7400 **13.** 4200 **17a.** def. of subtr. **b.** Dist. Prop. **c.** addition

19. $25 \cdot 1.7 \cdot 4$
$= 25 \cdot 4 \cdot 1.7$ Comm. Prop. of Mult.
$= (25 \cdot 4) \cdot 1.7$ Assoc. Prop. of Mult.
$= 100 \cdot 1.7$ mult.
$= 170$ mult.

21. $8 + 9m + 7$
$= 9m + 8 + 7$ Comm. Prop. of Add.
$= 9m + (8 + 7)$ Assoc. Prop. of Add.
$= 9m + 15$ add.

25. $2 + g\left(\frac{1}{g}\right) = 2 + 1$ Inv. Prop. of Mult.
$= 3$ add.

27. $(3^2 - 2^3)(8759) = (9 - 8)(8759)$ mult.
$= [9 + (-8)](8759)$ def. of subtr.
$= 1(8759)$ add.
$= 8759$ Ident. Prop. of Mult.

33. no **35.** yes **41.** No; $(5 - 3) - 1 = 2 - 1 = 1$, while $5 - (3 - 1) = 5 - 2 = 3$. **43.** No; $16 \div (4 \div 2) = 16 \div 2 = 8$, while $(16 \div 4) \div 2 = 4 \div 2 = 2$. **59.** $6 + 5k$ **61.** $-10p - 35$ **65.** $7 + [m + (-17)]$ **67.** $\frac{1}{2}\left(\frac{b}{4}\right)$ **69.** 7 **71.** $-\frac{1}{4}$

Lesson 1-9 pp. 62–65

EXERCISES **1.** (4, 5) **3.** (−5, 0)

5–8. 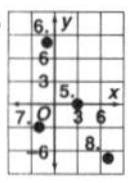

9. II **11.** IV **13.** I **15.** No; the point is on the y-axis, not in Quadrant III. **17.** neg. correlation **19.** no correlation **21.** (5, 0) **23.** (−3, −2), (1, 3), (2, −4)

25. 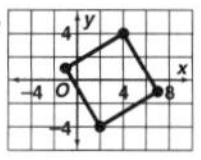 square

27. 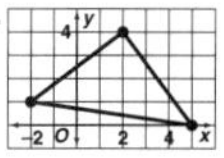 isosceles triangle

29. Neg. correlation; the more classes you take, the more work you have, so the less free time you have. **31.** No correlation; baby's length at birth is not related to its birthday.

47. $x - 4(2x + 1) - 3$
$= x - 8x - 4 - 3$ Dist. Prop.
$= 1x - 8x - 4 - 3$ Ident. Prop. of Mult.
$= 1x + (-8x) + (-4) + (-3)$ def. of subtr.
$= [1x + (-8x)] + [(-4) + (-3)]$ Assoc. Prop. of Add.
$= [1 + (-8)]x + (-4) + (-3)$ Dist. Prop.
$= -7x + (-4) + (-3)$ add.
$= -7x + (-7)$ add.
$= -7x - 7$ def. of subtr.

49. $8b + 7a - 4b - 9a$
$= 8b + 7a + (-4b) + (-9a)$ def. of subtr.
$= 8b + (-4b) + 7a + (-9a)$ Comm. Prop. of Add.
$= [8b + -4b] + [7a + -9a]$ Assoc. Prop. of Add.
$= [8 + (-4)]b + [7 + (-9)]a$ Dist. Prop.
$= 4b + (-2)a$ add.
$= 4b - 2a$ def. of subtr.

51. $\begin{bmatrix} 9 & -13 \\ 19 & -1 \end{bmatrix}$ **53.** $\begin{bmatrix} 3.1 & -0.7 & 21 \\ -4.9 & -4.7 & -2.1 \\ -1 & -7 & 8 \end{bmatrix}$ **55.** true **57.** true

Chapter Review pp. 67–69

1. term **2.** evaluate **3.** algebraic expression **4.** rational **5.** absolute value **6.** matrix **7.** reciprocal **8.** rational number **9.** x-coordinate **10.** scatter plot **11.** neg. correlation **12.** power **13.** Let n = the number, $5 + 3n$. **14.** Let n = the number, $30 - n$. **15.** Let n = the number, $\frac{7}{n}$. **16.** Let n = the number, $n(12)$. **17.** 9 **18.** 64 **19.** 4 **20.** 8 **21.** real numbers, rational numbers **22.** real numbers, irrational numbers **23.** real numbers, rational numbers **24.** real numbers, rational numbers, natural numbers, whole numbers, integers **25.** real numbers, rational numbers, natural numbers, whole numbers, integers **26.** −17 **27.** −5 **28.** 9.9 **29.** 24.9

30. −12 **31.** 0 **32.** 10 **33.** −40 **34.** $-\frac{5}{9}$ **35.** 2 **36.** $-\frac{5}{4}$ **37.** $\frac{23}{18}$ **38.** $4m + 3$ **39.** $b + 10$ **40.** $-5w + 20$ **41.** $36 - 27j$ **42.** $-3 + 10y$ **43.** $-2r + 1$ **44.** $35b + 5$ **45.** $7 - 25v$ **46.** $9t - \frac{6}{5}$ **47.** $-18 + 9m$ **48.** $-4 + x$ **49.** $10g + 1.5$ **50.** Assoc. Prop. of Add. **51.** Ident. Prop. of Add. **52.** Comm. Prop. of Mult. **53.** Dist. Prop.

54. $19 + 56\left(\frac{1}{56}\right) = 19 + 1$ Inv. Prop. of Mult.
$= 20$ add.

55. $-12p + 45 - 7p$
$= -12p + 45 + (-7p)$ def. of subtr.
$= -12p + (-7p) + 45$ Comm. Prop. of Add.
$= [-12 + (-7)]p + 45$ Dist. Prop.
$= -19p + 45$ add.

56. $24abc - 24bac$
$= 24abc - 24abc$ Comm. Prop. of Mult.
$= 24abc + (-24abc)$ def. of subtr.
$= [24 + (-24)]abc$ Dist. Prop.
$= (0)abc$ Inv. Prop. of Add.
$= 0$ Mult. Prop. of Zero

57. $4 \cdot 13 \cdot 25 \cdot 1$
$= 4 \cdot 25 \cdot 13 \cdot 1$ Comm. Prop. of Mult.
$= (4 \cdot 25) \cdot (13 \cdot 1)$ Assoc. Prop. of Mult.
$= 100 \cdot 13$ mult.
$= 1300$ mult.

58. (−4, 1) **59.** (2, −2) **60.** (3, 0) **61.** (−1, −1)

62. 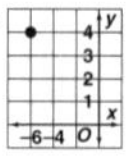

63. 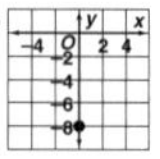

64. 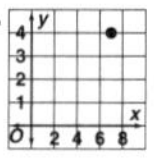

65a. 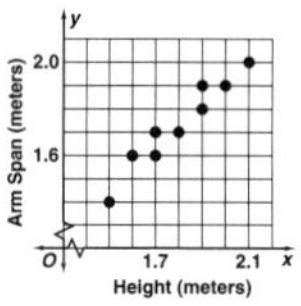

b. pos. correlation

Chapter 2

Lesson 2-1 pp. 77–80

EXERCISES **1.** 8 **3.** 13 **11.** 4 **13.** −57 **19.** $38\frac{3}{4} + g = 41\frac{1}{2}$; $2\frac{3}{4}$ in. **21.** 500 **23.** −18 **29.** −9 **31.** −10 **41.** −15 **43.** 8 **53.** No; 96.26 is close to 100 and 62.74 is close to 60, so the difference is close to 40. **57.** $-\frac{3}{8}$ **71.** 189 = e − 1048; 1237 engineers **73.** $17x = 106.25$, \$6.25 **77.** 44 **79.** 92 **91.** *A* **92.** *C* **93.** *B* **94.** *D* **95.** $5a - 15$ **96.** $-12 - 2y$ **97.** $9 + \frac{1}{2}m$ **98.** $8ac - 10c$ **99.** 6 **100.** 41 **101.** −13

Lesson 2-2 pp. 84–86

EXERCISES **1.** −10 **3.** −1 **17.** $2n + 4028 = 51{,}514$; 23,743 books **19.** $39.95 + 0.35m = 69.70$; 85 min **21.** −16 **23.** −85 **37.** Add. Prop. of Eq., Simplify., Mult. Prop. of Eq., Simplify. **39.** Subtr. Prop. of Eq., Simplify., Div. Prop. of Eq., Simplify. **41.** 75 **43.** 1

53. $7 - 3k - 7 = -14 - 7$ Subtr. Prop. of Eq.
$-3k = -21$ Simplify.
$\frac{-3k}{-3} = \frac{-21}{-3}$ Div. Prop. of Eq.
$k = 7$ Simplify.

55. $\frac{-y}{2} + 14 - 14 = -1 - 14$ Subtr. Prop. of Eq.
$\frac{-y}{2} = -15$ Simplify.
$\frac{-y}{2}(-2) = -15(-2)$ Mult. Prop. of Eq.
$y = 30$ Simplify.

57. $0.8c - 500 = 4650$; \$6437.50 **59.** 43 **61.** 2 **67.** 15.5 **69.** 31.5 **71.** The neg. sign was dropped; −1. **87.** 12 **88.** 15 **89.** −9 **90.** 6 **91.** 33 **92.** $11\frac{2}{5}$ **93.** 6 **94.** 4 **95.** 6 **96.** −11 **97.** 12

Lesson 2-3 pp. 91–94

EXERCISES **1.** 9 **3.** $5\frac{4}{7}$ **11.** $x + 9 + x = 25$; 8 ft by 9 ft **13.** 8 **21.** 11 **23.** 46 **31.** 21 **33.** 3.5 **39.** 2 **41.** 5 **55.** $4\frac{2}{3}$ **57.** 92 mi **61.** 25 **75.** 16 **77.** −19 **83.** 150 **85.** 90 **89.** 27 **91.** −4

Lesson 2-4 pp. 98–100

EXERCISES **1.** 9 **3.** 3 **17.** 200 min **19.** 8 ft **21a.** Answers may vary. Sample:
0: $9 = 9$
3: $-9 = -9$
−4: $33 = 33$
−6: $45 = 45$ **b.** identity

23. no solution **25.** identity **29.** 0 **31.** 10 **39.** $1200 + 9b = 25b$; 75 bags **41.** $a = 3, b = 5, c = 7, d = 11$ **43.** $a = 3, b = 6, c = 5, d = \frac{1}{3}$ **45.** The student subtracted y from both sides instead of adding y to both sides; 5.3. **65.** −4 **67.** $-6\frac{2}{3}$ **71.** $-\frac{4}{5}, -\frac{5}{8}, -\frac{3}{5}$ **73.** 8.02, 8.1, 8.3

Lesson 2-5 pp. 107–110

EXERCISES **1a.** Let w = width **b.** $\ell = w + 3$ **c.** $2w + 2(w + 3) = 30$; 6 **d.** 9 in. **3.** 9 cm; 18 cm

5. C 7a. Let n = the first integer. b. 2 c. $n + 2$ d. $n + n + 2 = 56$; 27, 29 11. $1\frac{17}{30}$ h 13a. x; $3 - x$ b. $320x = 280(3 - x)$, $1\frac{2}{5}$ h 15. 15 mi/h; 20 mi/h 17. 14 cm 19. −31, −29, −27 41. 0 43. $-\frac{1}{3}$ 47. −12 49. 54

Lesson 2-6 pp. 111–113

EXERCISES 1. $r = \frac{C}{2\pi}$ 3. $\ell = \frac{P}{2} - w$ 9. $y = -2x + 5$ 11. $y = -4x + 3$ 17. $x = \frac{c}{d}$ 19. $z = a + y$ 25a. $H = \frac{N}{7L}$ b. 11 ft 27a. $p = \frac{I}{rt}$ b. \$3000 c. If the interest at 3.5% for 4 yr is \$420, the principal is \$3000.00. 29. $b = \frac{A}{h}$ 31. $p = \frac{r + b}{a}$ 41a. $n = \frac{S}{180} + 2$ b. 5; 7; 4; 9 51. 71, 72, 73 53. [−60 9] 55. $\begin{bmatrix} -15.6 & 27 & 3 \\ 0 & 24 & -28.5 \end{bmatrix}$

Extension pp. 116–117

1. $SA = 2\pi rh + 2\pi r^2$ 3. 340 in.^{2} 9. $V = \ell wh$ 11. 282.74 ft^3

Lesson 2-7 pp. 121–123

EXERCISES 1. 12; 11; 10; median 3. 63; 52; none; median 5. 5.9 7. 125 9. 18 11. 20

15.

15	3 7
16	
17	5 6
18	4 6

15 | 3 means 15.3

17.

0	2 8
1	4
2	2 6
3	5
4	3 5

0 | 2 means 0.2

19. Type A: 0.30, 0.31, 0.23 and 0.31, 0.18; Type B: 0.4175, 0.44, 0.31, 0.24 21. −3.1, −2, −1 and −2, 15 37. $x = y - 4$ 39. $x = \frac{y - 4}{10}$ 41. −144 43. $-\frac{2}{3}$

Chapter Review pp. 125–127

1. identity 2. solution 3. inverse operations 4. Solutions of equivalent equations 5. consecutive integers 6. C 7. D 8. A 9. B 10. 16 11. −36 12. 31 13. 24 14. 26 15. 4.25 16. 12 17. 2 18. 4 19. 3 20. 5 21. 3 22. 2 23. 11 24. $\frac{1}{2}$ 25. −9 26. 18 27. −12 28. 9 29. −10 30. Let x = number of people; $6x + 3 = 27$; 4 people

31. $314 = -n + 576$
$314 - 576 = -n + 576 - 576$ Subtr. Prop. of Eq.
$-262 = -n$ Simplify.
$-1(-262) = -1(-n)$ Mult. Prop. of Eq.
$262 = n$ Simplify.

32. $-\frac{1}{4}w - 1 = 6$
$-\frac{1}{4}w - 1 + 1 = 6 + 1$ Add. Prop. of Eq.
$-\frac{1}{4}w = 7$ Simplify.
$-4(-\frac{1}{4}w) = -4(7)$ Mult. Prop. of Eq.
$w = -28$ Simplify.

33. $3h - 4 = 5$
$3h - 4 + 4 = 5 + 4$ Add. Prop. of Eq.
$3h = 9$ Simplify.
$\frac{3h}{3} = \frac{9}{3}$ Div. Prop. of Eq.
$h = 3$ Simplify.

34. −125 35. 6 36. −7 37. −18 38. 4 39. $-\frac{1}{2}$ 40. $\frac{3}{2}$ 41. 2 42. 0 43. 0 44. $\frac{3}{2}$ 45. −2 46. no solution 47. identity 48. 20 49. 10 50. identity 51. no solution 52. $2x + 2(x - 6) = 72$; width = 15 cm, length = 21 cm 53. $4.25x + 2.50 = 15.25$; 3 games 54. $b = \frac{2A}{h}$ 55. $x = \frac{y - b}{m}$ 56. $d = \frac{C}{\pi}$ 57a. $I = \frac{E}{R}$ b. 40 amperes 58. 1.9 h or 1 h 54 min 59. 36.75 m 60. 193, 194, 195 61. −68, −66, −64 62. 6.75 h or 6 h 45 min 63. 52 64. 85, 85, 87 65. 30.6, 27, 24 66. 2.3, 2.3, 2.3 67. 42.1, 42, 37 68. 3.8 km 69. 19 items 70. 6 people 71. 18, 18.4, 19.9

Chapter 3

Lesson 3-1 pp. 136–138

EXERCISES 1. yes 3. yes 5. no 9a. no b. no c. yes 11a. no b. no c. no 15. C 17. D 19. −1 0 1 2 3 21. −7 −6 −5 −4 −3 −2

27–35. Choice of variable may vary. 27. $x > -3$ 29. $x \geq 1$ 33. Let s = number of students. $s \leq 48$ 35. Let w = number of watts. $w \leq 60$ 39. b is greater than 0. 41. z is greater than or equal to −5.6. 51. Answers may vary. Sample: For $x = -1$, $3(-1) + 1 = -3 + 1 = -2$. $-2 \not> 0$.

55. $b \leq -5$ −6 −5 −4 −3 −2 −1 0

57. $a < 5$ 2 3 4 5 6

59. −2 −1 0 1 2 61. 0 1 2 3 4 5

63. −2 0 2 4 6 8 64. "At least" is translated as ≥. "At most" is translated as ≤. 65. $x \geq 2451$ 81. $y = 5x + 4$ 87. $I = \frac{V}{R}$ 89. $b = P - a - c$ 91. Commutative Property of Multiplication

Lesson 3-2 pp. 142–144

EXERCISES 1. 5 3. 4.3 5. $t < 1$ −2 −1 0 1 2

Selected Answers

7. $d \geq 10$ 8 9 10 11 12 13

21. $\frac{5}{3}$ 23. $w \leq 5$; 3 4 5 6 7 8

25. $b > -7$; −8 −6 −4 −2 0 2

39. $s + 637 \leq 2000$, \$1363 41. $r + 17 + 12 \geq 50$, 21 reflectors 43. Subtract 9 from each side. 45. $w \geq 11$ 47. $y < 3.1$ 71. at least \$15.50 75. $x \geq 1$ 77. $t \leq -3$ 99. Let c = length of octopus in feet. $c \leq 10$ 101. Let a = average. $a \geq 90$ 103. 13 105. −12 113. 7 115. 31

Lesson 3-3 pp. 149–151

EXERCISES 1. $t \geq -4$; −6 −4 −2 0 2

3. $w \leq -2$; −3 −2 −1 0 1

17. $t < -3$; −5 −4 −3 −2 −1 0 1

19. $w \leq -5$; −8 −6 −4 −2 0 2

29. $4.5c \geq 300$, 67 cars 31–33. Answers may vary. Samples are given. 31. −2, −3, −4, −5 33. −3, −4, −5, −6 39. Multiply each side by −4 and reverse the inequality symbol. 41. Divide each side by 5. 45. −2 47. 4 51. x and y are equal. 53–55. Estimates may vary. 53. $j > -6$ 55. $s \geq 28$ 59. $d \leq -7$ 61. $s < -\frac{1}{4}$ 75. Yes; in each case, y is greater than 6. 91. $w < -\frac{1}{8}$ 93. $d > 4$ 99. $n = -2$ 101. Prop. of Opposites 103. Ident. Prop. of Add.

Lesson 3-4 pp. 155–158

EXERCISES 1. $d \leq 4$ 3. $x > -2\frac{1}{2}$ 11. $27 \geq 2s + 8$ and $s \leq 9.5$, so the two equal sides must be no longer than 9.5 cm. 13. $j \geq 1$ 15. $h > 5$ 23. $t \leq -1$ 25. $n \geq 2$ 35. $q \leq -2$ 37. $x < 1\frac{1}{3}$ 41. Subtract 7 from each side. 43. Add 2 to each side, then multiply each side by −5, and reverse the inequality sign. 47. $6 - (r + 3) < 15$, $r > -12$ 49. $3(z + 2) > 12$, $z > 2$ 53a. maximum b. no more than 135 55. E 57. A 61. $r < 5\frac{1}{2}$ 63. $s \leq 4.4$ 79. Add $2x$ to each side rather than subtract $2x$, so $x \leq \frac{2}{5}$. 93. $y \geq -8$ 95. $t \geq -3$ 101. −16 103. 24

Extension p. 160

1. −5 −4 −3 −2 −1 0 1 3. −1 0 1 2 3 4

Lesson 3-5 pp. 163–165

EXERCISES 1. $-4 < x$ and $x < 6$ or $-4 < x < 6$; −6 −4 −2 0 2 4 6 8

3. $23 < c < 23.5$; 22 23 24

5. $-5 < j < 5$; −10 −5 0 5 10

7. $2 < n \leq 6$; −2 0 2 4 6 8

21. $x < 3$ or $x > 7$; −2 0 2 4 6 8

23. $b < 100$ or $b > 300$; 0 100 300

25. $k < -5$ or $k > -1$; −6 −5 −4 −3 −2 −1 0 1

27. $a \leq 4$ or $a > 5$; 2 3 4 5 6 7

35. $x < -3$ or $x \geq 2$ 37. $-4 \leq x \leq 3$ 39. $h < -7$ or $h > 4$ 41. $r < 16$ or $r > 25$ 45. all real numbers except 5 47. $2.5 < x < 7.5$ 49. $7 < x < 49$ 51. $66 \leq C \leq 88$ 53. Charlotte: $29 \leq C \leq 90$, Detroit: $15 \leq D \leq 83$ 65. $n \leq 3$ 67. $x = -1$ 69. identity

Lesson 3-6 pp. 167–169

EXERCISES 1. −2, 2 3. $-\frac{1}{2}, \frac{1}{2}$ 13. 3, 13 15. −3, 1 23. $k < -2.5$ or $k > 2.5$; −4 −3 −2 −1 0 1 2 3 4

25. $-8 < x < 2$; −8 −6 −4 −2 0 2

35. between 12.18 mm and 12.30 mm, inclusive

37. −9, 9 39. $-1\frac{1}{2}, 1\frac{1}{2}$ 53. $|n| > 7.5$

55. $|n + 1| \geq 3$ 57. 39%, 45% 63. $|x - 2| = 4$

65. $|x - 12\frac{1}{2}| = 3\frac{1}{2}$ 87. $-282 \leq e \leq 20{,}320$

89. −3 91. 5 95. −2.5, −2, 0, 3, π 97. 0.001, 0.009, 0.01, 0.011

Extension p. 173

1. Symmetric Prop. of Equality 7. Add. Prop. of Ineq., Add. Prop. of Ineq., Transitive Prop. of Ineq.

Chapter Review pp. 175–177

1. C 2. B 3. A 4. C 5. D 6. −1 0 1 2 3 4

7. −6 −5 −4 −3 −2 −1 0 1

8. 5 6 7 8 9 10 11 12

9. −2 −1 0 1 2 3 4

10. $n < -2$ 11. $n \geq -3.5$ 12. $n > -6$ 13. $n \geq 2$ 14. Let p = number of people, $p \geq 600$. 15. Let n = number of people, $n \leq 15$. 16. Let t = temperature in degrees Fahrenheit, $t < 32$.

17. $h > -1$; −3 −2 −1 0 1 2

18. $t < -5$; −8 −7 −6 −5 −4 −3

19. $m \geq -3$; −4 −3 −2 −1 0 1

20. $w \geq -2$; −4 −3 −2 −1 0 1

21. $q > -2.5$; −4 −3 −2 −1 0 1

22. $y > -14$; −15 −10 −5 0 5

23. $n \leq 15$; −5 0 5 10 15 20

24. $d \geq 4$; −2 0 2 4 6

25. $-2 \leq t$; −6 −4 −2 0 2 4 6

26. $0 < c$; −2 −1 0 1 2

27. $2.5 \geq u$; −1 0 1 2 3 4

28. $-9 < p$; −10 −8 −6 −4 −2 0 2

29. $3.50 + 2.75 + x \leq 12.00$, $x \leq 5.75$

30. $7.25h \geq 200$, $h \geq 27.586$ You must work at least 28 h.

31. $n > -2$ 32. $k \leq -\frac{1}{2}$ 33. $b < 40$ 34. $c \leq -2$ 35. $m < -6$ 36. $t > 3$ 37. $x \geq 2$ 38. $y \leq -56$ 39. $x < \frac{8}{3}$ 40. $190 + 0.04x \geq 500$, $x \geq 7750$

41. −4 −2 0 2 4 42. −4 −3 −2 −1 0 1 2 3

43. −4 −2 0 2 4 6

44. $-2 \leq z < 4$, −4 −2 0 2 4 6

45. $-\frac{5}{2} \leq d < 4$, −3 −2 −1 0 1 2 3 4 5

46. $-\frac{3}{2} \leq b < 0$, −4 −3 −2 −1 0 1

47. $t \leq -2$ or $t \geq 7$, −2 0 2 4 6 8

48. $2 \leq a < 5$, 1 2 3 4 5 6

49. $2 \leq a < 4$, 1 2 3 4 5 6 50. $75 \leq t \leq 89$

51. $|n + 2| > 3$ 52. $|n - 12| \leq 5$ 53. 5 or −5 54. $n \leq -6$ or $n \geq 2$ 55. $-3 \leq x \leq 3$ 56. $-9.6 < m < 9.6$ 57. $x < 3$ or $x > 4$ 58. 6.5 or −12.5 59. 8 60. all real numbers 61. no solution 62. $k < -7$ or $k > -3$ 63. −5 or 1 64. $z \leq -0.25$ or $z \geq 0.25$ 65. $2.74 \leq d \leq 2.86$ 66. $19.6 \leq \ell \leq 20.4$

Chapter 4

Lesson 4-1 pp. 185–188

EXERCISES 1. \$9.50/h 3. 131 cars/week 7. A 9. B 11. 480 13. 10,800 15. 11.25 17. 25.2 31. 105.6 km 33. $8\frac{11}{12}$ 35. $-3\frac{1}{2}$ 39. 18.75 41. 18.25 45. 15 mi/h 47. 1 mi/h 51. 10.5 mm 53. 3 55. −16 61. −8.4 63. about 750 students 67. 4 people/mi^2, 2485 people/mi^2, 78 people/mi^2

71. 48 v 83. 0 2 4 6 8 10 12 14

85. −5 −4 −3 −2 −1 0 1 2 3

89. s = students, $s \geq 235$ 91. w = weight (lb), $w > 20$ 93. 0 1 2 3 4 5 6 95. 6 97. −5

Lesson 4-2 pp. 192–195

EXERCISES 1. $\overline{AB} \cong \overline{PQ}, \overline{BC} \cong \overline{QR}, \overline{CA} \cong \overline{RP}$; $\angle A \cong \angle P, \angle B \cong \angle Q, \angle C \cong \angle R$ 3. 3.125 ft 5. 80 in. 9. 12 ft 11. 87.5 mi 13. 325.5 mi 17. 4 in. by 6 in. 19. 2 in. by 3 in. 21. 33.75 in. 25. 9 ft by 12 ft 27. 216 ft^2 33. $a = 8, b = 6, c = 10$ 35. 400,400 km 41. 4.5 43. $-22\frac{6}{7}$ 45. $b < -4$ 47. $m < -4$

Lesson 4-3 pp. 200–202

EXERCISES 1. 50% 3. $33\frac{1}{3}$% 7. 8 9. 21 13. $\frac{40}{100} = \frac{20}{x}$, 50 15. $\frac{15}{100} = \frac{24}{x}$, 160 21. $25 = 0.50x$; 50 23. $45 = n \cdot 60$; 75% 27. 200% 29. 300% 33. 100 35. 150 39. $\frac{75}{100} = \frac{3}{x}$, 4 41. $x = 0.002(900)$, 1.8 45. 62; 50% is 61 and 51.3% > 50%. 47. 73; 10% is 74 and 9.79% < 10%. 49. \$297.00 51. \$3896.00 53a. \$74.25 b. 3.75% c. 6 yr 55. \$1250.00 57. 2 yr 67. $13\frac{1}{3}$ mi 69. 90 mi

71. $b < -4$; −7 −6 −5 −4 −3 −2

73. $h > -21$; −22 −20 −18 −16 −14

Selected Answers

Lesson 4-4 pp. 207–209

EXERCISES 1. 50%; increase 3. 25%; increase 13. 39% 15. 0.5 ft 17. 0.005 g 19. 19.25 cm^2, 29.25 cm^2 21. 46.75 in.^{2}, 61.75 in.^{2} 25. 25% 27. 12.5% 29a. 48 cm^3 b. 74.375 cm^3 c. 28.125 cm^3 d. 26.375 cm^3 e. 55% 31. 22%; decrease 33. 175%; increase 39. 2% 41. 1 mm 45. 24.5 cm^2, 25.5 cm^2 47. 54.1 in.^{2}, 54.3 in.^{2} 49. 11% 61–63. Equations may vary. 61. $\frac{x}{100} = \frac{13}{15}$, 87% 63. $\frac{x}{100} = \frac{96}{32}$, 300% 67. $q \geq -17$

Lesson 4-5 pp. 214–217

EXERCISES 1. $\frac{1}{2}$ 3. $\frac{1}{6}$ 11. $\frac{5}{6}$ 13. 1 15. 24% 17. 15% 23. $\frac{1}{6}$ 25. $\frac{1}{3}$ 27. $\frac{1}{2}$ 29. $\frac{1}{450}$ 33. 1% 37a. $\frac{3}{4}$ b. $\frac{2}{5}$ c. $\frac{3}{20}$ 39. $\frac{3}{16}$ 41. $\frac{7}{16}$ 43. $\frac{1}{3}$ 55. 25%; increase 57. 40%; increase

61. $-3 \leq t \leq 4$; −4 −3 −2 −1 0 1 2 3 4

63. $h < 2$ or $h > 5$; 0 1 2 3 4 5 6

67. 6.17, 5, 5 69.

3	4 7 9
4	1 9
6	5
7	1

Technology p. 218

1. Answers may vary. Sample: Yes, as long as they are 40% of the data, any 4 numbers will suffice.

Lesson 4-6 pp. 222–224

EXERCISES 1. $\frac{1}{36}$ 3. $\frac{1}{18}$ 9. $\frac{4}{81}$ 11. $\frac{1}{9}$ 15. $\frac{2}{11}$ 17. $\frac{1}{55}$ 21. $\frac{2}{7}$ 23. $\frac{1}{6}$ 25. $\frac{1}{9}$ 31. Indep.; the data set hasn't changed. 33a. 0.58 b. 0.003248 35. 0.0036 37. $\frac{1}{10}$ 51. $\frac{4}{21}$ 53. $\frac{8}{21}$ 55. 2 57. No solution; abs. value can't be negative.

Extension p. 225

1. Not good; not everyone in a barber shop or salon is a teenager. 3. No; the sample was biased toward athletic activities such as biking.

Chapter Review pp. 227–229

1. rate 2. cross products 3. percent of change 4. greatest possible error 5. an outcome 6. complement of an event 7. independent 8. sample space 9. unit rate 10. percent of increase 11. 150 mi/h 12. 3.41 mi/h 13. 0.23 mi/h 14. 2 15. 2.3 16. −6 17. 20 18. 6 19. 5 20. 7.5 m 21. 19.5 m 22. 36 ft 23. 12.9 24. 2.5 25. 800% 26. 850 27. 3.75% 28. \$220 29. about 13%; increase 30. 25%; decrease 31. about 33%; decrease 32. Answers may vary. Sample: It costs a restaurant \$.11 to make a cup of tea, which it sells for \$.75. The percent of increase is about 582%. 33. about 5.4% 34. 0 35. $\frac{5}{6}$ 36. $\frac{1}{3}$ 37. $\frac{1}{6}$ 38a. $\frac{1}{4}$ b. Sample: P(not 3 heads) means the chances of getting 0, 1, 2, or 4 heads. 39. $\frac{11}{14}$ 40. dependent; $\frac{2}{45}$ 41. independent; $\frac{1}{20}$ 42. Answers may vary. Sample: In probability, two events are dependent if the outcome of one influences the outcome of the other. In everyday language, if one person is dependent on another, the first person relies on the second for support. 43. Indep.; the result of one number cube does not affect the other. 44. Dep.; once you select one sock, there are fewer socks when you make the second selection.

Chapter 5

Lesson 5-1 pp. 238–240

EXERCISES 1. Labels may vary. Sample is given.

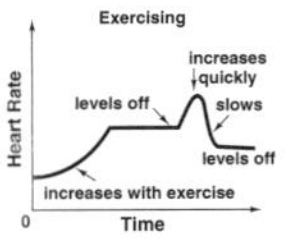

5.

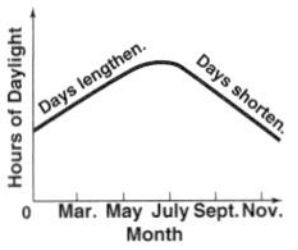

9. C; the temperature increases steadily and then alternates cooling and warming as the oven turns off and on during a cooking cycle.

Selected Answers

Page 811

11a.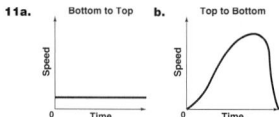

No; the graphs are different because you have a constant speed traveling up but not down.

15a.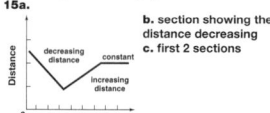
b. section showing the distance decreasing
c. first 2 sections

27. $\frac{1}{36}$ 29. $\frac{1}{12}$ 33. $x < 8$ 35. $x > -4$
39. 17 41. −15

Lesson 5-2 pp. 244–246
EXERCISES 1. {4, 5, 6}, {3, 6, 7, 19} 3. {−2, 2, 3}, {−3, −2, 3} 7. yes 9. no 11. no 13. yes 15. 4 17. 9 23. {0.5, 53} 25. {−27, −7, −2, 8, 48} 27. no 29. yes; {−4, −1, 0, 3}; {−4} 35. {−13.8, −1, 5} 37. {−0.75, 0, 12.69} 39. no 55. 30 mi 57. 7.5 mi 61. 33.5, 33.5, none, 3 63. $\frac{52}{9}$, 5, 5, 11

Lesson 5-3 pp. 249–252
EXERCISES 1. C 3. B
5–7. Tables may vary. Samples are given.
5. 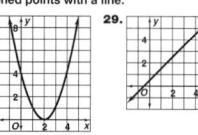 $y = -x + 2$
7.
13a. $M = 3.5h$
d. (Answers may vary. Sample is given.) about 8.5 h

15. 17.
25. Answers may vary. Sample: Make a table to find values for $f(x)$ when $x = -2$, 0, and 2. Then graph the ordered pairs $(x, f(x))$ and join the graphed points with a line.
27. 29.
41a. $.71 b. about 12 min 43. B 53. {−5, 1, 11.5}
55. {−6.5, 4, 10}
63. No sol.; $9 = 10 - 1$ and $|b|$ cannot be −1.
65. −7, 7 71. 48 km 73. 100.8 km

Technology p. 253
EXERCISES 1. {−9, 6, 15, 27} 3. $y = 3$, $x = 1.5$
5. $y = 2.16$, $x = -1.8$

Lesson 5-4 pp. 256–259
EXERCISES 1. B 3. C 11. $d(n) = 45n$
13. $e(n) = 6.37n$ 17a. $f(x) = 0.19x$ b. $1.52
19. $f(x) = 1000x$ 21a. $C(a) = 10a + 1$ b. $31
c. 61; the total cost of 12 books
25–27. Tables may vary. Samples are given.
25. 27. $f(x) = \frac{1}{2}x$
43. Tables may vary. Sample is given.
49. 2%; increase
51. 83%; decrease

Lesson 5-5 pp. 264–267
EXERCISES 1. no 3. yes; −2 11. $y = \frac{1}{5}x$
13. $y = \frac{5}{8}x$ 23. Choices of variables may vary.

Page 812

$E(h) = 7.10h$ 25. no 27a. $\frac{50}{20}$ or $\frac{5}{2}$ b. $\frac{50}{20} = \frac{130}{20}$, 52 lb
29. $y = \frac{1}{8}x$ 31. $y = -\frac{36}{25}x$ 33. $y = 9x$
41. 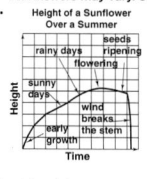 $y = \frac{5}{2}x$
45a. $\frac{32}{5}$ b. $b = \frac{3}{12}w$ 61. $y = \frac{1}{3}x$
63. $y = \frac{1}{8}x$ 65. $c \le -1.8$
67. $a \ge 16.6$

Lesson 5-6 pp. 270–272
EXERCISES 1. "Add 2 to the previous term"; 12, 14. 3. "Add 2 to the first term, 3 to the second term and continue, adding 1 more each time"; 18, 24. 13. 13 15. −11 23. −3, 15, 39 25. 17, 44, 80 35. $3\frac{1}{4}$, $3\frac{1}{2}$ 37. $\frac{4}{9}$, $\frac{4}{81}$ 47. $4500, $4350, $4200, $4050, $3900; the balance after 4 payments 49. No; there is no common difference. 51. No; there is no common difference. 57. 4.5, −4.5, −22.5 59. 1, $2\frac{3}{4}$, $5\frac{1}{4}$ 63. value of new term = value of previous term + 6 65. value of new term = value of previous term − 2.5 83. $y = 24x$ 85. $y = 0.14x$ 91. {−19, −3, 9} 93. {2, 4, 10}

Chapter Review
1. C 2. D 3. A 4. E 5. B 6. G 7. F
8. Answers may vary. Sample: A computer rental costs $2.50/h. If you start with a fixed amount of money, the longer you work on the computer, the less money you will have left.
9. Answers may vary. Sample: A residential thermostat senses when the temperature in the room falls below the set level. The heater is turned on until the temperature is 3°F above the set level. The heater is then turned off. The graph shows the air temperature rising while the heater is working, and falling after the heater is turned off.
10. Answers may vary. Sample: An elevator is on the second floor. Someone gets in, goes to the 11th floor, and gets off.
11–14. Answers may vary. Samples are given.
11. Height of a Sunflower Over a Summer

12. Number of People in a Restaurant
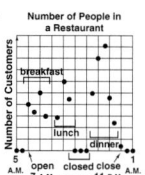
13. Number of Vehicles that Enter the School Parking Lot
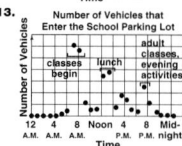
14. Bags of Peanuts Sold During a Baseball Game
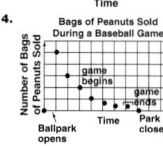
15. {−23, −7, −3, 13} 16. {1, 3, 3.5, 5.5}
17. {1, 2, 17, 26} 18. {−10, 2, 5, 17} 19. no
20. yes 21. yes 22. no 23. A relation is a function when each value of the domain corresponds to exactly one value of the range.
24–27. Tables may vary. Samples are given.
24. 25.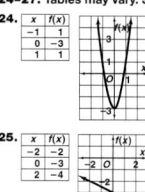

Page 813

26.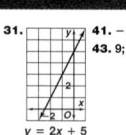
27. 28. $f(x) = x + 1$ 29. $f(x) = -x$ 30. $f(x) = x + 3.5$ 31. $S(r) = 0.1r$ 32. $c = 27 + 0.2b$ 33. yes; −3 34. no 35. no 36. yes; $\frac{2}{5}$
37. $y = \frac{1}{5}x$ 38. $y = x$ 39. $y = 2x$ 40. $y = -3x$ 41. yes; $y = -2x$ 42. no 43. yes; $y = \frac{1}{8}x$
44. 68.4 kg 45. 132.5 lb 46. "Add −9 to the previous term"; 63, 54, 45. 47. "Add 3 to the previous term"; 17, 20, 23. 48. "Add 11 to the previous term"; 56, 67, 78. 49. $-\frac{1}{2}$; 7, $6\frac{1}{2}$, 6
50. −2; −4, −6, −8 51. 13; 53, 66, 79
52. 3, 13, 17 53. 10, 25, 31 54. 4.5, 12, 15
55. −2, −17, −23 56. yes; 42, 49, 56 57. no

Chapter 6
Lesson 6-1 pp. 282–289
EXERCISES 1. 3; the temperature increases 3°F each hour. 3. $-\frac{1}{15}$ gal/mi 7. $\frac{1}{2}$ 9. $\frac{2}{3}$ 11. 2 13. $-\frac{3}{2}$
23. undefined 25. undefined 27. $\frac{9}{10}$ in./month
29. 30 mi/hr 31. $\frac{2}{3}$ 33. −20
37. 41a. $\frac{2}{3}$ b. $\frac{2}{3}$ 45. JK: $-\frac{1}{2}$; KL: 2; ML: $-\frac{1}{2}$; MJ: 2 49. −6 51. 4 55. true 57. true
61a. 111; $111/h b. 56 customers per hour 77. $p = 4.95q - 232$
79. $\frac{1}{2}$ 83. −4 85. 7

Technology p. 290
1a. $y = 2x + 1$ b. $y = \frac{1}{2}x + 1$ 3. Answers may vary. Sample: Changing m affects the slope of the graph. 5. (0, 1); (0, −2); (0, 2)

Lesson 6-2 pp. 294–296
EXERCISES 1. −2; 1 3. 1; $-\frac{5}{4}$ 11. $y = 3x + 2$
13. $y = 1$ 23. $y = \frac{3}{4}x + 2$ 25. $y = \frac{1}{2}x + \frac{1}{2}$

29. 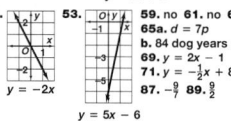 $y = \frac{2}{3}x - 1$
31. $y = 2x + 5$
41. −3; 2 43. 9; $\frac{1}{2}$
51. 53. $y = 5x - 6$ $y = -2x$
59. no 61. no 63. I
65a. $d = 7p$ b. 84 dog years
69. $y = 2x - 1$
71. $y = -\frac{1}{2}x + 8$ 87. $-\frac{9}{7}$ 89. $\frac{5}{2}$
91. 4.8 billion

Lesson 6-3 pp. 301–303
EXERCISES 1. 18; 9 3. −6; 30 11. C
13. 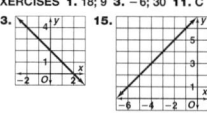 15.
19. horizontal 21. horizontal
23. 25. 27. $-3x + y = 1$ 29. $x - 2y = 6$
37a. Answers may vary. Sample: x = time walking; y = time running b. $3x + 8y = 15$
39. 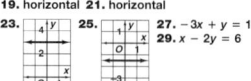 41.
47a. $3x + 7y = 28$
49. $y = \frac{2}{5}x + 10$
51. $y = -\frac{4}{5}x - 3$ 57. $-3x$ instead of $3x$
59. $y = -2$ 61. $x = -2$ 71. no 73. 5. 4 75. 4
77. −0.5

Page 814

Lesson 6-4 pp. 307–309
EXERCISES 1. 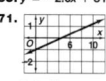 3.
11. $y - 2 = -\frac{2}{3}(x - 4)$ 13. $y + 7 = -\frac{3}{4}(x + 2)$
9–21. Answers may vary for the point indicated by the equation. 19. $y = 1(x + 1)$; $y = x + 1$
21. $y + 2 = -\frac{6}{5}(x - 4)$; $y = -\frac{6}{5}x + \frac{14}{5}$ 31. Yes; answers may vary. $y - 9 = -2(x + 4)$
33. no 35. no 37–39. Answers may vary for point indicated by the equation. 37. $y + 3 = \frac{5}{2}(x - 1)$ 39. $y - 4 = \frac{3}{2}(x - 1)$; $-3x + 2y = 5$
55. $y = -2.6x + 315.6$ 57. y-intercept changes
71. 73.
77. $\frac{2}{3}$; $\frac{3}{2}$ $\frac{1}{5}$; $\frac{11}{5}$ 79. −0.05; −3.35; −3.4

13a.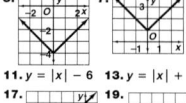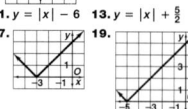
b. Answers may vary. Sample: $y = 0.9386x + 13{,}790$ c. 143,800,000 d. Answers may vary. Sample: No, the year is too far in the future.
17. $y = 0.37x - 28.66$; $12.04 billion
19a. (2, 3) and (6, 6); $y = 0.75x + 1.5$
b. $y = 0.75x + 1.21$ 25. $y - 5 = -x$
27. $y + 4 = -\frac{1}{2}(x - 3)$ 31. $x < 5$ 33. $x \le -5$

Lesson 6-5 pp. 314–316
EXERCISES 1. $\frac{1}{2}$ 3. 1 7. no, different slopes
9. yes, same slopes and different y-intercepts
13. $y = 6x$ 15. $y = -2x - 1$ 19. $-\frac{1}{2}$ 21. $-\frac{9}{5}$
25. $y = -\frac{1}{2}x$ 27. $y = 3x - 10$ 31. $y = \frac{5}{3}x + 1$
33. parallel 35. neither 43. $y = -\frac{4}{5}x - \frac{19}{5}$; $y = -\frac{4}{5}x + \frac{3}{5}$ 45. x; $y = 2x$ 49. about 5
51. Answers may vary. Sample: $\frac{5}{2} \cdot \left(-\frac{1}{5}\right) \ne -1$
55. No; the slopes are not neg. reciprocals.
57. False; the product of two positive numbers can't be −1. 61. The slope of $\overrightarrow{JK}$ is $\frac{1}{8}$. The slope of $\overrightarrow{KL}$ is −2. The slope of $\overrightarrow{LM}$ is $\frac{1}{8}$. The slope of $\overrightarrow{JM}$ is −4. The quadrilateral is not a parallelogram.
81. $y = -4x - 8$ 83. $y + 9 = -\frac{2}{3}(x + 1)$
85. −9; −17; −25 89. yes 91. yes

Lesson 6-6 pp. 320–323
EXERCISES 1–3. Trend lines may vary. Samples are given. 1. $y - 52.5 = 2(x - 91)$
3. $y - 16.4 = 0.64(x - 69.9)$
7. $y = -1.06x + 92.31$; −0.9701709306
9. $y = -2.29x + 613.93$; −0.8108238756

Lesson 6-7 pp. 327–329
EXERCISES 1. Answers may vary. Sample: same shape, shifted 3 units up 3. Answers may vary. Sample: same shape, shifted 7 units down
5. 7.
11. $y = |x| - 6$ 13. $y = |x| + 2$
17. 19.
23. $y = |x - 9|$ 25. $y = |x + \frac{5}{2}|$
29. 33. $y = -|x + 2.25|$ 35. $y = -|x - 4|$
37. 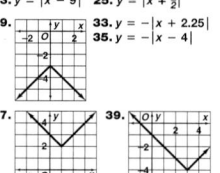 39.
49. $y = 5000x - 413{,}000$
51. $\begin{bmatrix} 12 & 6 \\ 2 & 6 \end{bmatrix}$ 53. $\begin{bmatrix} 2.5 & 14.0 \\ -2.0 & 10.7 \end{bmatrix}$

Top-left quadrant

Chapter Review pp. 331–333

1. perpendicular lines 2. parallel lines
3. translation 4. slope 5. y-intercept 6. 8 oz/mo
7. 3.375 in./wk 8. 5; the speed is 5 mi/h. 9. −1.25;
gasoline decreases 1.25 gal for each hour of
driving time. 10. 150; the height is at a
constant level of 150 ft. 11. $\frac{1}{4}$ 12. undefined 13. 1

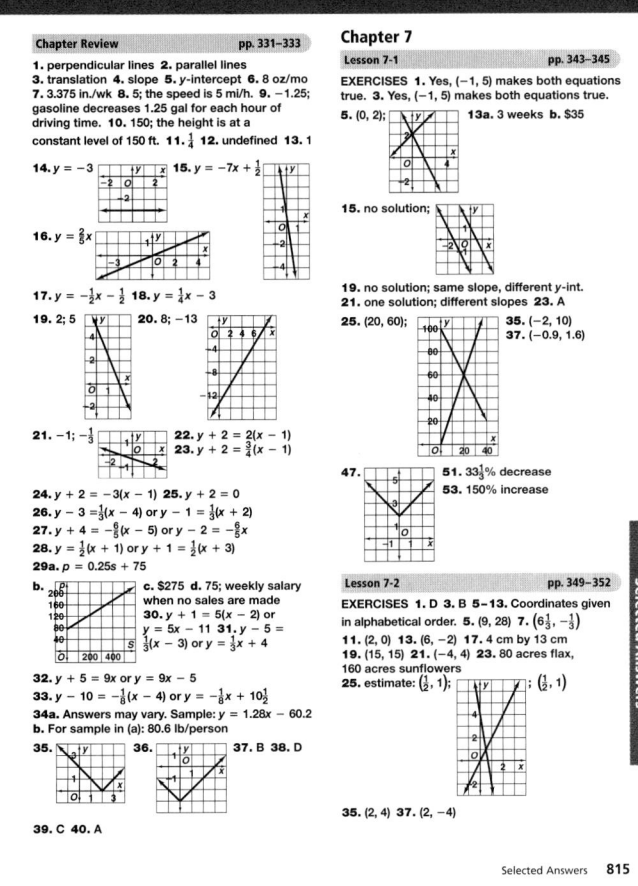

14. $y = -3$ 15. $y = -7x + \frac{1}{2}$

16. $y = \frac{2}{5}x$

17. $y = -\frac{1}{2}x - \frac{1}{2}$ 18. $y = \frac{1}{4}x - 3$

19. 2; 5 20. 8; −13

21. −1; $-\frac{1}{3}$ 22. $y + 2 = 2(x - 1)$
23. $y + 2 = \frac{3}{4}(x - 1)$

24. $y + 2 = -3(x - 1)$ 25. $y + 2 = 0$
26. $y - 3 = \frac{1}{3}(x - 4)$ or $y - 1 = \frac{1}{3}(x + 2)$
27. $y + 4 = -\frac{6}{5}(x - 1)$ or $y = -\frac{6}{5}x$
28. $y = \frac{1}{2}(x + 1)$ or $y + 1 = \frac{1}{2}(x + 3)$
29. $p = 0.25x + 75$
b. [graph] c. $275 d. 75; weekly salary
when no sales are made
30. $y + 1 = 5(x - 2)$ or
$y = 5x - 11$ 31. $y - 5 = \frac{1}{3}(x - 3)$ or $y = \frac{1}{3}x + 4$

32. $y + 5 = 9x$ or $y = 9x - 5$
33. $y - 10 = -\frac{1}{8}(x - 4)$ or $y = -\frac{1}{8}x + 10\frac{1}{2}$
34a. Answers may vary. Sample: $y = 1.28x - 60.2$
b. For sample in (a): 80.6 lb/person

35. [graph] 36. [graph] 37. B 38. D

39. C 40. A

Top-middle quadrant

Chapter 7

Lesson 7-1 pp. 343–345

EXERCISES 1. Yes, (−1, 5) makes both equations
true. 3. Yes, (−1, 5) makes both equations true.
5. (0, 2); [graph] 13a. 3 weeks b. $35

15. no solution; [graph]

19. no solution; same slope, different y-int.
21. one solution; different slopes 23. A
25. (20, 60); [graph] 35. (−2, 10)
37. (−0.9, 1.6)

47. [graph] 51. 33$\frac{1}{3}$% decrease
53. 150% increase

Lesson 7-2 pp. 349–352

EXERCISES 1. D 3. B 5–13. Coordinates given
in alphabetical order. 5. (9, 28) 7. $(6\frac{1}{3}, -\frac{1}{3})$
11. (2, 0) 13. (6, −2) 17. 4 cm by 13 cm
19. (15, 15) 21. (−4, 4) 23. 80 acres flax,
160 acres sunflowers
25. estimate: $(\frac{1}{2}, 1)$; [graph]; $(\frac{1}{2}, 1)$

35. (2, 4) 37. (2, −4)

Top-right quadrant

51. (12, 10); [graph] 55. [graph]

Lesson 7-3 pp. 356–359

EXERCISES 1. (1, 3) 3. (5, −17) 7a. $x + y = 20$,
$x - y = 4$ b. 12 and 8 9. (−5, 1) 11. $(-2, -\frac{6}{5})$
15a. $30w + \ell = 17.65$, $20w + 3\ell = 25.65$
b. $.39 for a wallet size, $5.95 for an 8 × 10
17. (−1, −3) 19. (2, −2) 23–25. Choice of
method may vary. Samples are given. 23. (−1, −2);
substitution; both solved for y 25. (10, 2);
substitution; one eq. solved for x 33. (10, −6)
35. (−15, −1) 39. 9 51. (6, 26) 53. (9, −5) 55. $\frac{2}{9}$
57. 71 59. −44

Technology pp. 360–361

1. [77] 3. $\begin{bmatrix} 624 & -2008 \\ 1442 & -512 \\ 125 & -1297 \end{bmatrix}$ 5. (5.6, 1.3)

7. (9.8, −36.6)

Lesson 7-4 pp. 365–368

EXERCISES 1a. $4a + 5b = 6.71$
b. $5a + 3b = 7.12$ c. pen: $1.19, pencil: $.39

3a.
a	b	24
0.04a	0.08b	0.05(24)

b. $a + b = 24$; $0.04a + 0.08b = 1.2$ c. 18 kg A,
6 kg B 5. 600 games 7a. $s + c = 2.75$
b. $s - c = 1.5$ c. 2.125 mi/h d. 0.625 mi/h
9–11. Answers may vary. Samples are given.
9. Substitution; one eq. is solved for t.
11. Elimination; subtract to eliminate m.
15a. $t = 99 - 3.5m$; $t = 0 + 2.5m$; $t = 41.25°$,
$m = 16.5$ min b. After 16.5 min, the temp. of
either piece will be 41.25°C. 19a. 42 mi/h
b. 12mi/h 29. (4, 1) 31. $(3, \frac{3}{2})$ 33. 1 35. −2
39. $-8 < n \le 3$ [number line]

Lesson 7-5 pp. 373–376

EXERCISES 1. no 3. yes 7. A 9. B

11. [graph]

19. $y \le \frac{2}{3}x - \frac{7}{3}$ 21. $y \le \frac{2}{3}x - \frac{8}{3}$

23a. $3x + 5y \le 48$
b. [graph] c. Answers may vary.
Sample: 8 blue and 4 gold,
2 blue and 8 gold, 12 blue
and 2 gold d. No; you
cannot buy −2 rolls of
paper.

25. [graph] 35. $x \le -3$

39. $y < 0$; [graph] 43. $y < x + 2$
55. about 775 games
57. 5 59. 11

61. 8, 18 63. 12 65. 11

Lesson 7-6 pp. 380–384

EXERCISES 1. no 3. no 5. [graph]

17. $y \ge -\frac{1}{2}x - 2$ and $y \le \frac{1}{2}x + 2$

19. $y \le -\frac{2}{3}x - 4$ and $y \ge \frac{1}{2}x - 3$
21. [graph]

23. $x + y \ge 50$, $4x + 3y \le 180$
[graph] 25. $x \le 3$, $x \ge -3$, $y \le 3$, $y \ge -3$
27. $y \ge \frac{2}{3}x - 2$, $y < \frac{2}{3}x + 2$
31a. triangle b. (2, 2), (−4, −1),
(−4, 2) c. 9 units²

Bottom-left quadrant

35a. $x \ge 1$, $10.99x + 4.99y \le 45$
[graph] b. (3, 0), (3, 1), (3, 2), (4, 0)
53. [graph]

59. $\frac{5}{2}$ 61. −8 63. $-\frac{1}{5}$ 65. $\frac{10}{9}$ 69. $f(x) = x + 6$

Technology p. 385

1. [graph]

Chapter Review pp. 387–389

1. elimination 2. solution of the system of linear
equations 3. system of linear inequalities
4. solution of the inequality 5. substitution
6. A 7. No; (2; 5) only satisfies one equation.
8. Infinitely many; the equations are equivalent.
9. Answers may vary. Sample: systems with
noninteger solutions.
10. [graph] (1, 2) 11. [graph] (−1, 2)

12. [graph] 13. [graph] (1, −1)

no solution
14. (−2, 5) 15. $(-4\frac{1}{2}, -6)$ 16. $(-1\frac{1}{6}, -\frac{5}{6})$ 17. (2, 2)
18. Answers may vary. Sample: There is no
solution when you get a false equation such as
0 = 2. There are infinitely many solutions when
you get a true equation such as 5 = 5.
19a. $x + y = 24$, $4x + 5y = 100$ b. (20, 4)
c. 20 4-point, 4 5-point 20. (−6, 23) 21. (1, −1)
22. (6, 4) 23. $(5\frac{5}{11}, 1\frac{7}{11})$ 24. $x + y = 34$,
$2x + 4y = 110$; 13 chickens and 21 cows
25. $10\frac{5}{9}$ fl oz 26. 63° and 27° 27. 18 ft by 39 ft

28. $1.29 29. 154 km/h
30. [graph] 31. [graph]

32. [graph] 33. [graph] 34. $x \ge 4$

35. $y \le 3x + 3$ 36. $2x + 3y \ge -6$
37. [graph] 38. [graph]

39. [graph] 40. [graph]

41. $y \le 3$, $y > x$ 42. $y > -2x + 2$, $y > \frac{4}{5}x - 4$
43. $x > -1$, $y \le x + 54$ 44. $y \le -\frac{2}{3}x + 3$,
$y \ge -\frac{1}{2}x - 1$ 45. Answers may vary.
Sample: $x \ge -1$, $y \le 5$, $x \le 5$, $x + y \ge 7$, $y \ge -1$

Chapter 8

Lesson 8-1 p. 397–399

EXERCISES 1. −1 3. $\frac{1}{25}$ 13. −2 15. 0; −3
17. 3a 19. x^7 33. $\frac{3}{25}$ 35. $-\frac{1}{5}$ 45a. $20.48; $.32
b. No; the value of the allowance rapidly
becomes very great. 47. pos. 51. 10^{-1} 53. 10^{-3}
57. 0.000001 59. 0.03 61a. $5^{-2}, 5^{-1}, 5^0, 5^1, 5^2$
b. 5^4 c. $\frac{a^p}{1}$ 63. 45 65. 40 69. $\frac{2}{9}$ 71. $\frac{1}{16}$

Bottom-right quadrant

73.
a	4	$\frac{1}{4}$	6	$\frac{1}{2}$	2
a^{-1}	$\frac{1}{4}$	3	$\frac{1}{6}$	$\frac{8}{7}$	0.5

75. A, B, D

77. No; $3x^{-2} \cdot 3x^2 = 9 \cdot x^0 = 9$. The product of
reciprocals should be 1. 79a. 1 correct, 0.4096; 2
correct, 0.1536; 3 correct, 0.0256; 4 correct,
0.0016 b. 0 or 1 95. [graph] 99. $y = 5x - 2$
101. $y = -\frac{3}{11}x - 17$

Lesson 8-2 pp. 402–404

EXERCISES 1. No; 55 > 10. 3. No; 0.9 < 1.
34. 5400 36. 1×10^1 53. 4 55. $\frac{2}{3}$
58. [graph]

Lesson 8-3 pp. 407–410

EXERCISES 1. 2^{10} or 1024 3. 1 7. c^5 9. $\frac{10}{7}$
17. $45x^7y^6$ 19. $x^{10}y^2$ 23. 6×10^9 25. 3.4×10^{-5}
29. 1.08×10^{21} dollars 31. 9 33. −3 41. $4x^4$
43. $4c^4$ 45. $12a^7$ 47. $3b \cdot 4 \cdot 2^2$ 49. 8.0×10^5
51. 1.2×10^{-4} 59. 7.65×10^{14} 61. 7.039305 ×
10^{-7} 63. about 6.7×10^{33} molecules 65. x^3
67. $5c^3$ 85. 1.28×10^6 87. 9.0×10^{-5}
93. [graph] 97. −1; 7; 13
99. −6.8; −22.8; −34.8

Lesson 8-4 pp. 413–415

EXERCISES 1. c^{10} 7. $\frac{1}{t^4}$ 9. $625y^4$ 11. $49a^2$
17. x^{16} 19. 1 23. 1.6×10^{11} 25. 8×10^{-30}
31. 8.57375×10^{-10} m³ 33. −4 35. −3 41. The
student who wrote $x^5 + x^5 = 2x^5$ is correct; x^5
times x^5 is x^{10}. 43. $243x^3$ 45. $30x^2$ 51a. $24x^2$;
$96x^2$ b. 4 times c. $8x^3$; $64x^3$ d. 8 times 53. $(ab)^5$
55. $(2xy)^2$ 59a. about 5.15×10^{14} m² b. about
3.60×10^{14} m² c. about 1.37×10^{18} m² 75. a^8b^3
77. $-4t^5$ 79. $(4\frac{2}{3}, 1\frac{1}{3})$ 81. (−9, −5) 83. 6
85. $-\frac{9}{11}$

Lesson 8-5 pp. 420–422

EXERCISES 1. 7 3. −3 5. $\frac{1}{4}$ 7. $\frac{1}{t}$ 13. 5×10^7
15. 6×10^2 19a. 3.86×10^{11} h; 2.65×10^8 people

b. about 1457 h c. about 4.0 h 21. $\frac{9}{25}$ 23. $\frac{32x^5}{y^3}$
29. $\frac{3}{2}$ 31. $\frac{9}{4}$ 37. 5^3 simplifies to 125. 39. Each
term should be raised to the 4th power and
simplified. 43. $\frac{1}{16m^{12}}$ 45. a^6 53. $\frac{8^5c^5}{b^3}$ 55. 5
63a. The student treated $\frac{6^4}{5}$ as $(\frac{6}{5})^4$. b. 125
65. $(\frac{m}{n})^7$ 67. 10^{10} 75. dividing powers with the
same base, def. of neg. exponent 77. mult.
powers with the same base 91. $27y^6$ 93. $\frac{t^{20}}{r^8}$
99. (0, 0) 101. (3, 5)
[graph]

Lesson 8-6 pp. 427–429

EXERCISES 1. 4 3. 0.1 7. 40, 80, 160 9. 20.25,
30.375, 45.5625 13. geometric 15. geometric
19. 5; 135; 10,935 21. 5; −135; −10,935
25. $A(n) = 6 \cdot 0.5^{n-1}$; 0.375 27. $A(n) = 7 \cdot (1.1)^{n-1}$;
9.317 29a. $A(n) = 100 \cdot (0.64)^{n-1}$
b. about 10.74 cm 31. 1, 0.2, 0.04;
$A(n) = 625 \cdot (0.2)^{n-1}$ 33. 1, −0.5, 0.25;
$A(n) = 16 \cdot (-0.5)^{n-1}$ 37. arithmetic; 3, 1, −1
39. geometric; 1.125, 0.5625, 0.28125
41a. $A(n) = 36 \cdot (0.9)^{n-1}$ b. 6; $n = 1$ corresponds
to the first swing, because $A(1) = 36$. c. 21.3 cm
55. a^4 57. $\frac{1}{16a_{20}}$ 63. 2.467×10^{-3} 65. $y = \frac{8}{3}x$
67. $y = -\frac{7}{8}x$

Lesson 8-7 pp. 432–435

EXERCISES 1. 216 3. 2.5 9. $160,000; $320,000
11. $16,000, $32,000 13. C 15. B 17. C
19. [graph] 21. [graph]

25. 0.04, 0.2, 1, 5, 25, 125;
increase 27. 100, 10, 1, 0.1,
0.01, 0.001; decrease

37a.
x	y
1	−2
2	4
3	−8
4	16
5	−32

39. $f(t) = 200 \cdot t^2$
41. $f(x) = 100x^2$
57. −3; 567, −1701, 5103
59. $-\frac{1}{3}; \frac{1}{9}, -\frac{1}{27}$
63. $y = 3x + 1$
65. $y = 0.4x - 3.8$

Technology p. 436

1a. $y = 26.87(0.83)^x$
b.
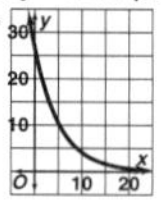
c. 0.65
3a. $y = 31.53(0.89)^x$ **c.** 0.03

Lesson 8-8 pp. 441–446

EXERCISES **1.** 20; 2 **3.** 10,000; 1.01 **7.** 1.05 **9.** 1.0875 **11.** 0.75%, 0.25% **13.** 1.125%; 0.375% **17.** \$16,661.35 **19.** \$28,338.18 **21a.** 3 half-lives **b.** 3.125 mCi **23.** 0.1 **25.** 0.9 **27.** exp. decay **29.** exp. decay **31.** $y = 130{,}000 \cdot (1.01)^x$; about 142,179 people **33.** $y = 2400 \cdot (1.07)^x$; \$4721.16 **35a.** $y = 584 \cdot (1.065)^x$; \$2057.81 **37.** Neither; it is not just one straight line. **39.** Neither; it decreases and and then increases, unlike an exponential function.
41. exponential function

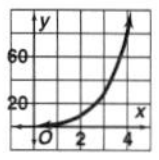

45. 4 half-lives
47a. $y = 6{,}284{,}000 \cdot (1.01)^x$
b. 7,667,674 people **49.** 88%
51. 46.1%

61.
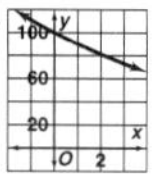
63. 7.28×10^{11} gal

Chapter Review

1. exponential growth **2.** growth factor **3.** Scientific notation **4.** exponential decay **5.** decay factor **6.** Compound interest **7.** common ratio **8.** interest period **9.** geometric sequence **10.** exponential function **11.** $\frac{d^6}{b^4}$ **12.** $\frac{y^8}{x^2}$ **13.** $\frac{7h^3}{k^8}$ **14.** $\frac{q^4}{p^2}$ **15.** $\frac{625}{16}$ or $39\frac{1}{16}$ **16.** $-\frac{1}{8}$ **17.** $-\frac{1}{8}$ **18.** $\frac{1}{49y^4}$ **19.** $\frac{9x^2}{w^4y^7}$ **20.** 36 **21.** $\frac{4}{9}$ **22.** $\frac{9}{8}$ or $1\frac{1}{8}$ **23.** 1 **24.** 108 **25.** C **26.** No; for values other than 0, $(-3b)^4 = 81b^4 \neq -12b^4$. **27.** No; 950 > 10. **28.** No; 72.35 > 10. **29.** yes **30.** No; 0.84 < 1. **31.** 2.793×10^6 mi **32.** 1.89×10^8 cars and trucks **33.** $2d^5$ **34.** $q^{12}r^4$ **35.** $-20c^4m^2$ **36.** 1.34^2 or 1.7956 **37.** $\frac{243x^2y^{14}}{64}$ **38.** $-\frac{4}{3r^{10}z^8}$

39. about 7.8×10^3 pores **40.** Answers may vary. Sample: Simplify $(2a^{-2})^{-2}(-3a)^2$; $\frac{9a^6}{4}$. **41.** $\frac{1}{w^3}$ **42.** $\frac{1}{64}$ **43.** $7x^2$ **44.** $\frac{n^{35}}{v^{21}}$ **45.** $\frac{c^3}{e^{11}}$ **46.** 2×10^{-3} **47.** 2.5×10^1 **48.** 5×10^{-5} **49.** 3×10^3 **50.** Answers may vary. Sample: Simplify and use div. prop: $\left(\frac{a^2}{2}\right)^{-3}$; use raising a quot. to a power prop.: $\frac{a^{-6}}{2^{-3}}$; use the def. of neg. exp.: $\frac{2^3}{a^6}$ or $\frac{8}{a^6}$ **51.** 0.1 **52.** 3 **53.** $-\frac{1}{2}$ **54.** geometric; $\frac{25}{4}, \frac{25}{16}, \frac{25}{64}$ **55.** neither; −30, −25, −19 **56.** arithmetic; 42, 49, 56 **57.** 6, 12, 24, 48 **58.** 7.5, 5.625, 4.21875 **59a.** 2430 bacteria **b.** about 180 min **60.** $a = 100, b = 1.025$ **61.** $a = 32, b = 0.75$ **62.** $a = 0.4, b = 2$ **63.** growth; 3 **64.** growth; 1.5 **65.** decay; 0.32 **66.** decay; $\frac{1}{4}$

67.
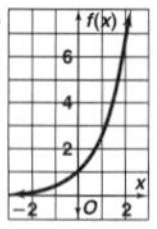
68.
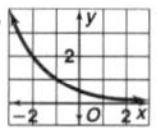
69.
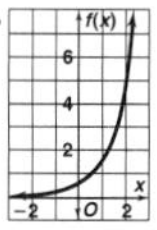
70.
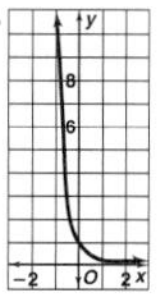

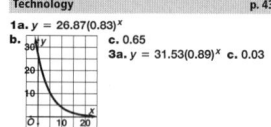

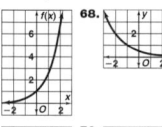

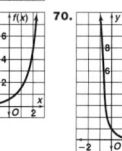

71. about 8.2 mg

Chapter 9

Lesson 9-1 pp. 459–461

EXERCISES **1.** 1 **3.** 0 **9.** quadratic trinomial **11.** cubic trinomial **15.** $-3x^2 + 4x$; quadratic binomial **17.** $c^2 + 4c - 2$; quadratic trinomial **21.** $8m^2 + 15$ **23.** $8w^2 - 3w + 4$ **29.** $b + 1$ **31.** $7n^4 + n^3$ **35.** $18y^2 + 5y$ **37.** $-7z^3 + 6z^2 + 2z - 5$ **39.** $28c - 16$ **43.** $-x^4 + x^3 + 15x$ **45.** $-h^{10} - 5h^9 + 8h^5 + 2h^4$ **49.** $5x + 18$ **51.** No; both terms of a binomial cannot be constants. **63.** 2 **65.** 5 **67.** exponential growth **69.** exponential growth **71.** 7^{18} **73.** $36x^5$ **79.** $y = |x| + 5$ **81.** $y = |x| - 12$

Selected Answers

Lesson 9-2 pp. 463–465

EXERCISES **1.** $8m^2 + 48m$ **3.** $63k^2 + 36k$ **13.** 3 **15.** 12 **19.** $2(3x - 2)$ **21.** $5(2x^3 - 5x^2 + 4)$ **25.** Karla; Kevin multiplied $-2x$ by 3 instead of −3. **27.** $-12a^3 + 15a^2 - 27a$ **29.** $-60c^3 + 36c^2 - 48c$ **33a.** $A = 16\pi x^2 - 4x^2$ **b.** $A = 4x^2(4\pi - 1)$ **35.** $24x(x^2 - 4x + 2)$ **37.** $x^2(5x^2 + 4x + 3)$ **51.** $-3x^2 + 10$ **53.** $5g^2 - g$ **57.** $\frac{1}{5}$ **59.** $-\frac{1}{8}$ **65.** (3, 2) **67.** (1, 6)

Lesson 9-3 pp. 469–472

EXERCISES **1.** 30 **3.** 7 **5.** $x^2 + 7x + 10$ **7.** $k^2 + k - 42$ **11.** $r^2 + 2r - 24$ **13.** $x^2 - x - 42$ **21.** $-2x^2 + 5x + 48$ **23.** $a^3 - 6a^2 + 9a - 4$ **25.** $3k^3 + 19k^2 - 33k + 56$ **27.** $2t^3 - 17t^2 + 36t - 15$ **29.** $48w^3 - 28w^2 - 2w + 2$ **31.** $p^2 + p - 56$ **33.** $25c^2 - 40c - 9$ **39a.** $2x^2 + 12x + 16$ **b.** $12x + 16$ **c.** 10 ft by 5 ft **43.** $1.5x^2 + 2.5x - 1$ **45.** $n^3 + 15n^2 + 56n$ **65.** $3c^2 - 27c$ **67.** $3y^2 - 10y$ **73.** $x(3x - 11)$ **75.** $n^2(9 - n)$ **81.** $\frac{1}{27}$ **83.** $\frac{1}{3w^5}$

Lesson 9-4 pp. 477–479

EXERCISES **1.** $c^2 + 2c + 1$ **3.** $4v^2 + 44v + 121$ **11.** 9801 **13.** 91,204 **15.** $x^2 - 16$ **17.** $d^2 - 49$ **21.** 899 **23.** 2496 **27.** $(10x + 15)$ units^2 **29.** $25p^2 - 10pq + q^2$ **31.** $x^2 - 14xy + 49y^2$ **45.** $p^2 - 81q^2$ **47.** $49b^2 - 64c^2$ **65.** $2x^2 - 23x + 66$ **67.** $3y^2 + 4y + 1$ **73.** 8.713×10^3 **75.** 6.8952×10^4

Lesson 9-5 pp. 483–485

EXERCISES **1.** 5 **3.** 7 **5.** $(r + 3)(r + 1)$ **7.** $(k + 3)(k + 2)$ **17.** 5 **19.** 9 **21.** $(x + 4)(x - 1)$ **23.** $(y + 5) \cdot (y - 4)$ **31.** B **33.** $(t + 9v)(t - 2v)$ **35.** $(p - 8q) \cdot (p - 2q)$ **39–41.** Answers may vary. Samples are given. **39.** 18; $(x - 6)(x + 3)$, 28; $(x - 7)(x + 4)$, 10; $(x - 5)(x + 2)$ **41.** 7; $(x + 4)(x + 3)$, 8; $(x + 6)(x + 2)$, 13; $(x + 12)(x + 1)$ **43.** $(k + 2)(k + 8)$ **45.** $(n - 4) \cdot (n + 14)$ **55.** $4x^2 + 12x + 5$; $(2x + 1)(2x + 5)$ **73.** $w^2 - 12w + 36$ **75.** $4q^2 + 28q + 49$ **81.** 6 weeks **83a.** 81 basic players, 48 deluxe players **b.** \$9719.19

85.
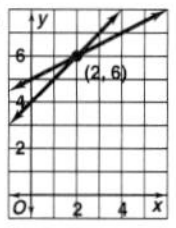

Lesson 9-6 pp. 487–489

EXERCISES **1.** $(2n + 1)(n + 7)$ **3.** $(11w - 3)(w - 1)$ **13.** $(2t - 3)(t + 1)$ **15.** $(2q + 3)(q - 7)$ **29.** Answers may vary. Sample: 18; $(5m - 4) \cdot (3m + 6)$, 54; $(5m - 2)(3m + 12)$, 117; $(5m - 1) \cdot (3m + 24)$ **33.** $(9p + 4)(6p + 7)$ **35.** $(7x - 2) \cdot (2x - 7)$ **45.** $(7p - 3q)(7p + 12q)$ **46.** $54h(2g - 1) \cdot (g - 1)$ **55.** $(t - 4)(t - 3)$ **57.** $(m - 3)(m - 12)$ **63.** 7921 **65.** 815,409 **67.** 1599 **69.** 39,996 **71.** $\frac{1}{2}$, 4, 16 **73.** $\frac{1}{81}, \frac{1}{3}$, 3

77.
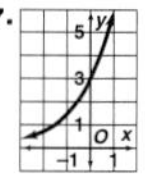

Lesson 9-7 pp. 493–495

EXERCISES **1.** $(c + 5)^2$ **3.** $(h + 6)^2$ **7.** $(2m + 5)$ **9.** $(5g - 4)$ **11.** $(8r - 9)^2$ **13.** $(x + 2)(x - 2)$ **23.** $(7y + 2)(7y - 2)$ **25.** $(2m + 9)(2m - 9)$ **31.** $3(m + 2)(m - 2)$ **33.** $3(x + 8)^2$ **39.** 11, 9 **41.** 15, 5 **45.** $25(2v + w)(2v - w)$ **47.** $7(2c + 5d)^2$ **55a.** $4(x + 5)(x - 5)$ **b.** $4(x + 5)(x - 5)$ **73.** $(2d + 1)(d + 5)$ **75.** $(2t + 1)(2t + 7)$ **83.** 29; 37; 45; $-11 + 8n$ **85.** 0.02; 0.002; 0.0002; $2000 \cdot \left(\frac{1}{10}\right)^n$ **91a.** $y = 11.4x + 64.8$ **b.** 93 **c.** 79

Lesson 9-8 pp. 499–501

EXERCISES **1.** $2m^2$; 3 **3.** $2z^2$; −5 **5.** $(2n^2 + 1) \cdot (3n + 4)$ **7.** $(3t + 1)(3t - 1)(3t + 5)$ **11.** $2(2v^2 + 1) \cdot (3v - 8)$ **13.** $2(m^2 + 2)(10m - 9)$ **17.** $(6p + 5) \cdot (2p + 1)$ **19.** $(6n - 1)(3n + 10)$ **27.** $5k$, $(k + 2)$, and $(k + 4)$ **29.** $2(10t^2 - 11)(3t - 10)$ **31.** $4(3x - 7y) \cdot (x + 2y)$ **35.** $(7w^2 - 4)(2w + 7)$ **37.** $2(2t^2 + 3) \cdot (11t - 1)$ **39.** $2w$, $(6w + 5)$, and $(7w + 1)$ **55.** $(r + 3)^2$ **57.** $2(t + 3)^2$ **63.** b^4 **65.** t^{15} **71.** 1.6×10^{21} **73.** 4.9×10^{-11} **79.** (1, 5) **81.** (0.5, 5)

Chapter Review pp. 503–505

1. A **2.** D **3.** E **4.** C **5.** B **6.** $-6y^2 + 8y + 2$; quadratic trinomial **7.** $9h^2 + 1$; quadratic binomial **8.** $3k^5 + k$; fifth degree binomial **9.** $7t^2 + 8t + 9$; quadratic trinomial **10.** x^2y^2; fourth degree monomial **11.** $x^3 + x^2 + 5$; cubic trinomial **12.** Answers may vary. Sample: $3z^4 - 5z^2 + 1$; 4 **13.** $-b^5 + 2b^3 + 6$ **14.** $8g^4 - 5g^2 + 11g + 5$ **15.** $7x^3 + 8x^2 - 3x + 12$ **16.** $t^3 - 5t^2 + 12t - 8$ **17.** $4y^2 + 3y + 4$ **18.** $7w^5 - 5w^4 - 7w^3 + w^2 + 3w - 3$ **19.** $-40x^2 + 16x$ **20.** $35g^3 + 15g^2 - 45g$

21. $-40t^4 + 24t^3 - 32t^2$ **22.** $5m^3 + 15m^2$ **23.** $-6w^4 - 8w^3 + 20w^2$ **24.** $-3b^3 + 5b^2 + 10b$ **25.** $3x$; $3x(3x^3 + 4x^2 + 2)$ **26.** $4t^2$; $4t^2(t^3 - 3t + 2)$ **27.** $10n^3$; $10n^3(4n^2 + 7n - 3)$ **28.** 2; $2(k^4 + 2k^3 - 3k - 4)$ **29.** $3d$; $3d(d - 2)$ **30.** $2m^2$; $2m^2(5m^2 - 6m + 2)$ **31.** 5; $5(2v - 1)$ **32.** $4w$; $4w(3w^2 + 2w + 5)$ **33.** $3d^3$; $3d^3(6d^2 + 2d + 3)$ **34.** 12; if the GCF of x and y is 3, the GCF of $4x$ and $4y$ is $4 \cdot 3$ or 12. **35.** Kim; 4, m, and n are factors of both monomials. The GCF is their product. **36.** $x^2 + 8x + 15$ **37.** $15v^2 - 29v - 14$ **38.** $6b^2 + 11b - 10$ **39.** $-k^2 + 5k - 4$ **40.** $p^3 + 3p^2 + 3p + 2$ **41.** $4a^2 - 21a + 5$ **42.** $y^3 - 9y^2 + 18y + 8$ **43.** $3x^2 + 10x + 8$ **44.** $-2h^3 + 11h^2 - 6h + 5$ **45.** $q^2 - 8q + 16$ **46.** $4k^6 + 20k^3 + 25$ **47.** $64 - 9t^4$ **48.** $4m^4 - 25$ **49.** $w^2 - 16$ **50.** $16g^4 - 25h^8$ **51.** $(2x + 1)(x + 4)$; $2x^2 + 9x + 4$ **52.** No; $(x - y)^2 = x^2 - 2xy + y^2 \neq x^2 - y^2$. **53.** $(x + 2)(x + 1)$ **54.** $(y - 7)(y - 2)$ **55.** $(x - 5) \cdot (x + 3)$ **56.** $(2w - 3)(w + 1)$ **57.** $(b - 3)(b - 4)$ **58.** $(2t - 1)(t + 2)$ **59.** $(x + 6)(x - 1)$ **60.** $2(3x + 2)(x + 1)$ **61.** $(7x + 2)(3x - 4)$ **62.** $(3x - 2)(x + 1)$ **63.** $(15y + 1)(y + 1)$ **64.** $(15y - 1)(y - 1)$ **65.** $(q + 1)^2$ **66.** $(b + 4)(b - 4)$ **67.** $(x - 2)^2$ **68.** $(2t + 11)(2t - 11)$ **69.** $(2d - 5)^2$ **70.** $(3c + 1)^2$ **71.** $(3k + 5)(3k - 5)$ **72.** $(x + 3)^2$ **73.** $6(2y + 1) \cdot (2y - 1)$ **74.** $\frac{1}{2}d + 1$ **75.** The factors are equal. **76.** No; only the square $(5u + 6)^2$ would have $25u^2$ and 36 as the first and last terms, however $2(5u)(6) \neq 65u$. **77.** $4x^2$; −2 **78.** $3k^2$; −2 **79.** $24y^2$; −4 **80.** $10n^3$; 7 **81.** $(3x^2 + 4)(2x + 1)$ **82.** $5y^2(2y + 3)(2y - 3)$ **83.** $3(3g - 1)(g + 2)$ **84.** $(3c - d)(2c - d)$ **85.** $(11k + 1)(k + 2)$ **86.** $3(u + 6)(u + 1)$ **87.** $(5p + 3)(3p + 1)$ **88.** $3(u - 6)(u - 1)$ **89.** $(h^2 - 3)(15h + 11)$ **90.** $(5x + 7)(6x^2 - 1)$ **91.** $4s^2t(3s - 1)(s + 2)$ **92.** $(x^2 + 2)(2x + 7)$ **93.** $2p$, $(p + 5)$, and $(3p + 4)$

Chapter 10

Lesson 10-1 pp. 513–516

EXERCISES **1.** (2, 5); max. **3.** (2, 1); min.

5.
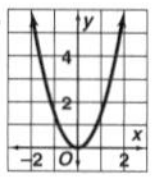
11. $f(x) = \frac{1}{3}x^2$, $f(x) = x^2$, $f(x) = 5x^2$
13. $f(x) = -\frac{2}{3}x^2$, $f(x) = -2x^2$, $f(x) = -4x^2$

15.
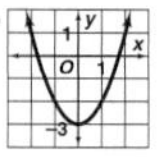
21. E **23.** F **27.** The graph of $y = 2x^2$ is narrower.
29. The graph of $y = 1.5x^2$ is narrower.

31.
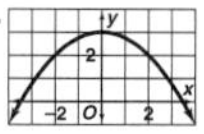
35.
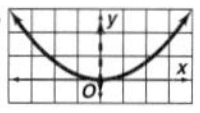

41. M **43.** M **55.** $(3a^2 - 2)(5a - 6)$ **57.** $(y + 2)(y - 2)(y + 3)$ **61.** $9n^2 - 63n$ **63.** $12m^6 - 4m^5 + 20m^2$

Lesson 10-2 pp. 520–523

EXERCISES **1.** $x = 0$, (0, 4) **3.** $x = 4$, (4, −25) **5.** B **7.** C

11.
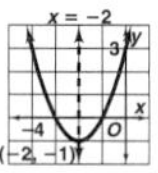

15a. 20 ft **b.** 400 ft^2

17.
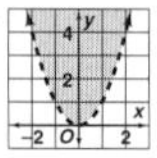
23.
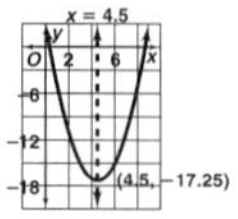

33. Answers may vary. Sample: **33.** $y = -3x^2$ **37a.** \$12.50 **b.** \$10,000 **39.** 26 units^2 **51.** C **53.** F **57.** $c^2 - 5c - 36$ **59.** $20t^2 + 17t + 3$

Lesson 10-3 pp. 526–528

EXERCISES **1.** 13 **3.** $\frac{1}{3}$ **13.** irrational **15.** irrational **17.** 5 and 6 **19.** −12 and −11 **21.** 3.46 **23.** 107.47 **25.** 0.93 **27.** 0 **29.** $\pm\frac{3}{7}$ **41.** $-\frac{2}{5}$ **43.** 1.26

67.
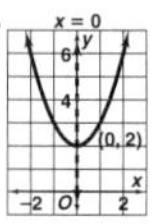

73. $9t^2 - 25$ **75.** $x^2 + 26x + 169$ **81.** −2 **83.** $-\frac{3}{4}$

Selected Answers

Lesson 10-4 pp. 531–534

EXERCISES

1.
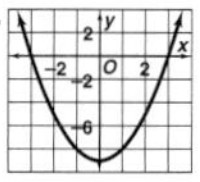
±3

11. ±21 **13.** 0 **19.** $x^2 = 256$; 16 m **21.** $\pi r^2 = 80$; 5.0 cm **23.** none **25.** one **29.** $\pm\frac{3}{7}$ **31.** ±2.8 **41.** 6.3 ft **51.** 3 **53.** 40 **59.** $(x + 4)(x + 1)$ **61.** $(a + 5)(a - 2)$ **65.** 3.6135×10^6 **67.** -8.12×10^0 **69.** 701,000

Technology p. 535

1. 10.78, 13.22 **3.** −2, 1.5 **5.** 0.28, 17.72 **7.** −12, 6

Lesson 10-5 pp. 538–540

EXERCISES **1.** 3, 7 **3.** 0, −1 **7.** 1, −4 **9.** 0, 8 **13.** −3, −5 **15.** 0, 6 **23.** 5 **25.** base: 10 ft, height: 22 ft **27.** $2q^2 + 22q + 60 = 0$; −6, −5 **29.** $4y^2 + 12y + 9 = 0$; $-\frac{3}{2}$ **35.** 8 in. × 10 in. **41.** 0, 4, 6 **43.** 0, 3 **57.** $x^2 = 320$; 17.9 ft **59.** $(2x + 3)(x + 5)$ **61.** $(4t - 3)(t + 2)$

Lesson 10-6 pp. 544–546

EXERCISES **1.** 49 **3.** 400 **7.** 4, −12 **9.** −5, −17 **13.** 7, −5 **15.** 11, 1 **19.** 1 **21.** $\frac{81}{100}$ **23.** 5, −1 **25a.** $(2x + 1)(x + 1)$ **b.** $2x^2 + 3x + 1 = 28$ **c.** 3 **27.** −3, −4 **29.** 6, 2 **39.** 5.16, −1.16 **41.** 5.6 ft by 14.2 ft **51.** −6, −5 **53.** $-\frac{8}{3}, \frac{8}{3}$ **57.** $(t - 11)^2$ **59.** $(4c + 3)^2$ **65.** r^{12} **67.** $-y$

Lesson 10-7 pp. 550–552

EXERCISES **1.** −1, −1.5 **3.** 1.5 **11.** 10.42, 1.58 **13.** 1.14, −0.77 **17a.** $0 = -16t^2 + 50t + 3.5$ **b.** $t \approx 3.2$; 3.2 s **19.** Factoring or square roots; the equation is easily factorable and there is no x term. **21.** Quadratic formula; the equation cannot be factored. **25.** 0.87, −1.54 **27.** 1.28, −2.61 **33a.** 7 ft × 8 ft **b.** $x(x + 1) = 60$, 7.26 ft × 8.26 ft **37.** 13.44 cm and 7.44 cm **47.** 1.54, 8.46 **49.** 0.1,− 6.1 **51.** $(3z - 2)(z + 4)$ **53.** $(6v - 5)(2v + 7)$ **55.** $(5t + 3)(3t + 2)$

Lesson 10-8 pp. 556–558

EXERCISES **1.** A **3.** B **5.** 1 **7.** 2 **17.** No; the discriminant is negative. **19.** 0 **21.** 2

25a. $S = -0.75p^2 + 54p$ **b.** no **c.** \$36 **31.** no **33.** yes; 1, −1.25 **49.** 0.5, −1.5 **51.** 0.61, −0.27 **55.** \$1093.81 **57.** \$6104.48 **59.** arithmetic **61.** arithmetic

Lesson 10-9 pp. 563–566

EXERCISES

1.
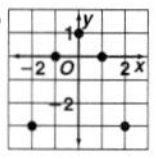
quadratic

7. quadratic; $y = 1.5x^2$ **9.** quadratic; $y = 2.8x^2$

13a.
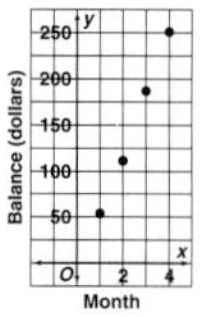

linear

b. 65, 64, 64; yes **c.** 64 **d.** $y = 64x - 5$ **15a.** 41, 123, 206 **b.** 82, 83 **c.** $d = 41t^2$ **d.** 256.25 cm **19.** $y = 0.875x^2 - 0.435x + 1.515$ **21.** $y = 2.125x^2 - 4.145x + 2.955$ **27a.** quadratic **b.** $d = 13.6t^2$ **c.** 54.4 ft **35.** 0

37.
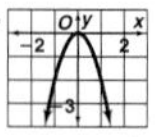

43. 0.125 **45.** $\frac{2}{27}$

Extension p. 567

1. Both graphs have the same shape, go through the origin, and lie in Quadrants I and III. The graph of $y = x^3$ is narrower than the graph of $y = \frac{1}{3}x^3$. **3.** Yes; the sign of a changes which quadrants the graphs are in, and the larger $|a|$, the narrower the graph.

5a.
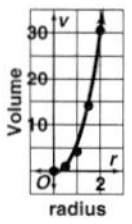

b. about 1.3 ft

Chapter Review pp. 569–571

1. parabola **2.** completing the square
3. principal square root **4.** vertex **5.** discriminant
6–9. Answers may vary. Samples are given.
6. $y = -2x^2$ **7.** $y = 2x^2$ **8.** $y = x^2$ **9.** $y = \frac{1}{2}x^2$

10. 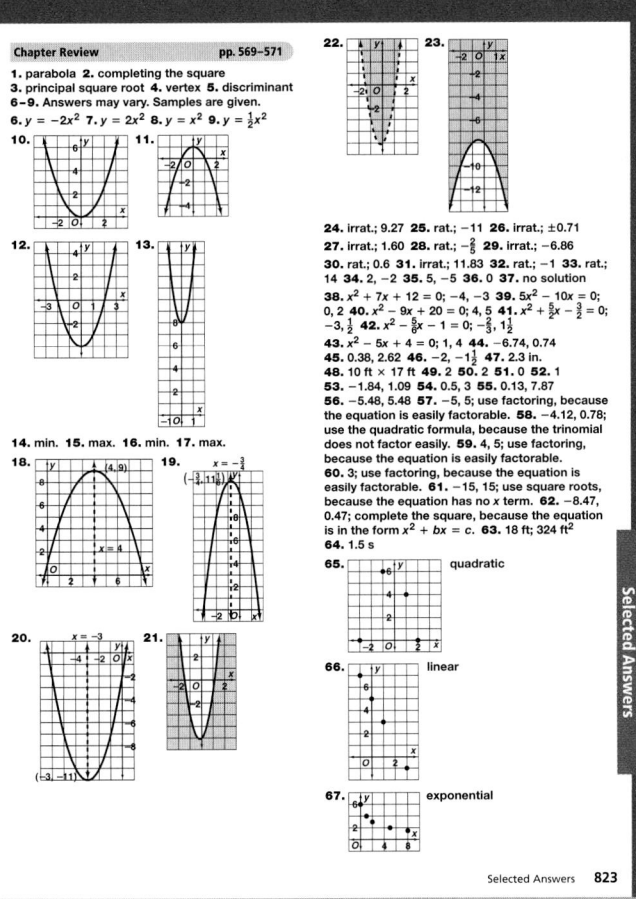 **11.**

12. **13.**

14. min. **15.** max. **16.** min. **17.** max.

18. **19.** $x = -\frac{3}{4}$

20. $x = -3$ **21.**

22. **23.**

24. irrat.; 9.27 **25.** rat.; −11 **26.** irrat.; ±0.71
27. irrat.; 1.60 **28.** rat.; −$\frac{2}{5}$ **29.** irrat.; −6.86
30. rat.; 0.6 **31.** irrat.; 11.83 **32.** rat.; −1 **33.** rat.;
14 **34.** 2, −2 **35.** 5, −5 **36.** 0 **37.** no solution
38. $x^2 + 7x + 12 = 0$; −3, −4 **39.** $5x^2 - 10x = 0$;
0, 2 **40.** $x^2 - 9x + 20 = 0$; 4, 5 **41.** $x^2 + \frac{5}{2}x - \frac{3}{2} = 0$;
−3, $\frac{1}{2}$ **42.** $x^2 - \frac{5}{2}x - 1 = 0$; −$\frac{3}{8}$, $1\frac{1}{2}$
43. $x^2 - 5x + 4 = 0$; 1, 4 **44.** −6.74, 0.74
45. 0.38, 2.62 **46.** −2, −$1\frac{1}{2}$ **47.** 2.3 in.
48. 10 ft × 17 ft **49.** 2 **50.** 2 **51.** 0 **52.** 1
53. −1.84, 1.09 **54.** 0.5, 3 **55.** 0.13, 7.87
56. −5.48, 5.48 **57.** −5, 5; use factoring, because
the equation is easily factorable. **58.** −4.12, 0.78;
use the quadratic formula, because the trinomial
does not factor easily. **59.** 4, 5; use factoring,
because the equation is easily factorable.
60. 3; use factoring, because the equation is
easily factorable. **61.** −15, 15; use square roots,
because the equation has no x term. **62.** −8.47,
0.47; complete the square, because the equation
is in the form $x^2 + bx = c$. **63.** 18 ft; 324 ft²
64. 1.5 s

65. quadratic

66. linear

67. exponential

68. quadratic

69. $y = 5(2)^x$ **70.** $y = 3x - 2$ **71.** $y = (x + 1)^2$
72. $y = \frac{1}{2}(10^x)$

Chapter 11

Lesson 11-1 pp. 578–581

EXERCISES 1. $10\sqrt{2}$ **3.** $5\sqrt{3}$ **13.** 20 **15.** $11\sqrt{2}$
25. 3 mi **27.** 17 mi **29.** $\frac{3\sqrt{3}}{3}$ **31.** $\frac{2\sqrt{30}}{11}$ **37.** $\frac{3}{2}$
39. $-2\sqrt{5}$ **45.** $\sqrt{5}$ **47.** $\frac{2\sqrt{10n}}{5n}$ **53.** not simplest
form; radical in the denominator of a fraction
55. Simplest form; radicand has no perfect-
square factors other than 1. **57.** 30 **59.** $\frac{3\sqrt{2}}{4}$
69. $-3 \pm 3\sqrt{2}$ **71.** $\frac{2 \pm \sqrt{10}}{3}$ **85.** exponential;
$y = 4(2.5)^x$
87.

$x = -1$

$(-4, -40)$

91. $3v^2 - v - 9$ **93.** $-3b^2 - 23b - 21$

Lesson 11-2 pp. 587–590

EXERCISES 1. 10 **3.** 17 **7.** 4 **9.** 12 **17.** no
19. yes **23.** no **25.** yes **27.** $\frac{4}{15}$ or 0.3 **29.** 6
33. yes **35.** yes **37.** 4.2 cm **39.** 559.9 **41.** 9.7
45. 12.8 ft **49.** A figure is a square; the figure is a
rectangle; if a figure is a rectangle then the figure
is a square; false. **51.** An angle is a right angle;
its measure is 90°; if the measure of an angle is
90°, then it is a right angle; true. **53.** 6 in. **67.** $\frac{\sqrt{6}}{3}$
69. $2b^2\sqrt{10b}$ **73.** 8 and 9 **75.** 11 and 12
77. irrational **79.** rational **81.** $12a^2 + 15a$
83. $-10p^4 + 26p^3$

Lesson 11-3 pp. 594–597

EXERCISES 1. 15 **3.** 10 **7.** 16 **9.** (1, 6) **11.** (0, 0)
15. (−4, 4) **17.** 10.6 **19.** $AB \approx 4.1$; $BC \approx 3.2$;
$AC = 5$ **21.** $RS \approx 3.2$; $ST \approx 5.7$; $RT \approx 5.1$
25a. $OR = \sqrt{29}$, $ST = \sqrt{29}$ **b.** $\frac{5}{2}$; $\frac{5}{2}$ **c.** yes
31a. 38.1 mi **b.** 20 mi, 21.2 mi **c.** 15 min, 16 min
33a. $R(-27, -5)$ **b.** $PR = \sqrt{13} \approx 3.6$ $RQ = \sqrt{13} \approx 3.6$ **49.** 10.2 **51.** 3.5 **55.** −10, 10 **57.** −5,
5 **61.** $v^2 + 2v - 35$ **63.** $8w^4 + 19w^2 + 11$

Extension pp. 598–599

1. 7.1 cm **3.** 9.9 ft **5.** 28.4 ft **7.** $x \approx 6.9$ cm;
$y = 8$ cm **9.** $x \approx 5.2$ m; $y = 6$ m

Lesson 11-4 pp. 600–602

EXERCISES 1. $5\sqrt{6}$ **3.** $-2\sqrt{5}$ **7.** yes **9.** no
11. $-3\sqrt{3}$ **13.** $-2\sqrt{5}$ **17.** $9 + \sqrt{3}$ **19.** $3\sqrt{5} +$
$2\sqrt{3}$ **23.** $58 - 10\sqrt{30}$ **25.** $43 + 4\sqrt{30}$
29. $-6\sqrt{2}$ **31.** $\frac{3(\sqrt{10} + \sqrt{5})}{5}$ **35.** $-\frac{4}{3}$; −1.3
37. 7.4 ft **39.** $6\sqrt{2} + 6\sqrt{3}$ or $6(\sqrt{2} + \sqrt{3})$
41. $8 + 2\sqrt{15}$ **47.** $\frac{\sqrt{10}}{10}$ **49.** $(10 + 10\sqrt{2})$ units
55. 9.1% **57.** 15.5% **77.** 6.7 units **79.** (3, 5)
81. 0, 7 **83.** −9, −3 **87.** $b^2 + 22b + 121$
89. $25g^2 - 49$

Lesson 11-5 pp. 607–609

EXERCISES 1. 4 **3.** 36 **7.** 576 ft **9.** 4.5 **11.** 7
15. 2 **17.** none **21.** 3 **23.** no solution **29a.** 25
b. 11.25 **33.** 1600 ft **35.** no solution **37.** 1, 6
63. $3\sqrt{2} + 4\sqrt{3}$ **65.** 32 **69.** 8.4, −0.4 **71.** −10.7,
0.7 **75.** $(m - 13)(m - 1)$ **77.** $(2p + 1)(p + 7)$

Lesson 11-6 pp. 616–619

EXERCISES 1. $x \geq 2$ **3.** $x \geq 0$
11.

x	$f(x)$
0	0
1	2
4	4

17. D **19.** C
21. **31.** $x \leq 4$; $y \geq 0$ **35.** Translate
the graph of $y = \sqrt{x}$ 10 units
down. **37.** Translate the graph
of $y = \sqrt{x}$ 9 units right.

39.

x	$f(x)$
0	0
1	4
4	5.7
4	8

47. B **49.** A **55.** False; only combine like terms.
57. False; $x = -1$. **71.** 73. 14.76 **77.** 4 − $\sqrt{39}$,
$4 + \sqrt{39}$ **79.** $\frac{-1 - \sqrt{11}}{3}$, $\frac{-1 + \sqrt{11}}{3}$
83. $(3x - 5)(x + 2)$ **85.** $2(x - 8)(x + 3)$

Extension p. 620

1. 10 **2.** 5 **3.** 2 **4.** 343 **5.** 4 **6.** 16 **7.** 125 **8.** 256
9. x^2 **10.** b **11.** $m^{\frac{8}{5}}$ **12.** m **13.** $a^{\frac{5}{6}}$ **14.** $k^{\frac{3}{4}}$
15. $216y^{\frac{21}{2}}$ **16.** $27c^6$

Lesson 11-7 pp. 621–624

EXERCISES 1. $\frac{3}{5}$ **3.** $\frac{3}{4}$ **7.** 0.5299 **9.** 1.2799
13. 10.4 **15.** 38.1 **19.** about 172 ft **21.** about
0.4 mi **23.** $B = 15$; $\sin A = \frac{8}{17}$; $\cos A = \frac{15}{17}$;
$\tan A = \frac{8}{15}$ **25.** $AC \approx 6$; $AB \approx 8$ **27.** $BC \approx 6$;
$AB \approx 18$ **29.** about 55 m **31a.** 1,720,000 ft
b. 326 mi **33.** about 6.8 m **35.** 4.5 **37.** $q \approx 6.1$;
$r \approx 7.9$ **39a.** about 252 ft **b.** about 377 ft
41. about 203 ft

51.

55. 0 **57.** $(n - 20)(n + 20)$
59. $(10p - 7)(10p + 7)$

Chapter Review pp. 629–631

1. conjugates **2.** legs **3.** rationalize
4. extraneous solution **5.** like radicals
6. Pythagorean Theorem **7.** sine **8.** angle of
elevation **9.** distance formula **10.** midpoint
11. $48\sqrt{2}$ **12.** $\frac{4\sqrt{21}}{11}$ **13.** $20c^2\sqrt{6}$ **14.** $\frac{10\sqrt{13}}{13}$
15. $10\sqrt{2}$ cm by 70$\sqrt{2}$ cm **16.** 5.8 **17.** 7.8
18. 14.8 **19.** 9.8 **20.** yes **21.** no **22.** about 85 ft
23. 5 units **24.** 8.2 units **25.** 10.8 units
26. Answers may vary. Sample:

$\sqrt{32}$ (or about 5.7) units

27. (0.5, 5.5) **28.** $(5\frac{1}{2}, 4\frac{1}{4})$ **29.** $2\sqrt{7}$ **30.** $5\sqrt{5}$
31. $\sqrt{6}$ **32.** $2\sqrt{5}$ **33.** $10 - 10\sqrt{2}$
34. $-1 + 2\sqrt{14}$ **35.** $3 + 8\sqrt{3}$ **36.** $17\sqrt{7}$
37. $\sqrt{6} + \sqrt{3}$ **38.** 2 **39.** 16 **40.** 4 **41.** 81 **42.** 1
43. 7 **44.** $5\sqrt{5}$ cm **45.** 2.93 in.
46.

x	y
0	0
0.5	0.5
2	1
4	1.4
8	2

47.

x	y
0	0
1	$\frac{1}{2}$
4	1
9	$1\frac{1}{2}$

48.

x	y
0	0
1	$\frac{1}{2}$
2	1
8	2

49.

x	y
0	0
1	2
2	3

50. $x \geq 0$; **51.** $x \geq 2$;

52. $x \geq -1$; **53.** $x \geq 0$;

54. $AC \approx 10$; $BC \approx 7$ **55.** $AB \approx 29$; $AC \approx 28$
56. $AB \approx 10$; $BC \approx 6$ **57.** $AC \approx 24$; $BC \approx 5$
58. about 55 ft

Chapter 12

Lesson 12-1 pp. 640–642

EXERCISES 1. $xy = 18$ **3.** $xy = 56$ **11.** 15 **13.** 7
23. 13.3 mi/h **25.** inverse variation; $xy = 60$
27. Direct variation; the ratio $\frac{cost}{pound}$ is constant at
$1.79. **29.** Inverse variation; the product of the
length and width remains constant with an area
of 24 square units. **31.** 1.1; $rt = 1.1$ **33.** 1; $ab = 1$
37. Inverse variation; the product of the rate and
the time is always 150. **39.** 121 ft **41.** direct
variation; $y = 0.4x$; 8 **43.** inverse variation;
$xy = 48$; 0.5 **47.** 10.2 L **57.** $\frac{15}{17}$ **59.** $\frac{8}{17}$ **63.** 12.0
65. 10.6 **69.** $(5x + 2)(3x + 7)$

Technology p. 643

1.

11a.

b. Adding translates the graph up, subtracting
translates the graph down.

Lesson 12-2 pp. 648–650

EXERCISES
1.

7. 2 **9.** 2 **11.** $x = -1$, $y = 0$ **13.** $x = 0$, $y = 2$
15. $x = 0$; **21.** $x = 0$, $y = 5$;

27. absolute value function with vertex (4, 0)
29. line with slope $\frac{1}{4}$, y-int. 0 **35.** moves graph
1 unit to the left **37.** lowers graph 15 units
43. $x = 0$, $y = 0$;

53. 17.8 lumens; 1.97 lumens **69.** $xy = 16$
71. $xy = 21.08$ **73.** 1 **75.** $3(d - 6)(d + 6)$
77. $(t^2 + 3)(t - 1)$

Extension p. 651

1. −1 **3.** gets very small; gets very large
5. 0 **7.** 2

Lesson 12-3 pp. 654–656

EXERCISES 1. $\frac{2a + 3}{4}$ **3.** $\frac{1}{3}$ **7.** $\frac{2}{9}$ **9.** $\frac{1}{m - 1}$ **17.** $\frac{-4}{t + 1}$
19. $-\frac{1}{2}$ **23.** 13 min **25.** $\frac{2r - 1}{r - 5}$ **27.** $\frac{5t - 4}{3t - 1}$
35a. I. $\frac{2b + 4h}{bh}$ **II.** $\frac{2h + 2r}{rh}$ **b.** $\frac{4}{9}$; $\frac{5}{9}$ **39.** $\frac{1}{4}$
41. $\frac{t + 3}{3(t + 2)}$
55. vertical asymptote: $x = 4$
horizontal asymptote: $y = 0$;

57. $10\sqrt{2}$ **59.** $2\sqrt{2}$ **61.** $y = x^2$, $y = -2x^2$,
$y = 3x^2$

Lesson 12-4 pp. 657–659

EXERCISES 1. $\frac{35x}{36}$ **3.** $\frac{40}{3s^5}$ **7.** $\frac{2c}{c - 1}$ **9.** $\frac{6}{t}$
13. $4(t + 1)(t + 2)$ **15.** $\frac{(x - 1)(x - 2)}{3}$ **17.** $\frac{-2d}{6d^2}$
19. $\frac{1}{s} + 4$ **21.** 6 **23.** $-\frac{1}{3}$ **27.** $\frac{11}{7k - 15}$ **29.** $t + 3$
31. $\frac{3t - \frac{5}{3}}{7t^2}$ **39.** $132.96 **41.** $\frac{x - 2}{4(x + 7)}$ **43.** $\frac{2}{a + 5}$
59. $\frac{b - 5}{2}$ **61.** $\frac{7}{9}$ **69.** 5.3 **71.** 11
75.

$x = 5$

$(5, -27)$

Lesson 12-5 pp. 664–666

EXERCISES 1. $x^4 - x^3 + x^2$ **3.** $3c^2 + 2c - \frac{1}{3}$
7. $x - 3$ **9.** $n - 1$ **13.** $5t - 50$
15. $b^2 - 3b - 1 + \frac{3}{3b - 1}$ **19.** $(r^2 + 5r + 1)$ cm
21. $b + 12 + \frac{1}{b + 4}$ **23.** $10w - 681 + \frac{49,046}{w + 72}$
27. $3x + 2 - \frac{1}{2x}$ **29.** $2b^2 + 2b + 10 + \frac{10}{b - 1}$

47a. $t = \frac{d}{r}$ **b.** $t^2 - 7t + 12$
59. $\frac{(t-5)(3t+1)(2t+11)}{(2t-55)(t+1)(3t)}$ **61.** $\frac{(x+5)(x+4)^2}{(x+7)(x+8)^2}$
63. 9.4 **65.** 17.9 **69.** 17 **71.** 63.25

Lesson 12-6 pp. 669–671

EXERCISES **1.** $\frac{9}{2m}$ **3.** $\frac{n+2}{n+3}$ **13.** $2x^2$ **15.** $7z$
17. $\frac{35+6a}{15a}$ **19.** $\frac{18+20x^2}{15x^8}$ **23.** $\frac{17m-47}{(m+2)(m-7)}$
25. $\frac{a^2+12a+15}{4(a+3)}$ **31.** $\frac{h^2+h+1}{2t^2-7}$ **33.** $\frac{-3-x-z}{xy^2z}$
45. $\frac{8x^2-1}{x}$ **47.** $\frac{-3x-5}{x(x-5)}$ **59.** $\frac{x^2}{2} + 2x - 1$ **61.** 6
63. no solution **65.** ± 3.9

Lesson 12-7 pp. 675–677

EXERCISES **1.** −2 **3.** −1 **17.** ≈12.7 min
19. 10, −10 **21.** 4 **25.** $\frac{1}{2}$, 2 **27.** −5, 2 **37.** 20 Ω
39. 20 Ω **53.** $-\frac{3}{x^2y^2z}$ **55.** $\frac{-4k-61}{(k-4)(k+10)}$
57. 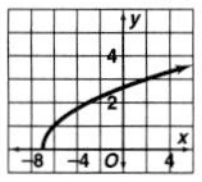 **63.** 8, 11 **65.** −8, 6

Lesson 12-8 pp. 682–685

EXERCISES

1. 10 choices
Shirt 1 → Tie 1 → S1, T1
→ Tie 2 → S1, T2
→ Tie 3 → S1, T3
→ Tie 4 → S1, T4
→ Tie 5 → S1, T5
Shirt 2 → Tie 1 → S2, T1
→ Tie 2 → S2, T2
→ Tie 3 → S2, T3
→ Tie 4 → S2, T4
→ Tie 5 → S2, T5
3a. 8, 10, 10, 10 **b.** 8,000,000 telephone numbers
5. 3,628,800 orders **7.** 1680 **9.** 360 **15.** 5040
17. ${}_8P_6$ **19.** ${}_8P_4$ **21a.** 24 **b.** $\frac{1}{24}$ **23.** 3 **25.** 5
27a. 260,000 license plates **b.** 23,920,000 license plates **29a.** 17,576 codes **b.** 17,526 codes **41.** 3
43. −10, 1 **47.** $BC \approx 34$, $AC \approx 54$ **49.** $AB \approx 48$, $AC \approx 7$ **51.** no solution **53.** $-\frac{7}{2} \pm \frac{\sqrt{97}}{2}$

Lesson 12-9 pp. 689–691

EXERCISES **1.** 1 **3.** 15 **11.** 220 **13.** $\frac{1}{5040}$ **15a.** 56 **b.** 1 **c.** $\frac{1}{56}$ **d.** $\frac{5}{28}$ **17.** 1 **19.** 4 **21.** permutation, since order *is* important **27.** 8 **41.** 12 **43.** 840
47. 2 **49.** $\frac{1}{10}$ **53.** −6.81, 0.81 **55.** −5.46, 1.46

Chapter Review pp. 693–695

1. rational expression **2.** asymptote
3. permutation **4.** rational equation **5.** inverse variation **6.** $xy = 6$ **7.** $xy = 9$ **8.** $xy = 4.4$ **9.** 4
10. 2.5 **11.** 18.75 **12.** inverse; $xy = 70$
13. direct; $y = 8.2x$ **14.** inverse; $xy = 3$
15. $y = 0, x = 0$; **16.** $y = 0, x = 0$;

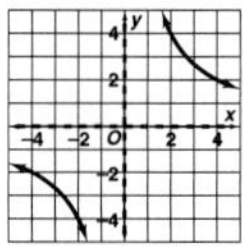

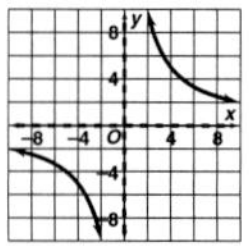

17. $y = 0, x = 5$; **18.** $y = 2, x = 0$;

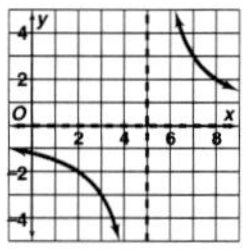

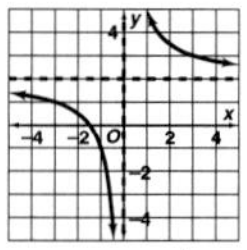

19. Answers may vary. Sample: $y = \frac{1}{x+1}$
20. The graph of $f(x) = \frac{5}{x+3}$ gets closer and closer to the lines $x = -3$ and $y = 0$. **21.** $x - 2$
22. $\frac{x}{4x+3}$ **23.** 6 **24.** $\frac{-3}{t(t-1)}$ **25.** $\frac{1}{2z-3}$ **26.** $\frac{x+2}{x+4}$
27. $\frac{24m}{(m-3)(m+1)}$ **28.** 12 **29.** $3(n+2)$
30. $\frac{1}{2(2e+1)}$ **31.** $2x - 4$ **32.** $3x^4 + 4x^3 - 1$
33. $50x^2 - 7x + \frac{1}{x}$ **34.** $x + 7 - \frac{5}{x+1}$
35. $x + 4 - \frac{32}{x+4}$ **36.** $2x^2 - 7x + 4$ **37.** $\frac{8x-4}{x-7}$
38. $\frac{7x+24}{28x}$ **39.** $\frac{15x^2+13x+27}{(3x-1)(2x+3)}$ **40.** $\frac{-3m+10}{(m+1)(m-1)}$
41. C **42.** 24 **43.** $-\frac{4}{35}$ **44.** 9 **45.** −14 **46.** −21
47. 2 **48.** ≈ 6 min **49.** 60 **50.** 1680 **51.** 360
52. 20 **53.** 3024 **54a.** 160 possible area codes **b.** 640 new area codes **55.** 6 **56.** 210 **57.** 36
58. 165 **59.** 5 **60.** 4 combinations
61. 3003 ways

Extra Practice

CHAPTER 1 **1.** Let T = total length, e = edge length; $T = 12e$. **3.** Let A = area, ℓ = length; $A = 12\ell$. **5.** 28 **7.** 9 **17.** < **19.** < **25.** −11
27. $-\frac{32}{15}$ **49.** $-16x + 12$ **51.** $8 - 4t$
60–65. 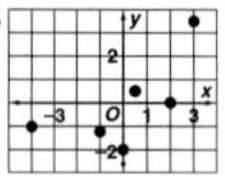

CHAPTER 2 **1.** 14 **3.** 8 **21.** t = test score; $\frac{87+84+85+t}{4} = 90$; no **23.** 1 **25.** −2 **39.** $\frac{A}{\ell}$
41. $\frac{ht}{p-m}$
47. mean = 39.375
median = 38
mode = 35
49. mean = 6.3
median = 6
modes = 5, 8

CHAPTER 3 **1.** $w > -3$; 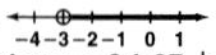
27. $5 < w < 7$ **29.** $m \le 4$ or $m > 8.4$ **37.** $|x| < 2$
39. $|x + 4| < 1$ **43.** $t > 1$ or $t < -1$;
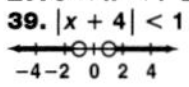

CHAPTER 3 **1.** −8 **3.** 48 **17.** $10x = 4$, 40% **19.** $1.2x = 6$, 500% **29.** 16% increase **31.** 200% increase **41.** 2.8%
43. 16.7% **45.** $\frac{5}{54}$ **47.** 0 **51.** $\frac{1}{12}$ **53.** $\frac{5}{24}$ **55.** $\frac{1}{12}$

CHAPTER 5 **1.**
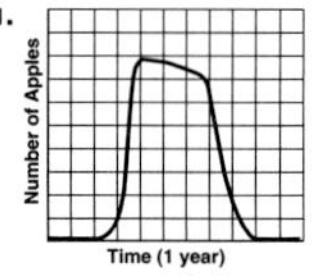

5. {−29, −11, −5, 13} **7.** {5, −1, 1, 19} **15.** no
17. yes
19. 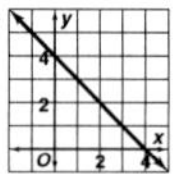 **21.** $f(x) = x + 2$
23. $f(x) = x - 7$

27. 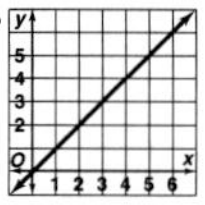 $y = x$

33. 33, 66 **35.** −1, 2

CHAPTER 6 **1.** 0.2 m/yr **3.** 1.6 mm/s
5. slope = 6, y-intercept = 8
7. slope = 0, y-intercept = 4
9. x-intercept = 2, y-intercept = 12
11. x-intercept = −6, y-intercept = 3
13. $y - 6 = -5(x - 4)$ **15.** $y - 5 = \frac{1}{2}(x - 8)$
21. 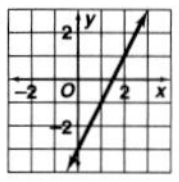 **29.** $y = \frac{3}{2}x + 2$
31. $y = x + 6$
37. $4x - y = -17$
39. $4x - 3y = 25$

45a–b. 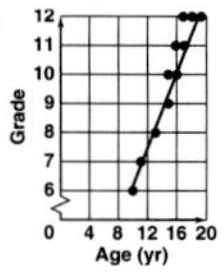

c. grade = 0.720 · age − 1.118
47. 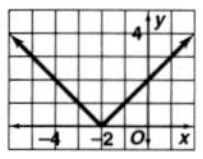

CHAPTER 7 **1.** (4, −3);
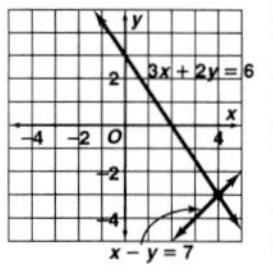

5. $x = 1, y = -1$
7. $x = 6, y = 13$
9. $x = 4, y = -9$
13. $x + y = 12$, $5x + y = 32$, 5 nickels, 7 pennies
15. $2x + 2y = 74$, $7x + 2y = 159$, length: 20 ft, width: 17 ft
19. 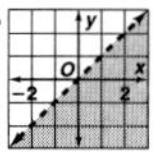 **25.** 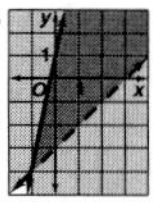

CHAPTER 8 **1.** $\frac{1}{64t^6}$ **3.** $(4.5)^2$ **17.** 9 **19.** 144
25. 3.4×10^7 **27.** 1.5×10^3 **33.** 8,050,000
35. 900,000,000 **41.** 1.5; 40.5, 60.75
43. 0.2; −0.008, −0.0016
49. $\{\frac{1}{3}, 1, 3, 9\}$; increase **51.** $\{\frac{2}{3}, 1, \frac{3}{2}, \frac{9}{4}\}$; increase
61. exponential growth; growth factor = 8
63. exponential decay; decay factor = $\frac{1}{2}$
69. $y = 200(1.04)^x$; \$243.33
71. $y = 3000(0.92)^x$; \$2336.06

CHAPTER 9 **1.** $2x^3 + 4x^2 - 11x + 11$
3. $6m^3 + m + 4$ **11.** $4b^3 + 12b$ **13.** $32m^2 - 40m$
19. $t^2(t^4 - t^3 + t^2 + 1)$ **21.** $4c^2(3c^3 - c + 4)$
27. $-5c^2 + 7c + 6$ **29.** $w^3 + 4w^2 + 3w - 2$
39. $(3x - 1)(2x + 5)$, $6x^2 + 13x - 5$
41. $(x - 3)(x - 1)$ **43.** $(v - 1)(v + 2)$
65. $(y + 3)(3y^2 - 1)$ **67.** $(w - 3)(w^2 + 3)$

CHAPTER 10 **1.** narrower **3.** wider and reflected over the x-axis **9.** $x = 0$, (0, 0) **11.** $x = 0$, (0, −3)
19. 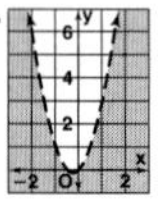 **21.** ±5 **23.** ±8 **33.** 6, −6
35. 10, −10 **61.** 2 **63.** 1

67. 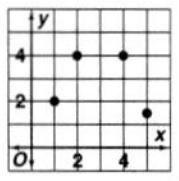 quadratic

CHAPTER 11 **1.** $\frac{\sqrt{3}}{3}$ **3.** $\frac{5\sqrt{2}}{3}$ **21.** no; $16 + 25 \neq 49$
23. no; $6^2 + 9^2 \neq 13^2$ **29.** 10 **31.** 10.8
33. 5.1; $\left(\frac{3}{2}, \frac{11}{2}\right)$ **35.** 1.4; $\left(\frac{9}{2}, -\frac{1}{2}\right)$ **43.** 5 **45.** 4
51. $x \ge -5$; 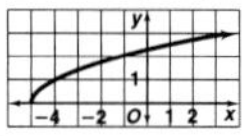

57. $\frac{9}{41}$ **59.** $\frac{9}{40}$ **63.** 0.9511 **65.** 1.1106 **67.** 201 m

CHAPTER 12 **1.** 70 **3.** 0.8 **7.** 8.1 **9.** 2
13. $x = 0, y = 0$; 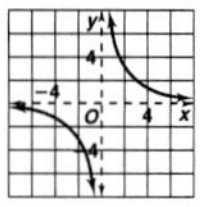

21. $\frac{t}{4}$ **23.** 4 **37.** $2x^2 + 5x + 2$ **39.** $3x^2 - 7x + 6$
41. 8 **43.** −1 **53.** 42 **55.** 8

Algebra Skills Handbook

p. 714 **1.** 10 games **3.** 9 tacks

p. 715 **1.** 17 and 19, or −19 and −17 **3.** 33, 34, 35, and 36 **5.** 24 years old **7.** mother: 38 yr; son: 16 yr; daughter: 7 yr **9.** regular tickets: 80; student tickets: 110

p. 716 **1.** 81 books **3.** 36 stories **5.** 7.2 m
7. 6 ways

p. 717 **1.** 21 lockers **3.** about 370,000,000 times
5. 63 games **7.** 32 and 33

p. 718 **1.** dog: K. C.; horse: Bo; bird: Cricket; cat: Tuffy **3.** Alexa, Karin, Heather, Annette, Tanya, Garo **5.** 126 players

p. 719 **1.** 6 **3.** 21 pencils **5.** 11 mi **7.** 290 mi
9. $4\frac{3}{4}$ mi east, 2 mi north

p. 710 **1.** composite **3.** composite **5.** prime
7. composite **9.** composite **11.** composite
13. composite **15.** composite **17.** composite
19. 1, 2, 23, 46 **21.** 1, 11 **23.** 1, 3, 9, 27 **25.** 1, 5, 41, 205 **27.** 1, 2, 3, 4, 6, 8, 12, 24 **29.** 1, 2, 4, 8, 11, 22, 44, 88 **31.** 1, 3, 61, 183 **33.** 1, 2, 7, 14, 49, 98
35. 1, 59 **37.** $2 \cdot 3 \cdot 3$ **39.** $3 \cdot 3 \cdot 3$ **41.** $2 \cdot 2 \cdot 2 \cdot 2 \cdot 2 \cdot 2$
43. $2 \cdot 2 \cdot 5 \cdot 5$ **45.** $2 \cdot 2 \cdot 3 \cdot 7$ **47.** $11 \cdot 11$

p. 721 **1.** 2 **3.** 24 **5.** 3 **7.** 7 **9.** 5 **11.** 21 **13.** 80
15. 33 **17.** 60 **19.** 240 **21.** 150 **23.** 40

p. 722 **1.** 2, 4 **3.** 3, 5 **5.** 3, 5, 9 **7.** 2 **9.** 2, 3, 4, 6, 8, 9 **11.** none **13.** 3, 5 **15.** 2, 3, 4, 6, 8, 9 **17.** 2, 4
19. 15 **21.** Answers may vary. Sample: $a + 1$ is not divisible by 2. Dividing by 2 will leave a remainder of 1.

p. 723 **1.** \$350 **3.** \$300 **5.** \$17.00 **7.** 7.10 **9.** 7.00
11. \$30.80

p. 724 **1.** $\frac{8}{14}, \frac{12}{21}, \frac{16}{28}, \frac{20}{35}, \frac{24}{42}$ **3.** $\frac{6}{16}, \frac{9}{24}, \frac{12}{32}, \frac{15}{40}, \frac{18}{48}$
5. $\frac{10}{12}, \frac{15}{18}, \frac{20}{24}, \frac{25}{30}, \frac{30}{36}$ **7.** 9 **9.** 48 **11.** 2 **13.** 9 **15.** 3
17. no **19.** no **21.** no **23.** $\frac{1}{2}$ **25.** $\frac{2}{3}$ **27.** $\frac{2}{5}$ **29.** $\frac{1}{3}$
31. $\frac{2}{5}$ **33.** $\frac{3}{4}$

p. 725 **1.** 0.3 **3.** 0.2 **5.** $0.\overline{714285}$ **7.** $0.\overline{5}$
9. $0.\overline{285714}$ **11.** 0.16 **13.** $\frac{7}{100}$ **15.** $\frac{7}{8}$ **17.** $6\frac{1}{3}$ **19.** $\frac{7}{9}$
21. $\frac{3}{8}$ **23.** $6\frac{12}{25}$

p. 726 **1.** $\frac{5}{7}$ **3.** 3 **5.** $10\frac{7}{15}$ **7.** $6\frac{2}{9}$ **9.** $6\frac{7}{33}$ **11.** $9\frac{2}{3}$
13. $13\frac{7}{16}$ **15.** $56\frac{11}{15}$ **17.** $\frac{3}{5}$ **19.** $1\frac{2}{7}$ **21.** $2\frac{3}{8}$ **23.** $3\frac{1}{3}$
25. $9\frac{4}{63}$ **27.** $2\frac{1}{6}$ **29.** $7\frac{5}{6}$

p. 727 **1.** $\frac{3}{10}$ **3.** $8\frac{5}{8}$ **5.** $3\frac{1}{2}$ **7.** $25\frac{3}{10}$ **9.** $2\frac{4}{5}$ **11.** 6
13. $9\frac{5}{6}$ **15.** $5\frac{15}{16}$ **17.** $\frac{8}{9}$ **19.** $\frac{18}{25}$ **21.** $13\frac{1}{3}$ **23.** $\frac{5}{6}$ **25.** 26
27. $1\frac{1}{3}$ **29.** $\frac{1}{3}$

p. 728 **1.** 56% **3.** 602% **5.** 820% **7.** 14.3%

9. 11.1% **11.** 75% **13.** 0.07 **15.** 0.009 **17.** 0.83
19. 0.15 **21.** 0.0003 **23.** 3.65 **25.** $\frac{19}{100}$ **27.** $4\frac{1}{2}$
29. $\frac{16}{25}$ **31.** $\frac{6}{25}$ **33.** $\frac{3}{800}$ **35.** $\frac{3}{5}$ **37.** $\frac{1}{50}$ **39.** $\frac{33}{50}$ **41.** $1\frac{1}{4}$

p. 729 **1.** 6^4 **3.** $5 \cdot 2^4$ **5.** $4^2 \cdot 3^2 \cdot 2$ **7.** 64 **9.** 144
11. 3267 **13.** $(1 \cdot 10^3) + (2 \cdot 10^2) + (5 \cdot 10^1) + (4 \cdot 10^0)$
15. $(8 \cdot 10^4) + (3 \cdot 10^3) + (4 \cdot 10^2) + (1 \cdot 10^0)$

p. 730 **1.** 100°, obtuse **3.** 180°, straight
5–12. Check students' work. **13.** Check students' work.

p. 731 **1.** 22 cm **3.** 24 cm^2 **5.** 216 cm^3
7. 351.68 cm^3

p. 732 **1.** 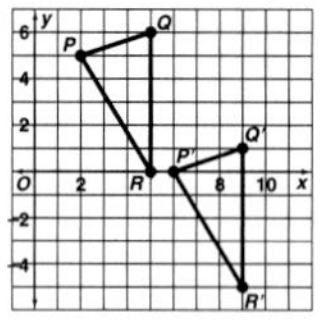

3. $(x, y) \to (x - 2, y - 1)$ **5.** $(x, y) \to (x + 4, y + \frac{1}{2})$
7. $(x, y) \to (x + 2, y + 5)$ **9.** $(x, y) \to (x + 6, y - 1)$
11. $(x, y) \to (x - 1, y + 1)$

p. 733 **1.** 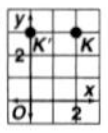 **3.** 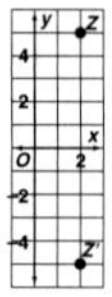

5. 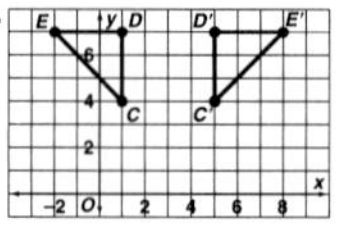

7. 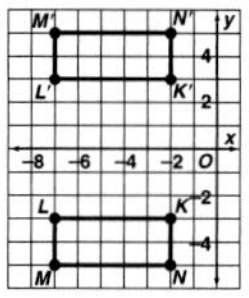 **9.** $x = 1$

p. 734 **1.** 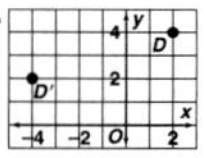 **3.** 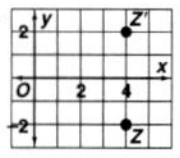

5a. 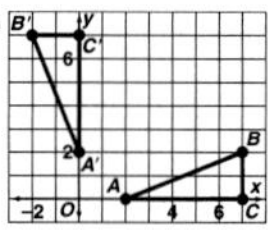

b. 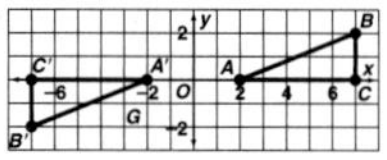

7a. 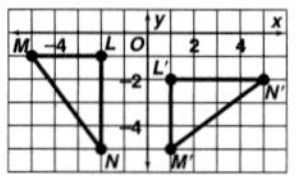

b. 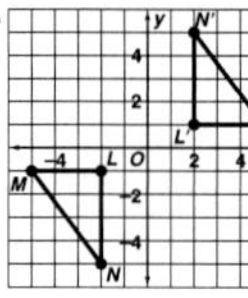 **9.** 90°

p. 735 **1.** 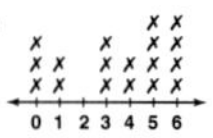 **3.** 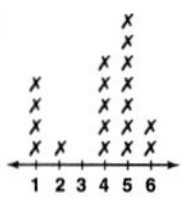

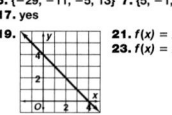

5.

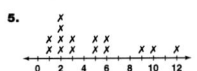

The line plot shows that most of the numbers are concentrated around 2, the maximum is 12, and the minimum is 1.

p. 736 1.

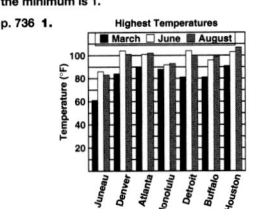

Highest Temperatures

p. 737 1a. 30–39 **b.** 15 students **c.** Answers may vary. Sample: If it actually took 50–59 minutes, the student might estimate by saying 1 hour. **d.** No; you don't know where inside each interval the answers are.

p. 738 1.

Market Share

The rap/hip hop category is growing faster.

p. 739 1a.

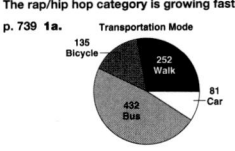

Transportation Mode

135 Bicycle
252 Walk
432 Bus
81 Car

b. 50% **c.** 3 times

p. 740 1.

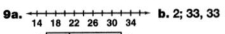

3.

9a.

 b. 2; 33, 33

c. 21 h; 23 h; both are much less than the 29-h typical week.

p. 741 1. Circle graph; the categories seem to cover how an average family spends all of its money in October. A circle graph also shows the percentage of a category more easily than a bar graph. **3.** Scatter plot; the levels of emissions most likely increase as the age of a car increases. A double bar graph would only be used if the data had an additional subject.

p. 742 1a. The graph implies that the runner's time on the 10-mile run was more than cut in half in six weeks, while actually the runner's time decreased by about 14%. **b.** Add a break on the vertical axis, or redraw the graph with the vertical axis starting at zero.

p. 743 1.

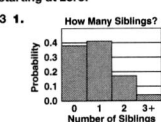

How Many Siblings?

3a.

Rolling Two Number Cubes

Sum	Probability
2	$\frac{1}{36}$
3	$\frac{2}{36}$
4	$\frac{3}{36}$
5	$\frac{4}{36}$
6	$\frac{5}{36}$
7	$\frac{6}{36}$
8	$\frac{5}{36}$
9	$\frac{4}{36}$
10	$\frac{3}{36}$
11	$\frac{2}{36}$
12	$\frac{1}{36}$

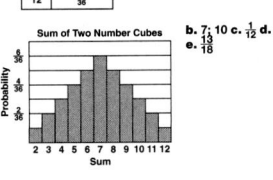

Sum of Two Number Cubes

b. 7; 10 **c.** $\frac{1}{12}$ **d.** $\frac{1}{6}$ **e.** $\frac{13}{18}$

p. 744 1. Use a coin. Let heads represent a book being a trade paperback. Flip the coin six times to represent one trial. Six rolls represent one trial. Count the number of trials that had only heads.

p. 745 1. Good sample; it uses the systematic method. **3.** Good sample; it is a random sample. **5.** Not biased; the question makes no assumptions and does not attempt to persuade you.

p. 746 1. ±10% **3.** ±3% **5.** 400 **7.** about 6 ft 5 in. tall

p. 747 1. = A2 + B2 + C2 **3.** = 1/2 ∗ B2 ∗ C2 **5.a.** D3 **b.** E4

CHAPTER 1

LESSON 1-8

page 55 Check Understanding

1a. Ident. Prop. of Mult.; m is mult. by the mult. identity, 1.

  b. Assoc. Prop. of Add.; the grouping of the terms changes.

  c. Assoc. Prop. of Mult.; the grouping of the factors changes.

  d. Ident. Prop. of Add.; the ident. for add., 0, is added.

  e. Comm. Prop. of Mult.; the order of the factors changes.

  f. Comm. Prop. of Add.; the order of the terms changes.

pages 56–58 Exercises

19. $25 \cdot 1.7 \cdot 4$
    $= 25 \cdot 4 \cdot 1.7$ Comm. Prop. of Mult.
    $= (25 \cdot 4) \cdot 1.7$ Assoc. Prop. of Mult.
    $= 100 \cdot 1.7$ mult.
    $= 170$ mult.

20. $-5(7y)$
    $= [-5(7)]y$ Assoc. Prop. of Mult.
    $= -35y$ mult.

21. $8 + 9m + 7$
    $= 9m + 8 + 7$ Comm. Prop. of Add.
    $= 9m + (8 + 7)$ Assoc. Prop. of Add.
    $= 9m + 15$ add.

22. $12x - 3 + 6x$
    $= 12x + (-3) + 6x$ def. of subtr.
    $= 12x + 6x + (-3)$ Comm. Prop. of Add.
    $= (12 + 6)x + (-3)$ Dist. Prop.
    $= 18x + (-3)$ add.
    $= 18x - 3$ def. of subtr.

23. $29c + (-29c)$
    $= [29 + (-29)]c$ Dist. Prop.
    $= 0 \cdot c$ Inv. Prop. of Add.
    $= 0$ Mult. Prop. of Zero

24. $43\left(\frac{1}{43}\right) + 1 = 1 + 1$
        Inv. Prop. of Mult.
    $= 2$ add.

27. $(3^2 - 2^3)(8759)$
    $= (9 - 8)(8759)$ mult.
    $= [9 + (-8)](8759)$ def. of subtr.
    $= 1(8759)$ add.
    $= 8759$ Ident. Prop. of Mult.

28. $(7^6 - 6^5)(8 - 8)$
    $= (7^6 - 6^5)[8 + (-8)]$ def. of subtr.
    $= (7^6 - 6^5) \cdot 0$ Inv. Prop. of Add.
    $= 0$ Mult. Prop. of Zero

29. $4 + 6(8 - 3m)$
    $= 4 + 48 - 18m$ Dist. Prop.
    $= 4 + 48 + (-18m)$ def. of subtr.
    $= (4 + 48) + (-18m)$ Assoc. Prop. of Add.
    $= 52 + (-18m)$ add.
    $= 52 - 18m$ def. of subtr.

30. $5\left(w - \frac{1}{5}\right) - w(9)$
    $= 5\left(w - \frac{1}{5}\right) - 9w$ Comm. Prop. of Mult.
    $= 5(w) - 5\left(\frac{1}{5}\right) - 9w$ Dist. Prop.
    $= 5w - 1 - 9w$ Inv. Prop. of Mult.
    $= 5w + (-1) + (-9w)$ def. of subtr.

    $= 5w + (-9w) + (-1)$ Comm. Prop. of Add.
    $= [5w + (-9w)] + (-1)$ Assoc. Prop. of Add.
    $= [5 + (-9)]w + (-1)$ Dist. Prop.
    $= -4w + (-1)$ add.
    $= -4w - 1$ def. of subtr.

40. No; $3 - 5 = -2$, while $5 - 3 = 2$.

41. No; $(5 - 3) - 1 = 2 - 1 = 1$, while $5 - (3 - 1) = 5 - 2 = 3$.

42. No; $1 \div 2 = \frac{1}{2}$, while $2 \div 1 = 2$.

43. No; $16 \div (4 \div 2) = 16 \div 2 = 8$, while $(16 \div 4) \div 2 = 4 \div 2 = 2$.

46. Answers may vary. Sample: The sandwich tastes the same whether the peanut butter or the jelly is on top. This is like the Comm. Prop. of Add., because you can add the peanut butter and jelly in either order.

LESSON 1-9

page 59 Check Skills You'll Need

1.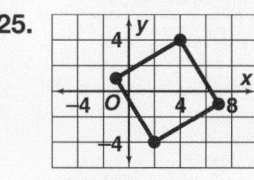

2.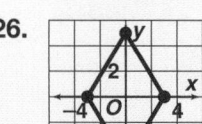

3.

4.

pages 62–65 Exercises

16.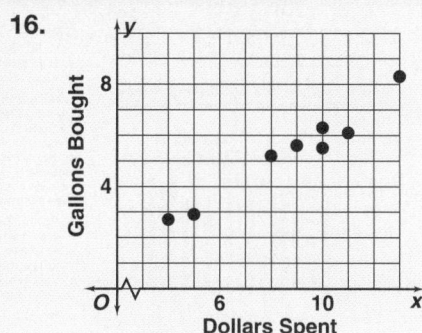

25.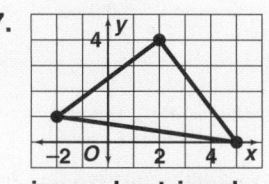

square

26.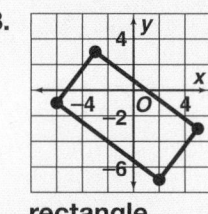

rhombus

27.

isosceles triangle

28.

rectangle

29. Neg. correlation; the more classes you take, the more work you have, so the less free time you have.

30. Pos. correlation; the greater the number of cars, the higher the pollution levels for a city.

31. No correlation; baby's length at birth is not related to its birthday.

32. Pos. correlation; the more you exercise, the more calories you burn.

33. Answers may vary. Samples: Pos. correlation; the number of hours a person earning an hourly wage works and the size of the paycheck.

Neg. correlation; the number of people working on a project and the time it takes to complete the project.
No correlation; person's height and the length of his or her hair.

page 70   Chapter Test

19–20. Answers may vary.

19. $10x + 3(\frac{1}{3} - x)$
$= 10x + 1 - 3x$ Dist. Prop.
$= 1 + 10x - 3x$ Comm. Prop. of Add.
$= 1 + (10 - 3)x$ Dist. Prop.
$= 1 + 7x$ subtr.

20. $(3^3 - 3^3)(1 - 2^2)$
$= (3^3 + (-3^3))(1 - 2^2)$ def. of subtr.
$= 0(1 - 2^2)$ Inv. Prop. of Add.
$= 0$ Mult. Prop. of Zero

27. Answers may vary. Sample:
$-\frac{2}{3}, 1.5, 1, -\frac{1}{6}$

$-\frac{2}{3}, -\frac{1}{6}, 1, 1.5$

page 71   Standardized Test Prep

6. [2] No.
1.07 euros = 1 U.S. dollar
$40 \div 1.07 \approx \$37.38$
The price is about \$37, which is not reasonable.

[1] correct answer, no work shown

7. [2] 0.70 pounds = 1 U.S. dollar
$15 \div 0.70 \approx \$21.43$

[1] correct answer, no work shown

8. [2] $2 \cdot 20 + 30 = 70$
No, the temperature is 70°F, which is cool for a beach day.

[1] correct temperature, but no conclusion

9. [2] Celsius $= \frac{(\text{Fahrenheit} - 30)}{2}$

[1] incorrect formula but reasonable attempt shown

CHAPTER 2

LESSON 2-2

page 81   Check Skills You'll Need

1. 9; Add. Prop. of Eq.
2. 5.2; Subtr. Prop. of Eq.
3. 14; Add. Prop. of Eq.
4. 33; Add. Prop. of Eq.
5. 32; Mult. Prop. of Eq.
6. 3; Div. Prop. of Eq.
7. $\frac{1}{5}$; Div. Prop. of Eq.
8. -9; Mult. Prop. of Eq.
9. $3\frac{3}{4}$; Subtr. Prop. of Eq.

CHAPTER 3

LESSON 3-2

pages 142–145   Exercises

17. $m < -1.6$

18. $b < \frac{1}{2}$

19. $n > 3$
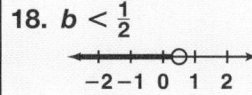

23. $w \le 5$;

24. $m > -8$;

25. $b > -7$;

26. $a \le -6$;

27. $r \ge -6$;

28. $k \le 1$;

29. $x < -1$;

30. $p > -6$;

31. $z \ge -1$;

32. $y < 5.5$;

33. $m > -1\frac{1}{2}$

34. $a \le -0.3$;

35. $p > -7$;

36. $h \le -\frac{1}{2}$

37. $d > -1.5$;

38. $t < -\frac{1}{2}$

69a. Let n = points scored on floor exercises. $8.8 + 7.9 + 8.2 + n \ge 34.0$; $n \ge 9.1$

b. Your sister must score 9.1 points or more to qualify for regional gymnastics competition.

page 178   Chapter Test

11. $z \le 2$;

12. $-4 \ge y$;

13. $x > -6$;

14. $u < 4$;

15. $t \le 2$;

16. $w \ge 1$;

17. $m > -4$

18. $y < 2.5$;

19. $x \leq 2$ or $x \geq 8$;

$$\begin{array}{c}\text{[number line: solid dots at 2 and 8, shading left of 2 and right of 8]}\\ -6\ -4\ -2\ \ 0\ \ 2\ \ 4\ \ 6\ \ 8\ \ 10\end{array}$$

20. $-3 < h < 2$;

$$\begin{array}{c}\text{[number line: open dots at }-3\text{ and }2\text{, shading between]}\\ -4\ -3\ -2\ -1\ \ 0\ \ 1\ \ 2\ \ 3\end{array}$$

21. $-6 < b \leq -3$;

$$\begin{array}{c}\text{[number line: open dot at }-6\text{, solid dot at }-3\text{, shading between]}\\ -7\ \ -6\ \ -5\ \ -4\ \ -3\ \ -2\end{array}$$

22. $-2.5 < q < 3$;

$$\begin{array}{c}\text{[number line: open dot at }-2.5\text{, open dot at 3, shading between]}\\ -4\ -3\ -2\ -1\ \ 0\ \ 1\ \ 2\ \ 3\ \ 4\end{array}$$

23. $n < -5$ or $n \geq -1$;

$$\begin{array}{c}\text{[number line: open dot at }-5\text{, solid dot at }-1\text{, shading left of }-5\text{ and right of }-1\text{]}\\ -6\ -5\ -4\ -3\ -2\ -1\ \ 0\ \ 1\end{array}$$

24. $k \geq 4$ and $k < 7.5$;

$$\begin{array}{c}\text{[number line: solid dot at 4, open dot at 7.5, shading between]}\\ -2\ \ 0\ \ 2\ \ 4\ \ 6\ \ 8\ \ 10\end{array}$$

page 179   Standardized Test Prep

6. [2] **a.** Let x = number of miles.
Let k = number of meters.
$k = 1610x$
$k = 1610(24,859.82)$
$\quad = 40,024,310.2$
The circumference of Earth around the poles is 40,024,310.2 meters.

b. The distance from a pole to the equator is $\frac{1}{4}(40,024,310.2)$ meters, which equals 10,006,077.55 meters. One ten millionth of this number is about 1 meter. So the unit of measure is close to the Academy of Sciences' original definition.

[1] correct conclusion but incomplete explanation

7. [2] **a.** Number of minutes in a day is $24 \text{ h} \cdot \frac{60 \text{ min}}{1 \text{ h}} = 1440 \text{ min}$
$\frac{24,901.55 \text{ mi}}{1440 \text{ min}} \approx 17.3 \text{ mi/min}$
The line separating night from day travels at the rate of 17.3 mi/min.

b. For all people not living on the equator, the line is moving slower because the numerator, the circumference at that latitude, is smaller than the circumference at the equator.

[1] correct conclusion, but incomplete explanation

CHAPTER 4

LESSON 4-3

page 196   Investigation

4.

$$\frac{x}{100} = \frac{27}{36},\ 75\%$$

5.

$$\frac{x}{100} = \frac{15}{60},\ 25\%$$

6.

$$\frac{80}{100} = \frac{40}{n},\ 50$$

7.

$$\frac{20}{100} = \frac{8}{n},\ 40$$

8.

$$\frac{25}{100} = \frac{13}{n},\ 52$$

9.

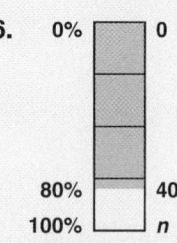

$$\frac{x}{100} = \frac{42}{63},\ 66\tfrac{2}{3}\%$$

page 231   Standardized Test Prep

16. [2] $\frac{3}{5}p = 21$

$\frac{5}{3} \cdot \frac{3}{5}p = \frac{5}{3} \cdot 21$

$p = 35$

So, about 35 paintings by Vermeer are known to exist.

[1] equation solved, but answer not rounded

17. [2] $20 raise:
$80 + $20 = $100
20% raise:
$80 \cdot 0.2 = 16$
$80 + $16 = $96
Accept the $20 raise because it will give a greater weekly salary.

[1] both new salaries given without explanation of which to accept

---

CHAPTER 5

LESSON 5-1

page 236   Check Understanding

1.

$$\text{[graph: Distance from Home vs. Time — walking, waiting for ride, riding up to "at school", riding, walking down]}$$

pages 238–240   Exercises

1–4. Labels may vary. Samples are given.

1.

$$\text{[graph: Heart Rate vs. Time — "Exercising": increases with exercise, levels off, increases quickly, slows, levels off]}$$

2.

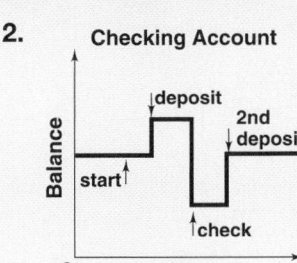

Checking Account

3.

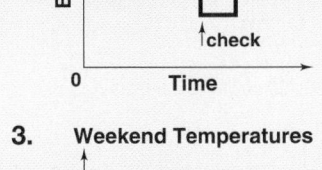

Weekend Temperatures

4.

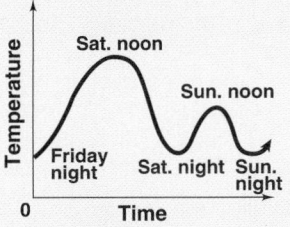

Hair Length

5–8. Graphs may vary. Samples are given.

5.

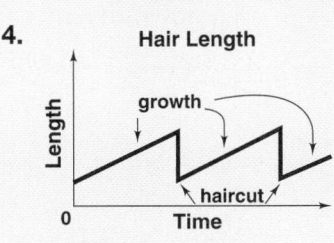

6.

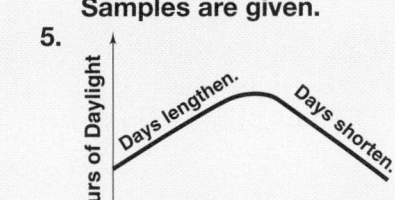

7.

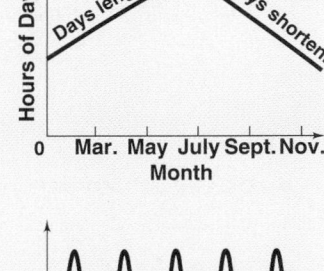

Pulse Rate During a Scary Movie

8.

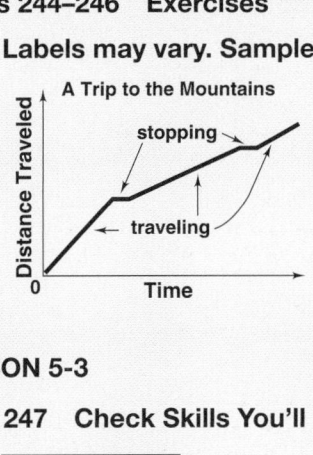

Between Classes

11a.

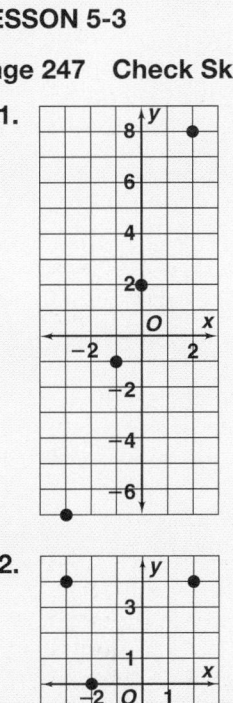

Bottom to Top

b.

Top to Bottom

No; the graphs are different because you have a constant speed traveling up but not down.

LESSON 5-2

page 241   Check Skills You'll Need

1.

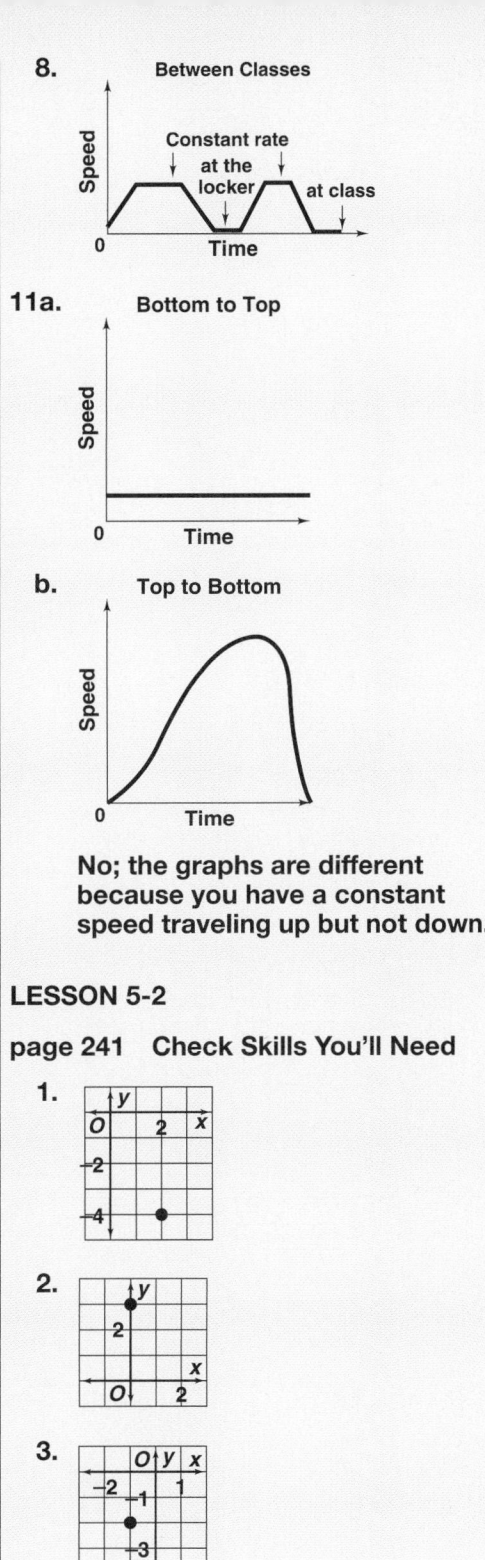

2.

3.

4.

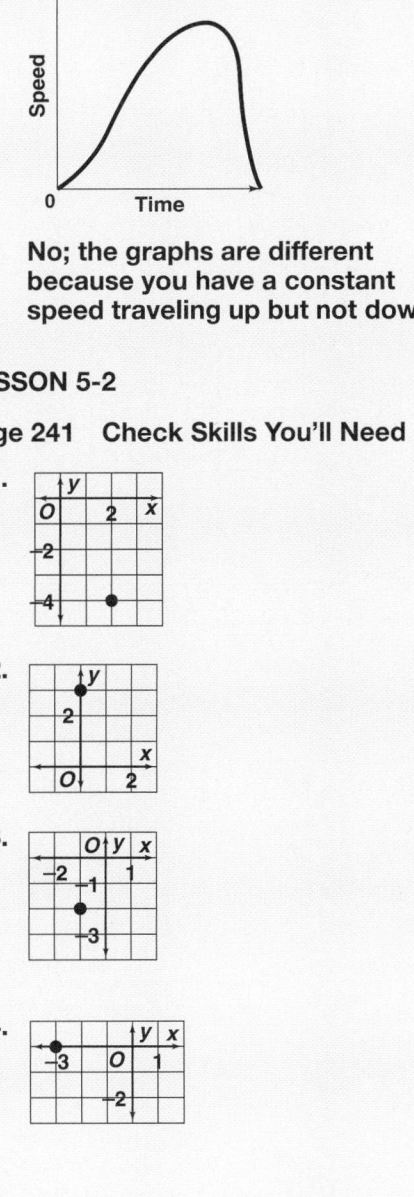

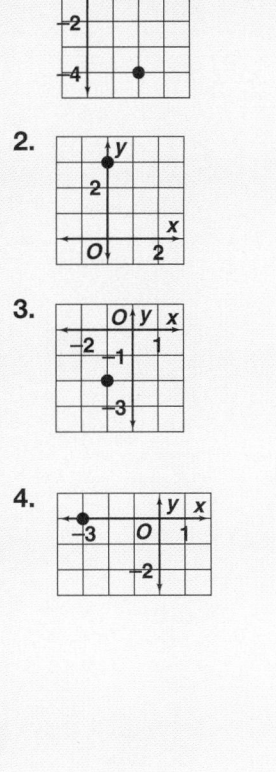

pages 244–246   Exercises

54.   Labels may vary. Sample:

A Trip to the Mountains

LESSON 5-3

page 247   Check Skills You'll Need

1.

2.

3.

pages 248–249   Check Understanding

1.   Tables may vary. Sample:

x	f(x)
0	4
1	7
−1	1
−2	−2

2a. Tables may vary. Sample:

c	P(c)
0	300
100	550
200	800
300	1050
500	1550

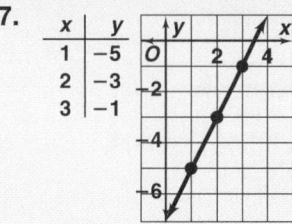

3a. Tables may vary. Sample:

x	y
-2	1
-1	0
0	-1
1	0
2	1

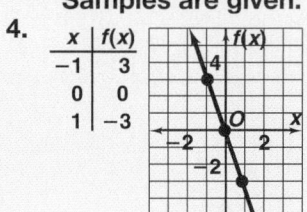

b. Tables may vary. Sample:

x	f(x)
-2	3
-1	0
0	-1
1	0
2	3

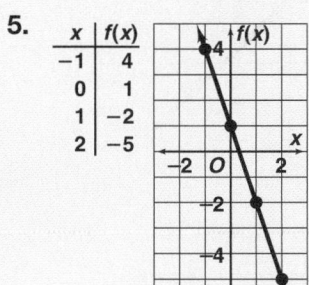

pages 249–252 Exercises

4–12. Tables may vary. Samples are given.

4.

x	f(x)
-1	3
0	0
1	-3

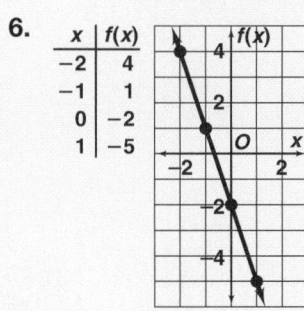

5.

x	f(x)
-1	4
0	1
1	-2
2	-5

6.

x	f(x)
-2	4
-1	1
0	-2
1	-5

7.

x	y
1	-5
2	-3
3	-1

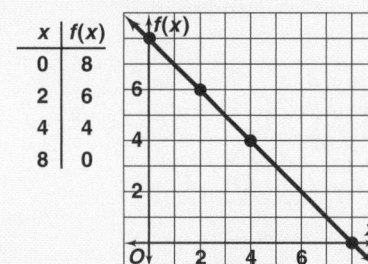

8.

x	f(x)
0	8
2	6
4	4
8	0

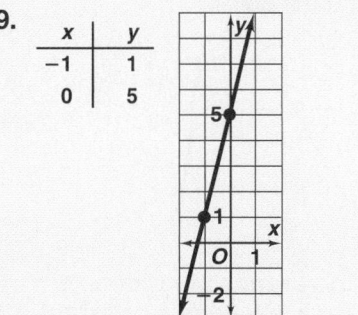

9.

x	y
-1	1
0	5

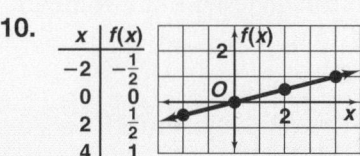

10.

x	f(x)
-2	$-\frac{1}{2}$
0	0
2	$\frac{1}{2}$
4	1

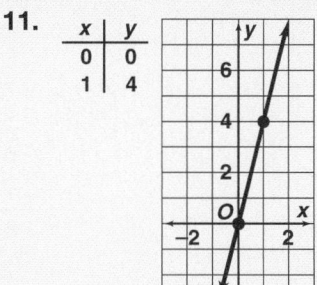

11.

x	y
0	0
1	4

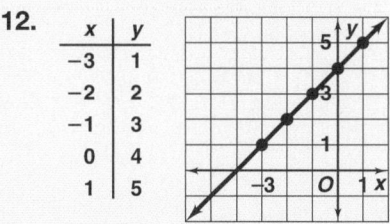

12.

x	y
-3	1
-2	2
-1	3
0	4
1	5

13c.

Money Earned Babysitting

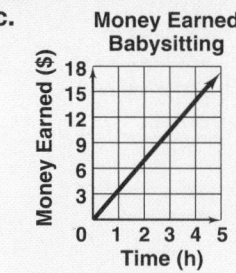

15.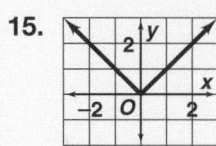

16.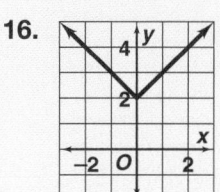

17.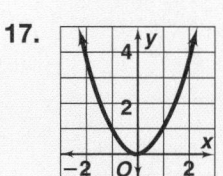

18.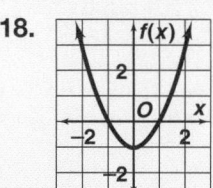

19.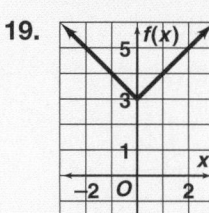

20.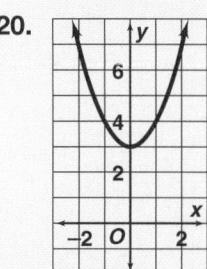

21.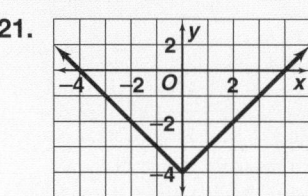

T774

22.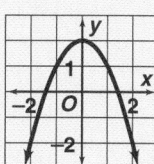

23.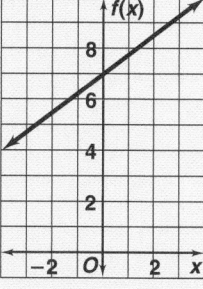

26.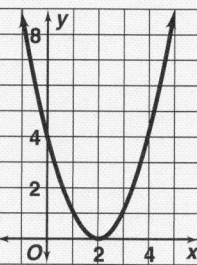

27.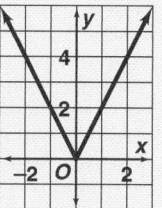

28.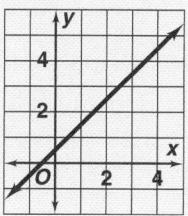

29.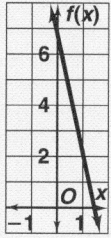

30.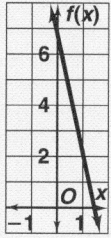

31.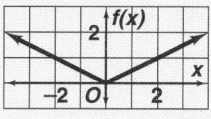

32.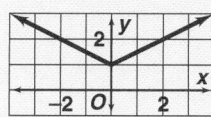

33.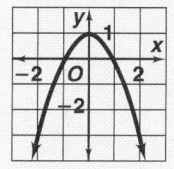

34.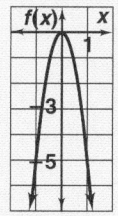

35.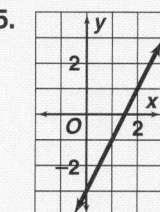

36.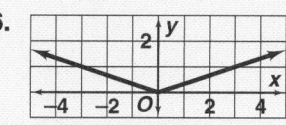

37.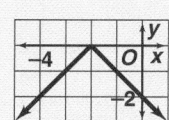

38a. 55.2 gal

b.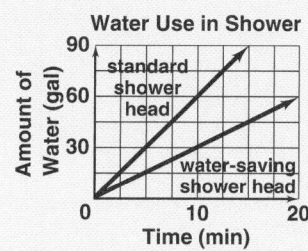

Water Use in Shower

40b.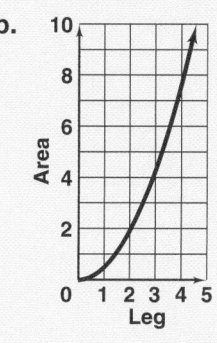

42a.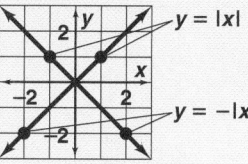

44a.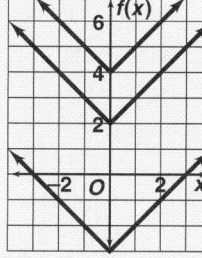

LESSON 5-4

page 254   Check Skills You'll Need

1–6. Tables may vary.
Samples are given.

1.

x	f(x)
−1	−6
0	−1
1	4
2	9
3	14

2.

x	y
−2	10
−1	7
0	4
1	1
2	−2

3.

t	g(t)
−2	−7.4
−1	−7.2
0	−7
1	−6.8
2	−6.6

4.

x	y
−2	−7
−1	−3
0	1
1	5
2	9

5.

x	f(x)
−2	8
−1	7
0	6
1	5
2	4

6.

d	c(d)
−2	−1.1
−1	−0.1
0	0.9
1	1.9
2	2.9

page 256–259 Exercises

42–47. Tables may vary.
Samples are given.

42.

x	f(x)
−1	−4
0	−3
1	−2
2	−1
3	0

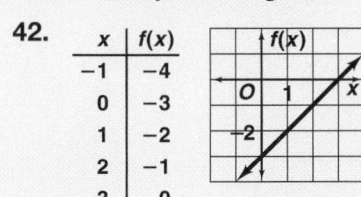

43.

x	y
−1	6
0	5
2	3
4	1
5	0

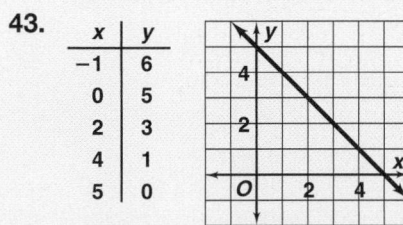

44.

x	g(x)
−1	4
0	3
1	2
2	1
3	0

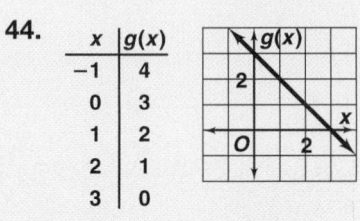

45.

x	f(x)
−1	−5
0	−3
1	−1
2	1
3	3

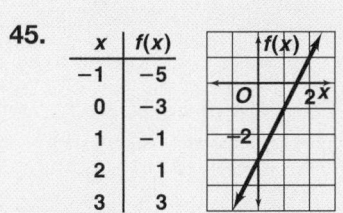

46.

x	y
−2	1
−1	−1
0	−3
1	−1
2	1

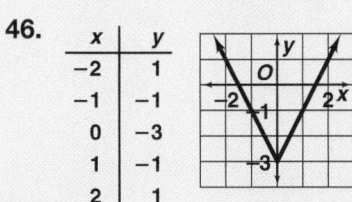

47.

x	y
−2	5
−1	−1
0	−3
1	−1
2	5

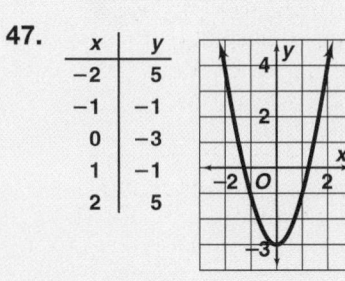

pages 275–277 Chapter Review

11–14. Answers may vary.
Samples are given.

11.

Height of a Sunflower Over a Summer

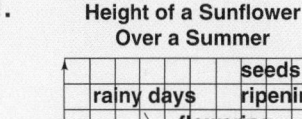
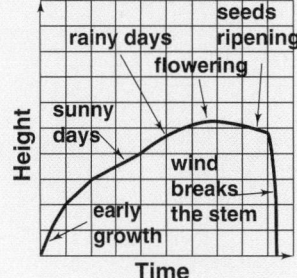

12.

Number of People in a Restaurant

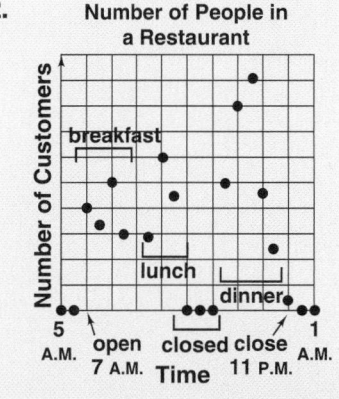

13.

Number of Vehicles that Enter the School Parking Lot

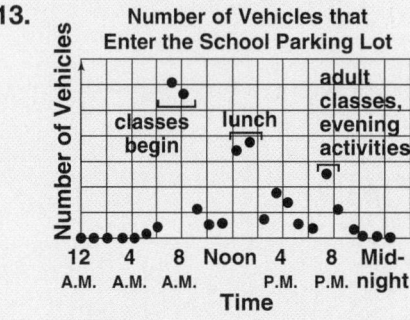

14.

Bags of Peanuts Sold During a Baseball Game

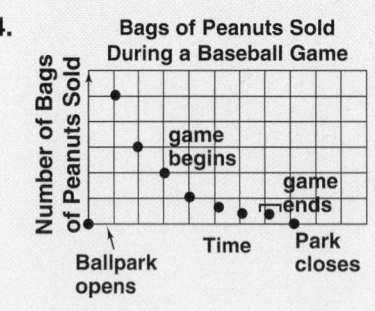

page 278 Chapter Test

1–2. Answers may vary.
Samples are given.

1.

Speed During Bike Ride

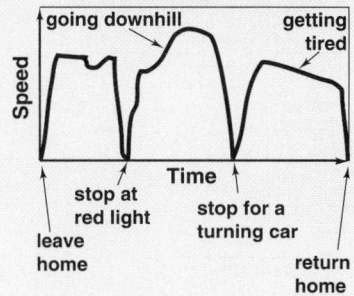

2.

Amount of Milk During Lunchtime

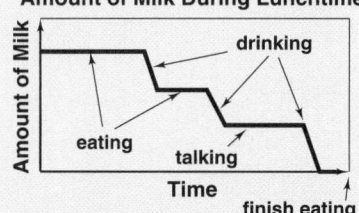

8.

x	f(x)
−2	−6
0	−3
2	0
4	3

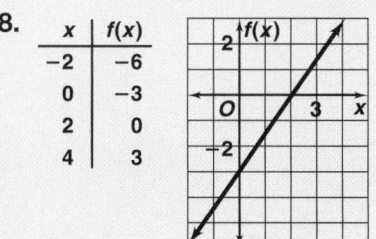

9.

x	f(x)
−2	0
−1	3
0	4
1	3
2	0
3	−5

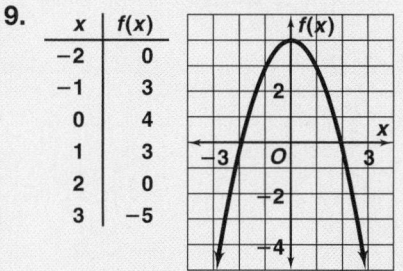

page 279 Standardized Test Prep

8. **[2] Yes; Amtrak carries 100,404 riders on the Boston–New York run, and this is 30% of train and air passengers.**

30% of total is 100,404.
$0.30x = 100,404$
$x = 334,680$

If the total stays the same and Amtrak ridership doubles, the percentage will also double.

$A = 2(100,404)$
$= 200,808$

The percent is
$\frac{200,808}{334,680} = 0.60$ or 60%.

[1] correct answer, but no explanation

CHAPTER 6

LESSON 6-2

page 293   Check Understanding

5.
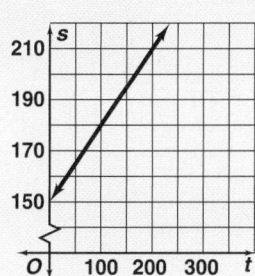

pages 294–296   Exercises

54.
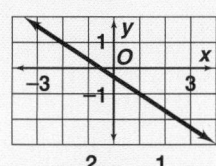

$$y = -\frac{2}{3}x - \frac{1}{3}$$

55.
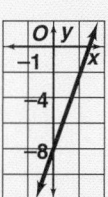 $y = 6x - 8$

57a.
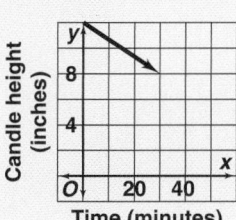

LESSON 6-3

page 299   Check Understanding

3a.
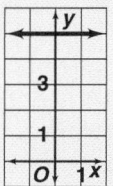

3b.
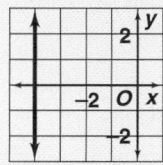

3c.

3d.
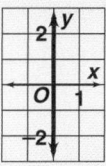

pages 301–303   Exercises

23.
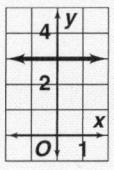

24.
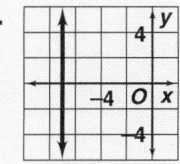

25.
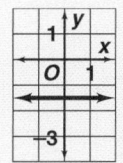

26.
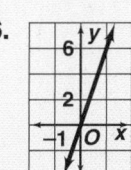

46.
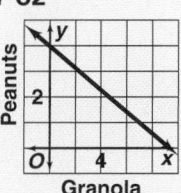

47b. **7 oz**
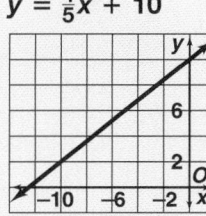

49. $y = \frac{4}{5}x + 10$

50. $y = \frac{6}{7}x + 3$
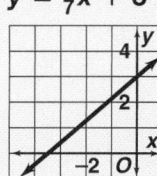

51. $y = -\frac{4}{5}x - 3$
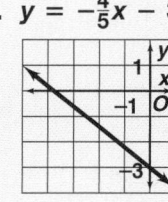

52. $y = \frac{5}{9}x - \frac{5}{3}$
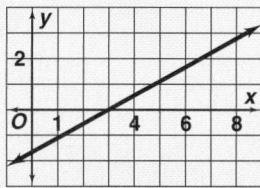

53. $y = -\frac{16}{11}x - 8$
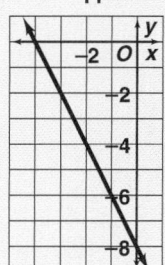

54. $y = \frac{1}{9}x - \frac{2}{3}$
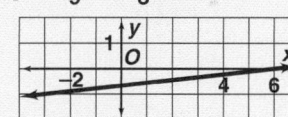

62b.
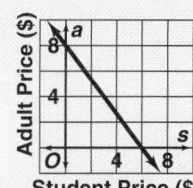

Answers may vary. Sample:
$s = \$2.00$, $a = \$5.33$;
$s = \$3.00$, $a = \$4.00$;
$s = \$6.00$, $a = \$0.00$
$s = \$3.00$ and
$a = \$4.00$ because they are
whole dollar amounts, and
adults pay more.

69. [4] a. $48x + 56y = 2008$

b.

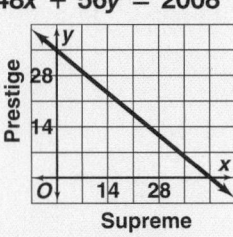

c. Answers will include three of the following:
1 Supreme, 35 Prestige;
8 Supreme, 29 Prestige;
15 Supreme, 23 Prestige;
22 Supreme, 17 Prestige;
29 Supreme, 11 Prestige;
36 Supreme, 5 Prestige

[3] correct equation and graph

[2] wrong equation, but a corresponding correct graph

[1] correct equation only

LESSON 6-4

pages 307–309 Exercises

1.

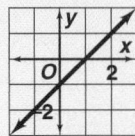

2.

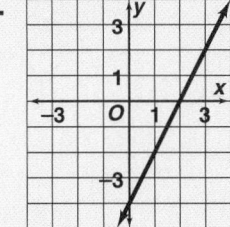

3.

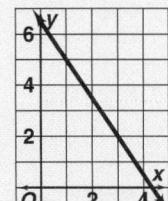

4.

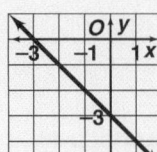

5.

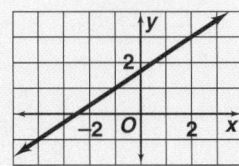

6.

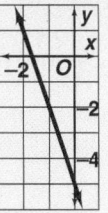

7.

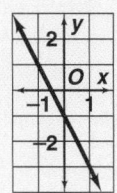

8.

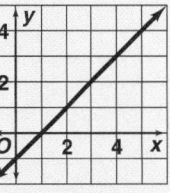

9.

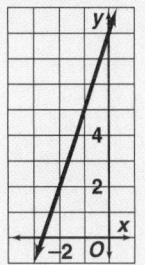

LESSON 6-6

page 318 Check Skills You'll Need

1.

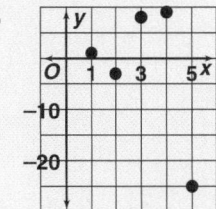

2.

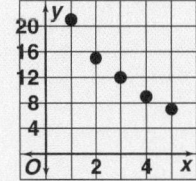

page 319 Check Understanding

1.

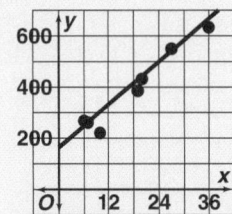

Answers may vary.
Sample: $y = 14x + 166$;
362 Calories

1. $y - 27 = 4.7(x - 5)$;
about 154 min

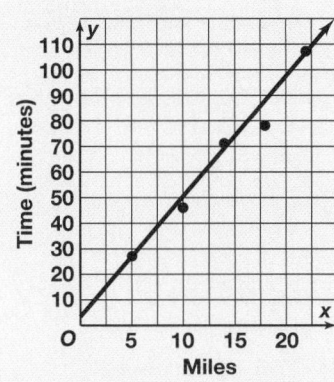

2. $y = -248.55x + 501,190.07$;
$r = -0.9854908654$

LESSON 6-7

page 325 Check Skills You'll Need

5.

x	y
0	6
1	5
2	4
3	3

6.

x	y
0	1
1	2
2	3
3	4

7.

x	y
0	1
1	2
-1	0
-2	1

page 326 Additional Examples

4a.

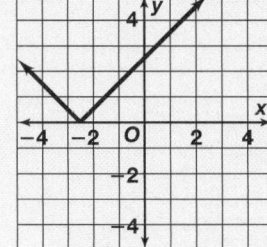

b.

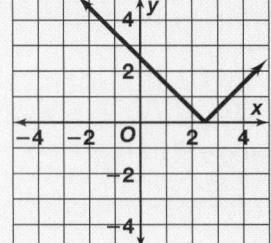

pages 327–329 Exercises

1. Answers may vary. Sample: same shape, shifted 3 units up

2. Answers may vary. Sample: same shape, shifted 3 units down

3. Answers may vary. Sample: same shape, shifted 7 units down

28. 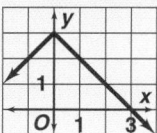 29.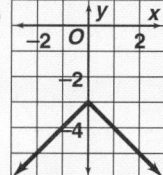

30. 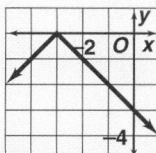 31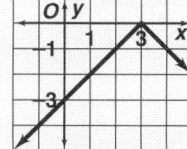

42a.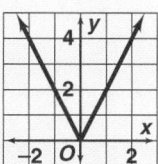

b. 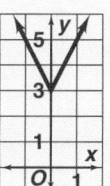 c.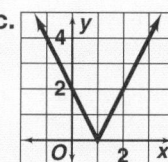

d.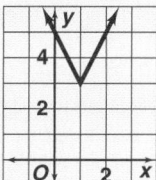

48. [4] a–b.

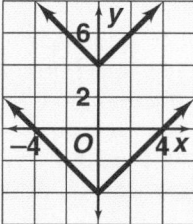

c. Part (a) graph is shifted 8 units up to get part (b) graph.

[3] one incorrect graph but correct answer to part (c) based on graphs drawn OR incorrect answer based on correct graphs

[2] both graphs incorrect but correct answer to part (c) based on graphs drawn

[1] both graphs incorrect and no answer given for part (c)

page 334   Chapter Test

5.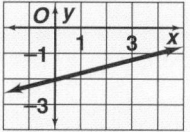

6.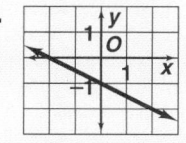

7.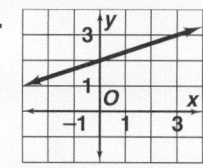

8.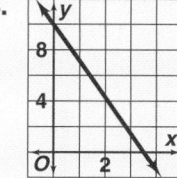

31b. intercepts: 6; −30

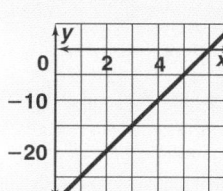

34.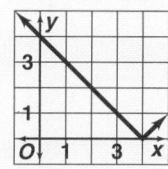

35.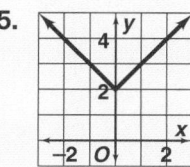

36a. $y = 0.0436x + 15.34$ (for 1967 = 67)

b. For sample in (a): 20,100 municipalities

37a. $y = -0.197x + 31.95$ (for 1967 = 67)

b. For sample in (a): 10,300 school districts

page 336   Standardized Test Prep

15. [2] Find the slope: $\frac{4 - (-1)}{3 - 2} = \frac{5}{1}$

Find the equation:
$y - 4 = 5(x - 3)$
$y - 4 = 5x - 15$
$y = 5x - 11$
(OR equivalent work using $y + 1 = 5(x - 2)$)

[1] one computational error OR no work shown

16. [2] $y + 3 = -\frac{5}{2}(x - 2)$
$y + 3 = -\frac{5}{2}x + 5$
$y = -\frac{5}{2}x + 2$

[1] one computational error OR no work shown

17. [2] $-3 \le 2x + 1 < 7$
$-4 \le 2x < 6$
$-2 \le x < 3$

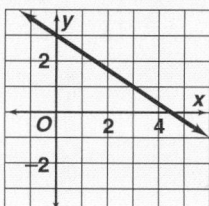

[1] incorrect graph OR no work shown

CHAPTER 7

pages 338   Diagnosing Readiness

14.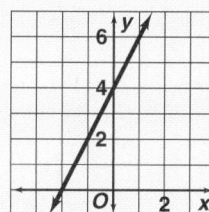

15.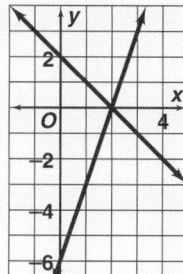

LESSON 7-1

page 340   Check Skills You'll Need

4.

T779

5.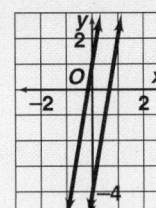

6.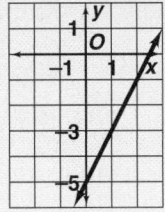

10.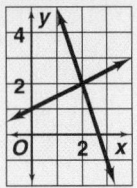

29.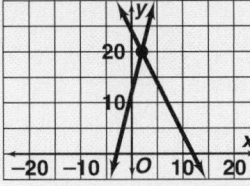

7.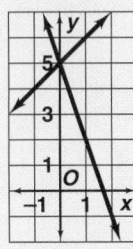

11.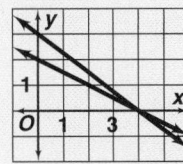

30.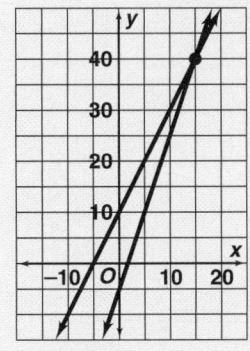

page 340 Check Understanding

1a. (−1, 4);
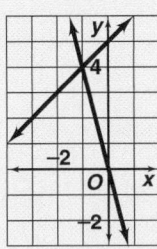

12.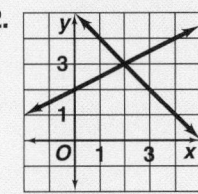

31.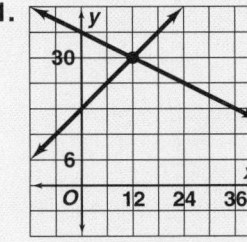

15.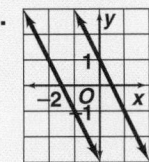

1b. (−2, 3);
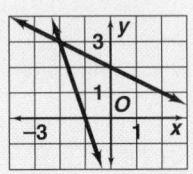

16.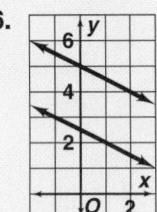

32.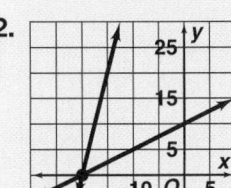

pages 343–345 Exercises

6.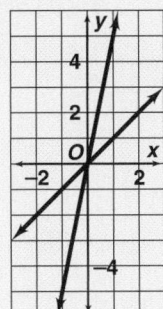

17.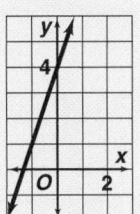

33a. time on the horizontal and distance on the vertical

b. Red represents the tortoise because it shows distance changing steadily over time. Blue represents the hare because it is steeper than the other line at the ends but shows no change in distance while the hare is napping.

c. The point of intersection shows when the tortoise passed the sleeping hare.

7. 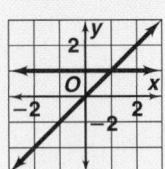   **8.**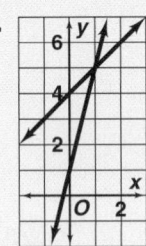

18.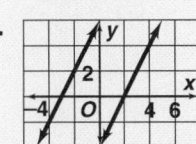

25.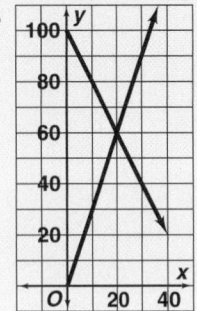

39. a. $c = 100 + 50t$;
$c = 50 + 75t$; (2, 200);

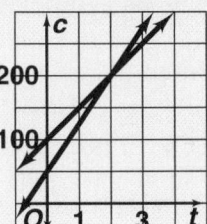

9.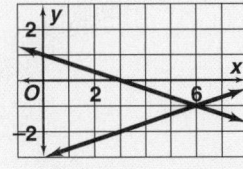

b. The cost of renting either studio for 2 h is the same, $200.

LESSON 7-2

pages 349–352   Exercises

25. estimate: $\left(\frac{1}{2}, 1\right)$;

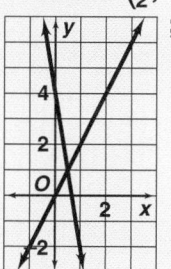

$\left(\frac{1}{2}, 1\right)$

26. estimate: $(-2, 3)$;

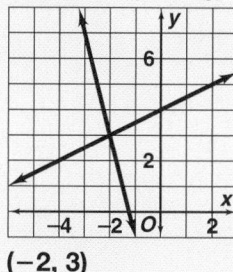

$(-2, 3)$

27. estimate: $(-1, 1)$;

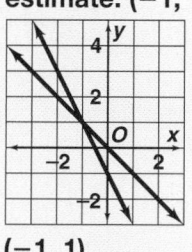

$(-1, 1)$

28. estimate: $(-3.5, -3.5)$;

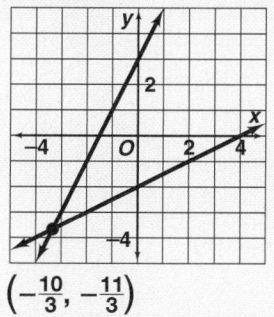

$\left(-\frac{10}{3}, -\frac{11}{3}\right)$

29. estimate: $\left(-\frac{3}{4}, 4\frac{3}{4}\right)$;

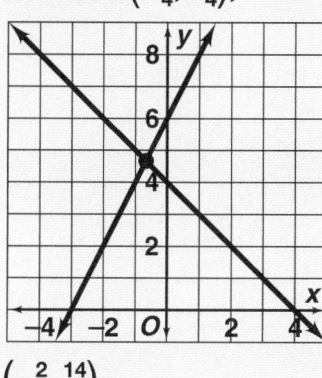

$\left(-\frac{2}{3}, \frac{14}{3}\right)$

30. estimate: $(-4, 0)$;

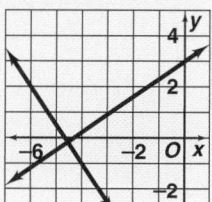

$\left(-\frac{50}{11}, -\frac{2}{11}\right)$

33b.

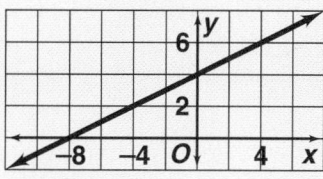

34b.

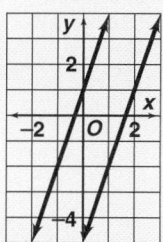

56.

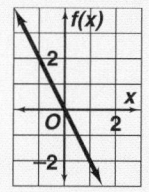

57.

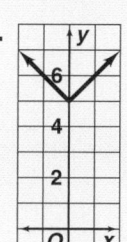

58.

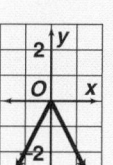

59.

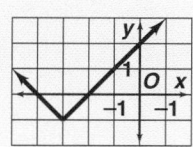

LESSON 7-5

page 370   Investigation

1.

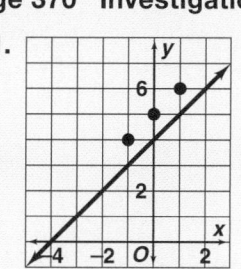

2. Answers may vary. Sample: (0, 5), (1, 6), and (−1, 4) all result in a true statement.

3. Answers may vary. Sample: (0, 1), (1, 2), and (2, 4) all result in a false statement.

pages 373–376   Exercises

18.

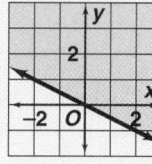

19. $y \leq \frac{2}{3}x - \frac{7}{3}$;

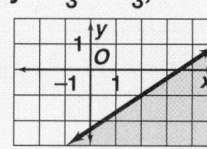

20. $y \geq \frac{5}{3}x - 2$;

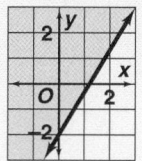

21. $y \leq \frac{2}{3}x - \frac{8}{3}$;

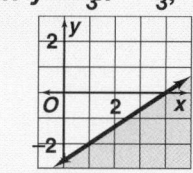

22. $y < -\frac{3}{2}x - 2$;

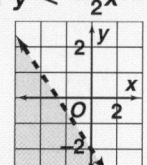

23b.

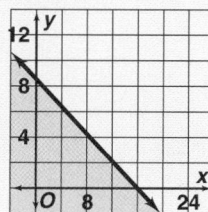

c. Answers may vary. Sample: 8 blue and 4 gold, 2 blue and 8 gold, 12 blue and 2 gold

d. No; you cannot buy −2 rolls of paper.

24b.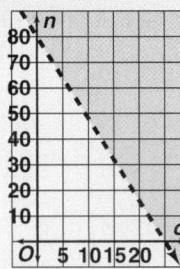

c. Answers may vary. Sample:
30 canvas and 10 nylon,
26 canvas and 20 nylon,
35 canvas and 10 nylon

d. Domain and range values must be positive integers, since you cannot buy portions of packs or a negative number of packs.

54. [2] First, graph the solid line $y = 3x - 4$. Then shade below the line.

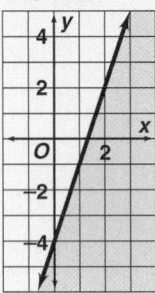

[1] correct graph given, no explanation

LESSON 7-6

page 377   Check Skills You'll Need

1. (2, 0);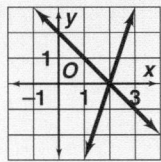

2. no solution;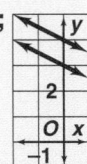

3. (4, 0);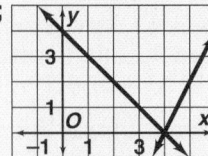

4.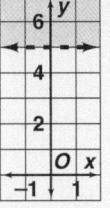

5.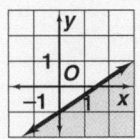

6.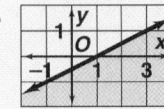

pages 380–384   Exercises

4.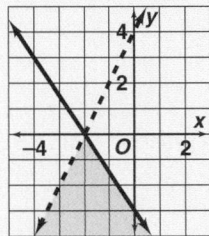

5.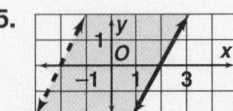

6.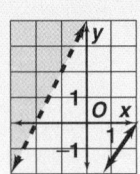

7.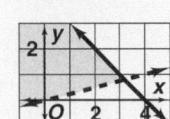

8.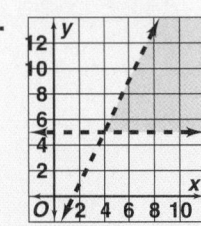

9.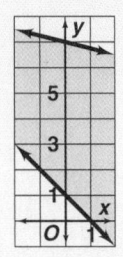

10.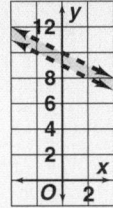

14.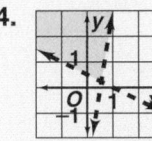

15.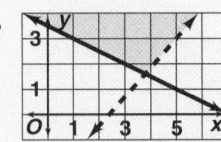

20a. $1.5f + 2.5c < 9.50$,
$f + c \geq 4$

b.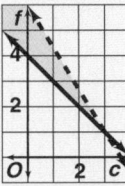

21.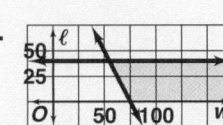

22b.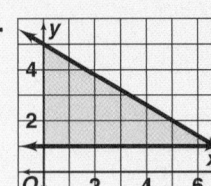

c. 2 books and 6 CDs; no, (2, 6) is not in the shaded region.

23. $x + y \geq 50$,
$4x + 3y \leq 180$

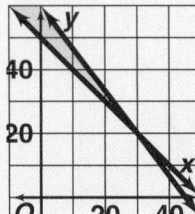

33a. trapezoid

b. (0, −4), (0, 2), (2, −4), (2, 0)

c. 10 units^2

34a. triangle

b. (2, −3), (2, 2), (7, −3)

c. 12.5 units^2

35a. $x \geq 1$,
$10.99x + 4.99y \leq 45$

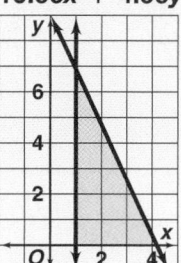

37a.

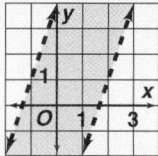

b. No; they are parallel.

43a. $s + d > 10$,
$s + d < 20, d \geq 3$,
$10d + 0.15s < 60$

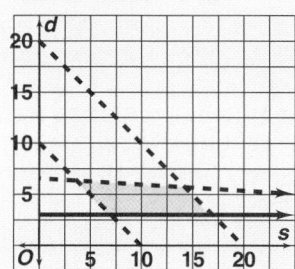

b. Answers may vary.
Sample: (8, 4.5); 12.5 g;
gold: $45.00, silver: $1.20

47b.

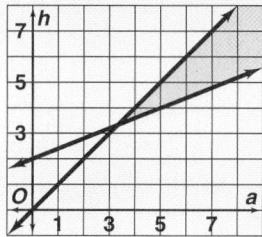

48a. $180x + 240y \geq 2700$

$x + y \leq 17$

$x > y$

$y \geq 4$

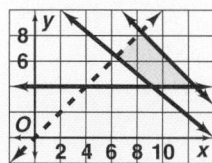

b. Answers may vary. Sample:
10 14-in. drums and
6 18-in. drums

55.

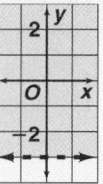

56.

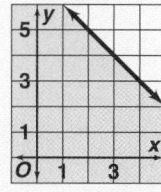

57.

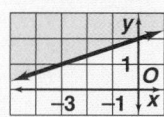

58.

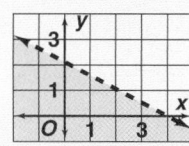

page 385   Technology

1.

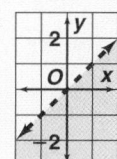

2.

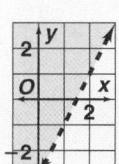

3.

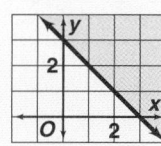

4.

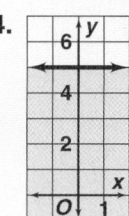

page 390   Chapter Test

1.

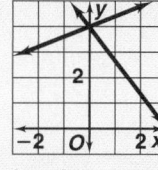

$(2, -1)$

2.

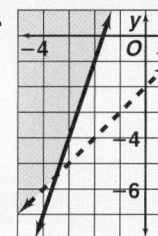

$(0, 4)$

20. Answers may vary. Sample: You
solve a system of linear equations
by finding a single point that
satisfies all the equations in the
system. You solve a system of
linear inequalities by graphing a
region that contains points that
satisify all the inequalities in the
system.

22.

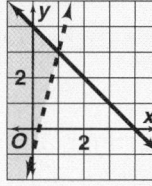

23.

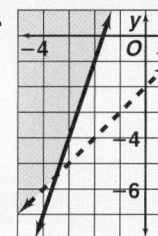

24.

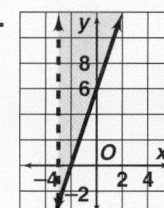

25.

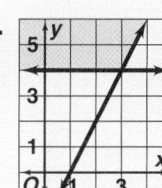

27a. $0.10d + 0.25q < 5.00$

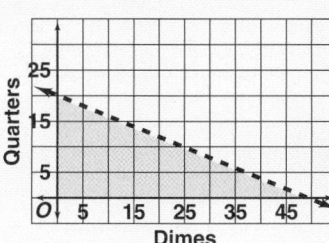

b. 49 items

c. 19 items

28a. $w \le 30$, $2\ell + 2w \le 180$

b.

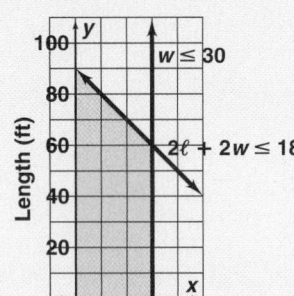

page 391   Standardized Test Prep

7. [2] Yes, the percent of change is over 4000%.

$$\frac{938.9 - 22.6}{22.6} = \frac{916.3}{22.6}$$

$$\approx 40.54$$

The percent of change is actually over 4054%.

[1] minor calculation error

8. [2] Let x = years after 1985, y = millions of CDs; $y = 65.45x + 22.6$; $y = 65.45(25) + 22.6 = 1658.85$, about 1659 million CDs.

[1] minor calculation error OR not predicting number sold in 2010

CHAPTER 8

LESSON 8-5

pages 420–423   Exercises

83.

Distance From the Sun (kilometers)

Planet	Maximum : Minimum
Mercury	$6.97 \times 10^7 : 4.59 \times 10^7 \approx 1.52$
Venus	$1.089 \times 10^8 : 1.075 \times 10^8 \approx 1.01$
Earth	$1.521 \times 10^8 : 1.471 \times 10^8 \approx 1.03$
Mars	$2.491 \times 10^8 : 2.067 \times 10^8 \approx 1.21$
Jupiter	$8.157 \times 10^8 : 7.409 \times 10^8 \approx 1.10$
Saturn	$1.057 \times 10^9 : 1.347 \times 10^9 \approx 1.12$
Uranus	$3.004 \times 10^9 : 2.739 \times 10^9 \approx 1.10$
Neptune	$4.537 \times 10^9 : 4.457 \times 10^9 \approx 1.02$
Pluto	$7.375 \times 10^9 : 4.425 \times 10^9 \approx 1.67$

LESSON 8-7

page 430   Check Skills You'll Need

1.

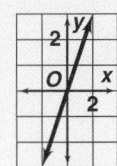

2.

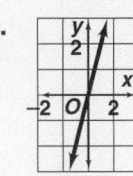

3.

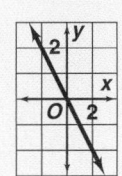

page 431   Additional Examples

3.

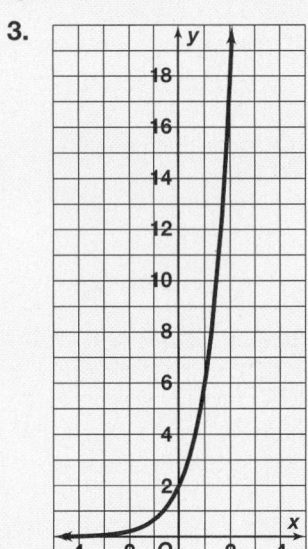

4.

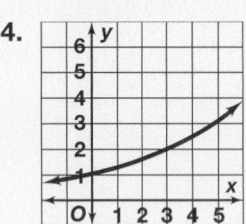

pages 432–435   Exercises

34a.

Time	Number of 20-min Time Periods	Pattern	Number of Bacteria Cells
Initial	0	75	75
20 min	1	$75 \cdot 2$	$75 \cdot 2^1 = 150$
40 min	2	$75 \cdot 2 \cdot 2$	$75 \cdot 2^2 = 300$
60 min	3	$75 \cdot 2 \cdot 2 \cdot 2$	$75 \cdot 2^3 = 600$
80 min	4	$75 \cdot 2 \cdot 2 \cdot 2 \cdot 2$	$75 \cdot 2^4 = 1200$
100 min	5	$75 \cdot 2 \cdot 2 \cdot 2 \cdot 2 \cdot 2$	$75 \cdot 2^5 = 2400$
120 min	6	$75 \cdot 2 \cdot 2 \cdot 2 \cdot 2 \cdot 2 \cdot 2$	$75 \cdot 2^6 = 4800$
140 min	7	$75 \cdot 2 \cdot 2 \cdot 2 \cdot 2 \cdot 2 \cdot 2 \cdot 2$	$75 \cdot 2^7 = 9600$

page 436   Technology

1b.

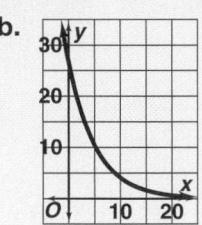

page 450   Chapter Test

28.

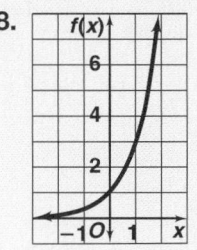

page 451   Standardized Test Prep

17. [4] Yes; because rectangles have opposite sides that are parallel and adjacent sides that are perpendicular, 2 slopes must be equal and the remaining 2 slopes must be their negative reciprocals.

[3] yes, with an explanation that neglects to mention either parallel or perpendicular

[2] yes, with a vague explanation

[1] yes, with no explanation

CHAPTER 9

LESSON 9-2

pages 463–465   Exercises

5. $18x^2 + 2x^3$

6. $-p^3 + 11p^2$

7. $12x^4 - 2x^3 + 10x^2$

8. $36y^5 + 32y^4 - 44y^2$

9. $-45c^5 + 40c^4 + 25c^3$

10. $-42q^7 + 14q^3 + 49q^2$

11. $-3g^{11} + 18g^9 - 15g^7$

12. $-40x^9 - 12x^8 + 28x^6$

LESSON 9-3

pages 469–472   Exercises

62. [2] $8v^3 + 2v^2 + 3v - 1$; multiply each term of $(2v^2 + v + 1)$ by $4v$, and then multiply each term of $(2v^2 + v + 1)$ by -1. Add the products.

[1] incorrect calculation OR incorrect explanation

63. [4] $[(2n + 6)(5n - 2)] -$
$[(3n + 2)(n + 2)] =$
$[10n^2 + 26n - 12] -$
$[3n^2 + 8n + 4] =$
$7n^2 + 18n - 16$

[3] appropriate methods, but with one computational error

[2] incorrect products subtracted correctly OR correct products subtracted incorrectly

[1] correct answer, without work shown

LESSON 9-4

page 474   Investigation

1. Row 1: $x^2 + 16x + 64$, $y^2 + 10y + 25$, $4p^2 + 12p + 9$
Row 2: $d^2 - 6d + 9$, $t^2 - 2t + 1$, $81r^2 - 36r + 4$
Row 3: $x^2 - 16$, $k^2 - 81$, $9c^2 - 49$

2. Row 1: The product is the first term of each binomial squared plus two times the product of the first and last terms of each binomial plus the last term of each binomial squared.
Row 2: The product is the first term of each binomial squared minus two times the product of the first and last terms of each binomial plus the last term of each binomial squared.
Row 3: The product is the first term of each binomial squared minus the last term of each binomial squared.

3. $p^2 + 12p + 36$
$v^2 - 10v + 25$
$x^2 - 64$

pages 477–479   Exercises

57a.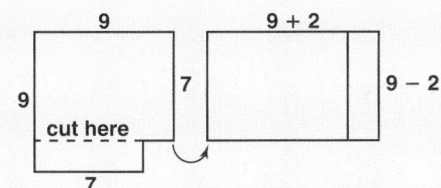

b.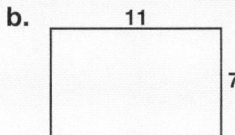

LESSON 9-5

page 481   Check Skills You'll Need

1. 1, 2, 3, 4, 6, 8, 12, 24

2. 1, 2, 3, 4, 6, 12

3. 1, 2, 3, 6, 9, 18, 27, 54

4. 1, 3, 5, 15

5. 1, 2, 3, 4, 6, 9, 12, 18, 36

6. 1, 2, 4, 7, 8, 14, 28, 56

7. 1, 2, 4, 8, 16, 32, 64

8. 1, 2, 3, 4, 6, 8, 12, 16, 24, 32, 48, 96

LESSON 9-6

pages 487–489   Exercises

28. Answers may vary. Sample:
41; $(4g + 1)(g + 10)$
14; $(4g + 10)(g + 1)$
22; $(2g + 1)(2g + 10)$

29. Answers may vary. Sample:
18; $(5m - 4)(3m + 6)$
54; $(5m - 2)(3m + 12)$
117; $(5m - 1)(3m + 24)$

30. Answers may vary. Sample:
8; $(7g - 4)(5g + 4)$
559; $(35g - 1)(g + 16)$
46; $(7g - 2)(5g + 8)$

32. Answers may vary. Sample:
Factor out the GCF, 2, first. Look at the factors of 25 and 8 to find a combination that will give you a sum of -45. $2(25x^2 - 45x + 8) = 2(5x - 1)(5x - 8)$.

43. Answers may vary. Sample:
$5x^2 - 12x + 4 = (5x - 2)(x - 2)$;
$9x^2 - 12x + 3 = 3(3x - 1)(x - 1)$;
$16x^2 - 12x + 2 = 2(4x - 1)(2x - 1)$

78.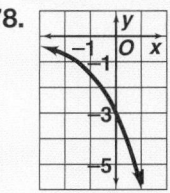

79.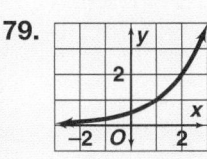

80.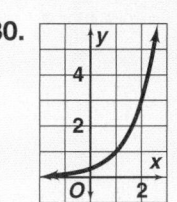

LESSON 9-7

page 490   Investigation

1. $(x + 3)(x + 3)$,
$(x + 9)(x + 1)$,
$(m + 3)(m + 12)$,
$(m + 6)(m + 6)$,
$(k + 25)(k + 1)$,
$(k + 5)(k + 5)$

2a. $x^2 + 6x + 9$;
$m^2 + 12m + 36$;
$k^2 + 10k + 25$

b. The middle term is the sum of the identical factors.

page 506   Chapter Test

11. $-8b^3 + 24b^2 + 56b$

12. $-5t^3 - t^2$

13. $9q^4 - 3q^2 + 12q$

14. $2c^6 + 8c^4$

15. $x^2 + 7x + 6$

16. $d^2 + d - 12$

17. $2h^2 - 9h + 4$

18. $6m^2 + m - 35$

26. Multiply each term of the first polynomial by each term of the second polynomial. Then combine like terms. Example:
$(x + 3)(x^2 - x + 1) =$
$x^3 - x^2 + x + 3x^2 - 3x + 3 = x^3 + 2x^2 - 2x + 3$

27. $x(3x + 5)$; $(3x^2 + 5x)$ m^2

28. $w(w - 2)(4w + 3)$;
$(4w^3 - 5w^2 - 6w)$ in.^{3}

31. $(w - 7)(w + 2)$

32. $(g + 5)^2$

33. $(3k + 4)^2$

34. $(n + 10)(n - 10)$

35. $(y - 2)^2$

36. $(2x + 7)(2x - 7)$

37. $(2p + 81)(2p + 1)$

38. $13(c + 2)(c - 2)$

45. $(3n^2 + 1)(4n + 5)$

46. $2(2x - 3)(x - 1)$

47. $(x^2 + 5)(x - 5)$

48. $(3r^2 - 2)(2r - 3)$

49. $(2y + 1)(2y - 1)(3y + 7)$

50. $(n^2 - 2)(3n - 4)$

CHAPTER 10

LESSON 10-1

page 510   Check Skills You'll Need

5.
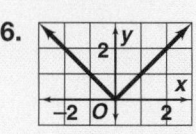

6.
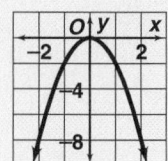

7.
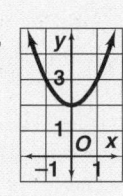

page 510   Investigation

2–3. Answers may vary. Samples are given.

2a. Both graphs are U-shaped with the lowest points at the origin.

b. $y = 3x^2$ is narrower than $y = x^2$.

3. $y = \frac{1}{3}x^2$ will be U-shaped with its lowest point at the origin. It will be wider than $y = x^2$.

pages 511–512   Check Understanding

2.

x	$f(x) = -2x^2$	(x, y)
0	$-2(0)^2 = 0$	$(0, 0)$
1	$-2(1)^2 = -2$	$(1, -2)$
2	$-2(2)^2 = -8$	$(2, -8)$

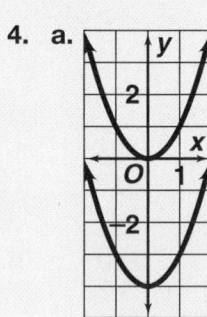

4. a.

The graph of $y = x^2 - 4$ has the same shape as the graph of $y = x^2$, but it is shifted down 4 units.

page 511   Additional Examples

2.
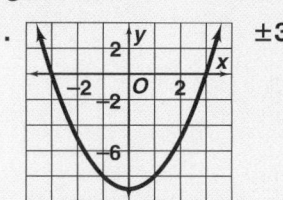

page 512   Additional Examples

4.
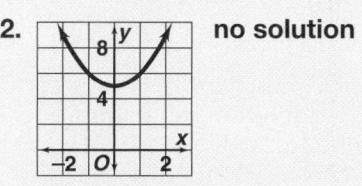

5.
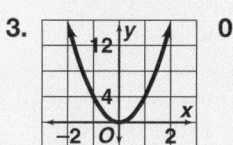

pages 513–516   Exercises

47a.
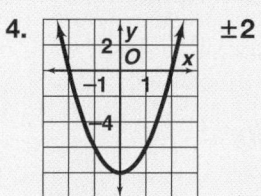

49a.
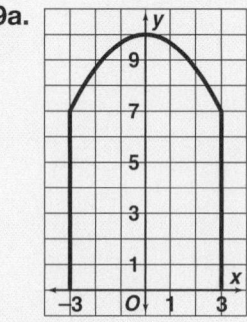

b.
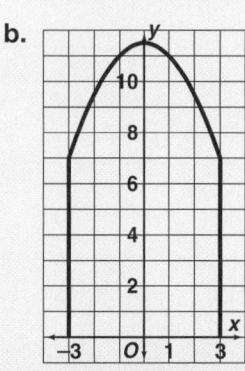

LESSON 10-2

pages 520–523   Exercises

44.
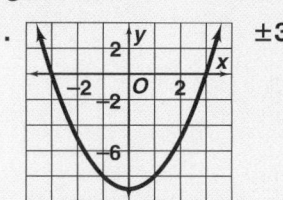

LESSON 10-3

pages 531–534   Exercises

1. ± 3

2. no solution

3. 0

4. ± 2

5. no solution
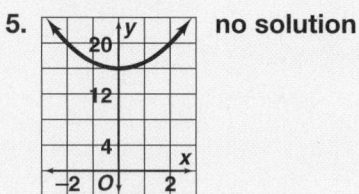

6. ± 3
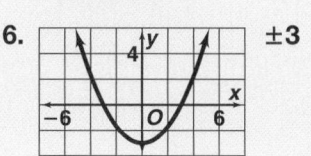

7. no solution
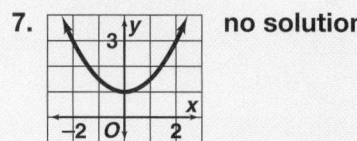

8. 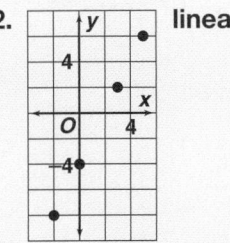 0

9. 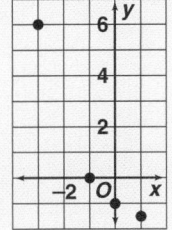 ±2

LESSON 10-9

pages 563–566   Exercises

1. 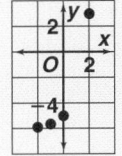 quadratic

2. linear

3. exponential

4. quadratic

5. exponential

6. 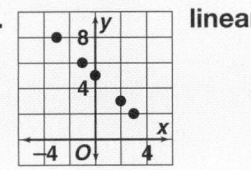 linear

13a. 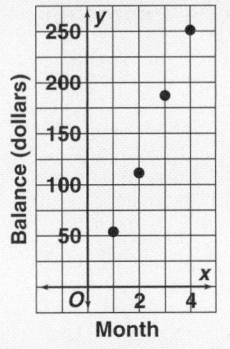 linear

pages 569–571   Chapter Review

10.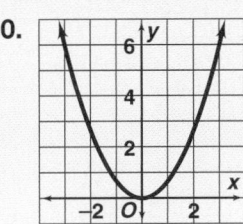

11.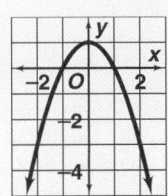

12.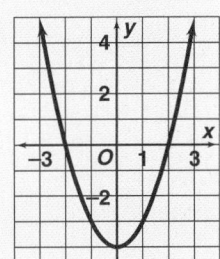

13.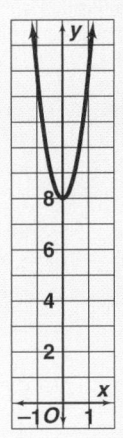

9.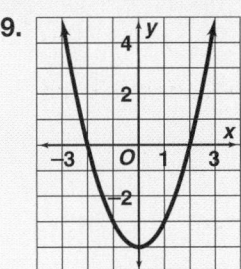

10.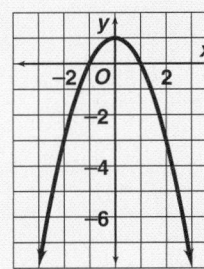

11.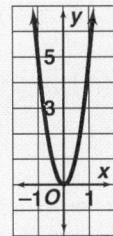

12.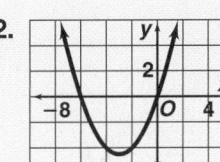

13.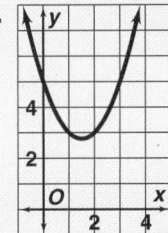

14.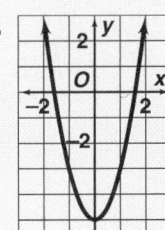

20.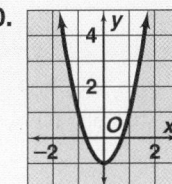

21.

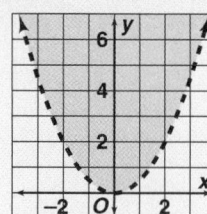

41. Answers may vary.
Sample: $y = -x^2 + 4$;

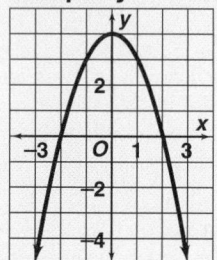

page 573 Standardized Test Prep

14. [2] $(2w - 6)w = 140$
    $2w^2 - 6w - 140 = 0$
    $w^2 - 3w - 70 = 0$
    $(w - 10)(w + 7) = 0$
            $w = 10$
    10 m by 14 m

[1] correct answer but no work shown

15. [2] straight line, U-shaped curve that opens in any direction, V-shaped curve that opens up or down (OR equivalent descriptions)

[1] two correct descriptions

16. [2] $9a + 3b - 3 - 4a + 7 - 8b$
    $= (9 - 4)a + (3 - 8)b - 3 + 7$
    $= 5a - 5b + 4$

[1] correct answer but no work shown

17. vertex: $\left(\frac{3}{8}, -\frac{9}{16}\right)$

x-intercepts: 0 and $\frac{3}{4}$

axis of symmetry: $x = \frac{3}{8}$

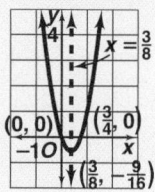

CHAPTER 11

LESSON 11-4

pages 603–606   Exercises

74. [2] $(3\sqrt{5} - \sqrt{2})(\sqrt{5} + 5\sqrt{2}) =$
    $3\sqrt{25} + 15\sqrt{10} - \sqrt{10} - 5\sqrt{4} =$
    $3(5) + 15\sqrt{10} - \sqrt{10} - 5(2) =$
    $15 + 15\sqrt{10} - \sqrt{10} - 10 =$
    $5 + 14\sqrt{10}$

[1] correct technique, but with a computational error

75. [4] $\dfrac{5}{\sqrt{7} + \sqrt{21}} \cdot \dfrac{\sqrt{7} - \sqrt{21}}{\sqrt{7} - \sqrt{21}}$

Multiply the numerator and the denominator by the conjugate of the denominator.

$\dfrac{5(\sqrt{7} - \sqrt{21})}{7 - 21}$ Simplify the denominator.

$\dfrac{5(\sqrt{7} - \sqrt{21})}{-14}$

[3] correct steps but answer not completely simplified

[2] correct technique, but with a computational error

[1] correct answer but no work shown

LESSON 11-5

pages 610–612   Exercises

61. [2] $\sqrt{15 - 5x} = \sqrt{4x - 3}$
    $15 - 5x = 4x - 3$
    $-9x = -18$
    $x = 2$
Check: $\sqrt{15 - 5(2)} \overset{?}{=} \sqrt{4(2) - 3}$
    $\sqrt{5} = \sqrt{5} \checkmark$

The solution is 2.

[1] correct technique with a minor error OR correct answer, no work shown

LESSON 11-6

page 614   Check Skills You'll Need

1.

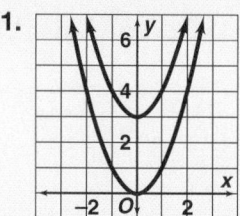

2.

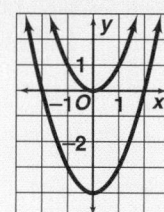

page 615   Check Understanding

2a.

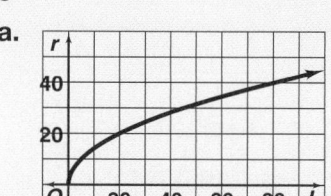

page 615   Additional Examples

2.

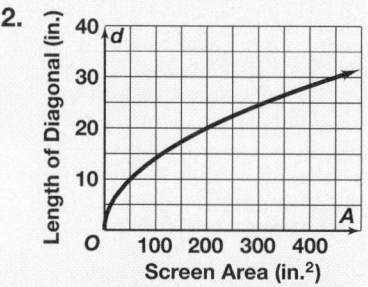

3.

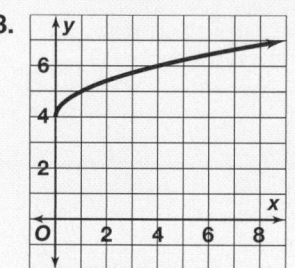

4.

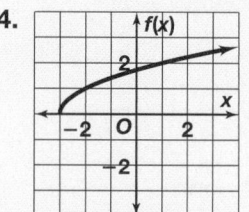

pages 616–619   Exercises

21.

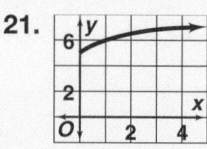

22.

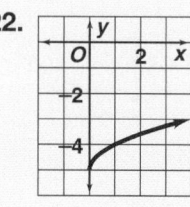

23.

24.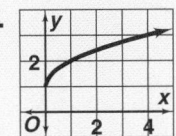

25.

26.

27.

28.

29.

38.

x	y
2.5	0
3.5	1
6.5	2

39.

x	f(x)
0	0
1	4
4	5.7
4	8

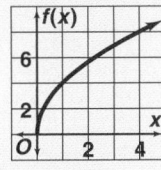

40.

x	y
−6	0
−5	1
−2	2
0	2.4

41.

x	y
0	0
2	1
4	1.4
8	2

42.

x	y
2	3
3	4
6	5

43.

x	f(x)
−2	−4
−1	−3
2	−2

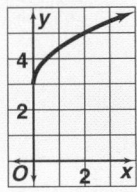

44.

x	y
0	3
1	4.4
2	5
3	5.4

45.

x	y
−3	1
−2	2.4
−1	3
0	3.4

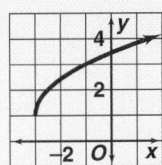

46.

x	y
1	−2
2	−0.3
3	0.4
4	1

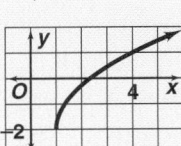

page 632   Chapter Test

37. $x \geq 0$;

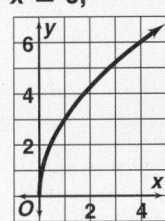

38. $x \geq 0$;

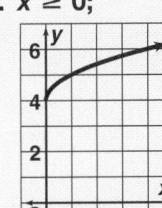

39. $x \geq 4$;

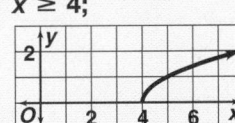

40. $x \geq -9$;

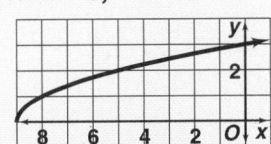

6. [2] a. $\frac{-b}{2a}$ is the maximum,

so $\frac{-3000}{2(-250)} = 6$

They can increase the price by a factor of six.

b. $r = 40,000 + 3000(6) - 250(6)^2 = 49,000$

The maximum revenue is $49,000.

c. $1000 - 50(6) = 1000 - 300 = 700$

The maximum number of sales is 700.

d. $40 + 5(6) = 40 + 30 = 70$

Carlos and Anna should charge $70 per game.

[1] appropriate methods, but one computational error

7. [2] The table shows what happens as the price decreases

Price	Number Sold	Revenue
$40	1000	$40,000
$30	1100	$33,000
$20	1200	$24,000

The decrease in price does not result in an increase in revenue. So Carlos and Anna should not decrease the price OR equivalent explanation.

[1] correct conclusion but insufficient explanation

CHAPTER 12

LESSON 12-1

page 643   Technology

1.
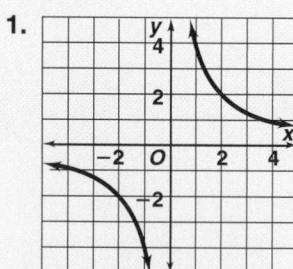

2.
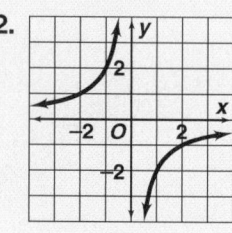

3.
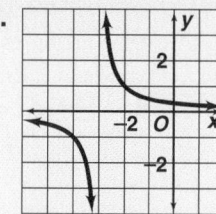

4.
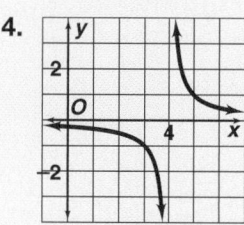

5.
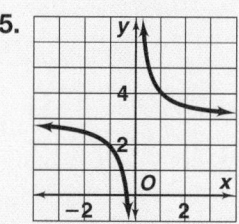

6.
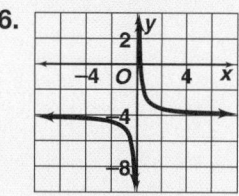

7.
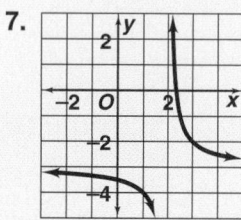

8.
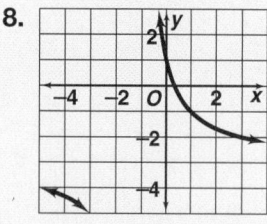

9.
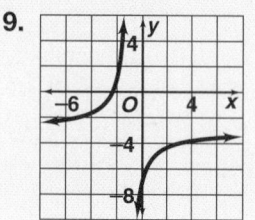

10a.
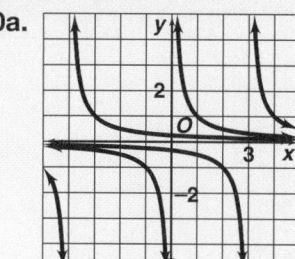

b. Adding translates the graph left, subtracting translates the graph right.

11a.
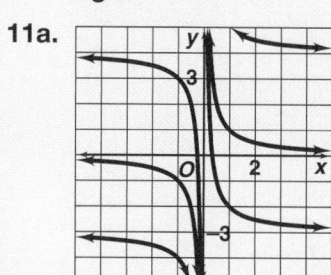

LESSON 12-2

pages 648–650   Exercises

14. $x = 0$;
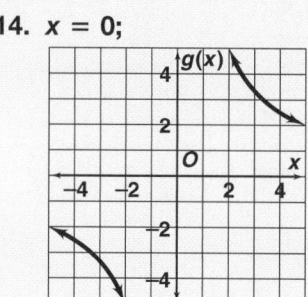

15. $x = 0$;
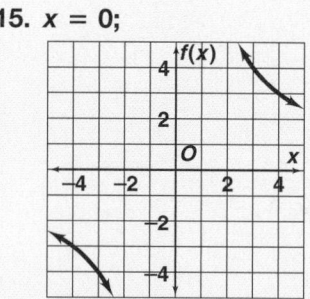

16. $x = -1$;
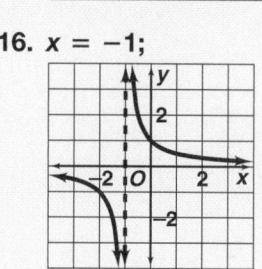

17. $x = 5$;

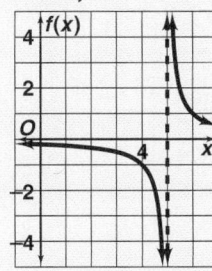

18. $x = -4$;

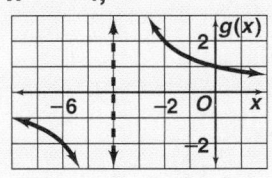

19. $x = -4$;

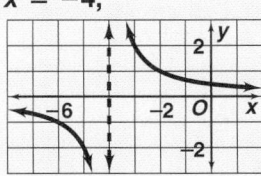

20. $x = 0, y = -5$;

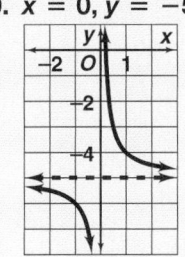

21. $x = 0, y = 5$;

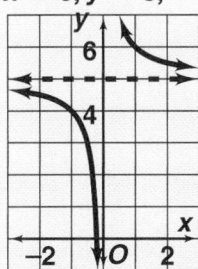

22. $x = 0, y = -6$;

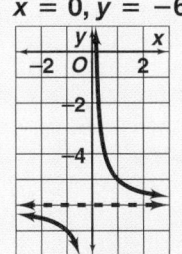

23. $x = -1, y = 4$;

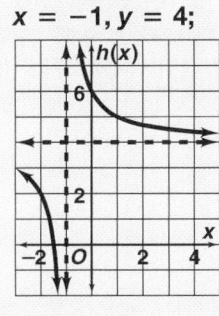

24. $x = 3, y = -5$;

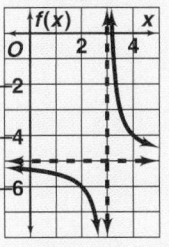

25. $x = 1, y = -2$;

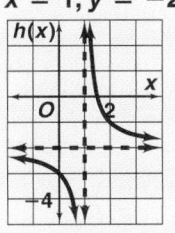

43. $x = 0, y = 0$;

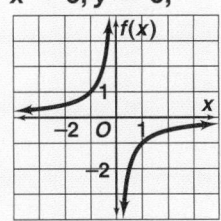

44. $x = 0, y = 0$;

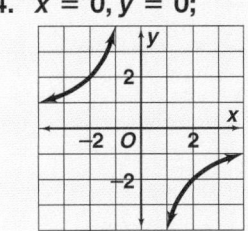

45. $x = -4, y = 0$;

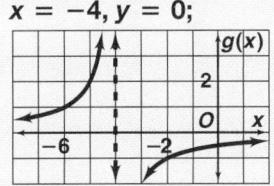

46. $x = 0, y = 1$;

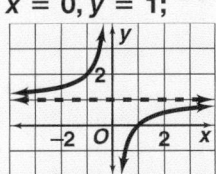

47. $x = -1, y = 4$;

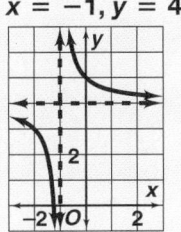

48. $x = -1, y = -3$;

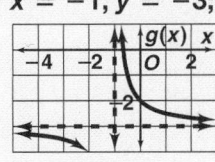

49. $x = 1, y = 3$;

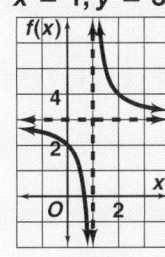

50. $x = -5, y = 1$;

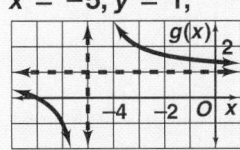

51. $x = 3, y = -2$;

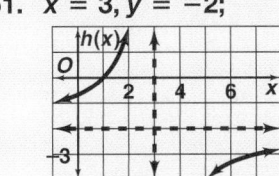

56. The graph of $y = \frac{3}{x}$ and $y = -\frac{3}{x}$ are both composed of two curves with asymptotes $x = 0$ and $y = 0$. The graph of $y = -\frac{3}{x}$ is a reflection of the graph of $y = \frac{3}{x}$ over the y-axis.

57.

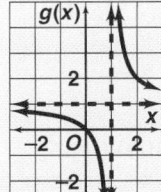

58.

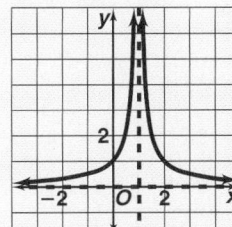

59.

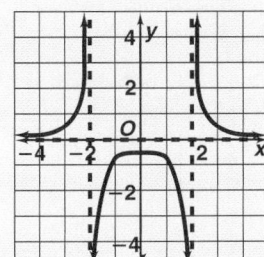

60.

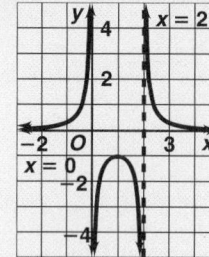

page 651 Extension

9a.

Term Number	Term
1	4
2	$3\frac{1}{2}$
3	$3\frac{1}{4}$
4	$3\frac{1}{8}$
5	$3\frac{1}{16}$
6	$3\frac{1}{32}$
7	$3\frac{1}{64}$

b.

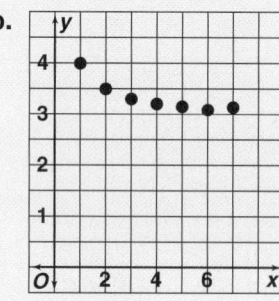

10a.

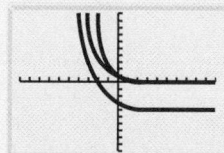

Xmin = −10,   Xmax = 10
Ymin = −10,   Ymax = 10

b. Answers may vary.
Sample: Exponential decay functions have a limit as x gets larger, but not as x gets smaller.

LESSON 12-5

page 662   Check Skills You'll Need

4. $2x^2 + 10x + 12$

5. $-3n^2 + 11n + 20$

6. $6a^3 - 21a^2 + 2a - 7$

pages 664–666   Exercises

56. [2]

$$\begin{array}{r} x^2 + 3x + 2 \\ 2x - 1\overline{)2x^3 + 5x^2 + x - 2} \\ \underline{2x^3 - x^2} \\ 6x^2 + x \\ \underline{6x^2 - 3x} \\ 4x - 2 \\ \underline{4x - 2} \\ 0 \end{array}$$

$$\begin{array}{r} x + 1 \\ x + 2\overline{)x^2 + 3x + 2} \\ \underline{x^2 + 2x} \\ x + 2 \\ \underline{x + 2} \\ 0 \end{array}$$

The width is $x + 1$.

[1] one computational error OR correct answer with no work shown

pages 693–695   Chapter Review

15. $y = 0, x = 0;$

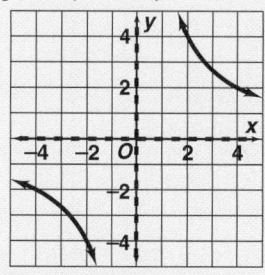

16. $y = 0, x = 0;$

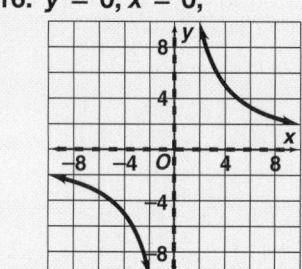

17. $y = 0, x = 5;$

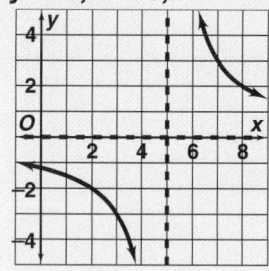

18. $y = 2, x = 0;$

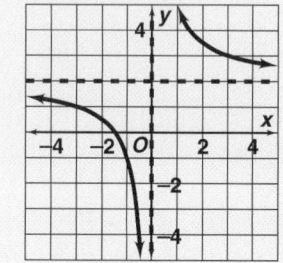

page 696   Chapter Test

7. $x = 0; y = 0$

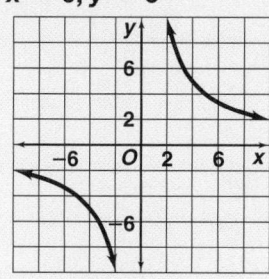

8. $x = 0; y = 0$

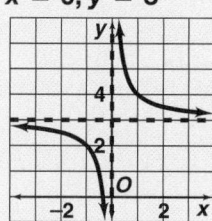

9. $x = 0; y = 3$

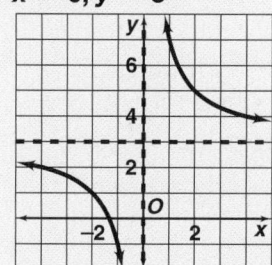

10. $x = 0; y = 3$

11. Answers may vary. Sample: In direct variation and in inverse variation, the variables are related to each other by a constant. But in direct variation, that number is the ratio of any corresponding pair of input and output values. Distance traveled varies directly with average speed. In inverse variation, that number is the product of any corresponding pair of input and output values. The cost per person of splitting a $14 pizza varies inversely with the number of people who are sharing it.

61. [2] asymptotes: $x = 2$, $y = 1$

$y = \dfrac{5}{0 - 2} + 1 = -\dfrac{3}{2}$

y-int. is $-\dfrac{3}{2}$.

$0 = \dfrac{5}{x - 2} + 1$

$-1 = \dfrac{5}{x - 2}$

$x - 2 = -5$

$x = -3$

x-int. is -3.

[1] asymptotes or intercepts only

62. [2] a. $\dfrac{32 - 42}{42} \approx -0.2380$

23.8%

[1] appropriate methods, but with one computational error

63. [2] No; when

$\dfrac{x}{x - 7} - \dfrac{2}{x - 7} = \dfrac{5}{x - 7}$

is multiplied by the LCD, $x - 7$, the resulting equation is $x - 2 = 5$. However, the solution 7 is extraneous.

[1] appropriate answer but no explanation

64. [2] $x - 472 = 1634$
$x = 2106$
2578

[1] value of x found correctly but $x + 472$ not found

65. [4] a. $t - 19 = \dfrac{19 - 40}{150 - 300}(\ell - 150)$

$t - 19 = \dfrac{7}{50}(\ell - 150)$

$t - 19 = \dfrac{7}{50}\ell - 21$

$t = \dfrac{7}{50}\ell - 2$

b. $t = \dfrac{7}{50}(200) - 2$

$t = 26$; 26 mm

c. $61 = \dfrac{7}{50}\ell - 2$

$63 = \dfrac{7}{50}\ell$

$450 = \ell$; 450 mm

[3] appropriate methods, but with one computational error

[2] incorrect equation used correctly OR correct equation used incorrectly

[1] no work shown

66. [4] $\cos 28° = \dfrac{BC}{7}$

$BC = 7 \cos 28° \approx 6.18$

$\sin 28° = \dfrac{AC}{7}$

$AC = 7 \sin 28° \approx 3.29$
(OR equivalent solution)

[3] correct equations, but error using calculator

[2] only one side found correctly

[1] no work shown

67. [4]

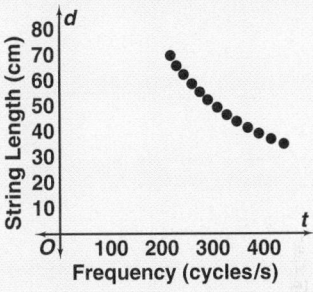

The data appear to show a linear trend but are not exactly linear; each day has a unique closing price (OR equivalent explanation).

[3] correct graph with incorrect explanation OR one error in graph

[2] graph axes not labeled

[1] no graph with some explanation

Activity 1

b.

Fret	Position (cm)
0	70.0
1	66.1
2	62.4
3	58.9
4	55.6
5	52.4
6	49.5
7	46.7
8	44.1
9	41.6
10	39.3
11	37.1
12	35.0

Activity 3

a.

Note	Frequency	Length (cm)
A	220.0	70.0
A#	233.1	66.1
B	246.6	62.4
C	261.6	58.9
C#	277.2	55.6
D	293.7	52.4
D#	311.1	49.5
E	329.6	46.7
F	349.2	44.1
F#	370.0	41.6
G	392.0	39.3
G#	415.3	37.1
A	440.0	35.0

Frequency vs. String Length

b.

Note	Fret number	Frequency
A	0	220.0
A#	1	233.1
B	2	246.6
C	3	261.6
C#	4	277.2
D	5	293.7
D#	6	311.1
E	7	329.6
F	8	349.2
F#	9	370.0
G	10	392.0
G#	11	415.3
A	12	440.0

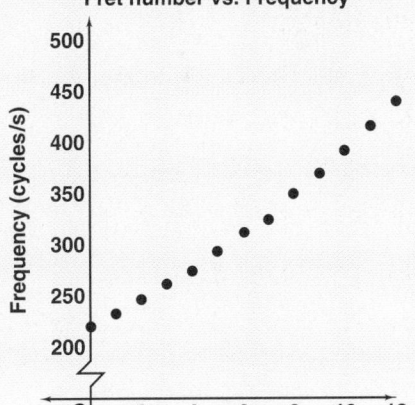

Fret number vs. Frequency

EXTRA PRACTICE

CHAPTER 5

page 706   Extra Practice

26. 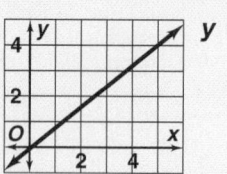 $y = \frac{4}{5}x$

27. 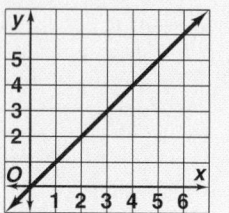 $y = x$

28. 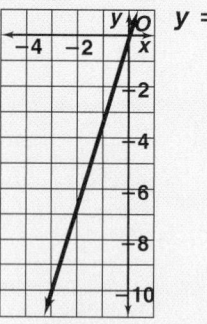 $y = \frac{10}{3}x$

29. 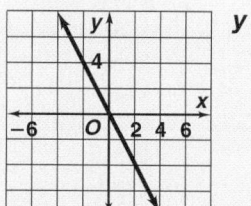 $y = -2x$

30. 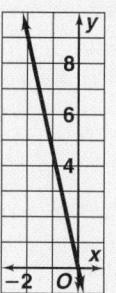 $y = -\frac{9}{2}x$

31. 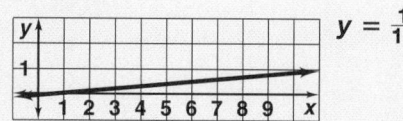 $y = \frac{1}{11}x$

CHAPTER 6

page 707   Extra Practice

37. $4x - y = -17$

38. $x - y = 0$

39. $4x - 3y = 25$

40. $2x - y = -3$

41. $x - 2y = 24$

42. $5x - 2y = 12$

43. $y = -1$

44. $x = 4$

45a–b.

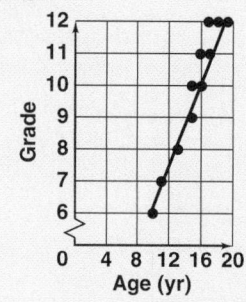

c. grade $= 0.720 \cdot$ age $- 1.118$

46.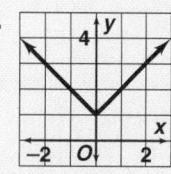

47.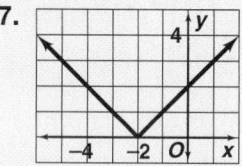

48.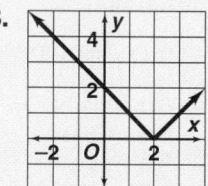

49.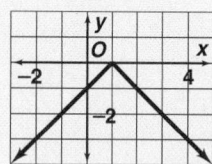

50.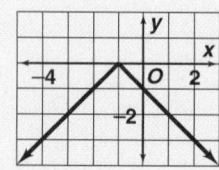

51.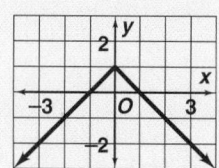

52.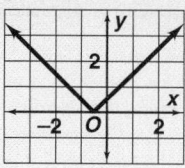

53.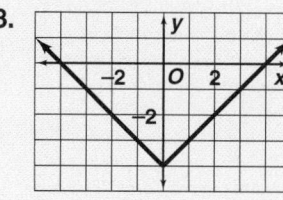

CHAPTER 11

page 712   Extra Practice

51. $x \geq -5$;

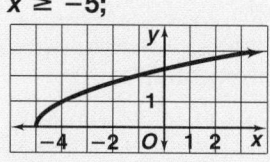

52. $x \geq 0$;

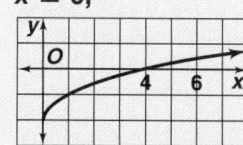

53. $x \geq -1$;

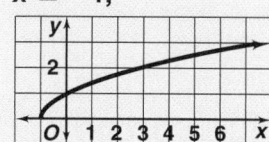

54. $x \geq 0$;

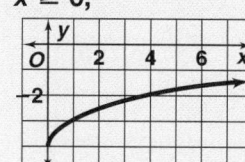

55. $x \geq 3$;

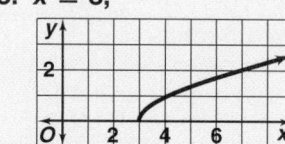

56. $x \geq 0$;

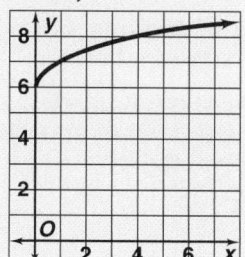

T794

Index

Teacher's Edition entries appear in blue type.

A

Absolute value
   defined, 20
   evaluating, 35–36
   finding, 20–22, 44
   simplifying, 33–34
   symbol for, 22

Absolute value equation(s)
   graphing, 325–329, 333
   solving, 167–172, 177, 178, 234

Absolute value function, 249, 647

Absolute value inequality
   graphing, 168–170, 178
   solving, 167–172, 177, 178

ACT. *See* Standardized Test Prep.

Acute angle, 730

Addend, 25

Addition
   Associative Property of, 54, 69
   Commutative Property of, 54, 55, 56, 69
   of fractions, 634, 726
   Identity Property of, 24, 54, 55
   Inverse Property of, 24–25, 54
   of like radicals, 600
   of matrices, 27, 28, 29, 30
   of polynomials, 459–461
   of rational expressions, 667–671, 694
   of real numbers, 24–31, 68, 280
   solving equations using, 74–76, 77, 78, 79, 95
   solving inequalities using, 140–141
   solving systems using, 353–354

Addition Property
   of Equality, 74, 75, 95, 353
   of Inequality, 140–141

Additional Examples, Teacher's Edition pages
   5, 11, 12, 18, 19, 20, 25, 26, 27, 33, 34,
   39, 40, 48, 49, 55, 61, 62, 75, 76, 83, 89,
   90, 97, 98, 105, 106, 112, 119, 120, 135,
   136, 142, 148, 155, 162, 163, 168, 169,
   183, 184, 190, 191, 198, 199, 205, 206,
   212, 213, 221, 237, 243, 248, 249, 255,
   256, 263, 264, 269, 270, 283, 284, 285,
   292, 293, 299, 300, 305, 306, 312, 313,
   319, 326, 341, 342, 348, 354, 355, 356,
   363, 364, 371, 372, 379, 380, 395, 396,
   401, 402, 406, 407, 412, 413, 418, 419,
   425, 426, 431, 439, 440, 457, 458, 463,
   468, 469, 476, 482, 487, 491, 492, 497,
   498, 511, 512, 518, 519, 525, 530, 537,
   543, 549, 555, 561, 562, 579, 580, 585,
   586, 592, 593, 601, 602, 608, 609, 615,
   623, 624, 637, 638, 639, 645, 646, 647,
   653, 658, 663, 668, 673, 674, 680, 681,
   687, 688

Additive inverse, 24, 54

Advanced Learner, 2D, 72D, 132D, 180D,
   234D, 280D, 338D, 392D, 454D, 508D,
   576D, 634D, Teacher's Edition pages 5,
   10, 18, 25, 33, 38, 48, 55, 60, 75, 82, 89,
   97, 104, 112, 119, 135, 141, 147, 154,
   162, 168, 183, 190, 198, 205, 212, 220,
   237, 242, 248, 255, 262, 269, 283, 292,
   299, 305, 312, 319, 326, 341, 348, 354,
   363, 371, 378, 395, 401, 406, 412, 418,
   425, 431, 438, 457, 463, 468, 475, 482,
   487, 491, 497, 511, 518, 525, 530, 537,
   542, 548, 555, 560, 579, 585, 592, 601,
   608, 615, 622, 637, 645, 653, 658, 663,
   668, 673, 680, 687

Airspeed, 669

Algebra at Work. *See also* Connections.
   airline pilot, 94
   auto mechanic, 606
   businessperson, 368
   cartographer, 224
   cell physiologist, 416
   electrician, 671
   marketing director, 159

Algebra tiles, 32, 34, 36, 46, 81, 95, 126, 129, 220,
   221, 222, 250, 280, 346, 466, 480, 541, 683

Algebraic expression(s)
   defined, 4
   evaluating, 10–12, 13, 14, 15
   multiplying powers in, 406
   simplifying, 48–49, 50–53, 417–418
   writing, 4–8, 42, 180

Algebraic reasoning, 173

Alternative Assessment, Teacher's Edition
   pages 7, 14, 22, 30, 36, 43, 52, 57, 64, 79,
   85, 93, 100, 109, 114, 122, 138, 144, 150,
   158, 165, 171, 187, 194, 201, 208, 216,
   223, 239, 245, 251, 259, 266, 273, 289,
   296, 302, 308, 316, 323, 328, 344, 351,
   358, 367, 375, 384, 398, 404, 410, 416,
   422, 428, 434, 443, 460, 465, 471, 478,
   484, 489, 494, 500, 515, 522, 527, 533,
   539, 545, 551, 557, 565, 582, 589, 596,
   605, 611, 618, 626, 641, 649, 655, 660,
   665, 670, 676, 684, 690

Alternative Method, Teacher's Edition pages
   11, 19, 27, 39, 46, 48, 83, 112, 147, 155,
   162, 183, 199, 220, 242, 243, 263, 312,
   324, 350, 365, 369, 372, 414, 425, 438,
   458, 463, 487, 542, 579, 603, 637,
   673, 680

Analysis
   of data. *See* Data Analysis.
   dimensional, 182, 183, 185, 186, 187
   of errors, 29, 51, 79, 85, 92, 100, 124, 137, 150,
      158, 174, 193, 239, 244, 245, 288, 295, 302,
      358, 374, 408, 414, 421, 459, 464, 493, 504,
      532, 545, 557, 589, 604, 628, 655, 659, 670
   of graphs, 237
   of special types of systems, 342

Angle(s)
   acute, 730
   classifying, 730
   corresponding, 190
   defined, 730
   of depression, 624, 625, 627
   of elevation, 623–624, 625, 626, 627
   interior, 114
   measuring, 730

   obtuse, 730
   right, 215, 730
   straight, 730
   supplementary, 79
   vertex of, 730
   vertical, 97

Answer(s)
   eliminating, 502
   guessing and testing, 715
   to Instant Check System, 804–832
   multiple correct answers, 386
   Selected, 804–832

Applications. *See* Connections.

Area
   defined, 731
   of rectangle, 13, 51, 64, 115, 151, 208, 209, 217,
      504, 505, 663
   of square, 209, 247, 491, 505
   of trapezoid, 12, 15, 70, 113, 470, 533
   of triangle, 64, 111, 251, 665

Area model, 462, 467, 474, 484, 485, 488

Arithmetic sequences, 269–273, 277, 425

Armstrong, Lance, 184

Assessment. *See also* Instant Check System,
      Open-Ended, Test-Taking Strategies.
   Chapter Review, 67–69, 125–127, 175–177,
      227–229, 275–277, 331–333, 387–389,
      447–449, 503–505, 569–571, 629–631,
      693–695
   Chapter Test, 70, 128, 178, 230, 278, 334, 390,
      450, 506, 572, 632, 696
   Check Understanding, 4, 5, 6, 10, 11, 12, 17,
      18, 19, 20, 25, 26, 27, 32, 33, 34, 38, 39, 40, 41,
      47, 48, 49, 55, 56, 60, 61, 62, 75, 76, 77, 82, 83,
      88, 89, 90, 97, 98, 103, 104, 105, 106, 107,
      111, 112, 113, 119, 120, 121, 134, 135, 136,
      140, 141, 142, 147, 148, 149, 153, 154, 155,
      161, 162, 163, 167, 168, 169, 182, 183 184,
      185, 186, 190, 191, 197, 198, 199, 200, 204,
      205, 206, 212, 213, 220, 221, 236, 237, 241,
      242, 243, 248, 249, 254, 255, 262, 263, 264,
      268, 269, 270, 283, 284, 285, 292, 293, 299,
      300, 305, 306, 307, 311, 312, 313, 319, 320,
      325, 326, 327, 340, 341, 342, 348, 349, 353,
      354, 355, 356, 363, 364, 371, 372, 378, 379,
      380, 395, 396, 400, 401, 402, 405, 406, 407,
      412, 413, 418, 419, 424, 425, 426, 427, 430,
      431, 432, 438, 439, 440, 441, 457, 458, 462,
      463, 467, 468, 469, 475, 476, 477, 481, 482,
      483, 486, 487, 491, 492, 496, 497, 498, 511,
      512, 513, 518, 519, 524, 525, 526, 530, 531,
      536, 537, 542, 543, 548, 549, 550, 555, 560,
      561, 562, 563, 578, 579, 580, 581, 585, 586,
      587, 592, 593, 600, 601, 602, 607, 608, 609,
      614, 615, 622, 623, 624, 637, 638, 639, 644,
      645, 646, 648, 652, 653, 654, 657, 658, 659,
      662, 663, 664, 667, 668, 669, 672, 673, 674,
      680, 681, 682, 687, 688
   Checkpoint Quiz, 31, 58, 94, 115, 151, 166, 195,
      217, 246, 267, 303, 324, 352, 376, 416, 435,
      472, 495, 534, 558, 597, 619, 656, 685
   Cumulative Review, 129, 231, 335, 451, 573,
      697–699

Index

Mixed Review, 8, 15, 23, 31, 36, 44, 53, 58, 65, 80, 86, 94, 101, 110, 115, 123, 139, 145, 151, 159, 166, 172, 188, 195, 202, 209, 217, 224, 240, 246, 252, 259, 267, 273, 289, 297, 303, 309, 317, 324, 329, 345, 352, 359, 368, 376, 384, 399, 404, 410, 416, 423, 429, 435, 444, 461, 465, 472, 479, 485, 489, 495, 501, 516, 523, 528, 534, 540, 546, 552, 558, 566, 583, 590, 597, 606, 612, 619, 627, 642, 650, 656, 661, 666, 671, 677, 685, 691

Standardized Test Prep, 8, 15, 22, 31, 36, 44, 52–53, 58, 65, 71, 80, 86, 93, 101, 110, 115, 123, 129, 139, 145, 150, 158–159, 166, 171–172, 179, 188, 194–195, 202, 209, 216–217, 224, 231, 240, 245–246, 251–252, 258–259, 266, 272–273, 279, 289, 297, 303, 309, 317, 323–324, 329, 335, 345, 352, 359, 367–368, 375, 384, 391, 399, 404, 409–410, 415–416, 423, 429, 434–435, 444, 451, 461, 465, 472, 479, 485, 489, 494–495, 500–501, 507, 516, 523, 528, 534, 539–540, 546, 552, 557–558, 566, 573, 583, 590, 596, 605–606, 612, 618–619, 627, 633, 642, 650, 655–656, 661, 666, 671, 677, 684–685, 691, 697–699

Associative Property
  of Addition, 54, 55, 69
  of Multiplication, 54, 55, 69
Asymptote, 644–650, 666, 693, 696
  horizontal, 646, 649
  vertical, 645–646, 648, 649
Average. *See* Mean(s), Median, Mode.
Axes, 59, 69
Axis of symmetry, 511, 514, 518, 520, 521, 567, 568, 569

B _____

Back-to-back stem-and-leaf plot, 121, 122
Bar Graphs, 736
Base
  defined, 9
  for exponent, 11, 729
Basic Algebra, 2D, 72D, 132D, 180D, 234D, 280D, 338D, 392D, 454D, 508D, 576D, 634D
Bauelos, Romana Acosta, 273
Best fit, line of, 319–324, 329, 333, 334, 436, 495
Below-Level Learner, 2D, 72D, 132D, 180D, 234D, 280D, 338D, 392D, 454D, 508D, 576D, 634D, Teacher's Edition pages 5, 10, 18, 25, 33, 38, 48, 55, 60, 75, 82, 89, 97, 104, 112, 119, 135, 141, 147, 154, 162, 168, 183, 190, 198, 205, 212, 220, 237, 242, 248, 255, 262, 269, 283, 292, 299, 305, 312, 319, 326, 341, 348, 354, 363, 371, 378, 395, 401, 406, 412, 418, 425, 431, 438, 457, 463, 468, 475, 482, 487, 491, 497, 511, 518, 525, 530, 537, 542, 548, 555, 560, 579, 585, 592, 601, 608, 615, 622, 637, 645, 653, 658, 663, 668, 673, 680, 687
Binomials
  dividing polynomials by, 663, 665
  dividing trinomials by, 665
  as factors of trinomials, 480
  multiplying, 466–472, 474–480, 504, 508
  square of, 474–476, 477, 478, 479

Block Scheduling, 2A, 72A, 132A, 180A, 234A, 280A, 338A, 392A, 454A, 508A, 576A, 634A
Box-and-Whisker plots, 740
Boyle's Law, 641
Brackets, 12, 45
Break-even point, finding, 363–364

C _____

Calculator. *See also* Graphing calculators.
  angle of depression, 624
  angle of elevation, 623
  combinations, 687
  compound interest, 439
  distance, 592
  evaluating, 438
  exercises, 207, 409, 526, 527, 542, 543, 564, 625–627
  exponential growth, 438
  golden ratio, 602
  hints, 12, 319, 341, 400, 408, 438, 525, 592
  permutations, 681
  Pythagorean Theorem, 585
  quadratic equation, 531
  quadratic formula, 548
  scientific notation, 400
  simplifying, 12, 409, 519
  square roots, 525, 526, 527, 531, 542, 543, 548, 579
  trigonometric ratios, 622–624
Careers. *See* Connections.
Careers, Teacher's Edition pages 6, 41, 62, 79, 136, 193, 220, 258, 287, 341, 382, 432, 477, 514, 617, 659
CD-ROM. *See* iText.
Celsius temperature, 43, 71, 112, 113
Center, of circle, 593
Central tendency, measures of, 118–123
Certain event, 211
Challenge Exercises. *See* Enrichment.
Change
  percent of, 204–209, 228, 229, 230
  rate of, 282–289, 331
Chapter Review, 67–69, 125–127, 175–177, 227–229, 275–277, 331–333, 387–389, 447–449, 503–505, 569–571, 629–631, 693–695
Chapter Test, 70, 128, 178, 230, 278, 334, 390, 450, 506, 572, 632, 696
Check for reasonableness, 76, 82, 97, 99, 154, 349, 354, 537, 563, 673
Checkpoint, 2C, 72C, 132C, 180C, 234C, 280C, 338C, 392C, 454C, 508C, 576C, 634C, Teacher's Edition pages 31, 58, 94, 115, 151, 166, 195, 217, 246, 267, 303, 324, 352, 376, 416, 435, 472, 495, 534, 558, 597, 619, 656, 685
Check Skills You'll Need. *See* Instant Check System.
Check Skills You'll Need, 2C–D, 72C–D, 132C–D, 180C–D, 234C–D, 280C–D, 338C–D, 392C–D, 454C–D, 508C–D, 576C–D, 634C–D, Teacher's Edition pages 4, 9, 17, 24, 32, 37, 47, 54, 59, 74, 81, 88, 90, 103, 111, 118, 134, 140, 146,

153, 161, 167, 182, 189, 197, 204, 211, 219, 236, 241, 247, 254, 261, 268, 282, 291, 298, 304, 311, 318, 325, 340, 347, 353, 362, 370, 377, 394, 400, 405, 411, 417, 424, 430, 437, 456, 462, 467, 474, 481, 486, 490, 496, 510, 517, 524, 529, 536, 541, 547, 554, 559, 578, 584, 591, 600, 607, 614, 621, 636, 644, 652, 657, 662, 667, 672, 679, 686
Check solutions, 75
Check Understanding. *See* Instant Check System.
Checkpoint Quiz. *See* Instant Check System.
Chu Shih-Chieh, 501
Cierva, Juan de la, 540
Circle
  area of, 116–117
  center of, 593, 594
  circumference of, 113, 127, 640
  expressions for the area of, 471
  pi(π) defined by, 18
  and probability, 214, 215
  radius of, 531, 532
Circle graphs, 739
Classification
  of angles, 730
  of combinations, 696
  of numbers, 17–19, 20–21, 68
  of permutations, 696
  of polynomials, 457
Closure, Teacher's Edition pages 5, 12, 20, 27, 34, 40, 49, 55, 76, 83, 90, 98, 106, 112, 120, 136, 142, 148, 155, 163, 169, 184, 191, 199, 206, 213, 221, 237, 243, 249, 256, 264, 270, 285, 293, 300, 306, 313, 319, 326, 342, 348, 356, 364, 372, 380, 396, 402, 407, 413, 419, 426, 431, 440, 458, 463, 469, 476, 482, 487, 492, 498, 512, 519, 525, 530, 537, 543, 549, 555, 562, 580, 586, 593, 602, 609, 615, 624, 639, 647, 653, 658, 663, 668, 674, 681, 688
Closure properties, 57
Cobb, Jewel Plummer, 416
Coefficient
  correlation, 319–320, 333
  defined, 49
  zero, 663
Combination(s), 686–691, 695
  classifying, 696
  counting, 687, 695
  defined, 686, 695
  using in probability, 688–689
Combination notation, 687
Common difference, 269, 272, 277
Common ratio, 424–429, 449
Communication. *See* Critical Thinking, Investigation, Reading Math, Writing.
Commutative Property
  of Addition, 54, 55, 56, 69
  of Multiplication, 49, 54, 69
Compatible numbers, 199
Complement of an event, 212, 214
Completing the square, 541–546, 570, 685
Composite numbers, 454, 720
Compound events, probability of, 219–224

Compound inequalities, 161–166, 177, 338

Compound interest, 438–439, 449, 558, 660, 698

Computers
  exercises, 144, 403, 415, 420, 682, 697
  simulations, 218
  spreadsheets, 100, 334, 338, 456, 557

Conclusion, 586

Conditional, 586

Congruent triangles, 100

Conjecture, 268, 271, 275, 277. *See also* Make a Conjecture.

Conjugates, 601–602, 630

Connections
  Careers
    airline pilot, 94
    archaeologist, 35, 595
    auto mechanic, 606
    businessperson, 368
    carpenter, 79, 89, 93, 99, 543
    cartographer, 224
    cartoonist, 21
    cell physiologist, 416
    demographer, 551, 564
    electrical engineer, 577
    electrician, 251, 671
    firefighter, 585, 617
    helicopter pilot, 594
    marketing director, 159
    mathematician, 501
    mechanic, 79, 606
    medical researcher, 443
    nutritionist, 64
    photographer, 649
    physician, 209
    physician's assistant, 78
    police officer, 615
    quality control inspector, 169
    recording engineer, 248
    surveyor, 641
    urban planner, 313
    wildlife manager, 122
    woodworker, 543
    zoologist, 379
  Interdisciplinary
    art, 29, 101, 195, 231, 602
    astronomy, 194, 401, 404, 407, 408, 422, 423, 448, 450
    biology, 265, 277, 287, 404, 407, 431, 433, 449, 478
    botany, 127
    chemistry, 29, 162, 366, 401, 408, 440, 442, 489, 603, 677
    civics, 202
    geography, 415
    geology, 408
    history, 14, 42, 53. *See also* Point in Time.
    language arts, 239, 250
    music, 5, 271, 358, 391
    physics, 8, 130, 245, 264, 265, 413, 428, 435, 527, 533, 555, 556, 564, 565, 583, 586, 587, 588, 611, 616, 671
    science, 22, 127, 164, 229, 277, 309, 409
    zoology, 379, 562
  Mathematics
    geometry, 9, 14, 15, 51, 63, 64, 70, 75, 79, 85, 92, 97, 98, 100, 103, 108, 109, 111, 114, 126, 144, 156, 158, 165, 166, 179, 190, 193, 194, 215, 250, 251, 265, 288, 296, 302, 316, 322, 349,

    350, 366, 367, 375, 382, 388, 408, 409, 414, 428, 459, 460, 464, 468, 470, 471, 477, 491, 494, 500, 504, 505, 506, 515, 532, 533, 535, 538, 539, 545, 551, 571, 572, 589, 593, 594, 595, 596, 604, 610, 632, 640, 660, 663, 665, 690, 699
    Mental Math, 50, 56, 63, 94, 136, 156, 349, 476–477, 493, 532, 556
    number theory, 272, 478
    probability, 232–233, 210–224, 229, 374, 634, 655, 660, 688–689, 696, 699
    statistics. *See* Data Analysis.
  Real-World
    advertising, 257, 276, 319, 345, 618
    after-school work, 158
    agriculture, 200, 223, 350, 352, 388
    air travel, 138, 145, 237, 364–365, 366, 367, 388, 641, 669, 676
    airplanes, 94, 169, 283, 295
    animals, 183, 186, 205, 214, 241, 244, 296, 323, 331, 379, 403, 431, 452–453, 475, 478, 513, 522, 562, 718
    archaeology, 35, 595
    architecture, 193, 252, 516, 522, 627
    aviation, 99, 594, 624, 625, 626
    baking, 653, 654, 698
    banking, 28, 30, 31, 70, 76, 114, 115, 144, 171, 343, 352, 365, 438, 439, 441, 443, 444, 450
    baseball, 113, 209, 232–233, 383, 538, 598, 630, 681
    basketball, 51, 80, 145, 427, 718
    bicycling, 130, 172, 184, 186, 195, 217, 239, 265, 267, 384, 640, 671, 715
    birds, 186, 318
    birthdays, 215
    blood type, 218
    bowling, 126, 127
    boxes, 150, 410
    budgets, 143, 176, 372, 373, 374
    bungee jumping, 515
    business, 23, 93, 97, 99, 129, 157, 159, 244, 283, 288, 322, 358, 363, 365, 366, 376, 382, 383, 456, 516, 521, 556, 563, 618, 695
    cable service, 390
    car rentals, 335
    carpentry, 79, 89, 93, 99, 209, 543
    carpooling, 639
    cars, 62, 79, 93, 128, 187, 323, 350, 442, 448, 450, 564, 606
    catalog order, 82
    catering, 682
    clocks, 533
    college costs, 507
    commissions, 94, 114, 157, 176, 201, 293, 451
    communications, 343
    community service, 142, 148, 151, 158, 178, 198, 200, 673
    commuting, 236, 240, 435, 639
    comparison shopping, 182
    computers, 144, 403, 415, 682, 697
    construction, 89, 93, 113, 288, 470, 521, 526, 538, 539, 589, 641, 655
    consumers, 202, 367, 381
    cooking, 238, 263
    credit cards, 443
    deliveries, 172, 293
    density, 22
    design, 532, 545, 608

    distance-rate-time problems, 159, 166, 236–237, 237, 279, 364, 366, 367, 608, 610, 648, 669, 670, 671, 714, 719
    diving, 521, 589
    ecology, 434
    education, 390, 442, 450, 460, 507
    electrical engineering, 187, 557, 671
    electricity, 109, 187, 266, 358, 413, 450, 676
    energy, 413, 436, 588
    engineering, 105, 187, 557, 626
    entertainment, 43, 80, 85, 86, 101, 128, 420
    environment, 207
    equipment rentals, 92, 97, 101, 115, 128, 258, 288
    exercise, 301, 670
    finance, 201, 228, 230, 421, 432, 471, 558, 719
    fire rescue, 585, 617
    fireworks, 519
    fitness, 99, 301, 670
    flight, 99, 594, 624, 625, 626
    flowers, 230
    food, 14, 64, 84, 129, 256, 258, 278, 302, 372, 381, 640, 653, 654, 680, 682, 684, 691, 695
    football, 21, 26, 28, 70, 549
    fractal geometry, 428
    framing, 13, 101, 532
    fund-raising, 149, 301, 302
    games, 212, 220, 221, 224, 230, 365, 376, 476, 477, 478
    garage sales, 390
    gardens and gardening, 202, 335, 390, 470, 515, 520, 539, 544, 556, 570, 675
    gas mileage, 266
    grades, 119–120, 123, 144, 160, 322, 451
    gravity, 515
    groceries, 52, 55
    ground speed, 669
    guitars, 700–701
    gymnastics, 143
    Habitat for Humanity, 636
    hair, 186
    handshake problem, 690
    hat sales, 399
    health care, 114, 157, 165, 166, 259, 403
    helicopters, 540, 594
    hiking, 595, 596, 685
    hobbies, 29, 228, 626
    home improvements, 556
    iguanas, 244
    indirect measurement, 191
    insecticides, 390
    insurance, 85
    interest, 201, 228, 230, 438–439, 441, 443, 444, 558, 660
    investing, 34, 93, 507, 604
    jewelry, 359, 383
    jobs, 30, 149, 176, 255, 682
    juries, 687, 689
    land area, 215
    landmarks, 237, 435, 552, 579
    landscaping, 515, 572
    law, 687, 689
    lawn care, 7
    levers, 638
    libraries, 84, 85, 252
    license plates, 683, 691
    light, 649
    loan payments, 660
    locks, 690

manufacturing, 99, 122, 169, 170, 177, 178, 213, 217, 373, 465, 537, 538, 588
maps, 59
medicine, 78, 409, 422, 438, 440, 443
meeting expenses, 157
metallurgy, 362–363
milk consumption, 200, 440
model building, 169, 464
mole, 408
money, 7, 28, 52, 71, 76, 202, 222, 223, 303, 365, 368, 390, 688, 689, 716, 719
music industry, 5, 248, 344, 391
NASDAQ exchange, 684
nature, 513, 625, 626
navigation, 59, 625
newspaper layout, 582
nutrition, 64, 80, 302, 695
office supplies, 217
optical fibers, 366
pace, 187
packaging, 587, 610, 611
painting, 274, 532, 641, 676
Panama Canal, 267, 444
paper folding, 428
parade banner, 154
parking costs, 239
parks, 12, 78, 122, 126, 157, 313
party supplies, 388
passwords, 682, 683
pets, 296, 522, 718
photocopying, 432, 433, 695
photography, 29
physical therapy, 207
pizza, 680, 691
plants, 341
plumbing, 278
population, 187, 215, 322, 324, 396, 404, 416, 421, 431, 433, 435, 437, 441, 442, 443, 444, 460, 551, 562, 564, 566
postage, 256, 380
power, 610
pricing products, 633
profit, 244, 255, 366
publishing, 363–364
pulse rate, 165
pyramids, 336–337
quality control, 169, 171, 213
radio, 215, 649, 684
recreation, 97, 114, 126, 127, 296, 596, 626
recycling, 158, 418
rent, 91
restaurants, 258, 357, 384, 451
roads, 284, 289
rock climbing, 26
rowing, 670
running, 187, 335, 351
safe loads, 142, 150, 158, 178
sailing, 538, 587
sales, 5, 6, 11, 13, 70, 114, 143, 149, 159, 201, 202, 204, 208, 209, 231, 257, 294, 297, 303, 355, 358, 366, 367, 390, 399
sales tax, 78, 201
scale model, 255
school musical, 138
school supplies, 53, 55, 365, 639
selecting representatives, 221, 223
shipping, 267, 380, 444
shopping, 48, 55, 56
sightseeing, 579

skating, 240, 321
soccer, 344, 717
softball, 230
solar heating, 588
space, 527, 574–575
spark plugs, 223
speed of cheetah, 183
sports, 14, 26, 28, 35, 51, 52, 70, 78, 80, 113, 126, 127, 145, 172, 184, 186, 187, 208, 209, 230, 344, 383, 426, 427, 522, 526, 538, 549, 550, 589, 595, 630, 640, 670, 671, 681, 682, 685, 717, 718
spreadsheets, 100, 338, 344, 456, 557
stock exchange, 684
stock price, 34
student council, 683
surveying, 641
surveys, 230
swimming, 681
taxes, 78, 150, 201, 368
telemarketing, 94
telephone service, 84, 92, 93, 99, 245, 251, 421, 682, 695
television, 420
temperature, 26, 28, 31, 36, 39, 43, 70, 71, 80, 85, 86, 112–113, 120, 123, 165, 239, 321, 366, 401
tennis, 522, 526
ticket sales, 128, 354, 357
tiling a floor, 150, 151
time zones, 273
tipping, 258
trains, 279, 716
transportation, 64, 236, 240, 271, 349, 368, 595, 699
travel, 71, 105, 106–107, 108, 109, 110, 115, 123, 127, 128, 138, 145, 237, 335, 364–365, 366, 367, 388, 640, 641, 642, 644, 669, 676, 680, 684, 698
trees, 188, 214, 716
urban planning, 12, 313, 531
vacations, 143, 358
vertical motion, 551, 571
videos, 350
volleyball, 522
volunteerism, 673
wages and earnings, 14, 79, 110, 202, 209, 227, 230, 231, 250, 255, 265, 273, 293, 335, 382, 641
water conservation, 250, 429
water supply, 198
water usage, 166, 257
weather and climate, 41, 78, 165, 171, 177, 208, 238, 263, 276
weight, 76, 239, 303
wildlife management, 122

Connections to Math, Teacher's Edition pages 12, 22, 75, 157, 164, 188, 191, 194, 265, 272, 293, 317, 382, 409, 470, 497, 550, 610, 645

Connections to other Disciplines, Teacher's Edition pages 22, 26, 33, 39, 83, 122, 183, 207, 265, 306, 321, 378, 401, 409, 464, 520, 532, 555, 585, 602, 604, 622, 654, 680

Consecutive integers, 104, 107, 108, 109, 115, 127, 129

Constant, 49
of variation, 262, 277, 637, 640, 693, 696
Converse, 586
of the Pythagorean Theorem, 586
Conversion factor, 182
Coordinate(s)
defined, 59
identifying, 59–60, 62, 63
range of, 241, 276, 392
reading, 284
x-, 59–60, 62, 69
y-, 59–60, 62, 69, 560
Coordinate plane, 59–65, 69, 234
Correlation, 62, 63–64, 65, 69, 70
Correlation coefficient, 319–320, 333
Corresponding angles, 190
Corresponding sides, 190
Cosine, 621–622, 631
Cost, formula for, 11, 13
Counterexamples, 18–19, 20, 23, 57, 65
Counting methods, 679–685, 688–689
Critical Thinking, 5, 13, 14, 15, 19, 21, 25, 30, 35, 43, 46, 52, 57, 62, 63, 79, 86, 92, 100, 108, 109, 119, 120, 122, 136, 137, 138, 144, 149, 156, 158, 162, 167, 169, 171, 187, 191, 193, 201, 208, 209, 210, 212, 215, 221, 225, 239, 244, 245, 248, 251, 257, 265, 271, 283, 287, 296, 302, 308, 314, 322, 323, 342, 345, 351, 358, 367, 370, 373, 374, 380, 387, 390, 394, 397, 398, 401, 403, 409, 413, 415, 421, 422, 428, 432, 434, 438, 447, 457, 460, 464, 470, 478, 480, 484, 488, 494, 499, 504, 505, 512, 513, 515, 521, 522, 526, 527, 532, 544, 546, 551, 552, 556, 557, 565, 567, 589, 592, 596, 604, 608, 609, 611, 615, 617, 618, 622, 641, 644, 649, 654, 659, 665, 670, 675, 680, 682, 683, 684, 687, 689, 690, 691

Cross products, 183–184, 227, 234
Cross Products Property, 184
Cross-curriculum connections. *See* Connections.
Cube(s)
number, 210, 211, 214, 216, 220, 222, 223, 224, 227, 229, 231, 240, 289, 374, 451, 476
surface area of, 414, 471, 528, 534
volume of, 414
Cubic function, 567
Cumulative Review, 129, 231, 335, 451, 573, 697–699
Curie, Marie, 440
Cylinder
surface area of, 14, 116–117
volume of, 14, 113, 465, 500, 572, 610, 631

D

Data
finding patterns in, 37, 397, 428, 434
fitting exponential curves to, 436
mean of, 120, 121–123
modeling, 561–566
range of, 120, 121, 127
writing linear equations from, 300, 306–307, 318–324
Data Analysis
exercises, 186, 209, 215, 216, 300, 441, 565

mean, 118, 119–120, 121–123, 127, 576
median, 118, 119–120, 121–123, 127
mode, 118, 119–120, 121–123, 127
scatter plots, 61–62, 63, 64, 69, 70, 280, 318–324
statistics, 441, 746
stem-and-leaf plots, 120–121, 122, 123, 127, 128, 129, 216
surveys, 186, 745

Data collection, 123, 216, 323, 336, 444, 565, 618, 737, 739

Data updates, 27, 128, 319, 320, 321, 324, 333, 334, 564

Decay, exponential, 439–445, 449

Decay factor, 440, 449

Decimals
fractions as, 19, 392, 725, 728
in gridded-response exercises, 66
solving equations containing, 90–91
writing as percent, 180, 728

Decrease, percent of, 204, 207, 217, 228, 229, 230

Deductive reasoning, 56, 57, 83, 126

Degree, 457, 503

Denominators
least common (LCD), 668, 669, 670, 671, 694, 695, 726
like, 667–668
monomial, 668
polynomial, 668–669
rationalizing, 581, 601–602, 630
unlike, 668–669

Density
formula for, 22
population, 187

Dependent events, 221, 222, 223, 229

Dependent variables, 248, 276

Depression, angle of, 624, 625, 627

Diagnosing Readiness. *See* Instant Check System.

Diagnosing Readiness, 2C–D, 72C–D, 132C–D, 180C–D, 234C–D, 280C–D, 338C–D, 392C–D, 454C–D, 508C–D, 576C–D, 634C–D, Teacher's Edition pages 2, 72, 132, 180, 234, 280, 338, 392, 454, 508, 576, 634

Diagram(s)
drawing, 89, 104, 193, 194, 195, 196, 330, 350, 352, 366, 376, 426, 479, 489, 521, 522, 538, 623, 624, 714
mapping, 242, 244
as problem solving strategy, 89, 103, 104, 193, 194, 195, 196, 330, 350, 352, 366, 376, 426, 479, 489, 521, 522, 538, 623, 624, 714
as test-taking strategy, 330
tree, 680
Venn, 18

Difference of squares, 476–477, 478, 492, 601

Dimensional analysis, 182, 183, 185, 186, 187

Direct variation, 261–266, 277, 638–639, 640, 641, 696

Discriminant, 554–558, 571, 576

Distance
finding on maps, 191, 192–193, 195, 246
finding using trigonometric ratios, 621–627, 631

Distance formulas, 15, 104, 364, 527, 579, 582, 591–592, 594, 595, 596, 610, 630

Distance-rate-time problems, 104–107, 108, 109, 110, 115, 127, 128, 159, 236–237, 279, 364, 366, 367, 648, 669, 670, 671, 714, 719

Distributive Property, 46–53, 55, 56, 57, 69, 80, 88, 180
multiplication of binomials using, 467–468, 504
simplifying radical expressions, 601
solving inequalities using, 154, 155
using substitution and, 348, 350, 363
using to simplify equations, 89–91

Diversity, Teacher's Edition pages 25, 29, 89, 142, 205, 263, 300, 344, 406, 457, 542, 608, 669

Dividend, 662

Divisibility, 722

Division
of fractions, 180, 727
of inequalities by negative numbers, 371
of polynomials, 662–666, 694
of powers, 417–418, 448
of rational expressions, 658, 659, 660, 661, 694
of real numbers, 40–44, 68, 72
simplifying radicals with, 580
solving equations using, 76–77
solving inequalities using, 148–149
using reciprocal, 41

Division Property
of Equality, 77, 83, 95
of Inequality, 148–149
of Square Roots, 580

Divisor, 662

Domain
defined, 241, 276
finding, 241–242, 614, 616, 617, 632, 634
finding range from, 392
of square root functions, 614, 616, 617, 631, 632

Dorling Kindersley. *See* Real-World Snapshots.

Dorling Kindersley. See Real-World Snapshots.

E

Earth, geometry of, 179

Einstein, Albert, 413

Element of a matrix, 27

Elevation, angle of, 623–624, 625, 626, 627

Eliminating answers, 502

Elimination method, solving systems using, 353–359, 362, 388

English Learners, Teacher's Edition pages 10, 16, 25, 66, 75, 98, 120, 135, 160, 163, 168, 190, 203, 205, 212, 238, 258, 262, 283, 292, 321, 354, 363, 366, 409, 421, 440, 475, 491, 514, 532, 548, 568, 587, 595, 602, 625, 639, 651, 668, 681

Enrichment. *See also* Extensions.
Challenge exercises, 8, 14–15, 22, 30, 36, 43–44, 52, 57, 64, 79–80, 86, 93, 100, 109–110, 114, 123, 138, 144, 150, 158, 165, 171, 187, 194, 202, 209, 216, 223, 239–240, 245, 251, 258, 266, 272, 289, 296, 302, 309, 316, 323, 328–329, 345, 351, 358–359, 367, 375, 383, 399, 404, 409, 415, 422, 428, 434, 443–444, 460, 464–465, 471, 478–479, 484, 488, 494, 500, 515–516, 522, 527–528, 533, 539, 545–546, 551–552, 557, 565, 583, 598, 596, 605, 611, 618, 627, 642, 649–650, 655, 661, 665–666, 670, 676–677, 684, 690–691

Enrichment, 2D–E, 72D–E, 132D–E, 180D–E, 234D–E, 280D–E, 338D–E, 392D–E, 454D–E, 508D–E, 576D–E, 634D–E

Equality
Addition Property of, 74, 75, 95, 353
Division Property of, 77, 83, 95
Multiplication Property of, 76–77, 83, 183
Reflexive Property of, 173
Subtraction Property of, 74, 75, 83, 95, 354
Symmetric Property of, 173
Transitive Property of, 173

Equation(s)
absolute value, 167–172, 177, 178, 234, 325–329, 333
with decimals, 90–91
defined, 5
equivalent, 75, 101, 129
with fractions, 90
with grouping symbols, 89, 91, 92,
identity, 98, 99, 110, 126, 128
for inverse variation, 637, 640, 641
linear. *See* Linear equation(s).
linear functions and, 102, 243, 291–293, 332
of lines, 318–324
literal, 111, 127
modeling, 81, 95
modeling relationships with equations and formulas, 5–8, 72
multi-step, 88–94, 132
with no solutions, 98, 99, 100, 110, 128, 170, 531, 532, 544, 558, 609, 611, 612
one-step, 74–80, 132, 180
with only variables, transforming, 112
of parallel lines, 312, 313, 333
percent, 197–202
problem solving and, 103–110
quadratic, 529–552, 609
radical, 607–612, 630–631, 634
rational, 672–677, 695
solution of, 75, 125
solving using addition and subtraction, 74–76
solving using multiplication and division, 76–77
solving using properties of equality, 75
solving using reciprocals, 77
standard form of, 300
two-step, 81–85, 126, 132
using graphs to solve and check, 102
with variables on both sides, 96–101
writing, 5–6, 72, 89, 97, 99, 104–106, 234, 300

Equivalent equations, 75, 101, 129

Equivalent fractions, 724

Equivalent inequalities, 140, 176

Eratosthenes, 179

Error(s)
greatest possible, 205, 206, 207
percent, 205–206, 207, 208

Error Analysis, 29, 51, 79, 85, 92, 100, 124, 137, 150, 158, 174, 193, 239, 244, 245, 288, 295, 302, 358, 374, 408, 414, 421, 459, 464, 493, 504, 532, 545, 557, 589, 604, 628, 655, 659, 670

Index

Error Prevention, Teacher's Edition pages 5, 13, 15, 21, 26, 29, 35, 38, 42, 45, 46, 49, 55, 63, 77, 82, 92, 97, 106, 112, 116, 123, 135, 137, 143, 147, 156, 160, 164, 170, 172, 185, 193, 199, 200, 206, 212, 213, 221, 240, 244, 248, 250, 257, 262, 269, 286, 292, 307, 313, 315, 320, 327, 342, 348, 350, 354, 355, 361, 366, 371, 373, 381, 385, 396, 397, 403, 408, 415, 421, 427, 433, 441, 445, 458, 459, 463, 466, 470, 475, 477, 480, 482, 483, 488, 492, 493, 497, 499, 502, 513, 521, 526, 531, 535, 538, 542, 548, 550, 553, 556, 563, 581, 586, 587, 588, 594, 603, 609, 616, 622, 640, 645, 654, 659, 663, 669, 675, 682, 683, 689

Estimation
  of answers, 628, 723
  of area, 521
  exercises, 78, 86, 149, 199, 201, 230, 250, 416, 443, 448, 521, 723
  of percents, 199–200, 201
  of solution to system, 347
  of square roots, 525
  as test-taking strategy, 628

Evaluating
  exponential expressions, 396
  exponential functions, 430–431, 449
  expressions, 10–12, 13, 14, 26, 29, 39, 40, 41, 68, 226, 234, 392, 508
  function rules, 508
  functions, 243
  identifying solutions of inequalities by, 134–135
  rational expressions, 653–654

Event(s)
  certain, 211
  complement of, 212, 214
  compound, probability of, 219–224
  defined, 211, 229
  dependent, 221, 222, 223, 229
  impossible, 211
  independent, 220, 221, 222, 223, 229, 660, 680
  odds in favor of, 215
  relating graphs to, 236–240

Expanded form, 729

Experimental probability, 212–213, 214, 229

Exponent(s)
  base of, 11, 729
  defined, 9, 729
  division properties of, 417–423, 454
  evaluating expressions with, 10, 11, 12, 13
  expanded form of, 729
  multiplication properties of, 405–416, 454
  negative, 394–399
  scientific notation, 400–404, 406–407, 448
  simplifying expressions with, 9, 10, 11, 12, 13, 729
  zero as, 394–399, 447

Exponential curve(s), fitting to data, 436

Exponential decay, 439–444, 449

Exponential expression(s), 395–396, 419

Exponential function(s), 430–435, 559–566, 647
  evaluating, 430–431, 449
  graphing, 431–432
  limits of, 651

Exponential growth, 437–439, 441–444, 449

Exponential model, 559, 560, 561, 562, 571

Expressions
  algebraic, 4–8, 10–12, 42, 48–49, 180, 406, 417–418
  evaluating, 10–12, 26, 39, 40, 41, 42, 68, 226, 234, 392, 508
  exponential, 395–396, 419
  rational, 652–656
  simplifying, 9–15, 39–40, 41–44, 48–49, 50–53, 56, 395–396, 417–418, 419, 454, 634

Extended-response exercises, 174, 195, 216, 252, 272, 303, 324, 329, 345, 359, 384, 423, 451, 472, 501, 516, 534, 546, 566, 573, 606, 627, 642, 666, 699

Extensions
  Algebraic Reasoning, 173
  Cubic Functions, 567
  Determining Limits, 651
  Developing Geometric Formulas, 116–117
  Interpreting Solutions, 160
  Rational Exponents, 620
  Sampling, 225
  Special Right Triangles, 598–599

Extra Practice, 702–713

Extraneous solutions, 609, 630–631

Extremes of a proportion, 183

F

Factor(s)
  conversion, 182
  decay, 440, 449
  greatest common (GCF), 463, 504, 721, 724
  growth, 437, 449
  perfect-square, 578–579
  prime, 579

Factorial, 681

Factoring, 508
  difference of squares, 492
  by grouping, 496–501
  perfect-square trinomial, 490–491, 493–495, 505
  polynomial, 463, 496–497, 504–505
  quadratic equation, 536–540
  quadratic expression, 673
  rational expression, 653, 657
  trinomial, 480–491, 493–495, 497–501, 504–505
  using models, 480

Fahrenheit temperature, 43, 71, 86, 112, 113

Families of functions, 647

Fibonacci Sequence, 272

FOIL (First, Outer, Inner, Last), 468, 492, 504, 601

Foot-pounds, 207

Formulas
  for airplane's lift capabilities, 94
  for area, 12, 13, 468
  for area of rectangle, 13, 51, 115, 663
  for area of trapezoid, 12, 15, 470, 533
  for area of triangle, 111, 251, 640, 665
  for aspect ratio of hang glider, 114
  for batting average, 113
  for bike travel, 130
  for circumference of a circle, 640
  for converting temperature scales, 43, 71, 86, 112, 113

for cost, 11, 13
for density, 22
for distance, 15, 104, 364, 527, 579, 582, 591–592, 594, 595, 596, 610, 630
for electrical circuit, 127
for energy-mass relationship, 413
for engine efficiency, 606
geometric, 111, 116–117, 756
for height, 43
for intensity of light, 649
for interior angle sum of polygon, 114
for length of pendulum, 533
for midpoint, 114, 593, 594, 595, 596, 630
for number of combinations, 695
for odds in favor, 215
for perimeter of pentagon, 250
for perimeter of rectangle, 9, 103, 129, 154
for power, 610
for probability, 211–214, 216, 229, 688
quadratic, 547–552, 558, 571
recursive, 272
for resistance in a parallel circuit, 671
for sales commission, 114
for simple interest, 114, 392
for slope, 284, 331
for speed, 615
for surface area of cube, 528, 534
for surface area of cylinder, 14, 116–117
for surface area of rectangular prism, 116–117
for surface area of sphere, 532
for time of an orbit, 611
for traffic light, 115
for transmission, 130
transformed, 111–115, 280
for velocity, 611, 616
for vertical motion, 549, 550, 551
for volume, 13, 14
for volume of air in lungs, 114
for volume of cylinder, 14, 465, 572, 610, 631
for volume of rectangular prisms, 117, 665
for volume of sphere, 14, 478, 567

45-45-90 triangles, 598

Fraction(s)
  adding, 634, 726
  converting to decimals, 19, 392, 725, 728
  dividing, 180, 727
  equivalent, 724
  in gridded-response exercises, 66
  improper, 727
  like, 726
  multiplying, 180, 727
  ordering, 19–21
  simplifying, 580, 724
  solving equations containing, 90
  subtracting, 634, 726
  unit, 53
  unlike, 726
  writing as percent, 180, 728

Fraction bar, 12, 40

Frequency, 735, 739

Fulcrum, 638

Function(s), 241–246
  absolute value, 249, 647
  cubic, 567
  defined, 242, 276
  evaluating, 243
  exponential, 430–435, 449, 559–566, 647, 651
  families of, 647

graphing, 247–253, 280, 508
identifying, 241–242, 648
limits of, 651
linear. *See* Linear functions.
quadratic, 510–523, 559–566, 569, 570, 647
radical, 647
rational, 643–650, 651, 693–694
signum, 251
square root, 614–619, 631, 632
three views of, 248–249
types of, 647

Function notation, 243, 276

Function rules, 244, 246, 247–259
defined, 243, 276
evaluating, 508
for geometric sequences, 425–426
graphs and, 247–253
tables and, 247–253
writing, 254–259, 338

G

Gateway Arch (St. Louis), 552

GCF (greatest common factor), 463, 504, 721, 724

Geometric formulas, 111, 116–117

Geometric sequences, 424–429, 449

Geometry. See also angle, area, circle,
perimeter, rectangle, right triangle,
sphere, surface area, volume.
examples, 12, 19, 97, 103, 11, 116–117, 154,
169, 190–191, 206, 379, 468, 473, 491, 498,
531, 537, 543, 592–593, 598–599, 613, 663
exercises, 6, 13–15, 51, 63–65, 70, 79, 85, 91–92,
98, 100, 107–109, 110, 113–117, 126, 129,
138, 144, 151, 153, 156, 158, 165, 171, 177,
192–195, 206–209, 215, 228, 250–251, 256,
265, 288, 296, 302, 316, 317, 322, 350, 352,
359, 366, 367, 381–382, 388, 408–409, 414,
428, 459–460, 464–465, 470–473, 477, 479,
493–495, 499–501, 504–506, 515, 528,
532–533, 539–540, 544–546, 551, 570–573,
589, 594–599, 604, 610, 632, 640, 655, 660,
665, 690, 699, 708, 710
fractal, 428

Glossary, 751–779

Golden ratio, 602

Golden rectangle, 158

Graph(s), 59–65
of absolute value equations, 325–329, 333
analyzing, 2, 237
axes of, 59, 69
bar, 736
box-and-whisker, 740
choosing appropriate, 741
circle, 739
choosing model with, 559–561, 571
of exponential functions, 431–432
finding rate of change using, 283
finding slope using, 284–285
of functions, 247–253, 280, 508
of inequalities, 135–136, 137, 138, 370
interpreting, 236–237
of inverse variations, 637, 640, 641
line, 738
of linear equations, 293, 338
of linear functions, 248–251, 261, 298–299
of linear inequalities, 370–372, 373–375, 385, 389

of lines using intercepts, 299
misleading, 742
quadratic, 510–518, 569
of quadratic inequalities, 519, 520, 570
of rational functions, 643–650, 693–694
relating to events, 236–240
scatter plots, 61–62, 63, 64, 69, 70, 280,
318–324
sketching, 237
solving quadratic equations with, 530, 535
solving systems of linear equations using,
340–345, 362, 387
solving systems of linear inequalities using,
377–379, 385, 389
of square root functions, 614–619, 631
translating, 325–329, 333
using point-slope form, 305
using to solve and check equations, 102
writing equation from, 292

Graphing calculator
CALC feature, 102, 319, 341, 535
counting combinations, 687
EDIT feature, 319
equation of line of best fit, 319, 321, 322, 323,
329, 333, 436, 564
exercises, 45, 63, 102, 253, 315, 322, 323, 324,
343, 434, 436, 538, 564, 611, 643, 649, 675
fitting exponential curves to data, 436, 564
function rules, tables, and graphs, 253
GRAPH feature, 253
graphing linear inequalities, 385
graphing rational functions, 643, 675
hints, 319, 341
Investigating $y = mx + b$, 290
MATH key, 687
matrices, 45, 360–361
Matrix feature, 360
MODE key, 643
permutation notation, 681, 682, 683
quadratic equation, 512, 514, 515, 520, 523,
535, 564
randInt(feature, 218
simulation, 218
SIN key, 622
solving system by graphing, 341, 343, 344
STAT screen, 319, 323, 436
TABLE feature, 253, 341, 535, 643
TBLSET feature, 253, 535
TRACE feature, 253, 341, 643
using graphs to solve and check equations, 102
VARS key, 436
WINDOW screen, 253, 535
X^{-1} key, 361
Y= feature, 102
ZOOM feature, 102, 253, 315, 341

Greatest common factor (GCF), 463, 504,
721, 724

Greatest possible error, 205, 206, 207

Gridded-response exercises, 66, 86, 123, 129, 150,
202, 231, 245, 309, 335, 352, 399, 451, 494,
528, 573, 596, 684

Griffith-Joyner, Florence, 208

Grouping, factoring by, 496–500

Grouping symbols, 11–12, 13, 14, 33, 89, 91, 92

Growth, exponential, 437–439, 441–444, 449

Growth factor, 437, 449

Guess and Test. *See* Try, Test, and Revise.

H

Half-life, 440, 445, 449

Hands-On Activities, 2D, 72D, 132D, 180D,
234D, 280D, 338D, 392D, 454D, 576D,
634D, Teacher's Edition pages 4, 9, 17,
24, 32, 37, 47, 54, 59, 74, 81, 88, 90, 103,
111, 118, 134, 140, 146, 153, 161, 167,
182, 189, 197, 204, 211, 219, 236, 241,
247, 254, 261, 268, 282, 291, 298, 304,
311, 318, 325, 340, 347, 353, 362, 370,
377, 394, 400, 405, 411, 417, 424, 430,
437, 456, 462, 467, 474, 481, 486, 490,
496, 510, 517, 524, 529, 536, 541, 547,
554, 559, 578, 584, 591, 600, 607, 614,
621, 636, 644, 652, 657, 662, 667, 672,
679, 686

Height, formula for, 43

Hints. *See* Calculator Hint, Graphing Calculator
Hint, Need Help, Problem Solving Hints.

Histogram, 737

History and math. *See* Point in Time.

Horizontal asymptote, 646, 649

Horizontal line, 285, 286, 299

Horizontal translation, 327, 333, 615, 631

Hypotenuse, 584, 630

Hypothesis, 586

I

Identity, 98, 99, 110, 126, 128

Identity Property
of Addition, 24, 54, 55
of Multiplication, 38, 54, 57

If-then statements, 586

Impossible event, 211

Improper fractions, 727

*Inclusion, Teacher's Edition pages 19, 97, 117,
141, 173, 191, 248, 253, 265, 350, 369,
395, 497, 512, 601, 681*

Inclusive, 161

Increase, percent of, 204–205, 217, 228, 229, 230

Independent events, 220, 221, 222, 223, 229,
660, 680

Independent variables, 248, 276

Indirect measurement, 191

Inductive reasoning, 268, 270, 271, 277

Inequalities, 134–179
absolute value, 168–172, 177, 178
compound, 161–166, 177, 338
defined, 19
equivalent, 140, 176
graphs of, 135–136, 137, 138, 370
linear. *See* Linear inequalities.
multiplying or dividing by negative
numbers, 371
multi-step, 153–159
properties of, 140–141, 146–149, 154, 155
quadratic, 519, 520
solution of, 134–135, 140–160, 175
solving using addition and subtraction,
140–145

solving using multiplication and division, 146–151
symbols for, 19, 21, 154

Infinite, 141

Input-output table, 243

Instant Check System
answers to, 781–797
Check Skills You'll Need, 4, 9, 17, 24, 32, 37, 47, 54, 59, 74, 81, 88, 90, 103, 111, 118, 134, 140, 146, 153, 161, 167, 182, 189, 197, 204, 211, 219, 236, 241, 247, 254, 261, 268, 282, 291, 298, 304, 311, 318, 325, 340, 347, 353, 362, 370, 377, 394, 400, 405, 411, 417, 424, 430, 437, 456, 462, 467, 474, 481, 486, 490, 496, 510, 517, 524, 529, 536, 541, 547, 554, 559, 578, 584, 591, 600, 607, 614, 621, 636, 644, 652, 657, 662, 667, 672, 679, 686
Check Understanding, 4, 5, 6, 10, 11, 12, 17, 18, 19, 20, 25, 26, 27, 32, 33, 34, 38, 39, 40, 41, 47, 48, 49, 55, 56, 60, 61, 62, 75, 76, 77, 82, 83, 88, 89, 90, 97, 98, 103, 104, 105, 106, 107, 111, 112, 113, 119, 120, 121, 134, 135, 136, 140, 141, 142, 147, 148, 149, 153, 154, 155, 161, 162, 163, 167, 168, 169, 182, 183 184, 185, 186, 190, 191, 197, 198, 199, 200, 204, 205, 206, 212, 213, 220, 221, 236, 237, 241, 242, 243, 248, 249, 254, 255, 262, 263, 264, 268, 269, 270, 283, 284, 285, 292, 293, 299, 300, 305, 306, 307, 311, 312, 313, 319, 320, 325, 326, 327, 340, 341, 342, 348, 349, 353, 354, 355, 356, 363, 364, 371, 372, 378, 379, 380, 395, 396, 400, 401, 402, 405, 406, 407, 412, 413, 418, 419, 424, 425, 426, 427, 430, 431, 432, 438, 439, 440, 441, 457, 458, 462, 463, 467, 468, 469, 475, 476, 477, 481, 482, 483, 486, 487, 491, 492, 496, 497, 498, 511, 512, 513, 518, 519, 524, 525, 526, 530, 531, 536, 537, 542, 543, 548, 549, 550, 555, 560, 561, 562, 563, 578, 579, 580, 581, 585, 586, 587, 592, 593, 600, 601, 602, 607, 608, 609, 614, 615, 622, 623, 624, 637, 638, 639, 644, 645, 646, 648, 652, 653, 654, 657, 658, 659, 662, 663, 664, 667, 668, 669, 672, 673, 674, 680, 681, 682, 687, 688
Checkpoint Quiz, 31, 58, 94, 115, 151, 166, 195, 217, 246, 267, 303, 324, 352, 376, 416, 435, 472, 495, 534, 558, 597, 619, 656, 685
Diagnosing Readiness, 2, 72, 132, 180, 234, 280, 338, 392, 454, 508, 576, 634
Instant Check System, 2C, 72C, 132C, 180C, 234C, 280C, 338C, 392C, 454C, 508C, 576C, 634C

Integers, 17–18, 20, 21, 23
adding, 24–31, 68, 72
consecutive, 104, 107, 108, 109, 115, 127, 129
multiplying, 37–38
subtracting, 32–36, 68, 72

Intercepts
x-, 298–299, 301, 302, 529
y-, 291, 292, 298, 299, 301, 302

Interdisciplinary Connections. *See* Connections.

Interest
compound, 438–439, 449, 558, 660, 698
exercises, 114, 201, 228, 230, 392, 438–439, 441, 443, 444, 558, 660
simple, 114, 201, 392, 773

Interest period, 438

Interior angles, 114

Internet links (Take It to the Net), 8, 15, 22, 27, 31, 36, 44, 53, 58, 65, 67, 70, 71, 80, 86, 93, 94, 101, 110, 115, 123, 125, 128, 131, 139, 145, 150, 159, 166, 172, 175, 178, 179, 188, 195, 202, 209, 217, 224, 227, 230, 233, 240, 246, 252, 259, 266, 273, 275, 278, 279, 289, 297, 303, 309, 317, 319, 320, 324, 329, 331, 333, 334, 337, 345, 352, 359, 368, 375, 384, 387, 390, 391, 399, 404, 410, 416, 423, 429, 435, 444, 447, 450, 453, 461, 465, 472, 479, 485, 489, 495, 501, 503, 506, 507, 516, 523, 528, 534, 540, 546, 552, 558, 564, 566, 569, 572, 575, 583, 590, 596, 606, 612, 619, 627, 629, 632, 633, 642, 650, 656, 661, 666, 671, 677, 685, 691, 693, 696, 697, 701

Interpreting solutions, 160

Intervention, 2C, 72C, 132C, 180C, 234C, 280C, 338C, 392C, 454C, 508C, 576C, 634C, Teacher's Edition pages 2, 4, 9, 17, 24, 32, 37, 47, 54, 59, 72, 74, 81, 88, 90, 103, 111, 118, 132, 134, 140, 146, 153, 161, 167, 180, 182, 189, 197, 204, 211, 219, 234, 236, 241, 247, 254, 261, 268, 280, 282, 291, 298, 304, 311, 318, 325, 338, 340, 347, 353, 362, 370, 377, 392, 394, 400, 405, 411, 417, 424, 430, 437, 454, 456, 462, 467, 474, 481, 486, 490, 496, 508, 510, 517, 524, 529, 536, 541, 547, 554, 559, 576, 578, 584, 591, 600, 607, 614, 621, 634, 636, 644, 652, 657, 662, 667, 672, 679, 686

Inverse
additive, 24, 54
multiplicative, 40–41, 54

Inverse operations, 75, 125

Inverse Property
of Addition, 24, 54
of Multiplication, 40–41, 54

Inverse variation, 636–642, 693
defined, 637, 693
direct variation vs., 638–639, 640, 641, 696
equation for, 637, 640, 641, 642
graphs of, 637, 641, 642

Investigation
Compound Events, 219
Determining Order, 679
Direct Variation, 261–262
Distributive Property, 46
Estimating Solutions, 347
Exploring Rate of Change, 282
Exploring Special Products, 474
Exponents, 394
Finding *x*-intercepts, 529
Functions, 247
Graphing Inequalities, 370
Intercepts, 298
Inverse Variation, 636
Modeling Equations, 95
Modeling Percents, 196
Multiplying Each Side of an Inequality, 146
Multiplying Integers, 37
Order of Operations, 9
Perfect-Square Trinomials, 490
Plotting Quadratic Curves, 510
Powers of Powers, 411
Proportions in Triangles, 189

Pythagorean Theorem, 584
Solving Systems Using Algebra Tiles, 346
Trigonometric Ratios, 621
Understanding Probability, 210
Using Models to Factor, 480
Using Models to Multiply, 466
Using Polynomials, 456
Using a Table to Solve an Equation, 96
Using a Transformed Formula, 111

Irrational number, 18, 68, 525, 526, 570

Isosceles right triangle, 598

iText, 2, 4, 9, 17, 24, 31, 32, 37, 47, 54, 58, 59, 72, 74, 81, 88, 94, 103, 111, 115, 118, 132, 134, 140, 146, 151, 153, 161, 166, 167, 180, 182, 189, 195, 197, 204, 211, 216, 219, 234, 236, 241, 246, 247, 254, 261, 267, 268, 280, 282, 291, 298, 303, 304, 311, 318, 324, 325, 338, 340, 347, 352, 353, 362, 370, 376, 377, 392, 394, 400, 405, 411, 416, 417, 424, 430, 435, 437, 454, 456, 462, 467, 472, 474, 481, 486, 490, 495, 496, 508, 510, 517, 524, 529, 534, 536, 541, 547, 554, 558, 559, 576, 578, 584, 591, 597, 600, 607, 614, 619, 621, 634, 636, 644, 652, 656, 657, 662, 667, 672, 679, 685, 686

J _____

Johnson, Lyndon B., 252

Justifying Steps, 56–57, 83, 84, 126, 173

K _____

Kelvin, 401

L _____

Laws
Boyle's, 641
of Large Numbers, 213
Ohm's, 127, 266

Learning Styles, See also Alternative Method, Diversity, English Learners, Error Prevention, Inclusion, Math Tip, Teaching Tip.
2D, 72D, 132D, 180D, 234D, 280D, 338D, 392D, 454D, 576D, 634D
Auditory Learners, Teacher's Edition pages 78, 89, 136, 198, 221, 242, 294, 305, 326, 363, 395, 406, 468, 475, 519, 553, 580, 640
Hands-On Activities, Teacher's Edition pages 4, 9, 17, 24, 32, 37, 47, 54, 59, 74, 81, 88, 90, 103, 111, 118, 134, 140, 146, 153, 161, 167, 182, 189, 197, 204, 211, 219, 236, 241, 247, 254, 261, 268, 282, 291, 298, 304, 311, 318, 325, 340, 347, 353, 362, 370, 377, 394, 400, 405, 411, 417, 424, 430, 437, 456, 462, 467, 474, 481, 486, 490, 496, 510, 517, 524, 529, 536, 541, 547, 554, 559, 578, 584, 591, 600, 607, 614, 621, 636, 644, 652, 657, 662, 667, 672, 679, 686
Technology Activities, Teacher's Edition pages 4, 9, 17, 24, 32, 37, 47, 54, 59, 74, 81, 88, 90, 103, 111, 118, 134, 140, 146, 153, 161, 167, 182, 189, 197, 204, 211, 219, 236, 241, 247, 254, 261, 268, 282, 291, 298, 304, 311, 318, 325, 340, 347,

353, 362, 370, 377, 394, 400, 405, 411, 417, 424, 430, 437, 456, 462, 467, 474, 481, 486, 490, 496, 510, 517, 524, 529, 536, 541, 547, 554, 559, 578, 584, 591, 600, 607, 614, 621, 636, 644, 652, 657, 662, 667, 672, 679, 686

Tactile Learners, Teacher's Edition pages 10, 19, 25, 34, 49, 60, 89, 105, 106, 116, 141, 168, 205, 210, 213, 220, 260, 274, 299, 342, 346, 371, 412, 457, 468, 473, 512, 514, 586, 610, 638, 687

Visual Learners, Teacher's Edition pages 18, 39, 48, 49, 60, 95, 104, 112, 148, 154, 184, 190, 192, 198, 248, 270, 284, 310, 312, 378, 385, 406, 468, 492, 537, 549, 560, 579, 580, 613, 623, 673, 678

Least common denominator (LCD), 668, 669, 670, 671, 694, 695, 726

Least common multiple (LCM), 668, 721, 726

Legs, of right triangle, 584, 630

Lesson Quiz, Teacher's Edition pages 7, 14, 22, 30, 36, 43, 52, 57, 64, 79, 85, 93, 100, 109, 114, 122, 138, 144, 150, 158, 165, 171, 187, 194, 201, 208, 216, 223, 239, 245, 251, 259, 266, 273, 289, 296, 302, 308, 316, 323, 328, 344, 351, 358, 367, 375, 384, 398, 404, 410, 416, 422, 428, 434, 443, 460, 465, 471, 478, 484, 489, 494, 500, 515, 522, 527, 533, 539, 545, 551, 557, 565, 582, 589, 596, 605, 611, 618, 626, 641, 649, 655, 660, 665, 670, 676, 684, 690

Lesson Resources, Teacher's Edition pages 4, 9, 17, 24, 32, 37, 47, 54, 59, 74, 81, 88, 90, 103, 111, 118, 134, 140, 146, 153, 161, 167, 182, 189, 197, 204, 211, 219, 236, 241, 247, 254, 261, 268, 282, 291, 298, 304, 311, 318, 325, 340, 347, 353, 362, 370, 377, 394, 400, 405, 411, 417, 424, 430, 437, 456, 462, 467, 474, 481, 486, 490, 496, 510, 517, 524, 529, 536, 541, 547, 554, 559, 578, 584, 591, 600, 607, 614, 621, 636, 644, 652, 657, 662, 667, 672, 679, 686

Library of Congress, 85

Like fractions, 726

Like radicals, 600, 630

Like terms, 49, 69, 72, 88–89

Limit, 651

Line(s)
  of best fit, 319–324, 329, 333, 334, 436, 495
  equations of, 318–324

Linear equation(s), 291–309
  defined, 291
  graphing, 293, 332, 338
  point-slope form of, 304–309, 332
  slope-intercept form of, 291–297, 332, 340
  standard form of, 298–303, 332
  systems of. *See* Systems of linear equations.
  writing, 291–292, 306–307

Linear function(s), 647
  equations and, 102, 243, 291–293, 332
  graphs of, 248–251, 261, 298–299
  tables and, 248, 261, 263–264, 283
  three views of, 248

Linear inequalities, 370–385

defined, 371, 389
  graphing, 370–372, 373–378, 385, 389
  solutions of, 371, 389
  systems of, 377–384, 385, 389

Linear model, 559, 560, 571

Line graphs, 738

Line plots, 735

Literal equation, 111, 127

Look for a Pattern, 716

Loroupe, Tegla, 187

M

Make a Conjecture, 22, 37, 43, 251, 411, 643, 651

Make a Table, 716

Manipulatives
  algebra tiles, 32, 34, 36, 46, 81, 95, 126, 129, 220, 221, 222, 250, 280, 346, 466, 480, 541, 683
  calculators. *See* Calculator, Graphing calculator.
  cards, 219, 222
  checkers, 220, 230
  coins, 229, 350
  dominoes, 224
  graph paper, 589, 621
  marbles, 222, 224, 230, 231, 359
  number cubes, 210, 211, 214, 216, 220, 222, 223, 224, 227, 229, 231, 240, 289, 374, 451, 476
  protractor, 730
  ruler, 193

Map(s)
  creating, 224
  finding distances on, 191, 192–193, 195, 246

Mapping diagram, 242, 244

Math Background, 2B, 72B, 132B, 180B, 234B, 280B, 338B, 392B, 454B, 508B, 576B, 634B, Teacher's Edition pages 5, 10, 18, 25, 33, 38, 48, 55, 60, 75, 82, 89, 97, 104, 112, 119, 135, 141, 147, 154, 162, 168, 183, 190, 198, 205, 212, 220, 237, 242, 248, 255, 262, 269, 283, 292, 299, 305, 312, 319, 326, 341, 348, 354, 363, 371, 378, 395, 401, 406, 412, 418, 425, 431, 438, 457, 463, 468, 475, 482, 487, 491, 497, 511, 518, 525, 530, 537, 542, 548, 555, 560, 579, 585, 592, 601, 608, 615, 622, 637, 645, 653, 658, 663, 668, 673, 680, 687

Math in the Media, 21, 30, 79, 202, 404, 444, 527, 551, 552, 641

Math Tip, Teacher's Edition pages 10, 18, 40, 49, 76, 87, 90, 104, 135, 154, 168, 183, 199, 214, 215, 225, 255, 260, 263, 284, 289, 295, 319, 327, 356, 371, 374, 379, 397, 399, 409, 412, 418, 425, 457, 464, 482, 491, 492, 518, 528, 544, 548, 555, 564, 567, 588, 592, 599, 608, 628, 651, 653, 674, 688

Matrices
  adding, 27, 28, 29, 30, 45
  defined, 27
  multiplying, 43, 360–361
  subtracting, 35
  technology, 45

Matzeliger, Jan, 14

Maximum point of parabola, 511, 513, 569, 570

Mean(s)
  defined, 118, 127
  finding, 119–120, 121–123, 127, 576
  of proportions, 183

Means-extremes property of proportions, 184

Measurement
  of angles, 730
  exercises, 259, 414, 615
  finding percent error in, 206–207
  indirect, 191
  instruments for, 403

Measures of central tendency, 118–123

Median
  defined, 118, 127
  finding, 119–120, 121–123, 127

Median-median method, 323

Mental Math, 50, 56, 63, 94, 136, 156, 349, 476–477, 493, 532, 556

Midpoint, 593, 630

Midpoint formula, 593, 594, 595, 596, 630

Minimum point of parabola, 511, 513, 569, 570

Mixed numbers, 727

Mixed Review, 8, 15, 23, 31, 36, 44, 53, 58, 65, 80, 86, 94, 101, 110, 115, 123, 139, 145, 151, 159, 166, 172, 188, 195, 202, 209, 217, 224, 240, 246, 252, 259, 267, 273, 289, 297, 303, 309, 317, 324, 329, 345, 352, 359, 368, 376, 384, 399, 404, 410, 416, 423, 429, 435, 444, 461, 465, 472, 479, 485, 489, 495, 501, 516, 523, 528, 534, 540, 546, 552, 558, 566, 583, 590, 597, 606, 612, 619, 627, 642, 650, 656, 661, 666, 671, 677, 685, 691

Mode, 119–120, 121–123
  defined, 118, 127

Model(s)
  choosing, 559–566, 571
  exponential, 559, 560, 561, 562, 571
  linear, 559, 560, 571
  quadratic, 513, 559, 560, 561, 571
  using to factor, 480
  using to multiply, 466

Modeling
  data, 561–566
  equations, 81, 95
  exponential decay, 440–441
  with formulas, 5–8
  percents, 196
  relationships with equations and formulas, 5–8
  scale, 255
  using tiles, 32, 34, 36, 46, 81, 95, 126, 129, 220, 221, 222, 250, 280, 346, 466, 480, 541, 683

Monomial(s)
  defined, 456
  degree of, 457
  distributing, 462
  dividing polynomials by, 662
  factoring out, 463

Multiple, 668, 721, 726

Multiple choice exercises, 8, 15, 22, 31, 36, 44, 52, 58, 65, 80, 93, 101, 110, 115, 129, 139, 145, 158, 166, 171, 188, 194, 209, 216, 224, 231, 240, 251, 258, 266, 272, 289, 297, 303, 317,

323, 329, 335, 345, 359, 367, 375, 384, 404, 409, 415, 423, 429, 434, 444, 446, 451, 461, 465, 472, 479, 485, 489, 500, 516, 523, 533, 539, 546, 552, 557, 566, 573, 583, 590, 605, 612, 618, 627, 642, 650, 655, 661, 666, 671, 677, 691, 697–698

Multiple correct answers, 386

Multiple Representations, 247–249, 250, 251, 254, 261, 300, 318, 320, 321, 322, 323, 341, 431–432, 436, 511, 512–513, 543, 544, 561–562, 564, 565, 614, 615, 616, 617, 644–646

Multiplication
Associative Property of, 54, 55, 57, 69
of binomials, 466–472, 474–480, 504, 508
Commutative Property of, 54, 69
of fractions, 180, 727
Identity Property of, 38, 54, 56
of inequalities by negative numbers, 371
of integers, 37
Inverse Property of, 40–41, 54, 57
of matrices, 360–361
of polynomials, 462, 468, 504
of powers, 405–406, 448
of radicals, 579
of rational expressions, 657–661, 694
of real numbers, 37–44, 68, 72
scalar, 43
with scientific notation, 402, 406–407
solving equations using, 76–77
solving inequalities using, 146–147
solving systems using, 354–356
of trinomial and binomial, 469
using models for, 466

Multiplication Counting Principle, 679–680, 682, 695

Multiplication Property
of Equality, 76–77, 83, 183
of exponents, 405–416, 454
of Inequality, 146–147
of negative one, 38, 48–50, 52, 55, 83
of Square Roots, 578–579, 600, 601, 629
of zero, 38, 55

Multiplicative inverse, 40–41, 54

Multi-step equation, 88–93, 132

Multi-step inequality, 153–159

Multi-step proportion, 185

N

NCTM, 2A, 72A, 132A, 180A, 234A, 280A, 338A, 392A, 454A, 508A, 576A, 634A

Natural numbers, 17

Need Help?, 19, 33, 56, 77, 81, 83, 88, 90, 97, 100, 137, 147, 156, 163, 167, 170, 183, 186, 197, 199, 242, 251, 272, 282, 299, 305, 340, 353, 364, 370, 371, 402, 406, 430, 459, 462, 463, 476, 491, 519, 525, 548, 557, 581, 591, 600, 601, 614, 657, 660, 662, 663, 664, 674

Negative correlation, 62, 63–65, 69, 70

Negative exponent, 394–399

Negative number, 371, 447

Negative reciprocal, 312–313

Negative slope, 286

Negative square root, 524, 570

No correlation, 61, 63, 64, 69, 70

No solution
equations with, 98, 99, 110, 128, 170, 530, 531, 532, 544, 558, 571, 609, 611, 612
systems with, 342

Notation
combination, 687
function, 243, 276
permutation, 681–682
scientific, 400–404, 406–407, 448
standard, 400–401

Number(s)
classifying, 17–22, 68
compatible, 199
composite, 454, 720
irrational, 18, 68, 525, 526, 570
Large Numbers, Law of, 213
mixed, 727
natural, 17
negative, 371, 447
prime, 720
rational, 17–22, 68, 72, 132, 525, 526, 570, 672
real. *See* Real numbers.
in scientific notation, 400–404, 406–407, 448
whole, 17–18, 20–21

Number cubes, 210, 211, 214, 216, 220, 222, 223, 224, 227, 229, 231, 240, 289, 374, 451, 476

Number line
absolute value and, 20
addition on, 25
opposites, 20
subtraction on, 32–34

Number patterns, 268–273

Number theory, 272, 478

O

Obtuse angle, 730

Odds in favor, 215

Ohm's Law, 127, 266

One-step equation, 74–80, 132, 180

Open sentence, 5

Open-Ended, 8, 15, 20, 22, 29, 35, 42, 51, 63, 70, 73, 78, 85, 92, 100, 109, 114, 122, 128, 137, 144, 150, 157, 165, 171, 178, 187, 193, 202, 208, 215, 216, 223, 229, 230, 244, 250, 253, 258, 265, 271, 272, 278, 288, 296, 302, 308, 315, 322, 334, 344, 346, 350, 358, 366, 375, 382, 383, 389, 390, 398, 403, 408, 414, 421, 427, 433, 442, 444, 448, 450, 460, 464, 470, 478, 484, 488, 493, 494, 500, 503, 506, 515, 521, 527, 533, 539, 545, 551, 556, 565, 569, 572, 582, 588, 595, 598, 604, 610, 616, 626, 630, 632, 641, 649, 654, 656, 659, 665, 670, 676, 683, 690, 694, 696, 730

Operations
inverse, 75, 125
order of, 9–10, 12–13, 68, 72, 392
with radical expressions, 600–606

Opposites, 20–22

Order
determining, 679
of operations, 9–15, 68, 72, 392

Ordered pair, 59, 69

Ordering
fractions, 19, 21

numbers, 21, 22
quadratic functions, 512, 513

Origin, 59

Outcome, 211

Outlier, 118, 119

P

Pacing Options, 2A, 72A, 132A, 180A, 234A, 280A, 338A, 392A, 454A, 508A, 576A, 634A

Parabola(s), 510–516
axis of symmetry of, 511
comparing widths of, 512
defined, 510, 569
maximum point of, 511, 513, 569, 570
minimum point of, 511, 513, 569, 570
symmetry of, 511, 514, 518, 520, 521, 567, 568, 569
vertex of, 511, 513, 520, 521, 569

Parallel lines
defined, 311, 332
identifying, 311–312, 315, 316
writing equations of, 312, 313, 332, 333

Parallelogram, 316, 594

Parentheses, 11, 13

Pascal's Triangle, 271, 501

Patterns, 37, 42, 43, 96, 185, 187, 209, 250, 268–273, 306, 308, 318, 319, 325, 329, 394, 397, 411, 428, 429, 434, 584, 621, 665, 716

Pentagon, perimeter of, 250

People and math
Lance Armstrong, 184
Romana Acosta Bauelos, 273
Chu Shih-Chieh, 501
Juan de la Cierva, 540
Jewel Plummer Cobb, 416
Marie Curie, 440
Albert Einstein, 413
Eratosthenes, 179
Florence Griffith-Joyner, 208
Lyndon B. Johnson, 252
Tegla Loroupe, 187
Jan Matzeliger, 14
Rocky Reifenstuhl, 53
Judith A. Resnik, 297
A. Henry Rhind, 53
Naoko Takahashi, 187
Jan Vermeer, 231
Leonardo da Vinci, 195

Percent(s)
of change, 204–209, 228, 229, 230
of decrease, 204, 207, 217, 228, 229, 230
defined, 197, 728
estimating, 199–200, 201
finding, 196, 197
greater than one hundred percent, 199
of increase, 204–205, 207, 217, 228, 229, 230
modeling, 196
writing as decimal, 180, 728
writing as fraction, 180, 728
writing numbers as, 180

Percent equation, 197–202

Percent error, 205–206, 207, 208

Percent proportion, 196–202

Perfect square, 525, 570

Perfect-square factors, 578–579

Perfect-square trinomial, 490–491, 493–495, 505

Perimeter
- defined, 731
- of pentagon, 250
- of rectangle, 9, 64, 89, 91, 92, 100, 101, 103, 107, 108, 115, 129, 154, 160, 166, 349, 350, 352, 379, 381
- and similarity, 193
- of square, 113, 247
- of triangle, 101, 109, 110, 156, 165

Permutation(s)
- classifying, 696
- and combinations, 686–687
- defined, 681, 695
- finding, 681–685, 695
- using in probability, 688

Permutation notation, 681–682

Perpendicular lines, 312, 313, 314, 315, 316, 332, 333

Pi (π), 18

Point(s)
- finding slope using, 285
- graphing, 60, 62

Point in Time
- Ahmes Papyrus, 53
- Romana Acosta Bauelos, 273
- Chu Shih-Chieh, 501
- Juan de la Cierva, 540
- Judith A. Resnik, 297

Point-slope form, 304–309, 332

Polynomial(s), 456–505
- adding, 459–461
- classifying, 457
- defined, 457, 503
- degree of, 457, 503
- describing, 456–457
- dividing, 662–666, 694
- dividing rational expressions by, 658–659
- factoring, 463, 496–497, 504–505
- factoring by grouping, 496–501
- modeling factoring of, 480
- modeling multiplication of, 466
- multiplying, 462, 468, 504
- multiplying rational expressions by, 658
- standard form of, 457, 506
- subtracting, 459–461

Population, 225

Population density, 187

Positive correlation, 62–64, 69, 70

Power(s). *See also* Exponent(s).
- defined, 9
- dividing, 417–418, 448
- multiplying, 405–406, 448
- multiplying equations with decimals by power of ten, 90
- powers of, 411–412, 448
- raising products to, 412–413, 448
- raising quotients to, 418–419, 448
- simplifying, 12, 395, 412–413.

Presentation Assistant Plus, 2F, 72F, 132F, 180F, 234F, 280F, 338F, 392F, 454F, 508F, 576F, 634F

Prime factor, 579

Prime factorization, 720

Prime numbers, 720

Principal square root, 524, 570

Prism. *See* Rectangular prism.

Probability, 210–225
- of compound events, 219–224
- defined, 211, 229
- distributions, 743
- exercises, 214–217, 222–224, 229, 374, 634, 655, 660, 696, 699
- experimental, 212–213, 214, 229
- formulas for, 211–216, 229, 660, 665, 688
- ratios and, 211–217
- theoretical, 211–212, 214, 229
- using combinations in, 688–689
- using permutations in, 688

Problem solving
- for distance-rate-time problems, 104–110, 115, 127, 128, 159, 236–237, 279, 364, 366, 648, 669, 671, 714, 719
- equations and, 103–110
- using trigonometric ratios, 623–624

Problem Solving Hints, 9, 103, 113, 138, 149, 194, 223, 266, 316, 328, 358, 375, 427, 469, 497, 511, 527, 579, 609, 675

Problem Solving Strategies
- Draw a Diagram, 89, 103, 104, 193, 194, 195, 196, 330, 350, 352, 366, 376, 426, 479, 489, 521, 522, 538, 623, 624, 714
- Look for a Pattern, 716
- Make a Table, 716
- Solve a Simpler Problem, 717
- Try, Test, and Revise, 715
- Use Logical Reasoning, 718
- Work Backward, 719

Product(s)
- cross, 183–184, 227, 234
- raising to a power, 412–413, 448
- sign of, 37, 38
- simplifying radical expressions involving, 578–579, 601–602, 629

Professional Development, 2B, 72B, 132B, 180B, 234B, 280B, 338B, 392B, 454B, 508B, 576B, 634B, Teacher's Edition pages 4, 9, 17, 24, 32, 37, 47, 54, 59, 74, 81, 88, 90, 103, 111, 118, 134, 140, 146, 153, 161, 167, 182, 189, 197, 204, 211, 219, 236, 241, 247, 254, 261, 268, 282, 291, 298, 304, 311, 318, 325, 340, 347, 353, 362, 370, 377, 394, 400, 405, 411, 417, 424, 430, 437, 456, 462, 467, 474, 481, 486, 490, 496, 510, 517, 524, 529, 536, 541, 547, 554, 559, 578, 584, 591, 600, 607, 614, 621, 636, 644, 652, 657, 662, 667, 672, 679, 686

Program Resources, 2E, 72E, 132E, 180E, 234E, 280E, 338E, 392E, 454E, 508E, 576E, 634E

Properties. *See also* Addition Property, Multiplication Property, Subtraction Property.
- associative, 54–57, 69
- closure, 57
- commutative, 54, 55, 56, 57, 69
- Cross Products, 184
- of discriminant, 555
- distributive. *See* Distributive Property.
- of equality, 74, 75–77, 79, 83, 95, 173, 353, 354
- graph of quadratic function, 517
- identifying and using, 54–58
- identity, 24, 38, 54–57
- inverse, 24–25, 40–41, 54
- of real numbers, 54–58
- using to solve two-step equations, 81–83, 126
- Zero-Product, 536–540, 570, 673.

Proportion(s), 183–202
- cross products of, 183–184
- defined, 183, 227
- means of, 183
- means-extremes property of, 184
- multi-step, 185
- percent equations and, 198–202
- rational, 674, 675
- similar figures and, 189–196
- solving, 183–185, 576
- in triangles, 189–190, 194, 228

Protractor, 730

Punnett square, 475, 478

Pyramid(s)
- surface area of, 116–117

Pythagorean Theorem, 584–590, 628, 630
- converse of, 586

Pythagorean triple, 588

Q

Quadrants, 59, 60, 62, 69

Quadratic curve, 510

Quadratic equation, 529–552, 609
- choosing appropriate method for solving, 549–550
- defined, 530
- factoring, 536–540
- finding roots of, 535
- number of real solutions of, 554–555
- solving by completing the square, 541–546, 570, 685
- solving by graphing, 530, 535
- solving using square roots, 530–533
- standard form of, 530, 570

Quadratic expression, factoring, 673

Quadratic formula, 547–552, 558, 571

Quadratic function(s), 510–523, 569
- defined, 510, 647
- graph of, 510–518, 569
- ordering, 512, 513
- standard form of, 510

Quadratic graph, 510–518, 569
- axis of symmetry of, 511
- maximum point of, 511, 513, 569, 570
- minimum point of, 511, 513, 569, 570
- vertex of, 511
- x-intercepts of, 529

Quadratic inequality, graphing, 519, 520, 570

Quadratic model, 513, 559, 560, 561, 571

Quadrilateral, 595, 596

Quantitative comparison exercises, 226, 231, 258, 266, 289, 317, 335, 410, 423, 451, 461, 479, 540, 558, 573, 590, 612, 650, 656, 699

Questions
- answering the question asked, 692
- extended-response, 174
- gridded-response, 66
- quantitative comparison, 226
- short-response, 124

Quotient(s), 662
  raising to a power, 418–419, 448
  sign of, 40
  simplifying radical expressions involving, 580–581, 601–602, 629

R _____

Radical(s), 578–583
  combining, 600
  isolating, 607
  like, 600, 603, 630
  multiplying, 579
  simplifying by dividing, 580
  simplifying fractions within, 580
  unlike, 600
Radical equation, 607–612, 630–631, 634
Radical expression, 578–583
  defined, 578
  operations with, 600–606
  simplifying, 578–583, 601–602, 629, 630, 656
Radical function, 647
  See also Square root function.
Radicand, 524, 548, 578
Random sample, 225
Range
  of coordinates, 241, 276, 392
  of data, 120, 121, 125
Rate(s). *See also* Distance-rate-time problems.
  of change, 282–289, 331
  converting, 182
  defined, 182
  ratios and, 182–183
  unit, 182–183
Ratio(s)
  applying to probability, 211–217
  common, 424–429, 449
  defined, 182, 227
  golden, 602
  rates and, 182–183
  trigonometric, 621–627, 631
Rational equation, 672–677
  defined, 672, 695
  solving, 672–674
Rational expression
  adding and subtracting, 667–671, 694
  defined, 652, 694
  dividing, 658, 659, 660, 661, 694
  evaluating, 653–654
  factoring, 653, 657
  multiplying, 657–661, 694
  simplifying, 652–656
Rational function
  defined, 644, 693
  graphing, 643–650, 693–694
  limits of, 651
Rational number, 17–22, 34, 68, 72, 132, 525, 526, 570, 672
  defined, 17
Rational proportion, 674
Rationalizing, 581, 601–602, 630
Reading and Math Literacy, 2D, 72D, 132D, 180D, 234D, 280D, 338D, 392D, 454D, 576D, 634D, Teacher's Edition pages 4, 31, 58, 67, 74, 94, 115, 125, 134, 151, 166, 175, 182, 195, 217, 227, 236, 246, 267, 275, 282, 303, 324, 331, 340, 352,

376, 387, 394, 416, 435, 447, 456, 472, 495, 203, 510, 534, 558, 569, 578, 597, 619, 629, 636, 656, 685, 693
Reading Comprehension, 202, 444, 552
  Geometry of Earth, 179
  Music to Our Ears, 391
  Pricing Products, 633
  Saving for College, 507
  Train Math, 279
  Travel Math, 71
Reading Math
  Hints, 4, 5, 18, 19, 40, 75, 90, 106, 134, 135, 141, 150, 161, 184, 201, 211, 212, 243, 257, 262, 268, 284, 285, 305, 342, 347, 359, 363, 366, 395, 443, 457, 470, 524, 548, 580, 584, 611, 637, 657, 673, 681
  Reading to Analyze Errors, 152
  Reading a Diagram, 473
  Reading an Example, 16, 678
  Reading a Formula, 203
  Reading a Graph, 260, 445
  Reading Math Vocabulary, 310
  Reading for Problem Solving, 87, 369, 613
  Understanding Vocabulary, 67, 125, 175, 227, 275, 331, 387, 447, 503, 569, 629, 693
  Using a Formula, 553
Real number(s), 525
  adding, 24–31, 68, 280
  defined, 18
  dividing, 40–44, 68, 72
  multiplying, 37–44, 68, 72
  properties of, 54–58
  subtracting, 32–36, 68, 280
Real-World Connections. *See* Connections.
Real-World Snapshots
  Applying Formulas, 574–575
  Applying Functions, 700–701
  Applying Probability, 232–233
  Applying Slope, 336–337
  Applying Systems of Equations, 452–453
  Applying Variation, 130–131
Real-World Snapshots, 2D, 72D, 132D, 180D, 234D, 280D, 338D, 392D, 454D, 508D, 576D, 634D, Teacher's Edition pages 130–131, 232–233, 336–337, 452–453, 574–575, 700–701
Reasonableness, check for, 76, 82, 97, 99, 154, 349, 354, 537, 563, 673
Reasoning. *See also* Critical Thinking, Error Analysis, Justifying Steps, Make a Conjecture, Patterns.
  Algebraic, 173
  deductive, 56–57, 83, 84, 126, 173
  exercises, 20, 21, 22, 29, 30, 43, 52, 57, 63, 64, 122, 144, 150, 158, 164, 210, 270, 271, 272, 308, 422, 428, 478, 557, 595, 650, 655, 684
  inductive, 268, 270, 277
  logical, 718
Reciprocal(s)
  defined, 41, 395
  division using, 41, 395, 658
  negative, 312–313
  of nonzero number, 147
  using to solve equations, 77
Rectangle
  area of, 13, 51, 64, 115, 151, 208, 209, 217, 504, 505, 663

golden, 158
  identifying, 316
  perimeter of, 9, 64, 89, 91, 92, 100, 101, 103, 107, 108, 115, 129, 154, 160, 166, 349, 350, 352, 379, 381
Rectangular prism
  surface area of, 116–117
  volume of, 113, 409, 471, 498, 501, 505, 665
Recursive formula, 272
Reflections, 733
Reflexive Property of Equality, 173
Reifenstuhl, Rocky, 53
Relations, 241–246, 276
Replacement set, 160
Resistance, 676
Resnik, Judith A., 297
Reteaching, 2D–E, 72D–E, 132D–E, 180D–E, 234D–E, 280D–E, 338D–E, 392D–E, 454D–E, 508D–E, 576D–E, 634D–E
Review. *See* Assessment, Extra Practice, Skills Handbook.
Review Chart, Teacher's Edition pages 129, 231, 335, 451, 573, 697, 698, 699
Rhind, A. Henry, 53
Rhombus, 316, 595
Right angle, 215, 730
Right triangle, 316
  hypotenuse of, 584, 630
  identifying, 586
  isosceles, 598
  legs of, 584, 630
  Pythagorean Theorem and, 584–590, 628, 630
Roots, of equation, 535. *See also* Square root(s), Square root function.
Rotations, 734
Rubric-based responses. *See* Extended response exercises *and* Short response exercises.

S _____

Sample space, 211, 229
Sampling, 225
SAT. *See* Standardized Test Prep.
Scalar, 43, 45
Scalar multiplication, 43
Scale, 191, 192, 193, 195, 228, 246
Scale drawing, 191
Scale model, 255
Scatter plot, 61–64, 318–324
  analyzing data using, 280
  defined, 61, 69
  making, 61–62, 63, 64, 69, 70, 318–319
Scientific calculator. *See* Calculator.
Scientific notation, 400–404, 448
  multiplying numbers in, 402, 406–407
  using, 401–402
  writing numbers in, 400–401
Segment, midpoint of, 593, 594, 596, 630
Selected Answers, 804–832
Sequence, 269–273
  arithmetic, 269–273, 277, 425
  defined, 269, 277
  Fibonacci, 272

function rules for, 425–426
geometric, 424–429, 449
terms of, 269–270, 277, 392, 426–427

Short-response exercises, 124, 139, 145, 159, 166, 172, 188, 195, 209, 217, 224, 231, 240, 246, 252, 258, 266, 272, 289, 297, 303, 317, 335, 345, 359, 368, 375, 384, 404, 410, 415, 429, 435, 444, 451, 461, 465, 472, 479, 485, 489, 500, 523, 534, 540, 546, 552, 558, 566, 573, 583, 590, 606, 619, 627, 642, 650, 656, 661, 666, 671, 677, 691, 699

Sides, 190

Sierpinski's Triangle, 428

Sign
of product, 38
of quotient, 40
of sum, 25

Signum function, 251

Similar figures, 189–196, 228
scale, 255

Simple interest, 114, 201, 392, 773

Simpler problem, solving, 717

Simplifying
defined, 9
exponential expressions, 395–396, 394, 395, 399, 419
expressions, 9–15, 39, 41–44, 47–53, 56, 395–396, 417–418, 419, 454, 634
fractions, 580, 582, 724
like radicals, 600, 603, 630
powers, 12, 395, 412–413
products and quotients, 578–583, 601–602, 629
radical expressions, 578–583, 601–602, 629, 630, 656
rational expressions, 652–656, 694
square root expressions, 524–525, 526

Simulations, 218, 744

Sine, 621–622, 625, 631

Skill maintenance. *See* Mixed Review.

Skills Handbook, 714–748
Adding and Subtracting Fractions, 726
Bar Graphs, 736
Box-and-Whisker Plots, 740
Choosing an Appropriate Graph, 741
Circle Graphs, 739
Conducting a Survey, 745
Divisibility, 722
Draw a Diagram, 714
Exponents, 729
Factors and Multiples, 721
Fractions and Decimals, 725
Fractions, Decimals, and Percents, 728
Histograms, 737
Interpreting Statistical Results, 746
Line Graphs, 738
Line Plots, 735
Look for a Pattern, 716
Make a Table, 716
Measuring and Classifying Angles, 730
Misleading Graphs, 742
Multiplying and Dividing Fractions, 727
Perimeter, Area, and Volume, 731
Prime Numbers and Composite Numbers, 720
Probability Distributions, 743
Reflections, 733
Rotations, 734

Simplifying Fractions, 724
Simulations, 744
Solve a Simpler Problem, 717
Spreadsheets, 747
Translations, 732
Try, Check, Revise, 715
Use Logical Reasoning, 718
Using Estimation, 723
Work Backward, 719

Slope, 284–289, 331
defined, 284
finding using graph, 284–285
finding using points, 285
formula for, 284, 331
identifying, 292
negative, 286
of parallel lines, 311
of perpendicular lines, 312
positive, 286

Slope-intercept form, 291–297, 332, 340

Solution(s)
of absolute value equation, 167–168, 177, 178, 234
of absolute value inequality, 167–172, 177, 178
"Cannot Be Determined," 568
of compound inequality, 162–163, 177, 338
defined, 75, 125
of distance-rate-time problem, 104–107, 108, 109, 110, 115, 127, 128, 159, 236–237, 279, 364, 366, 367, 648, 669, 670, 671, 714, 719
of equation, 75, 125
of equation containing decimals, 90–91
of equation containing fractions, 90
of equation with no solutions, 98, 99, 110, 128, 170, 530, 531, 532, 544, 558, 571, 609, 611, 612
of equation with variables on both sides, 96–101
extraneous, 609, 610, 630–631
with grouping symbols, 89–91
of inequality, 134–135, 140–160, 175
interpreting, 160
of linear inequality, 371, 389
of multi-step equation, 88–93, 132
of multi-step inequality, 153–159
of one-step equation, 74–80, 132, 180
of quadratic equations, 530–531, 535, 541, 542, 548
of radical equation, 607–612, 630–631, 634
of system of linear equations, 340–368, 387, 388
of system of linear inequality, 377–380, 385, 389
of system with infinitely many solutions, 342
of system with no solutions, 342
of two-step equation, 81–85, 126, 132
using Addition Property of Equality, 74, 75, 95, 353
using deductive reasoning, 83, 126
using graph for, 102
using multiplication and division, 76–77
using properties, 81–83
using reciprocals, 77
using Subtraction Property of Equality, 74, 75, 83, 95, 354

Spanish Support, 2D–E, 72D–E, 132D–E, 180D–E, 234D–E, 280D–E, 338D–E, 392D–E, 454D–E, 508D–E, 576D–E,

634D–E, Teacher's Edition pages 4, 8, 9, 15, 17, 23, 24, 31, 32, 36, 37, 44, 47, 53, 54, 58, 59, 65, 67, 70, 71, 73, 74, 80, 81, 86, 88, 94, 96, 101, 103, 110, 111, 115, 118, 123, 125, 128, 129, 134, 139, 140, 145, 146, 151, 153, 159, 161, 166, 167, 172, 175, 178, 179, 182, 188, 189, 195, 197, 202, 204, 209, 211, 217, 219, 224, 227, 230, 231, 236, 240, 241, 246, 247, 252, 254, 259, 261, 267, 268, 273, 275, 278, 279, 281, 289, 291, 297, 298, 303, 304, 309, 311, 317, 318, 324, 325, 329, 331, 334, 335, 340, 345, 347, 352, 353, 359, 362, 368, 370, 376, 377, 384, 387, 390, 391, 394, 399, 400, 404, 405, 410, 411, 416, 417, 423, 424, 429, 430, 435, 437, 444, 447, 450, 451, 456, 461, 462, 465, 467, 472, 474, 479, 481, 485, 486, 489, 490, 495, 496, 501, 503, 506, 507, 510, 516, 517, 523, 524, 528, 529, 534, 536, 540, 541, 546, 547, 552, 554, 558, 559, 566, 569, 572, 573, 578, 583, 584, 590, 591, 597, 600, 606, 607, 612, 614, 619, 621, 627, 629, 632, 633, 636, 642, 644, 650, 652, 656, 657, 661, 662, 666, 667, 671, 672, 677, 679, 685, 686, 691, 693, 696, 697

Solve a Simpler Problem, 717

Sphere
surface area of, 415, 532
volume of, 14, 478, 567

Spreadsheets, 100, 344, 456, 557, 747

Square(s)
area of, 209, 491, 505
of binomials, 474–476, 477, 478
completing, 541–546, 570, 685
difference of, 476–477, 478, 492, 601
perfect, 525, 570
perimeter of, 113, 247
Punnett, 475, 478
of trinomial, 478

Square root(s), 18, 524–528, 570. *See also* Radical(s).
defined, 524, 570
Division Property of, 580
estimating and using, 525–526
finding, 524–525, 576
Multiplication Property of, 578–579, 600, 601, 629
negative, 524, 570
principal, 524, 570
solving quadratic equations using, 530–531, 532, 533
table of, 750

Square root expressions, simplifying, 524–525, 526

Square root function, 614–619, 631
defined, 614
finding domain of, 614, 616, 617, 631, 632
graphing, 614–619, 631
translating graphs of, 615, 631

Standard form
of linear equation, 298–303, 332
of polynomial, 457, 506
of quadratic equation, 530, 570
of quadratic function, 510
writing equations in, 300

Standard notation, 400–401

Standardized Test Prep
    Cumulative Review, 129, 231, 335, 451, 573, 697–699
    Exercises, 8, 15, 22, 31, 36, 44, 52–53, 58, 65, 71, 80, 86, 93, 101, 110, 115, 123, 139, 145, 150, 158–159, 166, 171–172, 179, 188, 194–195, 202, 209, 216–217, 224, 240, 245–246, 251–252, 258–259, 266, 272–273, 279, 289, 297, 303, 309, 317, 323–324, 329, 345, 352, 359, 367–368, 375, 384, 391, 399, 404, 409–410, 415–416, 423, 429, 434–435, 444, 461, 465, 472, 479, 485, 489, 494–495, 500–501, 507, 516, 523, 528, 534, 539–540, 546, 552, 557–558, 566, 583, 590, 596, 605–606, 612, 618–619, 627, 633, 642, 650, 655–656, 661, 666, 671, 677, 684–685, 691
    Reading Comprehension, 71, 179, 202, 279, 391, 444, 507, 552, 633

Standardized Test Prep, 2C, 72C, 132C, 180C, 234C, 280C, 338C, 392C, 454C, 508C, 576C, 634C, Teacher's Edition pages 8, 15, 23, 31, 36, 44, 53, 58, 65, 67, 71, 80, 86, 94, 101, 110, 115, 123, 125, 129, 139, 145, 151, 159, 166, 172, 175, 179, 188, 195, 202, 209, 217, 224, 227, 231, 240, 246, 252, 259, 267, 273, 275, 279, 289, 297, 303, 309, 317, 324, 329, 331, 335, 345, 352, 359, 368, 376, 384, 387, 391, 399, 404, 410, 416, 423, 429, 435, 444, 447, 451, 461, 465, 472, 479, 485, 489, 495, 501, 503, 507, 516, 523, 528, 534, 540, 546, 552, 558, 566, 569, 573, 583, 590, 597, 606, 612, 619, 627, 629, 633, 642, 650, 656, 661, 666, 671, 677, 685, 691, 693, 697

Statistics. *See* Data Analysis.

Statue of Liberty, 237

Stem-and-leaf plot, 120–121, 122, 123, 127, 128, 129, 216

Straight angle, 730

Subscript, 284

Substitution method, 347–352, 362, 363, 388

Subtraction
    applying, 34
    of fractions, 634, 726
    of integers, 32–36, 68, 72
    of matrices, 35
    of polynomials, 459–461
    of rational expressions, 667–671, 694
    of real numbers, 32–36, 68, 280
    solving equations using, 74–76
    solving inequalities using, 141–142
    solving systems using, 353–354

Subtraction Property
    of Equality, 74, 75, 83, 95, 354
    of Inequality, 141–142

Sum, sign of, 25

Supplementary angles, 79

Surface area
    of cube, 414, 528, 534
    of cylinder, 14, 116–117
    of pyramid, 116–117
    of rectangular prism, 116–117
    of sphere, 415, 532

Survey, conducting, 745

Symbol(s)
    absolute value, 167, 168
    grouping, 11–12, 14, 33, 89, 91, 92
    for inequality, 19, 21, 154
    for pi (π), 18
    for similarity, 190

Symbolic (algebraic) reasoning, 173

Symmetric Property of Equality, 173

Symmetry, axis of, 511, 518, 520, 521, 567, 568, 569

System(s) of linear equations, 340
    analyzing special types of, 342
    applications of, 362–368
    estimating solutions of, 347
    with infinitely many solutions, 342
    with no solutions, 342
    solving, 340–361, 387, 388
    writing, 362–368

System(s) of linear inequalities, 377–384
    defined, 377, 389
    solutions of, 377, 389
    solving by graphing, 377–379, 385, 389
    writing and solving, 379–380, 389

T

Tables
    direct variations and, 263–264, 276
    finding rate of change using, 283
    function rules and, 247–253
    linear functions and, 248, 261, 263–264, 283
    making, 96, 215, 223, 298, 306, 344, 365, 584, 621, 716
    of square roots, 750
    of squares, 750
    of trigonometric ratios, 751
    using to solve a problem, 96, 187
    writing equations using, 306
    writing function rule for, 254, 257, 259

Takahashi, Naoko, 187

Take It to the Net. *See* Internet links.

Tangent, 621–622, 623, 624, 631

Teaching Tip, Teacher's Edition pages 40, 48, 51, 55, 60, 76, 82, 84, 95, 102, 119, 124, 142, 148, 154, 184, 196, 198, 199, 210, 215, 218, 226, 237, 242, 248, 262, 286, 290, 294, 300, 315, 346, 355, 364, 380, 386, 395, 412, 419, 426, 436, 438, 446, 466, 469, 475, 476, 480, 491, 497, 502, 511, 525, 537, 568, 585, 593, 615, 622, 623, 637, 639, 643, 653, 663, 673

Technology. *See also* Calculator, Computers, Graphing calculator, Internet Links, iText.
    exercise, 409
    Finding Roots, 535
    Fitting Exponential Curves to Data, 436
    Function Rules, Tables, and Graphs, 253
    Graphing Linear Inequalities, 385
    Graphing Rational Functions, 643
    Investigating $y = mx + b$, 290
    Matrices, 45
    Multiplying Matrices and Solving Systems, 360–361
    Simulations, 218
    Using Graphs to Solve and Check Equations, 102

Technology Activities, 2D, 72D, 132D, 180D, 234D, 280D, 338D, 392D, 454D, 576D, 634D, Teacher's Edition pages 4, 9, 17, 24, 32, 37, 47, 54, 59, 74, 81, 88, 90, 103, 111, 118, 134, 140, 146, 153, 161, 167, 182, 189, 197, 204, 211, 219, 236, 241, 247, 254, 261, 268, 282, 291, 298, 304, 311, 318, 325, 340, 347, 353, 362, 370, 377, 394, 400, 405, 411, 417, 424, 430, 437, 456, 462, 467, 474, 481, 486, 490, 496, 510, 517, 524, 529, 536, 541, 547, 554, 559, 578, 584, 591, 600, 607, 614, 621, 636, 644, 652, 657, 662, 667, 672, 679, 686

Technology Resources, 2E–F, 72E–F, 132E–F, 180E–F, 234E–F, 280E–F, 338E–F, 392E–F, 454E–F, 508E–F, 576E–F, 634E–F

Technology Tip, Teacher's Edition pages 61, 97, 121, 168, 206, 253, 269, 301, 341, 343, 360, 418, 422, 426, 433, 436, 523, 560, 567, 601, 610

Temperature scales, 43, 71, 86, 112, 113

Term(s)
    defined, 49
    like, 49, 69, 72, 88–89
    of sequence, 269–270, 277, 392, 426–427

Test Prep, 2C, 72C, 132C, 180C, 234C, 280C, 338C, 392C, 454C, 508C, 576C, 634C

Test-Taking Strategies
    Answering the Question Asked, 692
    Choosing "Cannot Be Determined," 568
    Drawing a Diagram, 330
    Eliminating Answers, 502
    Finding Multiple Correct Answers, 386
    Making Quantitative Comparisons, 226
    Testing Multiple Choices, 446
    Using Estimation, 628
    Using a Variable, 274
    Writing Extended Responses, 174
    Writing Gridded Responses, 66
    Writing Short Responses, 124

Test-Taking Strategies, 2C, 72C, 132C, 180C, 234C, 280C, 338C, 392C, 454C, 508C, 576C, 634C, Teacher's Edition pages 66, 124, 174, 226, 274, 330, 386, 446, 502, 568, 628, 692

Theoretical probability, 211–212, 214, 229

30-60-90 triangles, 599. *See also* Right triangles.

Tiles, 32, 34, 36, 46, 81, 95, 126, 220, 221, 222, 250, 280, 346, 466, 480, 683

Time. *See* distance-rate-time problems.

Time Savers, 2F, 72F, 132F, 180F, 234F, 280F, 338F, 392F, 454F, 508F, 576F, 634F

Transformations, 732, 733, 734

Transformed formulas, 111–115, 280

Transitive Property of Equality, 173

Translation, 325–329, 333, 732
    of graphs of square root functions, 615, 631
    horizontal, 327, 333, 615, 631
    vertical, 326, 333, 615, 631

Trapezoid(s)
    area of, 12, 15, 70, 113, 470, 533
    midpoints of segments of, 596

Tree diagram, 680

Trend. *See* correlation.

Trend line, 61, 62, 64, 318–324, 334

Triangle(s)
area of, 64, 111, 251, 665
congruent, 100
45-45-90, 598
Pascal's, 271, 501
perimeter of, 101, 109, 110, 156, 165
proportions in, 189–190, 194, 195
right. *See* Right triangles.
Sierpinski's, 428
similar, 190
sum of angles of, 92
30-60-90, 599

Triangle Inequality Theorem, 144

Triangular numbers, 464

Trigonometric ratios, 621–627, 631
cosine, 621–622, 631
defined, 621, 631
finding, 621–622, 625–627
sine, 621–622, 631
solving problems using, 623–624
table of, 751
tangent, 621–622, 623, 624, 631

Trinomial(s)
dividing by binomials, 665
factoring, 480–491, 493–495, 497–501, 504–505
factoring by grouping, 497–501
multiplication of, 469
perfect-square, 490–491, 493–495, 505
square of, 478

Try, Check, Revise, 715

Two-step equation, 81–85, 126, 132

Two-Year Algebra, 2A, 72A, 132A, 180A, 234A, 280A, 338A, 392A, 454A, 508A, 576A, 634A

U

Uniform motion, 104

Unit analysis, 182

Unit fractions, 53

Unit rates, 182–183

Unlike fractions, 726

Unlike radicals, 600

Update
data, 27, 128, 319, 320, 321, 324, 333, 334, 564

Use Logical Reasoning, 718

V

Value, absolute. *See* Absolute value.

Variable(s), 4–8
on both sides of equation, 96–101
defined, 4, 68
defining in terms of another, 103
dependent, 248, 276
independent, 248, 276
as test-taking strategy, 274
transforming equations with only variables, 112

Variation
constant of, 262, 277, 637, 640, 693, 696
direct, 261–267, 277, 638–639, 640, 641, 696
inverse, 636–642, 693, 696

Venn diagram, 18

Vermeer, Jan, 231

Vertex
defined, 511, 569, 730
identifying, 511, 513, 520, 521

Vertical angles, 97

Vertical asymptote, 645–646, 648, 649

Vertical line, 285, 286, 299

Vertical-line test, 242, 244, 245, 276

Vertical motion formula, 549, 550, 551

Vertical translation, 326, 333, 615, 631

Vinci, Leonardo da, 195

Volume
of air in lungs, 114
of cube, 414
of cylinder, 14, 113, 465, 572, 610, 631
defined, 731
finding percent error in calculating, 206
formulas for, 13, 14, 113, 114, 465, 471, 567, 572, 610, 631, 665
percent error in calculating, 206, 207, 208
of rectangular prism, 113, 409, 471, 498, 501, 505, 665
of rectangular solid, 660
and similarity, 194
of sphere, 14, 567

W

Whole numbers, 17–18, 20–21

Working backward, 208, 209, 375, 446, 608, 719

Writing
algebraic expressions, 4–8, 6, 42, 180
decimals as percents, 180, 728
equations, 5–6, 72, 89, 97, 99, 104–106, 234, 300

equations from graphs, 292
equations of parallel lines, 312, 313, 333
equations using tables, 306
Exercises, 7, 13, 14, 22, 29, 35, 42, 51, 57, 64, 70, 79, 85, 100, 109, 114, 122, 128, 137, 144, 150, 156, 164, 171, 178, 187, 194, 201, 208, 215, 222, 229, 230, 239, 245, 250, 257, 265, 270, 271, 276, 278, 288, 296, 302, 303, 316, 322, 344, 350, 358, 366, 374, 383, 386, 388, 390, 397, 403, 409, 415, 421, 427, 434, 443, 448, 450, 460, 464, 470, 478, 484, 488, 493, 500, 506, 514, 522, 527, 533, 538, 545, 551, 557, 564, 571, 572, 582, 588, 595, 605, 610, 611, 616, 617, 619, 632, 641, 649, 655, 660, 665, 670, 675, 683, 690, 694, 696, 699
Extended Responses, 174
fractions as percent, 180, 728
function rules, 254–259, 338
function rules from tables, 254, 257, 259
Gridded Responses, 66
linear equations, 291–292, 306–307
linear equations from data, 306–307
linear equations in standard form, 300
numbers in scientific notation, 400–401
percents as decimals, 180, 728
percents as fractions, 180, 728
Short Responses, 124
systems of equations, 362–368
systems of linear inequalities, 379–380, 389

X

x-axis, 59, 69

x-coordinate, 59, 60, 62, 69

x-intercept, 298–299, 529

Y

y-axis, 59, 69

y-coordinate, 59, 60, 62, 69, 560

y-intercept, 291, 292, 299

Z

Zero
dividing by, 41
as exponent, 394–399, 447
Multiplication Property of, 38, 55

Zero coefficient, 663

Zero pair, 81

Zero-Product Property, 536–540, 570, 673

Acknowledgments

STAFF CREDITS

The people who made up the High School Mathematics team—representing design services, editorial, editorial services, market research, marketing services, online services & multimedia development, production services, project office, and publishing processes—are listed below. Bold type denotes the core team members.

Leora Adler, Carolyn Artin, Stephanie Bradley, **Peter Brooks,** Amy D. Breaux, Judith Buice, Ronit Carter, **Lisa J. Clark,** Bob Cornell, Sheila DeFazio, Marian DeLollis, Jo DiGiustini, Delphine Dupee, Emily Ellen, Janet Fauser, Debby Faust, Suzanne Feliciello, Frederick Fellows, Jonathan Fisher, **Paula Foye,** Paul Frisoli, Patti Fromkin, Melissa Garcia, Jonathan Gorey, Jennifer Graham, Barbara Hardt, Daniel R. Hartjes, Richard Heater, Kerri Hoar, Jayne Holman, Karen Holtzman, Angela Husband, Carolyn Lock, Kevin Jackson-Mead, Al Jacobson, Misty-Lynn Jenese, Diahanne Lucas, Cathie Maglio, Cheryl Mahan, Barry Maloney, Ann McSweeney, **Eve Melnechuk,** Meredith Mascola, Sandy Morris, **Cindy Noftle,** Marsha Novak, **Marie Opera,** Jill Ort, Michael Oster, Steve Ouellette, Dorothy M. Preston, Rashid Ross, Donna Russo, **Malti Sharma, Dennis Slattery,** Emily Soltanoff, **Deborah Sommer,** Kathryn Smith, Lisa Smith-Ruvalcaba, Mark Tricca, Nate Walker, Diane Walsh, **Joe Will,** Amy Winchester, Carol Zacny

Cover Design: Brainworx Studio
Cover Photos: Fern, Corbis; Rollercoaster, Robin Smith/Stone/ Getty Images, Inc.
Technical Illustration: Nesbitt Graphics, Inc.
Photo Research: Sue McDermott, Magellan Visual Research

ILLUSTRATION

Argosy Illustration: 104, 105, 106, 157, 282, 295
Kim Barnes: 344
Ken Batelman: 381, 522, 531, 624
John Edwards and Associates: 244, 264, 308, 396, 401, 415
Ellen Korey-Lie: 63
Annette LeBlanc: 171
Ron Magnes: 109
Lisa Manning: 112, 123
Steve McEntee: 364
Morgan Cain & Associates: 27, 61, 64, 136, 182, 194, 539, 545
Matthew Pippin: 51
Roberto Portocarrero: 320
Brucie Rosch: 8, 17, 22; 34, 74, 120, 140, 193b, 201, 202, 357, 444, 456, 533
Phil Scheuer: 29
Kathryn Smith: 223, 358, 686

Neil Stewart: 438, 439
Roberta Warshaw: 6, 259, 315, 618, 660, 669, 679, 683
J/B Woolsey and Associates: 191t, 192, 232, 233
XNR Productions: 138, 158, 187, 191b, 193t, 322, 680

PHOTOGRAPHY

Front Matter

Page ix, Bob Daemmrich/The Image Works; **vii,** Hal Beral/Visuals Unlimited; **viii,** Michelle Bridwell/PhotoEdit; **x,** Frank Lane/Parfitt/Stone/Getty Images, Inc.; **xi,** Rob Atkins/The Image Bank/Getty Images, Inc.; **xii,** Joseph McBride/Stone/Getty Images, Inc.; **xiii,** Wilfried Krecichwost/Stone/Getty Images, Inc.; **xiv,** Jeff Greenberg/Omni-Photo Communications, Inc.; **xv,** Ron Kimball; **xvi,** R. D. Rubic/Precision Chromes, Inc.; **xvii,** Zefa/London/Corbis Stock Market; **xviii,** Nancy Richmond/The Image Works

Chapter One

Pages 2, 3, Chris Noble/Stone/Getty Images, Inc.; **5,** Jon Riley/Stone/Getty Images, Inc.; **7,** Bob Daemmrich/Stock Boston; **12,** Steve Bronstein/The Image Bank/Getty Images, Inc.; **13,** PhotoEdit; **14 both,** The Granger Collection; **17,** Arnulf Husmo/Stone/Getty Images, Inc.; **20,** Dugald Bremner/Stone/Getty Images, Inc.; **21,** © Bill Amend/Universal Press Syndicate; **26,** John Elk, III/Stock Boston; **29,** Russ Lappa; **30,** © 1980 by Thaves. Distributed from www.thecomics.com; **35,** Hal Beral/Visuals Unlimited; **39,** Nicholas Devore III/Bruce Coleman, Inc.; **43,** Courtesy of Cedar Point/Photo by Dan Feicht; **48,** Corbis; **51,** Alan Thornton/Stone/Getty Images, Inc.; **53,** British Museum/Michael Holford; **55,** Russ Lappa; **59,** Klaus Lahnstein/Stone/Getty Images, Inc.; **62,** Russ Lappa; **64,** Bill Aron/PhotoEdit

Chapter Two

Pages 72, 73, Bohemian Nomad Picturemakers/Corbis; **76,** Howard Grey/FPG/Getty Images, Inc.; **79,** ©Baloo/Rothco; **82,** Russ Lappa; **85,** SuperStock; **89,** Kevin R. Norris/Stone/Getty Images, Inc.; **92,** VCL/Alistair Berg/FPG/Getty Images, Inc.; **94,** David Frazier/Stone/Getty Images, Inc.; **97,** Michelle Bridwell/PhotoEdit; **99,** Russ Lappa; **105,** The Image Works; **114,** Chuck Piper/Visuals Unlimited; **119,** R. Krubner/H. Armstrong Roberts; **122,** Fred Whitehouse/Animals Animals/Earth Scenes; **130,** Philip Gatward/Dorling Kindersley; **130–131,** Philip Gatward /Dorling Kindersley; **131 tr,** Michael Dinneen/AP/Wide World Photos; **131 br,** Philip Gatward/Dorling Kindersley; **131 tl, 131 bl,** Jane Stockman/Dorling Kindersley

Chapter Three

Pages 132, 133, V.C.L./FPG/Getty Images, Inc.; **136,** Tony Freeman/PhotoEdit; **138,** Poulides/Thatcher/Stone/Getty Images, Inc.; **142,** Karl Weatherly/Corbis; **143,** Clive Brunskill/Allsport/Getty Images, Inc.; **144,** Corbis Stock Market; **148,** Jon Chomitz; **150,** Doug Sokell/Visuals Unlimited; **154,** Russ Lappa; **157,** Robin L. Sachs/PhotoEdit; **158,** Stone/Getty Images, Inc.; **159,** Mug Shots/Corbis Stock Market; **162,** Bob Daemmrich/Stock Boston; **165,** Michael Newman/PhotoEdit; **169,** Bob Daemmrich/The Image Works

Chapter Four

Pages 180, 181, David Madison/Stone/Getty Images, Inc.; **183,** Frank Lane/Parfitt/Stone/Getty Images, Inc.; **184,** Reuters New Media, Inc./Corbis; **186,** Charles Gupton/Corbis Stock Market; **189 both,** Russ Lappa; **198,** Larry Ulrich/Stone/Getty Images, Inc.; **200,** Wolfgang Kaehler/Corbis; **205,** Don Mason/Corbis Stock Market; **206,** Russ Lappa; **208,** NOAA; **209,** Mulvehill/The Image Works; **210 both, 212,** Russ Lappa; **213,** Lawrence Migdale/Stock Boston; **215,** PhotoEdit; **216,** Duomo Photography, Inc.; **220,** Russ Lappa; **222,** Mark Thayer; **223,** Peter Timmermans/Stone/Getty Images, Inc.; **224,** Bob Daemmrich; **232,** Jim Mone/AP/Wide World Photos; **232–233,** The Brearley Collection; **233,** © 1992 Ron Vesely/MLBPhotos

Chapter Five

Pages 234, 235, Getty Images, Inc.; **237 l,** Kit Kittle/Corbis; **237 r,** PhotoDisc, Inc.; **239 all,** Russ Lappa; **241,** Daryl Balfour/Stone/Getty Images, Inc.; **245,** Michael Newman/PhotoEdit; **248,** Stephen Frisch/Stock Boston; **255,** Seth Resnick/Stock Boston; **258,** SuperStock; **263,** Rob Atkins/The Image Bank/Getty Images, Inc.; **265,** Jim West/The Image Works; **271,** David Young-Wolff/PhotoEdit; **273,** UPI/Bettman

Chapter Six

Pages 280, 281, SuperStock; **284 l,** Martyn Goddard/Corbis; **284 r,** Chris Cheadle/Stone/Getty Images, Inc.; **286,** Joseph McBride/Stone/Getty Images, Inc.; **288,** David H. Wells/The Image Works; **291,** Ryan McVay/PhotoDisc, Inc./Getty Images, Inc.; **293,** Mark Thayer; **295 b,** Reprinted by permission: Tribune Media Services; **295 t,** Willie Maldonado/ Stone/Getty Images, Inc.; **296,** Tim Davis/Stone/Getty Images, Inc.; **297 both,** NASA; **300,** Myrleen Ferguson/PhotoEdit; **302,** Kenneth W. Fink/Photo Researchers, Inc.; **306,** Tom Stock/Stone/Getty Images, Inc.; **311,** Alan Thornton/Stone/Getty Images, Inc.; **313,** Charles Gupton/Stock Boston; **315,** Zoom/Allsport/Getty Images, Inc.; **321,** Mike Powell/Allsport/Getty Images, Inc.; **327,** Russ Lappa; **337 br,** Peter Hayman/Dorling Kindersley; **337 t,** Geoff Brightling/Dorling Kindersley; **337 bl,** Shaun Egan/Stone/Getty Images, Inc.

Chapter Seven

Pages 338, 339, AP/Wide World Photos; **341,** SuperStock; **349,** Annie Griffiths Belt/Corbis; **350,** Wilfried Krecichwost/ Stone/Getty Images, Inc.; **354,** Robert Brenner/PhotoEdit; **357 l,** Tony Freeman/PhotoEdit; **357 the rest,** Prentice Hall; **358,** Corel Corp.; **362,** Index Stock Imagery; **366,** Don Johnson/Corbis Stock Market; **367,** Steve McCutcheon/Visuals Unlimited; **368,** Brian Smith/Stock Boston; **372,** Spencer Grant/Picture Cube; **373,** Tamara Reynolds/Stone/Getty Images, Inc.; **374,** Aaron Stevenson/Silver Burdett Ginn; **379,** Steven Kline/Bruce Coleman, Inc.; **380 t,** Silver Burdett Ginn; **380 b,** Leonard de Selva/Corbis; **382,** John Eastcott, Frank Pedrick/The Image Works; **383,** Omni-Photo Communications

Chapter Eight

Pages 392, 393, John Lund/Stone/Getty Images, Inc.; **403,** Frans Lanting/Minden Pictures; **404,** Bill Amend/Universal Press Syndicate; **407,** Andrew Syred/Science Photo Library/Photo Researchers, Inc.; **409,** Maxine Hall/Corbis; **413,** The Granger Collection; **416,** Courtesy of Dr. Jewel Plummer Cobb;

421 m, Jessica Wecker/Photo Researchers, Inc.; **421 t,** PhotoDisc, Inc.; **421 b,** Chris Koonts/Transparencies, Inc.; **426,** Richard Megna/Fundamental Photographs; **428,** Richard Megna/Fundamental Photographs; **431,** John Carnemolla/ANT Photo Library; **432,** Corbis; **435,** PhotoEdit; **437,** Jeff Greenberg/Omni-Photo Communications, Inc.; **440,** Jonathan Nourok/PhotoEdit; **443,** Phototake; **452,** Dave King/Dorling Kindersley; **453 l,** Tim Flach/Getty Images, Inc.; **453 r,** David Madison/Getty Images, Inc.

Chapter Nine

Pages 454, 455, Mark Bacon/Alamy.com; **456,** The Image Bank/Getty Images, Inc.; **460,** Chuck Savage/Corbis Stock Market; **464,** Patrick Ingrand/Stone/Getty Images, Inc.; **471,** Cesar Lucas Abreu/The Image Bank/Getty Images, Inc.; **475,** Ron Kimball; **478,** Lynn M. Stone; **501,** Needham Research Institute

Chapter Ten

Pages 508, 509, NASA; **511,** Richard Megna/Fundamental Photographs; **513,** James H. Robinson/Animals Animals/Earth Scenes; **514 l,** Stone/Getty Images, Inc.; **514 r,** Prentice Hall; **515,** C Squared Studios/PhotoDisc/Getty Images, Inc.; **519,** R. D. Rubic/Precision Chromes, Inc.; **521,** Agence Vandystadt/Allsport; **522,** Jose Carrillo/PhotoEdit; **526,** David Austen/Stone/Getty Images, Inc.; **527 t,** NASA; **527 b,** Reprinted by permission: Tribune Media Services; **531,** Gene Peach/The Picture Cube/Index Stock Imagery; **532,** A. Ramey/Stock Boston; **538,** Michael Keller/FPG International/Getty Images, Inc.; **540 l,** The Granger Collection; **540 r,** UPI/Corbis/Bettman; **543,** Michael Pole/Corbis; **547,** Andy Lyons/Allsport/Getty Images, Inc.; **551,** Close to Home by John McPherson/Universal Press Syndicate; **552,** SuperStock; **555,** Jeff Sherman/FPG International/Getty Images, Inc.; **557,** SuperStock; **562,** Animals Animals/Earth Scenes; **565,** Russ Lappa; **574,** NASA

Chapter Eleven

Pages 576, 577, AFP/Corbis; **579,** Telegraph Colour Library/FPG International/Getty Images, Inc.; **585,** Spencer Jones/FPG International/Getty Images, Inc.; **588,** AFP/Corbis; **595,** Wesley Bocxe/Photo Researchers, Inc.; **602,** © ABC/Mondrian Estate/Holtzman Trust/Haags Gemeentemuseum; **605,** © Tribune Media Services, Inc. All Rights Reserved. Reprinted with permission.; **606,** Ron Sherman/Stock Boston; **608,** Zefa/London/ Corbis Stock Market; **611,** David Young Wolff/PhotoEdit; **615,** PhotoEdit; **617,** Kelly-Mooney Photography/Corbis; **618,** David Young-Wolff/PhotoEdit; **623,** Joe McDonald/Bruce Coleman, Inc.; **626,** Eye Ubiquitous/Corbis

Chapter Twelve

Pages 634, 635, John William Banagan/The Image Bank/Getty Images, Inc.; **636,** Nancy Richmond/The Image Works; **638,** David Young-Wolff/PhotoEdit; **641 l,** Bruce Roberts/Photo Researchers, Inc.; **641 r,** Close to Home by John McPherson/Universal Press Syndicate; **649,** Mark Joseph/Stone/Getty Images, Inc.; **653,** Antman/The Image Works; **655,** SuperStock; **670,** Bob Daemmrich/The Image Works; **671,** Frank Pedrick/The Image Works; **673,** Billy E. Barnes/PhotoEdit; **676 both, 677,** Richard Haynes; **682,** Billy E. Barnes/PhotoEdit; **687,** J. Pickerell/The Image Works; **688 both,** U.S. Mint; **690 t,** David Young-Wolff/PhotoEdit; **690,** Prentice Hall School Division; **700,** Neal Preston/Corbis; **700–701 the rest,** Dorling Kindersley